THE SIXTEENTH
MARCEL GROSSMANN MEETING

On Recent Developments in Theoretical and Experimental
General Relativity, Astrophysics and Relativistic Field Theories

PART A

THE SIXTEENTH
MARCEL GROSSMANN MEETING

On Recent Developments in Theoretical and Experimental
General Relativity, Astrophysics and Relativistic Field Theories

Proceedings of the MG16 Meeting
on General Relativity
Online, 5–10 July 2021

Editors

Remo Ruffini
University of Rome "La Sapienza", Rome, Italy
International Center for Relativistic Astrophysics Network (ICRANet), Pescara, Italy

Gregory Vereshchagin
International Center for Relativistic Astrophysics Network (ICRANet), Pescara, Italy

Series Editor

Remo Ruffini
University of Rome "La Sapienza", Rome, Italy
International Center for Relativistic Astrophysics Network (ICRANet), Pescara, Italy

NEW JERSEY • LONDON • SINGAPORE • BEIJING • SHANGHAI • HONG KONG • TAIPEI • CHENNAI

Published by

World Scientific Publishing Co. Pte. Ltd.

5 Toh Tuck Link, Singapore 596224

USA office: 27 Warren Street, Suite 401-402, Hackensack, NJ 07601

UK office: 57 Shelton Street, Covent Garden, London WC2H 9HE

Library of Congress Cataloging-in-Publication Data
Names: Marcel Grossmann Meeting on General Relativity (16th : 2021 : Online) |
　　Ruffini, Remo, editor. | Vereshchagin, Gregory, editor.
Title: The sixteenth Marcel Grossmann meeting on recent developments in theoretical and experimental
　　general relativity, astrophysics, and relativistic field theories : proceedings of the MG16 meeting on
　　general relativity online, 5–10 July 2021 / editors: Remo Ruffini, University of Rome "La Sapienza",
　　Rome, Italy, International Center for Relativistic Astrophysics Network (ICRANet), Pescara, Italy,
　　Gregory Vereshchagin, International Center for Relativistic Astrophysics Network (ICRANet), Pescara, Italy.
Other titles: Proceedings of the MG16 meeting on general relativity online, 5–10 July 2021
Description: New Jersey : World Scientific, [2023] | Includes bibliographical references.
Identifiers: LCCN 2022047088 | ISBN 9789811269769 (set ; hardcover) | ISBN 9789811266584 (v. 1) |
　　ISBN 9789811266591 (v. 2) | ISBN 9789811266607 (v. 3) | ISBN 9789811266614 (v. 4) |
　　ISBN 9789811269776 (set ; ebook)
Subjects: LCSH: General relativity (Physics)--Congresses. | Gravitation--Congresses. |
　　Quantum gravity--Congresses. | Cosmology--Congresses. | Astrophysics--Congresses.
Classification: LCC QC173.6 .M37 2021 | DDC 523.01--dc23/eng/20220929
LC record available at https://lccn.loc.gov/2022047088

British Library Cataloguing-in-Publication Data
A catalogue record for this book is available from the British Library.

Copyright © 2023 by Editors

All rights reserved.

This is an Open Access volume published by World Scientific Publishing Company. It is distributed under the terms of the Creative Commons Attribution-Non Commercial 4.0 (CC BY-NC) License. Further distribution of this work is permitted, provided the original work is properly cited.

For any available supplementary material, please visit
https://www.worldscientific.com/worldscibooks/10.1142/13149#t=suppl

Typeset by Stallion Press
Email: enquiries@stallionpress.com

Printed in Singapore

THE MARCEL GROSSMANN MEETINGS
Series Editor: REMO RUFFINI

Publications in the Series of Proceedings

Proceedings of the Sixteenth Marcel Grossmann Meeting on General Relativity
(Virtual Meeting, 2021)
Edited by G. Vereshchagin, R. Ruffini
World Scientific, 2022

Proceedings of the Fifteenth Marcel Grossmann Meeting on General Relativity
(Rome, Italy, 2018)
Edited by E.S. Battistelli, R.T. Jantzen, R. Ruffini
World Scientific, 2022

Proceedings of the Fourteenth Marcel Grossmann Meeting on General Relativity
(Rome, Italy, 2015)
Edited by M. Bianchi, R.T. Jantzen, R. Ruffini
World Scientific, 2017

Proceedings of the Thirteenth Marcel Grossmann Meeting on General Relativity
(Stockholm, Sweden, 2012)
Edited by K. Rosquist, R.T. Jantzen, R. Ruffini
World Scientific, 2015

Proceedings of the Twelfth Marcel Grossmann Meeting on General Relativity
(Paris, France, 2009)
Edited by T. Damour, R.T. Jantzen, R. Ruffini
World Scientific, 2012

Proceedings of the Eleventh Marcel Grossmann Meeting on General Relativity
(Berlin, Germany, 2006)
Edited by H. Kleinert, R.T. Jantzen, R. Ruffini
World Scientific, 2007

Proceedings of the Tenth Marcel Grossmann Meeting on General Relativity
(Rio de Janiero, Brazil, 2003)
Edited by M. Novello, S. Perez-Bergliaffa, R. Ruffini
World Scientific, 2005

Proceedings of the Ninth Marcel Grossmann Meeting on General Relativity
(Rome, Italy, 2000)
Edited by V.G. Gurzadyan, R.T. Jantzen, R. Ruffini
World Scientific, 2002

Proceedings of the Eighth Marcel Grossmann Meeting on General Relativity
(Jerusalem, Israel, 1997)
Edited by T. Piran
World Scientific, 1998

Proceedings of the Seventh Marcel Grossmann Meeting on General Relativity
(Stanford, USA, 1994)
Edited by R.T. Jantzen and G.M. Keiser
World Scientific, 1996

Proceedings of the Sixth Marcel Grossmann Meeting on General Relativity
(Kyoto, Japan, 1991)
Edited by H. Sato and T. Nakamura
World Scientific, 1992

Proceedings of the Fifth Marcel Grossmann Meeting on General Relativity
(Perth, Australia, 1988)
Edited by D.G. Blair and M.J. Buckingham
World Scientific, 1989

Proceedings of the Fourth Marcel Grossmann Meeting on General Relativity
(Rome, Italy, 1985)
Edited by R. Ruffini
World Scientific, 1986

Proceedings of the Third Marcel Grossmann Meeting on General Relativity
(Shanghai, People's Republic of China, 1982)
Edited by Hu Ning
Science Press – Beijing and North-Holland Publishing Company, 1983

Proceedings of the Second Marcel Grossmann Meeting on General Relativity
(Trieste, Italy, 1979)
Edited by R. Ruffini
North-Holland Publishing Company, 1982

Proceedings of the First Marcel Grossmann Meeting on General Relativity
(Trieste, Italy, 1975)
Edited by R. Ruffini
North-Holland Publishing Company, 1977

SPONSORS

International Center for Relativistic Astrophysics Network (ICRANet)
International Center for Relativistic Astrophysics (ICRA)

FREEDOM OF MOVEMENT FOR SCIENTISTS

The Marcel Grossmann Meetings were founded with the premise that scientists of all nations have a right to meet to exchange knowledge independent of national borders.

ACKNOWLEDGEMENTS

We acknowledge the outstanding job done before, during and after the meeting by the ICRANet/ICRA administrative and secretarial staff: Cristina Adamo, Silvia Latorre, Elisabetta Natale, and Cinzia di Niccolo. Finally this meeting and its proceedings could not have functioned without the dedicated IT support of the ICRANet system manager Gabriele Brandolini, with some temporary assistance from Domenico La Selva and Damiano Verzulli. We would like to thank Linda Kwan from World Scientific for valuable assistance during preparation of these proceedings.

ORGANIZING BODIES
OF THE SIXTEENTH MARCEL GROSSMANN MEETING

INTERNATIONAL ORGANIZING COMMITTEE

Blair David, Choquet Bruhat Yvonne, Damour Thibault, De Bernardis Paolo, Everitt C. W. Francis, Fryer Chris, Haensch Theodor, Henneaux Marc, Jones Christine, Kerr Roy, Kleinert Hagen, Kunz Jutta, Laemmerzahl Claus, Longair Malcolm, Mirabel Felix, Mirzoyan Razmik, Piran Tsvi, Rueda Jorge, Ruffini Remo (chair), Sasaki Misao, Sato Humitaka, Sunyaev Rashid, 't Hooft Gerard, Weinberg Steven, Yau Shing-Tung, Zhang Bing

LOCAL ORGANIZING COMMITTEE

Adamo Cristina, Bianco Carlo Luciano, Brandolini Gabriele A., di Niccolo Cinzia, Latorre Silvia, La Selva Domenico, Li Liang, Loppini Alessandro, Natale Elisabetta, Verzulli Damiano, Vereshchagin Gregory (chair), Wang Yu

INTERNATIONAL COORDINATING COMMITTEE

ALBANIA: Hafizi M. - ARGENTINA: Arguelles C., Scoccola C., Reula O., Romero G.E. - ARMENIA: Sahakyan N. - AUSTRALIA: Blair D., Ju L., Lun A., Manchester D., Melatos A., Quinn P., Scott S.M., Steele J.D. - AUSTRIA: Aichelburg P.C., Schindler S. - BELARUS: Kilin S., Prakapenia M., Siutsou I. - BELGIUM: Henneaux M. - BOLIVIA: Aguirre C.B. - BOSNIA: Pasic V. - BRAZIL: Barres de Almeida U., Coelho Goulart J., Dalmolin F.T., de Lima Rafael C.R., Guzzo M., Maia C., Malheiro M., Romero Filho C.A., Shellard R.C., Zen Vasconcellos C. - BULGARIA: Yazadjiev S. - CANADA: Singh D., Smolin L., Turok N. - CHILE: Bauer F., Bunster W.C., Giacomini A. - CHINA (MAINLAND): Cai R., Cai Y., Cao Z., Chang J., Chen J., Chen X., Dai Z., Feng L.-L., Han W., Jing Y., Li T.-P., Lin W., Lou Y.-Q., Luo J., Mei J., Tam T., Wang A., Wang Y., Wu X.-P., Wu Y.-L., Yuan Y.-F., Zhang B.-B., Zhang S.-N., Zhao G. - CHINA (TAIWAN): Chen Chiang-Mei, Chen Pisin, Lee Da-Shin, Lee Wo-Lung, Ni Wei-Tou - COLOMBIA: Bargueño de Retes P., Gonzalez G., Higuera Garzon M.A., Núñez L., Romano A.E., Valenzuela Toledo C.A., Zuluaga J.I. - CROATIA: Dominis Prester D., Karlica M., Milekovic M., Smolcic V., Smolic I., Suric T. - CUBA: Perez Martinez A., Pérez Rojas H. - CZECH REPUBLIC: Bicak J., Stuchlik Z. - DENMARK: Naselsky P. - ECUADOR: Contreras E. - EGYPT: Tawfik A.N., Wanas M.I. - ESTONIA: Einasto J., Saar E. - FINLAND: Poutanen J., Volovik G. - FRANCE: Brillet A., Buchert T., Chardonnet P., Coullet P., de Freitas Pacheco J.A., Deruelle N., Iliopoulos J., Lamanna G., Mignard F. - GEORGIA: Lavrelashvili George, Machabeli Giorgi - GERMANY: Biermann P., Blumlein J., Di Piazza A., Fritzsch H., Genzel R., Gilmozzi R., Hasinger G., Hehl F., Keitel C., Kiefer C., Mirzoyan R.,

Neugebauer G., Nicolai H., Renn J., Ringwald A., Ruediger A. - GREECE: Batakis N.A., Cotsakis S., Vagenas E.C. - HUNGARY: Fodor G., Levai P. - ICELAND: Bjornsson G., Jakobsson P. - INDIA: Chakrabarti S.K., Iyer B., Padmanabhan T., Souradeep T. - IRAN: Baghram S., Bavarsad E., Eslam Panah B., Firouzjahi H., Haghighat M., Mansouri R., Mashhoon B., Shakeri S., Sobouti Y., Taghi Mirtorabi M. - IRELAND: O'Murchada N. - ISRAEL: Milgrom M., Nakar E., Pe'er A., Piran T. - ITALY: Belinski V., Bianchi M., Bianco C.L., Cherubini C., Della Valle M., Falciano S., Filippi S., Haardt F., Menotti P., Merafina M., Pani P., Ricci F., Treves A., Vereshchagin G.V., Vitale S., Xue S.- S. - JAPAN: Fujimoto M.-K., Makishima K., Nakamura T., Sato K., Shibata M. - KAZAKHSTAN: Abishev M., Aimuratov Y., Boshkayev K., Mychelkin E.G., Spitaleri C. - KOREA (PYEONGYANG): Kim J.S. - KOREA (SEOUL): Kim S.P., Kim S.-W., Lee H.K., Lee H.-W., van Putten M. - KYRGYZSTAN: Gurovich V.Ts. - LIBYA: Gadri M. - MEXICO: Breton N., Cervantes-Cota J.L., Fraija Cabrera N.I., García-Diaz A.A., Macías Alvarez A., Mielke Eckehard W., Quevedo H., Rodriguez L.F. - NETHERLANDS: Slagter R. - NEW ZEALAND: Visser M., Wiltshire D. - NORWAY: Elgaroy O., Fonseca Mota D., Knutsen H. - PAKISTAN: Qadir A., Qamar S. - PERU: Vargas T. - POLAND: Belczynski K., Demianski M., Lewandowski Jerzy, Nurowski P., Sokolowski L. - PORTUGAL: Costa M., Da Silva A., Lemos J.P.S., Lobo F., Moniz P., Silva L.O. - ROMANIA: Visinescu M. - RUSSIA: Aksenov A., Arkhangelskaja I., Bisnovatyi-Kogan G., Blinnikov S., Chechetikin V.M., Cherepaschuk A.M., Khriplovich I., Lipunov V.M., Lukash V.N., Novikov I., Rudenko V.N., Starobinsky A.A. - SERBIA: Djordjevic G., Jovanovic P., Knezevic Z., Pankov-Hzvojevic M., Popovic L., Prodanovic T., Sijacki D., Simic S. - SLOVAKIA: Balek V. - SLOVENIA: Cadez A., Gomboc A., Zavrtanik D. - SOUTH AFRICA: Larena J., Maharaj S. - SPAIN: Elizalde E., Ibanez J., Perez M.J., Verdaguer E. - SWEDEN: Abramowicz M.A., Marklund M., Ryde F. - SWITZERLAND: Durrer R., Jetzer P. - TURKEY: Aliev A., Gurses M. - UKRAINE: Novosyadlyj B., Zaslavskii O., Zhuk A. - UNITED ARAB EMIRATES: Fernini I. - UNITED KINGDOM: Cruise A.M., Frenk Carlos S., Green M., Mavromatos N., Perry M., Willingale R. - USA: Abel T., Ashtekar A., Bardeen J., Carlstrom J., Cornish N., Dermer C., Fan X., Flanagan E., Fraschetti F., Fryer C., Incera V., Jantzen R.T. (chairperson), Kolb R., Laguna P., Lousto C., Madau Piero, Mathews Grant, Matzner Richard, Melia Fulvio, Mester John, Michelson Peter, Nordtvedt Kenneth, Parker Leonard, Pretorius F., Pullin J., Shapiro I., Shapiro S., Shoemaker D., Smoot G., Stiavelli M., Teukolsky S., van Nieuwenhuizen P., Zhang B. - UZBEKISTAN: Ahmedov B., Zalaletdinov R.M. - VATICAN CITY: Gionti G. - VENEZUELA: Fuenmayor E. - VIETNAM: Long H.N.

MARCEL GROSSMANN AWARDS

Sixteenth Marcel Grossmann Meeting

Institutional Awards

"for the creation of the world's best X-ray map of the entire sky, for the discovery of millions of previously unknown accreting supermassive black holes at cosmological redshifts, for the detection of X-rays from tens of thousands of galaxy clusters, filled mainly with dark matter, and for permitting the detailed investigation of the growth of the large-scale structure of the universe during the era of dark energy dominance".

S.A. LAVOCHKIN ASSOCIATION
- presented to its Designer General **Alexander Shirshakov**

MAX PLANCK INSTITUTE FOR EXTRATERRESTRIAL PHYSICS (MPE)
- presented to Professor **Peter Predehl**, Principal Investigator of eROSITA

SPACE RESEARCH INSTITUTE (IKI) OF THE RUSSIAN ACADEMY OF SCIENCES
- presented to Professor **Rashid Sunyaev,** Principal Investigator of SRG Observatory in Russia

Individual Awards

DEMETRIOS CHRISTODOULOU
"For his many lasting contributions to the foundation of mathematical physics including the dynamics of relativistic gravitational fields. Notably for: contributing in 1971, at the age of 19, to derive with Remo Ruffini the mass-energy formula of black holes as a function of their angular momentum, charge and irreducible mass. Christodoulou turned then to the study of partial differential equations and mathematical physics, to which he remained dedicated for the rest of his career. Highlights in this area include the theoretical discovery of the nonlinear memory effect of gravitational waves (Phys. Rev. Letters 1991), the monograph (1993) in collaboration with Sergiu Klainerman on the global nonlinear stability of the Minkowski spacetime, the monograph (2009) on the formation of black holes in pure general relativity by imploding gravitational waves, and the monographs (2007 and 2019) on the formation and further development of shocks in fluids."

GERARD 't HOOFT
"for his persistent devotion to the study of the quantum field theory boundary conditions at the black hole horizon".

TSVI PIRAN
"for extending Relativistic astrophysics across international frontiers, a true companion in the search for the deeper meaning of Einstein's great theory".

STEVEN WEINBERG
"for unwavering support for the MG meetings since their inception, a true companion in the search for the deeper meaning of Einstein's great theory".

Each recipient is presented with a silver casting of the TEST sculpture by the artist A. Pierelli. The original casting was presented to His Holiness Pope John Paul II on the first occasion of the Marcel Grossmann Awards.

15th Marcel Grossmann Meeting
July 2018, Rome, Italy

Institutional Awards

PLANCK SCIENTIFIC COLLABORATION (ESA)
"for obtaining important constraints on the models of inflationary stage of the Universe and level of primordial non-Gaussianity; measuring with unprecedented sensitivity gravitational lensing of Cosmic Microwave Background fluctuations by large-scale structure of the Universe and corresponding B-polarization of CMB, the imprint on the CMB of hot gas in galaxy clusters; getting unique information about the time of reionization of our Universe and distribution and properties of the dust and magnetic fields in our Galaxy"

- presented to Jean-Loup Puget, the Principal Investigator of the High Frequency Instrument (HFI)

HANSEN EXPERIMENTAL PHYSICS LABORATORY AT STANFORD UNIVERSITY
"to HEPL for having developed interdepartmental activities at Stanford University at the frontier of fundamental physics, astrophysics and technology"

- presented to Research Professor Leo Hollberg, HEPL Assistant Director

Individual Awards

LYMAN PAGE
"for his collaboration with David Wilkinson in realizing the NASA Explorer WMAP mission and as founding director of the Atacama Cosmology Telescope"

RASHID ALIEVICH SUNYAEV
"for the development of theoretical tools in the scrutinising, through the CMB, of the first observable electromagnetic appearance of our Universe"

SHING-TUNG YAU
"for the proof of the positivity of total mass in the theory of general relativity and perfecting as well the concept of quasi-local mass, for his proof of the Calabi conjecture, for his continuous inspiring role in the study of black holes physics"

14th Marcel Grossmann Meeting
July 2015, Rome, Italy

Institutional Award

EUROPEAN SPACE AGENCY (ESA)
"for the tremendous success of its scientific space missions in astronomy, astrophysics, cosmology and fundamental physics which have revolutionized our knowledge of the Universe and hugely benefited science and mankind"

- presented to its Director General Johann-Dietrich Woerner

Individual Awards

KEN'ICHI NOMOTO
"for heralding the role of binary systems in the evolution of massive stars"

MARTIN REES
"for fostering Research in black holes, gravitational waves and cosmology"

YAKOV G. SINAI
"for applying the mathematics of chaotic systems to physics and cosmology"

SACHIKO TSURUTA
"for pioneering the physics of hot neutron stars and their cooling"

FRANK C.N. YANG
"for deepening Einstein's geometrical approach to physics in the best tradition of Paul Dirac and Hermann Weyl"

T.D. LEE (award received by Yu-Qing Lou on behalf of Prof. T.D. Lee)
"for his work on white dwarfs motivating Enrico Fermi's return to astrophysics and guiding the basic understanding of neutron star matter and fields"

13th Marcel Grossmann Meeting
July 2012, Stockholm, Sweden

Institutional Award

ALBANOVA
for its innovative status as a joint institute established by Stockholm University and the Royal Institute of Technology and for fostering contributions to cosmology and astrophysics in the profound scientific tradition established by Oskar Klein.

- presented to the Rector of Stockholm University, Prof. Kåre Bremer.

Individual Awards

DAVID ARNETT
for exploring the nuclear physics and yet unsolved problems of the endpoint of thermonuclear evolution of stars, leading to new avenues of research in physics and astrophysics.

VLADIMIR BELINSKI and I.M. KHALATNIKOV
for the discovery of a general solution of the Einstein equations with a cosmological singularity of an oscillatory chaotic character known as the BKL singularity.

FILIPPO FRONTERA
for guiding the Gamma-ray Burst Monitor Project on board the BeppoSAX satellite, which led to the discovery of GRB X-ray afterglows, and to their optical identification.

12th Marcel Grossmann Meeting
July 2009, Paris, France

Institutional Award

INSTITUT DES HAUTES ÉSTUDES SCIENTIFIQUE (IHÉS)
for its outstanding contributions to mathematics and theoretical physics, and notably for having renewed basic geometrical concepts, and having developed new mathematical and physical aspects of spacetime.

- presented to Prof. Jean-Pierre Bourguignon

Individual Awards

JAAN EINASTO
for pioneering contributions in the discovery of dark matter and cosmic web and fostering research in the historical Tartu Observatory.

CHRISTINE JONES
for her fundamental contributions to the X-ray studies of galaxies and clusters tracing their formation and evolution and for her role in collaborations using clusters to study dark matter and in analyzing the effects of outbursts from supermassive black holes on the intracluster gas.

MICHAEL KRAMER
for his fundamental contributions to pulsar astrophysics, and notably for having first confirmed the existence of spin-orbit precession in binary pulsars.

11th Marcel Grossmann Meeting
July 2006, Berlin, Germany

Institutional Award

FREIE UNIVERSITÄT BERLIN
for the successful endeavor of re-establishing — in the spirit of the Humboldt tradition — freedom of thinking and teaching within a democratic society in a rapidly evolving cosmos

- presented to Dr. Dieter Lenzen, President of FUB

Individual Awards

ROY KERR
for his fundamental contribution to Einstein's theory of general relativity: "The gravitational field of a spinning mass as an example of algebraically special metrics."

GEORGE COYNE
for his committed support for the international development of relativistic astrophysics and for his dedication to fostering an enlightened relationship between science and religion.

JOACHIM TRUMPER
for his outstanding scientific contributions to the physics of compact astrophysical objects and for leading the highly successful ROSAT mission which discovered more than 200,000 galactic and extragalactic X-ray sources: a major step in the observational capabilities of X-ray astronomy and in the knowledge of our universe.

10th Marcel Grossmann Meeting
July 2003, Rio de Janeiro, Brazil

Institutional Award

CBPF (Brazilian Center for Research in Physics)
for its role as a teaching and research institution and as a place originating fundamental physics ideas in the exploration of the universe.

- presented to its founders Cesar Lattes, Josè Leite Lopez and Jayme Tiomno

Individual Awards

YVONNE CHOQUET-BRUHAT AND JAMES W. YORK, JR.
for separate as well as joint work in establishing the mathematical framework for proving the existence and uniqueness of solutions to Einstein's gravitational field equations.

YUVAL NE'EMAN
for his contributions to science, epistimology, mathematics and physics from subnuclear to space sciences.

9th Marcel Grossmann Meeting
July 2000, Rome, Italy

Institutional Award

SOLVAY INSTITUTES

for identifying and recording in discussions by the protagonists the crucial developments of physics and astrophysics in the twentieth century.

- presented to Jacques Solvay

Individual Awards

CECILLE AND BRYCE DEWITT

for promoting General Relativity and Mathematics research and inventing the "summer school" concept.

RICCARDO GIACCONI

for opening, five successive times, new highways for exploring the Universe.

ROGER PENROSE

for extending the mathematical and geometrical foundations of General Relativity.

8th Marcel Grossmann Meeting
June 1997, Jerusalem

Institutional Award

HEBREW UNIVERSITY
for its role as a cradle of Science and Humanities and for hosting the manuscripts of Albert Einstein.

- presented to M. Magidor, President of the Hebrew University of Jerusalem

Individual Awards

TULLIO REGGE
for his contributions to the interface between mathematics and physics leading to new fields of research of paramount importance in relativistic astrophysics and particle physics.

FRANCIS EVERITT
for leading the development of extremely precise space experiments utilizing superconducting technology to test General Relativity and the Equivalence Principle.

7th Marcel Grossmann Meeting
June 1994, Stanford, USA

Institutional Award

SPACE TELESCOPE SCIENCE INSTITUTE
for its critical role in the direction and operation of the Hubble Space Telescope, a truly unique international laboratory for the investigation and testing of general relativity in the context of modern astrophysics and cosmology.

- presented to Peter Stockman

Individual Awards

SUBRAHMANYAN CHANDRASEKHAR
for his contributions to the analysis of gravitational phenomena from Newton to Einstein and especially for leading the way to relativistic astrophysics with the concept of critical mass for gravitational collapse.

JIM WILSON
for having built on his experience in nuclear physics, thermonuclear reactions, and extensive numerical simulation to create a new testing ground for the novel concepts of relativistic astrophysics.

6th Marcel Grossmann Meeting
June 1991, Kyoto, Japan

Institutional Award

RITP

for keeping alive first in Hiroshima and them in Kyoto research in relativity, cosmology, and relativistic field theory and the development of a school of international acclaim.

- presented to Professor K. Tomita

Individual Awards

MINORU ODA

for participating in the pioneering work of the early sixties in X-ray astronomy and for his subsequent molding of an agile and diversified Japanese scientific space program investigating the deepest aspects of relativistic astrophysics.

STEPHEN HAWKING

for his contributions to the understanding of spacetime singularities and of the large scale structure of the Universe and of its quantum origins.

5th Marcel Grossmann Meeting
August 1988, Perth, Australia

Institutional Award

THE UNIVERSITY OF WESTERN AUSTRALIA
for its contributions to relativistic astrophysics.

- presented to the Vice Chancellor, Professor Robert Smith

Individual Awards

SATIO HAYAKAWA
for his contributions to research in gamma, X-ray and infrared radiation as well as cosmic rays.

JOHN ARCHIBALD WHEELER
for his contributions to geometrodynamics and Einstein's visions.

4th Marcel Grossmann Meeting
July 1985, Rome, Italy

Institutional Award

THE VATICAN OBSERVATORY
for its contributions to the origin and development of astrophysics.

- presented to His Holiness Pope John Paul II

Individual Awards

WILLIAM FAIRBANK
for his work in gravitation and low temperature physics.

ABDUS SALAM
for his work in unifying fundamental interactions.

Institutional Awards for the Spektrum-Roentgen-Gamma (SRG) mission

"for the creation of the world's best X-ray map of the entire sky, for the discovery of millions of previously unknown accreting supermassive black holes at cosmological redshifts, for the detection of X-rays from tens of thousands of galaxy clusters, filled mainly with dark matter, and for permitting the detailed investigation of the growth of the large-scale structure of the universe during the era of dark energy dominance".

S.A. LAVOCHKIN ASSOCIATION
- presented to its Designer General **Alexander Shirshakov**

MAX PLANCK INSTITUTE FOR EXTRATERRESTRIAL PHYSICS (MPE)
- presented to Professor **Peter Predehl**, Principal Investigator of eROSITA

SPACE RESEARCH INSTITUTE (IKI) OF THE RUSSIAN ACADEMY OF SCIENCES
- presented to Professor **Rashid Sunyaev**, Principal Investigator of SRG Observatory in Russia

On Tuesday June 29, 2021, the following 31 astro-ph appeared:

1. https://arxiv.org/abs/2106.14517
2. https://arxiv.org/abs/2106.14518
3. https://arxiv.org/abs/2106.14519
4. https://arxiv.org/abs/2106.14520
5. https://arxiv.org/abs/2106.14521
6. https://arxiv.org/abs/2106.14522
7. https://arxiv.org/abs/2106.14523
8. https://arxiv.org/abs/2106.14524
9. https://arxiv.org/abs/2106.14525
10. https://arxiv.org/abs/2106.14526
11. https://arxiv.org/abs/2106.14527
12. https://arxiv.org/abs/2106.14528
13. https://arxiv.org/abs/2106.14529
14. https://arxiv.org/abs/2106.14530
15. https://arxiv.org/abs/2106.14531
16. https://arxiv.org/abs/2106.14532
17. https://arxiv.org/abs/2106.14533
18. https://arxiv.org/abs/2106.14534
19. https://arxiv.org/abs/2106.14535
20. https://arxiv.org/abs/2106.14536
21. https://arxiv.org/abs/2106.14537
22. https://arxiv.org/abs/2106.14541
23. https://arxiv.org/abs/2106.14542
24. https://arxiv.org/abs/2106.14543
25. https://arxiv.org/abs/2106.14544
26. https://arxiv.org/abs/2106.14545
27. https://arxiv.org/abs/2106.14546
28. https://arxiv.org/abs/2106.14547
29. https://arxiv.org/abs/2106.14548
30. https://arxiv.org/abs/2106.14549
31. https://arxiv.org/abs/2106.14550

S.A. LAVOCHKIN ASSOCIATION
presented to its Designer General **Alexander Shirshakov**

Dr Alexander Shirshakov

S.A. Lavochkin Association created the Navigator space platform carrying German eRosita and Russian ART-XC X-Ray Telescopes, organized the launch of SRG Orbital X-Ray Observatory to the second Lagrangian point of the Sun-Earth system at a distance of 1.5 million km from the Earth and managed the observatory flight and the daily reception of its scientific data on Earth for 23.5 months.

Dr Alexander Shirshakov, Designer General of the S.A. Lavochkin Association, is specialized in design, manufacture, testing, launch and control of S/C for scientific purposes. Among those S/C launched, there are the «Radiostron» Astrophysical Observatory (2011) and the «Spektr-RG» space observatory (2019), while the planned S/C launches are «Luna-25» and «Exomars».

Dr Shirshakov started his career in 1973, working as an engineer of the State Unitary Enterprise «NPO named by S.A. Lavochkin» in Khimki (Russian Federation). Starting from 1989 he has played multiple roles within the Lavochkin Association, been appointed head of the group, head of the sector, head of department, deputy head of the complex, head of the branch, director of the center, deputy head of the Design Bureau, deputy General Designer and deputy General Director.

Dr Shirshakov is an editorial board Member of the reviewed edition of «Vestnik of Lavochkin Association». Since 2017, he is also member of the General Designer council. He has been awarded Honored Mechanical engineer of the Russian Federation as well as Agency-level award of the Russian Federal Space Agency.

MAX PLANCK INSTITUTE FOR EXTRATERRESTRIAL PHYSICS (MPE)
presented to Professor **Peter Predehl**, Principal Investigator of eROSITA

Professor Peter Predehl

eROSITA is the soft X-ray telescope on-board the Russian-German Spektr-RG mission which was successfully launched from Baikonur on July 13, 2019 and placed in a halo orbit around the L2 point. 30 years after ROSAT, eROSITA performs an all-sky survey with an unprecedented sensitivity, spectral and angular resolution. Clusters of galaxies are the largest collapsed objects in the Universe. Their formation and evolution is dominated by gravity, i.e. Dark Matter, while their large scale distribution and number density depends on the geometry of the Universe, i.e. Dark Energy. X-ray observations of clusters of galaxies provide information on the rate of expansion of the Universe, the fraction of mass in visible matter, and the amplitude of primordial fluctuations which are the origin of clusters of galaxies and the whole structure of the universe. eROSITA has been designed to detect at least 100.000 clusters of galaxies and to detect systematically more than 3 million obscured accreting Black Holes. eROSITA will also allow to study the physics of galactic X-ray source populations, like pre-main sequence stars, supernova remnants and X-ray binaries. The eROSITA telescope consists of seven identical Wolter-1 mirror modules. A novel detector system has been developed by MPE on the basis of the successful XMM-Newton pn-CCD technology. MPE is the scientific lead institute of eROSITA, responsible for the development of the instrument, the operation, the analysis software and data archive. Peter Predehl led this development as Principal Investigator of eROSITA and German lead scientist of the SRG mission for more than 15 years until the completion of the first of eight surveys in 2020. At this time eROSITA has already discovered more than 1 million X-ray sources, more than all X-ray observatories of the last 50 years together. This demonstrates that the design goals of the mission will easily be fulfilled.

SPACE RESEARCH INSTITUTE (IKI) OF THE RUSSIAN ACADEMY OF SCIENCES
presented to Professor **Rashid Sunyaev**

Professor Rashid Sunyaev

Space Research Institute (IKI) of the Russian Academy of Sciences was responsible for developing the overall concept and scientific program of the SRG Orbital observatory and played a leading role in developing the ART-XC telescope and the entire SRG observatory as part of the Russian space science program carried out by Roskosmos Corporation in the interests of the Russian Academy of Sciences.

During the flight to the L2 point of the Sun-Earth system, SRG with German (eRosita) and Russian (ART-XC named after Mikhail Pavlinsky) X-ray Telescopes aboard performed calibrations and long duration Performance Verification observations of a dozen of targets and deep fields. Starting in the middle of December 2019, the SRG scanned the whole sky three times. During these scans, SRG discovered two million point X-ray sources: mainly quasars, stars with hot and bright coronae, and more than 30 thousand clusters of galaxies. There is a competition and synergy in the search for clusters of galaxies between SRG and the ground-based Atacama Cosmology and South Pole Telescopes, which are searching for clusters of galaxies in microwave spectral band using Sunyaev-Zeldovich effect.

SRG provided the X-Ray map of the whole sky in hard and soft bands, the last is now the best among existing. The huge samples of the X-ray selected quasars at the redshifts up to $z = 6.2$ and clusters of galaxies will be used for well-known cosmological tests and detailed study of the growth of the large scale structure of the Universe during and after reionization. SRG/eRosita is discovering every day several extragalactic objects which increased or decreased their brightness more than 10 times during half of the year after the previous scan of the same one-degree wide strip on the sky. A significant part of these objects has observational properties similar to the Events of Tidal Disruption of a star orbiting in the vicinity of the supermassive black hole. ART-XC discovered a lot of bright galactic and extragalactic transients.

Rashid Sunyaev is the Principal Investigator of SRG mission in Russia, director-emeritus of the Max-Planck Institute for Astrophysics and Maureen and John Hendricks distinguished visiting professor of the Institute for Advanced Study, Princeton.

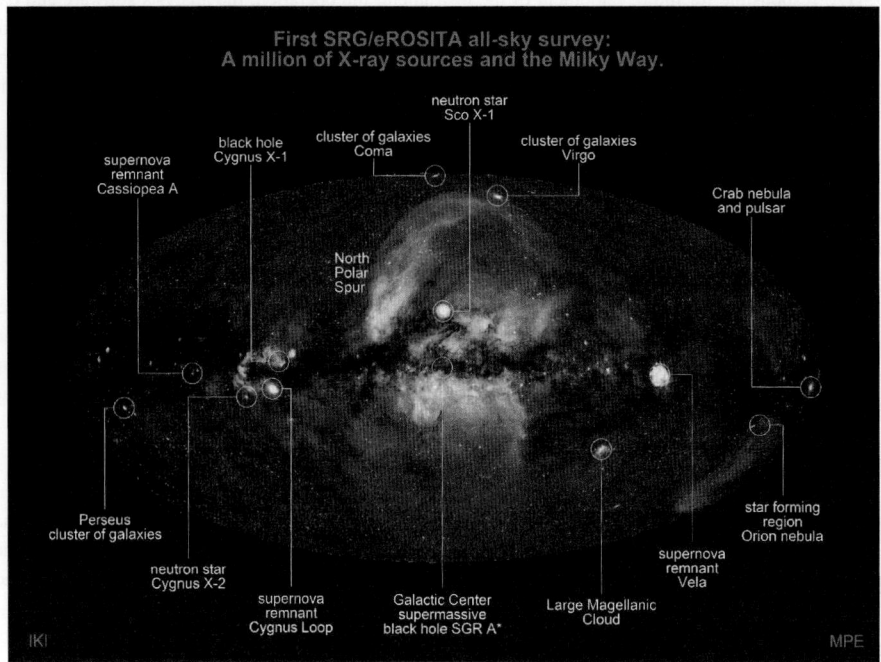

Individual Awards

Professor **DEMETRIOS CHRISTODOULOU**

"For his many lasting contributions to the foundation of mathematical physics including the dynamics of relativistic gravitational fields. Notably for: contributing in 1971, at the age of 19, to derive with Remo Ruffini the mass-energy formula of black holes as a function of their angular momentum, charge and irreducible mass. Christodoulou turned then to the study of partial differential equations and mathematical physics, to which he remained dedicated for the rest of his career. Highlights in this area include the theoretical discovery of the nonlinear memory effect of gravitational waves (Phys. Rev. Letters 1991), the monograph (1993) in collaboration with Sergiu Klainerman on the global nonlinear stability of the Minkowski spacetime, the monograph (2009) on the formation of black holes in pure general relativity by imploding gravitational waves, and the monographs (2007 and 2019) on the formation and further development of shocks in fluids."

Professor Demetrios Christodoulou

It was back in 1967 that Achille Papapetrou mentioned the case of the 16-year-old Demetrios Christodoulou to John Archibad Wheeler. Wheeler interviewed Demetrios in Paris and brought him immediately to Princeton where he was registered as an undergraduate at the university. After one year he entered the graduate school and started collaborating with me. At the time I was working with Wheeler on the effective potential approach to geodesics co-rotating and counter-rotating (see e.g. reference in The Classical Theory of Fields (Landau and Lifshitz, 1980) in the Kerr metric (later renamed as ISCO; see e.g. (Gravitation Misner, Thorne, Wheeler. 1973). In parallel, Frank Zerilli was working on the gravitational radiation emitted by the fall of a test particle in a Schwarzschild black hole (Zerilli 1970). From these limited conceptual arena Charles Misner and later Kip Thorne launched a program for the detection of gravitational waves on the Earth; see e.g. Misner 1974, Abbott et al. 2016, Abbott et al. 2017. See however Davis et al. 1972, Rodriguez et al. 2018 and J.A. Rueda et al. 2018.

A new approach started with the arrival of Demetrios: he was just creating mathematics following his needs. We identified the reversible and irreversible transformations of a Kerr black hole. Wheeler advanced a thermodynamic analogy. I addressed the need of identifying the concept of irreducible mass (from the Italian "irriducibile"), and was Demetrios's contribution to integrate, overnight, the differential equation for infinitesimal reversible transformations which led to the finite mass-energy formula of a Kerr black hole. That evening, while walking back home through IAS woods, I expressed to Wheeler the great relevance of the newly found formula by Demetrios and proposed to let Demetrios be the single author of this article, admiring his great mathematical talent. Wheeler agreed. The Editor of PRL objected since in that two pages article the Fig. 2 by Wheeler and myself was still unpublished. Actually that Fig. 2 followed a discussion I previously had with Penrose in Florence (Penrose 1961) which allowed us to present there, for the first time, a "Penrose Process". Some difficulties in achieving this process were obvious from the example in Fig. 2, which Roger later recognized himself (Penrose & Floyd 1971). The Editor finally agreed on our written request and the paper appeared on September 17, 1970 (Christodoulou, 1970). On January 1971 appeared my article with Johnny introducing the Black Hole (Ruffini & Wheeler, 1971), with the new physics we were developing in Princeton, including the concept of the "ergosphere". On march 1 1971 we submitted the mass formula of the Kerr Newmann metric, including the relation between the surface area of the horizon and the irreducible (Christodoulou & Ruffini, 1971). On March 11, 1971 the same results were independently confirmed by Steven Hawking, extending further the applicability of our equation (Hawking 1971).

The thesis was successfully discussed by a committee including Eugene Wigner (see Fig. 1), one of the closest collaborators of Albert Einstein and David Wilkinson (see Fig. 2), the head of the NASA WMAP mission, and Johnny and myself as supervisors. The new message was clear: Black Holes, far from being a sink of energy, were energy sources emitting "in principle" 50% of their mass energy, being extractable (Christodoulou & Ruffini, 1971).

Fig. 1 and Fig. 2: Demetrios during his thesis presentation with Eugene Wigner (Fig. 1) and David Wilkinson (Fig.2). Johnny and I were supervisors, ready to intervene in case of need, but no need of intervention was necessary! Wigner elaborated the aphorism of Niels Bohr "Interesting = wrong" in the most definite "very interesting if true = totally wrong".

Demetrios turned soon to the study of partial differential equations and mathematical physics, to which he dedicated for the rest of his career and results were published in four monographs: (Christodoulou and Klainerman 1994, Christodoulou 2007, Christodoulou 2009, Christodoulou 2019). In 1968, Johnny proposed to Demetrios the collapse of a "geon" composed of massless scalar field as a second topic for his thesis. It took almost forty years for him to solve this problem, extended by Demetrios to the focusing of gravitational waves leading to black hole formation (Christodoulou 2009).

Fig. 3: Prof. Remo Ruffini receiving the Cressy Morrison Award of the New York Academy of Sciences, 1972 for the discovery of the first Black Hole in our galaxy Cygnus X1.

A "long march" started on 12 December 1970 with the launch of the Uhuru satellite by Riccardo Giacconi. Early in 1971 an almost daily conversation with him and Herb Gursky at the Smithsonian Astrophysical Observatory, leading to the discovery of binary X-ray sources. This was soon followedby the announcement of Cygnus X1 identified as the first black hole in our galaxy (Ruffini 1973); see e.g. Gursky & Ruffini 1975, which contained as well the first publicannouncement of the Discovery of Gamma Ray burst, as well as Giacconi & Ruffini 1980, 2009; see Figs. 3 and 4).

Fig. 4: In the second row, from left to right, there are, among others: E. T. Newman, S. Chandrasekhar (Nobel 1983), R. Giacconi (Nobel 2002), R. Ruffini, A. Treves, A. Hewish (Nobel 1974), D. Arnett, J.H. Taylor (Nobel 1993), J. Wilson, R. Penrose (Nobel 2020), as well as J. Bahcall, T. Damour, T. Piran et al.

Today, after fifty years, this "long march" has reached a definite result: through the grandest observational multi-wavelength effort in the history of mankind, from space, ground and underground observatories, we are finally finding evidence that black holes are "alive" and their "extractable energy" in our mass formula (Christodoulou & Ruffini, 1971), is the energy source of the most energetic cosmological sources: gamma ray bursts (GRBs),the active galactic nuclei (AGNs) as well as the ultra-high energy cosmic rays (UHECRs) (Ruffini et al. 2021 and references therein). Their "inner engine", has three independent components: 1) a Kerr black hole which is neither in a stationary state nor in vacuum, 2) a background magnetic field aligned with the black hole rotation axis, and 3) an extremely diluted fully ionized plasma (Moradi et al. 2021).There is no role in this inner engine for ISCO. Indeed a new electro dynamical field equations describe the synchrotron radiation emitted close to the black hole horizon, they point to a discrete and repetitive emission of "blackholic quanta" in the MeV and in the GeV. The magnitudes and the emission time scales of these quanta, for M87 and GRB 130427A, are expressed as a function of the above three parameters (Rueda & Ruffini, 2021). A long lasting GeV emission with a luminosity decreasing as a temporal power law, allows for the first time in GRBs, the determination of the black hole mass and spin as well as their time evolution perfectly fulfilling our mass energy formula (Christodoulou & Ruffini, 1971): a long lasting emission process profoundly different from the traditional process of continued gravitational contraction.

Remo Ruffini

Professor GERARD 't HOOFT

"for his persistent devotion to the study of the quantum field theory boundary conditions at the black hole horizon".

Professor Gerard 't Hooft

Prof. Gerard 't Hooft has been a full Professor at the Utrecht University (the Netherlands), since 1977. Nowadays, he is an Emeritus Professor at that University. During his career, he has paid extended scientific visits to CERN (Geneva), Harvard, Stanford, Princeton and Duke University, NC. In 1999, together with M. Veltman, he received the Nobel Prize in Physics, awarded by The Royal Swedish Academy of Sciences, *"For elucidating the quantum structure of electroweak interactions in physics"*.

Prof. 't Hooft's main subjects of research includes:

– Gauge Theories for the sub-atomic particles and forces, various aspects and ingredients of what is now called "The Standard Model of the sub-atomic particles: renormalizability, topological features such as magnetic monopoles and instantons, 1/N expansions.

– Theories for the quantization of the gravitational force and black holes: producing models for the quantum properties of a black hole, as derived from Standard Model and General Relativity alone; its topological features such as antipodal identification.

– Fundamental theories underlying quantum mechanics, in particular returning determinism and reality to the dynamics of the tiniest material entities in his universe.

Prof. 't Hooft has been awarded the Wolf Prize of the State of Israel (1982), the Pius XI Medal (Vatican City, 1983), the Lorentz Medal (KNAW Amsterdam, 1986) as well as the Spinoza Premium (Netherlands Organization for Scientific Research NWO, 1995).

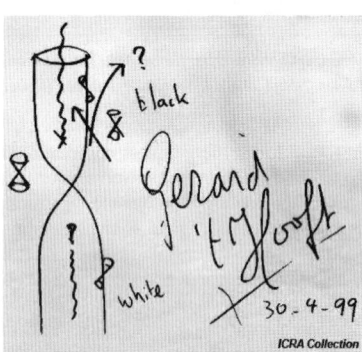

Fig. 2: The signature of Gerard 't Hooft on the wall of ICRA Room 301 (April 4, 1999).

A special event took place at ICRA on April 30, 1999. Prof. Ruffini invited Gerard 't Hooft to Rome to discuss a boundary condition for a quantum field on the black hole horizon, a topic Prof. Ruffini discussed in a previous article "Black-hole evaporation in the Klein-Sauter-Heisenberg-Euler formalism" with Thibault Damour (Phys. Rev. D 14, 332, 1976), but which needed to be examined in more detail. Prof. Ruffini planned to direct Gerard's attention to some specific aspects of this problem. Because we have traditionally been very attentive in spending ICRA travel funds, ICRA offered Gerard to come to Rome on a reduced fare weekend ticket arriving Friday and departing Monday. He had a great relaxing weekend together with Prof. Ruffini following his seminar, which among other things allowed Gerard to sign the wall in our ICRA Room (see Fig. 2), and during this splendid Rome spring weekend he also was able to find a missing factor of 2 in a formula in Prof. Ruffini's 1971 paper with Demetri Christodoulou on the black hole mass formula. The following October, Gerard received the Nobel prize, which meant that we could no longer get away with bringing him to Rome on a cheap ticket! Ever since Gerard has been in our MG IOC helping us with the preparation of the meetings. We are very happy to announce this MG16 Award to Gerard 't Hooft with the motivating phrase *"for his persistent devotion to the study of the quantum field theory boundary conditions at the black hole horizon"*.

Remo Ruffini

Professor **TSVI PIRAN**

"for extending relativistic astrophysics across international frontiers, a true companion in the search for the deeper meaning of Einstein's great theory".

Professor Tsvi Piran

Tsvi Piran is the emeritus Schwartzmann professor at the Hebrew University of Jerusalem. He obtained his PhD in Physics, in 1976 from the Hebrew University working on the collisional Penrose process. Piran returned to the Hebrew University at 1981after being a post doc at Oxford and Texas and a long-term member at the IAS at Princeton. In 1982 he initiated and directed the first ever summer school on Gravitational Waves that took place at Les Houches. Piran was a visiting professor at Harvard, Columbia and New York and a Moore scholar at Caltech.

Piran's research deals with numerous aspects of relativistic astrophysics, ranging from the foundation of numerical relativity to modeling of observer relativistic phenomena and analytic work on the fate of gravitational collapse. Piran's research work focuses mostly on black holes and in particular on gamma-ray bursts. He was among the first to point out their cosmological origin and their association with merging neutron stars and heavy r-process nucleo synthesis. Piran's achievements were recognized in the 2019 EMET prize for Physics.

Professor **STEVEN WEINBERG**

"for unwavering support for the MG meetings since their inception, a true companion in the search for the deeper meaning of Einstein's great theory".

Professor Steven Weinberg. Photo courtesy of Matt Valentine.

Steven Weinberg is a member of the Physics and Astronomy Departments at The University of Texas at Austin. His research has covered a broad range of topics in quantum field theory, elementary particle physics and cosmology. He has been honored with numerous awards, including the Nobel Prize in Physics, the National Medal of Science, the Heinemann Prize in Mathematical Physics and in 2020, the Breakthrough Prize. He is a member of the US National Academy of Sciences, Britain's Royal Society, and other academies in the USA and abroad. The American Philosophical Society awarded him the Benjamin Franklin Medal, with a citation that said he is "considered by many to be the preeminent theoretical physicist alive in the world today." His books for physicists include *Gravitation and Cosmology*, the three-volume work *The Quantum Theory of Fields*, *Cosmology* and published in April of 2021, *Foundations of Modern Physics*. Educated at Cornell, Copenhagen, and Princeton, he also holds honorary degrees from sixteen other universities. He taught at Columbia, Berkeley, M.I.T., and Harvard, where he was Higgins Professor of Physics, before coming to Texas in 1982.

Fig. 1: Chuo Pei Yuan and Cheng Ning Yang at MG2 in Trieste, Italy (1979).

The Sixteenth Marcel Grossmann Meeting (MG16) is a very special one in many respects: it will take place during a pandemic and in spite of the many difficulties, we have decided not to postpone it but to organize it as a virtual meeting. As described on the MG series webpage, these meetings started in 1975 with the first meeting at the International Centre for Theoretical Physics (ICTP) in Trieste (Italy) that I organized with Nobel Prize winner Abdus Salam. A second meeting followed in 1979, with a significantly larger participation including Nobel Laurate Cheng Ning Yang and a Chinese delegation led by Chuo Pei Yuan (see Fig. 1), including Fang Li-Zhi who had accompanied me during my entire first visit to China in 1979. The first truly international MG meeting followed in 1982 in Shanghai (China):this represented an especially important step forward both for the meeting and for China. A multi-millennia *"motto"* in China, which was then proclaimed on banners everywhere, read *"Friends from all over the world are welcomed"*.

We were soon at an impasse over the participation of scientists from Israel, since no diplomatic relations existed between China and Israel at that time and the Israeli scientists were not to be allowed to attend the meeting. A long negotiation began. The boundary conditions were clearly set by Steven Weinberg, a member of the present MG16 IOC: no MG meetings on Einstein's theory of general relativity could occur without the participation of Israeli scientists. The intervention of Yuval Ne'emann, also a member of the MG IOC then as well as the Minister of Science of Israel (see Fig.2), proposed a compromise that would admit at least one Israeli scientist. I went to Beijing alone, meeting every morning for a week with 12 Chinese representatives led by Chuo Pei Yuan going over all possible options. I stayed in an isolated villa not far from Tiananmen Square, accompanied by the 3 volumes of Matteo Ricci (RI MA TO) to keep me company. No solution was in sight the entire week. At the last moment, just before my departure, an agreement was finally reached allowing two Israeli scientists into China. The historic compromise would admit Gerard Tauber and Tsvi Piran into China using a special

Fig. 2: From right to left: Chaim Weizmann, President of Israel; Yuval Ne'emann, Minister of Science of Israel; R. Ruffini.

ICRA travel document I had proposed for them to be able to participate in the meeting, accepted by the Chinese Ambassador in Rome. This modified the thousand-year Chinese *"motto"* to read *"Scientists from all over the world are welcomed"*. The event was extremely beneficial for China and signaled the truly international nature of the MG meetings.

I kept on meeting Tauber in the years which followed (see Fig. 3). Soon after, Yuval Ne'emann visited China. The development of bilateral relations, including military cooperation and economical tights, grow exponentially until the establishment of normal diplomatic relations between Israel and China in 1992.

Fig. 3: From right to left: Arrigo Finzi, Remo Ruffini, Gerard Tauber and Konrad Bleuler.

Fig. 4: Albert Einstein, Hideki Yukawa and John. A. Wheeler with a handwritten dedication to Remo Ruffini "To Remo Ruffini, companion in the search for the deeper meaning of Einstein great theory. With warm regards, John Wheeler 5 April 1968".

Given their key role played in the foundations of the MG meetings, I am very happy to propose on behalf of the MG16 IOC, two special Marcel Grossmann Individual Awards: one to Steven Weinberg for *"for unwavering support for the MG meetings since their inception, a true companion in the search for the deeper meaning of Einstein's great theory"* and another one to Tsvi Piran, *"for extending Relativistic astrophysics across international frontiers, a true companion in the search for the deeper meaning of Einstein's great theory"*, in the words of John A. Wheeler's photo dedication to me (see Fig. 4).

Remo Ruffini

PREFACE

Since 1975, the Marcel Grossmann Meetings on Recent Developments in Theoretical and Experimental General Relativity, Gravitation, and Relativistic Field Theories have been organized in order to provide opportunities for discussing recent advances in gravitation, general relativity and relativistic field theories, emphasizing mathematical foundations, physical predictions and experimental tests. The objective of these meetings is to elicit exchange among scientists that may deepen our understanding of spacetime structures as well as to review the status of ongoing experiments aimed at testing Einstein's theory of gravitation either from the ground or from space. Previous meetings have been held in Trieste (MG1: 1975) and (MG2: 1979), Shanghai (MG3: 1982), Rome (MG4: 1985, MG9: 2000), Perth (MG5: 1988), Kyoto (MG6: 1991), Stanford (MG7: 1994), Jerusalem (MG8: 1997), Rio (MG10: 2003), Berlin (MG11: 2006), Paris (MG12: 2009), Stockholm (MG13: 2012), MG14 in 2015 and MG15 in 2018 both in Rome.

Due to the COVID-19 pandemic spreading in the last two years the decision was taken to organize the Sixteenth Marcel Grossmann meeting for the first time in history entirely online. Despite numerous challenges, related to the organization of large worldwide event, MG16 showed the strongest ever interest from the scientific community with a record-breaking number of almost 1200 registered participants and of more than 1000 speakers.

The traditional six-day schedule has been modified to account for different time zones of the speakers and each day the program of the meeting was divided in three blocks with the reference to the Central European Summer Time. The first block was starting at 06:30 in the morning, allowing comfortable time for speakers from Asia and Oceania. The second block was held in the daytime in Europe and Africa. The third block was starting in the afternoon and ending at 19:30 allowing accommodation of the speakers from the Americas. Each day the blocks of plenary sessions were interchanging with the blocks of about 30 parallel sessions each, making this one of the most intense MG meetings ever. All this was possible thanks to recent developments in communication technologies. The Indico open-source software was selected as a web platform for this meeting, while Zoom platform was adopted for the video-conferencing. The meeting was streamed on ICRANet YouTube channel.

The meeting started on Monday July 5 with the Award ceremony. The individual awards went to Demetrios Christodoulou, Tsvi Piran, Gerard 't Hooft and Steven Weinberg, while the Institutional Awards went to the S.A. Lavochkin Association, to the Max Planck Institute for Extraterrestrial Physics – MPE and to the Space Research Institute IKI of the Russian Academy of Sciences. Overall there were 54 plenary talks, 4 public lectures and 5 roundtables and about 90 parallel sessions. The plenary session "Events in Relativistics Astrophysics" on Monday have seen the contributions from Rashid Sunyaev, Michael Kramer, James Miller-Jones, Felix Mirabel. The public lectures were delivered by Razmik Mirzoyan, Asghar Qadir and Mohammad Bagheri. Plenary talks on Tuesday session "Black holes and the Quantum" by Juan Maldacena, Ahmed Almheiri, Gerard 't Hooft, Mihalis Dafermos, Sergiu Klainerman, Abhay Ashtekar and Frank Wilczek were bracketed by two roundtables on "New results from SRG/eRosita" with the participation of Andrea Merloni, Prof. Rashid Sunyaev, Alexander Lutovinov, Chandreyee Maitra, Esra Bulbul and "Solar neutrinos and Borexino" with the participation of Gianpaolo Bellini and Wick Haxton. Plenary talks on Wednesday in the session "Lambda CDM tensions" by George Efstathiou, Scolnic Daniel, Marc Kamionkowski, Wendy Freedman, Priya Natarajan and Licia Verde were followed by the roundtable "Precision cosmology" with the participation of Licia Verde, Marc Kamionkowski, Piero Rosati, and the public lecture by Francis Halzen. Two blocks of Thursday plenary sessions "Black holes in GRBs" and "Precision tests" included the talks by Roy Kerr, Yuan Ha, Lorenzo Amati, Elena Pian, Carlos Raúl Argüelles, Di Li, Jianglai Liu, Claus Lämmerzahl, Gerhard Heinzel and Ignazio Ciufolini and were followed by the roundtable "GRB 170817A and GRB 190829A" with the participation of Eleonora Troja, Liang Li, Rahim Moradi, Jorge Armando Rueda Hernandez. Two plenary blocks on Friday "Massive stars" and "Physics behind stellar collapse" included the talks by Selma de Mink, Norbert Langer, Jiri Bicak and Tomáš Ledvinka, Ivan De Mitri, Rahim Moradi and Giancarlo Cella. Finally, two plenary blocks on Saturday "Current and future missions" have seen the talks by Shuang-Nan Zhang, Weimin Yuan, Makoto Tashiro, Ruoyu Liu, Jean-Luc Atteia, Jim Hinton and Nicholas White and were followed by the roundtable "What is in our Galactic center" with the participation of Reinhard Genzel, Carlos Raúl Argüelles, Andreas Krut, Jorge Armando Rueda Hernandez, Eduar Becerra Vergara. The program of the meeting can be found at the official website http://www.icra.it/mg/mg16 and at ICRANet Indico website https://indico.icranet.org/event/1/.

These proceedings include about 400 papers containing the results presented at the Sixteenth Marcel Grossmann meeting. The plenary papers from the meeting have been published in International Journal of Modern Physics D as they were submitted. The table of contents includes also the links to YouTube videos with talks given at the meeting and cover plenary talks, public lectures, roundtables and all parallel sessions. The general link to the videos from MG16 is: https://www.youtube.com/watch?v=QFe1lsSid-o&list=PLr5RLbSWSonsaOnZukBDs0qsNIWM8AvRF.

As the editors we would like to express our gratitude to all the chairpersons of the parallel sessions at MG16, who peer-reviewed the papers submitted for these proceedings, as well as to the ICRANet secretariat office and in particular to Cinzia di Niccolo, Elisabetta Natale and Yasmina Di Domizio, as well as to ICRANet system manager Gabriele Brandolini for their help in preparation of this publication.

Remo Ruffini and Gregory Vereshchagin
November 2021

Contents

Publications in this Series	v
Sponsors and Acknowledgements	vii
Organizing Committees	ix
Marcel Grossmann Awards	xi
Preface	xxxvi

PART A
PLENARY SESSIONS

New results from testing relativistic gravity with radio pulsars *Michael Kramer*	3
Dragging of inertial frames by matter and waves *Jiří Bičák and Tomáš Ledvinka*	22
Probes of the progenitors, engines and physics behind stellar collapse *Chris L. Fryer*	39
The observation of high-energy neutrinos from the cosmos: Lessons learned for multimessenger astronomy *Francis Halzen*	59
The first results of PandaX-4T *Jianglai Liu on behalf of the PandaX Collaboration*	85
XRISM: X-ray imaging and spectroscopy mission *Makoto S. Tashiro and the XRISM team*	95
The SVOM mission *J.-L. Atteia, B. Cordier and J. Wei on behalf of the SVOM Collaboration*	104
Quantum field theory with boundary conditions at the horizons *Gerard 't Hooft*	133

The development of general relativity and the cosmological constant
Asghar Qadir 143

The irreducible mass of Christodoulou-Ruffini-Hawking mass formula
Yuan K. Ha 154

Reshaping our understanding on structure formation with the quantum nature of the dark matter
C. R. Argüelles, E. A. Becerra-Vergara, A. Krut et al. 164

First results of LHAASO
Ruo-Yu Liu for the LHAASO Collaboration 180

On the MG16 awards 2021
Remo Ruffini 196

The white dwarf binary merger model of GRB 170817A
J. A. Rueda, R. Ruffini, Liang Li et al. 217

PARALLEL SESSIONS

Accretion

• MHD Processes Near Compact Objects
Chairperson: Sergey Moiseenko
YouTube link: https://youtu.be/2WMTg06ZmV8

A semi-implicit multidimensional unstructured gas dynamical solver for astrophysical applications
Ilya A. Kondratyev and Sergey G. Moiseenko 242

Magnetized neutron stars propagating through a non-uniform ISM
O. D. Toropina, M. M. Romanova and R. V. E. Lovelace 255

Calculation of the kinetic coefficients of arbitrary degenerate electrons in magnetized dense matter
M. V. Glushikhina and G. S. Bisnovatyi-Kogan 264

Modeling of magnetic fields of accretion discs, using no-z- and RZ-approximations
M. V. Pashentseva and E. A. Mikhailov 272

• Accretion Discs and Jets
Chairpersons: Audrey Trova and Shokoufe Faraji
YouTube link: https://youtu.be/29Wj9RCVEKw

Limiting effects in tori clusters
D. Pugliese and Z. Stulchik 280

Hydrodynamical transport of angular momentum in accretion disks
in the presence of nonlinear perturbations due to noise
Subham Ghosh and Banibrata Mukhopadhyay 295

Properties of accretion disc models in the background quadrupole
Shokoufe Faraji 307

Magnetized tori around a uniformly accelerating black hole
Shokoufe Faraji and Audrey Trova 317

Multifrequency behaviour of high mass X-ray binaries
(Time lag between optical and X-ray outbursts)
Franco Giovannelli 321

Active Galactic Nuclei

• The Black Hole in M87
Chairpersons: Brian Punsly and Jorge Rueda
YouTube link: https://youtu.be/l1lTgksyJag

Rotation of the crescent image of M87* and polarization of its ESE hotspot
Krzysztof Nalewajko 339

Magnetic reconnection in jet-accretion disk systems
*Chandra B. Singh, Elisabete M. de Gouveia Dal Pino,
Luis H. S. Kadowaki et al.* 344

• Machine Learning in Astronomy: AGN, Transient Events, Cosmology and Others
Chairpersons: Rahim Moradi and Yu Wang
YouTube link: https://youtu.be/ErqrmMZQsBk

Exact fractal model of the universe and possible machine learning
methods for the verification of the fractality
A. A. Kirillov, E. P. Savelova and P. O. Vladykina 352

Estimating the photometric redshifts of galaxies and QSOs using
regression techniques in machine learning
A. Momtaz, M. H. Salimi and S. Shakeri 368

Deep learning in quasar physics
*F. Rastegar Nia, M. T. Mirtorabi, R. Moradi, Y. Wang
and A. Vafaei Sadr* 382

Cosmological density field emulation and gravitational wave inference
based on dimensionality reduction and supervised machine learning
Miguel Conceição, António da Silva and Alberto Krone-Martins ... 391

Unsupervised photometric detection of galaxy cluster candidates in
large surveys
Ana Carvalho, Alberto Krone-Martins and Antonio da Silva 409

• **Multiwavelength and Multi-Messenger Observations of Active Galactic Nuclei**
Chairpersons: Paolo Giommi and Narek Sahakyan

YouTube link: https://youtu.be/-Hyu2NQsExg

Time-dependent lepto-hadronic modeling of the emission processes in
blazar jets
S. Gasparyan, D. Bégué and N. Sahakyan 429

Multiwavelength study of high-redshift blazars
G. Harutyunyan and D. Israyelyan 445

Alternative Theories

• **Extended Theories of Gravity and Quantum Cosmology**
Chairpersons: Yi-Fu Cai and Wentao Luo

YouTube links: https://youtu.be/ADRr9DfV5zM
https://youtu.be/eOzpiC1cFkU
https://youtu.be/kYzJds_JIp8

Quantum gravity phenomenology from thermodynamics of spacetime
A. Alonso-Serrano and M. Liška 462

Gauge theory of gravity based on the correspondence between
the 1st and the 2nd order formalisms
David Benisty 479

$U(1)$ local strings in hybrid metric-Palatini gravity
Tiberiu Harko, Francisco S. N. Lobo and Hilberto M. R. da Silva 485

Inflationary supersymmetric FRLW quantum cosmology
N. E. Martínez-Pérez, C. Ramirez and V. M. Vázquez-Báez 499

Effective $f(R)$ actions for modified loop quantum cosmologies
Ana Rita Ribeiro, Daniele Vernieri and Francisco S. N. Lobo 517

Probing multiverse using gravitational wave observations
Moe Kukihara and Kazuhiro Hayama 531

Operator ordering ambiguity in observables of quantum cosmology
Harkirat Singh Sahota and Kinjalk Lochan 538

Decoupled quark stars in self-interacting Brans-Dicke gravity
M. Sharif and Amal Majid 548

Big-bounce in projectively invariant Nieh-Yan models: The Bianchi I case
*Flavio Bombacigno, Simon Boudet, Gonzalo J. Olmo
and Giovanni Montani* 561

Late time cosmology with derivatives of matter Lagrangian
Shahab Shahidi 576

On the semiclassical and quantum picture of the Bianchi I polymer dynamics
E. Giovannetti, G. Montani and S. Schiattarella 588

Quantum corrections to the Bianchi II transition under local rotational invariance
Sara F. Uria, David Brizuela and Ana Alonso-Serrano 597

- **Mathematical Problems of Relativistic Physics: Classical and Quantum**
Chairpersons: A. Shadi Tahvildar-Zadeh and Michael Kiessling

YouTube links: https://youtu.be/9Dr3M9Kb2jo
https://youtu.be/gMOykpapJ5A

The hypercomplex medium as storage of physical equations
Alexander P. Yefremov 605

The Maxwell-Bopp-Landé-Thomas-Podolsky-Einstein system for a static point source
Érik Amorim 619

On recent developments in the theory of relativistic dissipative fluids
V. Hoang 627

Adiabatic solutions in general relativity as null geodesics on the space of boundary diffeomorphisms
Emine Şeyma Kutluk 635

The point spectrum of the Dirac Hamiltonian on the zero-gravity Kerr-Newman spacetime
M. Kiessling, E. Ling and A. S. Tahvildar-Zadeh 648

Causal fermion systems: Classical gravity and beyond
Felix Finster 661

Newman-Penrose-Debye formalism for fields of various spins in pp-wave backgrounds
Aleksandr Kulitskii and Elena Yu Melkumova 679

Gravitational geometric phase
*Banibrata Mukhopadhyay, Tanuman Ghosh and
Soumya Kanti Ganguly* 689

Retarded potentials and radiation in odd dimensions
D. V. Gal'tsov and M. Khlopunov 699

Wave propagation in the anti-deSitter optical metric
D. García-Peláez and C. S. López-Monsalvo 713

New approaches to constrained dynamics and Hamilton-Jacobi
procedures in general relativity
D. Salisbury, J. Renn and K. Sundermeyer 719

Orientability of space from electromagnetic quantum fluctuations
N. A. Lemos and M. J. Rebouças 725

Essential self-adjointness of Dirac operators under the influence of
general-relativistic gravity
Michael K.-H. Kiessling, A. Shadi Tahvildar-Zadeh and Ebru Toprak 736

• **Wormholes, Energy Conditions and Time Machines**
Chairpersons: Francisco Lobo and Diego Rubiera-Garcia

YouTube links: https://youtu.be/tu_3Wqcd9Ys
https://youtu.be/NqN1c-2fv8Y

Relic magnetic wormholes as possible source of toroidal magnetic
fields in galaxies
A. A. Kirillov and E. P. Savelova 743

Wormhole geometries induced by action-dependent Lagrangian theories
Ismael Ayuso, Francisco S. N. Lobo and José P. Mimoso 756

Gravitational lensing by wormholes in binary systems
S. Pietroni 774

Hyper-fast positive energy warp drives
E. W. Lentz 779

From black-bounce to traversable wormhole, and beyond
Alex Simpson 787

Tractor beams, pressor beams, and stressor beams within the context
of general relativity
Matt Visser, Jessica Santiago and Sebastian Schuster 808

A singularity theorem for evaporating black holes
E.-A. Kontou, B. Freivogel and D. Krommydas 822

Circularly symmetric thin-shell wormholes in F(R) gravity with
(2+1)-dimensions
Cecilia Bejarano, Ernesto F. Eiroa and Griselda Figueroa-Aguirre 831

Warp drive dynamic solutions considering different fluid sources
*Osvaldo L. Santos-Pereira, Everton M. C. Abreu and
Marcelo B. Ribeiro* 840

Symmetries and geometry of spacetime: Towards a new paradigm
Francisco Cabral, Francisco S. N. Lobo and Diego Rubiera-Garcia 856

- **Theories of gravity: Alternatives to the cosmological and particle standard models**
Chairpersons: Stefano Bellucci and Orlando Luongo

YouTube links: https://youtu.be/-aQcrYoQfBM
https://youtu.be/WsCwPb5OQhY
https://youtu.be/JMnrUfBgqVU
https://youtu.be/pPhZY-bbsew

Thermodynamics of scalar-tensor gravity: A new approach
Valerio Faraoni 876

Two body dynamics in a quadratic modification of general relativity
Soham Bhattacharyya 883

Alternatives to Λ: Torsion, generalized couplings, and scale invariance
C. J. A. P. Martins, C. M. J. Marques, C. B. D. Fernandes et al. 907

Model-independent test of scalar-tensor gravity theory by
reconstructing scalar mode of GW170817
Yuya Gushima and Kazuhiro Hayama 921

Cosmology in the novel scalar-tensor representation of $f(R,T)$ gravity
Tiago B. Gonçalves, João Luís Rosa and Francisco S. N. Lobo 932

On the interaction between electromagnetic, gravitational, and plasma
related perturbations on LRS class II spacetimes
P. Semrén 943

Condition for expansion-collapse duality between Einstein and
Jordan frames
Dipayan Mukherjee, H. K. Jassal and Kinjalk Lochan 958

The model of dark energy based on the quantum-mechanical
uncertainty relation
Yu. V. Dumin 967

- **Conformal Dilaton Gravity and Related Issues**
Chairperson: Reinoud Jan Slagter

YouTube link: https://youtu.be/A3Ygi3YBs5A

Conformal dilaton gravity, antipodal mapping and black hole physics
on a warped spacetime
R. J. Slagter 978

From neutrino masses to the full size of the universe — Some
intriguing aspects of the tetron model
B. Lampe 999

Summary parallel session AT5
Reinoud Jan Slagter 1014

- **Horava-Lifshitz Gravity**
Chairperson: Anzhong Wang

YouTube links: https://youtu.be/vPT1dH1zITE
https://youtu.be/5z7zhpiDOpw

Boundary conditions for the Klein-Gordon field on Lifshitz spacetimes
Lissa de Souza Campos 1017

Dynamical system analysis of Bianchi-I spacetimes in $f(R)$ gravity
Saikat Chakraborty, Kazuharu Bamba and Alberto Saa 1026

Cosmological implications in modified Hořava-Lifshitz gravity
Abdul Jawad, Kazuharu Bamba and Farwa Khurshid 1038

Finite action principle and wormholes
Jan Chojnacki and Jan Kwapisz 1046

Strange quark stars in Hořava gravity
Grigoris Panotopoulos 1054

Shadows of Kerr-like black holes in $4D$ Einstein–Gauss–Bonnet
gravity and constraints from EHT observations
Sushant G. Ghosh and Rahul Kumar Walia 1069

Wormhole interaction in 2d Horǎva-Lifshitz quantum gravity
Jan Ambjørn, Yuki Hiraga, Yoshiyasu Ito and Yuki Sato 1084

Nature of singularities in vector-tensor theories of gravity
V. H. Satheeshkumar 1095

Hořava-Lifshitz and Einstein-Æther gravity in the light of Event Horizon Telescope observations of M87*
Emmanuel N. Saridakis 1104

Hořava-Lifshitz gravity in $(3+1)$ dimensions coupled with anisotropic matter and possible constraints from GRB 170817A
Tao Zhang and Fu-Wen Shu 1112

Summary of the parallel session AT6
Anzhong Wang 1119

• **Ghost-Free Models of Modified Gravity: Massive Gravity, Horndeski and DHOST Theories, Other Related Models; Their Properties and Solutions**
Chairpersons: Dmitry Gal'tsov and Michael Volkov

YouTube links: https://youtu.be/l8KHUPnT2D8
https://youtu.be/48OHIKpgNqs

Non-local R^2-like inflation, gravitational waves and Non-Gaussianities
K. Sravan Kumar 1124

Palatini kinetic scalar-tensor theory: Analytical and numerical solutions
D. V. Gal'tsov and D. S. Bushuev 1136

PART B

Black Holes: Theory and Observations/Experiments

• **Theoretical and Observational Studies of Astrophysical Black Holes**
Chairperson: Alexander Zakharov

YouTube links: https://youtu.be/fiv_MH-N2kw
https://youtu.be/GYoOb17GvE8

Reconstruction of a star motion in the vicinity of black hole from the redshift of the electromagnetic spectrum
S. O. Komarov and A. K. Gorbatsievich 1151

Shadows of hairy Kerr black holes and constraints from M87*
Sushant G. Ghosh and Misba Afrin 1167

Displacement memory and BMS symmetries
Shailesh Kumar 1179

Physical black holes in semiclassical gravity
Sebastian Murk and Daniel R. Terno 1196

- **Black Hole Thermodynamics**
  Chairperson: Hernando Quevedo

  YouTube links: https://youtu.be/XmZDf5mrXQk
  https://youtu.be/amseL2qykfk

Information recovery from evaporating rotating charged black holes
Zhi-Wei Wang, Samuel L. Braunstein and Saurya Das 1212

Black hole thermodynamics from entanglement mechanics
S. Mahesh Chandran and S. Shankaranarayanan 1223

Thermodynamics of charged black hole
M. Sharif and Amjad Khan 1238

Rindler trajectories and Rindler horizons in the Schwarzschild spacetime
Kajol Paithankar and Sanved Kolekar 1250

Linear growth of the two-point function for the Unruh state in $1+1$ dimensional black holes
Paul R. Anderson, Zachary P. Scofield and Jennie Traschen 1255

Stress-energy tensor for a quantized scalar field in a four-dimensional black hole that forms from the collapse of a null shell
Shohreh Gholizadeh Siahmazg, Paul R. Anderson, Raymond D. Clark and Alessandro Fabbri 1265

Microscopic model building for black hole membranes from constraints of symmetry
Swastik Bhattacharya and S. Shankaranarayanan 1275

Einstein-Maxwell-Dilaton-Axion mass formulas for black holes with struts and strings
Dmitri Gal'tsov, Gérard Clément and Igor Bogush 1291

- **Black Holes in Alternative Theories of Gravity**
  Chairpersons: Jutta Kunz and Kamal Hajian

  YouTube links: https://youtu.be/FRNGJKhiw7c
  https://youtu.be/Tjfmuut1Eo0

Holography for rotating black holes in $f(T)$ gravity
Masoud Ghezelbash 1308

Infinitely degenerate exact Ricci-flat solutions in $f(R)$ gravity
Semin Xavier, Jose Mathew and S. Shankaranarayanan 1319

Universe in a black hole with spin and torsion
Nikodem Popławski 1327

Asymptotically flat black hole solution in modified gravity
Surajit Kalita and Banibrata Mukhopadhyay 1337

Shadow of a charged black hole surrounded by an anisotropic matter field
Javier Badía and Ernesto F. Eiroa 1343

Constraining modified gravity theories with physical black holes
Sebastian Murk 1351

Penrose suggestion as to pre-Planck-era black holes showing up in present universe data sets discussed, with a possible candidate as to GW radiation which may provide initial CMBR data
A. W. Beckwith 1359

Summary of the parallel session BH3
Kamal Hajian and Jutta Kunz 1372

Binaries

• Explosive Events Associated with Compact-Object Binary Mergers
Chairpersons: Chris Belczynski and Jorge Rueda

YouTube links: https://youtu.be/Dwq1ZU3gKrg
https://youtu.be/nw02ylI6R2M

Uncertainties in kilonova modeling
C. L. Fryer, C. J. Fontes, O. Korobkin et al. 1391

• Post-Newtonian and Post-Minkowskian Corrections for Binary Gravitating Systems
Chairperson: Johannes Bluemlein

YouTube link: https://youtu.be/wfiLG5r08yE

Tutti-Frutti method: Recent developments in the PN/PM/SF treatment of the gravitational two-body problem
Donato Bini and Andrea Geralico 1405

• Multichannel Studies of Nonstationary Relativistic Stars
Chairperson: Vladimir Lipunov

YouTube link: https://youtu.be/usn2PlU_qFA

GRB observations on cubesate satellites in the Universat–SOCRAT project
Sergey I. Svertilov, Michail I. Panasyuk, Vitaly V. Bogomolov et al. 1412

Multiwavelength observations of GRB160625B by MASTER,
Lomonosov, Konus-Wind and three stage collapse
V. M. Lipunov, V. A. Sadovnichy, M. I. Panasyuk et al. 1429

The role of the magnetic fields in GRB outflows
N. Jordana-Mitjans, C. G. Mundell, S. Kobayashi et al. 1449

MASTER optical observations of the blazar TXS0506+056 during the IC170922A
V. M. Lipunov, K. Zhirkov, V. G. Kornilov et al. 1467

Boson Stars

• Scalar Fields in Cosmology
Chairpersons: Carlos Herdeiro and Alfredo Macias

YouTube links: https://youtu.be/SyLoguueGKk
https://youtu.be/f9nuo8Jvw-w

A short review on nonlinear perturbation theory of structure formation for modified gravity
Jorge L. Cervantes-Cota and Alejandro Aviles 1474

Testing modified gravity theories with marked statistics
Alejandro Aviles 1494

Dark matter as condensed phase of generic bosons
Elías Castellanos and Jorge Mastache 1513

Cosmic Microwave Background

• Cosmic Backgrounds from Radio to Far-IR
Chairperson: Carlo Burigana

YouTube link: https://youtu.be/4e3Cj5wahck

New Planck tSZ map and its cosmological analysis
H. Tanimura, M. Douspis and N. Aghanim 1527

The CMB dipole: Eppur si muove
R. M. Sullivan and D. Scott 1532

High angular resolution Sunyaev Zel'dovich observations: The case of MISTRAL
E. S. Battistelli, E. Barbavara, P. de Bernardis et al. 1542

Cosmological and astrophysical results exploiting magnification bias with high-z sub-millimetre galaxies
L. Bonavera, M. M. Cueli and J. Gonzalez-Nuevo 1557

The impact of the Lorentz symmetry violation on the CMB polarization
Seddigheh Tizchang, Rohoollah Mohammadi and She-Sheng Xue 1571

Cosmic backgrounds from the radio to the far-infrared: Recent results and perspectives from cosmological and astrophysical surveys
Carlo Burigana, Elia Sefano Battistelli, Laura Bonavera et al. 1579

- **New Horizons in Cosmology with CMB Spectral Distortions**

Chairpersons: Jens Chluba and Andrea Ravenni

YouTube links: https://youtu.be/uBYLO4Smw3o
https://youtu.be/5oAPfzAe35k

CMB μT cross-correlations as a probe of PBH scenarios
Ogan Özsoy and Gianmassimo Tasinato 1609

Theoretical and numerical aspects of CMB spectral distortions from non-thermal energy injections
Sandeep Kumar Acharya, Jens Chluba and Abir Sarkar 1628

BISOU: A balloon project to measure the CMB spectral distortions
B. Maffei, M. H. Abitbol, N. Aghanim et al. 1633

Cosmic microwave background spectral distortions constraints on decaying dark matter particles and axion-like particles using *COBE/FIRAS* and *EDGES*
Boris Bolliet 1645

The COSmic Monopole Observer (COSMO)
S. Masi, E. Battistelli, P. de Bernardis et al. 1654

- **Status of the H_0 and σ_8 Tensions: Theoretical Models and Model-Independent Constraints**

Chairpersons: Joan Solà Peracaula and Adrià Gómez-Valent

YouTube links: https://youtu.be/VNWZ1Bzjus4
https://youtu.be/zEBOCwvetKE
https://youtu.be/nzgC7qV9H_Y

Measuring the Hubble constant H_0 from gravitational lensing
Liliya L. R. Williams 1672

Extra components consistency in the Hubble tension and BBN
Osamu Seto and Yo Toda 1686

Gravitational anomalies, axions and a string-inspired running vacuum model in Cosmology
Nick E. Mavromatos 1693

Early and not so early dark energy. What do cosmological observations tell us about them?
Adrià Gómez-Valent, Ziyang Zheng, Luca Amendola, Valeria Pettorino and Christof Wetterich 1713

Renormalized ρ_{vac} without m^4 terms
Cristian Moreno-Pulido and Joan Solà Peracaula 1733

BD-ΛCDM and running vacuum models: Theoretical background and current observational status
Javier de Cruz Pérez, Joan Solà Peracaula, Adrià Gómez-Valent and Cristian Moreno-Pulido 1752

Cosmological tensions: Hints for a new concordance model?
E. Di Valentino 1770

Solving both H_0 and σ_8 tensions in $f(T)$ gravity
Emmanuel N. Saridakis 1783

Precision Cosmology and Hubble tension in the era of LSS surveys
G. Fanizza 1792

• **Effects of Primordial Perturbations Enhancement: From Black Holes Formation to CMB Anomalies**
Chairpersons: Antonio Enea Romano and Krzysztof Turzynski
YouTube link: https://youtu.be/frjjONXbd1M

Primordial black holes arise when the inflaton falls
Keisuke Inomata 1803

Effects of the modification of gravity on the production of primordial black holes
Sergio Andrés Vallejo Peña 1809

Cosmic Strings

• **Cosmic Strings**
Chairpersons: Reinoud Jan Slagter and Batool Imtiaz
YouTube link: https://youtu.be/ZpaU82ZUHzM

$U(1)$ local strings in generalized hybrid metric-Palatini gravity
Hilberto M. R. da Silva, Tiberiu Harko, Francisco S. N. Lobo and João Luís Rosa 1820

New evidence of the azimuthal alignment of quasars spin vector in Large Quasar Groups and cosmic strings
R. J. Slagter 1835

Summary parallel session cosmic strings I
Reinoud Jan Slagter and Batool Imtiaz 1848

- **From Cosmic Strings to Superstrings**
Chairpersons: Carlos Martins and Ivan Rybak
YouTube link: https://youtu.be/LJFtV_4aSAg

Scaling solutions of wiggly cosmic strings
A. R. R. Almeida and C. J. A. P. Martins 1851

High resolution calibration of string network evolution
J. R. C. C. C. Correia and C. J. A. P. Martins 1871

Radiation from Global Cosmic Strings using adaptive mesh refinement
Amelia Drew and E. P. S. Shellard 1891

Analysing the scaling density of axion strings
A. Lopez-Eiguren 1898

Electroweak axion string and superconductivity
Yu Hamada, Yoshihiko Abe and Koichi Yoshioka 1912

Dark Energy and Large Scale Structure

- **Dark Energy and the Accelerating Universe**
Chairpersons: Alexei Starobinky and David Polarski
YouTube links: https://youtu.be/JZEPRS_rqbE
https://youtu.be/3aG_AT4UzWE
https://youtu.be/ZlTWquG-pFk

Hints for the $H_0 - r_d$ tension in uncorrelated Baryon Acoustic Oscillations dataset
Denitsa Staicova 1923

Observational constraints on nonlinear matter extensions of general relativity
E.-A. Kolonia and C. J. A. P. Martins 1935

Constraining the dark energy-dark matter interaction model using low-redshift observations
Archana Sangwan, Joseph P. J. and S. Shankaranarayanan 1948

On the evolution of inhomogeneous perturbations in the ΛCDM model and $f(R)$ modified gravity theories
T. Schiavone and G. Montani 1961

Soft dark energy and soft dark matter
Emmanuel N. Saridakis 1970

A simple parametrisation for coupled dark energy
Vitor da Fonseca, Nelson J. Nunes and Tiago Barreiro 1979

- **Cosmography with Gravitational Lensing**
Chairpersons: Claudio Grillo and Mimoza Hafizi

YouTube link: https://youtu.be/FXplIAvUDBM

A tale of two double quasars: Hubble constant tension or biases?
L. J. Goicoechea and V. N. Shalyapin 1990

Dark Matter

- **Interacting Dark Matter**
Chairpersons: Nikolaos Mavromatos

YouTube links: https://youtu.be/zOshKJlwD-Y
https://youtu.be/JR44dh2GYik

Dark energy and dark matter unification from dynamical space time: BBN constraints
D. Benisty 2005

Entropy and irreversible processes in gravity and cosmology
Llorenç Espinosa-Portalés and Juan García-Bellido 2013

LHC experiments for long-lived particles of the dark sector
Vasiliki A. Mitsou 2029

Constraining the interactions in the dark sector with cosmological data
Adrià Gómez-Valent, Valeria Pettorino and Luca Amendola 2050

Running vacuum interacting with dark matter or with running gravitational coupling. Phenomenological implications
Joan Solà Peracaula 2069

Dark matter properties from the Fornax globular cluster timing: Dynamical friction and cored profiles
D. Blas 2089

Growth of linear perturbations in a universe with superfluid dark matter
S. Banerjee, S. Bera and D. F. Mota 2101

Interacting dark sector in the late Universe: Mapping fields and fluids, and observational signatures
Joseph P. J. and S. Shankaranarayanan 2119

The role of self interactions in the cosmological evolution of warm dark matter
R. Yunis, C. R. Argüelles, D. López Nacir et al. 2127

Interaction energy between a charged medium and its electromagnetic field as a dark matter candidate
Mayeul Arminjon 2139

- **Dark Matter Searches with Liquid Xenon and Argon Detectors and Self Gravitating Systems and Dark Matter**

Chairpersons: Marco Merafina and Soroush Shakeri and She-Sheng Xue

YouTube link: https://youtu.be/H9oGYnGq9pI

The maximum mass of dilute axion stars
Pierre-Henri Chavanis 2149

A dark matter solution for the XENON1T electron excess and the galactic center 511 keV line
Yasaman Farzan 2174

Preliminary results of rich galaxy clusters' spatial distribution analysis on CfA2 Redshift Survey data: Compact objects or dark matter presence at redshift less 0.032
I. V. Arkhangelskaja, A. M. Galper, L. N. Khanh and D. N. Dorosheva 2189

- **Dark Matter: Beyond ΛCDM**

Chairpersons: Carlos Argüelles and Andreas Krut

YouTube links: https://youtu.be/hdKeo5L7pYE
https://youtu.be/i0IPHXzmV-s

Probing the nature of dark matter with Milky Way subhaloes
M. R. Lovell 2202

Addressing classical cosmological back-reaction with multiple scales
Yonadav Barry Ginat 2217

Imaging formation process for DM profiles
Omar de J. Cabrera-Rosas and Tonatiuh Matos 2222

The self-gravitating Fermi gas in Newtonian gravity and general relativity
Pierre-Henri Chavanis 2230

- **Dark Matter and Rare Processes**

Chairpersons: Carlos Rita Bernabei and Zurab Berezhiani

YouTube links: https://youtu.be/wheVrbETP_0
https://youtu.be/dVdZ4TIDxt0

The dark matter: DAMA/LIBRA and its perspectives
R. Bernabei, P. Belli, V. Caracciolo et al. 2252

Dark matter directionality approach
R. Bernabei, P. Belli, V. Caracciolo et al. 2272

Collapse models under test by high sensitivity γ-ray and X-ray measurements
C. Curceanu, Kristian Piscicchia, Massimiliano Bazzi et al. 2288

Leptophilic dark matter at linear colliders
P. S. Bhupal Dev 2296

DM6 session: Dark matter and rare processes
R. Bernabei and Z. Berezhiani 2316

• **The Nature of Galactic Halos**
Chairpersons: Francesco De Paolis and Asghar Qadir
YouTube link: https://youtu.be/qIwVnNxi0n0

Primordial black holes as dark matter candidates in the Galactic halo
Lindita Hamolli, Mimoza Hafizi, Francesco De Paolis and Achille A. Nucita 2319

Giant cosmic ray halos around M31 and the Milky Way
S. Recchia, S. Gabici, F. A. Aharonian and V. Niro 2335

A nearly complete census of intergalactic gas using the kinematic Sunyaev-Zel'dovich effect
Chaves-Montero, Jonás 2345

Searching for Intermediate Mass Black Holes in the Milky Way's galactic halo
A. Franco, A. A. Nucita, F. De Paolis, F. Strafella and M. Maiorano . . . 2352

Virial clouds evolution from the last scattering up to the formation of first stars
Noraiz Tahir, Asghar Qadir, Muhammad Sakhi and Francesco De Paolis 2360

Testing Weyl-modified gravity on M31 and Milky Way
Muhammad Bilal and Asghar Qadir 2365

PART C

Education

• **Teaching Einsteinian Physics to School Students**
Chairpersons: David Blair and Matteo Luca Ruggiero
YouTube links: https://youtu.be/W-WV6J8kprg
https://youtu.be/UHYpwKQ09SU

Teaching relativity: A paradigm change
F. Herrmann and M. Pohlig 2371

Teaching relativity: Computer-aided modeling
F. Herrmann and M. Pohlig 2381

Solstices and Equinoxes in 1703 at the meridian line of St. Maria degli Angeli in Rome, and the stellar aberration of Sirius
Costantino Sigismondi and Silvia Pietroni 2388

Positional astrometry at arcsecond accuracy using historical instruments, with light equipment
Costantino Sigismondi and Lorenzo Ricciardi 2398

Daily, seasonal, and equinoctial solar paths on a school soccer field
Costantino Sigismondi 2411

Teaching relativity at the AstroCamp
C. J. A. P. Martins 2415

Sungrazing comets as General Relativistic gravitational probes
Silvia Pietroni and Costantino Sigismondi 2424

The three Summer solstice's markers of 1721 unveiled in the Basilica of Santa Maria degli Angeli in Rome
Costantino Sigismondi 2428

Einstein-First: Bringing children our best understanding of reality
A. Popkova, K. Adams, S. Boublil et al. 2438

Exact Solutions

• Exact Solutions in Four and Higher Dimensions
Chairpersons: David Blair and Matteo Luca Ruggiero
YouTube link: https://youtu.be/GHZUS5-4gVQ

Kundt spacetimes in the Einstein–Gauss–Bonnet theory
R. Švarc, J. Podolský and O. Hruška 2453

Exact decoupled solutions in curvature-matter coupled gravity
M. Sharif and Fizza Furqan 2464

Tolman-Oppenheimer-Volkov conditions beyond spherical symmetry
José P. Mimoso, Alan Maciel and Morgan Le Delliou 2479

A spherically symmetric stiff fluid spacetime in light of cosmic structure formation
Daniele Gregoris 2497

- **Exact Solutions (Including Higher Dimensions)**
Chairperson: Susan Scott

YouTube link: https://youtu.be/-hJjJvmmOew

Three-parameter solution for the null-surface formulation in
2+1 dimensions
Tina A. Harriott and J. G. Williams 2510

New exact stationary cylindrical anisotropic fluid solution of GR
M.-N. Célérier 2522

Early Universe

- **Quantum Fields**
Chairperson: Andrei Lebed

YouTube links: https://youtu.be/BLaTp0r0TkQ
https://youtu.be/ZifgaSDy5Vc

Hydrodynamic representation and energy balance for the Dirac and
Weyl fermions in curved space-times
Tonatiuh Matos, Omar Gallegos and Pierre-Henri Chavanis 2533

Breakdown of the Equivalence Principle for a composite quantum body
A. G. Lebed 2551

Extended DeWitt-Schwinger subtraction scheme, heavy fields and
decoupling
Antonio Ferreiro and Jose Navarro-Salas 2557

Renormalization and decoupling for the Yukawa model in curved
spacetime
Sergi Nadal-Gisbert, Antonio Ferreiro and José Navarro-Salas 2562

Trace anomaly and evaporation of spherical black holes
P. Meda 2573

On decay of the false Unruh vacuum
A. Shkerin 2587

Behaviour of noise kernel in de Sitter and FRW space-times
Ankit Dhanuka and Kinjalk Lochan 2600

Breaking Buchdahl: Ultracompact stars in semiclassical gravity
*Julio Arrechea, Carlos Barceló, Raúl Carballo-Rubio and
Luis J. Garay* 2608

Einstein anomaly with tensors of odd order in six dimensional curved space
Kohei Yamamoto and Satoshi Yajima 2619

Quantum memory and BMS symmetries
Sanved Kolekar and Jorma Louko 2623

• **Topological Methods, Global Existence Problems, and Spacetime Singularities**
Chairperson: Spiros Cotsakis
YouTube link: https://youtu.be/H8Itnc_C10c

Gravitational singularities, scattering maps for bouncing, and structure-preserving algorithms
Philippe G. LeFloch 2630

Brane-world asymptotics in a nonlinear fluid bulk
I. Antoniadis, S. Cotsakis and Ifigeneia Klaoudatou 2645

Primordial synchronization of Mixmaster spatial points
Spiros Cotsakis 2657

• **The Early Universe**
Chairperson: Stefano Ansoldi
YouTube links: https://youtu.be/m80hHWgOlFs
https://youtu.be/6tyaZ8MMVtw

Quintessential inflation from Lorentzian slow roll
David Benisty 2663

Condensed light, quantum black holes and L-CDM cosmology: Experimentally suggested and tested unified approach to dark matter, dark energy, cosmogenesis and two-stage inflation
Victor Borsevici 2672

Helical magnetic fields lead to baryogenesis
Ashu Kushwaha and S. Shankaranarayanan 2692

Polymer Quantization of the Isotropic Universe: Comparison with the Bounce of Loop Quantum Cosmology
G. Barca, E. Giovannetti, F. Mandini and G. Montani 2700

General relativistic evolution equations for density perturbations in open, flat and closed FLRW universes and the problem of structure formation
Pieter G. Miedema 2708

Constraining beyond ΛCDM models with 21cm intensity mapping
forecast observations combined with latest CMB data
M. Berti 2726

Entropy and irreversible processes in gravity and cosmology
Llorenç Espinosa-Portalés and Juan García-Bellido 2737

Fundamental Interactions and Stellar Evolution

• Why and How the Sun and the Stars Shine: The Borexino Experiment

Chairpersons: Giampaolo Bellini, Dmitry Naumov, Gioacchino Ranucci, Gemma Testera

YouTube links: https://youtu.be/hh5wDnM8miU
https://youtu.be/TG-HgBf7W4s
https://youtu.be/HLiis2LFeEs

Experimental detection of the CNO cycle
B. Caccianiga, N. Rossi, G. Testera et al. 2753

Borexino detector performances
A. Caminata, M. Agostini, K. Altenmüller et al. 2765

Study of antineutrinos from the Earth and the Cosmos with the
Borexino detector
Sandra Zavatarelli, M. Agostini, K. Altenmuller et al. 2774

Unveiling the engine of the Sun: Measurements of the *pp*-chain solar
neutrinos with Borexino
D. Guffanti, A. C. Re and O. Smirnov 2785

Electron neutrino survival probability in the energy range
200 keV–15 MeV
Marco Pallavicini on behalf of the Borexino Collaboration 2804

The relevance of pp-chain and CNO-cycle neutrino measurements for
solar physics
F. L. Villante and A. M. Serenelli 2815

Role of the CNO cycles in stars
A. Ianni 2835

Geoneutrino observation
Tadao Mitsui for the KamLAND Collaboration 2840

Synthesis of the session: Why and how the Sun and the stars shine
Gianpaolo Bellini 2845

- **Rotation in Stellar Evolution**
Chairperson: Georges Meynet
YouTube link: https://youtu.be/9LNoiwa0nv8

The internal rotation of low-mass stars from solar and stellar seismology
G. Buldgen and P. Eggenberger 2848

The rotation of supermassive stars
L. Haemmerlé 2865

Fast Transients

- **What Can We Learn from a Growing Sample of Fast Radio Bursts?**
Chairpersons: Duncan Lorimer, Victoria Kaspi and Bing Zhang
YouTube links: https://youtu.be/yo4n1SgfUrQ
https://youtu.be/NwGooPauhjU

Cosmology with high-redshift FRBs
A. Fialkov 2880

- **Non Standard Cosmological Probes**
Chairpersons: Duncan Lorimer, Victoria Kaspi and Bing Zhang
YouTube links: https://youtu.be/EEFUgiFeMck
https://youtu.be/Ryb15AINfMs

Closing the cosmological loop with the redshift drift
*C. J. A. P. Martins, C. S. Alves, J. Esteves, A. Lapel
and B. G. Pereira* 2890

Gamma-Ray Bursts as potential cosmological probes
L. Izzo 2906

Surface brightness fluctuations: The method and future applications
Michele Cantiello 2915

Preliminary results of analysis of Ia supernovae redshift distributions
on data of the Asiago Supernova and Open Supernova Catalogues
I. V. Arkhangelskaja 2930

- **Photospheric Emission in GRBs**
Chairpersons: Gregory Vereshchagin and Damien Bégué
YouTube links: https://youtu.be/ZifnzoUXIFc
https://youtu.be/n7vWAVhFXiU

Understanding prompt emission: Where do we stand?
Asaf Pe'er 2946

On explaining prompt emission from GRB central engines with
photospheric emission model
M. Bhattacharya and P. Kumar 2957

Monte Carlo simulations of photospheric emission in Gamma Ray Bursts
T. M. Parsotan and D. Lazzati 2972

The photosphere emission spectrum of hybrid relativistic outflow for
Gamma-Ray Bursts
Yan-Zhi Meng, Jin-Jun Geng and Xue-Feng Wu 2982

On diffusive photospheres in Gamma-Ray Bursts
G. V. Vereshchagin 2989

Summary of the parallel session GB3
G. V. Vereshchagin and D. Bégué 3002

- **High and Very High Energy Emission from Gamma-Ray Bursts**
Chairpersons: Francesco Longo and Fabian Schüssler

YouTube links: https://youtu.be/ZUkLyyYowaM
https://youtu.be/zwN1mNVeUzA

Synchrotron and synchrotron self-Compton emission components in
GRBs detected at very high energies
Jagdish C. Joshi, Vikas Chand and Soebur Razzaque 3009

The VERITAS gamma-ray burst follow-up program
D. Ribeiro for the VERITAS Collaboration 3017

MAGIC view of Gamma-Ray Bursts at very high energies
A. Berti on behalf of the MAGIC Collaboration 3030

Prospects for VHE monitoring of gamma-ray bursts with SWGO
G. La Mura, U. Barres de Almeida, R. Conceição et al. 3041

Theoretical implications on the very high energy emission from
GRB 190114C
*D. Miceli, A. Berti, Z. Bosnjak et al. on behalf of the
MAGIC Collaboration* 3052

AGILE and GRBs: 13 years of observations
A. Ursi on behalf of the AGILE Team 3062

Searching for Gamma-Ray Bursts with the High-Altitude Water
Cherenkov (HAWC) observatory
K. L. Engel for the HAWC Collaboration 3074

- **Electromagnetic Counterparts of Compact Binary Mergers**
Chairpersons: Jonathan Granot and Paz Beniamini

YouTube link: https://youtu.be/AS7bwaT48us

CALET search for gamma-ray counterparts of gravitational wave events
Masaki Mori for the CALET Collaboration 3084

- **Unusual and New Types of Gamma-Ray Bursts**
Chairperson: Binbin Zhang

YouTube link: https://youtu.be/VrF0iU8Q6us

Off-axis jet scenario for early afterglow emission of low-luminosity Gamma-Ray Burst GRB 190829A
Yuri Sato, Kaori Obayashi, Ryo Yamazaki, Kohta Murase and Yutaka Ohira 3095

- **Gamma-Ray Burst Correlations: Observational Challenges and Theoretical Interpretation**
Chairpersons: Maria Giovanna Dainotti and Liang Li

YouTube links: https://youtu.be/gcEy2h6y1jg
https://youtu.be/m2pCT6RAmI0
https://youtu.be/GTCvcVhBjN4

GRB prompt phase spectra under backscattering dominated model
Mukesh Kumar Vyas, Asaf Pe'er and David Eichler 3101

Applying models of pulsar wind nebulae to explain X-ray plateaux following short Gamma-Ray Bursts
L. C. Strang and A. Melatos 3107

Searching for strange quark planets
Xu Wang, Yong-Feng Huang and Bing Li 3118

Probe the universe by using Gamma-Ray Bursts with X-ray plateaus
Fan Xu and Yong-Feng Huang 3124

A new perspective on cosmology through Supernovae Ia and Gamma Ray Bursts
B. De Simone, V. Nielson, E. Rinaldi and M. G. Dainotti 3130

Theory of plateau phase in Gamma-Ray Bursts
Asaf Pe'er 3141

Exploring the canonical behaviour of long Gamma-Ray Bursts using an intrinsic multi-wavelength afterglow correlation
S. R. Oates, J. L. Racusin, M. De Pasquale et al. 3150

- **GRB 170817A and Binary Models**
Chairpersons: Marica Branchesi and Giulia Stratta
YouTube link: https://youtu.be/FRBvkaLX5WU

Kilonova emission observed so far: A comparison with AT2017gfo
A. Rossi 3162

- **Binary-Driven Hypernovae of Type 1, 2 and 3**
Chairpersons: Carlo Luciano Bianco, Christian Cherubini and Simonetta Filippi
YouTube link: https://youtu.be/8IFLfget3C0

Neutrinos and gamma-ray production from proton-proton interactions in binary-driven hypernovae framework
S. Campion, J. D. Melon Fuksman and J. A. Rueda Hernandez 3172

General relativistic turbulence in spherically symmetric core-collapse supernovae simulations
L. Boccioli, G. J. Mathews and E. P. O'Connor 3184

Gravitational Waves

- **Sources of Gravitational Waves**
Chairperson: Andrew Melatos
YouTube links: https://youtu.be/Lr8b9nKsFm4
https://youtu.be/xuqJOXPDyVY
https://youtu.be/qzOrgojHsMg
https://youtu.be/KCJoWMd71pE

Mountain formation by repeated, inhomogeneous crustal failure in a neutron star
A. D. Kerin and A. Melatos 3194

Gravitational waves from neutrino mass generating phase transitions
Nobuchika Okada and Osamu Seto 3206

Efficiency of registration of chirp bursts and signals of collapsing stars by the Euro-Asian network of GW interferometers
V. N. Rudenko, S. L. Andrusenko, D. P. Krichevskiy and G. D. Manucharyan 3219

Joint analysis method on gravitational waves and low-energy neutrinos to detect core-collapse supernovae
O. Halim, C. Casentini, M. Drago et al. 3228

- **Mid-frequency Gravitational Waves (0.1–10 Hz): Sources and Detection Methods**
Chairperson: Wei-Tou Ni
YouTube link: https://youtu.be/sJ6A7a73Vxw

A cryogenic and superconducting inertial sensor for the Lunar Gravitational–Wave Antenna, the Einstein Telescope and Selene-physics
F. Badaracco, J. V. van Heijningen, E. C. Ferreira and A. Perali 3245

Space gravitational wave antenna DECIGO and B-DECIGO
S. Kawamura and the DECIGO working group 3254

Summary of the parallel session GW2
Dongfeng Gao, Wei-Tou Ni, Jin Wang et al. 3261

- **Numerical Relativity and Gravitational Wave Observations**
Chairperson: Nigel Bishop
YouTube links: https://youtu.be/eZPytAU4Zmk
https://youtu.be/th-3KqkxDnU

Salient features of the optimised PyCBC IMBH search
Koustav Chandra, Archana Pai, V. Villa-Ortega et al. 3277

Matter shells modifying gravitational wave signals
Monos Naidoo, Nigel T. Bishop and Petrus J. van der Walt 3286

Odd-dimensional gravitational waves from a binary system on a three-brane
D. V. Gal'tsov and M. Khlopunov 3301

Developments in numerical relativity and gravitational wave observations
Nigel T. Bishop 3309

High Energy

- **Very High Energy Gamma Rays**
Chairpersons: Razmik Mirzoyan and Alessandro De Angelis
YouTube link: https://youtu.be/jHM1RH20ZyM

Insights into the Galactic Center environment from VHE gamma-ray observations with ground-based facilities
C. Fruck 3316

The TAIGA experiment
M. Tluczykont, I. I. Astapov, A. K. Awad et al. 3324

Science perspectives of the Southern Wide-field Gamma-ray Observatory (SWGO)
K. L. Engel for the SWGO Collaboration 3343

- **Future Missions for High-Energy Astrophysics**
Chairpersons: Filippo Frontera and Shaolin Xiong
YouTube link: https://youtu.be/JgDsZX6RUkU

Laue lenses: Focusing optics for hard X/soft Gamma-ray astronomy
L. Ferro, M. Moita, P. Rosati et al. 3355

ASTENA: A mission concept for a deep study of the transient
gamma-ray sky and for nuclear astrophysics
*E. Virgilli, F. Frontera, P. Rosati et al. on behalf of the
ASTENA Collaboration* 3368

Polarimetric prospects of a new hard X-soft gamma-ray space mission
for next decades
M. Moita, L. Ferro, F. Frontera et al. 3385

- **The SRG Mission: First Results from eROSITA and ART-XC**
Chairperson: Andrea Merloni
YouTube link: https://youtu.be/l0t1B716UcM

Prospect for WHIM detection in the cosmic web by *SRG/eROSITA*
H. Tanimura and N. Aghanim 3400

- **eXTP – Enhanced X-Ray Timing and Polarimetry Mission**
Chairpersons: Marco Feroci and Fangjun Lu
YouTube link: https://youtu.be/3d08eKmsImI

The role of eXTP in the multi-messenger astronomy era
G. Stratta and Gor Oganesyan 3403

- **Observations of HE and UHE Cosmic Rays**
Chairpersons: Ivan De Mitri and Fabio Gargano
YouTube link: https://youtu.be/l9DZyBMWO5c

CALET on the ISS: The first 5 years
Pier Simone Marrocchesi for the CALET Collaboration 3427

The fluxes of charged cosmic rays as measured by the DAMPE satellite
Paolo Bernardini on behalf of the DAMPE Collaboration 3442

Recent results from the Pierre Auger Observatory
E. Roulet for the Pierre Auger Collaboration 3449

The HERD space mission
F.C.T. Barbato on behalf of the HERD Collaboration 3455

PART D

History of Relativity

- **The "Fall and Rise" of Betelgeuse**
Chairperson: Costantino Sigismondi
YouTube link: https://youtu.be/VmbrE2gYmOM

The observation of the stars in daytime and near the horizon
Costantino Sigismondi and Paolo Ochner 3471

Fall and Rise of Betelgeuse: The summary of HR1 session
Costantino Sigismondi and Paolo Ochner 3475

Photometry of Betelgeuse at daylight
Otmar Nickel 3479

Evidence for dynamical changes in Betelgeuse using multi-wavelength data
Sneha Kachhara, Sandip V. George, Ranjeev Misra and G. Ambika 3485

The curious case of Betelgeuse
Jacco Th. van Loon 3494

Variable stars observed from city sites: The 2500 AAVSO-SGQ database
Costantino Sigismondi and Paolo Ochner 3501

Betelgeuse: An introductory course to observational astronomy
Costantino Sigismondi and Tiziana Pompa 3507

The meridian line of the Vatican obelisk to study the stellar aberration
Costantino Sigismondi and Lorenzo Ricciardi 3513

Betelgeuse, Sirius and the stars in the roman *Settecento*
Costantino Sigismondi 3519

- **History of Relativity, Gravitation and Cosmology**
Chairperson: Luis Crispino
YouTube link: https://youtu.be/RNbPUSp95PQ

On Einstein's last bid to keep a stationary cosmology
Salvador Galindo-Uribarri and Jorge L. Cervantes-Cota 3536

Jayme Tiomno: Relativity, gravity, cosmology, and the
Marcel Grossmann Meetings
William D. Brewer 3547

A look inside Feynman's route to gravitation
M. Di Mauro, S. Esposito and A. Naddeo 3563

Towards detecting gravitational waves: A contribution by
Richard Feynman
M. Di Mauro, S. Esposito and A. Naddeo 3576

Stellar gravitational collapse, singularity formation and theory breakdown
Kiril Maltsev 3596

The Hamilton-Jacobi analysis by Peter Bergmann and Arthur Komar
of classical general relativity
D. Salisbury 3626

- **Time and Philosophy in Physics**
Chairperson: Shokoufe Faraji

YouTube link: https://youtu.be/986v-V5JJEk

The passage of time and top-down causation
Barbara Drossel 3631

Explaining time's passage
Jonathan J. Dickau 3646

A glimpse to Feynman's contributions to the debate on the
foundations of quantum mechanics
M. Di Mauro, S. Esposito and A. Naddeo 3657

Summary of the parallel session HR3
Shokoufe Faraji 3671

Neutron Stars

- **Dense Matter in Compact Stars**
Chairpersons: Alessandro Drago and Jorge Rueda

YouTube links: https://youtu.be/U5Yr0oDVhqY
https://youtu.be/MvMDFh-1_bc

Massive compact stars in the two-families scenario
P. Char, A. Drago and G. Pagliara 3677

Quasi-universality of the magnetic deformation of neutron stars in
general relativity and beyond
J. Soldateschi, N. Bucciantini and L. Del Zanna 3684

Screening and elastic properties of the NS crust in the OCP
approximation
D. Barba González, C. Albertus Torres and M. A. Pérez-García ... 3703

Tidal deformability as a probe of dark matter in neutron stars
D. Rafiei Karkevandi, S. Shakeri, V. Sagun and O. Ivanytskyi ... 3713

Binary neutron star mergers with quark matter equations of state
Atul Kedia, Hee Il Kim, Grant Mathews and In-Saeng Suh 3732

Probing dense matter physics with transiently-accreting neutron stars: The case of source MXB 1659-29
Melissa Mendes, Andrew Cumming, Charles Gale and Farrukh J. Fattoyev 3736

• Compact Stars as Laboratories for Testing Strong Gravity
Chairpersons: Aurora Perez Martinez and César Augusto Zen Vasconcellos

YouTube link: https://youtu.be/C1KGecdNEfs

Vacuum properties and astrophysical implications
A. Pérez Martínez, M. Pérez-Garcia, E. Rodríguez Querts and A. Romero Jorge 3756

Testing extended theories of gravity with GRBs
L. Mastrototaro 3762

• Pulsar Power in Physics and Astrophysics and Pulsars and Pulsar Systems at High Energies
Chairpersons: Andrea Possenti and Pak-Hin Tam

YouTube links: https://youtu.be/gAG29DZwUbM
https://youtu.be/ytdUBFrViHI

News and views regarding PSR J1757–1854, a highly-relativistic binary pulsar
A. D. Cameron, M. Bailes, V. Balakrishnan et al. 3774

On the origin of the unique isolated X-Ray pulsar 1E 161348-5055 with 6.7 hr. spin period
V. Yu. Kim 3785

Advantages of including globular cluster millisecond pulsars in Pulsar Timing Arrays
M. Maiorano, F. De Paolis, A. A. Nucita and A. Franco 3791

Searching for pulsars in globular clusters with the MeerKAT Radio Telescope
F. Abbate on behalf of the MeerTIME/TRAPUM Collaboration 3799

Precision Tests

• Gravitational Lensing and Shadows
Chairpersons: Perlick Volker and Oleg Tsupko

YouTube links: https://youtu.be/6DXXWpMJ3IQ
https://youtu.be/F-K1gXn71_Y
https://youtu.be/B-V8r2HMztw

Gravitational lensing by rotating Simpson–Visser black holes
Sushant G. Ghosh and Shafqat Ul Islam 3812

Killing tensors in foliated spacetimes and photon surfaces
Igor Bogush, Kirill Kobialko and Dmitri Gal'tsov 3827

Decoding black hole metrics from the interferometric pattern of relativistic images
V. Bozza 3839

Symplectic evolution of an observed light bundle
N. Uzun 3844

Shadow of black holes with a plasma environment in 4D Einstein-Gauss-Bonnet gravity
Javier Badía and Ernesto F. Eiroa 3856

Aspects of neutrino mass hierarchy in gravitational lensing
Himanshu Swami 3865

Photon regions in stationary axisymmetric spacetimes and umbilic conditions
K. V. Kobialko and D. V. Gal'tsov 3874

Gravitational lensing by charged accelerating black holes
Torben C. Frost 3885

- **Experimental Gravitation**
Chairpersons: Angela di Virgilio and Claus Lammerzahl

YouTube link: https://youtu.be/mXcxztQ0nyk
https://youtu.be/tE3gIUBviTc

A manmade experiment aimed to clarify the gravity law in the Solar system
Alexander P. Yefremov and Alexandra A. Vorobyeva 3905

Gravitomagnetic field generation using high permittivity materials in superconducting magnetic energy storage devices
G. V. Stephenson 3910

Large ring laser gyroscopes: Geometry stabilization and laser control
U. Giacomelli, N. Beverini, G. Carelli et al. 3920

Dark gravitomagnetism with LISA and gravitational waves space detectors
A. Tartaglia, M. Bassan, G. Pucacco, V. Ferroni and D. Vetrugno 3929

Light rays in the Solar system experiments: Phases and displacements
Pravin Kumar Dahal and Daniel R. Terno 3942

The Ginger project – preliminary results
C. Altucci, F. Bajardi, A. Basti et al. 3956

• **Variation of the Fundamental Constants, Tests of the Fundamental Symmetries and Probes of the Dark Sector**
Chairpersons: Angela Victor Flambaum and Yevgeny Stadnik
YouTube links: https://youtu.be/NAZA-0tWHak
https://youtu.be/juhDGBJ12Lg
https://youtu.be/zxGgDP2sn60

Varying fundamental constants and dark energy in the ESPRESSO era
C. J. A. P. Martins 3963

• **Dragging is Never Draggy: MAss and CHarge Flows in GR**
Chairperson: Oldrich Semerak
YouTube link: https://youtu.be/ho31IgLNxu8

Testing the general relativistic nature of the Milky Way rotation curve with Gaia DR2
Mariateresa Crosta 3970

Spinning cylinders in general relativity: A canonical form for the Lewis metrics of the Weyl class
L. Filipe O. Costa, José Natário and N. O. Santos 3982

Magnetized black holes: The role of rotation, boost, and accretion in twisting the field lines and accelerating particles
Ondřej Kopáček and Vladimír Karas 3999

Spinning particle: Is Newton-Wigner the only way?
V. Witzany 4010

Gravitomagnetic resonance and gravitational waves
Matteo Luca Ruggiero and Antonello Ortolan 4019

Quantum Gravity

• **Loop Quantum Gravity**
Chairpersons: Marcin Kisielowski and Jerzy Lewandowski
YouTube links: https://youtu.be/VaLPseYWh9E
https://youtu.be/WFIgMqrQ07U

Studying the EPRL spinfoam self-energy
Pietropaolo Frisoni 4026

A spin foam framework for the black-to-white hole transition
Farshid Soltani 4045

Holographic properties of the bulk-to-boundary transmission of information in regions of quantum space
Eugenia Colafranceschi 4062

- **Quantum Gravity Phenomenology**
Chairpersons: Giovanni Amelino-Camelia and Jerzy Kowalski-Glikman

YouTube links: https://youtu.be/vYnVb2zNl0o
https://youtu.be/icK8z80Hm-Y
https://youtu.be/svXLa0yhyYY

Minimal length discretization and properties of modified metric tensor and geodesics
Abdel Nasser Tawfik, Fady T. Farouk, F. Salah Tarabia and Muhammad Maher 4074

The structure of the multiverse from the entanglement entropy
Samuel Barroso Bellido 4082

Effective field theory from relativistic Generalized Uncertainty Principle
Vasil N. Todorinov, Saurya Das and Pasquale Bosso 4088

Stelle gravity as the limit of quantum gravity with maximal momentum
V. Nenmeli, S. Shankaranarayanan, V. Todorinov and S. Das 4107

Baryon asymmetry and minimum length
Saurya Das, Mitja Fridman, Gaetano Lambiase and Elias C. Vagenas ... 4114

On quantum gravity and quantum gravity phenomenology
Douglas Edmonds, Djordje Minic and Tatsu Takeuchi 4126

WKB approach to the gravity-matter dynamics: A cosmological implementation
G. Maniccia and G. Montani 4146

Natural evidence for fuzzy sphere noncommutative geometry: Super-Chandrasekhar white dwarfs
Surajit Kalita, T. R. Govindarajan and Banibrata Mukhopadhyay 4159

A model of polymer gravitational waves: Theory and some possible observational consequences
Angel Garcia-Chung, James B. Mertens, Saeed Rastgoo, Yaser Tavakoli and Paulo Vargas Moniz 4166

- **Loop Quantum Gravity: Cosmology and Black Holes**
Chairpersons: Jorge Pullin and Parampreet Singh

YouTube links: https://youtu.be/CAuAK31Ukho
https://youtu.be/JlYnEzRiRR0

Primordial power spectrum from a matter-ekpyrotic scenario in loop quantum cosmology
Bao-Fei Li, Sahil Saini and Parampreet Singh 4178

The primordial power spectra in modified loop quantum cosmology
Bao-Fei Li, Javier Olmedo, Parampreet Singh and Anzhong Wang 4188

Primordial perturbations in kinetically dominated regimes of classical and quantum cosmology
B. Elizaga Navascués, R. Jiménez-Llamas and G. A. Mena Marugán 4193

Revisiting the Hamiltonian formalism of the Ashtekar–Olmedo–Singh black hole model
Alejandro García-Quismondo and Guillermo A. Mena Marugán 4211

A comparison of different choices of clocks in a reduced phase space quantization in loop quantum cosmology with an inflationary potential using effective techniques
Kristina Giesel, Bao-Fei Li and Parampreet Singh 4228

Initial conditions in LQC/mLQCs
Bao-Fei Li, Parampreet Singh and Anzhong Wang 4234

Holonomy corrections in effective midisuperspace models
A. Alonso-Bardaji and D. Brizuela 4239

Infrared signatures of quantum bounce in collapsing geometry
Harkirat Singh Sahota and Kinjalk Lochan 4247

Effective black hole interior and the Raychadhuri equation
Keagan Blanchette, Saurya Das, Samantha Hergott and Saeed Rastgoo . . . 4256

Effect of loop quantization prescriptions on the physics of non-singular gravitational collapse
Kristina Giesel, Bao-Fei Li and Parampreet Singh 4267

Summary of the parallel session QG3
Jorge Pullin and Parampreet Singh 4272

Strong Field

- **Strong Electromagnetic and Gravitational Field Physics: From Laboratories to Early Universe**

Chairpersons: Sang Pyo Kim and She-Sheng Xue

YouTube links: https://youtu.be/kexqTayqFiU
https://youtu.be/laymGp6x9Hg

Reliable equations of state of viscous strong and electroweak matter *A. Tawfik*	4277
Neutral fermion pair production by Sauter-like magnetic step *T. C. Adorno, Zi-Wang He, S. P. Gavrilov and D. M. Gitman*	4290
On the magnetic field screening in strong crossed electromagnetic field *S. Campion, J. A. Rueda Hernandez, S.-S. Xue and R. Ruffini*	4306
Particle creation by strong fields and quantum anomalies *José Navarro-Salas*	4317
Constraints on the non-minimal coupling of electromagnetic fields from astrophysical observations *Susmita Jana and S. Shankaranarayanan*	4326
New partial resummation of the QED effective action *Silvia Pla and José Navarro-Salas*	4337
Can a detector detect soft photons *Sanved Kolekar and Jorma Louko*	4347
Breaking of the adiabatic invariance in the production of particles by strong fields *P. Beltrán-Palau, A. Ferreiro, J. Navarro-Salas and S. Pla*	4352
Dynamics of relativistic electrons in non-uniform magnetic fields and its applications in quantum computing and astrophysics *Srishty Aggarwal and Banibrata Mukhopadhyay*	4362
Validity of the semiclassical approximation in 1+1 electrodynamics: Numerical solutions to the linear response equation *Ian M. Newsome*	4374
On Kerr black hole perfect MHD processes in Doran coordinates *C. Cherubini, S. Filippi, A. Loppini et al.*	4387
Tadpole contribution to magnetic photon-graviton conversion *N. Ahmadiniaz, F. Bastianelli, F. Karbstein and C. Schubert*	4393

- **The Effects of (Non)Linear Electrodynamics on the Properties of Astrophysical/Gravitational Compact Objects**
  Chairperson: Seyed Hossein Hendi
  YouTube link: https://youtu.be/SAIAXtQhavE

  Correspondence of gamma radiation coming from GRBs and magnetars based on the effects of nonlinear vacuum electrodynamics
  Tursynbek Yernazarov, Medeu Abishev and Yerlan Aimuratov 4401

  Absorption of massless scalar waves by electrically charged regular black holes
  Marco A. A. de Paula, Luiz C. S. Leite and Luís C. B. Crispino 4410

White Dwarfs

- **White Dwarf Explosions**
  Chairpersons: Robert Fisher and María Pilar Ruiz Lapuente
  YouTube links: https://youtu.be/ndaW6u2xuOo
  https://youtu.be/IwjYaQaqJeI

  Modeling Type Ia supernovae with explosions in white dwarfs near and below the Chandrasekhar mass
  Friedrich K. Röpke, Florian Lach, Sabrina Gronow et al. 4420

  Type Ia supernovae and their explosive nucleosynthesis: Constraints on progenitors
  Shing-Chi Leung and Ken'ichi Nomoto 4427

  Charged polarized white dwarfs with finite temperature as a possible source of type Ia supernovae
  Sílvia P. Nunes, José D. V. Arbañil and Manuel Malheiro 4447

- **White Dwarfs, Magnetic Compact Stars and Nuclear Astrophysics**
  Chairpersons: Manuel Malheiro and Jaziel Goulart Coelho
  YouTube link: https://youtu.be/onicFElJQnA

  CTCV J2056-3014 and other fast-spinning white dwarfs
  C. V. Rodrigues, R. Lopes de Oliveira, A. Bruch et al. 4453

  Gravitational waves from fast-spinning white dwarfs
  M. F. Sousa, J. C. N. de Araujo and J. G. Coelho 4461

  Highly magnetized white dwarfs: Implications and current status
  B. Mukhopadhyay, M. Bhattacharya, A. J. Hackett et al. 4475

  Electron captures and stability of white dwarfs
  N. Chamel, L. Perot, A. F. Fantina et al. 4488

Massive hot white dwarfs: Consequences of finite temperature in the structure and on the onset of instabilities
Sílvia P. Nunes, José D. V. Arbañil and Manuel Malheiro 4508

A study of the infrared emission of SGR/AXPs in a disk scenario and its implications for their origin
Sarah Villanova Borges 4514

Particle acceleration and high energy emission in the white dwarf binaries AE Aquarii and AR Scorpii
P. J. Meintjes, S. T. Madzime, Q. Kaplan et al. 4522

Study the effects of anisotropy on the highly magnetized white dwarfs
Debabrata Deb, Banibrata Mukhopadhyay and Fridolin Weber 4532

List of Participants   4545

PART A

PART A

New results from testing relativistic gravity with radio pulsars

Michael Kramer

Max-Planck-Institut für Radioastronomie
Auf dem Hügel 69, 53177 Bonn, Germany
mkramer@mpifr-bonn.mpg.de

We experience a golden era in testing and exploring relativistic gravity. Whether it is results from gravitational wave detectors, satellite or lab experiments, radio astronomy plays an important complementary role. Here one can mention the cosmic microwave background, black hole imaging and, obviously, binary pulsars. This talk will concentrate on the latter and new results from studies of strongly self-gravitating bodies with unrivalled precision. This presentation compares the results to other methods, discusses implications for other areas of relativistic astrophysics and will give an outlook of what we can expect from new instruments in the near future.

Keywords: Pulsars; Neutron stars; Black holes; Gravitational-wave astrophysics; Experimental tests of gravitational theories

PACS numbers: 97.60.Gb; 97.60.Jd; 97.60.Lf; 04.30.Tv; 04.80.Cc

1. Introduction

The latest Marcel-Grossmann Meeting has showed once more that gravity can be explored and tested in many different ways. Whether it is via lab experiments on Earth, in the Solar system or in outer space. Whether it is via radio astronomy, optical/infrared astronomy, high-energy observations or gravitational wave detectors. Nearly all experiments use techniques that were not even remotely thinkable at the time, when Einstein conceived general relativity (GR). And yet, all these experiments that the theory has been confronted with, seem to confirm GR's predictions. Obviously, the phenomena of Dark Matter and Dark Energy, or the incompatibility of GR with quantum physics, justify the search for alternatives and the continuing search for experiments that may eventually show a flaw in Einstein's theory.

In this endeavour it is important to complement the different approaches as they test different regimes of gravity, in each of which one may find a deviation for a given theory. This is illustrated in Figure 1. In the solar systems, gravity tests are made in the quasi-stationary weak-field regime, often involving satellite experiments of high precision (e.g. Ref. 1). The quasi-stationary strong-field regime can be probed with experiments such as stellar orbits around Sgr A* (e.g. Ref. 2) or radio images of black holes (Ref. 3). But also pulsar experiments contribute to this regime, and indeed they already allow precision tests of the radiative properties of gravity (e.g. Ref. 4), as we also show in the following. Using radio pulsars

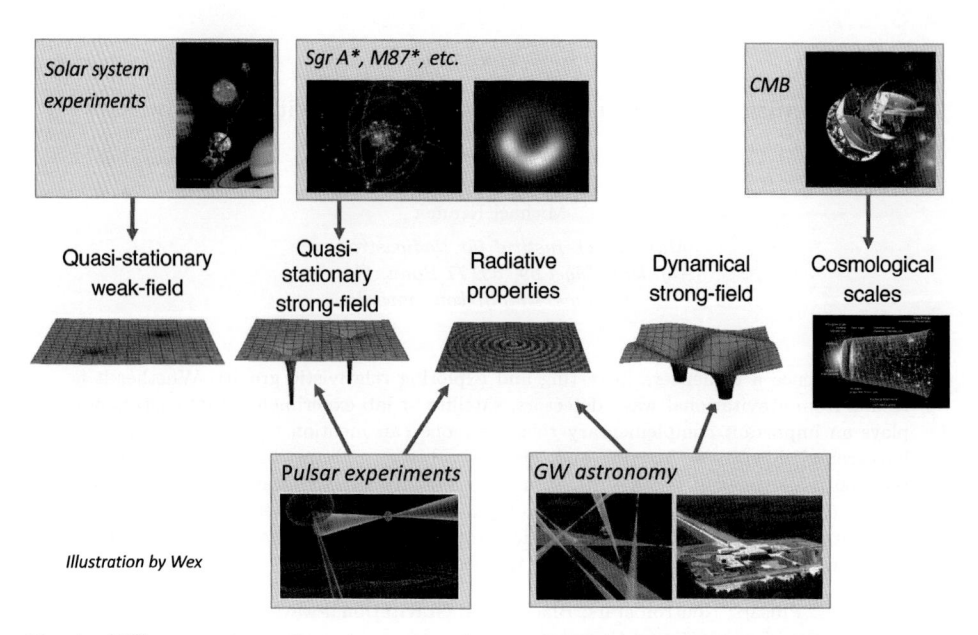

Fig. 1. Different regimes of gravity tests and examples of methods and experiments that allow tests in those.

also as galaxy-sized gravitational wave (GW) detectors (e.g. Refs. 5), one also enters the dynamical strong-field regime, where obviously also the Earth-bound GW detectors are operating (e.g. Ref. 6). Finally, theories should also be tested on the largest scales, which can be done, for instance, with studies of the cosmic microwave background (CMB).

We note that in most of these experimental methods (certainly in those examples given here) radio astronomy plays a crucial role. In the following, we will concentrate on recent results involving radio pulsars.

2. Testing gravity with pulsars

The most common, and most well known way, of testing gravity with pulsars is via a technique called pulsar timing.[7] Less common but still powerful is the usage of pulse structure data that allow us to probe precessional effects when the line-of-sight through the emission beam is changing, modifying the observed pulse properties like width or generally pulse shape.[8] In extreme cases, the pulsar may completely disappear from our view after a while.[9,10]

In pulsar timing one makes use of the often very stable rotation of a pulsar that leads to a regularity in the emitted pulsed signal, caused by a lighthouse effect, that rivals the best atomic clocks on Earth. As an observer on Earth, we can measure the arrival time of the pulses at the telescope and infer from it the motion of the

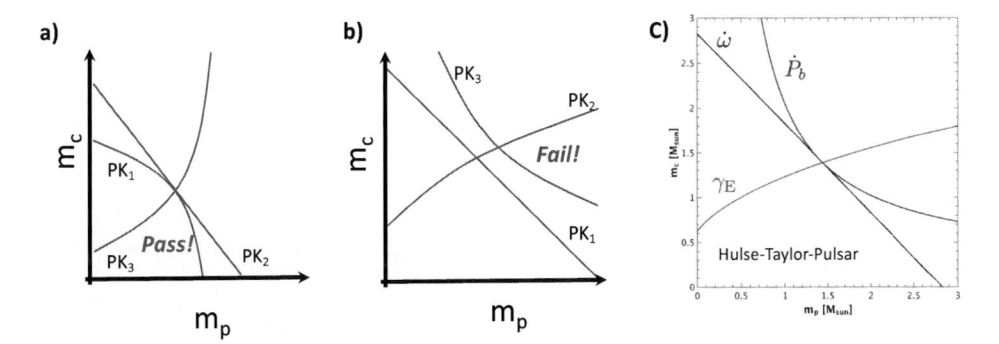

Fig. 2. Gravity tests using binary pulsars performed via the measurements of Post-Keplerian (PK) parameters and their graphical representation in a mass-mass diagram. a) all PK parameter lines insect in a single point: the test is passed. b) the lines do not intersect in a single point: the theory fails the test. c) Example for the Hulse-Taylor pulsar, here shown for general relativity.

pulsar in a binary orbit. The timing precision that is attainable (i.e. better than 100 ns in many cases) is provided by following the rotational phase of the pulsar in a coherent fashion, making measurements more precise as the time baseline increases. In a similar way, tracking the orbital phase reveals periodic and secular deviations from a simple Keplerian orbit, expressed in the so called Post-Keplerian (PK) parameters.[8,11,12] Those can typically be expressed as functions of the Keplerian parameters and the two unknown masses of the binary system. Once two PK parameters can be measured, the two masses can be determined within the framework of a given theory and the value of further PK parameters can be predicted. Once that is done, the predictions can be compared with similar measurements and the theory, hence, can be tested.

One can express such a test in a graphical form, where each PK parameter describes a line in a diagram with the values of two unknown masses as its axes. Two PK parameter lines define an intersection point through which every other PK parameter line must pass. If that is not the case, the theory determining the lines is falsified and needs to be rejected. The measurement uncertainties in the PK parameters is expressed as the width of the PK lines in the mass-mass diagram. See Figure 2.

2.1. The Double Pulsar

We demonstrate the power of pulsar timing using the best laboratory currently known, the so called "Double Puslar".[13,14] The system consists of two active radio pulsars – a currently still unique feature of the system – orbiting each other in 147 min. The recycled (old) pulsar (A) in the system has a period of 23 ms, the non-recycled (young) pulsar (B) a period of 2.8 s. An important feature of the system is its edge-on geometry (see Figure 3) that also leads to 30-s long eclipses and our

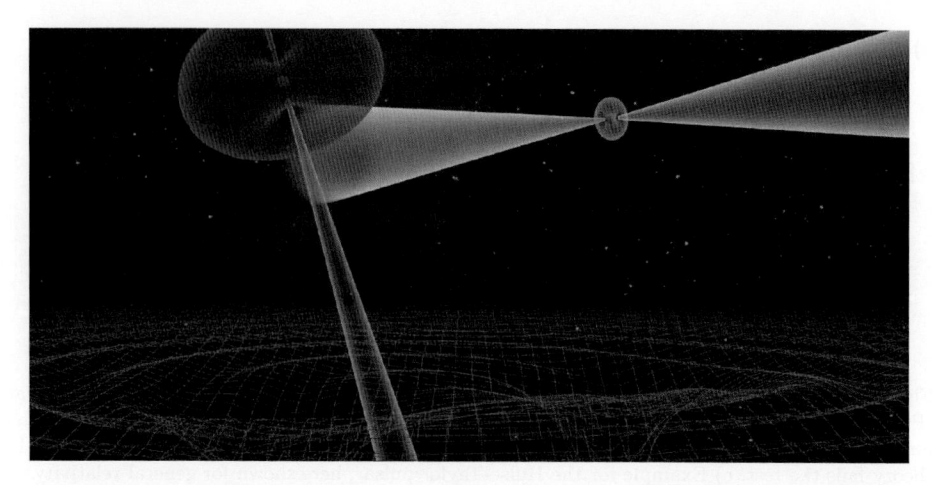

Fig. 3. Artistic impression of the Double Pulsar. Here, two active radio pulsars orbit each other in 147 min in a slightly eccentric orbit ($e = 0.09$). One pulsar is old and recycled ($P = 23$ ms), while the second pulsar is young ($P = 2.8$ s). Figure is not to scale.

ability to measure light-propagation effects (see below). The previous gravity tests with the system made usage of the ratio of the masses of the two pulsars, that can be directly (i.e. theory independently to 1PN order) measured from the two semi-major axes the pulsars' orbit around the common centre of mass.[4] Meanwhile the data have improved very significantly in both precision and length. The latest results were presented by Kramer et al. (Ref. 15), reporting the measurement of, in total, seven PK parameters.

What is important and different to previous experiments, the measurement precision is now so high that for the first time higher-order contributions need to be taken into account for some of the PK parameters. This includes the contribution of the A pulsar's effective mass loss (due to spin-down) to the observed orbital period decay, a relativistic deformation of the orbit, and the effects of the equation of state of super-dense matter on some of the observed PK parameters via relativistic spin-orbit coupling. The system also provides the currently most precise test of general relativity's quadrupolar description of GWs, validating GR's prediction at a level of 1.3×10^{-4} with 95% confidence.[15] As indicated, the impact of the mass loss due to rotational spin-down is taken into account in this result. Interestingly, as the pulsar is losing rotational energy, and while $E = mc^2$, the slow-down corresponds to a mass loss of 8.4 Million tons per second or 3.2×10^{-21} of the mass of A per second.

2.1.1. *Light propagation*

The edge-on geometry of the system allows not only a test of relativistic spin-precession as discussed in Section 3, but it also leads to a "Shapiro-delay", i.e. the a delay in the measured arrival time as the photons have to propagate in the curved

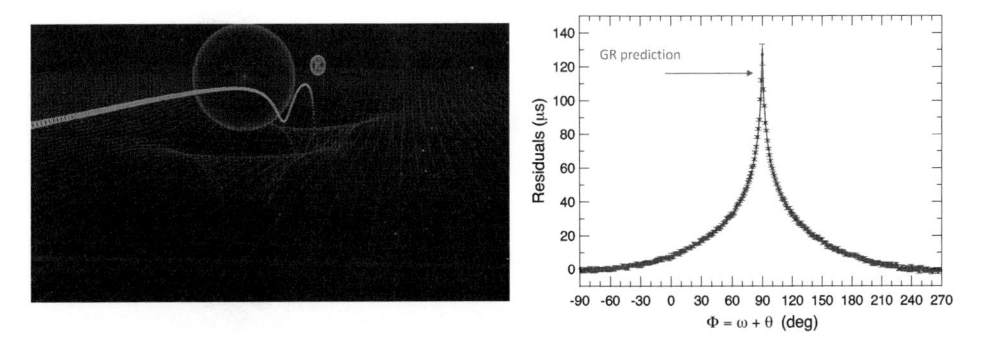

Fig. 4. Shapiro delay measurement in the Double Pulsar. The curvature of spacetime around the companion B (see artistic impression on the left, not to scale) leads to a delay in the arrival times of the pulses of pulsar A (right).

spacetime near the companion pulsar. We illustrate this effect in Figure 4. The data points follow the prediction of GR (red line) remarkable well (at a level of 4×10^{-4} with 95% confidence.[15] This agreement with the data is, however, only achieved when next-to-leading order effects are taking into account: at the 1.5PN limit one has to take into account that the speed of light is finite and that pulsar B moves during the flight time of the photos across the orbit. See Figure 5.

When comparing the Shapiro delay curve with precision data, another effect needs to be considered which relates to the fact the pulsar is indeed a lighthouse rather than a pulsating or oscillating object. This effect is aberration, which for pulsar timing means in principle a delay in arrival time that depends on orbital phase and on the orientation of the pulsar with respect to the orbit and the observer.[12,16] Due to the geometry of the Double Pulsar that does, however, not lead to separately measurable, additional PK parameters.[15] Nevertheless and most interestingly, given the precision obtained in the measurements, the curved spacetime encountered by the photons near superior conjunction leads to a deflection of the signal in the gravitational field of pulsar B. This gravitational signal deflection leads to a small change in the proper angle of emission, which in turn leads to a lensing correction to the classical ("longitudinal") aberration. See Ref. 15 for details. As a result, only those photons reach the observer on Earth that are emitted slightly earlier (or later, respectively) in pulsar rotational phase, before (and after, respectively) superior conjunction. The measurement shown in Figure 6 not only demonstrates the lighthouse character of pulsars but also indicates a prograde alignment of the pulsar spin relative to the total angular momentum vector.

2.1.2. Orbital deformation, lense-thirring effect and moment-of-inertia

A further effect that is observed in the Double Pulsar and that is now required to be considered in the data analysis is a relativistic deformation of the orbit. The presence of the effect[11,12] was already seen by Weisberg & Huang (Ref. 17). In

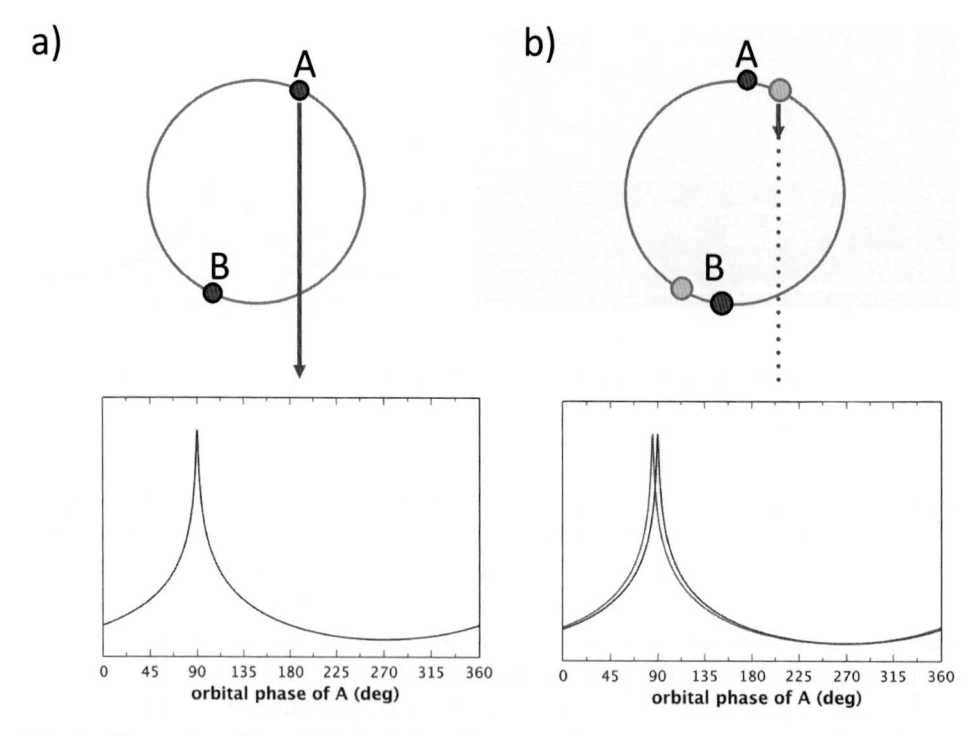

Fig. 5. Illustration of the physical origin and impact of the next-to-leading order (1.5PN) contribution to the Shapiro delay. a) Previously, a "static" Shapiro delay was implemented in timing formula, assuming the position of the companion pulsar B to be fixed during the propagation of A's photons. b) In reality, pulsar B moves during the flight time of the photons, which effectively leads to a small shift in the Shapiro delay curve at the 1.5PN level. Illustration by N. Wex.

this case, ignoring this subtle effect would (wrongly) suggest a tension between the measured "Einstein delay" and its prediction by GR. See Kramer et al. (Ref. 15) for details.

As already indicated, the extreme precision of the experiment now also needs to incooperate the effects of the equation of state (EoS) of super-dense matter on some of the observed post-Keplerian parameters via relativistic spin-orbit coupling. Indeed, the most precisely measured PK parameter, $\dot{\omega}$, representing the precession of the orbit, has a contribution from the Lense-Thirring effect due to the rotation of pulsar A at the 2PN level, which is more than 30 times larger than our measurement error. However, a calculation of the Lense-Thirring contribution requires the knowledge of the Moment-of-Inertia of pulsar A, I_A, which comes with a significant uncertainty due to our imperfect knowledge of the EoS for neutron star matter. To constrain I_A one can use constraints on the EoS obtained from the double neutron star merger GW170817[18] and determine precise measurements for the pulsars. Alternatively, one can ignore any existing constraints on the EoS of neutrons stars to simultaneously determine the pulsar masses, m_A, m_B, and I_A, assuming GR to be

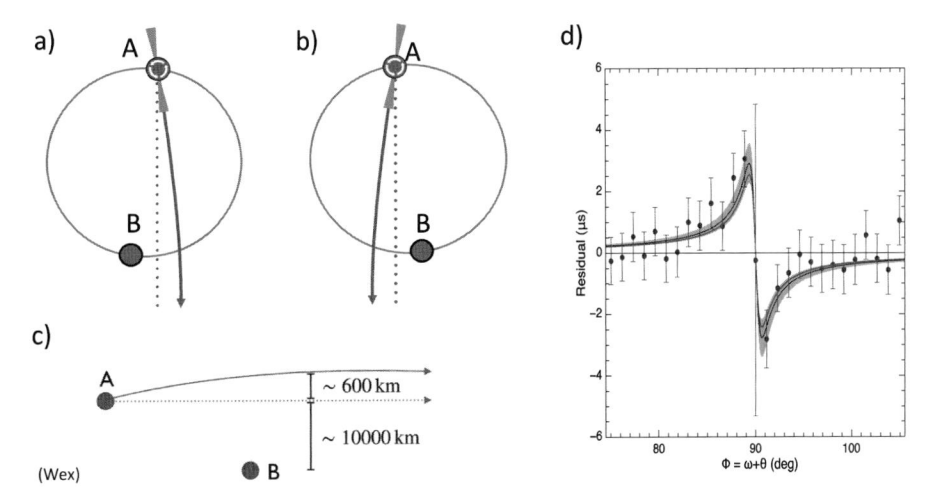

Fig. 6. Illustration and measurement of another next-to-leading order effect that needs to be taken into account for the Shapiro delay. In this case, aberrational light bending due to the curvature of spacetime around pulsar B is considered. a) Before superior conjunction, the photons have to be emitted at a slightly later rotational phase than usual to compensate for the light bending near B to reach the observer on Earth. b) After superior conjunction, the photons have to be emitted slightly earlier, respectively. c) The light bending contributes an additional 600 km to the total impact distance. d) Residuals observed near superior conjunction (i.e. periastron, $\Phi = 0$ deg), when this effect is *not* taken into account. The red curve shows the theoretical prediction arising from this effect, and the black curve corresponds to the best fit, with a 2σ range indicated by the light grey band. This effect allows us to infer the spin direction of pulsar A, indicating a prograde orientation. See Kramer et al. (2021) for details.

the correct theory of gravity. In this case, simply based on pulsar timing, one finds for the the MoI $I_A < 3.0 \times 10^{45}$ g cm^2 with 90% confidence,[15] which in turn can be directly compared to the results derived from the GW170817 LIGO/Virgo merger and from NICER X-ray timing. Using a universal relation, like the one in Ref. 19, one can convert the obtained probability distribution of I_A into a probability distribution for A's radius. With 90% confidence, this gives an upper limit for A's radius of 22 km, a value outside any physically valid EoS but purely based on the arrival times measurements of pulses.[15]

In summary, the Double Pulsar allows to test conservative aspects of the orbital dynamics of two strongly self-gravitating masses up to 2PN order, including a $\sim 1\sigma$ constraint on the Lense-Thirring contribution, which in turn can be used to constrain the MoI of pulsar A under the assumption of GR. The experiments allow to test the propagation of photons in the gravitational field of a strongly self-gravitating (material) body, with next-to-leading-order contributions being clearly present in the timing data, confirmed with a precision of about 10%. We can also test the radiative aspects of GR, yielding a test at 2.5PN level in the equations of motion with a precision of 1.3×10^{-4} (95% C.L.). In terms of overall fractional precision, this is the most precise test of GR's predictions for GW emission

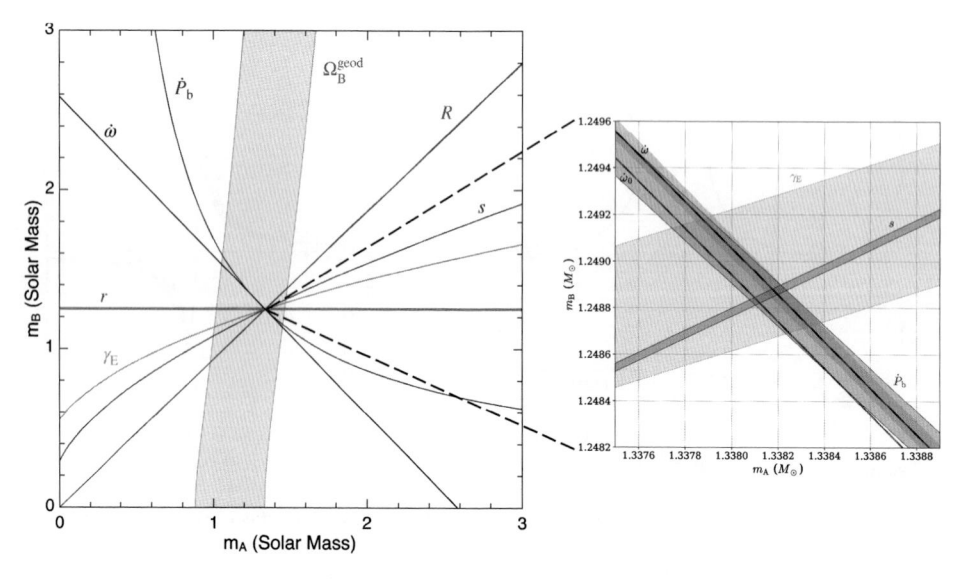

Fig. 7. Mass-mass diagram for the Double Pulsar as presented by Kramer et al. (2021). The right panel is a zoomed-in version of the intersection point of the PK parameter lines in the left panel. The shift of the line for the PK-parameter $\dot\omega$ when ignoring the Lense-Thirring effect ($\dot\omega_0$) is clearly visible. See text for details.

currently available. These tests are summarized in the mass-mass diagram shown in Figure 7.

3. Relativistic spin-precession

A gyroscope freely falling in curved spacetime suffers a precession with respect to a distant observer. Experiments made in Solar System provide precise weak-field tests and confirm it, e.g. with Lunar Laser Raning or GRAVITY Probe-B. In a binary pulsar system, the pulsar - also being a gyroscope - we observe, strictly speaking, a mixture of different contributions to relativistic spin-orbit coupling. One contribution comes from the motion of the first body around the centre of mass of the system (deSitter-Fokker precession), while the other comes from the dragging of the internal frame at internal frame at the first body due to the translational motion of the companion.[20] This resulting relativistic spin-precession causes nevertheless the expected effect: the pulsar precesses about the total angular momentum, which as a result changes the relative orientation of the pulsar towards Earth with potentially observable consequences as predicted by Damour & Ruffini in Ref. 21 even before the publication of the discovery of the Hulse-Taylor binary pulsar.[22] We note that the orbital angular momentum is expected to be much larger than that of a pulsar in the system, so that the orbital spin practically represents a fixed direction in space. Hence, effectively the pulsar precesses about the orbital angular momentum.

The precession rate, $\Omega_{\rm SO}$, is another PK as introduced above. Assuming GR to be valid, it is given by[23]

$$\Omega_{\rm SO} = T_\odot^{2/3} \left(\frac{2\pi}{P_{\rm b}}\right)^{5/3} \frac{m_{\rm A}(4m_{\rm B}+3m_{\rm A})}{2(m_{\rm B}+m_{\rm A})^{4/3}} \frac{1}{1-e^2}. \qquad (1)$$

The effect of relativistic sin precession on pulsar timing is in principle measurable due to a change in the aberration parameters with time.[8] Much more obvious, and hence easier to measure, are the consequences of the changing line-of-sight as the pulsar precesses. We expect changes in the pulse shape (e.g. in simply the measured width, but also more dramatic changes) and especially in the measured linearly polarised emission which is a sensitive probe of the pulsar geometry.[21,24] Such measurements have indeed enabled the detection of spin precession in a number of relativistic binaries. After the first detection in the Hulse-Taylor pulsar B1913+16[9,25] and later in PSR B1534+12,[26,27] it is now possible to convert long-term observations in precise quantitative tests of spin precession and, hence, test of the "effacement" property of a spinning body.

3.1. *Spin precession in the Double Pulsar*

A prime example to study relativistic spin precession is, again, the Double Pulsar. Here, we have two active pulsars, both of which could, in principle show the effects of precession. However, it turns out that the supernova explosion creating the second-born pulsar, B, was a low-kick supernova which left the pre-Supernova orientation of the orbital angular momentum vector unchanged. The spin of pulsar A, having been aligned with the orbital spin during its recycling period, is therefore still aligned with it, so that precession for A is not expected. Indeed, so far, profile changes for A have not been detected, suggesting that A's misalignment angle is less than 3 deg.[28,29]

In contrast, secular changes in the pulse shape and the orbital visibility windows of pulsar B were observed soon after its discovery,[30] providing early evidence for spin precession of B. Around 2008, the pulsar vanished from our view when our line-of-sight moved out of the emission beam.[10] B will eventually re-appear. The exact epoch for this to happen depends on the actual beam shape, but despite a precession period of 71 years (see Table 1), it could happen relatively soon.[10,31]

Meanwhile, it has been possible to track the orientation of the spin axis of pulsar B in a rather fortuitous way: Breton et al. (Ref. 32) studied the time evolution of the ~ 30-s long eclipses of A that are caused by the blocking rotating magnetosphere of B at superior conjunction. This absorption of the background emission, presumably by synchrotron self-absorption,[33] is not complete, but because of the torus-shaped dipolar magnetosphere[a] the light from the background pulsar A is visible every half-turn or full-turn of pulsar B, depending on the orientation of the spin-axis and,

---

[a]Deviations from a purely dipolar-shaped magnetosphere do exist and are observed. Indeed, about 50% of the magnetosphere is "missing" but for the remaining parts, the torus shape appears more than adequate, as the successful modelling shows. See, for instance Ref. 34.

hence, the magnetosphere. Applying a simple but successful geometrical model,[33] Breton et al. were able to explain the observed modulation of A's lightcurve during the eclipse phase in great detail. Model-fitting indicates a constant magnetic inclination angle and constant misalignment angle, while the azimuthal spin angle is changing with a rate of $\Omega_{\rm SO,B} = 4.77^{+0.66}_{-0.65}°$ yr^{-1}, in agreement with general relativity[32] (see Table 1).

3.2. PSR J1906+0746 – The currently best test

A further observational consequence of relativistic spin precession is its impact on the polarisation properties of binary pulsars. Here, two separate but related aspects are observable.

The first aspect is due to the changing line-of-sight within the pulsar beam. According to the rotating vector model (RVM),[24] we expect an S-like swing of the position angle of the linearly polarised emission component of the studied pulsar. The closer the line-of-sight approaches the magnetic axis, the steeper is the expected S-swing. In general, the shape of the S-swing depends on four quantities: the magnetic inclination angle, α, between the spin and magnetic axes, the impact angle between our line-of-sight and the magnetic axis, β, the pulse phase, ϕ, and, finally, the absolute (reference) position angle, Ψ_0, which is obtained at $\phi = 0$ and identical to the orientation of the pulsar spin-axis projected on the plane of the sky. Such a measurement was first achieved for PSR B1534+12,[26,27] where the impact angle β was observed to change with time.

The second consequence is the change of Ψ_0 due to the changing orientation of the pulsar spin and the resulting projection on the sky.[35] This change of the absolute position angle is periodic, with a period equal to the precessional period. Note that there is also a small contribution due to orbital aberration, which we will ignore here. We note that the measured absolute position angle will be affected by Faraday rotation due to propagation in the magnetised ionised interstellar medium. But this effect can, in principle, be measured and removed.

It is the additional information provided by the change in absolute position angle that allows to break some degeneracies and to potentially determine the true orbital inclination angle, i (rather than $180 - i$, as pulsar timing only provides $\sin i$). Modelling the evolution of the position angle swing in the described way requires in total only four free parameters, i.e. the precession rate, $\Omega_{\rm SO}$, the misalignment angle between pulsar spin and total angular momentum vector, δ, the precession reference phase, $\Phi_{\rm SO}^0$, and the magnetic inclination angle of the pulsar, α. A requirement for precession to occur is $\delta > 0$, a measurement of which is very useful to study the formation of the system (see Refs. 34 and 35 for a detailed discussion on this topic).

Both aspects just described are relevant for the beautiful case of PSR J1906+0746. This pulsar is an almost perfect orthogonal rotator, and so this pulsar was discovered with the emission from both magnetic poles being visible

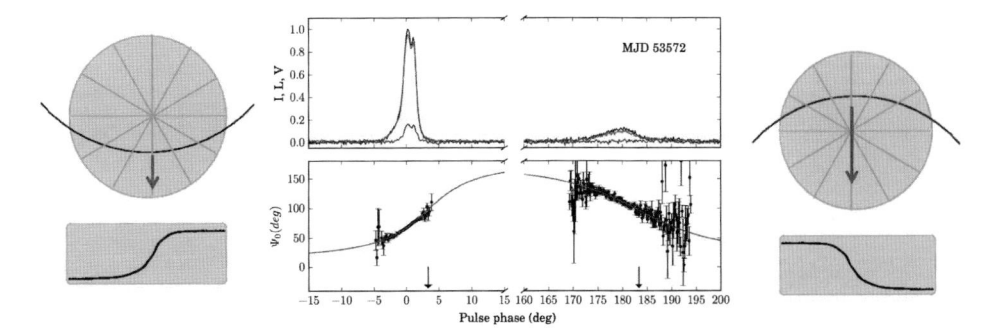

Fig. 8. Pulse profile of PSR J1906+0746 as observed by Desvignes et al. (2019) shown in the middle panel. Both magnetic poles (schematics left and right) were originally visible after discovery. Their observed emission is highly linearly polarised (red line), with a position angle swing (middle lower panel) that resembles a textbook-like rotating vector model. The pulsar also shows a modest amount of circularly polarised emission (middle upper panel, blue line). At the left pole, our line-of-sight moves out of the beam, while at the right pole our line-of-sight crossed the magnetic pole during the long-term monitoring of this source.

(see Figure 8). The emission's high degree of linear polarisation reveals a perfect RVM-like behaviour of the measured position angle that was studied by Desvignes et al. (Ref. 36). Fitting those to the RVM as a function of time using the precessional RVM model[35] described above, allows to measure the precession rate to $\Omega_{SO} = 2.17 \pm 0.11$ deg/yr which is in perfect agreement with the expectation from GR (see Table 1). This test is the currently best test of relativistic spin-precession for strongly self-gravitating bodies.

The study of the position angle reveals even more: Apart from providing measurements of the geometry of the system ($i = 45 \pm 3$ deg, $\alpha = 99.4 \pm 0.2$ deg, $\delta = 104 \pm 9$ deg), the evolution of the position angle swing with time shows how its slope becomes steeper when our lines-of-sight approaches the magnetic pole. It also shows how it swaps sign in slope when crossing the pole, and how it becomes flatter again when moving away from the pole[36] (see right of Figure 9). This is the first unequivocal evidence that the RVM is correct and that the position angle swing of pulsars is in principle determined by the geometry of the pulsar and its fieldlines. Deviation may, however, still occur in cases due to propagation effects or modifications to the field line structure in the emission region.

Furthermore, we can reconstruct the emission beams of the pulsar as projected on the sky and as shown in the left two panels of Figure 9). As the light of sight crosses the two beams, we can obtain "tomographic" images, albeit incomplete ones due to lack of observations in part of the beam. We note from the middle panel, showing the pole that is responsible for the (initially) weaker pulse component in Figure 8, that the emission beam is active on either side of the pole, ruling out models that predict radio emission to be restricted to one side of the pole. Secondly, the emission pattern is not symmetric in the latitudinal direction relative

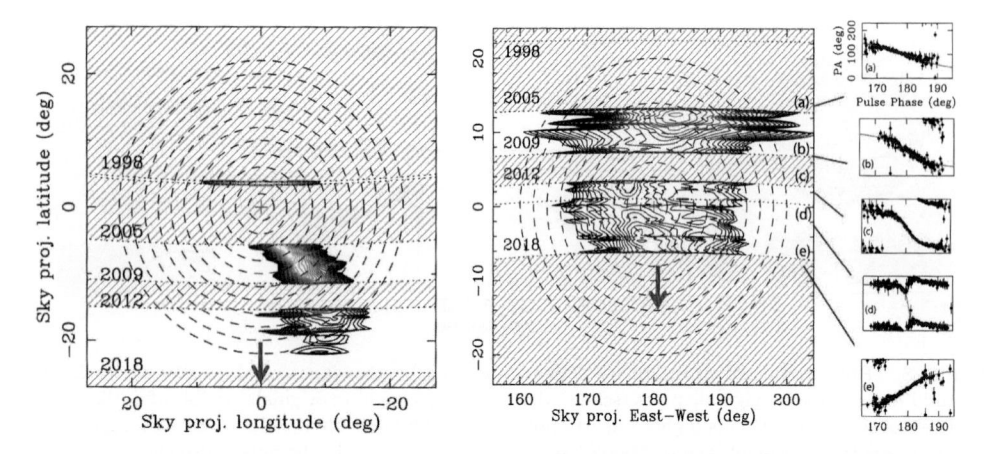

Fig. 9. Beam pattern of the two magnetic poles of PSR J1906+0746 as projected on the sky and observed by Desvignes et al.[36] The beams are reconstructed from observations spanning more than 10 years, when our line-of-sight moved in the indicated direction above both poles. For the right beam, our line-of-sight crossed the magnetic pole. The resulting position angle swing shown on the right evolves with time as expected from the rotating vector model (see text for details). For the left beam, the emission becomes weaker to the beam edge and the initially much stronger component (see Figure 8) is hardly detectable anymore and will soon vanish completely.

to the pole. When looking more closely at our data, we also notice that above the pole itself the emission is reduced, matching theoretical predictions for the current density in the polar cap for an orthogonal rotator.[37] What is also not visible in these total intensity plots shown here (see Ref. 36 for details) is an interesting behaviour of the polarisation characteristics more generally: the handedness of the circularly polarised emission changes when crossing the pole, the fractional linear polarization overall decreases with increasing distance to the beam centre, and finally, emission heights inferred from polarisation data increase from very low emission heights near the pole to emission heights of several hundreds of kilometres at the beam edge, again consistent with theoretical expectations[38] and inferred more indirectly from other pulsars.[39,40]

In summary, somewhat unexpectedly, an experiment designed to test theories of gravity and to tests predictions made by Thibault Damour and Remo Ruffini nearly 50 years ago, leads to unique insight into the emission physics of pulsars.

3.3. *Relativistic spin precession in other pulsars*

Today, spin precession has been routinely observed in all those binary pulsars, where we can expect the pulsar spin to be misaligned with the orbital momentum vector (i.e. systems where we observe the young pulsar or where the last supernova explosion in the system imparted a large kick onto the newly born neutron star) and where the precession rate is high enough due to a sufficient compactness of the orbit. Using the precession rate as given in GR, Eqn. 1, we provide a list of pulsars where we would expect to observe spin precession. Table 1 gives the corresponding values, sorted by decreasing rate. We note that for the vast majority of sources, spin precession has been detected (see Ref 41). The second highest rate is expected for the highly accelerated binary pulsar J1757−1854 discovered with in the High Time Resolution Universe Survey.[42] As presented by Cameron et al. in this conference, first signs of profile changes may already be present but further data are needed. If this is confirmed, the first top-6 pulsars (and seven out of eight) have all been observed to undergo spin precession. The only other exception in the table is PSR J1756−2251. Here the spin may be aligned with the orbital momentum vector, but studies are in progress to revisit this pulsar with larger precision and longer time baseline.[43]

Table 1. Binary pulsar systems where relativistic spin precession is expected or observed, ordered according to the precession rate as expected from general relativity. Pulsars marked with an asterisk have been identified of showing spin precession.

PSR	P(ms)	P_b (d)	x(lt-s)	e	Ω_p (deg yr^{-1})
J0737−3039A/B*	22.7/2770	0.10	1.42/1.51	0.09	4.8/5.1
J1757−1854	22.50	0.18	2.24	0.61	3.1
J1906+0746*	144.1	0.17	1.42	0.09	2.2
B2127+11C*	30.5	0.34	2.52	0.68	1.9
J1141−6545*	394.0	0.20	1.89	0.17	1.4
B1913+16*	59.0	0.33	2.34	0.62	1.2
J1756−2251	28.5	0.32	2.76	0.18	0.8
B1534+12*	37.9	0.42	3.73	0.27	0.5

4. Further recent tests with radio pulsars

In this work, we have so far concentrated on a few prominent, perhaps even spectacular recent examples of using pulsars for testing strong-field gravity. Much more can be studied, including fundamental concepts, such as the Universality of Free Fall (UFF) and the Strong Equivalence Principle (SEP), the possible variation of fundamental constants, or bounds on the graviton mass. We can also test specific alternatives to GR. Here, we refer to recent reviews (see Refs. 44, 45 for more in-depth discussions) and we point to other contributions of the MG16 meeting. Here, we will only highlight some recent examples.

4.1. Universality of Free Fall (UFF)

The UFF can be tested in the various regime that we discussed in context of Figure 1. In the solar system, we refer to the superb measurement using test masses aboard the MICROSCOPE satellite that was launched in April 2016 and operated until October 2018. The results indicate that any violation of the weak equivalence principle, Δ, is smaller than $\Delta < 10^{-15}$ (see Ref. 1).

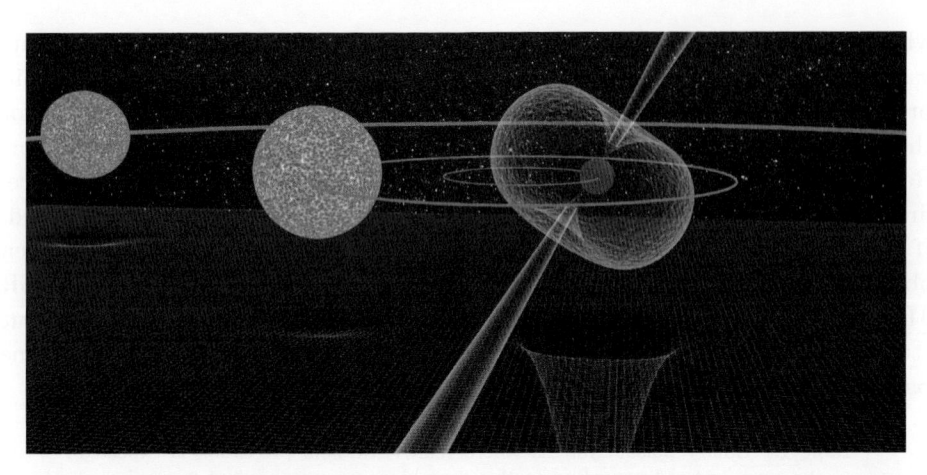

Fig. 10. Artistic impression of the Triple System, where a 2.7-ms pulsar, PSR J0337+1715, and a $0.20M_\odot$ white dwarf are in an inner 1.63-day orbit, while being orbited themselves by a second $0.41M_\odot$ white dwarf in 327 days. The figure is not to scale.

The Earth-Moon system allows to test the fall of two bodies with different gravitational self-energy, $\epsilon = E_{\rm grav}/mc^2$, where $E_{\rm grav}$ is the Newtonian gravitational binding energy, in the gravitational field of the Sun. For the Earth $\epsilon_E = -4.6 \times 10^{-10}$ and for the Moon, $\epsilon_M = -0.2 \times 10^{-10}$. The fall can be measured with Lunar Laser Ranging and limits on a deviation are currently at $\Delta < 2 \times 10^{-13}$.[46,47] Comparing this to the gravitational self-energy of the involved bodies, a limit on the violation of the SEP in the weak field of the solar system is $\Delta/\epsilon < 0.04\%$.

Pulsars allow us to test the SEP for strongly-self gravitating bodies, i.e. $\epsilon = -0.13$. The idea was already presented by Damour & Schäfer in 1991 (Ref. 48) who proposed to study the possible variation of the orbits of pulsar-white dwarf systems as they fall in the gravitational potential of the Milky Way. The discovery of a Triple System,[49] a pulsar with two White Dwarf (WD) companions, allows an important variation of this experiment, leading to a much more stringent test (see Figure 10).

The 2.7-ms pulsar, also known as PSR J0377+1715 is in a 1.63-day orbit with a WD of mass $0.2M_\odot$. This inner binary system is orbited by a second, more massive WD ($0.41M_\odot$) in a 327-day orbit. As pointed out already by Freire et al. (Ref. 50), in such a case, the pair of bodies with different gravitational self-energy falls in the gravitational potential of the outer WD, providing a much stronger field than that of the Milky Way. Archibald et al. (Ref. 51) presented the result of such an experiment and derived a limit of $\Delta < 2 \times 10^{-6}$. This may appear weaker than the weak-field limit from the solar system, but the SEP should apply for both weak- and strong-field conditions. Hence, when referring to a corresponding $\Delta/\epsilon < 0.002\%$, the importance of this measurement becomes clear.

Even more recently, Voisin et al. (Ref. 52) presented an important improvement on the experiment, using a completely independent data set. The improvements arise from a more uniformly sampled data set but also from an improved theoretical treatment that incorporates the interesting parameter Δ directly into the analysis of the timing data set. The result is a limit of $\Delta = (+0.5 \pm 1.8) \times 10^{-6}$ at 95% confidence level. While the numerical improvement upon Ref. 51 is 30%, this result is statistics-limited and avoids limitation by systematics as previously encountered.

We complete this section by also referring to recent results and proposals for further experiments to test the UFF also towards dark matter. See Ref. 53 for more details.

4.2. *Alternative theories of gravity*

Despite the successes of GR when being confronted with experimental data, GR may not be our final answer in describing gravity on a macroscopic scale. Given a number of unsolved questions (e.g. dark matter, dark energy, inflation) or its incompatibility with quantum mechanics, is still possible that we encounter an experiment that contradicts GR's predictions. In this case, we would learn important and substantial lessons, and so it is important to explore all regimes presented in Figure 1, probing different aspects of the predictions of GR and alternative theories with different methods. For instance, observations with GW detectors are able to test the highly dynamical strong-field regime and radiative aspects of gravity, but they are not able to test aspects of light-propagation in strong fields. This may be eventually possible with images from super-massive black holes, but the curvature of spacetime is many orders of magnitude smaller than around stellar compact objects. This, on the other hand, and other aspects can be tested with binary pulsars.

The close agreement of the Double Pulsar experiment with the predictions of GR shown in Section 2.1 allows us to place tight constraints on various alternatives to GR. Kramer et al. (Ref. 15) used their recent results to study both "Damour–Esposito-Farése" (DEF) gravity and Bekenstein's tensor-vector-scalar theory (TeVeS).[54] The latter is a MONDian relativistic gravity theory that evades the need for dark matter in galaxies by a modification of GR. Even though this theory has been ruled out already with observations of GWs,[55] Ref. 15 points out that pulsar experiments are still useful to test the aspects of scalar field in the theory.

DEF is a two-parameter mono-scalar-tensor gravity,[56] containing GR as a limit with the two parameters $\alpha_0 = \beta_0 = 0$. As other alternative of GR, DEF violates the SEP, which should result in observable dipolar GWs and a location-dependent gravitational constant. We would measure such phenomena in the form of different functional dependencies of the PK parameters as described in Section 2 (see e.g. Ref. 57). Moreover, in certain regions of the parameter space, DEF gravity shows genuine non-perturbative strong-field effects that are only present in NSs and therefore are not testable in the weak-field regime of the solar system. Hence, one can convert our observational results into constraints for the parameters α_0–β_0. This is done by Ref. 15 as shown in Figure 11. It demonstrates that pulsar tests are complementary to each other as well as to other methods.

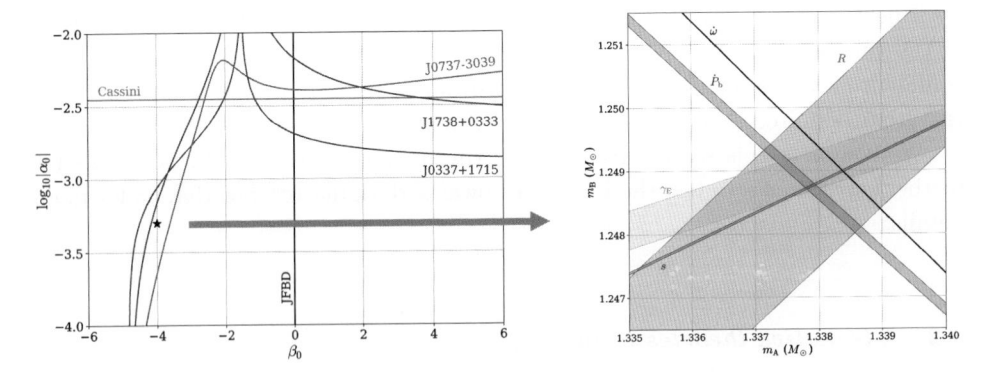

Fig. 11. (Left) Diagram displaying the α_0–β_0 parameter space of DEF gravity. Different experiments provide constraints shown as lines. Parameter space above a line is ruled out. In addition to constraints from the Cassini spacecraft, the figure includes constraints from limits on the existence of dipolar GW emission obtained from PSR J1738+0333, and constraints from the Triple System and the Double Pulsar as described earlier. GR is contained in this parameter space at ($\alpha_0 = 0, \beta_0 = 0$). The Jordan-Fierz-Brans-Dicke (JFBD) theory is also contained along the vertical ($\beta_0 = 0$)-line. (Right) Every point in the left parameter space corresponds to a specific DEF theory and different realisations of the PK parameters. For a specific choice as an example, indicated by the star in the left figure, one obtains a mass-mass diagram that can be compared to Figure 7. Here, the PK lines fail to intersect in a single point and the specific theory should be rejected. This is already visible by the star's position in the left diagram, left and above the Double Pulsar line. This specific theory, however, would have passed other existing constraints as indicated. See Kramer et al. (2021) for details and references therein.

5. Conclusions

In this contribution, I have tried to summarise some recent key results in probing strong-field gravity using pulsars. In the past three years, the results have not only improved dramatically in precision, but also new effects could be studied. Pulsar continue to play an important role and complement other experiments which have only become possible in the recent years. This includes terrestrial GW detection as well as the imaging of black holes. What is unique about pulsars is the incredible precision that we can obtain in pulsar timing experiments. This is perhaps best demonstrated by the fact that we now have to consider the mass loss of a pulsar spinning down and the interior structure of neutron stars when we one to interpret our results.

Figure 12 attempts to bring the pulsar experiments into context with others. The chosen parameters plotted are a deliberate choice, as they clearly demonstrate that pulsars probe strong-field gravity, as pointed out by many authors in the past (e.g. Ref. 58). It also shows the size of the parameter space to be probed. Future telescopes, like the Square Kilometre Array (SKA), will contribute many more experiments and exciting constraints, as first results with MeerKAT clearly demonstrate.[43] The best is still to come.

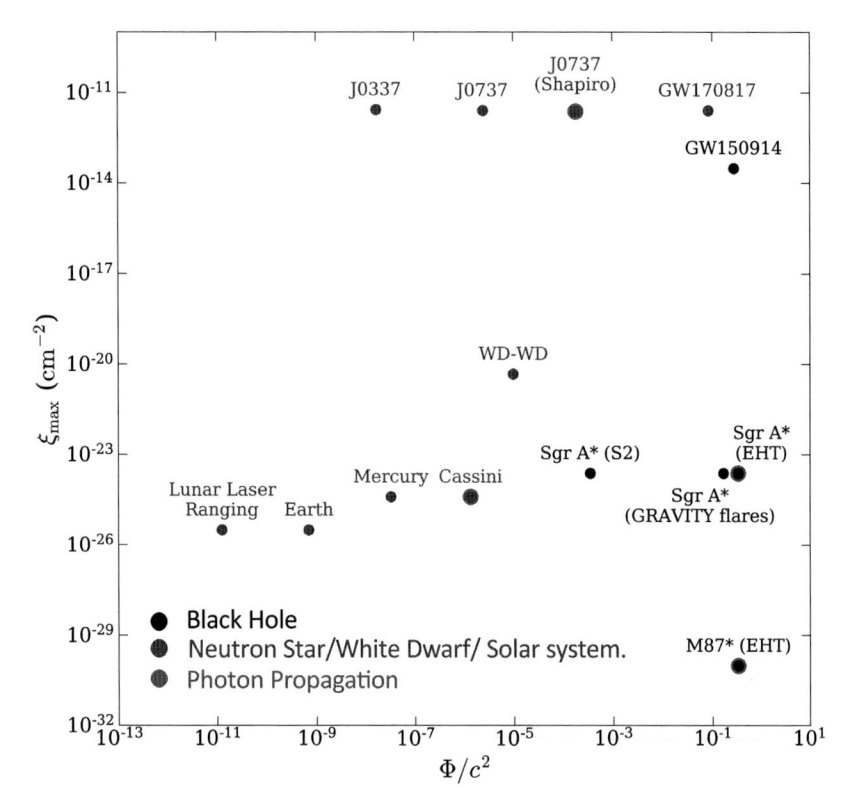

Fig. 12. Parameter space to compare different gravity experiments. While several possible combinations for 2-D diagrams are possible, none is complete in capturing all quantities relevant for gravity tests, and therefore each of them always gives an incomplete comparison. Adopting the plot from Kramer et al. (2021), we show the gravitational potential and the maximum spacetime curvature in a system, distinguishing between weakly and strongly self-gravitating masses amongst material bodies. Experiments that directly probe the coupling between gravitational and electromagnetic fields, i.e. the propagation of photons in a curved spacetime, are highlighted by red circles. We also mark experiments involving black holes as black dots. See Kramer et al. for a discussion of the choice of parameters and further details.

Acknowledgments

I am grateful to the organisers for inviting me to give the presentation. I thank my co-authors in the recent Double Pulsar work and in particular Norbert Wex for providing figures.

References

1. P. Touboul, G. Métris, M. Rodrigues, Y. André, Q. Baghi, et al. *Phys. Rev. Lett.* **119** (December 2017) 231101.
2. Gravity Collaboration,, *A&A* **615** (July 2018) L15.
3. Event Horizon Telescope Collaboration,, *ApJ* **875** (April 2019) L1.

4. M. Kramer, I. H. Stairs, R. N. Manchester, M. A. McLaughlin, A. G. Lyne, et al., R. D., *Science* **314** (2006) 97.
5. S. Chen, R. N. Caballero, Y. J. Guo, A. Chalumeau, K. Liu, et al., *MNRAS* **508** (December 2021) 4970.
6. B. P. Abbott, LIGO Scientific Collaboration and Virgo Collaboration, *Phys. Rev. Lett.* **116** (February 2016) 061102.
7. D. R. Lorimer and M. Kramer, *Handbook of Pulsar Astronomy* (Cambridge University Press, Cambridge, England, 2005).
8. T. Damour and J. H. Taylor, *Phys. Rev. D* **45** (1992) 1840.
9. M. Kramer, *ApJ* **509** (1998) 856.
10. B. B. P. Perera, M. A. McLaughlin, M. Kramer, I. H. Stairs, R. D. Ferdman, et al., *ApJ* **721** (October 2010) 1193.
11. T. Damour and N. Deruelle, *Ann. Inst. H. Poincaré (Physique Théorique)* **43** (1985) 107.
12. T. Damour and N. Deruelle, *Ann. Inst. H. Poincaré (Physique Théorique)* **44** (1986) 263.
13. M. Burgay, N. D'Amico, A. Possenti, R. N. Manchester, A. G. Lyne, et al., *Nature* **426** (December 2003) 531.
14. A. G. Lyne, M. Burgay, M. Kramer, A. Possenti, R. N. Manchester, et al., *Science* **303** (2004) 1153.
15. M. Kramer, I. H. Stairs, R. N. Manchester, N. Wex, A. Deller, W. Coles and et al., *Physical Reviews X* **in press** (December 2021).
16. L. L. Smarr and R. Blandford, *ApJ* **207** (1976) 574.
17. J. M. Weisberg and Y. Huang, *ApJ* **829** (September 2016) 55.
18. LIGO Scientific Collaboration, Virgo Collaboration, et al., *Phys. Rev. Lett.* **119** (October 2017) 161101.
19. J. M. Lattimer, *Universe* **5** (June 2019) 159.
20. G. Boerner, J. Ehlers and E. Rudolph, *A&A* **44** (1975) 417.
21. T. Damour and R. Ruffini, *Academie des Sciences Paris Comptes Rendus Ser. Scie. Math.* **279** (1974) 971.
22. R. A. Hulse and J. H. Taylor, *ApJ* **195** (1975) L51.
23. B. M. Barker and R. F. O'Connell, *ApJ* **199** (1975) L25.
24. V. Radhakrishnan and D. J. Cooke, *Astrophys. Lett.* **3** (1969) 225.
25. J. M. Weisberg, R. W. Romani and J. H. Taylor, *ApJ* **347** (1989) 1030.
26. Z. Arzoumanian, Radio observations of binary pulsars: Clues to binary evolution and tests of general relativity, PhD thesis, Princeton University (1995).
27. I. H. Stairs, S. E. Thorsett, J. H. Taylor and Z. Arzoumanian, Geodetic precession in PSR B1534+12, in *Pulsar Astronomy - 2000 and Beyond, IAU Colloquium 177*, eds. M. Kramer, N. Wex and R. Wielebinski (Astronomical Society of the Pacific, San Francisco, 2000), pp. 121–124.
28. R. N. Manchester, M. Kramer, A. Possenti, A. G. Lyne, M. Burgay, et al., *ApJ* **621** (March 2005) L49.
29. R. D. Ferdman, I. H. Stairs, M. Kramer, R. P. Breton, M. A. McLaughlin, et al., *ApJ* **767** (April 2013) 85.
30. M. Burgay, A. Possenti, R. N. Manchester, M. Kramer, M. A. McLaughlin, et al., *ApJ* **624** (May 2005) L113.
31. A. Noutsos, G. Desvignes, M. Kramer, N. Wex, P. C. C. Freire, et al., *A&A* **643** (November 2020) A143.
32. R. P. Breton, V. M. Kaspi, M. Kramer, M. A. McLaughlin, M. Lyutikov, et al., *Science* **321** (July 2008) 104.

33. M. Lyutikov and C. Thompson, *ApJ* **634** (December 2005) 1223.
34. M. Kramer and I. H. Stairs, *Ann. Rev. Astr. Ap.* **46** (September 2008) 541.
35. M. Kramer and N. Wex, *Class. Quant Grav.* **26** (April 2009) 073001.
36. G. Desvignes, M. Kramer, K. Lee, J. van Leeuwen, I. Stairs, et al, *Science* **365** (September 2019) 1013.
37. S. E. Gralla, A. Lupsasca and A. Philippov, *apj* **851** (December 2017) 137.
38. R. Yuen and D. B. Melrose, *PASA* **31** (October 2014) e039.
39. Y. Gupta and R. T. Gangadhara, *ApJ* **584** (2003) 418.
40. S. Johnston and M. Kramer, *MNRAS* **490** (December 2019) 4565.
41. M. Kramer, *International Journal of Modern Physics D* **23** (December 2014) 1430004.
42. A. D. Cameron, D. J. Champion, M. Kramer, M. Bailes, E. D. Barr, et al., *MNRAS* **475** (March 2018) L57.
43. M. Kramer, I. H. Stairs, V. Venkatraman Krishnan, P. C. C. Freire, F. Abbate, et al., *MNRAS* **504** (June 2021) 2094.
44. L. Shao and N. Wex, *Science China Physics, Mechanics, and Astronomy* **59** (September 2016) 699501.
45. N. Wex and M. Kramer, *Universe* **6** (September 2020) 156.
46. J. G. Williams, S. G. Turyshev and D. H. Boggs, *International Journal of Modern Physics D* **18** (January 2009) 1129.
47. F. Hofmann and J. Müller, *Classical and Quantum Gravity* **35** (February 2018) 035015.
48. T. Damour and G. Schäfer, *Phys. Rev. Lett.* **66** (1991) 2549.
49. S. M. Ransom, I. H. Stairs, A. M. Archibald, J. W. T. Hessels, D. L. Kaplan, et al., *Nature* **505** (January 2014) 520.
50. P. C. C. Freire, M. Kramer and N. Wex, *Classical and Quantum Gravity* **29** (September 2012) 184007.
51. A. M. Archibald, N. V. Gusinskaia, J. W. T. Hessels, A. T. Deller, D. L. Kaplan, et al., *Nature* **559** (2018) 73.
52. G. Voisin, I. Cognard, P. C. C. Freire, N. Wex, L. Guillemot, G. Desvignes, M. Kramer and G. Theureau, *A&A* **638** (June 2020) A24.
53. L. Shao, N. Wex and M. Kramer, *Phys. Rev. Lett.* **120** (June 2018) 241104.
54. J. D. Bekenstein, *Phys. Rev. D* **70** (October 2004) 083509.
55. S. Boran, S. Desai, E. O. Kahya and R. P. Woodard, *Physical Reviews D* **97** (February 2018) 041501.
56. T. Damour and G. Esposito-Farese, *Phys. Rev. Lett.* **70** (1993) 2220.
57. T. Damour and G. Esposito-Farese, *Phys. Rev. D* **54** (1996) 1474.
58. C. M. Will, *Living Reviews in Relativity*, **17** (2014), 4.

Dragging of inertial frames by matter and waves

Jiří Bičák

Tomáš Ledvinka

Institute of Theoretical Physics, Charles University
V Holešovičkách 2, Prague, Czech Republic

We review and analyze four specific general-relativistic problems in which gravitomagnetism plays the important role: the dragging of magnetic fields around rotating black holes, dragging inside a collapsing slowly rotating spherical shell of dust, compared with the dragging by rotating gravitational waves. We demonstrate how the quantum detection of inertial frame dragging can be accomplished by using the Unruh-DeWitt detectors. Finally, we shall briefly show how "instantaneous Machian gauges" can be useful in the cosmological perturbation theory.

Keywords: Einstein equations, Gravitomagnetism, Cosmology

PACS numbers:04.20.-q,98.80.-k

1. Introduction

The relativistic effect of the dragging of inertial frames is associated with the profound criticism of the Newtonian concepts of absolute space and time by Mach. It was this criticism which appears to be one of the most influential for Einstein in the creation of general relativity. Ernst Mach (1838-1916) was born very close to Brno (like Kurt Goedel), today Czech Republic, formerly Austria-Hungary. He was professor at the Charles-Ferdinand University in Prague for 28 years and his influence on Prague physics indirectly also led to the stay of Albert Einstein in Prague.

Let us illustrate Mach's ideas by just one thought from his most influential work:

> [The] investigator ... must feel the need of ... knowledge of the immediate connections, say, of the masses of the universe. There will hover before him as an ideal insight into the principles of the whole matter, from which accelerated and inertial motions will result in the same way *(Science of mechanics)*.

Keeping the Mach tradition, on the 150th anniversary of the birth of Ernst Mach, the international conference was organized in September 1988 at the Charles University in Prague. The conference papers are published in the book [1], including several contributions by some leading scientists, philosophers and historians of science. The meeting was inspiring for Julian Barbour and Herber Pfister who, during the meeting, decided to organize the meeting on just Mach's principle. A comprehensive volume [2], based on the conference at Tübingen in July 1993, includes not only many contributions by leading experts but also detailed texts recording many discussions.

Prague and Brno historically became attractive places for a number of influential scientists. Here we naturally recall the stay of Albert Einstein at the Karls-Ferdinand University from April 1911 until July 1912. His invitation to Prague was strongly supported by Mach's Prague pupils. Einstein wrote several pioneering papers showing the route to the final version of General Relativity, in particular in his answer to Max Abraham how a future theory of gravity should look like and, in the best known paper from Prague, he forecasted the light bending (we refer, e.g., to [3] for details). From the point of view of dragging, however, it is most interesting that it was in Prague where this phenomenon was first discussed, albeit based on Einstein's Prague preliminary version of general relativity. In his work [4] he considers a shell of matter and its influence on a mass point placed in its center as the shell starts to accelerate. In his words: *This suggests that the entire inertia of a mass point is an effect of the presence of all other masses, which is based on a kind of interaction with the latter. (This is exactly the same point of view that E. Mach advanced in his astute investigations on this subject.)*

Experiments

A nice experiment to measure rotational dragging was suggested by Braginsky, Polnarev and Thorne in 1984 [5]. The plane of a Foucault pendulum at the South Pole will be fixed with respect to "fixed stars" around which on average will not produce the dragging of the pendulum into the rotation. However, slowly rotating "very close" Earth does produce the effect of $\omega_{\text{drag}} = 2J/R^3$, where J and R are angular momentum and radius of the Earth—see Fig. 1 left.

Most sophisticated experiment to confirm the dragging of inertial frames by the rotating Earth is, of course, Gravity Probe B.

The idea of placing a gyroscope on a free orbit around the Earth was conceived independently by L. J. Schiff and G. E. Pugh. In fact, the gyros (the "most spherical balls" produced by man) were four. There was also a telescope in the satellite with the gyros which was pointing towards the Guide Star—see Fig. 1. The launch occurred on April 20, 2004, and lasted 16 months. The first results appeared in April 2007 but the complete analysis was finished only in 2015 (see [6]). The measured frame dragging effect, -37.2 ± 7.2 mas y^{-1}, confirmed the general-relativistic prediction -39.2 ± 0.2 mas y^{-1}. The relatively large error was caused primarily by random patches of electric charge on rotors (gyros) and their housing.

A very nice experiment demonstrating the dragging effects on the nodal rates of 3 laser-ranged satellites using the Earth gravity field model produced by space mission GRACE was performed by the group of I. Ciufolini (see his plenary talk at this conference, contribution by D. Lucchesi in the Section PT5; see also the book on Gravitomagnetism by I. Ciufolini and J. A. Wheeler [7]).

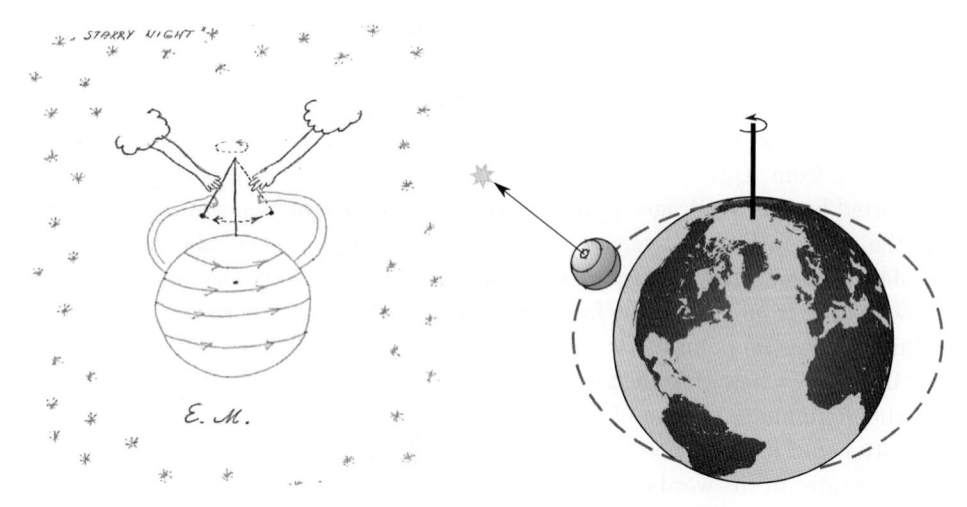

Fig. 1. *Left:* Dragging of the pendulum plane observed at the pole seen as a Machian competition between masses of distant stars and Earth. *Right:* A gyroscope on the polar orbit. Its axis changes direction both due to the geodesic precision ($\approx$ 6600mas y^{-1}) and due to frame dragging induced by Earth rotation ($\approx$ 39mas y^{-1}). This change with respect to a distant "guide" star was measured by the Gravity Probe B space experiment.

2. Magnetic fields, Meissner effect and dragging

Consider first the magnetic test field B_0 which is uniform at infinity and aligned with the hole rotation axis. Solution of Maxwell's equations on the background geometry of a rotating (Kerr) black hole with boundary condition of uniformity at infinity and finiteness at the horizon yields the field components; from these the lines of force are defined as lines tangent to the Lorentz force experienced by test magnetic/electric charges at rest with respect to locally non-rotating frames (preferred by the Kerr background field). The field lines are plotted in Fig. 2 for $a = 0.5M$ and in the extreme case when $a = M$. Notice that only weak expulsion occurs in the former case. There is a simple analytic formula for the flux across the hemisphere of the horizon, see [8–10]:

$$\Phi = B_0 \pi r_+^2 \left(1 - \frac{a^4}{r_+^4}\right), \qquad (1)$$

where $r_+ = M + (M^2 - a^2)^{1/2}$. As a consequence of the coupling of magnetic field to frame-dragging effects of the Kerr geometry the electric field of a quadrupolar nature arises. Its field lines are shown in Fig. 3. Again the field lines are expelled: while even with $a = 0.95M$ it is still not very distinct, the expulsion becomes complete in the extreme case. One can demonstrate that total flux expansion takes place for all axisymmetric stationary fields around a rotating black hole [9, 10]. In Fig. 4 the field lines of a current loop in the equatorial plane are shown. The Meissner-type effect arises also for charged (Reissner-Nordström) black holes as shown in Fig. 4 right.

Although extremely charged black holes ($e^2 = M^2$) are probably not important in astrophysics they may be significant in fundamental physics (as, for example, very special supersymmetric BPS states mass of which does not get any quantum corrections). In the charged case the electromagnetic perturbations are in general coupled to gravitational perturbations, the resulting formalism is involved. Nevertheless, one may construct explicit solutions, at least in stationary cases. From these the magnetic field lines follow as in the Kerr case. The magnetic field lines of a dipole located far away from the hole look like in a flat space, however, when the dipole is close to the horizon, the expulsion in the extreme case is evident (Fig. 4 right). Due to the coupling of perturbations closed field lines appear without any electric current inside; see [11] for details. There exist exact models (exact solutions of the Einstein-Maxwell equations) representing in general rotating, charged black holes immersed in an axisymmetric magnetic field. The expulsion takes place also within this exact framework - see [12–14]. Recently, the Meissner effect was also demonstrated for extremal black-hole solutions in higher dimensions in string theory and Kaluza-Klein theory. The question of the flux expulsion from the horizons of extreme black holes in more general frameworks is not yet understood properly. The authors of [15] "believe this to be a generic phenomenon for black holes in theories with more complicated field content, although a precise specification of the dynamical situations where this effect is present seems to be out of reach."

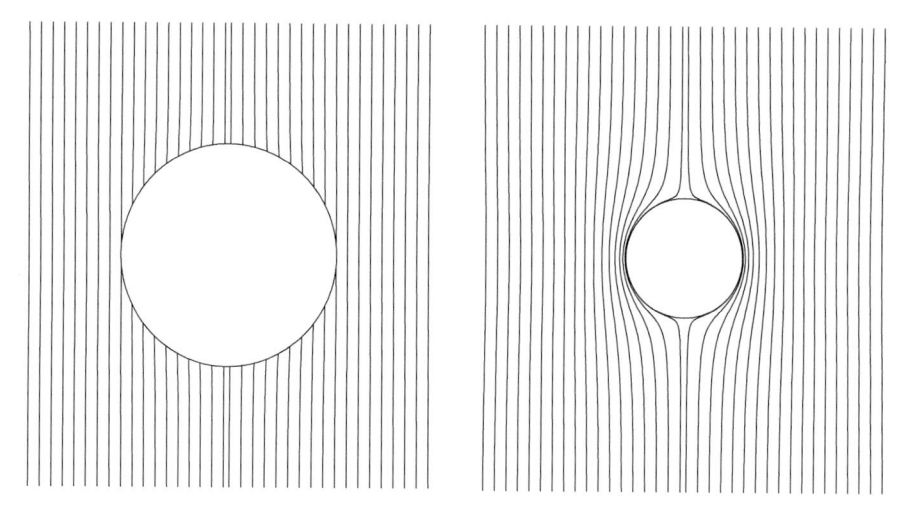

Fig. 2. Field lines of the test magnetic field uniform at infinity and aligned with the hole rotation axis. Two cases with a = 0.5M (left) and a = M (right) are shown.

The flux expulsion does not occur when the configuration is not axially symmetric. The electromagnetic field occurring when a Kerr black hole is placed in an

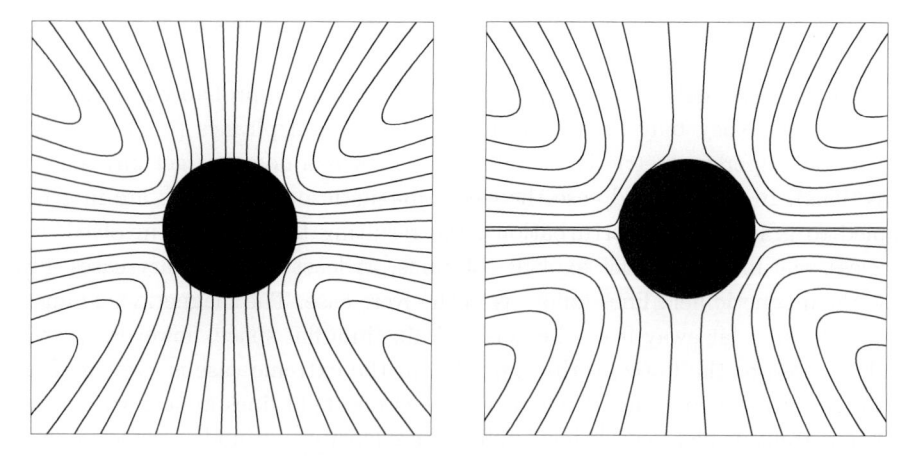

Fig. 3. Field lines of the electric field induced by the "rotating geometry" of Kerr black hole in asymptotically uniform test magnetic field; $a = 0.95M$ (left), and $a = M$ (right).

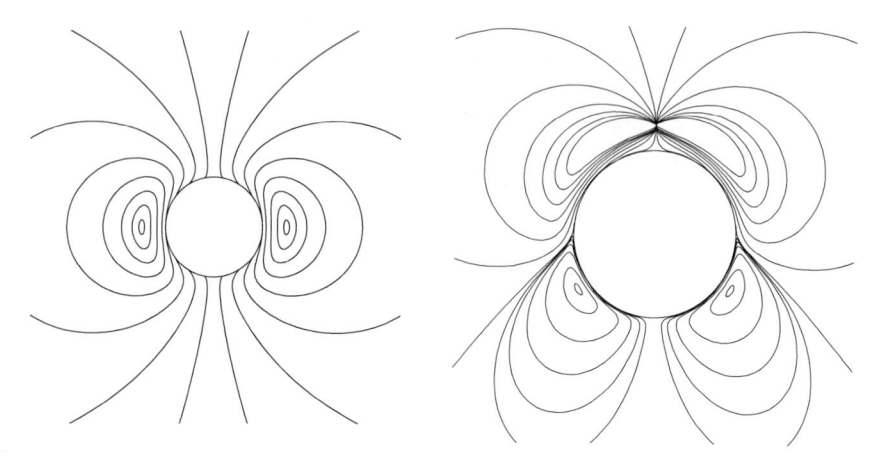

Fig. 4. *Left:* Field lines of the test magnetic field of a current loop in the equatorial plane of the Kerr spacetime with $a = 0.995M$. *Right:* Field lines of the test magnetic field of a magnetic dipole placed near the extreme Rissner-Nordström black hole.

originally uniform magnetic field without assuming the alignment of the direction of the magnetic field and the axis of symmetry of the black hole was first given in [16] (see also [17], [9]).

The properties of these "oblique" fields and their possible astrophysical relevance were already studied in the contribution [12] to the 5th Marcel Grossmann Meeting in Perth. They were then much developed in a number of important papers by V. Karas and his group appearing until today. Here we mention just few results and refer to the paper by V. Karas given in the Session PT5 of this MG16 meeting. One of the effects of the rotation on the fields which are asymptotically uniform and perpendicular to the rotation axis is the dragging of field lines by rotation and, as a consequence, the appearance of critical points where the field vanishes as seen in Fig. 5.

Fig. 5. Field lines in the equatorial plane of the Kerr black hole with color indicating the intensity of the field. Field lines which are asymptotically uniform and perpendicular to the rotation axis are dragged by rotation in vacuum (no conductive medium around). The horizon is in the center as a point. The critical point appears where the field vanishes (approx. at 11 hours). The figure is taken from [18].

In the most recent work, Karas *et al* realized that due to the presence of the plasma in the accretion flows and differential rotation even weak electromagnetic fields are crucial. Although magnetic fields within the accretion flow are turbulent in almost empty funnels around the rotation axis they can be organized on large scales and it is from here where they can accelerate the charged particles and produce collimated jets. Most recently, Karas and Kopáček conclude that inclined field (its oblique component) leads to more efficient acceleration and larger final Lorentz factors of escaping particles; see [19] and number of references therein. For an leading expert view on formation of jets and black-hole shadow in case of M87, see the contribution of R. Blandford to the Session PT5 of this MG16 meeting.

3. Dragging by a slowly rotating, collapsing spherical shell

A spherical shell in slow rotation and collapse (see Fig. 6) produces slightly perturbed Schwarzschild spacetime outside with the metric

$$ds^2 \doteq \left(1 - \frac{2M}{r}\right) dt^2 - \left(1 - \frac{2M}{r}\right)^{-1} dr^2 - r^2 \, d\theta^2 - r^2 \, (d\phi - \omega dt)^2 \,. \quad (2)$$

Here ω is the frame dragging potential given by $\omega = 2J/r^3$, J is fixed (small) total angular momentum of the shell. At the shell's surface $r = r_s$ is decreasing as shell collapses and $\omega_s = 2J/r_s^3$ is increasing. Notice (Fig. 6) that $\Omega = d\phi_s/dt$ is the angular velocity of the shell, $r_s^2 \Omega^2$ is neglected.

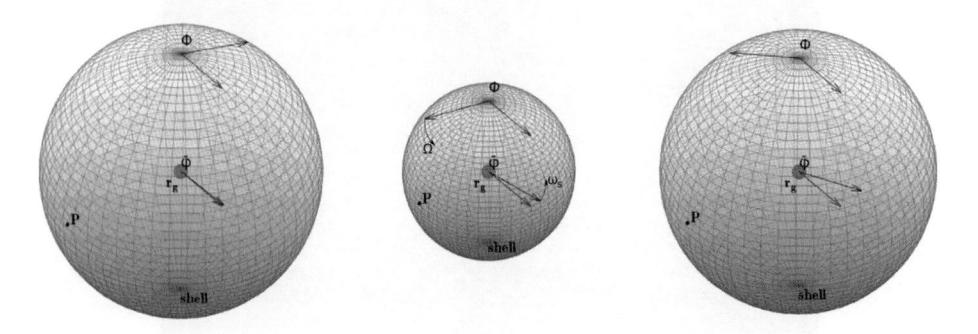

Fig. 6. Dragging of a gyroscope inside a slowly rotating, collapsing and rebouncing thin shell. Angular velocities of the vectors indicating the shell rotation Ω and the central inertial frame rotation ω_s are shown in the middle panel. See [21] for details. (Stills from the animation https://utf.mff.cuni.cz/~ledvinka/psi/a1.mp4 by W. Barker.)

The spacetime inside the shell is flat in this approximation. Its metric $ds^2 = dt^2 - dr^2 - r^2 \, d\theta^2 - r^2 \sin^2\theta \, d\bar\phi^2$ can be joined across the shell to the metric outside. Because $d\bar\phi = d\phi - \omega_s \, dt$, the local *inertial* frames (LIFs) inside ($\bar\phi = $ const.) all rotate rigidly with the same angular velocity w.r.t. the observers at rest relative to infinity ("static observers" with $\phi = $ const). Thus $d\bar\phi/dt = 0$ implies the time-dependent angular velocity $d\phi/dt = \omega_s(t)$ of the rigid rotation.

As measured *in LIF's* own proper time the rate of rotation is

$$\frac{d\phi}{d\bar{t}} = \bar\omega_s = \omega_s \frac{dt}{d\bar{t}}\bigg|_s . \quad (3)$$

Static observers inside experience *Euler acceleration* (Coriolis $\sim \omega_s^2$, centrifugal $\sim \omega_s^2$) and the congruence of their *worldlines* twists. Rate of rotation $\bar\Omega_\tau$ of the shell itself measured in its proper comoving time τ is

$$\bar\Omega_\tau = \frac{3r_s}{4m_s}\omega_s = \frac{3J}{2m_s r_s^2}. \quad (4)$$

Many details about this system can be found in Refs. [20–22].

4. Quantum detection of inertial frames dragging

Recently, we studied quantum Unruh-DeWitt detectors [23] and their suitability, at least in principle, for the detection of the dragging of inertial frames [24] and for the detection of a conicity of space [25]. We have shown, for the first time as far as we know, that the dragging of inertial frames (as well as conicity) can be observed by a quantum detector. We studied the response function of UdW detector placed in a slowly rotating shell which has flat spacetime inside and slowly rotating Kerr metric outside, as discussed in the previous Section. (Here we assume the shell to be stationary, not collapsing.)

The detector is a two-state system with energy gap Ω and the field-interaction Hamiltonian $\hat{H}(\tau) = \lambda \chi(\tau) \hat{\mu}(\tau) \otimes \hat{\Psi}(x(\tau))$, where $\chi(\tau)$ is switching function of the detector (ensuring that the interaction duration is $\Delta \tau = \pi/k$), $x(\tau)$ its worldline, $\hat{\mu}(\tau)$ its monopole momentum operator and λ is the coupling constant. We assume the detector-field system is in initial state $|0\rangle_D |0\rangle_\Phi$. Then the transition probability P to $|1\rangle_D$ is

$$P = \lambda^2 \mathcal{F} + O(\lambda^4). \qquad (5)$$

The response function $\mathcal{F}$ of the detector turns out to be

$$\mathcal{F} = \int_{-\infty}^{\infty} \int_{-\infty}^{\infty} \chi(\tau_1)\chi(\tau_2) e^{-i\Omega(\tau_2-\tau_1)} W(x(\tau_1), x(\tau_2)) \, d\tau_1 \, d\tau_2, \qquad (6)$$

where the Wightman function of the field is

$$W(x(\tau_1), x(\tau_2)) = {}_\Phi\langle 0| \hat{\phi}(x(\tau_2)) \hat{\phi}(x(\tau_1)) |0\rangle_\Phi. \qquad (7)$$

We show that the response function picks up the presence of rotation even though the spacetime inside the shell is flat and the detector is locally inertial. The detector can distinguish between the static situation when the shell is non-rotating and the stationary case when the shell rotates and the dragging of inertial frames, i.e. gravitomagnetic effects, arise. Moreover, it can do so when the detector is switched on for a finite time interval within which a light signal cannot travel to the shell and back to convey the presence of rotation.

The summary of the results for quantum detection of the dragging of inertial frames is taken from the publication [24]. (See also the contribution of W. Cong in the Session PT5 at MG 16.)

5. Dragging effects of gravitational waves

Rotating gravitational waves can also become a source of the dragging. The situation when the central frame is surrounded by rotating gravitational waves was for the first time modeled assuming the translational symmetry along z-axis in [26, 27]. Although this assumption implies unbounded energy of the gravitational waves and the spacetime is not asymptotically flat, the problem can be treated analytically as the master equation for the single function describing the gravitational wave has

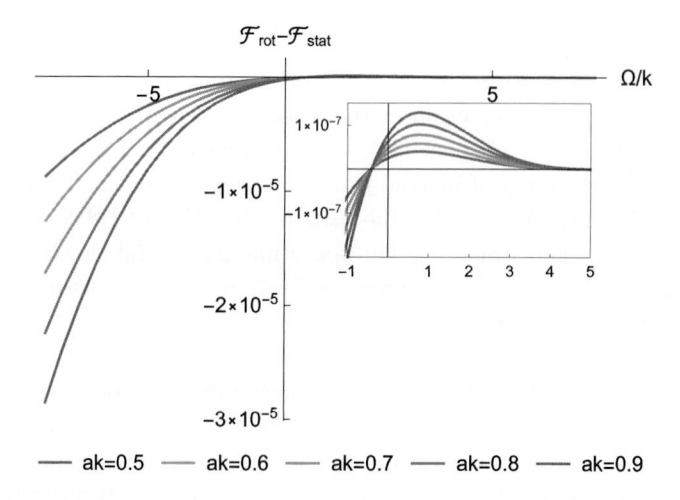

Fig. 7. Comparison with the detector in a static shell. Detector response function inside a slowly rotating shell is plotted for several values of the shell angular momentum $J = Ma$ appearing in the dimensionless parameter ak, where k is the frequency of detector switching function $\chi(\tau)$. The difference $\mathcal{F}_{rot} - \mathcal{F}_{stat}$ is plotted as a function of the energy gap Ω of the detector. Shell mass M and radius R radius satisfy $Mk = 1$, $Rk = 3$, detector is placed at $r_d = 0.5/k$ from the center.

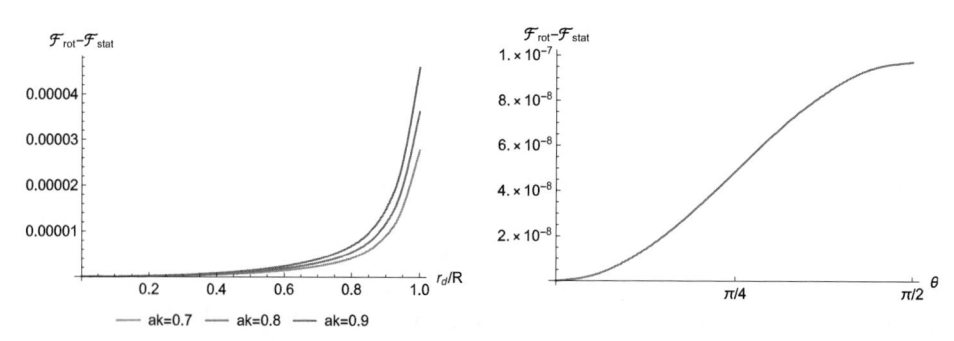

Fig. 8. Detected difference between rotating and static shell depends of the distance of the detector from the center (left) and on the spherical angular coordinate θ of the detector. Remaining parameters are described in Fig. 7.

the form of a flat-space wave equation $\Box\psi(t, \rho, \varphi) = 0$. Given a particular solution to this equation, other metric functions appearing in the line element

$$ds^2 = e^{2\gamma - 2\psi}(dt^2 - d\rho^2) - W^2 e^{-2\psi}(d\varphi + \omega\, dt)^2 - e^{2\psi} dz^2 \qquad (8)$$

can be determined from the Einstein equations. In particular, averaging of their $t - \varphi$ component identifies $\langle \psi_{,t} \psi_{,\phi} \rangle$ as a source of the dragging of the inertial frames on the axis and for ψ in the form of a cylindrical shell the central frame rotation is then found in a closed form. The analogy with angular momentum transport in spiral galaxies is discussed in [27].

A similar problem permitting asymptotic flatness was then studied in [21, 28]. The gravitational waves are assumed to form a spherical shell described again by a single scalar function $\psi(t, \mathbf{x})$ satisfying flat-space wave equations $\Box \psi = 0$ which this time appears only as the first order approximation of the full Einstein equations. The spacetime metric (in which we now use signature $-+++$)

$$g_{\mu\nu} = \eta_{\mu\nu} + h^{(1)}_{\mu\nu} + h^{(2)}_{\mu\nu} + \dots \tag{9}$$

is decomposed into a flat Minkowski metric $\eta_{\mu\nu} = \text{diag}(-1, 1, r^2, r^2 \sin^2 \theta)$ in spherical coordinates t, r, θ, φ, and the first and second-order perturbations $h^{(1)}_{\mu\nu}$ and $h^{(2)}_{\mu\nu}$. Then the first-order metric perturbations due to linearized gravitational waves appear the source of the second order perturbations

$$G^{(1)}_{\mu\nu}[h^{(2)}] = -G^{(2)}_{\mu\nu}[h^{(1)}, h^{(1)}], \tag{10}$$

where $G^{(2)}_{\mu\nu}[h^{(1)}, h^{(1)}]$ contains terms of the Einstein tensor $G_{\mu\nu}$ quadratic in the first-order perturbations.

Assuming the Regge-Wheeler gauge the function ψ then directly determines $h^{(1)}_{t\theta}, h^{(1)}_{t\varphi}, h^{(1)}_{r\theta}$, and $h^{(1)}_{r\varphi}$, with remaining first-order perturbations vanishing, and the effects of the linearized gravitational waves are then determined by the analysis of the second-order terms. To make space approximately flat for the central observer

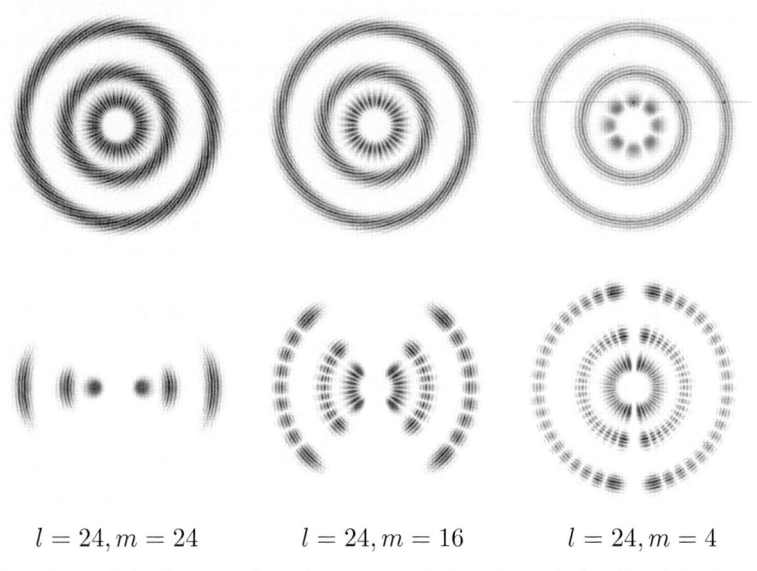

Fig. 9. Snapshots of the function ψ in the equatorial plane $\theta = \pi/2$ (top) and in the meridional plane $\varphi = 0, \pi$ (bottom) at three distinct times $t = 0, 2a, 4a$. The well-known behavior of spherical harmonics $Y_{lm} \sim \sin^{|m|} \theta$ means that for higher m the first order perturbations vanish not only near the center where we study the frame dragging but also along the z axis. The top right plot also shows the position of a null particle with $\mathbf{r} = a\hat{\mathbf{y}} + t\hat{\mathbf{x}}$ at given times to illustrate the localization of the wave at radii $r \approx \sqrt{a^2 + t^2}$. (We denote Cartesian unit vectors $\hat{\mathbf{x}}, \hat{\mathbf{y}}$, red/blue color indicates positive/negative ψ.)

and his inertial frame, $h^{(1)}_{\mu\nu}$ is assumed to vanish near the origin. Assuming a particular gauge, the quantity determining the central frame dragging can be determined from a quantity satisfying an elliptic equation, in a way similar to other situations. The central-frame rotation appears in the perturbation approach as a $l = 1, m = 0$ component in the expansion of $h^{(2)}_{\mu\nu}$ into mutually orthogonal spherical tensor harmonics. Then a projection of Eq. (10) into the relevant $m = 0$ tensor harmonic function resembles an averaging and yields

$$\frac{1}{2}\left[h_0^{(2)\prime\prime} - \frac{l(l+1)}{r^2}h_0^{(2)} - \dot{h}_1^{(2)\prime} - \frac{2}{r}\dot{h}_1^{(2)}\right] = \frac{1}{l(l+1)}\int_0^{2\pi}\int_0^{\pi} G_{t\varphi}^{(2)}[h^{(1)}, h^{(1)}]\partial_\theta Y_{l0}\, d\theta\, d\varphi,$$

where $h_0^{(2)}$ determines $h_{t\theta}^{(2)}, h_{t\varphi}^{(2)}$, and $h_1^{(2)}$ determines $h_{r\theta}^{(2)}, h_{r\varphi}^{(2)}$ components of the second-order metric perturbations. Dots and primes denote the time and radial derivatives. The rotation of the central frame $d\tilde\varphi = d\varphi - \omega_0 dt$ appears as $h_{t\varphi}^{(2)} = -\omega_0 r^2 \sin^2\theta$, so it is determined by the behavior of $h_0^{(2)}$ at $r = 0$. Using a global change of coordinate $\varphi \to \varphi + \delta\varphi^{(2)}(t,r)$, we can set

$$h_1^{(2)} = 0, \quad \text{i.e.,} \quad h_{r\varphi}^{(2)} = 0. \tag{11}$$

Near the center we then have the Minkowski metric in spherical coordinates with the dominating perturbation corresponding to the slow rigid rotating of the central frame with angular velocity $\omega_0(t)$. Fixing the gauge condition (11), $h_{1\,l=1,m=0}^{(2)} = 0$, prohibits any radial dependence of an additional coordinate transformation $\varphi \to \varphi + \delta\varphi^{(2)}(t,r)$ and the angle φ in the center and thus also the central frame rotation ω_0 is determined *unambiguously* with respect to spatial infinity. We find

$$\omega_0 = \frac{1}{4\pi}\iiint R_{t\varphi}^{(2)}[h^{(1)}, h^{(1)}]\frac{\sin\theta}{r}dr\, d\theta\, d\varphi. \tag{12}$$

To investigate further a particular closed-form solution ψ of the wave equation, it has been chosen in the form of a shell of null radiation converging toward the origin, bouncing at the minimal radius $r \approx a$, and then expanding back to infinity (see Fig. 9). This allowed us to evaluate the integral (12) and find the explicit (though lengthy) formula for ω_0. Assuming $l \gg 1$ it simplifies to

$$\omega_0(t) \doteq \frac{\omega_0^{\max}}{\left(1 + \frac{t^2}{a^2}\right)^{3/2}}. \tag{13}$$

In the same limit, we show in [21] that the frame dragging is determined by the angular momentum of the gravitational wave L_z and that the long exact formula can be approximated by $\omega_0^{\max} \doteq 2L_z/a^3$. The angular momentum of the linearized gravitational waves is defined using the effective stress energy tensor

$$L_z = -\int T_{t\varphi}^{\text{eff}}\, d^3x, \quad T_{t\varphi}^{\text{eff}} = \frac{1}{8\pi}G_{t\varphi}^{(2)}[h^{(1)}, h^{(1)}]. \tag{14}$$

We can see that (12) and (14) differ by a factor r^3 inside the integral. This explains why the approximate relation (13) holds: because for $l \gg 1$ the function ψ is localized around a thin shell with radius $r(t) \doteq \sqrt{a^2 + t^2}$ (see Fig. 9), the factor r^3 can

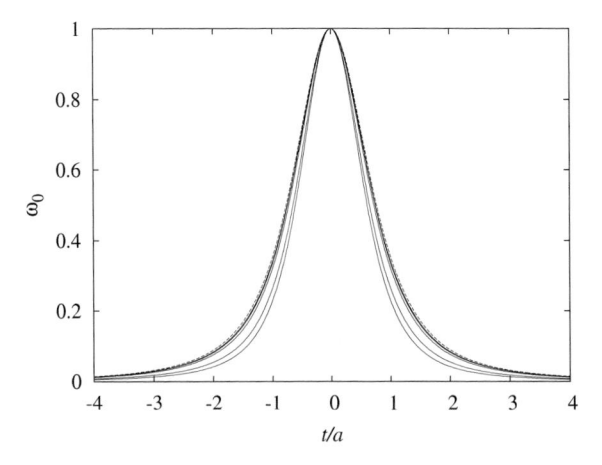

Fig. 10. The dependence of the normalized angular velocity of the central inertial frame $\omega_0(l,1;t)/\omega_0(l,1;t=0)$ on the parameter $l = 2,3,10,20,30$ (from inside to out). The dependence (13) is shown as a dashed line.

be put in front of the integral. The time dependence of $\omega_0(t)$ on the parameter l is shown in Fig. 10.

In an asymptotically flat spacetime we have two special flat-space worldlines categories — the one of the central observer and that of a cautious observer who slowly retreats to $r \gg a$ so that she never meets significant metric perturbations. The discrepancy between the orientation of the gyroscopes following these worldlines

$$\Delta\varphi_0 = \int_{-\infty}^{\infty} \omega_0(t)\, dt \qquad (15)$$

can be seen as an illustration of the dependence of the parallel transport on the chosen worldline. In Fig. 11 we illustrate $\Delta\varphi_0$ as an obvious implication of the spacetime curvature due to the rotating gravitational waves. Thus, although the immediate value of ω_0 involves instantaneous effects, its integral (15) representing the total rotation of the central gyroscope is a well-defined observable quantity. In the approximation $l \gg 1$ we then obtain $\Delta\varphi_0 \doteq 2a\omega_0^{\max} \doteq 4L_z/a^2$. Such a simple relation is not available for dragging by a massive rotating shell, because its dynamics is not as unambiguous as that of gravitational radiation.

6. On the dragging of inertial frames and Mach's principle in cosmology

In our treatment of the dragging of inertial frames in a cosmological context we shall mostly confine ourselves to the linear (cosmological) perturbation theory, rather than to exact models. Our inspiration will be Mach's principle as generally formulated by Hermann Bondi in his classical book [29]: ...*all motions, velocities, rotations and accelerations are relative; local inertial frames are determined through*

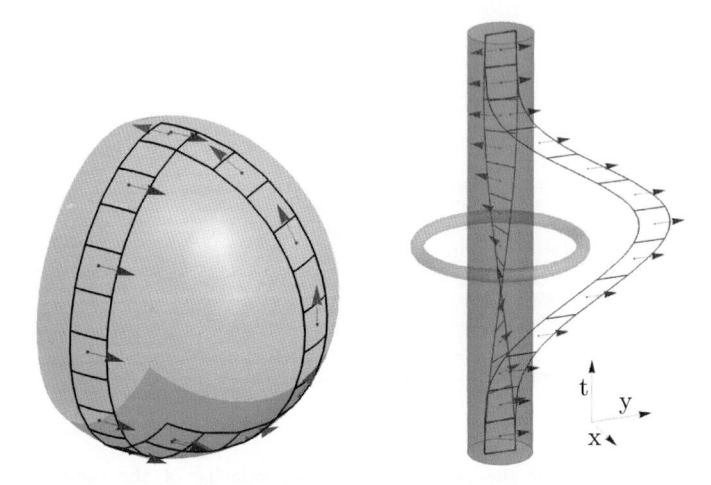

Fig. 11. *Left:* The fundamental dependence of parallel transport on the chosen path is usually demonstrated on a spherical surface naturally embedded in three-dimensional flat Euclidean space. Here we use neighborhoods of two meridians as an example of two approximately flat patches which yield mismatch when vector from the south pole is extended into both patches. *Right:* In our spacetime with rotating gravitational waves we also have two approximately flat patches. The spacetime is asymptotically flat which in the figure is symbolized by the blue "ladder" with arrows indicating "fixed" direction of a gyroscope. Because the gravitational waves do not reach the center, there is also approximately flat region near the center. Its worldtube is depicted as a gray cylinder. The gravitational waves are shown at the moment they are the strongest ($t = 0$) as a blue torus encircling the central observer. The rotation of the central inertial frame (and gyroscopes there) is illustrated by the twist of the red spacetime-coordinate "ladder" and the gyroscope orientation. The mismatch of gyroscope directions at the top demonstrates the meaning of Eq. (15) as the implication of a particular form of spacetime curvature accompanying the rotating gravitational wave.

distributions of energy and momentum in the Universe by some weighted averages of the apparent motions.

We started to realize such a "Machian program" in [30]. We first analysed frame-dragging effects due to slowly, rigidly rotating, but collapsing or expanding spheres in the (inhomogeneous) Lemaître-Tolman-Bondi universes, and we analysed the dragging effects of the vector perturbations of the FLRW universes described in a special gauge such that three (momentum) constraint equations enabled us to determine instantaneously metric perturbations h_{0k} ($k = 1, 2, 3$) in terms of energy-momentum perturbations δT_{0k} and show how such averages are to be taken. In closed universes a linear combination of six Killing vectors (three rotations plus three quasitranslations) may be added to the h_{0k}. We also obtain the solutions of the three constraint equations when angular momenta corresponding to the three rotations and quasimomenta corresponding to the three quasitranslations of the sources (determined by δT_{0k}) are given. No absolute rotations exist in closed universe, only differences of rotation rates are determinable — in accord with Mach's ideas that 'all motions are relative'. (If the velocities of the bodies, described by perturbations of perfect fluid, are given, the metric perturbations are determined uniquely.) The last result is related to the fundamental fact that six globally conserved quantities, corresponding to the six Killing vectors in a FLRW universe, must all vanish if considered for the whole closed universe.

It was, among others, an attempt to understand Mach's principle in cosmological perturbation theory, which inspired us to formulate conservation laws even for large perturbations with respect to curved backgrounds [31]. The resulting 'KBL superpotential' (using the designation by Julia and Silva in their profound analysis [32]), was found, after applying certain natural criteria, to be unambigous and most satisfactory in spacetimes with or without a cosmological constant, in any spacetime dimension. It also found applications in various studies of generation of cosmological perturbations (see [33] for references). For the recent generalization to the Horndeski theory, see [34].

In a more recent paper [33] we studied general linear perturbations of the FLRW universes from a 'Machian perspective'. This led us to investigate both rotations and accelerations of local inertial frames in perturbed universes. We first introduced congruences of cosmological observers' worldlines, defined their acceleration, rotation (twist, vorticity), shear and expansion in general, and then considered perturbed FLRW models ($g_{\mu\nu} = g_{\mu\nu}^{\text{FLRW}} + h_{\mu\nu}$). We found that un-accelerated and non-rotating local inertial frames (LIFs) are determined by $h_{00,l}, h_{0l,m}, h_{0l,0}$.

We developed all the perturbed Einstein equations in a general gauge 'ab initio', without assuming harmonic decompositions. Introducing the standard conformal time in FLRW universes, putting tildas over all the perturbation quantities, introducing the traceless part of h_k^l and notation

$$\tilde{h}_{Tk}^l = \tilde{h}_k^l - \tfrac{1}{3}\delta_k^l \tilde{h}_n^n, \qquad \mathcal{T}_k = \nabla_l \tilde{h}_{Tk}^l, \qquad \mathcal{K} = \tfrac{3}{2}\dot{a}\tilde{h}_{00} + \tfrac{1}{2}a\dot{\tilde{h}}_n^n - \nabla_l \tilde{h}_0^l, \qquad (16)$$

where ∇_l is the covariant derivative associated with the spatial FLRW background metric f_{kl}, a is the expansion factor, dot the derivative w.r.t. standard cosmological time t whereas the prime denotes the derivative with respect to conformal time η, $adt = d\eta$. Using $\nabla^2 = f^{kl}\nabla_{kl}$, $k = 0, \pm 1$ for the curvature index and $\mathcal{H} = aH$, H being the standard Hubble parameter, we find Einstein's equations for perturbations to obtain the form

$$a^2 \kappa \delta \tilde{T}_0^0 = a^2 \delta \tilde{G}_0^0 = \tfrac{1}{3}\nabla^2 \tilde{h}_n^n + k\tilde{h}_n^n - 2\mathcal{H}\mathcal{K} - \tfrac{1}{2}\nabla_k \mathcal{T}^k, \qquad (17)$$

$$a^2 \kappa \delta \tilde{T}_k^0 = a^2 \delta \tilde{G}_k^0 = \tfrac{1}{2}\nabla^2 \tilde{h}_{k0} + k\tilde{h}_{k0} + \tfrac{1}{6}\nabla_{kl}\tilde{h}_0^l + \tfrac{2}{3}\nabla_k \mathcal{K} - \tfrac{1}{2}(\mathcal{T}_k)', \qquad (18)$$

$$a^2 \kappa \left(\delta \tilde{T}_0^0 - \delta \tilde{T}_n^n\right) = a^2 \left(\delta \tilde{G}_0^0 - \delta \tilde{G}_n^n\right) = \nabla^2 \tilde{h}_{00} + 3a\left(\tfrac{1}{a}\mathcal{H}\right)' \tilde{h}_{00} + \tfrac{2}{a}(a\mathcal{K})', \qquad (19)$$

and

$$a^2 \kappa \left(\delta \tilde{T}_k^l - \tfrac{1}{3}\delta_k^l \delta \tilde{T}_n^n\right) = a^2 \delta \tilde{G}_{Tk}^l = \ldots . \qquad (20)$$

We do not write down fully the last equation since it describes waves and is not important for the determination of LIFs.

To see how the LIFs can be determined by surrounding matter instantaneously on certain time-slices we use some specific gauges which we call the "Machian gauges". We give three examples of such gauges. For example, by putting $\mathcal{T}_k = 0$ and $\mathcal{K} = 0$, the first three equations become (hyper-) elliptic and the quantities determining LIFs can be found instantaneously when the (perturbations of) matter distribution are given. The gauge conditions $\mathcal{T}_k = 0$, fixing spatial coordinates, are associated with the "transverse-traceless" gauges in the linearized gravity and minimal-shear condition in numerical relativity. We assume these conditions to be valid in all three Machian gauges. In the first Machian gauge we choose the time slices to be so that $\mathcal{K} = 0$. This implies the "constant mean curvature slices", and it coincides with Bardeen's uniform-Hubble expansion gauge. In other two Machian gauges, together with the same gauge condition on spatial coordinates, we require "uniform-intrinsic scalar curvature condition" and the "minimal-shear hypersurface condition" (called the Poisson gauge by Bertschinger in 1995). In [33] these gauges are discussed in detail. In particular it is shown that they admit much less residual freedom than the synchronous gauge, frequently used in cosmology.

These Machian gauges have been considered in the group of D. Wiltshire, in particular, in [35], in the review [36] and, most recently, by his students M. Williams [37] and R. Gaur [38] in the context of the Post-Newtonian Cosmology.

We believe that dragging effects and Machian ideas will remain the source of inspiration.

Acknowledgments

We acknowledge the partial support from Grant No. GAČR 21/11268S.

References

1. V. Prosser and J. Folta (eds.), *Ernst Mach and the Development of Physics* (Universitas Carolina Pragensis, Karolinum, Prague, 1991).
2. J. B. Barbour and H. Pfister (eds.), *Mach's Principle: From Newton's Bucket to Quantum Gravity* (Birkhäuser, Boston, 1995).
3. J. Bičák, *Einstein in Prague: Relativity Then and Now*, in *General Relativity, Cosmology and Atrophysics*, Fundamental Theories of Physics 177, eds. J. Bičák and T. Ledvinka (Springer, Cham, 2014), p. 33.
4. A. Einstein, Gibt es eine Gravitationswirkung, die der electrodynamischen Induktionswirkung analog ist?, *Vierteljahrsschrift für gerichtliche Medizin und öffentliches Sanitätswesen* **44**, 37–40 (1912).
5. V. B. Braginskii, A. G. Polnarev and K. S. Thorne, Foucault pendulum at the south pole - Proposal for an experiment to detect the Earth's general relativistic gravitomagnetic field, *Phys. Rev. Lett.* **53**, p. 863 (1984).
6. C. W. F. Everitt et al., The Gravity Probe B test of general relativity, *Class. Quantum Grav.* **32**, 224001 (2015).
7. I. Ciufolini and J. A. Wheeler, *Gravitation and Inertia* (Princeton University Press, 1995).
8. A. R. King, J. P. Lasota and W. Kundt, Black holes and magnetic fields, *Phys. Rev. D* **12**, p. 3037 (1975).

9. J. Bičák and V. Janiš, Magnetic fluxes across black holes, *Mon. Not. R. Astron. Soc.* **212**, p. 899 (1985).
10. J. Bičák and T. Ledvinka, Electromagnetic fields around black holes and Meissner effect, *Nuovo Cimento B Serie* **115**, p. 739 (2000).
11. J. Bičák and L. Dvořák, Stationary electromagnetic fields around black holes. III. General solutions and the fields of current loops near the Reissner-Nordström black hole, *Phys. Rev. D* **22**, p. 2933 (1980).
12. J. Bičák and V. Karas, The influence of black holes on uniform magnetic fields, in *Proceedings of the 5th Marcel Grossmann Meeting on General Relativity*, Part B, eds. D. Blair and M. Buckingham (World Scientific, Singapore, 1989), p. 1199.
13. V. Karas and D. Vokrouhlický, On interpretation of the magnetized Kerr-Newman black hole., *Journal of Mathematical Physics* **32**, p. 714 (1991).
14. V. Karas and Z. Budínová, Magnetic Fluxes Across Black Holes in a Strong Magnetic Field Regime, *Physica Scripta* **61**, p. 253 (2000).
15. A. Chamblin, R. Emparan and G. W. Gibbons, Superconducting p-branes and extremal black holes, *Phys. Rev. D* **58**, 084009 (1998).
16. J. Bičák and L. Dvořák, Stationary electromagnetic fields around black holes. II. General solutions and the fields of some special sources near a Kerr black hole., *General Relativity and Gravitation* **7**, p. 959 (1976).
17. M. D. Pollock and W. P. Brinkmann, The Interaction between a Weak Magnetic Field and a Black Hole, *Proceedings of the Royal Society of London Series A* **356**, p. 351 (1977).
18. V. Karas, O. Kopáček and D. Kunneriath, Influence of frame-dragging on magnetic null points near rotating black holes, *Class. Quantum Grav.* **29**, 035010 (2012).
19. V. Karas and O. Kopáček, Near horizon structure of escape zones of electrically charged particles around weakly magnetized rotating black hole: Case of oblique magnetosphere, *Astronomische Nachrichten* **342**, p. 357 (2021).
20. J. Katz, D. Lynden-Bell and J. Bičák, Instantaneous inertial frames but retarded electromagnetism in rotating relativistic collapse, *Class. Quantum Grav.* **15**, p. 3177 (1998).
21. W. Barker, T. Ledvinka, D. Lynden-Bell and J. Bičák, Rotation of inertial frames by angular momentum of matter and waves, *Class. Quantum Grav.* **34**, 205006 (2017).
22. H. Pfister and M. King, *Inertia and Gravitation*, Lecture Notes in Physics 897 (Springer, Cham, 2015).
23. B. S. DeWitt, Quantum gravity: the new synthesis, in *General Relativity: An Einstein centenary survey*, eds. S. W. Hawking and W. Israel (University Press, Cambridge, 1979).
24. W. Cong, J. Bičák, D. Kubizňák and R. B. Mann, Quantum detection of inertial frame dragging, *Phys. Rev. D* **103**, 024027 (2021).
25. W. Cong, J. Bičák, D. Kubizňák and R. B. Mann, Quantum detection of conicity, *Physics Letters B* **820**, 136482 (2021).
26. J. Bičák, J. Katz and D. Lynden-Bell, Gravitational waves and dragging effects, *Class. Quantum Grav.* **25**, 165017 (2008).
27. D. Lynden-Bell, J. Bičák and J. Katz, Inertial frame rotation induced by rotating gravitational waves, *Class. Quantum Grav.* **25**, 165018 (2008).
28. J. Bičák, J. Katz, T. Ledvinka and D. Lynden-Bell, Effects of rotating gravitational waves, *Phys. Rev. D* **85**, 124003 (2012).
29. H. Bondi, *Cosmology* (Cambridge University Press, London, 1960).
30. D. Lynden-Bell, J. Katz and J. Bičák, Mach's principle from the relativistic constraint equations, *Mon. Not. R. Astron. Soc.* **272**, p. 150 (1995). Errata **277**, 1600(E) (1995).

31. J. Katz, J. Bičák and D. Lynden-Bell, Relativistic conservation laws and integral constraints for large cosmological perturbations, *Phys. Rev. D* **55**, p. 5957 (1997).
32. B. Julia and S. Silva, Currents and superpotentials in classical gauge theories: II. Global aspects and the example of affine gravity, *Class. Quantum Grav.* **17**, p. 4733 (2000).
33. J. Bičák, J. Katz and D. Lynden-Bell, Cosmological perturbation theory, instantaneous gauges, and local inertial frames, *Phys. Rev. D* **76**, 063501 (2007).
34. J. Schmidt and J. Bičák, Covariant conserved currents for scalar-tensor Horndeski theory, *Journal of Mathematical Physics* **59**, 042501 (2018).
35. D. L. Wiltshire, Cosmological equivalence principle and the weak-field limit, *Phys. Rev. D* **78**, 084032 (2008).
36. D. L. Wiltshire, What is dust?—Physical foundations of the averaging problem in cosmology, *Class. Quantum Grav.* **28**, 164006 (2011).
37. M. Williams, Post-Newtonian Cosmology, dissertation, University of Canterbury, (New Zealand, 2020).
38. R. Gaur, Perturbation Theory and Averages in Inhomogeneous Cosmologies, Master's thesis, University of Canterbury (2021).

Probes of the progenitors, engines and physics behind stellar collapse

Chris L. Fryer

Center for Theoretical Astrophysics, Los Alamos National Laboratory,
Los Alamos, NM 87545, USA
E-mail: fryer@lanl.gov
https://ccsweb.lanl.gov/astro/index.html

SN are one of the most powerful explosions in the universe and astronomers have invoked the collapse of a stellar core down to a neutron star as a potential power source behind these cosmic blasts. The current paradigm behind core-collapse SN relies on convection in the region just above the newly formed neutron star. This engine was driven and confirmed by observations. We review this observational evidence, and the potential for further observational constraints in this paper.

Keywords: SNe; neutron star; black hole

PACS numbers: 97.60.Bw, 97.60.Jd, 97.60.Lf

1. Core-Collapse SNe (CCSNe)

The SN field was established Baade and Zwicky coined the term "Super-nova" (SN) to explain the most powerful class of novae.[1] Shortly thereafter, Zwicky also proposed what has become one of the standard energy sources behind these cosmic explosions: the collapse of the core of a massive star down to a neutron star.[2] Zwicky argued that this core-collapse SNe (CCSN) mechanism would tap the potential energy released when the core of a massive star collapsed down to a neutron star. The details of how this works has taken nearly 90 years to work out.

Over the past 8-9 decades, scientists have continued to refine the basic model behind CCSN. Stellar models focused on identifying which stars would produce cores that would collapse down to SNe. Stars are powered by nuclear fusion in their cores and the most massive stars can undergo a series of nuclear burning phases, where the ashes of the previous phase are fused in the next burning phase, until an iron core is produced. Iron is maximally compact, its fusion does not generate energy and the contraction of the iron core causes electron capture and the collapse of the core. This collapse only stops when the core forms a proto-neutron star, realizing the engine proposed by Zwicky.

1-dimensional simulations of stellar evolution have allowed astronomers to piece together the detailed evolution of these successive burning stages. This evolution is capture in a diagram developed by Kippenhahn.[3] Figure 1 shows the Kippenhahn diagram describing the evolution of a $22\,M_\odot$ star.[4] These Kippenhahn diagrams contain a wealth of information. The top curve denotes the mass of the star as a

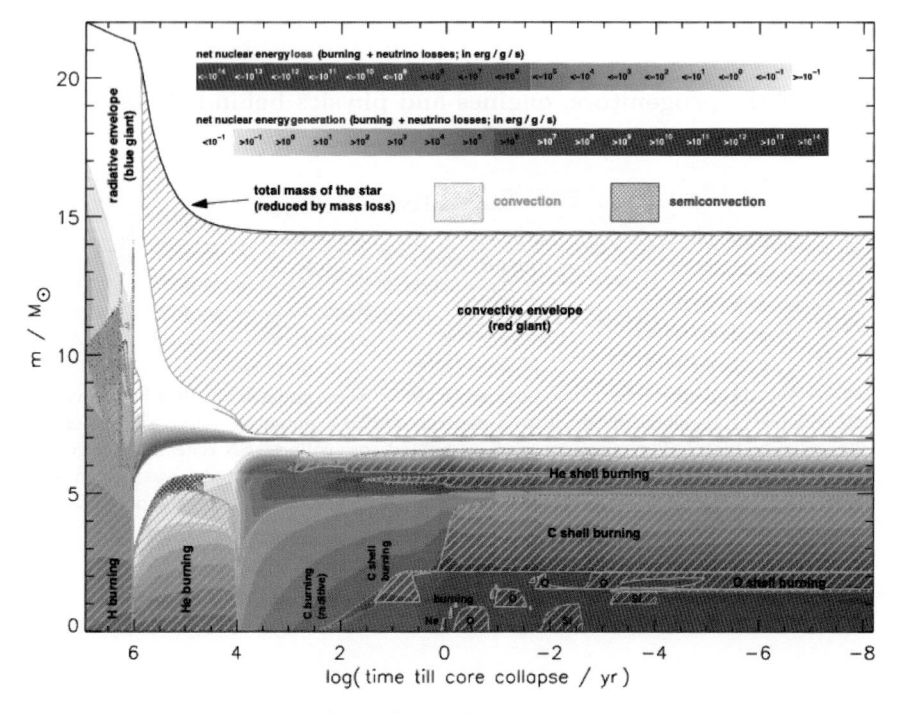

Fig. 1. Enclosed mass vs. time before collapse of a 22 M$_\odot$ star. This diagram encapsulates the entire life of the star. It color codes energy deposition from fusion and energy losses from neutrinos. Hash marks denote convection and the top line denotes mass loss from winds.

function of time. The lower-left corner shows the hydrogen burning core which lasts until a million years prior to collapse. The next phase is the helium core burning phase that lasts until 10,000 y prior to collapse. At the end of helium core burning, the core collapses and helium begins to fuse in a shell layer above this core. In the last 100 y, the star goes through a series of carbon, oxygen and silicon core and shell burning, building up an iron core. The timescales and the evolution of the core can all be learned from this diagram.

This iron core is supported by a combination of thermal and electron-degeneracy pressure. As the mass of this iron core continues to grow, the core contracts. Ultimately, electrons in the core capture onto protons, removing the support pressure and causing a runaway collapse. This collapse proceeds until the core reaches nuclear densities and neutron degeneracy pressure and nuclear forces halt the collapse. The collapse of the iron core to this proto-neutron star releases nearly 100 times the energy needed to drive the observed explosion. When the collapse halts, it can produce a strong bounce and preliminary 1-dimensional calculations of this collapse phase produced weak explosions.[5] These explosions did not match the observed energies and were missing critical pieces of physics, most importantly, the neutrino

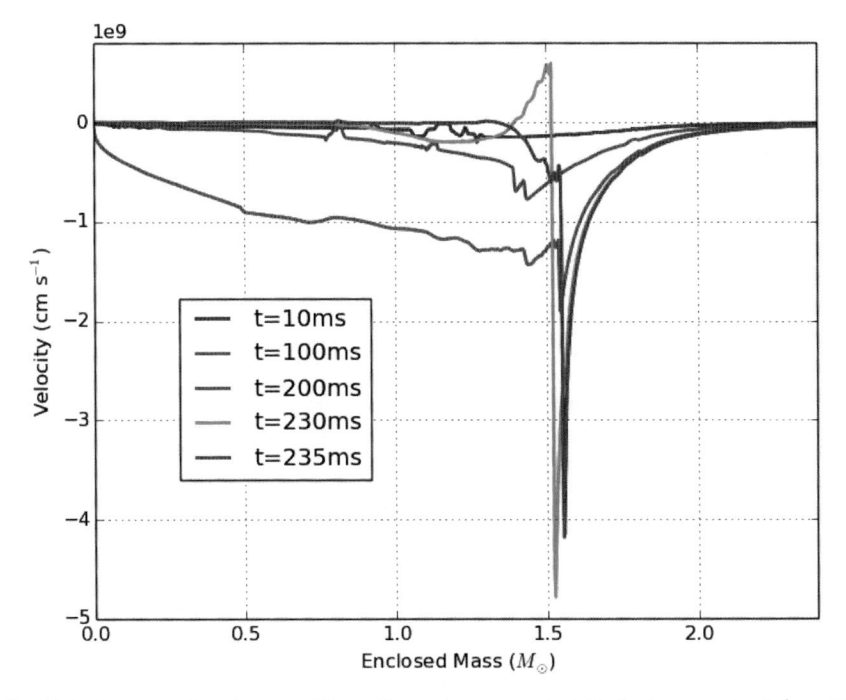

Fig. 2. Velocity vs. enclosed mass of the collapse, bounce and stall of a bounce shock for a 15 M$_\odot$ star at a series of times in the collapse. As the core begins to collapse, the infall accellerates until bounce. Shortly after the bounce, the bounce shock stalls. The different lines show this evolution.

physics. In the bounce, most of the potential energy converted into neutrinos and, as long as the neutrinos are trapped, the bounce shock propagates outward. But when the neutrinos in the outward-moving shock can escape, much of the bounce energy is lost, causing this shock to stall. Figure 2 shows the velocity evolution of a sample core collapse, bounce and bounce shock stall.

Although scientists realized that tapping the neutrinos leaking out of the core would be one way to revive the explosion, the diffusion of neutrinos was too slow to revive the shock. The first mention of convection in CCSN focused on using this convection to transport the neutrinos to the edge of the proto-neutron star, allowing the neutrinos to more quickly deposit their energy into the stalled shock.[6,7] Although this convection can play a role in our models, this is not the convection that has formed the basis for the current paradigm in SNe. The critical convection behind the convection-enhanced neutrino-driven SN engine is convection above the proto-neutron star, in the region between the edge of the proto-neutron star and the stalled shock. This paper focuses on this currently favored convection-enhanced paradigm, both the observational evidence leading to its development (Sec. 2) and the current and ongoing measurements confirming this paradigm (Sec. 3).

2. Observed Asymmetries and the Birth of the Convective Paradigm

Due to the difficulty in including all of the physics in SN models, most SN-engine simulations until the 1990s were 1-dimensional. But, with better observations of SNe and their remnants, astronomers began to demonstrate that these explosions were anything but spherically-symmetric.= In this section, we review the observations the led to the development of the convection-enhanced neutrino-driven SN explosion engine that is the current paradigm for normal SNe.

2.1. *Observed Asymmetries that Drove the Convective Paradigm*

Observations of SN remnants, both ejecta and remnant, have long argued for an asymmetries in the SN engine. Large asymmetries have been observed in many of the observed SN remnants. In spherically symmetric models, the ejecta from the SN is expected to follow the same elemental abundance layered distribution that was produced in the stellar evolution with the iron peak elements in the center with the elements getting lighter as we move out in the ejecta. The distribution in the Cassiopeia A SN remnant not only displays heavier elements further out than lighter elements but also a sizable amount of mixing,[8] suggesting an asymmetry in the explosion mechanism. Determining whether this mixing was due to asymmetries in the explosion or in the blastwave propagation through the surrounding medium,[9] along with limitations in the requirements to observe these abundances (shock-heating requirements, out-of-equilibrium atomic physics), limited the constraints these observations placed on the engine.

Another observational indication that the explosion mechanism in core collapse had large asymmetries is the observed distribution pulsar velocities with some pulsars moving faster than $1000\,\mathrm{km\,s^{-1}}$.[10] The high velocities observed in the pulsar velocity distribution suggests that these "kicks" are imparted onto the neutron stars during formation. One of the leading mechanisms behind these kicks is the asymmetric explosion of a SN engine. In this mechanism, the newly-formed compact remnant is kicked in the opposite direction of the ejecta conserving linear momentum. But a wide range of models have been proposed to explain these kicks (for a review, see[11]) and many don't require an asymmetric SN explosion. Like SN remnants, although suggestive, pulsar velocities were not definitive proof of supernova asymmetries.

Observations of SN 1987A provided this evidence and drove SN engine theorists to begin to actively gain new insight into the CCSN engine. First and foremost, SN 1987A provided essential confirmation of the basic core-collapse idea. Although theorists had argued that a CCSN could be produced by stars above $\sim 10\,\mathrm{M_\odot}$, no definitive proof existed until 1987, when a star in the Large Magellanic Cloud collapsed. Prior to its collapse, this star had been observed and its identification of this progenitor, Sanduleak -69 202, providing the first irrefutable evidence that at least some SNe are produced through the death of massive stars.[12] In addition, a burst of neutrinos were detected from this nearby SN at a rate that can only be produced with a compact object (either formation or a merger).[13,14] These two observations definitively demonstrated that at least some SNe are produced by the core-collapse to a compact object of a massive star.

Although SN 1987A solidified the foundation of the CCSN engine, it also raised a number of a new issues: the star was a blue, not a red, supergiant as predicted by models (we now believe this to be due to binary effects), the gamma-rays from the decay of radioactive nickel appeared much sooner than expected and the line profiles from these gamma-rays and infra-red lines (of the iron) were both broader than expected as well as being redshifted (instead of blue-shifted). From infra-red to gamma-rays, SN 1987A was showing the limitations of our spherically symmetric model. Scientists immediately realized that by artificially mixing out nickel produced in the innermost ejecta of 1-dimensional models, they could explain the early rise time of gamma-ray signal.[15] However, this artificial mixing did not explain the redshifted lines. In addition, producing the extent of mixing needed to explain the observations was difficult to achieve with simple Rayleigh-Taylor mixing developing in a symmetric shock propagated through the stellar profile.[16,17]

These difficulties led scientists to turn their attention to the engine itself and, instead of focusing on convection in the proto-neutron star, they focused on the region between the edge of the neutron star and the stalled shock. The unstable entropy gradient produced as the shock stalled led to convection in this region.[18,19] After a few preliminary studies, the first 2-dimensional calculations found this convection could change the fizzle produced by a 1-dimensional model into a strong explosion.[20] These instabilities evolved into low-mode convection which could both facilitate the extensive mixing and explain the pulsar kicks.[21] Three-dimensional models followed soon after,[22] including 3-dimensional explosion models that demonstrated that very low-mode convection could also explain the redshifted lines features.[23,24] This initiated a broad set of scientific work studying the SN engine that we will discuss in the next section.

2.2. *Evolution of the SN Engine*

Before we discuss the details of the convective engine, let's review the basic steps behind this leading paradigm:[25]

(i) **Onset of Collapse:** The iron core of a massive star because so massive that it compresses to densities that cause electrons to capture onto protons, removing electron degeneracy pressure. This causes further compression and accelerates the electron capture, driving a runaway collapse (Fig 2).

(ii) **Bounce** This runaway collapse proceeds until the core reaches nuclear densities where nuclear forces and neutron degeneracy pressure halt the collapse, causing the infalling core to bounce. The bounce shock moves out through the star (Fig 2).

(iii) **Stall of the Shock:** Most of the energy in the shock is stored in neutrinos. When the neutrinos are no longer trapped in the core, the shock loses energy and stalls at ∼100-200 km (Fig 2).

(iv) **Convective Engine:** The region between the compact core and the stalled shock is unstable to a range of instabilities, including Rayleigh-Taylor convection. This convection transports energy deposited at its base and transfers it outward to push against the infalling star. At the same time, it transports mass piling up at the stalled shock and allows it to convect to the core, releasing further potential energy and reducing the pressure that must be overcome at the stalled shock. These two effects, not modeled in 1-dimensional models, make it easier to drive an explosion (Fig 3).

(v) **Shock Launch:** When the pressure in the convective engine can overcome the ram pressure of the infalling star, an explosion is launched. The shock will be highly asymmetric (Rayleigh-Taylor tends to evolve to the largest mode possible in a convective region, Standing Accretion Shock Instabilities also produce low-mode convection). This aspherical shock will allow further accretion after its launch, allowing further energy deposition. But the neutrino-energy deposition will decrease as the density above the proto-neutron star decreases.

Here we focus most of our discussion on the convective engine. Figure 3 shows a 2-dimensional slice of a 3-dimensional simulation. This image shows both the high-entropy upflows and the low-entropy downflows. During the 15-20 y after the first 2-dimensional simulation of this engine, most studies focused on reproducing these results. Additional instabilities were studied, most notably the standing accretion shock instability (SASI).[26] The primary difference between these two mechanisms is the growth time of the instability and the latter interpretation of the convective motions is favored by models where the turbulence growth is slow. Simulations with more rapid convective growth argue for Rayleigh-Taylor instabilities.

The growth time is a key feature in the final result, both in the explosion energy and the remnant mass, so understanding this convection is critical. Unfortunately, a number of numerical artifacts make it difficult to model this convection. We can not resolve the convection and artificial viscosity (either explicitly state in smooth particle hydrodynamics or implicit in the numerical advection of grid-based codes). This growth time can be estimated analytically and we can test our calculations against this analysis. The growth time of this convection is on order of the inverse of the Brunt-Väisäla frequency:

$$T_{\text{growth}} = \sqrt{-\omega_{\text{BV}}^2} \tag{1}$$

where ω_{BV} is given by:p

$$\omega_{\text{BV}}^2 = -g_{\text{eff}} \left(\frac{1}{\rho} \frac{\partial \rho}{\partial r} - \frac{1}{\rho c_s^2} \frac{\partial P}{\partial r} \right) \tag{2}$$

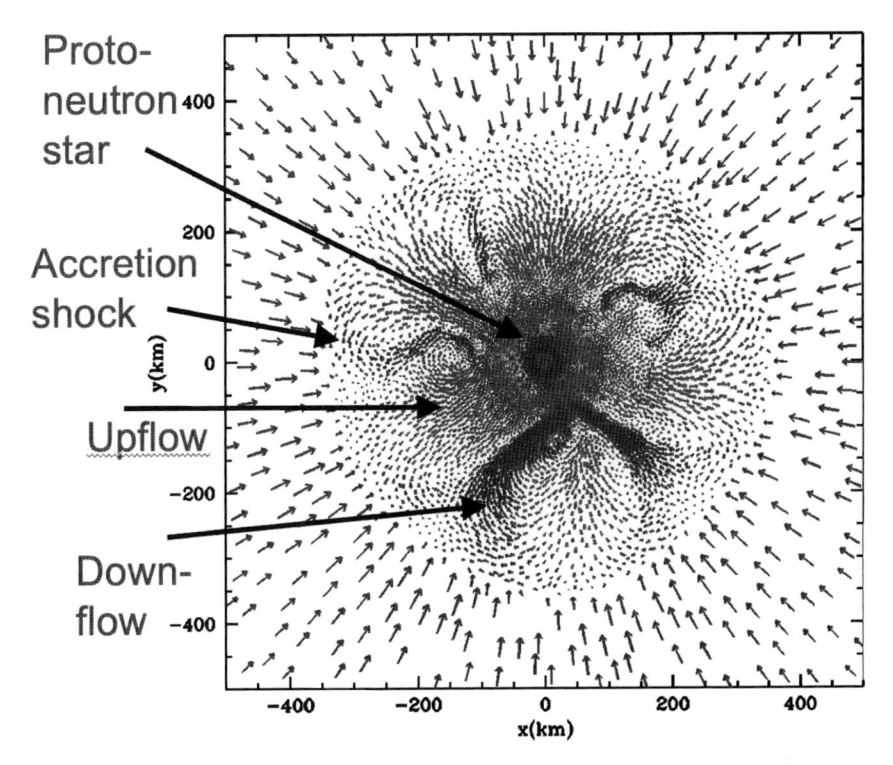

Fig. 3. Slice of a 3-dimensional convective engine. In this simulation, the convective region now extends to 300 km. The color-coding denotes entropy with red being high entropy and blue being low entropy. The vectors denote velocity magnitude (length) and direction. The proto-neutron star is in the inner 30 km. Material piles up at the top of the convective region near the stalled shock and the flows down in streams to the core.

where c_s is the sound speed, P is the pressure and $g_{\text{eff}} = -\partial\Phi/\partial r + v_r \partial v_r/\partial r$ is the effective gravity with Φ is the gravitational potential and v_r is the radial velocity. For the region above the proto-neutron star, the growth time can be approximated by:

$$T_{\text{growth}} \approx \sqrt{-\frac{GM_{\text{PNS}}}{r_{\text{PNS}}^2}\frac{\Delta S}{S\Delta r}} \qquad (3)$$

where G is the gravitational constant, M_{PNS}, r_{PNS} are mass and radius of the newly-formed, proto-neutron star, S is the entropy and ΔS is the change in entropy of a distance Δr in the region between the proto-neutron star and the stalled shock. With these conditions, we find the post-bounce convective growth-time to be on order of a few milliseconds.[25] All current calculations have growth times that are much longer than this prediction.

It could be that this simple analysis underestimates the growth time. We can further test the growth term by comparing our growth times to different prescriptions

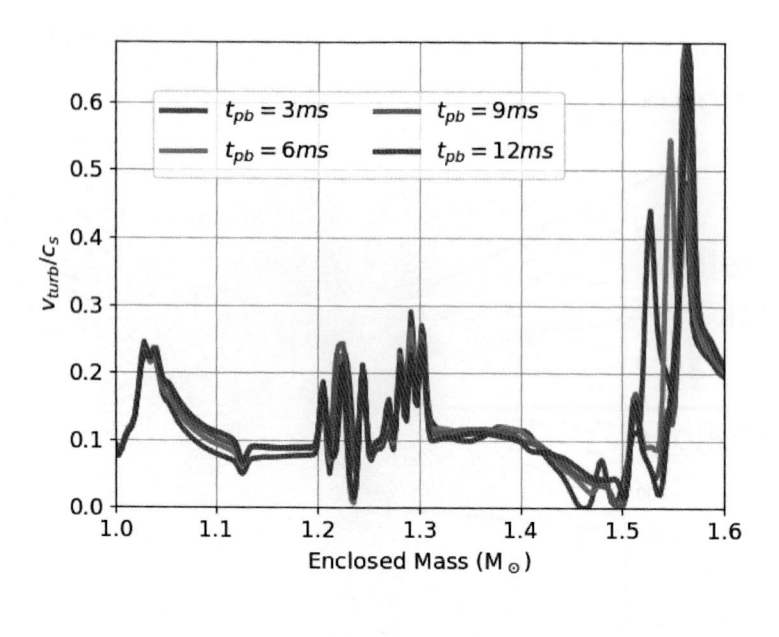

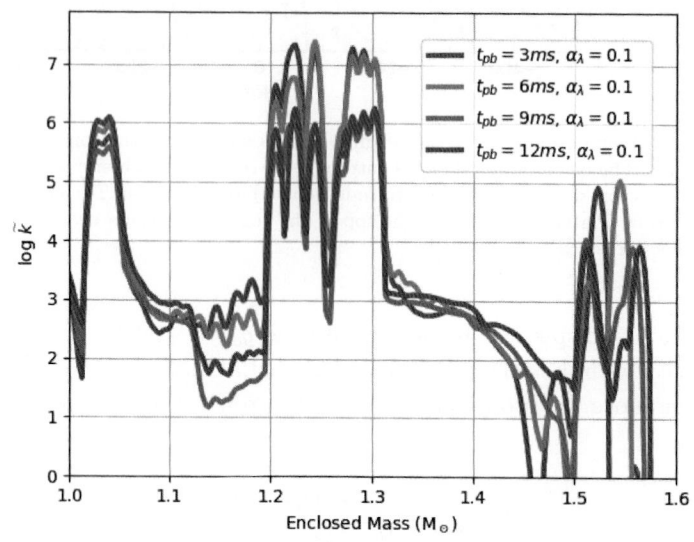

Fig. 4. Growth of turbulence, sound speed from mixing-length theory[27] and turbulent energy from a Reynolds Averaged Navier Stokes solution.[28] Strong turbulence develops in less than 10 ms.

(Fig 4) developed both in astrophysics (mixing-length theory[27]) and engineering (a Reynolds Averaged Navier Stokes solution[28]). Using 1-dimensional collapse models, these prescriptions also predict a very quick growth time for the instabilities: within a few ms, the Rayleigh-Taylor convection is strong with velocities/turbulent energies reaching a sizable fraction of the sound speed limit. Again, current models do not reproduce these growth times. Until we match these growth times, our simulations will not be quantitatively accurate, but they can help us study many of the trends with respect to different physics in the SN engine. They can also be used to study qualitative features in the SN explosion.

Beyond insufficient resolution, what else can be missing in these convective models. One of the most important is the initial seeds used to drive the explosion. The initial 2- and 3-dimensional models used smooth particle hydrodynamics.[20,22] The initial setup conditions have an intrinsic stochasticity in the density and these initial studies argued that these perturbations were on par with the convective inhomogeneities of the progenitor star. Later studies focused on very extreme instabilities in an attempt to produce the observed neutron star kicks.[29,30] An interesting feature of this neutron-star kick mechanism is that, unlike most other kick mechanisms, it predicts that lower-mass progenitors will produce the strongest neutron star kicks. Observations can potentially confirm or refute this kick mechanism. More recent studies have modeled the stellar convection at the final stages of a star's life, following this burning through collapse to produce more consistent simulations of these convective seeds.[31] In all cases, these models found, as expected by analytic theories, that these seeds accelerated the growth of convection.

Active areas of research in the convective engine includes increased-resolution models to better understand the limitations of the numerical methods modeling this convection. But a number of more physics-informed models are also being developed to better understand convective in the collapsed core. These methods will lead to better implementation of subgrid models that can help capture effects like the turbulent pressure. Much more work must be done to understand convection and core-collapse engine theorists are bringing a wide array of numerical and analysis tools to improve our understanding of this engine.

3. Confirmation and Ongoing Constraints of the Convective Engine

Even with the limitations of the convective-enhanced neutrino-driven engine, we are able to make predictions from this model both to test it as a model and use observational features to help improve our understanding. Here we review current observational comparisons that have solidified this standard paradigm. We also discuss upcoming observations that will further test the engine, providing valuable insight into the explosion engine. Like 1987A, we expect upcoming observations to not only constrain this engine, but perhaps provide the evidence to pursue new insight into this developing engine.

3.1. *Explaining SN Energies*

Prior to the development of the convection-enhanced SN explosion mechanism, explaining why CCSNe tap only ∼1% of the total potential energy released in the collapse of the core was one of the most baffling conundrums of the SN engine. But the convection-enhanced SN engine provided a natural explanation for this observation. The energy in the convective region continues to increase only until its energy is sufficient to overcome the ram pressure of the infalling material. The accretion rate of this infalling material and the time it takes the engine to overcome its ram pressure dictates the explosion energy. Figure 5 shows the energy required to overcome the ram pressure as a function of time in the collapse for a series of different progenitor stars. In all cases, this energy lies between a few tenths to a few times 10^{51}erg[a].

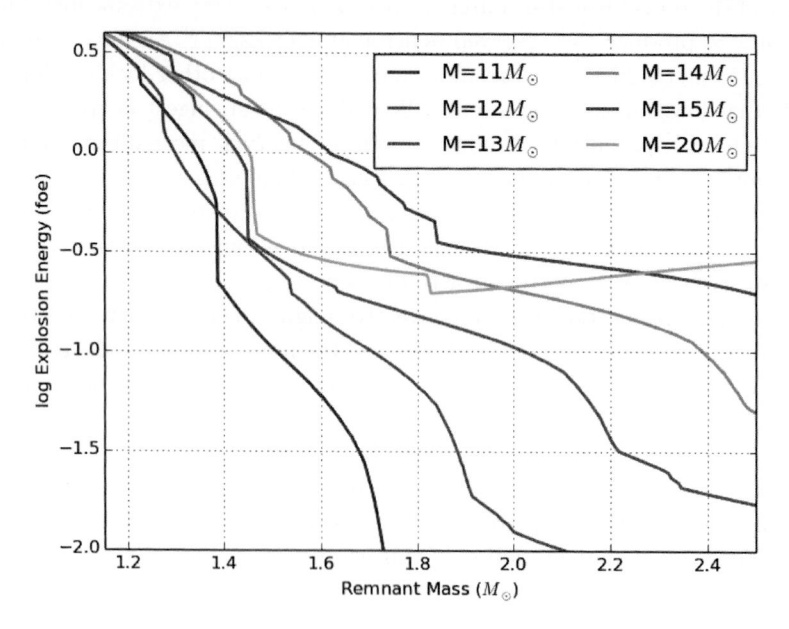

Fig. 5.   Explosion energy vs. enclosed mass for different stellar models.

The power of this natural explanation for the explosion energy is often underappreciated in the astronomy community. Let's compare it to the leading alternative engine for SNe, the magnetar-engine scenario. In this scenario, strong magnetic fields tap the rotation energy of the SN to power the explosion. The rotational energy is given by:

$$E_{\text{magnetar}} = 2/5 M_{\text{PNS}} R_{\text{PNS}}^2 \Omega_{\text{PNS}}^2 \qquad (4)$$

where M_{PNS}, R_{PNS}, and Ω_{PNS} are the mass, radius and rotation rate of the protomagnetar. When the explosion is launched (which must be in the first $\sim$ second after collapse so that the core does not accrete too much to collapse to a black hole), R_{PNS} is roughly 30 km. If the proto-neutron star contracts to form a 10 km

---

[a]Ten to the Fifty One Erg was termed a "foe" by Hans Bethe. This unit is also known as a Bethe.

neutron star spinning at 100 ms, we'd expect an average SN energy of 5×10^{47} erg instead of the observed $0.1-3 \times 10^{51}$ erg. Only the rare, fastest spinning stars would produce strong SNe.

3.2. Predicting SN Progenitors

One of the great successes of the convective-engine paradigm is its prediction of which stars produce strong SN explosions versus which collapse to form black holes. Under the convective paradigm, whether or not the convective engine can produce an explosion depends upon whether the energy of the convective engine can grow fast enough to overcome the ram pressure of the infalling material. A successful explosion is a race between the energy deposition timescale and the collapse timescale from accretion. If we ignore stellar winds, massive stars will have larger cores with higher accretion rates. This means that the timescale to collapse decreases and there is less time to develop convection and drive an explosion. In addition, the energy needed to overcome the higher accretion ram pressure is higher. Unless the engine becomes more efficient, these stars will not explode. Assuming minimal winds, the convective engine predicted that stars more massive than $\sim 23\,M_\odot$ would either fail to explode or produce weak explosions.[32]

Shortly thereafter, observations of SN lightcurves argued that most SN had ejecta masses above 15-20 $M_\odot$.[33] The magnetar model could produce explosions with such high ejecta masses, suggesting it might be the better standard SN engine. In this case, however, the analysis of the SN light-curves was wrong. As the sample of observed progenitors increased, it became clear that the vast majority of SN are produced from stars less massive that 20 $M_\odot$,[34] confirming the first prediction (vs. post-diction) of the convective engine and providing another strike for the magnetar model.

3.3. Compact Remnant Distribution

For the convective-engine paradigm, the mass of the compact remnant formed in CCSN can be described through a series of phases each of which depend on different properties of the explosion. The compact remnant initially forms during the collapse bounce phase. Typically, the mass of this bounce core is low (roughly $1.1\,M_\odot$[35]). As the convective engine develops, the core continues to accrete mass. Both the progenitor mass (that determines the infalling mass accretion rate with time) and the time it takes for this engine to develop dictates the mass of the core at the launch of the explosion. Finally, the explosion energy determines how much material ultimately falls back onto the compact core. All of these effects are important in determining the final compact remnant mass.

Observations of the compact remnant mass distribution provide insight into these explosion properties. Initially, observations argued for a remnant mass distribution that peaked strongly at two separate masses: a peak at $\sim 1.4\,M_\odot$ and another peak at $\sim M_\odot$.[36] These highly-peaked mass distributions are difficult to reproduce within convective-engine paradigm, especially when including the fallback of material after the launch of the launch.[37] Fallback occurs because the SN blastwave must drive the entire star to explode. As it decelerates, some of the ejecta can decelerate sufficiently that this material can not escape the gravitational potential of the star. This fallback has been studied both analytically and through a series of simulations,[38,39] demonstrating that fallback accretion decreases following a power-law time evolution: $\dot{M}_{\text{fallback}} \propto ^{-5/3}$. The amount of integrated fallback depends on the explosion energy and the progenitor structure (and hence, its mass).

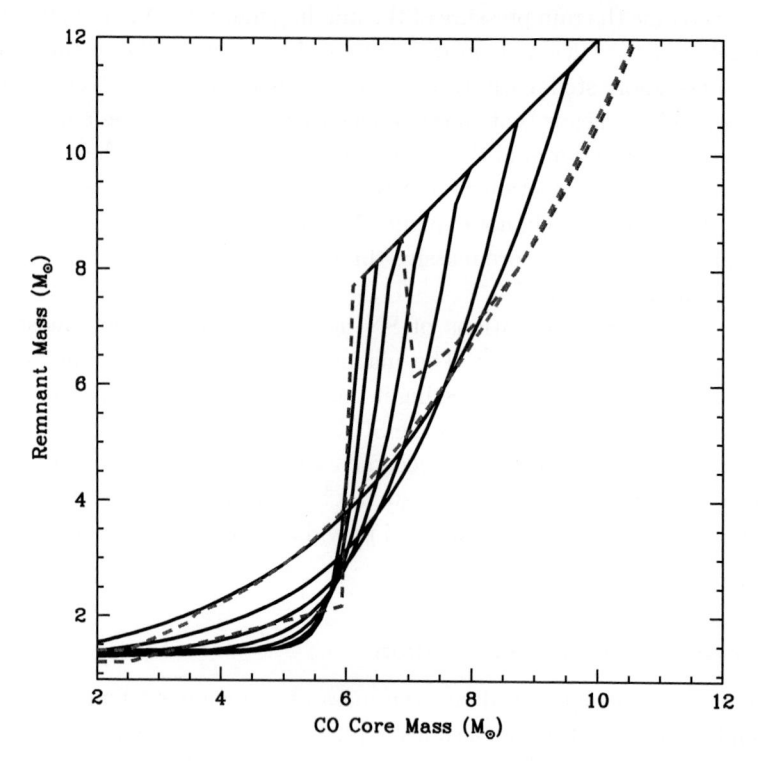

Fig. 6. Remnant mass as a function of CO core mass for rapid/slow convective models[35] along with a parameterized growth time model. The steeper the rise in remnant mass (caused by faster convective growth time), the deeper the mas gap produced.

One of the key observational constraints from the compact remnant mass distribution is the gap between neutron stars and black holes. Observations of neutron stars and black holes (binary pulsars and X-ray binaries) argued for an absence of neutron stars in the compact mass region lying between 2.5 and $4\,M_\odot$. Whether this was an observational bias or due to low-number statistics has been a matter of debate for many years. If the gap exists, it places strong constraints on the growth time of the convection.[35] Figure 6 shows the compact remnant mass as a function of the CO core mass while varying the convective growth time (and, hence, the injection time of the energy). Producing a pristine mass gap requires very rapid and strong explosions to avoid falllback filling in this gap. It is possible that fallback will drive further outflows that then limit further fallback such that, even though fallback occurs, the amount of mass accreted is limited.[40] Until recently, the mass gap favored rapid explosions, affecting both our understanding of the SN engine and predictions for a wide range of SN properties. However, gravitational wave observations suggest that the mass gap region is not as pristine as originally believed[41] and, because of this, the constraints on the convective growth time are less stringent (we will discuss this further in section 3.6).

With all of the current observations, we must consider the observational biases. One of the potential observational biases of the mass gap is that the observed compact mass distribution is limited to systems in close binaries. Any comparison of the predictions of the remnant mass distribution to the observed mass distribution must include calculations of these binaries and are limited by the associated uncertainties of binary population synthesis.[42–44]

3.4. SN Ejecta Remnants

The ejecta from CCSNe form another form of remnant as the ejecta in the SN blastwave propagates through the interstellar medium. As we discussed in Section 2.1, the morphology of these ejecta remnants provided the first hints that the SN engine must be aspherical. Although these remnants are highly aspherical, it is often difficult to extract properties of the explosive engine from other effects in the propagation of a SN remnant. As also we discussed in section 2.1, the effects of the propagation through the circumstellar medium and the modeling of the atomic physics in these non-local thermodynamic equilibrium conditions can make it difficult to tie the properties of the remnant to the explosion itself. Nonetheless, remnants can prove powerful probes of the SN explosion and its engine.

First, let's better understand the difficulties through the example of analyses of the Cassiopeia A SN remnant. As the blastwave propagates through the circumstellar medium, it decelerates, causing a reverse shock to progress inward (in mass coordinates) through the remnant, lighting up the material and allowing astronomers to probe properties of the explosion.[45,46] But the morphology of the shock can be shaped by the circumstellar medium[9] and the masses and properties inferred (masses, abundance rations) depend on assumptions in the atomic physics, i.e.[47] Cassiopeia A demonstrates the pitfalls of such an analysis. Images and analysis of the shock-heated material in Cassiopeia A suggests a jet-like explosion, suggesting a magnetar and disk model.[8] To verify this conclusion, astronomers developed another probe of this morphology by, instead of observing shocked material, observing material through the decay of radioactive material produced in the explosion. In particular, the NuStar satellite mapped out the ^{44}Ti production from the SN producing this remnant. ^{44}Ti is ideally suited as a probe of the central engine. It is produced in the innermost ejecta where ^{56}Ni is produced. It has a long enough half-life to be observed in SN remnants (unlike ^{56}Ni whose half-life is too short) and, because it is unstable (unlike iron), we know the observed ^{44}Ti was produced in the explosion. This innermost material may not yet be affected by the surrounding medium, especially if the reverse shock has yet to reach it. What the ^{44}Ti observations of the Cassiopeia A SN remnant showed was a clumpy distribution mimicking the convective motions in the SN engine.[48,49] This is the most direct observation to date proving the convection-enhance neutrino-driven SN engine. At least for this SN remnant, the engine is not matched by the magnetar model. Although limited to velocity imaging, the ^{44}Ti observations of SN 1987A suggest the same convective engine.[50]

Although these NuStar observations of remnants through the decay photons from radioactive elements provide a direct probe, the number of remnants that can be observed in such a manner is limited. Even with next generation gamma-ray detectors like COSI mission,[51] increasing the number of remnants with resolved images of the ^{44}Ti will be difficult. However, there exists a wealth of data of shock-heated material and combined with infra-red observations (and increasingly sophisticated models of the atomic physics), SN remnants will become an increasingly powerful probe of the SN engine. SN remnants measure key elements in the explosion that probe both the progenitor and the explosion energy. To demonstrate this, figure 7 shows the abundance fraction versus enclosed ejecta mass for two 1-dimensional SN explosions of a 15 M$_\odot$ star.[52] The abundances in this plot span the typically-observed abundances in SN remnants. The different observed abundances probe different aspects of the SN and different regions in the progenitor star. For example, Fe is produced in the innermost ejecta and is very sensitive to the explosion energy. Si, S, Ca, and Ar are produced just above the iron ejecta also probe the explosion energy. O, Mg, and Ne yields are produced even further out and are better probes of the progenitor because their production is much less sensitive to the explosion energy.

3.5. *Nucleosynthetic Yields*

Nucleosynthetic yields provide an excellent probe of the SN engine, especially of the elements produced near the engine (e.g. iron peak and heavier isotopes). As we discussed in Section 3.4, SN remnants provide a measure of the nucleosynthetic yields and their morphology. These remnant measurements probe the progenitor, explosion energy, and morphology of the explosion. ^{44}Ti observations are not only more direct probes (because the physics behind its analysis is more straightforward). The sensitivity of the ^{44}Ti production on the electron fraction of the inner ejecta[53] also means that it can probe the conditions in the convective region (and the properties of the neutrinos, including neutrino oscillations) in this region.

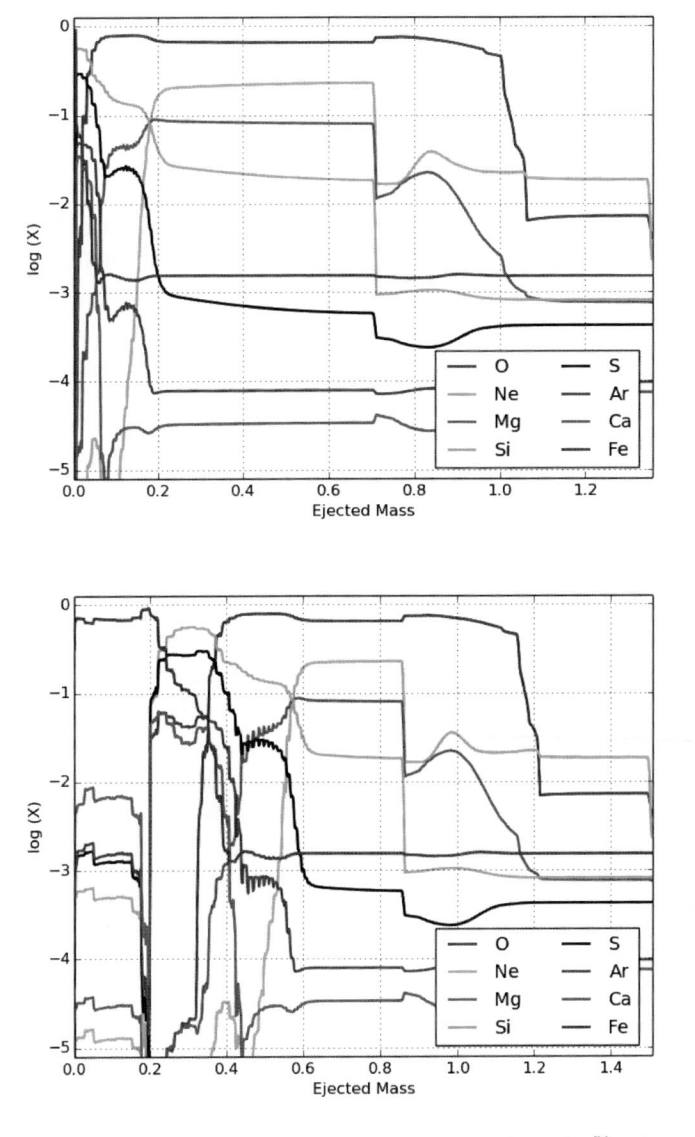

Fig. 7. Nucleosynthetic yiels from an 0.82 (top) and 1.86 (bottom) foe (10^{51} erg) explosion of a a 15 M$_\odot$ star. O, Mg, Ne are produced in stellar evolution and the supernova shock primarily destroys these abundances. Si, S, Ar, Ca are produced at the base of the C/O layer and their production depends somewhat on the SN explosion energy. Iron is produced in the core from shock-driven Si burning. It is very sensitive to the explosion energy, both to drive the nuclear fusion and to avoid falling back onto the proto-neutron star.

But remnants aren't the only way we can measure nucleosynthetic yields. Based on isotopic ratios, scientists have identified a set of pre-solar dust grains produced by SNe. With the detailed isotopic ratios and relative element abundances, scientists can begin to probe the detailed yields from SNe.[54–56] In addition, galactic chemical evolution, which measures the evolution of the abunadances as a function of metallicity, can be used to both determine which transients form different elements and the variation in their production rates.[57,58]

3.6. *Neutrinos and Gravitational Waves*

The neutrino detection of SN 1987A provided conclusive evidence that at least some SNe are produced in the formation of a compact remnant. Neutrinos remain one of the most direct probes of the SN engine. With a detailed neutrino spectrum, scientists can not only probe the nature of the proto-neutron star (and the nuclear matter equation of state) and the neutrino physics (including neutrino oscillations). Unfortunately, neutrinos are difficult to detect and, to date, SN 1987A remains the only SN detected in neutrinos. With hyperKamiokande, scientists expect to observer SNe out to 1 Mpc.[59] This can increase the neutrino detection rate, but for the detailed spectra to do most of the neutrino SN science will still require a Galactic SN.

Gravitational waves provide another[53] probe different physics of the inner engine: the rotation and the convection. To measure convection, we need a nearby SN, well within the Milky Way.[60] But, fast rotating collapses can be seen further out (in extreme cases, out to 1 Mpc).[61] With next generation detectors, a Galactic SN would produce a strong enough signal to measure the growth and extent of the SN mixing and the expected rate of fast-spinning collapses is sufficiently high that we will begin to place constraints on the angular momentum in stars (determining the importance of rotation in the SN engine). Next generation detectors will increase the number of mass-constraints on compact objects 100-fold, providing an extremely accurate mass distribution of compact objects (in close binary systems). With these masses, we can constrain the mixing in the SN engine (see Section 3.3).

3.7. *SN Light Curves and Early-Time Emission*

We have already discussed issues with using SN light-curves. One of the primary difficulties in studying the engines and progenitors of SNe from the SN light-curve lies in the fact that most of the emission occurs long after the SN blastwave has broken out of the star and interactions with the surrounding medium blur the features (and in particular the extent of the asymmetries) in the explosion and its progenitor star. Observing the emission from the SN blastwave as it breaks out of the star provides a much more direct probe of the explosion (asymmetries) and progenitor (convection, radii, and mass loss).[62–64] Figure 8 shows the early emission from a SN as it breaks out of the photosphere of a Wolf-Rayet star. This emission is driven by shocks produced as the SN blastwave propagates first through the convective envelope, then down the transition region from stellar edge to wind and then through the clumpy wind. By characterizing this emission, astronomers will probe the properties of the star, in particular, the convection in the stellar envelope (convection is a key uncertainty of massive star evolution) and stellar mass-loss (which alters the structure of the star and can change its final fate). This emission also prov ides a probe of the SN asymmetries. Ultrasat[65] and SIBEX[66,67] satellite missions are being developed to obtain a large number of this early-time SN emission.

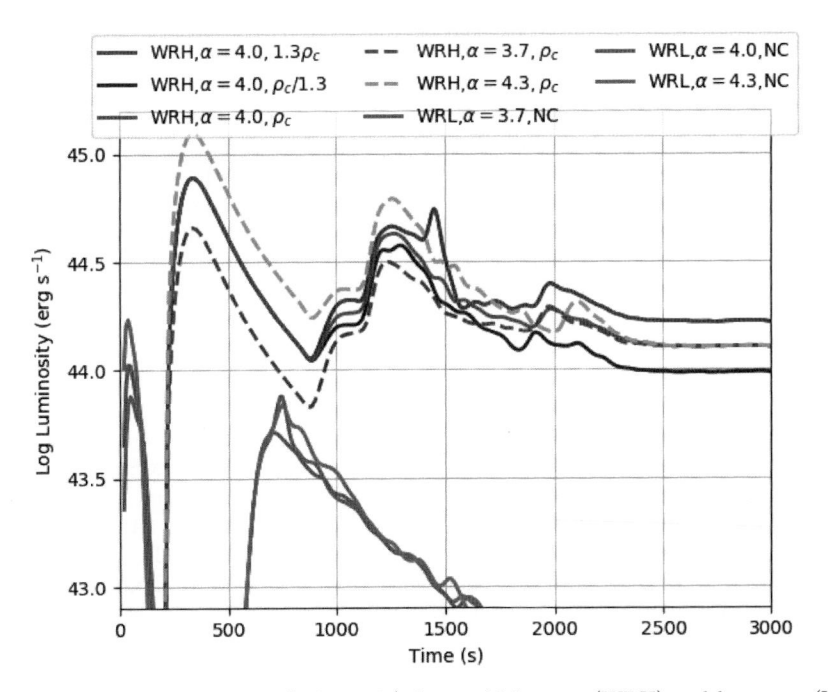

Fig. 8. Shock breakout emission (bolometric) from a high mass (WRH) and low mass (WRL) Wolf-Rayet progenitor star varying properties of the wind (with and without clumps) and the density slope of the transition region ($\rho = \rho_0 r^{-\alpha}$). Signal without clumps (NC) are compared to those with a wind clump density that varies by 30%. This emission is predominantly in the X-ray and UV bands.

4. Conclusion

In this paper, we reviewed the broad set of observations that led to, confirmed, and have constrained the convective-enhanced neutrino-driven SN engine paradigm. We have also outlined the the future observations that will place further constraints. For our understanding of the SN engine, the future is bright.

Acknowledgments

This section should come before the References. Dedications and funding information may also be included here.

References

1. W. Baade and F. Zwicky, *Proceedings of the National Academy of Science* **20** (May 1934) 254.
2. F. Zwicky, *ApJ* **88** (November 1938) 522.
3. R. Kippenhahn, S. Temesváry and L. Biermann, *Zeitschrift für Astrophysik* **46** (January 1958) 257.
4. A. Heger, S. E. Woosley, C. L. Fryer and N. Langer, Massive Star Evolution Through the Ages, in *From Twilight to Highlight: The Physics of Supernovae*, eds. W. Hillebrandt and B. Leibundgut (January 2003), p. 3.
5. S. A. Colgate and R. H. White, *ApJ* **143** (March 1966) 626.
6. R. I. Epstein, *MNRAS* **188** (August 1979) 305.
7. J. R. Wilson and R. W. Mayle, *Physics Reports* **163** (January 1988) 63.
8. U. Hwang, J. M. Laming, C. Badenes, F. Berendse, J. Blondin, D. Cioffi, T. DeLaney, D. Dewey, R. Fesen, K. A. Flanagan, C. L. Fryer, P. Ghavamian, J. P. Hughes, J. A. Morse, P. P. Plucinsky, R. Petre, M. Pohl, L. Rudnick, R. Sankrit, P. O. Slane, R. K. Smith, J. Vink and J. S. Warren, *ApJ Letters* **615** (November 2004) L117.
9. J. M. Blondin, P. Lundqvist and R. A. Chevalier, *ApJ* **472** (November 1996) 257.
10. J. M. Cordes and D. F. Chernoff, *ApJ* **505** (September 1998) 315.
11. C. L. Fryer and A. Kusenko, *ApJ Supp* **163** (April 2006) 335.
12. R. M. West, A. Lauberts, H. E. Jorgensen and H. E. Schuster, *Astronomy and Astrophysics* **177** (May 1987) L1.
13. K. Hirata, T. Kajita, M. Koshiba, M. Nakahata, Y. Oyama, N. Sato, A. Suzuki, M. Takita, Y. Totsuka, T. Kifune, T. Suda, K. Takahashi, T. Tanimori, K. Miyano, M. Yamada, E. W. Beier, L. R. Feldscher, S. B. Kim, A. K. Mann, F. M. Newcomer, R. van, W. Zhang and B. G. Cortez, *Physical Review Letters* **58** (April 1987) 1490.
14. R. M. Bionta, G. Blewitt, C. B. Bratton, D. Casper, A. Ciocio, R. Claus, B. Cortez, M. Crouch, S. T. Dye, S. Errede, G. W. Foster, W. Gajewski, K. S. Ganezer, M. Goldhaber, T. J. Haines, T. W. Jones, D. Kielczewska, W. R. Kropp, J. G. Learned, J. M. Losecco, J. Matthews, R. Miller, M. S. Mudan, H. S. Park, L. R. Price, F. Reines, J. Schultz, S. Seidel, E. Shumard, D. Sinclair, H. W. Sobel, J. L. Stone, L. R. Sulak, R. Svoboda, G. Thornton, J. C. van der Velde and C. Wuest, *Physical Review Letters* **58** (April 1987) 1494.
15. P. A. Pinto and S. E. Woosley, *ApJ* **329** (June 1988) 820.
16. D. Arnett, B. Fryxell and E. Mueller, *ApJ Letters* **341** (June 1989) L63.
17. M. Herant and W. Benz, *ApJ Letters* **370** (April 1991) L81.
18. M. Herant and W. Benz, *ApJ* **387** (March 1992) 294.
19. M. Herant, W. Benz and S. Colgate, *ApJ* **395** (August 1992) 642.
20. M. Herant, W. Benz, W. R. Hix, C. L. Fryer and S. A. Colgate, *ApJ* **435** (November 1994) 339.
21. M. Herant, *Space Science Reviews* **74** (November 1995) 335.
22. C. L. Fryer and M. S. Warren, *ApJ Letters* **574** (July 2002) L65.
23. A. L. Hungerford, C. L. Fryer and M. S. Warren, *ApJ* **594** (September 2003) 390.
24. A. L. Hungerford, C. L. Fryer and G. Rockefeller, *ApJ* **635** (December 2005) 487.
25. C. L. Fryer and P. A. Young, *ApJ* **659** (April 2007) 1438.
26. J. M. Blondin, A. Mezzacappa and C. DeMarino, *ApJ* **584** (February 2003) 971.
27. E. Böhm-Vitense, *Zeitschrift für Astrophysik* **46** (January 1958) 108.
28. D. Livescu, J. R. Ristorcelli, R. A. Gore, S. H. Dean, W. H. Cabot and A. W. Cook, *Journal of Turbulence* **10** (January 2009) 13.
29. A. Burrows and J. Hayes, *Physical Review Letters* **76** (January 1996) 352.
30. C. L. Fryer, *ApJ Letters* **601** (February 2004) L175.

31. C. E. Fields and S. M. Couch, *ApJ* **901** (September 2020) 33.
32. C. L. Fryer, *ApJ* **522** (September 1999) 413.
33. M. Hamuy, *ApJ* **582** (January 2003) 905.
34. S. J. Smartt, *ARA&A* **47** (September 2009) 63.
35. C. L. Fryer, K. Belczynski, G. Wiktorowicz, M. Dominik, V. Kalogera and D. E. Holz, *ApJ* **749** (April 2012) 91.
36. S. E. Thorsett and D. Chakrabarty, *ApJ* **512** (February 1999) 288.
37. C. L. Fryer and V. Kalogera, *ApJ* **554** (June 2001) 548.
38. R. A. Chevalier, *ApJ* **346** (November 1989) 847.
39. C. L. Fryer, *New Astron.* **50** (October 2006) 492.
40. C. L. Fryer, S. A. Colgate and P. A. Pinto, *ApJ* **511** (February 1999) 885.
41. A. et al., *arXiv e-prints* (August 2021) arXiv:2108.01045.
42. C. L. Fryer, S. E. Woosley and D. H. Hartmann, *ApJ* **526** (November 1999) 152.
43. M. Dominik, K. Belczynski, C. Fryer, D. E. Holz, E. Berti, T. Bulik, I. Mandel and R. O'Shaughnessy, *ApJ* **759** (November 2012) 52.
44. P. Drozda, K. Belczynski, R. O'Shaughnessy, T. Bulik and C. L. Fryer, *arXiv e-prints* (September 2020) arXiv:2009.06655.
45. J. C. Raymond, *ARA&A* **22** (January 1984) 75.
46. S. P. Reynolds, *ARA&A* **46** (September 2008) 89.
47. J. C. Raymond, B. C. Koo, Y. H. Lee, D. Milisavljevic, R. A. Fesen and I. Chilingarian, *ApJ* **866** (October 2018) 128.
48. B. W. Grefenstette, F. A. Harrison, S. E. Boggs, S. P. Reynolds, C. L. Fryer, K. K. Madsen, D. R. Wik, A. Zoglauer, C. I. Ellinger, D. M. Alexander, H. An, D. Barret, F. E. Christensen, W. W. Craig, K. Forster, P. Giommi, C. J. Hailey, A. Hornstrup, V. M. Kaspi, T. Kitaguchi, J. E. Koglin, P. H. Mao, H. Miyasaka, K. Mori, M. Perri, M. J. Pivovaroff, S. Puccetti, V. Rana, D. Stern, N. J. Westergaard and W. W. Zhang, *Nature* **506** (February 2014) 339.
49. B. W. Grefenstette, C. L. Fryer, F. A. Harrison, S. E. Boggs, T. DeLaney, J. M. Laming, S. P. Reynolds, D. M. Alexander, D. Barret, F. E. Christensen, W. W. Craig, K. Forster, P. Giommi, C. J. Hailey, A. Hornstrup, T. Kitaguchi, J. E. Koglin, L. Lopez, P. H. Mao, K. K. Madsen, H. Miyasaka, K. Mori, M. Perri, M. J. Pivovaroff, S. Puccetti, V. Rana, D. Stern, N. J. Westergaard, D. R. Wik, W. W. Zhang and A. Zoglauer, *ApJ* **834** (January 2017) 19.
50. S. E. Boggs, F. A. Harrison, H. Miyasaka, B. W. Grefenstette, A. Zoglauer, C. L. Fryer, S. P. Reynolds, D. M. Alexander, H. An, D. Barret, F. E. Christensen, W. W. Craig, K. Forster, P. Giommi, C. J. Hailey, A. Hornstrup, T. Kitaguchi, J. E. Koglin, K. K. Madsen, P. H. Mao, K. Mori, M. Perri, M. J. Pivovaroff, S. Puccetti, V. Rana, D. Stern, N. J. Westergaard and W. W. Zhang, *Science* **348** (May 2015) 670.
51. J. A. Tomsick, S. E. Boggs, A. Zoglauer, E. Wulf, L. Mitchell, B. Phlips, C. Sleator, T. Brandt, A. Shih, J. Roberts, P. Jean, P. von Ballmoos, J. Martinez Oliveros, A. Smale, C. Kierans, D. Hartmann, M. Leising, M. Ajello, E. Burns, C. Fryer, P. Saint-Hilaire, J. Malzac, F. Tavecchio, V. Fioretti, A. Bulgarelli, G. Ghirlanda, H.-K. Chang, T. Takahashi, K. Nakazawa, S. Matsumoto, T. Melia, T. Siegert, A. Lowell, H. Lazar, J. Beechert and H. Gulick, *arXiv e-prints* (September 2021) arXiv:2109.10403.
52. S. Andrews, C. Fryer, W. Even, S. Jones and M. Pignatari, *ApJ* **890** (February 2020) 35.
53. G. Magkotsios, F. X. Timmes, A. L. Hungerford, C. L. Fryer, P. A. Young and M. Wiescher, *ApJ Supp* **191** (November 2010) 66.
54. L. R. Nittler, S. Amari, R. S. Lewis, R. M. Walker and E. Zinner, *Meteoritics* **30** (September 1995) 557.

55. A. N. Nguyen and S. Messenger, *ApJ* **784** (April 2014) 149.
56. J. Schulte, M. Bose, P. A. Young and G. S. Vance, *ApJ* **908** (February 2021) 38.
57. B. Côté, M. Eichler, A. Arcones, C. J. Hansen, P. Simonetti, A. Frebel, C. L. Fryer, M. Pignatari, M. Reichert, K. Belczynski and F. Matteucci, *ApJ* **875** (April 2019) 106.
58. M. N. Ishigaki, T. Hartwig, Y. Tarumi, S.-C. Leung, N. Tominaga, C. Kobayashi, M. Magg, A. Simionescu and K. Nomoto, *MNRAS* **506** (October 2021) 5410.
59. K. e. a. Abe, *arXiv e-prints* (January 2019) arXiv:1901.03750.
60. C. L. Fryer and K. C. B. New, *Living Reviews in Relativity* **14** (January 2011) 1.
61. C. L. Fryer, D. E. Holz and S. A. Hughes, *ApJ* **565** (January 2002) 430.
62. E. Waxman and B. Katz, Shock Breakout Theory, in *Handbook of Supernovae*, eds. A. W. Alsabti and P. Murdin 2017, p. 967.
63. C. L. Fryer, C. J. Fontes, J. S. Warsa, P. W. A. Roming, S. X. Coffing and S. R. Wood, *ApJ* **898** (August 2020) 123.
64. C. M. Irwin, I. Linial, E. Nakar, T. Piran and R. Sari, *MNRAS* (September 2021).
65. I. Sagiv, A. Gal-Yam, E. O. Ofek, E. Waxman, O. Aharonson, S. R. Kulkarni, E. Nakar, D. Maoz, B. Trakhtenbrot, E. S. Phinney, J. Topaz, C. Beichman, J. Murthy and S. P. Worden, *AJ* **147** (April 2014) 79.
66. P. W. A. Roming, T. A. Pritchard, J. L. Prieto, C. S. Kochanek, C. L. Fryer, K. Davidson, R. M. Humphreys, A. J. Bayless, J. F. Beacom, P. J. Brown, S. T. Holland, S. Immler, N. P. M. Kuin, S. R. Oates, R. W. Pogge, G. Pojmanski, R. Stoll, B. J. Shappee, K. Z. Stanek and D. M. Szczygiel, *ApJ* **751** (June 2012) 92.
67. P. Roming, C. Fryer, A. Bayless and J. De la Rosa, Shock Breakout and Shock Interaction Mission, in *43rd COSPAR Scientific Assembly. Held 28 January - 4 February*, (January 2021), p. 1640.

The observation of high-energy neutrinos from the cosmos: Lessons learned for multimessenger astronomy

Francis Halzen

Department of Physics, University of Wisconsin–Madison, Madison, WI 53705, US

The IceCube neutrino telescope discovered PeV-energy neutrinos originating beyond our Galaxy with an energy flux that is comparable to that of GeV-energy gamma rays and EeV-energy cosmic rays. These neutrinos provide the only unobstructed view of the cosmic accelerators that power the highest energy radiation reaching us from the universe. We will review the results from IceCube's first decade of operations, emphasizing the measurement of the diffuse multiflavored neutrino flux from the universe and the identification of the supermassive black hole TXS 0506+056 as a source of cosmic neutrinos and, therefore, cosmic rays. We will speculate on the lessons learned for multimessenger astronomy, among them that extragalactic neutrino sources may be a relatively small subset of the cosmic accelerators observed in high-energy gamma rays and that these may be gamma-ray-obscured at the times that they emit neutrinos.

Keywords: Neutrinos; cosmic rays; multimessenger astronomy.

PACS numbers: 95.55.Vj; Neutrino; muon; pion; and other elementary particle detectors; cosmic ray detectors

1. Neutrino Astronomy: A Brief Introduction

The shortest wavelength radiation reaching us from the universe is not radiation at all; it consists of cosmic rays—protons and high-energy nuclei. Some reach us with extreme energies exceeding 10^8 TeV from a universe beyond our Galaxy that is obscured to gamma rays and from which only neutrinos reach us as astronomical messengers.[1] Their origin is still unknown but the identification of a supermassive black hole powering a cosmic-ray accelerator[2,3] represents a breakthrough towards a promising path for resolving the century-old puzzle of the origin of cosmic rays: multimessenger astronomy.

The rationale for searching for cosmic-ray sources by observing neutrinos is straightforward: in relativistic particle flows near neutron stars or black holes, some of the gravitational energy released in the accretion of matter is transformed into the acceleration of protons or heavier nuclei, which subsequently interact with ambient radiation or matter to produce pions and other secondary particles that decay into neutrinos. For instance, when protons interact with intense radiation fields near the source via the photoproduction processes

$$p + \gamma \to \pi^0 + p \quad \text{and} \quad p + \gamma \to \pi^+ + n\,, \tag{1}$$

both neutrinos and gamma rays are produced with roughly equal rates; while neutral pions decay into two gamma rays, $\pi^0 \rightarrow \gamma+\gamma$, the charged pions decay into three high-energy neutrinos (ν) and antineutrinos ($\bar{\nu}$) via the decay chain $\pi^+ \rightarrow \mu^+ + \nu_\mu$ followed by $\mu^+ \rightarrow e^+ + \bar{\nu}_\mu + \nu_e$. The fact that cosmic neutrinos are inevitably accompanied by high-energy photons transforms neutrino astronomy into multimessenger astronomy.

A main challenge of multimessenger astronomy is to separate these photons, which we will refer to as *pionic* photons, from photons radiated by electrons that are accelerated along with the cosmic ray protons. Another challenge is to identify the electromagnetic energy associated with the pionic photons because they do not reach our telescopes with their initial energy. They suffer losses in interactions with the extragalactic background light (EBL), predominantly with microwave photons, via the process $\gamma + \gamma_{cmb} \rightarrow e^+ + e^-$. Importantly, they may also lose energy in the source. As is the case when constructing a neutrino beam in a particle physics laboratory, neutrinos require a target that transforms the energy of the proton beam into neutrinos. Powerful neutrino sources within reach of IceCube's sensitivity require a dense target that is likely to be opaque to pionic gamma rays. Additionally losing energy in the source, these may reach Earth with MeV energies or below. We will review the accumulating indications that cosmic neutrinos originate in gamma-obscured sources with their associated multimessenger signals emerging below the detection thresholds of high-energy gamma-ray satellites and ground-based TeV gamma-ray telescopes.[4,5]

2. High-Energy Cosmic Neutrinos

Close to the National Science Foundation's research station located at the geographical South Pole, the IceCube project[6] transformed one cubic kilometer of natural Antarctic ice into a Cherenkov detector. The deep ice of the Antarctic glacier constitutes the detector, forming both support structure and Cherenkov medium. Below a depth of 1,450 meters, a cubic kilometer of glacial ice has been instrumented with 86 cables called "strings," each of which is equipped with 60 optical sensors; see Fig. 1. Each digital optical module (DOM) consists of a glass sphere containing a photomultiplier and the electronics board that captures and digitizes the light signals locally using an onboard computer; see Fig. 2. The digitized signals are given a global time stamp accurate to 2 ns and are subsequently transmitted to the surface. Processors at the surface continuously collect the time-stamped signals from the optical modules, each of which functions independently. The digital messages are sent to a string processor and a global event trigger. They are sorted into the Cherenkov radiation patterns that are emitted by muon tracks produced by muon neutrinos interacting in the ice, or by secondary particle showers initiated by electron and tau neutrinos. These reveal the flavor, energy, and direction of the incident neutrino.[7]

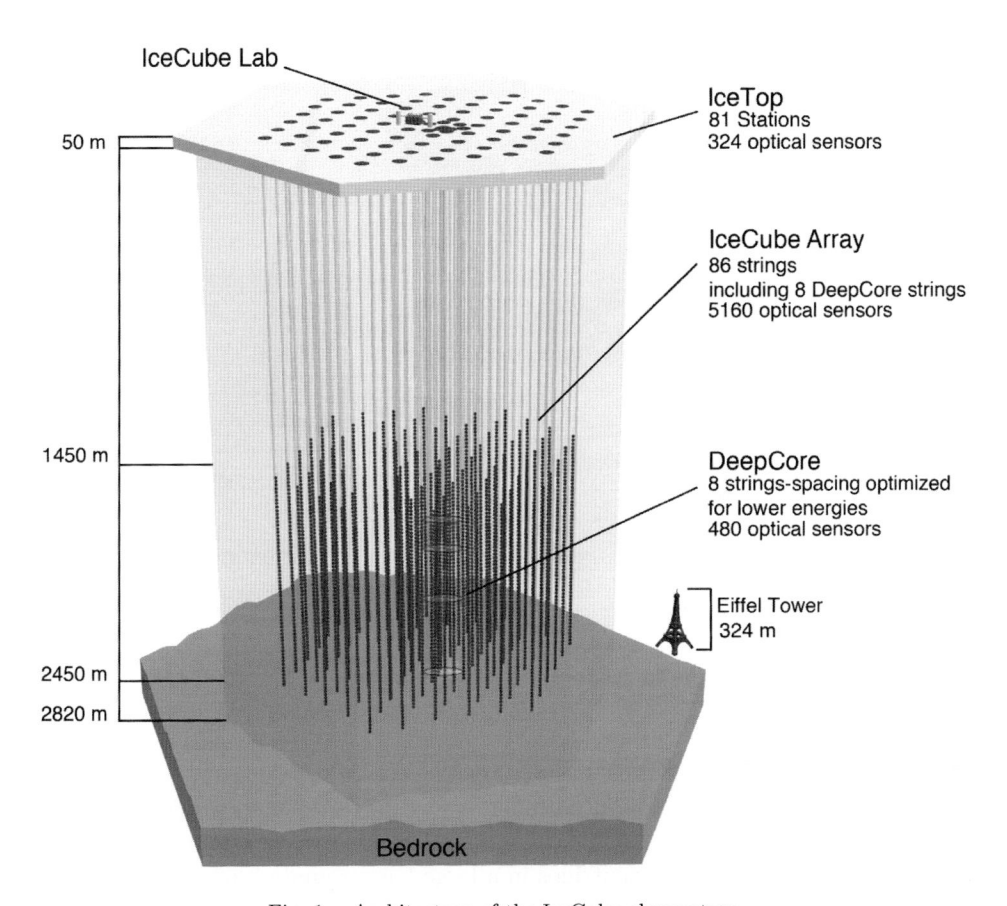

Fig. 1. Architecture of the IceCube observatory.

Constructed between 2004 and 2010, IceCube has now taken 10 years of data with the completed detector.

The arrival direction of a secondary muon track, or of an electromagnetic shower initiated by an electron or tau neutrino, is reconstructed from the arrival times of the Cherenkov photons at the optical sensors, while the number of photons is a proxy for the energy deposited by secondary particles in the detector. Although the detector only records the energy of the secondary muon inside the detector, from Standard Model physics we can infer the energy spectrum of the parent neutrino.

Tracks resulting from muon neutrino interactions can be pointed back to their sources with a $\leq 0.4°$ angular resolution for the highest energy events. In contrast, the reconstruction of cascade directions, in principle possible to within a few degrees, is still in the development stage in IceCube, achieving 8° resolution.[8,9] On the other hand, determining the shower energy from the observed light pool is straightforward, and a resolution of better than 15% can be achieved. For illustration, we contrast

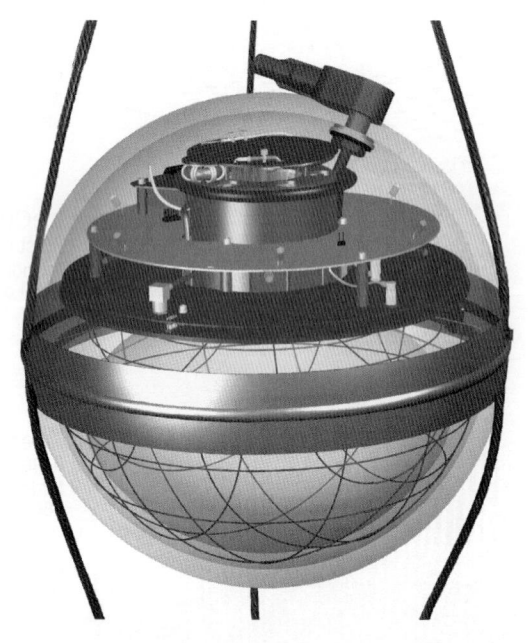

Fig. 2. Digital optical module showing the down-facing 10-inch photomultiplier and the associated electronics that digitize the light signals.

in Fig. 3 the Cherenkov patterns initiated by an electron (or tau) neutrino of 1 PeV energy (top) and a neutrino-induced muon losing 2.6 PeV energy while traversing the detector (bottom).

IceCube identifies cosmic neutrinos in a large background of muons and neutrinos produced by cosmic rays interacting in the atmosphere. Two principal methods are used to separate neutrinos of cosmic origin from the background of atmospheric muons and neutrinos. The first method reconstructs muon tracks reaching the detector from directions below the horizon, the second identifies neutrinos of all flavors that interact inside the instrumented volume of the detector; examples of events are shown in Fig. 3. We will describe these methods in turn.

2.1. *Muon Neutrinos Through the Earth*

Detecting particles from directions below the horizon has the immediate advantage of eliminating the overwhelming background of cosmic-ray muons that reach the detector from above. The tracks are separated from the background of atmospheric muons using the Earth as a filter. IceCube thus collects samples of muon neutrinos with high purity, typically well above 99%, at a rate of more than 100,000 per year. The neutrino energies cover more than six orders of magnitude, from ~ 5 GeV in the highly instrumented inner core, labeled DeepCore in Fig. 1, to extreme energies beyond 10 PeV. IceCube thus measured the atmospheric neutrino flux over more than five orders of magnitude in energy with a result that is consistent with theoretical

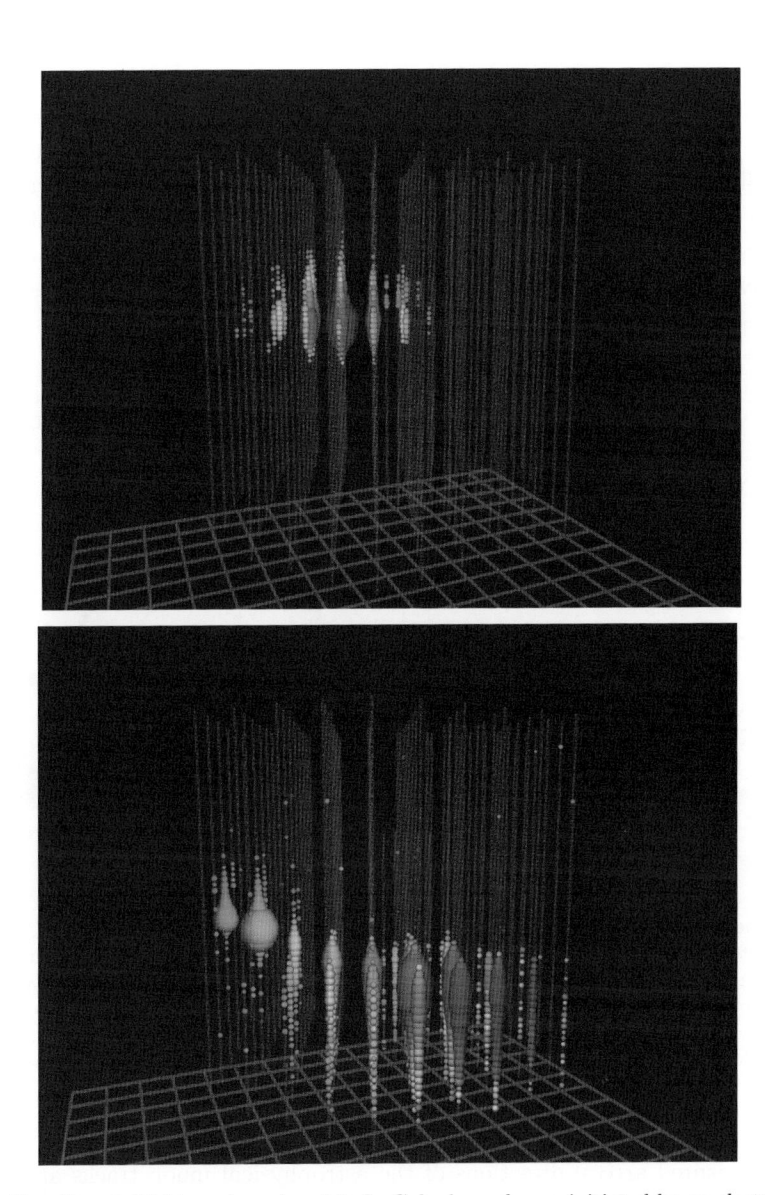

Fig. 3. **Top Panel:** Light pool produced in IceCube by a shower initiated by an electron or tau neutrino of 1.14 PeV, which represents a lower limit on the energy of the neutrino that initiated the shower. White dots represent sensors with no signal. For the colored dots, the color indicates arrival time, from red (early) to purple (late) following the rainbow, and size reflects the number of photons detected. **Bottom Panel:** A muon track coming up through the Earth, traverses the detector at an angle of 11° below the horizon. The deposited energy, i.e., the energy equivalent of the total Cherenkov light of all charged secondary particles inside the detector, is 2.6 PeV.

calculations. Muon neutrinos can be detected even when interacting outside the detector because of the kilometer range of the secondary muons. More importantly, IceCube has observed an excess of neutrino events at energies beyond 100 TeV[10–12] that cannot be accounted for by the atmospheric flux at the 5.6σ level. A recent measurement of the energy flux covering 9.5 years of data was performed yielding a sample of 650,000 neutrinos with 99.7% purity; see Fig. 4. The excess cosmic neutrino flux (red) over the atmospheric background (purple) is well described by a power law with a spectral index of -2.37 ± 0.09 and a normalization at 100 TeV neutrino energy of $(1.36^{+0.24}_{-0.25}) \times 10^{-18}\,\mathrm{GeV}^{-1}\mathrm{cm}^{-2}\mathrm{sr}^{-1}\mathrm{s}^{-1}$.[13] The residual atmospheric muon background is small (yellow). For more details, see Ref. 14.

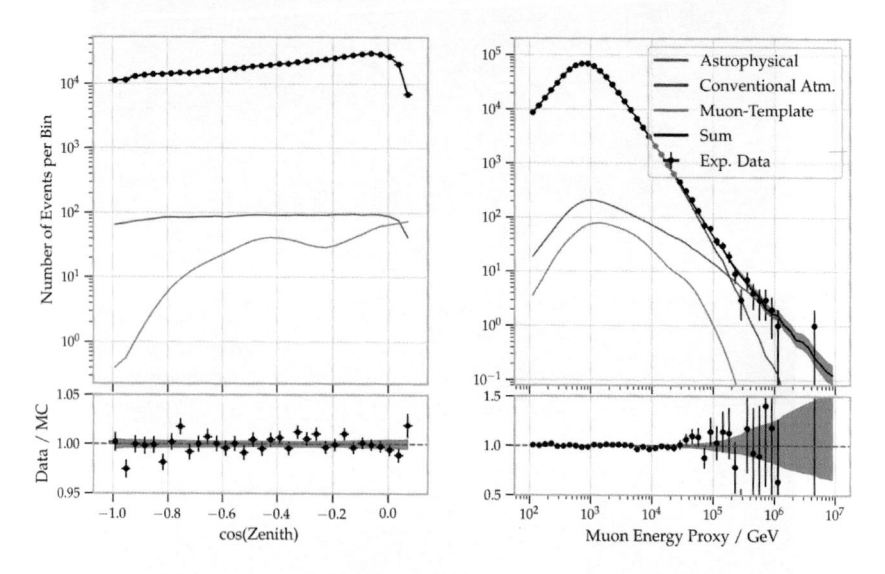

Fig. 4. The distributions of muon tracks arriving from the Northern Hemisphere, i.e., with declination greater than $-5°$, for the period 2010-18,[13] are shown as a function of reconstructed zenith (left) and muon energy (right). The full data set consists of about 650,000 neutrino events with a purity of 99.7%. Best fits to the low-energy atmospheric and high-energy astrophysical components of the neutrino flux are superimposed. Statistical errors are shown as crosses, the grey bands in the ratio plots show an estimate of the systematic error obtained by varying all fit-parameters within their uncertainties.

The measured arrival directions of the astrophysical muon tracks are isotropically distributed over the sky. Surprisingly, there is no evidence for a correlation to nearby sources in the Galactic plane; IceCube observes a diffuse flux of extragalactic sources. Only after collecting 10 years of data[15] did the first evidence emerge at the 3σ level that the neutrino sky is not isotropic. The anisotropy results from four sources—TXS 0506+056 among them (more about that source later)—that emerge as point sources of neutrinos with a p-value of less than 0.01 (pretrial); see Fig. 5. The strongest of these sources is the nearby active galaxy NGC 1068, also known as Messier 77, which, independently, also emerges as the most significant source in a list of about a hundred candidates that had been preselected by the collaboration as targets of interest.

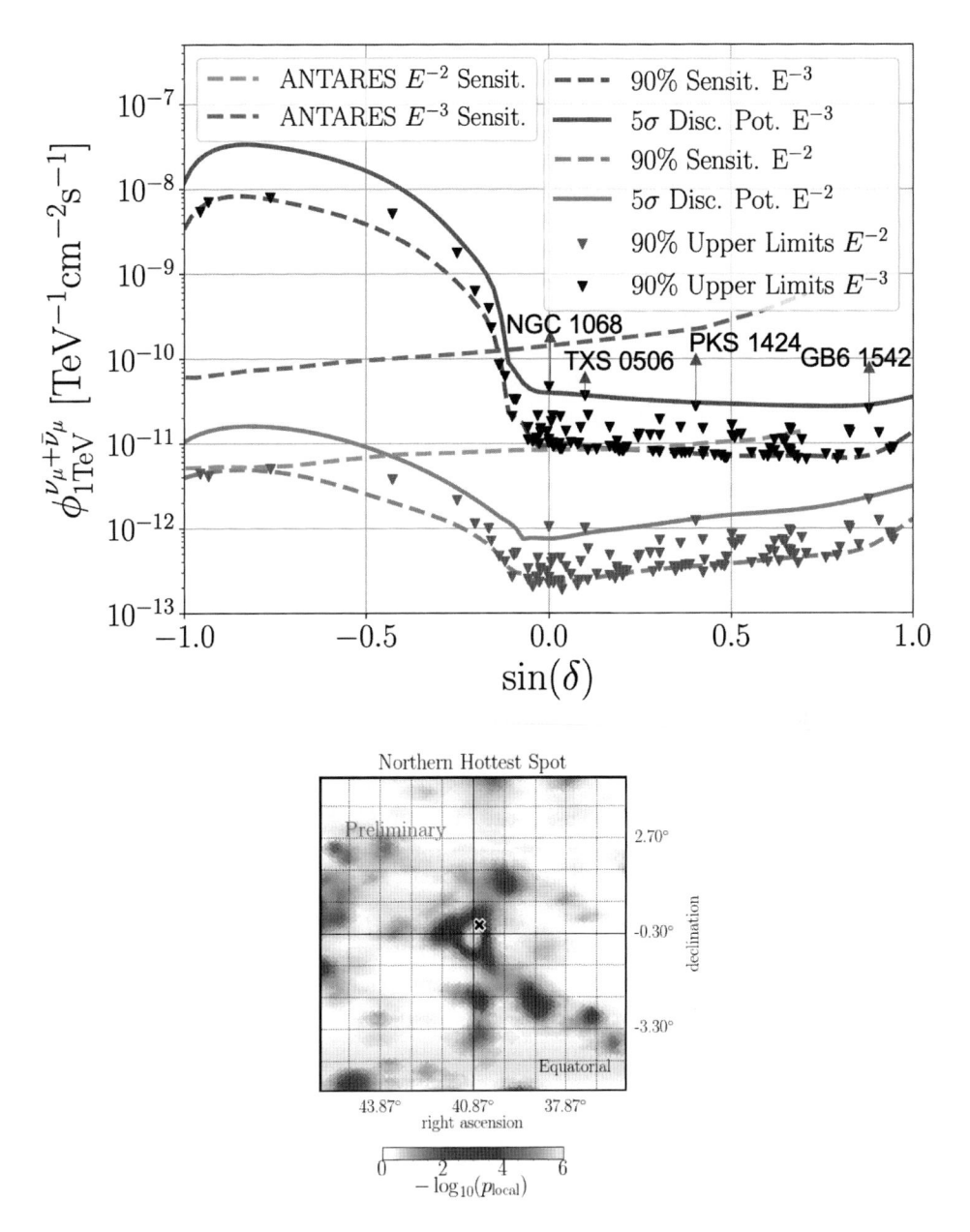

Fig. 5. **Top Panel:** Upper limits on the flux from candidate point sources of neutrinos in 10 years of IceCube data assuming two spectral indices of the flux.[15] Also shown as triangles are limits on a preselected list of about one hundred candidate sources. Four sources exceed the 4σ level (pretrial) and collectively result in a 3σ anisotropy of the sky map. **Bottom Panel:** Association of the hottest source in the sky map as well as in the list of preselected candidate sources with the active galaxy NGC 1068.

2.2. Neutrinos Interacting Inside the Instrumented Volume

The second method for separating cosmic from atmospheric neutrinos exclusively identifies high-energy neutrinos interacting inside the instrumented volume of the detector, so-called starting events. After only two years of operation, IceCube used this method to make the initial discovery of an extragalactic flux of cosmic neutrinos[1] with an energy flux, $E^2 dN/dE$, in the local universe that is, surprisingly, similar to that in gamma rays.[16,17] Using this method, one divides the instrumented volume of ice into an outer veto shield and a ~ 500-megaton inner fiducial volume. The advantage of focusing on neutrinos interacting inside the instrumented volume of ice is that the detector functions as a total absorption calorimeter,[8] allowing for a good energy measurement that separates cosmic from lower-energy atmospheric neutrinos. In contrast to the first method, neutrinos from all directions in the sky and of all flavors can be identified, including both muon tracks and secondary showers produced by charged-current interactions of electron and tau neutrinos and neutral current interactions of neutrinos of all flavors. A sample event with a light pool of roughly one hundred thousand photoelectrons extending over more than 500 meters is shown in the top panel of Fig. 3.

The starting event samples revealed the first evidence for neutrinos of cosmic origin.[1,18] Events with PeV energies and with no trace of coincident muons that reveal either the decay products of a parent meson or an accompanying atmospheric shower are highly unlikely to be of atmospheric origin. The present seven-year data set contains a total of 60 neutrino events with deposited energies ranging from 60 TeV to 10 PeV that are likely to be of cosmic origin. The deposited energy and zenith dependence of the high-energy starting events[12,19] is compared to the atmospheric background in Fig. 6. A purely atmospheric explanation of the observation is excluded at 8σ.

The flux of cosmic neutrinos has by now also been characterized with a range of other methods. Their results agree, pointing at extragalactic sources whose flux has equilibrated in the three neutrino flavors after propagation over cosmic distances,[21] with $\nu_e : \nu_\mu : \nu_\tau \sim 1 : 1 : 1$. Fig. 7 shows the measurement of the cosmic neutrino flux of a recent analysis that specializes to showers only. These have been isolated from the atmospheric background down to energies below 10 TeV.[22] The energy spectrum of $E^{-2.5}$ agrees with the measurement using upgoing muons with a spectral index of $E^{-2.4}$ above an energy of ~ 100 TeV.[12] In general, analyses reaching lower energies exhibit larger spectral indices with the updated 7.5 years starting-event sample,[19] yielding a spectral index value of -2.87 ± 0.2 for the 68.3% confidence interval.

2.3. Cosmic Tau Neutrinos

We should comment at this point that there is yet another method to conclusively identify neutrinos that are of cosmic origin: the observation of high-energy tau neutrinos. Tau neutrinos are produced in the atmosphere by the oscillations of muon neutrinos into tau neutrinos, but only for neutrino energies well below 100 GeV.

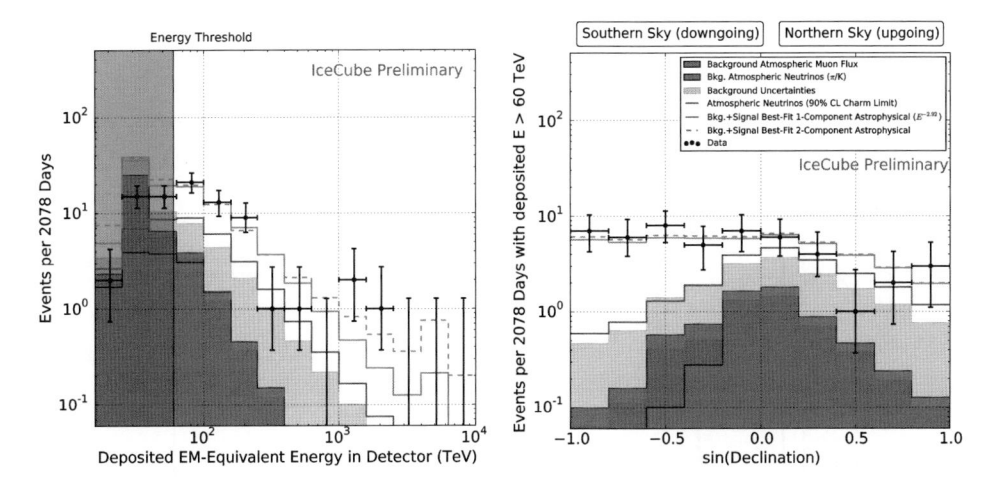

Fig. 6. **Left Panel:** Deposited energies, by neutrinos interacting inside IceCube, observed in six years of data.[12] The grey region shows uncertainties on the sum of all backgrounds. The atmospheric muon flux (blue) and its uncertainty is computed from simulation to overcome statistical limitations in our background measurement and scaled to match the total measured background rate. The atmospheric neutrino flux is derived from previous measurements of both the π, K, and charm components of the atmospheric spectrum.[20] Also shown are two fits to the spectrum, assuming a simple power-law (solid gray) and a broken power-law (dashed gray). **Right Panel:** The same data and models, but now showing the distribution of events with deposited energy above 60 TeV in declination. At the South Pole, the declination angle δ is equivalent to the distribution in zenith angle θ related by the identity, $\delta = \theta - \pi/2$. It is clearly visible that the data is flat in the Southern Hemisphere, as expected from the contribution of an isotropic astrophysical flux.

Above that energy a tau neutrino must be of cosmic origin, produced in cosmic accelerators with a neutrino flux with a tau fraction of approximately one third. Tau neutrinos produce two spatially separated showers in the detector, one from the interaction of the tau neutrino and the second from the decay of the secondary tau produced.[23] The mean decay length of the tau lepton is $\lambda_\tau = (E_\tau/m)\,c\tau \approx 50\,\text{m} \times (E_\tau/\text{PeV})$, where m, τ, and E_τ are the mass, lifetime, and energy of the tau, respectively. Two such candidate events have been identified.[24] An event with a decay length of 17 m and a probability of 98% of being produced by a tau neutrino is shown in Fig. 8. The energies of the two showers are 9 TeV and 80 TeV.

Yet another independent confirmation of the observation of neutrinos of cosmic origin appeared in the form of the Glashow resonance event shown in Fig. 9. The event was identified in a dedicated search for partially contained showers of very high energy.[25] The reconstructed energy of the shower is 6.3 PeV, which matches the laboratory energy for the production of a weak intermediate W^- in the resonant interaction of an electron antineutrino with an atomic electron: $\bar{\nu}_e + e^- \to W^- \to q + \bar{q}$. Given its high energy, the initial neutrino is cosmic in origin; it represents an independent discovery of cosmic neutrinos at the level of 5σ. Assuming the Standard Model cross section, we expect 1.55 events in the data sample searched, assuming an antineutrino:neutrino ratio of 1:1 characteristic of a cosmic source producing

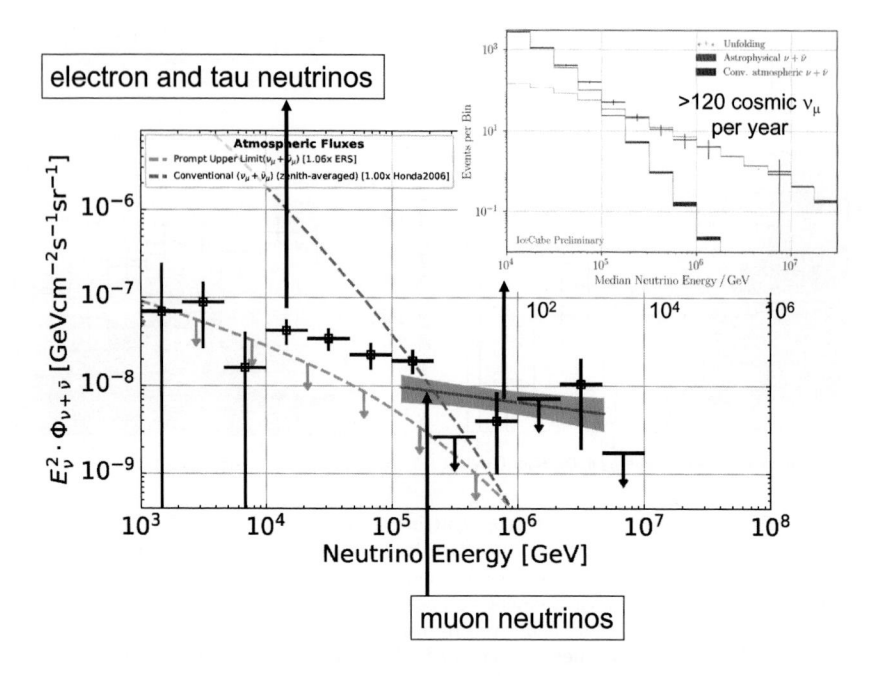

Fig. 7. The flux of cosmic muon neutrinos[12] inferred from the eight-year upgoing-muon track analysis (red solid line) with 1σ uncertainty range (shaded range; from fit shown in upper-right inset) is compared with the flux of showers initiated by electron and tau neutrinos.[22] The measurements are consistent assuming that each neutrino flavor contributes an identical flux to the diffuse spectrum.

an equal number of pions of all three electric charges. Taking into account the detector's energy resolution, the probability that the event is produced off resonance by deep inelastic scattering is only 0.01, assuming a spectrum with a spectral index of $\gamma = -2.5$. Furthermore, the presence of both muons and an electromagnetic shower is consistent with the hadronic decay of a W^- produced on the Glashow resonance.[25]

The observation of a Glashow resonance event indicates the presence of electron antineutrinos in the cosmic neutrino flux. Its unique signature provides a method to disentangle neutrinos from antineutrinos; their ratio distinguishes accelerators that produce neutrinos via pp and $p\gamma$ interactions and is also sensitive to their magnetic field.[25]

Finally, data from the ANTARES experiment are consistent with the observation of a flux of cosmic origin although with limited statistical significance.[26]

3. Multimessenger Astronomy

The most important message emerging from the IceCube measurements may not be apparent yet: the prominent role of neutrinos relative to photons in the extreme

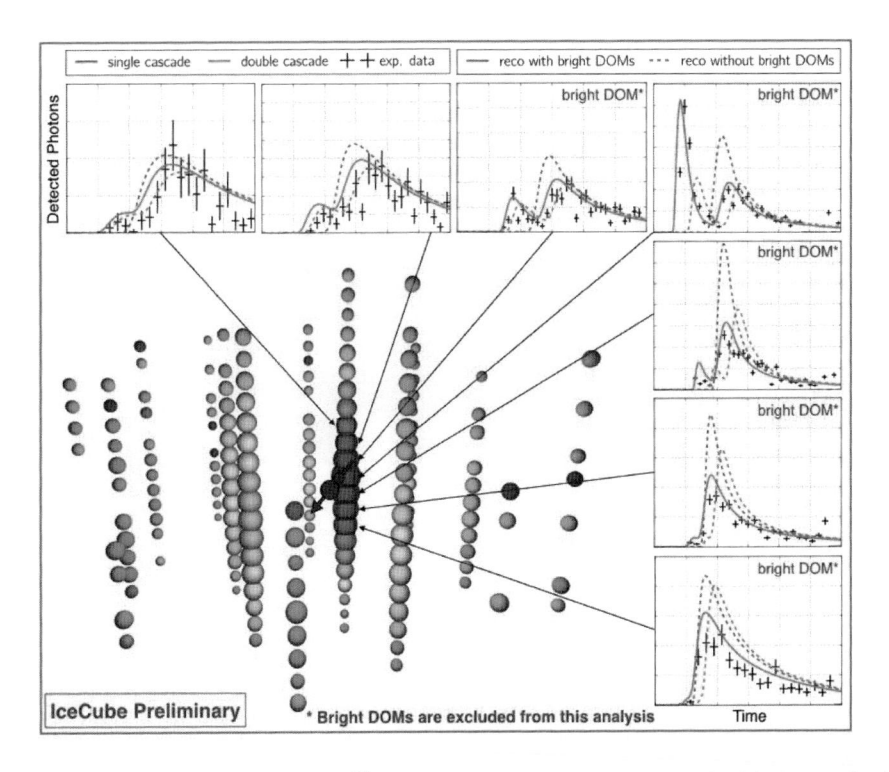

Fig. 8. Event view of a tau neutrino.[24] The Cherenkov photons associated with the production and subsequent decay of the tau neutrino are identified by the double-peaked photon count as a function of time for the bright DOMs, for instance, the one shown in the top-right corner. The best fit (solid line) corresponds to a 17 m decay length and is far superior to fits assuming a single electromagnetic or hadronic shower (dashed lines).

universe. Photons are inevitably produced in association with neutrinos when accelerated cosmic rays produce both neutral and charged pions in interactions with target material in the vicinity of the accelerator. While neutral pions decay into two gamma rays, $\pi^0 \to \gamma + \gamma$, the charged pions decay into three high-energy neutrinos (ν) and antineutrinos ($\bar{\nu}$) via the decay chain $\pi^+ \to \mu^+ + \nu_\mu$ followed by $\mu^+ \to e^+ + \bar{\nu}_\mu + \nu_e$ and the charged-conjugate process. On average, the four final state leptons equally share the energy of the charged pion. With these approximations, gamma rays and neutrinos carry on average 1/2 and 1/4 of the energy of the parent pion.

Modeling of gamma ray observations generally indicated that the flux in pionic photons would be relatively small compared to a dominant flux of photons radiated by electrons in electromagnetic processes, synchrotron radiation, and inverse Compton scattering. These were generally assumed to dominate the energy production of sources in the Galaxy and beyond. IceCube observations show that this is not the case. To illustrate this point, we show in Fig. 10 the energy fluxes, $E^2 dN/dE$, of neutrinos and gamma rays in the universe. Clearly, the energy flux of cosmic

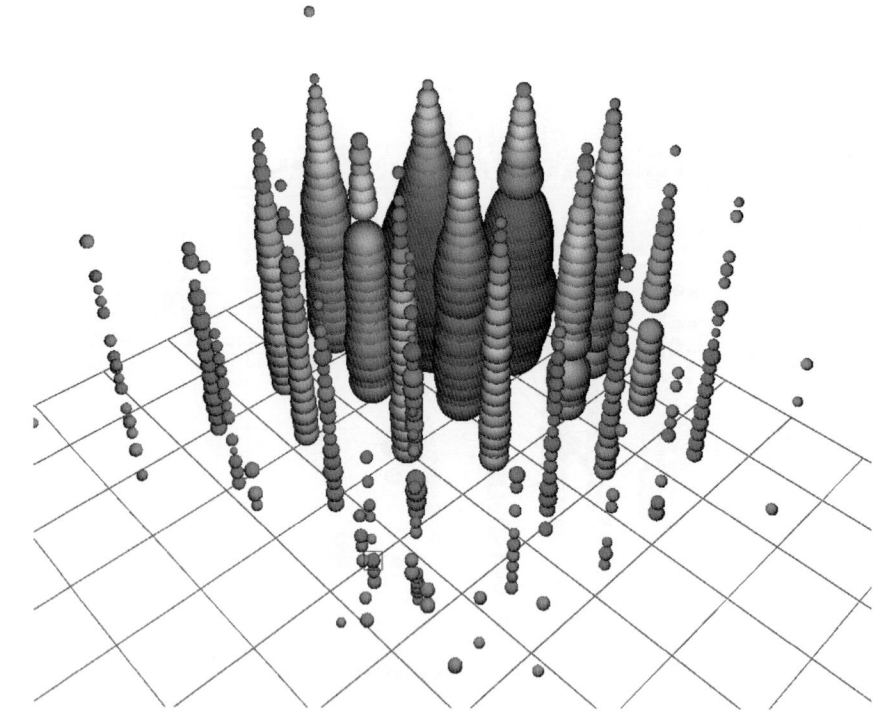

Fig. 9. Particle shower created by the Glashow resonance.[25] Its energy is reconstructed at the resonant energy for the production of a weak intermediate boson W^- in the interaction of an antielectron neutrino with an atomic electron in the ice. The properties of the secondary muons produced in the particle shower are consistent with the hadronic decay of a W^- boson.

neutrinos is comparable to the one for the highest energy gamma rays observed by the NASA Fermi satellite.[16] This already indicates a more prominent role of hadronic processes than routinely anticipated. We will look at this match of the neutrino and gamma-ray energies in more detail.

The neutrino production rate Q_{ν_α} (with typical units GeV^{-1}s^{-1} and with the subscript α labeling the neutrino flavor) can be related to the one for charged pions Q_π by

$$\sum_\alpha E_\nu Q_{\nu_\alpha}(E_\nu) \simeq 3\left[E_\pi Q_{\pi^\pm}(E_\pi)\right]_{E_\pi \simeq 4E_\nu}, \qquad (2)$$

while, similarly, the production rate of pionic gamma rays is related to the one for neutral pions by

$$E_\gamma Q_\gamma(E_\gamma) \simeq 2\left[E_\pi Q_{\pi^0}(E_\pi)\right]_{E_\pi \simeq 2E_\gamma}. \qquad (3)$$

Pion production in the interactions of cosmic rays with photon fields proceeds resonantly via the processes $p + \gamma \to \Delta^+ \to \pi^0 + p$ and $p + \gamma \to \Delta^+ \to \pi^+ + n$.

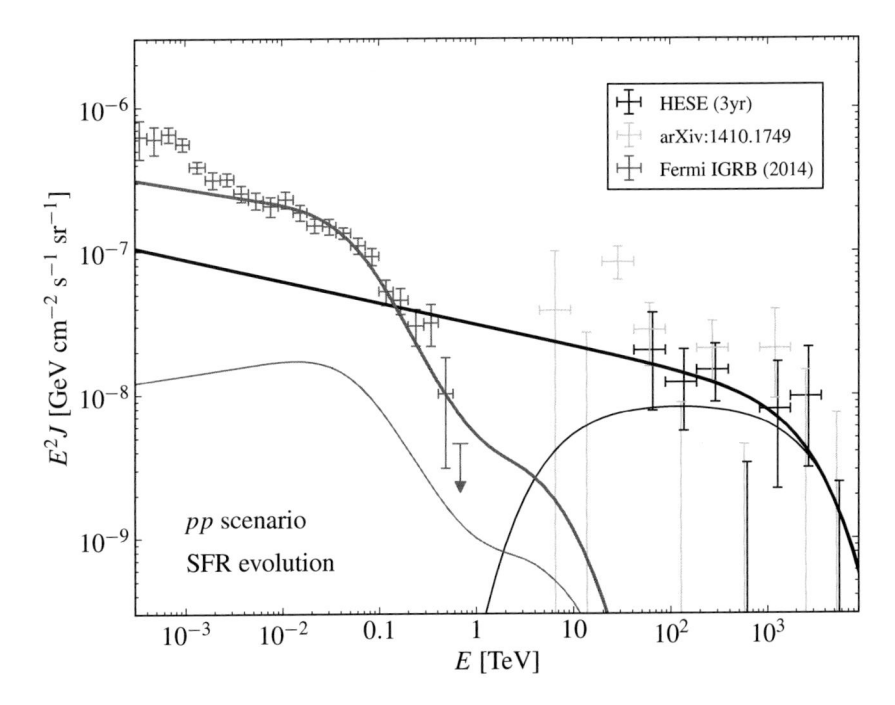

Fig. 10. A calculation illustrating that the photon flux that accompanies the neutrino flux (thick black line) measured by IceCube matches the gamma-ray flux (thick red line) observed by Fermi. We assume a $E^{-1.5}$ energy spectrum, star-formation redshift evolution and, importantly, gamma-ray transparent sources, i.e., pionic photons lose energy in the EBL but not in their sources. The black data points are early IceCube measurements.[27,28] The result suggests that the decay products of neutral and charged pions from pp interactions may be significant components of the nonthermal radiation in the extreme universe.[29] (Introducing the cutoff on the high-energy flux, shown in the figure, does not affect the result.) The calculation is compared to an identical calculation adopting a spectral shape characteristic for the production of cosmic neutrinos on a gamma-ray target in the source (thin lines). While the pionic gamma-ray energy flux is now suppressed relative to the Fermi observations, the neutrino energy spectrum underestimates the IceCube observations and the conclusion that the sources are likely obscured is recovered after correct normalization to the most up to date measurements.[29]

These channels produce charged and neutral pions with probabilities 2/3 and 1/3, respectively. However, the additional contribution of nonresonant pion production changes this ratio to approximately 1/2 and 1/2. In contrast, cosmic rays interacting with matter produce equal numbers of pions of all three charges: $p + p \to n_\pi [\pi^0 + \pi^+ + \pi^-] + X$, where n_π is the pion multiplicity. We thus obtain a charge ratio $K_\pi = n_{\pi^\pm}/n_{\pi^0} \simeq 2$ and 1 for pp and $p\gamma$ interactions, respectively.

Eqs. 2 and 3 can now be combined to obtain a direct relation between the gamma-ray and neutrino production rates:

$$\frac{1}{3} \sum_\alpha E_\nu^2 Q_{\nu_\alpha}(E_\nu) \simeq \frac{K_\pi}{4} \left[E_\gamma^2 Q_\gamma(E_\gamma) \right]_{E_\gamma = 2E_\nu}, \qquad (4)$$

where the factor 1/4 accounts for the fact that two gamma rays are produced in the neutral pion decay with twice the energy of the accompanying neutrino, $\langle E_\nu \rangle / \langle E_\gamma \rangle \simeq 1/2$. Note that the relative production rate of gamma rays and neutrinos only depends on the ratio of charged-to-neutral pions produced without any reference to the cosmic-ray beam that initiates their production in the target. This powerful relation follows from the fact that pion production conserves isospin and nothing else.

Before applying this relation to data, one must recall that the universe is transparent to extragalactic neutrinos but not to the accompanying gamma rays. These will interact with microwave photons and other components of the extragalactic background light (EBL) to initiate an electromagnetic cascade that reaches Earth in the form of multiple photons of lower energy. The electromagnetic shower subdivides the initial PeV photon energy into multiple photons with GeV to TeV energies by the time it reaches Earth.[30,31] If the source itself is opaque to gamma rays, the high-energy gamma rays will lose energy even before reaching the EBL to possibly emerge at Earth below the threshold of Fermi, at MeV energies and below.

In order to underscore the power of the multimessenger connection between photons and neutrinos, we first calculate the gamma-ray flux accompanying the diffuse cosmic neutrino flux observed by IceCube, which we describe by a power law with spectral index of -2.15, consistent with the neutrino data above an energy of 100 TeV. The result is shown in Fig. 10 assuming gamma-ray transparent sources and equal multiplicities of all three pion charges, i.e., $K_\pi = 2$. The cascaded gamma-ray energy flux resulting from the pionic photons accompanying the neutrino flux matches the energy flux of extragalactic gamma rays measured by Fermi.

Clearly, in this illustration, the slope and overall normalization of the neutrino spectrum have been adjusted to not exceed the isotropic extragalactic gamma-ray background observed by the Fermi satellite. We conclude that the high-energy cosmic neutrino flux above 100 TeV shown in Fig. 10 saturates the Fermi measurement for the highest photon energies; higher normalization and larger spectral index of the neutrino flux will result in a gamma-ray flux that exceeds the Fermi observations. Fitting the IceCube data with a $E^{-2.5}$ spectral index, closer to the present observations, results in larger neutrino energy fluxes at energies below 100 TeV for both neutrinos and their accompanying photons. After cascading in the EBL, the latter exceeds the Fermi observations. There is no conflict here; in this case, we conclude that the assumption that the sources themselves are transparent to photons is untenable. The resolution is as mentioned above, that the photons lose energy in the source even before entering the EBL and, as a result, reach Earth with energies that are below the detection threshold of the Fermi satellite, at MeV energy or below.

Alternatively, the target for producing the neutrinos may be photons. This changes the value of K_π and, more importantly, the shape of the energy spectrum; for a detailed discussion, see, for instance, Ref. 32. Yielding an energy spectrum that peaks near PeV energies, as shown in Fig. 10, the contribution to the Fermi flux is suppressed at lower energies relative to the power law assumed in Fig. 10. However, as was the case for pp interactions, fits that do not exceed the Fermi data tend not to accommodate the cosmic neutrino spectrum below 100 TeV. This is illustrated in Fig. 10 where we obtain a neutrino spectrum well below the Fermi observations at the price of not fitting the overall normalization of the neutrino data. If sources of the TeV-PeV neutrinos are transparent to gamma rays with respect to two-photon annihilation, tensions with the isotropic diffuse gamma-ray background measured by Fermi seem unavoidable, independently of the production mechanism.[29]

The conclusion is inescapable that the energy fluxes of neutrinos and gamma rays in the extreme universe are qualitatively the same. Furthermore, the IceCube observations point at contributions to the diffuse flux from gamma-obscured sources.

We therefore anticipate that multimessenger studies of gamma-ray and neutrino data will be a powerful tool to identify and study the cosmic ray accelerators that produce cosmic neutrinos. Accordingly, IceCube has developed methods, most promising among them the real-time multiwavelength observations with astronomical telescopes, to identify the sources and build on the discovery of cosmic neutrinos to launch a new era in astronomy.[33,34]

An important lesson for multiwavelength astronomy is that strong high-energy gamma-ray emitters may not be the best candidate neutrino sources. For instance, IceCube does not observe neutrinos from gamma-ray bursts, but this result covers a sample of bursts that are strong gamma-ray emitters.[35] A handful of bursts have been identified that are obscured in gamma rays and may instead provide the key to detecting a neutrino signal. The strongest sources in the 10-year IceCube sky map, the galaxies NGC 1068 and TXS 0506+O56, are gamma-ray-obscured sources at least at the time that they emitted neutrinos. We will discuss this next.

Interestingly, the common energy density of photons and neutrinos is also comparable to that of the ultra-high-energy extragalactic cosmic rays.[36]

4. Identifying Neutrino Sources: The Supermassive Black Hole TXS 0506+056

Phenomenological studies[37,38] and recent data analyses[39–41] have converged on the fact that Fermi's extragalactic gamma-ray flux shown in Fig. 10 is dominated by blazars, AGN with jets pointing at Earth. It is tempting to conclude, based on the matching energy fluxes of photons and neutrinos discussed in the previous section, that the unidentified neutrino sources contributing to the diffuse neutrino flux have already been observed as strong gamma-ray emitters. This is not the case. A dedicated IceCube study[42] correlating the arrival directions of cosmic neutrinos with Fermi blazars shows no evidence of neutrino emission from these sources. The limit leaves room for a contribution of Fermi blazars to the diffuse cosmic neutrino flux below the 10% level. Surprisingly, the multimessenger campaign launched by the neutrino alert IC-170922A[2] identified the first source of cosmic neutrinos as a Fermi "blazar." We will discuss how the multiwavelength data shed light on the apparent contradiction.

Since 2016, the IceCube multimessenger program has grown from issuing Galactic supernova alerts[43] and matching neutrinos with early LIGO/Virgo gravitational wave candidates to a steadily expanding set of automatic filters that select in real time rare, very high energy neutrino events that are likely to be cosmic in origin.[44] Within less than one minute of stopping in the instrumented Antarctic ice, the arrival directions of the neutrinos are reconstructed and automatically sent to the Gamma-ray Coordinate Network for potential follow-up by astronomical telescopes.

4.1. *Observation of a Cosmic Neutrino Source: TXS 0506+056*

On September 22, 2017, the tenth such alert, IceCube-170922A,[45] reported a well-reconstructed muon that deposited 180 TeV inside the detector, corresponding to a most probable energy of the parent neutrino of 290 TeV. Its arrival direction was aligned with the coordinates of a known Fermi blazar, TXS 0506+056, to within $0.06°$. The source was "flaring" with a gamma-ray flux that had increased by a factor of seven in recent months. A variety of estimates converged on a probability on the order of 10^{-3} that the coincidence was accidental. The identification of the neutrino with the source reached the level of evidence, but not more. What clinched the association was a series of subsequent observations, culminating with the optical observation of the source switching from an "off" to an "on" state two hours after the emission of IC-170922A, conclusively associating the neutrino with TXS 0506+056.[46] The sequence of observations can be summarized as follows:

- The redshift of the host galaxy, a known blazar, was measured to be $z \simeq 0.34$.[47] It is important to realize that nearby blazars like the Markarian sources are at a distance that is ten times closer, and therefore TXS 0506+056, with a similar flux despite the greater distance, is one of the most luminous sources in the universe. This suggests that it belongs to a special class of sources that accelerate proton beams in dense environments, revealed by the neutrino. That the source is special eliminates any conflict between its observation and the lack of correlation between the arrival directions of IceCube neutrinos and the bulk of the blazars observed by Fermi.[42] Such limits implicitly assume that all sources in an astronomical category are identical, and this is a strong, unstated assumption as underscored by this observation.
- Originally detected by NASA's Swift[48] and Fermi[49] satellites, the alert was followed up by ground-based air Cherenkov telescopes.[50] MAGIC detected the emission of gamma rays with energies exceeding 100 GeV starting several days after the observation of the neutrino.[51] Given its distance, this establishes the source as a relatively rare TeV blazar.
- Informed where to look, IceCube searched its archival neutrino data up to and including October 2017 for evidence of neutrino emission at the location of TXS 0506+056.[3] When searching the sky for point sources of

neutrinos, two analyses have been routinely performed: one that searches for steady emission of neutrinos and one that searches for flares over a variety of timescales. Evidence was found for 19 high-energy neutrino events on a background of fewer than 6 in a burst lasting 110 days. This burst dominates the integrated flux from the source over the last 9.5 years of archival IceCube data, leaving the 2017 flare as a second subdominant feature. We note that this analysis applied a published prescription to data; the chance that this observation is a fluctuation is small.

- Radio interferometric images[52,53] of the source revealed a jet that loses its tight collimation beyond 5 milliarcseconds running into material or intense radiation fields that are likely to be the target for producing the neutrinos. The nature of the target is still a matter of debate. Speculations include the merger with another galaxy that may supply plenty of material to interact with the jet of the dominant galaxy. Alternatively, the jet may interact with the dense molecular clouds of a star-forming region or simply with supermassive stars in the central region of the host galaxy.[52,53] Also, in a so-called structured jet, the accelerated protons may catch up and collide with a slower moving and denser region of jetted photons. Additionally, the VLBA data reveal that the neutrino burst occurs at the peak of enhanced radio emission at 15 GHz, which started five years ago; see Fig. 11. The radio flare may be a signature of a galaxy merger; correlations of radio bursts with the process of merging supermassive black holes have been anticipated.[54]

- The MASTER robotic optical telescope network has been monitoring the source since 2005 and detected its strongest time variation in the last 15 years to occur two hours after the emission of IC170922, with a second variation following the 2014-15 burst.[46] The blazar switches from the "off" to the "on" state two hours after the emission of the neutrino. After an episode of monitoring the uniformity of their observations of the source in the first quarter of 2020, they argue that the time variation detected on September 22, 2017 conclusively associates the source with the neutrino.[46]

Additionally, it is important to note the fact that the high-energy photon and neutrino spectra covering the 2014 burst are consistent with a hard E^{-2} spectrum, which is expected for a cosmic accelerator. In fact, the gamma-ray spectrum shows a hint of flattening beyond E^{-2} during the 110-day period of the 2014 burst.[55,56]

In summary, both the multiwavelength campaign[2] and the observation of an earlier burst of the same source in archival neutrino data provide statistically independent[3] evidence for the association of neutrinos with TXS 0506+056 at the 3 and 3.7σ level, respectively. The significances contributed by the optical and TeV associations on timescales of hours and days are not taken into account, and it is not straightforward to do so because of their a posteriori nature. We conclude, however, that the association of neutrinos with the source summarized above is compelling.

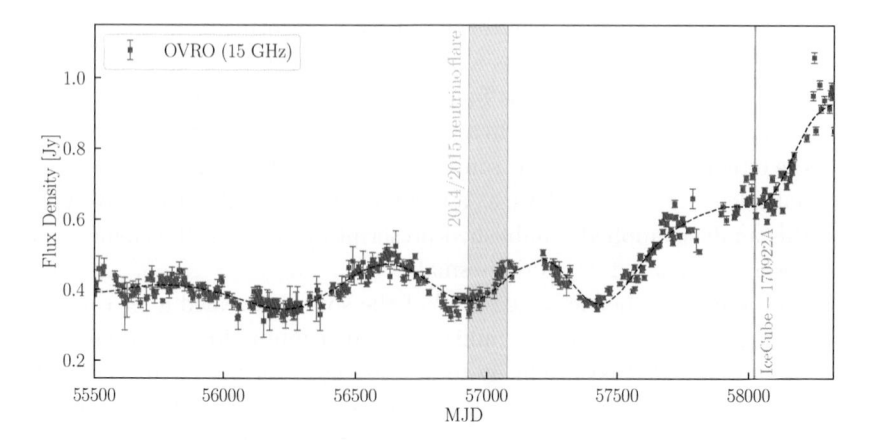

Fig. 11. TXS 0506+056 radio light curve from Owen Valley Radio Observatory (OVRO) at 15 GHz (red). The dashed line illustrates the pattern of the radio flux density. The 2014/15 110-day neutrino flare (yellow band) and the IceCube-170922A episodes are shown.

Other IceCube alerts have triggered intriguing observations. Following up on a July 31, 2016, neutrino alert, the AGILE collaboration, which operates an orbiting X-ray and gamma-ray telescope, reported a day-long blazar flare in the direction of the neutrino one day before the neutrino detection.[57] A tentative but very intriguing association of an IceCube alert[58] has been made with a tidal disruption event, an anticipated source of high-energy neutrino emission. Even before IceCube issued automatic alerts, in April 2016, the TANAMI collaboration argued for the association of the highest energy IceCube event at the time, dubbed "Big Bird," with the flaring blazar PKS B1424-418.[59] Interestingly, the event was produced at a minimum of the Fermi flux,[5] indicating a gamma-ray-obscured source. AMANDA, IceCube's predecessor, observed[60] three neutrinos in coincidence with a rare flare of the blazar 1ES 1959+650 detected by the Whipple telescope in 2002.[61] However, none of these identifications reach the significance of the observations triggered by IC-170922A.

4.2. *The Blueprint of the TXS 0506+056 Beam Dump?*

Blazars are accelerators with their jets pointing at Earth. The gamma-ray community has developed a routine procedure for modeling their spectrum with two components: a lower energy component produced by synchrotron radiation by the electron beam and a high-energy component resulting from the inverse Compton scattering of (possibly the same) photons by accelerated electrons; for a recent discussion, see Ref. 62. Such a source cannot accommodate the TXS observations for two reasons: an electron beam does not produce pions that decay into neutrinos, and, even with the presence of protons in the beam, a target is required to produce the parent pions. It is also evident that a source that emits high-energy gamma rays is transparent to $\gamma\gamma$ absorption and unlikely to host the target material to produce neutrinos. The opacity for $\gamma\gamma$ interactions to absorb photons is typically two orders of magnitude larger than the one for $p\gamma$ interactions to produce pions and neutrinos.[63]

With the opacity to photons about two orders of magnitude larger, the target producing the neutrinos is unlikely to be transparent to TeV photons, only to photons with tens of GeV energy, and that is indeed what is observed by Fermi at the time of the 2014 flare. There is also evidence that, temporarily, TXS 0506+056 was a gamma-ray-obscured source at the time the IC-170922A neutrino was emitted. The optical observations show a dramatic transition of the blazar from the "off" to the "on" state two hours after the emission of the neutrino, resulting additionally in the doubling of its total optical luminosity.[46] Also at the time of IC-170922 the ground-based atmospheric gamma-ray telescopes observed rapid variations in the flux around the time of the neutrino emission,[2] with the gamma-ray emission observed by MAGIC only emerging after several days.[51]

A more direct indication that strong neutrino emitters are gamma-ray-obscured is indicated by a more recent alert, IC-190730A, sent by IceCube on July 30, 2019. A well-reconstructed 300-TeV muon neutrino was observed in spatial coincidence with the blazar PKS 1502+106.[64] With a reconstructed energy just exceeding that of IC-170922A, it is the highest energy neutrino alert so far. OVRO radio observations[65] show that the neutrino is coincident with the peak flux density of a flare at 15 GHz that started five years prior,[66] matching the similar long-term radio outburst of TXS 0506+056 at the time of IC-170922A; see Fig. 11. Even more intriguing is the fact that the gamma-ray flux observed by Fermi shows a clear minimum at the time that the neutrino is emitted; see Fig. 12. We infer that at this time the jet meets the target that produces the neutrino. Inevitably, the accompanying high-energy gamma rays will be absorbed and the bulk of their electromagnetic energy will cascade down to energies below the Fermi threshold, i.e., MeV or below. Accumulating evidence indicates that cosmic neutrinos are produced by temporarily gamma-suppressed blazars or some other category of AGN.

The coincidence of the two highest energy alerts to date with extended periods of radio emission has led to the speculation that all,[67] or at least some,[68] cosmic neutrinos originate in radio-bright galaxies. The significance of the correlation and its physical origin, if any,[69] are debated.

We suggest that neutrino sources are special, with properties unlikely to match any astronomical classification; astronomical observations catalog accelerators, not neutrino sources. If the neutrino flux observed from TXS 0506+056 over the last decade were typical of all blazars, these would overproduce the total diffuse flux observed by IceCube by well over an order of magnitude.[63] The diffuse neutrino flux limits the density of such sources in the universe to $\sim 5 \times 10^{-10}$ per Mpc^3, i.e., about 5% of all blazars, and more likely an even smaller fraction of all AGN.[4] Attempts by IceCube and others to find a correlation between the directions of high-energy neutrinos and *all* Fermi blazars must inevitably be unsuccessful, as was the case in Ref. 42.

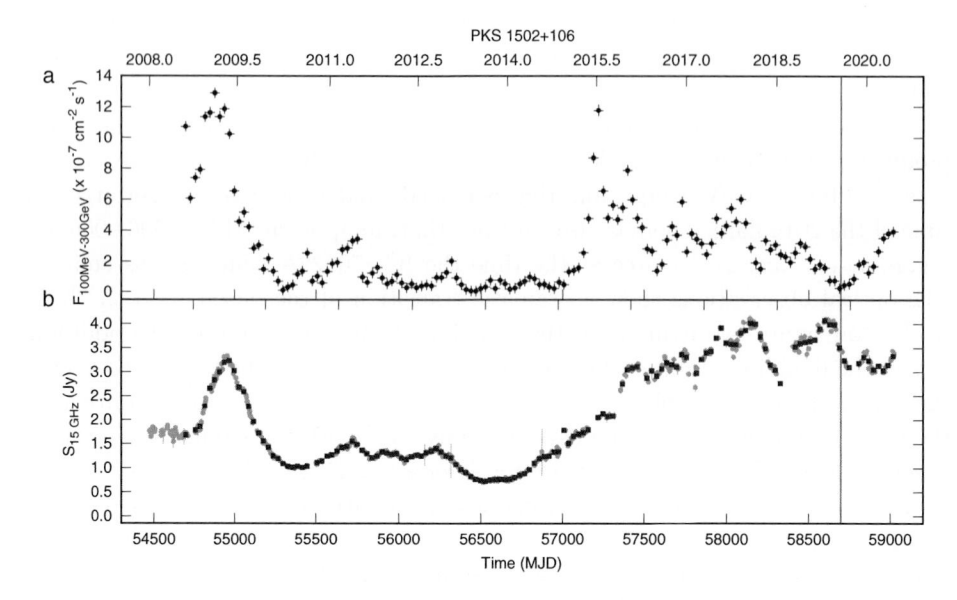

Fig. 12. Temporal variation of the γ-ray and radio brightness of PKS 1502+106.[5] **Top Panel:** Fermi-LAT likelihood light curve integrated between 100 MeV and 300 GeV (marked by black dots with error bars). **Bottom Panel:** OVRO flux density curve of PKS 1502+106 plotted with light blue dots, which is superimposed by the radio flux density curve binned to the Fermi-LAT light curve (marked with dark blue squares). The detection time of the neutrino IC-190730A is labeled by a vertical purple line.

The nature of this special class of sources has not been settled. One straightforward explanation could be that a subclass of AGN, selected by redshift evolution, are powerful proton accelerators producing neutrinos in the past and no longer active today. This assumption accommodates the relatively large redshift of TXS 0506+056, which would be the closest among a set of sources that only accelerated cosmic rays at early redshifts.[70]

Alternatively, in merging galaxies there is plenty of material for accelerated cosmic rays to interact with the jet of the dominant galaxy. Merger activity in active galaxies in not uncommon. The fresh material provides optically thick environments and allows for rapid variation of the Lorentz factors. A cursory review of the literature on the production of neutrinos in galaxy mergers is sufficient to conclude that they can indeed accommodate the observations of both the individual sources discussed above and the total flux of cosmic neutrinos.[71–73] Besides mergers, some form of structured jet where the accelerated protons collide with a slower moving and denser region of jetted photons is a possibility. The jet could also interact with dense molecular clouds of a star-forming region or simply with supermassive stars in the central region of the host galaxy.[52,53]

The observation that the energy flux in neutrinos and very high energy cosmic rays are similar supports the fact that cosmic rays must be highly efficient at producing neutrinos, requiring a large target density that renders them opaque to high-energy gamma rays. A consistent picture emerges with the source opacity $\tau_{p\gamma}$ exceeding a value of 0.8,[4,63] resulting in a gamma-ray cascade where photons lose energy in the source before cascading to yet lower energies in the extragalactic background light. Some of their energy emerges below the Fermi threshold by the time they reach Earth. This is consistent with the discussion in the previous section that the multimessenger relation between neutrinos and gamma rays points at obscured sources.

We previously mentioned the evidence emerging from 10 years of IceCube data that the arrival directions of cosmic neutrinos are no longer isotropic.[74] The anisotropy results from four sources—TXS 0506+056 among them—that show evidence for clustering above the 4σ level (pretrial). The strongest of these sources is the nearby active galaxy NGC 1068. There is evidence for shocks near the core and for molecular clouds with column density reaching $\sim 10^{25}$ cm^{-2}.[75] Similar to TSX 0506+056, a merger onto the black hole is observed—either with a satellite galaxy or, more likely, with a star-forming region[76] accounting for the molecular clouds. This major accretion event may be the origin of the increased neutrino emission.

Although it is obviously challenging to provide a final conclusion on the origin of neutrinos and cosmic rays, we should not lose sight of the fact that high-energy neutrino astronomy exists and that IceCube has demonstrated it has the tools to reveal the extreme universe with more data, or, more realistically, with a larger detector.

5. From Discovery to Astronomy: Larger Telescopes with Better Angular Resolution

Neutrino astronomy has reached a stage that reminds us of the time when Trevor Weekes's 11-meter ground-based Cherenkov telescope had established one convincing TeV source: the Crab. Even today we do not know how the Crab produces gamma rays that track the pulsations of the pulsar at TeV energy. We have to take the lead on TeV astronomy: building more and better telescopes.

Following the pioneering work of DUMAND,[77] several neutrino telescope projects were initiated in the Mediterranean Sea and in Lake Baikal in the 1990s.[78–81] In 2008, the construction of the ANTARES detector off the coast of France was completed. It demonstrated the feasibility of neutrino detection in the deep sea and has provided a wealth of technical experience and design solutions for deep-sea components. An international collaboration has started construction of a multi-cubic-kilometer neutrino telescope in the Mediterranean Sea, KM3NeT.[82] KM3NeT in its second phase[82] will consist of two units for astrophysical neutrino observations, each consisting of 115 strings carrying more than 2,000 optical modules. Since April 2021, six are operational and taking data.[83]

A parallel effort is underway in Lake Baikal with the construction of the deep underwater neutrino telescope Baikal-GVD (Gigaton Volume Detector).[84] The first

GVD cluster was upgraded in the spring of 2016 to its final size: 288 optical modules, a geometry of 120 meters in diameter and 525 meters high, and an instrumented volume of 6 Mton. Each of the eight strings consists of three sections with 12 optical modules. At this time, 7 of the 14 clusters have been deployed, reaching a sensitivity close to the diffuse cosmic neutrino flux observed by IceCube.

IceCube itself is deploying seven new strings at the bottom of the detector array that have been designed as an incremental extension of the DeepCore detector and as a test bed for the technologies of a next-generation detector. The new instrumentation will dramatically boost IceCube's performance at the lowest energies, increasing the samples of atmospheric neutrinos by a factor of ten. New calibration devices will advance our understanding of the response of the light sensors in both current and new strings, resulting in improved reconstructions of cascade events, better identification of tau neutrinos, and an enhanced pointing resolution of muon neutrinos that could approach the 0.1 degree level for the highest energy events of cosmic origin. The improved calibration of the existing sensors will also enable a reanalysis of more than ten years of archival data and significantly increase the discovery potential for neutrino sources before the construction of a second-generation instrument.

Further progress requires a larger instrument. Therefore, as a next step, IceCube proposes to instrument $10\,\text{km}^3$ of glacial ice at the South Pole, capitalizing on the large absorption length of light in ice to thereby increase IceCube's sensitive volume by an order of magnitude.[85] This large gain is made possible by the unique optical properties of the Antarctic glacier revealed by the construction of IceCube. Exploiting the extremely long photon absorption lengths in the deep Antarctic ice, the spacing between strings of light sensors will be increased from 125 to close to 250 meters without significant loss of performance of the instrument at TeV energies and above. The instrumented volume can therefore grow by one order of magnitude while keeping the instrumentation and its budget at the level of the current IceCube detector. The new facility will increase the rates of cosmic events from hundreds to thousands over several years. The superior angular resolution of the longer muon tracks will allow for the discovery of cosmic neutrino sources, currently seen at the $\sim 3\sigma$ level in the 10-year sky map; see Fig. 5.

Acknowledgements

Discussion with collaborators inside and outside the IceCube Collaboration, too many to be listed, have greatly shaped this presentation. Thanks. I would like to single out Markus Ahlers, Qinrui Liu and Ali Kheirandish for contributing to aspects of this manuscript. This research was supported in part by the U.S. National Science Foundation under grants PLR-1600823 and PHY-1913607 and by the University of Wisconsin Research Committee with funds granted by the Wisconsin Alumni Research Foundation.

References

1. IceCube Collaboration (M. G. Aartsen et al.), *Science* **342** (2013) 1242856, arXiv:1311.5238 [astro-ph.HE].
2. Liverpool Telescope, Swift/NuSTAR, MAGIC, H.E.S.S., AGILE, Kiso, VLA/17B-403, INTEGRAL, Kapteyn, Subaru, HAWC, Fermi-LAT, ASAS-SN, VERITAS, Kanata, IceCube Collaboration (M. G. Aartsen et al.), *Science* **361** (2018) eaat1378, arXiv:1807.08816 [astro-ph.HE].
3. IceCube Collaboration (M. G. Aartsen et al.), *Science* **361** (2018) 147, arXiv:1807.08794 [astro-ph.HE].
4. F. Halzen and A. Kheirandish, *Front. Astron. Space Sci.* **6** (2019) 32.
5. E. Kun, I. Bartos, J. B. Tjus, P. L. Biermann, F. Halzen and G. Mező, *The Astrophysical Journal Letters* **911** (Apr 2021) L18.
6. IceCube Collaboration (M. G. Aartsen et al.), *JINST* **12** (2017) P03012, arXiv:1612.05093 [astro-ph.IM].
7. F. Halzen, *Eur. Phys. J.* **C46** (2006) 669, arXiv:astro-ph/0602132 [astro-ph].
8. IceCube Collaboration Collaboration (M. Aartsen et al.), *JINST* **9** (2014) P03009, arXiv:1311.4767 [physics.ins-det].
9. T. Yuan, *TeV Particle Astrophysics 2017 (TeVPA2017), Columbus, Ohio, USA* (2017).
10. IceCube Collaboration (M. G. Aartsen et al.), *Phys. Rev. Lett.* **115** (2015) 081102, arXiv:1507.04005 [astro-ph.HE].
11. IceCube Collaboration (M. G. Aartsen et al.), *Astrophys. J.* **833** (2016) 3, arXiv:1607.08006 [astro-ph.HE].
12. IceCube Collaboration (M. G. Aartsen et al.), *PoS* **ICRC2017** (2017) arXiv:1710.01191 [astro-ph.HE].
13. IceCube Collaboration (J. Stettner), *PoS* **ICRC2019** (2020) 1017, arXiv:1908.09551 [astro-ph.HE].
14. J. B. Stettner, Measurement of the energy spectrum of astrophysical muon-neutrinos with the IceCube Observatory, dissertation, RWTH Aachen University (2021). pp. 1 Online–Ressource : Illustrationen, Diagramme. Veröffentlicht auf dem Publikationsserver der RWTH Aachen University; Dissertation, RWTH Aachen University, 2021.
15. IceCube Collaboration (M. G. Aartsen et al.), *Phys. Rev. Lett.* **124** (2020) 051103, arXiv:1910.08488 [astro-ph.HE].
16. Fermi-LAT Collaboration (M. Ackermann et al.), *Astrophys. J.* **799** (2015) 86, arXiv:1410.3696 [astro-ph.HE].
17. K. Fang and K. Murase, *Nature Phys.* **14** (2018) 396, arXiv:1704.00015 [astro-ph.HE], [Nature Phys.14,no.4,396(2018)].
18. IceCube Collaboration Collaboration (M. Aartsen et al.), *Phys.Rev.Lett.* **111** (2013) 021103, arXiv:1304.5356 [astro-ph.HE].
19. R. Abbasi, M. Ackermann, J. Adams, J. Aguilar, M. Ahlers, M. Ahrens, C. Alispach, A. Alves, N. Amin, K. Andeen and et al., *Physical Review D* **104** (Jul 2021).
20. IceCube Collaboration Collaboration (M. Aartsen et al.), *Phys.Rev.* **D89** (2014) 102001, arXiv:1312.0104 [astro-ph.HE].
21. IceCube Collaboration (M. G. Aartsen et al.), *Phys. Rev. Lett.* **114** (2015) 171102, arXiv:1502.03376 [astro-ph.HE].
22. IceCube Collaboration (M. G. Aartsen et al.), *Phys. Rev. Lett.* **125** (2020) 121104, arXiv:2001.09520 [astro-ph.HE].
23. J. G. Learned and S. Pakvasa, *Astropart.Phys.* **3** (1995) 267, arXiv:hep-ph/9405296 [hep-ph].

24. IceCube Collaboration (R. Abbasi *et al.*), *to be published in Phys. Rev. Lett.* (11 2020) arXiv:2011.03561 [hep-ex].
25. IceCube Collaboration (M. G. Aartsen *et al.*), *Nature* **591** (2021) 220.
26. A. Albert, M. André, M. Anghinolfi, G. Anton, M. Ardid, J.-J. Aubert, J. Aublin, T. Avgitas, B. Baret, J. Barrios-Martí and et al., *The Astrophysical Journal* **853** (Jan 2018) L7.
27. IceCube Collaboration (M. Aartsen *et al.*), *Phys.Rev.Lett.* **113** (2014) 101101, arXiv:1405.5303 [astro-ph.HE].
28. IceCube Collaboration (M. G. Aartsen *et al.*), *Phys. Rev.* **D91** (2015) 022001, arXiv:1410.1749 [astro-ph.HE].
29. K. Murase, M. Ahlers and B. C. Lacki, *Phys.Rev.* **D88** (2013) 121301, arXiv:1306.3417 [astro-ph.HE].
30. R. J. Protheroe and T. Stanev, *Monthly Notices of the Royal Astronomical Society* **264** (09 1993) 191.
31. M. Ahlers, L. Anchordoqui, M. Gonzalez-Garcia, F. Halzen and S. Sarkar, *Astropart.Phys.* **34** (2010) 106, arXiv:1005.2620 [astro-ph.HE].
32. S. Yoshida and K. Murase, *Physical Review D* **102** (Oct 2020).
33. IceCube, MAGIC, VERITAS Collaboration (M. G. Aartsen *et al.*), *JINST* **11** (2016) P11009, arXiv:1610.01814 [hep-ex].
34. IceCube Collaboration (M. G. Aartsen *et al.*), *Astropart. Phys.* **92** (2017) 30, arXiv:1612.06028 [astro-ph.HE].
35. IceCube Collaboration (M. G. Aartsen *et al.*), *Astrophys. J.* **843** (2017) 112, arXiv:1702.06868 [astro-ph.HE].
36. Pierre Auger Collaboration, A. Aab *et al.*, The Pierre Auger Observatory: Contributions to the 34th International Cosmic Ray Conference (ICRC 2015), in *Proceedings, 34th International Cosmic Ray Conference (ICRC 2015): The Hague, The Netherlands, July 30-August 6, 2015*, (2015). arXiv:1509.03732 [astro-ph.HE].
37. M. Ajello *et al.*, *Astrophys. J.* **751** (2012) 108, arXiv:1110.3787 [astro-ph.CO].
38. M. Di Mauro, F. Donato, G. Lamanna, D. A. Sanchez and P. D. Serpico, *Astrophys. J.* **786** (2014) 129, arXiv:1311.5708 [astro-ph.HE].
39. Fermi-LAT Collaboration (M. Ackermann *et al.*), *Phys. Rev. Lett.* **116** (2016) 151105, arXiv:1511.00693 [astro-ph.CO].
40. H.-S. Zechlin, A. Cuoco, F. Donato, N. Fornengo and A. Vittino, *Astrophys. J. Suppl.* **225** (2016) 18, arXiv:1512.07190 [astro-ph.HE].
41. M. Lisanti, S. Mishra-Sharma, L. Necib and B. R. Safdi, *Astrophys. J.* **832** (2016) 117, arXiv:1606.04101 [astro-ph.HE].
42. IceCube Collaboration (M. G. Aartsen *et al.*), *Astrophys. J.* **835** (2017) 45, arXiv:1611.03874 [astro-ph.HE].
43. IceCube Collaboration (R. Abbasi *et al.*), *Astron. Astrophys.* **535** (2011) A109, arXiv:1108.0171 [astro-ph.HE], [Erratum: Astron.Astrophys. 563, C1 (2014)].
44. IceCube Collaboration (R. Abbasi *et al.*), *Astrophys. J.* **910** (2021) 4, arXiv:2012.04577 [astro-ph.HE].
45. C. Kopper and E. Blaufuss, *GRB Coordinates Network, Circular Service, No. 21916, #1 (2017)* **21916** (2017).
46. V. M. Lipunov, V. G. Kornilov, K. Zhirkov, E. Gorbovskoy, N. M. Budnev, D. A. H. Buckley, R. Rebolo, M. Serra-Ricart, R. Podesta, N. Tyurina, O. Gress, Y. Sergienko, V. Yurkov, A. Gabovich, P. Balanutsa, I. Gorbunov, D. Vlasenko, F. Balakin, V. Topolev, A. Pozdnyakov, A. Kuznetsov, V. Vladimirov, A. Chasovnikov, D. Kuvshinov, V. Grinshpun, E. Minkina, V. B. Petkov, S. I. Svertilov, C. Lopez, F. Podesta,

H. Levato, A. Tlatov, B. Van Soelen, S. Razzaque and M. Böttcher, *ApJLett* **896** (June 2020) L19, arXiv:2006.04918 [astro-ph.HE].
47. S. Paiano, R. Falomo, A. Treves and R. Scarpa, *Astrophys. J.* **854** (2018) L32, arXiv:1802.01939 [astro-ph.GA].
48. P. A. E. A. Keivani, J. A. Kennea, D. B. Fox, D. F. Cowen, J. P. Osborne, F. E. Marshall and Swift-IceCube Collaboration, *The Astronomer's Telegram* **10792** (September 2017).
49. Y. T. Tanaka, S. Buson and D. Kocevski, *The Astronomer's Telegram* **10791** (September 2017).
50. R. Mirzoyan, *The Astronomer's Telegram* **10817** (October 2017).
51. MAGIC Collaboration (S. Ansoldi *et al.*), *Astrophys. J. Lett.* **863** (2018) L10, arXiv:1807.04300 [astro-ph.HE].
52. S. Britzen, C. Fendt, F. Böttcher, F. Jaron, I. N. Pashchenko, A. Araudo, O. Karas and O. Kurtanidze, *Mem. Soc. Ast. It.* **90** (2019) 77.
53. E. Kun, P. L. Biermann and L. Á. Gergely, *Monthly Notices of the Royal Astronomical Society: Letters* **483** (Nov 2018) L42–L46.
54. L. Á. Gergely and P. L. Biermann, *The Astrophysical Journal* **697** (May 2009) 1621.
55. P. Padovani, P. Giommi, E. Resconi, T. Glauch, B. Arsioli, N. Sahakyan and M. Huber, *Mon. Not. Roy. Astron. Soc.* **480** (2018) 192, arXiv:1807.04461 [astro-ph.HE].
56. S. Garrappa *et al.*, *8th International Fermi Symposium* (2018).
57. F. Lucarelli *et al.*, *Astrophys. J.* **846** (2017) 121, arXiv:1707.08599 [astro-ph.HE].
58. R. Stein, S. v. Velzen, M. Kowalski, A. Franckowiak, S. Gezari, J. C. A. Miller-Jones, S. Frederick, I. Sfaradi, M. F. Bietenholz, A. Horesh and et al., *Nature Astronomy* **5** (Feb 2021) 510–518.
59. M. Kadler, F. Krauß, K. Mannheim, R. Ojha, C. Müller, R. Schulz, G. Anton, W. Baumgartner, T. Beuchert, S. Buson and et al., *Nature Physics* **12** (Apr 2016) 807–814.
60. IceCube Collaboration (E. Bernardini), *Nucl. Instrum. Meth. A* **567** (2006) 418.
61. VERITAS Collaboration (M. K. Daniel *et al.*), *Astrophys. J.* **621** (2005) 181, arXiv:astro-ph/0503085 [astro-ph].
62. J. Biteau, E. Prandini, L. Costamante, M. Lemoine, P. Padovani, E. Pueschel, E. Resconi, F. Tavecchio, A. Taylor and A. Zech, *Nature Astronomy* **4** (January 2020) 124–131.
63. F. Halzen, A. Kheirandish, T. Weisgarber and S. P. Wakely, *Astrophys. J.* **874** (2019) L9, arXiv:1811.07439 [astro-ph.HE].
64. V. Lipunov, E. Gorbovskoy, V. Kornilov, N. Tyurina, F. Balakin, V. Vladimirov, P. Balanutsa, A. Kuznetsov, D. Vlasenko, I. Gorbunov, A. Pozdnyakov, D. Zimnukhov, V. Senik, A. Chasovnikov, V. Grinshpun, T. Pogrosheva, R. Rebolo, M. Serra, R. Podesta, C. Lopez, F. Podesta, C. Francile, H. Levato, D. Buckley, O. Gress, N. M. Budnev, O. Ershova, A. Tlatov, D. Dormidontov, V. Yurkov, A. Gabovich and Y. Sergienko, *The Astronomer's Telegram* **12971** (July 2019) 1.
65. S. Kiehlmann, T. Hovatta, M. Kadler, W. Max-Moerbeck and A. C. S. Readhead, *The Astronomer's Telegram* **12996** (August 2019) 1.
66. V. Karamanavis, L. Fuhrmann, T. P. Krichbaum, E. Angelakis, J. Hodgson, I. Nestoras, I. Myserlis, J. A. Zensus, A. Sievers and S. Ciprini, *Astronomy and Astrophysics* **586** (February 2016) A60, arXiv:1511.01085 [astro-ph.HE].
67. A. V. Plavin, Y. Y. Kovalev, Y. A. Kovalev and S. V. Troitsky, *Astrophys. J.* **908** (2021) 157, arXiv:2009.08914 [astro-ph.HE].
68. T. Hovatta *et al.*, *Astron. Astrophys.* **650** (2021) A83, arXiv:2009.10523 [astro-ph.HE].

69. B. Zhou, M. Kamionkowski and Y.-f. Liang, *Phys. Rev. D* **103** (2021) 123018, arXiv:2103.12813 [astro-ph.HE].
70. A. Neronov and D. Semikoz, *Journal of Experimental and Theoretical Physics* **131** (Aug 2020) 265–272.
71. K. Kashiyama and P. Mészáros, *Astrophys.J.* **790** (2014) L14, arXiv:1405.3262 [astro-ph.HE].
72. C. Yuan, P. Mészáros, K. Murase and D. Jeong, *Astrophys. J.* **857** (2018) 50, arXiv:1712.09754 [astro-ph.HE].
73. C. Yuan, K. Murase and P. Mészáros, *Astrophys. J.* **878** (2019) 76, arXiv:1810.04155 [astro-ph.HE].
74. IceCube Collaboration, T. Carver, Ten years of All-sky Neutrino Point-Source Searches, in *36th International Cosmic Ray Conference (ICRC 2019) Madison, Wisconsin, USA, July 24-August 1, 2019*, (2019). arXiv:1908.05993 [astro-ph.HE].
75. A. Marinucci *et al.*, *Mon. Not. Roy. Astron. Soc.* **456** (2016) L94, arXiv:1511.03503 [astro-ph.HE].
76. S. García-Burillo, F. Combes, A. Usero, S. Aalto, M. Krips, S. Viti, A. Alonso-Herrero, L. K. Hunt, E. Schinnerer, A. J. Baker, F. Boone, V. Casasola, L. Colina, F. Costagliola, A. Eckart, A. Fuente, C. Henkel, A. Labiano, S. Martín, I. Márquez, S. Muller, P. Planesas, C. Ramos Almeida, M. Spaans, L. J. Tacconi and P. P. van der Werf, *Astronomy and Astrophysics* **567** (July 2014) A125, arXiv:1405.7706 [astro-ph.GA].
77. DUMAND Collaboration Collaboration (J. Babson *et al.*), *Phys.Rev.* **D42** (1990) 3613.
78. BAIKAL Collaboration (I. A. Belolaptikov *et al.*), *Astropart. Phys.* **7** (1997) 263.
79. NESTOR Collaboration Collaboration (G. Aggouras *et al.*), *Astropart.Phys.* **23** (2005) 377.
80. ANTARES Collaboration Collaboration (J. Aguilar *et al.*), *Astropart.Phys.* **26** (2006) 314, arXiv:astro-ph/0606229 [astro-ph].
81. E. Migneco, *J.Phys.Conf.Ser.* **136** (2008) 022048.
82. KM3NeT Collaboration (S. Adrian-Martinez *et al.*), *J. Phys.* **G43** (2016) 084001, arXiv:1601.07459 [astro-ph.IM].
83. A. Sinopoulou, R. Coniglione, R. Muller and E. Tzamariudaki, Atmospheric neutrinos with the first detection units of km3net/arca (2021).
84. A. D. Avrorin *et al.*, *Phys. Part. Nucl.* **46** (2015) 211.
85. IceCube-Gen2 Collaboration (M. G. Aartsen *et al.*), *J. Phys. G* **48** (2021) 060501, arXiv:2008.04323 [astro-ph.HE].

The first results of PandaX-4T

Jianglai Liu*

School of Physics & Astronomy and Tsung-Dao Lee Institute, Shanghai Jiao Tong University,
Shanghai, 200240, China
E-mail: jianglai.liu@sjtu.edu.cn
* On behalf of the PandaX Collaboration

Dark matter, an invisible substance which constitutes 85% of the matter in the observable universe, is one of the greatest puzzles in physics and astronomy today. Dark matter can be made of a new type of fundamental particle, not yet observed due to its feeble interactions with visible matter. In this talk, we present the first results of PandaX-4T, a 4-ton-scale liquid xenon dark matter observatory, searching for these dark matter particles from deep underground. We will briefly summarize the performance of PandaX-4T, introduces details in the data analysis, and present the latest search results on dark matter-nucleon interactions.

Keywords: Dark Matter; WIMPs; Liquid xenon; PandaX-4T.

1. Introduction

The detection of the weakly-interacting-massive-particles (WIMPs) has been outlined by Goodman and Witten in 1985.[1] Yet, in the direct detection of dark matter, we have not seen convincing signals. At the large mass region (approximately 100 GeV/c^2 and above), the front runners are xenon-based experiments.[2–4] The sensitivities of these experiments, roughly speaking, correspond to a few events per tonne per year.

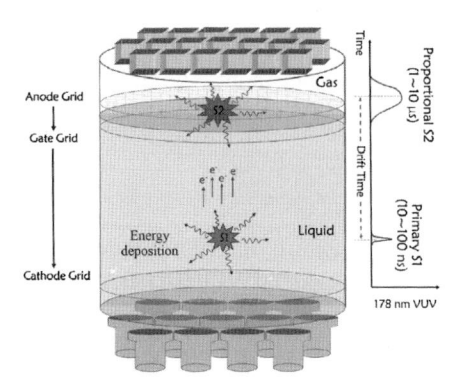

Fig. 1. Working principle of a two-phase TPC.

All of these xenon experiments are based on a tank of liquid xenon cooled at negative one hundred degrees. The detector is the so-called Time Projection

Chamber (TPC), capable of measuring both the energy deposition and its location, utilizing the detection of prompt scintillation photons ($S1$) and delayed electroluminescence signals due to ionized electrons ($S2$). See Fig. 1. The interaction of dark matter and xenon nucleus produces nuclear recoils (NR), and the background gamma rays produce electron recoils (ER). The ratio of $S1$ and $S2$ is a natural discriminant for ER background.

The three dark matter experiments with xenon TPC are LUX-ZEPLIN (LZ), XENONnT and PandaX-4T. LZ is located at the 4850 feet level of the Sanford Underground Research Facility in Lead, SD, containing seven active tonnes of liquid xenon. At the Laboratori Nazionali del Gran Sasso (LNGS) of INFN in Italy, the XENONnT detector is an upgrade to XENON1T, with an active mass of six tonnes. Both LZ and XENONnT are under active preparation. The experiment I am going to focus here, PandaX-4T, with 3.7 tonnes of active mass, is located in China Jinping Underground Laboratory (CJPL), southwest of China, 2400 meters underneath a rock mountain.

CJPL is the deepest underground laboratory in the world. CJPL-I has a small space and only holds two experiments, PandaX and CDEX (China Dark matter Experiment), to detect dark matter with different methods. CJPL-II has a much expanded lab space, with eight experimental halls, each with a dimension of 65 m long and 14×14 m² cross section. Currently, there are three experimental halls in occupation, PandaX, CDEX and JUNA (Jingping Underground lab for Nuclear Astrophysics).

2. The PandaX Experiment

The PandaX collaboration is formed in 2009. Up to now, we have undergone two completed phases. The first phase, PandaX-I, had 120 kg of xenon target. The second, PandaX-II, has 580 kg of xenon target. In particularly, PandaX-II has produced several leading results on the direct detection of dark matter. Since the August of 2019, the new generation of the experiment, PandaX-4T, was officially moved into CJPL-II.

2.1. *Results of PandaX-II*

In 2019, we finished the full exposure of 130 ton·day of PandaX-II. As shown in Fig. 2(a), the data set was increased by a factor of 2.5 in sensitivity for WIMPs,[5] in comparison with the results in 2017.[8] But the upper limit is worsened due to background fluctuation. For ER signals, we are looking directly for the solar axion signal and the anonymous neutrino magnetic moment from the solar neutrinos. In light of the recent XENON1T excess, in this region, the data are contaminated by the tritium background, with limited sensitivity to confirm or refute XENON1T (Fig. 2(b)).[6] Fig. 2(c) gives a new search using an extremely low threshold data by giving up $S1$ and only taking $S2$. This pushes the energy threshold down to 80 eV.

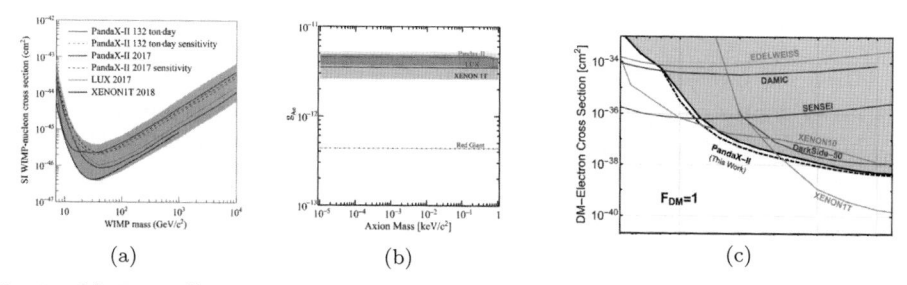

Fig. 2. (a) The 90% confidence level upper limits vs. WIMP mass for the spin-independent WIMP-nucleon elastic scattering cross sections from the full exposure data of PandaX-II, overlaid with that from PandaX-II 2017, LUX 2017, and XENON1T 2018;[5] (b) A search of solar axion-electron coupling constant g_{Ae} in PandaX-II, in comparison with other experiments;[6] (c) 90% C.L. upper limits (solid: the constant model, dashed: NEST 2.0) on WIMP-electron scattering cross section from PandaX-II data for a point-like interaction.[7]

Therefore, we can look for the direct scatterings of WIMPs and electrons. Because of the low threshold, we have the best sensitivity around 25 MeV/c^2 in WIMP mass for a point-like interaction, which was unexplored previously.[7]

2.2. *Overview of PandaX-4T*

For the newly deployed PandaX-4T experiment, a 900 m^3 water tank is acting as the shielding of the central detector. The detector resides in a platform at the middle of this tank. At the center of the detector, there is a TPC with a 1.2 m height and 1.2 m diameter, holding 3.7 tonnes liquid xenon. On the top and bottom, it is covered by roughly 400 channels of 3-in PMTs.

The preparation of PandaX-4T started in April, 2018, after the permission from the CJPL management. The installation of the entire apparatus was completed on May, 2020. The commissioning run extended from Nov. 28, 2020 to Apr. 16, 2021, of which the data will be reported here.

Most of our instrumentation severing the detector is located in a 10000-class clean room. All the TPC assemblies were carried out in a 1000-class clean room. To avoid the contamination of radon, the air going into the 1000-class clean room were purified by a radon removal system.

3. Performance of PandaX-4T Commissioning

3.1. *Cryogenics*

The cryogenics is very stable during the commissioning. In fact, the heat load of the system is only 50 W, much smaller than the maximum cooling power 580 W by design. We have two circulation loops trying to clean out the electronegative outgassing from the detector with a rate of 40 kg/h. Through out the stable running period, the pressure and the temperature are stable within 0.5% and 0.1 K, respectively.

3.2. Electronics and DAQ

We utilize a triggerless electronics system. Every channel is read out separately by a faster digitizer whenever the signal is above 1/3 photonelectron (PE), with a sampling rate of 250 MS/s. The average single photon efficiency is around 95%, and the maximum bandwidth of the DAQ is 450 MB/s.

3.3. TPC operation conditions

As illustrated in Fig. 1, between the anode and the gate is a 10 mm amplification region for the ionized electrons. Between the gate and the cathode is the drifting region, with a maximum drift distance of 1.2 m. Below the cathode, we have a 10 cm shielding region to suppress the background from bottom PMTs. During the operations, the HVs on the electrodes were set at a few different values to avoid excessive discharges.

3.4. Data taking history

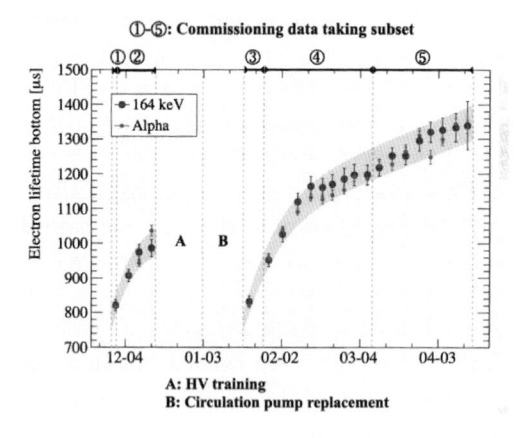

Fig. 3. Electron lifetime for different commissioning data taking subset.

Electronegative impurities tend to attach ionized electrons, leading to an exponential attenuation of the $S2$ signals vs. drift time. The purity of the liquid is characterized by the mean attenuation time, i.e. the electron lifetime. Using internal gamma or alpha peaks, the extracted electron lifetime also gives the vertical correction for $S2$. In total, we have a stable data running period of 95 days, and as shown in Fig. 3, the electron life time is kept around 1000 μs. In comparison, the maximum drift time in the TPC is about 840 μs.

3.5. Calibration

Calibration is one of the most important aspects. PandaX-4T adopted three main methods. One is the gas source injection, where we can load in radioactive ^{83m}Kr and ^{220}Rn into the detector. They are short-lived, but uniformly distributed in the detector. Second is the external calibration loops, where a source can go into these loops at three different height of the TPC. Lastly, we have a Deuteron-Deuteron (D-D) fusion generator for neutrons. It produces semi-monoenergetic neutrons, which are then beamed directly into the detector.

- Uniformity correction with ^{83m}Kr. When ^{83m}Kr radioactive sources are loaded into the detector, they uniformly distribute in the detector with a characteristic 41.5 keV energy, based on which the uniformity of $S1$ and $S2$ can be calibrated. For $S2_b$, the RMS variation in the fiducial volume is 12% and for $S1$, the RMS variation 20%. The measured energy resolution is 6.8%.

For the energy reconstruction, event-by-event we use a linear combination of $S1$ and $S2$ according to Eq. 1.

$$E = 13.7\text{eV} \times \left(\frac{S1}{\text{PDE}} + \frac{S2_b}{\text{EEE} \times \text{SEG}} \right), \qquad (1)$$

in which PDE, EEE and SEG are corresponding to the photon detection efficiency, electron extraction efficiency and single electron gain, respectively.

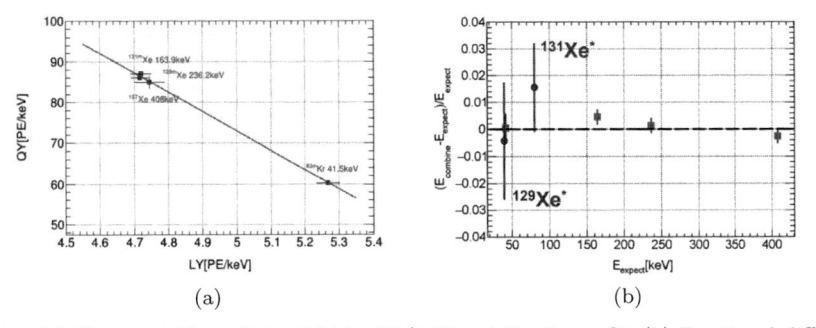

Fig. 4. (a) Charge yield vs. light yield in PE/keV and the linear fit. (b) Fractional differences between the reconstructed and expected energy. Blue squares represent uniformly distributed electron recoil peaks, ^{131m}Xe(164 keV), ^{129m}Xe(236 keV), ^{127}Xe(408 keV) and ^{83m}Kr(41.5 keV). Blue points in (b) represent de-excitation gammas from ^{129}Xe*(39.6 keV) and ^{131}Xe*(80.2 keV) after neutron activation, with the NR components subtracted from $S1$ and $S2$, which are not used in the linear fit.

SEG can be obtained using the smallest $S2$ signals identified in the data. The uniform distribution to the detector is only 13% for the RMS variation. The top and bottom ratio for these low energy is also very stable. Then with various ER peaks in the data, we can fit for PDE and EEE using Eq. 1, as shown in Fig. 4(a). Just for the check, the reconstruction energy, after applying these two

fitted parameters, shows on Fig. 4(b). The red points have been used in the fit. We use two more independent data points produced by illuminating xenon with neutrons and looking at de-excitation gamma rays. They are also at the zero line, but with a large uncertainty because the de-excitation energy contains some of the nuclear energy component.
- Nuclear recoil calibration with D-D neutrons.

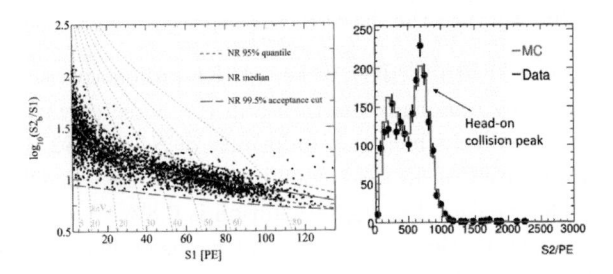

Fig. 5. D-D neutron calibration. The left picture shows $\log_{10} S2/S1$ over $S1$; The right plot gives the one-dimensional projection of $S2$, which is in agreement with MC expectation.

The other aspect of the calibration is to determine the low energy response of the detector, particularly relevant to the dark matter search. If dark matter interacts with xenon, and produces a low energy nuclear recoil, the best calibration should come from the neutrons. Fig. 5 summarizes the neutron recoil calibration with the D-D neutron band. D-D neutron band can generate a monoenergetic neutron around 2.2 MeV. The data set is used in combination with the AmBe data set, another neutron source, to tune the parameters, such as the light yield, charge yield, as well as fluctuations in the signal model.

4. ER calibration with ^{220}Rn

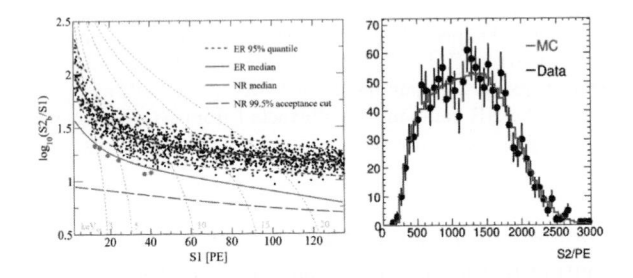

Fig. 6. ^{220}Rn calibration. In the left plot, purple solid line is the medium of neutron calibration. The right plot gives the one-dimensional projection of $S2$, which is in agreement with the MC data.

ER calibration is critical for us to understand the majority of the background. The ER response is calibrated by injecting ^{220}Rn into the detector, which only have 55 s life time. One of the decay progeny ^{212}Pb is a beta emitter, producing a flat energy spectrum at low energy. We characterize the rejection power by simply counting how many events are leaked underneath the nuclear recoil medium line. As shown in Fig. 6, the full rejection power is 0.43%, with roughly 50% uncertainty.

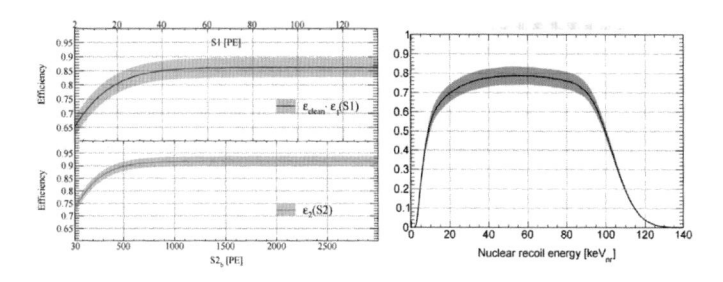

Fig. 7. Selection efficiency. The left picture shows the data quality cut efficiency for $S1$ an $S2_b$; The right plot gives the efficiency vs. nuclear recoil energy.

Using the same electron or nuclear recoil low energy data set, we can determine the efficiency for both $S1$ and $S2$. As illustrated in Fig. 7, at the plateau region, we have an efficiency of around 78%@40 keV.

4.1. *Backgrounds*

The major background components considered in the dark matter analysis are the following:

The first is the material background from the detector. If we bin our detector into several regions, the top, the bottom, the outer and the center, the background component is different. Comparing the expectation from the data, the overall agreement is around 14%. After converting all these high energy events into the low energy in the dark matter region, it is a minor background with 33 events expected.

^{222}Rn background, distributed uniformly into a detector, is important. They can come out of the surface of an emanation material. However, ^{222}Rn can be identified easily through their decay progeny. There are alphas that one can identify, as well as α-β coincidence signals. We find that the rate of radon is about 5 μBq/kg. This number is improved by six times from PandaX-II. The extracted background is estimated to be 347±190 events.

^{85}Kr, another noble gas, is used to be a major problem for the earlier generation of PandaX. Using a delayed coincidence technique, the krypton level is measured to be 0.33 ppt, improved about twenty times from PandaX-II. The residual ^{85}Kr background is estimated to 53±34 events.

^{127}Xe normally do not exist in the xenon. It is produced when xenon is exposed too longer on the surface. Through the characterized gamma and X-rays in the electron-capture process, we can track them in the detector. The half live of ^{127}Xe is only 36 days, and will decay soon. The background in the dark matter region is the 5 keV K-shell X-rays. Actually, we can tag these X-rays through the 33 keV L-shell X-rays. The expected events of ^{127}Xe background is estimated to be 9±2.

Tritium background is unfortunately identified in our data. They are likely originated from a calibration at the end of PandaX-II, where we loaded tritium into the detector, trying to calibrate the detector and see how well we can remove them. Unfortunately, the removal is probably inefficient, leaving some residuals in PandaX-4T. In our fit, we left this contaminant to be floated, resulting into about 5×10^{-24} mol/mol concentration, a value that one cannot see with direct assay measurement.

Surface background is related to radon. Radon progeny can attach to the surface of the detector. These events can be clearly identified from the data by looking for αs with abnormally small $S2$. Because they are closed to the PTFE reflector, we can get both the position distribution and the $S2$ distributions to estimate how much of these backgrounds could leak underneath the dark matter search window. The expected background for these wall surface is estimated to be 0.6±0.2.

Neutron background generates directly nuclear recoil. For these neutron background, once they enter the detector, they could multi-scatter, and eventually get capture onto xenon, producing high energy capture signals. Both processes are bench-marked by neutron source calibration. In the end, the neutron background is estimated to be 1.3±0.6.

Accidental background is formed by random coincidence between uncorrelated $S1$ and $S2$. Therefore, cuts imposing the diffusion relations observed in data are effective in removing them. The expected accidental background was suppressed by two times in comparison with PandaX-II. It is estimated to be 2.4±0.5.

Fiducial volume determination utilizes the expected background from detector materials, as well as a combination of the radon background and the tritium background that is measured *in-situ*, to maximize a figure-of-merit related to the search sensitivity. The fiducial mass is settled at 2.67 tonnes.

5. Results

Fig. 8 shows the dark matter candidates within the fiducial volume and dark matter selection window. There are 1058 candidates in total. Six events are identified below the NR median curve. Candidates are uniformly distributed in the fiducial volume, which is expected if backgrounds are dominated by the tritium and radon. A fit to the data is consistent with background-only hypothesis, with a goodness-of-fit p-value of 0.7.

Based on the fit, we therefore set the bound on the spin-independent WIMP-nucleon scattering, summarized in Fig. 9. With a 0.63 tonne·year, we have a

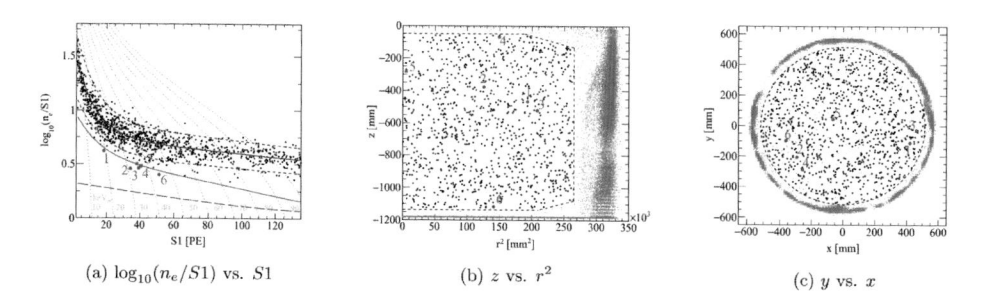

Fig. 8. Distributions of the final dark matter candidates in $\log_{10}(n_e/S1)$ vs. $S1$ (a), z vs. r^2 (b), and y vs. x (c). n_e is the number of electrons derived from $S2$ so that different run sets under different gate conditions can be plotted on the same graph. In (a), the solid blue and red lines are the ER and NR medians, respectively, and the dashed blue lines are the corresponding 95% quantiles of ER events. The dashed violet line represents the 99.5% NR acceptance cut. The nuclear recoil energy in keV$_{nr}$ are indicated with the grey dashed lines. The six ER events located below the NR median line are highlighted in brown. In (b) and (c), the dashed lines are projections of the fiducial volume, and black (light grey) dots represent events inside (outside).

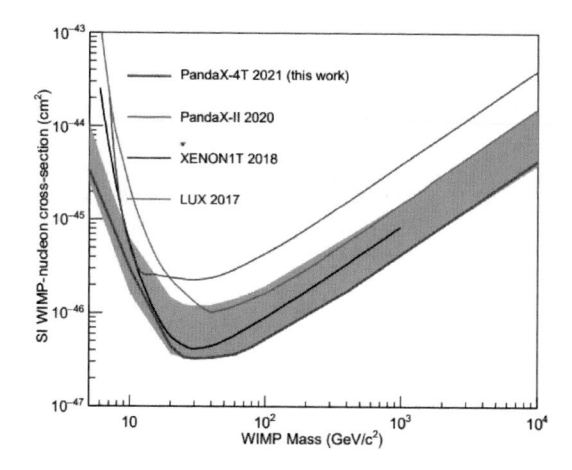

Fig. 9. The 90% C.L. upper limit vs. m_χ for the SI WIMP-nucleon elastic cross section from PandaX-4T commissioning data (red), overlaid with that from LUX 2017,[4] XENON1T 2018[3] and PandaX-II 2020.[5] The green band represents the $\pm 1\sigma$ sensitivity band.

sensitivity which is improved from the previous PandaX-II final analysis by 2.8 times at 40 GeV/c^2. Comparing the results (red line) with XENON1T, we are slightly edged, for example, at 40 GeV/c^2 where our exclusion limit is 1.3 times stronger. With this data, we can also dive into previously unexplored territory, such as approaching the low energy neutrino floor, and getting deeper into the SUSY parameter space.

6. Conclusion and Outlook

As mentioned, we have completed the first commissioning run of PandaX-4T with a 0.63 tonne·year exposure. PandaX-4T has produced the strongest WIMP-nucleon interaction constraint.[2] This demonstrates the physics potential of a highly sensitive multi-ton liquid xenon detector. PandaX-4T is currently performing an offline tritium removal campaign, aiming to reduce the electron recoil background by at least two-fold. In parallel, the collaboration is developing the plan for the next generation xenon experiment at CJPL.

References

1. M. W. Goodman and E. Witten, Detectability of certain dark-matter candidates, *Phys. Rev. D* **31**, 3059 (Jun 1985).
2. Y. Meng, Z. Wang, Y. Tao *et al.*, Dark Matter Search Results from the PandaX-4T Commissioning Run (2021).
3. E. Aprile *et al.*, Dark Matter Search Results from a One Ton-Year Exposure of XENON1T, *Phys. Rev. Lett.* **121**, p. 111302 (2018).
4. D. S. Akerib *et al.*, Results from a search for dark matter in the complete LUX exposure, *Phys. Rev. Lett.* **118**, p. 021303 (2017).
5. Q. Wang, A. Abdukerim, W. Chen *et al.*, Results of dark matter search using the full PandaX-II exposure, *Chinese Physics C* **44**, p. 125001 (Nov 2020).
6. X. Zhou, X. Zeng, X. Ning, *et al.*, A Search for Solar Axions and Anomalous Neutrino Magnetic Moment with the Complete PandaX-II Data, *Chinese Physics Letters* **38**, p. 011301 (Jan 2021).
7. C. Cheng, P. Xie, A. Abdukerim *et al.*, Search for Light Dark Matter–Electron Scattering in the PandaX-II Experiment, *Physical Review Letters* **126** (May 2021).
8. X. Cui, A. Abdukerim, W. Chen *et al.*, Dark matter results from 54-ton-day exposure of pandax-ii experiment, *Physical Review Letters* **119**, p. 181302 (Oct 2017).

XRISM: X-ray imaging and spectroscopy mission

Makoto S. Tashiro

The Institute of Space and Astronautical Science, JAXA
Tsukuba, Ibaraki, Kanagawa, 305-8505, Japan
Department of Physics, Saitama University
Sakura-ku, Saitama, Saitama, 338-8570, Japan
tashiro@mail.saitama-u.ac.jp

and the XRISM team

The X-Ray Imaging and Spectroscopy Mission (XRISM) is a JAXA/NASA X-ray observatory with collaboration from ESA and several institutes and academic institutions worldwide. It is proposed to fulfill the promise of high-resolution X-ray spectroscopy with imaging once realized but unexpectedly terminated by a mishap of ASTRO-H/Hitomi. XRISM carries two sets of X-ray Mirror Assemblies and is equipped on the focal plane with a 6 × 6 pixelized X-ray micro-calorimeter array and an aligned X-ray CCD camera. With the combination of high-resolution spectroscopy imaging and the broader field of view, XIRSM is expected to pioneer a new horizon of the Universe in X-ray astrophysics. Aiming to launch the satellite in the Japanese Fiscal Year 2022, we fabricate the instruments and test for the satellite integration starting at the beginning of 2022. The paper reports the development status, reviewing the science objectives and the operation plan.

Keywords: X-ray astronomy; observation satellite; spectroscopy; imaging

1. Overview of XRISM

The X-ray imaging and spectroscopy mission — XRISM[1,2] is a recovery mission of ASTRO-H Hitomi[3] launched on February 17, 2016. After the launch and following the commissioning of the onboard instruments, Hitomi started observation. However, due to a series of mishaps in the attitude control system, Hitomi was forced to stop operation on March 26. The observation period was only one month, but the results clearly show the X-ray microcalorimeter epoch-making capability. The observation was terminated before opening the gate valve. The valve was equipped to protect the sensor assembly from the atmosphere on the ground, but the gate valve limited the bandpass below ~ 2 keV. Even with the limitation in the low energy band, the unprecedented energy resolution enables us to measure the plasma turbulence velocity and detect weak lines of rare metals with a few ks exposure. The obtained spectrum is a highlight obtained from the Perseus cluster of galaxies.[4]

The central concept of XRISM is to maximize the X-ray micro-calorimeter science since it is an entirely new scientific field. We chose a conservative combination with the CCD camera to strengthen the science. Table 1 summarizes of required specifications of the instruments of XRISM.

Table 1. XRISM mission instruments specifications

Parameters	Resolve	Xtend
Feild of view	$\geq 2.9' \times 2.9'$	$\geq 22' \times 22'$
Angular resolution[†]	$\leq 1.7'$	$\leq 1.7'$
Effective area at 6 keV	≥ 210 cm^2	≥ 300 cm^2
Imaging pixel format	6×6	1280×1280
Energy range	0.3 – 12 keV	0.4 – 13 keV
Energy resolution[‡]	≤ 7 eV (goal 5 eV)	≤ 250 eV*

†: The half power diameter
‡: The full width half maximum at 6 keV
*: At the end of mission life.

1.1. *Resolve*

The critical device of XRISM — the X-ray microcalorimeter realizes the high-resolution spectroscopy with imaging by the X-ray Mirror Assembly (XMA). The XMA is a Wolter-I X-ray mirror of their reflectors' figure in conical approximation. The reflectors of the mirror are made of heat formed aluminum sbstrate followed by epoxy replication on gold-sputtered smooth Pyrex clindrical mandrels. The XMA is developed and fabricated by NASA/Goddard Space Flight Center (GSFC). The imaging spectroscopy telescope of XRISM is named "Resolve."[5] The device measures phonons induced by a penetrated X-ray photon. The X-ray photon heats the mercury tellurized absorber by a few mK, and the temperature rise is measured by the attached silicon thermometer in the accuracy of μK. All the pixelized detectors are cooled down to 50 mK to reduce both heat capacity and thermal noise. The equipped adiabatic de-magnetized refrigerator (ADR) and liquid helium realize the extremely low temperature at the sensor in the vacuum dewar, whose thermal shields are cooled by Joule-Tomson coolers and two-stage Stirring coolers. The detector system is placed on the focal plane of an X-ray mirror assembly, and the 6×6 pixels realize a moderate imaging capability and unprecedented energy resolution. The Resolve telescope is emphasized with the high energy resolution of 7 eV FWHM at 6 keV. The energy resolution allows us to measure the velocity dispersion of the iron line in the accuracy of 100 km s^{-1}.

The detector assembly and the ADR cooling system are developed by NASA/GSFC, while JAXA and Sumitomo Heavy Industry (SHI) develop and provide the vacuum dewar and the mechanical cooling systems.

1.2. *Xtend*

The wide-field X-ray CCD imager with the identical XMA constitutes the "Xtend" telescope, which covers the same energy band of Resolve with a 200 μm thick back-illuminated CCDs.[6] The X-ray CCD, operated at the temperature of −110°C utilizing the one-stage Stirling cooler, covers almost the same energy band from oxygen lines to highly ionized irons. The device was developed for the Hitomi/SXI and employed by XRISM with a slight modification. The CCD is produced by Hamamatsu Photonics, is calibrated by the Xtend team of XRISM, and is installed in a camera body electronics by Mitsubishi Heavy Industry (MHI).

The spacecraft of 2.3 tons is 7.9 m long, 9.2 m wide, and the baseplate diameter is about 3 m. It is designed to work for three years with cryogen of Resolve. After three years, we can conduct cryogen-free operation with installed mechanical coolers.

2. Science Cases

The high energy resolution and weak line detection capability of Resolve exceed the previous observatories above 0.8 keV. The Xtend is excellent in grasp capability, which is the product of effective area and the solid angle of field of view. With the combination of a narrow field of view, Resolve, Xtend is useful for producing reliable scientific outputs with the brand new X-ray micro-calorimeter system. The science cases with X-ray microcalorimeter are summarized in ASTRO-H White Papers.[7–23]

2.1. *Structure formation of cluster of galaxies*

The precision of cluster cosmology depends on the accuracy of the mass measurements. One of the most important ways of measuring cluster masses is based on hydrostatic equilibrium — the assumption that the thermal pressure alone supports the hot gas against the cluster's gravity. However, numerical simulations show that the macroscopic motions of the intra-cluster medium (ICM) may provide significant non-thermal pressure support, up to 25 – 30% at the radius at which the cluster mass density is 200 times the critical density of the universe (r_{200}).

Hitomi observed the Perseus core, which is dominated by the central massive galaxy NGC 1275, to reveal the macroscopic motion of the ICM (Fig. 1. By measuring the line doppler broadening, the Hitomi succeeded in showing that the turbulent velocity dispersion is 164 ± 10 km s^{-1} as mentioned.[4] This kinetic pressure is less than 10% of the thermal pressure on a scale of 60 kpc. XRISM will continue Hitomi's legacy by measuring velocities of gas motions and the non-thermal pressure contribution with an accuracy of a few percent in many relaxed, bright galaxy clusters. Velocity measurements up to r_{2500}, for even a small sample of nearby relaxed clusters, will significantly improve the constraints on dark energy and other cosmological parameters.[17]

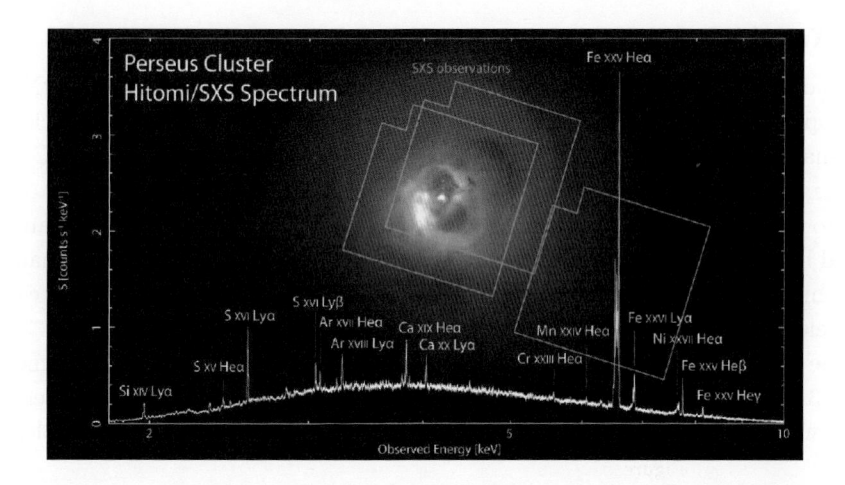

Fig. 1. Chandra image[24] and the Hitomi SXS spectrum from Perseus cluster of galaxies.[4,25] The blue boxes in the image indicates the field of view of Hitmoi SXS. Hitomi observed the central region and obtained the high resolution spectrum. Evaluating the Fe-K lines width, the Hitomi collaboration[4] reveals the turbulent velocity dispersion of 164 ± 10 km s^{-1}.[a]

2.2. Transportation of energy and matters

XRISM will conduct spatially and spectrally investigation on the Active Galactic Nucleus (AGN) feedback.[19] Figure 2 left panel shows Chandra X-ray image of the core region of the Virgo cluster of galaxies dominated by the central galaxy M 87, which highlights the complexity of structures in the gas. We focus that the 1 keV gas indicates uplifted gas produced by the AGN feedback. These structures will be resolved by the Resolve utilizing the imaging spectroscopy capability. Each white box (6 × 6) shows the field of view of Resolve, and by mapping, XRISM will observe both the uplifted gas structure and surrounding ICM. Figure 2 right shows a simulated Resolve spectrum of one of the regions with the expected outflows in M 87 assuming a 100 ks exposure. The spectrum resolves the contributions from the different thermal components to the Fe-L line complex and allows us to distinguish uplifted cool gas from the ambient hot ICM.

The chemical evolution of the universe reflects the history of billions of supernovae. Resolve will detect weak lines from rare elements in the ICM, such as Na, Al, Cr, and Mn. Al and Na are sensitive tracers of the metallicity of the underlying stellar population. Also, Cr and Mn can be used to probe the characteristics of SN Ia progenitors, resulting in information about the chemical enrichment history of the ICM and the universe.

---

[a]Credit: ISAS/JAXA https://www.isas.jaxa.jp/feature/forefront/190924.html.

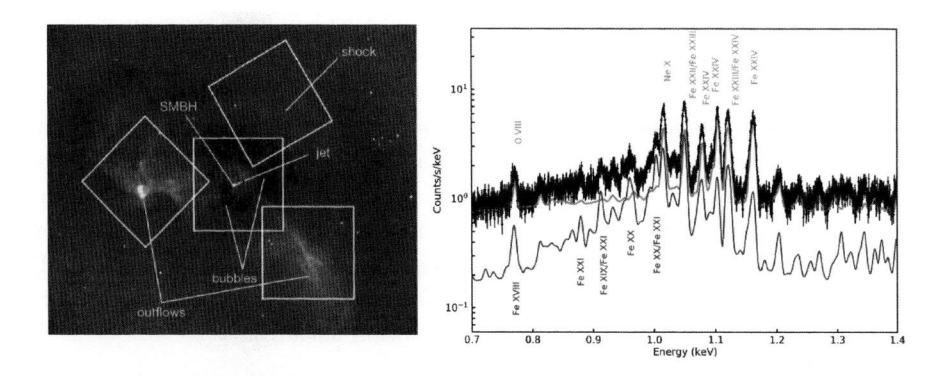

Fig. 2. Spatially and spectrally resolving AGN feedback with XRISM. Reprinted by courtesy of the authors from Figure 5 of "Science of XRISM"[30] which is updated from an ASTRO-H White Paper.[17] **Left:** Chandra X-ray image of the core region of the Virgo cluster, including the central galaxy M 87, divided by a spherically symmetric model of surface brightness. The image highlights the complexity of structures in the gas produced by the AGN feedback.[28, 29] Each white box (2.9′ × 2.9′) shows the field of view of Resolve. The two regions point at the cool and bright structures, such as the shock and the center of M 87. **Right:** a 100 ks simulated Resolve spectrum of one of the regions with outflows (left box) in M 87. The spectrum shows the contributions from the different thermal components to the Fe-L line complex.

2.3. *Relativistic objects*

XRISM will revolutionize our understanding of accreting SMBHs, starting from how cold gas flows in from the interstellar medium (ISM) of the galaxy down to the inner accretion flow where matter is affected by the strong gravity of the black hole.[18]

Relativistic Doppler broadening and gravitational redshifts in the accretion disks surrounding black holes have been investigated for decades.[26] In particular, the ASCA observation of MCG–6-30-15 opened our observational view of a broad Fe K line in AGN X-ray spectra.[27] The implication of the broad line is immense, as it may provide a way of measuring an elusive fundamental parameter of a black hole — spin. As such, the broad Fe-K line has ignited debate and continued interest.

Rapid time variability shown in the following observations, including the X-ray reverberation mapping or quasar microlensing, improved our understandings. They indicate that the broad Fe K line is produced by reprocessing the inner accretion disk within $\sim 10R_g$. However, the details of the inner disk radius and kinematics of the flow are still highly debated.

By disentangling the expected contributions from other spectral features — narrow emission from the outer disk and torus or absorption through ionized outflows along our line of sight —, XRISM probes properties of the inner accretion flow to estimate the black hole spin. Thus, we will clearly understand how much material is making it to the black hole and how much material is removed through massive outflows.

Figure 3 left chart shows Fe-K line prole of MCG–6-30-15 as seen in 300 ks by XMM-Newton pn (blue) and Chandra HETGS (green), along with a Resolve simulation in red. The red XRISM spectrum alone shows clear spectral features in this Fe-K energy band. The middle chart shows The ratio of the XMM pn spectrum to a power-law model t between 2 and 4 keV, and 7.5 and 10 keV. The pn spectrum can be well described either by pure relativistic reflection with an inclination of 5 deg (blue) or by relativistic reflection with an inclination of 75 deg with additional emission and absorption, including an ultrafast outflow of $v_{out} = 0.13\ c$ (red). The right panel shows that XRISM will easily distinguish between these two scenarios since it resolves the narrow emission and absorption features.

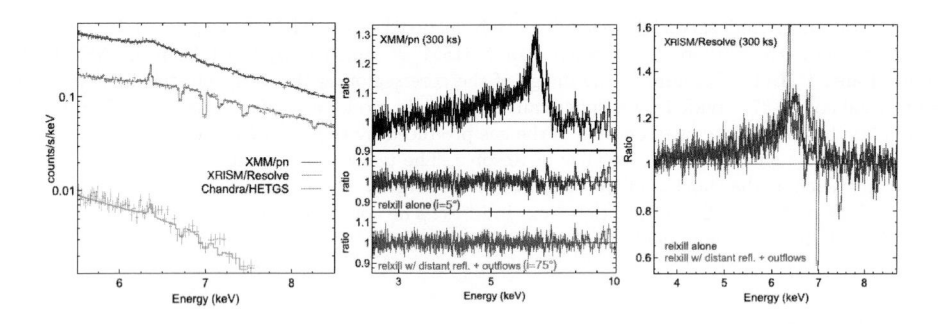

Fig. 3. Reprinted by courtesy of the authors from Figure 6 of "Science of XRISM." **Left**: Fe-K line prole of MCG–6-30-15 as seen in 300 ks by XMM-Newton pn (blue) and Chandra HETGS (green), along with a Resolve simulation in red. **Middle:** The ratio of the XMM pn spectrum to a power-law model fit between 2–4 keV and 7.5 – 10 keV. The pn spectrum can be equally well described by pure relativistic reflection with an inclination of 5 deg (shown in blue) or by relativistic reflection with an inclination of 75 deg with additional emission and absorption, including an ultrafast outflow of $v_{out} \sim 0.13\ c$ (shown in red). **Right:** XRISM will easily distinguish between these two scenarios, as the narrow emission and absorption will be resolved.[30]

The relativistic redshift on a compact object surface is also one of the scientific targets of XRISM. Here we show an example of the symbiotic star detected by Swift/BAT T Coronae Borealis (T CrB), which is a recurrent nova.[9] This fact and the hard BAT spectrum indicate that its white dwarf is exceptionally massive, around 1.35 solar mass.

T CrB exhibits a strong 6.4 keV Fe-K line, partly from the reflection of the white dwarf surface. Therefore, T CrB is an ideal target to investigate the compact object's mass and radius by measuring the gravitational redshift. This simulated spectrum is guided using the 46 ks Suzaku observation obtained in 2006.[31] The XIS data were reproduced well with a model absorbed by a partial covering absorber, with a single, narrow Gaussian at 6.396 keV. If it is, the inset shows that the XRISM Resolve has the statistical quality necessary to detect the expected gravitational redshift of 4 eV of the neutral iron-K line (Fig. 4).

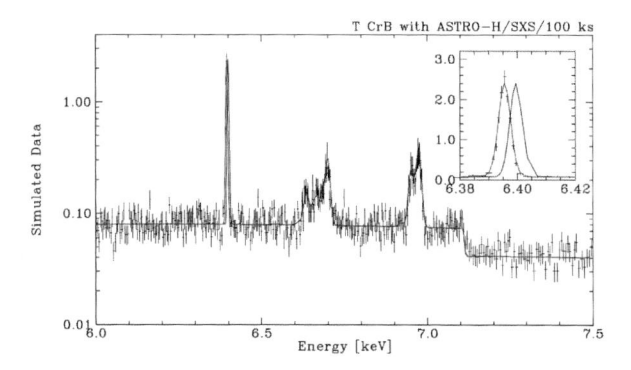

Fig. 4. Simulated 100 ks observation of T Cr B in the Fe-Kα region. The inset showing a close-up spectrum around the energy of 6.4 keV. It shows the Resolve has a capability to detect the expected gravitational redshift of 4 eV (see text). Reprinted by courtesy of the authors from Figure 2 of "ASTRO-H White Paper – White Darf"[9]

3. Mission Status and Observation Plan

All the instruments produced under the international collaboration are being delivered to the JAXA Tsukuba Space Center. The Resolve calorimeter sensor insert was delivered and installed in the dewar produced in SHI, Japan. The integrated dewar system equipped with the mechanical coolers was transferred to Tsukuba Space Center with the cooler drivers. The XMA is under calibration and is planned to be delivered to Japan in January 2022. All CCD chips for the Xtend were screened in Osaka University and were integrated into the camera system at MHI. The camera was transferred to Tsukuba Space Center. In 2022, these mission instruments will be installed on the satellite in the first half. Then we conduct the proto-flight test. XRISM will be launched in the Japanese Fiscal Year 2022 or the early calendar year 2023 from Tanegashima Space Center.

Table 2. XRISM observation phases

Initial phase	3 months
critical operation	∼ 1 week
comissioning	until 3 months after launch
Nominal phase	until 3 years after launch
initial calibration & test observations	1 month
calibration & performance verification observation	6 months
nominal observation (Guest observations)	26 months

Observation phases defined in the operation plan are summarized in Table 2. At the beginning of the nominal observation phase, the performance verification (PV) observations are conducted. The initial observation phase is planned to verify the performance to show the XRISM capability to the astrophysics community. The PV observation target objects list was recently released on the XRISM website for researchers.[b] The XRISM Science Team consists of contributors to develop instruments, data processing software, and calibration and observation plan to carry out the PV observations. In addition to the XRISM Science Team, unlike Hitomi, XRISM introduced the XRISM Guest Scientist Program to the PV phase observation. The XGSs will be solicited by the three agencies — JAXA, NASA, and ESA independently — in 2022 and contribute to PV observation planning, data analysis, and produce science output with the XRISM Science Team. The guest observer phase is open 10 months after the launch. The announcement of opportunity for the guest observations is planned to be submitted at the end of the commissioning.

The approved nominal mission term is 3 years. After the 3 years, the XRISM project is to have a mission completion review. At the moment, if the satellite, including the mechanical cooling system, functions well and the mission extension review approve, the latter phase operation will be conducted in the latter half of the 2020s.

Acknowledgments

XRISM is a JAXA mission joint with NASA in collaboration with ESA. The XRISM Science Team studies the science cases described in this paper based on the previous research by the ASTRO-H Science Working Group.

References

1. M. S. Tashiro et al, Concept of X-ray Astronomy Recovery Mission (XARM), in *Proc. SPIE: Space Telescopes and Instrumentations 2018: Ultraviolet and Gamma-Ray*, **10699** eds. J-W. A. den Herder, S. Nikzad, (2018) id. 1069922.
2. M. S. Tashiro et al, Status of X-ray Imaging and Spectroscopy Mission (XRISM), in *Proc. SPIE: Space Telescopes and Instrumentations 2020: Ultraviolet and Gamma-Ray*, **11444** eds. J-W. A. den Herder, S. Nikzad, K. Nakazawa (2020) id. 1144422.
3. T. Takahashi et al., *Journal of Astronomical Telescopes, Instruments, and Systems*, **4** (2018) id. 021402.
4. Hitomi Collaboration, *Nature*, **535** (2016) 117.
5. Y. Ishisaki et al., Status of resolve instrument for X-ray imaging telescope (Xtend) onboard X-ray Astronomy Recovery Mission (XARM), in *Proc. SPIE: Space Telescopes and Instrumentations 2018: Ultraviolet and Gamma-Ray*, **10699** eds. J-W. A. den Herder, S. Nikzad, (2018) id. 1069924.
6. K. Hayashida et al, Soft X-ray imaging telescope (Xtend) onboard X-ray Astronomy Recovery Mission (XARM), in *Proc. SPIE: Space Telescopes and Instrumentations 2018: Ultraviolet and Gamma-Ray*, **10699** eds. J-W. A. den Herder, S. Nikzad, (2018) id. 1069923.

---

[b] https://xrism.isas.jaxa.jp/research/

7. T. Takahashi et al., ASTRO-H Space X-ray Observatory White Paper, *arXiv*, (2014) 1412.2351.
8. Y. Tsuboi et al., ASTRO-H Space X-ray Observatory White Paper - Stars – Accretion, Shocks, Charge Exchange and Magnetic Phenomena, *arXiv*, (2014) 1412.1162.
9. K. Mukai et al., ASTRO-H Space X-ray Observatory White Paper - White Dwarf, *arXiv*, (2014) 1412.1163.
10. C. Done et al., ASTRO-H Space X-ray Observatory White Paper - Low-mass X-ray Binaries, *arXiv*, (2014) 1412.1164.
11. S. Kitamoto et al., ASTRO-H Space X-ray Observatory White Paper - Accreting Pulsars and Related Sources, *arXiv*, (2014) 1412.1165.
12. J. Miller et al., ASTRO-H Space X-ray Observatory White Paper - Stellar-Mass Black Holes, *arXiv*, (2014) 1412.1173.
13. J. P. Hughes et al., ASTRO-H Space X-ray Observatory White Paper - Young Supernova Remnants, *arXiv*, (2014) 1412.1169.
14. K. S. Long et al., ASTRO-H Space X-ray Observatory White Paper - Old Supernova Remnants and Pulsar Wind Nebulae, *arXiv*, (2014) 1412.1166.
15. K. Koyama et al., ASTRO-H Space X-ray Observatory White Paper - Plasma Diagnostic and Dynamics of the Galactic Center Region, *arXiv*, (2014) 1412.1170.
16. F. Paerels et al., ASTRO-H Space X-ray Observatory White Paper - High Resolution Spectroscopy of Interstellar and Circumgalactic Gas in the Milky Way and Other Galaxies, *arXiv*, (2014) 1412.1174.
17. T. Kitayama et al., ASTRO-H Space X-ray Observatory White Paper - Clusters of Galaxies and Related Sources, *arXiv*, (2014) 1412.1176.
18. C. Reynolds et al., ASTRO-H Space X-ray Observatory White Paper - AGN Reflection, *arXiv*, (2014) 1412.1177.
19. J. S. Kaastra et al., ASTRO-H Space X-ray Observatory White Paper - AGN Reflection, *arXiv*, (2014) 1412.1171.
20. R. K. Smith et al., ASTRO-H Space X-ray Observatory White Paper - New Spectral Features, *arXiv*, (2014) 1412.1172.
21. F. Aharonian et al., ASTRO-H Space X-ray Observatory White Paper - Shock and Acceleration, *arXiv*, (2014) 1412.1175.
22. P. Coppi et al., ASTRO-H Space X-ray Observatory White Paper - Broad-band Spectroscopy and Polarimetry, *arXiv*, (2014) 1412.1190.
23. M. S. Tashiro et al., ASTRO-H Space X-ray Observatory White Paper - Chemical Evolution in High-z Universe, *arXiv*, (2014) 1412.1179.
24. I. Zhuravleva, et al.,, NASA/CXC/Stanford.
25. Hitomi Collaboration, *Nature*, **551** (2017) 478.
26. A. C Fabian, et al., *MNRAS* **238** (1989) 729.
27. Y. Tanaka et al., *Nature* **6533** (1995) 659.
28. W, Forman et al.., *ApJ.* **665** (2007) 1057.
29. A. Simionescu et al., *A&A* **482** (2008) 97.
30. XRISM Science Team, Science with the X-ray Imaging and Spectroscopy Mission (XRISM), *arXiv*, (2020) 2003.04962.
31. G. J. M. Luna et al., RS Ophiuchi (2006) and the Recurrent Nova Phenomenon ASP Conference Series, **401** (2007) 342.

The SVOM mission

On behalf of the *SVOM* collaboration

J.-L. Atteia[1], B. Cordier[2], J. Wei[3]

[1] *IRAP, Université de Toulouse, CNRS, CNES, UPS, (Toulouse), France*
E-mail: jean-luc.atteia@irap.omp.eu

[2] *Lab AIM - CEA, CNRS, Université Paris-Saclay,
Université de Paris, 91191, Gif-sur-Yvette, France*
E-mail: bertrand.cordier@cea.fr

[3] *Key Laboratory of Space Astronomy and Technology, National Astronomical Observatories,
Chinese Academy of Sciences, Beijing 100101, People's Republic of China*
E-mail: wjy@nao.cas.cn

The Sino-French space mission *SVOM* is mainly designed to detect, localize and follow-up Gamma-Ray Bursts and other high-energy transients. The satellite, to be launched mid 2023, embarks two wide-field gamma-ray instruments and two narrow-field telescopes operating at X-ray and optical wavelengths. It is complemented by a dedicated ground segment encompassing a set of wide-field optical cameras and two 1-meter class follow-up telescopes. In this contribution, we describe the main characteristics of the mission and discuss its scientific rationale and some original GRB studies that it will enable.

Keywords: *SVOM*; High-Energy Astrophysics; Multi-Messenger Astrophysics; Gamma-Ray Bursts.

1. Why a New Gamma-Ray Burst Mission?

SVOM (Space-based multi-band astronomical Variable Objects Monitor) is a Sino-French mission devoted to the study of gamma-ray bursts (GRBs) to be launched in 2023.[1] Its main goals are the detection and multi-wavelength study of high-energy transients, and the search for the electromagnetic counterparts of non-photonic transient sources detected in gravitational waves or neutrinos. Before describing *SVOM* in Section 2, we briefly discuss in this section the rationale for a new GRB mission in the coming years.

1.1. *High-energy Astrophysics*

The astrophysics of high-energy transients is essential for the study of several major questions of modern astrophysics.

High-energy transients offer a unique view at extreme stellar explosions with relativistic jets. High-energy observations reveal the presence of a 'central engine' able to launch relativistic jets, and as such they are essential to clarify key issues like the complex zoology of GRBs (which encompasses long and short duration GRBs, low-luminosity GRBs and ultra-long GRBs), the nature of the GRB-supernova (SN) connection or the distribution of GRB beaming angles. The jets themselves raise several unanswered questions, like their composition and geometry, the nature of the central engine (a magnetar or a black hole?) and the mechanism of their acceleration, the physical processes explaining their high radiative efficiency, and their role in the acceleration of Very High-Energy cosmic rays. The jets have their origin in the universal accretion/ejection mechanism that takes place around accreting compact objects. However, GRB jets being extremely relativistic with Lorentz factors of the order of one hundred, they probe a regime that is not accessible with other phenomena.

Sometimes, high-energy transients are associated with the birth of stellar mass black holes (BHs). BH astrophysics has emerged as a major topic after the discovery of dozens of binary black hole mergers by the LIGO Scientific Collaboration and Virgo Collaboration (LVC).[2] Black hole demography and zoology, their mass & spins distribution and their birth places are key questions which are now actively studied. In this context, GRBs are of high interest because they offer a complementary view on the birth of stellar mass BHs across the history of the universe.

Gamma-ray bursts are so intense that some of them are detectable out to high redshift ($z \geq 5$).[3] They illuminate regions of the young universe (at z=6 the universe is about 950 Myr old), pinpointing galaxies that would otherwise remain undetectable and measuring their chemical enrichment and physical state, as well as the properties of the intergalactic medium at such high redshifts. Additionally, the history of GRB formation provides crucial insight into the formation rate of massive stars in the early universe, and pushing the redshift limit a bit further may permit the identification of GRBs from the first generation of stars (usually called population III stars) giving us a glimpse at the formation of the first stellar mass black holes. The current GRB samples probably contain a small fraction of very distant GRBs that have not been recognized in the absence of NIR spectra of their afterglows, this emphasizes the need for fast NIR followup of GRB afterglows.

Neutron stars (NSs) are prolific sources of high-energy transients, which can be emitted by very different mechanisms in accreting neutron stars, magnetars and in mergers of neutron stars. Fundamental questions like the equation of state of neutron star, the mass gap between neutrons stars and black holes, the radiation process of magnetars are active fields of research which require continued observations of violent phenomena involving neutron stars.

Finally, GRBs are powerful tools to test the Lorentz invariance over very large distances and they may also become a privileged tool for cosmography if we manage to standardize them.

1.2. *Multi-messenger Astrophysics*

The detection of transient gravitational wave signals from cosmic explosions has opened a new window on violent phenomena involving compact objects like neutron stars and black holes. The complementarity of gravitational wave (GW) astrophysics and HE astrophysics has been wonderfully illustrated by the joint detection of GW170817 and GRB 170817A[4] followed by the discovery of the kilonova AT 2017gfo. These discoveries opened the era of multi-messenger astrophysics. This new context raises new questions for HE astrophysicists, like the geometry of the jets of short GRB, the compared demography of BNS mergers and short GRBs, the compared demography of BBH mergers and long GRBs, the masses of BHs involved in galactic HE transients, in BBH mergers and in GRBs, the photonic emission of BNS mergers, BHNS mergers, and BBH mergers, the delay between a merger and the emergence of a GRB, or the comparison of the speed of gravitational waves with the speed of light. This non-comprehensive list illustrates a renewed interest for transient HE observations in the multi-messenger era.

1.3. *A Rich Instrumental Panorama*

Additional motivations to develop new instruments for the exploration of the transient high-energy sky are the diversity of sources that emit bursts of HE photons, the fact that some of them are rare events that do not repeat, and the rapid evolution of the instrumental panorama.

The transient manifestations of black holes at high energies involve galactic and extragalactic X-ray binaries, GRBs of all types, Active Galactic Nuclei (AGNs), Relativistic Tidal Disruption Events (TDEs), and possibly BHNS mergers. Neutron stars, on the other hand, manifest themselves as galactic and extragalactic X-ray binaries, magnetars or soft gamma repeaters eventually associated with FRBs, and of course as BNS mergers. The diversity of these manifestations calls for different observing strategies, in terms of energy range, sensitivity, pointing strategy, follow-up, etc., which cannot be accommodated with a single mission.

The construction of novel missions is further justified by the fact that the coming years are expected to be a golden age for transient sky astronomy and for multi-messenger astrophysics, with a number of large facilities surveying the sky for photons at all wavelengths and for non-photonic messengers. In the electromagnetic domain, we can mention the Cherenkov Telescope Array (CTA[5]), the High-Altitude Water Cherenkov Observatory (HAWC[6]) and the Large High Altitude Air Shower Observatory (LHAASO[7]) for Very High-Energy gamma-rays. In X-rays, eROSITA[8] will establish a reliable map of the X-ray sky, allowing the fast identification of new sources. In the visible the already operating Zwicky Transient Facility (ZTF[9]) and the future Vera Rubin Observatory[10] will map the visible transient sky every night allowing meaningful comparisons with the transient high-energy sky. In the meantime, new spectrometers on large telescopes, like SOXS[11] or NTE[a] will increase our capacity to measure the redshifts of extragalactic transients. In the radio domain, the counterparts of HE transients will be observed with very good sensitivity with

---

[a]https://nte.nbi.ku.dk/

the precursors of SKA, like ASKAP[12] or MEERKAT,[13] while instruments like the Canadian Hydrogen Intensity Mapping Experiment (CHIME[14]) or the Commensal Real-time ASKAP Fast Transients Survey (CRAFT[15]) will monitor the transient radio sky for Fast Radio Bursts (FRBs).

The true revolution, however, comes from the instruments looking for non-photonic messengers from violent events, in particular the gravitational waves interferometers LIGOâ VIRGO, GEO and KAGRA, which have opened the exploration of the transient gravitational wave universe.[16] As shown with the detection of GW170817 and GRB 170817A, the joint operation of gravitational wave detectors and HE detectors brings crucial information on transient gravitational wave sources. The field of neutrino astronomy is also evolving very quickly and the large neutrinos observatories like ICECUBE[17] or KM3NeT[18] have started to constrain the physics of GRB jets.[19]

After this short introduction, we now present the SVOM mission (Section 2) and some of its science capabilities for the study of GRBs (Section 3).

2. The *SVOM* Mission

The *SVOM* mission (Figure 1) is the result of a bilateral collaboration between France (CNES) and China (CAS, CNSA).[20,21] It involves several research institutes from these two countries and contributions from the University of Leicester, the Max Planck Institut für Extraterrestische Physik and the Universidad Nacional Autónoma de México. *SVOM* is led by J.Y. Wei from NAOC in China and B. Cordier from CEA in France. The mission has been designed to survey the high-energy sky and to follow-up cosmic transients at optical and X-ray wavelengths. It encompasses a space segment, with four instruments embarked onboard a low Earth orbit satellite and a strong ground segment[22] with two sets of wide-field optical cameras, two 1-meter class ground follow-up telescopes, and a network of $\sim$ 45 VHF receiving stations distributed along the footprint of the orbit. The launch of *SVOM* is scheduled mid 2023 with three years of nominal operations and a possible extension of two years.

The main science drivers of *SVOM* are high-energy transient astrophysics with a focus on gamma-ray bursts, multi-messenger astrophysics, and time domain astronomy. The "core program" is dedicated to GRB detection and follow-up, aiming to improve our understanding of these phenomena. Between GRBs, *SVOM* will carry out other programs driven by the narrow-field instruments: a target of opportunity program focused on multi-messenger astrophysics and a general program focused on multi-wavelength astronomy. A detailed description of the *SVOM* mission and its science objectives can be found in Wei et al.[1] and in the website of the mission[b]. We now briefly describe the space and ground instruments developed for *SVOM*.

---

[b]http://www.svom.fr/

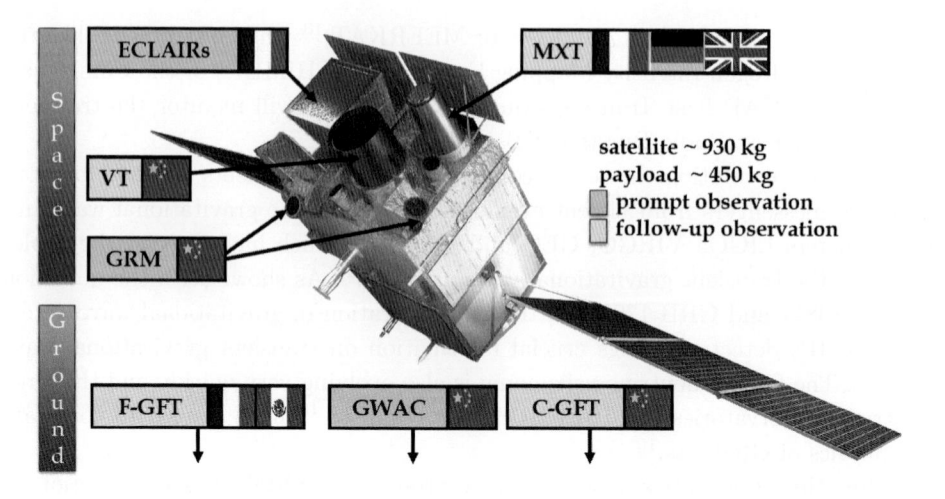

Fig. 1. Outline of the *SVOM* mission, showing the satellite and the space and ground instruments.

2.1. *Space-based Instruments*

2.1.1. *Gamma-Ray Monitor – GRM*

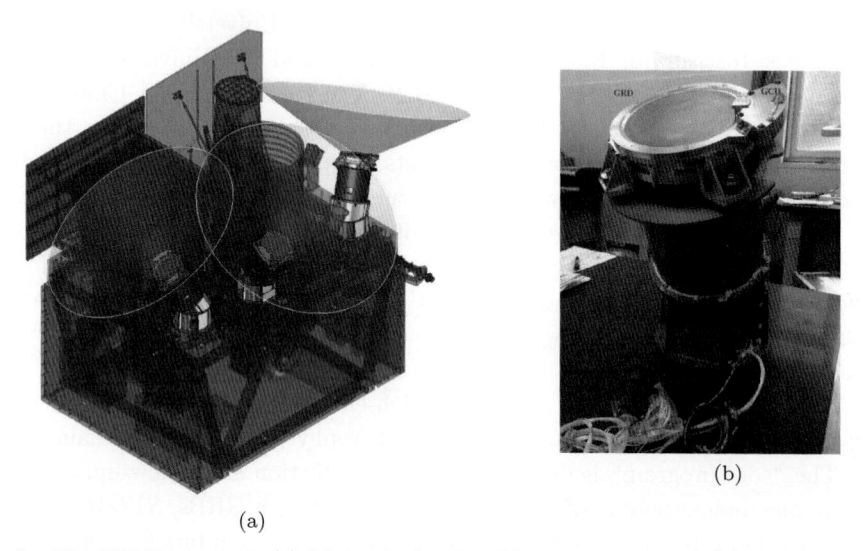

Fig. 2. The GRM instrument. (a) Schematic drawing showing the position and orientation of the three GRD detectors on the science platform. (b) One of three GRD detection modules of the GRM.

The Gamma-ray monitor (GRM) is a wide-field gamma-ray spectrometer.[23–25] It encompasses three NaI-based detection modules (called GRDs) looking at different regions of the sky. The pointing directions of the three GRDs are 30° from the pointing axis of the satellite and they are separated by 120° in azimuth (Figure 2). The main characteristics of the instrument are given in Table 1. The GRM allows the detection of GRBs with a good sensitivity within a large field of view (2.6 sr), a feature which is especially important for the detection of short/hard GRBs in the era of transient gravitational wave detectors. It will also nicely complement ECLAIRs to measure the GRB spectral parameters over a large energy range (4 keV–5 MeV).[26]

Table 1. GRM main characteristics.

Energy range (keV)	15 – 5000
Number of GRD modules	3
Detection area (cm^2, 1 of 3 modules)	200
Field of View (sr, all 3 modules)	2.6
Expected GRB rate (yr^{-1})	90 ($\sim$ 17% short[27])
Additional features	14 detection times from 5 ms to 40 seconds in 5 energy bands
	6 mm plastic scintillator to monitor particles & reject particle events
	Crude localization capability

2.1.2. *ECLAIRs*

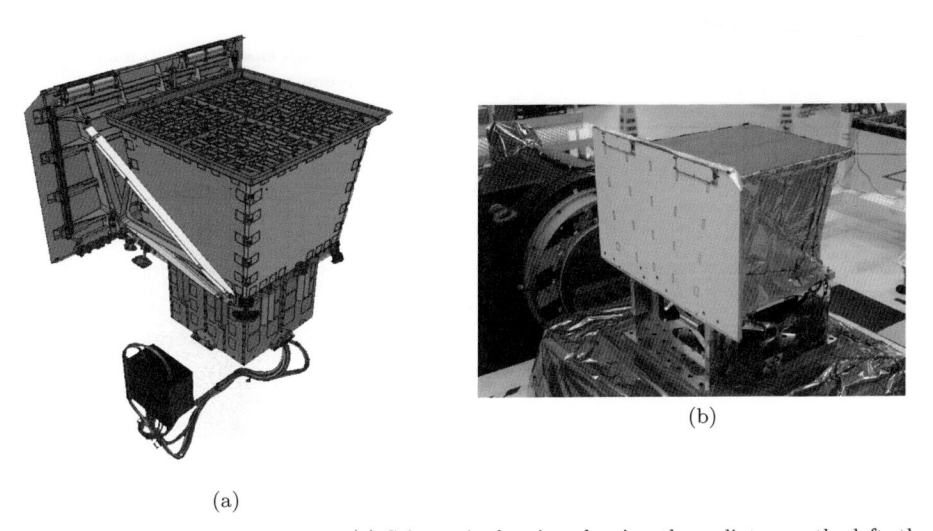

Fig. 3. The ECLAIRs instrument. (a) Schematic drawing showing the radiator on the left, the coded mask (dark blue), the shield (light blue), the detection plane electronics (grey) and the onboard calculator (black). The detection plane itself is not visible, it is located 45 cm below the coded mask at the bottom of the shield. (b) ECLAIRs during vibration tests.

ECLAIRs is the hard X-ray imager and trigger of SVOM. The instrument is based on a coded-mask placed in front of a CdTe detection plane with 6400 4x4 mm^2

pixels,[28,29] its main characteristics are summarized in Table 2. An interesting feature of ECLAIRs is its low energy threshold at 4 keV. Reaching this threshold was a significant technological challenge for the detectors and their readout electronics, but also for the mask, whose holes have to be transparent at these energies, and for the trigger software which has to deal with non-GRB transient sources (e.g. X-ray bursters), which are numerous at energies of a few keV. When it detects an excess in a sky image, ECLAIRs sends an alert to the satellite in order to start a slew towards the source (if the conditions are met) and to start followup with the onboard narrow-field instruments MXT & VT. In parallel, the alert is broadcast by the onboard VHF antennas allowing to trigger followup observations from the ground. All the photons detected by ECLAIRs are sent to the ground, allowing to look for faint transients with improved detection methods after a typical delay of few hours.

Table 2. ECLAIRs main characteristics.

Energy range (keV)	4.0 – 150.0
Detection area (cm^2)	1000
Number of CdTe detectors	6400
Median FWHM at 60 keV (keV)	1.3
Field of View (total, sr)	2.0
Mask open fraction (%)	40
Localisation accuracy at detection limit (arcminute)	12.0
Expected GRB rate (yr^{-1})	65
Additional features	18 detection times from 10 ms to 20 min. in 3 energy bands

2.1.3. *Microchannel X-ray Telescope – MXT*

The Microchannel X-ray Telescope (MXT) is a focusing X-ray telescope using an innovative focusing "Lobster-Eye" micro-pores optics and a fully-depleted framestore silicon pnCCD camera read out by two ASICs.[30,31] Its main characteristics are summarized in Table 3. The MXT will observe the X-ray afterglow promptly, improving ECLAIRs localization by a factor $\geq 10^3$.

Table 3. MXT main characteristics.

Energy range (keV)	0.2 – 10.0
Focal length (cm)	100
Field of View (arcminute)	64 x 64
Effective area (cm^2 at 1 keV)	27
Energy resolution at 1.5 keV (eV)	80
Localisation accuracy (arcsecond) (for 50% of GRBs, within 5 minutes of the trigger)	13.0
Additional features	Micro-pores "Lobster Eye" optics with square 40 μm pores Silicon pnCCD based camera

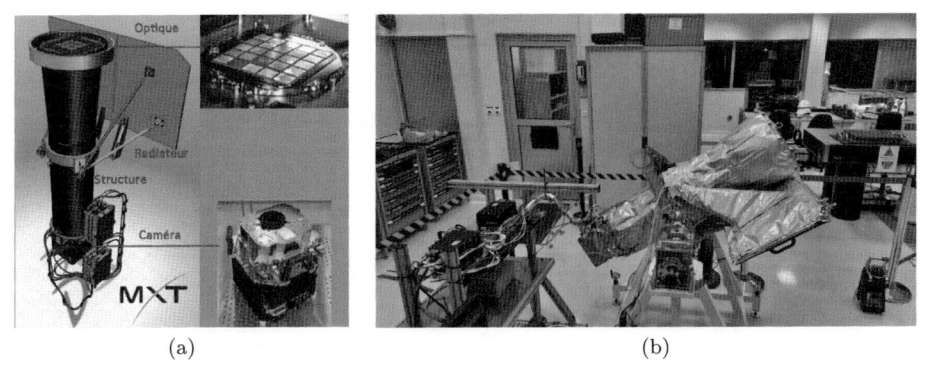

Fig. 4. The MXT instrument. (a) Schematic drawing showing the radiator in light blue, the lobster eye optics (top inset), the shield (black), the camera (bottom inset), and the onboard calculator. (b) MXT during tests.

2.1.4. *Visible Telescope – VT*

The Visible Telescope (VT) is a Ritchey-Chretien optical telescope with two channels, able to detect GRBs up to redshift z ∼ 6.5.[32,33] It will observe SVOM GRBs quickly (in less than 5 minutes), providing an arcsecond localization of the afterglow or a deep limit ($M_v = 22.5$) very quickly after the burst.

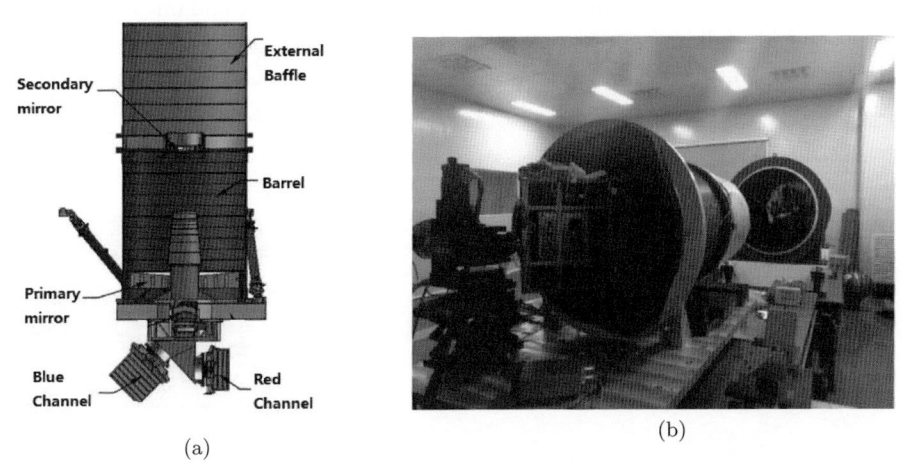

Fig. 5. The VT instrument. (a) Schematic drawing showing the various components except the onboard calculator. (b) VT during tests.

Table 4. VT main characteristics.

Diameter (mm)	400
Focal length (mm)	3600
Two channels	blue (400-650 nm) and red (650-1000 nm)
Field of View (arcminute)	26 x 26
Localisation accuracy (arcsecond)	≤ 1.0
Sensitivity (300 s integration)	$M_v = 22.5$
Additional features	Ritchey-Chretien telescope
	Two 2k x 2k CCD detectors
	Will detect 80% of ECLAIRs GRBs
	Fully covers ECLAIRs error boxes

2.2. *Ground-based Instruments*

2.2.1. *Ground Wide Angle Cameras – GWAC*

The Ground Wide Angle Cameras (GWAC)[34] is a set of several units, each made of 4 wide-angle optical cameras (called JFoV) and a small photographic camera (called FFoV) on a single fast-moving mount (Fig. 6). Each unit covers instantaneously about 12% of the ECLAIRs field of view, five of them have been installed at Xinglong Observatory (China) and 4 more will be installed at Muztagh Ata Observatory (China). The characteristics of JFoV and FFoV cameras are given in Table 5, the FFoV extends the optical flux coverage by ∼ 6 mag in R-band, at the bright end. GWACs will scan the entire accessible sky each night to detect optical transients, offering the unique capability to detect precursor optical emission for *SVOM* GRBs. Three robotic telescopes on the same site (two 60 cm diameter and one 30 cm diameter) can quickly follow interesting events detected by GWAC. The GWACs are in commissioning phase, they have already participated in the search for counterparts of gravitational wave events during the O2 and O3 runs of LIGO/VIRGO.[35]

Fig. 6. Four GWAC units at the Xinglong Observatory (on the right of the picture).

Table 5. GWAC main characteristics.

Number of units	5 (Xinglong) + 4 (Muztagh Ata)
Number of telescopes per unit	4 (JFoV) + 1 (FFoV)
Diameter (mm)	180 (JFoV) – 35 (FFoV)
Detector	4k x 4k CCD (JFoV) – 3k x 3k CCD (FFoV)
Field of View (degrees)	12.8 x 12.8 (JFoV) – 30 x 30 (FFoV)
Sensitivity (σ)	R $\sim$ 16 (JFoV) – R $\sim$ 12 (FFoV)
Location	Xinglong and Muztagh Ata Observatories (China)
Additional features	Self triggering capability
	The FFoV performs guiding.

2.2.2. Ground Followup Telescopes – GFT

Two Ground Followup Telescopes (GFT, Fig. 7) aim at observing quickly the high-energy transients detected by *SVOM*, to precisely measure their light curves and their positions. The two GFTs are respectively located in China and Mexico, about 120° apart in longitude, to maximise the probability of immediate observations in response to *SVOM* alerts. Upon reception of an alert, the GFT which is in the night (if any) will start observing the source - if it is above the horizon - in less than 1 minute. The GFTs will also be used to perform joint observations with the satellite as well as non-*SVOM* observations. The main characteristics of the Chinese GFT (CGFT[c]) and of the French-Mexican GFT (Colibri[36]) are given in Table 6.

Table 6. GFTs main characteristics.

	C-GFT	Colibri
Diameter (mm)	1200	1300
Focal ratio	8	3.75
Number of channels	3 (g ; r ; i)	3 (g/r/i ; z/y ; J/H)
Field of View (arcminute)	21 x 21	26 x 26 (grizy) ; 21 x 21 (JH)
Sensitivity (r channel, 300 s, 10σ)	$m_{AB} \approx 20$	$m_{AB} \approx 22$

2.3. The Mission

2.3.1. Orbit and Pointing Strategy

The *SVOM* satellite will be launched by a Long March 2C launch vehicle, on a 29° inclined orbit, at an altitude of 630 km. The pointing strategy has been designed to favour the detection of extragalactic transients and their immediate observability by ground based telescopes. This calls for a nearly anti-solar pointing (Fig. 8a) with some excursions to avoid SCO-X1 and the galactic plane.[37] In the following this pointing strategy is called "the B1 law". The resulting 1 year sky coverage of ECLAIRs is shown in Fig. 8b, it favours the galactic poles, with exposure times

---
[c]https://www.svom.eu/en/#filter=.instrumentsarticle.portfolio217load

Fig. 7. The two GFTs. (a) Chinese GFT at Jilin observatory. (b) French-Mexican GFT (aka Colibri) under test at the "Observatoire de Haute Provence" in France, before its installation at the Mexican National Astronomical Observatory in San Pedro Mártir.

reaching 3 to 4 Ms. The B1 law will be the rule during the nominal part of the mission (the first three years), with three exceptions: to point GRBs detected onboard, to point targets of opportunity, and to observe few remarkable sources as part of the general program (cf. Section 2.3.2).

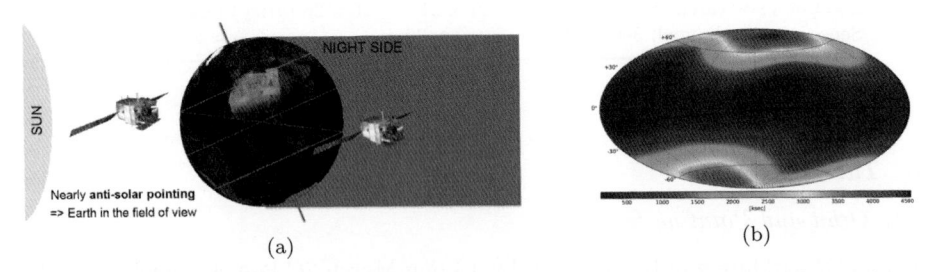

Fig. 8. *SVOM* pointing strategy. (a) Illustration of the anti-solar pointing that allows telescopes on the night side of the Earth to observe SVOM alerts promptly. (b) ECLAIRs one year exposure map in galactic coordinates.

2.3.2. *Observing Programs*

The observing time of *SVOM* is divided into three components: the *Core Program* (CP), which is the observation of HE transients detected onboard, the *General*

Program (GP), which is the observation of pre-selected sources close to the B1 law with the narrow field instruments, and the *Target of Opportunity* program (ToO) to observe active sources upon request from the ground.[1] The GP is selected by a TAC every six months and uploaded every week for the next two weeks. The ToOs are approved by the PIs of the mission and uploaded as soon as possible (see Sec. 2.3.3). Figure 9 shows the time allocated to each of the three programs during the nominal mission and during the extended mission.

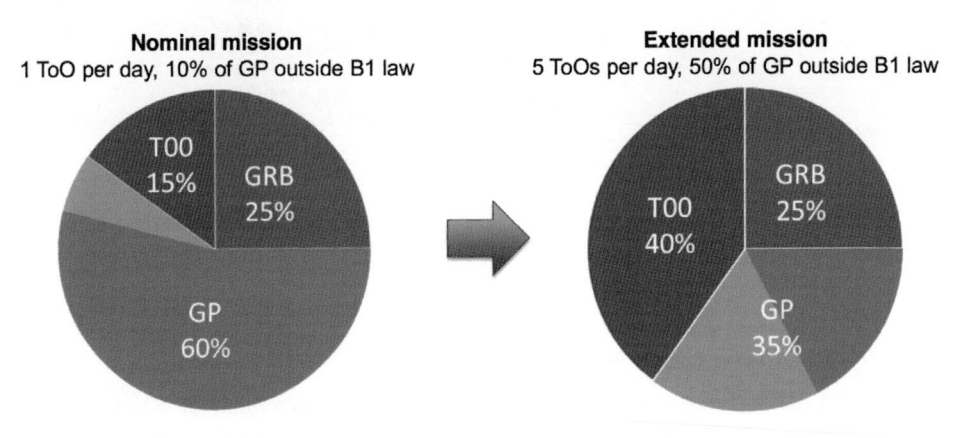

Fig. 9. Fraction of observing time attributed to the three observing programs of SVOM. Left: during the nominal 3-yr observing phase. Right: during the 2-yr extended phase. Light green indicates the time devoted to the General Program outside the B1 law.

2.3.3. *Alerts and ToOs*

SVOM alerts will be distributed promptly to the community through the GCN network. Alerts can report a count rate excess or the detection of a new source or both. The detection of a count rate excess triggers the construction of a sky image and the search for a new source. A catalog of known sources onboard permits differentiating new transients from known sources,[38] the slew threshold for known sources is set very high in order to slew towards a known source only when it is in a truly exceptional state. Alerts validated onboard will be broadcast by two onboard VHF antennas, hopefully detected by one of the $\sim$ 45 VHF receiving stations distributed around the world (Fig. 10) and forwarded to the French Science Center, which will format them as GCN Notices and VOEvents and transmit them immediately to the GCN.[39]

On the way up, commands can be sent quickly to *SVOM* with the Beidou short messages communication service.[40] This will be used to program target of opportunity observations towards active high-energy sources or towards neutrinos or gravitational waves transient sources.

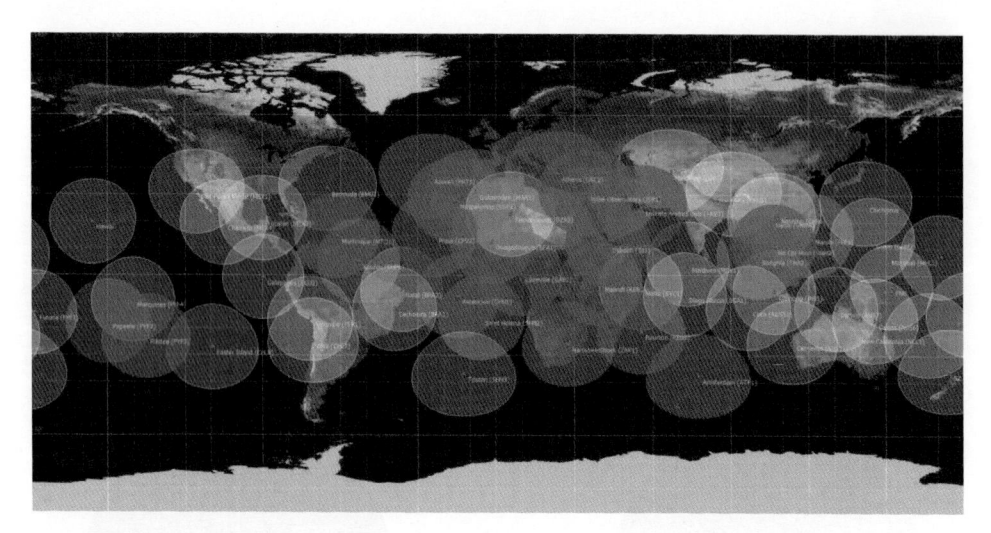

Fig. 10. *SVOM* network of VHF receiving stations. In green the stations installed and fully operational at the end of 2021.

2.3.4. *Burst Advocates and Instrument Specialists*

Like other GRB missions (e.g. *Swift* or *Fermi*), the management of *SVOM* alerts will be assigned to *Burst Advocates* who will survey all activities connected with the alert, act as points of contact for the non-*SVOM* world, and eventually take decisions about the follow-up of the source. Considering the large number of space and ground instruments involved in the detection and follow-up of transients and the number of burst advocates needed to ensure the proper follow-up of the alerts, it is needed to complement the pool of burst advocates with a few *Instrument Specialists* (2 or 3 per instrument) that can be contacted at any time by a burst advocate who has questions about the details of an instrument's operation.

2.3.5. *Mission Status*

All *SVOM* instruments have been constructed, they have undergone environment testing and full characterization, which have demonstrated their nominal performance. They are ready to be shipped to Shanghai to be integrated on the satellite in the first half of 2022. The full satellite will then undergo complete testing, before the launch planned mid 2023. The complex *SVOM* system (satellite operations and programming, observation sequences with and without triggers, satellite slews, alert reception and distribution, data management, etc.) has also been tested during extensive "system tests" lasting several days, that reproduced realistic operating conditions. These tests have demonstrated the capability of the *SVOM* collaboration to manage all aspects of this complex mission.

3. *SVOM* & GRB Science

We conclude this presentation with a subjective list of GRB science topics that could make good progress in the coming years thanks to *SVOM*. A presentation of the complete list of scientific objectives of the mission can be found in Wei et al.[1]

3.1. *GRB detection*

Thanks to its low energy threshold and a thorough onboard image processing, ECLAIRs will be particularly sensitive to long and soft GRBs. As such, it provides a unique opportunity to increase the sample of X-Ray Flashes[41,42] (XRFs) that may hold the key to the connection between SNIbc supernovae and classical long GRBs. This is also the guarantee to detect several high-redshift GRBs ($z \geq 5$) during the nominal mission,[1] despite the relatively small size of ECLAIRs. This is important because SVOM has the potential to quickly identify high-z GRBs as explained below.

The pointing strategy of the satellite will guarantee long periods of stable pointing, allowing the detection of long, faint transients like the ultra-long GRBs. A study by Dagoneau et al.[43] shows that *SVOM* may double the number of detected UL-GRBs (Figure 11b), allowing detailed multi-WL studies of these mysterious events and their host galaxies.

Finally, all ECLAIRs and GRM photons are sent to the ground, allowing the construction of various delayed off-line triggers that will benefit of more computation power than available onboard and a much better knowledge of the context (solar activity, particles, pre- and post- count-rate evolution...), and could be used to search for classical HE transients with better sensitivity as well as new types of HE transients.

3.2. *Physics of the Prompt Emission*

The unique combination of observations with GRM, ECLAIRs and GWAC for some GRBs will provide a unique coverage of the prompt emission. The systematic broadband time-resolved spectroscopy of the prompt GRB emission with ECLAIRs+GRM (and occasionally GWAC) will offer a renewed view of this phase, allowing to disentangle the role of the photosphere from internal shocks and other dissipation processes[26] (Figure 11a). For some GRBs, the prompt coverage may be extended to VHE gamma-rays with Fermi/LAT and CTA, allowing crucial diagnostic on the physics of GRB relativistic jets.[44,45]

3.3. *Physics of the Afterglow*

SVOM has two features that will permit to study the physics of GRB afterglows systematically with more detailed data. The first one is a good coverage of the prompt-afterglow transition for GRBs longer than 2-3 minutes, in X-rays thanks to

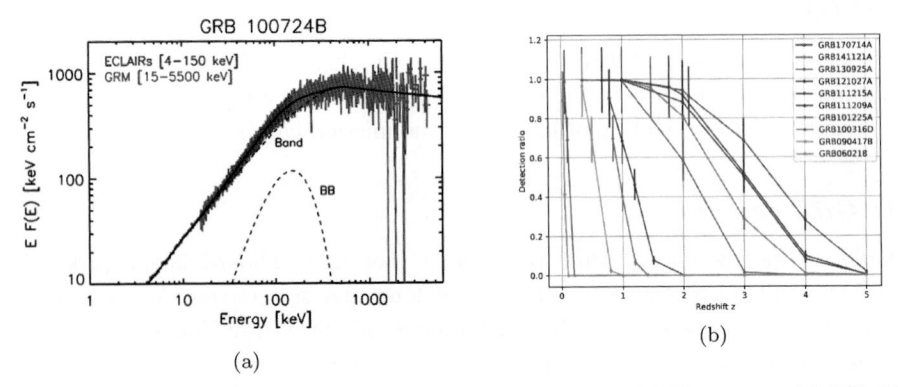

Fig. 11. Predicted *SVOM* performance. (a) Joint reconstruction of GRB spectra with ECLAIRs and GRM.[26] (b) ECLAIRs sensitivity to ultra-long GRBs.[43]

the overlap of ECLAIRs and MXT energy ranges, and in the optical thanks to the combination of GWAC + GFT + VT. The second is the multi-wavelength coverage of the afterglow with MXT, VT and GFT, with a good sensitivity balance between VT & MXT, ensuring that $\sim 70\%$ of the afterglows of *SVOM* GRBs will be detected by both instruments. In addition, it is expected that most *SVOM* GRBs will have their redshift measured (see below), giving us access to the energetics of the bursts.

3.4. *Redshifts of GRBs*

SVOM will provide arcsecond GRB localizations in less than 5 minutes with the GFTs and the VT, and the majority of *SVOM* GRBs will be immediately observable with telescopes in the night hemisphere. These localizations will permit fast spectroscopic observations with mid- or large-size telescopes with the goal of measuring the redshifts of a large fraction ($\geq 2/3$) of *SVOM* GRBs. *SVOM* will also provide quick indications of intermediate redshift GRBs[46] ($3 \leq z \leq 6$), and of high-z GRBs candidates, when the afterglow is undetected in the VT. In all cases, dark bursts in the VT will indicate GRBs of interest, deserving additional observations with powerful telescopes.

3.5. *SN-less GRBs*

The detection of two SN-less GRBs with *Swift* in 2006[47–50] raised a lot of attention, since the association of long GRBs with SNIbc was by then considered secure. In 2011, another SN-less GRB was detected by *Swift*: GRB 111005A[51] at 57 Mpc (z=0.01326). These events raise the question of the nature of SN-less GRBs: are they the result of the explosion of the core of a massive star or a merger? Since GRB 111005A was well within the detection volume of GW detectors for NSNS or BHNS mergers and easily detectable with ECLAIRs (Figure 12), the occurrence of

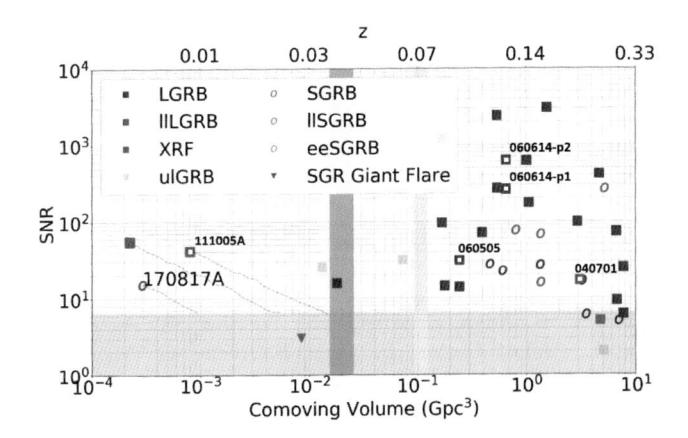

Fig. 12. ECLAIRs on-axis count SNR for GRBs in the local universe ($z \lesssim 0.3$). The orange horizontal band represents the detection limit of ECLAIRs at SNR = 6.5. The green and yellow bands represent the O4 LIGO detection limits for NS-NS and BH-NS mergers respectively. The light grey trails represent the evolution of the on-axis count SNR with the redshift.[52]

another event of this type within the field of view of ECLAIRs during the operation of GW interferometers would provide crucial data to solve this mystery.[52]

4. Conclusion

The operation of *SVOM* simultaneously with powerful instruments in the 2020's decade will certainly bring new crucial data for our understanding of GRBs. We have already mentioned the diagnostic brought by gravitational waves for nearby events, like short GRBs, sub-luminous GRBs or XRFs. We can also mention the search for GRBs coincident in time and direction with afterglow candidates that will be detected by the Vera Rubin Observatory. The operation of *SVOM* simultaneously with large neutrino detectors like ICECUBE or KM3NeT may also bring its share of surprises. Last but not least, the discovery of VHE gamma-ray emission from GRBs by HESS and MAGIC raises the hope to increase the number of such detections with CTA in the SVOM era, revealing key information about the composition and physical processes at work in ultrarelativistic jets.

Observing GRBs, AGNs, TDEs and transient sources of gravitational waves, SVOM will become a key player in the fields of High-Energy Astrophysics, Time Domain Astronomy and Multi-Messenger Astrophysics, after its launch mid-2023.

References

1. J. Wei, B. Cordier, S. Antier, P. Antilogus, J. L. Atteia, A. Bajat, S. Basa, V. Beckmann, M. G. Bernardini, S. Boissier, L. Bouchet, V. Burwitz, A. Claret, Z. G. Dai, F. Daigne, J. Deng, D. Dornic, H. Feng, T. Foglizzo, H. Gao, N. Gehrels, O. Godet, A. Goldwurm, F. Gonzalez, L. Gosset, D. Götz, C. Gouiffes, F. Grise, A. Gros,

J. Guilet, X. Han, M. Huang, Y. F. Huang, M. Jouret, A. Klotz, O. La Marle, C. Lachaud, E. Le Floch, W. Lee, N. Leroy, L. X. Li, S. C. Li, Z. Li, E. W. Liang, H. Lyu, K. Mercier, G. Migliori, R. Mochkovitch, P. O'Brien, J. Osborne, J. Paul, E. Perinati, P. Petitjean, F. Piron, Y. Qiu, A. Rau, J. Rodriguez, S. Schanne, N. Tanvir, E. Vangioni, S. Vergani, F. Y. Wang, J. Wang, X. G. Wang, X. Y. Wang, A. Watson, N. Webb, J. J. Wei, R. Willingale, C. Wu, X. F. Wu, L. P. Xin, D. Xu, S. Yu, W. F. Yu, Y. W. Yu, B. Zhang, S. N. Zhang, Y. Zhang and X. L. Zhou, The Deep and Transient Universe in the SVOM Era: New Challenges and Opportunities - Scientific prospects of the SVOM mission, *arXiv e-prints* , p. arXiv:1610.06892 (October 2016).

2. R. Abbott, T. D. Abbott, S. Abraham, F. Acernese, K. Ackley, A. Adams, C. Adams, R. X. Adhikari, V. B. Adya, C. Affeldt, M. Agathos, K. Agatsuma, N. Aggarwal, O. D. Aguiar, L. Aiello, A. Ain, P. Ajith, S. Akcay, G. Allen, A. Allocca, P. A. Altin, A. Amato, S. Anand, A. Ananyeva, S. B. Anderson, W. G. Anderson, S. V. Angelova, S. Ansoldi, J. M. Antelis, S. Antier, S. Appert, K. Arai, M. C. Araya, J. S. Areeda, M. Arène, N. Arnaud, S. M. Aronson, K. G. Arun, Y. Asali, S. Ascenzi, G. Ashton, S. M. Aston, P. Astone, F. Aubin, P. Aufmuth, K. AultONeal, C. Austin, V. Avendano, S. Babak, F. Badaracco, M. K. M. Bader, S. Bae, A. M. Baer, S. Bagnasco, J. Baird, M. Ball, G. Ballardin, S. W. Ballmer, A. Bals, A. Balsamo, G. Baltus, S. Banagiri, D. Bankar, R. S. Bankar, J. C. Barayoga, C. Barbieri, B. C. Barish, D. Barker, P. Barneo, S. Barnum, F. Barone, B. Barr, L. Barsotti, M. Barsuglia, D. Barta, J. Bartlett, I. Bartos, R. Bassiri, A. Basti, M. Bawaj, J. C. Bayley, M. Bazzan, B. R. Becher, B. Bécsy, V. M. Bedakihale, M. Bejger, I. Belahcene, D. Beniwal, M. G. Benjamin, T. F. Bennett, J. D. Bentley, F. Bergamin, B. K. Berger, G. Bergmann, S. Bernuzzi, C. P. L. Berry, D. Bersanetti, A. Bertolini, J. Betzwieser, R. Bhandare, A. V. Bhandari, D. Bhattacharjee, J. Bidler, I. A. Bilenko, G. Billingsley, R. Birney, O. Birnholtz, S. Biscans, M. Bischi, S. Biscoveanu, A. Bisht, M. Bitossi, M. A. Bizouard, J. K. Blackburn, J. Blackman, C. D. Blair, D. G. Blair, R. M. Blair, O. Blanch, F. Bobba, N. Bode, M. Boer, Y. Boetzel, G. Bogaert, M. Boldrini, F. Bondu, E. Bonilla, R. Bonnand, P. Booker, B. A. Boom, R. Bork, V. Boschi, S. Bose, V. Bossilkov, V. Boudart, Y. Bouffanais, A. Bozzi, C. Bradaschia, P. R. Brady, A. Bramley, M. Branchesi, J. E. Brau, M. Breschi, T. Briant, J. H. Briggs, F. Brighenti, A. Brillet, M. Brinkmann, P. Brockill, A. F. Brooks, J. Brooks, D. D. Brown, S. Brunett, G. Bruno, R. Bruntz, A. Buikema, T. Bulik, H. J. Bulten, A. Buonanno, R. Buscicchio, D. Buskulic, R. L. Byer, M. Cabero, L. Cadonati, M. Caesar, G. Cagnoli, C. Cahillane, J. Calderón Bustillo, J. D. Callaghan, T. A. Callister, E. Calloni, J. B. Camp, M. Canepa, K. C. Cannon, H. Cao, J. Cao, G. Carapella, F. Carbognani, M. F. Carney, M. Carpinelli, G. Carullo, T. L. Carver, J. Casanueva Diaz, C. Casentini, S. Caudill, M. Cavaglià, F. Cavalier, R. Cavalieri, G. Cella, P. Cerdá-Durán, E. Cesarini, W. Chaibi, K. Chakravarti, C. L. Chan, C. Chan, K. Chandra, P. Chanial, S. Chao, P. Charlton, E. A. Chase, E. Chassande-Mottin, D. Chatterjee, D. Chattopadhyay, M. Chaturvedi, K. Chatziioannou, A. Chen, H. Y. Chen, X. Chen, Y. Chen, H. P. Cheng, C. K. Cheong, H. Y. Chia, F. Chiadini, R. Chierici, A. Chincarini, A. Chiummo, G. Cho, H. S. Cho, M. Cho, S. Choate, N. Christensen, Q. Chu, S. Chua, K. W. Chung, S. Chung, G. Ciani, P. Ciecielag, M. Cieślar, M. Cifaldi, A. A. Ciobanu, R. Ciolfi, F. Cipriano, A. Cirone, F. Clara, E. N. Clark, J. A. Clark, L. Clarke, P. Clearwater, S. Clesse, F. Cleva, E. Coccia, P. F. Cohadon, D. E. Cohen, M. Colleoni, C. G. Collette, C. Collins, M. Colpi, M. Constancio, L. Conti, S. J. Cooper, P. Corban, T. R. Corbitt, I. Cordero-Carrión, S. Corezzi, K. R. Corley, N. Cornish, D. Corre, A. Corsi, S. Cortese, C. A. Costa, R. Cotesta, M. W. Coughlin, S. B. Coughlin, J. P. Coulon, S. T. Countryman, B. Cousins, P. Couvares, P. B. Covas, D. M.

Coward, M. J. Cowart, D. C. Coyne, R. Coyne, J. D. E. Creighton, T. D. Creighton, M. Croquette, S. G. Crowder, J. R. Cudell, T. J. Cullen, A. Cumming, R. Cummings, L. Cunningham, E. Cuoco, M. Curyło, T. D. Canton, G. Dálya, A. Dana, L. M. DaneshgaranBajastani, B. D'Angelo, B. Danila, S. L. Danilishin, S. D'Antonio, K. Danzmann, C. Darsow-Fromm, A. Dasgupta, L. E. H. Datrier, V. Dattilo, I. Dave, M. Davier, G. S. Davies, D. Davis, E. J. Daw, R. Dean, D. DeBra, M. Deenadayalan, J. Degallaix, M. De Laurentis, S. Deléglise, V. Del Favero, F. De Lillo, N. De Lillo, W. Del Pozzo, L. M. DeMarchi, F. De Matteis, V. D'Emilio, N. Demos, T. Denker, T. Dent, A. Depasse, R. De Pietri, R. De Rosa, C. De Rossi, R. DeSalvo, O. de Varona, S. Dhurandhar, M. C. Díaz, M. Diaz-Ortiz, N. A. Didio, T. Dietrich, L. Di Fiore, C. DiFronzo, C. Di Giorgio, F. Di Giovanni, M. Di Giovanni, T. Di Girolamo, A. Di Lieto, B. , GWTC-2: Compact Binary Coalescences Observed by LIGO and Virgo during the First Half of the Third Observing Run, *Physical Review X* **11**, p. 021053 (April 2021).

3. G. Vedrenne and J.-L. Atteia, *Gamma-Ray Bursts* 2009.
4. B. P. Abbott, R. Abbott, T. D. Abbott, F. Acernese, K. Ackley, C. Adams, T. Adams, P. Addesso, R. X. Adhikari, V. B. Adya, C. Affeldt, M. Afrough, B. Agarwal, M. Agathos, K. Agatsuma, N. Aggarwal, O. D. Aguiar, L. Aiello, A. Ain, P. Ajith, B. Allen, G. Allen, A. Allocca, P. A. Altin, A. Amato, A. Ananyeva, S. B. Anderson, W. G. Anderson, S. V. Angelova, S. Antier, S. Appert, K. Arai, M. C. Araya, J. S. Areeda, N. Arnaud, K. G. Arun, S. Ascenzi, G. Ashton, M. Ast, S. M. Aston, P. Astone, D. V. Atallah, P. Aufmuth, C. Aulbert, K. AultONeal, C. Austin, A. Avila-Alvarez, S. Babak, P. Bacon, M. K. M. Bader, S. Bae, P. T. Baker, F. Baldaccini, G. Ballardin, S. W. Ballmer, S. Banagiri, J. C. Barayoga, S. E. Barclay, B. C. Barish, D. Barker, K. Barkett, F. Barone, B. Barr, L. Barsotti, M. Barsuglia, D. Barta, S. D. Barthelmy, J. Bartlett, I. Bartos, R. Bassiri, A. Basti, J. C. Batch, M. Bawaj, J. C. Bayley, M. Bazzan, B. Bécsy, C. Beer, M. Bejger, I. Belahcene, A. S. Bell, B. K. Berger, G. Bergmann, J. J. Bero, C. P. L. Berry, D. Bersanetti, A. Bertolini, J. Betzwieser, S. Bhagwat, R. Bhandare, I. A. Bilenko, G. Billingsley, C. R. Billman, J. Birch, R. Birney, O. Birnholtz, S. Biscans, S. Biscoveanu, A. Bisht, M. Bitossi, C. Biwer, M. A. Bizouard, J. K. Blackburn, J. Blackman, C. D. Blair, D. G. Blair, R. M. Blair, S. Bloemen, O. Bock, N. Bode, M. Boer, G. Bogaert, A. Bohe, F. Bondu, E. Bonilla, R. Bonnand, B. A. Boom, R. Bork, V. Boschi, S. Bose, K. Bossie, Y. Bouffanais, A. Bozzi, C. Bradaschia, P. R. Brady, M. Branchesi, J. E. Brau, T. Briant, A. Brillet, M. Brinkmann, V. Brisson, P. Brockill, J. E. Broida, A. F. Brooks, D. A. Brown, D. D. Brown, S. Brunett, C. C. Buchanan, A. Buikema, T. Bulik, H. J. Bulten, A. Buonanno, D. Buskulic, C. Buy, R. L. Byer, M. Cabero, L. Cadonati, G. Cagnoli, C. Cahillane, J. Calderón Bustillo, T. A. Callister, E. Calloni, J. B. Camp, M. Canepa, P. Canizares, K. C. Cannon, H. Cao, J. Cao, C. D. Capano, E. Capocasa, F. Carbognani, S. Caride, M. F. Carney, J. Casanueva Diaz, C. Casentini, S. Caudill, M. Cavaglià, F. Cavalier, R. Cavalieri, G. Cella, C. B. Cepeda, P. Cerdá-Durán, G. Cerretani, E. Cesarini, S. J. Chamberlin, M. Chan, S. Chao, P. Charlton, E. Chase, E. Chassande-Mottin, D. Chatterjee, K. Chatziioannou, B. D. Cheeseboro, H. Y. Chen, X. Chen, Y. Chen, H. P. Cheng, H. Chia, A. Chincarini, A. Chiummo, T. Chmiel, H. S. Cho, M. Cho, J. H. Chow, N. Christensen, Q. Chu, A. J. K. Chua, S. Chua, A. K. W. Chung, S. Chung, G. Ciani, R. Ciolfi, C. E. Cirelli, A. Cirone, F. Clara, J. A. Clark, P. Clearwater, F. Cleva, C. Cocchieri, E. Coccia, P. F. Cohadon, D. Cohen, A. Colla, C. G. Collette, L. R. Cominsky, J. Constancio, M., L. Conti, S. J. Cooper, P. Corban, T. R. Corbitt, I. Cordero-Carrión, K. R. Corley, N. Cornish, A. Corsi, S. Cortese, C. A. Costa, M. W. Coughlin, S. B. Coughlin, J. P. Coulon, S. T. Countryman, P. Couvares, P. B. Covas,

E. E. Cowan, D. M. Coward, M. J. Cowart, D. C. Coyne, R. Coyne, J. D. E. Creighton, T. D. Creighton, J. Cripe, S. G. Crowder, T. J. Cullen, A. Cumming, L. Cunningham, E. Cuoco, T. Dal Canton, G. Dálya, S. L. Danilishin, S. D'Antonio, K. Danzmann, A. Dasgupta, C. F. Da Silva Costa, V. Dattilo, I. Dave, M. Davier, D. Davis, E. J. Daw, B. Day, S. De, D. DeBra, J. Degallaix, M. De Laurentis, S. Deléglise, W. Del Pozzo, N. Demos, T. Denker, T. Dent, R. De Pietri, V. Dergachev, R. De Rosa, R. T. DeRosa, C. De Rossi, R. DeSalvo, O. de Varona, J. Devenson, S. Dhurandhar, M. C. Díaz, L. Di Fiore, M. Di Giovanni, T. Di Girolamo, A. Di Lieto, S. Di Pace, I. Di Palma, F. Di Renzo, Z. Doctor, V. Dolique, F. Donovan, K. L. Dooley, S. Doravari, I. Dorrington, R. Douglas, M. Dovale Álvarez, T. P. Downes, M. Drago, C. Dreissigacker, J. C. Driggers, Z. Du, M. Ducrot, P. Dupej, S. E. Dwyer, T. B. Edo, M. C. Edwards, A. Effler, P. Ehrens, J. Eichholz, S. S. Eikenberry, R. A. Eisenstein, R. C. Essick, D. Estevez, Z. B. Etienne, T. Etzel, M. Evans, T. M. Evans, M. Factourovich, V. Fafone, H. Fair, S. Fairhurst, X. Fan, S. Farinon, B. Farr, W. M. Farr, E. J. Fauchon-Jones, M. Favata, M. Fays, C. Fee, H. Fehrmann, J. Feicht, M. M. Fejer, A. Fernandez-Galiana, I. Ferrante, E. C. Ferreira, F. Ferrini, F. Fidecaro, D. Finstad, I. Fiori, D. Fiorucci, M. Fishbach, R. P. Fi, Multi-messenger Observations of a Binary Neutron Star Merger, *ApJ* **848**, p. L12 (October 2017).

5. Cherenkov Telescope Array Consortium, B. S. Acharya, I. Agudo, I. Al Samarai, R. Alfaro, J. Alfaro, C. Alispach, R. Alves Batista, J. P. Amans, E. Amato, G. Ambrosi, E. Antolini, L. A. Antonelli, C. Aramo, M. Araya, T. Armstrong, F. Arqueros, L. Arrabito, K. Asano, M. Ashley, M. Backes, C. Balazs, M. Balbo, O. Ballester, J. Ballet, A. Bamba, M. Barkov, U. Barres de Almeida, J. A. Barrio, D. Bastieri, Y. Becherini, A. Belfiore, W. Benbow, D. Berge, E. Bernardini, M. G. Bernardini, M. Bernardos, K. Bernlöhr, B. Bertucci, B. Biasuzzi, C. Bigongiari, A. Biland, E. Bissaldi, J. Biteau, O. Blanch, J. Blazek, C. Boisson, J. Bolmont, G. Bonanno, A. Bonardi, C. Bonavolontà, G. Bonnoli, Z. Bosnjak, M. Böttcher, C. Braiding, J. Bregeon, A. Brill, A. M. Brown, P. Brun, G. Brunetti, T. Buanes, J. Buckley, V. Bugaev, R. Bühler, A. Bulgarelli, T. Bulik, M. Burton, A. Burtovoi, G. Busetto, R. Canestrari, M. Capalbi, F. Capitanio, A. Caproni, P. Caraveo, V. Cárdenas, C. Carlile, R. Carosi, E. Carquín, J. Carr, S. Casanova, E. Cascone, F. Catalani, O. Catalano, D. Cauz, M. Cerruti, P. Chadwick, S. Chaty, R. C. G. Chaves, A. Chen, X. Chen, M. Chernyakova, M. Chikawa, A. Christov, J. Chudoba, M. Cieślar, V. Coco, S. Colafrancesco, P. Colin, V. Conforti, V. Connaughton, J. Conrad, J. L. Contreras, J. Cortina, A. Costa, H. Costantini, G. Cotter, S. Covino, R. Crocker, J. Cuadra, O. Cuevas, P. Cumani, A. D'Aì, F. D'Ammando, P. D'Avanzo, D. D'Urso, M. Daniel, I. Davids, B. Dawson, F. Dazzi, A. De Angelis, R. de Cássia dos Anjos, G. De Cesare, A. De Franco, E. M. de Gouveia Dal Pino, I. de la Calle, R. de los Reyes Lopez, B. De Lotto, A. De Luca, M. De Lucia, M. de Naurois, E. de Oña Wilhelmi, F. De Palma, F. De Persio, V. de Souza, C. Deil, M. Del Santo, C. Delgado, D. della Volpe, T. Di Girolamo, F. Di Pierro, L. Di Venere, C. Díaz, C. Dib, S. Diebold, A. Djannati-Ataï, A. Domínguez, D. Dominis Prester, D. Dorner, M. Doro, H. Drass, D. Dravins, G. Dubus, V. V. Dwarkadas, J. Ebr, C. Eckner, K. Egberts, S. Einecke, T. R. N. Ekoume, D. Elsässer, J. P. Ernenwein, C. Espinoza, C. Evoli, M. Fairbairn, D. Falceta-Goncalves, A. Falcone, C. Farnier, G. Fasola, E. Fedorova, S. Fegan, M. Fernandez-Alonso, A. Fernández-Barral, G. Ferrand, M. Fesquet, M. Filipovic, V. Fioretti, G. Fontaine, M. Fornasa, L. Fortson, L. Freixas Coromina, C. Fruck, Y. Fujita, Y. Fukazawa, S. Funk, M. Füßling, S. Gabici, A. Gadola, Y. Gallant, B. Garcia, R. Garcia López, M. Garczarczyk, J. Gaskins, T. Gasparetto, M. Gaug, L. Gerard, G. Giavitto, N. Giglietto, P. Giommi, F. Giordano, E. Giro, M. Giroletti, A. Giuliani,

J. F. Glicenstein, R. Gnatyk, N. Godinovic, P. Goldoni, G. Gómez-Vargas, M. M. González, J. M. González, D. Götz, J. Graham, P. Grandi, J. Granot, A. J. Green, T. Greenshaw, S. Griffiths, S. Gunji, D. Hadasch, S. Hara, M. J. Hardcastle, T. Hassan, K. Hayashi, M. Hayashida, M. Heller, J. C. Helo, G. Hermann, J. Hinton, B. Hnatyk, W. Hofmann, J. Holder, D. Horan, J. Hörandel, D. Horns, P. Horvath, T. Hovatta, M. Hrabovsky, D. Hrupec, T. B. Humensky, M. Hütten, M. Iarlori, T. Inada, Y. Inome, S. Inoue, T. Inoue, Y. Inoue, F. Iocco, K. Ioka, M. Iori, K. Ishio, Y. Iwamura, M. Jamrozy, P. Janecek, D. Jankowsky, P. Jean, I. Jung-Richardt, J. Jurysek, P. Kaaret, S. Karkar, H. Katagiri, U. Katz, N. Kawanaka, D. Kazanas, B. Khélifi, D. B. Kieda, S. Kimeswenger, S. Kimura, S. Kisaka, J. Knapp, J. Knödlseder, B. Koch, K. Kohri, N. Komin, K. Kosack, M. Kraus, M. Krause, F. Krauß, H. Kubo, G. Kukec Mezek, H. Kuroda, J. Kushida, N. La Palombara, G. Lamanna, R. G. Lang, J. Lapington, O. Le Blanc, S. Leach, J. P. Lees, J. Lefaucheur, M. A. Leigui de Oliveira, J. P. Lenain, R. Lico, M. Limon, E. Lindfors, T. Lohse, S. Lombardi, F. Longo, M. López, R. López-Coto, C. C. Lu, F. Lucarelli, P. L. Luque-Escamilla, E. Lyard, M. C. Maccarone, G. Maier, P. Majumdar, G. Malaguti, D. Mandat, G. Maneva, M. Manganaro, S. Mangano, A. Marcowith, J. Marín, S. Markoff, J. Martí, P. Martin, M. Martínez, G. Martínez, N. Masetti, S. Masuda, G. Maurin, N. Maxted, D. Mazin, C. Medina, A. Melandri, S. Mereghetti, M. Meyer, I. A. Minaya, N. Mirabal, R. Mirzoyan, A. Mitchell, T. Mizuno, R. Moderski, M. M, *Science with the Cherenkov Telescope Array* 2019.

6. A. Albert, R. Alfaro, C. Alvarez, J. R. A. Camacho, J. C. Arteaga-Velázquez, K. P. Arunbabu, D. Avila Rojas, H. A. Ayala Solares, V. Baghmanyan, E. Belmont-Moreno, S. Y. BenZvi, C. Brisbois, K. S. Caballero-Mora, T. Capistrán, A. Carramiñana, S. Casanova, U. Cotti, S. Coutiño de León, E. De la Fuente, R. Diaz Hernandez, L. Diaz-Cruz, B. L. Dingus, M. A. DuVernois, M. Durocher, J. C. Díaz-Vélez, R. W. Ellsworth, K. Engel, C. Espinoza, K. L. Fan, K. Fang, M. F. Alonso, H. Fleischhack, N. Fraija, A. Galván-Gámez, D. Garcia, J. A. García-González, F. Garfias, G. Giacinti, M. M. González, J. A. Goodman, J. P. Harding, S. Hernandez, J. Hinton, B. Hona, D. Huang, F. Hueyotl-Zahuantitla, P. Hüntemeyer, A. Iriarte, A. Jardin-Blicq, V. Joshi, D. Kieda, A. Lara, W. H. Lee, H. León Vargas, J. T. Linnemann, A. L. Longinotti, G. Luis-Raya, J. Lundeen, R. López-Coto, K. Malone, V. Marandon, O. Martinez, I. Martinez-Castellanos, J. Martínez-Castro, J. A. Matthews, P. Miranda-Romagnoli, J. A. Morales-Soto, E. Moreno, M. Mostafá, A. Nayerhoda, L. Nellen, M. Newbold, M. U. Nisa, R. Noriega-Papaqui, L. Olivera-Nieto, N. Omodei, A. Peisker, Y. Pérez Araujo, E. G. Pérez-Pérez, Z. Ren, C. D. Rho, C. Rivière, D. Rosa-González, E. Ruiz-Velasco, H. Salazar, F. Salesa Greus, A. Sandoval, M. Schneider, H. Schoorlemmer, F. Serna, G. Sinnis, A. J. Smith, R. W. Springer, P. Surajbali, K. Tollefson, I. Torres, R. Torres-Escobedo, T. N. Ukwatta, F. Ureña-Mena, T. Weisgarber, F. Werner, E. Willox, A. Zepeda, H. Zhou, C. de León, J. D. Álvarez and HAWC Collaboration, 3HWC: The Third HAWC Catalog of Very-high-energy Gamma-Ray Sources, *ApJ* **905**, p. 76 (December 2020).

7. X. Bai, B. Y. Bi, X. J. Bi, Z. Cao, S. Z. Chen, Y. Chen, A. Chiavassa, X. H. Cui, Z. G. Dai, D. della Volpe, T. Di Girolamo, G. Di Sciascio, Y. Z. Fan, J. Giacalone, Y. Q. Guo, H. H. He, T. L. He, M. Heller, D. Huang, Y. F. Huang, H. Jia, L. T. Ksenofontov, D. Leahy, F. Li, Z. Li, E. W. Liang, P. Lipari, R. Y. Liu, Y. Liu, S. Liu, X. Ma, O. Martineau-Huynh, D. Martraire, T. Montaruli, D. Ruffolo, Y. V. Stenkin, H. Q. Su, T. Tam, Q. W. Tang, W. W. Tian, P. Vallania, S. Vernetto, C. Vigorito, J. . C. Wang, L. Z. Wang, X. Wang, X. Y. Wang, X. J. Wang, Z. X. Wang, D. M. Wei, J. J. Wei, D. Wu, H. R. Wu, X. F. Wu, D. H. Yan, A. Y. Yang, R. Z. Yang,

Z. G. Yao, L. Q. Yin, Q. Yuan, B. Zhang, B. Zhang, L. Zhang, M. F. Zhang, S. S. Zhang, X. Zhang, Y. Zhao, X. X. Zhou, F. R. Zhu and H. Zhu, The Large High Altitude Air Shower Observatory (LHAASO) Science White Paper, *arXiv e-prints* , p. arXiv:1905.02773 (May 2019).
8. P. Predehl, R. Andritschke, V. Arefiev, V. Babyshkin, O. Batanov, W. Becker, H. Böhringer, A. Bogomolov, T. Boller, K. Borm, W. Bornemann, H. Bräuninger, M. Brüggen, H. Brunner, M. Brusa, E. Bulbul, M. Buntov, V. Burwitz, W. Burkert, N. Clerc, E. Churazov, D. Coutinho, T. Dauser, K. Dennerl, V. Doroshenko, J. Eder, V. Emberger, T. Eraerds, A. Finoguenov, M. Freyberg, P. Friedrich, S. Friedrich, M. Fürmetz, A. Georgakakis, M. Gilfanov, S. Granato, C. Grossberger, A. Gueguen, P. Gureev, F. Haberl, O. Hälker, G. Hartner, G. Hasinger, H. Huber, L. Ji, A. v. Kienlin, W. Kink, F. Korotkov, I. Kreykenbohm, G. Lamer, I. Lomakin, I. Lapshov, T. Liu, C. Maitra, N. Meidinger, M. Menz, A. Merloni, T. Mernik, B. Mican, J. Mohr, S. Müller, K. Nandra, V. Nazarov, F. Pacaud, M. Pavlinsky, E. Perinati, E. Pfeffermann, D. Pietschner, M. E. Ramos-Ceja, A. Rau, J. Reiffers, T. H. Reiprich, J. Robrade, M. Salvato, J. Sanders, A. Santangelo, M. Sasaki, H. Scheuerle, C. Schmid, J. Schmitt, A. Schwope, A. Shirshakov, M. Steinmetz, I. Stewart, L. Strüder, R. Sunyaev, C. Tenzer, L. Tiedemann, J. Trümper, V. Voron, P. Weber, J. Wilms and V. Yaroshenko, The eROSITA X-ray telescope on SRG, *A&A* **647**, p. A1 (March 2021).
9. E. C. Bellm, S. R. Kulkarni, M. J. Graham, R. Dekany, R. M. Smith, R. Riddle, F. J. Masci, G. Helou, T. A. Prince, S. M. Adams, C. Barbarino, T. Barlow, J. Bauer, R. Beck, J. Belicki, R. Biswas, N. Blagorodnova, D. Bodewits, B. Bolin, V. Brinnel, T. Brooke, B. Bue, M. Bulla, R. Burruss, S. B. Cenko, C.-K. Chang, A. Connolly, M. Coughlin, J. Cromer, V. Cunningham, K. De, A. Delacroix, V. Desai, D. A. Duev, G. Eadie, T. L. Farnham, M. Feeney, U. Feindt, D. Flynn, A. Franckowiak, S. Frederick, C. Fremling, A. Gal-Yam, S. Gezari, M. Giomi, D. A. Goldstein, V. Z. Golkhou, A. Goobar, S. Groom, E. Hacopians, D. Hale, J. Henning, A. Y. Q. Ho, D. Hover, J. Howell, T. Hung, D. Huppenkothen, D. Imel, W.-H. Ip, Ž. Ivezić, E. Jackson, L. Jones, M. Juric, M. M. Kasliwal, S. Kaspi, S. Kaye, M. S. P. Kelley, M. Kowalski, E. Kramer, T. Kupfer, W. Landry, R. R. Laher, C.-D. Lee, H. W. Lin, Z.-Y. Lin, R. Lunnan, M. Giomi, A. Mahabal, P. Mao, A. A. Miller, S. Monkewitz, P. Murphy, C.-C. Ngeow, J. Nordin, P. Nugent, E. Ofek, M. T. Patterson, B. Penprase, M. Porter, L. Rauch, U. Rebbapragada, D. Reiley, M. Rigault, H. Rodriguez, J. van Roestel, B. Rusholme, J. van Santen, S. Schulze, D. L. Shupe, L. P. Singer, M. T. Soumagnac, R. Stein, J. Surace, J. Sollerman, P. Szkody, F. Taddia, S. Terek, A. Van Sistine, S. van Velzen, W. T. Vestrand, R. Walters, C. Ward, Q.-Z. Ye, P.-C. Yu, L. Yan and J. Zolkower, The Zwicky Transient Facility: System Overview, Performance, and First Results, *PASP* **131**, p. 018002 (January 2019).
10. Ž. Ivezić, S. M. Kahn, J. A. Tyson, B. Abel, E. Acosta, R. Allsman, D. Alonso, Y. AlSayyad, S. F. Anderson, J. Andrew, J. R. P. Angel, G. Z. Angeli, R. Ansari, P. Antilogus, C. Araujo, R. Armstrong, K. T. Arndt, P. Astier, É. Aubourg, N. Auza, T. S. Axelrod, D. J. Bard, J. D. Barr, A. Barrau, J. G. Bartlett, A. E. Bauer, B. J. Bauman, S. Baumont, E. Bechtol, K. Bechtol, A. C. Becker, J. Becla, C. Beldica, S. Bellavia, F. B. Bianco, R. Biswas, G. Blanc, J. Blazek, R. D. Blandford, J. S. Bloom, J. Bogart, T. W. Bond, M. T. Booth, A. W. Borgland, K. Borne, J. F. Bosch, D. Boutigny, C. A. Brackett, A. Bradshaw, W. N. Brandt, M. E. Brown, J. S. Bullock, P. Burchat, D. L. Burke, G. Cagnoli, D. Calabrese, S. Callahan, A. L. Callen, J. L. Carlin, E. L. Carlson, S. Chandrasekharan, G. Charles-Emerson, S. Chesley, E. C. Cheu, H.-F. Chiang, J. Chiang, C. Chirino, D. Chow, D. R. Ciardi, C. F. Claver, J. Cohen-Tanugi, J. J.

Cockrum, R. Coles, A. J. Connolly, K. H. Cook, A. Cooray, K. R. Covey, C. Cribbs, W. Cui, R. Cutri, P. N. Daly, S. F. Daniel, F. Daruich, G. Daubard, G. Daues, W. Dawson, F. Delgado, A. Dellapenna, R. de Peyster, M. de Val-Borro, S. W. Digel, P. Doherty, R. Dubois, G. P. Dubois-Felsmann, J. Durech, F. Economou, T. Eifler, M. Eracleous, B. L. Emmons, A. Fausti Neto, H. Ferguson, E. Figueroa, M. Fisher-Levine, W. Focke, M. D. Foss, J. Frank, M. D. Freemon, E. Gangler, E. Gawiser, J. C. Geary, P. Gee, M. Geha, C. J. B. Gessner, R. R. Gibson, D. K. Gilmore, T. Glanzman, W. Glick, T. Goldina, D. A. Goldstein, I. Goodenow, M. L. Graham, W. J. Gressler, P. Gris, L. P. Guy, A. Guyonnet, G. Haller, R. Harris, P. A. Hascall, J. Haupt, F. Hernandez, S. Herrmann, E. Hileman, J. Hoblitt, J. A. Hodgson, C. Hogan, J. D. Howard, D. Huang, M. E. Huffer, P. Ingraham, W. R. Innes, S. H. Jacoby, B. Jain, F. Jammes, M. J. Jee, T. Jenness, G. Jernigan, D. Jevremović, K. Johns, A. S. Johnson, M. W. G. Johnson, R. L. Jones, C. Juramy-Gilles, M. Jurić, J. S. Kalirai, N. J. Kallivayalil, B. Kalmbach, J. P. Kantor, P. Karst, M. M. Kasliwal, H. Kelly, R. Kessler, V. Kinnison, D. Kirkby, L. Knox, I. V. Kotov, V. L. Krabbendam, K. S. Krughoff, P. Kubánek, J. Kuczewski, S. Kulkarni, J. Ku, N. R. Kurita, C. S. Lage, R. Lambert, T. Lange, J. B. Langton, L. Le Guillou, D. Levine, M. Liang, K.-T. Lim, C. J. Lintott, K. E. Long, M. Lopez, P. J. Lotz, R. H. Lupton, N. B. Lust, L. A. MacArthur, A. Mahabal, R. Mandelbaum, T. W. Markiewicz, D. S. Marsh, P. J. Marshall, S. Marshall, M. May, R. McKercher, M. McQueen, J. Meyers, M. Migliore, M. Miller, D. J. Mills, C. Miraval, J. Moeyens, F. E. Moolekamp, D. G. Monet, M. Moniez, S. Monkewitz, C. Montgomery, C. B. Morrison, F. Mueller, G. P. Muller, F. Muñoz Arancibia, D. R. Neill, S. P. Newbry, J.-Y. Nief, A. Nomerotski, M. Nordby, P. O'Connor, J. Oliver, S. S. Olivier, K. Olsen, W. O'Mullane, S. Ortiz, S. Osier, R. E. Owen, R. Pain, P. E. Palecek, J. K. Parejko, J. B. Parsons, N. M. Pease, J. M. Peterson, J. R. Peterson, D. L. Petravick, M. E. Libby Petrick, C. E. Petry, F. Pierfederici, S. Pietrowicz, R. Pike, P. A. Pinto, R. Plante, S. Plate, J. P. Plutchak, P. A. Price, M. Prouza, V. Radeka, J. Rajagopal, A. P. Rasmussen, N. Regnault, K. A. Reil, D. J. Reiss, M. A. Reuter, S. T. Ridgway, V. J. Riot, S. Ritz, S. Robinson, W. Roby, A. Roodman, W. Rosing, C. Roucelle, M. R. Rumore, S. Russo, A. Saha, B. Sassolas, T. L. Schalk, P. Schellart, R. H. Schindler, S. Schmidt, D. P. Schneider, M. D. Schneider, W. Schoening, G. Schumacher, M. E. Schwamb, J. Sebag, B. Selvy, G. H. Sembroski, L. G. Seppala, A. Serio, E. Serrano, R. A. Shaw, I. Shipsey, J. Sick, N. Silvestri, C. T. Slater, J. A. Smith, R. C. Smith, S. Sobhani, C. Soldahl, L. Storrie-Lombardi, E. Stover, M. A. Strauss, R. A. Street, C. W. Stubbs, I. S. Sullivan, D. Sweeney, J. D. Swinbank, A. Szalay, P. Takacs, S. A. Tether, J. J. Thaler, J. G. Thayer, S. Thomas, A. J. Thornton, V. Thukral, J. Tice, D. E. Trilling, M. Turri, R. Van Berg, D. Vanden Berk, K. Vetter, F. Virieux, T. Vucina, W. Wahl, L. Walkowicz, B. Walsh, C. W. Walter, D. L. Wang, S.-Y. Wang, M. Warner, O. Wiecha, B. Willman, S. E. Winters, D. Wittman, S. C. Wolff, W. M. Wood-Vasey, X. Wu, B. Xin, P. Yoachim and H. Zhan, LSST: From Science Drivers to Reference Design and Anticipated Data Products, *ApJ* **873**, p. 111 (March 2019).
11. P. Schipani, R. Claudi, S. Campana, A. Baruffolo, S. Basa, S. Basso, E. Cappellaro, E. Cascone, R. Cosentino, F. D'Alessio, V. De Caprio, M. Della Valle, A. de Ugarte Postigo, S. D'Orsi, R. Franzen, J. Fynbo, A. Gal-Yam, D. Gardiol, E. Giro, M. Hamuy, M. Iuzzolino, D. Loreggia, S. Mattila, M. Munari, G. Pignata, M. Riva, S. Savarese, B. Schmidt, S. Scuderi, S. Smartt and F. Vitali, The new SOXS instrument for the ESO NTT, **9908**, p. 990841 (August 2016).
12. S. Johnston, R. Taylor, M. Bailes, N. Bartel, C. Baugh, M. Bietenholz, C. Blake, R. Braun, J. Brown, S. Chatterjee, J. Darling, A. Deller, R. Dodson, P. Edwards,

R. Ekers, S. Ellingsen, I. Feain, B. Gaensler, M. Haverkorn, G. Hobbs, A. Hopkins, C. Jackson, C. James, G. Joncas, V. Kaspi, V. Kilborn, B. Koribalski, R. Kothes, T. Landecker, E. Lenc, J. Lovell, J. P. Macquart, R. Manchester, D. Matthews, N. McClure-Griffiths, R. Norris, U. L. Pen, C. Phillips, C. Power, R. Protheroe, E. Sadler, B. Schmidt, I. Stairs, L. Staveley-Smith, J. Stil, S. Tingay, A. Tzioumis, M. Walker, J. Wall and M. Wolleben, Science with ASKAP. The Australian square-kilometre-array pathfinder, *Experimental Astronomy* **22**, 151 (December 2008).

13. R. S. Booth, W. J. G. de Blok, J. L. Jonas and B. Fanaroff, MeerKAT Key Project Science, Specifications, and Proposals, *arXiv e-prints* , p. arXiv:0910.2935 (October 2009).

14. CHIME/FRB Collaboration, M. Amiri, K. Bandura, P. Berger, M. Bhardwaj, M. M. Boyce, P. J. Boyle, C. Brar, M. Burhanpurkar, P. Chawla, J. Chowdhury, J. F. Cliche, M. D. Cranmer, D. Cubranic, M. Deng, N. Denman, M. Dobbs, M. Fandino, E. Fonseca, B. M. Gaensler, U. Giri, A. J. Gilbert, D. C. Good, S. Guliani, M. Halpern, G. Hinshaw, C. Höfer, A. Josephy, V. M. Kaspi, T. L. Landecker, D. Lang, H. Liao, K. W. Masui, J. Mena-Parra, A. Naidu, L. B. Newburgh, C. Ng, C. Patel, U. L. Pen, T. Pinsonneault-Marotte, Z. Pleunis, M. Rafiei Ravandi, S. M. Ransom, A. Renard, P. Scholz, K. Sigurdson, S. R. Siegel, K. M. Smith, I. H. Stairs, S. P. Tendulkar, K. Vanderlinde and D. V. Wiebe, The CHIME Fast Radio Burst Project: System Overview, *ApJ* **863**, p. 48 (August 2018).

15. J.-P. Macquart, M. Bailes, N. D. R. Bhat, G. C. Bower, J. D. Bunton, S. Chatterjee, T. Colegate, J. M. Cordes, L. D'Addario, A. Deller, R. Dodson, R. Fender, K. Haines, P. Hall, C. Harris, A. Hotan, S. Johnston, D. L. Jones, M. Keith, J. Y. Koay, T. J. W. Lazio, W. Majid, T. Murphy, R. Navarro, C. Phillips, P. Quinn, R. A. Preston, B. Stansby, I. Stairs, B. Stappers, L. Staveley-Smith, S. Tingay, D. Thompson, W. van Straten, K. Wagstaff, M. Warren, R. Wayth, L. Wen and CRAFT Collaboration, The Commensal Real-Time ASKAP Fast-Transients (CRAFT) Survey, *PASA* **27**, 272 (June 2010).

16. B. P. Abbott, R. Abbott, T. D. Abbott, S. Abraham, F. Acernese, K. Ackley, C. Adams, V. B. Adya, C. Affeldt, M. Agathos, K. Agatsuma, N. Aggarwal, O. D. Aguiar, L. Aiello, A. Ain, P. Ajith, T. Akutsu, G. Allen, A. Allocca, M. A. Aloy, P. A. Altin, A. Amato, A. Ananyeva, S. B. Anderson, W. G. Anderson, M. Ando, S. V. Angelova, S. Antier, S. Appert, K. Arai, K. Arai, Y. Arai, S. Araki, A. Araya, M. C. Araya, J. S. Areeda, M. Arène, N. Aritomi, N. Arnaud, K. G. Arun, S. Ascenzi, G. Ashton, Y. Aso, S. M. Aston, P. Astone, F. Aubin, P. Aufmuth, K. Aultoneal, C. Austin, V. Avendano, A. Avila-Alvarez, S. Babak, P. Bacon, F. Badaracco, M. K. M. Bader, S. W. Bae, Y. B. Bae, L. Baiotti, R. Bajpai, P. T. Baker, F. Baldaccini, G. Ballardin, S. W. Ballmer, S. Banagiri, J. C. Barayoga, S. E. Barclay, B. C. Barish, D. Barker, K. Barkett, S. Barnum, F. Barone, B. Barr, L. Barsotti, M. Barsuglia, D. Barta, J. Bartlett, M. A. Barton, I. Bartos, R. Bassiri, A. Basti, M. Bawaj, J. C. Bayley, M. Bazzan, B. Bécsy, M. Bejger, I. Belahcene, A. S. Bell, D. Beniwal, B. K. Berger, G. Bergmann, S. Bernuzzi, J. J. Bero, C. P. L. Berry, D. Bersanetti, A. Bertolini, J. Betzwieser, R. Bhandare, J. Bidler, I. A. Bilenko, S. A. Bilgili, G. Billingsley, J. Birch, R. Birney, O. Birnholtz, S. Biscans, S. Biscoveanu, A. Bisht, M. Bitossi, M. A. Bizouard, J. K. Blackburn, C. D. Blair, D. G. Blair, R. M. Blair, S. Bloemen, N. Bode, M. Boer, Y. Boetzel, G. Bogaert, F. Bondu, E. Bonilla, R. Bonnand, P. Booker, B. A. Boom, C. D. Booth, R. Bork, V. Boschi, S. Bose, K. Bossie, V. Bossilkov, J. Bosveld, Y. Bouffanais, A. Bozzi, C. Bradaschia, P. R. Brady, A. Bramley, M. Branchesi, J. E. Brau, T. Briant, J. H. Briggs, F. Brighenti, A. Brillet, M. Brinkmann, V. Brisson,

P. Brockill, A. F. Brooks, D. A. Brown, D. D. Brown, S. Brunett, A. Buikema, T. Bulik, H. J. Bulten, A. Buonanno, D. Buskulic, C. Buy, R. L. Byer, M. Cabero, L. Cadonati, G. Cagnoli, C. Cahillane, J. C. Bustillo, T. A. Callister, E. Calloni, J. B. Camp, W. A. Campbell, M. Canepa, K. Cannon, K. C. Cannon, H. Cao, J. Cao, E. Capocasa, F. Carbognani, S. Caride, M. F. Carney, G. Carullo, J. Casanueva Diaz, C. Casentini, S. Caudill, M. Cavaglià, F. Cavalier, R. Cavalieri, G. Cella, P. Cerdá-Durán, G. Cerretani, E. Cesarini, O. Chaibi, K. Chakravarti, S. J. Chamberlin, M. Chan, M. L. Chan, S. Chao, P. Charlton, E. A. Chase, E. Chassande-Mottin, D. Chatterjee, M. Chaturvedi, K. Chatziioannou, B. D. Cheeseboro, C. S. Chen, H. Y. Chen, K. H. Chen, X. Chen, Y. Chen, Y. R. Chen, H. P. Cheng, C. K. Cheong, H. Y. Chia, A. Chincarini, A. Chiummo, G. Cho, H. S. Cho, M. Cho, N. Christensen, H. Y. Chu, Q. Chu, Y. K. Chu, S. Chua, K. W. Chung, S. Chung, G. Ciani, A. A. Ciobanu, R. Ciolfi, F. Cipriano, A. Cirone, F. Clara, J. A. Clark, P. Clearwater, F. Cleva, C. Cocchieri, E. Coccia, P. F. Cohadon, D. Cohen, R. Colgan, M. Colleoni, C. G. Collette, C. Collins, L. R. Cominsky, M. Constancio, L. Conti, S. J. Cooper, P. Corban, T. R. Corbitt, I. Cordero-Carrión, K. R. Corley, N. Cornish, A. Corsi, S. Cortese, C. A. Costa, R. Cotesta, M. W. Coughlin, S. B. Coughlin, J. P. Coulon, S. T. Countryman, P. Couvares, P. B. Covas, E. E. Cowan, D. M. Coward, M. J. Cowart, D. C. Coyne, R. Coyne, J. D. E. Creighton, T. D. Creighton, J. Cripe, M. Croquette, S. G. Crowder, T. J. Cullen, A. Cumming, L. Cunningham, E. Cuoco, T. Dal Canton, G. Dálya, S. L. Danilishin, S. D'Antonio, K. Danzmann, A. Dasgupta, C. F. da Silva Costa, L. E. H. Datrier, V. Dattilo, I. Dave, M. Davier, D. Davis, E. J. Daw, D. Debra, M. Deenadayalan, J. Degallaix, M. de Laurentis, S. Deléglise, W. D. Pozzo, L. M. Demarchi, N. Demos, T. Dent, R. de Pietri, J. Derby, R. De Rosa, C. de Rossi, R. Desalvo, O. de Varona, S. Dhurandhar, M. C. Díaz, T. Dietrich, L. di Fiore, M. di Giovanni, T. di Girolamo, A. di Lieto, B. Ding, S. di Pace, I. di Palma, F. di Renzo, A. Dmitriev, Z. Doctor, K. Doi, F. Donovan, K. L. Dooley, S. Doravari, I. Dorrington, T. P. Downes, M. Drago, J. C. Driggers, Z. Du, J. G. Ducoin, P. Dupej, S. E. Dwyer, P. J. Easter, T. B. Edo, M. C. Edwards, A. Effler, S. Eguchi, P. Ehrens, J. Eichholz, S. S. Eikenberry, M. Eisenmann, R. A. Eisenstein, Y. Enomoto, R. C. Essick, H. Estelles, D. Estevez, Z. B. Etienne, T. Etzel, M. Evans, T. M. Evan, Prospects for observing and localizing gravitational-wave transients with Advanced LIGO, Advanced Virgo and KAGRA, *Living Reviews in Relativity* **23**, p. 3 (September 2020).
17. IceCube Collaboration, Evidence for High-Energy Extraterrestrial Neutrinos at the IceCube Detector, *Science* **342**, p. 1242856 (November 2013).
18. S. Adrián-Martínez, M. Ageron, F. Aharonian, S. Aiello, A. Albert, F. Ameli, E. Anassontzis, M. Andre, G. Androulakis, M. Anghinolfi, G. Anton, M. Ardid, T. Avgitas, G. Barbarino, E. Barbarito, B. Baret, J. Barrios-Martí, B. Belhorma, A. Belias, E. Berbee, A. van den Berg, V. Bertin, S. Beurthey, V. van Beveren, N. Beverini, S. Biagi, A. Biagioni, M. Billault, M. Bondì, R. Bormuth, B. Bouhadef, G. Bourlis, S. Bourret, C. Boutonnet, M. Bouwhuis, C. Bozza, R. Bruijn, J. Brunner, E. Buis, J. Busto, G. Cacopardo, L. Caillat, M. Calamai, D. Calvo, A. Capone, L. Caramete, S. Cecchini, S. Celli, C. Champion, R. Cherkaoui El Moursli, S. Cherubini, T. Chiarusi, M. Circella, L. Classen, R. Cocimano, J. A. B. Coelho, A. Coleiro, S. Colonges, R. Coniglione, M. Cordelli, A. Cosquer, P. Coyle, A. Creusot, G. Cuttone, A. D'Amico, G. De Bonis, G. De Rosa, C. De Sio, F. Di Capua, I. Di Palma, A. F. Díaz García, C. Distefano, C. Donzaud, D. Dornic, Q. Dorosti-Hasankiadeh, E. Drakopoulou, D. Drouhin, L. Drury, M. Durocher, T. Eberl, S. Eichie, D. van Eijk, I. El Bojaddaini, N. El Khayati, D. Elsaesser, A. Enzenhöfer, F. Fassi, P. Favali, P. Fermani, G. Ferrara, C. Filippidis, G. Frascadore, L. A. Fusco, T. Gal, S. Galatà, F. Garufi, P. Gay, M. Gebyehu,

V. Giordano, N. Gizani, R. Gracia, K. Graf, T. Grégoire, G. Grella, R. Habel, S. Hallmann, H. van Haren, S. Harissopulos, T. Heid, A. Heijboer, E. Heine, S. Henry, J. J. Hernández-Rey, M. Hevinga, J. Hofestädt, C. M. F. Hugon, G. Illuminati, C. W. James, P. Jansweijer, M. Jongen, M. de Jong, M. Kadler, O. Kalekin, A. Kappes, U. F. Katz, P. Keller, G. Kieft, D. Kießling, E. N. Koffeman, P. Kooijman, A. Kouchner, V. Kulikovskiy, R. Lahmann, P. Lamare, A. Leisos, E. Leonora, M. L. Clark, A. Liolios, C. D. Llorens Alvarez, D. Lo Presti, H. Löhner, A. Lonardo, M. Lotze, S. Loucatos, E. Maccioni, K. Mannheim, A. Margiotta, A. Marinelli, O. Mariş, C. Markou, J. A. Martínez-Mora, A. Martini, R. Mele, K. W. Melis, T. Michael, P. Migliozzi, E. Migneco, P. Mijakowski, A. Miraglia, C. M. Mollo, M. Mongelli, M. Morganti, A. Moussa, P. Musico, M. Musumeci, S. Navas, C. A. Nicolau, I. Olcina, C. Olivetto, A. Orlando, A. Papaikonomou, R. Papaleo, G. E. Păvălaş, H. Peek, C. Pellegrino, C. Perrina, M. Pfutzner, P. Piattelli, K. Pikounis, G. E. Poma, V. Popa, T. Pradier, F. Pratolongo, G. Pühlhofer, S. Pulvirenti, L. Quinn, C. Racca, F. Raffaelli, N. Randazzo, P. Rapidis, P. Razis, D. Real, L. Resvanis, J. Reubelt, G. Riccobene, C. Rossi, A. Rovelli, M. Saldaña, I. Salvadori, D. F. E. Samtleben, A. Sánchez García, A. Sánchez Losa, M. Sanguineti, A. Santangelo, D. Santonocito, P. Sapienza, F. Schimmel, J. Schmelling, V. Sciacca, M. Sedita, T. Seitz, I. Sgura, F. Simeone, I. Siotis, V. Sipala, B. Spisso, M. Spurio, G. Stavropoulos, J. Steijger, S. M. Stellacci, D. Stransky, M. Taiuti, Y. Tayalati, D. Tézier, S. Theraube, L. Thompson, P. Timmer, C. Tönnis, L. Trasatti, A. Trovato, A. Tsirigotis, S. Tzamarias, E. Tzamariudaki, B. Vallage, V. Van Elewyck, J. Vermeulen, P. Vicini, S. Viola, D. Vivolo, M. Volkert, G. Voulgaris, L. Wiggers, J. Wilms, E. de Wolf, K. Zachariadou, J. D. Zornoza and J. Zúñiga, Letter of intent for KM3NeT 2.0, *Journal of Physics G Nuclear Physics* **43**, p. 084001 (August 2016).
19. N. Senno, K. Murase and P. Mészáros, Choked jets and low-luminosity gamma-ray bursts as hidden neutrino sources, *Phys. Rev. D* **93**, p. 083003 (April 2016).
20. F. Gonzalez and S. Yu, SVOM: a French/Chinese cooperation for a GRB mission, **10699**, p. 1069920 (July 2018).
21. K. Mercier, F. Gonzalez, M. Jouret-Perl, J.-L. Atteia, P. Mandrou, R. Pons, S. Basa, B. Cordier, D. Götz, F. Pinsard, S. Schanne, C. Lachaud, J. Wei and S. Zhang, The French payload on-board the SVOM French-Chinese mission, **9144**, p. 914422 (July 2014).
22. L. Chaoul, V. Mousset and G. Quenouille, Svom french ground segment : Mission, science & instrument centres.
23. Y. Dong, B. Wu, Y. Li, Y. Zhang and S. Zhang, SVOM gamma ray monitor, *Science China Physics, Mechanics, and Astronomy* **53**, 40 (January 2010).
24. D.-H. Zhao, B.-B. Wu, L.-M. Song, Y.-W. Dong, S. Schanne, B. Cordier and J.-T. Liu, Onboard GRB trigger algorithms of SVOM-GRM, *Research in Astronomy and Astrophysics* **13**, 1381 (November 2013).
25. X. Wen, J. Sun, J. He, R. Song, E. Wang, P. Zhou, Y. Dong, X. Liu, J. Liu, L. Li, H. Shi, R. Wang, B. Wu, L. Zhang and S. Zhang, Calibration study of the Gamma-Ray Monitor onboard the SVOM satellite, *Nuclear Instruments and Methods in Physics Research A* **1003**, p. 165301 (July 2021).
26. M. G. Bernardini, F. Xie, P. Sizun, F. Piron, Y. Dong, J. L. Atteia, S. Antier, F. Daigne, O. Godet, B. Cordier and J. Wei, Scientific prospects for spectroscopy of the gamma-ray burst prompt emission with SVOM, *Experimental Astronomy* **44**, 113 (October 2017).
27. A. von Kienlin, C. A. Meegan, W. S. Paciesas, P. N. Bhat, E. Bissaldi, M. S. Briggs, E. Burns, W. H. Cleveland, M. H. Gibby, M. M. Giles, A. Goldstein, R. Hamburg,

C. M. Hui, D. Kocevski, B. Mailyan, C. Malacaria, S. Poolakkil, R. D. Preece, O. J. Roberts, P. Veres and C. A. Wilson-Hodge, The Fourth Fermi-GBM Gamma-Ray Burst Catalog: A Decade of Data, *ApJ* **893**, p. 46 (April 2020).

28. O. Godet, G. Nasser, J. . Atteia, B. Cordier, P. Mandrou, D. Barret, H. Triou, R. Pons, C. Amoros, S. Bordon, O. Gevin, F. Gonzalez, D. Götz, A. Gros, B. Houret, C. Lachaud, K. Lacombe, W. Marty, K. Mercier, D. Rambaud, P. Ramon, G. Rouaix, S. Schanne and V. Waegebaert, The x-/gamma-ray camera ECLAIRs for the gamma-ray burst mission SVOM, **9144**, p. 914424 (July 2014).

29. S. Schanne, N. Dagoneau, F. Château, H. Le Provost, F. Daly, S. Anvar, S. Antier, A. Gros and B. Cordier, The SVOM ECLAIRs gamma-ray burst trigger, *Mem. Soc. Astron. Italiana* **90**, p. 267 (January 2019).

30. D. Götz, J. Osborne, B. Cordier, J. Paul, P. Evans, A. Beardmore, A. Martindale, R. Willingale, P. O'Brien, S. Basa, C. Rossin, O. Godet, N. Webb, J. Greiner, K. Nandra, N. Meidinger, E. Perinati, A. Santangelo, K. Mercier and F. Gonzalez, The microchannel x-ray telescope for the gamma-ray burst mission SVOM, **9144**, p. 914423 (July 2014).

31. K. Mercier, F. Gonzalez, D. Götz, M. Boutelier, N. Boufracha, V. Burwitz, M. C. Charmeau, P. Drumm, C. Feldman, A. Gomes, J. M. Le Duigou, N. Meidinger, A. Meuris, P. O'Brien, J. Osborne, P. Pasqier, L. Perraud, J. F. Pearson, F. Pinsard, E. Raynal and R. Willingale, MXT instrument on-board the French-Chinese SVOM mission, **10699**, p. 1069921 (July 2018).

32. C. Wu, Y. L. Qiu and H. B. Cai, SVOM Visible Telescope: Performance and Data Process Scheme, **279**, 421 (September 2012).

33. X. Fan, G. Zou, Y. Qiu, Z. Pang, H. Zhao, Q. Chen, Y. Pan and H. Yuan, Optical design of the visible telescope for the SVOM mission, *Appl. Opt.* **59**, p. 3049 (April 2020).

34. X. Han, Y. Xiao, P. Zhang, D. Turpin, L. Xin, C. Wu, H. Cai, W. Dong, L. Huang, Z. Kang, N. Leroy, H. Li, Z. Li, X. Lu, Y. Qiu, B. E. Stahl, J. Wang, X. Wang, Y. Xu, Y. Yang, Y. Zhao, R. Zhang, W. Zheng, Y. Zheng and J. Wei, The Automatic Observation Management System of the GWAC Network. I. System Architecture and Workflow, *PASP* **133**, p. 065001 (June 2021).

35. D. Turpin, C. Wu, X.-H. Han, L.-P. Xin, S. Antier, N. Leroy, L. Cao, H.-B. Cai, B. Cordier, J.-S. Deng, W.-L. Dong, Q.-C. Feng, L. Huang, L. Jia, A. Klotz, C. Lachaud, H.-L. Li, E.-W. Liang, S.-F. Liu, X.-M. Lu, X.-M. Meng, Y.-L. Qiu, H.-J. Wang, J. Wang, S. Wang, X.-G. Wang, J.-Y. Wei, B.-B. Wu, Y.-J. Xiao, D.-W. Xu, Y. Xu, Y.-G. Yang, P.-P. Zhang, R.-S. Zhang, S.-N. Zhang, Y.-T. Zheng and S.-C. Zou, The mini-GWAC optical follow-up of gravitational wave alerts - results from the O2 campaign and prospects for the upcoming O3 run, *Research in Astronomy and Astrophysics* **20**, p. 013 (January 2020).

36. D. Corre, S. Basa, A. Klotz, A. M. Watson, M. Ageron, P. Ambert, F. Ángeles, J. L. Atteia, P. E. Blanc, O. Boulade, J. Boy, E. Cadena, B. Cordier, S. Cuevas Cardona, F. Dolon, D. Dornic, D. Dubreuil, A. S. Farah, L. Figueroa, J. Floriot, J. Fuentes-Fernández, P. Gallais, E. Jiménez-Bailón, R. Langarica Lebre, J. F. Le Borgne, W. H. Lee, A. Le Van Suu, M. Marcos, R. Mathon, C. Meessen, J. L. Ochoa, E. Pallier, J. Platzer, F. Quirós, S. Ronayette, D. Turpin, H. Valentin and S. D. Vergani, End-to-end simulations for COLIBRI, ground follow-up telescope for the SVOM mission., **10705**, p. 107051R (July 2018).

37. B. Cordier, F. Desclaux, J. Foliard and S. Schanne, SVOM pointing strategy: how to optimize the redshift measurements?, **1000**, 585 (May 2008).

38. N. Dagoneau, S. Schanne, J. Rodriguez, J. L. Atteia and B. Cordier, Onboard catalogue of known X-ray sources for SVOM/ECLAIRs, *A&A* **645**, p. A18 (January 2021).
39. S. D. Barthelmy, P. Butterworth, T. L. Cline, N. Gehrels, F. Marshall, T. Takeshima, V. Connaughton, R. M. Kippen, C. Kouveliotou and C. R. Robinson, The GRB coordinates network (GCN): A status report, **428**, 99 (May 1998).
40. G. Li, S. Guo, J. Lv, K. Zhao and Z. He, Introduction to global short message communication service of beidou-3 navigation satellite system, *Advances in Space Research* **67**, 1701 (2021).
41. C. Barraud, J. F. Olive, J. P. Lestrade, J. L. Atteia, K. Hurley, G. Ricker, D. Q. Lamb, N. Kawai, M. Boer, J. P. Dezalay, G. Pizzichini, R. Vanderspek, G. Crew, J. Doty, G. Monnelly, J. Villasenor, N. Butler, A. Levine, A. Yoshida, Y. Shirasaki, T. Sakamoto, T. Tamagawa, K. Torii, M. Matsuoka, E. E. Fenimore, M. Galassi, T. Tavenner, T. Q. Donaghy, C. Graziani and J. G. Jernigan, Spectral analysis of 35 GRBs/XRFs observed with HETE-2/FREGATE, *A&A* **400**, 1021 (March 2003).
42. T. Sakamoto, D. Q. Lamb, N. Kawai, A. Yoshida, C. Graziani, E. E. Fenimore, T. Q. Donaghy, M. Matsuoka, M. Suzuki, G. Ricker, J. L. Atteia, Y. Shirasaki, T. Tamagawa, K. Torii, M. Galassi, J. Doty, R. Vanderspek, G. B. Crew, J. Villasenor, N. Butler, G. Prigozhin, J. G. Jernigan, C. Barraud, M. Boer, J. P. Dezalay, J. F. Olive, K. Hurley, A. Levine, G. Monnelly, F. Martel, E. Morgan, S. E. Woosley, T. Cline, J. Braga, R. Manchanda, G. Pizzichini, K. Takagishi and M. Yamauchi, Global Characteristics of X-Ray Flashes and X-Ray-Rich Gamma-Ray Bursts Observed by HETE-2, *ApJ* **629**, 311 (August 2005).
43. N. Dagoneau, S. Schanne, J.-L. Atteia, D. Götz and B. Cordier, Ultra-Long Gamma-Ray Bursts detection with SVOM/ECLAIRs, *Experimental Astronomy* **50**, 91 (July 2020).
44. MAGIC Collaboration, V. A. Acciari, S. Ansoldi, L. A. Antonelli, A. Arbet Engels, D. Baack, A. Babić, B. Banerjee, U. Barres de Almeida, J. A. Barrio, J. Becerra González, W. Bednarek, L. Bellizzi, E. Bernardini, A. Berti, J. Besenrieder, W. Bhattacharyya, C. Bigongiari, A. Biland, O. Blanch, G. Bonnoli, Ž. Bošnjak, G. Busetto, A. Carosi, R. Carosi, G. Ceribella, Y. Chai, A. Chilingaryan, S. Cikota, S. M. Colak, U. Colin, E. Colombo, J. L. Contreras, J. Cortina, S. Covino, G. D'Amico, V. D'Elia, P. da Vela, F. Dazzi, A. de Angelis, B. de Lotto, M. Delfino, J. Delgado, D. Depaoli, F. di Pierro, L. di Venere, E. Do Souto Espiñeira, D. Dominis Prester, A. Donini, D. Dorner, M. Doro, D. Elsaesser, V. Fallah Ramazani, A. Fattorini, A. Fernández-Barral, G. Ferrara, D. Fidalgo, L. Foffano, M. V. Fonseca, L. Font, C. Fruck, S. Fukami, S. Gallozzi, R. J. García López, M. Garczarczyk, S. Gasparyan, M. Gaug, N. Giglietto, F. Giordano, N. Godinović, D. Green, D. Guberman, D. Hadasch, A. Hahn, J. Herrera, J. Hoang, D. Hrupec, M. Hütten, T. Inada, S. Inoue, K. Ishio, Y. Iwamura, L. Jouvin, D. Kerszberg, H. Kubo, J. Kushida, A. Lamastra, D. Lelas, F. Leone, E. Lindfors, S. Lombardi, F. Longo, M. López, R. López-Coto, A. López-Oramas, S. Loporchio, B. Machado de Oliveira Fraga, C. Maggio, P. Majumdar, M. Makariev, M. Mallamaci, G. Maneva, M. Manganaro, K. Mannheim, L. Maraschi, M. Mariotti, M. Martínez, S. Masuda, D. Mazin, S. Mićanović, D. Miceli, M. Minev, J. M. Miranda, R. Mirzoyan, E. Molina, A. Moralejo, D. Morcuende, V. Moreno, E. Moretti, P. Munar-Adrover, V. Neustroev, C. Nigro, K. Nilsson, D. Ninci, K. Nishijima, K. Noda, L. Nogués, M. Nöthe, S. Nozaki, S. Paiano, J. Palacio, M. Palatiello, D. Paneque, R. Paoletti, J. M. Paredes, P. Peñil, M. Peresano, M. Persic, P. G. Prada Moroni, E. Prandini, I. Puljak, W. Rhode, M. Ribó, J. Rico, C. Righi, A. Rugliancich, L. Saha, N. Sahakyan, T. Saito, S. Sakurai, K. Satalecka, K. Schmidt, T. Schweizer, J. Sitarek,

I. Šnidarić, D. Sobczynska, A. Somero, A. Stamerra, D. Strom, M. Strzys, Y. Suda, T. Surić, M. Takahashi, F. Tavecchio, P. Temnikov, T. Terzić, M. Teshima, N. Torres-Albà, L. Tosti, S. Tsujimoto, V. Vagelli, J. van Scherpenberg, G. Vanzo, M. Vazquez Acosta, C. F. Vigorito, V. Vitale, I. Vovk, M. Will, D. Zarić and L. Nava, Teraelectronvolt emission from the γ-ray burst GRB 190114C, *Nature* **575**, 455 (November 2019).

45. H. Abdalla, R. Adam, F. Aharonian, F. Ait Benkhali, E. O. Angüner, M. Arakawa, C. Arcaro, C. Armand, H. Ashkar, M. Backes, V. Barbosa Martins, M. Barnard, Y. Becherini, D. Berge, K. Bernlöhr, E. Bissaldi, R. Blackwell, M. Böttcher, C. Boisson, J. Bolmont, S. Bonnefoy, J. Bregeon, M. Breuhaus, F. Brun, P. Brun, M. Bryan, M. Büchele, T. Bulik, T. Bylund, M. Capasso, S. Caroff, A. Carosi, S. Casanova, M. Cerruti, T. Chand, S. Chandra, A. Chen, S. Colafrancesco, M. Curyło, I. D. Davids, C. Deil, J. Devin, P. deWilt, L. Dirson, A. Djannati-Ataï, A. Dmytriiev, A. Donath, V. Doroshenko, J. Dyks, K. Egberts, G. Emery, J. P. Ernenwein, S. Eschbach, K. Feijen, S. Fegan, A. Fiasson, G. Fontaine, S. Funk, M. Füßling, S. Gabici, Y. A. Gallant, F. Gaté, G. Giavitto, L. Giunti, D. Glawion, J. F. Glicenstein, D. Gottschall, M. H. Grondin, J. Hahn, M. Haupt, G. Heinzelmann, G. Henri, G. Hermann, J. A. Hinton, W. Hofmann, C. Hoischen, T. L. Holch, M. Holler, D. Horns, D. Huber, H. Iwasaki, M. Jamrozy, D. Jankowsky, F. Jankowsky, A. Jardin-Blicq, I. Jung-Richardt, M. A. Kastendieck, K. Katarzyński, M. Katsuragawa, U. Katz, D. Khangulyan, B. Khélifi, J. King, S. Klepser, W. Kluźniak, N. Komin, K. Kosack, D. Kostunin, M. Kreter, G. Lamanna, A. Lemière, M. Lemoine-Goumard, J. P. Lenain, E. Leser, C. Levy, T. Lohse, I. Lypova, J. Mackey, J. Majumdar, D. Malyshev, V. Marandon, A. Marcowith, A. Mares, C. Mariaud, G. Martí-Devesa, R. Marx, G. Maurin, P. J. Meintjes, A. M. W. Mitchell, R. Moderski, M. Mohamed, L. Mohrmann, C. Moore, E. Moulin, J. Muller, T. Murach, S. Nakashima, M. de Naurois, H. Ndiyavala, F. Niederwanger, J. Niemiec, L. Oakes, P. O'Brien, H. Odaka, S. Ohm, E. de Ona Wilhelmi, M. Ostrowski, I. Oya, M. Panter, R. D. Parsons, C. Perennes, P. O. Petrucci, B. Peyaud, Q. Piel, S. Pita, V. Poireau, A. Priyana Noel, D. A. Prokhorov, H. Prokoph, G. Pühlhofer, M. Punch, A. Quirrenbach, S. Raab, R. Rauth, A. Reimer, O. Reimer, Q. Remy, M. Renaud, F. Rieger, L. Rinchiuso, C. Romoli, G. Rowell, B. Rudak, E. Ruiz-Velasco, V. Sahakian, S. Sailer, S. Saito, D. A. Sanchez, A. Santangelo, M. Sasaki, R. Schlickeiser, F. Schüssler, A. Schulz, H. M. Schutte, U. Schwanke, S. Schwemmer, M. Seglar-Arroyo, M. Senniappan, A. S. Seyffert, N. Shafi, K. Shiningayamwe, R. Simoni, A. Sinha, H. Sol, A. Specovius, M. Spir-Jacob, Ł. Stawarz, R. Steenkamp, C. Stegmann, C. Steppa, T. Takahashi, T. Tavernier, A. M. Taylor, R. Terrier, D. Tiziani, M. Tluczykont, C. Trichard, M. Tsirou, N. Tsuji, R. Tuffs, Y. Uchiyama, D. J. van der Walt, C. van Eldik, C. van Rensburg, B. van Soelen, G. Vasileiadis, J. Veh, C. Venter, P. Vincent, J. Vink, H. J. Völk, T. Vuillaume, Z. Wadiasingh, S. J. Wagner, R. White, A. Wierzcholska, R. Yang, H. Yoneda, M. Zacharias, R. Zanin, A. A. Zdziarski, A. Zech, A. Ziegler, J. Zorn, N. Żywucka, F. de Palma, M. Axelsson and O. J. Roberts, A very-high-energy component deep in the γ-ray burst afterglow, *Nature* **575**, 464 (November 2019).
46. J. Wang, Y.-L. Qiu and J.-Y. Wei, A pilot study of catching high-z GRBs and exploring circumburst environment in the forthcoming SVOM era, *Research in Astronomy and Astrophysics* **20**, p. 124 (August 2020).
47. M. Della Valle, G. Chincarini, N. Panagia, G. Tagliaferri, D. Malesani, V. Testa, D. Fugazza, S. Campana, S. Covino, V. Mangano, L. A. Antonelli, P. D'Avanzo, K. Hurley, I. F. Mirabel, L. J. Pellizza, S. Piranomonte and L. Stella, An enigmatic

long-lasting γ-ray burst not accompanied by a bright supernova, *Nature* **444**, 1050 (December 2006).
48. J. P. U. Fynbo, D. Watson, C. C. Thöne, J. Sollerman, J. S. Bloom, T. M. Davis, J. Hjorth, P. Jakobsson, U. G. Jørgensen, J. F. Graham, A. S. Fruchter, D. Bersier, L. Kewley, A. Cassan, J. M. Castro Cerón, S. Foley, J. Gorosabel, T. C. Hinse, K. D. Horne, B. L. Jensen, S. Klose, D. Kocevski, J.-B. Marquette, D. Perley, E. Ramirez-Ruiz, M. D. Stritzinger, P. M. Vreeswijk, R. A. M. Wijers, K. G. Woller, D. Xu and M. Zub, No supernovae associated with two long-duration γ-ray bursts, *Nature* **444**, 1047 (December 2006).
49. A. Gal-Yam, D. B. Fox, P. A. Price, E. O. Ofek, M. R. Davis, D. C. Leonard, A. M. Soderberg, B. P. Schmidt, K. M. Lewis, B. A. Peterson, S. R. Kulkarni, E. Berger, S. B. Cenko, R. Sari, K. Sharon, D. Frail, D. S. Moon, P. J. Brown, A. Cucchiara, F. Harrison, T. Piran, S. E. Persson, P. J. McCarthy, B. E. Penprase, R. A. Chevalier and A. I. MacFadyen, A novel explosive process is required for the γ-ray burst GRB 060614, *Nature* **444**, 1053 (December 2006).
50. N. Gehrels, J. P. Norris, S. D. Barthelmy, J. Granot, Y. Kaneko, C. Kouveliotou, C. B. Markwardt, P. Mészáros, E. Nakar, J. A. Nousek, P. T. O'Brien, M. Page, D. M. Palmer, A. M. Parsons, P. W. A. Roming, T. Sakamoto, C. L. Sarazin, P. Schady, M. Stamatikos and S. E. Woosley, A new γ-ray burst classification scheme from GRB060614, *Nature* **444**, 1044 (December 2006).
51. M. J. MichałowskI, D. Xu, J. Stevens, A. Levan, J. Yang, Z. Paragi, A. Kamble, A.-L. Tsai, H. Dannerbauer, A. J. van der Horst, L. Shao, D. Crosby, G. Gentile, E. Stanway, K. Wiersema, J. P. U. Fynbo, N. R. Tanvir, P. Kamphuis, M. Garrett and P. Bartczak, The second-closest gamma-ray burst: sub-luminous GRB 111005A with no supernova in a super-solar metallicity environment, *A&A* **616**, p. A169 (September 2018).
52. B. Arcier, J. L. Atteia, O. Godet, S. Mate, S. Guillot, N. Dagoneau, J. Rodriguez, D. Gotz, S. Schanne and M. G. Bernardini, Detection of short high-energy transients in the local universe with SVOM/ECLAIRs, *Ap&SS* **365**, p. 185 (December 2020).

Quantum field theory with boundary conditions at the horizons[*]

Gerard 't Hooft

Faculty of Science, Department of Physics,
Institute for Theoretical Physics,
Princetonplein 5, 3584 CC Utrecht, The Netherlands
g.thooft@uu.nl

A procedure to derive a unitary evolution law for a quantised black hole has been proposed by the author. The proposal implies several assumptions, which seem almost unavoidable to this author. We start off with the question how to describe the energy eigenstates of a black hole. The background metric required for this cannot be the Vaidya metric let alone the metric proposed by Hawking, who included the effect of the final evaporation of the black hole. This however leads to the formation if firewalls at both the future and the past event horizon, unless one anticipates the effects that the firewalls have. These effects can be handled as new boundary conditions at the horizons, describing the flow of the participating particles. It is subsequently explained how these boundary conditions must involve the antipodes of the outside world. Imposing unitarity and continuity then automatically leads to a unique, unitary evolution operator. We exhibit the resulting, quite coherent picture.

Keywords: Quantum black hole; past and future event horizon; firewall; Penrose diagram; eternal black hole; time slices; entanglement; vector representation; Shapiro shift; Cauchy surface; boundary condition; antipodal identification.

1. Introduction

There is a general agreement that a theoretical study of black holes in a regime, where quantum mechanical effects play a role, is important for a more complete understanding of general relativity and/or some modifications of this theme, in its relation to quantum mechanics.[1,2] There are several problems and disagreements, however. What is the classical limit from where one should start adding quantum corrections? The first thing many investigators assume is that there is a classical metric describing a black hole from beginning to end, and after that, the dynamical variables should be subject to some quantum mechanical replacement.[3] This should give the "quantum black hole".

However, there is a difficulty concerning the way these quantum variables would evolve. First, in accordance with the no-hair theorem, the evolution of these

---

[*]Based on a talk presented at the Sixteenth Marcel Grossmann Meeting on Recent Developments in Theoretical and Experimental General Relativity, Astrophysics and Relativistic Field Theories, online, July 2021.

"quantum corrections" would quickly fade away, together with all other quantum field theoretical degrees of freedom. There seems to be just a single state that survives: the Hartle–Hawking state.[4] We do have evolution in this Hartle–Hawking state in a quantum mechanical manner, which is why investigators did continue along such directions, but, entanglement or not, only a single state seems to survive, and this appears to be incompatible with unitarity.

Second, if there is a quantum mechanical evolution law, it should also apply both during the initial implosion and the final puff of the evaporation process. These depend on quantum processes, and demanding their tie evolution to be fixed destroys unitarity.

Third, the quantum states will be entangled with particles entering or leaving the scene far from the black hole.

There is a way out of these difficulties, which is to consider more carefully how ingoing particles assemble near the past event horizon, and how the emitted Hawking particles are prepared near the future event horizon. They form what has become to be known as *firewalls*.[5–7] This is the subject of the present investigation. Already years ago, the author reported about what seems to be considerable progress along these lines,[8] but there continue to be communication barriers that should be overcome.

Particle states emerging from the past event horizon will be shown here to generate a rich spectrum of different possible quantum states of out-going particles, and, considering the equally rich spectrum of in-going particles, the quantum mechanical interactions between the two horizons can be seen to restore unitarity.

There will be limitations to what we can do presently, as will be briefly explained later.

2. The Background Metric

The Penrose diagram[9,10] for the eternal black hole is depicted in Fig. 1(a). This diagram is the unique analytic extension of the Schwarzschild metric that solves Einstein's equations without matter effects added. In line of arguments just sketched above, and clarified further below, this is the only metric that we believe can be used for the quantum theory.

The metric often considered in quantum speculations for black holes, is the Vaidya metric of the kind sketched in Fig. 1(b). It was suspected to be superior since it includes the black hole formation process, so it may seem to contain more freely adjustable parameters that can be subject to quantisation.

Adding to that the gravitational effects of the Hawking evaporation, Hawking proposed to substitute this by Fig. 1(c). This diagram,[11] like the others, has the singularity at $r = 0$ absorbing in-going material, which is problematic since unitarity would demand information to be returned in the entire process. Anyway, one should

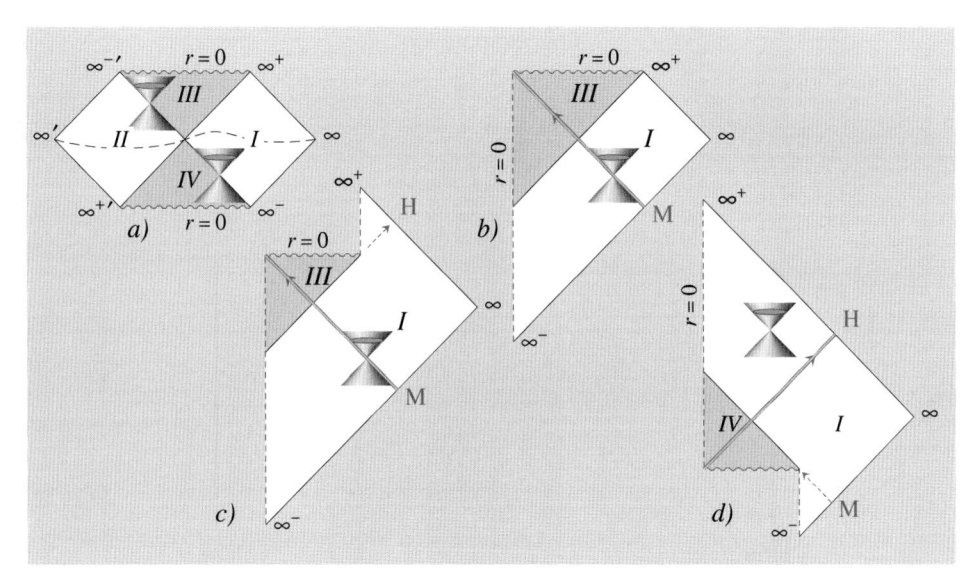

Fig. 1. Different Penrose diagrams for the Schwarzschild black hole. M stands for matter moving in, H for Hawking radiation going out. See text.

realise that the underlying equations, both for general relativity and for quantum mechanics, are invariant under time reversal, so that Fig. 1(d) should at least be considered as possibility as well.

We shall later conclude that only Fig. 1(a) can be used for the quantum process, but the arguments will be more convincing after we have treated the details of our theory. At this point, let us emphasise here that Fig. 1(a) for the eternal black hole is the most suitable one to use for the description of the stationary modes of a black hole, in particular its energy eigenstates, which make use of beams of in-going and out-going particles asymptotically far away, so as to make up for the evaporation.

To set up our program, we momentarily return to Schwarzschild coordinates, we divide the Schwarzschild time coordinate t in equal slices, each lasting for at most one period $\Delta t \approx M_{\rm BH}$ in Planck units, see Fig. 2. Within each of these time slices, the physical variables are defined to consist of all standard model particles and the slightly hidden degrees of freedom such as dark matter and gravitons. These particles are following their (quantum) trajectories, but, and this is essential for our procedure, particles that venture too close to either the future or the past horizon, will *not* be included. The idea is that such particles will become more manifestly observable in future or past slices (where they belong).

This paper is about stitching these slices back together in order to get the complete picture. Particularly at the horizons, this is a nontrivial procedure.

There may be some misunderstanding as to the quantum state of the Hawking particles. The Hawking particles are seen to be entangled, and as such it may appear

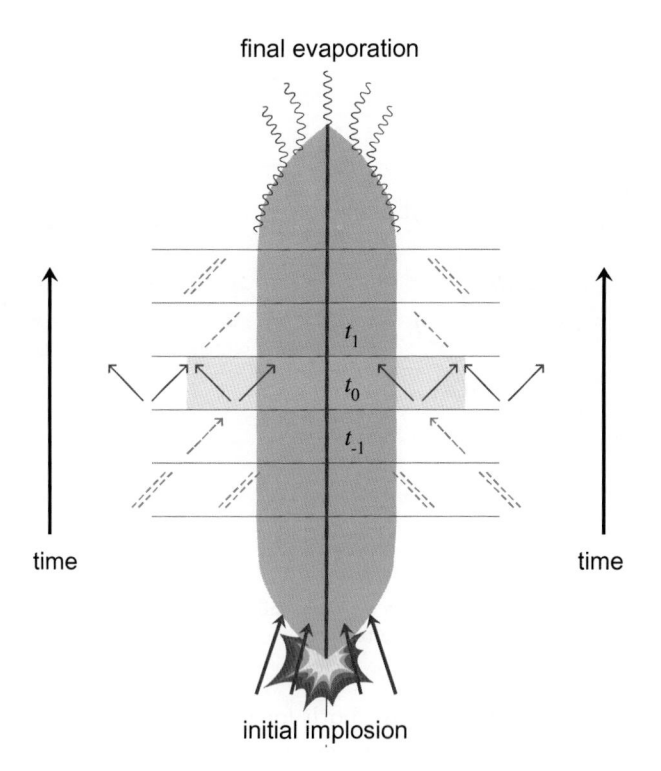

Fig. 2. Slicing the Schwarzschild coordinates in sequences of short periods. The quantum variables can be defined on each slice, lasting not longer than $\mathcal{O}(M_{\text{BH}})$ in Planck units.

that they can only form a single quantum state. This happens only, however, if none of the Hawking particles are subject to observation, and if nothing is thrown into the black hole for large stretches in time. This will become more clear below.[a]

Quantum field theory (QFT), projected on this background of time-slices, will reveal how particles propagate and interact. At any safe distance (of the order of a couple of Planck lengths), the outcomes of QFT calculations will be decisive as to what happens. Up to this point, it should be clear that the metric of an eternal black hole serves just fine as a background.

However, particles inevitably will approach the horizons more closely. There are particles entering the future event horizon, and particles emerging from the past event horizon. A theory is needed that *dictates* how particles appear out of the past horizon, and how, if at all, this is determined by the in-going ones.

At this point, it seems that Hawking's original calculation[1] cannot be the entire story since it puts all out-particles into just one state, the Hartle–Hawking state.

---

[a]For a better understanding of these aspects of quantum mechanics, it may be helpful to view quantum mechanics itself as a *vector representation* of physically observable objects, see the author's ideas about this, in Refs. 12 and 13.

In contrast, we expect that different states of particles entering the future horizon should lead to different states of out-particles.

It suffices to produce a prescription that holds just for a few Planck lengths away from the intersection point of future and past event horizons. There, we expect "something" that causes in-particles to bounce against, or turn into, out-particles. So-far, in this treatment, we have only used the physically accessible or observable part of the Schwarzschild metric. Quantum gravity has been used only in its perturbative regime, so it only enters in the form of some stray gravitons. But now, this is going to change.

What has been found is that *interactions* between in- and out-particles can do the job. We need interactions that become sufficiently strong only at tiny distances. Which force acts more strongly at close distances than the renormalizable interactions in the Standard Model? Of course, the answer is: the gravitational force.

3. The In–Out Interaction Caused by Gravity

Indeed, the gravitational effect of an in-going particle on an out-going one is that the wave function of the out-particle is modified. This is illustrated in Fig. 3: the dashed arrowline marked "in", going through the future event horizon very early in time, carries a large momentum δp^-. Coming from region (IV) in the diagram, a Hawking particle was on its way out (wiggled line marked "out"). Due to δp^-, a shock wave[14] from the in-particle drags the out-particle along, displacing it by a distance δu^-, which is proportional to δp^- and a Green function $F(\theta)$ depending on the transverse, angular, distance θ between the particles. This function $F(\theta)$ has been calculated.[15]

This effect is closely related to the Shapiro effect,[16] the fact that a light or radio signal from an astrophysical source or a spacecraft, grazing the Sun, experiences a delay due the solar gravitational field. All Hawking particles are delayed in a different way, depending on their transverse positions, and so it happens that the entire quantum state describing the out-particles is modified.

The modification operator is easy to calculate, in principle

$$U = e^{i\delta p^- \sum_{\text{out}} p^+_{\text{out}} GF(\theta_{\text{out}})} = e^{i \sum_{\text{in,out}} p^+_{\text{out}} p^-_{\text{in}} GF(\theta_{\text{out}}, \varphi_{\text{out}}, \theta_{\text{in}}, \varphi_{\text{in}})},$$
(3.1)

where G is Newton's constant, and furthermore, in the second part we replaced δp^- by $\sum_{\text{in}} p^-_{\text{in}}$ since *all* in-particles have this effect on *all* out-particles.

It must be emphasised that the dependence of U on the in-particle momenta increases exponentially with Schwarzschild time, because, the later the time t where we study the particles in the background metric, the closer the older in-particles squeeze against the past horizon, so the larger their influence will be. The very first in-particles in fact were the particles that formed the black hole by imploding. Since they came in very early, their exponentiated in-momenta p^- are gigantic, in terms

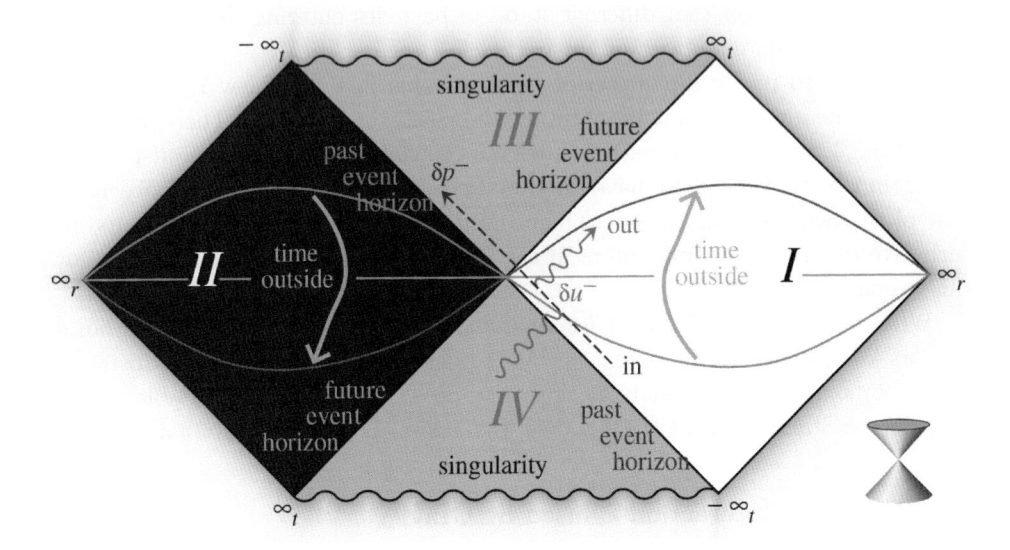

Fig. 3. The Penrose diagram for the eternal black hole, see text. Light cones everywhere in the diagram are oriented the same way as the one shown.

of the Penrose coordinates for the particles later in time, *but this is nothing to worry about*: they caused the wave functions of the early out particles to be separated by equally large separation variables u^-_{out}.

The increase of u^- changes from exponential to linear in time as soon as the out-particles move out of the direct gravitational influence of the black hole. They are joining the other distant out-particles that no longer play any role for us. Our complete quantum states of course include the early out-going particles, and our calculations show that they are entangled with the later particles, but from this moment onwards we can just re-arrange the basis of quantum states for the out-particles, and describe their wave functions any way we please.

The reader may have felt something strange in the emerging picture: the time dependence of all particle states is such that the outgoing particles move away exponentially from the past and future event horizons, but there are *two* regions in which they can escape. The Penrose diagram used so-far is twice the size of the universe that we usually consider as the home universe of this black hole. We labelled these two regions (I) and (II) in Fig. 3. What happens to a particle that makes its way out in region (II)? If we ignore it, we make a mistake. The operator U derived in Eq. (3.1) is the operator for the Fourier transform (apart from the Green function F that will be treated later). *The Fourier transformation process is unitary*, which means that we can use it to describe a unitary quantum evolution of the black hole, *but it is only unitary if we consider in- and out-wave functions to cover the entire line* $[-\infty, +\infty]$, and not just the half-lines that form the boundaries of region (I) or region (II) of a black hole.

Indeed, the Shapiro effect can easily transport the geodesic of a particle across the other horizon. This is the real reason why we are destined to use the entire, double, Penrose diagram for our considerations. Before disclosing the *physical* role of region (II), we sketch the picture obtained so-far.

A time boost for an outside observer, $t \Rightarrow t + \Delta t$, corresponds to a *Lorentz boost*, $(u^+, u^-) \Rightarrow (u^+ e^{-t/4GM_{\text{BH}}}, u^- e^{t/4GM_{\text{BH}}})$ for an observer close to the origin of this diagram. This implies that Cauchy surfaces for the particles in the regions (I) and (II) take the shape of the green curve in Fig. 3, that evolves into and beyond the red curve as time continues.

The Cauchy surfaces never enter into the regions (III) or (IV) in the Penrose diagram. They pivot around the origin. This is where our procedure contrasts with other work.[3]

However, we do have to pay for this — in an interesting way. Our general finding is that, when particles go into and out of the black hole, they cause shifts along the horizons. During black hole formation, these shifts are large. Effectively, we are using the eternal Penrose diagram, but the *boundary conditions*, by which the horizons connect different domains of the spacetime metric, are strongly affected by the gravitational force: the Shapiro effect.

Now, we have to address the question what region (II) stands for physically. It cannot just be ignored. It also cannot just be there to describe another black hole. That other black hole would not only be strongly entangled with the first one, as some investigators argue, but the two black holes exchange information. Entangled particles do *not* exchange information without violating locality.

Mathematically, it is easy to "cure" our theory. We have to find an isometry transformation in spacetime, whose square is the identity. We can write it as $\mathbb{Z}_2$. One such transformation is the identity itself, or, regions (I) and (II) are then assumed to represent the same spacetime. Our problem is then that this does not work since the Shapiro shift would not commute with such a mapping, or, it would generate cusp singularities near the origin. However, such cusp singularities do not arise if we accompany the $\mathbb{Z}_2$ mapping with an antipodal mapping:

$$(\theta, \varphi) \leftrightarrow (\pi - \theta, \varphi + \pi). \tag{3.2}$$

In flat Minkowski spacetime, this would also generate a cusp singularity at the origin, but for Schwarzschild (and its rotating and charged relatives), it does not. This is because in the entire spacetime that we are using, $r \geq 2\text{GM}_{\text{BH}}$ so that angular positions never come close to their antipodes. Only deep inside the regions (III) and (IV), $r \to 0$, and points coincide with their antipodes. We never venture more than infinitesimal distances into these unphysical regions.

Nevertheless, at the beginning of this paragraph, we put the word "cure" in quotation marks. The fact that a solution looks mathematically pleasing does not automatically mean that it embodies the physical solution.

This antipodal mapping procedure may help us to avoid the "quantum no-cloning" condition, but does it? We do see a potential danger. In region (II), compared with the time variable for a local observer, the arrow of time for the distant observer will flip over. *Time runs backwards there!* This means that, if, near the antipodes, an observer sees a particle, the same particle will appear to move backwards in time, or, have negative energy, when viewed by an observer in region (II).

Our resolution to that problem is to redefine energy by a constant. A particle in region (II) has energy $E_{\text{II}} = E^{\max} - E_{\text{I}}$, where $E^{\max}$ is the *energy of the "antivacuum" state*. The antivacuum is the state completely filled with particles, having the largest possible amount of energy.

Better understanding is obtained by adhering to expansions in partial harmonics, item 9 in the next section, but this we leave for future considerations.

4. On the Complete Theory

We hope the above can serve as a more elaborate explanation as to the various ingredients for a consistent theory of quantum black holes. It can be viewed as a "package deal": there are several postulates that by now sound natural and unavoidable by this author, but seem to meet with considerable skepticism from other researchers:

(1) Up to a few Planck lengths from the horizon, matter particles may be handled using conventional quantum field theory, only during small time steps, each lasting for the "scrambling time", $T_{\text{scrambl}} = \mathcal{O}(M_{\text{BH}})$. This is far too short to include collapsing matter or late evaporation. These would act as projection operators that ruin unitarity. In practice, we can only handle modest amounts of matter going in and/or out during any of these short time spans.
(2) One has to use the metric of the eternal black hole as background.
(3) The metric must be divided by $\mathbb{Z}_2$, to restore a single asymptotic region.
(4) The only way to do that is by *antipodal identification*.
(5) Time outside runs *backwards* in region (II). This implies that the local states to be compared with the black hole states must approach the *antivacuum* in region (II). Creating a particle near the black hole corresponds to creating a particle in (I) or annihilating a particle in (II).
(6) During the time stretch around time $t \approx t_0$ for the distant observer, in-particles at $t \ll t_0$ are seen to generate a Shapiro shift along the past event horizon; out-particles at $t \gg t_0$ generate Shapiro shift along future event horizon.
These form *firewalls* that can be removed by re-arranging the corrections at the horizons (cut-and-paste procedures that effectively modify the boundary conditions there).
(7) This links the *positions* of the out particles to the momenta on the in-particles, and *vice versa*. That opens the way to define a unitary evolution law.
(8) Initial imploding matter and the final evaporating matter have decisive effects at the horizons; rather than merely shifting the geodesics, these may *initiate*

the links between the antipodes there. Initial and final black holes are mere *seeds*, to be described as gravitational *instantons*. This is as yet a suspicion; it is not known how to substantiate that with calculations.

(9) To do explicit calculations, it is advisable to expand the in-going momenta and the out-going momenta or positions at the horizons in *spherical harmonics* for optimal use of linearity of the equations. The Green function $F(\theta, \varphi, \theta', \varphi')$ then diagonalises, much like Schrödinger's equation for the hydrogen atom.

Note that these spherical harmonics are not to be confused; in our case, we are dealing with *operators*. Since these operators involve all of the in-going and out-going particles, it is not appropriate to try to "second quantise" them. At every (ℓ, m), we have only one position operator and one momentum operator.

The mathematics works correctly only when these views are all combined. In particular, we may *only* compare states in a background metric to states as seen from the outside, if the mapping on the Cauchy surfaces is 1 to 1.

This enforced the antipodal mapping (it cannot be avoided).

Note that this mapping keeps all information visible on the Cauchy surfaces; we have no information loss.

The procedure described above can lead to an accurately defined scattering matrix linking every in-state to an out state in a unitary manner. Unitarity may follow because, at every (ℓ, m) mode, where ℓ must be odd because of the antipodal identification, the Fourier transformation is a unitary operation.

It is important to emphasise that the Shapiro effect only acts on energy and momentum, not on other quantum numbers. This means that further analysis is needed to establish how data other than positions and momenta are transported across horizons.

Thus, we are not yet ready to consider the complete Standard Model to describe the interactions in the immediate vicinity of the black hole. This is somewhat reminiscent to the situation in string theory. This theory also requires first to characterise all its excited states in terms of momentum and/or position operators, while its relation with the Standard Model can only be established by extensive studies of the relevant symmetry groups and algebras.

A new energetic generation of young students and ambitious postdocs is asked for to continue research along these lines.

References

1. S. W. Hawking, *Commun. Math. Phys.* **43** (1975) 199.
2. G. 't Hooft, *Nucl. Phys. B* **256** (1985) 727.
3. S. B. Giddings, *Phys. Lett. B* **754** (2016) 39, https://doi.org/10.1016/j.physletb.2015.12.076.
4. J. B. Hartle and S. W. Hawking, *Phys. Rev. D* **13** (1976) 2188.
5. A. Almheiri, D. Marolf, J. Polchinski and J. Sully, *J. High Energy Phys.* **1302** (2013) 062, arXiv:1207.3123 [hep-th].
6. D. Marolf, *Rept. Prog. Phys.* **80** (2017) 092001, arXiv:1703.02143 [gr-qc].

7. J. Polchinski, arXiv:1609.04036 [hep-th].
8. G. 't Hooft, *Foundations Phys.* **47** (2017) 1503, arXiv:1612.08640 [gr-qc].
9. R. Penrose, *Phys. Rev. Lett.* **10** (1963) 66.
10. S. W. Hawking and G. F. R. Ellis, *The Large Scale Structure of Space-time* (Cambridge University Press, Cambridge, 1973).
11. J. B. Hartle, *Generalized Quantum Theory and Black Hole Evaporation*, in *Black Holes and High Energy Astrophysics*, eds. H. Sato and N. Sugiyama (Universal Academy Press, Tokyo, 1998), arXiv:grqc/9808070.
12. G. 't Hooft, *The Cellular Automaton Interpretation of Quantum Mechanics*, Fundamental Theories of Physics, Vol. 185 (Springer International Publishing, 2016), http://arxiv.org/abs/1405.1548.
13. G. 't Hooft, arXiv:2103.04335[quant-ph].
14. P. C. Aichelburg and R. U. Sexl, *Gen. Relativ. Gravit.* **2** (1971) 303.
15. T. Dray and G. 't Hooft, *Nucl. Phys. B* **253** (1985) 173.
16. I. I. Shapiro, *Phys. Rev. Lett.* **13** (1964) 789.

The development of general relativity and the cosmological constant

Asghar Qadir
Abdus Salam School of Mathematical Sciences
Government College University Lahore, Pakistan
E-mail: asgharqadir46@gmail.com

There is much talk of a "mysterious form of energy", called "dark energy" that forms the bulk of the energy content of the Universe. Perhaps the most mysterious aspect of it is why it should be regarded as mysterious in the first place. This question is discussed in the context of the development of relativity and relativistic cosmology. It will be argued that there is no good reason to treat it as other than Einstein's cosmological constant.

Keywords: Cosmological constant; dark energy; geodesic equation; geodesic deviation; Einstein equations; Planck units; vacuum energy.

1. Introduction

It is often taken that there is no need to hark back to a subject and one only needs to consider current developments. However, people like Julian Barbour[1] point out that the past debates and the process of the development of a subject might provide the correct direction in which to proceed. He was talking of the problem of combining quantum theory and general relativity, which has not been achieved despite the best efforts of the best scientists for about a century. This problem is at the base of, or contributes significantly to, many other important problems that Physics is facing today. I would agree with Barbour that when we are so badly stuck, we should look back to see where we took a wrong turn. Very often we do not realize that some hidden assumptions have been made and proceed forward in various erroneous directions. We should look back lest, in our headlong rush forward, we miss the lessons lying in the past. This is especially true if it is argued that we cannot require experimental verification because it is beyond our current technology, and must instead rely on the concept of "naturalness" — reminiscent of Aristotle's "self-evident truths". This argument is appealed to for the attempted merger of the two major theories, which have so far resisted a union — the so-called "quantum-gravity problem". The problem is exacerbated by the current trend to publish as much as possible, which encourages wild speculation, instead of scientific progress based on adequate experimental evidence. One might fruitfully apply the same caution, to look back, for other recent developments.

I am, here, concerned with the so-called "dark-energy problem". In an attempt to see significant effects of his general theory of relativity, Albert Einstein applied it to the Universe in the large.[2] The equations in his seminal paper on general relativity[3] implied a non-static Universe, and he firmly believed that it should be static (see[4] for a more detailed explanation of why he believed it). In this paper he added a constant to his Lagrangian and obtained a static Universe model. However, in 1929 Edwin Hubble found that further away galaxies are redder. Treating the reddening as a Doppler shift, he deduced the Hubble Law,[5] that galaxies are generally receding from us at a rate proportional to their distance. (Einstein called his modification "the greatest blunder of my life".) This fitted with Friedmann's solutions for Einstein's field equations,[6] which provided three universe models: two expanding forever; and one contracting later; but all expanding at more or less the same decreasing rate currently. Thus, if the scaling factor for the distance between galaxies is given by $a(t)$, the Hubble parameter that relates the speed of expansion with the distance is $H = \dot{a}(t)/a(t)$. As the scale is increasing this is positive. However, the dimensionless acceleration $q = a(t)\ddot{a}(t)/\dot{a}^2(t)$, would be negative. For the model which contracts later, H would become zero later, and then negative.

Observations strongly supported the Friedmann models, but the fact that the Universe consists mainly of hydrogen and helium and all other elements are essentially "cooked" in stars, seemed to be a stumbling block in the theory till George Gamow[7] suggested that there must have been radiation in the early Universe that stopped nucleosynthesis but allowed some deuterium, tritium, helium$_3$ and normal helium to form. Later observations further supported the Friedmann open model.[8] Gamow's "hot big bang model predicted that there would then be a remnant of that radiation still left over as the Universe cooled. A rough estimate was of 3°K. It was confirmed in 1965 when Penzias and Wilson discovered a microwave background radiation,[9] which turned out be in a Planck spectrum, as predicted. Fitting the observed primordial abundance of elements with the radiation gave very precise estimates of the amount of baryonic matter in the early Universe.

In 1997 new observations of the further reaches of the Universe, obtained by studying type Ia supernovae, indicated that the Universe is expanding at an exponential rate.[10,11] As it happens, much earlier in 1927, Georges Lemaître[12] had independently derived the Friedmann solutions, but with an extra feature allowing for an exponential expansion in later times. He had derived the solution using Einstein's equations with a cosmological constant. This was what Perlmutter and Reiss[10,11] had referred to. Nevertheless, a flurry of papers appeared in the journals about evidence for a "mysterious form of dark energy", despite the fact that Riess' paper explicitly mentions the cosmological constant. In this paper I will try to demonstrate that it is because of not looking back to the past, that theory is still blundering down *dark* blind alleys, instead of accepting the obvious solution. It is that, and *the dark side of the force*, forcing many people to publish many papers. The current standard model of cosmology[13] is called the ΛCDM model, the CDM stands for "Cold Dark Matter" — and the "Λ" is Einstein's "greatest blunder"!

2. Generalizing Special Relativity

Soon after Einstein published his paper on special relativity,[14] his one-time teacher Hermann Minkowski (whose classes he had skipped), wrote the theory in terms of a four-dimensional spacetime (a space with an indefinite metric).[15] Einstein was not pleased with the development at the time, regarding the physics of the theory as being obfuscated by the mathematical formalism. However, the theory was restricted to uniform linear motion, and he needed to generalize it. On considering small accelerations along the direction of motion he was able to derive the physical consequence of a deflection of light due to gravity, which amounts to a bending of a straight line by acceleration. He considered uniform circular motion and found that it entailed a change in the geometry implying that one needed non-Euclidean geometry (see for example[16] for an explanation of the reasoning).

Isaac Newton[17] had defined the world-view that held sway before Einstein, according to which there is an absolute space and an absolute time, whereby space exists in itself independent of any matter or any observer in it. God was explicitly given the role of the Universal observer to provide reality to space. Time was taken to "flow at a constant rate". What sense would that phrase make? A stream can flow at a constant rate, meaning that in equal intervals of time the particles in the stream would flow equal distance. How could points of *time* flow at a constant rate in equal units of *time*? When Einstein had challenged this so-called "common sense" view with his special theory, non-physicists found it impossible to come to terms with the new view. However, while he challenged the absolute time more directly, and allowed lengths to decrease for moving observers, he had not altered the basic picture of a rigid grid. With a change of geometry that picture would become untenable. Before the Newtonian revolution, the world-view of Aristotle (c. 350 BC) held sway. In that view, space only existed as the distance between bodies. To give it reality, Aristotle had postulated an all-pervading aether. Further, time only gave a chronology of events, and precise measures of time were not assumed. If Newton's absolute grid had to go, then we should expect space to be defined by its matter content. Measures of space and time would depend on the procedures specified to measure them and would not be automatically defined.

Einstein had another problem, this time with Newton's law of gravitation. According to it, if a body moves away from its position, another body will *instantaneously* feel the change in the gravitational force between the two bodies. However, this militates against the basic precept of his special theory, as *all* information must obey the speed of light limit. Somehow, Aristotle's aether would be needed. However, he had managed to get rid of the luminiferous aether. As such, the spacetime would have to carry the information across at a speed limited by that of light. Instead of being Newton's rigid grid, or a rotated version of it (causing distances to appear shrunk), Einstein needed a more malleable spacetime that could be distorted by its matter content. Over time it became clear to him that he needed to use the geometry taught by Minkowski that he had skipped.

3. The Einstein-Grossmann Collaboration

Einstein had already arrived at the key to his generalization by, what he had called "the happiest thought of my life". This was the realization that gravity would not be felt in a freely falling frame, since all objects would fall together, as Galileo had shown. Hence, in that frame a ball released would not fall but float. This led him to a prediction of the bending of light by gravity,[18] as an experimenter in a fixed frame would see light sent across a falling lift hit the other side lower than if the lift is falling.[16] The effect turns out to be half what he later derived from the full general theory. He proposed that the effect could be seen by looking at the bending of the light from a star near the edge of the solar disc, seen during a full solar eclipse. (Fortunately for him, World War I broke out and prevented the expedition to observe the solar eclipse in South America. By the time it finally became possible, he had the correct answer.) In that paper he also obtained the gravitational red-shift, which is unaltered in the full theory. However, the effect is so small that it was not till 1956 (after Einstein's death) that the experiment could actually be performed and not till 1959 that the effect was finally verified.[19]

His friend, Marcel Grossmann (who is commemorated in these meetings) had not only attended Minkowski's lectures, but was proficient in non-Euclidean geometry, so Einstein asked him to help. Though Einstein had tried other non-Euclidean extensions of Geometry, Grossmann taught him Riemann's extension using differential calculus — what is nowadays called differential, or Riemannian, geometry. This turned out to be especially fruitful. Though "the happiest thought" had come earlier, in many ways "the happiest *development*" came in the first paper of their collaboration,[20] where Newtonian's scalar gravitational potential is replaced by the geometrical metric tensor. Thus *the spacetime itself becomes the medium to carry the gravitational field*, participating in dynamics as was needed. This set the base for the theory. In it, the gravitational "force" is nothing but the curvature of the four-dimensional spacetime. Paths are bent due to the warping of the spacetime, rather than a mysterious force acting instantaneously from a distance. In the second paper of the collaboration,[21] the basic field equations were set up and shown to be covariant. This was well before the derivation of the equations from a variational principle. In it, the Einstein tensor was defined by using the divergence-free condition for the conservation of the stress-energy tensor and the second Bianchi identities. However, they limited themselves to those transformations that left the determinant of the metric tensor invariant. In other words, instead of the symmetry group being $GL(4)$, $SL(4)$ was used. Since that reduces one of the degrees of freedom, the field equations were not correctly identified there.

There remains a crucial step in obtaining the field equations that was not made explicit in their derivation. How do we suddenly jump to relating the curvature tensor to the stress-energy tensor, without it coming from the bending of the path due to the presence of matter-energy as the warping of the spacetime? I will derive them the way I think Einstein must have done, but unfortunately left hidden.

4. Derivation of the Einstein Field Equations by Using Geodesic Deviation

To follow the argument, one needs to think of one of a family of observers looking at another observer of the same family, i.e. both in the same frame. I hope the reader will bear with me while I go through basic differential geometry, so that the reasoning can be seen in full clarity. The observers will follow *geodesics*, the straightest available paths. If the tangent vector to the path is **t**, treating it as a derivative operator, $\mathbf{t}(\mathbf{t}) = 0$, so that the direction does not change, i.e. $d\mathbf{t}/ds = 0$. This is the *geodesic equation*. In terms of the components of **t**, $t^a = dx^a/ds$, where x^a is the position vector of the observer, the geodesic equation is $t^b t^a_{;b} = 0$, where the summation convention that repeated indices are summed over, has been used and ";" is the covariant derivative, $t^a_{;b} = t^a_{,b} + \Gamma^a_{bc} t^c$, "," being the partial derivative $\partial/\partial x^a$. Thus, in this index notation, the geodesic equation becomes

$$\ddot{x}^a + \Gamma^a_{bc} \dot{x}^b \dot{x}^c = 0 , \tag{1}$$

where Γ^a_{bc} is the Christoffel symbol, given in terms of the metric tensor, g_{bc}, by

$$\Gamma^a_{bc} = \Gamma^a_{cb} = \frac{1}{2} g^{ad}(g_{bd,c} + g_{cd,b} - g_{bc,d}) , \tag{2}$$

and g^{ad} is the inverse of g_{bd}, so that $g_{bd} g^{ad} = \delta^a_b$.

Let **p** represent the position vector of observer B, as seen by observer A. If the geodesics are radial lines on a plane and A is an ant moving outward at a constant rate on one line at angle θ_A, looking at an ant B on another line at θ_B, **p** will increase at a constant rate as the two move out, so $\ddot{\mathbf{p}} = 0$. Instead, let A be a jet plane flying due South on longitude ϕ_A and B another on longitude ϕ_B. For the sake of definiteness, let them both start at a latitude θ_1 in the northern hemisphere. Even if the two jets fly at the same speed **p** will increase, $\dot{\mathbf{p}} > 0$, as θ decreases, but the rate of increase of $\dot{\mathbf{p}}$ will *decrease* at a constant rate, i.e. $\ddot{\mathbf{p}} < 0$. As the rate of change of position is the velocity, $\dot{\mathbf{p}}$ is the velocity and *its* rate of change, $\ddot{\mathbf{p}}$, is the acceleration, $\mathcal{A}$. Thus curvature is seen to be related to acceleration in kinematic terms. To see precisely how the two are related, one needs to require that the position vector **p** be "carried along" by the tangent vector to the geodesic, **t**. We say that **p** is *Lie transported* along **t**. In the above example, if A starts at point P and goes on to point Q, then the position vector of B at Q will be given by $\mathbf{t}(\mathbf{p})$. Further, if B starts at R and ends at S, then S is given by $\mathbf{p}(\mathbf{t})$. But the position of S relative to Q is also given by $\mathbf{t}(\mathbf{p})$. Hence they commute, i.e. $\mathbf{t}(\mathbf{p}) = \mathbf{p}(\mathbf{t})$.

The curvature of a space over a small area is measured by carrying a vector field, v^a along one direction in the locally flat coordinate system and then the other, and subtracting the result from carrying it in the reverse order. (Carrying along the map, rather than on the curved space itself, is called *parallel transport*.) This is seen most easily on the surface of the Earth with one direction along a line of longitude and the other a line of latitude. Carrying equal *distances* and not angles (which would be the case for Lie transport), as defined in the local coordinate system of a map, the rectangle carrying the vector will not close, because the cosine of the latitude will enter into the distance. Also the final direction of the vector will be different for the two, as it gets "twisted around more at a higher latitude than a lower one. Thus the Riemann curvature tensor is defined in index notation by

$$2v^a{}_{;[c;d]} = R^a{}_{bcd}v^b , \qquad (3)$$

where $S_{[ab]} = (S_{ab} - S_{ba})/2!$.

For our purposes we need to use a four-dimensional spacetime. Since the geodesic of A is the path of a test particle, **t** must be a timelike vector, and since **p** is the position vector of a neighbouring test particle seen at some time in the rest-frame of A, it must be a spacelike vector. I use the metric signature convention $(+, -, -, -)$, so that $\mathbf{t}.\mathbf{t} > 0 > \mathbf{p}.\mathbf{p}$. Thus the physical acceleration of B relative to A is

$$\mathcal{A} = \ddot{\mathbf{p}} = \mathbf{t}[\mathbf{t}(\mathbf{p})] . \qquad (4)$$

In the geometrical context it is called the *geodesic deviation*. We now use the Lie transport and geodesic equations to get the relation between the curvature tensor and the acceleration.[4] First, we use the Lie transport for the acceleration, written in index notation, by commuting the expression inside the bracket to get

$$\mathcal{A}^\mu = t^\rho(t^\nu p^\mu_{;\nu})_{;\rho} = t^\rho(p^\nu t^\mu_{;\nu})_{;\rho} , \qquad (5)$$

and then expand the bracket to obtain

$$\mathcal{A}^\mu = t^\rho p^\nu_{;\rho} t^\mu_{;\nu} + t^\rho p^\nu t^\mu_{;\nu;\rho} . \qquad (6)$$

Next, we use the Lie transport equation again for the first term to write it as

$$\mathcal{A}^\mu = p^\rho t^\nu_{;\rho} t^\mu_{;\nu} + t^\rho p^\nu t^\mu_{;\nu;\rho} . \qquad (7)$$

Notice that

$$p^\rho(t^\nu t^\mu_{;\nu})_{;\rho} = p^\rho t^\nu_{;\rho} t^\mu_{;\nu} + p^\rho t^\nu t^\mu_{;\nu;\rho} , \qquad (8)$$

so we and add and subtract $p^\rho t^\nu t^\mu_{;\nu;\rho}$, using the positive part to rewrite the first term and obtain

$$\mathcal{A}^\mu = p^\rho(t^\nu t^\mu_{;\nu})_{;\rho} - p^\rho t^\nu t^\mu_{;\nu;\rho} + t^\rho p^\nu t^\mu_{;\nu;\rho} . \qquad (9)$$

Now use the geodesic equation to get rid of the first term. Interchanging dummy indices and using the definition of the Riemann tensor, we finally arrive at

$$\mathcal{A}^\mu = -R^\mu{}_{\nu\rho\pi} t^\nu p^\rho t^\pi . \qquad (10)$$

If the curvature is due to gravity, then this is the tidal acceleration, or the acceleration of one test particle as seen by an observer on the other. If the mass of the test particle is m, $m\mathcal{A}^\mu$ is the tidal force, which is the gravitational force equivalent to the curvature, which has been called the pseudo-Newtonian, or ψN-, force.[4,22]

Since the acceleration is taken to be physically "caused" by the distribution of matter and energy, represented by the stress-energy tensor, $T^{\mu\nu}$, and geometrically by the Riemann tensor, $R^{\mu}{}_{\nu\rho\pi}$, the two must be functionally related. Thus

$$T^{\mu\nu} = f^{\mu\nu}(R^{\alpha}{}_{\beta\gamma\delta}) \,. \tag{11}$$

The problem is that the former is a second rank tensor while the latter is a fourth rank tensor. The trace of the Riemann tensor, called the *Ricci* tensor, $R_{\beta\delta} = R^{\alpha}{}_{\beta\alpha\delta}$, is a second rank tensor which could be used in place of the Riemann tensor. Further, for mass-energy conservation the stress-energy tensor must be divergence-free, i.e. $T^{\mu\nu}{}_{;\nu} = 0$, which requires that $f^{\mu\nu}{}_{;\nu} = 0$. Now the Riemann tensor satisfies the second Bianchi identities (for a proof of which, see for example[4])

$$R^{\alpha}{}_{\beta\gamma\delta;\epsilon} + R^{\alpha}{}_{\beta\epsilon\gamma;\delta} + R^{\alpha}{}_{\beta\delta\epsilon;\gamma} = 0 \,, \tag{12}$$

contracting which yields the divergence-free *Einstein* tensor

$$\mathcal{E}_{\beta\delta} = R_{\beta\delta} - \frac{1}{2}g_{\beta\delta}R \,, \tag{13}$$

$R = g^{\mu\nu}R_{\mu\nu}$ being the *Ricci scalar*. Integrating $f^{\mu\nu}{}_{;\nu} = 0$, the simplest function $f^{\mu\nu}$ would be a constant, which means a constant times the covariantly constant metric tensor, $g^{\mu\nu}$, but that would "throw the baby out with the bath-water". The simplest meaningful expression is to add in a constant times the Einstein tensor, which yields the relation between curvature and matter-energy as

$$R_{\mu\nu} - \frac{1}{2}g_{\mu\nu}R + \Lambda g_{\mu\nu} = \kappa T_{\mu\nu} \,, \tag{14}$$

where Λ is a constant of integration and the overall proportionality constant, κ, is put in with the matter-energy tensor, rather than the geometrical tensor.

5. What Difference Does It Make?

So what have we achieved? Just an alternate derivation of the Einstein field equations with a cosmological constant? I believe that this derivation had already been arrived at by Einstein. Undoubtedly, Einstein first *published* his field equations by using the variational principle. If he had got them earlier by this method, why did he not publish that derivation? I think that he felt that the Physics community was not so readily adopting the geometrical work of Grossmann and him, and wanted a derivation that would convince the community, and so waited till he had the field theoretic derivation worked out. Why would he not, then, have inserted the cosmological constant in there? There seem to be some letters between Hilbert and him that indicate he *had* done so in an earlier draft, but removed it later. The reason would be that the jewel in the crown of relativity was the explanation of the perihelion shift of Mercury by a theory with no free parameters. Had he put in the cosmological constant, there *would* be a free parameter. He was convinced that the theory was right. In this derivation the cosmological constant would *have to be there*.

In the derivation from the variational principle, it would have to be inserted by hand and so Hilbert was not getting it.

Even if this was the original derivation by Einstein, what difference does it make in any case? The point is that if we accept that Einstein inserted the constant later, by hand for his paper on cosmology a couple of years later,[2] it appears artificial and not part of the original theory, that had been verified. I have made much of the constant of integration coming with the geometry and not with the (physical) stress-energy tensor. It could, apparently, equally well have been inserted on the right side of the equation. In that case it would be an all-pervasive vacuum energy and not part of the geometry. Thus, it would need to be included in quantization. It is then assumed that the renormalization effect would come at the cut-off where quantum gravity takes over. On dimensional arguments one can argue that neither quantum mechanics nor relativity can be neglected when $\hbar, G, c^{-1}$ are non-negligible. Using them to make dimensional quantities, we get *Planck units*. It is further argued that "hence quantum gravity will set in *at* the Planck scale". Using the Planck energy density, which has the same units as the cosmological constant, *one gets a value about 126 orders of magnitude off from observation!* Hawking called this "the worst prediction in the history of Physics", and one cannot but agree with him. However, the original argument says that it must be invoked *by* the Planck scale, not *at* it. There is no reason that it should not set in *well before* the Planck scale. As I mentioned earlier, there is no theory of quantum gravity in any case, so one can only say what a valid theory for it *might* say. In that context Husain and Qureshi[23] have pointed out that the claimed problem does not arise. They point out that the argument is based on quantization of energy that is well defined in Minkowski space but is ambiguous in an arbitrarily curved spacetime. *There is no vacuum instability problem.*

So, what difference did the history make, if Einstein *had* got the cosmological constant earlier? It would have been perceived as part of the geometry, as a constant curvature, and the question of quantizing it would not arise till we had a "quantum geometrical" description of spacetime. One could then try to see what it would say, if anything, about the matter. The point is that it may be just our perception of what is "natural" that leads to the problems.

6. Conclusion and Discussion

In this paper it has been argued that it makes a huge difference whether the cosmological constant is regarded as part of the geometry or part of the stress-energy tensor. In the former role, as shown by Willem de Sitter,[24] it yields a static, constant curvature spacetime. Though this universe model does not change with time, an observer looking at the geodesic of a neighbouring test particle sees it accelerating *away* and so sees an expansion of this universe. Transforming to a cosmological time, using which one could talk of what is happening in a distant part of this universe "at the same time", the expansion would seem to be exponential (see for example[4]).

Put with the stress-energy tensor it would be an all-pervasive vacuum energy which gives a repulsive force for positive Λ.

Which way *should* it be looked at? Well, it was the expression involving the curvature that had to be determined, and so it is natural to keep the constant on the left side of the equation with the geometry. There is then no energy field causing the expansion — which appears as a kinematic effect. As such it cannot be considered for quantization without quantizing the rest of the spacetime. In that case the renormalization of the quantization of the rest of the curvature might, for example, balance that of the cosmological constant, so that there would be no net renormalization effect. I am not claiming that this *must* be so, only that we do not know and it could even be so. In fact, Maxwell had pointed out that his electromagnetic force, and hence energy, is opposite to the gravitational. Thus all gravitational effects should be expected to behave opposite to electromagnetic effects. Now the net mass-energy, material and gravitational, of the Universe is zero. That is what made it possible for Brout et al.[25] to propose that the Universe may be a vacuum fluctuation. In fact, have argued that there is reason to believe that any quantum gravitational effect should act opposite to other quantum fields.[26]

The current speculation is that the exponential expansion is due to a "mysterious form of dark energy" with thoroughly counter-intuitive properties. In fact, in some ways it is reminiscent of the luminiferous aether with any number of properties inserted by hand, with no evidence for them. This introduces any number of free parameters, reminiscent of Aristotle's epicycles. Regardless of these problems, let us go ahead and see what the claim is. The argument goes that if it were due to a cosmological constant, it would be orders of magnitude too small — *hence it must be zero*. You might well wonder how zero would be closer to the Planck value than the small observed value? Surely, that should be infinitely many orders of magnitude off! Why should it be zero in any case? If there is a constant appearing in the equations, should one not naturally look to the observational data to provide the value? The response normally given is that "it must be zero for some hitherto unknown reason, which will emerge later, but in the meantime we should assume that it is zero."

The standard model of cosmology is called the "Λ-CDM model", of which the latter stands for "cold dark matter" and the former for the cosmological constant. Thus, within observational errors, the data gives a behaviour of the Universe identical with what would be expected with a cosmological constant. To argue that it is a dynamical field seems perverse. Alternatively, we can say that the Almighty has set it to behave that way just to confuse us — transferring the perversity to Him (as we tend to do for most of our sins). Perhaps He is busting a rib up in Heaven, laughing at how "He has confused these arrogant blighters!" Why do we not simply accept the obvious explanation of the cosmological constant and determine it, just as we do Newton's constant of gravity? I am forced to conclude that it is because we would then eliminate a whole spew of papers and students supervised, based on wild speculations. In this conference "the Hubble tension" has been taken to imply that the "dark energy" underwent a phase transition and started to behave like the cosmological constant.[27] The essence of the argument was because "the ΛCDM is correct, and if it does not fit at the very early stage then the Λ cannot be constant", despite the fact, as pointed out,[28] that the accuracy of the measurements for it are not yet sufficient for any definite conclusion. As we have no idea of the Physics of the CDM, why should there not be a phase transition for *it*? That would appear to be far more natural as matter *does* undergo phase transitions. Because people have got wedded to "the mysterious dark energy" — the dark side of the force.

Acknowledgments

I am most grateful for very useful comments to Francesco De Paolis, Viqar Husain, Babar Qureshi and Khalid Saifullah. I am also most grateful to the Organizing Committee of MG 16 for providing me a Registration fee waiver to participate in the Virtual Meeting.

References

1. J.B. Barbour, *The Discovery of Dynamics: A Study from a Machian Point of View of the Discovery and the Structure of Dynamical Theories* (Oxford University Press 2001).
2. A. Einstein, "Kosmologische betrachtungen zur allgemeinen relativitätstheorie", *Preuss. Akad. der Wissen. Sitz.* **1917 (part 1)** 142–152.
3. A. Einstein, "Zur allgemeinen relativitätstheorie", *Preuss. Akad. der Wissen. Sitz.* **1915 (part 2)** 844–847; "Grundlage der allgemeinen relativitätstheorie", *Annalen der Physik* **49** (1915) 769–822.
4. A. Qadir, *Einstein's General Theory of Relativity* (Cambridge Scholars Publishing 2020).
5. E. Hubble, "A relation between distance and radial velocity among extra-galactic nebulae", *Proc. Nat. Acad. Sci.* **15** (1929) 168–173.
6. A. Friedman, "Über die krümmung des raumes", *Z. Phys.* **10** (1922) 377–386.
7. G. Gamow, "The evolution of the Universe", *Nature* **162** (1970) 680–682.
8. A. Sandage, "Distances to galaxies, the Hubble constant, the Friedmann time and the edge of the World", *Proc. Symp. on the Galaxy and Distance Scale, in Quart. Jour. Roy. Astron. Soc.* **13** (1972) 282–296; "Observational tests of world models", *Ann. Rev. Astron. & Astrophys.* **26** (1988) 561–630.
9. A.A. Penzias and R.W. Wilson, "A measurement of excess antenna temperature at 4080 Mc/s", *Astrophys. Jour.* **142** (1965) 419–421.
10. S. Perlmutter et al, "Measurements of the cosmological parameters Ω and Λ from the first seven supernovae at $z \geq 0.35$", *Astrophys. Jour.* **483** (1997)m565–581.
11. A.G. Reiss et al., "Observational evidence from supernovae for an accelerating Universe and a cosmological constant", *Astron. Jour.* **116** (1998) 1009–10038.
12. G. Lemâitre, "Un Univers homogène de masse constante et de rayon croissant rendant compte de la vitesse radiale des nébuleuses extra-galactiques", *Annales de la Société Scientifique de Bruxelles* **47** (1927) 49–59.
13. P.J.E. Peebles, *Principles of Physical Cosmology* (Princeton University Press 2019).
14. A. Einstein, "Zur elektrodynamik bewegter körper", *Annalen der Physik* **17** (1905) 891–921.

15. H. Minkowski, "Das relativitätsprinzip", *Annalen der Physik* **352** (1907) 927–938; "Die grundgleichungen für die elektromagnetischen Vorgänge in bewegten Körpern", *Nachrichten der Gesellschaft der Wissenschaften zu Göttingen, Mathematisch-Physikalische Klasse* (1908) 53–111; "Raum und Zeit", *Jahresbericht der Deutschen Mathematiker-Vereinigung* **18** (1909) 75–88.
16. A. Qadir, *Relativity: An Introduction to the Special Theory* (World Scientific 1989).
17. I. Newton, *Philosophiae Naturalis Principia Mathematica* S. Pepys Reg. Soc. Praeses 1686.
18. A. Einstein, "Relativitätsprinzip und die aus demselben gezogenen folgerungen", *Jahrbuch der Radioaktivität* **4** (1907) 411–462.
19. R.V. Pound and G.A. Rebka Jr., "Gravitational red-shift in nuclear resonance", *Phys. Rev. Lett.* **3** 439–441.
20. A. Einstein and M. Grossmann, "Entwurf einer verallgemeinerten relativitätstheorie und eine theorie der gravitation: I. Physikalischer teil von A. Einstein; II. Mathematischer teil von M. Grossmann", *Zeitschrift für Mathematik und Physik*, **62** (1913) 225–261.
21. A. Einstein and M. Grossmann, "Kovarianzeigenschaften der Feldgleichungen der auf die verallgemeinerte Relativitätstheorie gegründeten Gravitationstheorie", *Zeitschrift für Mathematik und Physik*, **63** (1914) 215–225.
22. A. Qadir, "General relativity in terms of forces", *Proc. Third Regional Conference on Mathematical Physics*, eds. F. Hussain and A. Qadir (World Scientific 1990) pp. 481–490; "The gravitational force in general relativity", *M.A.B. Bég Memorial Volume*, eds. A. Ali and P.A. Hoodbhoy (World Scientific 1991) pp.159–178.
23. V. Husain and B. Qureshi, "Ground state of the Universe and the cosmological constant. A nonperturbative analysis", *Phys. Rev. Lett.* **116** (2016) 061302 (6 pages).
24. W. de Sitter, "On Einstein's theory of gravitation and its astronomical consequences", *Mon. Not. Roy. Astron. Soc.* **78** (1917) 3–28.
25. R. Brout, F. Englert and E. Gunzig, "The creation of the Universe as a quantum phenomenon", *Ann. Phys.* **115** (1978) 78–106.
26. A. Qadir, "On the reality of Hawking radiation", *Int. J. Mod. Phys. D* **28** (2019) 2040001 (11 pages).
27. M. Kamionkowski, "The Hubble tension", talk on Wednesday 07/07 at 16.40.
28. W. Freedman, "The Hubble constant tension", talk on Wednesday 07/07 at 17.15.

The irreducible mass of Christodoulou-Ruffini-Hawking mass formula

Yuan K. Ha

Department of Physics, Temple University
Philadelphia, Pennsylvania 19122 U.S.A.
E-mail: yuanha@temple.edu

We reveal three new discoveries in black hole physics previously unexplored in the Hawking era. These results are based on the remarkable 1971 discovery of the irreducible mass of the black hole by Christodoulou and Ruffini, and subsequently confirmed by Hawking.
1. The Horizon Mass Theorem shows that the mass at the event horizon of any black hole: neutral, charged, or rotating, depends only on twice its irreducible mass observed at infinity.
2. The External Energy Conjecture proposes that the electrostatic and rotational energy of a general black hole exist completely outside the horizon due to the nature of the irreducible mass.
3. The Moment of Inertia Property shows that every Kerr black hole has a moment of inertia. When the rotation stops, there is an irreducible moment of inertia as a result of the irreducible mass.
Thus after 50 years, the irreducible mass has gained a new and profound significance. No longer is it just a limiting value in energy extraction, it can also determine black hole dynamics and structure. What is believed to be a black hole is a physical body with an extended structure. Astrophysical black holes are likely to be massive compact objects from which light cannot escape.

Keywords: Black holes; quasi-local energy; irreducible mass; Kerr metric; moment of inertia.

1. 50th Anniversary 1971–2021

This article is to celebrate the 50th anniversary of the discovery of the mass-energy formula of a Kerr-Newman black hole in 1971 by introducing three new results recently found in black hole physics. Surprisingly, these results all invove the concept of the irreducible mass.

First, congratulations to Demetrios Christodoulou and Remo Ruffini for their remarkable discovery of the *irreducible mass*[1] of the black hole and confirmed by Hawking,[2] one of the most important concepts in black hole physics.

This year is also the 50th anniversary of the renormalization of Yang-Mills theory[3] in 1971. Congratulations to Gerard 't Hooft and the late Martinus Veltman for their elucidation of the quantum structure of electroweak interactions, one of the great achievements in 20th Century physics.

The irreducible mass formula discovered by Christodoulou and Ruffin in 1971 is the following:[1]

$$M^2 = \left(M_{irr} + \frac{Q^2}{4GM_{irr}}\right)^2 + \frac{J^2 c^2}{4G^2 M_{irr}^2}. \tag{1}$$

Here M is the total mass of the Kerr-Newman black hole, M_{irr} is the irreducible mass; Q is the electric charge and J is the angular momentum. All quantities are reckoned according to the distant observer. When Q and J are zero, the irreducible mass is the mass of a Schwarzschild black hole. 50 years later, the irreducible mass has gained unexpected new and profound significance besides energy extraction. It can also determine black hole dynamics and structure.

It is especially appropriate to explain the many definitions of a black hole in physics.[4] The mathematical black hole in general relativity has a singularity hidden by a horizon. However, neither singularity nor horizon has been observed. Compact objects like the one at the center of our galaxy are also called black holes in common usuage, even though their nature is still unknown. This is pointed out in the 2020 Nobel Prize in Physics citation. To Roger Penrose, the citation is 'for the discovery that black hole formation is a robust prediction of the general theory of relativity'. To Reinhard Genzel and Andrea Ghez, the citatation is 'for the discovery of a supermassive compact object at the center of our galaxy'. The term black hole is avoided. Strictly speaking, the black hole has not been discovered, but only a black hole-like object has been observed in astyrophysics. The Laplace 'dark star' introduced the concept of the black hole as a massive body from which light cannot escape due to its strong gravity.

Between 1965–1985, several important theorems on classical black holes were gradually discovered. They are known as:

(1) Singularity Theorem (1965),[5]
(2) Area Non-decrease Theorem (1972),[6]
(3) Uniqueness Theorem (1975),[7]
(4) Positive Energy Theorem (1983).[8]

These theorems have been well discussed for many years in general relativity and accepted as basic properties of the classical black hole. In recent years, three new results on black holes previously unexplored in the Hawking era are found. They were developed using the quasi-local energy approach and angular momentum consideration. Remarkably, they all contain the irreducible mass of Christodoulou and Ruffini. They are:

(5) Horizon Mass Theorem (2005),[9]
(6) External Energy Conjecture (2017),[10]
(7) Moment of Inertia Property (2018).[11]

These results are derived completely within general relativity and therefore legitimate. They add new properties to the classical black hole with potential to resolve several long-standing paradoxes in black hole physics.

2. Horizon Mass Theorem

Theorem. *For neutral and charged black holes, the horizon mass is always twice the irreducible mass observed at infinity.*

For rotating black holes, the horizon mass is found to be extremely close to twice the irreducible mass for all rotations. It is conjectured that a rigorous proof will eventually show that the horizon mass is exactly twice the irreducible mass.

In notation, it is simply

$$M(r_+) = 2M_{irr} \qquad (2)$$

where r_+ is the horizon radius of the black hole. The theorem relates the mass of a black hole observed at the event horizon to its irreducible mass observed at infinity. The irreducible mass does not contain electrostatic and rotational energy. The Horizon Mass Theorem is the final outcome of quasi-local mass applied to black holes.

The quasi-local energy is one of the most important concepts in general relativity after decades of searching for a consistent definition of gravitational energy. It was finally obtained in 1993. The Brown and York expression[12] for quasi-local energy is given in terms of the total mean curvature of a surface bounding a volume for a gravitational system in four-dimensional spacetime. The total energy E, including binding energy, is given in the form of an integral,

$$E = \frac{c^4}{8\pi G} \int_{^2B} d^2x \sqrt{\sigma}(k - k^0), \qquad (3)$$

where σ is the determinant of the metric defined on the two-dimensional surface ^2B; k is the trace of the extrinsic curvature of the surface, and k_0, the trace of the curvature of a reference space. For asymptotically flat reference spacetime, k^0 is taken to be zero. The expression in Eq.(3) is the basis for establishing the Horizon Mass Theorem.

For a Schwarzschild black hole, the total energy contained in a sphere enclosing the black hole at a coordinate distance r is calculated,[12-14]

$$E(r) = \frac{rc^4}{G}\left[1 - \sqrt{1 - \frac{2GM}{rc^2}}\right]. \qquad (4)$$

At the Schwarzschild radius, $r = r_+ = 2GM/c^2$, the above equation reduces to

$$E(r) = \left(\frac{2GM}{c^2}\right)\frac{c^4}{G} = 2Mc^2, \qquad (5)$$

giving the first case of the Horizon Mass Theorem in Schwarzschild spacetime, i.e. $M(r_+) = 2M$.

For a Reissner-Nordström black hole enclosed within a radius at coordinate r, the total energy calculated is now [9],

$$E(r) = \frac{rc^4}{G}\left[1 - \sqrt{1 - \frac{2GM}{rc^2} + \frac{GQ^2}{r^2c^4}}\right]. \tag{6}$$

Here M is the total mass of the black hole including electrostatic energy observed at infinity, and Q is the electric charge.

The irreducible mass is the final mass of the black hole when its charge is neutralized by adding oppositely charged particles, extracting energy from the black hole. It is defined as in electrostatics,

$$M = M_{irr} + \frac{Q^2}{4GM_{irr}}. \tag{7}$$

Inverting the equation to solve for M_{irr}, we find

$$M_{irr} = \frac{M}{2} + \frac{M}{2}\sqrt{1 - \frac{Q^2}{GM^2}}. \tag{8}$$

The horizon radius of a Reissner-Nordström black hole is known to be

$$r_+ = \frac{GM}{c^2} + \frac{GM}{c^2}\sqrt{1 - \frac{Q^2}{GM^2}}. \tag{9}$$

Combining Eq.(6) and Eq.(9), we find the mass contained within the horizon to be

$$\frac{E(r_+)}{c^2} = M(r_+) = M + M\sqrt{1 - \frac{Q^2}{GM^2}}, \tag{10}$$

i.e. $M(r_+) = 2M_{irr}$. This is the second case of the Horizon Mass Theorem in Reissner-Nordström spacetime. It is seen that the horizon mass of the charged black hole depends only on the energy of the black hole when it is neutral.

We proceed next to the case for a slowly rotating black hole with mass M and angular momentum J. The total energy contained within a sphere of radius r can only be given by an approximate expression. This is due to the complexity of the Kerr metric, and more importantly, due to the fact that the Kerr metric only has axial symmetry instead of spherical symmetry. At the horizon, it is found that,[15]

$$E(r) = \frac{rc^4}{G}\left[1 - \sqrt{1 - \frac{2GM}{rc^2} + \frac{\alpha^2}{r^2}}\right]$$

$$+ \frac{\alpha^2 c^4}{6rG}\left[2 + \frac{2GM}{rc^2} + \left(1 + \frac{2GM}{rc^2}\right)\sqrt{1 - \frac{2GM}{rc^2} + \frac{\alpha^2}{r^2}}\right] + \cdots \tag{11}$$

where $\alpha = J/Mc$ is the angular momentun length paranneter. The leading term of the expression is similar to the energy expression in the Reissner-Nordström case, suggesting that the mass at the horizon is twice the irreducible mass. The next term depends on α^2, adding a small contribution to the leading term.

The irreducible mass of a Kerr black hole is the final mass when its rotational energy is completely extracted by adding external particles, such as in the Penrose process.[16] It is given in the form

$$M_{irr}^2 = \frac{M^2}{2} + \frac{M^2}{2}\sqrt{1 - \frac{J^2c^2}{G^2M^4}}. \tag{12}$$

The horizon radius in this case is,

$$r_+ = \frac{GM}{c^2} + \frac{GM}{c^2}\sqrt{1 - \frac{J^2c^2}{G^2M^4}}. \tag{13}$$

An approximate relation for the horizon energy is therefore found,

$$E(r_+) \approx 2M_{irr} + O(\alpha^2). \tag{14}$$

The conclusion is that there is very little rotational energy insiide the Kerr black hole.

It is natural to extend the quasi-local energy investigation to include higher rotations, and logically, all rotations. However, a severe challenge appeared at this stage and progress on black hole rotation in this approach stopped. The calculations became extremely difficult to perform. No analytical expression or numerical evaluation could achieve an *exact* expression for the horizon mass of the Kerr black hole. An analysis of the horizon mass in the teleparallel equivalent formulation of general relativity[17] reveals that it is strikingly close to twice the irreducible mass $2M_{irr}$ for all range of the parameter $0 \leq \alpha < GM/c^2$. The tiny discrepancy is likely due to evaluating method and describing the spherical horizon region in a system with intrinsic axial symmetry. A general principle based on equipartition of energy at the horizon also suggests the horizon mass result for the Kerr black hole[18] by invoking one-half of the horizon mass for compensating the negative gravitational potential energy and the other half for supplying the irreducible mass.

We give a heuristic argument for the Horizon Mass Theorem with the area concept of a black hole.[9] It has been known from the Kerr metric that the area at the event horizon of a Kerr black hole for all rotations is[1]

$$A = 4\pi(r_+^2 + \alpha^2) = \frac{16\pi G^2 M_{irr}^2}{c^4}, \tag{15}$$

and the area of a Schwarzschild black hole of mass M_S and radius R_S is

$$A = 4\pi R_S^2 = 4\pi\left(\frac{2GM_S}{c^2}\right)^2 = \frac{16\pi G^2 M_S^2}{c^4}. \tag{16}$$

The two areas can be related by invoking Hawking's Area Non-decrease Theorem in the energy extraction process. The theorem asserts that the area of a Kerr black hole is the same as the area of the final Schwarzschild black hole when rotational energy is extracted in a smooth and reversible process. Since the horizon mass of the

Schwarzschild black hole is proven to be twice its asymptotic mass M_S, the horizon mass of the Kerr black hole in this process is therefore $2M_{irr}$. The result applies to all rotations. It is believed that a rigorous mathematical proof will eventually show that the horizon mass is *exactly* twice the irreducible mass.

The Horizon Mass Theorem is crucial for understanding processes occuring near the horizon, such as the merging of two black holes,[19] and quantum emission of Hawking radiation.[20]

3. External Energy Conjecture

Proposition. *The electrostatic energy and rotational energy of a general black hole exist completely outside the horizon.*

The conjecture is a direct consequence of the irreducible mass in the Horizon Mass Theorem.

By definition, the irreducible mass does not contain rotational energy or electrostatic energy. A rotating black hole does not have rotational energy inside the horizon; therefore rotational energy exists outside the surface. Similarly, an electrically charged black hole does not have electrostatic energy inside. Electrostatic energy exists only outside, like that of a conductor. When quantum particles carrying electric charges and spins reach the black hole, they are forbidden to enter inside. They can only stay outside or at the surface. Since all matter particles in Nature are quantum particles, this makes the interior of the black hole completely hollow. Classical particles do not exist in Nature; they are a tool in classical mechanics.

We may generalize the External Energy Conjecture to include other energies of a black hole and introduce a new paradigm.[11]

External Energy Paradigm:

> *All energies of a black hole are external quantities. They include: constituent mass, gravitational energy, electrostatic energy, magnetic energy, rotational energy, heat energy, etc.*

The validity of this paradigm will be demonstrated in the next section in which the moment of inertia of a black hole is presented.

4. Moment of Inertia Property

Statement. *A black hole with an angular momentum and an angular velocity at the event horizon has a moment of inertia given by:*

$$\text{coefficient} \times \text{Kerr mass} \times (\text{ergosphere radius})^2 \ .$$

When rotation stops, there is an irreducible moment of inertia given by:

$$\text{irreducible mass} \times (\text{Schwarzschild radius})^2 \ .$$

The result of this statement is derived solely from the Kerr metric and is therefore a *bona fide* property of general relativity. Every black hole has a moment of inertia, even when it is not rotating. Moment of inertia indicates structure of the black hole.

The Kerr metric[21] discovered in 1963 ushered in a new epoch in general relativity and in astrophysics. It is absolutely indispensable for the study of rotating black holes. We demonstrate the existence of moment of inertia uniquely from the Kerr metric, using angular momentum and angular velocity consideration. We present the Kerr metric in an *explicit* form of the Boyer-Lindquist coordinates[22] (t, r, θ, ϕ) so that the metric coefficients can be readily extracted for calculation. It contains two constants $\alpha = J/Mc$ and $m = GM/c^2$ for the stationary case,

$$ds^2 = \left(\frac{r^2 + \alpha^2 \cos^2\theta - 2mr}{r^2 + \alpha^2 \cos^2\theta}\right) c^2 dt^2 + \left(\frac{4m\alpha r \sin^2\theta}{r^2 + \alpha^2 \cos^2\theta}\right) cd\phi dt$$
$$- \frac{[(r^2 + \alpha^2)(r^2 + \alpha^2 \cos^2\theta) + 2mr\alpha^2 \sin^2\theta]}{r^2 + \alpha^2 \cos^2\theta} \sin^2\theta d\phi^2$$
$$-(r^2 + \alpha^2 \cos^2\theta)\left(d\theta^2 + \frac{dr^2}{r^2 + \alpha^2 - 2mr}\right). \qquad (17)$$

The Kerr spacetime rotates with different angular velocities at different locations. The angular velocity at a point is defined as the change in azimuthal angle ϕ with respect to the change in coordinate time t. It can be expressed in terms of the metric coefficients as

$$\Omega = \frac{d\phi}{dt} = -\frac{g_{t\phi}}{g_{\phi\phi}}. \qquad (18)$$

where $g_{t\phi} = g_{\phi t}$. At the equatorial region, $\theta = 90°$, the angular velocity expression at a distance r can be written as

$$\Omega = \frac{2m\alpha rc}{(r^2 + \alpha^2)r^2 + 2mr\alpha^2}. \qquad (19)$$

Further simplification can be achieved at the event horizon $r = r_+$, using the identity $r_+^2 + \alpha^2 = 2mr_+$, i.e.

$$\Omega_+ = \frac{\alpha c}{r_+^2 + \alpha^2}. \qquad (20)$$

In terms of actual physical quantities, we have an exact algebraic relation for the angular velocity of the Kerr black hole,

$$\Omega_+(J) = \frac{\frac{J}{M}}{\frac{2G^2 M^2}{c^4}\left[1 + \sqrt{1 - \frac{J^2 c^2}{G^2 M^4}}\right]}. \qquad (21)$$

Given an angular momentun J and a Kerr mass M determined by a distant observer, the angular velocity at the event horizon can be obtained in radians/sec.

Equivalently, we can express the angular momentum J in terms of the angular velocity Ω through the moment of inertia $I(\Omega)$ in the form

$$J(\Omega) = I(\Omega) \cdot \Omega. \tag{22}$$

We find, from Eq.(21), after substantial algebra,

$$J(\Omega_+) = \frac{M \left(\frac{2GM}{c^2}\right)^2}{1 + \left(\frac{2GM}{c^2}\right)^2 \frac{\Omega_+^2}{c^2}} \cdot \Omega_+. \tag{23}$$

The crucial step here is to extract a radius factor in the above relation. It is recognized that the factor $2GM/c^2$ is the ergosphere radius at the equator, since M is the Kerr mass which includes rotational energy. Accordingly, the moment of inertia of the Kerr black hole is

$$I(\Omega_+) = \frac{M \left(\frac{2GM}{c^2}\right)^2}{1 + \left(\frac{2GM}{c^2}\right)^2 \frac{\Omega_+^2}{c^2}}. \tag{24}$$

It is further recognized that the entire denominator in the above expression becomes a dimensionless number and acts as a numerical coefficient. The structure of the Kerr black hole is therefore,

coefficient × Kerr mass × (ergosphere radius)^2.

As angular momentum is continually reduced in the energy extraction process, a slowly rotating black hole is formed. In the static limit, the quantity $\Omega_+^2 \to 0$ first, the Kerr mass becomes the irreducible mass, $M \to M_{irr}$ and the coefficient becomes exactly equal to 1. The moment of inertia of a Schwarzschild black hole is derived. It is the limiting value of the moment of inertia of the Kerr black hole in Eq.(24), given by

$$I = M_S R_S^2. \tag{25}$$

There is an irreducible moment of inertia of the Kerr black hole as a result of the irreducible mass. It is the rotatonal analogue of the rest mass of a moving body $E = mc^2$.

A further observation that leads quickly to the irreducible moment of inertia is by considering the angular momentum definition in the Kerr metric $J = Mac$ and the angular velocity Ω_+ at the horizon found in Eq.(20). We find,

$$I = \frac{J}{\Omega_+} = M \left(r_+^2 + a^2\right) = \sqrt{M_{irr}^2 + M_{rot}^2} \left(r_+^2 + a^2\right). \tag{26}$$

As the rotational parameter $a \to 0$, the rotational mass $M_{rot} \to 0$; while the horizon radius $r_+ \to R_S$. In the limit, $I = M_{irr} R_S^2 = M_S R_S^2$. If one directly puts $J = 0$ and

$\Omega_+ = 0$ in the definition $I = J/\Omega_+$, one would get an undefined result $0/0$. The static limit of the Kerr black hole hole has the structure,

$$irreducible\ mass \times (Schwarzschild\ radius)^2.$$

A Schwarzschild black hole does not have an axis of rotation. Introducing an axis destroys its spherical symmetry. The center is therefore the point of symmetry. The moment of inertia $I = M_S R_S^2$ is a statement about the mass distribution of a body with respect to the center in that the total mass is to be located at the Schwarzschild radius. A natural interpretation is that the static black hole is a hollow massive shell. This would go against the Equivalence Principle and the Singularity Theorem. It is possible that the static black hole resulting from the energy extraction process of a Kerr black hole is fundamentally different from the original Schwarzschild black hole. The static black hole derived from a Kerr black hole may be a quasi-black hole. A quasi-black hole has the same exterior spacetime as that of the Schwarzschild black hole but without the conceptual difficulties associated with the latter.[23] Singularity does not exist because particles are forbidden to cross the horizon by the very presence of the moment of inertia. The black hole firewall is such a scenario.[24] The quasi-black hole would also provide a physical surface where electric charges can stay instead of hovering without cause in the case of the charged black hole. In addition, if the surface area is identified as the entropy of a black hole according to Bekenstein[25] and Hawking,[6] then it is logical to expect that all mass of the quasi-black hole is at the surface. The moment of inertia is a new property of the Kerr black hole.

5. Epilogue

After 50 years, the irreducible mass has progressed from the gedanken Penrose process to quantum energy extraction in gamma-ray bursts and active galactic nuclei emissions.[26] Instead of being a cold and inert body, the real black hole is a highly active object. The irreducible mass further plays a central role in newly discovered black hole properties. These results may resolve some of the long-standing paradoxes in black hole physics.

References

1. D. Christodoulou and R. Ruffini, *Phys. Rev. D* **4**, 3552 (1971).
2. S. W. Hawking, *Phys. Rev. Lett.* **26**, 1344 (1971).
3. G. 't Hooft and M. Veltman, *Nucl. Phys. B* **44**, 189 (1972).
4. E. Curiel, *Nature Astronomy* **3**, 27 - 34 (2019).
5. R. Penrose, *Phys. Rev. Lett.* **14**, 57 (1965).
6. S. W. Hawking, *Commun. Math. Phys.* **25**, 152 (1972).
7. D. C. Robinson, *Phy. Rev. Lett.* **34**, 905 (1975).
8. R. Schoen and S. T. Yau, *Commun. Math. Phys.* **65**, 45 (1979).

9. Y. K. Ha, *Int. J. Mod. Phys. D* **14**, 2219 (2005).
10. Y. K. Ha, *Mod. Phys. Lett. A* **32**, 1730021 (2017).
11. Y. K. Ha, *Int. J. Mod. Phys. A* **33**, No. 31, 1844025 (2018).
12. J. D. Brown and J. W. York, Jr., *Phys. Rev. D* **47**, 1407 (1993).
13. J. W. Maluf, *J. Math. Phys.* **36**, 4242 (1995).
14. Y. K. Ha, *Gen. Relativ. Gravit.* **35**, 2045 (2003).
15. E. A. Martinez, *Phys. Rev. D* **50**, 4920 (1994).
16. R. M. Floyd and R. Penrose, *Nature Phys. Sci.* **229**, 177 (1971).
17. J. W. Maluf, E. F. Martins and A. Kneip, *J. Math. Phys.* **37**, 6302 (1996).
18. N. Dadhich, *Curr. Sci.* **76**, 831 (1999).
19. B. P. Abbott el al., *Phys. Rev. Lett.* **116**, 061102 (2016).
20. S. W. Hawking, *Commun. Math. Phys.* **43**, 199 (1975).
21. R. P. Kerr, *Phys. Rev. Lett.* **11**, 237 (1963).
22. R. M. Boyer and R. W. Lindquist, *J. Math. Phys.* **8**, 265 (1967).
23. J. V. Narlikar and T. Padmanabhan, *Found. Phys.* **18**, No. 6, 639 (1988).
24. A. Almheiri, D. Maroff, J. Polchinski and J. Sully, *J. High Energy Phys.* **2013**, 62, (2013).
25. J. Bekenstein, *Lett. Nuovo. Cim.* **4**, 737 (1972).
26. R. Moradi, J. A. Rueda, R. Ruffini, Y. Wang, *A&A* **649**, A75 (2021)

Reshaping our understanding on structure formation with the quantum nature of the dark matter

C. R. Argüelles,[1,2,*] E. A. Becerra-Vergara,[2,3,4] A. Krut,[2] R. Yunis,[2,3] J. A. Rueda,[2,3,5,6] R. Ruffini[2,3,6]

[1] *Facultad de Ciencias Astronómicas y Geofísicas, Universidad Nacional de La Plata, Paseo del Bosque, B1900FWA La Plata, Argentina*
[2] *International Center for Relativistic Astrophysics Network – ICRANet, Piazza della Repubblica 10, 65122 Pescara, Italy*
[3] *ICRA, Dipartimento di Fisica, Sapienza Università di Roma, Piazzale Aldo Moro 5, 00185 Rome, Italy*
[4] *GIRG, Escuela de Física, Universidad Industrial de Santander, 680002, Cra 27 calle 9, Bucaramanga, Colombia*
[5] *ICRANet-Ferrara, Dip. di Fisica e Scienze della Terra, Università degli Studi di Ferrara, Via Saragat 1, 44122 Ferrara, Italy*
[6] *INAF, Istituto de Astrofisica e Planetologia Spaziali, Via Fosso del Cavaliere 100, 00133 Rome, Italy*
carguelles@fcaglp.unlp.edu.ar

We study the non-linear structure formation in cosmology accounting for the quantum nature of the dark matter (DM) particles in the initial conditions at decoupling, as well as in the relaxation and stability of the DM halos. Differently from cosmological N-body simulations, we use a thermodynamic approach for collisionless systems of self-gravitating fermions in General Relativity, in which the halos reach the steady state by maximizing a coarse-grained entropy. We show the ability of this approach to provide answers to crucial open problems in cosmology, among others: the mass and nature of the DM particle, the formation and nature of supermassive black holes in the early Universe, the nature of the intermediate mass black holes in small halos, and the *core-cusp* problem.

Keywords: Dark Matter; Galaxies: Super Massive Black Holes - Halos; Self-gravitating Systems: fermions

1. Introduction

In the particle DM paradigm, different particle candidates (e.g. WIMPS, axions, sterile neutrinos, etc.) have different early Universe histories that, in turn, translates into different evolution of primordial perturbations in the cosmic plasma which seeds the formation of galaxies at later stages.[1] The effects of the DM microphysics is, in these cases, often quantified only by the (linear) matter power spectrum: a measure of the distribution of density perturbations before non-linear processes are involved. Such non-linear processes typically include the gravitational collapse of primordial structures, key to the formation of the observed structures in the late Universe, such as galaxies and clusters.

From the point of view of structure formation, the quantum nature of particle DM has been traditionally involved only in the initial conditions before self-gravity comes into play, neglecting any role it may have in the dynamics of the formed systems. However, whether or not this DM microphysics affects the overall structure of DM halos has been questioned in recent works. That is, our ignorance about its potential (quantum) effects through the innermost regions of the halos and their stability, may represent a hole in our knowledge of these systems.

Indeed, the limited inner spatial resolution of DM halos inherent of cosmological N-body simulations implies huge uncertainties on the DM central distribution. It includes the open questions on how the DM is correlated with baryonic matter on such inner scales, and ultimately, how is the relation with the supermassive black hole (SMBH) at the center of large galaxies, and how they can co-exist in a steady state. Moreover, the use of classical point masses as the building blocks of matter (without considering the quantum nature of the particles) in traditional N-body simulations within the LCDM paradigm does not allow for any new possible sources of quantum-pressure in DM halos (e.g. as recently shown within 3D numerical simulations for bosons 2 or fermions 3). The arising of these quantum effects at the center of equilibrium systems of self-gravitating quantum particles (either bosons or fermions) is a long-known physical phenomenon.[4]

Motivated by these open issues, we here present an alternative mechanism of structure formation in cosmology based on thermodynamics of self-gravitating fermions. In such a scenario, the quantum nature of the DM particles is duly taken into account in the physics of decoupling in the early Universe (with corresponding effects in the linear power spectrum), as well as at DM halo formation and subsequent stability and morphology.

2. DM halo formation: A thermodynamic approach

The thermodynamic approach for DM halo formation used here is motivated by the seminal work of *Lynden-Bell* on violent relaxation.[5] This approach was originally applied for collisionless stellar systems, and few decades later extended to indistinguishable particles such as massive neutrinos in Ref. 6. Relevant extensions to Lynden-Bell theory allowing for out of equilibrium effects (i.e particle evaporation), were performed in Refs. 7, 8 using the framework of kinetic theory. Quasi-stationary solutions to such equations (see Eq. (2) below), lead to a most-probable, coarse-grained distribution function (DF) at (violent) relaxation, of more realistic applications than the original Lynden-Bell's version: a tidally truncated Fermi–Dirac DF of the form

$$\bar{f}(\epsilon \leq \epsilon_c) = \frac{1 - e^{(\epsilon-\epsilon_c)/kT}}{e^{(\epsilon-\mu)/kT} + 1}, \quad \bar{f}(\epsilon > \epsilon_c) = 0, \tag{1}$$

where $\epsilon = \sqrt{c^2p^2 + m^2c^4} - mc^2$ is the particle kinetic energy, μ is the chemical potential with the particle rest-energy subtracted off, T is the effective temperature, k is the Boltzmann constant, c is the speed of light, and m is the DM fermion mass. The full set of dimensionless-parameters of the model are defined by the temperature, degeneracy and cutoff parameters, $\beta = kT/(mc^2)$, $\theta = \mu/(kT)$ and $W = \epsilon_c/(kT)$, respectively (when these parameters are evaluated at the center of the configuration, they will be written with a subscript 0).

DM halos built upon such a fermionic DF in a cosmological framework, naturally lead to finite-sized halos which can be stable, extremely long-lived, and holding key implications to supermassive BH formation from DM as shown here (and detailed in Ref. 3).

In the limiting case of $\epsilon_c \gg \epsilon$, there is no particle escape, and (1) takes the form of the traditional (coarse-grained) Fermi-Dirac DF obtained in the original work of Lynden-Bell. Indeed, this DF is a stationary solution of the Vlasov-Poisson (VP) equation governing collisionless systems,[7] that is a solution of Eq. (2) shown below, with $\mathbf{J} = 0$, usually called 'VP dynamically-stable' solutions. The more realistic "tidally-truncated" DF (1) is another kind of quasi-stationary solution of the more general *convection-diffusion* kinetic equation (2), as demonstrated in Refs. 7, 9. This accounts for the 'microphysics' of the long-range particle-particle interactions[a] involved in the diffusion current $\mathbf{J}$, caused mainly by the rapid fluctuations of the gravitational potential (proper of violent relaxation processes):

$$\frac{\partial \bar{f}}{\partial t} + \mathbf{v}\frac{\partial \bar{f}}{\partial \mathbf{r}} - \nabla\Phi\frac{\partial \bar{f}}{\partial \mathbf{v}} = -\frac{\partial \mathbf{J}}{\partial \mathbf{v}}. \qquad (2)$$

When the gravitational fluctuations die down at the end of relaxation, the diffusion current approaches zero (i.e. no more evaporation), and the DF (1) remains as a stationary solution of the VP equation. Now, these dynamically-stable VP solutions can be easily used to build DM halos in (hydrostatic) equilibrium able to reproduce galaxy rotation curves (as shown in Refs. 10, 11). However, such analysis does not explain neither *how* such a collisionless self-gravitating system reaches the required steady state, nor if they maximize the coarse-grained entropy S of such a fermion-gas, nor if they are just transitional (unstable/unreachable) states. This stems from the fact that VP dynamical stability *does not* necessarily imply thermodynamical stability, therefore some dynamically stable solutions for DM halos in hydrostatic equilibrium can be more likely to occur in Nature than others!

---

[a]For isolated systems made of fermions, such a current can make (2) to be of the form of a fermionic Landau equation, conserving mass and energy, and continuously increase the Fermi-Dirac entropy functional (i.e. fulfilling H-theorem).[9]

In order to find dynamically and thermodynamically stable configurations of collisionless self-gravitating fermions in General Relativity (GR), able to model realistic DM halos, it is needed to solve the problem of finding solutions that maximize the global entropy $S = \int_0^R s(r)e^{\lambda/2}4\pi r^2 dr$ (at fixed total energy and particle number), where $s(r)$ is the entropy density given by the Gibbs-Duhem relation

$$s(r) = \frac{P(r) + \rho(r) - \mu(r)n(r)}{T(r)}, \quad (3)$$

$e^{\lambda/2}4\pi r^2 dr$ is the proper volume, being e^λ the spatial component of the spherically-symmetric spacetime metric: $ds^2 = e^\nu c^2 dt^2 - e^\lambda dr^2 - r^2 d\Theta^2 - r^2 \sin^2\Theta d\phi^2$, with (r, Θ, ϕ) the spherical coordinates, and ν and λ depend only on r.

The mass-energy density $\rho(r)$, pressure $P(r)$ and particle number density $n(r)$ are directly obtained as the corresponding integrals of $\bar{f}(p)$ over momentum space (bounded from above by $\epsilon \leq \epsilon_c$) as detailed in Ref. 3. This makes a four-parametric equation of state $(\rho(r), P(r))$ depending on (β, θ, W, m) according to the dimensionless parameters in (1). The stress-energy tensor is the one of a perfect fluid with the above density and pressure, so the self-gravitating configurations of fermions are solutions of the hydrostatic equilibrium equation, with the local $T(r)$ and $\mu(r)$ fulfilling, respectively, the Tolman and Klein equilibrium relations (see Ref. 3 for details). We shall analyze which of such solutions are thermodynamically stable and of astrophysical interest regarding realistic DM halos in cosmology.

The above stability analysis can be solved in an elegant manner via the 'Katz criterion'.[12] This allows to find the full set of thermodynamically-stable solutions (i.e. maxima of global entropy S) along the full series of equilibrium solutions of self-gravitating fermions. This is a powerful and rigorous method which relies only in the derivatives of the caloric curve given by total energy $E = c^2 M(R)$ vs. $1/T_\infty$ (like in Fig. 1), and without the need of calculating explicitly the (rather involving) second order entropy variations $\delta^2 S$. This is a commonly used method to calculate the stability of self-gravitating systems (see e.g. Refs. 9, 3). We work in the microcanonical ensemble applied for isolated systems since, as explained in detail in Ref. 9, it is the most appropriate for astrophysical applications. The relevant thermodynamic potential to be extremized in this ensemble is the coarse-grained entropy S.

In order for such a maximization entropy problem to be well defined, the self-gravitating solutions with given particle number $N = \int_0^R n(r)e^{\lambda/2}4\pi r^2 dr$ and total energy $E = c^2 M(R)$ must be bounded in radius, as occurring when working with the tidally-truncated DF (1). We recall this is not the case for the standard Fermi-Dirac DF (i.e coarse-grained solution of the VP equation), which instead leads to unbounded systems. Therefore, our approach is well posed and without the need to invoke unrealistic bounding boxes.[3]

3. Astrophysical & cosmological applications

We use the following method to assure that the fixed boundary conditions — such as N and corresponding $M(R)$ required to maximize the global entropy S — do correspond to values of a given fermionic halo in a realistic cosmological framework: **(i)** calculate the linear matter power spectrum for such fermionic (quantum) candidates; **(ii)** apply the corresponding Press-Schechter formalism to obtain the virial halo mass, $M_{\rm vir} \equiv M(R \equiv R_{\rm vir})$, with associated redshift $z_{\rm vir}$ for such a particle mass; and then **(iii)** use the the most probable coarse-grained DF (1) obtained at the end of violent relaxation (valid for that redshift), to obtain the full families of DM (equilibrium) profiles in agreement with above virial constraints. Having done this, we can analyze the (thermodynamic) stability of such halos using the Katz criterion in a given cosmological framework, and further check their astrophysical applications.

This strategy was recently applied in Ref. 3 within a WDM cosmology for fermion masses of $\mathcal{O}(10)$ keV, and exemplified here for an average DM halo of mass $M_{\rm vir} \approx 5 \times 10^{10} M_\odot$, which started to form at $z_{\rm vir} \approx 10$ according to the Press-Schechter formalism in our cosmological setup.

We show in Fig. 1 the caloric curve in dimensionless variables, $-\hat{M}$ vs. $1/\hat{T}_\infty$, for an average DM halo (with corresponding $\hat{N} = 76.25$, and $W_0 - \theta_0 = 24$ typical of average-size galaxies[3]) and for a particle mass of $m = 48$ keV. The stability analysis is based on the Katz criterion and follows the global procedure **(i-iii)** mentioned above. A practical *rule of thumb* to understand how the Katz criterion works is: (a) an unstable mode (coming from stable ones) arises when the caloric curve *rotates clockwise* (i.e. when the negative slope in the $(-\hat{M}, \hat{T}_\infty^{-1})$ curve becomes infinite for then turning into positive), (b) when the same curve *rotates counterclockwise* a stable mode has been re-gained (the later implying that a positive slope turned into negative just after becoming vertical). In this sense, once in a given unstable branch of the caloric curve, it is necessary as many counterclockwise turns of the curve as clockwise passed, to regain the thermodynamic stability (see Appendix A in Ref. 3 for details).

In Fig. 1, we display the full family of thermodynamically-stable (i.e. maxima of S) solutions in continuous-blue line, and the thermodynamically unstable ones (i.e. minimum or saddle points of S) in dotted-violet. Interestingly, there are two spiral features in this caloric curve. The upper one arises due to the fermion (quantum) degeneracy which avoids the *gravothermal catastrophe* typical of Boltzmannian distributions (as first shown for classical systems in Ref. 13). The second spiral feature is of relativistic origin and lead to the turning point criterion for gravitational collapse discussed below.

We now highlight the main conclusions of this stability analysis, and its cosmological and astrophysical consequences in three different subsections.

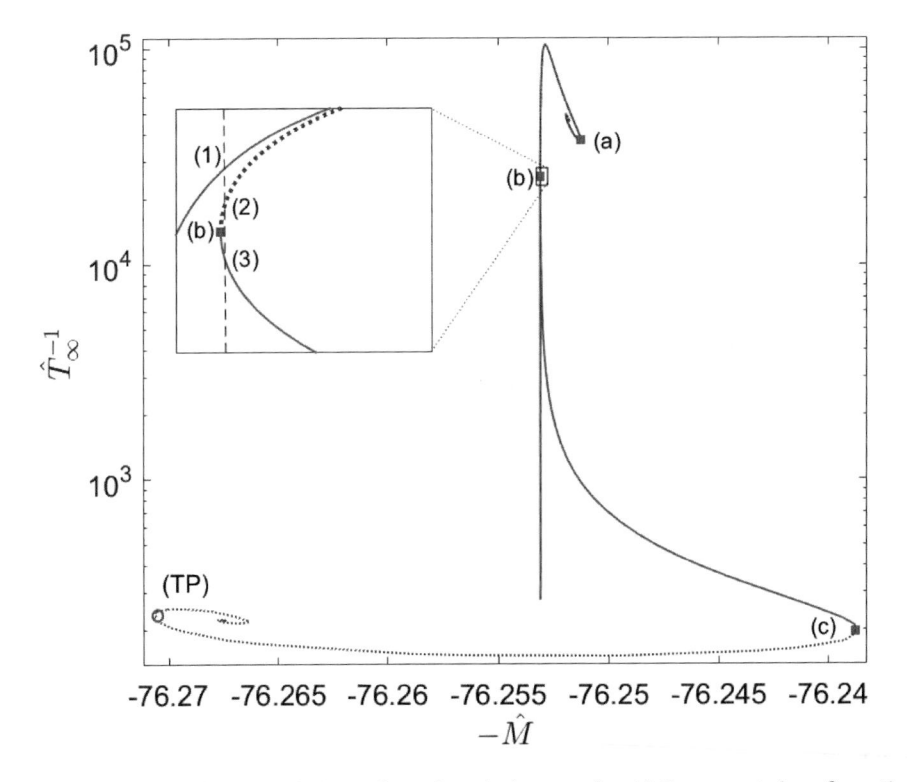

Fig. 1. Series of equilibrium solutions along the caloric curve for tidally-truncated configurations of $mc^2 = 48$ keV fermions, for typical DM halos of $M_{\rm vir} \approx 5 \times 10^{10} M_\odot$. The equilibrium states within the continuous-blue branches are thermodynamically (and dynamically) stable, while the dotted-violet branches — between (a) and (b) and after (c) — are unstable, according to the Katz criterion. Figure taken from Ref. 3.

3.1. *The shape of the fermionic DM halos*

We analyze from the caloric curve of Fig. 1 all the different kinds of density profiles for a conveniently fixed value of the total energy $\hat{M}$ (see vertical black-dashed line in the inset-box of Fig. 1, leading to the associated profiles of Fig. 2). There are two different families of stable and astrophysical DM profiles in a $\mathcal{O}(10)$ keV cosmology, arising from our (thermodynamic) halo-formation approach. They are either King-like, as the solution (1) in Fig. 1 (resembling the Burkert profile), or they develop a *core-halo* morphology (like the solution (3) in Fig. 1). Importantly, both kinds of solutions can agree with the observational DM surface density relation of galaxies (the latter $\propto \rho(r_{pl})\, r_h$, with $\rho(r_{pl})$ the density at plateau, and r_h the one-halo scale-length of such profiles), as demonstrated in Ref. 3. In the first case, the fermions are in the dilute regime (i.e. $\theta_0 \ll -1$) and correspond to a global maxima of entropy, while in the second case, the degeneracy pressure (i.e. Pauli principle) is holding the quantum core against gravity, and correspond to a local maxima of entropy. This kind of fermionic *core-halo* solutions are usually referred as the Ruffini-Argüelles-Rueda (RAR) model.[10,14] They are extremely long-lived, meta-stable states as demonstrated in Ref. 3, with a lifetime $\propto e^N$, and more likely to arise in Nature than the former as argued in Ref. 9.

Remarkably, solutions like (3) in Fig. 1 can fit the rotation curve in galaxies, such as in the case of the Milky Way as shown in Fig. 3, while their dense quantum core can work as an alternative to the SMBH in non-active galaxies.[10,11,15,16] Indeed, this latter statement was analyzed in the case of our own Galaxy in Ref. 15 within the extended RAR model for $mc^2 = 56$ keV. It has been there shown that the gravitational potential of the DM dense core of such a configuration leads to better fit of the orbits of the S2 and G2 objects around Sgr A*, with respect to the one obtained by the central BH model (see Figs. 4 and 5). Furthermore, a geodesic in the gravitational field of the DM profile of the extended RAR model naturally predicts the post-pericenter slowing down phenomenon observed in G2 (see Fig. 5), result that contrasts with the BH hypothesis where it has been proposed that G2 is being slowed down by a drag force caused by an accretion flow onto the massive BH over which G2 should move.[17,18] Finally, strengthening this DM interpretation of the Galactic Center, in Ref. 16, this result has been extended to the up-to-date astrometry data of the 17 best-resolved S-stars orbiting Sgr A*, achieving to explain the dynamics of the S-stars with similar (and some cases better) accuracy compared to a central BH model (see Fig. 6), strengthen the alternative nature of Sgr A*.

Another key consequence of such a thermodynamic approach for DM halo formation is that, on inner halo scales, the $\mathcal{O}(10)$ keV fermionic density profiles develops an extended plateau (similar to Burkert profiles, with or without the innermost quantum core depending on the degree of central degeneracy), thus not suffering from the core-cusp problem associated to the standard ΛCDM cosmology.[19] Interestingly, while in N-body simulations (within the CDM paradigm) it is possible to obtain 'cored' profiles when including for DM self-interactions (see e.g. Ref. 20), here the flatness on inner halo scales are obtained due to the fulfillment of an entropy maximization. The later can be achieved thanks to the long range particle-particle interactions involved in the diffusion-current term of equation (2) (see also footnote a) as shown here, or complementarily it could be enhanced by (short-range) DM self-interactions as well.

3.2. *Gravitational core-collapse of DM and SMBH formation*

Another striking consequence of the present DM halo formation approach is that it predicts a novel SMBH formation mechanism from DM. Namely, a galactic quantum core made of DM (like in solution (3) of Fig. 2) might become so densely packed that, above a threshold critical mass, the quantum pressure can not support it any longer against its own weight, leading to its gravitational collapse and forming a SMBH. Such threshold solution correspond to the last-stable configuration depicted

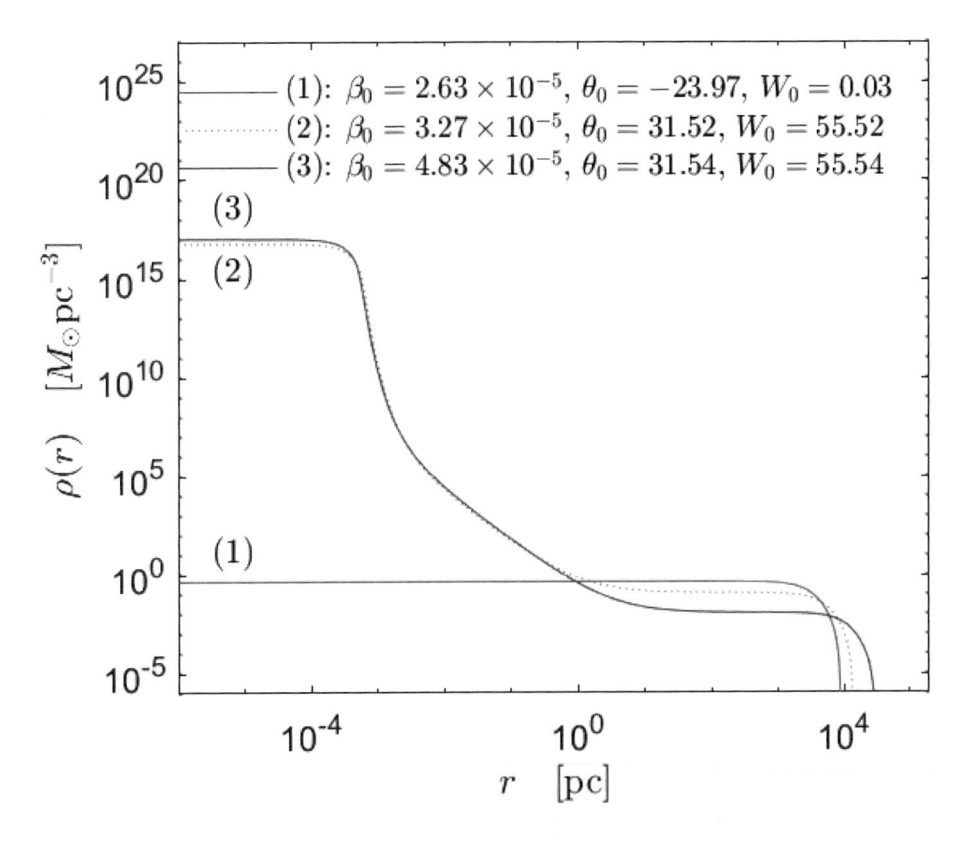

$$\text{(1): } \beta_0 = 2.63 \times 10^{-5}, \theta_0 = -23.97, W_0 = 0.03$$
$$\text{(2): } \beta_0 = 3.27 \times 10^{-5}, \theta_0 = 31.52, W_0 = 55.52$$
$$\text{(3): } \beta_0 = 4.83 \times 10^{-5}, \theta_0 = 31.54, W_0 = 55.54$$

Fig. 2. Density profiles for $mc^2 = 48$ keV corresponding with three different solutions along the caloric curve in Fig. 1 at a fixed energy. Only the profiles (1) (resembling a King distribution) and the *core-halo* one (3) are stable, while profile (2) is thermodynamically unstable. Solutions like (3) are successfully applied to explain the Milky Way rotatoin curve (see Fig. 3). They are stable, extremely long-lived and fulfill with different observational probes. Figure taken from Ref. 3.

by the point (c) in the caloric curve of Fig. 1, below which there is no possible accessible state (see Ref. 3 for details). Moreover, such a collapse occurs *prior* to the turning point in the (traditional) *total mass* vs. *central density* diagram (see Fig. 7). This result, occurring here for self-gravitating systems of neutral fermions at finite T_∞ in GR, agrees with similar findings within rotating perfect-fluid stars,[25] and generalizes the traditional result applied to compact objects (such as neutron stars) based on full degeneracy ($T \to 0$).

This kind of DM core-collapse can only occur when the total particle number exceeds the so-called Oppenheimer-Volkoff limit (i.e. $\hat{N} > \hat{N}_{\rm OV} \approx 0.4$, as fulfilled in the case here exemplified of $\hat{N} = 76.25$). However, as explained in Sec. 3.1, it can also exist a stable branch of *core-halo* solutions for such $\hat{N} > \hat{N}_{\rm OV}$ as exemplified through the solution (3) in Fig. 1, before the last stable one (c). This fact is characteristic of self-gravitating solutions of fermions at finite T (as in the RAR model), which

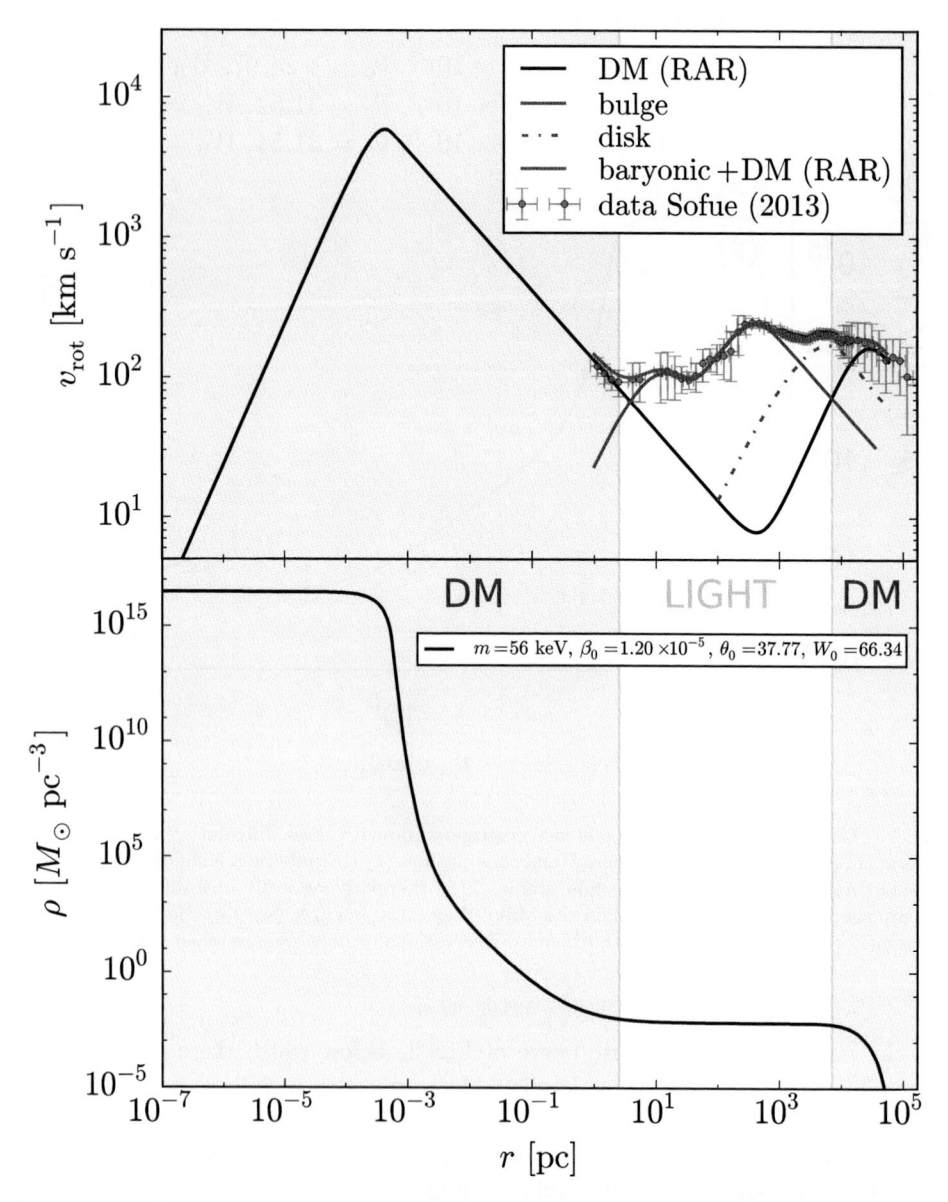

Fig. 3. Milky Way rotation curve and DM density profile within the core-halo DM RAR profiles for $mc^2 = 56$ keV, with a DM quantum core of mass of $M_c = M(r_c) = 3.5 \times 10^6 M_\odot$. Top: DM (black) and baryonic (bulge + disk) contribution to the rotation curve $v_{\rm rot}$ (total in red). Bottom: corresponding DM density profile. Figure taken from Ref. 15.

differ from the traditional $T \to 0$ limit where the system must necesarily collapse when $\hat{N} > \hat{N}_{\rm OV}$ (see Ref. 3 for further details).

In cases when $\hat{N} > \hat{N}_{\rm OV}$ as the one shown here, and for $mc^2 \approx 50$ keV, it is possible to form a SMBH of $M_c^{\rm cr} \approx 2 \times 10^8 M_\odot$ at the center of a realistic DM halo:

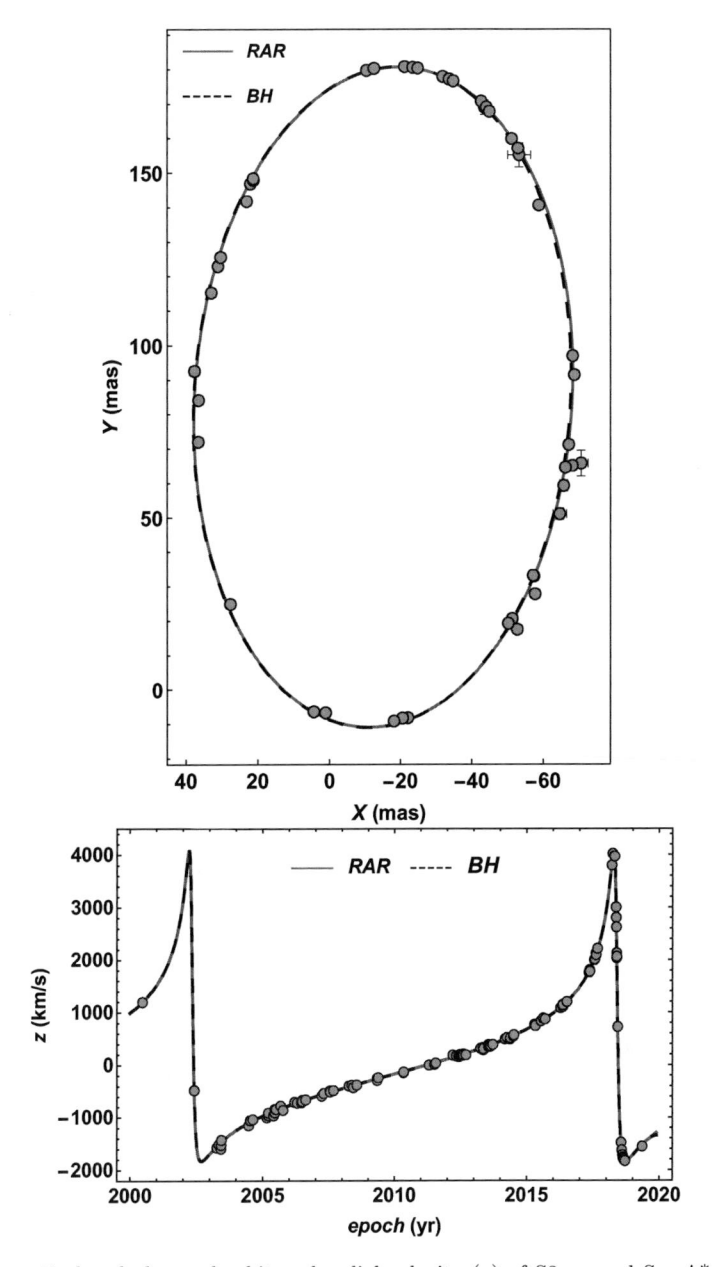

Fig. 4. Theoretical and observed orbit and radial velocity (z) of S2 around Sgr A* (wiht data taken from Ref. 21). Top panel: shows the projected orbit on the sky, X (Right Ascension) vs. Y (Declination). Bottom panel: shows the line–of–sight radial velocity as a function of time. The theoretical models are calculated by solving the equations of motion of a test particle in the gravitational field of: (i) a Schwarzschild BH of 4.075×10^6 $M_\odot$ (*black dashed curve*), and (ii) the fermionic DM distribution obtained from the core-halo RAR model with $mc^2 = 56$ keV fermions (*red curves*). Figure adapted from Ref. 15.

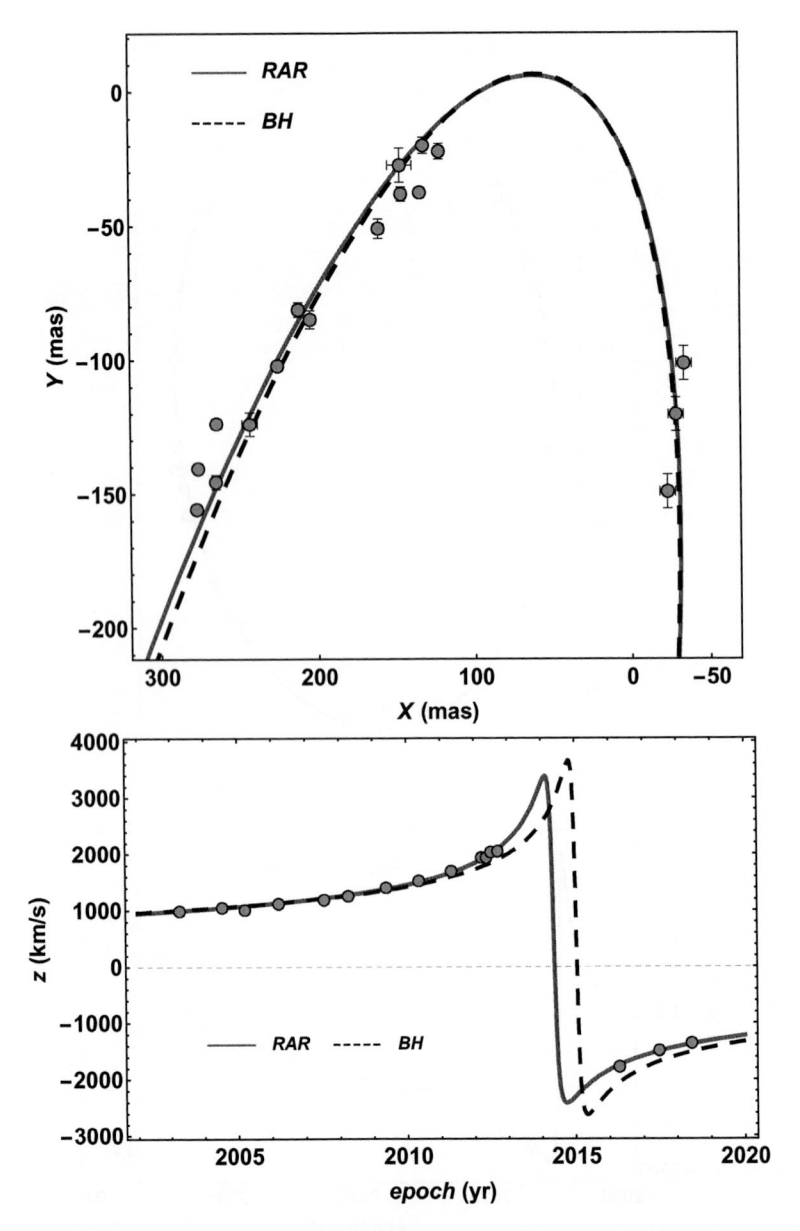

Fig. 5. Theoretical and observed orbit and line-of-sight radial velocity of G2 around Sgr A*. *Top panel*: shows the projected orbit on the sky, X (Right Ascension) vs. Y (Declination). *Bottom panel*: shows the redshift function z as a function of time. The theoretical models are calculated by solving the equations of motion of a test particle in the gravitational field of: (1) a Schwarzschild BH of 4.075×10^6 M$_\odot$ (*black dashed curve*), and (2) the DM distribution obtained from the extended RAR model for 56 keV fermions (*red curves*). The mass of the quantum core in the RAR model is 3.5×10^6 M$_\odot$. The observational data are taken from Refs. 17, 18, 22. Figure adapted from Ref. 15.

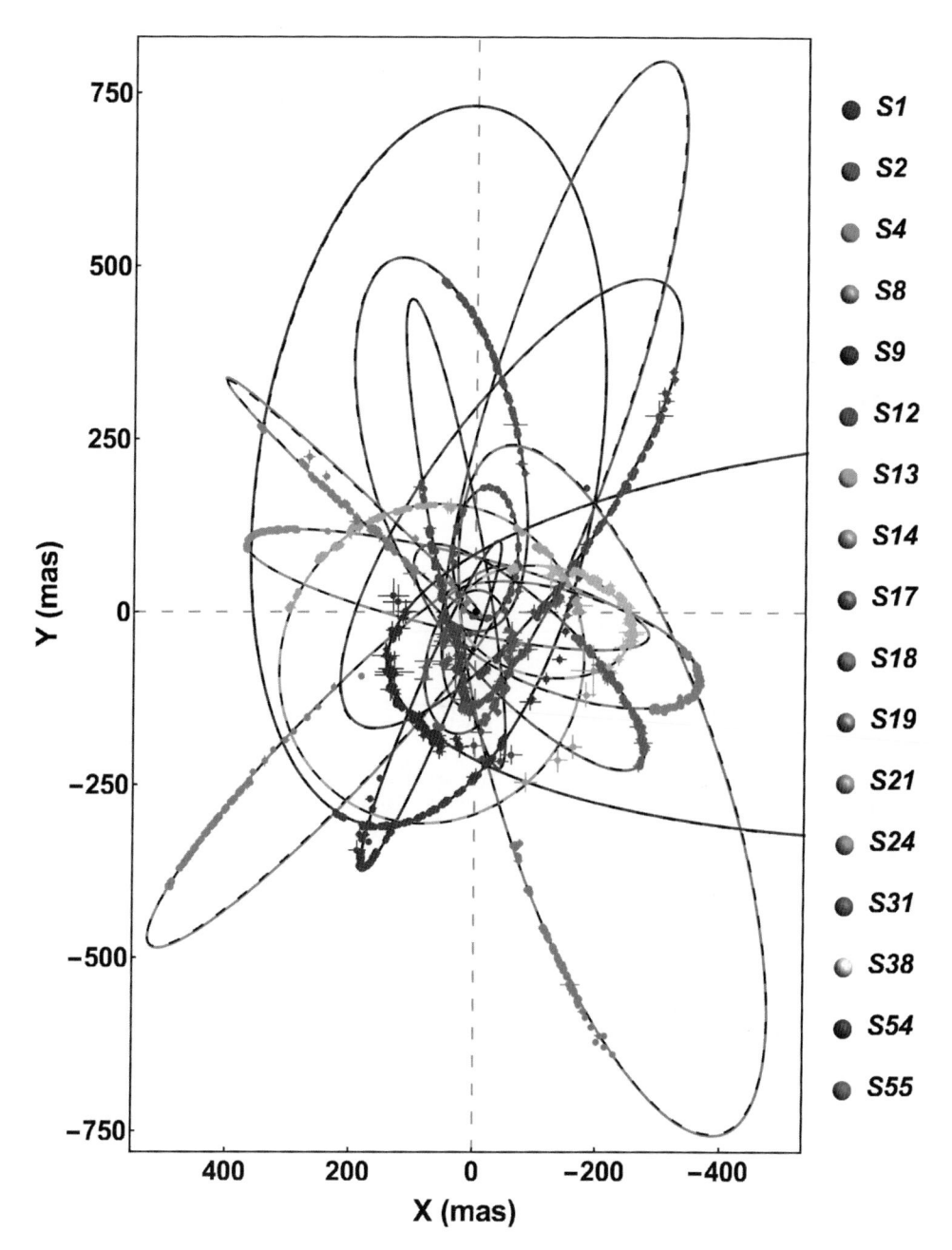

Fig. 6. Best-fit orbits for the 17 best-resolved S-star orbiting Sgr A*. It shows the projected orbit on the sky, X vs. Y, where X is right ascension and Y is declination. The *black dashed curves* correspond to the BH model and the *colored curves* to the RAR model for $m \approx 56$ keV fermions. The astrometric data was taken from Refs. 21, 23, 24. Figure taken from Ref. 16.

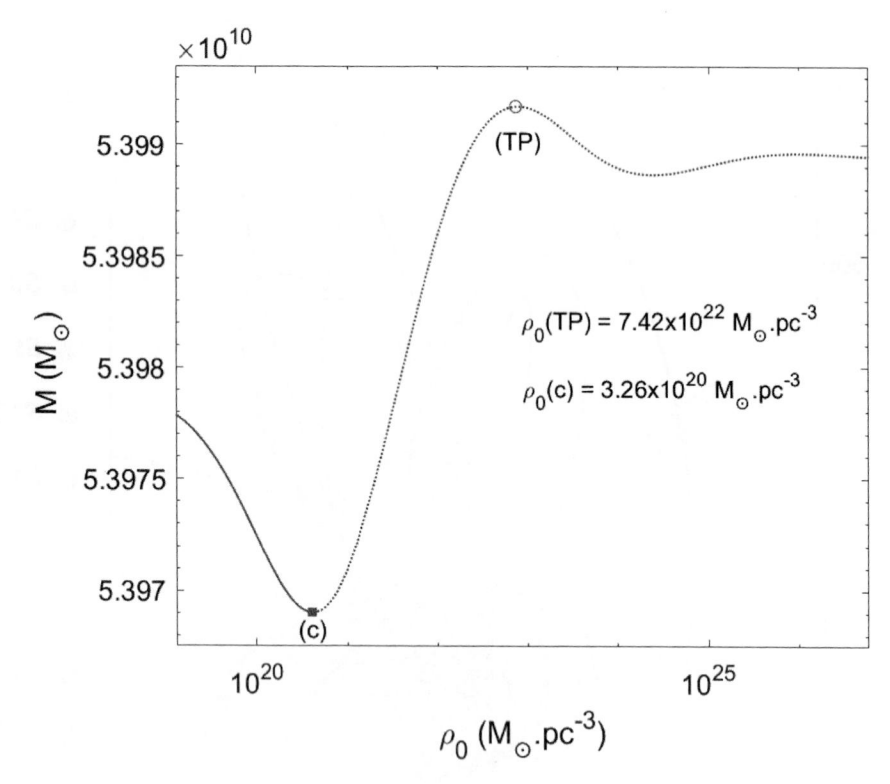

Fig. 7. Series of equilibrium states with $N > N_{OV}$ are shown along a ρ_0 vs. M curve, in correspondence with the caloric curve of Fig. 1. The last stable configuration at the onset of the core-collapse occurs at the minimum of this curve and *prior* to the turning point instability (corresponding with point (c) in Fig. 1). Such a critical solution has a critical core mass $M_c^{cr} \approx 2 \times 10^8 M_\odot$, and thus a forming a SMBH from DM core-collapse. Figure taken from Ref. 3.

that is, the last stable configuration at the onset of the core-collapse (point (c) in Fig. 1) correspond to a critical core mass $M_c^{cr} = 2.17 \times 10^8 M_\odot$, and thus a forming a SMBH from DM core-collapse (see Ref. 3 for more details). This is an interesting number, since the majority of the SMBHs are comprised within $\sim 10^8 M_\odot$,[26] in some way separating active from non-active galaxies. Moreover, the relevance of such a DM core-collapse scenario, is that it can occur within the high $z \sim 10$ Universe when such halos start to form, without the need of prior star formation or any BH seed mechanisms involving (likely unrealistic) super-Eddington accretion rates. This may provide the long-sought solution to the problem of SMBH formation in the early Universe, which deserves further detailed investigations.

Such a critical value triggering core-collapse can be written in a more familiar way in terms of the Planck mass m_{pl} and the fermion mass m as $N_{OV} \approx 0.398 \, m_{pl}^3/m^3$, corresponding to a critical (total) mass $M_{OV} \approx 0.384 \, m_{pl}^3/m^2$ which for $m \approx 50$ keV yields $M_{OV} \sim 10^8 M_\odot$. Therefore, equilibrium configurations of fermions at finite T_∞ with $M_{vir} < 10^8 M_\odot$ can not undergo core-collapse towards a

SMBH within the present scenario. Indeed, the caloric curves in such cases never develop a last-stable solution (like (c) in Fig. 1), nor the second spiral of relativistic origin as shown in Ref. 3.

The above numbers imply another intriguing consequence for this new theory: the critical mass for collapse into a massive BH can not be reached for smaller DM halos, for example those surrounding typical dwarf galaxies with $M_{\rm vir} \lesssim 10^8 M_\odot$. Instead, this $\hat{N} < \hat{N}_{\rm OV}$ scenario would leave smaller dwarf galaxies with a central DM nucleus with a mass typically of $M_c \sim 10^5 M_\odot$ (or less) as shown in Ref. 11, thus offering a natural explanation for the so called 'intermediate-mass BHs'. Such a DM quantum-core can still mimic the gravitational signatures of a central BH, whilst the dark matter outer halo could also explain the observed galaxy rotation curves.[11]

4. Conclusions

We have shown that mechanisms of DM halo formation based on entropy maximization in which the quantum (fermionic) nature of the particles is accounted for, may provide answers to crucial open problems in cosmology. In particular they allow: to constraint the mass of the DM particles, to provide a novel mechanisms of supermassive BH formation from DM core-collapse, to understand the nature of the intermediate mass black holes in small halos, and to provide a solution to the *core-cusp* problem.

The approach applied here (and detailed in[3]) for DM halo formation in terms of self-gravitating fermions is self-consistent: the nature and mass of the DM particle involved in the linear matter power spectrum calculations (as obtained in Ref. 3 within a CLASS code for WDM cosmology of $\mathcal{O}(10)$ keV), are the same building blocks at the basis of virialized DM configurations with its inherent effects in the *core-halo* profiles. Importantly, such a fermion mass would produce the same ΛCDM power-spectrum on scales down to $\mathcal{O}(\text{Mpc})$, hence providing the expected large-scale structure (see Appendix B in Ref. 3). Moreover, for such typical fermion masses the number of sub-halos in the corresponding WDM cosmology is not in tension with the number of Milky Way satellites,[27] while being consistent with Lyman-α forest observations.[28] Another relevant consequence is that the maximum entropy approach for structure formation applying here for $\mathcal{O}(10)$ keV particles, can naturally avoid the so called 'catch-22' tension arising for fermionic halos within (N-body simulation-based) WDM cosmologies.[29] That is, the resulting fermionic profiles within our approach allow for 'cored' density profiles in dwarfs with right sizes and masses, and at the same time in agreement with Lyman-α bounds.[11]

To conclude, we believe the results shown here open new insights in the formation and stability of DM halos. Moreover, the quantum degenerate core at the center of the stable DM configurations, and its eventual core-collapse, may play crucial roles in helping to understand the formation of SMBHs in the early Universe, or in mimicking its effects without the need of a singularity at all. The astrophysical consequences of the analysis here shown for $\mathcal{O}(10)$ keV — together with the recent results in Refs. 3, 10, 11, 15 — strongly suggest that such DM *core-halo* morphology are a very plausible scenario within the late stages of non-linear structure formation.

References

1. H. Mo, F. Van den Bosch and S. White, *Galaxy formation and evolution* (Cambridge University Press, 2010).
2. H.-Y. Schive, M.-H. Liao, T.-P. Woo, S.-K. Wong, T. Chiueh, T. Broadhurst and W. Y. P. Hwang, *Phys. Rev. Lett.* **113** (December 2014) 261302, arXiv:1407.7762 [astro-ph.GA].
3. C. R. Argüelles, M. I. Díaz, A. Krut and R. Yunis, *Mon. Not. R. Astron. Soc.* **502** (April 2021) 4227, arXiv:2012.11709 [astro-ph.GA].
4. R. RUFFINI and S. BONAZZOLA, *Phys. Rev.* **187** (Nov 1969) 1767.
5. D. Lynden-Bell, *Mon. Not. R. Astron. Soc.* **136** (January 1967) 101.
6. A. Kull, R. A. Treumann and H. Boehringer, *Astrophys. J.l* **466** (July 1996) L1, arXiv:astro-ph/9606057 [astro-ph].
7. P.-H. Chavanis, *Mon. Not. R. Astron. Soc.* **300** (November 1998) 981.
8. P.-H. Chavanis, *Physica A Statistical Mechanics and its Applications* **332** (February 2004) 89, arXiv:cond-mat/0304073 [cond-mat.stat-mech].
9. P.-H. Chavanis, M. Lemou and F. Méhats, *Phys. Rev. D* **92** (December 2015) 123527, arXiv:1409.7840 [astro-ph.CO].
10. C. R. Argüelles, A. Krut, J. A. Rueda and R. Ruffini, *Physics of the Dark Universe* **21** (September 2018) 82, arXiv:1810.00405 [astro-ph.GA].
11. C. R. Argüelles, A. Krut, J. A. Rueda and R. Ruffini, *Physics of the Dark Universe* **24** (March 2019) 100278.
12. J. Katz, *Mon. Not. R. Astron. Soc.* **189** (December 1979) 817.
13. P. H. Chavanis and J. Sommeria, *Mon. Not. R. Astron. Soc.* **296** (May 1998) 569.
14. R. Ruffini, C. R. Argüelles and J. A. Rueda, *Mon. Not. R. Astron. Soc.* **451** (July 2015) 622, arXiv:1409.7365 [astro-ph.GA].
15. E. A. Becerra-Vergara, C. R. Argüelles, A. Krut, J. A. Rueda and R. Ruffini, *Astron. & Astrophys.* **641** (September 2020) A34, arXiv:2007.11478 [astro-ph.GA].
16. E. A. Becerra-Vergara, C. R. Argüelles, A. Krut, J. A. Rueda and R. Ruffini, *Mon. Not. R. Astron. Soc.* **505** (July 2021) L64, arXiv:2105.06301 [astro-ph.GA].
17. P. M. Plewa, S. Gillessen, O. Pfuhl, F. Eisenhauer, R. Genzel, A. Burkert, J. Dexter, M. Habibi, E. George, T. Ott, I. Waisberg and S. von Fellenberg, *Astrophys. J.* **840** (May 2017) 50, arXiv:1704.05351.
18. S. Gillessen, P. M. Plewa, F. Widmann, S. von Fellenberg, M. Schartmann, M. Habibi, A. Jimenez Rosales, M. Bauböck, J. Dexter, F. Gao, I. Waisberg, F. Eisenhauer, O. Pfuhl, T. Ott, A. Burkert, P. T. de Zeeuw and R. Genzel, *Astrophys. J.* **871** (January 2019) 126.
19. J. S. Bullock and M. Boylan-Kolchin, *Annu. Rev. Astron. Astrophys.* **55** (August 2017) 343, arXiv:1707.04256 [astro-ph.CO].
20. R. Davé, D. N. Spergel, P. J. Steinhardt and B. D. Wandelt, *Astrophys. J.* **547** (February 2001) 574, arXiv:astro-ph/0006218 [astro-ph].
21. T. Do, A. Hees, A. Ghez, G. D. Martinez, D. S. Chu, S. Jia, S. Sakai, J. R. Lu, A. K. Gautam, K. K. O'Neil, E. E. Becklin, M. R. Morris, K. Matthews, S. Nishiyama, R. Campbell, S. Chappell, Z. Chen, A. Ciurlo, A. Dehghanfar, E. Gallego-Cano, W. E. Kerzendorf, J. E. Lyke, S. Naoz, H. Saida, R. Schödel, M. Takahashi, Y. Takamori,

G. Witzel and P. Wizinowich, *Science* **365** (August 2019) 664, arXiv:1907.10731 [astro-ph.GA].

22. K. Phifer, T. Do, L. Meyer, A. M. Ghez, G. Witzel, S. Yelda, A. Boehle, J. R. Lu, M. R. Morris, E. E. Becklin and K. Matthews, *Astrophys. J.l* **773** (August 2013) L13, arXiv:1304.5280 [astro-ph.GA].
23. S. Gillessen, P. M. Plewa, F. Eisenhauer, R. Sari, I. Waisberg, M. Habibi, O. Pfuhl, E. George, J. Dexter, S. von Fellenberg, T. Ott and R. Genzel, *Astrophys. J.* **837** (March 2017) 30, arXiv:1611.09144 [astro-ph.GA].
24. S. Gillessen, F. Eisenhauer, S. Trippe, T. Alexander, R. Genzel, F. Martins and T. Ott, *Astrophys. J.* **692** (February 2009) 1075, arXiv:0810.4674 [astro-ph].
25. K. Takami, L. Rezzolla and S. Yoshida, *Mon. Not. R. Astron. Soc.* **416** (September 2011) L1, arXiv:1105.3069 [gr-qc].
26. K. Gültekin, D. O. Richstone, K. Gebhardt, T. R. Lauer, S. Tremaine, M. C. Aller, R. Bender, A. Dressler, S. M. Faber, A. V. Filippenko, R. Green, L. C. Ho, J. Kormendy, J. Magorrian, J. Pinkney and C. Siopis, *Astrophys. J.* **698** (June 2009) 198, arXiv:0903.4897 [astro-ph.GA].
27. E. J. Tollerud, J. S. Bullock, L. E. Strigari and B. Willman, *Astrophys. J.* **688** (November 2008) 277, arXiv:0806.4381 [astro-ph].
28. V. Iršič, M. Viel, M. G. Haehnelt, J. S. Bolton, S. Cristiani, G. D. Becker, V. D'Odorico, G. Cupani, T.-S. Kim, T. A. M. Berg, S. López, S. Ellison, L. Christensen, K. D. Denney and G. Worseck, *Phys. Rev. D* **96** (July 2017) 023522, arXiv:1702.01764 [astro-ph.CO].
29. A. V. Macciò, S. Paduroiu, D. Anderhalden, A. Schneider and B. Moore, *Mon. Not. R. Astron. Soc.* **424** (August 2012) 1105, arXiv:1202.1282 [astro-ph.CO].

First results of LHAASO

Ruo-Yu Liu* for the LHAASO Collaboration

*School of Astronomy and Space Science, Nanjing University,
Nanjing, 210023, China*
*E-mail: ryliu@nju.edu.cn

The Large High Altitude Air Shower Observatory (LHAASO) has recently published the first results, including the discovery of 12 ultrahigh-energy gamma-ray sources (with emission above 100 TeV) above 7σ confidence level and a detailed analysis of Crab Nebula. This contribution gives a brief introduction to the LHAASO experiment and its recent discoveries.

Keywords: Gamma rays; Cosmic rays; Pulsar Wind Nebula

1. Introduction

The Large High Altitude Air Shower Observatory (LHAASO) is one of the key national science and technology infrastructure facilities of China, located in Mt. Haizi (29°21'27.6" N, 100°08'19.6" E, 4410 m above the sea level), Sichuan Province of China. It is a new generation instrument aiming for a deep investigation of the so-called "non-themral Universe" at extreme energies. The observatory consists of three detectors: the Water Cherenkov Detector Array (WCDA) for gamma rays in 0.5 – 10 TeV, the Kilometer Square Array (KM2A) for gamma rays in 10 TeV – 1 PeV, and the Wide Field Chenrenkov Telescope Array (WFCTA) for cosmic rays from 1 TeV – 1 EeV.

KM2A comprises an array of 5195 electron detectors (ED) made by scintillation tiles, and an array of 1188 underground muon detectors (MD) each of which is a pure water Cherenkov detector enclosed within a cylindrical concrete tank. Both arrays cover an area of 1 km^2 with an additional 0.3 km^2 skirt array used to identify showers falling outside the central region. Once charged particles in an air shower enter an ED, they lose energy and excite the scintillation medium to produce a large amount of scintillation photons, which will be recorded by photomultiplier tubes and used to determine the number of electromagnetic particles N_e in a shower. Each MD is enveloped by a steel lid underneath soil. The thickness of the overburden soil is 2.5 m to absorb the secondary electrons/positrons and gamma rays in showers. Thus particles that can reach the water inside and produce Cherenkov signals are almost exclusively muons, although a few very energetic electrons/positrons or gamma rays in the central part of showers may have a chance to penetrate through the screening soil layer. To reduce the possible pollution from the high energy electromagnetic particles near the shower core, only MDs with a distance farther than 15 m from the core are used to count the number of muons N_μ in a shower.

Each air shower event is composed of many ED and MD hits with timing and charge information. In the reconstruction of primary particle event, only the ED hits are used for direction, core location, and energy reconstruction. Both ED hits and MD hits are used for composition discrimination. Gamma-ray-induced showers are muon-poor while cosmic-ray-induced showers are muon-rich. Therefore, the ratio between the measured muons and electrons can be used to discriminate primary gamma rays from cosmic protons/nuclei, which is defined as

$$R = \log\left(\frac{N_\mu + 0.0001}{N_e}\right). \qquad (1)$$

0.0001 in the numerator is used to show the case with zero muon. Generally, a simple cut on the parameter R is used in the discrimination, where the detailed value of R depends on the energy of the reconstructed event and can be adjusted to maximize the detection efficiency.[1] This process is extremely important for the gamma ray detection because cosmic rays constitute the majority of the recorded events by KM2A and become a background for the gamma-ray observations. The rejection power of KM2A can be better than 10^4 above 100 TeV (i.e., reduce the background cosmic-ray flux by a factor higher than 10^4). The large collective area and the high rejection power make LHAASO the most sensitive detector for ultrahigh-energy (UHE) gamma rays with energy above 100 TeV.

Detection of UHE gamma-ray emission is crucial to understand the origin of Galactic cosmic rays. The measured cosmic-ray spectrum roughly maintains a power-law behaviour up to about 1 PeV. After that it shows a spectral break feature known as the "knee". This indicates the existence of astrophysical objects in our Galaxy capable of accelerating protons up to at least PeV energies (which is also known as proton "PeVatrons"). When these high-energy protons interact with matter inside or close to the accelerators, neutral pions are generated, which further decay into gamma-ray photons. These gamma-ray emission reveal the location of the cosmic-ray accelerators. Since each produced photon takes about 10% of the energy of the parent proton, we need to search for UHE gamma-ray sources in order to find out PeV cosmic-ray sources. In the rest of this artcile, we will introduce the first results of LHAASO, which are mainly based on[2] and.[3]

2. Discovery of 12 Ultrahigh-energy Gamma-ray Sources

The first results of LHAASO are mainly discovered by the half KM2A during the operation of 11 months in the year 2020. By reconstructing showers with zenith angle < 50°, we have detected 12 sources with emission above 100 TeV at the statistical significance exceeding 7σ level and the basic information of the sources are listed in Table. 1. All of these sources are located in the Galactic plane and hence very likely Galactic sources. Most of them show extended spatial structures with angular extensions up to 1°. Generally, there are multiple astrophysical objects proposed as potential PeVatron candidates in spatial association with these sources.

Table 1. UHE γ-ray sources. The celestial coordinates (R.A.,dec), the statistical significance of detection above 100 TeV (using a point-like template for the Crab Nebula and LHAASO J2108+5157 and 0.3° extension templates for other sources) are shown together with the corresponding differential photon fluxes at 100 TeV in unit of the Crab flux (1 CU=6.1×10^{-17} photons TeV^{-1} cm^{-2} s^{-1}) and the detected highest photon energies.

Source Name	R.A. (°)	dec (°)	Significance (σ) above 100 TeV	E_{Max} (PeV)	Flux (± error) (CU) at 100 TeV
LHAASO J0534+2202	83.55	22.05	17.8	0.88 ±0.11	1.00(0.14)
LHAASO J1825-1326	276.45	-13.45	16.4	0.42 ±0.16	3.57(0.52)
LHAASO J1839-0545	279.95	-5.75	7.7	0.21 ±0.05	0.70(0.18)
LHAASO J1843-0338	280.75	-3.65	8.5	$0.26^{+0.16}_{-0.10}$	0.73(0.17)
LHAASO J1849-0003	282.35	-0.05	10.4	0.35 ±0.07	0.74(0.15)
LHAASO J1908+0621	287.05	6.35	17.2	0.44 ±0.05	1.36(0.18)
LHAASO J1929+1745	292.25	17.75	7.4	$0.71^{+0.16}_{-0.07}$	0.38(0.09)
LHAASO J1956+2845	299.05	28.75	7.4	0.42 ±0.03	0.41(0.09)
LHAASO J2018+3651	304.75	36.85	10.4	0.27 ±0.02	0.50(0.10)
LHAASO J2032+4102	308.05	41.05	10.5	1.42 ±0.13	0.54(0.10)
LHAASO J2108+5157	317.15	51.95	8.3	0.43 ±0.05	0.38(0.09)
LHAASO J2226+6057	336.75	60.95	13.6	0.57 ±0.19	1.05(0.16)

Among these astrophysical objects, most of them are supernova remnants, pulsar wind nebulae and young massive star clusters.

The top-three brightest sources at 100 TeV are LHAASO J1825-1326, LHAASO J1908+0621 and LHAASO J2226+6057. The regions of the three sources have been extensively studied in the previous literature (e.g.,[4-27]). All of them are associated with both energetic pulsars and supernova remnants. Dense molecular clouds also appear in their region. LHAASO's observations extend their spectra up to several hundred TeV energies, demonstrating there exist efficient particle accelerators acting as PeV particle factories. The spectra present gradual softening towards high energies. The log-parabola function can describe the spectra better than power-law function, as can be seen in Fig. 1. However, we cannot tell whether these multi-hundred-TeV gamma rays arise from the leptonic process such as the inverse Compton (IC) scattering of electrons, or hadronic process such as the proton-proton (pp) collisions, based on the present data. Deep observations of multiwavelength instruments are needed to elucidate their natures.

We'd like to highlight that the energy of the most energetic photons detected from these sources is 1.42 ± 0.13 PeV in association with the Cygnus Cocoon, which is a energetic gamma-ray emitter at GeV – TeV band. It has been proposed that Cygnus Cocoon is powered by the O/B star association, Cygnus OB2, possibly via collisions of the stellar winds.[28-30] LHAASO's discovery may be considered as the evidence of Cygnus OB2 as a proton PeVatron.

It is also worth mentioning that among the 12 detected sources, there is a new source, LHAASO J2108+5157, without association with any of the previously detected very-high-energy sources. The position of its gamma-ray emission is correlated with a giant molecular cloud, which makes the hadronic origin of the gamma-ray emission possible. Detection of this source also implies that there could be much more new UHE gamma-ray sources hiding in our Galaxy than we previously expected. Future observations of LHAASO with longer exposure can hopefully discovered more UHE gamma-ray sources or PeVatron candidates. We stress that the 12 sources reported here are UHE gamma-ray sources with significant emission above 100 TeV. There are much more sources with significantly detected by KM2A above 20 TeV, such as LHAASO J0621+3755[31] and LHAASO J0341+5258.[32]

Note that the only point-like source discovered in this survey, i.e., LHAASO J0534+2202, which is also the only identified source, is the Crab Nebula. The highest-energy photon from Crab Nebula reaches 0.88 ± 0.11 PeV, demonstrating it as an electron PeVatron. We will show more detailed analysis on Crab Nebula in the next section.

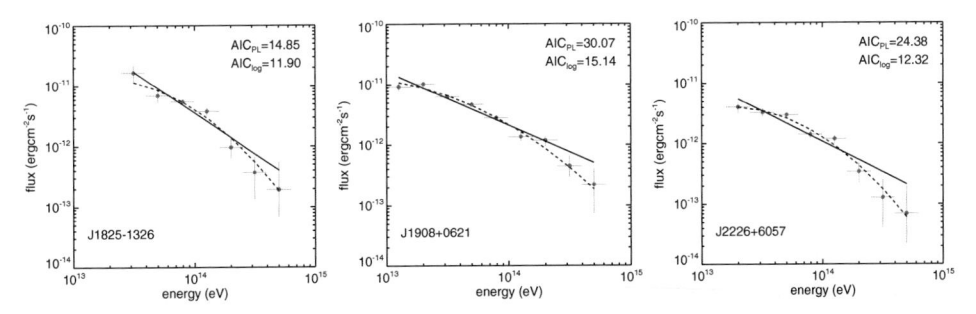

Fig. 1. The spectral energy distributions and significance maps of LHAASO J1825-1326 (panel a), LHAASO J1908+0621 (panel b), and LHAASO J2226+6057 (panel c) The spectral fits with a log-parabola function (solid lines) in the form of $(E/10 \text{ TeV})^{[-a-b \log(E/10\text{TeV})]}$ are compared with the power-law fits, $E^{-\Gamma}$: (a) $a = 0.92, b = 1.19$ vs $\Gamma = 3.36$; (b) $a = 2.27, b = 0.46$ vs $\Gamma = 2.89$, and (c) $a = 1.56, b = 0.88$ vs $\Gamma = 3.01$. The comparison of the two models with the Akaike Information Criterion[33] (AIC) gives: $\text{AIC}_{\text{LOG}} = 11.6$ and $\text{AIC}_{\text{PL}} = 14.8$ for LHAASO J1825-1326; $\text{AIC}_{\text{LOG}} = 15.1$ and $\text{AIC}_{\text{PL}} = 30.1$ for LHAASO J1908+0621; $\text{AIC}_{\text{LOG}} = 12.3$ and $\text{AIC}_{\text{PL}} = 24.4$ for LHAASO J2226+6057.

3. PeV Gamma rays from the Crab Nebula

The Crab Nebula was born from a supernova explosion occurring at Jul 4, 1054 A.D. It is the brightest pulsar wind nebula known so far, powered by the ultrarelativistic electron-positron wind launched by the Crab pulsar. It is a very important source in gamma-ray astronomy and considered as the standard candle. Previous observations revealed gamma-ray emission beyond 100 TeV.[34,35] LHAASO measured the spectrum of Crab Nebula in TeV – PeV range. The spectrum from 0.5 TeV to 13 TeV is measured using the WCDA pond, from September 2019 to October 2020. The KM2A data consists of that collected at the half array stage, which is the same as that used for the discovery of the twelve sources, and the data collected by three quarters of the array in about 3 months. The 0.88 PeV photon, as mentioned in the previous section, was detected on 11 January 2020. The shower of the event has also triggered WCDA. Coincidently, the event occurred after local midnight and was recorded by WFCTA. The derived energy is $0.92^{+0.28}_{-0.20}$ PeV which is well consistent with that derived from KM2A's measurement, and demonstrates that LHAASO can cross check the results using multiple detection techniques, ensuring reliable and accurate results. In the stage of the 3/4 KM2A, the highest-energy photon detected from the Crab Nebula has an energy of 1.12 PeV, arriving at 4 January 2021. The spectrum between 0.5 TeV to 1.1 PeV can be described by a log-parabola function, where the local slope softens from 2.5 around 1 TeV to 3.7 around 1 PeV.

The gradual softening of the spectrum is consistent with the prediction of IC radiation of electrons where the Klein-Nishina effect operates at the highest energies and softens the spectrum. For gamma-ray emission above 100 TeV, cosmic microwave background is the dominant target radiation field for the IC radiation. The relation between the average energy of upscattered IC photons (from 2.7K CMB) and the energy of the parent electrons can be given by

$$E_e \simeq 2.15(E_\gamma/1 \text{ PeV})^{0.77} \text{ PeV} . \qquad (2)$$

To account for 1.1 PeV photon via the IC radiation of electrons, the energy of electron needs to be about 2.3 PeV. The acceleration rate of electrons can be given by $\dot{E}_e = \eta e B c$,[36] where η is the ratio of the projection of the electric field to the mean magnetic field. Its value cannot exceed unity under the classical electrodynamics and ideal magnetohydrodynamics, and can be also regarded as the acceleration efficiency. On the other hand, electrons will lose energy via the synchrotron radiation when it propagates in the magnetic field. The maximum energy of electrons is then is determined by the balance between the acceleration and the energy loss rates, i.e.,

$$E_{e,\max} = 5.8\eta^{-1/2} (B/100\mu G)^{-1/2} \text{ PeV} \qquad (3)$$

On the other hand, in the framework of the standard one-zone model, fitting to the multiwavelength data from X-ray to PeV gamma-ray energies results in a magnetic field of $B = 112^{+15}_{-13} \mu G$, as shown in Fig. 2. According to the relation between E_γ and E_e given by Eq.(2), we find the electron acceleration in the Crab Nebula must proceed at an extreme efficiency

$$\eta = 0.16(B/112\mu G)(E_\gamma/1.1 \text{ PeV})^{1.54} \text{ PeV} . \qquad (4)$$

in the framework of the standard one-zone model. For comparison, at the diffusive shock acceleration in young supernova remnants,[37] η is smaller by at least 3 orders of magnitude.

Note that although the standard one-zone model can generally give an acceptable fit to the overall spectrum of the Crab Nebula, the presence of the intense flare at MeV/GeV band (also known as "Crab flare",[40,41]) implies fast acceleration and synchrotron cooling of sub-PeV/PeV electrons in compact (with size < 0.01 pc) highly magnetized (with $B \gtrsim 1$ mG) regions inside the nebula, and is thus inconsistent with the standard one-zone picture. Actually, in the spectral fitting of the KM2A data in the standard one-zone scenario, we find that the one-zone model does not agree very well with the measured flux in the energy range of $60-500$ TeV,

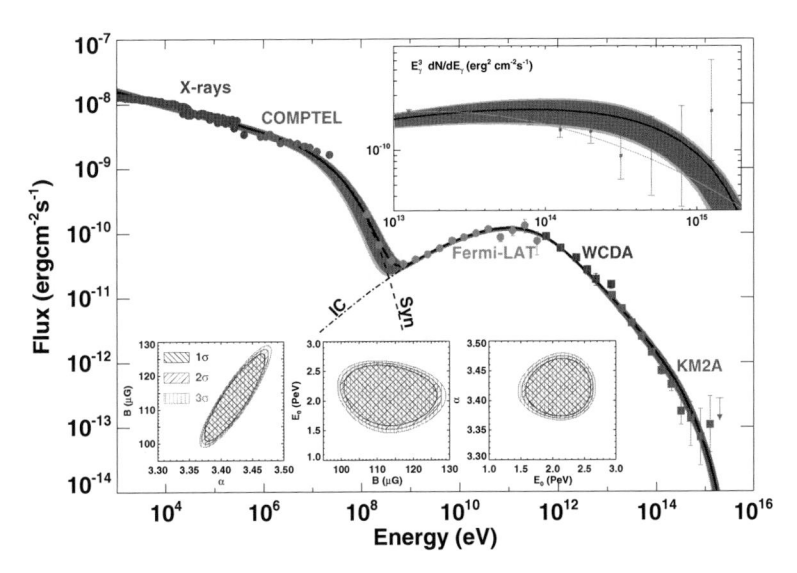

Fig. 2. **The Spectral Energy Distribution of the Crab Nebula.** The black curves represent the fluxes of the Synchrotron and IC components of radiation of an electron population calculated within the one-zone model. The electron spectrum above 1 TeV is assumed to be a power-law function terminated by an super-exponential cutoff, $E^{-\alpha}\exp[-(E/E_0)^2]$. The model's best fit parameters are: $\alpha = 3.42 \pm 0.05$, $E_0 = 2.15^{+0.55}_{-0.65}$ PeV, $B = 112^{+15}_{-13}$ μG. The total energy in electrons above 1 TeV is $W_e = 7.7 \times 10^{47}$ erg. A break in the electron spectrum at $E_b = 0.76$ TeV is assumed to provide a consistency with the GeV γ-ray and low-frequency synchrotron data. The dark-grey and light-grey shaded regions show the 1σ and 3σ error bands, respectively. The insets in the bottom exhibit the 2-dimensional projected parameter spaces of the free parameters α, B and E_0. The green curve presents the log-parabola spectral fitting. The purple and the magenta circles show the X-ray and the MeV emission of the Crab Nebula.[38] The orange circles represent the Crab observations by Fermi-LAT in the non-flare state.[39] The blue and red squares represent WCDA and KM2A measurements reported in.[3] The inserted figure in the top right corner zooms the fluxes above 10 TeV in the presentation of $E^3 dN/dE$.

nor it reproduces the spectral hardening above 500 TeV although the latter is not statistically sound at the present time. The fitting can be ameliorated by introducing a second spectral component, either produced by an extra population of PeV electrons or protons, which are accelerated presumably in different sites by different mechanisms. Based on the present observation, we expect that the full LHAASO array can detect 1 − 2 PeV photons from the Crab Nebula per year. Hopefully, we can accumulate sufficient statistics to clarify whether such a spectral hardening truly exists in 2 years.

4. Conclusion

LHAASO is a dual-purpose complex of particle detectors for the measurements of gamma rays in sub-TeV to PeV energy range and cosmic rays in TeV to EeV energy range. It is designed to be operating continuously and steadily for many years in order to accumulate a large data sets. The first results of LHAASO introduced here are probably only the tip of the iceberg, but they demonstrate LHAASO's potential to provide a deep insight into the mystery of cosmic-ray origin and related physics, especially when combined with the multiwavelength data of other instruments. The full LHAASO array has started to collect data since the end of July 2021. We anticipate more interesting discoveries by LHAASO in the coming years.

References

1. F. Aharonian, Q. An, Axikegu, L. X. Bai, Y. X. Bai, Y. W. Bao, D. Bastieri, X. J. Bi, Y. J. Bi, H. Cai, J. T. Cai, Z. Cao, Z. Cao, J. Chang, J. F. Chang, X. C. Chang, B. M. Chen, J. Chen, L. Chen, L. Chen, L. Chen, M. J. Chen, M. L. Chen, Q. H. Chen, S. H. Chen, S. Z. Chen, T. L. Chen, X. L. Chen, Y. Chen, N. Cheng, Y. D. Cheng, S. W. Cui, X. H. Cui, Y. D. Cui, B. Z. Dai, H. L. Dai, Z. G. Dai, Danzengluobu, D. Della Volpe, B. D. Piazzoli, X. J. Dong, J. H. Fan, Y. Z. Fan, Z. X. Fan, J. Fang, K. Fang, C. F. Feng, L. Feng, S. H. Feng, Y. L. Feng, B. Gao, C. D. Gao, Q. Gao, W. Gao, M. M. Ge, L. S. Geng, G. H. Gong, Q. B. Gou, M. H. Gu, J. G. Guo, X. L. Guo, Y. Q. Guo, Y. Y. Guo, Y. A. Han, H. H. He, H. N. He, J. C. He, S. L. He, X. B. He, Y. He, M. Heller, Y. K. Hor, C. Hou, X. Hou, H. B. Hu, S. Hu, S. C. Hu, X. J. Hu, D. H. Huang, Q. L. Huang, W. H. Huang, X. T. Huang, Z. C. Huang, F. Ji, X. L. Ji, H. Y. Jia, K. Jiang, Z. J. Jiang, C. Jin, D. Kuleshov, K. Levochkin, B. B. Li, C. Li, C. Li, F. Li, H. B. Li, H. C. Li, H. Y. Li, J. Li, K. Li, W. L. Li, X. Li, X. Li, X. R. Li, Y. Li, Y. Z. Li, Z. Li, Z. Li, E. W. Liang, Y. F. Liang, S. J. Lin, B. Liu, C. Liu, D. Liu, H. Liu, H. D. Liu, J. Liu, J. L. Liu, J. S. Liu, J. Y. Liu, M. Y. Liu, R. Y. Liu, S. M. Liu, W. Liu, Y. N. Liu, Z. X. Liu, W. J. Long, R. Lu, H. K. Lv, B. Q. Ma, L. L. Ma, X. H. Ma, J. R. Mao, A. Masood, W. Mitthumsiri, T. Montaruli, Y. C. Nan, B. Y. Pang, P. Pattarakijwanich, Z. Y. Pei, M. Y. Qi, D. Ruffolo, V. Rulev, A. Sáiz, L. Shao, O. Shchegolev, X. D. Sheng, J. R. Shi, H. C. Song, Y. V. Stenkin, V. Stepanov, Q. N. Sun, X. N. Sun, Z. B. Sun, P. H. T. Tam, Z. B. Tang, W. W. Tian, B. D. Wang, C. Wang, H. Wang, H. G. Wang, J. C. Wang, J. S. Wang, L. P. Wang, L. Y. Wang, R. N. Wang, W. Wang, W. Wang, X. G. Wang, X. J. Wang, X. Y. Wang, Y. D. Wang, Y. J. Wang, Y. P. Wang, Z. Wang, Z. Wang, Z. H. Wang, Z. X. Wang, D. M. Wei, J. J. Wei, Y. J. Wei, T. Wen, C. Y. Wu, H. R. Wu, S. Wu, W. X. Wu, X. F. Wu, S. Q. Xi, J. Xia, J. J. Xia, G. M. Xiang, G. Xiao, H. B. Xiao, G. G. Xin, Y. L. Xin, Y. Xing, D. L. Xu, R. X. Xu, L. Xue, D. H. Yan, C. W. Yang, F. F. Yang, J. Y. Yang, L. L. Yang, M. J. Yang, R. Z. Yang, S. B. Yang, Y. H. Yao, Z. G. Yao, Y. M. Ye, L. Q. Yin, N. Yin, X. H. You, Z. Y. You, Y. H. Yu, Q. Yuan, H. D. Zeng, T. X. Zeng, W. Zeng, Z. K. Zeng, M. Zha, X. X. Zhai, B. B. Zhang, H. M. Zhang, H. Y. Zhang, J. L. Zhang, J. W. Zhang, L. Zhang, L. Zhang, L. X. Zhang, P. F. Zhang, P. P. Zhang, R. Zhang, S. R. Zhang, S. S. Zhang, X. Zhang, X. P. Zhang, Y. Zhang, Y. Zhang, Y. F. Zhang, Y. L. Zhang, B. Zhao, J. Zhao, L. Zhao, L. Z. Zhao, S. P. Zhao, F. Zheng, Y. Zheng, B. Zhou, H. Zhou, J. N. Zhou, P. Zhou, R. Zhou, X. X. Zhou, C. G. Zhu, F. R. Zhu, H. Zhu, K. J. Zhu, X. Zuo and (Lhaaso Collaboration), Observation of the Crab Nebula with LHAASO-KM2A - a performance study, *Chinese Physics C* **45**, p. 025002 (February 2021).
2. Z. Cao, F. A. Aharonian, Q. An, L. X. Axikegu, Bai, Y. X. Bai, Y. W. Bao, D. Bastieri, X. J. Bi, Y. J. Bi, H. Cai, J. T. Cai, Z. Cao, J. Chang, J. F. Chang, X. C. Chang, B. M. Chen, J. Chen, L. Chen, L. Chen, L. Chen, M. J. Chen, M. L. Chen, Q. H. Chen, S. H. Chen, S. Z. Chen, T. L. Chen, X. L. Chen, Y. Chen, N. Cheng, Y. D. Cheng, S. W. Cui, X. H. Cui, Y. D. Cui, B. Z. Dai, H. L. Dai, Z. G. Dai, Danzengluobu, D. della Volpe, B. D'Ettorre Piazzoli, X. J. Dong, J. H. Fan, Y. Z. Fan, Z. X. Fan, J. Fang, K. Fang, C. F. Feng, L. Feng, S. H. Feng, Y. L. Feng, B. Gao, C. D. Gao, Q. Gao,

W. Gao, M. M. Ge, L. S. Geng, G. H. Gong, Q. B. Gou, M. H. Gu, J. G. Guo, X. L. Guo, Y. Q. Guo, Y. Y. Guo, Y. A. Han, H. H. He, H. N. He, J. C. He, S. L. He, X. B. He, Y. He, M. Heller, Y. K. Hor, C. Hou, X. Hou, H. B. Hu, S. Hu, S. C. Hu, X. J. Hu, D. H. Huang, Q. L. Huang, W. H. Huang, X. T. Huang, Z. C. Huang, F. Ji, X. L. Ji, H. Y. Jia, K. Jiang, Z. J. Jiang, C. Jin, D. Kuleshov, K. Levochkin, B. B. Li, C. Li, C. Li, F. Li, H. B. Li, H. C. Li, H. Y. Li, J. Li, K. Li, W. L. Li, X. Li, X. Li, X. R. Li, Y. Li, Y. Z. Li, Z. Li, Z. Li, E. W. Liang, Y. F. Liang, S. J. Lin, B. Liu, C. Liu, D. Liu, H. Liu, H. D. Liu, J. Liu, J. L. Liu, J. S. Liu, J. Y. Liu, M. Y. Liu, R. Y. Liu, S. M. Liu, W. Liu, Y. N. Liu, Z. X. Liu, W. J. Long, R. Lu, H. K. Lv, B. Q. Ma, L. L. Ma, X. H. Ma, J. R. Mao, A. Masood, W. Mitthumsiri, T. Montaruli, Y. C. Nan, B. Y. Pang, P. Pattarakijwanich, Z. Y. Pei, M. Y. Qi, D. Ruffolo, V. Rulev, A. Sáiz, L. Shao, O. Shchegolev, X. D. Sheng, J. R. Shi, H. C. Song, Y. V. Stenkin, V. Stepanov, Q. N. Sun, X. N. Sun, Z. B. Sun, P. H. T. Tam, Z. B. Tang, W. W. Tian, B. D. Wang, C. Wang, H. Wang, H. G. Wang, J. C. Wang, J. S. Wang, L. P. Wang, L. Y. Wang, R. N. Wang, W. Wang, W. Wang, X. G. Wang, X. J. Wang, X. Y. Wang, Y. D. Wang, Y. J. Wang, Y. P. Wang, Z. Wang, Z. Wang, Z. H. Wang, Z. X. Wang, D. M. Wei, J. J. Wei, Y. J. Wei, T. Wen, C. Y. Wu, H. R. Wu, S. Wu, W. X. Wu, X. F. Wu, S. Q. Xi, J. Xia, J. J. Xia, G. M. Xiang, G. Xiao, H. B. Xiao, G. G. Xin, Y. L. Xin, Y. Xing, D. L. Xu, R. X. Xu, L. Xue, D. H. Yan, C. W. Yang, F. F. Yang, J. Y. Yang, L. L. Yang, M. J. Yang, R. Z. Yang, S. B. Yang, Y. H. Yao, Z. G. Yao, Y. M. Ye, L. Q. Yin, N. Yin, X. H. You, Z. Y. You, Y. H. Yu, Q. Yuan, H. D. Zeng, T. X. Zeng, W. Zeng, Z. K. Zeng, M. Zha, X. X. Zhai, B. B. Zhang, H. M. Zhang, H. Y. Zhang, J. L. Zhang, J. W. Zhang, L. Zhang, L. Zhang, L. X. Zhang, P. F. Zhang, P. P. Zhang, R. Zhang, S. R. Zhang, S. S. Zhang, X. Zhang, X. P. Zhang, Y. Zhang, Y. Zhang, Y. F. Zhang, Y. L. Zhang, B. Zhao, J. Zhao, L. Zhao, L. Z. Zhao, S. P. Zhao, F. Zheng, Y. Zheng, B. Zhou, H. Zhou, J. N. Zhou, P. Zhou, R. Zhou, X. X. Zhou, C. G. Zhu, F. R. Zhu, H. Zhu, K. J. Zhu and X. Zuo, Ultrahigh-energy photons up to 1.4 petaelectronvolts from 12 γ-ray Galactic sources, *Nature* **594**, 33 (January 2021).

3. Z. Cao, F. A. Aharonian, Q. An, L. X. Axikegu, Bai, Y. X. Bai, Y. W. Bao, D. Bastieri, X. J. Bi, Y. J. Bi, H. Cai, J. T. Cai, Z. Cao, J. Chang, J. F. Chang, X. C. Chang, B. M. Chen, J. Chen, L. Chen, L. Chen, L. Chen, M. J. Chen, M. L. Chen, Q. H. Chen, S. H. Chen, S. Z. Chen, T. L. Chen, X. L. Chen, Y. Chen, N. Cheng, Y. D. Cheng, S. W. Cui, X. H. Cui, Y. D. Cui, B. Z. Dai, H. L. Dai, Z. G. Dai, Danzengluobu, D. della Volpe, B. D'Ettorre Piazzoli, X. J. Dong, J. H. Fan, Y. Z. Fan, Z. X. Fan, J. Fang, K. Fang, C. F. Feng, L. Feng, S. H. Feng, Y. L. Feng, B. Gao, C. D. Gao, Q. Gao, W. Gao, M. M. Ge, L. S. Geng, G. H. Gong, Q. B. Gou, M. H. Gu, J. G. Guo, X. L. Guo, Y. Q. Guo, Y. Y. Guo, Y. A. Han, H. H. He, H. N. He, J. C. He, S. L. He, X. B. He, Y. He, M. Heller, Y. K. Hor, C. Hou, X. Hou, H. B. Hu, S. Hu, S. C. Hu, X. J. Hu, D. H. Huang, Q. L. Huang, W. H. Huang, X. T. Huang, Z. C. Huang, F. Ji, X. L. Ji, H. Y. Jia, K. Jiang, Z. J. Jiang, C. Jin, D. Kuleshov, K. Levochkin, B. B. Li, C. Li, C. Li, F. Li, H. B. Li, H. C. Li, H. Y. Li, J. Li, K. Li, W. L. Li, X. Li, X. Li, X. R. Li, Y. Li, Y. Z. Li, Z. Li, Z. Li, E. W. Liang, Y. F. Liang, S. J. Lin, B. Liu, C. Liu, D. Liu, H. Liu, H. D. Liu, J. Liu, J. L. Liu, J. S. Liu, J. Y. Liu, M. Y. Liu, R. Y. Liu, S. M. Liu, W. Liu, Y. N. Liu, Z. X. Liu, W. J. Long, R. Lu, H. K. Lv, B. Q. Ma, L. L. Ma, X. H. Ma, J. R. Mao, A. Masood, W. Mitthumsiri, T. Montaruli, Y. C. Nan, B. Y. Pang, P. Pattarakijwanich, Z. Y. Pei, M. Y. Qi, D. Ruffolo, V. Rulev, A. Sáiz, L. Shao, O. Shchegolev, X. D. Sheng, J. R. Shi, H. C. Song, Y. V. Stenkin, V. Stepanov, Q. N. Sun, X. N. Sun, Z. B. Sun, P. H. T. Tam, Z. B. Tang, W. W. Tian, B. D. Wang, C. Wang, H. Wang, H. G. Wang, J. C. Wang, J. S. Wang, L. P. Wang, L. Y. Wang, R. N. Wang, W. Wang, W. Wang, X. G. Wang, X. J. Wang, X. Y. Wang, Y. D. Wang,

Y. J. Wang, Y. P. Wang, Z. Wang, Z. Wang, Z. H. Wang, Z. X. Wang, D. M. Wei, J. J. Wei, Y. J. Wei, T. Wen, C. Y. Wu, H. R. Wu, S. Wu, W. X. Wu, X. F. Wu, S. Q. Xi, J. Xia, J. J. Xia, G. M. Xiang, G. Xiao, H. B. Xiao, G. G. Xin, Y. L. Xin, Y. Xing, D. L. Xu, R. X. Xu, L. Xue, D. H. Yan, C. W. Yang, F. F. Yang, J. Y. Yang, L. L. Yang, M. J. Yang, R. Z. Yang, S. B. Yang, Y. H. Yao, Z. G. Yao, Y. M. Ye, L. Q. Yin, N. Yin, X. H. You, Z. Y. You, Y. H. Yu, Q. Yuan, H. D. Zeng, T. X. Zeng, W. Zeng, Z. K. Zeng, M. Zha, X. X. Zhai, B. B. Zhang, H. M. Zhang, H. Y. Zhang, J. L. Zhang, J. W. Zhang, L. Zhang, L. Zhang, L. X. Zhang, P. F. Zhang, P. P. Zhang, R. Zhang, S. R. Zhang, S. S. Zhang, X. Zhang, X. P. Zhang, Y. Zhang, Y. Zhang, Y. F. Zhang, Y. L. Zhang, B. Zhao, J. Zhao, L. Zhao, L. Z. Zhao, S. P. Zhao, F. Zheng, Y. Zheng, B. Zhou, H. Zhou, J. N. Zhou, P. Zhou, R. Zhou, X. X. Zhou, C. G. Zhu, F. R. Zhu, H. Zhu, K. J. Zhu and X. Zuo, Peta–electron volt gamma-ray emission from the crab nebula, *Science* **373**, 425 (2021).
4. A. J. B. Downes, T. Pauls and C. J. Salter, G 40.5-0.5 : A previously unrecognised supernova remnant in Aql., *A&A* **92**, 47 (December 1980).
5. J. Yang, J.-L. Zhang, Z.-Y. Cai, D.-R. Lu and Y.-H. Tan, Molecular Gas Distribution around the Supernova Remnant G40.5 0.5, *CJA&A* **6**, 210 (April 2006).
6. F. Aharonian, A. G. Akhperjanian, G. Anton, U. Barres de Almeida, A. R. Bazer-Bachi, Y. Becherini, B. Behera, W. Benbow, K. Bernlöhr, C. Boisson, A. Bochow, V. Borrel, I. Braun, E. Brion, J. Brucker, P. Brun, R. Bühler, T. Bulik, I. Büsching, T. Boutelier, S. Carrigan, P. M. Chadwick, A. Charbonnier, R. C. G. Chaves, A. Cheesebrough, L. M. Chounet, A. C. Clapson, G. Coignet, M. Dalton, M. K. Daniel, B. Degrange, C. Deil, H. J. Dickinson, A. Djannati-Ataï, W. Domainko, L. O'C. Drury, F. Dubois, G. Dubus, J. Dyks, M. Dyrda, K. Egberts, D. Emmanoulopoulos, P. Espigat, C. Farnier, F. Feinstein, A. Fiasson, A. Förster, G. Fontaine, M. Füßling, S. Gabici, Y. A. Gallant, L. Gérard, B. Giebels, J. F. Glicenstein, B. Glück, P. Goret, D. Hauser, M. Hauser, S. Heinz, G. Heinzelmann, G. Henri, G. Hermann, J. A. Hinton, A. Hoffmann, W. Hofmann, M. Holleran, S. Hoppe, D. Horns, A. Jacholkowska, O. C. de Jager, I. Jung, K. Katarzyński, U. Katz, S. Kaufmann, E. Kendziorra, M. Kerschhaggl, D. Khangulyan, B. Khélifi, D. Keogh, N. Komin, K. Kosack, G. Lamanna, J. P. Lenain, T. Lohse, V. Marandon, J. M. Martin, O. Martineau-Huynh, A. Marcowith, D. Maurin, T. J. L. McComb, M. C. Medina, R. Moderski, E. Moulin, M. Naumann-Godo, M. de Naurois, D. Nedbal, D. Nekrassov, J. Niemiec, S. J. Nolan, S. Ohm, J. F. Olive, E. de Oña Wilhelmi, K. J. Orford, M. Ostrowski, M. Panter, M. Paz Arribas, G. Pedaletti, G. Pelletier, P. O. Petrucci, S. Pita, G. Pühlhofer, M. Punch, A. Quirrenbach, B. C. Raubenheimer, M. Raue, S. M. Rayner, M. Renaud, O. Reimer, F. Rieger, J. Ripken, L. Rob, S. Rosier-Lees, G. Rowell, B. Rudak, C. B. Rulten, J. Ruppel, V. Sahakian, A. Santangelo, R. Schlickeiser, F. M. Schöck, R. Schröder, U. Schwanke, S. Schwarzburg, S. Schwemmer, A. Shalchi, J. L. Skilton, H. Sol, D. Spangler, L. Stawarz, R. Steenkamp, C. Stegmann, G. Superina, P. H. Tam, J. P. Tavernet, R. Terrier, O. Tibolla, C. van Eldik, G. Vasileiadis, C. Venter, L. Venter, J. P. Vialle, P. Vincent, M. Vivier, H. J. Völk, F. Volpe, S. J. Wagner, M. Ward, A. A. Zdziarski and A. Zech, Detection of very high energy radiation from HESS J1908+063 confirms the Milagro unidentified source MGRO J1908+06, *A&A* **499**, 723 (June 2009).
7. B. Bartoli, P. Bernardini, X. J. Bi, C. Bleve, I. Bolognino, P. Branchini, A. Budano, A. K. Calabrese Melcarne, P. Camarri, Z. Cao, R. Cardarelli, S. Catalanotti, C. Cattaneo, S. Z. Chen, T. L. Chen, Y. Chen, P. Creti, S. W. Cui, B. Z. Dai, G. D'Alí Staiti, Danzengluobu, M. Dattoli, I. De Mitri, B. D'Ettorre Piazzoli, T. Di Girolamo, X. H. Ding, G. Di Sciascio, C. F. Feng, Z. Feng, Z. Feng, F. Galeazzi, E. Giroletti, Q. B.

Gou, Y. Q. Guo, H. H. He, H. Hu, H. Hu, Q. Huang, M. Iacovacci, R. Iuppa, I. James, H. Y. Jia, Labaciren, H. J. Li, J. Y. Li, X. X. Li, G. Liguori, C. Liu, C. Q. Liu, J. Liu, M. Y. Liu, H. Lu, X. H. Ma, G. Mancarella, S. M. Mari, G. Marsella, D. Martello, S. Mastroianni, P. Montini, C. C. Ning, A. Pagliaro, M. Panareo, B. Panico, L. Perrone, P. Pistilli, X. B. Qu, F. Ruggieri, P. Salvini, R. Santonico, P. R. Shen, X. D. Sheng, F. Shi, C. Stanescu, A. Surdo, Y. H. Tan, P. Vallania, S. Vernetto, C. Vigorito, B. Wang, H. Wang, C. Y. Wu, H. R. Wu, B. Xu, L. Xue, Y. X. Yan, Q. Y. Yang, X. C. Yang, Z. G. Yao, A. F. Yuan, M. Zha, H. M. Zhang, J. Zhang, J. Zhang, L. Zhang, P. Zhang, X. Y. Zhang, Y. Zhang, Zhaxiciren, Zhaxisangzhu, X. X. Zhou, F. R. Zhu, Q. Q. Zhu, G. Zizzi and Argo-YBJ Collaboration, Observation of the TeV Gamma-Ray Source MGRO J1908+06 with ARGO-YBJ, *ApJ* **760**, p. 110 (December 2012).

8. E. Aliu, S. Archambault, T. Aune, B. Behera, M. Beilicke, W. Benbow, K. Berger, R. Bird, J. H. Buckley, V. Bugaev, J. V. Cardenzana, M. Cerruti, X. Chen, L. Ciupik, E. Collins-Hughes, M. P. Connolly, W. Cui, J. Dumm, V. V. Dwarkadas, M. Errando, A. Falcone, S. Federici, Q. Feng, J. P. Finley, H. Fleischhack, P. Fortin, L. Fortson, A. Furniss, N. Galante, D. Gall, G. H. Gillanders, S. Griffin, S. T. Griffiths, J. Grube, G. Gyuk, D. Hanna, J. Holder, G. Hughes, T. B. Humensky, P. Kaaret, M. Kertzman, Y. Khassen, D. Kieda, F. Krennrich, S. Kumar, M. J. Lang, A. S. Madhavan, G. Maier, A. J. McCann, K. Meagher, J. Millis, P. Moriarty, R. Mukherjee, D. Nieto, A. O'Faoláin de Bhróithe, R. A. Ong, A. N. Otte, D. Pandel, N. Park, M. Pohl, A. Popkow, H. Prokoph, J. Quinn, K. Ragan, J. Rajotte, G. Ratliff, L. C. Reyes, P. T. Reynolds, G. T. Richards, E. Roache, J. Rousselle, G. H. Sembroski, K. Shahinyan, F. Sheidaei, A. W. Smith, D. Staszak, I. Telezhinsky, K. Tsurusaki, J. V. Tucci, J. Tyler, A. Varlotta, V. V. Vassiliev, S. Vincent, S. P. Wakely, J. E. Ward, A. Weinstein, R. Welsing and A. Wilhelm, Investigating the TeV Morphology of MGRO J1908+06 with VERITAS, *ApJ* **787**, p. 166 (June 2014).

9. A. U. Abeysekara, A. Albert, R. Alfaro, J. R. Angeles Camacho, J. C. Arteaga-Velázquez, K. P. Arunbabu, D. Avila Rojas, H. A. Ayala Solares, V. Baghmanyan, E. Belmont-Moreno, S. Y. BenZvi, C. Brisbois, K. S. Caballero-Mora, T. Capistrán, A. Carramiñana, S. Casanova, U. Cotti, J. Cotzomi, S. Coutiño de León, E. De la Fuente, C. de León, S. Dichiara, B. L. Dingus, M. A. DuVernois, J. C. Díaz-Vélez, R. W. Ellsworth, K. Engel, C. Espinoza, H. Fleischhack, N. Fraija, A. Galván-Gámez, D. Garcia, J. A. García-González, F. Garfias, M. M. González, J. A. Goodman, J. P. Harding, S. Hernandez, J. Hinton, B. Hona, D. Huang, F. Hueyotl-Zahuantitla, P. Hüntemeyer, A. Iriarte, A. Jardin-Blicq, V. Joshi, S. Kaufmann, D. Kieda, A. Lara, W. H. Lee, H. León Vargas, J. T. Linnemann, A. L. Longinotti, G. Luis-Raya, J. Lundeen, R. López-Coto, K. Malone, S. S. Marinelli, O. Martinez, I. Martinez-Castellanos, J. Martínez-Castro, H. Martínez-Huerta, J. A. Matthews, P. Miranda-Romagnoli, J. A. Morales-Soto, E. Moreno, M. Mostafá, A. Nayerhoda, L. Nellen, M. Newbold, M. U. Nisa, R. Noriega-Papaqui, A. Peisker, E. G. Pérez-Pérez, J. Pretz, Z. Ren, C. D. Rho, C. Rivière, D. Rosa-González, M. Rosenberg, E. Ruiz-Velasco, F. Salesa Greus, A. Sandoval, M. Schneider, H. Schoorlemmer, G. Sinnis, A. J. Smith, R. W. Springer, P. Surajbali, E. Tabachnick, M. Tanner, O. Tibolla, K. Tollefson, I. Torres, R. Torres-Escobedo, L. Villaseñor, T. Weisgarber, J. Wood, T. Yapici, H. Zhang, H. Zhou and HAWC Collaboration, Multiple Galactic Sources with Emission Above 56 TeV Detected by HAWC, *PRL* **124**, p. 021102 (January 2020).

10. J. Li, R.-Y. Liu, E. de Oña Wilhelmi, D. F. Torres, Q.-C. Liu, M. Kerr, R. Bühler, Y. Su, H.-N. He and M.-Y. Xiao, Investigating the Nature of MGRO J1908+06 with Multiwavelength Observations, *ApJL* **913**, p. L33 (June 2021).
11. G. G. Pavlov, O. Kargaltsev and W. F. Brisken, Chandra Observation of PSR B1823-13 and Its Pulsar Wind Nebula, *ApJ* **675**, 683 (Mar 2008).
12. H. Uchiyama, H. Matsumoto, T. G. Tsuru, K. Koyama and A. Bamba, Suzaku Observation of HESS J1825-137: Discovery of Largely-Extended X-Rays from PSR J1826-1334, *PASJ* **61**, p. S189 (January 2009).
13. A. Van Etten and R. W. Romani, Multi-zone Modeling of the Pulsar Wind Nebula HESS J1825-137, *ApJ* **742**, p. 62 (Dec 2011).
14. F. Voisin, G. Rowell, M. G. Burton, A. Walsh, Y. Fukui and F. Aharonian, ISM gas studies towards the TeV PWN HESS J1825-137 and northern region, *MNRAS* **458**, 2813 (May 2016).
15. D. Khangulyan, A. V. Koldoba, G. V. Ustyugova, S. V. Bogovalov and F. Aharonian, On the Anomalously Large Extension of the Pulsar Wind Nebula HESS J1825-137, *ApJ* **860**, p. 59 (June 2018).
16. H. E. S. S. Collaboration, H. Abdalla, F. Aharonian, F. Ait Benkhali, E. O. Angüner, M. Arakawa, C. Arcaro, C. Armand, M. Arrieta, M. Backes, M. Barnard, Y. Becherini, J. Becker Tjus, D. Berge, K. Bernlöhr, R. Blackwell, M. Böttcher, C. Boisson, J. Bolmont, S. Bonnefoy, P. Bordas, J. Bregeon, F. Brun, P. Brun, M. Bryan, M. Büchele, T. Bulik, T. Bylund, M. Capasso, S. Caroff, A. Carosi, S. Casanova, M. Cerruti, N. Chakraborty, T. Chand, S. Chandra, R. C. G. Chaves, A. Chen, S. Colafrancesco, B. Condon, I. D. Davids, C. Deil, J. Devin, P. deWilt, L. Dirson, A. Djannati-Ataï, A. Dmytriiev, A. Donath, V. Doroshenko, L. O. C. Drury, J. Dyks, K. Egberts, G. Emery, J. P. Ernenwein, S. Eschbach, S. Fegan, A. Fiasson, G. Fontaine, S. Funk, M. Füßling, S. Gabici, Y. A. Gallant, F. Gaté, G. Giavitto, D. Glawion, J. F. Glicenstein, D. Gottschall, M. H. Grondin, J. Hahn, M. Haupt, G. Heinzelmann, G. Henri, G. Hermann, J. A. Hinton, W. Hofmann, C. Hoischen, T. L. Holch, M. Holler, D. Horns, D. Huber, H. Iwasaki, A. Jacholkowska, M. Jamrozy, D. Jankowsky, F. Jankowsky, L. Jouvin, I. Jung-Richardt, M. A. Kastendieck, K. Katarzyński, M. Katsuragawa, U. Katz, D. Kerszberg, D. Khangulyan, B. Khélifi, J. King, S. Klepser, W. Kluźniak, N. Komin, K. Kosack, M. Kraus, G. Lamanna, J. Lau, J. Lefaucheur, A. Lemière, M. Lemoine-Goumard, J. P. Lenain, M. Leser, T. Lohse, R. López-Coto, I. Lypova, D. Malyshev, V. Marandon, A. Marcowith, C. Mariaud, G. Martí-Devesa, R. Marx, G. Maurin, P. J. Meintjes, A. M. W. Mitchell, R. Moderski, M. Mohamed, L. Mohrmann, C. Moore, E. Moulin, T. Murach, S. Nakashima, M. de Naurois, H. Ndiyavala, F. Niederwanger, J. Niemiec, L. Oakes, P. O'Brien, H. Odaka, S. Ohm, M. Ostrowski, I. Oya, M. Panter, R. D. Parsons, C. Perennes, P. O. Petrucci, B. Peyaud, Q. Piel, S. Pita, V. Poireau, A. Priyana Noel, D. A. Prokhorov, H. Prokoph, G. Pühlhofer, M. Punch, A. Quirrenbach, S. Raab, R. Rauth, A. Reimer, O. Reimer, M. Renaud, F. Rieger, L. Rinchiuso, C. Romoli, G. Rowell, B. Rudak, E. Ruiz-Velasco, V. Sahakian, S. Saito, D. A. Sanchez, A. Santangelo, M. Sasaki, R. Schlickeiser, F. Schüssler, A. Schulz, H. Schutte, U. Schwanke, S. Schwemmer, M. Seglar-Arroyo, M. Senniappan, A. S. Seyffert, N. Shafi, I. Shilon, K. Shiningayamwe, R. Simoni, A. Sinha, H. Sol, A. Specovius, M. Spir-Jacob, Ł. Stawarz, R. Steenkamp, C. Stegmann, C. Steppa, T. Takahashi, J. P. Tavernet, T. Tavernier, A. M. Taylor, R. Terrier, L. Tibaldo, D. Tiziani, M. Tluczykont, C. Trichard, M. Tsirou, N. Tsuji, R. Tuffs, Y. Uchiyama, D. J. van der Walt, C. van Eldik, C. van Rensburg, B. van Soelen, G. Vasileiadis, J. Veh, C. Venter, P. Vincent, J. Vink, F. Voisin, H. J. Völk, T. Vuillaume, Z. Wadiasingh, S. J. Wagner, R. M. Wagner, R. White, A. Wierzcholska,

16. R. Yang, H. Yoneda, D. Zaborov, M. Zacharias, R. Zanin, A. A. Zdziarski, A. Zech, F. Zefi, A. Ziegler, J. Zorn and N. Żywucka, Particle transport within the pulsar wind nebula HESS J1825-137, *A&A* **621**, p. A116 (January 2019).
17. R.-Y. Liu and H. Yan, On the unusually large spatial extent of the TeV nebula HESS J1825-137: implication from the energy-dependent morphology, *MNRAS* **494**, 2618 (April 2020).
18. G. Principe, A. M. W. Mitchell, S. Caroff, J. A. Hinton, R. D. Parsons and S. Funk, Energy dependent morphology of the pulsar wind nebula HESS J1825-137 with Fermi-LAT, *A&A* **640**, p. A76 (August 2020).
19. A. Albert, R. Alfaro, C. Alvarez, J. R. A. Camacho, J. C. Arteaga-Velázquez, K. P. Arunbabu, D. A. Rojas, H. A. Ayala Solares, V. Baghmanyan, E. Belmont-Moreno, S. Y. BenZvi, C. Brisbois, T. Capistrán, A. Carramiñana, S. Casanova, U. Cotti, J. Cotzomi, E. D. l. Fuente, R. D. Hernandez, B. L. Dingus, M. A. DuVernois, M. Durocher, J. C. Díaz-Vélez, K. Engel, C. Espinoza, K. Fang, H. Fleischhack, N. Fraija, A. Galván-Gámez, D. Garcia, J. A. García-González, F. Garfias, G. Giacinti, M. M. González, J. A. Goodman, J. P. Harding, B. Hona, D. Huang, F. Hueyotl-Zahuantitla, P. Hüntemeyer, A. Iriarte, A. Jardin-Blicq, V. Joshi, G. J. Kunde, A. Lara, W. H. Lee, H. L. Vargas, J. T. Linnemann, A. L. Longinotti, G. Luis-Raya, J. Lundeen, K. Malone, V. Marandon, O. Martinez, J. Martínez-Castro, J. A. Matthews, P. Miranda-Romagnoli, E. Moreno, M. Mostafá, A. Nayerhoda, L. Nellen, M. Newbold, M. U. Nisa, R. Noriega-Papaqui, N. Omodei, A. Peisker, Y. P. Araujo, E. G. Pérez-Pérez, C. D. Rho, D. Rosa-González, H. Salazar, F. S. Greus, A. Sandoval, M. Schneider, F. Serna, R. W. Springer, K. Tollefson, I. Torres, R. Torres-Escobedo, F. Ureña-Mena, L. Villaseñor, E. Willox, H. Zhou and C. d. León, Evidence of 200 TeV Photons from HAWC J1825-134, *ApJL* **907**, p. L30 (February 2021).
20. J. P. Halpern, E. V. Gotthelf, K. M. Leighly and D. J. Helfand, A Possible X-Ray and Radio Counterpart of the High-Energy Gamma-Ray Source 3EG J2227+6122, *ApJ* **547**, 323 (January 2001).
21. R. Kothes, B. Uyaniker and S. Pineault, The Supernova Remnant G106.3+2.7 and Its Pulsar-Wind Nebula: Relics of Triggered Star Formation in a Complex Environment, *ApJ* **560**, 236 (October 2001).
22. V. A. Acciari, E. Aliu, T. Arlen, T. Aune, M. Bautista, M. Beilicke, W. Benbow, D. Boltuch, S. M. Bradbury, J. H. Buckley, V. Bugaev, Y. Butt, K. Byrum, A. Cannon, A. Cesarini, Y. C. Chow, L. Ciupik, P. Cogan, W. Cui, R. Dickherber, T. Ergin, S. J. Fegan, J. P. Finley, P. Fortin, L. Fortson, A. Furniss, D. Gall, G. H. Gillanders, E. V. Gotthelf, J. Grube, R. Guenette, G. Gyuk, D. Hanna, J. Holder, D. Horan, C. M. Hui, T. B. Humensky, P. Kaaret, N. Karlsson, M. Kertzman, D. Kieda, A. Konopelko, H. Krawczynski, F. Krennrich, M. J. Lang, S. LeBohec, G. Maier, A. McCann, M. McCutcheon, J. Millis, P. Moriarty, R. Mukherjee, R. A. Ong, A. N. Otte, D. Pandel, J. S. Perkins, M. Pohl, J. Quinn, K. Ragan, L. C. Reyes, P. T. Reynolds, E. Roache, H. J. Rose, M. Schroedter, G. H. Sembroski, A. W. Smith, D. Steele, S. P. Swordy, M. Theiling, J. A. Toner, V. V. Vassiliev, S. Vincent, R. G. Wagner, S. P. Wakely, J. E. Ward, T. C. Weekes, A. Weinstein, T. Weisgarber, D. A. Williams, S. Wissel, M. Wood and B. Zitzer, Detection of Extended VHE Gamma Ray Emission from G106.3+2.7 with Veritas, *ApJL* **703**, L6 (September 2009).
23. Y. Xin, H. Zeng, S. Liu, Y. Fan and D. Wei, VER J2227+608: A Hadronic PeVatron Pulsar Wind Nebula?, *ApJ* **885**, p. 162 (November 2019).
24. S. Liu, H. Zeng, Y. Xin and H. Zhu, Hadronic versus Leptonic Models for γ-Ray Emission from VER J2227+608, *ApJL* **897**, p. L34 (July 2020).

25. Tibet ASγ Collaboration, M. Amenomori, Y. W. Bao, X. J. Bi, D. Chen, T. L. Chen, W. Y. Chen, X. Chen, Y. Chen, S. W. Cirennima, Cui, L. K. Danzengluobu, Ding, J. H. Fang, K. Fang, C. F. Feng, Z. Feng, Z. Y. Feng, Q. Gao, Q. B. Gou, Y. Q. Guo, Y. Y. Guo, H. H. He, Z. T. He, K. Hibino, N. Hotta, H. Hu, H. B. Hu, J. Huang, H. Y. Jia, L. Jiang, H. B. Jin, K. Kasahara, Y. Katayose, C. Kato, S. Kato, K. Kawata, W. Kihara, Y. Ko, M. Kozai, G. M. Labaciren, Le, A. F. Li, H. J. Li, W. J. Li, Y. H. Lin, B. Liu, C. Liu, J. S. Liu, M. Y. Liu, W. Liu, Y. Q. Lou, H. Lu, X. R. Meng, K. Munakata, H. Nakada, Y. Nakamura, H. Nanjo, M. Nishizawa, M. Ohnishi, T. Ohura, S. Ozawa, X. L. Qian, X. B. Qu, T. Saito, M. Sakata, T. K. Sako, J. Shao, M. Shibata, A. Shiomi, H. Sugimoto, W. Takano, M. Takita, Y. H. Tan, N. Tateyama, S. Torii, H. Tsuchiya, S. Udo, H. Wang, H. R. Wu, L. Xue, Y. Yamamoto, Z. Yang, Y. Yokoe, A. F. Yuan, L. M. Zhai, H. M. Zhang, J. L. Zhang, X. Zhang, X. Y. Zhang, Y. Zhang, Y. Zhang, Y. Zhang, S. P. Zhao and X. X. Zhaxisangzhu, Zhou, Potential PeVatron supernova remnant G106.3+2.7 seen in the highest-energy gamma rays, *Nature Astronomy* **5**, 460 (January 2021).
26. C. Ge, R.-Y. Liu, S. Niu, Y. Chen and X.-Y. Wang, Revealing a peculiar supernova remnant G106.3+2.7 as a petaelectronvolt proton accelerator with X-ray observations, *The Innovation* **2**, p. 100118 (May 2021).
27. Y. Fujita, A. Bamba, K. K. Nobukawa and H. Matsumoto, X-Ray Emission from the PeVatron-candidate Supernova Remnant G106.3+2.7, *ApJ* **912**, p. 133 (May 2021).
28. C. J. Cesarsky and T. Montmerle, Gamma-Rays from Active Regions in the Galaxy - the Possible Contribution of Stellar Winds, *SSR* **36**, 173 (October 1983).
29. F. Aharonian, R. Yang and E. de Oña Wilhelmi, Massive stars as major factories of Galactic cosmic rays, *Nature Astronomy* **3**, 561 (March 2019).
30. A. M. Bykov, A. Marcowith, E. Amato, M. E. Kalyashova, J. M. D. Kruijssen and E. Waxman, High-Energy Particles and Radiation in Star-Forming Regions, *SSR* **216**, p. 42 (April 2020).
31. F. Aharonian, Q. An, L. X. Axikegu, Bai, Y. X. Bai, Y. W. Bao, D. Bastieri, X. J. Bi, Y. J. Bi, H. Cai, J. T. Cai, Z. Cao, Z. Cao, J. Chang, J. F. Chang, X. C. Chang, B. M. Chen, J. Chen, L. Chen, L. Chen, L. Chen, M. J. Chen, M. L. Chen, Q. H. Chen, S. H. Chen, S. Z. Chen, T. L. Chen, X. L. Chen, Y. Chen, N. Cheng, Y. D. Cheng, S. W. Cui, X. H. Cui, Y. D. Cui, B. Z. Dai, H. L. Dai, Z. G. Dai, Danzengluobu, D. Della Volpe, B. D'Ettorre Piazzoli, X. J. Dong, J. H. Fan, Y. Z. Fan, Z. X. Fan, J. Fang, K. Fang, C. F. Feng, L. Feng, S. H. Feng, Y. L. Feng, B. Gao, C. D. Gao, Q. Gao, W. Gao, M. M. Ge, L. S. Geng, G. H. Gong, Q. B. Gou, M. H. Gu, J. G. Guo, X. L. Guo, Y. Q. Guo, Y. Y. Guo, Y. A. Han, H. H. He, H. N. He, J. C. He, S. L. He, X. B. He, Y. He, M. Heller, Y. K. Hor, C. Hou, X. Hou, H. B. Hu, S. Hu, S. C. Hu, X. J. Hu, D. H. Huang, Q. L. Huang, W. H. Huang, X. T. Huang, Z. C. Huang, F. Ji, X. L. Ji, H. Y. Jia, K. Jiang, Z. J. Jiang, C. Jin, D. Kuleshov, K. Levochkin, B. B. Li, C. Li, C. Li, F. Li, H. B. Li, H. C. Li, H. Y. Li, J. Li, K. Li, W. L. Li, X. Li, X. Li, X. R. Li, Y. Li, Y. Z. Li, Z. Li, Z. Li, E. W. Liang, Y. F. Liang, S. J. Lin, B. Liu, C. Liu, D. Liu, H. Liu, H. D. Liu, J. Liu, J. L. Liu, J. S. Liu, J. Y. Liu, M. Y. Liu, R. Y. Liu, S. M. Liu, W. Liu, Y. N. Liu, Z. X. Liu, W. J. Long, R. Lu, H. K. Lv, B. Q. Ma, L. L. Ma, X. H. Ma, J. R. Mao, A. Masood, W. Mitthumsiri, T. Montaruli, Y. C. Nan, B. Y. Pang, P. Pattarakijwanich, Z. Y. Pei, M. Y. Qi, D. Ruffolo, V. Rulev, A. Sáiz, L. Shao, O. Shchegolev, X. D. Sheng, J. R. Shi, H. C. Song, Y. V. Stenkin, V. Stepanov, Q. N. Sun, X. N. Sun, Z. B. Sun, P. H. T. Tam, Z. B. Tang, W. W. Tian, B. D. Wang, C. Wang, H. Wang, H. G. Wang, J. C. Wang, J. S. Wang, L. P. Wang, L. Y. Wang, R. N. Wang, W. Wang, W. Wang, X. G. Wang, X. J. Wang, X. Y. Wang, Y. D. Wang, Y. J. Wang, Y. P. Wang, Z. Wang, Z. Wang, Z. H. Wang, Z. X. Wang,

D. M. Wei, J. J. Wei, Y. J. Wei, T. Wen, C. Y. Wu, H. R. Wu, S. Wu, W. X. Wu, X. F. Wu, S. Q. Xi, J. Xia, J. J. Xia, G. M. Xiang, G. Xiao, H. B. Xiao, G. G. Xin, Y. L. Xin, Y. Xing, D. L. Xu, R. X. Xu, L. Xue, D. H. Yan, C. W. Yang, F. F. Yang, J. Y. Yang, L. L. Yang, M. J. Yang, R. Z. Yang, S. B. Yang, Y. H. Yao, Z. G. Yao, Y. M. Ye, L. Q. Yin, N. Yin, X. H. You, Z. Y. You, Y. H. Yu, Q. Yuan, H. D. Zeng, T. X. Zeng, W. Zeng, Z. K. Zeng, M. Zha, X. X. Zhai, B. B. Zhang, H. M. Zhang, H. Y. Zhang, J. L. Zhang, J. W. Zhang, L. Zhang, L. Zhang, L. X. Zhang, P. F. Zhang, P. P. Zhang, R. Zhang, S. R. Zhang, S. S. Zhang, X. Zhang, X. P. Zhang, Y. Zhang, Y. Zhang, Y. F. Zhang, Y. L. Zhang, B. Zhao, J. Zhao, L. Zhao, L. Z. Zhao, S. P. Zhao, F. Zheng, Y. Zheng, B. Zhou, H. Zhou, J. N. Zhou, P. Zhou, R. Zhou, X. X. Zhou, C. G. Zhu, F. R. Zhu, H. Zhu, K. J. Zhu, X. Zuo, LHAASO Collaboration and X. Y. Huang, Extended Very-High-Energy Gamma-Ray Emission Surrounding PSR J 0622 +3749 Observed by LHAASO-KM2A, *PRL* **126**, p. 241103 (June 2021).

32. Z. Cao, F. Aharonian, Q. An, Axikegu, L. X. Bai, Y. X. Bai, Y. W. Bao, D. Bastieri, X. J. Bi, Y. J. Bi, H. Cai, J. T. Cai, Z. Cao, J. Chang, J. F. Chang, B. M. Chen, E. S. Chen, J. Chen, L. Chen, L. Chen, L. Chen, M. J. Chen, M. L. Chen, Q. H. Chen, S. H. Chen, S. Z. Chen, T. L. Chen, X. L. Chen, Y. Chen, N. Cheng, Y. D. Cheng, S. W. Cui, X. H. Cui, Y. D. Cui, B. D'Ettorre Piazzoli, B. Z. Dai, H. L. Dai, Z. G. Dai, Danzengluobu, D. d. Volpe, X. J. Dong, K. K. Duan, J. H. Fan, Y. Z. Fan, Z. X. Fan, J. Fang, K. Fang, C. F. Feng, L. Feng, S. H. Feng, Y. L. Feng, B. Gao, C. D. Gao, L. Q. Gao, Q. Gao, W. Gao, M. M. Ge, L. S. Geng, G. H. Gong, Q. B. Gou, M. H. Gu, F. L. Guo, J. G. Guo, X. L. Guo, Y. Q. Guo, Y. Y. Guo, Y. A. Han, H. H. He, H. N. He, J. C. He, S. L. He, X. B. He, Y. He, M. Heller, Y. K. Hor, C. Hou, H. B. Hu, S. Hu, S. C. Hu, X. J. Hu, D. H. Huang, Q. L. Huang, W. H. Huang, X. T. Huang, X. Y. Huang, Z. C. Huang, F. Ji, X. L. Ji, H. Y. Jia, K. Jiang, Z. J. Jiang, C. Jin, T. Ke, D. Kuleshov, K. Levochkin, B. B. Li, C. Li, C. Li, F. Li, H. B. Li, H. C. Li, H. Y. Li, J. Li, K. Li, W. L. Li, X. R. Li, X. Li, X. Li, Y. Li, Y. Z. Li, Z. Li, Z. Li, E. W. Liang, Y. F. Liang, S. J. Lin, B. Liu, C. Liu, D. Liu, H. Liu, H. D. Liu, J. Liu, J. L. Liu, J. S. Liu, J. Y. Liu, M. Y. Liu, R. Y. Liu, S. M. Liu, W. Liu, Y. Liu, Y. N. Liu, Z. X. Liu, W. J. Long, R. Lu, H. K. Lv, B. Q. Ma, L. L. Ma, X. H. Ma, J. R. Mao, A. Masood, Z. Min, W. Mitthumsiri, T. Montaruli, Y. C. Nan, B. Y. Pang, P. Pattarakijwanich, Z. Y. Pei, M. Y. Qi, Y. Q. Qi, B. Q. Qiao, J. J. Qin, D. Ruffolo, V. Rulev, A. Sáiz, L. Shao, O. Shchegolev, X. D. Sheng, J. Y. Shi, H. C. Song, Y. V. Stenkin, V. Stepanov, Y. Su, Q. N. Sun, X. N. Sun, Z. B. Sun, P. H. T. Tam, Z. B. Tang, W. W. Tian, B. D. Wang, C. Wang, H. Wang, H. G. Wang, J. C. Wang, J. S. Wang, L. P. Wang, L. Y. Wang, R. N. Wang, W. Wang, W. Wang, X. G. Wang, X. J. Wang, X. Y. Wang, Y. Wang, Y. D. Wang, Y. J. Wang, Y. P. Wang, Z. H. Wang, Z. X. Wang, Z. Wang, Z. Wang, D. M. Wei, J. J. Wei, Y. J. Wei, T. Wen, C. Y. Wu, H. R. Wu, S. Wu, W. X. Wu, X. F. Wu, S. Q. Xi, J. Xia, J. J. Xia, G. M. Xiang, D. X. Xiao, G. Xiao, H. B. Xiao, G. G. Xin, Y. L. Xin, Y. Xing, D. L. Xu, R. X. Xu, L. Xue, D. H. Yan, J. Z. Yan, C. W. Yang, F. F. Yang, J. Y. Yang, L. L. Yang, M. J. Yang, R. Z. Yang, S. B. Yang, Y. H. Yao, Z. G. Yao, Y. M. Ye, L. Q. Yin, N. Yin, X. H. You, Z. Y. You, Y. H. Yu, Q. Yuan, H. D. Zeng, T. X. Zeng, W. Zeng, Z. K. Zeng, M. Zha, X. X. Zhai, B. B. Zhang, H. M. Zhang, H. Y. Zhang, J. L. Zhang, J. W. Zhang, L. X. Zhang, L. Zhang, L. Zhang, P. F. Zhang, P. P. Zhang, R. Zhang, S. R. Zhang, S. S. Zhang, X. Zhang, X. P. Zhang, Y. F. Zhang, Y. L. Zhang, Y. Zhang, Y. Zhang, B. Zhao, J. Zhao, L. Zhao, L. Z. Zhao, S. P. Zhao, F. Zheng, Y. Zheng, B. Zhou, H. Zhou, J. N. Zhou, P. Zhou, R. Zhou, X. X. Zhou, C. G. Zhu, F. R. Zhu, H. Zhu, K. J. Zhu and X. Zuo, Discovery of a New Gamma-Ray Source, LHAASO J0341+5258, with Emission up to 200 TeV, *ApJL* **917**, p. L4 (August 2021).

33. H. Akaike, A New Look at the Statistical Model Identification, *IEEE Transactions on Automatic Control* **19**, 716 (January 1974).
34. M. Amenomori, Y. W. Bao, X. J. Bi, D. Chen, T. L. Chen, W. Y. Chen, X. Chen, Y. Chen, Cirennima, S. W. Cui, Danzengluobu, L. K. Ding, J. H. Fang, K. Fang, C. F. Feng, Z. Feng, Z. Y. Feng, Q. Gao, Q. B. Gou, Y. Q. Guo, H. H. He, Z. T. He, K. Hibino, N. Hotta, H. Hu, H. B. Hu, J. Huang, H. Y. Jia, L. Jiang, H. B. Jin, F. Kajino, K. Kasahara, Y. Katayose, C. Kato, S. Kato, K. Kawata, M. Kozai, Labaciren, G. M. Le, A. F. Li, H. J. Li, W. J. Li, Y. H. Lin, B. Liu, C. Liu, J. S. Liu, M. Y. Liu, Y. Q. Lou, H. Lu, X. R. Meng, H. Mitsui, K. Munakata, Y. Nakamura, H. Nanjo, M. Nishizawa, M. Ohnishi, I. Ohta, S. Ozawa, X. L. Qian, X. B. Qu, T. Saito, M. Sakata, T. K. Sako, Y. Sengoku, J. Shao, M. Shibata, A. Shiomi, H. Sugimoto, M. Takita, Y. H. Tan, N. Tateyama, S. Torii, H. Tsuchiya, S. Udo, H. Wang, H. R. Wu, L. Xue, K. Yagisawa, Y. Yamamoto, Z. Yang, A. F. Yuan, L. M. Zhai, H. M. Zhang, J. L. Zhang, X. Zhang, X. Y. Zhang, Y. Zhang, Y. Zhang, Y. Zhang, Zhaxisangzhu, X. X. Zhou and Tibet AS γ Collaboration, First Detection of Photons with Energy beyond 100 TeV from an Astrophysical Source, *PRL* **123**, p. 051101 (August 2019).
35. MAGIC Collaboration, V. A. Acciari, S. Ansoldi, L. A. Antonelli, A. Arbet Engels, D. Baack, A. Babić, B. Banerjee, U. Barres de Almeida, J. A. Barrio, J. Becerra González, W. Bednarek, L. Bellizzi, E. Bernardini, A. Berti, J. Besenrieder, W. Bhattacharyya, C. Bigongiari, A. Biland, O. Blanch, G. Bonnoli, Ž. Bošnjak, G. Busetto, R. Carosi, G. Ceribella, Y. Chai, A. Chilingaryan, S. Cikota, S. M. Colak, U. Colin, E. Colombo, J. L. Contreras, J. Cortina, S. Covino, V. D'Elia, P. da Vela, F. Dazzi, A. de Angelis, B. de Lotto, M. Delfino, J. Delgado, D. Depaoli, F. di Pierro, L. di Venere, E. Do Souto Espiñeira, D. Dominis Prester, A. Donini, D. Dorner, M. Doro, D. Elsaesser, V. Fallah Ramazani, A. Fattorini, G. Ferrara, D. Fidalgo, L. Foffano, M. V. Fonseca, L. Font, C. Fruck, S. Fukami, R. J. García López, M. Garczarczyk, S. Gasparyan, M. Gaug, N. Giglietto, F. Giordano, N. Godinović, D. Green, D. Guberman, D. Hadasch, A. Hahn, J. Herrera, J. Hoang, D. Hrupec, M. Hütten, T. Inada, S. Inoue, K. Ishio, Y. Iwamura, L. Jouvin, D. Kerszberg, H. Kubo, J. Kushida, A. Lamastra, D. Lelas, F. Leone, E. Lindfors, S. Lombardi, F. Longo, M. López, R. López-Coto, A. López-Oramas, S. Loporchio, B. Machado de Oliveira Fraga, C. Maggio, P. Majumdar, M. Makariev, M. Mallamaci, G. Maneva, M. Manganaro, K. Mannheim, L. Maraschi, M. Mariotti, M. Martínez, D. Mazin, S. Mićanović, D. Miceli, M. Minev, J. M. Miranda, R. Mirzoyan, E. Molina, A. Moralejo, D. Morcuende, V. Moreno, E. Moretti, P. Munar-Adrover, V. Neustroev, C. Nigro, K. Nilsson, D. Ninci, K. Nishijima, K. Noda, L. Nogués, S. Nozaki, S. Paiano, J. Palacio, M. Palatiello, D. Paneque, R. Paoletti, J. M. Paredes, P. Peñil, M. Peresano, M. Persic, P. G. Prada Moroni, E. Prandini, I. Puljak, W. Rhode, M. Ribó, J. Rico, C. Righi, A. Rugliancich, L. Saha, N. Sahakyan, T. Saito, S. Sakurai, K. Satalecka, K. Schmidt, T. Schweizer, J. Sitarek, I. Šnidarić, D. Sobczynska, A. Somero, A. Stamerra, D. Strom, M. Strzys, T. Suda, T. Surić, M. Takahashi, F. Tavecchio, P. Temnikov, T. Terzić, M. Teshima, N. Torres-Albà, L. Tosti, V. Vagelli, J. van Scherpenberg, G. Vanzo, M. Vazquez Acosta, C. F. Vigorito, V. Vitale, I. Vovk, M. Will and D. Zarić, MAGIC very large zenith angle observations of the Crab Nebula up to 100 TeV, *A&A* **635**, p. A158 (March 2020).
36. F. A. Aharonian, A. A. Belyanin, E. V. Derishev, V. V. Kocharovsky and V. V. Kocharovsky, Constraints on the extremely high-energy cosmic ray accelerators from classical electrodynamics, *PRD* **66**, p. 023005 (July 2002).
37. M. A. Malkov and L. O. Drury, Nonlinear theory of diffusive acceleration of particles by shock waves, *Reports on Progress in Physics* **64**, 429 (April 2001).

38. L. Kuiper, W. Hermsen, G. Cusumano, R. Diehl, V. Schönfelder, A. Strong, K. Bennett and M. L. McConnell, The Crab pulsar in the 0.75-30 MeV range as seen by CGRO COMPTEL. A coherent high-energy picture from soft X-rays up to high-energy gamma-rays, A&A **378**, 918 (November 2001).
39. M. Arakawa, M. Hayashida, D. Khangulyan and Y. Uchiyama, Detection of Small Flares from the Crab Nebula with Fermi-LAT, ApJ **897**, p. 33 (July 2020).
40. A. A. Abdo, M. Ackermann, M. Ajello, A. Allafort, L. Baldini, J. Ballet, G. Barbiellini, D. Bastieri, K. Bechtol, R. Bellazzini, B. Berenji, R. D. Blandford, E. D. Bloom, E. Bonamente, A. W. Borgland, A. Bouvier, T. J. Brand t, J. Bregeon, A. Brez, M. Brigida, P. Bruel, R. Buehler, S. Buson, G. A. Caliandro, R. A. Cameron, A. Cannon, P. A. Caraveo, J. M. Casand jian, Ö. Çelik, E. Charles, A. Chekhtman, C. C. Cheung, J. Chiang, S. Ciprini, R. Claus, J. Cohen-Tanugi, L. Costamante, S. Cutini, F. D'Ammando, C. D. Dermer, A. de Angelis, A. de Luca, F. de Palma, S. W. Digel, E. do Couto e Silva, P. S. Drell, A. Drlica-Wagner, R. Dubois, D. Dumora, C. Favuzzi, S. J. Fegan, E. C. Ferrara, W. B. Focke, P. Fortin, M. Frailis, Y. Fukazawa, S. Funk, P. Fusco, F. Gargano, D. Gasparrini, N. Gehrels, S. Germani, N. Giglietto, F. Giordano, M. Giroletti, T. Glanzman, G. Godfrey, I. A. Grenier, M. H. Grondin, J. E. Grove, S. Guiriec, D. Hadasch, Y. Hanabata, A. K. Harding, K. Hayashi, M. Hayashida, E. Hays, D. Horan, R. Itoh, G. Jóhannesson, A. S. Johnson, T. J. Johnson, D. Khangulyan, T. Kamae, H. Katagiri, J. Kataoka, M. Kerr, J. Knödlseder, M. Kuss, J. Lande, L. Latronico, S. H. Lee, M. Lemoine-Goumard, F. Longo, F. Loparco, P. Lubrano, G. M. Madejski, A. Makeev, M. Marelli, M. N. Mazziotta, J. E. McEnery, P. F. Michelson, W. Mitthumsiri, T. Mizuno, A. A. Moiseev, C. Monte, M. E. Monzani, A. Morselli, I. V. Moskalenko, S. Murgia, T. Nakamori, M. Naumann-Godo, P. L. Nolan, J. P. Norris, E. Nuss, T. Ohsugi, A. Okumura, N. Omodei, J. F. Ormes, M. Ozaki, D. Paneque, D. Parent, V. Pelassa, M. Pepe, M. Pesce-Rollins, M. Pierbattista, F. Piron, T. A. Porter, S. Rainò, R. Rando, P. S. Ray, M. Razzano, A. Reimer, O. Reimer, T. Reposeur, S. Ritz, R. W. Romani, H. F. W. Sadrozinski, D. Sanchez, P. M. S. Parkinson, J. D. Scargle, T. L. Schalk, C. Sgrò, E. J. Siskind, P. D. Smith, G. Spand re, P. Spinelli, M. S. Strickman, D. J. Suson, H. Takahashi, T. Takahashi, T. Tanaka, J. B. Thayer, D. J. Thompson, L. Tibaldo, D. F. Torres, G. Tosti, A. Tramacere, E. Troja, Y. Uchiyama, J. Vandenbroucke, V. Vasileiou, G. Vianello, V. Vitale, P. Wang, K. S. Wood, Z. Yang and M. Ziegler, Gamma-Ray Flares from the Crab Nebula, Science **331**, p. 739 (February 2011).
41. M. Tavani, A. Bulgarelli, V. Vittorini, A. Pellizzoni, E. Striani, P. Caraveo, M. C. Weisskopf, A. Tennant, G. Pucella, A. Trois, E. Costa, Y. Evangelista, C. Pittori, F. Verrecchia, E. Del Monte, R. Campana, M. Pilia, A. De Luca, I. Donnarumma, D. Horns, C. Ferrigno, C. O. Heinke, M. Trifoglio, F. Gianotti, S. Vercellone, A. Argan, G. Barbiellini, P. W. Cattaneo, A. W. Chen, T. Contessi, F. D'Ammand o, G. DeParis, G. Di Cocco, G. Di Persio, M. Feroci, A. Ferrari, M. Galli, A. Giuliani, M. Giusti, C. Labanti, I. Lapshov, F. Lazzarotto, P. Lipari, F. Longo, F. Fuschino, M. Marisaldi, S. Mereghetti, E. Morelli, E. Moretti, A. Morselli, L. Pacciani, F. Perotti, G. Piano, P. Picozza, M. Prest, M. Rapisarda, A. Rappoldi, A. Rubini, S. Sabatini, P. Soffitta, E. Vallazza, A. Zambra, D. Zanello, F. Lucarelli, P. Santolamazza, P. Giommi, L. Salotti and G. F. Bignami, Discovery of Powerful Gamma-Ray Flares from the Crab Nebula, Science **331**, p. 736 (February 2011).

On the MG16 awards 2021

Remo Ruffini

ICRA and Dipartimento di Fisica, Università di Roma La Sapienza
Piazzale Aldo Moro 5, I-00185 Roma, Italy
ruffini@icra.it

ICRANet
Piazza della Repubblica 10, I-65122 Pescara, Italy
ruffini@icra.it

INAF
Viale del Parco Mellini 84, 00136 Rome, Italy
ruffini@icra.it

On Monday July 5, 2021 took place the official ceremony for the attribution of the 4 MG16 Individual Awards to Demetrios Christodoulou, Gerard 't Hooft, Tsvi Piran and Steven Weinberg, as well as for the attribution of the 3 MG16 Institutional Awards to the Spektrum-Roentgen-Gamma (SRG) mission of the Max Planck Institute for Extraterrestrial Physics (MPE), of the Space Research Institute (IKI) of the Russian Academy of Sciences and of the S.A. Lavochkin Association. The MG Awards consist in a silver casting of the TEST sculpture by the artist Attilio Pierelli. The MG16 Awards were presented to the Awardees by Prof. Roy P. Kerr.

Keywords: Black Holes; mass energy formula; Horizons; International scientific cooperation; Scientific space missions

1. The MG Awards

Since 1985, the MG Awards have been attributed on the occasion of the Marcel Grossmann meetings. The MG Award consist in a silver casting of the TEST sculpture by the artist Attilio Pierelli.

On the occasion of the MG4 meeting (July 1985, Rome, Italy) the Institutional Award went to the Vatican Observatory (presented to His Holiness Pope John Paul II), while the Individual Awards went to William Fairbank and to Abdus Salam. On the occasion of the MG5 meeting (August 1988, Perth, Australia) the Institutional Award went to the University of Western Australia (presented to the then Vice Chancellor, Prof. Robert Smith) while the Individual Awards went to Satio Hayakawa and to John Archibal Wheeler. On the occasion of the MG6 meeting (June 1991, Kyoto, Japan) the Institutional Award went to the RITP (presented to Prof. K. Tomita) while the Individual Awards went to Minoru Oda and to Stephen Hawking. On the occasion of the MG7 meeting (June 1994, Stanford, USA) the

Institutional Award went to the Space Telescope Institute (presented to Prof. Peter Stockman) while the Individual Awards went to Subrahmanyan Chandrasekhar and to Jim Wilson. On the occasion of the MG8 meeting (June 1997, Jerusalem) the Institutional Award went to the Hebrew University (presented to the then President M. Magidor), while the Individual Awards went to Tullio Regge and to Francis Everitt. On the occasion of the MG9 meeting (July 2000, Rome, Italy) the Institutional Award went to the Solvay Institutes (presented to Jacques Solvay), while the Individual Awards went to Cecile and Bryce Dewitt, Riccardo Giacconi and Roger Penrose. On the occasion of the MG10 meeting (July 2003, Rio de Janeiro, Brazil) the Institutional Award went to the Brazilian Center for Research in Physics - CBPF (presented to its founders Cesar Lattes, Josè Leite Lopez and Jayme Tiomno), while the Individual Awards went to Yvonne Choquet-Bruhat, to James W. York, Jr and to Yuval Ne'eman. On the occasion of the MG11 meeting (July 2006, Berlin, Germany) the Institutional Award went to the Freie Universitaet Berlin (presented to the then President Dr. Dieter Lenzen), while the Individual Awards went to Roy Kerr, George Coyne and Joachim Trumper. On the occasion of the MG12 meeting (July 2009, Paris, France) the Institutional Award went to the Institut des hautes études scientifiques - IHES (presented to Prof. Jean-Pierre Bourguignon), while the Individual Awards went to Jaan Einasto, to Christine Jones and to Michael Kramer. On the occasion of the MG13 meeting (July 2012, Stockholm, Sweden) the Institutional Award went to Albanova (presented to the Rector of the f Stockholm University, Prof. Kåre Bremer), while the Individual Awards went to David Arnett, to Vladimir Belinski and I. M. Khalatnikov and to Filippo Frontera. On the occasion of the MG14 meeting (July 2015, Rome, Italy) the Institutional Award went to the European Space Agency - ESA (presented to its Director General Johann-Dietrich Woerner), while the Individual Awards went to Ken'ichi Nomoto, to Martin Rees, to Yakov G. Sinai and to Sachiko Tsuruta. The 2 additional MG14 Individual Awards to Frank C.N. Yang and to T.D. Lee have been delivered on the occasion of the International Conference on Gravitation and Cosmology/the fourth Galileo-Xu Guangqi meeting in Beijing on May 4, 2015. On the occasion of the MG15 meeting (July 2018, Rome, Italy) the Institutional Award went to the Planck scientific collaboration - ESA (presented to the Principal Investigator of the High Frequency Instrument (HFI) Jean-Loup Puget) and to the Hansen experimental physics laboratory at Stanford University (presented to its Assistant Director Leo Hollberg), while the Individual Awards went to Lyman Page, to Rashid Sunyaev and to Shing-Tung Yau.

2. MG16 Individual Awardees

The MG16 Individual Awards went to Demetrios Christodoulou, Gerard 't Hooft, Tsvi Piran and Steven Weinberg.

2.1. *Demetrios Christodoulou*

Motivation: Professor **Demetrios Christodoulou** received the MG16 Award *"For his many lasting contributions to the foundation of mathematical physics including the dynamics of relativistic gravitational fields. Notably for: contributing in 1971, at the age of 19, to derive with Remo Ruffini the mass-energy formula of black holes as a function of their angular momentum, charge and irreducible mass. Christodoulou turned then to the study of partial differential equations and mathematical physics, to which he remained dedicated for the rest of his career. Highlights in this area include the theoretical discovery of the nonlinear memory effect of gravitational waves (Phys. Rev. Letters 1991), the monograph (1993) in collaboration with Sergiu Klainerman on the global nonlinear stability of the Minkowski spacetime, the monograph (2009) on the formation of black holes in pure general relativity by imploding gravitational waves, and the monographs (2007 and 2019) on the formation and further development of shocks in fluids."*

Scientific and historical background: It was back in 1967 that Achille Papapetrou mentioned the case of the 16 year old Demetrios Christodoulou to John Archibad Wheeler. Wheeler interviewed Demetrios in Paris and brought him immediately to Princeton where he was registered as an undergraduate at the university. After only one year he entered the graduate school and started collaborating with me. At the time I was working with Wheeler on the effective potential approach to co-rotating and counter-rotating geodesics (see e.g. reference in The Classical Theory of Fields (Landau and Lifshitz, 1980) in the Kerr metric (later renamed as ISCO; see e.g. (Gravitation Misner, Thorne, Wheeler. 1973). In parallel, Frank Zerilli was working on the gravitational radiation emitted by a test particle falling into a Schwarzschild black hole (Zerilli 1970). From this limited conceptual arena Charles Misner and later Kip Thorne launched a program for the detection of gravitational waves on the Earth; see e.g. Misner 1974, Abbott et al. 2016, Abbott et al. 2017; see however Davis et al. 1972, Rodriguez et al. 2018 and J.A. Rueda et al. 2018. A new approach started with the arrival of Demetrios: he was just creating mathematics following his needs. We identified the reversible and irreversible transformations of a Kerr black hole. Wheeler advanced a thermodynamic analogy. I addressed the need to identify the concept of irreducible mass (from the Italian "irriducibile"), and was Demetrios's contribution to integrate, overnight, the differential equation for infinitesimal reversible transformations which led to the finite mass-energy formula for a Kerr black hole. That evening, while walking back home through the IAS woods, I expressed to Wheeler the great relevance of the newly found formula by Demetrios and proposed to let Demetrios be the single author of this article, admiring his great mathematical talent. Wheeler agreed. The Editor of PRL objected since in that two page article Fig. 2 by Wheeler and myself was still unpublished. Actually that Fig. 2 followed a discussion I previously had had with Penrose in Florence (Penrose 1969) which allowed us to present the "Penrose process" there. Some difficulties in achieving this process were obvious from the example in Fig. 2, which Roger later recognized himself (Penrose & Floyd 1971). The Editor finally agreed to our written request and the paper appeared on Sep 17, 1970 (Christodoulou, 1970). In January 1971 my article with Johnny *Introducing the Black Hole* (Ruffini & Wheeler, 1971) appeared with the new physics we were developing in Princeton, including the concept of the "ergosphere". On March 1, 1971 we submitted an article giving the mass formula for the Kerr-Newman metric, including the relation between the surface area of the horizon and the irreducible mass (Christodoulou & Ruffini, 1971) . On March 11, 1971 the same results were independently confirmed by Steven Hawking, extending further the applicability of our formula (Hawking 1971).

The thesis of Demetrios was successfully discussed by a committee including Eugene Wigner (see Fig. 1a), one of the closest collaborators of Albert Einstein and David Wilkinson (See Fig. 1b), the head of the NASA WMAP mission and Johnny and myself as supervisors. The new message was clear: black holes, far from being energy sinks, were energy sources able to emit "in principle" up to 50% of their mass energy as being extractable (Christodoulou & Ruffini, 1971).

Demetrios turned soon to the study of partial differential equations and mathematical physics, to which he dedicated for the rest of his career and results were published in four monographs: (Christodoulou and Klainerman 1994, Christodoulou 2007, Christodoulou 2009, Christodoulou 2019). In 1968, Johnny proposed to Demetrios the collapse of a "geon" composed of massless scalar field as a second

Fig. 1. Demetrios during his thesis presentation with Eugene Wigner (above) and David Wilkinson (below). Myself and Johnny were supervisors, ready to intervene in case of need, but no need of intervention was necessary! Wigner elaborated the aphorism of Niels Bohr "Interesting = wrong" in the most definite "very interesting, if true = totally wrong"

topic for his thesis. It took almost forty years for him to solve this problem, which he extended to the more difficult case of focusing gravitational waves leading to black hole formation (Christodoulou 2009).

A "long march" started on December 12, 1970 with the launch of the Uhuru satellite by Riccardo Giacconi. Early in 1971 an almost daily conversation with him and Herb Gursky at the Smithsonian Astrophysical Observatory led to the discovery of binary X-ray sources. This was soon followed by the announcement of Cygnus X1 identified as the first black hole in our galaxy (Ruffini 1973); see e.g. Gursky & Ruffini 1975 which also contained the first public announcement of the discovery of gamma ray bursts, as well as Giacconi & Ruffini 1980, 2009; see Fig. 2).

Fig. 2. In the second row, from left to right, there are, among others: E. T. Newman, S. Chandrasekhar, R. Giacconi, R. Ruffini, A. Treves, A. Hewish, D. Arnett, G. I. Taylor, J. Wilson, R. Penrose, as well as J. Bahcall, T. Damour, T. Piran et al.

Today, after fifty years this "long march" has reached a definite result: through the grandest observational multi-wavelength effort in the history of mankind, from space, ground and underground observatories, we are finally finding evidence that black holes are "alive" and their "extractable energy" in our mass formula (Christodoulou & Ruffini, 1971) is the energy source of the most energetic sources in our universe: gamma ray bursts (GRBs), active galactic nuclei (AGNs) as well as ultra-high energy cosmic rays (UHECRs) (Ruffini et al. 2021 and references therein). Their "inner engine" has three independent components: 1) a Kerr black hole which is neither in a stationary state nor in vacuum, 2) a background magnetic field aligned with the black hole rotation axis, and 3) an extremely diluted fully ionized plasma (Moradi et al. 2021). There is no role in this inner engine for ISCOs. Indeed new electrodynamical field equations describe the synchrotron radiation emitted close to the black hole horizon, and they point to a discrete and repetitive emission of "blackholic quanta" in the MeV and in the GeV. The magnitudes and the emission time scales of these quanta, for M87 and GRB 130427A, are expressed as a function of the above three parameters (Rueda & Ruffini, 2021). A long lasting GeV emission with a luminosity decreasing as a temporal power law allows for the first time for GRBs the determination of the black hole mass and spin as well as their time evolution perfectly fulfilling our mass energy formula (Christodoulou & Ruffini, 1971): a long lasting emission process profoundly different from the traditional process of continued gravitational contraction.

2.2. *Gerard 't Hooft*

Motivation: Professor **Gerard 't Hooft** received the MG16 Individual Award *"for his persistent devotion to the study of the quantum field theory boundary conditions at the black hole horizon"*.

Scientific and historical background:Prof. Gerard 't Hooft has been a full Professor at the Utrecht University (the Netherlands), since 1977. Nowadays, he is an Emeritus Professor at that University. During his career, he has paid extended scientific visits to CERN (Geneva), Harvard, Stanford, Princeton and Duke University, NC. In 1999, together with M. Veltman, he received the Nobel Prize in Physics, awarded by The Royal Swedish Academy of Sciences, *"For elucidating the quantum structure of electroweak interactions in physics"*. Prof. 't Hooft main subjects of research includes:

- Gauge Theories for the sub-atomic particles and forces, various aspects and ingredients of what is now called "The Standard Model" of the sub-atomic particles: renormalizability, topological features such as magnetic monopoles and instantons, 1/N expansions,
- Theories for the quantization of the gravitational force and black holes: producing models for the quantum properties of a black hole, as derived from Standard Model and General Relativity alone; its topological features such as antipodal identification,
- Fundamental theories underlying quantum mechanics, in particular returning determinism and reality to the dynamics of the tiniest material entities in his universe, Prof. 't Hooft has been awarded the Wolf Prize of the State of Israel (1982), the Pius XI Medal (Vatican city, 1983), the Lorentz Medal (KNAW Amsterdam, 1986) as well as the Spinoza Premium (Netherlands Organization for Scientific Research NWO, 1995).

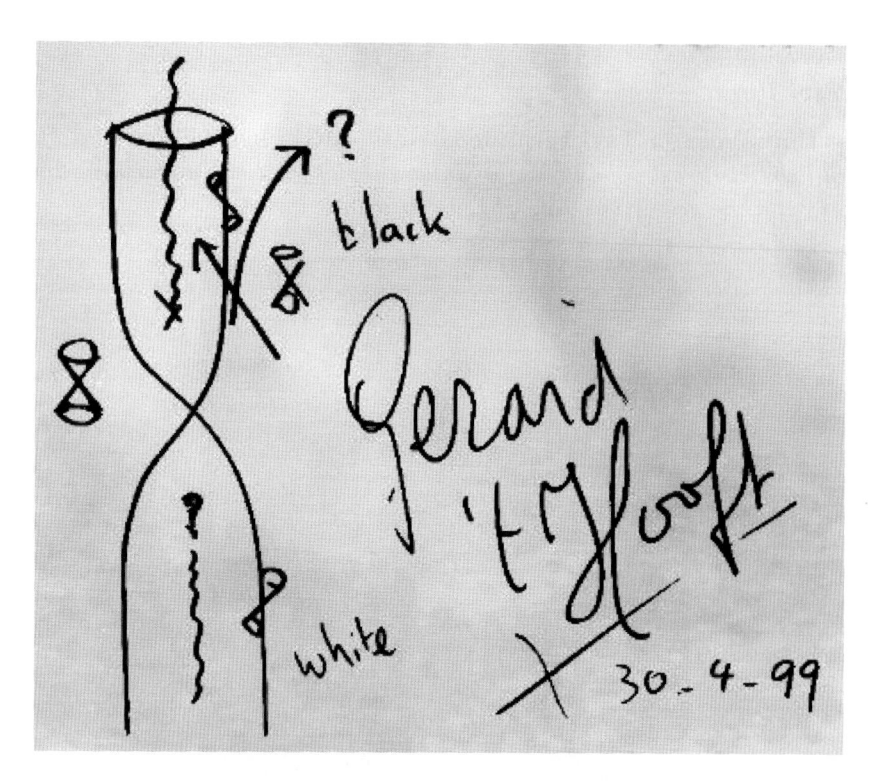

Fig. 3. The signature of Gerard 't Hooft on the wall of ICRA Room 301 (April 4, 1999).

A special event took place at ICRA on April 30, 1999. Prof. Ruffini invited Gerard 't Hooft to Rome to discuss a boundary condition for a quantum field on the black hole horizon, a topic Prof. Ruffini discussed in a previous article "Black-hole evaporation in the Klein-Sauter-Heisenberg-Euler formalism" with Thibault Damour

(Phys. Rev. D 14, 332, 1976), but which needed to be examined in more detail. Prof. Ruffini planned to direct Gerard's attention to some specific aspects of this problem. Because we have traditionally been very attentive in spending ICRA travel funds, ICRA offered Gerard to come to Rome on a reduced fare weekend ticket arriving Friday and departing Monday. He had a great relaxing weekend together with Prof. Ruffini following his seminar, which among other things allowed Gerard to sign the wall in our ICRA Room (see Fig. 3), and during this splendid Rome spring weekend he also was able to find a missing factor of 2 in a formula in Prof. Ruffini's 1971 paper with Demetri Christodoulou on the black hole mass formula. The following October, Gerard received the Nobel prize, which meant that we could no longer get away with bringing him to Rome on a cheap ticket! Ever since Gerard has been in our MG IOC helping us with the preparation of the meetings. We are very happy to announce this MG16 Award to Gerard 't Hooft with the motivating phrase *"for his persistent devotion to the study of the quantum field theory boundary conditions at the black hole horizon"*.

2.3. *Tsvi Piran*

Motivation: Professor **Tsvi Piran** received the MG16 Individual Award *"for extending Relativistic astrophysics across international frontiers, a true companion in the search for the deeper meaning of Einstein's great theory"*.

Scientific and historical background: Tsvi Piran is the emeritus Schwartzmann professor at the Hebrew University of Jerusalem. He obtained his PhD in

Physics, in 1976 from the Hebrew University working on the collisional Penrose process. Piran returned to the Hebrew University at 1981after being a post doc at Oxford and Texas and a long term member at the IAS at Princeton. In 1982 he initiated and directed the first ever summer school on Gravitational Waves that took place at Les Houches. Piran was a visiting professor at Harvard, Columbia and New York and a Moore scholar at Caltech. Piran's research deals with numerous aspects of relativistic astrophysics, ranging from the foundation of numerical relativity to modeling of observer relativistic phenomena and analytic work on the fate of gravitational collapse. Piran's research work focuses mostly on black holes and in particular on gamma-ray bursts. He was among the first to point out their cosmological origin and their association with merging neutron stars and heavy r-process nucleo synthesis. Piran's achievements were recognized in the 2019 EMET prize for Physics.

2.4. *Steven Weinberg*

Motivation: Professor **Steven Weinberg** received the MG16 Individual Award *"for unwavering support for the MG meetings since their inception, a true companion in the search for the deeper meaning of Einstein's great theory"*.

Scientific and historical background: Steven Weinberg is a member of the Physics and Astronomy Departments at The University of Texas at Austin. His research has covered a broad range of topics in quantum field theory, elementary particle physics and cosmology. He has been honored with numerous awards, including the Nobel Prize in Physics, the National Medal of Science, the Heinemann Prize in Mathematical Physics and in 2020, the Breakthrough Prize. He is a member of the US National Academy of Sciences, Britain's Royal Society, and other academies in the USA and abroad. The American Philosophical Society awarded him the Benjamin Franklin Medal, with a citation that said he is "considered by many to be the preeminent theoretical physicist alive in the world today." His books for physicists include *Gravitation and Cosmology*, the three-volume work *The Quantum Theory of Fields, Cosmology* and published in April of 2021, *Foundations of Modern Physics*. Educated at Cornell, Copenhagen, and Princeton, he also holds honorary degrees from sixteen other universities. He taught at Columbia, Berkeley, M.I.T., and Harvard, where he was Higgins Professor of Physics, before coming to Texas in 1982.

2.5. *Scientific and historical background for the Tsvi Piran and Steven Weinberg MG16 Awards*

The Sixteenth Marcel Grossmann Meeting (MG16) is a very special one in many respects: it will take place during a pandemic and in spite of the many difficulties, we have decided not to postpone it but to organize it as a virtual meeting. As described on the MG series webpage, these meetings started in 1975 with the first meeting at the International Centre for Theoretical Physics (ICTP) in Trieste (Italy) that I organized with Nobel Prize winner Abdus Salam. A second meeting followed in 1979, with a significantly larger participation including Nobel Laurate Cheng Ning Yang and a Chinese delegation led by Chuo Pei Yuan (see Fig. 4), including Fang Li-Zhi who had accompanied me during my entire first visit to China in 1979. The first truly international MG meeting followed in 1982 in Shanghai (China):this represented an especially important step forward both for the meeting and for China. A multi-millennia *"motto"* in China, which was then proclaimed on banners everywhere, read *"Friends from all over the world are welcomed"*.

We were soon at an impasse over the participation of scientists from Israel, since no diplomatic relations existed between China and Israel at that time and the Israeli scientists were not to be allowed to attend the meeting. A long negotiation began. The boundary conditions were clearly set by Steven Weinberg, a member of the present MG16 IOC: no MG meetings on Einstein's theory of general relativity could occur without the participation of Israeli scientists. The intervention of Yuval Ne'emann, also a member of the MG IOC then as well as the Minister of Science of Israel (see Fig. 5), proposed a compromise that would admit at least one Israeli scientist.

I went to Beijing alone, meeting every morning for a week with 12 Chinese representatives led by Chuo Pei Yuan going over all possible options. I stayed in an isolated villa not far from Tiananmen Square, accompanied by the 3 volumes of Matteo Ricci (RI MA TO) to keep me company. No solution was in sight the

Fig. 4. Chuo Pei Yuan and Cheng Ning Yang at MG2 in Trieste, Italy (1979).

entire week. At the last moment, just before my departure, an agreement was finally reached allowing two Israeli scientists into China. The historic compromise would admit Gerard Tauber and Tsvi Piran into China using a special ICRA travel document I had proposed for them to be able to participate in the meeting, accepted by the Chinese Ambassador in Rome. This modified the thousand year Chinese *"motto"* to read *"Scientists from all over the world are welcomed"*. The event was extremely beneficial for China and signaled the truly international nature of the MG meetings.

I kept on meeting Tauber in the years which followed (see Fig. 6). Soon after, Yuval Ne'emann visited China. The development of bilateral relations, including military cooperation and economical tights, grow exponentially until the establishment of normal diplomatic relations between Israel and China in 1992.

Given their key role played in the foundations of the MG meetings, I am very happy to propose on behalf of the MG16 IOC, two special Marcel Grossmann Individual Awards: one to Steven Weinberg for *"for unwavering support for the MG*

Fig. 5. From right to left: Chaim Weizmann, President of Israel; Yuval Ne'emann, Minister of Science of Israel; R. Ruffini.

meetings since their inception, a true companion in the search for the deeper meaning of Einstein's great theory" and another one to Tsvi Piran, "*for extending Relativistic astrophysics across international frontiers, a true companion in the search for the deeper meaning of Einstein's great theory*", in the words of John A. Wheeler's photo dedication to myself (see Fig. 7).

3. MG16 Institutional Awardees

The MG16 Institutional Awards to the Spektrum-Roentgen-Gamma (SRG) mission *"for the creation of the world's best X-ray map of the entire sky, for the discovery of millions of previously unknown accreting supermassive black holes at cosmological redshifts, for the detection of X-rays from tens of thousands of galaxy clusters, filled mainly with dark matter, and for permitting the detailed investigation of the growth of the large-scale structure of the universe during the era of dark energy dominance"* went to the S.A. Lavochkin Association (presented to its Designer General Alexander Shirshakov), to the Max Planck Institute for Extraterrestrial Physics - MPE (presented to Professor Peter Predehl, Principal Investigator of eROSITA) and to the Space Research Institute (IKI) of the Russian Academy of Sciences (presented to Professor Rashid Sunyaev, Principal Investigator of SRG Observatory in Russia).

Fig. 6. From right to left: Arrigo Finzi, Remo Ruffini, Gerard Tauber and Konrad Bleuler.

Fig. 7. Albert Einstein, Hideki Yukawa and John. A. Wheeler with a hand-written dedication to Remo Ruffini "To Remo Ruffini, companion in the search for the deeper meaning of Einstein great theory. With warm regards, John Wheeler 5 April 1968".

On Tuesday June 29, 2021, the following 31 Astro-Ph appeared:

(1) https://arxiv.org/abs/2106.14517
(2) https://arxiv.org/abs/2106.14518
(3) https://arxiv.org/abs/2106.14519
(4) https://arxiv.org/abs/2106.14520
(5) https://arxiv.org/abs/2106.14521
(6) https://arxiv.org/abs/2106.14522
(7) https://arxiv.org/abs/2106.14523
(8) https://arxiv.org/abs/2106.14524
(9) https://arxiv.org/abs/2106.14525
(10) https://arxiv.org/abs/2106.14526
(11) https://arxiv.org/abs/2106.14527
(12) https://arxiv.org/abs/2106.14528
(13) https://arxiv.org/abs/2106.14529
(14) https://arxiv.org/abs/2106.14530
(15) https://arxiv.org/abs/2106.14531
(16) https://arxiv.org/abs/2106.14532
(17) https://arxiv.org/abs/2106.14533
(18) https://arxiv.org/abs/2106.14534
(19) https://arxiv.org/abs/2106.14535
(20) https://arxiv.org/abs/2106.14536
(21) https://arxiv.org/abs/2106.14537
(22) https://arxiv.org/abs/2106.14541
(23) https://arxiv.org/abs/2106.14542
(24) https://arxiv.org/abs/2106.14543
(25) https://arxiv.org/abs/2106.14544
(26) https://arxiv.org/abs/2106.14545
(27) https://arxiv.org/abs/2106.14546
(28) https://arxiv.org/abs/2106.14547
(29) https://arxiv.org/abs/2106.14548
(30) https://arxiv.org/abs/2106.14549
(31) https://arxiv.org/abs/2106.14550

3.1. *S.A. Lavochkin Association*

The MG16 Institutional Award to the S.A. Lavochkin Association has been presented to its Designer General, **Alexander Shirshakov**.

S.A. Lavochkin Association created the Navigator space platform carrying German eRosita and Russian ART-XC X-Ray Telescopes, organized the launch of SRG Orbital X-Ray Observatory to the second Lagrangian point of the Sun-Earth system at a distance of 1.5 million km from the Earth and managed the observatory flight and the daily reception of its scientific data on Earth for 23.5 months.

Dr Alexander Shirshakov, Designer General of the S.A. Lavochkin Association, is specialized in design, manufacture, testing, launch and control of S/C for scientific purposes. Among those S/C launched, there are the *Radiostron* Astrophysical Observatory (2011) and the *Spektr-RG* space observatory (2019), while the planned S/C launches are *Luna-25* and *Exomars*.

Dr Shirshakov started his career in 1973, working as an engineer of the State Unitary Enterprise *NPO named by S.A. Lavochkin* in Khimki (Russian Federation). Starting from 1989 he has played multiple roles within the Lavochkin Association, been appointed head of the group, head of the sector, head of department, deputy head of the complex, head of the branch, director of the center, deputy head of the Design Bureau, deputy General Designer and deputy General Director.

Dr Shirshakov is an editorial board Member of the reviewed edition of *Vestnik of Lavochkin Association*. Since 2017, he is also member of the General Designer council. He has been awarded Honored Mechanical engineer of the Russian Federation as well as Agency-level award of the Russian Federal Space Agency.

3.2. *Max Planck Institute for Extraterrestrial Physics (MPE)*

The MG16 Institutional Award to the Max Planck Institute for Extraterrestrial Physics (MPE) has been presented to Professor Peter Predehl, the Principal Investigator of eROSITA.

eROSITA is the soft X-ray telescope on-board the Russian-German Spektr-RG mission which was successfully launched from Baikonur on July 13, 2019 and placed in a halo orbit around the L2 point. 30 years after ROSAT, eROSITA performs an all-sky survey with an unprecedented sensitivity, spectral and angular resolution. Clusters of galaxies are the largest collapsed objects in the Universe. Their formation and evolution is dominated by gravity, i.e. Dark Matter, while their large scale distribution and number density depends on the geometry of the Universe, i.e. Dark Energy. X-ray observations of clusters of galaxies provide information on the rate of expansion of the Universe, the fraction of mass in visible matter, and the amplitude of primordial fluctuations which are the origin of clusters of galaxies and the whole structure of the universe. eROSITA has been designed to detect at least 100.000 clusters of galaxies and to detect systematically more than 3 Million obscured accreting Black Holes. eROSITA will also allow to study the physics of galactic X-ray source populations, like pre-main sequence stars, supernova remnants and X-ray binaries. The eROSITA telescope consists of seven identical Wolter-1 mirror modules. A novel detector system has been developed by MPE on the basis of the successful XMM-Newton pn-CCD technology. MPE is the scientific lead institute of eROSITA, responsible for the development of the instrument, the operation, the analysis software and data archive. Peter Predehl led this development as Principal Investigator of eROSITA and German lead scientist of the SRG mission for more than 15 years until the completion of the first of eight surveys in 2020. At this time eROSITA has already discovered more than 1 Million X-ray sources, more than all X-ray observatories of the last 50 years together. This demonstrates, that the design goals of the mission will easily be fulfilled.

3.3. *Space Research Institute (IKI) of the Russian Academy of Sciences*

The MG16 Institutional Award to the Space Research Institute (IKI) of the Russian Academy of Sciences has been presented to Professor Rashid Sunyaev, the Principal Investigator of SRG Observatory in Russia.

The Space Research Institute (IKI) of the Russian Academy of Sciences was responsible for developing the overall concept and scientific program of the SRG Orbital observatory and played a leading role in developing the ART-XC telescope and the entire SRG observatory as part of the Russian space science program carried out by Roskosmos Corporation in the interests of the Russian Academy of Sciences.

During the flight to the L2 point of the Sun-Earth system, SRG with German (eRosita) and Russian (ART-XC named after Mikhail Pavlinsky) X-Ray Telescopes aboard performed calibrations and long duration Performance Verification observations of a dozen of targets and deep fields. Starting in the middle of December 2019, the SRG scanned the whole sky three times. During these scans, SRG discovered two million point X-Ray sources: mainly quasars, stars with hot and bright coronae, and more than 30 thousand clusters of galaxies. There is a competition and synergy in the search for clusters of galaxies between SRG and the ground-based Atacama Cosmology and South Pole Telescopes, which are searching for clusters of galaxies in microwave spectral band using Sunyaev-Zeldovich effect.

SRG provided the X-Ray map of the whole sky in hard and soft bands, the last is now the best among existing. The huge samples of the X-ray selected quasars at the redshifts up to z=6.2 and clusters of galaxies will be used for well-known cosmological tests and detailed study of the growth of the large scale structure of the Universe during and after reionization.

SRG/eRosita is discovering every day several extragalactic objects which increased or decreased their brightness more than 10 times during half of the year after the previous scan of the same one-degree wide strip on the sky. A significant part of these objects has observational properties similar to the Events of Tidal Disruption of a star orbiting in the vicinity of the supermassive black hole. ART-XC discovered a lot of bright galactic and extragalactic transients.

Rashid Sunyaev is the Principal Investigator of SRG mission in Russia, director-emeritus of the Max-Planck Institute for Astrophysics and Maureen and John Hendricks distinguished visiting professor of the Institute for Advanced Study, Princeton.

Fig. 8. The SRG space mission.

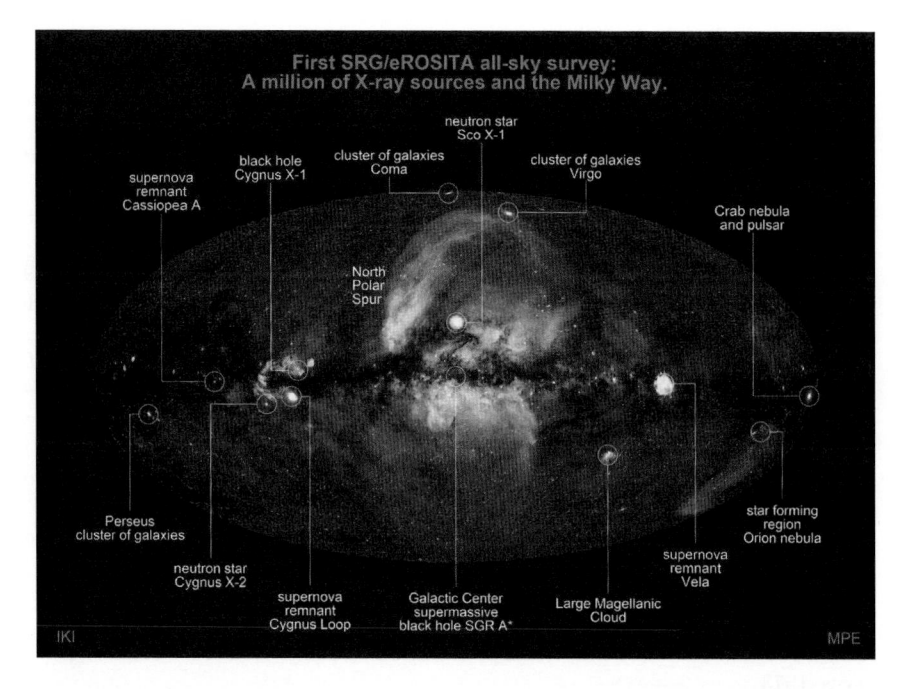

Fig. 9. First SRG/eROSITA all-sky survey, a million of X-ray sources and the Milky Way.

Acknowledgments

It gives me a great pleasure to thank the members of the International Organising Committee (IOC) of the MG meetings as well as members of the scientific and academic communities at large, for discussion and advices.

References

1. Landau, L. D., Lifshitz, E. M., The Classical Theory of Fields, 4th Edition, *Butterworth-Heinemann*, 1980
2. Misner, Charles W., Thorne, Kip S., Wheeler, John A., Gravitation, *San Francisco: W.H. Freeman and Co.*, 1973
3. F. Zerilli, Gravitational Field of a Particle Falling in a Schwarzschild Geometry Analyzed in Tensor Harmonics, *Phys. Rev. D 2, 2141*, 1970
4. Misner, C. W., Mechanisms for the Emission and Absorption of Gravitational Radiation, *Proceedings of the IAU Symposium, No. 64* 1974
5. Abbott B.P. et al., Improved Analysis of GW150914 Using a Fully Spin-Precessing Waveform Model, *Phys. Rev. X 6, 041014*, 2016
6. Abbott B.P. et al., GW170817: Observation of Gravitational Waves from a Binary Neutron Star Inspiral, *Phys. Rev. Lett. 119, 161101*, 2017
7. Davis M. et al., Can Synchrotron Gravitational Radiation Exist?, *Phys. Rev. Lett. 28, 1352*, 1972
8. Rodriguez et al., On the Final Gravitational Wave Burst from Binary Black Holes Mergers, *Astron. Rep. 62, 940–952*, 2018

9. Rueda J.A. et al., GRB 170817A-GW170817-AT 2017gfo and the observations of NS-NS, NS-WD and WD-WD mergers, *JCAP10 006*, 2018
10. Penrose R., Gravitational Collapse: the Role of General Relativity, *Rivista del Nuovo Cimento, Numero Speziale I, 252*, 1969
11. Penrose, R., Floyd, R. Extraction of Rotational Energy from a Black Hole, *Nature Physical Science 229*, 1971
12. Christodoulou D., Reversible and Irreversible Transformations in Black-Hole Physics, *Phys. Rev. Lett. 25, 1596*, 1970
13. Ruffini R., Wheeler J. A., Introducing the black hole, *Physics Today 24, 1, 30*, 1971
14. Christodoulou D., Ruffini R., Reversible Transformations of a Charged Black Hole, *Phys. Rev. D 4, 3552*, 1971
15. Hawking S.W., Gravitational Radiation from Colliding Black Holes, *Phys. Rev. Lett. 26, 1344*, 1971
16. Christodoulou D., Klainerman S., The Global Nonlinear Stability of the Minkowski Space (PMS-41), *Princeton Legacy Library*, 1994
17. Christodoulou D., The Formation of Shocks in 3-Dimensional Fluids, *EMS Monographs in Mathematics, European Mathematical Society*, 2007
18. Christodoulou D., The Formation of Black Holes in General Relativity, *EMS Monographs in Mathematics, European Mathematical Society*, 2009
19. Christodoulou D., The Shock Development Problem, *EMS Monographs in Mathematics, European Mathematical Society*, 2019
20. Ruffini R., Neutron stars and Black Holes in our Galaxy, *New York Academy of Sciences*, 1973
21. Gursky, H., Ruffini, R., Neutron Stars, Black Holes and Binary X-Ray Sources, *Springer Netherlands*, 1975
22. Giacconi, R.; Ruffini, R., Physics and astrophysics of neutron stars and black holes, *Bologna, Societa Italiana di Fisica; Amsterdam, North Holland Publishing Co.*, 1980
23. Rees M., Ruffini R., Wheeler J.A., Black Holes, Gravitational Waves and Cosmology, *CRC*, 2004
24. Ruffini R. et al., The morphology of the X-ray afterglows and of the jetted GeV emission in long GRBs, *Monthly Notices of the Royal Astronomical Society, Volume 504, Issue 4*, 2021
25. Rueda, J.A., Ruffini, R. The blackholic quantum, *Eur. Phys. J. C 80, 300*, 2021

The white dwarf binary merger model of GRB 170817A[*]

J. A. Rueda[†,‡,§,¶,††,¶¶], R. Ruffini[†,‡,∥,**], Liang Li[†,‡,‡‡],
R. Moradi[†,‡,‡‡], N. Sahakyan[§§] and Y. Wang[†,‡,‡‡]

[†]*ICRANet, Piazza della Repubblica 10, I-65122 Pescara, Italy*

[‡]*ICRA, Dipartimento di Fisica, Sapienza Università di Roma,
Piazzale Aldo Moro 5, I-00185 Roma, Italy*

[§]*ICRANet-Ferrara, Dipartimento di Fisica e Scienze della Terra,
Università degli Studi di Ferrara, Via Saragat 1,
I-44122 Ferrara, Italy*

[¶]*Dipartimento di Fisica e Scienze della Terra,
Università degli Studi di Ferrara,
Via Saragat 1, I-44122 Ferrara, Italy*

[∥]*Université de Nice Sophia-Antipolis,
Grand Château Parc Valrose, Nice, CEDEX 2, France*

[**]*INAF, Viale del Parco Mellini 84,
00136 Rome, Italy*

[††]*INAF, Istituto di Astrofisica e Planetologia Spaziali,
Via Fosso del Cavaliere 100, 00133 Rome, Italy*

[‡‡]*INAF – Osservatorio Astronomico d'Abruzzo,
Via M. Maggini snc, I-64100 Teramo, Italy*

[§§]*ICRANet-Armenia, Marshall Baghramian Avenue 24a,
Yerevan 0019, Republic of Armenia*
[¶¶]*jorge.rueda@icra.it*

Following the GRB 170817A prompt emission lasting a fraction of a second, 10^8 s of data in the X-rays, optical, and radio wavelengths have been acquired. We here present a model that fits the spectra, flux, and time variability of all these emissions, based on the thermal and synchrotron cooling of the expanding matter ejected in a binary white dwarf merger. The $10^{-3} M_\odot$ of ejecta, expanding at velocities of 10^9 cm s^{-1}, are powered by the newborn massive, fast rotating, magnetized white dwarf with a mass of $1.3 M_\odot$, a rotation period of $\gtrsim 12$ s, and a dipole magnetic field $\sim 10^{10}$ G, born in the merger of a $1.0 + 0.8 M_\odot$ white dwarf binary. Therefore, the long-lasting mystery of the GRB 170817A nature is solved by the merger of a white dwarf binary that also explains the prompt emission energetics.

Keywords: Gamma-ray bursts; white dwarfs; white dwarf mergers.

1. Introduction

GRB 170817A is a short gamma-ray burst (GRB) whose prompt emission lasts less than a second, as was detected by the gamma-ray burst monitor (GBM) onboard

---

[*]Based on a talk presented at the Sixteenth Marcel Grossmann Meeting on Recent Developments in Theoretical and Experimental General Relativity, Astrophysics and Relativistic Field Theories, online, July 2021.

the NASA Fermi Gamma-ray Space Satellite,[1,2] and confirmed by *INTEGRAL*.[3] It was subsequently associated with GW170817, a gravitational wave signal reported by the LIGO/Virgo Collaboration about 40 min after the Fermi-GBM circular.[4] These initial data were then associated with the optical-infrared-ultraviolet source AT 2017gfo, which started to be observed about 12 h ($\approx 4 \times 10^4$ s) after the GRB trigger.[5–8] Further data of GRB 170817A have been in the mean time acquired in the X-rays and in the radio from 10^6 s after the GRB trigger, and still ongoing.

It has been well established that short GRBs are produced by neutron star binary (NS-NS) mergers.[9–11] Therefore, it is not surprising that GRB 170817A was labeled as such from the very beginning,[1,4,12] despite the fact that it had been soon recognized that GRB 170817A was observationally very different from typical short GRBs.[2] Indeed, a comparison of GRB 170817A in the gamma-rays, X-rays and in the optical with typical short GRBs led[13] to suggest that GRB 170817A looks more like a white dwarf binary (WD-WD) merger rather than an abnormal, special or unique NS-NS merger.[14] Identified additional sources similar to GRB 170817A and have proposed an alternative interpretation of them as WD-WD mergers.

In the mean time, 10^8 s of data of GRB 170817A have been acquired in the X-rays, in the optical, and in the radio wavelengths, besides just the MeV radiation of the prompt emission. These observations have indeed led to alternative explanations. In fact

- The NS-NS merger interprets the associated optical counterpart AT 2017gfo as a nuclear *kilonova* produced by the decay of r-process, which yields in the matter ejected in the merger.[5–8]
- The experimental confirmation of the nuclear *kilonova* needs a univocal spectroscopic identification of the atomic species present in the ejecta.[15–19] This has not been achievable in view of lack of available accurate models of atomic spectra, the nuclear reaction network, density profile, and details of the radiative transport (opacity). Other mechanisms can also explain the photometric properties of AT 2017gfo, for instance the cooling of the expanding ejecta of a WD-WD merger.[13,20] We will further elaborate this scenario in this paper.
- The NS-NS merger leading to a jet propagating throughout the ejected matter appears in conflict with recent data by the *Chandra* X-ray Telescope at 10^7–10^8 s after the GRB trigger.[21,22]

In view of all the above, we here explore further and extend the suggestion by Ref. 13 of GRB 170817A being the product of a WD-WD merger, adding new observations all the way up to 10^8 s.

- The possibly observed re-brightening in the X-ray afterglow of GRB 170817A at 1000 days agrees with the predicted appearance of the pulsar-like activity of the newborn WD from a WD-WD merger.[13,20]

- The rate of GRB 170817A-like events is well explained by the rate of WD-WD mergers.[13,20]
- Interestingly, the host galaxy of GRB 170817, NGC 4993 distant at about 40 Mpc, is an old elliptical galaxy.[1] Elliptical old galaxies are amply recognized as preferred sites of type Ia supernovae produced by the so-called double-degenerate scenario, namely, by WD-WD mergers.[23,24]

The aim of this paper is to extend the treatment of Ref. 20 on WD-WD mergers, and exploit the analogy with the synchrotron emission in the X-rays, optical and radio bands in the afterglow of long GRBs[25–28] to determine the emission of WD-WD mergers across the electromagnetic spectrum. Then, we apply the above considerations to the luminosity in the X-rays, optical and radio wavelengths observed in the afterglow of GRB 170817A.

We here show the prominent role of rotation and its effect on the synchrotron emission from the interaction of the newborn rotating object with the ejected matter in the merger. This process is energetically predominant and has been neglected in traditional simulations of these merging systems. The ejected matter expands in the magnetic field of the newborn fast rotating WD, which injects rotational and accretion energy into the expanding ejecta. While expanding, the ejecta radiate energy across the electromagnetic spectrum due to thermal cooling and synchrotron emission. We evidence that the newborn WD becomes observable as a pulsar when the synchrotron radiation fades off. The amount of mass ejected, the mass, rotation period, and strength of the magnetic field of the newborn WD are the most important features that determine the electromagnetic emission of the system.

We show that the above process leads to a hard-to-soft evolution of the emitted radiation with specific decreasing luminosities that approach a distinct power-law behavior. The late-time luminosity is dominated by the pulsar activity of the newborn object, therefore the asymptotic power-law gives information on the parameters of the newborn central object. The total energy radiated during the whole evolution is dominated by the energy injected and radiated from the central WD, so it is covered by its rotational energy.[29] Energy and angular momentum conservation allow to infer, for instance, the spin and magnetic field of the newborn WD directly from the light-curve of the source, prior to any detailed fit of the observational data with the theoretical model (see Refs. 26–28, for the case of long GRBs).

We apply the above considerations to GRB 170817A and show the agreement of the WD-WD merger scenario with all the available observational multiwavelength data from the gamma-rays all the way down to the radio wavelengths. This paper is organized as follows. In Sec. 2, we formulate the general physical conditions of the WD-WD coalescence that constrain the parameters of the newborn WD formed at merger. Section 3 presents an estimate of a possible mechanism leading to a gamma-ray prompt emission in these mergers, and how it compares with GRB

1780817A. Section 4 is devoted to the analysis of the WD-WD post-merger early optical-infrared-ultraviolet emission by thermal cooling, and how it compares with AT 2017gfo. In Sec. 5, we present the theoretical model of the synchrotron emission powered by the newborn WD, and how it leads to a multiwavelength emission (from the radio to the gamma-rays). A comparison with the emission of GRB 170817A $t \gtrsim 10^6$ s is presented. We outline our conclusions in Sec. 6. We use cgs units throughout.

2. Merging Binary and Post-Merger Remnant

The fate of the central remnant of a WD-WD merger with a total mass near (below or above) the Chandrasekhar mass limit can be one of the three possibilities: (i) a stable newborn WD, (ii) a type Ia supernova, or (iii) a newborn neutron star. Sub-Chandrasekhar remnants can lead either to (i) and (ii), while super-Chandrasekhar remnants produce either (ii) or (iii). Super-Chandrasekhar remnants are supported by angular momentum, so they are less dense and metastable objects whose final fate is delayed until the excess of angular momentum is loss, e.g. via magnetic braking, inducing its compression.[30,31]

We are here interested in WD-WD mergers leading to stable, massive, sub-Chandrasekhar newborn WDs with a mass $\gtrsim 1.0 M_\odot$. These WDs can have rotation periods as short as ~ 0.5 s (see Ref. 32) and can also avoid the trigger of unstable burning leading to type Ia supernova providing its central density is kept under some critical value of a few 10^9 g cm^{-3}.[31]

Numerical simulations of WD-WD mergers show that the merged configuration has in general three distinct regions:[31,33–39] a rigidly rotating, central WD, on top of which there is a hot, convective corona with differential rotation, surrounded by a rapidly rotating Keplerian disk. Roughly, half of the mass of the secondary star, which is totally disrupted, goes to the corona while the other half goes to the disk. The above implies that little mass is ejected in the merger. Numerical simulations show that the amount of expelled mass is approximated by Ref. 39

$$m_{\rm ej} \approx h(q)\, M, \quad h(q) = \frac{0.0001807}{-0.01672 + 0.2463 q - 0.6982 q^2 + q^3}, \tag{1}$$

where

$$M = m_1 + m_2 = \left(\frac{1+q}{q}\right) m_2, \tag{2}$$

is the total binary mass, and $q \equiv m_2/m_1 \leq 1$ is the binary mass ratio. Equation (1) tells us that for a fixed total binary mass, the larger the mass symmetry, the smaller the mass that is ejected. Thus, for a fully symmetric mass ratio, $q = 1$, the amount of expelled matter becomes $m_{\rm ej} \approx 3.4 \times 10^{-4} M$.

WD-WD merger simulations show two important ingredients for our model. First, the central remnant (the newborn WD) is degenerate, namely, massive

($\gtrsim 1.0 M_\odot$), fast rotating, and magnetized.[31] Second, although the amount of expelled matter is negligible with respect to the total mass of the system, the ejecta are crucial for the electromagnetic emission in the post-merger evolution.

We start with a double WD with components of mass m_1 and m_2, with corresponding radii R_1 and R_2. We shall make use of the analytic mass-radius relation[40]

$$\frac{R_i}{R_\odot} = \frac{0.0225}{\bar{\mu}} \frac{\sqrt{1-(m_i/M_{\rm crit})^{4/3}}}{(m_i/M_{\rm crit})^{1/3}}, \qquad (3)$$

where $\bar{\mu} \approx 2$ is the molecular weight, and

$$M_{\rm crit} \approx \frac{5.816 M_\odot}{\bar{\mu}^2} \approx 1.4\, M_\odot, \qquad (4)$$

is the critical mass of (carbon) WDs, $M_\odot$ and $R_\odot$ are the solar mass and radius. Since little mass is expelled, we estimate the newborn WD mass as

$$m_{\rm wd} \approx M - m_d = m_1 + m_2 - m_d \approx \left(\frac{2+q}{2\,q}\right) m_2, \qquad (5)$$

where we have approximated the disk mass by $m_d \approx m_2/2$, according to numerical simulations. Combining Eqs. (2) and (5), we obtain

$$M \approx 2\left(\frac{1+q}{2+q}\right) m_{\rm wd}, \qquad (6)$$

and using Eqs. (1) and (6), we obtain

$$m_{\rm wd} \approx \left(\frac{2+q}{1+q}\right) \frac{m_{\rm ej}}{2\,h(q)}. \qquad (7)$$

As we shall see in Sec. 6, the above equations allow us to infer, from the inferred mass of the ejecta from the fit of the multiwavelength data of GRB 170817A, the parameters of the merging components and of the newborn WD.

3. The Prompt γ-Ray Emission

GRB 170817 was first detected by the GBM on board the *Fermi* satellite.[2] The gamma-ray emission was confirmed by *INTEGRAL*.[3]

GRB 170817A is as a short burst with a duration (T_{90}) of 2.048 s, as reported in the NASA/HEASARC database.[a] We performed a Bayesian spectral analysis of the *Fermi*-GBM data by using the Multi-Mission Maximum Likelihood Framework (3ML, see Ref. 41), and the best model is selected by comparing the deviance information criterion (DIC, see Refs. 42, 43). We first fit the data with a single power-law function, and obtained a DIC value of 3138. We then compare this model to the blackbody (Planck) spectrum over the same time interval, and obtained a DIC value of 3146. We also fit the data with a Comptonized (i.e. a cutoff power-law,

---
[a] https://heasarc.gsfc.nasa.gov/W3Browse/fermi/fermigbrst.html.

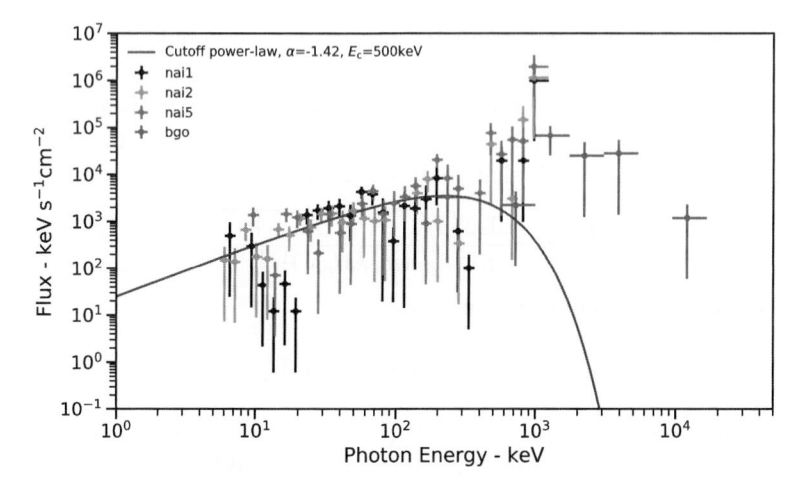

Fig. 1. Spectral fits of νF_ν spectrum for the entire pulse (-0.320 to 1.984 s) of the *Fermi*-GBM observation of GRB 170817A. This time interval is the best fit with a Comptonized function, with a cutoff energy $E_c = 500 \pm 317$ keV, $\alpha = -1.42 \pm 0.18$, and time-averaged flux is $(1.84 \pm 0.82) \times 10^{-7}$ erg s^{-1} cm^{-2} (see Sec. 3 for details of the data analysis).

hereafter CPL) function, and obtained a DIC value of 3128. The CPL model leads to a DIC improvement of 10 with respect to the power-law model, and of 18 with respect to the blackbody model, which suggests the CPL as the model that best fits the data. We refer to Refs. 44–48 for a detailed Bayesian analysis of the data and the reduction procedure applied to GRBs.

As discussed above, the entire pulse (-0.320 to 1.984 s) is best fitted by a CPL with a cutoff energy $E_c = 500 \pm 317$ keV and power-law index $\alpha = -1.42 \pm 0.18$ (see Fig. 1). The time-averaged flux is $(1.84 \pm 0.82) \times 10^{-7}$ erg s^{-1} cm^{-2}. With the measured cosmological redshift of $z = 0.009783$, corresponding to a source distance of ≈ 43 Mpc, the isotropic energy released in this time interval is estimated to be $(4.16^{+3.15}_{-1.84}) \times 10^{46}$ erg. The nonthermal energy released at energies above 1 MeV corresponds to only 2.82% of the emission corresponding to $\approx 1.17 \times 10^{45}$ erg. Therefore, most of the energy is released below MeV energies, which corresponds to $\approx 4.04 \times 10^{46}$ erg.

We here advance the possibility that the γ-ray prompt emission of GRB 170817A occurs from activity in the merged magnetosphere. We could think of the WD pulsar magnetosphere in an analogous way as the NS pulsar magnetosphere, therefore the presence of the strong magnetic field and rotation produces the presence of a electric field by Faraday (unipolar) induction.[49] Numerical simulations show that the merger forms a transient hot corona with temperatures 10^8–10^9 K that cools down rapidly mainly by neutrino emission.[31] Therefore, thermal production of e^+e^- pairs can occur for short time before it cools below the pair formation energy threshold. The charged particles are accelerated by the electric field to then follow the magnetic field lines generating both curvature and synchrotron photons. Since the magnetic field lines are curved, photon–photon collisions occur roughly in all directions, so the majority of the photons with energy in excess of $m_e c^2$ can decay into pairs again and generate a thermal plasma. A minority of photons escape along the rotation axis (see below), leading to the observed nonthermal emission above 1 MeV.

The cross-section of the $\gamma\gamma \to e^- e^+$ process is given by

$$\sigma_{\gamma\gamma} = \frac{3\sigma_T}{16}(1-\bar{\beta}^2)\left[2\bar{\beta}(\bar{\beta}^2 - 2) + (3 - \bar{\beta}^4)\ln\left(\frac{1+\bar{\beta}}{1-\bar{\beta}}\right)\right], \quad (8)$$

where $\sigma_T \approx 6.65 \times 10^{-25}$ cm^2 is the Thomson cross-section, and $\bar{\beta}$ is the e^- (or e^+) velocity (in units of c) in the center of momentum frame

$$\bar{\beta} \equiv \sqrt{1 - \frac{2}{\bar{\epsilon}_{\text{inc}}\bar{\epsilon}_{\text{tgt}}(1-\cos\theta)}}, \quad (9)$$

being $\bar{\epsilon}_{\text{inc,tgt}} \equiv \epsilon_{\text{inc,tgt}}/(m_e c^2)$ the normalized energy of the incident and target photons which collide making an angle θ measured in laboratory frame.

Photons emitted along the curved magnetic field lines are expected to be absorbed since they will be radiated nearly isotropically. In this case, $\langle\cos\theta\rangle \sim 0$ and the cross-section becomes maximal at $\bar{\epsilon}_{\text{inc}}\bar{\epsilon}_{\text{tgt}} \approx 4$, and $\sigma_{\gamma\gamma} \approx \sigma_T/4$. Under these conditions, the $\gamma\gamma$ optical depth is

$$\tau_{\gamma\gamma} \approx n_{\text{tgt}} \sigma_{\gamma\gamma} r \approx \frac{L_{\text{tgt}} \sigma_{\gamma\gamma}}{4\pi r c \epsilon_{\text{tgt}}} \approx \frac{L_{\text{tgt}} \bar{\epsilon}_{\text{inc}} \sigma_T}{64\pi r m_e c^3}, \quad (10)$$

where r is the source size and n_{tgt} is the density of target photons, which we have estimated as $n_{\text{tgt}} \approx L_{\text{tgt}}/(4\pi r^2 c \epsilon_{\text{tgt}})$, where L_{tgt} is the luminosity emitted at energies larger than the target photon energy.

For a transient hot corona, most photons are emitted at energies around the peak of the Planck spectrum, which for a temperature of a few 10^9 K implies $\epsilon_{\text{inc}} \sim \epsilon_{\text{tgt}} \sim 3kT \sim 1$ MeV. Assuming a source size $r \sim R_{\text{wd}} \sim 10^9$ cm, and a target luminosity $L_{\text{tgt}} \sim 4\pi R_{\text{wd}}^2 \sigma T^4 \sim 10^{51}$ erg s^{-1}, the optical depth (10) $\tau_{\gamma\gamma} \sim 10^{10}$.

The above conditions imply that most photons interact generating an optically thick pair plasma which explains the dominant blackbody component observed by *Fermi*-GBM. The observed nonthermal component is explained if $\approx 1\%$ of the photons escape from the system, which can occur near the rotation axis of the WD. There, the interaction angle could approach values as small as $\cos\theta \sim 1$, thereby reducing drastically the photon–photon cross-section.

4. Thermal Cooling of the Ejecta as Origin of the Kilonova

The second observed emission associated with GRB 170817A is the optical counterpart at about 0.5 d after the *Fermi*-GBM trigger, i.e. AT 2017gfo.[7,8,50,51] For the modeling of this thermal emission of the expanding ejecta, we must take into account that in a nonhomogeneous distribution of matter, the layers reach transparency at different times. For simplicity, we consider the ejected matter as a spherically symmetric distribution extending at radii $r_i \in [R_*, R_{\max}]$, with corresponding velocities $v_i \in [v_*, v_{\max}]$, in self-similar expansion

$$r_i(t) = r_{i,0} \hat{t}^n, \quad v_i(t) = n\frac{r_i(t)}{t} = v_{i,0}\hat{t}^{n-1}, \qquad (11)$$

where $\hat{t} \equiv t/t_*$, being $t_* \equiv nR_{*,0}/v_{*,0}$ the characteristic expansion timescale, which is the same for all layers in view of the condition of self-similarity. Here, $r_{i,0}$ and $v_{i,0}$ are the initial radius and velocity of the layer (so at times $t \ll t_*$ close to the beginning of the expansion. The case $n = 1$ corresponds to a uniform expansion.

The density at the position $r = r_i$ is given by

$$\rho(r_i) = \frac{(3-m)}{4\pi}\frac{m_{\text{ej}}}{R_{*,0}^3}\left[\left(\frac{R_{\max}}{R_*}\right)^{3-m} - 1\right]^{-1}\left(\frac{r_i}{R_*}\right)^{-m}\hat{t}^{-3n}, \qquad (12)$$

where m_{ej} is the total mass of the ejecta, and m is a positive constant. The distribution and time evolution given by Eq. (12) ensure that at any time the total mass of the ejecta, i.e. the volume integral of the density, is always equal to m_{ej}.

We divide the ejecta into N shells defined by the $N+1$ radii

$$r_{i,0} = R_{*,0} + i\frac{(R_{\max,0} - R_{*,0})}{N}, \quad i = 0, 1, ..., N, \qquad (13)$$

so the width and mass of each shell are, respectively, $\Delta r = (R_{\max,0} - R_{*,0})/N$, and

$$m_i = \int_{r_i}^{r_{i+1}} 4\pi r^2 \rho(r) dr \approx \frac{4\pi}{m-3} r_i^2 \rho(r_i) \Delta r, \qquad (14)$$

so in view of the decreasing density with distance, the inner layers are more massive than the outer layers. The number of shells to be used must be chosen to satisfy the constraint that the sum of the shells mass gives the total ejecta mass, i.e.

$$\sum_{j=1}^{N} m_j = m_{\text{ej}}, \qquad (15)$$

where we have introduced the discrete index $j = i+1$ to differentiate the counting of the shells from the counting of radii given by Eq. (13). In this work, we use $N = 100$ shells which ensures that Eq. (15) is satisfied with 99% of accuracy.

Under the assumption that the shells do not interact with each other, we can estimate the evolution of the ith shell from the energy conservation equation

$$\dot{E}_i = -P_i \dot{V}_i - L_{\text{cool},i} + H_{\text{inj},i}, \qquad (16)$$

where $V_i = (4\pi/3)r_i^3$, E_i, and P_i are the volume, energy, and pressure of the shell, while $H_{\text{inj},i}$ is the power injected into the shell, and

$$L_{\text{cool},i} \approx \frac{cE_i}{r_i(1+\tau_{\text{opt},i})}, \qquad (17)$$

is the bolometric luminosity radiated by the shell, being $\tau_{\text{opt},i}$ the optical depth.

Assuming a spatially constant, gray opacity throughout the ejecta, the optical depth of the radiation emitted by the ith layer is given by

$$\tau_{\text{opt},i} = \int_\infty^{r_i} \kappa\rho(r)dr = \int_{R_{\max}}^{r_i} \kappa\rho(r)dr = \tau_{i,0}\hat{t}^{-2n}, \tag{18}$$

$$\tau_{i,0} \equiv \frac{m-3}{m-1}\frac{\kappa m_{\text{ej}}}{4\pi R_{*,0}^2} \frac{\left[\left(\frac{R_*}{r_i}\right)^{m-1} - \left(\frac{R_*}{R_{\max}}\right)^{m-1}\right]}{\left[1 - \left(\frac{R_*}{R_{\max}}\right)^{m-3}\right]}, \tag{19}$$

where we have used Eq. (12), and κ is the opacity.

We adopt a radiation-dominated equation of state for the ejecta and, improving with respect to Ref. 20, accounting for the radiation pressure, i.e.

$$E_i = 3P_i V_i + L_{\text{cool},i}^{\text{abs}} \frac{r_i}{c}. \tag{20}$$

The power injected into the ejecta originates from the newborn central WD.[20] This energy is absorbed and thermalized becoming a heating source for the expanding matter. The power-law decreasing density (12) suggests that the inner the layer the more radiation it should absorb. In order to account for this effect, we weigh the heating source for each shell using the mass fraction, i.e.

$$H_{\text{inj},i} = \frac{m_i}{m_{\text{ej}}} H_{\text{inj}}, \tag{21}$$

where m_i is the shell's mass, and adopts the following form for the heating source:

$$H_{\text{inj}} = H_0\left(1 + \frac{t}{t_c}\right)^{-\delta}, \tag{22}$$

where H_0 and δ are model parameters. According to Ref. 20, power from fallback accretion with $H_0 \sim 10^{45}$ erg s^{-1}, $\delta \sim 1.3$, and $t_c \sim t_*$ (see Table 1), dominates the energy release from the newborn WD at these early-times.

The photospheric radius at a time t is given by the position of the shell that reaches transparency at that time. Namely, it is given by the position of the shell whose optical depth fulfills $\tau_{\text{opt},i}[r_i(t)] = 1$. Using Eq. (18), we obtain

$$R_{\text{ph}} = \frac{R_{\max,0}\hat{t}^n}{\left[1 + \frac{m-1}{m-3}\frac{4\pi R_{*,0}^2\left[1 - \left(\frac{R_*}{R_{\max}}\right)^{m-3}\right]}{\kappa m_{\text{ej}}}\left(\frac{R_{\max}}{R_*}\right)^{m-1}\hat{t}^{2n}\right]^{\frac{1}{m-1}}}. \tag{23}$$

Equation (23) shows that when the entire ejecta is optically thick, $R_{\text{ph}} = R_{\max}$. Then, the transparency reaches the inner shells all the way to the instant over which

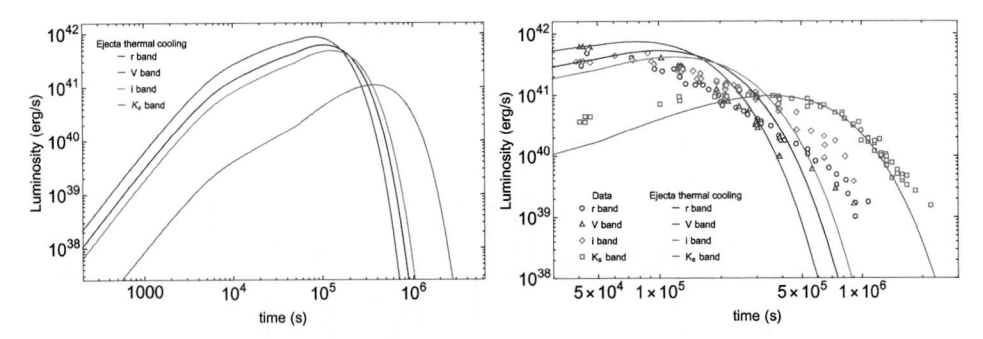

Fig. 2. Left: emission from the expanding, cooling ejecta at early-times in the visible (r and V) and in the infrared (i and K_s) bands, following the theoretical treatment of Sec. 6. Right: zoomed view of the left panel figure at the times relevant for the comparison with the observational data of AT 2017gfo.[7,8,50,51]

$R_{\rm ph} = R_*$, reached at $t = t_{{\rm tr},*}$, when the entire ejecta is transparent. The time $t_{{\rm tr},*}$ is found from the condition $\tau_{{\rm opt},*}[R_*(t_{{\rm tr},*})] = 1$, and is given by

$$\hat{t}_{{\rm tr},*} = \left\{ \frac{m-3}{m-1} \frac{\kappa m_{\rm ej}}{4\pi R_{*,0}^2} \left(\frac{R_*}{R_{\rm max}}\right)^{m-1} \frac{\left[\left(\frac{R_{\rm max}}{R_*}\right)^{m-1} - 1\right]}{\left[1 - \left(\frac{R_*}{R_{\rm max}}\right)^{m-3}\right]} \right\}^{\frac{1}{2n}}. \qquad (24)$$

At $t < t_{{\rm tr},*}$, the photospheric radius evolves as $R_{\rm ph} \propto t^{\frac{n(m-3)}{m-1}}$, while at later times, $R_{\rm ph} \propto t^n$. For the parameters of our system, $t_{{\rm tr},*} \sim 10^5$ s (see Fig. 2).

The bolometric luminosity is given by the sum of the luminosity of the shells

$$L_{\rm bol} = \sum_{j=1}^{N} L_{{\rm cool},j}, \qquad (25)$$

so the effective temperature of the thermal blackbody radiation, T_s, can be obtained from the Stefan–Boltzmann law, i.e.

$$T_s = \left(\frac{L_{\rm bol}}{4\pi R_{\rm ph}^2 \sigma}\right)^{1/4}, \qquad (26)$$

where σ is the Stefan–Boltzmann constant. The power per unit frequency, per unit area, is given by Planck's spectrum

$$B_\nu(\nu, t) = \frac{2\pi h \nu^3}{c^2} [e^{\frac{h\nu}{k_b T_s(t)}} - 1]^{-1}, \qquad (27)$$

where ν is the radiation frequency, h and k_b are the Planck and Boltzmann constants. Most of the thermal cooling is radiated in the visible, infrared and ultraviolet wavelengths, which we refer to as optical. Therefore, the spectral density

Table 1. Numerical values of the theoretical model parameters that determine the thermal cooling of the expanding ejecta which fits the data of AT 2017gfo shown in Fig. 2.

Parameter	Value
n	1.22
m	9.00
$m_{\rm ej}$ ($10^{-3} M_\odot$)	1.00
$R_{*,0}$ (10^{11} cm)	4.00
$v_{*,0}$ (10^9 cm s^{-1})	1.00
κ (cm^2 g^{-1})	0.20
H_0 (10^{45} erg s^{-1})	8.16
δ	1.30
t_c/t_*	1.00

(power per unit frequency) given by the thermal cooling at a frequency ν is

$$J_{\rm cool}(\nu,t) = 4\pi R_{\rm ph}^2(t) B_\nu(\nu,t), \qquad (28)$$

and the luminosity radiated in the frequency range $[\nu_1,\nu_2]$ can be then obtained as

$$L_{\rm cool}(\nu_1,\nu_2;t) = \int_{\nu_1}^{\nu_2} J_{\rm cool}(\nu,t)d\nu. \qquad (29)$$

Figure 2 shows the luminosity in the r, V, i, and K_s energy bands obtained from Eq. (29), and compares them with the corresponding observations of AT 2017gfo. For the fit of these data, we have set the parameters, as shown in Table 1.

The value of the parameter $v_{\rm max,0}$ does not have any appreciable effect in the evolution, so it cannot be constrained from the data. This happens because most of the mass is concentrated in the innermost layers, so they dominate the thermal evolution. For self-consistency of the model, we have set $v_{\rm max,0} = 2v_{*,0}$, a value that keeps the outermost shell velocity well below the speed of light at any time in the evolution. As for the initial value of the internal energy of the shells, $E_i(t_0)$, we have set them to the initial kinetic energy of each layer, $E_i = (1/2)m_i v_i(t_0)^2$.

There is a general agreement of the model with the observations, although it cannot catch any detailed observational feature. There are some extensions to the present model that can increase its accuracy. For instance, we can abandon the assumption of spherical expansion allowing the layers to have a latitude-dependent velocity. Such a detailed treatment goes beyond our present scope that is to show the broad agreement of a WD-WD merger model with the multiwavelength data but not a dedicated model of AT 2017gfo.

5. Synchrotron and WD Pulsar Radiation

We have shown above that the expanding matter reaches full transparency at about 10^5 s. After this time, the emission originated from the newborn WD as well as the one originated in the ejecta itself, become observable. We here follow the treatment in Ref. 28 for the explanation of the X-ray afterglow of long GRBs as originating from a newborn spinning NS powering the expanding SN. Here, we simulate the emission generated in the X-rays, in the optical, and in the radio by the synchrotron emission of electrons accelerated in the expanding magnetized ejecta, together with the emission of the newborn spinning WD pulsar.

We show below that synchrotron radiation originating in the merger ejecta dominates the emission up to nearly 10^8 s. We find evidence of the newborn WD pulsar emission, owing to magnetic dipole braking, in the X-ray luminosity at approximately 10^6 s, when the synchrotron radiation was not fully overwhelming yet, and then at times 10^8 s, when the synchrotron luminosity sufficiently decreased for the WD pulsar emission to be fully observed (see Fig. 4 for details).

5.1. *Synchrotron emission by the expanding ejecta*

In this model, a fraction of the kinetic energy of the merger ejecta is used to accelerate electrons that, owing to the presence of the magnetized medium provided by the newborn WD, convert their kinetic energy into synchrotron radiation. The electrons are continuously injected from the newborn WD into the ejecta. The magnetic field threading every ejecta layer evolves as

$$B_i(t) = B_{i,0} \left[\frac{r_{i,0}}{r_i(t)}\right]^\mu = \frac{B_{i,0}}{\hat{t}^{\mu n}}, \qquad (30)$$

where $B_i^{(0)}$ is the magnetic field strength at $r = r_{i,0}$, and μ gives the spatial dependence of the field at large distance from the newborn WD.

Because the electrons lose their energy very efficiently by synchrotron radiation (see details below), we can simplify our calculation by adopting that the radiation originates from the innermost layer of the ejecta, which we will denote to as R_*. The evolution of this layer, following Eq. (11), is given by $R_*(t) = R_{*,0}\hat{t}^n$, $v_*(t) = v_{*,0}\hat{t}^{n-1}$, $t_* = nR_{*,0}/v_{*,0}$, and the magnetic field at its varying position decreases with time as $B_*(t) = B_{*,0}\hat{t}^{-n}$.

The evolution of the distribution of radiating electrons is determined by the kinetic equation accounting for the particle energy losses[52]

$$\frac{\partial N(E,t)}{\partial t} = -\frac{\partial}{\partial E}[\dot{E}\, N(E,t)] + Q(E,t), \qquad (31)$$

where $Q(E,t)$ is the number of injected electrons per unit time, per unit energy, and $\dot{E}$ is the electron energy loss rate.

In our case, we assume electrons are subjected to adiabatic losses by expansion and synchrotron radiation losses, i.e.

$$-\dot{E} = \frac{E}{\tau_{\rm exp}} + \beta B_*(t)^2 E^2, \qquad (32)$$

where $\beta = 2e^4/(3m_e^4 c^7)$, $B(t)$ is the magnetic field, and

$$\tau_{\exp} \equiv \frac{R_*}{v_*} = \frac{t}{n} = \frac{t_*}{n}\hat{t}, \tag{33}$$

is the characteristic timescale of expansion.

In order to find the solution to the kinetic equation (31), we follow the treatment of Ref. 53, adapted to our specific physical situation. We consider a distribution of the injected particles following a power-law behavior, i.e.

$$Q(E,t) = Q_0(t) E^{-\gamma}, \quad 0 \le E \le E_{\max}, \tag{34}$$

where γ and $E_{\max}$ are parameters to be determined from the observational data, and $Q_0(t)$ can be related to the power released by the newborn WD and injected into the ejecta. We assume that the injected power has the form

$$L_{\rm inj}(t) = L_0 \left(1 + \frac{t}{t_q}\right)^{-k}, \tag{35}$$

where L_0, t_q, and k are model parameters. We have not chosen arbitrarily the functional form of Eq. (35), actually, both the powers released by magnetic dipole braking and by fallback accretion (see Eq. (22)) obey this sort of time evolution.

Therefore, the function $Q_0(t)$ can be found from

$$L_{\rm inj}(t) = \int_0^{E_{\max}} E\, Q(E,t) dE = \int_0^{E_{\max}} Q_0(t) E^{1-\gamma} dE = Q_0(t) \frac{E_{\max}^{2-\gamma}}{2-\gamma}, \tag{36}$$

which using Eq. (35) leads to

$$Q_0(t) = q_0 \left(1 + \frac{t}{t_q}\right)^{-k}, \tag{37}$$

where $q_0 \equiv (2-\gamma) L_0 / E_{\max}^{2-\gamma}$.

Having specified the evolution of the ejecta by Eq. (11) and the magnetic field by Eq. (30), as well as the rate of particle injection given by Eqs. (34) and (37), we can now proceed to the integration of the kinetic equation (31).

First, we find the evolution of a generic electron injected at time $t = t_i$ with energy E_i. Integration of Eq. (32) leads to the energy evolution

$$E = \frac{E_i (t_i/t)^n}{1 + \mathcal{M} E_i t_i^n \left[\frac{1}{\hat{t}_i^{n(1+2\mu)-1}} - \frac{1}{\hat{t}^{n(1+2\mu)-1}}\right]}, \tag{38}$$

where we have introduced the constant

$$\mathcal{M} \equiv \frac{\beta B_{*,0}^2 t_*^{1-n}}{n(1+2\mu)-1}, \tag{39}$$

which have units of 1/(energy × time^n). In the limit $t/t_* \gg 1$ and $n = 1$, Eq. (38) reduces to Eq. (3.3) of Ref. 53, and in the limit $t_* \to \infty$, reduces to the solution presented in Sec. 3 of Ref. 52 for synchrotron losses in a constant magnetic field.

The solution of Eq. (31) is given by

$$N(E,t) = \int_E^\infty Q[E_i, t_i(t, E_i, E)]\frac{\partial t_i}{\partial E}dE_i, \tag{40}$$

where the relation $t_i(t, E_i, E)$ is obtained from Eq. (38).

We can write $N(E,t)$ as a piecewise function of time, separating it into different time intervals that allow simplifications and approximations depending upon the physical situation at work, and on the behavior of the energy injection given by Eq. (37). All the observational data of GRB 170817A are contained in the time interval $t < t_b$ and at electron energies int he range $E_b < E < E_{\max}$ (see definition of t_b and E_b below) where synchrotron losses are dominant. Under these conditions, the solution of Eq. (40) is well approximated by

$$N(E,t) \approx \begin{cases} \dfrac{q_0}{\beta B_{*,0}^2(\gamma-1)}\hat{t}^{2\mu n}E^{-(\gamma+1)}, & t < t_q, \\[2mm] \dfrac{q_0}{\beta B_{*,0}^2(\gamma-1)}\left(\dfrac{t_q}{t_*}\right)^k \hat{t}^{2\mu n-k}E^{-(\gamma+1)}, & t_q < t < t_b, \end{cases} \tag{41}$$

and we have defined

$$E_b = \frac{\hat{t}^{2\mu n-1}}{\mathcal{M}t_*^n}, \quad t_b = t_*(\mathcal{M}t_*^n E_{\max})^{\frac{1}{2\mu n-1}}. \tag{42}$$

With the knowledge of $N(E,t)$, we can proceed to estimate the synchrotron spectral density (energy per unit time, per unit frequency) from $J_{\text{syn}}(\nu,t)d\nu = P_{\text{syn}}(\nu,E)N(E,t)dE$, where $P_{\text{syn}}(\nu,E)$ is the synchrotron power per unit frequency ν, radiated by a single electron of energy E. Most of the synchrotron radiation is emitted in a narrow range of frequencies around the so-called photon critical frequency, ν_{crit}. Thus, we can assume electrons emit the synchrotron radiation at

$$\nu \approx \nu_{\text{crit}} \approx \alpha B_* E^2, \tag{43}$$

where $\alpha = 3e/(4\pi m_e^3 c^5)$. This gives a relation between the electron energy and the radiation frequency, and $P_{\text{syn}}(\nu, E)$ can be approximated to the bolometric power

$$P_{\text{syn}}(\nu, E) \approx P_{\text{syn}}(\nu) = \beta B_*^2 E^2(\nu) = \frac{\beta}{\alpha}B_*\nu. \tag{44}$$

Within this approximation, the spectral density is

$$J_{\text{syn}}(\nu,t) \approx P_{\text{syn}}(\nu)N(E,t)\frac{dE}{d\nu}. \tag{45}$$

It can be seen from Eq. (41) that in each time and frequency interval we can write

$$N(E,t) = \eta\hat{t}^l E^{-p}, \tag{46}$$

where η and the power-law indexes l and p are known constants from Eq. (41). With this, the spectral density (45) becomes

$$J_{\text{syn}}(\nu,t) = \frac{\beta}{2}\alpha^{\frac{p-3}{2}}\eta B_{*,0}^{\frac{p+1}{2}}t^{\frac{2l-\mu n(p+1)}{2}}\nu^{\frac{1-p}{2}}. \tag{47}$$

The synchrotron luminosity in the frequencies $[\nu_1, \nu_2]$ can be then obtained as

$$L_{\rm syn}(\nu_1, \nu_2; t) = \int_{\nu_1}^{\nu_2} J_{\rm syn}(\nu, t) d\nu, \qquad (48)$$

which in a narrow frequency band from $\nu_1 = \nu$ to $\nu_2 = \nu + \Delta\nu$ where $\Delta\nu/\nu \ll 1$, can be well approximated as

$$L_{\rm syn}(\nu, t) \approx \nu J_{\rm syn}(\nu, t) = \frac{\beta}{2} \alpha^{\frac{p-3}{2}} \eta B_{*,0}^{\frac{p+1}{2}} t^{\frac{2l-\mu n(p+1)}{2}} \nu^{\frac{3-p}{2}}, \qquad (49)$$

where we have used Eq. (47).

5.2. WD evolution and pulsar emission

The central WD emits also pulsar-like radiation. We adopt a dipole + quadrupole magnetic field model.[54] In this model, the total luminosity of spindown is

$$\begin{aligned}L_{\rm sd} &= L_{\rm dip} + L_{\rm quad} \\ &= \frac{2}{3c^3} \Omega^4 B_{\rm dip}^2 R_{\rm wd}^6 \sin^2\chi_1 \left(1 + \xi^2 \frac{16}{45} \frac{R_{\rm wd}^2 \Omega^2}{c^2}\right), \end{aligned} \qquad (50)$$

where the parameter ξ defines the quadrupole to dipole strength ratio as

$$\xi \equiv \sqrt{\cos^2\chi_2 + 10\sin^2\chi_2} \frac{B_{\rm quad}}{B_{\rm dip}}, \qquad (51)$$

and the modes can be separated: $\chi_1 = 0$ and any value of χ_2 for the $m = 0$ mode, $(\chi_1, \chi_2) = (90°, 0°)$ for the $m = 1$ mode, and $(\chi_1, \chi_2) = (90°, 90°)$ for the $m = 2$ mode.

The WD evolution is obtained from the energy balance equation

$$-(\dot{W} + \dot{T}) = L_{\rm tot} = L_{\rm inj} + L_{\rm sd}, \qquad (52)$$

where W and T are, respectively, the gravitational and rotational energies of the newborn WD. We can obtain an analytic, sufficiently accurate solution of Eq. (52) by noticing the following. The power injected in electrons $L_{\rm inj}$ is larger than $L_{\rm sd}$ and has a shorter timescale with respect to the spindown timescale (see Eq. (35) and Fig. 5), so at $t < t_q$, we have $L_{\rm tot} \approx L_{\rm inj}$. At later times, $L_{\rm tot} \approx L_{\rm sd}$, so the luminosity should approach the spindown luminosity

$$L_{\rm sd} = L_{\rm sd,0}\left(1 + \frac{t}{\tau_{\rm sd}}\right)^{-s}, \qquad (53)$$

where $s = (n_b + 1)/(n_b - 1)$, being n_b the so-called braking index ($n_b = 3$ for a pure dipole and $n_b = 5$ for a pure quadrupole), and $\tau_{\rm sd}$ is the spindown timescale

$$\tau_{\rm sd} = \frac{1}{2\mathcal{A}\Omega_0^2}, \qquad (54)$$

being $\mathcal{A} = (2/3)(B_{\rm dip}^2 R_{\rm wd}^6)/(c^3 I)$, and Ω_0 the initial angular velocity of the WD.

With the above, Eq. (52) is integrated analytically accounting for changes in the WD structure. We describe the WD as an effective Maclaurin spheroid,[55] so the angular velocity, Ω, is related to the spheroid eccentricity, e, by

$$\Omega^2 = 2\pi G \rho g(e), \quad g(e) = \frac{(3-2e^2)(1-e^2)^{1/2}\arcsin(e)}{e^3} - \frac{3(1-e^2)}{e^2}, \quad (55)$$

where $\rho = 3m_{\rm wd}/(4\pi R_{\rm wd}^3)$ is the density of the sphere with the same volume of the spheroid, being $m_{\rm wd}$ and $R_{\rm wd}$ the corresponding values of the mass and radius of the WD. The total energy of the spheroid is also a function of the eccentricity as

$$E = T + W = \pi G \rho I_0 \mathcal{F}(e), \quad (56)$$

where $I_0 = (2/5) m_{\rm wd} R_{\rm wd}^2$, and

$$\mathcal{F}(e) = -2 + \frac{3(1-e^2)^{2/3}}{e^2} + \frac{(4e^2-3)(1-e^2)^{1/6}}{e^3}\arcsin(e) \approx -\frac{4e^2}{15}, \quad (57)$$

being the last line a series expansion of the function $\mathcal{F}$ which is accurate enough for low values of the eccentricity and which allows to give an analytic solution for the eccentricity as a function of time.

Then, integrating Eq. (52) and using Eqs. (56) and (57), we obtain

$$e(t) \approx \sqrt{\frac{15\Theta(t)}{4}}, \quad \Omega \approx \sqrt{2\pi G \rho \Theta(t)}, \quad (58)$$

where

$$\Theta(t) = -\mathcal{F}(e_0) + \mathcal{G}(t), \quad (59)$$

$$\mathcal{G}(t) = \frac{L_0 t_q}{\pi G \rho I_0 (k-1)}\left[\left(1+\frac{t}{t_q}\right)^{1-k}-1\right] + \frac{L_{\rm sd,0}\tau_{\rm sd}}{\pi G \rho I_0 (s-1)}\left[\left(1+\frac{t}{\tau_{\rm sd}}\right)^{1-s}-1\right], \quad (60)$$

where e_0 is the initial value of the spheroid eccentricity, and we have used that the function $g(e)$ in Eq. (55) satisfies $g(e) = -\mathcal{F}(e)$, at the order of our approximation. We recall that the moment of inertia changes with the eccentricity as $I = I_0(1-e^2)^{-1/3} \approx I_0(1+e^2/3)$. The corresponding parameters of the model that explains the afterglow emission at different wavelengths are presented in the next section.

6. Model Parameters from the Multiwavelength Data

We proceed to determine the model parameters that best fit the GRB 170817A afterglow. We list in Table 2 the value adopted for each parameter of the present model to fit the multiwavelength data of GRB 170817A shown in Fig. 3. We did not consider here data at MeV energies because it is only present in the prompt emission that we have already discussed in Sec. 3 and is explained by a different mechanism from the synchrotron radiation. There are observations in the 30 MeV–10 GeV energy band by AGILE[67] which give upper limits $\sim 10^{44}$–10^{45} erg s^{-1} in

Table 2. Numerical values of the theoretical model of synchrotron radiation of Sec. 5 that fit the multiwavelength observational data of GRB 170817A as shown in Fig. 3.

Parameter	Value
γ	1.13
k	2.70
μ	1.50
L_0 (10^{39} erg s^{-1})	1.80
$B_{*,0}$ (10^9 G)	1.00
$E_{\max}$ ($10^6\, m_e c^2$)	1.00
t_q (10^7 s)	1.22
ξ	0.00
$B_{\rm dip}$ (10^{10} G)	1.30
P (s)	12.21

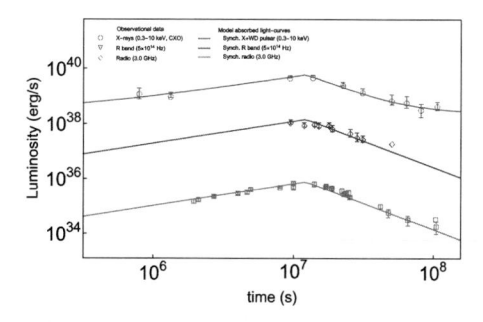

Fig. 3. Comparison of the theoretical (solid curves) light-curves with the observational data (points) of GRB 170817A, in selected energy bands from the radio to the gamma-rays. The radio data at 3 GHz have been taken from Refs. 56–63; the infrared (F606W HST band) data points are retrieved from Refs. 63–64; the X-ray (0.3–10 keV) data from CXO are taken from Ref. 66.

the time interval $\sim 10^3$–10^6 s. For the parameters of Table 2, no emission is indeed expected at these energies because the maximum synchrotron radiation frequency obtained from Eq. (43) falls below 10 GeV before $\sim 10^4$ s. The synchrotron luminosity vanishes at these energies at longer times.

Having discussed the gamma-rays, we turn now to the X-rays, optical and radio emission. Figure 3 compares the absorbed luminosity predicted by the model (see Sec. 4), as a function of time, in selected energy bands, with the corresponding observational data of GRB 170817A. We have here included the X-ray data the 0.3–10 keV energy band from the *Chandra* X-ray Observatory (CXO) including the latest observations,[66] the infrared data from the HST at $\approx 5 \times 10^{14}$ Hz,[63–65] and the radio data at 3 GHz.[56–63, 66]

The model shows a satisfactory fit of the data in the X-rays, optical and radio data, both where the luminosity rises, at times $t \sim 10^6$–10^7 s, and where it fades off, at $t \gtrsim 10^7$ s. We show a closer view in Fig. 4 of the X-rays, optical, and radio luminosities around the time of the peak luminosity. The synchrotron luminosity

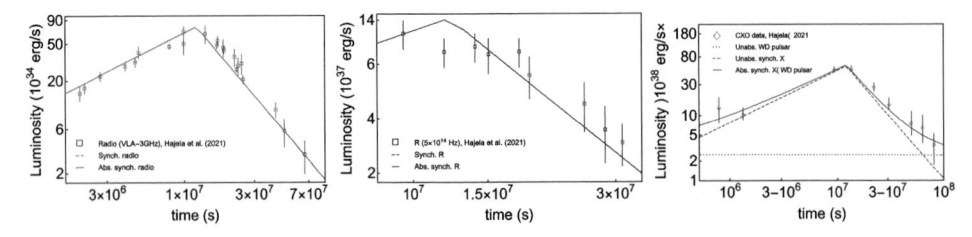

Fig. 4. Zoomed views of the radio (left), optical (center), and X-ray (right) luminosities around transparency. The dashed curves represent the unabsorbed luminosities. The dotted curve in the right panel shows the contribution from the newborn WD pulsar which causes the deviation from the pure synchrotron power-law luminosity at times $\gtrsim 3 \times 10^7$ s.

rises as a power-law while the energy injection is constant, i.e. up to $t \approx t_q = 1.2 \times 10^7$ s, while it decreases as a power-law at later times. Probably the most interesting feature that can be seen from these zoomed views appears in the X-ray emission, where we can see in addition to the synchrotron luminosity, evidence of the WD pulsar emission owing to the magnetic dipole braking. The contribution from the pulsar emission is seen first at $t \sim 10^6$ s when the synchrotron radiation is rising but is still comparable with the pulsar spindown luminosity. Then, the synchrotron luminosity takes over, reaches a peak at approximately 10^7 s, and then decreases. While the optical and radio counterparts continue to fade with time as dictated by the synchrotron radiation, the accuracy of the X-ray data of the CXO presented in Ref. 66 allows to identify a clear deviation in the X-rays at a few 10^7 s from such a power-law behavior. This is again the signature of the emergence of the WD pulsar emission.

We have used the entity of this deviation to constrain the WD pulsar parameters. Since the pulsar emission depends on the WD radius (see Sec. 5.2), we first estimated the mass of the newborn WD. To accomplish this task, we must apply the considerations of Sec. 2. From the inferred mass of the ejecta, $m_{\rm ej} = 10^{-3} M_\odot$ (see Table 1), we obtain an upper limit to the binary mass ratio via Eq. (7), by requesting that the newborn object be a stable, sub-Chandrasekhar WD, i.e. $m_{\rm wd} \lesssim 1.4 M_\odot$, which leads to $q \lesssim 0.87$. According to this maximum mass ratio and the ejecta mass value, Eq. (5) constraints the secondary mass to the range $m_2 \lesssim 0.85 M_\odot$. With the knowledge of q and m_2, Eq. (2) constrains the total binary mass to $M \lesssim 1.82 M_\odot$. Thus, the primary component must satisfy $m_1 \lesssim 0.97 M_\odot$.

We assume that the newborn WD is stable, therefore it might have a mass close but not equal to the Chandrasekhar mass, since some mass will be accreted via matter fallback. Hereafter, we shall adopt in our estimates $m_{\rm wd} \approx 1.3 M_\odot$, so a radius $R_{\rm wd} \approx 3.4 \times 10^8$ cm. With these WD structure parameters, we can proceed to constrain the magnetic field strength and rotation period.

The X-ray emission data show that deviation from the pure synchrotron emission behavior starts at $\approx 3 \times 10^7$ s, and extends up to when we have data, namely, up to $\approx 10^8$ s (see Fig. 4). This would suggest to chose this time for the spindown timescale

τ_{sd}, but at the moment it is only a lower limit to τ_{sd} because the luminosity did not reach yet the power-law given by the pulsar luminosity.

Hereafter, we assume a pure dipole (i.e. $\xi = 0$) because the fit of the X-ray emission does not require at the moment the quadrupole component (see Fig. 4). By eliminating the rotation angular velocity between the pulsar luminosity (50) and the spindown timescale (54), we can express the magnetic field strength as

$$B_{dip} = \frac{3^{1/2} c^{3/2} I}{2^{3/2} L_{sd}^{1/2} R_{wd}^3 \tau_{sd}}, \tag{61}$$

where I is the moment of inertia. We can use Eq. (61) to give an upper limit to B_{dip} by setting as values of L_{sd} and τ_{sd}, the values of the latest value of the X-ray luminosity data, i.e. $L_{sd} = L_X \approx 4.87 \times 10^{38}$ erg s^{-1}, and $\tau_{sd} \approx 10^8$ s. With this, we obtain an upper value $B_{dip,max} \approx 7.46 \times 10^{11}$ G. To this upper value of B_{dip}, it corresponds an upper value of the initial rotation period which can be obtained by calculating $P_0 = 2\pi/\Omega_0$ from Eq. (50), i.e.

$$P_0 = 2\pi \left(\frac{2 B_{dip}^2 R_{wd}^6}{c^3 L_{sd}} \right)^{1/4}, \tag{62}$$

from which we obtain $P_{0,max} \approx 75.25$ s. We can further constrain the rotation period by seeking for values of the magnetic field strength and rotation period in agreement with the model presented in Sec. 3 for the prompt emission. Such a mechanism is expected to release magnetic energy stored in the magnetosphere, i.e.

$$E_B \approx \frac{1}{6} B_{dip}^2 R_{wd}^3, \tag{63}$$

so we need a dipole magnetic field strength

$$B_{dip} = \left(\frac{6 E_B}{R_{wd}^3} \right)^{1/2} \approx \left(\frac{6 E_{prompt}}{R_{wd}^3} \right)^{1/2}. \tag{64}$$

If we assume that the entire energy of the prompt emission, $E_{prompt} \approx 4.16 \times 10^{46}$ erg (see Sec. 3) is paid by the magnetosphere energy, we obtain a magnetic field $B_{dip} = 9.61 \times 10^{10}$ G. If we require the magnetic field energy to cover only the nonthermal component of the prompt, i.e. 1.17×10^{45} erg (see Sec. 3), then the dipole magnetic field becomes 1.30×10^{10} G. For the above magnetic field values, Eq. (62) gives, respectively, $P_0 \approx 30$ s, and $P_0 \approx 12$ s. The WD pulsar luminosity shown in Figs. 3 and 5 corresponds to the latter case.

The energy released (and injected into the ejecta) by the fallback accretion phase is $E_{fb} = H_0 t_*/(\delta - 1) \approx 3.34 \times 10^{48}$ erg. Energy and angular momentum are transferred to the newborn WD during this phase, and since the rotational to gravitational energy ratio of a uniformly rotating WD is of the order of 10^{-2},[32] the newborn WD has gained about a few 10^{46} erg of rotational energy during this phase. This might produce at a rotation period decrease of the order of a second, which confirms that the WD must be already fast rotating at birth.

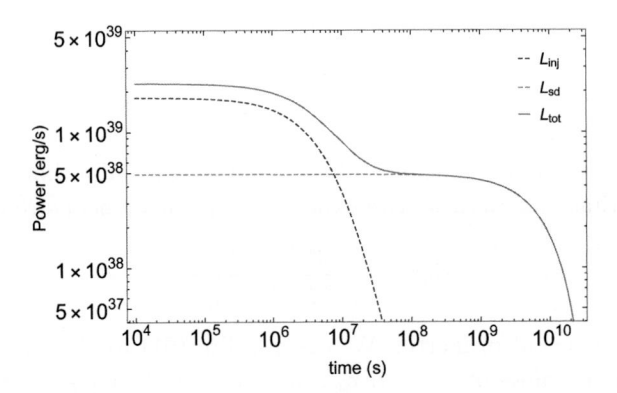

Fig. 5. Power injected into the ejecta by the newborn WD and the pulsar emission as given, respectively, by Eqs. (35) and (50). See the main text for further details.

In Fig. 5, we plot the power injected in energetic electrons from the WD, $L_{\rm inj}$, and the luminosity due to magnetic dipole braking, $L_{\rm sd}$. Both components release an energy of the order of 10^{46} erg. From the inferred rotation period of 12.21 s, the initial eccentricity turns out to be $e_0 \approx 0.39$, so the moment of inertia is about 5% bigger than the one of the equivalent spherical configuration. Using the evolution equations (58), we obtain that the moment of inertia, for instance from 10^4 s to 10^8 s, changes in about 0.03%. This small change in the structure of the WD, and the associated change in the rotational and gravitational energy, are sufficient to pay for the energy released by the ongoing magnetospheric phenomena responsible for the injection of particles into the ejecta and for the pulsar emission; see Sec. 5.2.

7. Conclusions

We have here addressed a self-consistent explanation of GRB 170817A, including its associated optical emission AT 2017gfo, based on a WD-WD merger. The most recent data of *Chandra* of the X-ray emission of GRB 170817A at $\sim 10^8$ s (~ 1000 d) after the GRB trigger,[21,22] indicate an X-ray re-brightening. This is explained by the emergence of the pulsar-like activity of the newborn WD (see Figs. 3 and 4), as predicted in Refs. 13, 20. We have here inferred that the newborn object is consistent with a massive ($\sim 1.3\,M_\odot$), fast rotating ($P \gtrsim 12$ s), highly magnetized ($B \sim 10^{10}$ G) WD, formed in a $1.0 + 0.8$ WD-WD merger (see Secs. 2 and 6).

The post-merger emission at different wavelengths is explained as follows. The prompt gamma-ray emission detected by the *Fermi*-GBM, with a luminosity of $\sim 10^{47}\,{\rm erg\,s^{-1}}$ and observed duration of $\lesssim 1$ s, can be explained by the transient hot corona produce at the merger. The high temperature produces photons that undergo $e^- e^+$ pair creation, the pairs are accelerated by the electric field induced by the 10^{10} G magnetic field an the WD rotation, thereby producing photons. The system is highly opaque to these photons (see Sec. 3) to the $\gamma\gamma$ pair production process. Only a small percentage of photons is expected to be able to escape from the system along the polar axis, leading to the small amount of nonthermal emission observed above 1 MeV, while the rest is expected to form a nearly thermal plasma.

The ejecta expand with velocities $\sim 10^9\,\mathrm{cm\,s^{-1}}$, and release energy by thermal cooling (see Sec. 4) and synchrotron radiation (see Sec. 5), powered by the newborn WD at the merger (see Sec. 5.2). Fallback accretion onto the newborn WD injects energy into the ejecta at early-times, heating up the ejecta. The ejecta is optically thick up to nearly 10^5, so the ejecta cool by diffusion while it expands. The thermal radiation is in agreement with the data of the early optical counterpart AT 2017gfo (see Fig. 2). This explanation is markedly different from the *nuclear kilonova* from decay of r-process synthesized heavy nuclei in an NS-NS merger ejecta.

The signature of the synchrotron radiation is identified from nearly 10^6 s, which explains the rising and decreasing luminosities with the same power-law slopes in the X-ray, optical and radio emissions (see Fig. 3 for details).

The X-ray data are essential for identifying the emergence of the newborn WD as a pulsar. We have shown evidence of the pulsar emission around 10^6 s and at late-times 10^8 s, causing the X-ray luminosity to deviate from the power-law emission of a pure synchrotron emission (see Figs. 3 and 4). These data reveal a rotation period $\gtrsim 12$ s, and magnetic field of $\sim 10^{10}$ G. The follow-up of the GRB 170817A X-ray emission in the next months/years to come is crucial to confirm this prediction.

Summarizing, GRB 170817A/AT 2017gfo are explained by a WD-WD merger. The $10^{-3} M_\odot$ expelled in the merger expand and radiates via thermal and synchrotron cooling. The former explains AT 2017gfo and the latter the late-time X-rays, optical and radio emission. In this line, the association of GW170417A with GRB 170817A[1] is not confirmed in our treatment based on the new data in the X-rays, optical, and in the radio up to 10^8 s. Therefore, we indicate the necessity to further inquire on the spacetime sequence of the early part of these events.

Indeed, WDs of parameters approaching the present ones have been already identified, e.g. the WD in V1460 Her with $P \approx 39$ s,[68] and the most recent observation of the WD in LAMOST J024048.51+195226.9 with $P \approx 25$ s.[69] WDs of similar properties have been proposed as a model of SGRs and AXPs.[70–73] Therefore, the newborn WD pulsar in GRB 170817A could show itself in the near future as an SGR/AXP in the GRB 170817A sky position.

References

1. B. P. Abbott *et al.*, *Astrophys. J. Lett.* **848** (2017) L12, arXiv:1710.05833 [astro-ph.HE].
2. A. Goldstein, P. Veres, E. Burns, M. S. Briggs, R. Hamburg, D. Kocevski, C. A. Wilson-Hodge, R. D. Preece, S. Poolakkil, O. J. Roberts, C. M. Hui, V. Connaughton, J. Racusin, A. von Kienlin, T. Dal Canton, N. Christensen, T. Littenberg, K. Siellez, L. Blackburn, J. Broida, E. Bissaldi, W. H. Cleveland, M. H. Gibby, M. M. Giles, R. M. Kippen, S. McBreen, J. McEnery, C. A. Meegan, W. S. Paciesas and M. Stanbro, *Astrophys. J. Lett.* **848** (2017) L14, arXiv:1710.05446 [astro-ph.HE].
3. V. Savchenko, C. Ferrigno, E. Kuulkers, A. Bazzano, E. Bozzo, S. Brandt, J. Chenevez, T. J. L. Courvoisier, R. Diehl, A. Domingo, L. Hanlon, E. Jourdain, A. von Kienlin,

P. Laurent, F. Lebrun, A. Lutovinov, A. Martin-Carrillo, S. Mereghetti, L. Natalucci, J. Rodi, J. P. Roques, R. Sunyaev and P. Ubertini, *Astrophys. J. Lett.* **848** (2017) L15, arXiv:1710.05449 [astro-ph.HE].
4. B. P. Abbott *et al.*, *Astrophys. J. Lett.* **848** (2017) L13, arXiv:1710.05834 [astro-ph.HE].
5. E. Pian *et al.*, *Nature* **551** (2017) 67, arXiv:1710.05858 [astro-ph.HE].
6. I. Arcavi, G. Hosseinzadeh, D. A. Howell, C. McCully, D. Poznanski, D. Kasen, J. Barnes, M. Zaltzman, S. Vasylyev, D. Maoz and S. Valenti, *Nature* **551** (2017) 64, arXiv:1710.05843 [astro-ph.HE].
7. P. S. Cowperthwaite *et al.*, *Astrophys. J. Lett.* **848** (2017) L17, arXiv:1710.05840 [astro-ph.HE].
8. M. Nicholl *et al.*, *Astrophys. J. Lett.* **848** (2017) L18, arXiv:1710.05456 [astro-ph.HE].
9. B. Paczynski, *Astrophys. J. Lett.* **308** (1986) L43.
10. D. Eichler, M. Livio, T. Piran and D. N. Schramm, *Nature* **340** (1989) 126.
11. R. Narayan, B. Paczynski and T. Piran, *Astrophys. J. Lett.* **395** (1992) L83, arXiv:astro-ph/9204001.
12. L. Li and Z.-G. Dai, *Astrophys. J.* **918** (2021) 52, arXiv:2106.04788 [astro-ph.HE].
13. J. A. Rueda, R. Ruffini, Y. Wang, Y. Aimuratov, U. Barres de Almeida, C. L. Bianco, Y. C. Chen, R. V. Lobato, C. Maia, D. Primorac, R. Moradi and J. F. Rodriguez, *J. Cosmol. Astropart. Phys.* **10** (2018) 006, arXiv:1802.10027 [astro-ph.HE].
14. C. Yue, Q. Hu, F.-W. Zhang, Y.-F. Liang, Z.-P. Jin, Y.-C. Zou, Y.-Z. Fan and D.-M. Wei, *Astrophys. J. Lett.* **853** (2018) L10, arXiv:1710.05942 [astro-ph.HE].
15. R. T. Wollaeger, C. L. Fryer, E. A. Chase, C. J. Fontes, M. Ristic, A. L. Hungerford, O. Korobkin, R. O'Shaughnessy and A. M. Herring, *Astrophys. J.* **918** (2021) 10, arXiv:2105.11543 [astro-ph.HE].
16. O. Korobkin, R. T. Wollaeger, C. L. Fryer, A. L. Hungerford, S. Rosswog, C. J. Fontes, M. R. Mumpower, E. A. Chase, W. P. Even, J. Miller, G. W. Misch and J. Lippuner, *Astrophys. J.* **910** (2021) 116, arXiv:2004.00102 [astro-ph.HE].
17. Y. L. Zhu, K. A. Lund, J. Barnes, T. M. Sprouse, N. Vassh, G. C. McLaughlin, M. R. Mumpower and R. Surman, *Astrophys. J.* **906** (2021) 94, arXiv:2010.03668 [astro-ph.HE].
18. J. Barnes, Y. L. Zhu, K. A. Lund, T. M. Sprouse, N. Vassh, G. C. McLaughlin, M. R. Mumpower and R. Surman, *Astrophys. J.* **918** (2021) 44, arXiv:2010.11182 [astro-ph.HE].
19. B. Côté, C. L. Fryer, K. Belczynski, O. Korobkin, M. Chruślińska, N. Vassh, M. R. Mumpower, J. Lippuner, T. M. Sprouse, R. Surman and R. Wollaeger, *Astrophys. J.* **855** (2018) 99, arXiv:1710.05875 [astro-ph.GA].
20. J. A. Rueda, R. Ruffini, Y. Wang, C. L. Bianco, J. M. Blanco-Iglesias, M. Karlica, P. Lorén-Aguilar, R. Moradi and N. Sahakyan, *J. Cosmol. Astropart. Phys.* **2019** (2019) 044, arXiv:1807.07905 [astro-ph.HE].
21. E. Troja, B. O'Connor, G. Ryan, L. Piro, R. Ricci, B. Zhang, T. Piran, G. Bruni, S. B. Cenko and H. van Eerten, arXiv e-prints (2021), arXiv:2104.13378 [astro-ph.HE].
22. E. Troja, H. van Eerten, B. Zhang, G. Ryan, L. Piro, R. Ricci, B. O'Connor, M. H. Wieringa, S. B. Cenko and T. Sakamoto, *Mon. Not. R. Astron. Soc.* **498** (2020) 5643, arXiv:2006.01150 [astro-ph.HE].
23. M. Livio and P. Mazzali, *Phys. Rep.* **736** (2018) 1, arXiv:1802.03125 [astro-ph.SR].
24. M. Della Valle and L. Izzo, *Astron. Astrophys. Rev.* **28** (2020) 3, arXiv:2004.06540 [astro-ph.SR].
25. R. Ruffini, R. Moradi, J. A. Rueda, L. Li, N. Sahakyan, Y. C. Chen, Y. Wang, Y. Aimuratov, L. Becerra, C. L. Bianco, C. Cherubini, S. Filippi, M. Karlica, G. J. Mathews,

M. Muccino, G. B. Pisani and S. S. Xue, *Mon. Not. R. Astron. Soc.* **504** (2021) 5301, arXiv:2103.09142 [astro-ph.HE].
26. J. A. Rueda, R. Ruffini, M. Karlica, R. Moradi and Y. Wang, *Astrophys. J.* **893** (2020) 148, arXiv:1905.11339 [astro-ph.HE].
27. Y. Wang, J. A. Rueda, R. Ruffini, L. Becerra, C. Bianco, L. Becerra, L. Li and M. Karlica, *Astrophys. J.* **874** (2019) 39, arXiv:1811.05433 [astro-ph.HE].
28. R. Ruffini, M. Karlica, N. Sahakyan, J. A. Rueda, Y. Wang, G. J. Mathews, C. L. Bianco and M. Muccino, *Astrophys. J.* **869** (2018) 101, arXiv:1712.05000 [astro-ph.HE].
29. L. Li, X.-F. Wu, W.-H. Lei, Z.-G. Dai, E.-W. Liang and F. Ryde, *Astrophys. J. Suppl.* **236** (2018) 26, arXiv:1712.09390 [astro-ph.HE].
30. L. Becerra, K. Boshkayev, J. A. Rueda and R. Ruffini, *Mon. Not. R. Astron. Soc.* **487** (2019) 812, arXiv:1812.10543 [astro-ph.SR].
31. L. Becerra, J. A. Rueda, P. Lorén-Aguilar and E. García-Berro, *Astrophys. J.* **857** (2018) 134, arXiv:1804.01275 [astro-ph.SR].
32. K. Boshkayev, J. A. Rueda, R. Ruffini and I. Siutsou, *Astrophys. J.* **762** (2013) 117, arXiv:1204.2070 [astro-ph.SR].
33. W. Benz, A. G. W. Cameron, W. H. Press and R. L. Bowers, *Astrophys. J.* **348** (1990) 647.
34. J. Guerrero, E. García-Berro and J. Isern, *Astron. Astrophys.* **413** (2004) 257.
35. P. Lorén-Aguilar, J. Isern and E. García-Berro, *Astron. Astrophys.* **500** (2009) 1193.
36. R. Longland, P. Lorén-Aguilar, J. José, E. García-Berro and L. G. Althaus, *Astron. Astrophys.* **542** (2012) A117, arXiv:1205.2538 [astro-ph.SR].
37. C. Raskin, E. Scannapieco, C. Fryer, G. Rockefeller and F. X. Timmes, *Astrophys. J.* **746** (2012) 62, arXiv:1112.1420 [astro-ph.HE].
38. C. Zhu, P. Chang, M. H. van Kerkwijk and J. Wadsley, *Astrophys. J.* **767** (2013) 164, arXiv:1210.3616 [astro-ph.SR].
39. M. Dan, S. Rosswog, M. Brüggen and P. Podsiadlowski, *Mon. Not. R. Astron. Soc.* **438** (2014) 14, arXiv:1308.1667 [astro-ph.HE].
40. M. Nauenberg, *Astrophys. J.* **175** (1972) 417.
41. G. Vianello, R. J. Lauer, P. Younk, L. Tibaldo, J. M. Burgess, H. Ayala, P. Harding, M. Hui, N. Omodei and H. Zhou, arXiv e-prints (2015) arXiv:1507.08343 [astro-ph.HE].
42. D. J. Spiegelhalter, N. G. Best, B. P. Carlin and A. Van Der Linde, *J. R. Stat. Soc. Series B* **64** (2002) 583.
43. E. Moreno, F. J. Vazquez-Polo and C. P. Robert, arXiv e-prints (2013), arXiv:1310.2905 [stat.ME].
44. L. Li, *Astrophys. J. Suppl.* **242** (2019) 16, arXiv:1810.03129 [astro-ph.HE].
45. L. Li, *Astrophys. J. Suppl.* **245** (2019) 7.
46. L. Li, *Astrophys. J.* **894** (2020) 100, arXiv:1908.09240 [astro-ph.HE].
47. L. Li, F. Ryde, A. Pe'er, H.-F. Yu and Z. Acuner, *Astrophys. J. Suppl.* **254** (2021) 35, arXiv:2012.03038 [astro-ph.HE].
48. L. Li and B. Zhang, *Astrophys. J. Suppl.* **253** (2021) 43, arXiv:2101.04325 [astro-ph.HE].
49. P. Goldreich and W. H. Julian, *Astrophys. J.* **157** (1969) 869.
50. E. Troja *et al.*, *Nature* **551** (2017) 71, arXiv:1710.05433 [astro-ph.HE].
51. D. Lazzati, D. López-Cámara, M. Cantiello, B. J. Morsony, R. Perna and J. C. Workman, *Astrophys. J. Lett.* **848** (2017) L6, arXiv:1709.01468 [astro-ph.HE].
52. N. S. Kardashev, *Sov. Astron.* **6** (1962) 317.
53. F. Pacini and M. Salvati, *Astrophys. J.* **186** (1973) 249.

54. J. Pétri, *Mon. Not. R. Astron. Soc.* **450** (2015) 714, arXiv:1503.05307 [astro-ph.HE].
55. S. Chandrasekhar, *Ellipsoidal Figures of Equilibrium* (1969).
56. K. D. Alexander, E. Berger, W. Fong, P. K. G. Williams, C. Guidorzi, R. Margutti, B. D. Metzger, J. Annis, P. K. Blanchard, D. Brout, D. A. Brown, H. Y. Chen, R. Chornock, P. S. Cowperthwaite, M. Drout, T. Eftekhari, J. Frieman, D. E. Holz, M. Nicholl, A. Rest, M. Sako, M. Soares-Santos and V. A. Villar, *Astrophys. J. Lett.* **848** (2017) L21, arXiv:1710.05457 [astro-ph.HE].
57. G. Hallinan, A. Corsi, K. P. Mooley, K. Hotokezaka, E. Nakar, M. M. Kasliwal, D. L. Kaplan, D. A. Frail, S. T. Myers, T. Murphy, K. De, D. Dobie, J. R. Allison, K. W. Bannister, V. Bhalerao, P. Chandra, T. E. Clarke, S. Giacintucci, A. Y. Q. Ho, A. Horesh, N. E. Kassim, S. R. Kulkarni, E. Lenc, F. J. Lockman, C. Lynch, D. Nichols, S. Nissanke, N. Palliyaguru, W. M. Peters, T. Piran, J. Rana, E. M. Sadler and L. P. Singer, *Science* **358** (2017) 1579, arXiv:1710.05435 [astro-ph.HE].
58. S. Kim *et al.*, *Astrophys. J. Lett.* **850** (2017) L21, arXiv:1710.05847 [astro-ph.HE].
59. K. P. Mooley, E. Nakar, K. Hotokezaka, G. Hallinan, A. Corsi, D. A. Frail, A. Horesh, T. Murphy, E. Lenc, D. L. Kaplan, K. de, D. Dobie, P. Chandra, A. Deller, O. Gottlieb, M. M. Kasliwal, S. R. Kulkarni, S. T. Myers, S. Nissanke, T. Piran, C. Lynch, V. Bhalerao, S. Bourke, K. W. Bannister and L. P. Singer, *Nature* **554** (2018) 207, arXiv:1711.11573 [astro-ph.HE].
60. K. P. Mooley, D. A. Frail, D. Dobie, E. Lenc, A. Corsi, K. De, A. J. Nayana, S. Makhathini, I. Heywood, T. Murphy, D. L. Kaplan, P. Chandra, O. Smirnov, E. Nakar, G. Hallinan, F. Camilo, R. Fender, S. Goedhart, P. Groot, M. M. Kasliwal, S. R. Kulkarni and P. A. Woudt, *Astrophys. J. Lett.* **868** (2018) L11, arXiv:1810.12927 [astro-ph.HE].
61. K. D. Alexander, R. Margutti, P. K. Blanchard, W. Fong, E. Berger, A. Hajela, T. Eftekhari, R. Chornock, P. S. Cowperthwaite, D. Giannios, C. Guidorzi, A. Kathirgamaraju, A. MacFadyen, B. D. Metzger, M. Nicholl, L. Sironi, V. A. Villar, P. K. G. Williams, X. Xie and J. Zrake, *Astrophys. J. Lett.* **863** (2018) L18, arXiv:1805.02870 [astro-ph.HE].
62. D. Dobie, D. L. Kaplan, T. Murphy, E. Lenc, K. P. Mooley, C. Lynch, A. Corsi, D. Frail, M. Kasliwal and G. Hallinan, *Astrophys. J. Lett.* **858** (2018) L15, arXiv:1803.06853 [astro-ph.HE].
63. L. Piro, E. Troja, B. Zhang, G. Ryan, H. van Eerten, R. Ricci, M. H. Wieringa, A. Tiengo, N. R. Butler, S. B. Cenko, O. D. Fox, H. G. Khandrika, G. Novara, A. Rossi and T. Sakamoto, *Mon. Not. R. Astron. Soc.* **483** (2019) 1912, arXiv:1810.04664 [astro-ph.HE].
64. J. D. Lyman *et al.*, *Nature Astronomy* **2** (2018) 751, arXiv:1801.02669 [astro-ph.HE].
65. G. P. Lamb, J. D. Lyman, A. J. Levan, N. R. Tanvir, T. Kangas, A. S. Fruchter, B. Gompertz, J. Hjorth, I. Mandel, S. R. Oates, D. Steeghs and K. Wiersema, *Astrophys. J. Lett.* **870** (2019) L15, arXiv:1811.11491 [astro-ph.HE].
66. A. Hajela *et al.*, arXiv e-prints (2021), arXiv:2104.02070 [astro-ph.HE].
67. F. Verrecchia *et al.*, *Astrophys. J. Lett.* **850** (2017) L27, arXiv:1710.05460 [astro-ph.HE].
68. I. Pelisoli, T. R. Marsh, R. P. Ashley, P. Hakala, A. Aungwerojwit, K. Burdge, E. Breedt, A. J. Brown, K. Chanthorn, V. S. Dhillon, M. J. Dyer, M. J. Green, P. Kerry, S. P. Littlefair, S. G. Parsons, D. I. Sahman, J. F. Wild and S. Yotthanathong, *Mon. Not. R. Astron. Soc.* **507** (2021) 6132, arXiv:2109.00553 [astro-ph.SR].

69. I. Pelisoli, T. R. Marsh, V. S. Dhillon, E. Breedt, A. J. Brown, M. J. Dyer, M. J. Green, P. Kerry, S. P. Littlefair, S. G. Parsons, D. I. Sahman and J. F. Wild, arXiv e-prints (August 2021), arXiv:2108.11396 [astro-ph.SR].
70. J. G. Coelho, D. L. Cáceres, R. C. R. de Lima, M. Malheiro, J. A. Rueda and R. Ruffini, *Astron. Astrophys.* **599** (2017) A87.
71. J. A. Rueda, K. Boshkayev, L. Izzo, R. Ruffini, P. Lorén-Aguilar, B. Külebi, G. Aznar-Siguán and E. García-Berro, *Astrophys. J. Lett.* **772** (2013) L24, arXiv:1306.5936 [astro-ph.SR].
72. K. Boshkayev, L. Izzo, J. A. Rueda Hernandez and R. Ruffini, *Astron. Astrophys.* **555** (2013) A151, arXiv:1305.5048 [astro-ph.SR].
73. M. Malheiro, J. A. Rueda and R. Ruffini, *PASJ* **64** (2012) 56, arXiv:1102.0653 [astro-ph.SR].

A semi-implicit multidimensional unstructured gas dynamical solver for astrophysical applications

Ilya A. Kondratyev*, Sergey G. Moiseenko

Space Research Institute RAS, Profsoyuznaya st., 84-32, Moscow, Russia, 117485
* E-mail: mrkondratyev95@gmail.com

National Research University "Higher School of Economics", Staraya Basmannaya st., 21/4 s. 5, Moscow, Russia, 105066

> Astrophysical problems such as modelling of core-collapse supernovae, collapse of protostellar clouds as well as other processes, involving collapsing matter, deal with regions (e.g. protostars, protoneutron stars), where a speed of sound has much larger values, than in remaining parts of a computational domain. A time-step in explicit numerical schemes, thus, has to be bounded by acoustic Courant-Friedrichs-Lewy condition, due to high speed of sound in these compact regions. In some cases, this condition can be very restrictive, and (semi-) implicit numerical schemes may outperform the explicit ones. We propose a semi-implicit solver on a collocated mesh for self-gravitating gas dynamical flows, in which only acoustic waves are treated implicitly. We use an operator-difference approach to construct difference analogues of vector differential operators on unstructured meshes in two and three dimensions, which allows us to save the conjugacy properties of the operators. A Rusanov-type dissipation was used to get monotonic flow profiles and usual linear flux reconstruction to improve an order of spatial approximation. Results of test calculations are presented.
>
> *Keywords*: Gas dynamics; semi-implicit schemes; self-gravity.

1. Introduction

Numerical simulations of astrophysical fluid flows is one of the key instruments, which allow us to explain a wide range of astronomical phenomena on the qualitative level, as well as to compare the theoretical predictions to observational data quantitatively. An astrophysics is rich for different types of gas and plasma flows in the case, when one can use ideal compressible fluid approximation without dissipation (e.g. Euler equations). The ideal flow is described in terms of hyperbolic systems of partial differential equations, for which the explicit schemes, such as Godunov-type finite volume,[1] can be successfully applied (see also textbooks[2,3]). Explicit SPH solvers are broadly used by astrophysical community as well.[4] But there are the problems, such as, for example, star formation from protostellar clouds, collapses of stars' iron cores and supernovae explosions, where the implicit or semi-implicit schemes may possibly outperform the explicit solvers. It is a common situation in astrophysical modelling, when the compact high-density regions of a collapsed matter with high speed of sound (such as protostars, protoneutron stars) appear in a computational domain, where the velocity of the flow is very low compared to the acoustic speed, so that we deal with low Mach number flows. At the same time, in other parts of the domain, the flow can be considered as compressible, strong shocks and other different flow discontinuities may form. The latter situation is common for e.g. a post-bounce evolution of core-collapse supernovae.[5] It also stands for magnetorotational supernove simulations, when we have small acoustic timescale and large magnetic field evolution timescale.[6,7] The mesh size during such astrophysical simulations is usually refined in the regions of collapsed objects up to several orders of magnitude, compared to the cell size on the outer boundary. The explicit solvers are restricted by Courant-Friedrichs-Lewy (CFL) condition. In the mentioned types of astrophysical flows, the global CFL condition comes mostly from the high sound speed from resolved collapsed objects and may be very restrictive, which makes such kind of simulations computationally expensive and challenging. Thus, the implicit treatment of acoustic waves in hydrodynamical schemes allows to increase timestep significantly, and hence, to reduce the computational cost of such astrophysical simulations.

Implicit evaluation of the pressure field is a common approach in incompressible flow simulations.[8] The idea to extend the semi-implicit to compressible flows was proposed in mid-80's by Casulli and Greenspan,[9] but only quite recently this approach was used to construct the so-called *All-Mach number solvers* for gas dynamics (see e.g. works[10–13] on structured and[14,15] on unstructured grids, and references therein) and for MHD equations,[16,17] written in conservative form. They are the pressure-based solvers by its nature, but they can work as high resolution shock-capturing methods as well in presence of discontinuities. The usage of semi-implicit solvers results to the solution of an elliptic equation with a Laplace-type operator for the pressure on each time-step, and it is very important to construct a consistent difference analogue of the solving differential problem, which provides the cheaply solvable linearized systems. To obtain a symmetric sign-definite matrices for the linear elliptic problems, we use a Support (basic) Operators Method (operator-difference approach)[19] to construct the difference analogues of differential operators in three dimensions. The support operators method has also many common features with mimetic finite difference[18] approach.

The idea of the support operators method is that the difference operators should be derived in the way to fulfil the same properties as the continuous operators. Thus, the constructed operators should satisfy the difference analogues of integral relations such as Green formula. This approach allows to obtain the so-called completely conservative fully implicit finite-difference schemes for gas dynamics and MHD equations[19] on unstructured grids. For 2D simulations of magnetorotational supernova explosion this method was used e.g. in[20] with a cell-nodal approximation[21,22] in the framework of Newtonian MHD with self-gravity.

The paper is organized as follows. In the next subsection we derive the nodal difference operators of gradient and divergence in three dimensions. In the 3-rd subsection we provide the description of the solving gravitational gas-dynamics system and derive a semi-implicit numerical scheme for these equations, and in the last subsections we present and discuss the results of numerical simulations of several benchmark problems in low and high Mach number regimes.

2. Difference analogues of differential operators

In the Support operators method the difference analogues of differential operators are built in pairs. Further we are going to consider only the nodal gradient and divergence operators, while the other difference analogues can be obtained in a similar way. To introduce difference GRAD and DIV operators one should define finite dimensional linear grid spaces and scalar products of grid functions in them. The first operator can be obtained using any numerical differencing technique, while the second one has to satisfy the grid analogue of the Green formula in corresponding grid space. Thus, the resulting operators are conjugated to each other. The GRAD operator can be derived in two different ways: either using the finite element approach with linear basis functions inside the tetrahedra (for 2D case see e.g.[23]) or with a finite volume approach using piecewise-constant basis functions on the nodal edge-based (median-dual) cells, as in Godunov-type methods on unstructured grids (see e.g.[24]). The grid gradient operator reads (for 3D case):

$$(\nabla_\times p)_j = -\frac{1}{12W_j} \sum_{i \in G_j} \sum_{k=1}^{4} \left(S_k \mathbf{n}_k p_k\right)_i, \qquad (1)$$

where p is a nodal scalar function, G_j is a set of tetrahedral cells adjoined to sought j-th node, i is a cell index, k is a node index inside the i-th cell, $\mathbf{n}_k$ and S_k are unit normal and area to the tetrahedron's triangular face, which does not contain the node k in its vertexes, and $W_j = \frac{1}{4} \sum_{i \in G_j} V_i$ is a "node" volume (the volume of a median-dual cell), V_i is a volume of i-th tetrahedron.

To obtain the consistent approximation of the divergence operator, the Green formula and its difference analogue should be used:

$$\int_V p\nabla \cdot \mathbf{v} dV + \int_V (\nabla p) \cdot \mathbf{v} dV = \oint_{\partial V} p\mathbf{v} \cdot \mathbf{dS},$$
$$\sum_{l=1}^{N_n} (\nabla_\times p)_l \cdot \mathbf{v}_l W_l + \sum_{k=1}^{N_n} p_k (\nabla_\times \cdot \mathbf{v})_k W_k = (\Phi \cdot \mathbf{v}, p), \qquad (2)$$

where ∇ and $\nabla \cdot$ are the gradient and the divergence operators correspondingly, $\mathbf{v}$ is a vector function, N_n is a total number of the nodes, and V is a volume of the computational domain. The surface integral in the right hand side of the formulae (2) correspond to the so-called *Boundary operator* Φ in a formalism of the support operators method. Its evaluation can be found in.[21,22,25] The boundary operator is used to formulate the boundary-value problems in the operator-difference form.

We do not consider it here, because in the solver we use ordinary finite volume boundary conditions via ghost cells approach.

To derive the DIV operator in the interior nodes of the computational domain, the Green formula in (2) is written without the integral in the right hand side. By substituting the grid gradient operator (1) in the analogue of the Green formula (2) and rearranging the terms, the following approximation for the divergence operator can be obtained

$$(\nabla_\times \cdot \mathbf{v})_j = -\frac{1}{12W_j} \sum_{i \in G_j} \sum_{k=1}^{4} \left(S_k \mathbf{n}_k \cdot \mathbf{v}_k\right)_i. \qquad (3)$$

We note, that the latter operator has the same form, as the initially derived gradient one (1) due to the usage of purely nodal approximation, while its form and stencil is different from the cell-nodal DIV operator. The divergence operator (3) is conjugated to (1), and thus, the grid Laplacian transforms into the symmetric and sign-definite matrix. The usage of the support operators technique allows to derive the full set of vector calculus operators in any geometry, which satisfy the conjugacy properties.

Finally, the difference analogues of differential operators can be written in a finite-volume form[26]

$$(\nabla_\times^{fw} p)_j = \frac{1}{W_j} \sum_{n \in H_j} \left(\frac{S_{nj} \mathbf{n}_{nj}(p_n + p_j)}{2}\right), \qquad (4)$$

where H_j is a set of neighbouring nodes to the sought node with index j, S_{nj} and $\mathbf{n}_{nj}$ are the area and the unit normal to the n-th face of the node-centred median-dual control volume. This approximation leads to exactly the same expression as (1).[26]

3. Semi-implicit numerical scheme for the equations of gas dynamics with gravitation

3.1. *Euler equations with self-gravity*

Gas dynamical equations with self-gravity can be written in the following conservative formulation:

$$\begin{aligned}
\frac{\partial \rho}{\partial t} + \nabla \cdot (\rho \mathbf{v}) &= 0, \\
\frac{\partial \rho \mathbf{v}}{\partial t} + \nabla \cdot (\rho \mathbf{v} \otimes \mathbf{v}) + \nabla P &= -\rho \nabla \Psi, \\
\frac{\partial \rho E}{\partial t} + \nabla \cdot \left(\rho \mathbf{v}\left(E + \frac{P}{\rho}\right)\right) &= -\rho \mathbf{v} \cdot \nabla \Psi, \\
\nabla \cdot \nabla \Psi &= 4\pi G \rho.
\end{aligned} \qquad (5)$$

In the system above, the first three equations without source terms in right hand sides correspond to ideal Euler equations, while the last one is the Poisson equation for a gravitational potential Ψ. The source terms correspond to presence of an acceleration by gravity, G is a gravitational constant. In ideal Euler equations (5) ρ is a mass density, $\mathbf{v}$ is a flow velocity; P is a pressure, $E = \frac{\mathbf{v}^2}{2} + E_{th}$ is a total energy density, E_{th} is an internal energy density. A thermodynamic equation of state is needed to close the system of equations (5). In this paper we consider only a perfect gas equation of state with an adiabatic index γ:

$$P = (\gamma - 1)\rho E_{th}. \tag{6}$$

Extension of a semi-implicit solver (see next subsection) to an arbitrary equation of state is straightforward and can be found in e.g.[11,12]

3.2. *Poisson solver*

The Poisson equation should be solved on each time-step to calculate the value of the gravitational potential, and hence, a gravitational force. The support operators method allows to construct a discrete Laplace operator in the form of a symmetric and sign-definite matrix. Purely nodal approximation requires the stencil, which consists of the second-order neighbours for each node. The boundary conditions are projected to the boundary nodes and included in the operator-difference form of the solving problem. For example, the Dirichlet boundary-value problem reads[21,22]

$$(I - \delta)\nabla_\times \cdot \nabla_\times (I - \delta)\Psi + (I - \delta)\nabla_\times \cdot \nabla_\times \delta\Psi_\gamma = 4\pi G(I - \delta)\rho, \tag{7}$$

where Ψ_γ is a boundary value of the gravitational potential, I is a unit operator, δ is an operator, which is equal to unity in the boundary nodes, and zero - in the interior ones.[22] For other types of boundary conditions (e.g. an absence of the force on the boundary) we solve the Poisson using the ghost cells approach. The resulting linear system can be solved with a matrix-free conjugate gradient method. The gravitational acceleration then can be calculated as a nodal gradient of the potential.

In Fig. 1 the solution of the Poisson equation is shown for the spherically-symmetric Gaussian-law solution $\Psi = \exp\left(-\frac{x^2+y^2+z^2}{2}\right)$ given by the function $f = \exp\left(-\frac{x^2+y^2+z^2}{2}\right)(x^2 + y^2 + z^2 - 3)$ in the right-hand side of the equation.

The cell-node approximation can also be used for the solution of the Poisson equation procedure. It allows to use a smaller stencil for the matrix, while the gradient of the potential still can be found with a purely nodal operator (4).

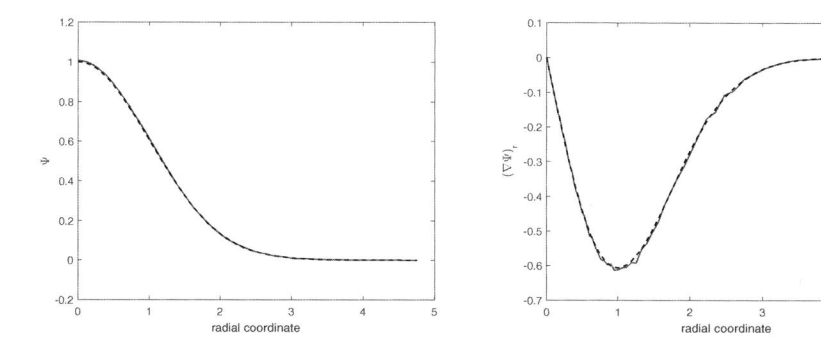

Fig. 1. The solution of the Poisson equation (blue lines, 1D plots are given for the X-axis) for the potential (left) and its gradient (right) together with an analytical solution (black lines). The computational domain is cube ($0 < x, y, z < 5$) with no force conditions on the symmetry boundaries and Dirichlet conditions on outer ones.

3.3. Hydro-solver

The difference gas dynamical system of equations can be written in the following form on a collocated mesh

$$\frac{\rho^{n+1} - \rho^n}{\tau} + \widetilde{\nabla}_\times \cdot (\rho^n \mathbf{v}^n) = 0,$$

$$\frac{\rho^{n+1}\mathbf{v}^{n+1} - \rho^n \mathbf{v}^n}{\tau} + \widetilde{\nabla}_\times \cdot (\rho^n \mathbf{v}^n \otimes \mathbf{v}^n) + \nabla_\times P^{n+1} = \mathbf{S}_v, \quad (8)$$

$$\frac{\rho^{n+1}E^{n+1} - \rho^n E^n}{\tau} + \widetilde{\nabla}_\times \cdot \left(\rho^n \mathbf{v}^n \frac{(\mathbf{v}^2)^n}{2}\right) + \nabla_\times \cdot \left(h^{n+1}\rho^{n+1}\mathbf{v}^{n+1}\right) = S_e,$$

where $h = E_{th} + \frac{P}{\rho} = \frac{\gamma P}{(\gamma-1)\rho}$ is a thermodynamic enthalpy. This system describes the flow evolution from time $t = t^n$ to $t = t^{n+1} = t^n + \tau$. The last terms in the left parts of the second and third equations in (8) should be evaluated implicitly according to,[9,11] which allows to treat implicitly only the acoustic waves in the gas dynamical system (5). The source terms are given by the formulae $\mathbf{S}_v = -\rho^{n+1}\nabla_\times\Psi$, $S_e = -\rho^{n+1}\mathbf{v}^n \cdot \nabla_\times\Psi$. The gravitational potential is solved for the density distribution on the $(n+1)$-th time-step. Note, that such separate treatment of acoustic waves is equivalent to the Toro-Vazquez flux splitting approach.[27]

The difference operator with tilde $\widetilde{\nabla}_\times \cdot$ in explicitly evaluated advective fluxes corresponds to an upwind monotonic scheme for advection. It is written together with a Rusanov-type numerical dissipation:

$$(\widetilde{\nabla}_\times \cdot \mathbf{F})_j = (\nabla_\times \cdot \mathbf{F})_j - \frac{1}{2W_j}\sum_{i \in H_j}\left(\left|\frac{\partial \mathbf{F}}{\partial \mathbf{u}}\right|\mathbf{n}_{ij}|S_{ij}(u_i - u_j)\right), \quad (9)$$

where dissipation is written in a finite-volume form (4), in which **u** and **F** are the vector of conservative variables and the flux vector correspondingly:

$$\mathbf{u} = (\rho, \rho\mathbf{v}, \rho E)$$
$$\mathbf{F} = (\rho\mathbf{v}, \rho\mathbf{v} \otimes \mathbf{v}, \rho\mathbf{v}E). \tag{10}$$

We use $|\frac{\partial \mathbf{F}}{\partial \mathbf{u}}| = \max(|\mathbf{v}|_i, |\mathbf{v}|_j)$, thus, dissipation coefficient is independent on the speed of sound.[11] The explicit advective scheme is implemented in the same manner, as the edge-based Godunov-type finite volume solvers on median-dual grids,[28] so that the advective fluxes **F** in (9) are calculated at the centres of the edges between the nodes.

The numerical scheme is conditionally stable with a milder CFL condition, which depend only on the flow velocity and not on the speed of sound:

$$\tau < \tau_{adv} = \min \frac{\Delta X}{2|\mathbf{v}|}, \tag{11}$$

where ΔX is a characteristic local mesh size.

By substituting the momentum from the momentum equation in (8) to the energy equation, we can obtain the following nonlinear equation:

$$\frac{P^{n+1}}{\gamma - 1} - \tau^2 \nabla_\times \cdot \left(h^{n+1} \nabla_\times P^{n+1} \right)$$
$$= \rho^n E^n - \rho^{n+1} \frac{(\mathbf{v}^2)^{n+1}}{2} - \tau \tilde{\nabla}_\times \cdot \left(\rho^n \mathbf{v}^n \frac{(\mathbf{v}^2)^n}{2} \right) + \tau S_e \tag{12}$$
$$- \tau \nabla_\times \cdot \left(h^{n+1} (\rho^n \mathbf{v}^n - \tau \tilde{\nabla}_\times \cdot (\rho^n \mathbf{v}^n \otimes \mathbf{v}^n) + \tau \mathbf{S}_v) \right),$$

The latter system is nonlinear, and the usual approach to solve it is a usage of nested Newton-type iterations (r-iterations, Picard iterations),[11,12] which converge rapidly (usually 2-3 iterations are enough). The resulting linearised system reads:

$$\frac{P^{n+1,r+1}}{\gamma - 1} - \tau^2 \nabla_\times \cdot \left(h^{n+1,r} \nabla_\times P^{n+1,r+1} \right)$$
$$= \rho^n E^n - \rho^{n+1} \frac{(\mathbf{v}^2)^{n+1,r}}{2} - \tau \tilde{\nabla}_\times \cdot \left(\rho^n \mathbf{v}^n \frac{(\mathbf{v}^2)^n}{2} \right) + \tau S_e \tag{13}$$
$$- \tau \nabla_\times \cdot \left(h^{n+1,r} (\rho^n \mathbf{v}^n - \tau \tilde{\nabla}_\times \cdot (\rho^n \mathbf{v}^n \otimes \mathbf{v}^n) + \tau \mathbf{S}_v) \right),$$

$$h^{n+1,r} = \frac{\gamma P^{n+1,r}}{(\gamma - 1)\rho^{n+1}}.$$

To obtain the solution from n-th time level to $n+1$-th, the following procedures should be done:

(I) solving the mass conservation equation in (8) with the explicit scheme and obtaining ρ^{n+1}

(II) solving the Poisson equation (7) with the density ρ^{n+1} for the gravitational potential and calculating the forces in the source terms of gas-dynamical system (8)

(III) defining $P^{n+1,1} = P^n$, $h^{n+1,1} = h^n$ and $\mathbf{v}^{n+1,1} = \mathbf{v}^n$

(IV) r-iterations, $r = \overline{1, r_p}$

    (a) Solving (13) and obtaining $P^{n+1,r+1}$
    (b) recalculating $h^{n+1,r+1}$ and calculating $\mathbf{v}^{n+1,r+1}$ from the momentum equation (8) using $P^{n+1,r+1}$

(V) defining $P^{n+1} = P^{n+1,r_p}$, $h^{n+1} = h^{n+1,r_p}$ and $\mathbf{v}^{n+1} = \mathbf{v}^{n+1,r_p}$

(VI) calculating the energy using a semi-implicit equation from the system (8).

This procedures allow to obtain a numerical solution of the gas-dynamical system (5) with a first order in space and time. In this study we use $r_p = 3$ Picard iterations.

To extend this scheme to higher order in space, we use the same approach as in explicit finite volume Godunov-type schemes on unstructured meshes, as it is done in e.g.[28] (see also[29] for a different approach). We apply a piecewise-linear reconstruction of conservative gas-dynamical variables in advection upwind fluxes (9) with Barth-Jespersen slope limiters,[24] thus, the explicit advective part of the solver is calculated with the second order in space. For this reason, the resulting order of spatial approximation of the scheme is higher, than one. Note, that the difference operators like (4) provide the second order in space on the mesh, consisting on equilateral tetrahedra (or equilateral triangles in 2D), because these operators are analogous to the usual central differences on the uniform grid, so that on such kind of meshes the solver has the second approximation order in space. High order in time approximation can be achieved either by employing explicit high order methods for the advective parts of the solving system, as was done in e.g.,[15] or by using the implicit-explicit Runge-Kutta methods.[13]

The linearised problem (13) has a matrix of a Laplace-type second order difference operator and, in addition, a diagonal, filled with the positive elements. The conjugated difference operators allow to obtain an easily reversible symmetric and positive definite matrix. We use a matrix-free conjugate gradient method to solve the system (13), which is very efficient.

It is also possible to make a discretization of the system (5) in time, substitute the expression for $\rho^{n+1}\mathbf{v}^{n+1}$ in the energy equation, and further discretize the energy equation in space.[13] The cell-node approximation and the Support operators method can be applied for the Laplace-type operator in (13), thus, making the matrix stencil more compact. Preliminary calculations show, that this approach is slightly more effective, as well as it provides a collocated pressure system, which is similar in properties to the staggered grid approach.[13]

4. Test computations

The code was developed in two variants: 2D and 3D Cartesian versions. We have tested our code in several benchmark problems in high and low Mach number regimes as well as simulated a test problem of a dust collapse to check the code's ability to simulate the flows with self-gravity.

In Fig. 2 the Sod shock tube problem solution is shown for the 3D (the first three pictures) and 2D versions of our code at the time $T = 0.45$ for the mesh with $N_x = 200$ nodes in X-direction and $N_y = N_z = 10$ ones in Y- and Z-directions. The initial conditions are as usual: $\rho(x < 1) = 0.125, P(x < 1) = 0.1$ and $\rho(x \geq 1) = 1, P(x \geq 1) = 1$, while the velocity is zero everywhere. The shock profile is about 4-5 cells thick. The solution is obtained by the conservative scheme, thus, the discontinuities have physically correct amplitudes and velocities.

In Fig. 3 the density profile of a slowly moving contact discontinuity is presented. The initial conditions are the following: $\mathbf{v} = (0.01, 0, 0), P = 3$ everywhere, while the density $\rho(x < 0.25) = 50, \rho(x \geq 0.25) = 1$. The problem is solved until the final time $T = 50$, which corresponds to the contact discontinuity located at $x = 0.75$.

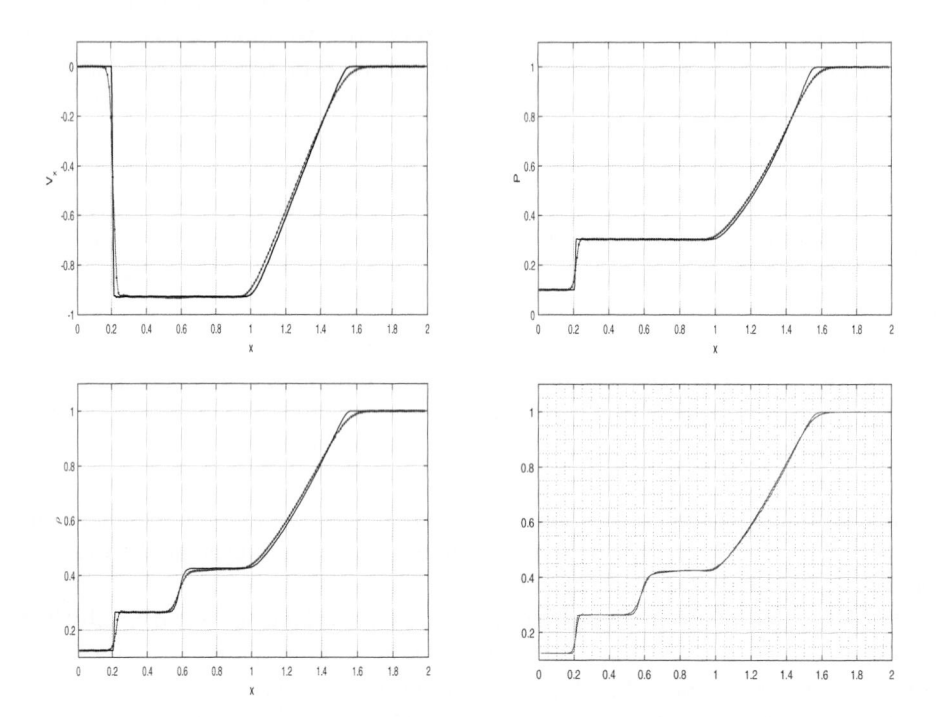

Fig. 2. Velocity, pressure and density fields (the first three figures, blue lines) of the gas in the Sod shock tube at time $T = 0.45$, compared to the reference solution given by a second-order explicit second-order local Lax-Friedrichs solver with Barth-Jespersen slope limiters (black lines) on a finer mesh with $N_x = 500$ nodes. On the last picture the density plot is shown for 2D explicit (red line) and 2D semi-implicit (blue line) solvers with the same mesh resolution.

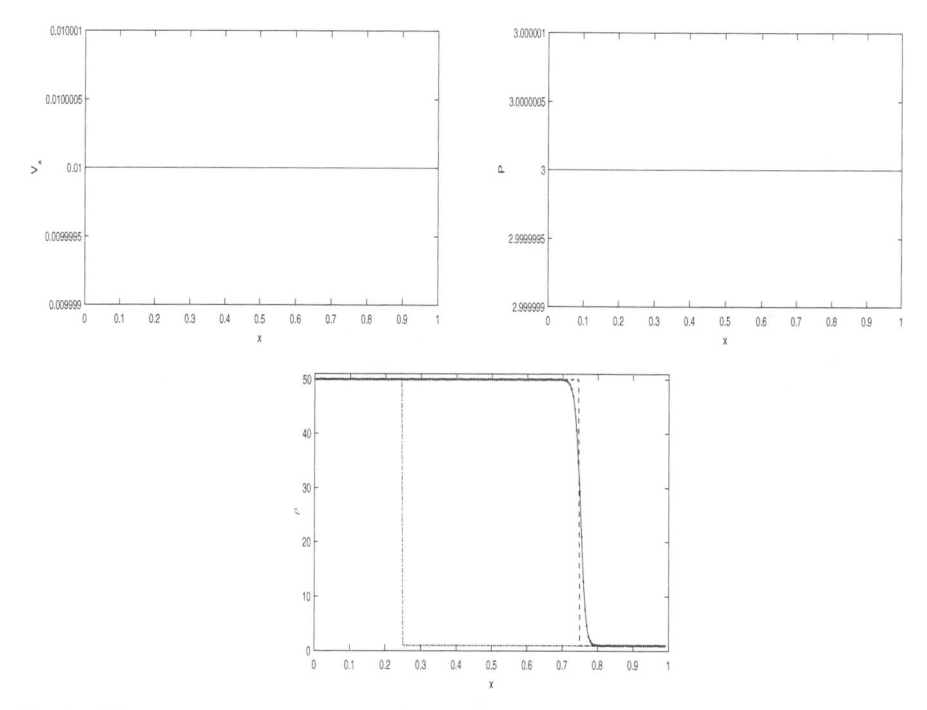

Fig. 3. Velocity, pressure and density fields of the gas in a slowly moving contact discontinuity problem at time $T = 50$. The blue lines correspond to our numerical solution, while the red dash-dotted line and dashed purple line are initial and final location of the contact discontinuity correspondingly.

The profile is smeared over ~ 10 grid points. On this problem, the semi-implicit scheme greatly outperforms the explicit solver by a factor of ~ 40. The time step τ_{adv} (11) is equal to $\sim 200 \tau_{CFL}$.

The next test is the Sedov-Taylor planar blast wave solution, which was performed in a 2D cylindrical geometry. The shock front location is $R \approx \sqrt{T}$. Fig. 4 shows the density and pressure profiles at $T = 0.2$. The 2D mesh, used in the simulations, is refined at the centre of explosion by a factor of 10. It has 8756 nodes. The numerical solution shows a good agreement with analytics. In the refined central part ($r = \sqrt{x^2 + y^2} \ll 1$) of the computational domain, the sound speed is greatly exceeds the velocity, while at $r \lesssim 1$ the strong high Mach number shock wave is pronounced. At the end of the simulation, the advective time-step was about 50 times higher, than the CFL time-step τ_{CFL}. In real astrophysical conditions this ratio of time-steps could be even higher.

The latter situation is more pronounced in 3D Sedov-Taylor blast wave problem, where the semi-implicit calculation (see Fig. 5) was at least 10 times faster, than the explicit solver, due to restrictive acoustic time-step in the centre of computational domain.

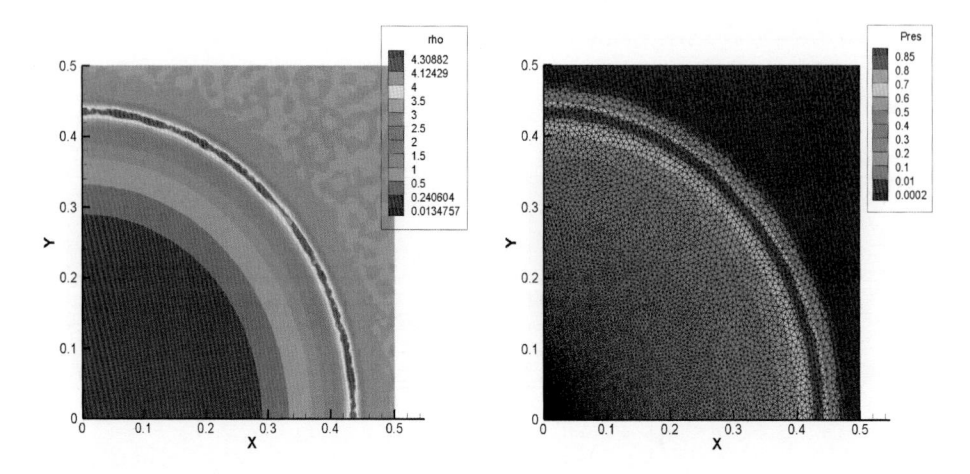

Fig. 4. Density (left) and pressure (right, together with the 2D mesh) of the gas in a planar Sedov-Taylor blast wave problem at time $T = 0.2$.

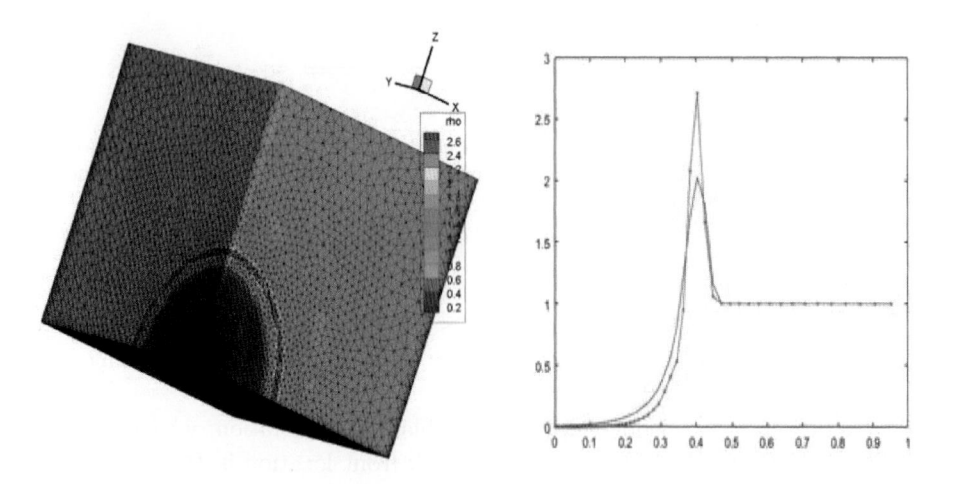

Fig. 5. Density (left) and its 1D slice (right, red line, together with the explicit solver calculation) of the gas in a 3D Sedov-Taylor blast wave problem at time $T = 0.1$.

We have tested our code including the self-gravity module and simulated a well-known problem on the spherical collapse of a pressureless star (dust collapse), which was originally considered in the paper by Colgate and White.[30] The octant-symmetric 3D results for the density at dimensionless time $T = 1.791$ are presented in Fig. 6. We use the system of units, which removes the multiplier $4\pi G$ in the Poisson equation for the gravitational potential (7). In these units the free-fall time $t_{ff} = \sqrt{\frac{3}{2}\frac{\pi}{2}} \approx 1.9238$. The initial cloud radius and density are equal to unity. We use the mesh, which is refined to the centre of the computational domain. The snapshot

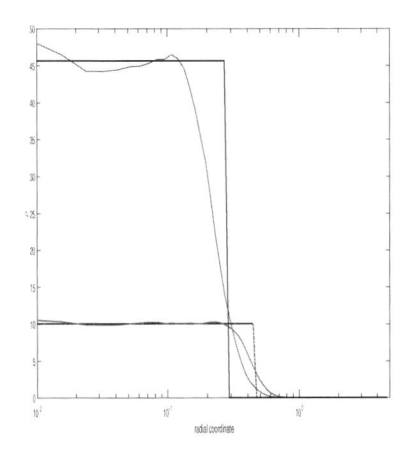

Fig. 6. Density of the gas in the dust collapse problem at time $T = 1.791$. Left panel correspond to 3D solution, while the right panel corresponds to 1D spherical plot (blue line - numerical solution, black dashed line - analytics) together with the solution at the time $T = 1.618$ (red line - numerical solution, black dotted line - analytics).

of our simulation in Fig. 6 shows a physically correct evolution of collapsing matter, although at the developed stage of the collapse the density field has a discrepancy from the analytical solution (blue line in Fig. 6, right) due to the high spatial and temporal steps. The initial spherically-symmetric conditions are also disturbed by unstructured mesh, and these disturbances tend to slight deviation from spherical symmetry.

5. Conclusion

In this paper we have constructed the semi-implicit nodal (edge-based) pressure-based solver for gravitational gas dynamics on unstructured tetrahedral meshes. The usage of the Support operators technique results to linear systems with symmetric and sign-definite matrices for the pressure system in semi-implicit gas-dynamical solver as well as for the Poisson equation for the gravitational potential. The code works efficiently both in low and high Mach number regimes, and its spatial accuracy is close to the second order. In future, we plan to apply this code to simulation of the post-bounce evolution of core-collapse supernovae. Further development of the code will be devoted to improvement of temporal accuracy, massive parallelization and inclusion of magnetic fields.

References

1. Godunov S.K., Mat. Sbornik, 47(89):3, 271 (1959)
2. Bisikalo D.V., Zhilkin A.G. and Boyarchuk A.A. "Gas dynamics of close binary stars", Moscow-Fiz.Mat.Lit. (in Russian) (2015)

3. Toro E.F., "Riemann Solvers and numerical methods for fluid dynamics: A practical introduction", Springer (2009)
4. Monaghan J.J., Annu. Rev. Astron. Astrophys., 30:543-74 (1992)
5. B. Mueller, Living reviews in computational astrophysics, 6, 3 (2020)
6. Ardeljan N.V., Bisnovatyi-Kogan G.S. and Moiseenko S.G., Mon. Not. R. Astron. Soc., 359, 333 (2005)
7. Obergaulinger M., Aloy M.Á., Mon. Not. R. Astron. Soc., 492 (4), 4613 (2020)
8. Harlow F.H. and Welch J.E., Physics of Fluids, 8, 2182 (1965)
9. Casulli V. and Greenspan D., International Journal for Numerical Methods in Fluids, 4, 11, 1001 (1984)
10. Cordier F., Degond P. and Kumbaro A., Journal of Computational Physics, 231, 5685 (2012)
11. Dumbser M., Casulli V., Applied Mathematics and Computation, 272, 479 (2016)
12. Boscheri W., Dimarco G., Loub'ere R., Tavelli M. and Vignal M.H., Journal of Computational Physics, 415, 109486 (2020)
13. Boscheri W. and Pareschi L., Journal of Computational Physics, 434, 110206 (2021)
14. Tavelli M. and Dumbser M., Journal of Computational Physics, 341, 341 (2017)
15. Busto S., Río-Martín L., Vázquez-Cendón M.E. and Dumbser M., Applied Mathematics and Computation, 402, 126117 (2021)
16. Dumbser M., Balsara D.S., Tavelli M. and Fambri F., International Journal for Numerical Methods in Fluids, 89 (1-2) 16 (2019)
17. Fambri F., arXiv:2012.11218 (2021)
18. Lipnikov K., Manzini G. and Shashkov M., Journal of Computational Physics, 257, 1163 (2014)
19. Samarskii A.A. and Popov Yu.P., "Difference methods for solving problems of gas dynamics" Moscow, Izdatel'stvo Nauka (in Russian) (1992)
20. Moiseenko S.G., Ardeljan N.V. and Bisnovatyi-Kogan G.S., Monthly Notices of the Royal Astronomical Society, 370 (1) 501 (2006)
21. Ardeljan N.V. and Kosmachevskii K.V., "Problems of Construction and Research of Conservative Difference Schemes for Magneto-gas-dynamics" Moscow - Moscow State University (in Russian) (1987)
22. Ardeljan N.V. and Kosmachevskii K.V., Comput. Math. Modelling, 6, 209 (1995)
23. Ardelyan N.V. and Sablin M.N., Comput. Math. Modelling, 14, 217 (2003)
24. Barth, T.J. and Jespersen D.C., The design and application of upwind schemes on unstructured meshes, AIAA Paper, 89-0366 (1989)
25. Kondratyev I.A. and Moiseenko S.G., Journal of Physics: Conf. Series, 1163, 012069 (2019)
26. Barth T.J., Numerical Aspects of Computing Viscous High Reynolds Number Flows on Unstructured Meshes, AIAA paper, 91-0721 (1991)
27. Toro E.F., Vázquez-Cendón M.E., Computers and fluids, 70, 1 (2012)
28. Barth T.J., A 3-D Upwind Euler Solver for Unstructured Meshes, AIAA paper, 91-1548CP (1991)
29. Kulikov I. Vorobyov E., Chernykh I. and Elbakyan V., Journal of Physics: Conf. Series, 1640, 012003 (2020)
30. Colgate S.A., White R.H., Astrophys. J., 143, 626 (1966)

Magnetized neutron stars propagating through a non-uniform ISM

O. D. Toropina

Space Research Institute, Russian Academy of Sciences
Profsoyuznaya 84/32, Moscow 117997, Russia
E-mail: toropina@iki.rssi.ru

M. M. Romanova and R. V. E. Lovelace

Department of Astronomy, Cornell University,
NY, 14853, Ithaca, USA

Many neutron stars propagate through the interstellar medium with supersonic velocities, and their magnetospheres interact with the interstellar medium (ISM), forming bow shocks and magnetotails. Using numerical MHD simulations, we investigated the propagation of a magnetized neutron stars through a non-uniform ISM, the interaction of the magnetospheres with the ISM and the influence of ISM density on the shape of the magnetosphere tail. We consider the interaction of magnetized neutron stars with small-scale and large-scale inhomogeneities in the ISM. We conclude that the inhomogeneities in the ISM can change the shapes of the bow shocks and magnetotails at different values of the magnetization.

Keywords: Neutron stars; magnetic field; PWN; ISM; MHD.

1. Introduction

The most dramatic bow shock nebulae are associated with the neutron stars. Pulsars emit winds of relativistic particles and magnetic fields, and are frequently surrounded by the pulsar wind nebulae. Most pulsars propagate supersonically through the interstellar medium, and their PWNs interact with the ISM, forming bow shocks and magnetotails. The bow shocks are often observed in the H_α spectral line.[2] Many interesting structures (bow shocks, very long tails, and jet-like features) are observed in the X-ray[5] and radio wavebands. A remarkable example of PWN is the Guitar Nebula discovered in 1992. It's powered by an ordinary NS, PSR B2224+65. This pulsar travels at an extraordinarily high velocity, about 1600 km/sec. It leaves behind a "tail" in the ISM, that looks like a guitar. The high-resolution observations in the H_α line show that the shape of the Nebula's head becomes wider with time. The variation in shape may be connected with the variation in the density of the ISM.[4]

Many of the PWN show irregularities in their shapes in the X-ray band, as well as very long tails (see review by Kargaltsev et al.[7]). Longer tails are observed in the radio band.[8] Two examples of PWN, observed in the X-ray and radio bands are presented on the Figure 1: the PWN associated with the pulsar PSR J1509-5850 and the Mouse Nebula, powered by the pulsar PSR J1747-2958.[6] These PWNs have extended tails in the X-ray band (red lines), and longer tails in the radio-band (blue lines). One can see that both the heads of the PWN and their tails have different unevenness in shapes.

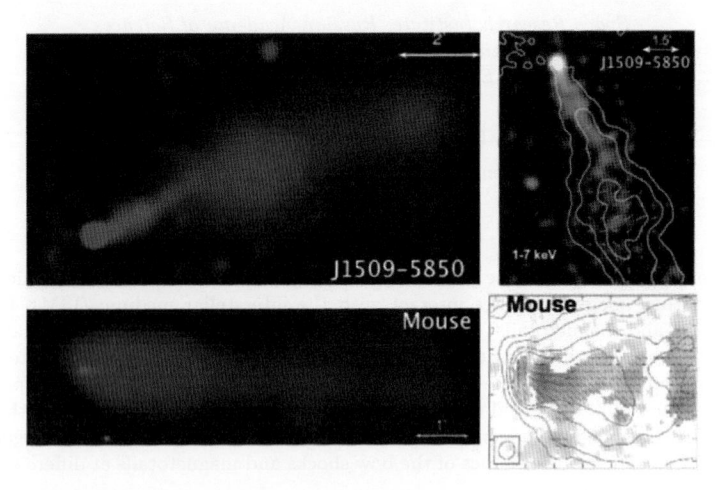

Fig. 1. X-ray and radio images of the very long pulsar tails, by Kargaltsev and Pavlov.[6] Right panels show the radio contours and the direction of the magnetic field. The red and blue colours in the left panels correspond to X-ray and radio, respectively.

When a pulsar or an isolated neutron star propagates supersonically through the ISM, then the PWN or magnetosphere of isolated star interacts with the ISM, forming a bow shock and magnetotails. In the bow shock, the energy of accelerated particles may dominate over magnetic energy. However, in the magnetotails, the magnetic energy may be comparable to or larger than the energy of the particles. Long and magnetically dominated magnetotails can to form in the PWN. They may be visible, if the accelerated particles propagate into the magnetotails, or invisible. In the simulation of the supersonic PWN, it is important to take into account both, the matter and the magnetic field components of the PWN.

Supersonic propagation of pulsars and isolated neutron stars through the ISM has been studied in a number of axisymmetric non-relativistic and relativistic hydrodynamic simulations (e.g., Bucciantini,[3] Barkov[1]). Most of the these simulations of the bow shocks propagating through an inhomogeneous ISM medium were performed in hydrodynamic approximation. Early we performed MHD simulation of supersonic propagation of magnetized isolated neutron stars in the homogeneous ISM.[9,10] Then we started MHD simulation of the bow shock PWN propagating through a non-uniform ISM.[12] Our aim is to consider this problem in axisymmetric MHD simulations at different magnetization values of the pulsar wind.

2. Model

We performed MHD simulations to investigated the supersonic propagation of magnetized isolated neutron star and PWNs through the non-uniform ISM. We used an axisymmetric, resistive MHD code, that incorporates the methods of local iterations and flux-corrected-transport.[13] The flow is described by the resistive MHD equations:

$$\frac{\partial \rho}{\partial t} + \nabla \cdot (\rho \mathbf{v}) = 0 ,$$

$$\rho \frac{\partial \mathbf{v}}{\partial t} + \rho(\mathbf{v} \cdot \nabla)\mathbf{v} = -\nabla p + \frac{1}{c}\mathbf{J} \times \mathbf{B} + \mathbf{F}^g ,$$

$$\frac{\partial \mathbf{B}}{\partial t} = \nabla \times (\mathbf{v} \times \mathbf{B}) + \frac{c^2}{4\pi\sigma}\nabla^2 \mathbf{B} ,$$

$$\frac{\partial(\rho\varepsilon)}{\partial t} + \nabla \cdot (\rho\varepsilon\mathbf{v}) = -p\nabla\cdot\mathbf{v} + \frac{\mathbf{J}^2}{\sigma} . \quad (1)$$

We assume axisymmetry ($\partial/\partial\phi = 0$), but calculate all three components of $\mathbf{v}$ and $\mathbf{B}$. The equation of state for an ideal gas, $p = (\gamma - 1)\rho\varepsilon$, where $\gamma = 5/3$ is the specific heat ratio and ε is the specific internal energy of the gas. The equations incorporate Ohm's law $\mathbf{J} = \sigma(\mathbf{E}+\mathbf{v}\times\mathbf{B}/c)$, where σ is the electric conductivity. The associated magnetic diffusivity, $\eta_m \equiv c^2/(4\pi\sigma)$, is assumed to be a constant. The gravitational force, $\mathbf{F}^g = -GM\rho\mathbf{R}/R^3$, is due to the star because the self-gravity of the accreting gas is negligible.

We use a cylindrical, inertial coordinate system (r, ϕ, z) with the $z-$axis parallel to the star's dipole moment μ and rotation axis $\mathbf{\Omega}$. The vector potential $\mathbf{A}$ is calculated so that automatically $\nabla \cdot \mathbf{B} = 0$ at all times. The intrinsic magnetic field of the star is taken to be an aligned dipole, with vector potential $\mathbf{A} = \mu \times \mathbf{R}/R^3$. A description of numerical model in detail can be found in.[11,12]

We measure length in units of the Bondi radius $R_B \equiv GM/c_s^2$, with c_s the sound speed at infinity, density in units of the density of the interstellar medium ρ, and magnetic field strength in units of B_0 which is the field at the pole of the numerical star. We measure time in units of $t_0 = (Z_{max} - Z_{min})/v_\infty$, which is the crossing time of the computational region with the star's velocity, v_∞.

3. Propagation of magnetized isolated neutron stars through non-uniform ISM

First, we consider a supersonic propagation of magnetized, isolated old neutron stars (IONS) through the non-uniform ISM, in particular through the a dense and cold cloud. Simulations were done for a number of values of the star's magnetic moments μ, the velocity of the star v and the density of the ISM cloud ρ. We received pictures of the flow of matter for different parameters μ, v and ρ. For all used parameters a magnetospheric radius of the star is much larger than accretion radius $R_m \gg R_{acc}$, so that matter cannot accretes onto neutron star surface. This case corresponds to the georotator regime for isolated neutron stars.

When a neutron star moving through an uniform medium with the density ρ_0, incoming matter forms a conical shock wave around the star. The magnetic field lines stretches in the direction of flow of matter out of the magnetospheric radius R_m and form a long tail of the magnetosphere. A picture of the matter flow one can see on top panel of the Figure 2. We observed a reconnection of magnetic field lines in the tail. Then a star passes through the non-uniform medium which is a cold and dense cloud, and the shape of the bow shock and the tail of the magnetosphere varies depending on the density and temperature of the ISM. The shape of the bow shock changes its width and the shape of the magnetotail gets multiple "bumps".

A typical example of the matter flow is represented on Figure 2. In this case Mach numbers $\mathcal{M} = v/c_s = 6$ and density of the cloud $\rho/\rho_0 = 6$. A central region of calculation at moments $t_1 = 0$, $t_2 = 0.33t_0$, $t_3 = 0.66t_0$ and $t_4 = 1.0t_0$ is shown, when t_0 is the crossing time of the computational region. On the left panel the background represents the logarithm of the density and solid lines are magnetic field lines. The length of the arrows is proportional to the poloidal velocity of the matter. We can see that with increasing density of the cloud the width of the bow shock and width of the tail decreases. Then with decreasing density of of the cloud the magnetosphere recovers its shape. Magnetic field lines are compressed by the dense incoming flow and form new reconnections in the tail. On the right panel the background represents the logarithm of the temperature. We can see that with decreasing temperature of the cloud the width of the bow shock and width of the tail decreases. Then with increasing temperature of of the cloud the magnetosphere recovers its shape.

Left panel on Figure 3 shows a density distribution across the magnetotail on the distance $z = 0.5$ and at the same time $t = 0.33t_0$, A solid line represents an uniform medium with constant density ρ_0. A maximum of the density correspond to the distance $r = 0.37$ approximately. A dotted line represents the cloud density $\rho/\rho_0 = 3$. A maximum of the density correspond to $r = 0.26$. A dashed line represents the cloud density $\rho/\rho_0 = 6$. A maximum of the density correspond to $r = 0.20$. We can see that with an increase in the density of the ISM the tail of the magnetosphere becomes more narrow and hollow.

Right panel on Figure 3 shows a temperature distribution across the magnetotail on same distance $z = 0.5$ and at the same time $t = 0.33t_0$. The solid line represents an uniform medium with constant density ρ_0. The dotted line represents the cloud density $\rho/\rho_0 = 3$ and a dashed line represents the cloud density $\rho/\rho_0 = 6$. For all three values of the density, the temperature is maximum at the Z axis, then decreases along R axis and forms a "step", and then becomes a constant. We can see that with a decrease in the temperature of the ISM the tail of the magnetosphere becomes more narrow and hollow.

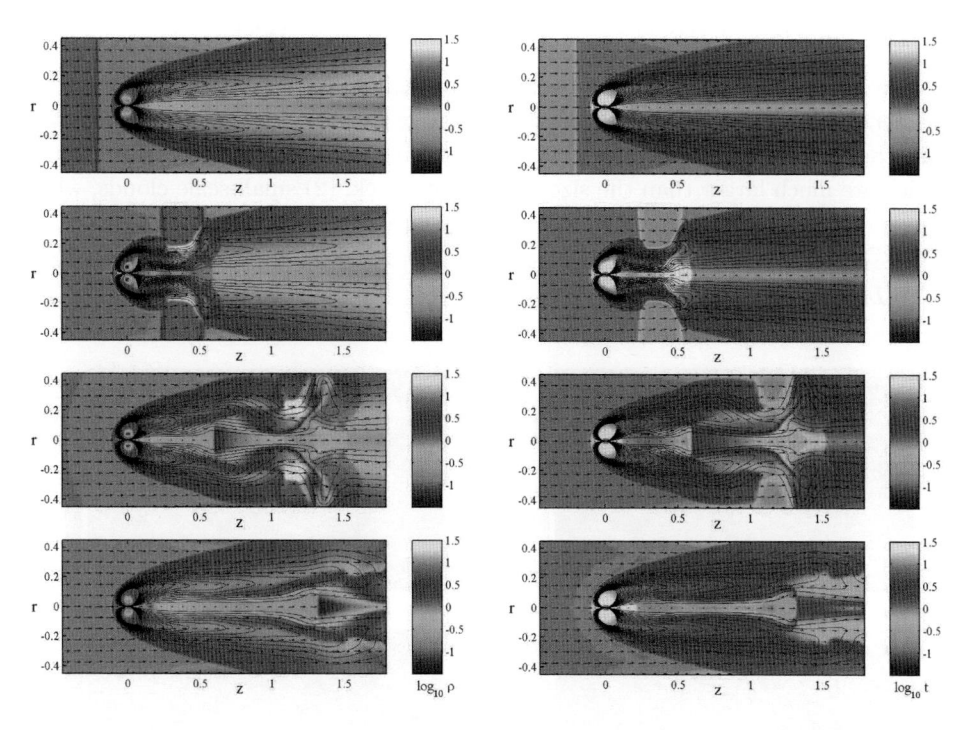

Fig. 2. The propagation of a neutron star with a magnetic field through the dense and cold cloud of interstellar medium. Mach numbers $\mathcal{M} = 6$ and dencity of the cloud $\rho/\rho_0 = 6$. Central region of matter flow at moments $t_1 = 0$, $t_2 = 0.33t_0$, $t_3 = 0.66t_0$ and $t_4 = 1.0t_0$ is shown. On the left panel the background represents the logarithm of the density the background represents the logarithm of density. Solid lines are magnetic field lines. The length of the arrows is proportional to the poloidal velocity. On the right panel the background represents the logarithm of the temperature.

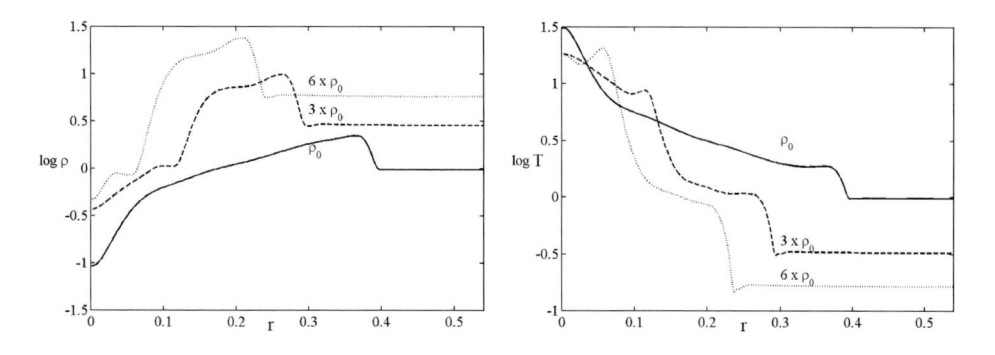

Fig. 3. Left panel: Distribution of the density across the magnetotail at the same time $t = 0.33t_0$ on the distance $z = 0.5$. Right panel: Distribution of the temperature across the magnetotail at the same time $t = 0.33t_0$ on the distance $z = 0.5$.

4. Propagation of PWN through the non-uniform ISM

We investigate the propagation of a PWN through an ISM with an inhomogeneous matter distribution. Observations point to large and small-scale inhomogeneities, and therefore we consider two types of imhomogeneities: (1) large-scale clouds, which are much larger than the size of the bow shock, (2) small-scale clouds, whose size is comparable with the width of the bow shock.

4.1. Large-scale cloud

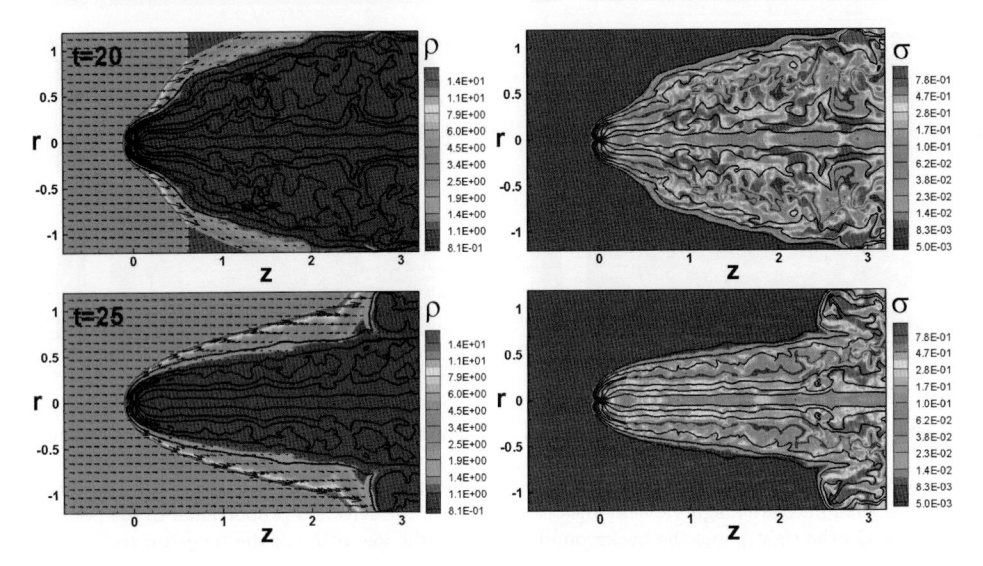

Fig. 4. *Left panels:* Propagation of a PWN of moderate magnetization through a large cloud of density $\rho_{\text{cloud}} = 3\rho_0$ at two moments in time. The background represents the logarithm of density. The solid lines are magnetic field lines. *Right panels:* Same, but the background shows magnetization σ.

Fig. 4 shows an example of propagation of a large cloud of density $\rho_{\text{cloud}} = 3\rho_0$ through the PWN in the model with a moderate magnetization. The left panels show that the cloud compresses the bow shock and the bow shock has a smaller opening angle (the Mach cone). The cloud is in pressure balance with the rest of the ISM, so that the sound speed in the cloud is three times lower than in the rest of the ISM. Therefore, the Mach number of the star inside the cloud is $M_{\text{new}} = v_p/c_s = 3M_{\text{old}} = 60$. This is why we observe a smaller opening angle of the Mach cone. The bottom left panel shows that after entering the cloud, the KH instability develops in the region of CD. This is an expected result: at larger Mach number, there is a larger difference between velocities of matter from two sides of the contact discontinuity. The right panels of Fig. 4 show that the region of high magnetization becomes more narrow after the passage of the cloud. Also, the region of high magnetization becomes less homogeneous (more patchy) due to the action of the KH instability. These simulations demonstrate that propagation through a large-scale cloud leads to a reconstruction of the magnetic field in space and to change in the value of the magnetic field. The tangled magnetic field may reconnect and the magnetic energy can be converted to the energy of accelerated particles and radiate. This may be a possible reason for the re-brightening of PWN magnetotails observed in X-ray.[7]

4.1.1. Small-scale inhomogeneities

Our simulations show that the KH instability frequently forms at the CD and produces some wavy structure of the bow shock. However, a wavy structure could also result from the interaction of the bow shock with the small-scale inhomogeneities in the ISM. To model the interaction of the small-scale inhomogeneities with the bow shock, we took models where the KH instability is weak and does not modify the shape of the bow shock.

We model small-scale inhomogeneities as a set of small clouds with Gaussian density distribution, with the maximum density of ρ_{max} and half-width of $\Delta r = 0.2$. To keep the pressure balance between the clouds and the rest of the ISM, we take the temperature in the cloud to be $T_{cloud} = T_{ISM} * \rho_0/\rho_{cloud}$. We experimented with clouds of different densities, and found that the shape of the bow shock varies significantly if the density in the cloud is $\rho_{cloud} \gtrsim 2\rho_0$. At $\rho_{cloud} = 2\rho_0$, a wavy structure starts to become visible, while at $\rho_{cloud} = 3\rho_0$, the bow shock changes its local shape significantly.

Fig. 5 shows a wavy variation of density in the bow shocks that appears after the propagation of clouds of density $\rho_{cloud} = 3\rho_0$ in the models with low and moderate magnetizations. Such an interaction with small-scale inhomogeneities may explain the wiggles in the shape of the bow shock observed in PSR J0742-2822 (see Fig. 1). In PSR J0742-2822, the estimated stand-off distance is $R_{sd} \approx 4.2 \times 10^{16} d/2\text{kpc}$ cm. The size of clouds in our model $R_{cl} \approx (2-4) R_{sd} \approx (0.8 - 1.6) \times 10^{17} d/2\text{kpc}$ cm. It may correspond to one of scales in turbulent ISM matter. We should note that an alternative explanation of these small-scale features in bow shocks can be connected with the KH instability. Currently, we cannot distinguish between these two mechanisms.

5. Conclusions

We performed MHD simulations of the supersonic propagation of magnetized neutron star and bow shock PWN propagating through a uniform and non-uniform ISM at different levels of magnetization. Our main findings are the following:

The fluctuations in the density or temperature leads to a change in shape of bow shock and the tail of the magnetosphere structure of the neutron star. With an increase in the density of the ISM the bow shock nebulae and the tail of the

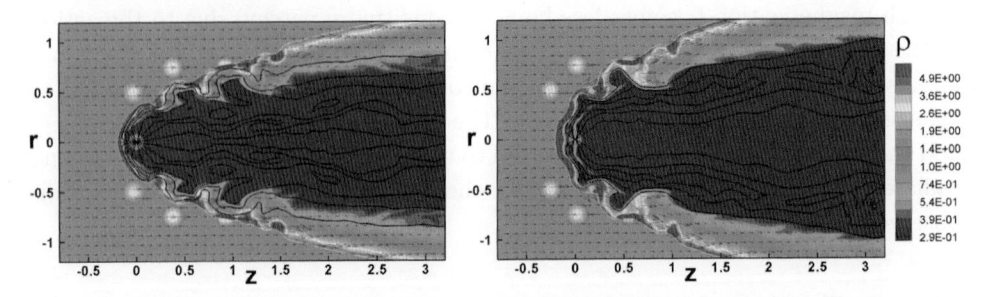

Fig. 5. Interaction of the bow shock with small-scale clouds of maximum density $\rho_{cloud} = 3\rho_0$ in the model with low σ (left panel) and in the model with medium σ (right panel). The background represents the logarithm of density. The solid lines are magnetic field lines.

magnetosphere become narrow and vice versa. A temperature dependence is opposite. With an increase in the temperature of the ISM the bow shock nebulae and the tail of the magnetosphere become wider. A presence of "bubbles" or "bumps" in the shape of bow shock and the magnetotail most likely indicates on the changing density or temperature of the ISM.

The interaction of the bow shock with a large-scale, dense cloud leads to the compression of the bow shock and the formation of a new bow shock with a smaller opening angle. The level of compression (the ratio between the original and final widths of the bow shock) is approximately the same for PWN of different magnetization.

The interaction of the bow shock with the small-scale inhomogeneities in the ISM leads to a wavy structure in the bow shock. The amplitude of the "waves" increases with the ratio ρ_{cloud}/ρ_0. For example, variation in the shape of the bow shock of pulsar PSR J0742-2822 can be explained by the propagation through a series of clouds with a density ratio of $\rho_{cloud}/\rho_0 \approx 3$. Small-scale clouds produce wavy shapes of the bow shocks in PWN of different magnetization.

Acknowledgements

We are grateful to V.V. Saveliev (IPM RAS) for the original version of MHD simulation program. This work was partially supported by RFBR grants 18-29-21021, 20-02-00455.

References

1. Barkov, M., & Lyutikov, M. 2018, MNRAS, eprint arXiv:1804.07327
2. Brownsberger, S., Romani, R.W., 2014, ApJ, Volume 784, Issue 2, article id. 154, 14 pp.
3. Bucciantini, N., 2002, A&A, 387, 1066
4. Chatterjee S. & Cordes J. M., 2004, ApJ, Volume 600, Issue 1, pp. L51
5. Kargaltsev, O., & Pavlov, G.G. 2010, AIPC, 1248, 25

6. Kargaltsev, O., Durant, M., Pavlov, G., Garmire, G. 2012, ApJ Supplement, Volume 201, Issue 2, article id. 37, 7 pp.
7. Kargaltsev, O., Pavlov, G.G., Klingler, N., & Rangelov, B. 2017, J. Plasma Phys., Vol. 83, pp. 1-25
8. Ng, C.-Y. et al. 2010, ApJ, 712, 596
9. Toropina, O.D., Romanova, M.M., Toropin, Yu.M.,& Lovelace, R. V. E. 2001, ApJ, 561, 964
10. Toropina O.D., Romanova M.M., Lovelace R.V.E., 2007, MNRAS 371, 569–576 (2006)
11. Toropina, O.D., Romanova, M.M., & Lovelace, R. V. E., 2012, MNRAS, Volume 420, Issue 1, pp. 810-816
12. Toropina O.D., Romanova M.M., Lovelace R.V.E., 2019, MNRAS, Volume 484, Issue 2, P. 1475–1486,
13. Zhukov, V. T., Zabrodin, A. V., & Feodoritova, O. B. 1993, Comp. Maths. Math. Phys., 33, No. 8, 1099

Calculation of the kinetic coefficients of arbitrary degenerate electrons in magnetized dense matter

M. V. Glushikhina[*,‡] and G. S. Bisnovatyi-Kogan[*,†,§]

[*]*Space Research Institute of Russian Academy of Sciences (IKI RAN), Profsoyuznaya str., 84/32, Moscow, 117997, Russia*
[†]*National Research Nuclear University (MEPhI), Kashirskoe Shosse, 31, Moscow, 115409, Russia*
[‡]*E-mail: m.glushikhina@iki.rssi.ru*
[§]*E-mail: gkogan@iki.rssi.ru*
www.iki.cosmos.ru

A solution of the Boltzmann equation is obtained for a magnetized plasma with arbitrary degenerate electrons and nondegenerate nuclei. For the arbitrary and non-degenerate electrons kinetic coefficients are obtained by solving Boltzmann equation by Chapman-Enskog method of successive approximations. The expressions have a considerably more complicated dependence on magnetic field than analogous dependences derived in previous publications on this subject.

Keywords: Neutron stars; magnetic field; kinetics.

1. Introduction

The transfer of heat and charge in a magnetized nondegenerate plasma plays an important role in describing its behavior both under laboratory conditions and in the structure and evolution of stars. Kinetic coefficients such as thermal conductivity, diffusion, thermal diffusion and diffusional thermal effect determine heat fluxes and current densities. Knowing the distribution of heat and current, one can calculate the magneto-thermal evolution, the distribution of the magnetic field and temperature over the surface of stars, or describe the behavior of plasma obtained and accelerated in laboratory conditions.

Here is presented results of solving Boltzmann equation by two methods. For arbitrary degeneracy case we used the Chapman–Enskog method of successive approximations. Tensors of thermal diffusion, diffusion and diffusional thermal effect are found by using an expansion of three polynomials.[1,2] In Lorentz approximation Boltzmann equation has an exact solution. It is shown by using Lorentzian gas as an example that the method has good convergence to the exact solution.

2. General equations

We use the Boltzmann equation for arbitrary-degenerate electrons in a magnetic field, taking into account the interaction of electrons with ions and with each other. Boltzmann equation describing the change in the electron distribution function f

over time in the presence of electric and magnetic fields, written as[3,4]

$$\frac{\partial f}{\partial t} + c_i \frac{\partial f}{\partial r_i} - \frac{e}{m_e}\left(E_i + \frac{1}{c}\varepsilon_{ikl}c_k B_l\right)\frac{\partial f}{\partial c_i} + J = 0. \tag{1}$$

Here $(-e), m_e$ — charge (negative) and electron mass, E_i, B_i — electric field strength and magnetic induction, ε_{ikl} completely antisymmetric Levi - Civita tensor, c — the speed of light. The collision integral J for nondegenerate electrons and singly charged ions, according to,[5–8] is written in the form:

$$J = J_{ee} + J_{eN} = \int [ff_1 - f'f_1']g_{ee}b\,db\,d\varepsilon dc_{1i} + \int [ff_I - f'f_I']g_{eI}b\,db\,d\varepsilon dc_{Ii}. \tag{2}$$

Here the impact parameter b and ε are the geometric parameters of the collision of particles with relative speeds g_{ee}, g_{eI}.

Integration in the electronic part of the collision integral in (2) is performed over the phase space incident particles (dc_{1i}) and their physical space ($b\,db\,d\varepsilon$).[5] Post-collision velocity functions are marked with strokes.

The transfer equations for the electron concentration total momentum and energy of electrons in a two-component mixture of electrons and kernels can be obtained in the usual way from Boltzmann equations in quasineutral plasma[3–5,9]

Here and in what follows, we assume the average mass velocity to be equal to the average ion velocity $c_{0i} = \langle c_{Ii}\rangle$, we also consider electric current and heat flux only from electrons.

The Boltzmann equation can be solved by using the Chapman-Enskog method of successive approximations.[5] This method is used when the distribution functions are close to their values in the state of thermodynamic equilibrium, and deviations are considered in a linear approximation. In a first approximation, we look for the distribution function f in the form $f = f_0[1 + \chi(1 - f_0)]$

The χ function allows the solution to be represented as:[1]

$$\chi = -A_i \frac{\partial \ln T}{\partial r_i} - n_e D_i d_i \frac{G_{5/2}}{G_{3/2}}, \tag{3}$$

where diffusion vector d_i:

$$d_i = \frac{\rho_N}{\rho}\frac{\partial \ln P_e}{\partial r_i} - \frac{\rho_e}{P_e}\frac{1}{\rho}\frac{\partial P_N}{\partial r_i} + \frac{en_e}{P_e}\left(E_i + \frac{1}{c}\varepsilon_{ikl}c_{0k}B_l\right). \tag{4}$$

$G_n = \frac{1}{\Gamma(n)}\int_0^\infty \frac{x^{n-1}dx}{1+exp(x-x_0)}$, $x_0 = \frac{\mu}{kT}$, here G_n is Fermi integral and μ is chemical potential. The functions A_i and D_i determine the heat flux and diffusion.

The collision integral similar to J_{ee} from (2) for strongly degenerate neutrons in nuclear matter is given in,[8] see also.[11] In the presence of non-degenerate heavy nuclei and highly degenerate neutrons, the contribution of collisions between them to the heat transfer and diffusion coefficients is negligible compared to neutron-nucleus collisions. The same situation holds for highly degenerate electrons. Therefore, for strongly degenerate electrons, the Lorentz approximation, taking into account collisions between light and heavy particles, is asymptotically accurate. Therefore, we can neglect J_{ee} compared to J_{eN}, and we can equate $J = J_{eN}$ in (2). In this case Boltzmann equation is solved in Lorentz approximation as it was shown in[1,12] and the components of four tensors of kinetic coefficients are calculated.

General expressions for the heat flux q_i, and the average directional (diffusion) electron velocity $\langle v_i \rangle$ are given by

$$q_i = -\lambda_{ij}\frac{\partial T}{\partial x_j} - n_e \nu_{ij} d_j = q_i^{(A)} + q_i^{(D)}, \qquad (5)$$

$$\langle v_i \rangle = -\mu_{ij}\frac{\partial T}{\partial x_j} - n_e \eta_{ij} d_j = \langle v_i^{(A)} \rangle + \langle v_i^{(D)} \rangle, \qquad (6)$$

where λ_{ij} and ν_{ij} are the tensors of thermal conductivity and diffusional thermal effect, and μ_{ij} and η_{ij} — thermal diffusion and diffusional tensors, respectively.[11,13] The indices (A) and (D) determine the heat fluxes and diffusion velocities of electrons determined by the temperature gradient $\partial T/\partial x_j$, and the diffusion vector d_j, respectively.

The method for finding the coefficients of the thermal conductivity tensor λ_{ij} for arbitrary degeneracy is described in detail in the work,[1] where analytical expressions are found for them. For strongly degenerate electrons, the coefficients of thermal diffusion, diffusion and diffusion thermal effect in the Lorentz approximation are found in.[12]

3. Exact solution in Lorentz approximation

The Lorentz approximation for solving the kinetic equation is used when the mass of light particles much less than the mass of heavy particles, and electron-electron collisions can be neglected. So we can neglect J_{ee} in comparison with J_{eN}, and we can equate $J = J_{eN}$ in the (2). In this approximation, the linearized Boltzmann equation has exact solution. This approximation works well for transport in metal, where strong electron degeneracy makes it possible to neglect electron-electron collisions. The Lorentz approximation can be used to check the approximate polynomial solution, since it makes it possible to trace the convergence of the approximate solution to the exact one with increasing degree of the polynomials. Solution in Lorentz's approximation was considered in different approaches,[5,16,17] see also.[15] For thermal conductivity, the convergence of a polynomial solution to an exact one was considered in,[1] if we consider only the heat flux connected with the temperature gradient, at zero value of the diffusive vector d_i from (5), (6) than we obtain the expression for the heat flux for the case $B = 0$ from[15] as:

$$q_i^A = -\frac{640k}{\Lambda}\frac{m_e(kT)^4}{n_N Z^2 e^4 h^3}\left(G_5 - \frac{1}{2}\frac{G_{5/2}}{G_{3/2}}G_4\right)\frac{\partial T}{\partial r_i}. \tag{7}$$

In the limiting cases the coefficient in (7) is reduces to

$$\lambda_e^l = \frac{40\sqrt{2}}{\pi^{3/2}\Lambda}k\frac{n_e}{n_N}\frac{(kT)^{5/2}}{e^4 Z^2\sqrt{m_e}} = \frac{320}{3\pi}\frac{k^2 T n_e}{m_e}\tau_{nd} \quad (ND)$$

$$= \frac{5}{64\Lambda}\frac{k^2 T n_e^2 h^3}{m_e^2 n_N Z^2 e^4} = \frac{5\pi^2}{6}\frac{k^2 T n_e}{m_e}\tau_d \quad (D). \tag{8}$$

Average frequency of electron-ion collisions ν_{ei} in[14] in the limiting case of non-degenerate electrons is written as

$$\nu_{ei} = \frac{4}{3}\sqrt{\frac{2\pi}{m_e}}\frac{Z^2 e^4 n_N \Lambda}{(kT)^{3/2}} \quad (ND)$$

$$= \frac{32\pi^2}{3}m_e\frac{Z^2 e^4 \Lambda n_N}{h^3 n_e} \quad (D). \tag{9}$$

Here indices (ND) and (D) determine non-degenerate and degenerate cases respectively.

Using the same approach as in,[1] we can find an exact solution in explicit form for the Lorentz approximation for the case $B = 0$:

$$\langle v_i^A\rangle = -\frac{128k}{\Lambda}\frac{m_e(kT)^3}{n_N n_e Z^2 e^4 h^3}\left(G_4 - \frac{5}{8}\frac{G_{5/2}}{G_{3/2}}G_3\right)\frac{\partial T}{\partial r_i}, \tag{10}$$

$$\langle v_i^D\rangle = -n_e\frac{G_{5/2}}{G_{3/2}}\eta_{ij}d_j = \frac{32}{\Lambda}\frac{m_e(kT)^4}{n_e n_N Z^2 e^4 h^3}\frac{G_{5/2}}{G_{3/2}}G_3 d_i, \tag{11}$$

$$q_i^D = -n_e\frac{G_{5/2}}{G_{3/2}}\nu_{ij}d_j = \frac{128}{\Lambda}\frac{m_e(kT)^5}{n_N Z^2 e^4 h^3}\frac{G_{5/2}}{G_{3/2}}G_4\frac{\partial T}{\partial r_i}. \tag{12}$$

In limiting cases, the coefficient in (10) reduces to

$$\mu_e^l = \frac{12k}{\pi^{3/2}\Lambda n_N}\frac{(kT)^{3/2}}{e^4 Z^2\sqrt{2m_e}} = \frac{16k}{m_e\pi}\tau_{nd} \quad (ND), \tag{13}$$

and the coefficients in (11), (12) are reduced to

$$\eta_e^l = \frac{32}{3\pi}\frac{kT}{n_e m_e \pi}\tau_{nd}, \quad \nu_e^l = -\frac{128(kT)^2}{3\pi m_e}\tau_{nd}. \tag{14}$$

The exact formulas in the Lorentz model are used by[5] to estimate the accuracy of the polynomial approximation. The contribution of electron-electron collisions to the thermal diffusion coefficient for different Z can be estimated from the graph of normalized three-polynomial thermal diffusion coefficients in the direction perpendicular to the magnetic field, introducing the quantity $Q_\perp^{(3l)}$, $U_\perp^{(3l)}$ and $W_\perp^{(3l)}$ defined as:

$$Q_\perp^{(3l)} = \frac{\mu_{nd}^{(13)}}{\mu_{e,nd}^l}, \qquad U_\perp^{(3l)} = \frac{\eta_{nd}^{(13)}}{\eta_e^l}, \qquad W_\perp^{(3l)} = \frac{\nu_{nd}^{(13)}}{\nu_e^l}. \qquad (15)$$

Here $\mu_{e,nd}^l$ is taken from the top line in (13), $\nu_{e,nd}^l$ and $\eta_{e,nd}^l$ are taken from (14). Curves for different Z, including $Z = \infty$, related to Lorentz approximation are shown in Fig. (1a) for thermodiffusion, on Fig. (1b) for diffusional thermal effect, on Fig. (2a) for diffusion and on Fig. (2b) thermal conductivity plots[1] are presented for comparison.

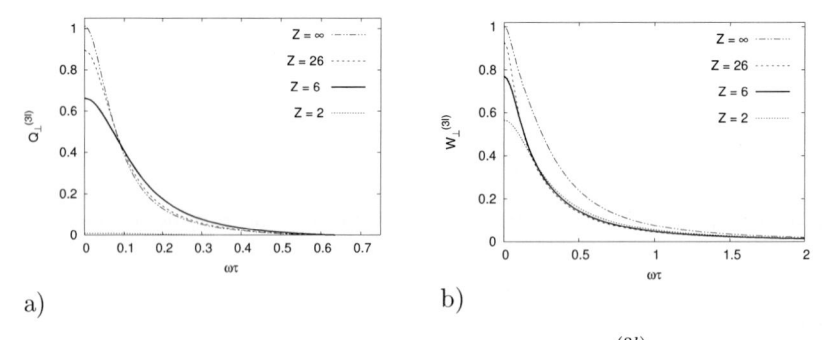

Fig. 1. On the (a) figure are presented the plots of the values of $Q_\perp^{(3l)}$ as functions of $\omega\tau$ in the three-polynomial approximation for nondegenerate plasma of helium ($Z = 2$), carbon ($Z = 6$), iron ($Z = 26$) in comparison with Lorentz plasma, formally corresponding to $Z = \infty$. The deviation from the Lorentzian plasma is due to the contribution of electron-electron collisions. On the right-side figure are plots of the values of the diffusional thermal effect $W_\perp^{(3l)}$ as a function of $\omega\tau$.

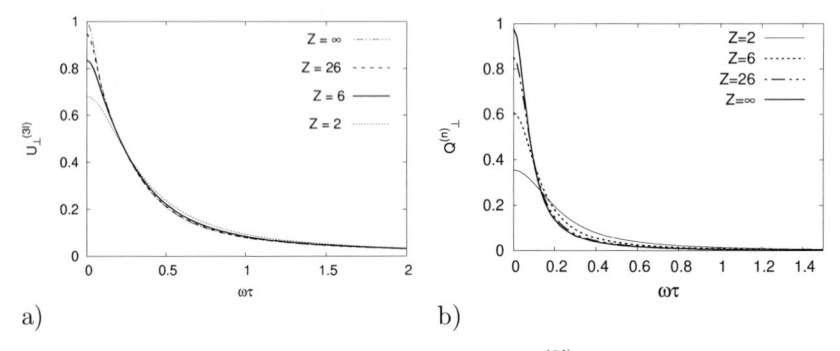

Fig. 2. On tthe (a) figure are plots of diffusion values of $U_\perp^{(3l)}$ as functions of $\omega\tau$ in the three-polynomial approximation for nondegenerate plasma of helium (Z=2), carbon (Z=6), iron (Z=26), for comparison with the Lorentz plasma, formally corresponding to $Z = \infty$. On the (b) figure are plots for heat conductivity coefficient from[1] as a function of $\omega\tau$, here: $Q_\perp^{(3l)} = \lambda_\perp^{(3)}/\lambda_\parallel^{lor}$.

4. Partially degenerate electrons

To examine the effect of degeneracy on the convergence of the polynomial approximation to the exact value, we compare the coefficients calculated by the method of successive approximations with the coefficients obtained as an exact solution in the Lorentz approximation. In a partially degenerate plasma, it is enough to simply calculate collision integral for electron-ion at $\mu = 0$ - chemical potential with the degeneracy level $DL = \epsilon_{fe}/kT = 1.011$. When compared with the exact solutions for heat conductivity and thermaldiffusion, obtained by the Lorentz method, the 3-polynomial solution for thermal conduction differs from the exact solution by about 13%, for thermal diffusion - by 7%. For non-degenerate electrons in the 3-polynomial approximation, the coefficient of thermal conductivity differs by 2.2%, and thermal diffusion by 1.3%.

For partial degeneracy, it is found that the 3-polynomial solution for diffusion differs from the exact one by 2.6%. For diffusion thermal effect: 3-polynomial by about 8%. For the nondegenerate case, the 3-polynomial approximation differs by 0.14% from the exact one for diffusion, and by 0.38% for the diffusion thermal effect. Detailed description of the calculations can be found in.[1,2] The accuracy of approximation by a series of orthogonal functions decreases with an increase in the degree of degeneracy.

5. Discussion

In this work, the tensors of the kinetic coefficients of diffusion, thermal diffusion, and diffusion thermal effect are found for nondegenerate electrons in a nonquantizing magnetic field. Tensors are obtained from the solution the kinetic Boltzmann equation by the classical Chapman–Enskog method using the expansion into Sonin polynomials and taking into account two and three terms of the expansion. Electron-ion and electron-electron collisions are taken into account. Tensors are written for an arbitrary local direction magnetic field and temperature gradient in the Cartesian coordinate system according to.[4]

Using the example of the Lorentz approximation, it was shown that the accuracy of the approximation by a series of orthogonal functions, similar to Sonin's polynomials, decreases with increasing degree of degeneracy.

For non-degenerate electrons, disregarding electron-electron collisions, the value of the thermal diffusion coefficient in the two-polynomial approximation underestimates the exact solution obtained in the Lorentz approximation at $B = 0$ by 26%, and in the three-polynomial approximation it overestimates by approximately 1%. For partially degenerate electrons, at $\mu = 0$, the two-polynomial solution underestimates the exact one by 28%, and the three-polynomial one underestimates the exact one by 7%. It should be noted that electron-electron collisions further decrease the coefficient values.

The diffusion coefficient value obtained from the two-polynomial approximation underestimates the exact solution by about 4%, and the three-polynomial solution underestimates the exact solution by 0.14% for nondegenerate electrons. In the case of partial degeneracy, the diffusion obtained from the two-polynomial solution underestimates the exact one by 0.4%, and the one obtained from the three-polynomial solution overestimates the exact one by 3%.

The diffusion thermal effect coefficient for nondegenerate electrons in the two-polynomial approximation underestimates the exact solution by 12%, and in the three-polynomial approximation overestimates the exact solution by 0.4%. With partial degeneracy of electrons, the two-polynomial solution underestimates the exact solution by 2.5%, and the three-polynomial solution overestimates the exact solution by 8%.

The Chapman–Enskog method can be used for a sufficiently dense gas (plasma), where the time between particle collisions is the smallest value among other characteristic times. In the presence of a magnetic field, in addition to the lifetime of the system and the characteristic time of changes, in the plasma parameters rotation time in the Larmor circle is added $\tau_L = 2\pi/\omega$. This time must be much less than τ, which leads to a condition under which the Chapman–Enskog method can be used, in the form $\omega\tau \ll 2\pi$. Therefore, this work can be successfully applied for $\omega\tau \lesssim 1$, and for large $\omega\tau$ only qualitative estimates can be obtained.

The coefficients can be used for calculation of heat fluxes and electric current in white dwarfs, on the surface of magnetized neutron star, as well as in the magnetized matter accreting to the magnetized neutron star or for describing plasma obtained in laboratory conditions.

References

1. G. S. Bisnovatyi-Kogan, M. V. Glushikhina, Plasma Physics Reports, **44**, 405 (2018).
2. M. V. Glushikhina, Plasma Physics Reports, **46**, 152 (2020).
3. G. S. Bisnovatyi-Kogan, Transport properties of partially ionized two-temperature plasma and isotropic corrections to Maxwellian distribution function (in Russian), Diploma Thesis, Moscow Institute of Physics and Technology (Soviet Union, 1964).
4. G. S. Bisnovatyi-Kogan, J. Appl. Mech. Tech. Phys., No. 3, 43 (1964).
5. *Chapmen S., Cowling T.G.* // Mathematical Theory of Nonuniform Gases, Cambrige, (1952).
6. E. Uehling, G. Uhlenbeck., Phys. Rev., **43**, 552 (1933).
7. E. Uehling, Phys. Rev., **46**, 917 (1934).
8. S. Z. Tomonaga, Z. Phys. **110**, 573 (1938).
9. W. Marshall, The kinetic theory of an ionized gas, At. Energy Res Estable, N T/R, 2419 (1960).
10. *Landau L. D., Lifshitz E. M.* // Statistical Physics. **5**, 3rd ed., Butterworth-Heinemann, 1980.
11. G. S. Bisnovatyi-Kogan, M. M. Romanova, JETP, **56**, 243 (1983).
12. G. S. Bisnovatyi-Kogan, M. V. Glushikhina, Plasma Physics Reports, **44**, 971 (2018).
13. *Kalikhman L. E.* // Elements of magnetohydrodynamics, Atomizdat, Moscow, 1964.

14. *Ginzburg V. A., Rukhadze A. A.* // Waves in Magnetoactive Plasma, M.: Nauka, 1970.
15. *Bisnovatyi-Kogan G.S* // Stellar Physics I: Fundamental Concepts and Stellar Equilibrium. Springer, 2001.
16. A. A. Wyller, Astrophisica Norvegica. **9**, 79 (1971).
17. A. A. Wyller, Astrophys. J., **184**, 517 (1973).

Modeling of magnetic fields of accretion discs, using no-z- and RZ-approximations

M. V. Pashentseva[1], E. A. Mikhailov[1,2]

[1] *Faculty of Physics, Lomonosov Moscow State University, Moscow, Russia*
[2] *P.N.Lebedev Physical Institute, Russia*

The evolution of the accretion discs surrounding different compact objects (such as white dwarfs, neutron stars and black holes) is closely connected with the magnetic fields and their features. It is highly likely that the magnetic field generation is connected with the dynamo action. As for the dynamo, we have a lot of specific models which have been constructed for different astrophysical objects. For accretion discs we can take the approaches that were used for galactic discs which have nearly the same shape. There are two main models. The first one is connected with no-z approximation which is based on the fact that the discs is quite thin. RZ-model describes the discs with large half-thickness and can be used for the objects where we should study the vertical structure of the magnetic field. Here we show the results obtained for the accretion discs which used both of these approaches and compare the results.

Keywords: Magnetic fields, accretion discs, dynamo theory, no-z model, RZ-model.

1. Introduction

The accretion discs surrounding different compact objects (such as black holes, neutron stars and white dwarfs), play an important role in different branches of astrophysics. Their structure and features is closely connected with the magnetic fields, which should have a strong influence on the motions in the disc.[1] Nowadays there are different approaches that describe the origin of magnetism of such objects. First of all, we should mention the transition of the field which is connected with the accreting matter.[2] Also there are some models which describe the field as a result of interaction between the central object and the accretion disc. However, observational data and theoretical models show that the field is highly likely to be generated by the dynamo mechanism.[3-5]

The dynamo mechanism is widely used to study the magnetic field evolution in different objects such as the Sun, stars, galaxies etc. The equations of the dynamo are quite difficult to be solved in explicit form. So there are different specific two-dimensional models which take into account geometrical features of the celestial body and allow us to simplify the problem. As for the galaxies, there is so-called no-z approximation,[6] which is based on the fact that the galactic disc is quite thin. So some of the partial derivatives can be changed by the algebraic expressions, and the z-component of the field can be taken from the solenoidality condition. This approach can be used to study magnetism of the accretion discs,[7,8] because their shape is quite close to the one of the galaxies. As for thick galactic discs, we can take the RZ-model, which uses another basic assumptions.[9] In this paper we study the magnetic field using this model, too. After that we compare the given results.

2. Dynamo

The dynamo is connected with transition of the energy of turbulent motions to the energy of the magnetic field.[10] If we are speaking about the large-scale magnetic field, it is based on two main effects. First of all, it is the alpha-effect which is connected with the helicity of the turbulent motions. It is connected with the rotation of the magnetic field. The second process is associated with the differential rotation which is caused by changing angular velocity (most of celestial bodies rotate with a non-solid law). They compete with the dissipative effects which destroy the large-scale structures of the field. So, dynamo is a threshold process: the field can grow only if the alpha-effect and differential rotation are more intensive than the dissipation. Otherwise the field will decay and the dynamo won't be able to generate significant fields.

The evolution of large-scale component of the field is described by the Steenbeck – Krause – Rädler equation, which has been obtained by averaging the magnetohydrodynamics equations by scales comparable with size the turbulent cells:[11]

$$\frac{\partial \vec{B}}{\partial t} = \nabla \left(\alpha \vec{B} \right) + \nabla \left[\vec{V}, \vec{B} \right] + \eta \Delta \vec{B},$$

This equation is rather difficult to be solved. So usually the researchers use specific two-dimensional models for every type of the objects: such as Parker dynamo for stars of torus dynamo for outer rings of galaxies.

2.1. *No-z approximation for accretion discs*

While studying the magnetic fields in the accretion discs, it is quite convenient to use the models which have been developed for the objects that have nearly the same geometrical shape (of course, taking into account sufficiently different lengthscales). As for the galactic discs, so-called no-z approximation is widely used. It studies the evolution of two components of the field (which lie in the equatorial plane), which makes the problem much easier. The z-component of the field is taken using the solenoidality condition. Also it is quite convenient to assume that the field is axisymmetric (as for the accretion discs it is even more reasonable than for the galactic ones).

If we study the accretion disc, we should take the keplerian law for the rotation velocity Ω[1]:

$$\Omega = \frac{(GM)^{\frac{1}{2}}}{r^{\frac{3}{2}}},$$

where M is the mass of the black hole, neutron star or white dwarf; r is the distance from the central object.

The equations should be solved for values $r_{in} < r < R$, where r_{in} is the inner radius and R is the outer one.

It is quite convenient to use the dimensionless units: all parameters are measured in their typical values. As for the magnetic field, some dimensionless parameters characterizing the dynamo regime are introduced.

R_α shows the intensity of the alpha-effect:

$$R_\alpha = \frac{\Omega(R)l^2}{\eta},$$

where Ω is the angular velocity of the disc and l is the typical size of the turbulent cell.

R_ω is connected with the differential rotation:

$$R_\omega = \frac{\Omega(R)h^2}{\eta},$$

λ corresponds to the ration between the lengthscales of the disc (half-thickness h and radius R):

$$\lambda = \frac{h}{R} = 0.037 r^{\frac{1}{8}} \left(1 - \sqrt{\frac{r_{in}}{r}}\right)^{\frac{3}{20}}.$$

Taking these assumptions into account, the equations for the magnetic field in dimensionless form look like this:

$$\frac{\partial B_r}{\partial t} = -R_\alpha B_\varphi \left(1 - \frac{B^2}{B^{*2}}\right) - \frac{\pi^2 B_r}{4} + \lambda^2 \left(\frac{\partial}{\partial r}\left(\frac{1}{r}\frac{\partial}{\partial r}(rB_r)\right)\right)$$
$$- \frac{V_0}{r\left(1 - \sqrt{\frac{r_{in}}{r}}\right)}\left(\frac{\partial B_r}{\partial r}\right), \quad (1)$$

$$\frac{\partial B_\varphi}{\partial t} = -\frac{3R_\omega}{2r^{\frac{3}{2}}} B_r - \frac{\pi^2 B_\varphi}{4} + \lambda^2 \left(\frac{\partial}{\partial r}\left(\frac{1}{r}\frac{\partial}{\partial r}(rB_\varphi)\right)\right) - \frac{V_0}{r\left(1 - \sqrt{\frac{r_{in}}{r}}\right)}\left(\frac{\partial B_\varphi}{\partial r}\right). \quad (2)$$

The equipartition field is assumed to be the following:[7]

$$B^* = 420 r^{\frac{-21}{16}} \left(1 - \sqrt{\frac{r_{in}}{r}}\right)^{\frac{17}{40}}.$$

It is included in the equations using the non-linearity coefficient $(1 - \frac{B^2}{B^{*2}})$.

As for the boundary conditions, we use the following ones:

$$\frac{\partial B_r}{\partial r}(R) = 0,$$

$$\frac{\partial B_\varphi}{\partial r}(R) = 0.$$

$$B_r(r_{in}) = 0,$$
$$B_\varphi(r_{in}) = 0.$$

Also we can take the zero derivative conditions on the inner boundary:[8]

$$\frac{\partial B_r}{\partial r}(r_{in}) = 0,$$
$$\frac{\partial B_\varphi}{\partial r}(r_{in}) = 0.$$

However, it has been shown that the results for the magnetic field will be nearly the same as for the model with zero field boundary condition.

The magnetic field for different inner radius is shown on figure 1. It can be seen that larger inner radius moves the field from the center. Also the time dependence is shown on figure 2.

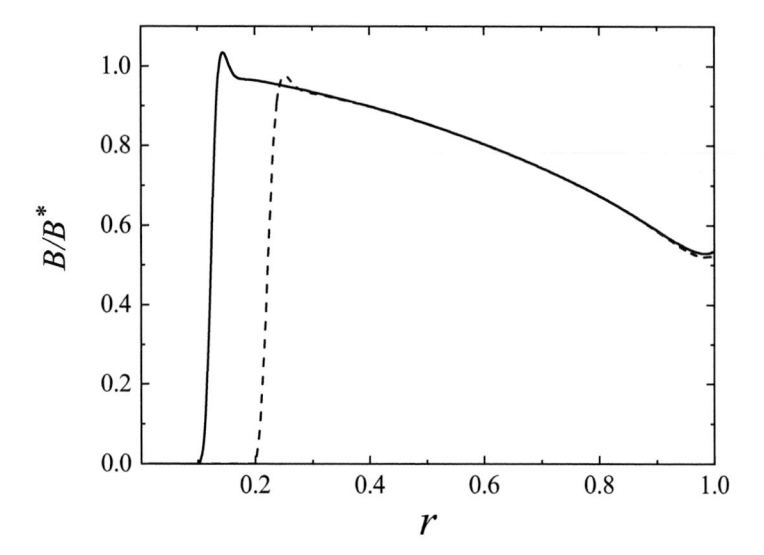

Fig. 1. The dependence of the magnetic field on the distance to the center of the accretion disk for different inner radius with zero boundary condition ($D_{eff} = 15$). Solid line shows the case, when $r_{in} = 0.1$ and the dotted line – the case $r_{in} = 0.2$.

3. RZ-model

No-z approximation has a lot of advantages for a wide spectra of objects (from galaxies to accretion discs). Unfortunately, it cannot be use for the objects where the vertical structure is more complicated than a standard law which is taken into

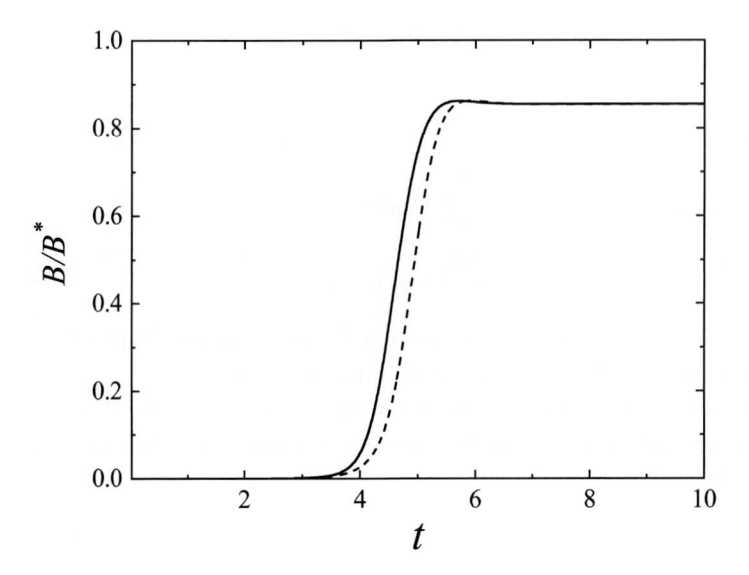

Fig. 2. Time dependence of the magnetic field for different r_{in} with zero boundary condition. Solid line shows the case, when $r_{in} = 0.1$ and the dotted line – the case $r_{in} = 0.2$.

account there. So, for thick discs we should take the RZ-approximation which describes the field using another approaches. Firstly these ideas have been used for the torus dynamo in outer rings of galaxies[12] and now there are results which can describe the whole disc.[9]

The magnetic field $\vec{B}$ can be presented as:

$$\vec{B} = B\vec{e_\varphi} + \nabla\left(A\vec{e_\varphi}\right),$$

where B is the azimuthal magnetic field and A is the azimuthal part of the vector potential of the magnetic field.

If we use this model, the Steenbeck – Krause – Rädler equation will take the following approximate form:

$$\frac{\partial A}{\partial t} = R_\alpha z B \left(1 - B^2\right) + \lambda^2 \Delta A - V\frac{\partial A}{\partial r},$$

$$\frac{\partial B}{\partial t} = R_\omega r \left(-\frac{3}{2}r^{\frac{5}{2}}\frac{\partial A}{\partial z}\right) + \lambda^2 \Delta B - V\frac{\partial B}{\partial r}.$$

All main dimensionless parameters here are the same as for the previous model. The equations are solved for $-h < z < h$, $r_{in} < r < R$, and the boundary conditions are:

$$A|_{t=0} = 0$$

$$B|_{t=0} = B_0 sin(\pi r) cos\left(\frac{\pi z}{h}\right)$$

$$\frac{\partial A(r,-h)}{\partial z} = 0.$$

The comparative results are shown on Fig 3. Here we can see both the field modeled using no-z approximation and the RZ-model. We can see that the field for the RZ-model reaches a bit larger values and the typical dependence is different, too.

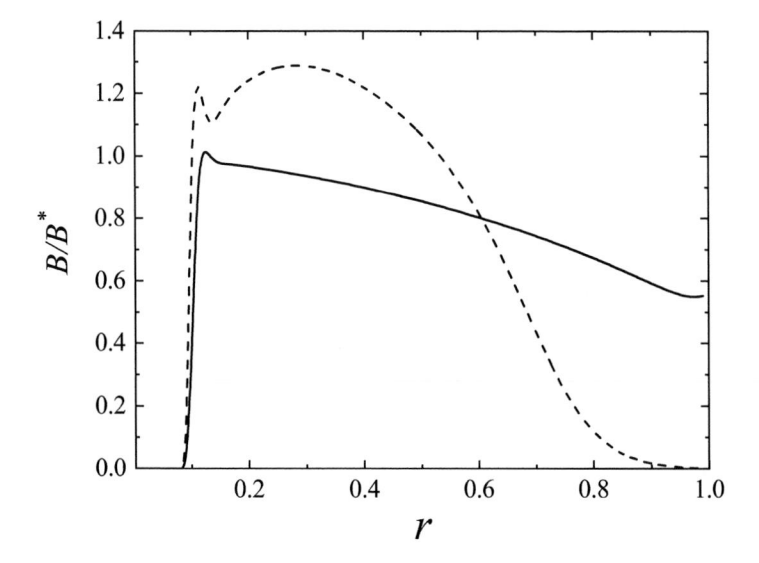

Fig. 3. Comparison of two models. Dashed line shows RZ-model and solid line shows no-z model.

Figure 4 shows the 2D-structure of the field. Here we can see the maximum of the magnetic field quite close to the inner boundary, and near the outer boundary the field decreases.

Also we have studied the connection between the dynamo number $D = R_\alpha R_\omega$ and the r-dependence of the field. It can be seen that for lower D the field is smaller, too.

4. Conclusion

In this work we have studied evolution of the magnetic field in accretion discs. We have used two different models taking into account different approaches to the dynamo. First of all, we studied the evolution of the magnetic field using the no-z approximation which has been developed for thin discs.[6] After that, we passed to

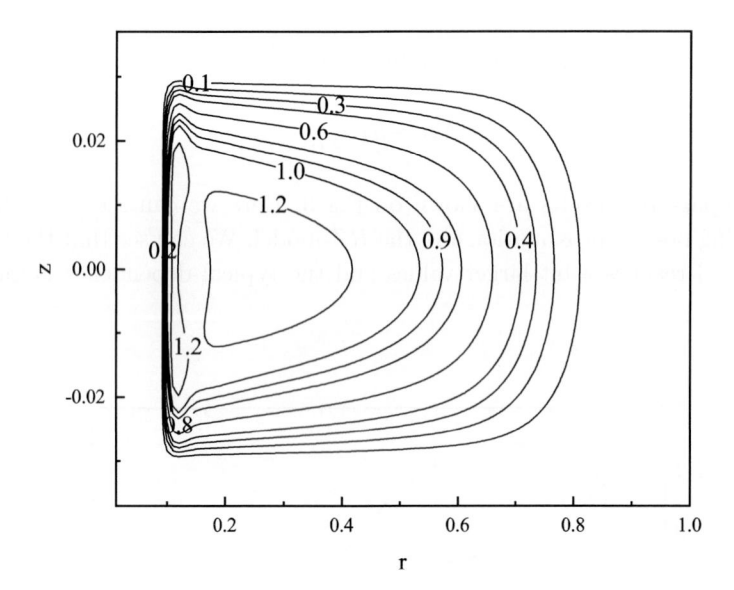

Fig. 4. The dependence of the magnetic field on r and z coordinates for RZ-model.

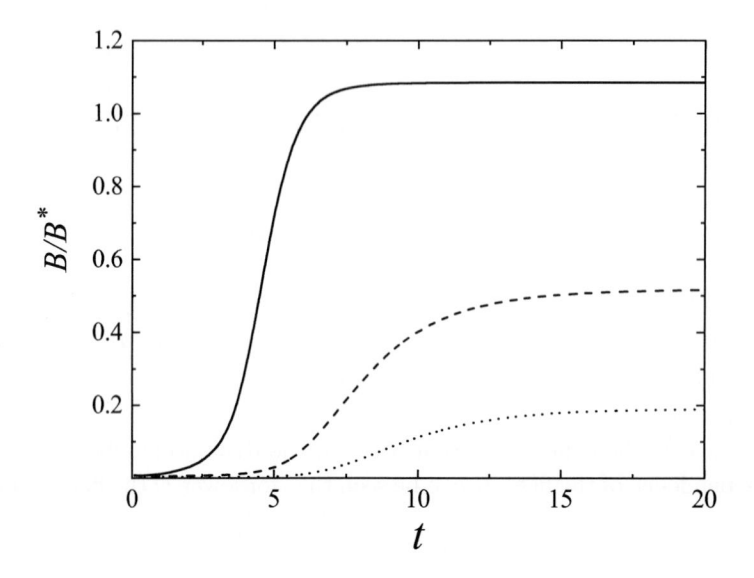

Fig. 5. Time dependence of the magnetic field for RZ-model for different D_{eff}. Solid line shows the case, when $D_{eff} = 15$, dashed line shows the case, when $D_{eff} = 9$, dotted line shows the case, when $D_{eff} = 7$.

the RZ-model, which takes into account z-dependence of the magnetic field, but it is more difficult to be solved from the numerical point of view. We can conclude that if we study thick discs, it is better to take the RZ-model, and for thin one we can take no-z approximation.

Work of M.P. was supported by a grant from the Fund for the Development of Theoretical Physics and Mathematics "BASIS", project 21-1-1-4-4.

References

1. N. I. Shakura, R. A. Sunyaev, Astron. Astrophys, 24, 337 (1973).
2. Okuzumi S., Takeuchi T., Muto T., ApJ, 785, 127 (2014).
3. Brandenburg A., Donner K.J. MNRAS, 288, L29 (1997).
4. von Rekowski B., Brandenburg A., Astronomy & Astrophysics, 420, 1 (2004).
5. Rüdiger R., Elstner D., Stepinsky T. F., Astron. Astrophys., 298, 934 (1995).
6. Moss D., Monthly Notices of the Royal Astronomical Society, 275, 1, 191 (1995).
7. Moss D., Sokoloff D., Suleimanov V., Astronomy & Astrophysics, 588, A18 (2016).
8. D. V. Boneva, E. A. Mikhailov, M. V. Pashentseva, D. D. Sokoloff, Astronomy and Astrophysics., 652, A38 (2021).
9. Mikhailov E. A., Pushkarev V. V., Research in Astronomy and Astrophysics, 21, 56 (2021).
10. Sokoloff D., Physics-Uspekhi 58, 601 (2015).
11. Krause F., Rädler K.-H., Berlin (1980).
12. Mikhailov E. A., Astrophysics., 61, 2, 147 (2018).

Limiting effects in tori clusters

D. Pugliese and Z. Stulchik

Research Centre for Theoretical Physics and Astrophysics
Institute of Physics, Silesian University in Opava,
Bezručovo náměstí 13, CZ-74601 Opava, Czech Republic
E-mail:d.pugliese.physics@gmail.com

We consider agglomerates of misaligned tori orbiting a supermassive black hole. The aggregate of tilted tori is modeled as a single orbiting configuration by introducing a leading function governing the distribution of toroids (and maximum pressure points inside the disks) around the black hole attractor. The orbiting clusters are composed by geometrically thick, pressure supported, perfect fluid tori. This analysis places constraints on the existence and properties of tilted tori and more general aggregates of orbiting disks. We study the constraints on the tori collision emergence and the instability of the agglomerates of tori with general relative inclination angles, the possible effects of the tori geometrical thickness and on the oscillatory phenomena. Some notes are discussed on the orbiting ringed structure in dependence of the dimensionless parameter ξ representing the (total) BH rotational energy extracted versus the mass of the BH, associating ξ to the characteristics of the accretion processes.

Keywords: Accretion disks; Accretion– jets; Black hole physics; Hydrodynamics

1. Introduction

We study agglomerates of tori orbiting one central Kerr super-massive black hole (SMBH), in two macro-configuration models: (i) as an equatorial-**R**inged **A**ccretion **D**isk (eRAD), where the toroids equatorial and symmetry planes coincide with the central Kerr BH equatorial plane;[1–9] (ii) as **R**inged **A**ccretion **D**isk (RAD), where the agglomerate is composed by misaligned (tilted) tori.[10–12]

The eRAD tori rotation orientation is a well defined quantity, and a couple of eRAD toroids can be both corotating or counter-rotating with respect to the central spinning BH, otherwise tori can have a relative alternate rotation orientation (with an inner corotating toroid and an outer counter-rotating toroid with respect to the central attractor or *viceversa*). Tori with different relative rotation orientation constitute an interesting case from the viewpoint of the constrains posed by the eRAD or RAD model, for example in the case of double tori accretion phase or also tori collision which depends generally on the spin-mass ratio of the central BH. It is clear that an orbiting tori aggregate model could be constructed considering a different disk model for each toroidal component. However in this analysis we mostly consider a Polish doughnut (PD) model. This is a well known geometrically thick disk model, widely used in literature in a variety of different applications.[1,13] Polish doughnut shows a remarkably good fitting of main morphological characteristics of thick disks also in comparison with more refined dynamical GRHD or

GRMHD models.[13] RAD is a "constraining-models", providing initial configurations for dynamical (GRMHD) situations. In general aggregates of toroidal structures orbiting one central BH attractor can result from different accreting phases of the SMBHs growing, where the infalling materials, having diverse angular momentum, may trace back the BH story.[2,5,14–23]

This paper is structured in two parts: In the first part, Sec. (2), we discuss the eRAD model, focusing on the model parameters and distribution of pressure and density critical points. We introduce the concept of leading function for the agglomeration describing the tori distribution around the central attractor.

The second part, Sec. (3), focuses on aggregates of misaligned tori (RAD), discussing explicit solutions of its inner structure and an adapted parametrization for the toroidal components.

2. The Equatorial Ringed Accretion Disks

2.1. *Leading function and geodesic structure*

A key step in the modelization of the orbiting agglomerate is to individuate an adapted "leading function", representing the tori location around the central attractor. For large part of this analysis, we can identify the leading function with the definition of fluid specific angular momentum ℓ. Different choices are the agglomerate leading functions also possibles as we see some examples in Sec. (2.4) and Sec. (3.1). In the Kerr spacetime there is

$$\ell \equiv \frac{L}{E} = -\frac{U_\phi}{U_t} = -\frac{g_{\phi\phi}U^\phi + g_{\phi t}U^t}{g_{tt}U^t + g_{\phi t}U^\phi} = -\frac{g_{t\phi} + g_{\phi\phi}\Omega}{g_{tt} + g_{t\phi}\Omega}, \tag{1}$$

$$\Omega \equiv \frac{U^\phi}{U^t} = -\frac{Eg_{\phi t} + g_{tt}L}{Eg_{\phi\phi} + g_{\phi t}L} = -\frac{g_{t\phi} + g_{tt}\ell}{g_{\phi\phi} + g_{t\phi}\ell},$$

where $g_{\alpha\beta}$ are metric components in the Boyer-Lindquist coordinates, U^α is the fluid four velocity, Ω is the fluid relativistic angular velocity and (E, L) are constants of motions–see for example.[1,2] In general, we may interpret E, for timelike geodesics, as representing the total energy of the test particle coming from radial infinity, as measured by a static observer at infinity, and L as the axial component of the angular momentum of the particle. (For the PD tori orbiting in a Kerr spacetime the set of results known as Von Zeipel theorem holds, therefore the fluid is barotropic and the surfaces of constant pressure coincide with the surfaces of constant density. In these spacetimes, the family of von Zeipel's surfaces does not depend on the particular rotation law of the fluid, $\Omega = \Omega(\ell)$, but on the background spacetime only.[24–28])

The leading function provides the distribution of the possible maximum points of pressure and density in the fluids surrounding the BH, which are identified as the RAD-"rings seeds", coincident with torus centers r_{center}, and eventually the minimum points of pressure of the fluids orbiting around the central attractor. The minimum points of pressure are associated to the cusps $r_\times$ of the PD torus Roche lobe and are regulated by the geodesic structure of the background, composed by the marginally stable circular orbit (r_{mso}), the marginally bounded circular orbit (r_{mbo}) and the marginally circular orbit (r_γ) which is also a photon orbit. (The cusp location in the PD model, located in the range $]r_{mbo},r_{mso}[$, could be related to the inner edge of an accreting torus.) In the RAD and eRAD models, the location of the maximum points of the pressure around the attractor are interpreted as "rings seeds", and are regulated by a set of radii, associated to the geodesics structure, located in the "stability region" at $r > r_{mso}$ and defined by

$$r^\pm_{(\mathrm{mbo})}: \ell^\pm(r^\pm_{\mathrm{mbo}}) = \ell^\pm(r^\pm_{(\mathrm{mbo})}) \equiv \ell^\pm_{\mathrm{mbo}}, \quad \text{with} \quad r^\pm_{(\gamma)}: \ell^\pm(r^\pm_\gamma) = \ell^\pm(r^\pm_{(\gamma)}) \equiv \ell^\pm_\gamma,$$

where $r^\pm_\gamma < r^\pm_{\mathrm{mbo}} < r^\pm_{\mathrm{mso}} < r^\pm_{(\mathrm{mbo})} < r^\pm_{(\gamma)}$

and $r^\pm_\mathcal{M}: \partial_r \partial_r \ell^\pm = 0$, with $r^\pm_{(\mathcal{M})}: \ell^\pm(r^\pm_{(\mathcal{M})}) = \ell^\pm(r^\pm_\mathcal{M}) \equiv \ell^\pm_\mathcal{M}.$ (2)

In here and in the following with $\mathcal{Q}^\pm$ we indicate quantities $\mathcal{Q}$ associated to counter-rotating ($\ell a < 0$) or corotating ($\ell a > 0$) structures respectively, with respect to the central BH spin a/M. In the following, for any quantity $\mathbf{Q}$ and radius $r_\bullet$ we adopt the notation $\mathbf{Q}_\bullet \equiv \mathbf{Q}(r_\bullet)$. Where more conveniently, we use dimensionless quantities where $r \to r/M$ and $a \to a/M$.

The leading function, solution of $\partial_r^2 \ell^\pm(r,\theta;a) = 0$ (where (r,θ,ϕ,t) are the Boyer-Lindquist coordinates of the Kerr metric), provides the point of maximum density of the rings seeds distribution around the BH.

The corotating and counter-rotating tori cusps orbital regions are shown in the Figs 1 for different BH attractors. In the Figs 1 the orbital regions for the ring seeds locations (tori centers) are also shown. The union of these regions provides the maximum rage of the location of the rings seeds and the maximum extension of the disks inner part (the region $[r_{inner}, r_{center}]$ where $r_\times \leq r_{inner}$ is the torus cusp and r_{inner} is the inner edge of the quiescent (i.e. not cusped torus)). The orbital strips in Figs 1 relative to the corotating and counter-rotating fluids, cross in different points depending on the BH spin–mass ratio and particularly for slower spinning attractors.

2.2. Ideal GRMHD and GRHD

Polish doughnuts have been realized in different ideal GRMHD and GRHD setups, where for the ideal GRMHD (infinitely conductive plasma) case there is

$$U_\alpha \nabla^\alpha \rho + (p+\rho)\nabla^\alpha U_\alpha = 0,$$
$$(p+\rho)U^\alpha \nabla_\alpha U^\gamma - \epsilon h^{\beta\gamma}\nabla_\beta p - \epsilon(\nabla^\alpha F_{\alpha\delta})F_\beta^\delta h^{\beta\gamma} = 0,$$
$$U^\alpha \nabla_\alpha s = 0.$$

(F_α^β is the Faraday tensor and ϵ is a quantity related to the metric signature[29,30]). The electric field does not affect the continuity equation or the equation for the

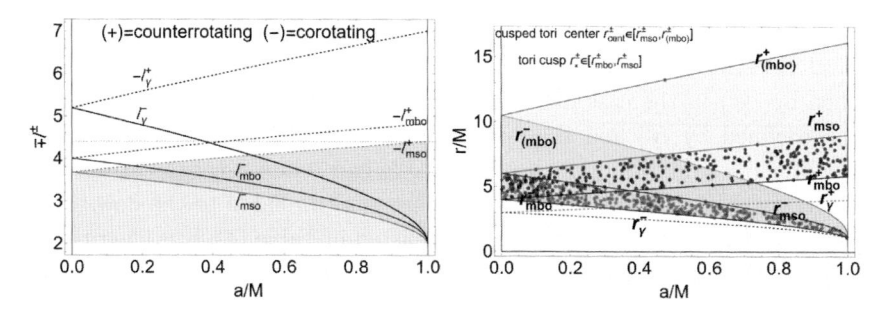

Fig. 1. Left: Fluid specific angular momentum $\ell^{\pm}$ of the eRAD tori, for corotating $(-)$, and counterrotating $(+)$, fluids, versus SMBH dimensionless spin a/M. Tori can form for $\mp\ell^{\pm} > \mp\ell^{\pm}_{mso}$ respectively. There is $\ell_{\bullet} \equiv \ell(r_{\bullet})$ for $r_{\bullet} = \{r_{mso}, r_{mbo}, r_{\gamma}\}$, r_{mso} is the marginally stable circular orbit, r_{mbo} is the marginally bounded orbit and r_{γ} the last circular (photon) orbit. Right: radii r_{mbo} and r_{mso} and the pair $r_{(mbo)}$ and $r_{(mso)}$ as functions of the dimensionless spin of the BH–see Eqs (2).

entropy. The entropy per particles s is conserved along the flow U^{α}, defined for *each* torus of the aggregate, and h^{β}_{α} is the metric on the 3-sheet orthogonal to flow direction U^{α}, defining the projector tensor (there is $\nabla_{\alpha}g_{\beta\gamma} = 0$). The inner ringed structure is defined by the boundary conditions determining the tori (edges)—see for more details.[9,29,31]

To simplify our discussion we consider in this analysis the GRHD scenario (see for example[1,13]). With the barotropic equation of state, $p = p(\rho)$, the set of GRHD equations for the PD model, reduces to the only constrain equation for the pressure (Euler equation):

$$\frac{\nabla_{\mu}p}{p+\rho} = -\nabla_{\mu}W + \frac{\Omega\nabla_{\mu}\ell}{1-\Omega\ell};$$

where $W = W(a;\ell;r,\theta)$ is an effective potential, function of (r,θ) for the Kerr metric (in the Boyer-Lindquist coordinates). The equation for the pressure critical points can be further simplified by considering ℓ as a model parameter, constant in each torus of the aggregate. In this setup the extreme points of pressure are the extremes of the potential W, and the leading function is given by the radial derivative of the effective potential. More precisely the tori parameters are the couple (ℓ, K) with $\ell = constant$ and $V_{eff} = K = constant$ for each torus, where $W = \ln V_{eff}$.

In this context, the eRAD leading function is $\ell(r) : \partial_r V_{eff} = 0$. The tori (Boyer) surfaces are equipressure surfaces (also surfaces of constant (p, ρ, ℓ, Ω)) and the fluids fill every equipressure surfaces.[32]

2.2.1. *The energy function and tori energetics*

The "energy function" $K(r) = V_{eff}(\ell(r))$ regulates, with the leading function $\ell(r)$, the RAD aggregate, where $K : K(r) =$ constant for each torus. More precisely, function $K(r,\theta;a) \equiv V_{eff}(\ell,r,\theta;a)|_{\ell(r,\theta;a)}$ determines the flow (and the torus) geometrical thickness, the tori extension on the equatorial plane, and it is uniquely identified by $\ell(r)$ in the case of cusped tori. The relation between the geometrical maxima (defined by K) and the density maxima (fixed by ℓ) is provided by the extreme of the leading function $\ell(r,\theta;a)$.[12] We can relate $K(r)$ to certain features of the tori energetics, evaluating some characteristics related to the flow thickness, as mass accretion rate or cusp luminosity as listed in Table (1). It is clear that these quantities depends on the details of the different tori models, but this analysis can provide an estimation of these quantities with respect to the flow co-rotation or counter-rotation, the dimensionless BH rotational energy (or dimensionless spin) and the tori location in the aggregate.[33]

Table 1. There is $\varpi = n+1$, with $\gamma = 1/n+1$ being the polytropic index, κ is the polytropic constant. Ω is the relativistic angular velocity. $W = \ln V_{eff}$ is the value of the equipotential surface, which is taken with respect to the asymptotic value, $W_\times = \ln K_\times$ is W at the cusp $r_\times$, while $W_s \geq W_\times$ and r_s is related to the accreiting flow thickness. $\mathcal{L}$ representing the total luminosity, $\dot{M}$ the total accretion rate where, for a stationary flow, $\dot{M} = \dot{M}_\times$, $\eta \equiv \mathcal{L}/\dot{M}c^2$ the efficiency, $\mathcal{D}(n,\kappa), \mathcal{C}(n,\kappa), \mathcal{A}(n,\kappa), \mathcal{B}(n,\kappa)$ are functions of the polytropic index and the polytropic constant. $\mathcal{L}_\times/\mathcal{L}$ is the fraction of energy produced inside the flow and not radiated through the surface but swallowed by central BH–see Figs 2

Quantities $\mathcal{O}(r_\times,r_s,n) \equiv q(n,\kappa)(W_s - W_\times)^{d(n)}$	Quantities $\mathcal{P} \equiv \frac{\mathcal{O}(r_\times,r_s,n)r_\times}{\Omega(r_\times)}$
$\mathcal{R}$-quantities: $\mathcal{R}_\times \equiv (W(r_s) - W_\times)^\varpi$	$\mathcal{N}$-quantities: $\mathcal{N}_\times \equiv \frac{r_\times(W(r_s)-W_\times)^\varpi}{\Omega(r_\times)}$
Enthalpy-flux: $\mathcal{D}(n,\kappa)(W_s - W_\times)^{n+3/2}$	**torus-accretion-rate:** $\dot{m} = \frac{\dot{M}}{\dot{M}_{Edd}}$
Mass-Flux: $\mathcal{C}(n,\kappa)(W_s - W_\times)^{n+1/2}$	**Mass-accretion-rates:** $\dot{M}_\times = \mathcal{A}(n,\kappa)r_\times \frac{(W_s-W_\times)^{n+1}}{\Omega(r_\times)}$
$\frac{\mathcal{L}_\times}{\mathcal{L}} = \frac{\mathcal{B}(n,\kappa)}{\mathcal{A}(n,\kappa)} \frac{W_s - W_\times}{\eta c^2}$	**Cusp-luminosity:** $\mathcal{L}_\times = \mathcal{B}(n,\kappa)r_\times \frac{(W_s-W_\times)^{n+2}}{\Omega(r_\times)}$

Evaluation of these quantities defined in Table (1) are in Figs 2 as functions of the BH dimensionless rotational energy for different models, fixed according to selected values of the fluid specific angular momentum ℓ (fixing the cusp location and the center of maximum density) and the $K_s \in]K_\times, 1[$, fixing the flow thickness at the cusp.[34]

2.3. The BH rotational energy

The BH rotational energy is related to the BH geometrical features through its irreducible mass M_{irr}. From the definition of irreducible mass $M_{irr}^2 = \left(M^2 + \sqrt{M^4 - J^2}\right)/2$, where M is the BH total (ADM) mass and the $J = aM$,

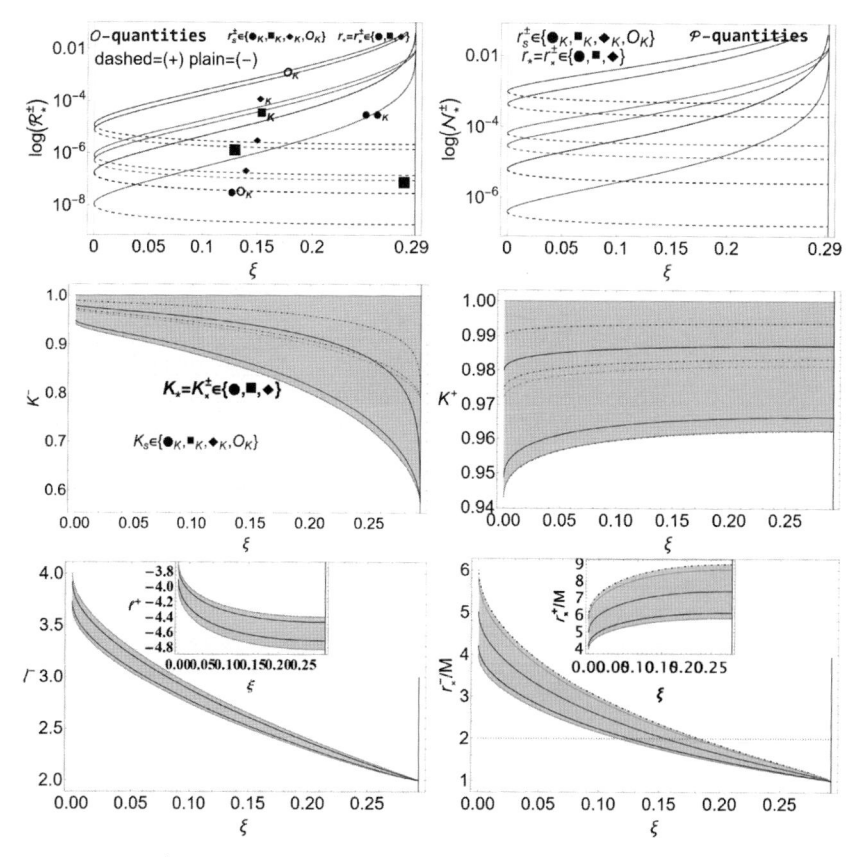

Fig. 2. Plots of $\mathcal{N}_\times^\pm \equiv r_\times (W^\pm(r_s) - W_\times^\pm)^\kappa (\Omega(r_\times^\pm))^{-1}$ for $\mathcal{P}$-quantities analysis and $\mathcal{R}_\times^\pm \equiv (W^\pm(r_s) - W_\times^\pm)^\kappa$ for $\mathcal{O}$-quantities analysis defined in Table (1) for corotating ((−)–continuum curves) and counterrotating ((+)–dashed curves) tori for different values of the cusps $r_* = r_\times^\pm \in \{\bullet, \blacksquare, \blacklozenge\}$ and radii $r_s \in \{\bullet_K, \blacksquare_K, \blacklozenge_K, O_K\}$, related to thickness of the accreting matter flow, where $\varpi = n+1$, with $\gamma = 1/n+1$ is the polytropic index, κ is the polytropic constant. Radii $(r_\times, r_s)$ and the associated angular momentum ℓ and K parameters are shown with $\{\bullet, \blacksquare, \blacklozenge, \bullet_K, \blacksquare_K, \blacklozenge_K, O_K\}$. Ω is the relativistic angular velocity. ξ is the dimensionless BH rotational energy.

the dimensionless rotational energy ξ is:

$$\xi \equiv \frac{M_{rot}}{M(0)} = 1 - \frac{\sqrt{1 + \sqrt{1 - \frac{J(0)^2}{M(0)^4}}}}{\sqrt{2}}, \tag{3}$$

$$\xi_\pm^\mp = 1 \pm \sqrt{\frac{r_\mp}{2}}, \quad \frac{\delta M_{irr}}{M_{irr}} = \frac{\delta M - \delta J \omega_H^+}{\sqrt{M(0)^2 - \frac{J(0)^2}{M(0)^2}}},$$

where $\xi \equiv \xi_-^+$, M_{rot} is the rotational mass, $r_\pm$ are the outer and inner BH horizons, ω_H^+ is the BH relativistic frequency (light-like limiting circular frequency evaluated at the BH outer horizon r_+). Thee BH dimensionless spin is $a(\xi) = \mathcal{A} \equiv 2\sqrt{-(\xi - 2)(\xi - 1)^2 \xi}$. The rotational energy ξ is governed by the constraint

$\delta M_{irr} \geq 0$ thus $(\delta M - \delta J \omega_H^+) \geq 0$, where $\xi = 1 - M_{irr}/M$, with quantities evaluated at an initial state (0). It is $\xi \in [0, \xi_\ell]$ where $\xi_\ell \equiv \frac{1}{2}(2 - \sqrt{2})$, limiting the total rotational energy extracted to a $\approx 29\%$ of the total mass M for a process leading an extreme Kerr BH to the static Schwarzschild BH.

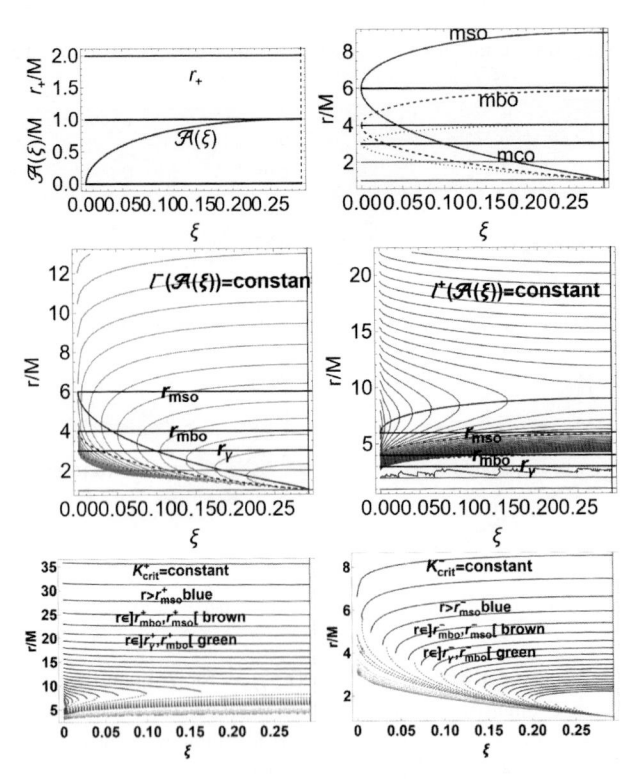

Fig. 3. Upper left panel: the BH outer horizon r_+ and the dimenionless BH spin function $\mathcal{A}(\xi)$, as functions of the dimensionless BH rotational energy ξ. Extreme Kerr BH corresponds to $\xi \approx 0.29$. Upper right panel: marginally bounded orbit mbo (dashed curves), marginally stable orbit mso (plain curves), marginally circular orbit mco (dotted curves) for corotating motion (blue curves) and counter-rotating motion (red curves) as functions of the parameter ξ. Center Bottom panels: the tori specific fluid angular momenta $\ell^{\mp}$ =constant for corotating (center left panel) and counter-rotating (center right panel) tori, the RAD energy function $K^{\pm}(r)$ =constant for the counter-rotating (bottom left panel) and corotating fluids (bottom right panel) as functions of ξ, where $r_\gamma^\pm$ is the last circular circular orbit (photon orbit) for counter-rotating (+) and corotating orbits (-).

In Figs 2 and Figs 3 the tori aggregates energetic characteristics at the state 0, prior a possible process involving the BH and its environment, are related to the BH rotational energy. The energetic parameter ξ and the angular relativistic velocity of the BH determine the BH state prior the transition-.[34–36] This analysis turns particularly relevant for the RAD model which, because of its inner discrete structure, can be characterized by phases of enhanced accretion rates. Furthermore, as each torus of the aggregate is a geometrically thick disk, each component can contribute with super-Eddington accretion rates, with the possibility of further effects as runaway instability,[37,38] or in the case of RAD composed by misaligned tori, the Bardeen-Petterson effect.[39]

2.4. *Magnetized tori: alternative leading function*

As mentioned in Sec. (2.1), the leading function is not necessary the fluid specific angular momentum. An example providing a different aggregate leading function is the case of orbiting agglomerates composed by magnetized tori with a "Komissarov" toroidal magnetic field.[40] In this case the eRAD aggregate leading function is a function $\mathcal{S}$, defined by the magnetic field parameters and proving the rings seeds locations, the minima of pressure (according to the conditions for the cusp formation), the maximum values of the $\mathcal{S}$-parameter for the formation of a tori couple and constrains on the eRAD inner structure in dependence on the tori relative rotation orientation. More precisely, let us consider the toroidal magnetic field: $B^\phi = \sqrt{2 p_B/A}$, where $A \equiv \ell^2 g_{tt} + 2\ell g_{t\phi} + g_{\phi\phi}$, and $p_B = \mathcal{M}\left(g_{t\phi}g_{t\phi} - g_{tt}g_{\phi\phi}\right)^{q-1} \hat{\omega}^q$ is the magnetic pressure, $\hat{\omega}$ is the fluid enthalpy, q and $\mathcal{M}$ are constant; The Euler equation can be written as

$$\frac{\partial_* p}{\rho+p} = G_*^{(f)} + G_*^{(em)}, \quad G_*^{\natural} = -\frac{\partial}{\partial *} W_*^{\natural}; \quad * = \{r, \theta\}, \quad \natural = \{(em), (f)\}, \tag{4}$$

$$\partial_\mu (W^{(f)} + W^{(em)}) = \partial_\mu [\ln V_{eff} + \mathcal{G}], \ \mathcal{G}(r, \theta) = \mathcal{S}\left(A V_{eff}^2\right)^{q-1}, \ \mathcal{S} \equiv \frac{q \mathcal{M} \hat{\omega}^{q-1}}{q-1}.$$

The RAD leading $\mathcal{S}$-function is

$$\mathcal{S}_{crit} \equiv -\frac{\Delta^{-\mathcal{Q}}}{\mathcal{Q}} f(a, \ell; r) \quad (\mathcal{Q} \equiv q-1),$$

where $f(a, \ell; r)$ is a function of the BH spin and fluid angular momentum[9,31] (there is $\Delta \equiv r^2 - 2Mr + a^2$).

3. Misaligned Tori

In this section we discuss the tori aggregates containing misaligned tori. To simply our discussion we consider misaligned tori orbiting a central static BH. In this case we can use different leading functions for the description of the aggregate introduced in Sec. (3.1). Tori geometrical thickness is discussed in Sec. (3.2). Frequency models in tori aggregates are considered in Sec. (3.2.1) and tori geometrical characteristics are deepened in Sec. (3.3) for quiescent (not cusped) tori in Sec. (3.3.1) and for cusped tori analyzed in Sec. (3.3.2).

3.1. *Leading functions*

In this section we introduce three definitions of leading functions for the tori aggregates–see.[11]

The critical $\bar{r}(r_i)$ and $r_\times^\varepsilon$ functions:

$$\bar{r}(r_i) = \frac{2r_i\left[\sqrt{2r_i - r_\gamma} + r_i - 1\right]}{(r_i - r_+)^2}, \quad r_\times^\varepsilon \equiv \frac{r_{center}\left(\sqrt{2r_{center} - r_\gamma} + 1\right)^2}{(r_{center} - r_+)^2}, \quad (5)$$

(solutions of $\ell(r) = \ell(r_p)$ for two orbits (r, r_p)). In this case the leading function is a relation between the extremes of pressure inside the tori $\bar{r}(r_i)$, or the cusp $r_\times^\varepsilon$ as function of the center of maximum pressure. The distance $r_{center} - r_\times$ increases with the tori distance in the aggregates from the central BH attractor.

Leading function $\ell_{crit}^o(K)$:
There is

$$\ell_{crit}^o(K) \equiv \sqrt{\frac{27K^4 - K(9K^2 - 8)^{3/2} - 36K^2 + 8}{2K^2(K^2 - 1)}}, \quad (6)$$

$$\ell_{crit}^i(K) \equiv \sqrt{\frac{27K^4 + K(9K^2 - 8)^{3/2} - 36K^2 + 8}{2K^2(K^2 - 1)}}, \quad (7)$$

where $\ell_{crit}^o(K) > \ell_{crit}^i(K) > \ell_{mso}$, $\ell_{crit}^i(K) \in [\ell_{mso}, \ell_\gamma[$.

In this case, notably the leading function, relating the two tori parameters ℓ and K, bas been split in function $\ell_{crit}^o(K)$, the leading function providing parameters (ℓ, K) at the tori centers (rings seeds), and function $\ell_{crit}^i(K)$ for the tori cusps.

Similarly we introduce the following alternative functions.

Tori critical radius $r_{crit}^o(K)$: There is

$$r_{crit}^o(K) \equiv -\frac{8}{K\left(\sqrt{9K^2 - 8} + 3K\right) - 4}, \quad r_{crit}^i(K) \equiv \frac{8}{K\left(\sqrt{9K^2 - 8} - 3K\right) + 4},$$

$$r_{crit}^i(K_\times) = r_\times, \quad r_{crit}^o(K_{center}) = r_{center} \quad (8)$$

similarly to $\ell_{crit}^o(K)$, the leading function is $r_{crit}^o(K)$, relating the center of maximum pressure (ring seed) and the K parameter at the torus center.

3.2. Geometrical thickness

Disk geometrical thickness is an important characteristic for the RAD tori. The eRAD is a geometrical thin disk composed by geometrical thick tori with an inner articulated ringed structure, combining some features of geometrical thick disks, inherited by its components and features typical of the geometrical thin disks in its global structure. Geometrical thickness is a relevant parameter in the comparison with other disks model, in the assessment of the torus vertical structure and the influence of a possible poloidal magnetic field, for the accretion mechanism and the study of tori oscillations. The definition of geometrical thickness adopted here coincides with the thickness **S** of the outer Roche lobe section of the PD torus. For large part of the (ℓ, K) range, cusped tori can be considered geometrically thin i.e. **S** < 1. There are classes of toroidal components with equal thickness. For example, in the "reference" case **S** $= 1$, distinguishing geometrically thin and geometrically thick disks, where there are couples of toroids with equal energy parameter K, regulating also the flow thickness.[10,11]

A further parameter for the evaluation of tori geometrical thickness is the dimensionless β_{crit}

$$\beta_{crit} = \frac{(r_{center} - 2)^2(r_{center} - r_\times)\sqrt{r_{center}r_\times - 2(r_{center} + 2r_\times)}}{r_{center}\sqrt{r_{center} - 3r_\times}\sqrt{r_\times - 2}},$$

emerging from the analysis of cusped tori oscillation.[41–43] Similarly to the leading function $\bar{r}(r_i)$ of Eq. (5), β_{crit} depends on the distance between the maximum and minimum point of pressure in the tori, which increases with the distance from the central attractor. For small β_{crit} ($\beta_{crit} \geq 0$), tori may be considered geometrically thin for radial and vertical oscillation, and can be described by the radial and vertical epicyclical frequencies from the hypothesis of thin (slender) tori, coincident therefore with the respective circular orbit frequencies.[42,44,45] The conditions for geometrical thin components according to definition **S** < 1 and conditions for geometrical thin tori according to β_{crit} coincide only for special conditions on ℓ and K parameters (therefore depending on the tori location in the agglomerate and their dimension), having tori with combined characteristics typical of geometrical thin and thick disks.[10]

3.2.1. Frequency models in tori aggregates

In the conditions where $\beta_{crit} \geq 0$, we can consider the circular orbit approximation for the oscillation frequencies. In[10] different frequency models are applied to the RAD structure, interpreted as a frame for the high–frequency (HF) Quasi-Periodic Oscillations (QPOs), assuming the geodesic (nearly circular geodesic motion) frequencies

$$\nu_r(r) = \nu_K(r)\sqrt{1 - \frac{r_{mso}}{r}}, \quad \nu_\theta(r) = \nu_K(r) \equiv \frac{1}{r^{3/2}}, \quad (9)$$

determined by the tori constraints. The frequencies (9) are combined for the fitting of resonance ratios, identifying the upper ν_U and lower ν_L frequencies from different oscillation models and assuming $(\nu_r(r), \nu_K(r))$ evaluated at different points r of the tori surfaces. Therefore in[10] we used the frequency models (**TD,RP,RE,WD**) listed Table (2), evaluated in different tori models. The twin peak quasi-periodic oscillations with resonant frequency ratios $\nu_U/\nu_L = \{3:2, 4:3, 5:4, 2:1, 3:1\}$ have been analyzed.[10]

Different components of the aggregates fit different frequency models, according to tori location in the aggregate with respect to the central attractor distinguishing therefore the toroidal components and the different torus active parts.[10] In the models of Table (2), the torus inner edge has been considered the active part of the emission process, the frequencies being evaluated at $r_{inner} > r_\times$ (for quiescent tori) or $r_{inner} = r_\times$ for cusped tori, and as ($\beta_{crit} \gtrsim 0, \mathbf{S} \ll 1$), the maximum of

Table 2. Frequency models and related tori models for the analysis of Sec. (3.2.1). Frequencies (ν_θ, ν_r) are in Eq. (9), the relativistic frequency $\nu_K = \Omega$, coincident with ν_θ in the static spacetime is in Eq. (1). The fluid specific angular momentum is ℓ and K is the energy parameter, r_{center} is the center of maximum density and pressure in the torus, r_{out} is the torus outer edge. The relativistic-precession model coincides in static BH also with the total precession models **TP**. Radius $r_{max}^\times$ is the cusped torus geometrical maximum of Eq. (13), where $r_{max}^o(r) \equiv r_{max}^\times$ as functions of ℓ. Radii $\bar{r}(r_i)$ and $r_\times^e$ are the aggregate leading functions of Eqs (5); function $\bar{r}(r_i)$ relates the critical points of pressure in each toroidal component of the aggregate, and function $r_\times^e$ provides the torus cusp as function of the torus center–see Eq. (5).

Frequency models	Tori models
(RP): $\nu_U = \nu_K$, $\nu_L = \nu_{per} \equiv \nu_K - \nu_r$; (relativistic-precession model)	**[(a)-model]**: function of r/M
	[(b)-model]: $r = r_{center}(\ell)$ function of $\ell \in [\ell_{mso}, \ell_{mbo}]$
(RE): $\nu_U = \nu_\theta$, $\nu_L = \nu_r$; (resonance epicyclic models)	**[(c)-model]**: for $r = r_{out}(\ell)$ functions of ℓ
(TD): $\nu_L = \nu_K$, $\nu_U = (\nu_K + \nu_r)$;	**[(d)-model]**: in $r = r_{max}^\times(\ell)$ function of ℓ
	[(e)-model]: for $r = r_\times^e$ function of r/M torus cusp or center
(tidal distortion model)	**[(f)-model]**: function of $\bar{r}(r_i)$
(WD): $\nu_L = 2(\nu_K - \nu_r)$, $\nu_U = (2\nu_K - \nu_r)$; (warped disk model)	**[(g)-model]**: for $r = r_{center}(K)$ function of K

pressure point, the outer edge and the geometrical maximum point have been also considered.[46–57]

3.3. Tori geometrical characteristics

Frequencies models of Table (2) have been evaluated on the outer r_{out} and the inner $r_\times$ tori edges, the tori geometrical maximum r_{max} and tori center r_{center}. The evaluation of the tori geometrical characteristics is relevant in the determination of inner ringed structure and tori collision. In this section we provide $(r_\times, r_{out}, r_{center}, r_{max})$, the torus height h and the inner Roche lobe maximum high. These quantities are functions of tori parameters (ℓ, K) for quiescent (not cusped) tori, considered in Sec. (3.3.1) and ℓ or K (or alternately the critical pressure points $r_\times$ and r_{center}) for cusped tori analyzed in Sec. (3.3.2).

3.3.1. Roche lobes in quiescent and cusped tori

For quiescent and cusped tori, we provide below the outer and inner torus edge and the tori elongations λ on the tori symmetry plane–see[11]

$$\textbf{Torus outer edge:} \quad r_{out} \equiv \frac{2\left[1 + \mathbb{K}\tau \cos\left(\frac{1}{3}\cos^{-1}(\alpha)\right)\right]}{3\mathbb{K}}, \tag{10}$$

$$\textbf{Tori elongation:} \quad \lambda \equiv \frac{2\tau \cos\left(\frac{1}{6}\left[2\cos^{-1}(\alpha) + \pi\right]\right)}{\sqrt{3}},$$

$$\textbf{Torus inner edge:} \quad r_{inner} \equiv \frac{2\left[1 - \mathbb{K}\tau \sin\left(\frac{1}{3}\sin^{-1}(\alpha)\right)\right]}{3\mathbb{K}}.$$

where $\mathbb{K} : K \equiv \sqrt{1-\mathbb{K}}$, $\mathcal{Q} \equiv \ell^2$ and $(\alpha, \mathbb{K}, \tau)$ are functions of (ℓ, K)–see.[11] (Note in the case of cusped tori $r_{inner} = r_\times$).

For the inner Roche lobe, the inner edge an the elongation of the lobe on the symmetry plane are

$$r^{BH}_{inner} \equiv \frac{2\left[\frac{1}{\mathbb{K}} - \tau \sin\left(\frac{1}{6}\left[2\cos^{-1}(\alpha) + \pi\right]\right)\right]}{3},$$

$$\lambda^{BH}_{inner} \equiv \frac{2}{3}\tau\left[\sin\left(\frac{1}{6}\left[2\cos^{-1}(\alpha) + \pi\right]\right) - \sin\left[\frac{1}{3}\sin^{-1}(\alpha)\right]\right]. \quad (11)$$

The geometrical maximum for the outer r^o_{max} and inner Roche lobes r^i_{max} are

Outer lobe : $\quad r^o_{max}(K, \ell) \equiv \sqrt{\frac{K^2\mathcal{Q}}{K^2 - 1} + 4\sqrt{\frac{2}{3}}\psi\cos\left[\frac{1}{3}\cos^{-1}(\psi_\pi)\right]},$

Inner lobe : $\quad r^i_{max}(K, \ell) \equiv \sqrt{\frac{K^2\mathcal{Q}}{K^2 - 1} - 4\sqrt{\frac{2}{3}}\psi\sin\left[\frac{1}{3}\sin^{-1}(\psi_\pi)\right]},$

and the torus height is

$$h^o_{max}(K, \ell) \equiv \sqrt{\frac{K^2\mathcal{Q}}{1 - K^2} + \mathbf{Z} - 4\sqrt{\frac{2}{3}}\psi\cos\left[\frac{1}{3}\cos^{-1}(\psi_\pi)\right]},$$

where $(\psi, \psi_\pi, \mathbf{Z})$ are functions of (ℓ, K).[11]

3.3.2. *Cusped tori*

In this section we specialize the analysis of Sec. (3.3.1) for cusped misaligned tori, which are described by one only independent parameter K or ℓ (or equivalently $r_\times$ or r_{center}).

We can express the critical points of pressure in the tori in terms of the parameter ℓ. The torus center and the point of minimum density (and hydrostatic pressure) are

$$r_{center}(\ell) \equiv \frac{1}{3}\left[\mathcal{Q} + 2L_\ell\cos\left(\frac{1}{3}\iota_a\right)\right], \quad r_\times(\ell) \equiv \frac{1}{3}\left[\mathcal{Q} - 2L_\ell\cos\left(\frac{1}{3}[\iota_a + \pi]\right)\right],$$

where $L_\ell, L_{\updownarrow}$ are functions of ℓ and $\mathcal{Q} \equiv \ell^2$.[11] The cusped torus outer edge is located at

$$r^\times_{out} \equiv \frac{2\ell^2\hat{\psi}_2}{3\ell^2\hat{\psi}_2 + \hat{\psi}_0^2(6 - \hat{\psi}_0)} + 2\hat{\psi}_4\sqrt{\frac{\ell^2\left[\hat{\psi}_0^2\left(3\ell^2\hat{\psi}_2(6 - \hat{\psi}_0) + \hat{\psi}_0^2(\hat{\psi}_0^2 - 12\hat{\psi}_0 + 36)\right) + 12\ell^2\hat{\psi}_2^2\right]}{3\left(3\ell^2\hat{\psi}_2 + \hat{\psi}_0^2(6 - \hat{\psi}_0)\right)^2}},$$

(where $(\hat{\psi}_0, \hat{\psi}_2)$ are functions of ℓ). Similarly to functions (ℓ^o, ℓ^i) of Eqs (6), the leading function can be expressed in terms of the energy function K as

$$K_{center}(\ell) \equiv \sqrt{\frac{\left[\mathcal{Q} + 2L_\ell \cos\left(\frac{\iota_a}{3}\right) - 6\right]\left[\mathcal{Q} + 2L_\ell \cos\left(\frac{\iota_a}{3}\right)\right]^2}{3\mathcal{Q}\left[3\ell^4 + 2(2\mathcal{Q} - 15)L_\ell \cos\left(\frac{\iota_a}{3}\right) - 39\mathcal{Q} + 2L_\ell^2 \cos\left(\frac{2\iota_a}{3}\right) + 54\right]}},$$

$$K_\times(\ell) \equiv \sqrt{\frac{\left[\mathcal{Q} - 2L_\ell \sin\left(\frac{\iota_b}{3}\right) - 6\right]\left(\mathcal{Q} - 2L_\ell \sin\left(\frac{\iota_b}{3}\right)\right)^2}{3\mathcal{Q}\left[3\ell^4 + 2(15 - 2\mathcal{Q})L_\ell \sin\left[\frac{\iota_b}{3}\right] - 39\mathcal{Q} - 2L_\ell^2 \cos\left(\frac{2\iota_b}{3}\right) + 54\right]}},$$

$$\iota_a \equiv \cos^{-1}(L_{\updownarrow}), \quad \iota_b \equiv \sin^{-1}(L_{\updownarrow}) \tag{12}$$

(here $L_{\updownarrow}$ is a function of the momentum ℓ). Function $K_{center}(\ell)$ describes the rings seeds, while $K_\times(\ell)$ refers the tori cusps ($\mathcal{Q} \equiv \ell^2$).

The cusped tori outer edge can be expressed as function of the cusp $r_\times$ as follows:

$$r^\times_{out}(r_\times) = \frac{2}{3}\left[\sqrt{\frac{(r_\times - r_{mso})^2 r_\times^2}{(r_\times - r_{mbo})^2}} \cos\left[\frac{1}{3}\cos^{-1}\mathbf{X}\right] + \frac{r_\times}{r_\times - r_{mbo}} + r_\times\right]$$

where $\mathbf{X}$ is a function of $r_\times$, and the the geometrical maxima of cusped tori for the outer (o) and inner (i) Roche lobes are

$$r^o_{max}(r) = \sqrt{4\sqrt{\frac{2}{3}}\psi_\lambda \cos\left[\frac{1}{3}\cos^{-1}\left(-\frac{3}{4}\sqrt{\frac{3}{2}}\psi_\lambda\psi_\sigma^2\right)\right] + \frac{r^2}{(r-r_\gamma)\psi_\sigma}}$$

$$r^i_{max}(r) = \sqrt{\frac{r^2}{(r-r_\gamma)\psi_\sigma} - 4\sqrt{\frac{2}{3}}\psi_\lambda \cos\left[\frac{1}{3}\left(\cos^{-1}\left[-\frac{3}{4}\sqrt{\frac{3}{2}}\psi_\lambda\psi_\sigma^2\right] + \pi\right)\right]},$$

(here r is the fluid pressure critical point where $\psi_\lambda, \psi_\sigma$ are functions of r).

The cusped torus height is

$$h^o_{max}(r_\times) = \left(-2\sqrt{6}\sqrt{\frac{(r_\times - r_\gamma)(r_\times - r_+)^2 r_\times^4}{(r_\times - r_{mbo})^3}} \sec\left[\frac{1}{3}\cos^{-1}(\psi_\rho)\right] + \right.$$

$$\left. \frac{9(r_\times - r_+)^2 r_\times^2 \sec^2\left[\frac{1}{3}\cos^{-1}(\psi_\rho)\right]}{8(r_\times - r_{mbo})(r_\times - r_\gamma)} + \frac{(r_\times - r_+)(5r_\times - 18)r_\times^2}{(r_\times - r_{mbo})^2}\right)^{1/2},$$

(ψ_σ is a function of $r_\times$.) Finally we can express the cusped tori geometrical thickness $\mathbf{S}_\times = 2h_\times/(\lambda_\times)$ in terms of the pressure critical points where $\lambda_\times$ is the cusped torus elongation on its symmetry plane and $h_\times$ the cusped torus height.

4. Conclusion

We explored models of tori clusters orbiting around a central SMBH, detailing the morphological characteristics of the toroidal components. Configurations considered here can be used as initial data for dynamical (time-dependent, evolutive) GRMHD analysis. A "leading function" as been used to constraint the tori distribution around the central attractor, together with the energy function $K(r)$ regulating the agglomerate stability (cusp emergence and tori collision), the flow thickness, mass accretion rate and cusp luminosity.

From the observational viewpoint the inner ringed structure offers several interesting scenarios arising from the unstable states associated to its inner activity, as the presence of multiple accretion points and inter disk shells of multiple jets. Eventually observational evidence of the RAD and the associated inter disk activity could be found in the obscuration of the X-ray emission spectrum, as a track of the agglomerate inner composition. An indication of the presence of multiple orbiting tori could be seen in an increasing BH accretion mass rate and the presence of interrupted phases of BH accretion, or in the emission associated to oscillation tori modes as in HF QPOs. The establishment of runaway instability and the tori self-gravity can be relevant further factors for eRAD tori agglomerate around SMBHs[37,38] and the Bardeen–Petterson effect is main relevant in the misaligned tori case.[39]

References

1. D. Pugliese & G. Montani, Phys. Rev. D, 91, 083011 (2015).
2. D. Pugliese & Z. Stuchlik, Astrophys. J. Suppl., 221, 2, 25 (2015).
3. D. Pugliese & Z.Stuchlík, Astrophys. J. Suppl., **223**, 2, 27 (2016).
4. D. Pugliese & Z. Stuchlik, JHEAp, 17, 1 (2018).
5. D. Pugliese & Z. Stuchlík,Class. Quant. Grav. **35**, 18, 185008 (2018).
6. D. Pugliese & Z. Stuchlík, Astrophys. J. Suppl., **229**, 2, 40 (2017).
7. D. Pugliese & Z. Stuchlik, Eur. Phys. J. **C 79** 4, 288, (2019).
8. D. Pugliese & Z. Stuchlík, Class. Quant. Grav., **35** 10, 105005 (2018)
9. D. Pugliese and G. Montani, Mon. Not. Roy. Astron. Soc., 476, 4, 4346 (2018).
10. D. Pugliese & Z. Stuchlik, Mon. Not. Roy. Astron. Soc., 493, 3, 4229–4255(2020).
11. D. Pugliese & Z. Stuchlik Class. Quant. Grav., 37 19, 195025 (2020).
12. D. Pugliese & Z. Stuchlik, to appear in PASJ (2021).
13. M. A. Abramowicz & P. C. Fragile, Living Rev. Relativity, 16, 1 (2013).
14. C. M. Violette Impellizzeri et al., Astrophys. J. L, 884, L28 (2019).
15. S. Dyda, R. V. E. Lovelace, et al., Mon. Not. Roy. Astron. Soc., **446**, 613-621 (2015).
16. C. Alig, M. Schartmann, A. Burkert, K. Dolag, Astrophys. J., 771, 2, 119 (2013).
17. J. M. Carmona-Loaiza, M. Colpi, M. Dotti et al., Mon. Not. Roy. Astron. Soc., 453, 1608 (2015).
18. R. V. E. Lovelace & T. Chou, Astrophys. J., 468, L25 (1996).
19. R. V. E. Lovelace, M. M. Romanova, P. Lii, et al. Comp. Astroph. Cosmology, 1-3, (2014).
20. C. Nixon, A. King, & D. Price, Mon. Not. Roy. Astron. Soc., 434, 1946 (2013).
21. S. Doğan, C. Nixon, A. King, et al., Mon. Not. Roy. Astron. Soc., 449, 1251 (2015).
22. C. Bonnerot, E. M. Rossi, G. Lodato, Mon. Not. Roy. Astron. Soc., 455, 2, 2253 (2016).

23. H. Aly, W. Dehnen, C. Nixon & A. King, Mon. Not. Roy. Astron. Soc., 449, 1, 65 (2015).
24. O. Zanotti & D. Pugliese, Gen. Rel. Grav., 47, 4, 44 (2015).
25. M. Kozłowski, M. Jaroszyński, M. A. Abramowicz, Astron. Astrophys., 63, 209 (1998).
26. M. A. Abramowicz, Acta. Astron., 21, 81, (1971).
27. S. K. Chakrabarti, Mon. Not. Roy. Astron. Soc., 245, 747 (1990).
28. S. K. Chakrabarti, Mon. Not. Roy. Astron. Soc., 250, 7 (1991).
29. D. Pugliese and G. Montani, Gen. Rel. Grav., 53, 5, 51 (2021).
30. D. Pugliese and J. A. Valiente Kroon, Gen.Rel.Grav. 44, 2785-2810 (2012).
31. D. Pugliese and G. Montani, EPL, 101, 1, 19001 (2013).
32. R. H. Boyer, Proc. Camb. Phil. Soc., **61**, 527 (1965).
33. M. A. Abramowicz, Astronomical Society of Japan, 37, 4, 727–734 (1985).
34. D. Puglese & Z. Stuchlik, Class. Quant. Grav., 38, 14, 145014 (2021).
35. R. A. Daly, APJ, 691, L72-L76, 1 (2009).
36. R. A. Daly and T. B. Sprinkle, Mon. Not. Roy. Astron. Soc., 438, 3233-3242 (2014).
37. M. A. Abramowicz, M. Calvani, L. Nobili, Nature, 302, 597 (1983).
38. J. A. Font and F. Daigne, Mon. Not. Roy. Astron. Soc. **334**, 383 (2002).
39. J. M. Bardeen, J. A. Petterson, Astrophys. J., 195, L65 (1975).
40. S. S. Komissarov, Mon. Not. Roy. Astron. Soc., 368, 993 (2006).
41. G. Török, K. Goluchová, J. Horák, et al., Mon. Not. Roy. Astron. Soc., **457**, L19 (2016).
42. O. Straub & E. Sramkova, Class. Quantum Grav., **26**, 055011 (2009).
43. M. A. Abramowicz, O. M. Blaes, J. Horak et al., Class. Quantum Grav., **23**, 1689 (2006).
44. K. Goluchova, J. Horak et al., MNRAS, 457, L19 (2016).
45. K. Goluchova, M. Urbanec et al., Astrophys. J., 833, 273 (2016).
46. Z. Stuchlìk, J. Schee, E. Šràmkovà & G. Török, Acta Astron. **67**, 181 (2017).
47. Z. Stuchlík & M. Kološ, A&A, **586**, A130 (2016).
48. Z. Stuchlík, P. Slaný & G. Török, A&A, **463**, 807 (2007).
49. G. Török & Z. Stuchlík, A&A, **437**, 775 (2005).
50. A. Kotrlová, E. Šrámková, G. Török et al, A&A, **607**, A69 (2017).
51. G. Török, K. Goluchová, M. Urbanec et al., Astrophys. J., **833**, 273 (2016).
52. E. Šrámková, G. Török, A. Kotrlová, et al., A&A, **578**, A90 (2015).
53. G. Török, A. Kotrlová, E. Šrámková et al., A&A, **531**, A59 (2011).
54. Z. Stuchlík, A. Kotrlová & G. Török, A&A, **525**, A82 (2011).
55. A. Kotrlová, Z. Stuchlík & G. Török, Class. Quantum Grav., **25**, 225016 (2008).
56. Z. Stuchlík, P. Slaný & P. Török, A&A, **470**, 401 (2007).
57. Z. Stuchlik, A. Kotrlová, G. Török, A&A, 552, A10 (2013).

Hydrodynamical transport of angular momentum in accretion disks in the presence of nonlinear perturbations due to noise

Subham Ghosh* and Banibrata Mukhopadhyay[†]

Department of Physics, Indian Institute of Science,
Bangalore, Karnataka, 560012, India
* subham@iisc.ac.in
[†] *bm@iisc.ac.in*

The origin of hydrodynamical instability and turbulence in the Keplerian accretion disk is a long-standing puzzle. The flow therein is linearly stable. Here we explore the evolution of perturbation in this flow in the presence of an additional force. Such a force, which is expected to be stochastic in nature hence behaving as noise, could result from thermal fluctuations (however small be), grain–fluid interactions, feedback from outflows in astrophysical disks, etc. We essentially establish the evolution of nonlinear perturbation in the presence of Coriolis and external forces, which is the modified Landau equation. We obtain that even in the linear regime, under suitable forcing and Reynolds number, the otherwise least stable perturbation evolves to a very large saturated amplitude, leading to nonlinearity and plausible turbulence. Hence, forcing essentially leads a linear stable mode to unstable. We further show that nonlinear perturbation diverges at a shorter time-scale in the presence of force, leading to a fast transition to turbulence. Interestingly, the emergence of nonlinearity depends only on the force but not on the initial amplitude of perturbation, unlike the original Landau equation-based solution.

Keywords: Accretion, accretion disks – hydrodynamics – instabilities – turbulence

1. Introduction

Origin of instability and plausible turbulence in Rayleigh stable flows, e.g., the Keplerian accretion flow, is a long-standing problem. While such flows are evident to be turbulent, they are linearly stable for any Reynolds number (Re). Although people[1,2] described the underlying flow in accretion disks to be turbulent with an effective turbulent viscosity, the origin of turbulence therein was not clear until Balbus and Hawley[3] proposed the idea of magnetorotational instability (MRI) following Velikhov[4] and Chandrasekhar.[5] MRI is a Magnetohydrodynamical (MHD) instability, and it operates due to the coupling between the weak magnetic field and the rotation of the fluid parcel. Although MRI is a popular instability mechanism, it poses several problems. There are astrophysical bodies where the ionization fraction is tiny as they are cold. In such systems, MRI gets suppressed.[6] Apart from that, beyond a certain value of the toroidal component of the magnetic field for compressible plasma, MRI gets suppressed.[7,8] There are several other cites too where MRI seizes to work or becomes suppressed.[9,10] We, therefore, venture for a hydrodynamical origin of nonlinearity and hence plausible turbulence in the accretion disk. Our emphasis is the conventional linear instability when perturbation grows exponentially, unlike the case of transient growth. We particularly consider here an extra force,[11] to fulfill our purpose. The examples[12] of the origin of such force in astrophysical context, particularly in accretion disks, could be: the interaction between the dust grains and fluid parcel in protoplanetary disks, back reactions of outflow/jet to accretion disks.

2. Formalism of the problem

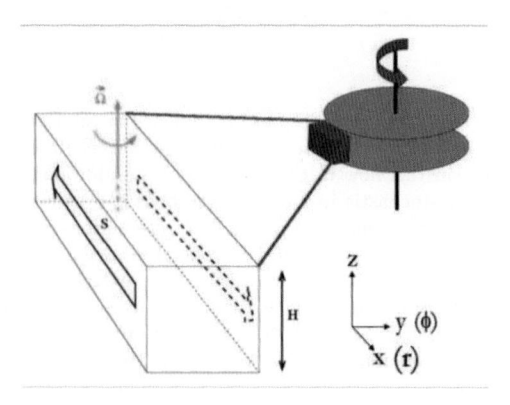

Fig. 1. Model picture of local cubical box in accretion disk where we perform the analysis (http://ipag.obs.ujf-grenoble.fr/ longarep/astrophysics.html). Within the box, the Cartesian coordinate x is along the radial cylindrical coordinate r (with respect to the center of the accretion disk), y is along ϕ, and z is same in both the systems.

To formulate the problem, we have considered a local box at a local patch in the accretion disk, as shown in the Fig. 1. Although the accretion disk possesses cylindrical geometry, In the local box, we study the motion of the local fluid element using the Cartesian coordinates. The one to one correspondence between the Cartesian (x, y, z) and cylindrical (r, ϕ, z) coordinates are shown in the Fig. 1. The Cartesian coordinates x, y, z are along the cylindrical coordinates r, ϕ, z. The details of the local formulation are in Mukhopadhyay et al.,[13,14] and Ghosh and Mukhopadhyay.[15] As we confine ourselves in the local region of the accretion disks, the corresponding flow has been considered incompressible.[9,13,16–18] The governing equations are the ensemble-averaged Orr-Sommerfeld and Squire equations in the presence of Coriolis force and an additional stochastic force,[12,19] which is delta correlated with nonzero mean. The Orr-Sommerfeld and Squire equations are obtained by eliminating the pressure term from the corresponding Navier-Stokes equations and utilizing the continuity equation for the incompressible flow. The governing equations are given by,

$$\left(\frac{\partial}{\partial t} + U\frac{\partial}{\partial y}\right)\nabla^2 u - U''\frac{\partial u}{\partial y} + \frac{2}{q}\frac{\partial \zeta}{\partial z} - \frac{1}{Re}\nabla^4 u + \Gamma_1 = NL^u, \qquad (1)$$

$$\left(\frac{\partial}{\partial t}+U\frac{\partial}{\partial y}\right)\zeta - U'\frac{\partial u}{\partial z} - \frac{2}{q}\frac{\partial u}{\partial z} - \frac{1}{Re}\nabla^2\zeta + \Gamma_2 = NL^\zeta, \quad (2)$$

where u and ζ are respectively the x-component of the velocity and vorticity perturbations after ensemble averaging, U the y-component of background velocity which for the present purpose of plane shear in the dimensionless units is $-x$, q the rotation parameter with $\Omega(r) \propto 1/r^q$, $\Omega(r)$ being the angular frequency of the fluid parcel at radius r, Γ-s are the corresponding constant means of stochastic forces (white noise with nonzero mean due to gravity making the system biased[11]) in the system described below, and NL-s are the non-linear terms due to the perturbation. The x-component of vorticity and the non-linear terms are given by

$$\zeta = \frac{\partial w}{\partial y} - \frac{\partial v}{\partial z}, \quad (3)$$

$$NL^u = -\nabla^2\{(\mathbf{u}' \cdot \nabla)u\} + \frac{\partial}{\partial x}\nabla \cdot \{(\mathbf{u}' \cdot \nabla)\mathbf{u}'\}, \quad (4)$$

$$NL^\zeta = -\frac{\partial}{\partial y}\{(\mathbf{u}' \cdot \nabla)w\} + \frac{\partial}{\partial z}\{(\mathbf{u}' \cdot \nabla)v\}, \quad (5)$$

where $\mathbf{u}' = (u, v, w)$, which is the perturbed velocity vector. For the complete description of the flow, equations 1 and 2 are supplemented with the equation of continuity, which is given by

$$\nabla \cdot \mathbf{u}' = 0, \quad (6)$$

To solve the governing equations, we have no-slip boundary conditions along x-direction,[12,13,20] i.e. $u = v = w = 0$ at $x = \pm 1$ or equivalently

$$u = \frac{\partial u}{\partial x} = \zeta = 0, \text{ at } x = \pm 1. \quad (7)$$

2.1. *Linear theory*

In the evolution of linear perturbation, let the linear solutions be

$$u = \hat{u}(x,t)e^{i\mathbf{k}\cdot\mathbf{r}}, \quad (8)$$
$$\zeta = \hat{\zeta}(x,t)e^{i\mathbf{k}\cdot\mathbf{r}}, \quad (9)$$

with $\mathbf{k} = (0, k_y, k_z)$ and $\mathbf{r} = (0, y, z)$. Substitute these in equations (1) and (2), neglecting non-linear terms, we obtain

$$\frac{\partial}{\partial t}Q + i\mathcal{L}Q + \Gamma = 0, \quad (10)$$

where

$$Q = \begin{pmatrix} \hat{u} \\ \hat{\zeta} \end{pmatrix}, \quad \mathcal{L} = \begin{pmatrix} \mathcal{L}_{11} & \mathcal{L}_{12} \\ \mathcal{L}_{21} & \mathcal{L}_{22} \end{pmatrix}, \quad \mathcal{D} = \frac{\partial}{\partial x}, \quad (11)$$

$$\mathcal{L}_{11} = (\mathcal{D}^2 - k^2)^{-1}\left[k_y U (\mathcal{D}^2 - k^2) - k_y U'' - \frac{1}{iRe}(\mathcal{D}^2 - k^2)^2\right],$$

$$\mathcal{L}_{12} = (\mathcal{D}^2 - k^2)^{-1}\frac{2k_z}{q},$$

$$\mathcal{L}_{21} = -\left(U' + \frac{2}{q}\right)k_z,$$

$$\mathcal{L}_{22} = k_y U - \frac{1}{iRe}(\mathcal{D}^2 - k^2),$$

and

$$\Gamma = e^{-i\mathbf{k}\cdot\mathbf{r}}\begin{pmatrix}(\mathcal{D}^2 - k^2)^{-1}\Gamma_1\\ \Gamma_2\end{pmatrix}. \tag{12}$$

Let us subsequently assume the trial solution of the equation (10) be

$$Q = AQ_x e^{-i\sigma t} - \frac{1}{\mathcal{D}_t + i\mathcal{L}}\Gamma, \tag{13}$$

where σ is the eigenvalue corresponding to the particular mode and it is complex having real (σ_r) and imaginary (σ_i) parts,

$$Q_x = \begin{pmatrix}\phi^u(x)\\ \phi^\zeta(x)\end{pmatrix} \tag{14}$$

and $\mathcal{D}_t$ stands for $\partial/\partial t$. Q_x is the eigenfunction corresponding to the homogeneous part of the equation (10), i.e., Q_x satisfies $\mathcal{L}Q_x = \sigma Q_x$. The first term of the right-hand side of the equation (13) is due to the homogeneous part of the equation (10), and the second term is due to the inhomogeneous part, i.e., the presence of Γ, of the same equation. Hence, Q is influenced by the force Γ. However, the typical eigenspectra for the Keplerian flow ($q = 1.5$), constant angular momentum flow ($q = 2$) and plane Couette flow ($q \to \infty$) for $Re = 2000$ and $k_y = k_z = 1$ are shown in the Fig. 2. Since $\mathcal{L}_{12}$ and $\mathcal{L}_{21}$ in the equation (11) are zero for the plane Couette flow and constant angular momentum flow, respectively, we obtain the same eigenspectra for both plane Couette, and constant angular momentum flows. We perform the whole analysis for the least stable modes for the respective flows, and these least stable modes are shown in the dotted box in Fig. 2.

2.2. Nonlinear theory

For the non-linear solution, following similar work but in the absence of force,[20-22] we assume the series solution for velocity and vorticity, i.e.

$$\psi = \sum_{n\to-\infty}^{\infty}\psi_n = \sum_{n\to-\infty}^{\infty}\bar{\psi}_n(t,x)e^{in(\mathbf{k}\cdot\mathbf{r}-\sigma_r t)}, \tag{15}$$

when obviously $\bar{\psi}_{-n} = \bar{\psi}_n^*$ and ψ could be any one of u and ζ.

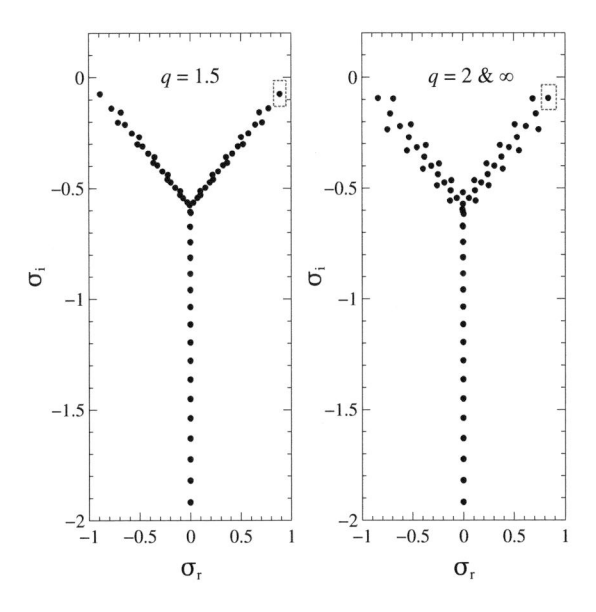

Fig. 2. Variation of σ_i with σ_r for $Re = 2000$ and $k_y = k_z = 1$ for the Keplerian flow ($q = 1.5$), constant angular momentum flow ($q = 2$) and plane Couette flow ($q \to \infty$). The latter two eigenspectra are identical. The dotted box represents the least stable mode for the respective cases.

We substitute these in equations (1) and (2) and collect the coefficients of the term $e^{i(\mathbf{k}\cdot\mathbf{r}-\sigma_r t)}$, to capture least nonlinear effect following, e.g.,,[12,20,22] from both sides and obtain

$$\frac{\partial Q_1}{\partial t} - i\sigma_r Q_1 + i\mathcal{L}Q_1 = NL_1, \tag{16}$$

where $NL_1 = \begin{pmatrix} \left(\mathcal{D}^2 - k^2\right)^{-1} NL_1^u \\ NL_1^\zeta \end{pmatrix}$ and $Q_1 = \begin{pmatrix} \bar{u}_1(x,t) \\ \bar{\zeta}_1(x,t) \end{pmatrix}$. We assume the solution for Q_1 to be

$$Q_1 = \sum_{m=1}^{\infty} A_{t,m} Q_{x,m} - \frac{1}{\mathcal{D}_t + i\mathcal{L}}\Gamma, \tag{17}$$

where m stands for various eigenmodes.

However, to the first approximation, our interest is in the least stable mode. Similar descriptions in two dimensions[20] without Γ and three-dimensional Keplerian disks[22] without Γ are already there in the in the literature and we mostly follow their formalism. We, therefore, omit the summation, and subscript m in the equation (17), and obtain

$$Q_1 = A_t Q_x - \frac{1}{\mathcal{D}_t + i\mathcal{L}}\Gamma. \tag{18}$$

We then substitute the equation (18) in the equation (16) and using biorthonormality between Q_x and its conjugate function $\tilde{Q}_x$, we obtain

$$\frac{dA_t}{dt} - \sigma_i A_t + \mathcal{N} = p|A_t|^2 A_t, \tag{19}$$

where

$$\mathcal{N} = \int_{-1}^{1} dx \tilde{Q}_x^{\dagger} \Gamma' \tag{20}$$

and

$$p = \int_{-1}^{1} dx \tilde{Q}_x^{\dagger} \mathcal{S}, \tag{21}$$

where

$$\Gamma' = -\Gamma + i\sigma_r \left(\frac{1}{\mathcal{D}_t + i\mathcal{L}}\right)\Gamma \tag{22}$$
$$= -\Gamma + i\sigma_r(t - i\mathcal{L}t^2)(1 + \mathcal{L}^2 t^2)^{-1}\Gamma,$$

$\mathcal{S}$ is the spatial contribution from the nonlinear terms. For the greater details, see Ghosh and Mukhopadhyay.[12]

Throughout the paper, Γ from the equation (12) has been decomposed as $\Gamma \rightarrow \Gamma \begin{pmatrix} 1 \\ 1 \\ 1 \end{pmatrix}$ by adjusting Γ_1 and Γ_2, as they are only the free parameters.

The evolution of $\mathcal{N}$ has been shown in Fig. 3 for the parameters mentioned in the figure. It shows that $\mathcal{N}$ becomes saturated beyond a certain time, and the saturation depends on Re. As Re increases, the saturation increases. Fig. 4 shows the variation of the least stable (the one in the dotted box in Fig. 2) as a function of Re in the case of the Keplerian flow. It tells us that the least stable mode approaches zero as Re is increased.

3. Results

Equation (19), which is a nonlinear equation, tells us about the evolution of the amplitude of the perturbation. To explore the evolution of linear and nonlinear perturbations, we use the equation (19) accordingly. For the evolution of the linear perturbation, we get rid of the nonlinear term in equation (19).

3.1. *Evolution of* $|A|_t$ *in the linear regime*

In the linear regime, the equation (19) becomes

$$\frac{dA_t}{dt} = \sigma_i A_t - \mathcal{N}. \tag{23}$$

This equation tells that at large t, $|A_t|$ becomes $|\mathcal{N}|/|\sigma_i|$.[12]

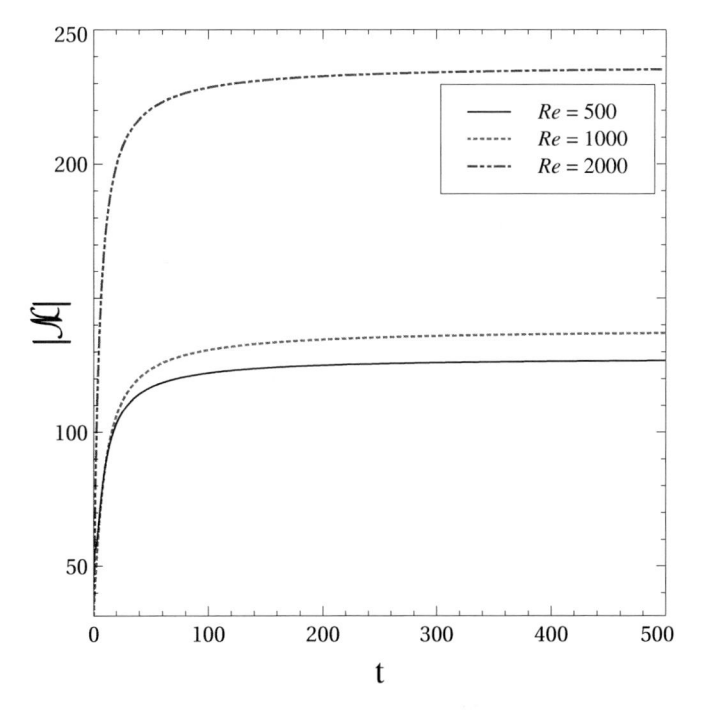

Fig. 3. Variation of $\mathcal{N}$ as a function of t for $Re = 500$, 1000 and 2000, for $\Gamma = 10^4$ and $k_y = k_z = 1$, corresponding to the respective least stable modes.

Fig. 5 shows the variation of $|A_t|$ as a function of t for various values of Re and Γ. Fig. 5 also suggests the scaling relation between saturated $|A_t|$ and Γ to be

$$|A_t| \propto \Gamma \tag{24}$$

for a fixed Re. Apart from that, we notice that for a fixed Γ, $|A|_t$ becomes saturated at $|\mathcal{N}|/|\sigma_i|$ beyond a certain time, and the saturation increases as Re increases. This saturation is independent of the initial condition.[12] This is because at a fixed Γ, $|\mathcal{N}|$ becomes saturated (see Fig. 3) at a fixed value, and the saturated value increases as Re increases, as well as $|\sigma_i|$ increases as Re increases (see Fig. 4). Now, in the accretion disk, Re is huge[19] ($\gtrsim 10^{14}$). The smaller Γ, therefore, can bring nonlinearity in the accretion disk, as for huge Re, $|\sigma_i|$ is infinitesimally small. Hence, $|\mathcal{N}|/|\sigma_i|$ becomes enormous. This huge saturation of $|A_t|$ could bring nonlinearity and hence plausibly turbulence in the underlying Keplerian flow.

3.2. Evolution of $|A_t|$ in the nonlinear regime

In the nonlinear regime, the evolution of $|A_t|$ is described by the equation (19). Fig. 6 describes the variation of $|A_t|$ as a function of t for nonlinear perturbation in the Keplerian flow. In the figure, $RE(A_t)$ and $IM(A_t)$ indicate the real and

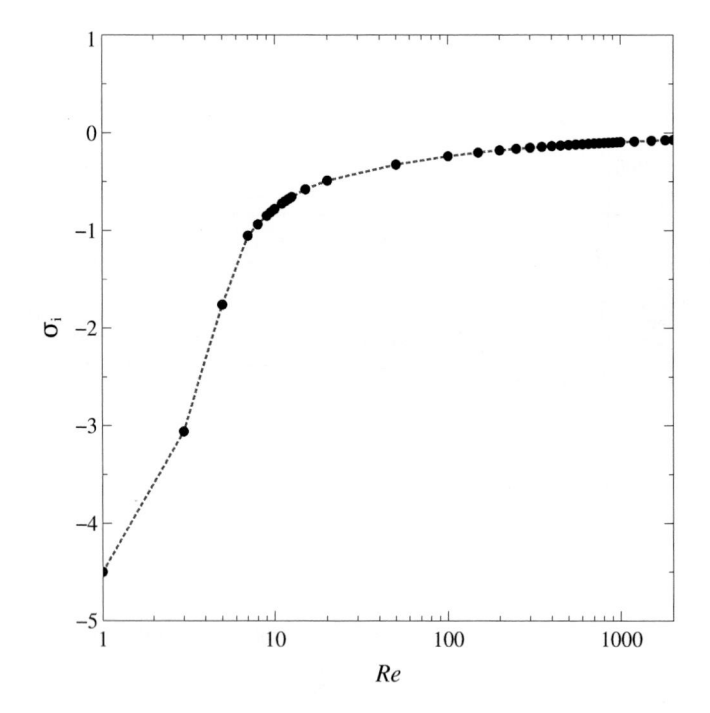

Fig. 4. Variation of the least stable σ_i as a function of Re for $k_y = k_z = 1$ in the Keplerian flow.

imaginary parts of initial A_t, respectively. It tells us that for $\Gamma = 0$, depending on the initial amplitude, $|A_t|$ may diverge (green line) or $|A_t|$ may decay (continuous black line) to zero from the initial amplitude. When there is no noise, i.e., $\Gamma = 0$, the diverging solution of $|A_t|$ occurs when the initial amplitude is beyond a critical amplitude.[12] It is apparent that the onset of the nonlinearity depends on the initial amplitude of perturbation in the absence of the force, but it does not depend on the same in the presence of force.[12] The divergence of $|A_t|$ and hence the onset of nonlinearity and plausible turbulence depends only on the strength of the force, as shown by dashed (magenta) line, compared to dot-dashed (blue) and dotted (red) lines, in Fig. 6.

4. Conclusion

If there is no extra force involved in the system, then the equation (19) becomes the usual Landau equation, which is

$$\frac{dA_t}{dt} = \sigma_i A_t + p|A_t|^2 A_t, \qquad (25)$$

which can be further recast to

$$\frac{d|A|^2}{dt} = k_1 |A|^2 + k_2 |A|^4, \qquad (26)$$

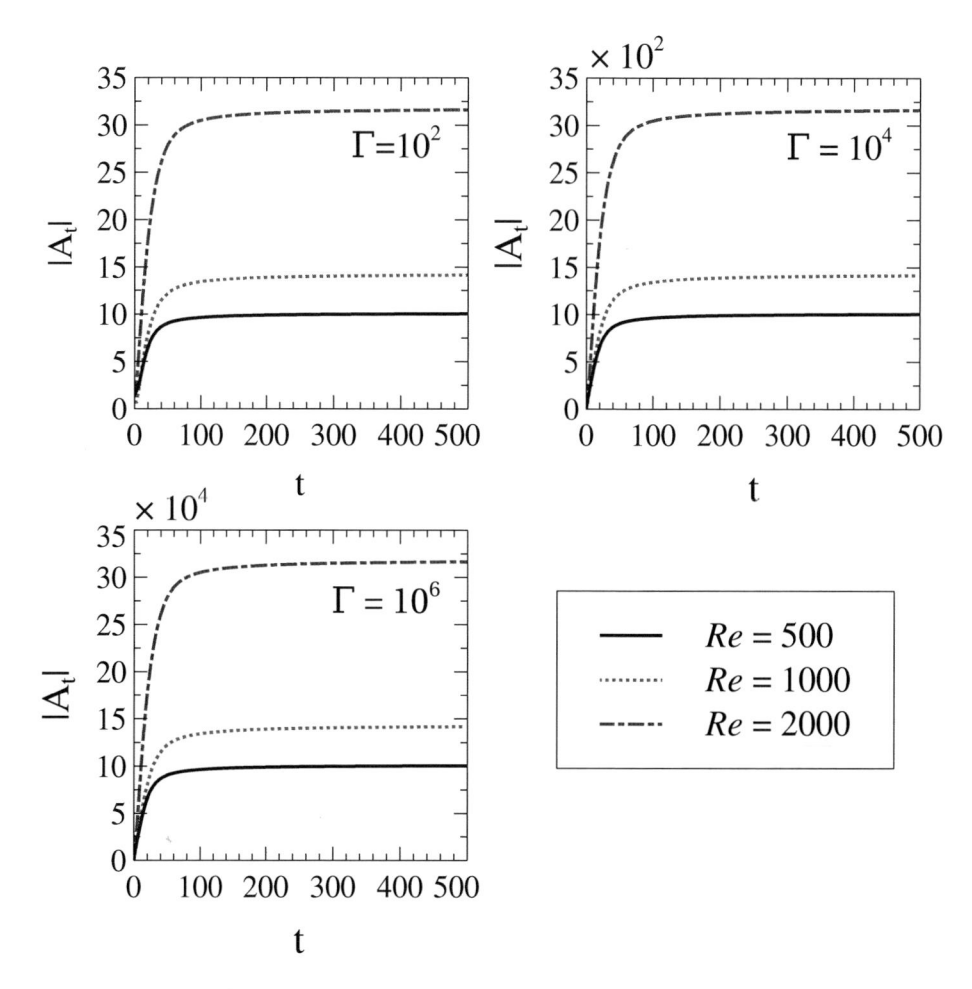

Fig. 5. Variation of $|A_t|$ as a function of t for three sets of Re and Γ with $k_y = k_z = 1$ for linear analysis in the Keplerian flow ($q = 1.5$).

where A is the amplitude of the nonlinear perturbations for the corresponding system, k_1 is $2\sigma_i$ and k_2 is the real part of $2p$, i.e., $2p_r$. Its solution is

$$|A|^2 = \frac{A_0^2}{-\frac{k_2}{k_1}A_0^2 + \left(1 + \frac{k_2}{k_1}A_0^2\right)e^{-k_1 t}}, \qquad (27)$$

where A_0 is the initial amplitude. Depending on the sign (positive/negative) of k_1 and k_2, there are four[21,23] different possible evolutions of $|A|$. These given below.

- In the present context of shear flows, k_1 (i.e., σ_i) is negative, but k_2 is positive. Therefore, there will be a threshold for initial amplitude A_i, determining the growth of perturbation. If the initial amplitude $A_0 < A_i$,

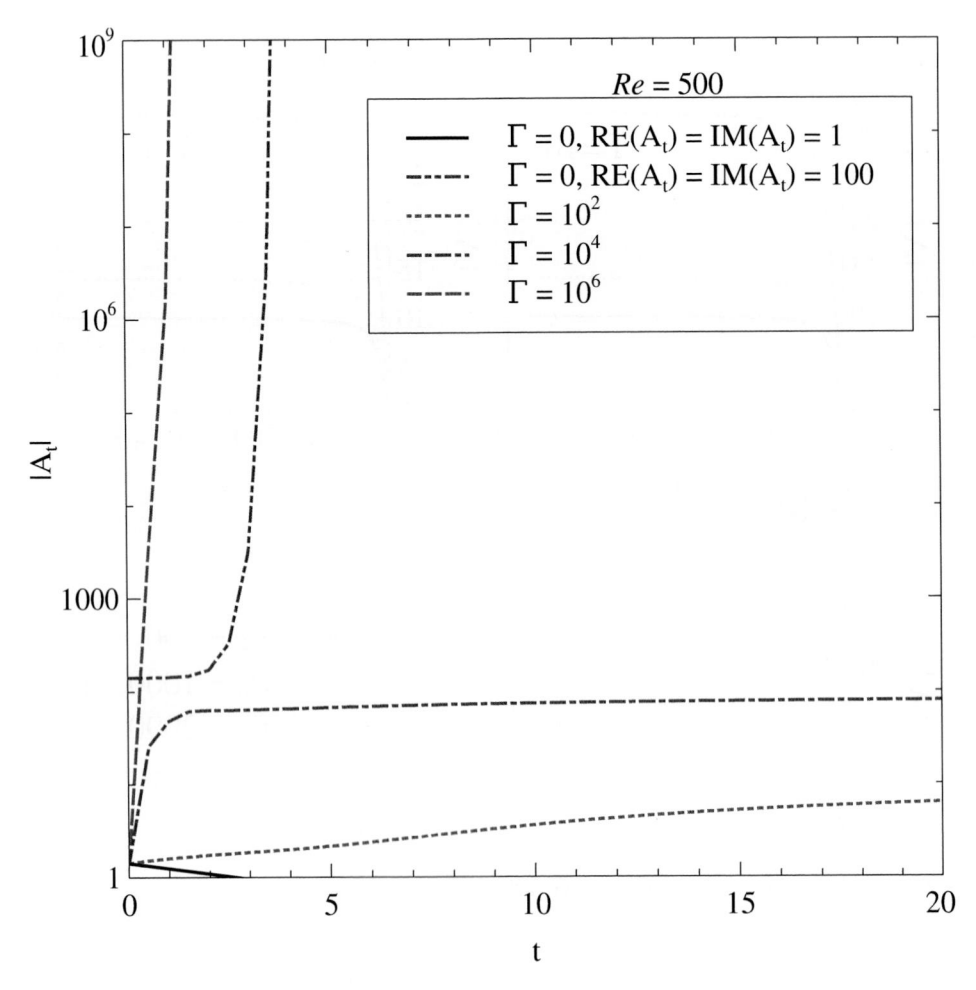

Fig. 6. Variation of $|A_t|$ as a function of t with $k_y = k_z = 1$ for nonlinear analysis in the Keplerian flow for $Re = 500$ and four different Γ. For $\Gamma \neq 0$, initial condition is $\text{RE}(A_t) = \text{IM}(A_t) = 1$.

then
$$|A|^2 \sim \frac{A_i^2 A_0^2 e^{k_1 t}}{A_i^2 - A_0^2} \qquad (28)$$

at a large t. Therefore, $|A|^2 \to 0$ for $A_0 < A_i$ at $t \to \infty$. However, if $A_0 > A_i$, then $|A|^2 \to \infty$ at $t \to \ln(1 - A_i^2/A_0^2)/k_1$.
- If both k_1 and k_2 would be positive, $|A|^2$ blows up after a finite time. Hence, there will be a fast transition to turbulence.
- On the other hand, if $k_1 > 0$ but $k_2 < 0$, then $|A|^2 \to k_1/|k_2|$ at $t \to \infty$. In this case, $|A|^2$ at a large t does not depend on A_0.
- Obviously, for k_1 and k_2 both negative, $|A|^2$ decays fast.

However, we have shown that the saturation in $|A_t|$ is $|\mathcal{N}|/|\sigma_i|$ in the linear regime. We have also argued that depending on Re and Γ, the system may already be in the nonlinear regime. The evolution of $|A_t|$ at the linear regime in our case, i.e., with extra force, is similar to that of $|A|$ from the equation (26), i.e. without force, for $k_1 > 0$ and $k_2 < 0$. In the Keplerian flow, k_1, i.e. σ_i, is negative, but k_2, i.e. p_r, could be positive. In the presence of extra force, the Landau equation modifies in such a way that the solution in the linear regime itself mimics the Landau equation without force (i.e., equation 26), however, with $k_1 > 0$ and $k_2 < 0$. Further, in the nonlinear regime, the amplitude A_t (i.e., with extra force included) diverges beyond a certain time, depending on Re and Γ. In the nonlinear regime, the Landau equation in the presence of extra force but negative k_1 (σ_i) is, therefore, mimicking the Landau equation without force but with positive k_1 and k_2. Essentially, the extra force effectively changes the sign of k_1 (i.e., σ_i) for the Landau equation without force. Speaking in another way, the very presence of extra force destabilizes the otherwise stable system. Thus, the presence of force plays an important role in developing nonlinearity and turbulence in the case of Rayleigh stable flows.

Acknowledgment

S.G. acknowledges DST India for INSPIRE fellowship. This work is partly supported by a fund of Department of Science and Technology (DST-SERB) with research Grant No. DSTO/PPH/BMP/1946 (EMR/2017/001226).

References

1. N. I. Shakura and R. A. Sunyaev, Black holes in binary systems. Observational appearance, *Astronomy & Astrophysics* **24**, 337 (1973).
2. D. Lynden-Bell and J. E. Pringle, The Evolution of Viscous Discs and the Origin of the Nebular Variables, *Monthly Notices of the Royal Astronomical Society* **168**, 603 (09 1974).
3. S. A. Balbus and J. F. Hawley, A powerful local shear instability in weakly magnetized disks. I - Linear analysis. II - Nonlinear evolution, *The Astrophysical Journal* **376**, 214 (July 1991).
4. E. Velikhov, Stability of an ideally conducting liquid flowing between rotating cylinders in a magnetic field, *Zhur. Eksptl'. i Teoret. Fiz.* **36** (05 1959).
5. S. Chandrasekhar, The Stability of Non-Dissipative Couette Flow in Hydromagnetics, *Proceedings of the National Academy of Science* **46**, 253 (February 1960).
6. X.-N. Bai, Wind-driven Accretion in Protoplanetary Disks. II. Radial Dependence and Global Picture, *The Astrophysical Journal* **772**, p. 96 (Aug 2013).
7. M. E. Pessah and D. Psaltis, The Stability of Magnetized Rotating Plasmas with Superthermal Fields, *The Astrophysical Journal* **628**, 879 (August 2005).
8. U. Das, M. C. Begelman and G. Lesur, Instability in strongly magnetized accretion discs: A global perspective, *Monthly Notices of the Royal Astronomical Society* **473**, 2791 (2018).
9. S. K. Nath and B. Mukhopadhyay, Origin of nonlinearity and plausible turbulence by hydromagnetic transient growth in accretion disks: Faster growth rate than magnetorotational instability, *Physical Review E* **92**, p. 023005 (August 2015).

10. T. Singh Bhatia and B. Mukhopadhyay, Exploring non-normality in magnetohydrodynamic rotating shear flows: Application to astrophysical accretion disks, *Physical Review Fluids* **1**, p. 063101 (October 2016).
11. S. K. Nath and B. Mukhopadhyay, A Pure Hydrodynamic Instability in Shear Flows and Its Application to Astrophysical Accretion Disks, *The Astrophysical Journal* **830**, p. 86 (October 2016).
12. S. Ghosh and B. Mukhopadhyay, Hydrodynamical instability with noise in the Keplerian accretion discs: modified Landau equation, *Monthly Notices of the Royal Astronomical Society* **496**, 4191 (August 2020).
13. B. Mukhopadhyay, N. Afshordi and R. Narayan, Bypass to Turbulence in Hydrodynamic Accretion Disks: An Eigenvalue Approach, *The Astrophysical Journal* **629**, 383 (August 2005).
14. B. Mukhopadhyay, R. Mathew and S. Raha, Growing pseudo-eigenmodes and positive logarithmic norms in rotating shear flows, *New Journal of Physics* **13**, p. 023029 (February 2011).
15. S. Ghosh and B. Mukhopadhyay, Forced linear shear flows with rotation: rotating couette-poiseuille flow, its stability and astrophysical implications (2021).
16. Yecko, P. A., Accretion disk instability revisited - transient dynamics of rotating shear flow, *Astronomy & Astrophysics* **425**, 385 (2004).
17. N. Afshordi, B. Mukhopadhyay and R. Narayan, Bypass to Turbulence in Hydrodynamic Accretion: Lagrangian Analysis of Energy Growth, *The Astrophysical Journal* **629**, 373 (August 2005).
18. F. Rincon, G. I. Ogilvie and C. Cossu, On self-sustaining processes in Rayleigh-stable rotating plane Couette flows and subcritical transition to turbulence in accretion disks, *Astronomy & Astrophysics* **463**, 817 (Mar 2007).
19. B. Mukhopadhyay and A. K. Chattopadhyay, Stochastically driven instability in rotating shear flows, *Journal of Physics A Mathematical General* **46**, p. 035501 (January 2013).
20. T. Ellingsen, B. Gjevik and E. Palm, On the non-linear stability of plane Couette flow, *Journal of Fluid Mechanics* **40**, 97 (1970).
21. P. Schmid, D. Henningson and D. Jankowski, Stability and Transition in Shear Flows. Applied Mathematical Sciences, *Applied Mechanics Reviews* **55**, p. B57 (2002).
22. S. R. Rajesh, Weakly non-linear stability of a hydrodynamic accretion disc, *Monthly Notices of the Royal Astronomical Society* **414**, 691 (June 2011).
23. P. G. Drazin and W. H. Reid, *Hydrodynamic Stability* September 2004.

Properties of accretion disc models in the background quadrupole

Shokoufe Faraji

University of Bremen, Center of Applied Space Technology and Microgravity (ZARM), 28359 Germany

We consider a static and axially symmetric metric containing two quadrupole parameters. In the present contribution, we study the quadrupole moments constraints on the properties of the relativistic accretion disc models, also explore the relation of oscillatory frequencies of charged particles to the frequencies of the twin high-frequency quasi-periodic oscillations observed in some microquasars. We also compare the results with Schwarzschild and Kerr metrics.

Keywords: Accretion discs; Quadrupole moment; Black hole physics; QPOs

1. Introduction

In this paper, we are interested in studying how the presence of quadrupole moments in the metric affects the nature of astrophysical properties. This metric may link the observable effects to the system due to taking these parameters as the new dynamical degrees of freedom.

The first static and axially symmetric solution of Einstein equation containing arbitrary quadrupole moment were described in.[1] Later, Zipoy and Voorhees[2,3] found an equivalent transformation which can be treated analytically. Later on, with introducing a new parameter is known as q-metric.[4] In this regard, quadrupoles can be seen as perturbation parameters of the Schwarzschild spacetime from a dynamical point of view. This metric represents the exterior gravitational field of an isolated static axisymmetric mass distribution. Of course, there are different ways of including quadrupole in the metric, but we consider ones that can be treated analytically. One simple and straightforward extension of q-metric involves introducing an external field in addition to the dynamical metric. This class of theories is referred to as generalized q-metric. The astrophysical motivation for choosing such fields is the possibility to constitute a reasonable model for a more realistic situation occurring in vicinity of compact objects.

This work studies thin and magnetized thick accretion disc models,[5] and quasi-periodic oscillations (QPOs)[6] in this static and axisymmetric background.

2. q-metric with an external source

Most of the astrophysical studies considered the Kerr black hole. However, here, we choose to work on the generalized q-metric that considers the existence of a static and axially symmetric external distribution of matter in its vicinity up to quadrupole like adding a magnetic surrounding.[7] In fact, due to their strong gravitational field, compact objects are not necessarily isolated or spherically symmetric as a response to their environments. This metric describes the outer of a deformed compact object up to quadrupole and reads as[8]

$$ds^2 = -\left(\frac{x-1}{x+1}\right)^{(1+\alpha)} e^{2\hat{\psi}} dt^2 + M^2(x^2-1)e^{-2\hat{\psi}}$$
$$\times \left(\frac{x+1}{x-1}\right)^{(1+\alpha)} \left[\left(\frac{x^2-1}{x^2-y^2}\right)^{\alpha(2+\alpha)} e^{2\hat{\gamma}}\right.$$
$$\left.\times \left(\frac{dx^2}{x^2-1} + \frac{dy^2}{1-y^2}\right) + (1-y^2)d\phi^2\right], \quad (1)$$

where $t \in (-\infty, +\infty)$, $x \in (1, +\infty)$, $y \in [-1, 1]$, $\phi \in [0, 2\pi)$, and in principle $\alpha \in (-1, \infty)$. Metric function $\hat{\psi}$ plays the role of gravitational potential, and once we have it by an integration of its explicit form, $\hat{\gamma}$ is obtained. These are given by

$$\hat{\psi} = -\frac{\beta}{2}\left[-3x^2y^2 + x^2 + y^2 - 1\right], \quad (2)$$

$$\hat{\gamma} = -2x\beta(1-y^2)$$
$$+ \frac{\beta^2}{4}(x^2-1)(1-y^2)(-9x^2y^2 + x^2 + y^2 - 1). \quad (3)$$

By its construction, this metric is valid locally.[9] This metric has two parameters aside from the mass; deformation parameter α and distortion parameter β, which are not independent of each other. These are chosen to be relatively small and connected to the q-metric and the surrounding external mass distribution, respectively. It can easily be checked that for vanishing β we recover the q-metric, and in the limits $\alpha = 0$ and $\beta \neq 0$ distorted Schwarzschild written in the prolate spheroidal coordinates,[9] and for $\alpha = 0$ and $\beta = 0$ we recover the Schwarzschild solution. The relation between the prolate spheroidal coordinates (t, x, y, ϕ), and the Schwarzschild coordinates (t, r, θ, ϕ) is

$$x = \frac{r}{M} - 1, \quad y = \cos\theta. \quad (4)$$

To the end, we explore this background by analyzing the thick and thin accretion disc models, and Quasi-periodic oscillations.

3. Accretion discs

In this analysis, we consider two well known Thin and Thick analytical models of accretion onto a compact object.

3.1. *Thin model*

The standard thin disc model has been used to explain a variety of observations where gas is cold and neutral. Therefore, the coupling between the magnetic field and gas is negligible. In general, observations provide the luminosity and the maximum temperature of the disc that fit the data model.

In this model, the steady axisymmetric fluid configuration is assumed. In addition, as a result of the geometrically thin assumption, effectively, all physical quantities only depend on the vertical distance from the equatorial plane and the radial distance to the central object so that we can consider vertically integrated quantities. Therefore, the two-dimensional disc structure can be decoupled to one-dimensional configurations. One is responsible for the radial quasi-Keplerian flow another for the vertical hydrostatic structure.[10,11]

Three fundamental equations govern the radial structure of the thin disc model

$$(\rho u^\mu)_{;\mu} = 0, \tag{5}$$

$$u_\mu T^{\mu\nu}{}_{;\nu} = 0, \tag{6}$$

$$h_{\mu\sigma}(T^{\sigma\nu})_{;\nu} = 0. \tag{7}$$

where u^μ is the four-velocity of the fluid and ρ is the rest mass density, $T^{\sigma\nu}$ is the stress-energy tensor containing non-vanishing shear part, and $h^{\mu\nu}$ is the projection tensor. These equations, together with the radial velocity, which is stated in terms of surface density and mass accretion rate, alpha viscosity prescription and heat flow, govern the radial structure of the disc.[10,11]

For the vertical profile in the comoving fluid frame, the force due to vertical pressure gradient is balanced with gravity, the centrifugal force, and vertically Euler force. The pressure is the sum of gas pressure from nuclei and the radiation pressure, which in practical is derived from the relativistic Euler equation.[12]

Finally, by solving this system of linear equations, one obtains a unique solution for considering positive temperature and pressure. Besides quadrupoles, three parameters describe a thin disc solution in this background, namely M, mass accretion rate $\dot{M}$, and viscosity parameter α. Consequently, the geometric configuration of an accretion disc located around this space-time depends explicitly on the value of the quadrupole parameter. An analysis shows the astrophysical quantities possess almost the same pattern. Figure 1 shows the temperature and flux profiles for different values of quadrupole parameters. As it shows, the intensity of these quantities is much higher closer to the central object and for negative values than Schwarzschild and positive values. This links to the location of ISCO, which is considered the inner edge of the thin accretion disc. For negative quadrupoles, ISCO is closer to the central object, pushing away for positive ones. Therefore, for negative values, the inner part of the disc is located closer to the central object, which causes more intense characteristics in all quantities. It means the behaviour of positive quadrupole moments is smoother than negative ones in general. We may compare this result with the Kerr solution if we consider the rotation parameter a kind of quadrupole counterpart in this background. In the Kerr background, the intensity of these quantities for co-rotating is also smaller than the counter-rotating case. However, the main difference in the Kerr background is this pattern is valid everywhere, not only closer to the inner part of the disc. Therefore, in general, there are distinguishable differences in both cases regarding observational data.[13]

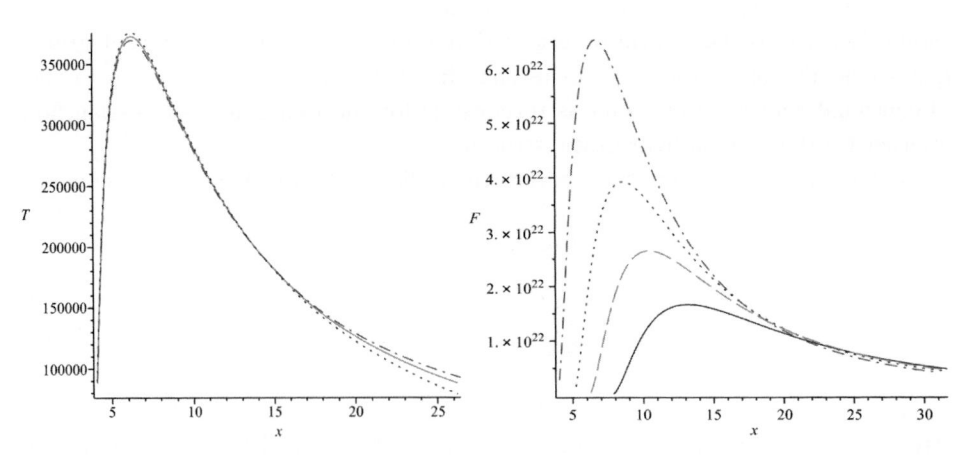

Fig. 1. The left plot is temperaturee T profile for $\alpha = -0.2$; blue line shows $\beta = -0.00001$, green one $\beta = 0$ (Schwarzschild), and red one $\beta = -0.00001$. The right plot is flux profile F for vanishing β (q-metric) and different values of α; from top $\alpha = -0.2$, $\alpha = 0$ (Schwarzschild), $\alpha = 0.2$, $\alpha = 0.5$.

3.2. Thick model

The thick disc model describes a general method of constructing perfect fluid equilibria in an axially symmetric and stationary background, which is the simplest analytical model of discs with no accretion flow and is radiatively inefficient. In this work, we considered its magnetic version. The evolution of an ideal magnetised fluid is described by the baryon conservation, energy-momentum conservation, and induction equation.[14,15] The final well known equation in this model reads as[16]

$$W - W_{\text{in}} + \frac{\kappa}{\kappa - 1}\frac{p}{w} + \frac{\eta}{\eta - 1}\frac{p_m}{w} = \int_{\ell_{in}}^{\ell} \frac{\Omega d\ell}{1 - \Omega \ell}, \qquad (8)$$

where $W = \ln|u_t|$, magnetic pressure and gas pressure are p_m and p, η and κ are parameters, and w is enthalpy. Therefore, one can construct this model by specifying Ω or ℓ to fix the geometry of the equipotential surfaces. In the constant case, the disc surface is fully determined by the choice of the potential in the inner part of the disc, W_{in}, independent of the magnetic field.[17] Thus, the value of angular momentum ,ℓ_0, determines the total potential.[16]

In this work we also considered two more angular momentum distributions; the power-law,[18] and the trigonometric function.[19] In the power-law distribution it is

assumed that
$$\Omega(\ell) = c\ell^n. \tag{9}$$

where by using this equation, the right hand side of the equation (8) can be calculated easily.[18] In the trigonometric function distribution, it is assumed that[19]

$$\ell(x,y) = \begin{cases} \ell_0 \left(\frac{\ell_K(x)}{\ell_0}\right)^\sigma (1-y^2)^\delta, & x \geq x_{\mathrm{ms}}, \\ \ell_0(\zeta)^{-\sigma}(1-y^2)^\delta, & x < x_{\mathrm{ms}}, \end{cases} \tag{10}$$

where $\ell_0 = \zeta \ell_K(x_{\mathrm{ms}})$, and ℓ_K is the Keplerian angular momentum in the equatorial plane, η, σ, and δ are parameters, and x_{ms} is the place of marginally stable orbit. In this model, one only needs to solve function F to obtain the solution[19]

$$\frac{\partial_x p}{\partial_y p} = \frac{\partial_x g^{tt} + \ell^2 \partial_x g^{\phi\phi}}{\partial_y g^{tt} + \ell^2 \partial_y g^{\phi\phi}} := -F(x,y). \tag{11}$$

Analysis of results shows that changing parameter β_c has a strong effect on the location and amplitude of the rest-mass density and spreading the matter through the disc for any chosen value of quadrupoles.

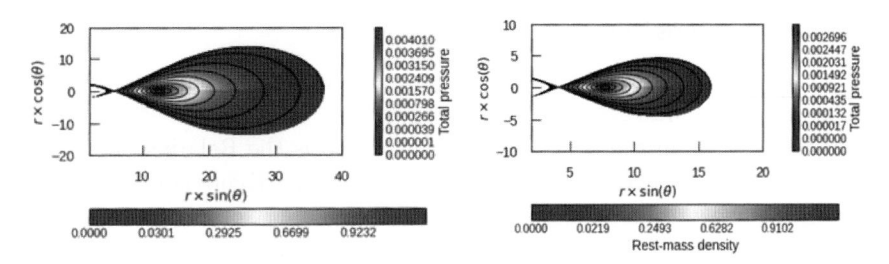

Fig. 2. The left plot is for $(\alpha, \beta) = (0.4, 0.000001)$, the right one is for $(\alpha, \beta) = (-0.1, 0.000001)$ with constant angular momentum.

In fact, a higher magnetic pressure causes the matter to concentrate more in the inner part of the disc. The rest-mass density maximum and its location also depend on the quadrupoles values. Although the effect of quadrupoles correlates with the other parameters, we can conclude that quadrupoles are more responsible for shifting the position of the disc and have a positive contribution to its radial extension. However, this effect for β is not easy to see, as the values of quadrupole parameters that we chose in our models are minimal.[20,21] Moreover, there is a possibility of having two tori in a row for any value of β but negative values for the parameter $\alpha \in (-0.5, -0.553]$. In Figure 3 this situation is plotted with constant angular momentum. However, with two other angular momentum distributions discussed in the paper it is also possible to have two tori.[20]

Furthermore, in the trigonometric distribution, the σ and δ parameters influence each other. However, one can say that σ is more responsible for the location and

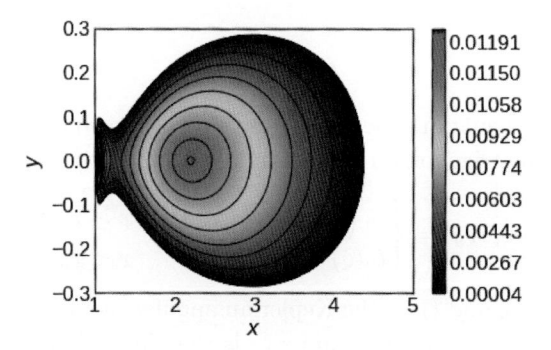

Fig. 3. Possibility to have two tori in a row for $\alpha \in (-0.5, -0.553]$ regardless of the β values.

amplitude of the rest-mass density, and δ affects the distribution of equidensity surfaces. In the case of the power-law distribution, steeper angular momentum tends to shrink the disc and decrease the amplitude of the rest-mass density and pushes away the location of its maximum simultaneously.

4. Quasi-periodic oscillations

Quasi-periodic oscillations (QPOs) of X-ray power spectral density have been observed at low (Hz) and high (kHz) frequencies.[22,23] There have been many models to explain QPOs in the past years. Among them is the Relativistic Precession Model (RPM), which relates the twin-peak QPOs to the Keplerian and periastron precession frequency on an orbit located in the inner part of the accretion disc.[24] Regarding, the high frequencies QPOs (the two-picks in Fourier power density spectra) are considered as the resonances between oscillation modes. Within the ratio 3 : 2 epicyclic resonance, the resonant frequencies are identified with frequencies of radial and vertical epicyclic axisymmetric modes.[25-27]

In this work, we are interested in the dynamics that occur when a static, axisymmetric central compact object is embedded in a weak uniform magnetic field of strength B aligned with the central body's symmetry axis and described by the ϕ-component of the vector potential[28]

$$A_\phi = \frac{1}{2} B(x^2 - 1) e^{-2\hat{\psi}} \left(\frac{x+1}{x-1}\right)^{(1+\alpha)}. \tag{12}$$

In addition, the specific energy and angular momentum of the particle read as[29]

$$E = \left(\frac{x-1}{x+1}\right)^{(1+\alpha)} e^{2\hat{\psi}} \frac{dt}{ds}, \tag{13}$$

$$L = (x^2 - 1) e^{-2\hat{\psi}} \left(\frac{x+1}{x-1}\right)^{(1+\alpha)} \left(\frac{d\phi}{ds} + Q\right), \tag{14}$$

where $Q := \frac{qB}{2m}$ is magnetic parameter. Further, the effective potential is

$$V_{\text{Eff}} = \left(\frac{x-1}{x+1}\right)^{(\alpha+1)} e^{2\hat{\psi}} \left[\epsilon + e^{-2\hat{\psi}} \left(\frac{x+1}{x-1}\right)^{\alpha} (1-y^2) \right.$$
$$\left. \times \left(\frac{Le^{2\hat{\psi}}}{(x+1)(1-y^2)} \left(\frac{x-1}{x+1}\right)^{\alpha} - Q(x+1)\right)^2\right], \quad (15)$$

The second term corresponds to the central force potential and electromagnetic potential energy. In what follows, we investigate the stability of circular motion in this background in the presence of a homogeneous magnetic field. We followed the method described in[30,31] and extend the result to this background. The results are in good agreement with these papers regarding vanishing quadrupoles, also rotation in their works.

We need to describe the more general class of orbits slightly deviated from the circular orbits in the equatorial plane x^μ using the perturbation expansion, $x'^\mu = x^\mu + \xi^\mu$. By considering this relation into the geodesic equation with non-vanishing external force and making the integration, for the t and ϕ components, up to linear order in ξ^μ, and we obtain[30,31]

$$\omega_x^2 = \partial_x U^x - \gamma^x{}_\eta \gamma^\eta{}_x, \quad (16)$$
$$\omega_y^2 = \partial_y U^y. \quad (17)$$

These equations describe radial and vertical oscillations of the charged particle about circular orbits. The sign of frequencies determines the dynamic ω_x^2 and ω_y^2 so that if they have a positive sign, we have a stable orbit; otherwise, even a minimal perturbation can cause a substantial deviation from the unperturbed orbit.

In Schwarzschild solution, the vertical epicyclic frequency is a monotonically decreasing function of x, and we have $\omega_x^2 < \omega_y^2 = \Omega^2$. On the contrary to the Schwarzschild case, the interesting situation in this background is to have various orderings among frequencies and thus different possibilities to reproduce the ratio of 3 : 2, also other ratios via different combinations of parameters[29] which is not the case in either Schwarzschild or in q-metric.

Among the various models of the resonance of accretion disc oscillations, we consider the group of QPO models (WD, TD, RP, Ep, Kp, RP1, RP2) considered in[32] and examined them in this background and compared with observational data of three microquasars XTE 1550-564, GRS 1915+105, and GRO 1655-40.[29,33] However, the physical details of these models are different and depend explicitly on the time evolution of the desired system. Indeed, the case of relatively slowly rotating XTE 1550-564 source is more compatible with our static set-up. However, different sets of parameters can fit the data even for the two other fast-rotating sources. An analysis shows for chosen parameters Q, α, and β, the best fit almost corresponds to RP2, RP, and RP1 models in low spin cases. Besides, results reveal that even the regular orbits for some combinations of parameters of metric turn to behave chaotically with a higher magnetic field.

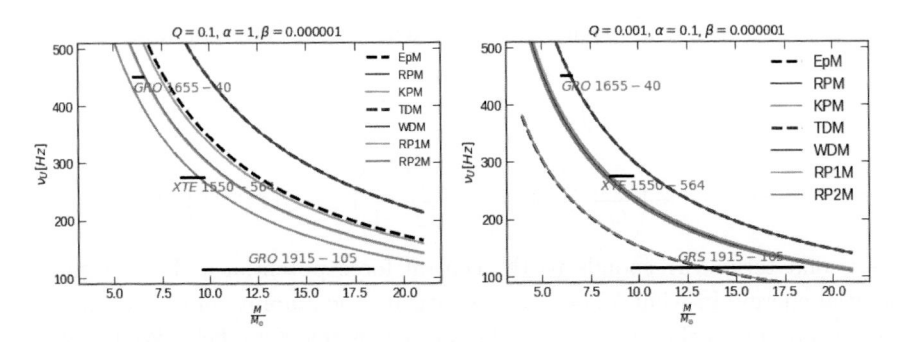

Fig. 4. The upper oscillation frequencies compared to the mass limits obtained from observations of three microquasars for some chosen parameters.

5. Conclusion

In this paper, we mentioned astrophysical features of two accretion disc models in the background of a compact object containing quadrupole moments. We have shown that the presence of quadrupoles changes the accretion disc's geometric properties in both models drastically. In particular, in the Thin accretion disc model, the spectral features would be significantly different and distinguishable in the observation from a black hole. The structure and the shape of the magnetized Thick accretion disc model are also influenced strongly by these parameters.

In addition, the dependency of these two parameters reflects into epicyclic frequencies of particles that cost substantial deviation from the correspondence quantities in the Schwarzschild case. In fact, the resonant phenomena of the radial and vertical oscillations at their frequency ratio 3 : 2 depending on chosen parameters, also in this background can be well related to the frequencies of the twin HF QPOs 3 : 2 observed in the microquasars. Although the fitting depends on the combination of parameters, we still can expect to have a better fitting for choosing a larger quadrupole moment in the combination.

Directions for the future could be adding the strong magnetic field which also influences the metric itself, considering rotation, studying the self-gravity of the Thin disc model, and studying the stability of this solution to extend this work. Further, this theoretical model can be served as the initial data for numerical simulations in the astrophysical setting.

References

1. H. Weyl, Zur gravitationstheorie, *Annalen der Physik* **359**, 117 (1917).
2. D. M. Zipoy, Topology of some spheroidal metrics, *Journal of Mathematical Physics* **7**, 1137 (1966).
3. B. H. Voorhees, Static axially symmetric gravitational fields, *Phys. Rev. D* **2**, 2119 (Nov 1970).

4. H. Quevedo, Mass Quadrupole as a Source of Naked Singularities, *International Journal of Modern Physics D* **20**, 1779 (Jan 2011).
5. M. A. Abramowicz and P. C. Fragile, Foundations of Black Hole Accretion Disk Theory, *Living Reviews in Relativity* **16**, p. 1 (January 2013).
6. A. R. Ingram and S. E. Motta, A review of quasi-periodic oscillations from black hole X-ray binaries: Observation and theory, *New Astronomy Reviews* **85**, p. 101524 (September 2019).
7. F. J. Ernst, Black holes in a magnetic universe, *Journal of Mathematical Physics* **17**, 54 (January 1976).
8. S. Faraji, A generalization of q-metric, *arXiv e-prints* , p. arXiv:2010.15723 (October 2020).
9. R. Geroch and J. B. Hartle, Distorted black holes., *Journal of Mathematical Physics* **23**, 680 (1982).
10. I. D. Novikov and K. S. Thorne, Astrophysics of black holes., 343 (1973).
11. D. N. Page and K. S. Thorne, Disk-Accretion onto a Black Hole. Time-Averaged Structure of Accretion Disk, *ApJ* **191**, 499 (July 1974).
12. M. A. Abramowicz, A. Lanza and M. J. Percival, Accretion Disks around Kerr Black Holes: Vertical Equilibrium Revisited, *ApJ* **479**, 179 (April 1997).
13. S. Faraji, Structure of the thin disk in the background of a distorted naked singularity versus a distorted static black hole, *arXiv e-prints* , p. arXiv:2011.06634 (November 2020).
14. A. M. Anile, *Relativistic fluids and magneto-fluids : with applications in astrophysics and plasma physics* (Oxford Univ. Press, 1989).
15. W. G. Dixon, *Special relativity: the foundation of macroscopic physics.* (Oxford Univ. Press, 1978).
16. S. S. Komissarov, Magnetized tori around kerr black holes: analytic solutions with a toroidal magnetic field, *Monthly Notices of the Royal Astronomical Society* **368**, p. 993–1000 (Apr 2006).
17. R. Okada, J. Fukue and R. Matsumoto, A model of astrophysical tori with magnetic fields, *PASJ* **41**, 133 (January 1989).
18. M. Wielgus, P. C. Fragile, Z. Wang and J. Wilson, Local stability of strongly magnetized black hole tori, *MNRAS* **447**, 3593 (March 2015).
19. L. Qian, M. A. Abramowicz, P. C. Fragile, J. Horák, M. Machida and O. Straub, The Polish doughnuts revisited. I. The angular momentum distribution and equipressure surfaces, *Astron Astroph* **498**, 471 (May 2009).
20. S. Faraji and A. Trova, Magnetised tori in the background of a deformed compact object, *Astron Astroph* **654**, p. A100 (October 2021).
21. S. Faraji and A. Trova, Effect of an external mass distribution on the magnetized accretion disk, *Phys. Rev.* **104**, p. 083006 (October 2021).
22. M. van der Klis, Millisecond Oscillations in X-ray Binaries, *Annu. Rev. Astron. Astrophys.* **38**, 717 (January 2000).
23. J. E. McClintock and R. A. Remillard, *Black hole binaries*, in *Compact stellar X-ray sources*, (Oxford, 2006), pp. 157–213.
24. L. Stella and M. Vietri, Lense-Thirring Precession and Quasi-periodic Oscillations in Low-Mass X-Ray Binaries, *ApJ* **492**, L59 (January 1998).
25. M. A. Abramowicz and W. Kluźniak, A precise determination of black hole spin in GRO J1655-40, *Astron Astroph* **374**, L19 (August 2001).
26. W. Kluzniak and M. A. Abramowicz, Strong-Field Gravity and Orbital Resonance in Black Holes and Neutron Stars — kHz Quasi-Periodic Oscillations (QPO), *Acta Physica Polonica B* **32**, p. 3605 (November 2001).

27. M. A. Abramowicz, D. Barret, M. Bursa, J. Horák, W. Kluźniak, P. Rebusco and G. Török, The correlations and anticorrelations in QPO data, *Astronomische Nachrichten* **326**, 864 (November 2005).
28. R. M. Wald, Black hole in a uniform magnetic field, *Phys. Rev. D* **10**, 1680 (Sep 1974).
29. S. Faraji and A. Trova, Dynamics of charged particles and QPO of related disk models in the background of a distorted, deformed compact object- I. embedded in a uniform magnetic field, *arXiv e-prints* , p. arXiv:2103.03229 (March 2021).
30. A. N. Aliev and D. V. Galtsov, Radiation from relativistic particles in nongeodesic motion in a strong gravitational field., *General Relativity and Gravitation* **13**, 899 (October 1981).
31. A. N. Aliev, D. V. Galtsov and V. I. Petukhov, Negative Absorption Near a Magnetized Black-Hole - Black-Hole Masers, *Astrophys. Space Sci.* **124**, 137 (1986).
32. G. Török, A. Kotrlová, E. Šrámková and Z. Stuchlík, Confronting the models of 3:2 quasiperiodic oscillations with the rapid spin of the microquasar GRS 1915+105, *Astron Astroph* **531**, p. A59 (July 2011).
33. S. Faraji and A. Trova, Quasi-periodic oscillatory motion of particles orbiting a distorted deformed compact object, *arXiv e-prints* , p. arXiv:2102.11871 (February 2021).

Magnetized tori around a uniformly accelerating black hole

Shokoufe Faraji, Audrey Trova

University of Bremen, Center of Applied Space Technology and Microgravity (ZARM), 28359 Germany

We generalize the relativistic accretion thick disc model to the background of a spinning charged accelerating black hole described by the C-metric to study the effects of this background on the disc model. We show the properties of this accretion disc model and its dependence on the initial parameters. This background can be distinguishable from the Kerr space-time by analyzing the observing features of accretion discs.

Keywords: C-metric; Magnetic field; Accretion disc; Black hole physics

1. Introduction

In this paper we investigate the spinning charged C-metric, with the aim of studying the properties of the well known magnetised Thick accretion disc model and the morphology of the equipotential surfaces.

The family of C-metric has accelerating nature and is considered as describing an accelerating black hole.[1] The spinning charged C-metric in Boyer-Lindquist-type coordinates[2] reads as

$$ds^2 = \frac{1}{\Omega^2}\left(-\frac{f}{\Sigma}\left[dt - a\sin^2\theta\frac{d\varphi}{K}\right]^2 \right.$$
$$\left. + \frac{\Sigma}{f}dr^2 + \Sigma r^2\frac{d\theta^2}{g} + \frac{g\sin^2\theta}{\Sigma r^2}\left[adt - (r^2+a^2)\frac{d\varphi}{K}\right]^2\right), \quad (1)$$

where

$$\Omega = 1 + \alpha r\cos\theta, \quad (2)$$

$$f(r) = \left(1 - \alpha^2 r^2\right)\left(1 - \frac{2m}{r} + \frac{e^2+a^2}{r^2}\right), \quad (3)$$

$$g(\theta) = (e^2+a^2)\alpha^2\cos^2\theta + 2m\alpha\cos\theta + 1, \quad (4)$$

$$\Sigma(r,\theta) = \frac{a^2}{r^2}\cos^2\theta + 1, \quad (5)$$

$$\xi = \alpha^2(e^2+a^2) + 1, \quad (6)$$

$$K = \xi + 2m\alpha, \quad (7)$$

where $t \in (-\infty, +\infty)$, $\theta \in (0, \pi)$, $r \in (0, +\infty)$. The metric has four independent parameters: the mass m, the electric charge e, the rotation a, and the so-called acceleration parameter α. In this metric $r = 0$ is the curvature singularity, and there is a conical singularity on the θ axis. The parameter K affects the distribution of conical defects in the space-time and allows φ to be 2π-periodic (see for example[3-5]).

Almost all studies with this metric are revolved around the coordinate ranges, which are dictated by the metric functions and their root configurations. The main constrains are

$$r_b = -\frac{1}{\alpha \cos \theta}, \tag{8}$$

$$e^2 + a^2 \leq m^2, \tag{9}$$

and

$$2m\alpha \leq \begin{cases} 2\sqrt{\xi - 1} & \xi > 2, \\ \xi & 0 < \xi \leq 2. \end{cases} \tag{10}$$

2. Properties of the disc model

The Thick accretion disc is an analytical model that provides a general method to build equilibrium configurations of the perfect fluid matter orbiting around a stationary and axially symmetric black hole.[6,7] In this procedure, we considered the approach of Komissarov[8] to attach a dynamically toroidal magnetic field to the model.

An analysis shows[9] that by increasing the acceleration parameter α, almost the possibility of having solutions decreases dramatically. On the contrary, the charge parameter e positively contributes to having solutions; mainly, its effect manifests more for a relatively large α. Furthermore, the possibility of having solutions for larger α depends on having large values for e, so the effect of higher α on the disc could be neutralized partially with the higher charge.

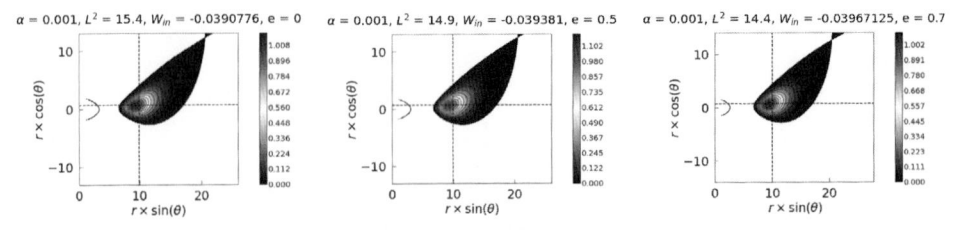

Fig. 1. Contour map of the rest-mass density of magnetised disc. The dashed lines point the center of the disc at $r_c = 10$. The discs are all highly magnetised disc.

The effect of rotation parameter a on having solutions is not strong compared to α but more substantial than the charge parameter e. In fact, parameter a, like α, has a negative effect on having solutions. In general, as e increases, we expect the matter is concentrated closer to the inner edge of the disc. On the contrary, the higher values of a spread the matter more through the disc. Moreover, Increasing a

decreases the size of the disc and change the distribution of matter. In addition, it shifts the disc farther from the compact object, contrary to an increase in e, which shift the disc closer to the central object.

For a fixed value of acceleration parameter α and vanishing rotation, the magnetization parameter does not influence the geometry of the disc; however, it changes the distribution of matter inside the disc and shifts the location of the rest-mass density maximum. In addition, we have a larger oriented disc for larger values of e.

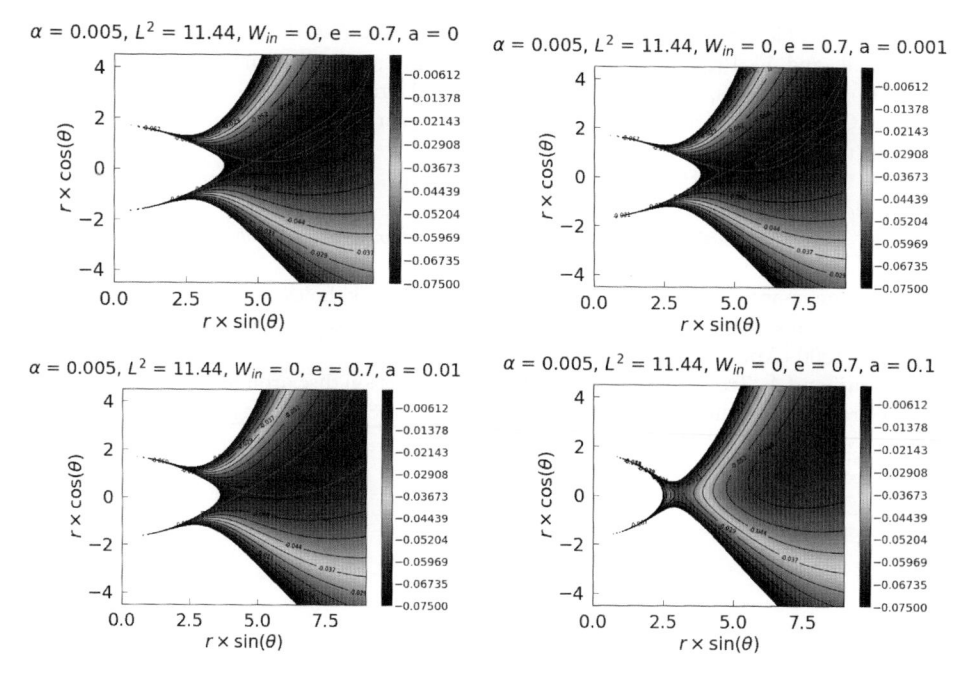

Fig. 2. Contour map of the equipotential surfaces. no solution for $\alpha = 0.005$ unless for high e and very low a. Show no solution for higher α and rotation.

3. Conclusion

In this work, we discussed the influence of the magnetisation parameter, charge e, rotation a, and accelerating parameter α in the spinning charged C-metric on the structure of the magnetised thick disc model.

In general, we can have the Thick disc model for relatively small values of α, while by increasing α, the disc structure becomes smaller and gradually vanishes. The same is true for a. On the contrary to these two parameters, an increase in e increases the disc size and possibility of having a solution. However, we should mention that the strength of the parameters are not the same, as α has the strongest and e has the weaker effect on the disc structure, in comparison.

A further step of this work can be a study on the oscillation of the disc in this setup which is in progress. In addition, this is interesting to examine the Thick disc model with different angular momentum profiles in this space-time.

References

1. W. Kinnersley and M. Walker, Uniformly accelerating charged mass in general relativity, *Phys. Rev. D* **2**, 1359 (Oct 1970).
2. K. Hong and E. Teo, A new form of the rotating C-metric, *Classical and Quantum Gravity* **22**, 109 (January 2005).
3. F. J. Ernst, Generalized c-metric, *Journal of Mathematical Physics* **19**, 1986 (1978).
4. J. Bičák and V. Pravda, Spinning C metric: Radiative spacetime with accelerating, rotating black holes, *Phys. Rev.* **60**, p. 044004 (August 1999).
5. J. B. Griffiths, P. Krtous and J. Podolský, Interpreting the C-metric, *Classical and Quantum Gravity* **23**, 6745 (December 2006).
6. A. M. Anile, *Relativistic fluids and magneto-fluids : with applications in astrophysics and plasma physics* (Oxford Univ. Press, 1989).
7. W. G. Dixon, *Special relativity: the foundation of macroscopic physics.* (Oxford Univ. Press, 1978).
8. S. S. Komissarov, Magnetized tori around kerr black holes: analytic solutions with a toroidal magnetic field, *Monthly Notices of the Royal Astronomical Society* **368**, p. 993–1000 (Apr 2006).
9. S. Faraji and A. Trova, Magnetised relativistic accretion disc around a spinning charged accelerating black hole, *arXiv e-prints*, p. arXiv:2108.07070 (August 2021).

Multifrequency behaviour of high mass X-ray binaries
(Time lag between optical and X-ray outbursts)

Franco Giovannelli

INAF - Istituto di Astrofisica e Planetologia Spaziali, Roma, Italy
Email: franco.giovannelli@iaps.inaf.it

In this work, without any claim to completeness, I will review the zoo of binary systems emitting X radiation, the multi-frequency behaviors of high-mass X-ray systems (HMXBs), with particular emphasis on the X-ray/Be system A 0535 + 26/HDE 245770, which for a favorable series of concomitant causes it is the most studied system. I will also discuss the time lag between events occurring in the high-energy and low-energy bands in galactic accreting systems.

Keywords: X-ray binaries; High mass X-ray binaries; individual: A 0535+26/HDE 245770; accretion, accretion disks

1. Introduction

Among X-ray emitters, X-ray binaries are cauldrons of fundamental physical processes which appear along practically the whole electromagnetic spectrum. The sub-class of X-ray transient sources show multifrequency behaviour which deserve particular attention in order to understand the causing physics. These binary systems consist of a compact star and an optical star, therefore there is a mutual influence between these two stars that drive the low energy (LE) (i.e. radio, IR, optical) and high energy (HE) (i.e. UV, X-ray, γ-ray) processes. The LE processes are produced mostly on the optical star and the HE processes mostly on the compact star, typically a neutron star. Thus it appears evident that through the study of LE processes it is possible to understand also the HE processes and vice versa. In this paper we will discuss this problem starting from the experimental evidence of a delay between LE and HE processes detected for the first time in the X-ray/Be system A0535+26/HDE245770 (e.g. Giovannelli & Sabau-Graziati;[40] Giovannelli, Bisnovatyi-Kogan & Klepnev[41] (here after GBK13); Giovannelli et al.[43]). This delay is common in cataclysmic variables (CVs) and other binary systems with either a neutron star or a black hole.

Giovannelli[30] published an extensive review about X-ray binary systems. Briefly we can summarize the main characteristics of these systems.

2. The zoo of X-ray binary systems

The trivial definition of X-ray binaries (XRBs) is that they are binary systems emitting X-rays. However it has been largely demonstrated that X-ray binary systems emit energy in IR, Optical, UV, X-ray, Gamma-ray and sometimes they show also valuable radio emission. They can be divided in sub-classes, namely:

1. High Mass X-ray Binaries (HMXB) in which the optical companion is an early type giant or supergiant star and the collapsed object is a neutron star or a black hole. They are concentrated around the galactic plane. The mass transfer is usually occurring via stellar wind; they show hard pulsed X-ray emission (from 0.069 to 1413 s) with $KT \geq 9$ keV; typical X-ray luminosity is ranging from 10^{34} to 10^{39} erg s^{-1}, and the ratio of X-ray to optical luminosity is $\sim 10^{-3}$–10. The HMXBs can be divided in two sub-classes:

1.1. Hard Transient X-ray Sources (HXTS) in which the neutron star is eccentrically (e $\sim$ 0.2–0.5) orbiting around a V-III luminosity-class Be star ($P_{orb} >$ 10 days); they show strong variable pulsed hard X-ray emission ($L_{Xmax}/L_{Xmin} >$ 100) with $KT \geq 17$ keV, and P_{spin} ranging from 0.069 to 1413 s; $L_X = 10^{34} - 10^{39}$ erg s^{-1}.

1.2. Permanent X-ray Sources in which the neutron star or black hole is circularly orbiting (e $\sim$ 0) around a giant or supergiant OB star ($P_{orb} <$ 10 days); they show an almost steady permanent pulsed hard X-ray emission ($L_{Xmax}/L_{Xmin} \ll$ 100), and P_{spin} ranging from 0.069 to 1413 s; $L_X \sim 10^{37}$ erg s^{-1}.

1.3. Supergiant X-ray Binaries (SGXBs): obscured sources, which display huge amount of low energy absorption produced by the dense wind of the supergiant companion, surrounded by a weakly magnetized neutron star.

1.4. Supergiant Fast X-ray transients (SFXT), a subclass of SGXBs and a new subclass of transients in which the formation of transient accretion discs could be partly responsible for the flaring activity in systems with narrow orbits. They show $L_{Xpeak} \approx 10^{36}$ erg s^{-1}, and $L_{Xquiecence} \approx 10^{32}$ erg s^{-1}.

2. Low Mass X-ray Binaries (LMXB) in which the optical companion is a low-mass-late-type star and the collapsed object is a neutron star or a black hole (P_{orb} from 41 min to 11.2 days). They are concentrated in the globular clusters, and in the halo around the galactic center. The mass transfer in these systems is usually occurring via Roche lobe overflow. Their emission in soft X-ray range is usually not pulsed with $KT \leq 9$ keV. Their X-ray luminosity is ranging from 10^{36} to 10^{39} erg s^{-1} and $L_X/L_{opt} \sim 10^2$–10^4; many LMXBs show Quasi Periodic Oscillations (QPOs) between 0.02 and 1000 seconds and few of them also pulsed X-ray emission, such as Her X1, 4U 1626-27 and GX 1+4.

Many LMXB show transient behaviour in the form irregular X-ray bursts, when their luminosity increases several tens or hundreds times. During these luminous stages, steady periodical signals, with millisecond periods, have been observed in several of them. In few of them ms X-ray pulsars have been discovered in quiescent stages between bursts. The ms X-ray pulsars in LMXB form a link between binary X-ray sources and recycled binary radio pulsars, with ms periods and low magnetic fields (Bisnovatyi-Kogan & Komberg[5]), which are formed on the place of these LMXB after ceasing of accretion, due to evolution of the companion star, transforming into low mass white dwarf, or a giant degenerate planet.

3. Cataclysmic Variables (CVs) in which the optical companion is a low-mass-late-type star and the compact object is a white dwarf. The detected CVs are spread roughly around the solar system at distance of 200-300 pc. Orbital periods are ranging from tens of minutes to about ten hours. The mass transfer is occurring either via Roche lobe overflow or via accretion columns or in an intermediate way depending on the value of the magnetic field. Typical X-ray luminosity is ranging from 10^{32} to 10^{34} erg s^{-1}. Updated reviews about CVs are those by Giovannelli[29] and Giovannelli & Sabau-Graziati.[42]

4. RS Canum Venaticorum (RS CVn) type systems, in which no compact objects are present and the two components are a F or G hotter star and a K star. Typical X-ray luminosity is ranging from 10^{30} to 10^{31} erg s^{-1}. Usually in the current literature they are excluded from the class of X-ray binaries since historically they were discovered as X-ray emitters only with the second generation of X-ray experiments.

In binary systems there are essentially two ways for accreting matter from one star to the other: via accretion disk or via stellar wind (Giovannelli & Sabau-Graziati,[37] adapted from Blumenthal & Tucker[7]) (left panel of Fig 1). But in some cases there is a third way which is a mixture between the two, as for instance in eccentric binary systems close to the periastron passage where a temporary accretion disk can be formed around the neutron star (e.g. Giovannelli & Ziółkowski[35]), like shown in the right panel of Fig. 1 (Giovannelli & Sabau-Graziati,[37] after Nagase[64]).

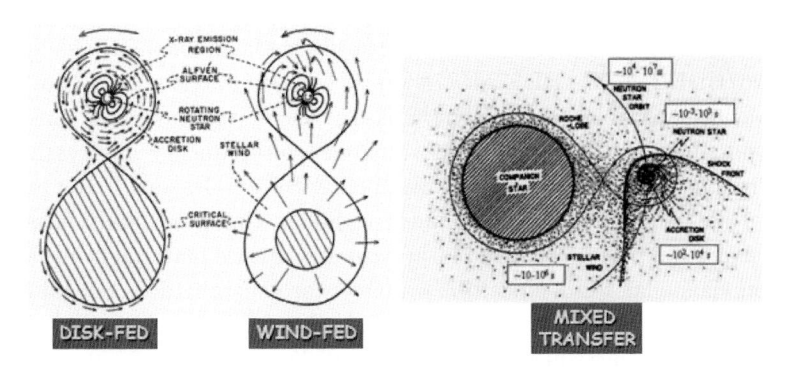

Fig. 1. Left panel: accretion in X-ray binary systems disk-fed and wind-fed (adopted from Giovannelli & Sabau-Graziati,[37] adapted from Blumenthal & Tucker[7]). Right panel: mixed transfer (adopted from Giovannelli & Sabau-Graziati,[37] after Nagase[64]).

XRBs are the best laboratory for the study of accreting processes thanks to their relative high luminosity in a large part of the electromagnetic spectrum. For this reason, multifrequency observations are fundamental in understanding their morphology and the physics governing their behaviour.

Because of the strong interactions between the optical companion and collapsed object, low and high energy processes are strictly related.

Often, it is easier to perform observations of low energy processes (e.g. in radio, near-infrared (NIR) and optical bands) since the experiments are typically ground-based, on the contrary to observations of high energy processes, for which experiments are typically space-based.

2.1. *High mass X-ray binaries*

Among the X-ray binaries, the class of High Mass X-ray Binaries (HMXBs) constitutes an important group for studying the interactions either via stellar wind either via accretion disk between the optical and the compact companions.

2.2. *X-ray/Be systems*

The X-ray/Be binaries are the most abundant group of massive X-ray binaries in the galaxy, with a total inferred number of between 10^3 and 10^4. The ones which do occasionally flare-up as transient X-ray/Be systems are only the "tip" of this vast "iceberg" of systems (van den Heuvel & Rappaport[46]). The mass loss processes are due to the rapid rotation of the Be star, the stellar wind and, sporadically, to the expulsion of casual quantity of matter essentially triggered by gravitational effects close to the periastron passage of the neutron star. The long orbital period (> 10 days) and a large eccentricity of the orbit (> 0.2) together with transient hard X-ray behavior are the main characteristics of these systems. Among the whole sample of galactic systems containing 114 X-ray pulsars (Liu, van Paradijs & van den Heuvel[56]), only few of them have been extensively studied. Among these, the system A 0535+26/HDE 245770 – HDE 245770 was nicknamed Flavia star by Giovannelli & Sabau-Graziati[36]) – is the best known thanks to concomitant favorable causes, which rendered possible forty six years of coordinated multifrequency observations, most of them discussed in the past by e.g. Giovannelli & Sabau-Graziati,[36] Burger et al.[9]), Piccioni et al.,[68] and later by Giovannelli & Sabau-Graziati[40] and Giovannelli et al.[43,44]). Accretion powered X-ray pulsars usually capture material from the optical companion via stellar wind, since this primary star generally does not fill its Roche lobe. However, in some specific conditions (e.g. the passage at the periastron of the neutron star) and in particular systems (e.g. A 0535+26/HDE 245770), it is possible the formation of a temporary accretion disk around the neutron star behind the shock front of the stellar wind. This enhances the efficiency of the process of mass transfer from the primary star onto the secondary collapsed star, as discussed by Giovannelli & Ziolkowski[35] and by Giovannelli et al.[38] in the case of A 0535+26.

Optical emission of HMXBs is dominated by that of the optical primary component, which is not, in general, strongly influenced by the presence of the X-ray source. The behavior of the primary stars can be understood in the classical (or almost) frame-work of the astrophysics of these objects, i.e. by the study of their spectra which will provide indications on mass, radius, and luminosity. Both groups of HMXBs (transient and permanent) differ because of the different origin of the mass loss process: in the first, the mass loss process occurs via a strong stellar wind and/or because of an incipient Roche lobe over-flow; in the second group, the mass transfer is probably partially due to the rapid rotation of the primary star and partially to stellar wind and sporadically to expulsions of a casual quantity of matter, essentially triggered by gravitational effects because of periastron passage where the effect of the secondary collapsed star is more marked. A relationship between orbital period of HMXBs and the spin period of the X-ray pulsars is shown in Fig. 2 (updated from Giovannelli & Sabau-Graziati[37] and from Corbet[20,21]). It allows to recognize three kinds of systems, namely disk-fed, wind-fed [$P_{pulse} \propto (P_{orb})^{4/7}$], and X-ray/Be systems [$P_{pulse} \propto (P_{orb})^2$].

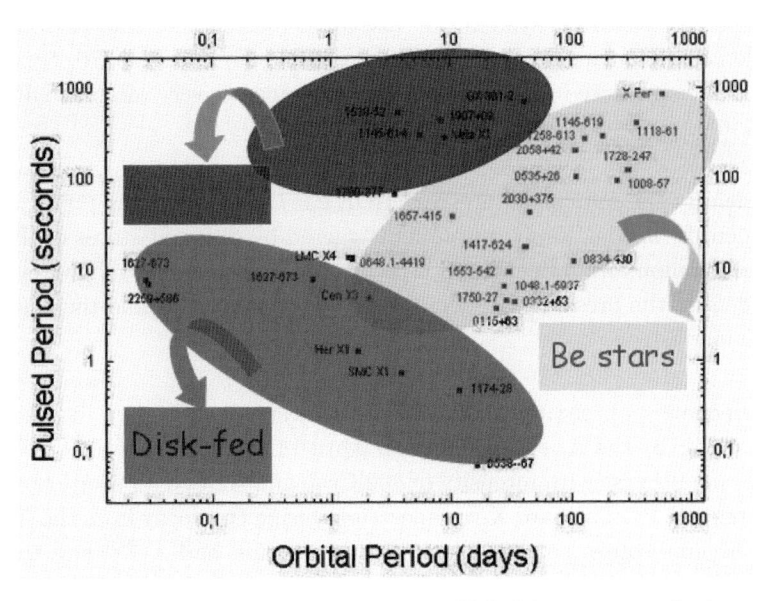

Fig. 2. Spin period vs orbital period for X-ray pulsars. Disk–fed systems are clearly separated by systems having as optical counterparts either OB stars or Be stars (adopted from Giovannelli & Sabau-Graziati,[37] after Corbet[20,21]).

Most of the systems having a Be primary star are hard X-ray (KT > 10 KeV) transient sources (HXTS). They are concentrated on the galactic plane within a band of ∼ 3.9°. The orbits are quite elliptic and the orbital periods large (i.e. A 0538-66: e = 0.7, P_{orb} = 16.6 days (Skinner et al.[76]); A 0535+26: e = 0.47 (Finger, Wilson & Hagedon[23]), P_{orb} = 111.0 days (Priedhorsky & Terrell[69]). The X-ray flux during outburst phases is of order 10-1000 times greater than during quiescent phases. For this reason, on the contrary, the stars belonging to the class of permanent X-ray sources, which do not present such strong variations in X-ray emission, can be also named "standard" high mass X-ray binaries. In X-ray/Be systems, the primary Be star is relatively not evolved and is contained within its Roche lobe. The strong outbursts occur almost periodically in time scales of the order of weeks-months. Their duration is shorter than the quiescent phases. During X-ray outbursts, spin-up phenomena in several systems have been observed (i.e. A 0535+26 and 4U 1118-61 (Rappaport & Joss[70]). The observed spin-up rates during the outbursts are consistent with torsional accretion due to an accretion disk (e.g. Ghosh[26]). So, the formation of a temporary accretion disk around the collapsed object should be possible during outburst phases (e.g. Giovannelli & Ziółkowski[35]).

3. Old & news from the transient X-ray/Be system A0535+26/HDE245770

The most studied HMXB system, for historical reasons and due to concomitant favourable causes, is the X-ray/Be system A 0535+26/HDE 245770. By means of long series of coordinated multifrequency measurements, very often simultaneously obtained, it was possible to:

- identify the optical counterpart HDE 245770 of the X-ray pulsar;
- identify various X-ray outbursts triggered by different states of the optical companion and influenced by the orbital parameters of the system;
- identify the presence of a temporary accretion disc around the neutron star at periastron.

Multifrequency observations of A 0535+26 started soon after its discovery as an X-ray pulsar by the Ariel-5 satellite on April 14, 1975 (Coe et al.[17]). The X-ray source was in outburst with intensity of ~ 2 Crab and showed a pulsation of ~ 104 s (Rosenberg et al.[73]). The hard X-ray spectrum during the decay from the April 1975 outburst became softer, so that the 19 May spectrum had $E^{-0.8}$ and the 1 June spectrum $E^{-1.1}$ (Ricketts et al.[71]). Between 13 and 19 April, 1975, as the nova brightened, the spectra showed some evidence of steepening. The best fit of the experimental data between roughly 27 and 28 April was compatible with an 8 keV black-body curve (Coe et al.[17]). The X-ray source decayed from the outburst with an e-folding time of 19 days in the energy range of 3-6 keV (Kaluzienski et al.[51]).

In the X-ray error box of the X-ray source A 0535+26, detected by Ariel V, were present 11 stars up to 23rd magnitude and one of them (HDE 245770) of magnitude around 9 showed the H_α and H_β in emission, H_γ filled in with emission, and H_δ, H_ϵ,..., H_{10} in absorption (Margon et al.[59]). A priori probability of finding a 9 mag star in such a field is 0.004, thus HDE 245770 was considered as the probable optical counterpart of A0535+26.

But in order to really associate this star with the X-ray pulsar, it was necessary to find a clear signature proving that the two objects would belong to the same binary system. This happened thanks to a sudden insight of the author, Franco Giovannelli (FG), who predicted the fourth X-ray outburst of A 0535+26 around mid December 1977. For this reason, Giovannelli's group was observing in optical HDE 245770 around the predicted period for the X-ray outburst of A 0535+26. Figure 3 shows the X-ray flux intensity of A 0535+26 as deduced by various measurements available at that time, with obvious meaning of the symbols used (Giovannelli[28]). FG's intuition was sparked by looking at the rise of the X-ray flux (red line) and at the 24th May 1977 measurement (red asterisk): he assumed that the evident rise of the X-ray flux would have produced an outburst similar to the first one, which occurred in 1975. Then with a simple extrapolation he predicted the fourth outburst, similar to the second: and this happened!

Optical photoelectric photometry of HDE 245770 showed significant light enhancement of the star relative to the comparison star BD +26 876 between Dec. 17 and Dec 21 (here after 771220-E) and successive fading up to Jan. 6 (Bartolini et al.[1]), whilst satellite SAS-3 was detecting an X-ray flare (Chartres & Li[16]). The observed enhancement of optical emission followed by the flare-up of the X-ray source gave a direct argument strongly supporting the identification of HDE 245770 – later nicknamed Flavia' star by Giovannelli & Sabau-Graziati[36] – with A 0535+26.

Soon after, with spectra taken at the Loiano 152 cm telescope with a Boller & Chivens 26767 grating spectrograph (831 grooves/mm II-order grating: 39 Å mm^{-1}) onto Kodak 103 aO plates, it was possible to classify HDE 245770 as O9.7IIIe star. This classification was so good that it survives even to the recent dispute attempts made with modern technology. The mass and radius of the star are 15 M$_\odot$ and 14 R$_\odot$, respectively; the distance to the system is 1.8 ± 0.6 kpc (Giangrande et al.[27]).

UV spectra taken with the IUE enabled the reddening of the system to be determined as E(B-V) = 0.75 ± 0.05 mag, the rotational velocity of the O9.7IIIe star ($v_{rot} \sin i = 230 \pm 45$ km s^{-1}), the terminal velocity of the stellar wind ($v_\infty \simeq 630$ km s^{-1}), the mass loss rate ($\dot{M} \sim 10^{-8}$ M$_\odot$ yr^{-1} in quiescence (Giovannelli et al.[33]). During the October 1980 strong outburst, the mass loss rate was $\dot{M} \sim 7.7 \times 10^{-7}$ M$_\odot$ yr^{-1} (de Martino et al.[61]).

Complete reviews of this system can be found in Giovannelli et al.,[34] Giovannelli & Sabau-Graziati,[36] and Burger et al.[9]

Briefly, the properties of this system, placed at a distance of 1.8 ± 0.6 kpc (Giangrande et al.[27]), can be summarized as follows: a hard X-ray transient, long-period X-ray pulsar – the secondary star – is orbiting around the primary O9.7IIIe star. The masses are of $\sim 1.5 \pm 0.3$ M$_\odot$ (Joss & Rappaport;[50] Thorsett et al.;[79] van Kerkwijk, van Paradijs, J. & Zuiderwijk[52]), and 15 M$_\odot$ (Giangrande et al.[27]) for the secondary and primary star, respectively. The eccentricity is e = 0.47 (Finger, Wilson & Hagedon[23]). Usually the primary star does not fill its Roche lobe (de Loore et al.[58]). However, the suggestion that there might be a temporary accretion disk

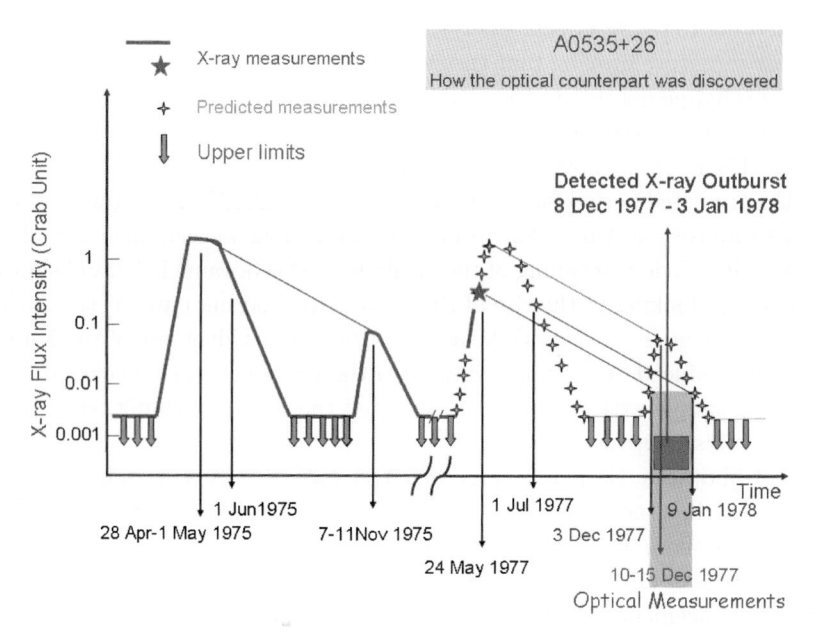

Fig. 3. X-ray flux versus time of A 0535+26. X-ray measurements are reported with red lines and asterisk, upper limits with green arrows, and predicted fluxes with light blue stars. Periods of real detected X-ray outburst and optical measurements are also marked (adopted from Giovannelli[28]).

around the X-ray pulsar when it approaches periastron (Giovannelli & Ziółkowski[35]) was confirmed by the X-ray measurements of Finger, Wilson & Harmon[24] and was discussed by Giovannelli et al.[38]

The first suggestion of Bartolini et al.[2] about the value of the orbital period ($P_{orb} = 110.856 \pm 0.002$ days), allowed Giovannelli & Sabau-Graziati[40] to discover a systematic delay (~ 8 days) of the X-ray outbursts with respect to the periastrons passages of the neutron star. Just a little before or simultaneously to the periastron, the system experiences an optical brightening ranging from ≈ 0.02 to ≈ 0.2 magnitudes.

The trigger of this discovery was the optical flare occurred at JD 2,444,944 (5th December 1981) (hereafter 811205-E; E stands for event) (Giovannelli et al.[34]) and followed by a short X-ray outburst (811213-E) (Nagase et al.[65]) – predicted by a private communication of Adriano Guarnieri (member of Giovannelli's group) to the team of Hakucho Japanise X-ray satellite. Unfortunately in the following years simultaneous optical and X-ray measurements were not always obtained around periastron passage. However, the available data were sufficient for showing the aforementioned systematic delay.

In order to explain and describe the 8-day delay between periastron passage and X-ray outbursts, GBK13 constructed a model adopting the orbital period determined by Priedhorsky & Terrell[69] from X-ray data ($P_{orb} = 111.0 \pm 0.4$ days), and the ephemeris $JD_{opt-outb} = JD_0(2,444,944) \pm n(111.0 \pm 0.4)$ days; the 111-day orbital period agrees within the error bars with many other determinations reported in the literature: from optical data (e.g. Guarnieri et al.;[45] de Martino et al.;[60] Hutchings;[47] Janot-Pacheco, Motch & Mouchet[48]), and from X-ray data (e.g. Nagase et al.;[65] Priedhorsky & Terrell;[69] Motch et al.;[63] Finger, Wilson & Harmon;[24] Coe et al.;[18] Finger et al.[25]).

4. Time delay between optical and X-ray outbursts in A 0535+26/HDE 245770

A description of the time–delay among many optical and X-ray events occurring around the periastron passages in the system A 0535+26/HDE 245770 have been presented in the papers by GBK13 and Giovannelli et al.[43,44] However, just to remark the importance of the experimental evidence of such a time–delay I will present a few more examples that in my opinion definitively support the validity of the model developed in GBK13. Briefly, the model is the following: in the vicinity of periastron the mass flux $\dot{M}$ increases (depending on the activity of the Be star) between $\approx 10^{-8}$ and $\approx 10^{-7}$ $M_\odot$ yr^{-1}. The outer part of the accretion disk – geometrically thin and optically thick without advection (Shakura & Sunyaev;[75] Bisnovatyi-Kogan[4]) – becomes hotter, therefore the optical luminosity (L_{opt}) increases. Due to large turbulent viscosity, the wave of the large mass flux is propagating toward the neutron star, thus the X-ray luminosity (L_x) increases due to the appearance of a hot accretion disk region and due the accretion flow channeled by the magnetic field lines onto magnetic poles of the neutron star. The time–delay τ is the time between the optical and X-ray flashes appearance. Figure 4 shows a sketch of this model.

By using the ephemerides given by GBK13, namely:

$$JD_{opt-outb} = JD_0(2,444,944) \pm n(111.0 \pm 0.4) \text{ days}$$

that fixed the reference point at the date 5th December 1981 (811205-E), it was possible to explain the behaviour of the system during the year 2014 (Giovannelli et al.[43]). It was possible not only to predict the arrival time of the X-ray outbursts following the optical flashes, but also the intensity I_x of the X-ray flares, thanks to the relationship I_x versus ΔV_{mag}, where ΔV_{mag} is the relative variations of the V magnitude of the Be star around the periastron passage with respect to the level before and after such a passage. This relationship is shown in Fig. 5 (adapted from Giovannelli et al.[44]).

An impressive strong optical event have been detected on March 19, 2010 (JD 2,455,275). On the basis of such a strong optical activity – especially H_γ in emission – Giovannelli, Gualandi & Sabau-Graziati[39] predicted the incoming X-ray outburst of A 0535+26, which actually occurred (Caballero et al.[11]). The X-ray intensity reached was 1.18 Crab on April 3, 2010 in the range 15–50 keV of BAT/SWIFT

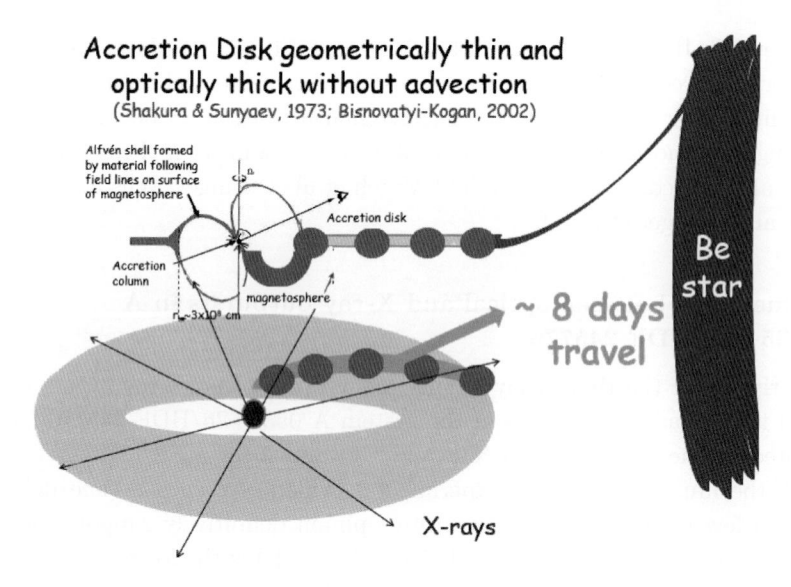

Fig. 4. Sketch of the viscous accretion disk model for explaining the time-delay between X-ray and optical flashes (adopted from:[41] GBK13).

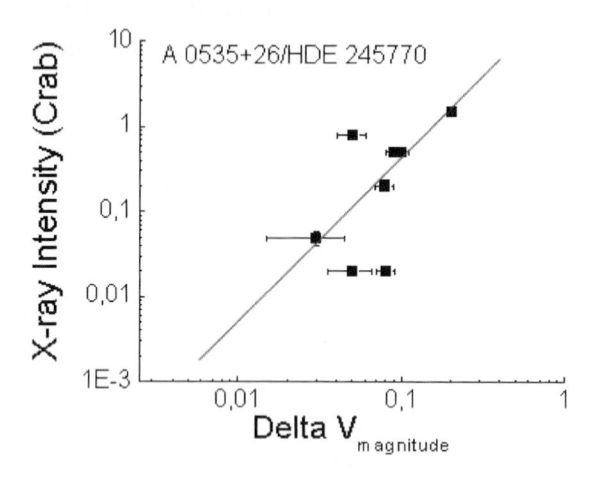

Fig. 5. Intensity of the X-ray flare of A 0535+26 versus the variation of V magnitude of HDE 245770 around the periastron passage (adapted from Giovannelli et al.[44]).

(Caballero et al.;[10–13] Caballero et al.[14]). Figure 6 shows the March–April 2010 event. The X-ray flare started about 8 days after the 93th periastron passage after the 811205-E, just when optical spectroscopy was performed by Giovannelli, Gualandi & Sabau-Graziati,[39] and reached the maximum about 12 days later and decayed in about 20 days roughly as occurred in 1975 when A0535+26 was discovered by the Ariel V satellite.

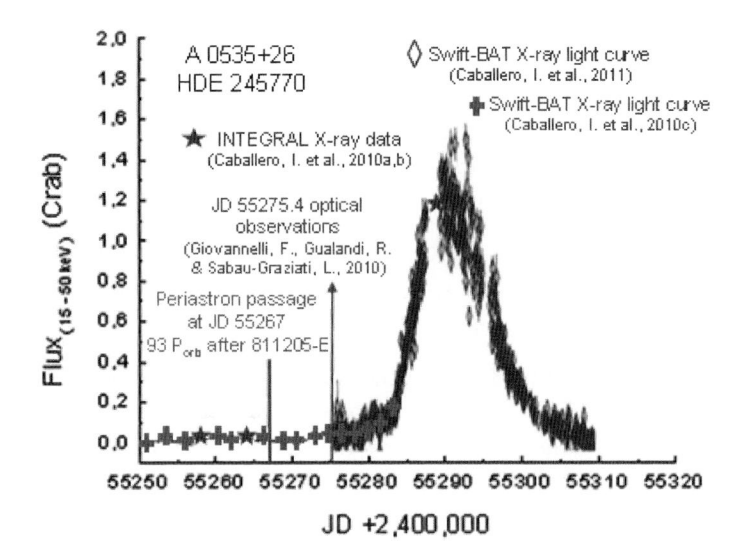

Fig. 6. The predicted March–April 2010 X-ray outburst of A 0535+26 (Giovannelli, Gualandi & Sabau-Graziati[39]) after the 93th passage at the periastron after 811205-E (Caballero et al.;[10–13] Caballero et al.[14]

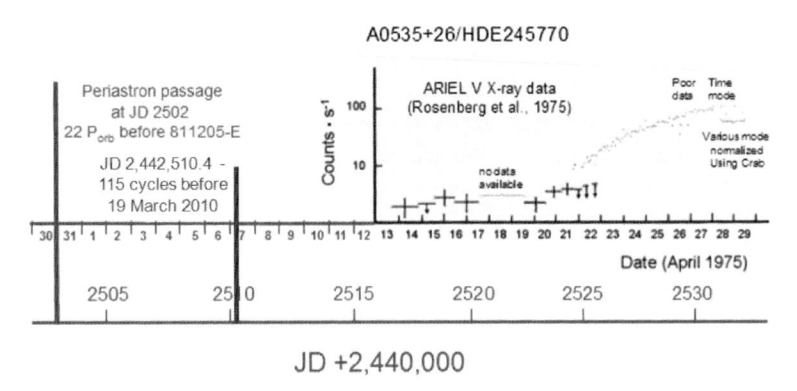

Fig. 7. The Periastron passage at the 22nd cycle before 811205-E (JD 2502) (red line) precedes of ∼ 14 days the X-ray outburst of A 0535+26 which starts approximatively on JD 2516 (after Rosenberg et al.[73]). The vertical blue line indicates the day April 7, 1975 (JD 2,442,510.4) just 115 cycles before the strong optical spectroscopic activity detected on March 19, 2010 (JD 2,455,275.4) (after:[41] GBK13).

The astonishing fact that definitively demonstrate the goodness of GBK13's ephemerides and the mechanism triggering the X-ray outburst with a time–delay with respect to the optical flare around the periastron passage is reported in Fig. 7. Indeed, in this figure, the measurements of the first detection of A 0535+26 by Ariel V satellite are reported. Unfortunately in 1975, around the time of the discovery of A 0535+26 no optical measurements are available for obvious reasons. The vertical red line indicates the time of the periastron passage following GBK13's ephemeris.

This passage occurred at the 22nd cycle before the 811205-E. The vertical blue line indicates the day April 7, 1975 (JD 2,442,510.4) just 115 cycles before the strong optical spectroscopic activity detected on March 19, 2010 (JD 2,455,275.4), that preceded the strong X-ray outburst reported in Fig. 6.

The similarity between the first X-ray outburst and that of March–April 2010 is evident, and the separation of the two events is exactly 115 cycles.

5. General model of time lag between optical and X-ray outbursts in binary accreting sources

In LMXBs (Low-Mass X-ray Binaries) the compact object can be either a neutron star or a black hole and the optical companion is a low mass star. The exchange of matter occurs via Roche lobe overflow, like shown in the left panel of Fig. 1. In HMXBs (High-Mass X-ray Binaries) the compact object can be either a neutron star or a black hole and the optical companion is a high mass star: giant or supergiant. The exchange of matter occurs mainly via stellar wind since usually the optical star does not fill its Roche lobe (Fig. 1, left panel). However, sometimes, the exchange of matter can occur in a mixed way because of the formation of an accretion disk around the compact object around the periatron passage (e.g. Giovannelli & Ziółkowski[35]) (Fig. 1, right panel).

As well known, X-ray/Be systems are formed by a compact star and an optical star. Obviously there is a mutual influence between the two stars. Low-energy (LE) processes influence high-energy (HE) processes and vice versa. Never confuse the effect with the cause. There is a general law in the Universe: **Cause and Effect**. The *Cause* generates an *Effect* and NOT vice versa!

It is right to remind that the mechanism proposed by GBK13 for explaining the X-ray-optical delay in A 0535+26/HDE 245770 is based on an enhanced mass flux propagation through the viscous accretion disk. This mechanism, known as UV-optical delay (the delay of the EUV flash with respect to the optical flash) was observed and modeled for cataclysmic variables (e.g. Smak;[77] Lasota[55]). Time delays have been detected also in several other X-ray transient binaries. This is the reason that urged Bisnovatyi-Kogan & Giovannelli[6] (BKG17) to generalize the aforementioned model, developed for the particular case of A 0535+26/HDE 245770 (Flavia' star). This general model provides the formula (1) of the time delay between the optical and X-ray flashes appearance in transient cosmic accreting sources:

$$\tau = 6.9 \frac{m^{2/3} \dot{m}^{1/15}}{\alpha^{4/5} (T_4)^{28/15}} \tag{1}$$

where:

$m = M/M_\odot$; $\dot{m} = \dot{M}/(10^{-8}\ M_\odot/\mathrm{yr})$; $T_4 = T_0/10^4$ K; α = viscosity, and T_0 = maximum temperature in optics.

By using this formula it is possible to obtain an excellent agreement between the experimental and theoretical delays found in:

- X-ray/Be system A0535+26/HDE245770: $\tau_{exp} \simeq 8$ days (GBK13); $\tau_{th} \simeq 8$ days;
- Cataclysmic variable SS Cygni; $\tau_{exp} = 0.9$–1.4 days (Wheatley, Mauche & Mattei[81]); $\tau_{th} \simeq 1.35$ days;
- Low-mass X-ray binary Aql X-1/V1333 Aql: $\tau_{exp} \sim 3$ days (Shahbaz et al.[74]); $\tau_{th} \simeq 3.2$ days
- Black hole X-ray transient GRO J1655-40: $\tau_{exp} \sim 6$ days (Orosz et al.[67]); $\tau_{th} \simeq 6.5$ days.

In this general formula the α-viscosity parameter plays an important role, and usually it is hard to be determined. However, if the other parameters are known, because experimentally determined, the formula (1) can be used for determining α, taking into account the experimental delay measured in a certain source.

Over the last couple of decades we have witnessed the discovery of a multitude of highly ionized absorbers in high-resolution X-ray spectra from both BH and NS XRBs. The first detections were obtained thanks to ASCA on the BH binaries GROJ1655-40 and GRS 1915+105. Narrow absorption lines in the spectra of these systems identified as Fe XXV and Fe XXVI indicated the first of many discoveries of photo-ionized plasmas in LMXBs (Chandra, XMM-Newton and Suzaku). Black hole hot accretion flows occur in the regime of relatively low accretion rates and are operating in the nuclei of most of the galaxies in the universe. One of the most important progress in recent years in this field is about the wind or outflow. This progress is mainly attributed to the rapid development of numerical simulations of accretion flows, combined with observations on, e.g., Sgr A*, the SMBH in the Galactic center. The mass loss from a BH via wind is related to the mass accretion rate onto the BH as (Yuan[82]):

$$\dot{M}_{wind}(r) = \dot{M}_{BH} \times (r/20r_g)^s \quad \text{with} \quad s \approx 1 \quad \text{and} \quad r_g = \frac{2GM_{BH}}{c^2} \qquad (2)$$

At this point it is useful to make a sort of summary about the number of XRBSs, including CVs. Liu, van Paradijs & van den Heuvel[56, 57] and Ziółkowski[84] report 315 galactic XRBs: 197 LMXBs (63%) and 118 HMXBs (37%), 72 of which are Be/X-ray systems; moreover there are 62 BH candidates. Coleiro & Chaty[19] report that in the Milky way there are ≥ 200 HMXBs. Ritter & Kolb[72] catalogue, in the 7.20 (Dec. 2013) version, reports 1166 CVs. Buckley[8] reports about the discoveries of 530 new CVs from MASTER-Network and 855 CVs from Catalina Real Time Survey (CRTS) (http://nesssi.cacr.caltech.edu/DataRelease/). Ferrario, de Martino & Gänsicke[22] report the number of MCVs as ≈ 250, and ~ 60 of which IPs, and considering those systems for which the magnetic field intensity has not yet been determined, their number is of ≈ 600. Table 1 shows the content of XRBSs, including CVs,

Table 1. Comparison of numbers of different classes of X-ray Binary Systems in the Milky Way and in the Magellanic Clouds (Ziółkowski;[84] Ferrario, de Martino & Gänsicke;[22] Buckley[8]).

Name of the Class	Milky Way	LMC	SMC
Total mass of the galaxy (in M_{SMC} units)	100	10	1
High Mass X-ray Binaries	118	26	83
in this Be/X-ray	72	19	79
Low Mass X-ray Binaries	197	2	-
Black Hole Candidates	62	2	-
Cataclysmic Variables	≈ 2000	-	-
in this MCVs	≈ 250	-	-
IPs	∼ 60	-	-
B not yet determined	≈ 600	-	-

in the Galaxy, and in the LMC and SMC (Ziółkowski;[84] Ferrario, de Martino & Gänsicke;[22] Buckley[8]). The mass are expressed in unit of SMC.

Some attempts of evaluation of the number of SBHs in the Galaxy have been done. For instance, taking into account the γ-ray emissivity of the Galaxy (1.3 $\times 10^{43}$ s^{-1} for E > 100 MeV) measured by the SAS II satellite (Strong, Wolfendale & Worral[78]) and the processes of disk-fed accretion onto black holes, Giovannelli, Karakuła & Tkaczyk[31,32] – considering a spherical accretion flow with a constant Mach number, corresponding to the adiabatic power $\gamma = 5/3$ – found a possible upper limits to the number of black holes (M ~ 10 M$_\odot$ and $\dot{M} \approx 10^{-8}$ M$_\odot$ yr^{-1}) of 10^{-5} - 10^{-4} of the total star population of the Galaxy for Mach's number 1 and 2, respectively.(*)

There is a class of intermediate-mass black holes (IMBHs), with masses > 100 M$_\odot$ up to $\approx 10^5$ M$_\odot$. It contains a dozen systems, as listed in Johnstone.[49] However, black holes with masses of several hundred to a few thousand solar masses remain elusive, as reported in a review by Casares & Jonker[15] where a deeply discussion about the mass measurements of SBHs and IMBHs is contained.

Supermassive black holes (SMBHs) are 10^6–10^{10} times more massive than our Sun and are found in the centers of galaxies (see the exhaustive review by Kormendy & Ho[54]). Most galaxies, and maybe all of them, harbor such a black hole. So in our region of the Universe, there are some 10^{11} SMBHs. The nearest one resides in the center of our Milky Way galaxy. The most distant one we know of resides in a quasar

---

(*)The Mach number is given by the ratio of the velocity of the gas to the local sound speed. In order to evaluate the temperature, concentration and velocity of the plasma near the black hole it is necessary to solve the system of equations describing the plasma motion (Michel[62]) taking into account the distance from the black hole in units of gravitational radius and the u = R-component of four velocity. Mach's number 1 and 2 correspond to different values of u_0^2 (1.0266 and 2.1213, respectively) at a distance r_0 from the black hole (Giovannelli, Karakuła & Tkaczyk[31,32]).

galaxy billions of lightyears away. SMBHs grow in size as they gorge on surrounding matter.

A list of BH candidates has been reported by Johnston[49] and provides the input for constructing the map of sky locations of BH candidates. Source list includes results reported in Kormendy & Gebhardt,[53] Orosz,[66] Tremaine et al.,[80] and Ziółkowski.[83]

6. Conclusions

The zoo of X-ray binary systems has been presented together with the main characteristics of the single constituent element. A particular emphasis has been devoted to the individual X-ray/Be system A 0535+26/HDE 245770 for which I discussed its history since its discovery by the Ariel-V satellite. Thanks to the long term survey of this system a delay between X-ray and optical flares has been recognized. This fact triggered the work for understanding the physical reasons of this phenomenon that allowed Bisnovatyi-Kogan & Giovannelli[6] to develop a model of time lag between optical and X-ray flashes for close-binary galactic sources with accretion disks.

The time lag in disk-accreting galactic close-binary sources is based on a sudden increase in the accretion flow that starts at the disk periphery and is related to the optical maximum. The massive accretion layer propagates to the central compact source as a result of the turbulent viscosity. The X-ray flash occurs when this massive layer reaches the inner hot regions of the accretion disk and falls into the central compact object. The matter in the accretion disk moves inside with a speed that is determined by the turbulent viscosity. They described this model quantitatively and derived an analytic formula that determines the value of the time lag. This formula gives results that agree well with observational values.

Acknowledgments

This research has made use of the NASA's Astrophysics Data System.

References

1. Bartolini, C., Guarnieri, A., Piccioni, A., Giangrande, A., Giovannelli, F.: 1978, IAU Circ. No. 3167.
2. Bartolini, C., Bianco, G., Guarnieri, A., Piccioni, A., Giovannelli, F.: 1983, *Hvar Obs. Bull.* **7(1)**, 159.
3. Bisnovatyi-Kogan, G.S.: 2002, in *Black Hole Astrophysics*, Proc. of the Sixth APCTP Winter School, Hyun Kyu Lee & Myeong-Gu Park (Eds.), World Scientific Publishing Co. Pte. Ltd., ISBN 9789812776761, pp. 187-206.
4. Bisnovatyi-Kogan, G.S.: 2011, *Stellar Physics 2: Stellar Evolution and Stability*, Berlin-Heidelberg: Springer-Verlag.
5. Bisnovatyi-Kogan, G.S., Komberg, B.V.: 1974, Sov. Astron. 18, 217.
6. Bisnovatyi-Kogan, G.S., Giovannelli, G.: 2017, A&A 599, A55, 7 pp. (BKG17).

7. Blumenthal, G.R., Tucker, W.H.: 1974, Ann. Rev. A&A 12, 23-46.
8. Buckley, D., 2015, talk at the Palermo Workshop on *"The Golden Age of Cataclysmic Variables and Related Objects - III"*.
9. Burger, M., van Dessel, E.L., Giovannelli, F., Sabau-Graziati, L., Bartolini, C. et al.: 1996, in *Multifrequency Behaviour of High Energy Cosmic Sources*, F. Giovannelli & L. Sabau-Graziati (eds.), Mem. SAIt. 67, 365.
10. Caballero, I., Lebrun, F., Rodriguez, J., Soldi, S., Mattana, F., et al.: 2010a, ATel. 2496.
11. Caballero, I., Santangelo, A., Pottschmidt, K., Klochkov, D., Rodriguez, J., et al.: 2010b, ATel. 2541.
12. Caballero, I., Pottschmidt, K., Barragán, L., Ferrigno, C., Klochkov, D., et al.: 2010c, Talk at CRSF Meeting, Tübingen 2010.
13. Caballero, I., Kretschmar, P., Pottschmidt, K., Santangelo, A., Wilms, J., et al.: 2010d, AIPC 1248, 147.
14. Caballero, I., Pottschmidt, K., Santangelo, A., Barragán, L., Klochkov, D., et al.: 2011, arXiv:1107.3417.
15. Casares, J., Jonker, P.G.: 2014, SSRv 183, 223-252.
16. Chartres, M., Li, F.: 1977, IAU Circ. No. 3154.
17. Coe, M. J., Carpenter, G.F., Engel, A.R., Quenby, J.J.: 1975, Nature 256, 630.
18. Coe, M.J., Reig, P., McBride, V.A., Galache, J.L., Fabregat, J.: 2006, MNRAS 368, 447.
19. Coleiro, A., Chaty, S.: 2013, ApJ 764, 185.
20. Corbet, R.H.D.: 1984, A&A 141, 91.
21. Corbet, R.H.D.: 1986, MNRAS 220, 1047.
22. Ferrario, L., de Martino, D., Gänsicke, B.T.: 2015, SSRv 191, 111-169.
23. Finger, M.H., Wilson, R.B., Hagedon, K.S. 1994 IAU Circ. No. 5931.
24. Finger, M.H., Wilson, R.B., Harmon, B.A.: 1996, ApJ 459, 288.
25. Finger, M.H., Camero-Arranz, A., Kretschmar, P., Wilson, C., and Patel, S.: 2006, BAAS 38, 359.
26. Ghosh, P.: 1994, in *The Evolution of X-Ray Binaries*, S.S. Holt & C.S. Day (Eds.), AIP Conf. Proc. 308, 439.
27. Giangrande, A., Giovannelli, F., Bartolini, C., Guarnieri, A., Piccioni, A.: 1980, A&A Suppl. Ser. 40, 289.
28. Giovannelli, F.: 2005, *The Impact of Multifrequency Observations in High Energy Astrophysics*, Ph. D. Thesis, University of Barcelona, Spain.
29. Giovannelli, F.: 2008, Ch. J. A&A Suppl. 8, 237-258
30. Giovannelli, F.: 2016, in *Proc. of the 4th Ann. Conf. on High Energy Astrophysics in Southern Africa (HEASA 2016)*. Online at http://pos.sissa.it/cgi-bin/reader/conf.cgi?confid=275, id. 31.
31. Giovannelli, F., Karakuła, S., Tkaczyk, W.: 1981, in *Origin of Cosmic Rays*, Setti, G., Spada, G. & Wolfendale, A.W. (Eds.), IAU Symp. 94, p. 335.
32. Giovannelli, F., Karakuła, S., Tkaczyk, W.: 1982, Acta Astron. 32, 121.
33. Giovannelli, F., de Loore, C., Bartolini, C., Burger, M., Ferrari-Toniolo, M., et al. 1982 in *Proc. of the Third European IUE Conference*, ESA SP-176, 233.
34. Giovannelli, F., Ferrari-Toniolo, M., Persi, P., Golynskaya, I.M., Kurt, V.G., et al.: 1985 in *Multifrequency Behaviour of Galactic Accreting Sources*, F. Giovannelli (ed.), Edizioni Scientifiche SIDEREA, Roma, p. 284.
35. Giovannelli, F., Ziółkowski, J.: 1990, AcA 40, 95-103.
36. Giovannelli, F., Sabau-Graziati, L.: 1992, SSRv 59, 1-81.
37. Giovannelli, F., Sabau-Graziati, L.: 2001, Ap&SS, 276, 67-80.

38. Giovannelli, F., Bernabei, S., Rossi, C., Sabau-Graziati, L.: 2007, A&A, 475, 651.
39. Giovannelli, F., Gualandi, R., Sabau-Graziati, L.: 2010, ATel. 2497.
40. Giovannelli, F., Sabau-Graziati, L.: 2011, Acta Polytechnica Vol. 51, No. 2., p. 21.
41. Giovannelli, F., Bisnovatyi-Kogan, G.S., Klepnev, A.S.: 2013, A&A 560, id.A1, 11 pp (GBK13).
42. Giovannelli, F., Sabau-Graziati, L.: 2015, in *The Golden Age of Cataclysmic Variables and Related Objects - II*, F. Giovannelli & L. Sabau-Graziati (Eds.), Acta Polytechnica, CTU Proc. ISSN 2336-5382, Vol. 2 No. 1, 3-20.
43. Giovannelli, F., Bisnovatyi-Kogan, G.S., Bruni, I., Corfini, G., Martinelli, F., Rossi, C.: 2015a, AcA 65, 107-116.
44. Giovannelli, F., Rossi, C., Bisnovatyi-Kogan, G., Bruni, I., Fasano, A., Salas Procas, J.: 2015b, Proc. of the *XI Multifrequency Behaviour of High Energy Cosmic Sources* Workshop (MULTIF15). Online at http://pos.sissa.it/cgi-bin/reader/conf.cgi?confid=246, id.39
45. Guarnieri, A., Bartolini, C., Piccioni, A., Giovannelli, F.: 1985, in *Multifrequency Behaviour of Galactic Accreting Sources*, F. Giovannelli (ed.), Frascati: CNR, Istituto di Astrofisica, Edizioni Scientifiche SIDEREA, Roma, p. 310.
46. van den Heuvel, E.P.J., Rappaport, S.: 1987, in *Physics of Be Stars*, A. Slettebak & T.P. Snow (eds.), Cambridge and New York, Cambridge University Press, Proc. of the IAU Coll. N. 92, p. 291.
47. Hutchings, J.B.: 1984, PASP 96, 312.
48. Janot-Pacheco, E., Motch, C., Mouchet, M.: 1987, A&A 177, 91.
49. Johnstone, Wm. R.: 2004, http://www.johnstonsarchive.net/relativity/bhctable.html
50. Joss, P.C., Rappaport, S.A.: 1984, Ann. Rev. Astron. Astrophys. 22, 537.
51. Kaluzienski, L.J., Holt, S.S., Boldt, E.A. Serlemitsos, P.J.: 1975, Nature 256, 633.
52. van Kerkwijk, M.H., van Paradijs, J., Zuiderwijk, E.J.: 1995, A&A 303, 497.
53. Kormendy, J., Gebhardt, K.: 2001, arXiv:astro-ph/0105230v1.
54. Kormendy, J., Ho, L.C.: 2013, Ann. Rev. A&A 51, 511-653.
55. Lasota, J.-P.: 2001, New Astron. Rev. 45, 449.
56. Liu, Q.Z., van Paradijs, J., van den Heuvel, E.P.J.: 2006, A&A 455, 1165.
57. Liu, Q.Z., van Paradijs, J., van den Heuvel, E.P.J.: 2007, A&A 469, 807.
58. de Loore, C., Giovannelli, F., van Dessel, E.L., Bartolini, C., Burger, M., et al.: 1984 A&A 141, 279.
59. Margon, B., Nelson, J., Chanan, G., Bowyer, S., Thorstensen, J.R.: 1977, ApJ 216, 811.
60. de Martino, D., Vittone, A., Giovannelli, F., Ciatti, F., Margoni, R., et al.: 1985, in *Multifrequency Behaviour of Galactic Accreting Sources*, Proceedings of the 1984 Frascati Workshop, Franco Giovannelli (ed.). Frascati: CNR, Istituto di Astrofisica, Ed. Scientifiche SIDEREA, Roma, p. 326.
61. de Martino, D., Waters, L.B.F.M., Giovannelli, F., Persi, P.: 1989, in *The 23rd ESLAB Symposium on Two Topics in X Ray Astronomy*, Volume 1 *X-Ray Binaries*, ESA SP 296, 519-520.
62. Michel, F.C.: 1972, Ap&SS 15, 153.
63. Motch, C., Stella, L., Janot-Pacheco, E., Mouchet, M.: 1991, ApJ 369, 490.
64. Nagase, F.: 1989, PASJ 41, no. 1, 1-79.
65. Nagase, F., Hayakawa, S., Kunieda, H., Makino, F., Masai, K., et al.: 1982, ApJ 263, 814.
66. Orosz, J.A.: 2002, arXiv:astro-ph/0209041v1.
67. Orosz, J.A., Remillard, R.A., Bailyn, C.D., McClintock, J.E.: 1997, ApJL 478, L83.

68. Piccioni, A., Bartolini, C., Bernabei, S., Guarnieri, A., Tarozzi, F., Valentini, G.: 1999, in *Frontier Objects in Astrophysics and Particle Physics*, F. Giovannelli & G. Mannocchi (Eds.), SIF, Bologna, Italy, 65, 195.
69. Priedhorsky, W.C., Terrell, J.: 1983, Nature 303, 681.
70. Rappaport, S., Joss, P.C.: 1981, in *X-Ray Astronomy with the Einstein Satellite*, R. Giacconi (ed.), D. Reidel Publ. Co., Dordrecht, Holland, p. 123.
71. Ricketts, M.J., Turner, M.J.L., Page, C.G., Pounds, K.A.: 1975, 256, 631-633.
72. Ritter, H., Kolb, U.: 2003, A&A 404, 301.
73. Rosenberg, F.D., Eyles, C.J., Skinner, G.K., Willmore, A.P.: 1975, Nature 256, 628.
74. Shahbaz, T., Bandyopadhyay, R.M., Charles, P.A., Wagner, R.M., Muhli, P., et al.: 1998, MNRAS 300, 1035.
75. Shakura, N.I., Sunyaev, R.A.: 1973, A&A 24, 337.
76. Skinner, G.K.,, Bedford, D.K., Elsner, R.F., Leahy, D., Weisskopf, M.C., Grindlay, J.: 1982, Nature, 297, 568-570.
77. Smak, J.: 1984, PASP 96, 5.
78. Strong, A.W., Wolfendale, A.W., Worral, D.M.: 1976, MNRAS 175, 23.
79. Thorsett, S.E., Arzoumanian, Z., McKinnon, M.M., Taylor, J.H.: 1993, ApJ 405, L29.
80. Tremaine, S., Gebhardt, K., Bender, R., Bower, G., Dressler, A. et al.: 2002, ApJ 574, 740-753.
81. Wheatley, P.J., Mauche, C.W., Mattei, J.A.: 2003, MNRAS 345, 49.
82. Yuan, F.: 2016, in *Astrophysics of Black Holes*, C. Bambi (Ed.), ApSSLibrary 440, 152-168.
83. Ziółkowski, J.: 2003, arXiv:astro-ph/0307307v1.
84. Ziółkowski, J.: 2013, Acta Polytechnica Vol 53, Suppl., 665.

Rotation of the crescent image of M87* and polarization of its ESE hotspot

Krzysztof Nalewajko

Nicolaus Copernicus Astronomical Center, Polish Academy of Sciences
Bartycka 18, 00-716 Warsaw, Poland
E-mail: knalew@camk.edu.pl

The first image of the black hole (BH) M87* obtained by the Event Horizon Telescope (EHT) has the shape of a crescent extending from the E to WSW position angles, with a tentative 'ESE hotspot'. Assuming that the BH spin vector is aligned with both the inner accretion axis and the projected direction of the kpc-scale relativistic jet, the position of the ESE hotspot is inconsistent with the axisymmetric accretion flow. Recent polarimetric EHT images of M87* show that the ESE hotspot is essentially unpolarized, which strongly supports its distinct origin. If the hotspot emission is due to the synchrotron radiation, its depolarization requires either isotropically tangled magnetic fields or an additional Faraday dispersion measure. The 6-day EHT observing campaign in April 2017 allowed in principle to detect orbital motions advancing by up to $\sim 60°$. The apparent rotation rate of the major axis of the EHT crescent image is consistent with the rotation rate of the Faraday-corrected polarization angle measured by the ALMA. However, the counterclockwise (CCW) sense of these rotations is opposite to the clockwise (CW) rotation of the plasma flows implied by the N-S brightness asymmetry, which might indicate that accretion in M87 is retrograde.

Keywords: Black hole physics; Galaxies:active; Galaxies:individual:M87; Relativistic processes.

1. Introduction

The Event Horizon Telescope (EHT) resolved at 1.3 mm the core M87* of the nearby (distance of $D \simeq 16.8$ Mpc) radio galaxy Virgo A (M87) into a crescent image of angular diameter of $\simeq 42$ μas, which corresponds to $\simeq 11$ gravitational radii $R_g = GM_{BH}/c^2$ for the black hole (BH) mass of $M_{BH} \simeq 6.5 \times 10^9 M_\odot$ (G is the gravitational constant, c is the speed of light, $M_\odot$ is the mass of the Sun; $R_g/c \simeq 8.9$ h).[1-6] M87* is thought to be the base of a relativistic jet observed in radio,[7-9] optical[10] and X-ray[11] bands, propagating in the WNW direction (position angle $\simeq 288°$) beyond the kpc scales. The inclination angle of the jet axis is estimated at $\simeq 17°$.[9] If the jet is powered by the Blandford-Znajek mechanism,[12] its direction of propagation should be aligned with the BH spin. Accreting plasma in the vicinity of spinning black hole would be forced to swirl with trans-relativistic velocities preferentially along the BH equatorial plane. The resulting difference in the Doppler beaming of emission should result in a roughly N-S brightness asymmetry of the crescent image. It is in fact observed by the EHT that the S side of the M87* crescent image is significantly brighter than the N side.

The angular extent of the M87* crescent is roughly from the E to WSW position angles. There is a hint of substructures in the angular brightness profiles that depends significantly on the image reconstruction method. The observed crescent may consist of the *proper crescent* extending from the SSE to WSW position angles and the *ESE hotspot*. Using simple axisymmetric models for the geometry of emitting regions, we have previously suggested that the proper crescent can be explained by emitting regions symmetric with respect to the BH spin/jet WNW axis, and that the ESE hotspot (opposite to the WNW jet) would be rather a localized perturbation of the accretion flow.[13] Such azimuthal perturbations are commonly observed in the results of GRMHD numerical simulations of magnetized BH accretion flows.[5,14,15]

2. Polarization of the ESE hotspot

More recently, the EHT Collaboration presented the first resolved polarimetric images of M87*.[16,17] These images show linear polarization at the level of $\sim 15\%$. In our interpretation, this polarization is largely limited the proper crescent, while the ESE hotspot is essentially unpolarized. Such a striking difference between the polarization properties of these two regions strongly supports their distinct origin.

The very low polarization degree of the ESE hotspot calls into question whether it is produced by the same emission mechanism (presumably synchrotron), whether it is optically thin (or a localized millimeter photosphere), or whether it involves ordered or tangled magnetic fields. It could also result from depolarization by an additional localized Faraday screen. Unresolved ALMA polarimetry simultaneous to the EHT campaign was performed in two bands — 1.3 mm and 3 mm — which allowed to estimate the simultaneous rotation measures as $\sim \pm 10^5$ rad/m^2.[18] Since depolarizing a 1.3 mm signal by factor e requires a dispersion measure of $\simeq 4 \times 10^5$ rad/m^2, depolarization of the ESE hotspot may require an additional dispersion measure of order $\sim 10^6$ rad/m^2. Such dispersion measures are plausible in the advection dominated accretion flow (ADAF) models[19] for the mass accretion rate of $\dot{M} \gtrsim 2 \times 10^{-3} M_\odot/\mathrm{yr}$.[20]

3. Rotation of the crescent image and net polarization vector

The 2017 EHT observing campaign spanned 6 days, resolved images were obtained from data recorded on April 5th, 6th, 10th and 11th. This time scale can be compared with the orbital period of a source propagating along the innermost stable circular orbit (ISCO) in Schwarzschild[a] metric: $P_{\mathrm{ISCO}} \simeq 92 R_g/c \simeq 34$ days. Hence, during the 6-day campaign one could expect to observe an orbital advance by $\sim 60°$. Note that the estimated viewing angle of the M87 jet is sufficiently small that equatorial accretion flows would be well aligned with the plane of the sky.

---

[a]The effect of BH spin is not included in this basic analysis, but it would be an obvious next level of sophistication.

For comparison, in the case of Sgr A* ($R_g/c \simeq 20$ s; $P_{\text{ISCO}} \simeq 31$ min) the VLTI/GRAVITY Collaboration detected orbital motion at the period of $P_{\text{GRAVITY}} \simeq 40$ min $\simeq 1.3 P_{\text{ISCO}}$,[21] which corresponds to a circular Schwarzschild geodesic of radius $R_{\text{circ}} \simeq 7.1 R_g$.

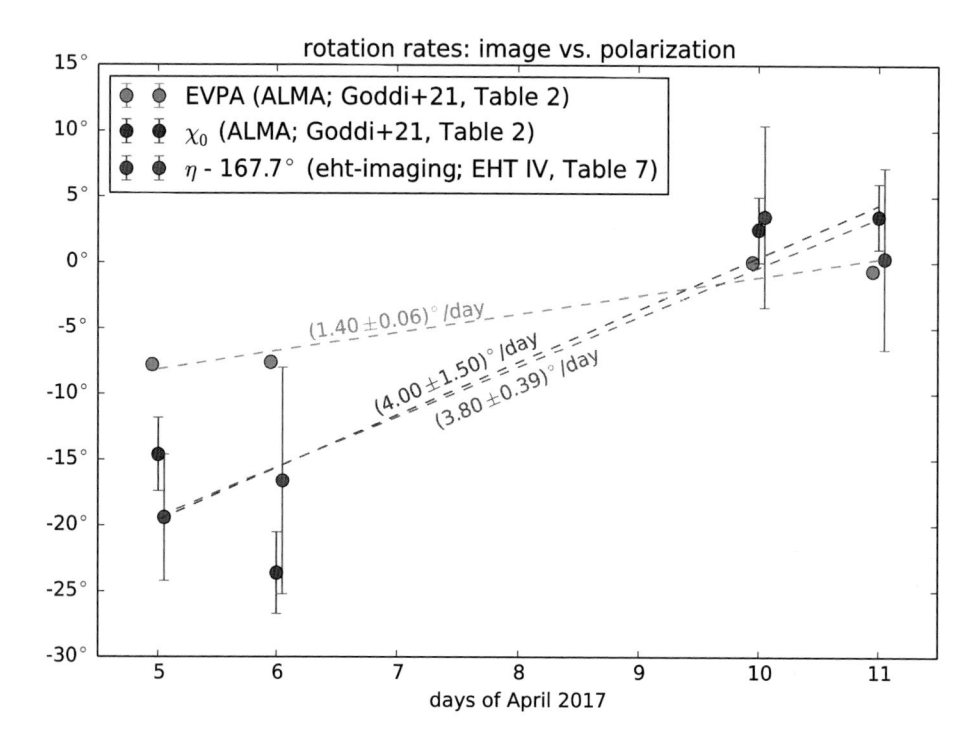

Fig. 1. Time evolution of the orientation angles of the total-intensity crescent image and net polarization. See the main text for details.

In Figure 1, we compare two kinds of orientation angles measured independently for each day of the M87 campaign. First, we consider the mean orientation angles η of the crescent image according to the `eht-imaging` algorithm from the Table 7 of EHT Paper IV.[4] This angle increases by $\simeq +23°$ between April 5th and April 10th, and the mean rotation rate is $(3.8 \pm 0.6)°$/day. Second, we consider the net polarization angles from the Table 2 of the ALMA Paper:[18] the observed angles EVPA, and the angles χ_0 corrected for Faraday rotation using the simultaneous rotation measure values. The EVPA increases by $\simeq +7.8°$ between April 5th and April 10th, while χ_0 increases by $\simeq +27°$ between April 6th and April 11th. The mean rotation rate is $(1.4 \pm 0.3)°$/day for the EVPA and $(4.0 \pm 1.2)°$/day for the χ_0. The rotation rate of the Faraday-corrected polarization angle is thus consistent with the rotation rate of the crescent. The rate of $3.9°$/day corresponds to the orbital period of $P \simeq 92$ days $\simeq 2.7 P_{\rm ISCO}$. The apparent rotation rate of the crescent image and net polarization would correspond to $R_{\rm circ} \simeq 11.6\, R_{\rm g}$.

The trend of increasing position angle measured from N to E corresponds to the counterclockwise (CCW) rotation on the sky for the relatively outer accretion flow. On the other hand, since the S side of the M87* image is clearly brighter than the N side, should this be attributed to the trans-relativistic Doppler beaming of the inner accretion flow (funnel wall), in light of the roughly W direction of the projected jet, the inner accretion flow (and the BH itself) should rotate in the clockwise (CW) direction on the sky. This situation of opposite outer and inner accretion flows corresponds to the bottom left panel of Figure 5 in EHT Paper V.[5] This would suggest that accretion in M87 is retrograde. And this in turn would constrain the range of GRMHD models listed in Table 2 of EHT Paper V[5] to two categories: the high-spin ($a_* = -0.94$) SANE models, and the medium-spin ($a_* = -0.5$) MAD models.

Acknowledgments

I thank Brian Punsly for motivating this contribution by inviting the author to speak at the Sixteenth Marcel Grossmann Meeting. I also thank Agata Różańska and Marek Sikora for discussions. This work was partially supported by the Polish National Science Centre grant 2015/18/E/ST9/00580.

References

1. Event Horizon Telescope Collaboration, First M87 Event Horizon Telescope Results. I. The Shadow of the Supermassive Black Hole, *ApJ* **875**, p. L1 (April 2019).
2. Event Horizon Telescope Collaboration, First M87 Event Horizon Telescope Results. II. Array and Instrumentation, *ApJ* **875**, p. L2 (April 2019).
3. Event Horizon Telescope Collaboration, First M87 Event Horizon Telescope Results. III. Data Processing and Calibration, *ApJ* **875**, p. L3 (April 2019).
4. Event Horizon Telescope Collaboration, First M87 Event Horizon Telescope Results. IV. Imaging the Central Supermassive Black Hole, *ApJ* **875**, p. L4 (April 2019).
5. Event Horizon Telescope Collaboration, First M87 Event Horizon Telescope Results. V. Physical Origin of the Asymmetric Ring, *ApJ* **875**, p. L5 (April 2019).
6. Event Horizon Telescope Collaboration, First M87 Event Horizon Telescope Results. VI. The Shadow and Mass of the Central Black Hole, *ApJ* **875**, p. L6 (April 2019).
7. W. Junor, J. A. Biretta and M. Livio, Formation of the radio jet in M87 at 100 Schwarzschild radii from the central black hole, *Nature* **401**, 891 (October 1999).
8. C. C. Cheung, D. E. Harris and L. Stawarz, Superluminal Radio Features in the M87 Jet and the Site of Flaring TeV Gamma-Ray Emission, *ApJ* **663**, L65 (July 2007).
9. R. C. Walker P. E. Hardee, F. B. Davies, C. Ly and W. Junor, The Structure and Dynamics of the Subparsec Jet in M87 Based on 50 VLBA Observations over 17 Years at 43 GHz, *ApJ* **855**, p. 128 (March 2018).
10. J. A. Biretta, W. B. Sparks and F. Macchetto, Hubble Space Telescope Observations of Superluminal Motion in the M87 Jet, *ApJ* **520**, 621 (August 1999).
11. A. S. Wilson and Y. Yang, Chandra X-Ray Imaging and Spectroscopy of the M87 Jet and Nucleus, *ApJ* **568**, 133 (March 2002).

12. R. D. Blandford and R. L. Znajek, Electromagnetic extraction of energy from Kerr black holes., *MNRAS* **179**, 433 (May 1977).
13. K. Nalewajko, M. Sikora and A. Różańska, Orientation of the crescent image of M 87*, *A&A* **634**, p. A38 (February 2020).
14. O. Porth, Y. Mizuno, Z. Younsi and C. M. Fromm, Flares in the Galactic Centre - I. Orbiting flux tubes in magnetically arrested black hole accretion discs, *MNRAS* **502**, 2023 (April 2021).
15. N. Scepi, J. Dexter and M. C. Begelman, Sgr A* X-ray flares from non-thermal particle acceleration in a magnetically arrested disc, *arXiv e-prints*, p. arXiv:2107.08056 (July 2021).
16. Event Horizon Telescope Collaboration, First M87 Event Horizon Telescope Results. VII. Polarization of the Ring, *ApJ* **910**, p. L12 (March 2021).
17. Event Horizon Telescope Collaboration, First M87 Event Horizon Telescope Results. VIII. Magnetic Field Structure near The Event Horizon, *ApJ* **910**, p. L13 (March 2021).
18. C. Goddi, I. Martí-Vidal, H. Messias, G. C. Bower, A. E. Broderick and et al., Polarimetric Properties of Event Horizon Telescope Targets from ALMA, *ApJ* **910**, p. L14 (March 2021).
19. D. P. Marrone, J. M. Moran, J.-H. Zhao and R. Rao, Interferometric Measurements of Variable 340 GHz Linear Polarization in Sagittarius A*, *ApJ* **640**, 308 (March 2006).
20. M. Mościbrodzka, J. Dexter, J. Davelaar and H. Falcke, Faraday rotation in GRMHD simulations of the jet launching zone of M87, *MNRAS* **468**, 2214 (June 2017).
21. Gravity Collaboration, Detection of orbital motions near the last stable circular orbit of the massive black hole SgrA*, *A&A* **618**, p. L10 (October 2018).

Magnetic reconnection in jet-accretion disk systems

Chandra B. Singh

*South-Western Institute for Astronomy Research, Yunnan University, University Town,
Chenggong District, Kunming 650500, People's Republic of China
E-mail: chandrasingh@ynu.edu.cn*

Elisabete M. de Gouveia Dal Pino, Luis H.S. Kadowaki and Tania E. Medina-Torrejón

*Instituto de Astronomia, Geofísica e Ciências Atmosféricas, Universidade de São Paulo,
Rua do Matão 1226, São Paulo, 05508-090, Brasil*

Yosuke Mizuno

*Tsung-Dao Lee Institute and School of Physics and Astronomy, Shanghai Jiao Tong University,
Shanghai 200240, People's Republic of China*

David Garofalo

*Department of Physics, Kennesaw State University,
Marietta GA 30060, USA*

Grzegorz Kowal

*Escola de Artes, Ciências e Humanidades - Universidade de São Paulo,
Av. Arlindo Béttio, 1000 – Vila Guaraciaba,
São Paulo, 03838-000, Brasil*

Black hole surroundings and relativistic jets host magnetically dominated regions and fast magnetic reconnection are likely to play an important role concerning astrophysical phenomena associated with such regions. In this contribution, we highlight the works related to turbulence-driven reconnection processes. These processes have been studied by us using analytical as well as numerical methods which showed that fast reconnection processes are powerful ways to giving rise to relativistic particles and associated non-thermal emissions around stellar-mass and supermassive black holes. The power released from the reconnection can even compete with those of extraction from black hole spin.

Keywords: Instabilities; Jets; Acceleration of Particles; Magnetic Reconnection; Magnetohydrodynamics; Numerical Methods

1. Introduction

Black holes are in a range of masses like 5-10 solar masses for stellar-mass to $10^6 - 10^{10}$ for supermassive black holes. Accretion disks, as well as relativistic jets, are quite common features for those black holes. Usually, relativistic jets can achieve high Lorentz factors and propagate several orders of magnitude in distances. Those are likely to be powered by the energy available from accretion disk or black hole spin. The base of the jets is supposed to be magnetically dominated which later becomes kinetically dominated so an efficient conversion is needed to explain this picture. So magnetic reconnection can be a viable mechanism to make it happen. Another issue that requires explanation is regarding very high emissions (up to TeV) from highly under luminous radio galaxies which might occur close to the base of the jet and from a very compact region in magnetized surroundings around black holes. As standard processes in sites like shocks are likely to be weak, so promising candidate is magnetic reconnection processes and requires due attention.

In the presence of turbulence, the first-order Fermi process in the fast reconnection sites or current sheets is likely to accelerate particles to high energies as shown in analytical[1] and numerical works.[2,3] It was shown that the particles trapped within current sheets were found to undergo exponential growth in energy with time and the corresponding energy spectrum was power-law with spectral indices $\sim$ 1-2. Such a mechanism is well-suited for addressing very high energy phenomena seen in a range of systems containing black holes like galactic black holes or microquasars(GBHs), active galactic nuclei (AGNs), and gamma-ray bursts(GRBs). In this contribution, we discuss further works showing the role of fast magnetic reconnection in accretion disks and jets in such systems containing black holes.

2. Magnetic reconnection around black holes

de Gouveia Dal Pino and Lazarian[1] proposed a model showing that the first-order Fermi process in the coronal region around a black hole can accelerate particles due to the power extraction from fast magnetic reconnection between lines anchored in the accretion disk and black hole horizon. That model could address the origin of radio flares in GBHs and AGNs and later extended to gamma emissions and larger samples as well.[4] Further, the fundamental plane black hole activity which correlates the radio and X-ray emissions could be easily explained in the framework of fast magnetic reconnection model. In those models, a standard disk with corona as a central source around the black hole was used which is suitable for close to Eddington sources. Later the scenario was revisited for taking care of sub-Eddington sources as well by considering thick magnetically dominated accretion flow (MDAF).[5]

Figure 1 shows the calculated turbulence-driven fast magnetic reconnection power and the observed radio and gamma-ray luminosities for more than 270 sources including XRBs, low luminous AGNs (LLAGNs), and GRBs.[5] The diamonds in red and green colours represent the radio emissions in the case of LLAGNs and XRBs respectively. Some XRBs (Cyg X-1 and Cyg X-3) and LLAGNs (Cen A, IC 310, Per A, and M87) are highlighted which have been studied extensively in multi-wavelength studies. The reconnection power is much greater than the observed radio luminosities which means only a small fraction of this power is enough to explain the radio emission for most of the sources. Observed gamma-ray luminosities for 23 sources are included, represented by red and green circles for LLAGNs and XRBs respectively. The circles represent the emissions of 4 radio galaxies, 2 XRBs, and several Seyfert galaxies (most with upper limits in GeV). It is seen that the released

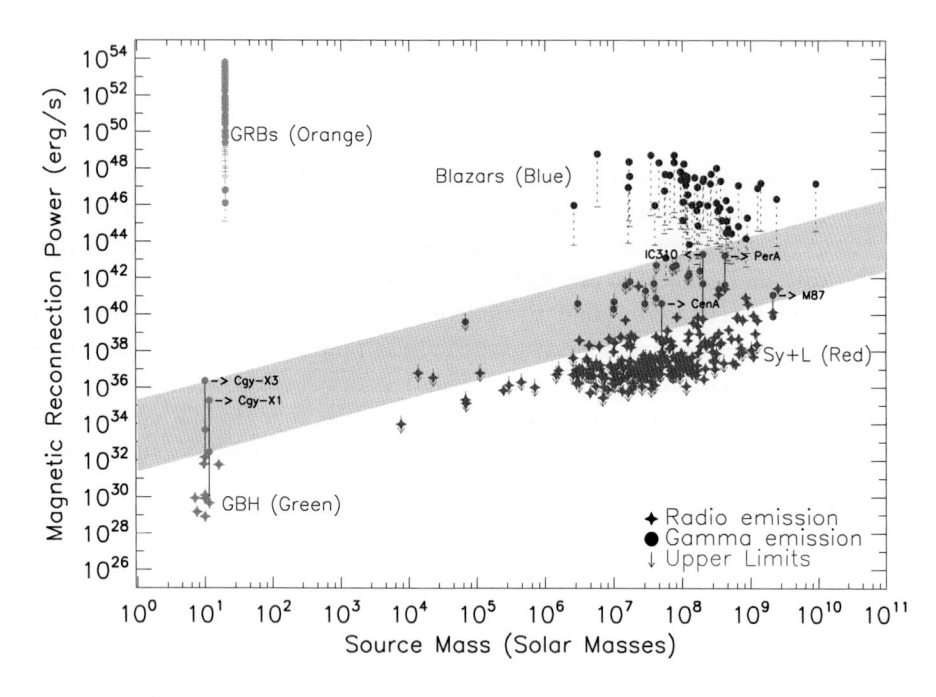

Fig. 1. Tubulent-driven magnetic power against black hole source mass compared to observed emissions of LLAGNs, GBHs, GRBs and blazars. In few cases, maximum and minimum values of gamma-ray luminosity are connected with a vertical black line that extends down to the radio emission. The inverted arrows for some sources indicate that the gamma-ray emission is an upper limit only. The gamma-ray emissions for blazars and GRBs are represented by blue and orange circles respectively. The vertical dashed lines correct the observed emissions by Doppler boosting effects (adopted from ref.[5]).

magnetic energy power is sufficient enough to produce gamma-ray emissions. The gamma-ray and radio emissions seem to be correlated and originating from the same core region around black holes and produced by the same acceleration mechanisms. However, the emissions of blazars and GRBs seem to originate along the jet rather than from the base of the jets. This is likely because the emissions from the core region of these sources are usually screened as the jets point towards our line of sight.

In another work,[6] we performed a semi-analytical comparison between black hole spin and fast magnetic reconnection power for accreting black holes based on fiducial astrophysical parameter space. Besides the rotational energy of the black hole, the fast reconnection power may play a similar role to power relativistic jets. Frame dragging effects of rotating black holes can lead to complicated magnetic structures and enhances the possibility of polarity inversion of the field lines leading to reconnection events and high energy emissions. The reconnection power is

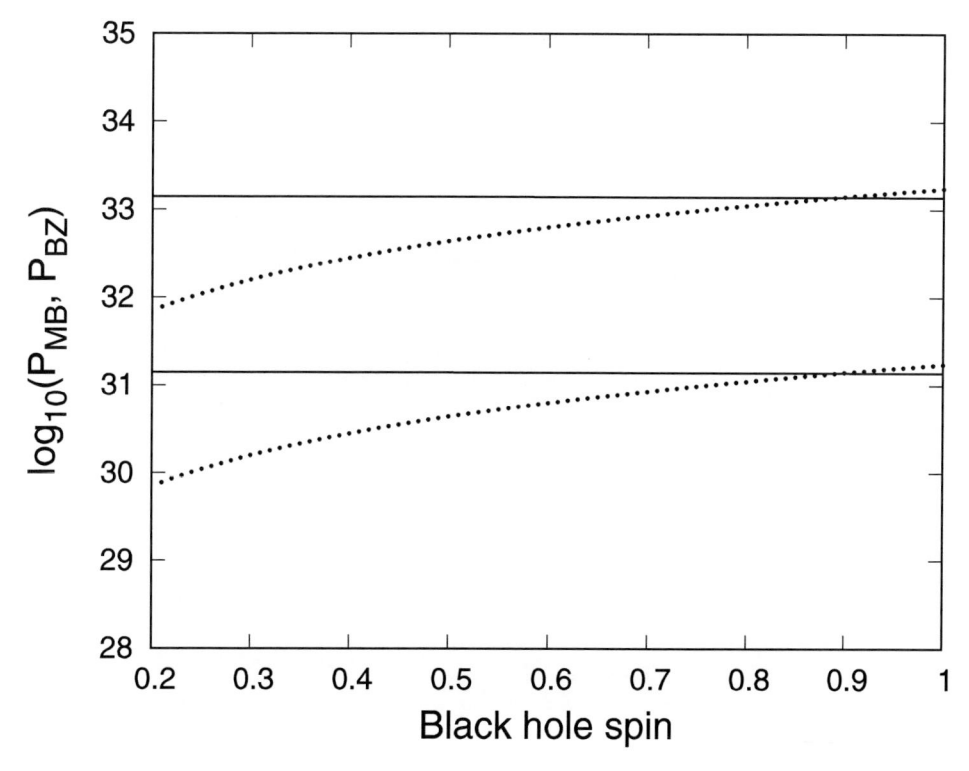

Fig. 2. Magnetic reconnection power P_{MB} and black hole spin power P_{BZ} ploted against black hole spin (adopted from ref.[6]).

a minimum close to the black hole and near the spin axis. It is likely to increase in magnitude with increase in the mass accretion rate. It may compete or even dominate the black hole spin power as shown in Fig. 2. It shows the maximum and minimum values for black hole spin and reconnection power as a function of black hole spin. The power available from the black hole spin and reconnection is comparable for rapidly rotating black holes and the same range of mass accretion rates. The black hole spin power obviously depends on the black hole rotation magnitude while the reconnection process seems to be independent of the black hole spin. The black hole spin-driven process gets suppressed in presence of reconnection. This may occur due to the destruction of large-scale magnetic fields following reconnection events. So state transitions from hard state to soft state can be triggered by this process.

3. Magnetic reconnection in relativistic jets

Using the three-dimensional relativistic magnetohydrodynamic code RAISHIN, we investigated the influence of radial density profile on the spatial development of the current-driven kink instability (CDKI) along magnetized rotating, relativistic jets.[7]

Decreasing density
$\Omega_0=2$, t=100

(a) density

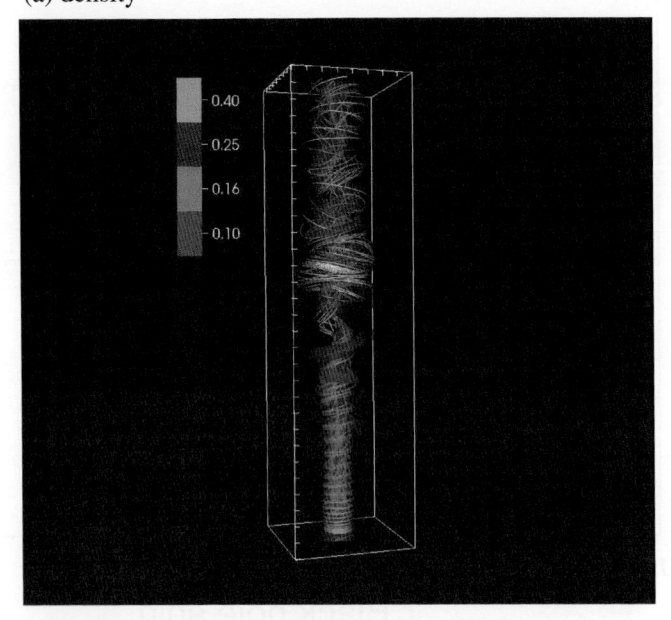

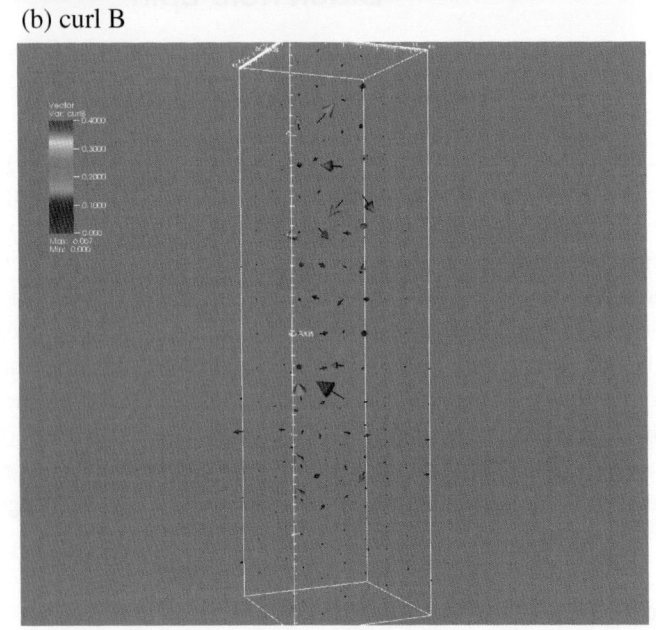

(b) curl B

Fig. 3. Current driven kink instability and fast magnetic reconnection in a relativistic magnetized jet for decreasing density profile (heavier jet) with angular velocity amplitude of $\Omega_o = 2$. The upper panel shows 3D density isosurfaces, and bottom panel the locations of maximum current density as tracer of reconnection sites at t = 100 (adopted from ref.[7]).

We studied light as well as heavy jets with respect to the environment depending on the density profile. Different angular velocity amplitudes have been also tested. The results show the propagation of a helically kinked structure along the jet and a relatively stable configuration for the lighter jets. The jets appear to be collimated by the magnetic field and the flow is accelerated due to the conversion of electromagnetic into kinetic energy. We also identified the regions of high current density in filamentary current sheets, indicative of magnetic reconnection, which are associated with the kink unstable regions (Fig. 3) and correlated to the decrease of the sigma parameter of the flow. We discuss the implications of our findings for Poynting-flux dominated jets in connection with the magnetic reconnection process. We find that fast magnetic reconnection may be driven by the kink-instability turbulence and govern the transformation of magnetic into kinetic energy thus providing an efficient way to power and accelerate particles in AGN and gamma-ray-burst relativistic jets.

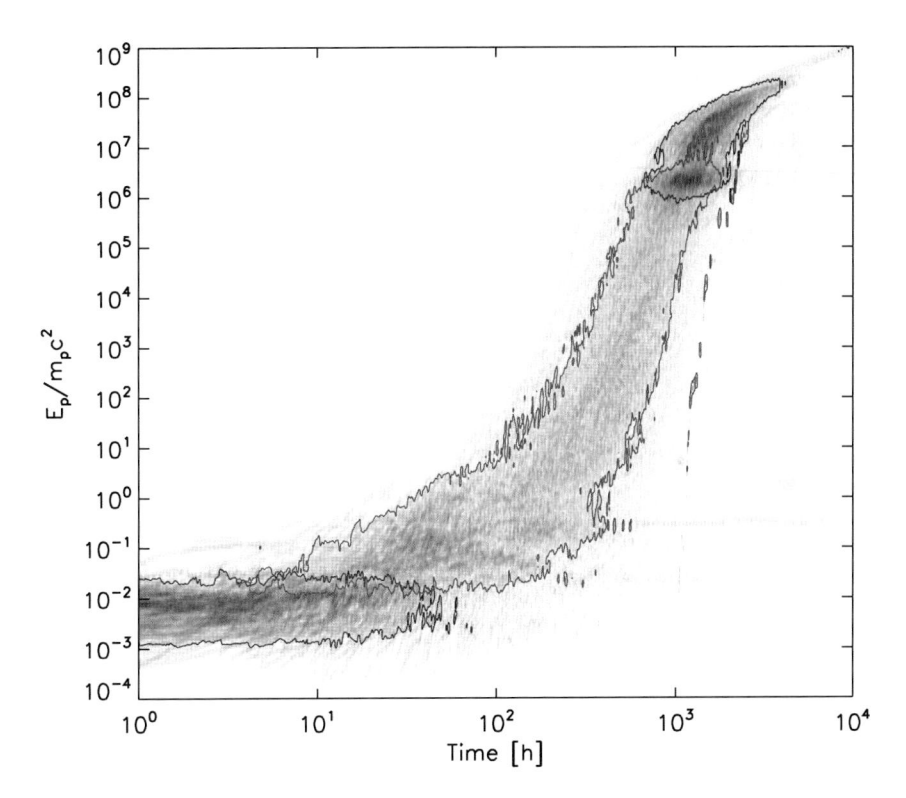

Fig. 4. Kinetic energy evolution, normalized by the proton rest mass energy, for the particles injected. Colours indicate which velocity component is being accelerated (red or blue for parallel or perpendicular component to the local magnetic field, respectively (adopted from ref.[8]).

Further, we also investigated the acceleration of particles injected in the jet subject to CDKI, which drives turbulence and fast magnetic reconnection.[8] Test protons injected in the nearly stationary snapshots of the jet, experience an exponential acceleration up to maximum energy. For a background magnetic field of $B \sim 0.1$ G, this saturation energy is $\sim 10^{16}$ eV, while for $B \sim 10$ G it is $\sim 10^{18}$ eV. The simulations also reveal a clear association of the accelerated particles with the regions of fast reconnection. In the early stages of the development of the non-linear growth of CDKI in the jet, when there are still no sites of fast reconnection, injected particles are also efficiently accelerated, but by magnetic curvature drift in the wiggling jet spine. However, they have to be injected with initial energy much larger than that required for particles to accelerate in reconnection sites. Fig. 4 shows which component of the velocity of the particles is being predominantly accelerated (red for the parallel and blue for the perpendicular component to the direction of the local magnetic field). We note that in the exponential regime, there is a clear dominance of the parallel component, characterizing an effective electric field mostly parallel to the reconnection layers, as expected, though the stochastic nature of the whole process also allows for the acceleration of the perpendicular component. The slower drift acceleration regimes, both in the beginning and after the exponential growth regime, are dominated by the acceleration in the vertical direction. We also obtained from the simulations an acceleration time due to reconnection with a weak dependence on the particles energy E, $t_A \propto E^{0.1}$. The energy spectrum of the accelerated particles develops a high energy tail with a power-law index $p \sim -1.2$ at the beginning of the acceleration, in agreement with earlier works. Our results provide an appropriate multi-dimensional framework for exploring this process in real systems and explain their complex emission patterns, especially in the very high energy bands and the associated neutrino emission recently detected in some blazars.

4. Summary and Conclusions

In this presentation, we discussed the role of magnetic reconnection in accretion-ejection phenomena around black holes based on results obtained in our theoretical and numerical studies. Our main conclusions can be summarized as follows:

1. Fast magnetic reconnection can play an important role in accretion/jet systems for particle acceleration, dissipation of magnetic energy, and conversion from magnetically dominated region to kinetically dominated region.
2. Power released by the fast magnetic reconnection can explain radio as well as gamma-ray emissions of XRBs and non-blazar AGNs as coming from the core around black holes with masses that span 10 orders of magnitude.
3. Black hole rotation and magnetic reconnection processes can drive jets of comparable power and even compete with each other.

4. The fast turbulent reconnection in magnetically dominated relativistic jets can be triggered by CDKI, possibly drive Fermi acceleration and lead to gamma-ray emissions as required by GRB and AGN blazar jets.

Acknowledgments

C.B.S. is supported by the National Natural Science Foundation of China under grant No. 12073021.

References

1. E. M. de Gouveia dal Pino and A. Lazarian, Production of the large scale superluminal ejections of the microquasar GRS 1915+105 by violent magnetic reconnection, *A&A*, **441**, 845 (2005).
2. G. Kowal, E. M. de Gouveia Dal Pino and A. Lazarian, Particle Acceleration in Turbulence and Weakly Stochastic Reconnection, *PRL*, **108**, 241102 (2012).
3. M. V. del Valle, E. M. de Gouveia Dal Pino and G. Kowal, Properties of the first-order Fermi acceleration in fast magnetic reconnection driven by turbulence in collisional magnetohydrodynamical flows, *MNRAS*, **463**, 4331 (2016).
4. L. H. S. Kadowaki, E. M. de Gouveia Dal Pino and C. B. Singh, The Role of Fast Magnetic Reconnection on the Radio and Gamma-ray Emission from the Nuclear Regions of Microquasars and Low Luminosity AGNs, *ApJ*, **802**, 113 (2015).
5. C. B. Singh, E. M. de Gouveia Dal Pino and L. H. S. Kadowaki, On the Role of Fast Magnetic Reconnection in Accreting Black Hole Sources, *ApJL*, **799**, L20 (2015).
6. C. B. Singh, D. Garofalo and E. M. de Gouveia Dal Pino, Magnetic reconnection and Blandford-Znajek process around rotating black holes, *MNRAS*, **478**, 5404 (2018).
7. C. B. Singh, Y. Mizuno and E. M. de Gouveia Dal Pino, Spatial Growth of Current-driven Instability in Relativistic Rotating Jets and the Search for Magnetic Reconnection, *ApJ*, **824**, 48 (2016).
8. T. E. Medina-Torrejón, E. M. de Gouveia Dal Pino, L. H. S. Kadowaki, G. Kowal, C. B. Singh and Y. Mizuno, Particle Acceleration by Relativistic Magnetic Reconnection Driven by Kink Instability Turbulence in Poynting Flux-Dominated Jets, *ApJ*, **908**, 193 (2021).

Exact fractal model of the universe and possible machine learning methods for the verification of the fractality

A. A. Kirillov, E. P. Savelova, P. O. Vladykina*

Department of Mathematical Modeling, Bauman Moscow State Technical University, Moscow, 105005, Russian Federation
* E-mail: vladykinapo@yandex.ru

We discuss the possibility that the topological structure of the Universe may possess fractal properties. Relic wormholes and their fractal distribution are predicted in a natural way by lattice quantum gravity models. This gives a new approach to some long-standing problems. Those are the nature of dark matter phenomena, the origin of Faber-Jackson and Tully-Fisher relations, and the observed deficit of baryons. We consider open Friedman model and construct an exact fractal model by means of a factorization of the space over a discrete subgroup of the group of motion. We derive some basic features of the resulting fractal space and discuss applications of machine learning methods for the verification of the fractal properties.

Keywords: Dark matter; wormholes; fractal distribution; baryon deficit.

1. Introduction

The nature of dark matter represents one of the most challenging problems of modern astrophysics. Particle physics suggests many possible candidates. The most promising are WIMPs (weakly interacting massive particles) which can be both new particles beyond the standard model, or particles composed from already known. However, such particles can hardly solve the problem. Indeed, experiments at LHC do not show the presence of particles beyond the standard model. Moreover, such particles should possess very exotic properties. Firstly, in the early Universe at the moment of recombination such particles have a rather high density but do not interact with baryons or radiation, otherwise they essentially change the observed CMB power spectrum of $\Delta T/T$. Secondly, in the modern Universe in centers of galaxies dark matter particles have much more modest densities but they should possess a sufficiently strong interaction with baryons to form the observed cored distribution of dark matter $\rho_{DM}(r) \sim const$ as $r \to 0$, where r is the distance to the center of a galaxy.[1–3] We recall that numerical investigations based on DM particles predict the presence of a cusp $\rho_{DM}(r) \sim 1/r$[4,5] in centers of galaxies which is the unavoidable consequence of the potential nature of initial velocities and the fact that DM particles interact via gravity only.

In principle, such a difficulty of DM models based on particles may be overcome in some of modified theories of gravity[6] which gain the popularity during the last decade.[7,8] However, any modification should be approved first from particle physics standpoint and most of such modifications can be rejected already at laboratory scales. In other words, most of such theories have pure academic interest and have no astrophysical applications.

One of the possible solutions of the problem is based on the fact that local topology of space may possess a rather complex or fractal structure.[9,10] It has two basic advantages. First, it does not require any modification of general relativity or the presence of additional dark matter component. And second, it gives the natural explanation to the empirical Tully-Fisher and Faber-Jackson relations[11,12] for rotation curves in galaxies. We point out that except the exotic scheme suggested by Milgrom,[13] where such relations were incorporated from the very beginning, the fractal topology gives the only natural explanation to such relations.[14]

The origin of fractal topological structure comes out directly from predictions of lattice quantum gravity models.[15–17] Indeed lattice models predict that at Planckian scales space-time has a foamy structure which possesses fractal properties. In particular, numerical investigations[17] show that spectral dimension of space-time runs from the value $D = 3/2$ at sub-Planckian scales to the value $D = 4$ on macroscopic scales. At very small scales the space-time foam can be described by a distribution of virtual wormholes.[18] At laboratory scales vacuum is stable which means that all virtual wormholes appear and disappear permanently. However if we believe that the early Universe underwent through an inflationary phase, we should expect that the exponential expansion very rapidly stretches all scales and some virtual wormholes do not decay. They temper and form initial conditions for the topological structure of space. The subsequent evolution of wormholes is the pure classical process. Spherically symmetric wormholes rapidly collapse, while toroidal and more complex wormholes may survive till the present days.[19,20] In other words, the present topological structure of space is an instant print of the space-time foam picture existing on Planck scales. Since the vacuum state possesses homogeneity and isotropy properties, the topology of our Universe inherits the same properties upon the freezing out on the inflationary stage.

The fractal structure of space can be described as follows. Consider an arbitrary point x in space and fix the geodesic distance R. Then the volume $V_x(R)$ of space which gets inside the geodesic ball, i.e., all points y which obey the inequality $\ell(y, x) < R$ (where $\ell(y, x)$ is the geodesic distance between x and y), scales with R as $V_x \sim R^d$, where $d = D - 1$. The homogeneity and isotropy of space requires that the function $V_x(R)$ and the dimension D do not depend on the initial point x.

The initial point x and omnidirectional geodesic lines, issued from the point x, define the extrapolated reference system which is used in astrophysics. The coordinate volume of such a system has always the dimension $D = 4$ which reflects the fact that locally space is Euclidean with the dimension $d = 3$ (i.e., R^3). We point out that the dependence on the redshift (cosmological evolution) and the choice of the background metric (open, flat, or closed model) somewhat changes the behavior of $V(R)$ and the definition of the dimension d, but rough features and the value $d = 3$ remains valid.

The situation changes when the space is filled with a distribution of wormholes. A part of geodesics go through wormhole throats and return to the same physical region of space or get into a remote region. Therefore, the behavior of $V(R)$ and the dimension d may change essentially. From the pure mathematical standpoint this signals to the fact that the extrapolated coordinate system stops to work (the same point may have multiple images), which requires to introduce additional atlases. In general the dimension evaluated in such a manner may either exceed or be less than the coordinate dimension $d = 3$. What kind of the dimension is realized for physical space depends on properties and the distribution of wormholes.

It is curious that the distribution of galaxies gives roughly the analogous picture. In a homogeneous space the number of galaxies reflects sufficiently well the behavior of the physical volume of space. The galaxy counts show the fractal behavior $N(R) \sim R^d$ with the dimension $d \approx 2$ up to the distances $R \sim 200 Mpc$[21,22] where $N(R)$ is the number of galaxies within the distance R. The maximal scale changes with the increase of precision. First estimates[23] for the scale upon which the distribution of galaxies switches to the homogeneity have the order $\sim 200 Mpc$. However more recent observations of SDSS[24] have found the existence of wall-type structures (Sloan Great Wall, etc.) on scales up to $0.1 R_H$, where R_H is the Hubble radius, see also.[25] Such super-large structures have posed a serious problem for the standard scenario of the structure formation. Recall that according to latter the largest scale on which inhomogeneities may develop is $300 Mpc$. Moreover, such structures seem to be inconsistent with the cosmological principle. We consider such data as an indirect evidence for the fractal (or at least complex) topological structure of space and the existence of relic wormholes. The development of perturbations and the formation of structures in the presence of relic wormholes is a rather complex problem which requires the further investigation.

We point out that in the flat space the light when passing through a wormhole throat is too scattered and may contribute only to the diffuse background radiation.[26] Most likely the scattered signal is too dim to observe a separate galaxy through wormhole throats. The exception may be only gigantic throats compared to the void and larger size. This means that the observed dimension counted by galaxies is always less than three $d < 3$. In particular, this may also explain the observed deficit of baryons.[27]

The fractal topological structure can be easily obtained in open Friedman models by means of a specific factorization of the negative curvature (Lobachevsky) space over a discrete subgroup of the group of motion of space.[19,20] We point out that the fractal distribution of baryonic matter does not necessarily indicate the existence of a fractal topological structure. However such a distribution requires specific initial conditions and, to be consistent with the observed homogeneity of the background, it requires the presence of dark matter which is dually distributed in space. The fractal topological structure, in turn, is the direct prediction of lattice quantum gravity models and, therefore, it has the most rigorous theoretical ground.

At first glance the basic disadvantage of the factorization is the presence of multiple images. Why do we not see images of the same galaxy? To find the answer is not difficult. First, our Universe has flat space. For small throats of wormholes (of the galaxy size or less) the additional images are very small and cannot be directly observed. Indeed, as it was demonstrated[30] in the flat model the intensity of an image I have the order $I \sim \frac{R^2}{L^2} I_0$, where R is the characteristic radius of the throat and L is the distance between the throat center and the original source and the ratio $\frac{R^2}{L^2} \leq 1$. It reaches the order of $\frac{R^2}{L^2} \sim 1$ only for very large throats. Moreover, the position of the image will be seen only in the second entrance into the wormhole and, therefore the image may have an arbitrary distance from the original. We point out that for fractal distribution over distances between entrances into the same wormhole the mean distance between entrances diverges.

Therefore, different images contribute only to the scattered background radiation. For gigantic wormholes all such images are too far from each other and we may see the same galaxy at different stages of its evolution. Therefore, it is impossible to recognize that we indeed see the same galaxy.

Thus the basic disadvantage is that the factorization requires the negative curvature space only, while the position of Doppler picks in the CMB spectrum favor for the flat space. In flat space such a factorization is impossible, while a fractal structure can be obtained by inserting fractal distribution of wormholes by onset or by means of deforming the metric of the factorized Lobachevsky space. We point out that such a deformation is not an unusual phenomenon. For example, if the inflation starts in an open model, then the factorization takes actually place at sub-Planck scales, while the subsequent particle production may change the value of the mean spatial curvature and produce flat or even closed space which depends on the rate of particle production.

In the flat space the presence of wormholes was shown to produce a specific modification of the standard Newton's law.[28, 29] If we interpret this as dark matter phenomenon, then we find the rigid relation between distribution of visible and dark components in a galaxy in the form $\rho_{DM}(k) = b(k)\rho_{vis}(k)$, where $\rho(k)$ is the Fourier components for dark and visible matter densities and $b(k)$ corresponds to the correction which depends on the distribution of wormholes around the galaxy. This gives the direct method for the determining of the correction $b(k)$ from observations and the subsequent modeling of the distribution of relic wormholes.

If our Universe is filled with relic wormholes, then how can we recognize this? To give an answer on such a question is not so easy. The investigation of possible independent effects related to the scattering of radiation on wormholes has revealed that almost all effects are well hidden under analogous effects related to the ordinary matter.[30] Here we see the three most promising possibilities. The first possibility relates to recently observed unexpected circular radio objects[31] and the possible role of torus-shaped wormholes in their origin.[32] The second relates to the gravitational wave Astronomy. In particular, several groups have claimed evidence for repeating echoes in the LIGO/Virgo observations of binary black hole mergers.[33–36] And such echoes can be generated by the near-horizon or other strong field effects related to black holes or wormholes.[37–39] We stress that the scattering of GWs by wormholes produces much stronger effects as compared to the scattering by ordinary matter objects, e.g., see discussions in,[40] which allows to disentangle such effects and detect wormholes.

The third and the most promising possibility lies in the application of machine leaning methods for detecting unusual structures produced by wormholes on the sky maps. The structures we should look for are the ring-type structures, which in general case have elliptical or even rectangular form. The latter may appear in regions where the mean curvature is negative, see Fig. 2. Besides, one should also look for multiple images of galaxies, etc..

2. Stable wormholes and factorization of the open model

As it was discussed above, relic wormholes are remnants of the inflationary stage. A-priori such wormholes may have an arbitrary form and geometric structure. Stable spherically symmetric wormholes cannot exist without an essential modification of general relativity. In general relativity static spherical wormholes require the presence of exotic matter which does not show up in physical systems and laboratory experiments. The exotic matter can be replaced by a proper modification of theory, e.g., see also a recent paper[41] and references therein, but any modification requires first a verification from particle physics point of view. Any deviation from general relativity is not detected yet, while quantum corrections may stabilize only wormholes of a Planck size.[42] Therefore, spherical wormholes collapse very soon upon the inflationary stage and form couples of primordial black holes.

Situation changes when we consider less symmetric configurations. It was demonstrated[19,20] that in open Friedman models a collection of stable wormholes can be constructed simply by means of a factorization of space over a discrete subgroup of the group of motions for the Lobachevsky space. The simplest wormhole here has the throat in the form of a torus and in such a scheme spherical wormholes do not appear at all. Such wormholes expand in the agreement with the expansion of space and, in other words, in the expanding co-moving reference frame they are static. This does not mean that they cannot collapse as the spherical configurations do. In particular, the development of density perturbations may enforce to collapse a whole region of space which contains such a wormhole throat. In what follows we briefly describe the factorization scheme.

2.1. *Factorization of the open Friedman model*

Consider the open Friedman model with the metric

$$ds^2 = dt^2 - a^2(t)dl^2, \tag{1}$$

where the space-like metic corresponds to the Lobachevsky space

$$dl^2 = d\chi^2 + \sinh^2\chi \left(\sin^2\theta d\varphi^2 + d\theta^2\right). \tag{2}$$

For the sake of illustration and simplicity we demonstrate the factorization for 2D sections of the space which correspond to a plane $d\varphi = 0$. Such a plane corresponds to two values of the polar angle $\varphi = \varphi_0$ and $\varphi = \varphi_0 + \pi$ which formally can be covered by the angles $\theta \in [0, 2\pi]$ where the range $\theta \in [\pi, 2\pi]$ corresponds to the half-plane $\varphi = \varphi_0 + \pi$. Using the coordinate transformation as

$$z = x + iy = i\frac{1-w}{1+w} \tag{3}$$

where $w = \tanh\frac{\chi}{2} e^{i\theta}$, we get the realization of the section in the form of the upper complex half-plane $Im\, z > 0$ which is the Klein model of the Lobachevsky plane $dl^2 = \frac{dx^2 + dy^2}{y^2}$. Consider two particular geodesic lines on the plane which correspond to semicircles $|z| = 1/R$ and $|z| = R$ with $R > 1$. Then the factorization can be determined by the map $z' = R^2 z$ which represents one of possible motions of the plane. The factorization means that any two points of the plane represent the same point, if they are connected by the relation

$$z_n = R^{2n} z, \; n = 0, \pm 1, \pm 2, ... \tag{4}$$

The above factorization corresponds to the cut along those two geodesic lines and subsequent gluing along them. The resulting space is a wormhole which connects two independent Lobachevsky planes (regions E_+ and E_-, see Fig. 1).

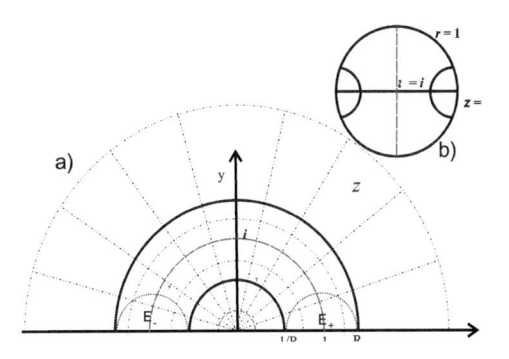

Fig. 1. a) The Lobachevsky plane. Dashed lines give the polar frame. The stripe between the two geodesic lines $r = 1/R$ and $r = R$ corresponds to the wormhole region. Regions below red dashed geodesics (semi-circles) correspond to two unrestricted Lobschevsky spaces $E_\pm$. The point $y = i$ corresponds to the center point of the wormhole throat ($\chi = 0$). The line $y = 0$ corresponds to infinity $\chi \to \infty$ for the plane. b) The same plane in coordinates $w = re^{i\theta}$, where $r = \tanh\frac{\chi}{2}$.

To understand how such a factorization looks in three dimensions let us return to the initial coordinates χ, θ, and φ. The geodesic lines $|z| = R$ and $|z| = 1/R$ are determined by

$$\tan^2\theta = \frac{\cosh^2\chi - \cosh^2\chi_0}{\cosh^2\chi \sinh^2\chi_0}, \tag{5}$$

where $R = e^{\chi_0}$ and χ_0 gives the shortest distance to the geodesic lines from the center point $\chi = 0$. The above equation corresponds to an arbitrary section $d\varphi = 0$ and describes two lines which can be seen in opposite directions $\theta = 0$ and $\theta = \pi$. Here the point $\chi = 0$ corresponds to the center of the throat (the point $z = i$ on Fig. 1). Using the symmetry with respect to the change of φ we find that in 3D space the above equation determines two semi-spheres (rigorously speaking they become semi-spheres in terms of the radial variable $r = \tanh\frac{\chi}{2}$ in which the infinity $\chi \to \infty$ becomes the sphere $r = 1$), while the factorization has the same form determined by (3) and (4). In this case the throat is not restricted. It is important that from the central point $\chi = 0$ such semi-spheres occupy the solid angles $\Delta\Omega = 2\pi\Delta\theta$ where $\Delta\theta$ can be found from (5) in the limit $\chi \to \infty$ which gives the asymptotic angles $\Delta\theta = 2\arctan(1/\sinh\chi_0)$. To get a restricted throat we have to place two more analogous semi-spheres e.g., in the orthogonal to $\theta = 0, \pi$ directions at a distance χ_1, see fig. 2. Moreover, the distances $\chi_{0,1}$ should be chosen in such a way that all

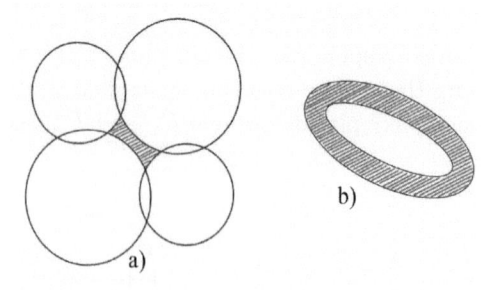

Fig. 2. a) The form of a throat as it is seen on sky in the open model. It represents the colored curved rectangle. Regions behind the circles are copies of the physical region. All additional images lay within the circles. b) The form of the throat as it is seen in flat models upon the deformation of the metric from the negative curvature space. The throat has the torus-like form and only part of the throat surface is seen. Additional images lay inside the surface of the torus.

four semi-spheres restrict a finite minimal section. It is also important that every semi-sphere envelopes a non-physical space, since every point within it represents an image of a point from the corresponding physical space.

Now let us consider how such a wormhole looks for a remote from the center of the throat observer. To this end we should simply shift the central point $\chi = 0$ from the middle of the throat. From qualitative standpoint the picture remains the same, every semi-sphere is determined by the same equation (5) but the distance to it χ_0 changes. Four such semi-spheres group and if they restrict a finite solid angle they form a remote wormhole. The angle they occupy on sky is $\Delta\theta \sim 2\exp(-\chi_0)$ and the throats (minimal sections) are seen as curved rectangles. We point out that from the topological standpoint throats are tori but in open model they will be seen on sky as rectangles. Such wormholes restore the torus-like form of throats only in the case when the space is additionally deformed or curved in such a way that the mean curvature becomes zero or positive one.

Above we have described the factorization which forms a wormhole that connects two independent (connected only through the throat) Lobachevsky spaces. To get a wormhole whose both entrances lay in the same region requires one more analogous map as described in.[19] In this case we get couples of such throats (groups of semi-spheres) on sky. Now to get a pure fractal picture we may construct a Cantor set on sky by placing such groups of semi-spheres of smaller and smaller solid angles.

2.2. *Stability of wormholes*

The factorization described previously requires the negative curvature space which corresponds to an open Friedman model, while the position of Doppler picks in the power CMB spectrum favor for the flat space. In flat space such a factorization is impossible. However a fractal structure can be obtained by inserting fractal distribution of wormholes or by deforming the metric of a factorized Lobachevsky space. The deformation of the Lobachevsky space can be obtained rather naturally during the inflationary stage. Indeed, if the space had initially a negative curvature, then during the inflation stage production of wormholes and particles took place. Therefore, particle production process could essentially change the value of spatial curvature and essentially deform the picture described above. In this sense we may expect to see a distribution of analogous wormholes even in flat space. We point out that contrary to the open model in flat space upon the deformation throat sections will look as torus- like shapes. This poses the problem how such wormholes may evolve in flat space. Spherical wormholes are unstable and collapse very quickly. The stability of torus-like wormholes is not investigated yet. There are only some encouraging results. For example, the existence and stability of static cylindrical wormholes without exotic matter was demonstrated recently in Refs.[43,44] We point out that the toroidal wormhole reduces to the cylindrical one in the limit when on of radii tends to infinity. Though the rigorous investigation of the behavior of toroidal wormholes during the cosmological evolution still is not completed, we may expect that such wormholes collapse much slower, than spherical wormholes do and may survive till the present days. As a result we get open or flat Friedman model filled with toroidal wormholes.

When we consider wormhole throats as objects of a finite size (e.g., they occupy a finite solid angle on sky) we may average out over possible random orientations of the throats in space. We point out that there are no strong physical arguments in favor for some particular characteristic size of wormholes, moreover, fractal structure of space-time at Planck scales predicts analogous fractal distribution over the throat sizes. In the case of the statistical averaging over possible orientations the spherical symmetry of the wormhole configuration restores and, therefore, estimates based on spherical wormholes should give correct predictions, at least to the leading order. In what follows we discuss the open Friedman model with almost zero value of the space curvature where wormholes can be considered simply as quasi-static objects expanding only due to the scale factor $a(t)$. The cosmological evolution of $a(t)$ follows the standard Friedman equations

$$H^2 + \frac{k}{a^2} = \frac{8\pi G}{3}\rho,$$

where $H = \dot{a}/a$ is the Hubble constant, $k = -1$, and ρ is the matter density (baryons plus radiation). The metric has the standard form $ds^2 = dt^2 - a^2(t)dl^2$, where the space-like part dl^2 corresponds to the Lobachevsky space.

The behavior of small perturbations in such a model is determined by the standard Lifshitz theory[45] with one exception. The basic equations for perturbations have local character and, therefore, do not depend on the topological structure of space. However possible solutions do. In particular, in comparison to the ordinary Lobachevsky space the space with wormholes represents a space with a specific factorization. For example in flat space the factorization over translations in one of directions gives the space which is simply the cylinder and one of coordinates becomes a periodic one. This means that corresponding modes are classified by a discrete wave numbers instead of continues ones and, therefore, some modes are absent. Analogously, the factorization of the open model selects only particular solutions among all possible solutions for the unrestricted space. Therefore, from qualitative and quantitative standpoint the evolution of perturbations will show essential deviations from the behavior in standard Friedman models. Analogous deviations are indeed observed and are interpreted as the presence of dark matter, or a modification of general relativity. According to Ref.[17] the Hausdorff dimension of space should be $1 < d \leq 3$. At laboratory scales we see that $d = 3$ and no deviations from the standard Newton's law are observed. The number of galaxies counts show that starting from galactic scales ($R \sim 5Kpc$) at least up to $200Mpc$ the Hausdorff dimension is $d \approx 2$ and at those scales we observe the phenomenon of dark matter.

Indeed, the simplest estimate for the Newton's law gives $F \propto \frac{GM}{S(R)}$, where M is the mass within the volume $V(R)$ (ball of the radius R) and $S(R) = \frac{dV(R)}{dR}$ is the square of the sphere surrounding the volume $V(R)$. In the case of a fractal law $V \sim R^d$ and $S \sim R^{d-1}$. The value $d \approx 2$ is in the very good agreement with observations of dark matter in the range of scales $5Kpc < R < 200Mpc$. The value $d \approx 1$ gives too strong the gravitational bind and such structures should decouple the cosmological expansion very early, or it even should be suppressed during the inflationary stage.

From one standpoint, stable toroidal wormholes do surely exist in negative curvature spaces (in the open model), while in the flat model their stability requires additional study. From other point, the position of the Doppler picks in the CMB ($\Delta T/T$) spectrum points out to the fact that our Universe is very close to the flat space, which means that the matter density is close to the critical value. Here, however, one should be especially careful in making estimates. First, the positions of picks are evaluated on the basis of the standard Friedman models when the possible factorization of the space is not taken into account (i.e., the possible presence of wormholes). Secondly, the presence of fluctuations $\Delta T/T \sim 10^{-5}$ means that at the moment of recombination analogous fluctuations are present in the metric and matter density $\Delta\Omega = \Omega - 1 \sim 10^{-5}$, where $\Omega = \rho/\rho_{cr}$ and $\rho_{cr} = 3H^2/(8\pi G)$ is the critical density. In other words, the space is split in regions of a positive ($\Omega > 1$, $k/a^2 \approx 10^{-5} H^2$) and negative ($\Omega < 1$, $k/a^2 \approx -10^{-5} H^2$) curvature. If in regions where $\Omega > 1$ the presence of stable wormholes requires the additional study, in the regions where $\Omega < 1$ stable wormholes do exist. Moreover, in the fractal Universe the observed mean value of the spatial curvature is somewhat different from the actual locall value. It contains the additional factor $V_{ph}(R)/V_{coor}(R)$, where $V_{ph}(R) \sim R^{D-1}$ is the actual physical volume of space, while $V_{coor}(R) \sim R^3$ is the coordinate, or extrapolated volume. In this estimate one should take the Hubble radius $R = R_H$, or the radius of the sphere of last scattering. In accordance to Ref.[6] the estimate $V_{ph}(R)/V_{coor}(R) \approx 10^{-5}$ is in the agreement with observations which means that at the moment of recombination the local value of the spatial curvature and the Hubble constant may have the same order ($k/a_{rec}^2 \approx H_{rec}^2$). We point out that the same value 10^{-5} characterizes the portion of actually observed baryons with respect to the value predicted by nucleosynthesis. Here we assume estimates of the number of baryons based only on counts of galaxies and discrete sources, while the diffuse background (e.g., the X-ray background) gives much higher estimate for such a ratio ~ 0.4.[46–48] In fractal picture the diffuse background does not rigorously reflects the actual number of baryons. It reflects merely the mean homogeneity and isotropy of space and the local density of baryons, while the actual number of baryons is proportional to the physical volume of space $N(R) \sim V_{ph}(R) \ll V_{coor}(R)$. In other words, rigorous estimates require further investigation.

3. Fractal distribution of wormholes and modification of Newton's law

The fractality of the topological structure of space requires the analogous fractal distribution of wormholes. At first glance the fractality is not consistent with the observed homogeneity and isotropy of the Universe. This however is not so, e.g., the diffuse background which appears due to the scattering on wormholes remains homogeneous and isotropic.[30] The basic feature of the fractal distribution is a scale - dependence of different mean values, such as mean density of wormhole throats n, the mean distance between entrances $\langle X \rangle$, the mean radius of the throat $\langle R \rangle$, etc.

Consider the simplest model suggested by us in Ref.,[28] which explicitly demonstrates that non-trivial topology can model effects of dark matter. The model is based on spherical wormholes, while actual stable wormholes should have torus like throats. We assume that throats are averaged over orientations then the spherical symmetry restores and such wormholes can be considered in the leading order as spherical ones.

In the case of weak gravitational fields and potential perturbations the Einstein's equations reduce to the Laplace equation for Newton's potential ($R_0^0 - \frac{1}{2}R = 8\pi T_0^0$)

$$\frac{1}{a^2}\Delta\phi = 4\pi G\left(\delta\rho + \frac{3}{c^2}\delta P\right),$$

where a is the scale factor, $\delta\rho$ and δP are perturbations in density and pressure respectively. The behavior of perturbations are determined by the Green function (Newton's law)

$$\Delta G(x, x') = 4\pi\delta(x - x').$$

In the Euclidean space the Newton's law gives $G_0 = -1/r$ (in the Fourier representation it gives $G_0 = -4\pi/k^2$). In the presence of wormholes the Green function changes.[28] It is convenient to describe corrections which appear due to wormholes by the presence of additional sources (fictitious sources). Then formally we may think that the space remains Euclidean, while proper periodic conditions on throats are accounted by the bias of sources

$$\Delta G(x, x') = 4\pi\left[\delta(x - x') + b(x - x')\right].$$

Here the bias function $b(x)$ describes corrections to the Newton's law which appear due to non-trivial topology of space. Indeed the presence of the bias $b(x - x')$ gives rise to the transformation

$$\frac{1}{r^2} \to \frac{2}{\pi}\int_0^\infty [1 + b(k)]\frac{\sin(kr) - kr\cos(kr)}{kr^2}dk.$$

The asymptotically flat rotation curves in galaxies require that the correction to the Newton's potential should have the logarithmic behavior, i.e. the gravitational acceleration should switch from $1/r^2$ to $1/r$. The above expression implies that at galaxy scales the bias behaves as $b(k) \sim 1/k^\alpha$ with $\alpha \sim 1$ and $b(x-x') \sim 1/(x-x')^2$. When considering a galaxy with surface mass density distribution $\rho_L(x)$ the bias $b(x - x')$ forms an effective dark matter halo in the form

$$\rho_{DM}(x) = \int b(x - x')\rho_L(x')d^3x'.$$

In particular, for $b(k) \sim 1/k^\alpha$ and an infinitely thin disc $\rho_L(x) = \sigma e^{-r/R_D}\delta(z)$ this expression gives the pseudo-isothermal halo $\rho_{DM} = \rho_0 R_C^2/(R_C^2 + r^2)$, where R_C is the radius of the core, e.g., see.[6,14]

For a homogeneous distribution of wormholes the bias function $b(x)$ was first considered in[28] and more general case was constructed in.[18] The bias is expressed via the distribution of wormholes which in the homogeneous and isotropic case is a function $F = nf(X, R)$, where n is the density of wormhole throats in space, X is the distance between entrances into a wormhole, and R is the throat radius. In the Fourier representation ($b(k) = \int b(r) e^{-i\mathbf{k r}}d^3r$) it has the form[29]

$$b(k) = n\overline{R}(k)\frac{4\pi}{k^2}(\nu(k) - 1),$$

where we define
$$\overline{R}(k) = \frac{1}{k}\int \widetilde{f}(0,R)\sin(kR)\,dR = -\frac{1}{k}\mathrm{Im}\int e^{-ikR}w(R)dR, \qquad (6)$$

$$\nu(k) = \frac{1}{k\overline{R}(k)}\int \widetilde{f}(k,R)\sin(kR)\,dR, \qquad (7)$$

and $\widetilde{f}(k,R) = \int f(X,R)e^{-i\mathbf{k}\mathbf{X}}d^3X$ is the Fourier transform for the distribution function over distances. Here $k = |\mathbf{k}|$ and the dependence of the above functions only on k reflects the isotropy of the distribution f. The physical meaning of these two functions $\overline{R}(k)$ and $\nu(k)$ become quite clear in the limit $kR \ll 1$, when throat radii assumed to be small as compared to the characteristic scales. Then we may set $\sin(kR) \approx kR$ and we find $\overline{R} \approx \int Rw(R)dR = \int Rf(X,R)\,d^3X dR$ which is simply the mean value of the throat radius. We point out that $\overline{R}(k)$ is proportional to the imaginary part of the characteristic function for the distribution over radii $w(R) = \widetilde{f}(0,R)$ (6) (which is $w(k) = \int e^{-ikR}w(R)dR$). Analogously the function $\nu(k) \approx (1/\overline{R})\int R\widetilde{f}(k,R)dR$ is the characteristic function for the distribution over the distances between throat entrances. In the most general case the effective radius $\overline{R}(k)$ has the dependence on scales and it admits both signs. Thus, the presence of a distribution of wormholes gives rise to the specific modification of the Newton's law and the true Green function becomes

$$G(k) = -\frac{4\pi}{k^2}(1 + b(k)).$$

Consider the simplest particular situation when all distances between throats have the same value X_0 and all throat radii be R_0, then we find the homogeneous and isotropic distribution in the form

$$f(X,R) = \frac{1}{4\pi X_0^2}\delta(|X| - X_0)\delta(R - R_0),$$

and the Fourier transform is

$$\widetilde{f}(k,R) = \delta(R - R_0)\frac{\sin kX_0}{kX_0}.$$

The effective radius and the characteristic function which correspond to such a distribution are

$$\overline{R}(k) = R_0\frac{\sin(kR_0)}{kR_0}, \quad \nu(k) = \frac{\sin kX_0}{kX_0},$$

and the bias is

$$b(k) = -\frac{4\pi}{k^2}nR_0\frac{\sin(kR_0)}{kR_0}\left(1 - \frac{\sin kX_0}{kX_0}\right).$$

We see that the bias $b(k)$ (and, therefore, corrections to the Newton's potential) alternates the sign with the change of scales. It is completely determined by three typical scales related to wormhole distribution, which are the density $n \sim 1/L_w^3$, the typical throat radius R_0, and the typical distance between entrances into throats X_0.

In the general case (of the isotropic and homogeneous distributions) the above expressions can be rewritten as follows

$$\overline{R}(k) = \frac{\langle \sin(kR) \rangle}{k}, \quad \nu(k) = \frac{1}{\overline{R}(k)} \left\langle \frac{\sin(kR)}{k} \frac{\sin kX}{kX} \right\rangle,$$

where the mean value is determined as $\langle g(X,R) \rangle = \int g(X,R)f(X,R)d^3XdR$. For normal distributions, when all momenta are finite, we may expand the above expressions in series and find

$$b(k) = \lambda \sum_{N=1}^{\infty} (-1)^N (kL_N)^{2(N-1)} \approx -\lambda \left(1 - (L_2k)^2 + (L_3k)^4 + ...\right), \quad (8)$$

where $\lambda = \frac{4\pi n}{6} \langle RX^2 \rangle$ and the characteristic scales L_N are determined via mean values as follows

$$(L_N)^{2(N-1)} = \frac{6}{\langle RX^2 \rangle} \sum_{l=0}^{N-1} \frac{\langle R^{2l+1} X^{2(N-l)} \rangle}{(2l+1)!(2(N-l)+1)!}.$$

The first term here determines the re-normalization of the gravitational constant, while next terms determine higher order corrections. The above analysis shows that using only normal distributions it is hardly possible to get the desirable form of corrections (observed in galaxies). This is confirmed by estimates presented in Introduction. Indeed, Gaussian distribution of wormholes is described by three typical scales those are $L_w \sim n^{-1/3}$ which characterizes the absolute value of corrections, R_0, and X_0. Starting from a typical scale $R > X_0$ $V_{phys}(R) \simeq V_{Coor}(R)$ and all corrections reduce to a some renormalization of gravitational constant, while at smaller intermediate scales ($R_0 < R < X_0$) corrections have more complex behavior (partial screening, e.g., see[28]). This indicates that we should consider more general fractal distributions.

In the case of fractal distributions such an expansion does not work, since all momenta may diverge, while the density of wormholes n is badly determined (its value also depends on scales). In this case we should directly work with characteristic functions $w(k)$ ($\overline{R}(k) = -Im\, w(k)/k$) and $\nu(k)$. Indeed, consider the simplest example when $w(k)$ and $\nu(k)$ are independent. Then every function can be expressed as

$$\nu(k) = \exp\left\{-(kL_1)^{\alpha_1}\left(1 - i\beta_1 \tan\left(\frac{\alpha_1 \pi}{2}\right)\right)\right\}, \quad (9)$$

where $\beta_1 \in [-1, 1]$ determines an asymmetry of the distribution e.g., see Ref.[49] And analogously

$$w(k) = \exp\left\{-(kL_2)^{\alpha_2}\left(1 - i\beta_2 \tan\left(\frac{\alpha_2 \pi}{2}\right)\right)\right\}, \quad (10)$$

with its own parameters L, β, and α. The last equation defines the effective radius as

$$\overline{R}(k) = -Im\frac{w(k)}{k} = -L_2 \frac{\exp\left(-(kL_2)^{\alpha_2}\right)}{kL_2}\sin\left[(kL_2)^{\alpha_2}\beta_2\tan\left(\frac{\alpha_2\pi}{2}\right)\right]. \quad (11)$$

In the case $\alpha = 2$ the above characteristic functions corresponds to the standard Gaussian distribution, while for $\alpha < 2$ the dispersion which corresponds to such a distribution diverges as

$$\sigma = \left.\frac{d^2}{dk^2}\ln\nu(k)\right|_{k=0} \propto k^{\alpha-2} \to \infty$$

as well as all higher momenta. The parameters α_i relates to the Hausdorff dimension of space D and it characterizes the fractal structure of $f(X, R)$. To avoid misunderstanding we also point out that the scales L_i do not characterize the mean value between entrances into throats, or the mean radius, since for fractal distributions such moments diverge. In such a case the decomposition in series presented above (8) does not work. In this case we should expand directly the characteristic functions (9), (11) themselves. In the region of sufficiently small scales $kL_i \gg 1$ (i.e., at very small distances) the function $b(k)$ quickly oscillates and vanishes $b(k) \to 0$. In this region of scales the standard Newton's law does work. At sufficiently big scales, i.e., in the limit $kL_i \ll 1$, we find the first leading term as

$$b(k) \approx 4\pi\chi\frac{(kL_2)^{\alpha_2-1}(kL_1)^{\alpha_1}}{(kL_3)^2} + \ldots = 4\pi\chi\left(k\widetilde{L}\right)^{\alpha_1+\alpha_2-3} + \ldots, \quad (12)$$

where $L_3 = 1/\sqrt{nL_2}$ and

$$\chi = \beta_2\tan\left(\frac{\alpha_2\pi}{2}\right)\left(1 - i\beta_1\tan\left(\frac{\alpha_1\pi}{2}\right)\right).$$

Corrections to the empirical Green function $b(k)$ can be restored directly from observations and by relations (6), (7) they determine the distribution of wormholes. In the present paper we do not analyze any actual data, since it requires an independent study. However some rough estimates can be obtained. Indeed, the first correction for the empirical Green function which follows from rotation curves[14] behaves roughly as $G_{emp} = -\frac{4\pi}{k^2}(1 + (k\widetilde{L})^{-\alpha})$ with $\alpha \simeq 1$ which determines parameters in (12) as $\chi \simeq 1$ ($\beta_1 = 0$), $\alpha_1 + \alpha_2 \simeq 2$, and $\widetilde{L} \sim 5Kpc$. As it was discussed in Ref.[14] the value of the parameter $\widetilde{L}$ may somewhat change from a galaxy to a galaxy which reflects the presence of initial inhomogeneities of the metric at the moment of recombination.

As it was demonstrated in[14] the bias in the form (12) and the homogeneity of total matter (baryon plus dark matter components)[6] straightforwardly lead to the origin of Tully-Fisher and Faber-Jackson relations. Therefore, this can be also considered as indirect indication of the fractal topological structure of space. Moreover, the recent SDSS data[24,25] show the traces of the fractal distribution of baryons up to scales $\sim 0.1R_H$.

4. Concluding remarks

As concluding remarks we point out to basic results of this paper. First, we have demonstrated that the most natural origin of dark matter phenomena relates to the existence of locally complex or fractal topological structure of our Universe. At extremely small (sub-Planckian) distances such a fractal structure is predicted by lattice quantum gravity models. During the inflationary period the topological fractal structure tempers and forms the initial conditions for the actual structure of space in Friedman models. One may imagine such a process as an instant enormous increase of a small (of the Planckian order) portion of space filled with virtual wormholes up to macroscopic scales. The stretched wormholes become real and form the initial topological structure, while their subsequent evolution is already governed by classical gravity. Spherical wormholes collapse and form primordial black holes, while torus-like wormholes may survive till the present days.

Secondly, the fractal structure is consistent with the apparent homogeneity and isotropy of space. The simplest rigorous model is the Lobachevsky space factorized over a discrete subgroup of the group of motion. The resulting space has a constant spatial curvature and it locally cannot be distinguished from Friedman model. However it is not a homogeneous space any more and in general it possesses a complex topological structure. The flat model can be obtained by a deformation (due to particle production) of the factorized Lobachevsky space. In this case the fractal topological structure will correspond to a specific distribution of relic wormholes which possesses fractal properties.

And finally, we have demonstrated that when the distribution of wormholes possesses fractal properties, corrections to the standard Newton's law have the necessary form to imitate carefully the presence of dark matter in galaxies. The empirical Green function restored from the analysis of rotation curves in galaxies allows directly restrict some of parameters of the fractal distribution of wormholes.

The rigorous verification of the fractal topological structure requires the use of machine leaning methods. Such methods allow for detecting unusual structures produced by wormholes on the sky maps. Those are the ring-type structures with a specific temperature profile, e.g., if a wormhole throat rotates, then due to the kinematic Sunaev-Zeldovich effect this produces a specific profile of T in CMB. In general case rings may have elliptical or rectangular form. Besides, the fractal structure predicts that galaxies may have multiple images given at different moments of their evolution. Such features cannot be detected without the use of machine leaning methods.

References

1. de Blok, W. J. G., Bosma A. *Astron. and Astrophys.* **385**, 816 (2002).
2. Gentile G., et al. *Mon. Not. RAS.* **351**, 903 (2004).
3. Salucci P., *Astron. Astrophys. Rev.* **27** 2 (2019).
4. Navarro J. F., Frenk C. S., White S. D. M. *The Astrophys. J.* **462** 563 (1996).

5. Diemand J., et. al. *Mon. Not. RAS.* **364** 665 (2005).
6. Kirillov A.A. *Phys. Lett. B* **632** 453 (2006).
7. Amendola L., et. al. *Living Rev. Relativ.* **21** 2 (2018).
8. Harko, T., & Lobo, F. Extensions of $f(R)$ Gravity: Curvature-Matter Couplings and Hybrid Metric-Palatini Theory. (Cambridge Monographs on Math. Phys., (2018)).
9. Kirillov A. A. and Savelova E. P. *Gravit. Cosmol.* **14** 256 (2008).
10. Kirillov A.A., Turaev D. *Phys. Lett. B* **656** 1 (2007).
11. Tully R.B., Fisher J.R., *Astron. and Astrophys.* **54** 661 (1977).
12. Faber S.M. and Jackson R.E., *Astrophys. J.* **206** 668 (1976).
13. Milgrom M. *Astrophys. J.* **270**, 365 (1983).
14. Kirillov A.A., Turaev D. *Mon. Not. RAS. L* **371**, 31 (2006).
15. Knizhnik V., Polyakov A., Zamolodchikov A. *Mod. Phys. Lett. A* **3** 819 (1988).
16. Kawai H., Kawamoo N., Mogami T., Watabiki Y. *Phys. Lett. B* **306** 19 (1993).
17. Ambjorn J., Jurkiewicz J., Loll R. *Phys. Rev. Lett.* **95**, 171301 (2005).
18. Savelova E.P. *Grav. Cosmol.* **21**, 48 (2015).
19. Kirillov A.A., Savelova E.P. *Int. J. Mod. Phys. D* **25**, 1650075 (2016).
20. Kirillov A.A., Savelova E.P. *Eur. Phys. J. C* **80**, 45 (2020).
21. Coleman P.H., Pietronero L. *Phys. Rep.* **213** 311 (1992).
22. Baryshev Yu. Teerikorpi P. *Discovery of Cosmic Fractals.* WS, (2002), Pages: 408.
23. Geller M. J. Huchra J. P. *Science* **246**, 897 (1989).
24. SDSS collaboration. *Astrophys. Journ. Suppl.*, **233** 25 (2017).
25. Horvath I. et al. *Astron. & Astrophys.*, **584** , A48 (2015).
26. Planck collaboration, Planck 2018 results - IV. *Astron. & Astrophys.* **641**, A4 (2020).
27. Fukugitai M., Hogan C.J., Peebles P.J.E. *Astrophys. J.* **503**, 518 (1998).
28. Kirillov A.A., Savelova E.P. *Phys. Lett. B* **660**, 93 (2008).
29. Kirillov A. A. and Savelova E. P. *Gravit. Cosmol.* **24**, 337 (2018).
30. Kirillov A. A. and Savelova E. P. *Universe* **4**, 35 (2018).
31. Norris, et al *Publications of the Astron. Soc. of Australia*, **38**, E003 (2021).
32. Kirillov A.A., Savelova E.P. *Eur. Phys. J. C* **80**, 810 (2020).
33. Abedi J., Dykaar H. and Afshordi N., *Phys. Rev. D,* **96**, 082004 (2017).
34. Conklin R. S., Holdom B. and Ren J., *Phys. Rev. D,* **98**, 044021 (2018).
35. Westerweck J. et al., *Phys. Rev. D,* **97**, 124037 (2018).
36. Abedi J. and Afshordi N., *JCAP,* **11**, 010 (2019).
37. Cardoso V, Franzin E, and Pani P, *Phys. Rev. Lett.* **116**, 171101 (2016).
38. Cardoso V., et al., *Phys. Rev. D,* **94**, 084031 (2016).
39. Cardoso V. and Pani P., *Living Rev. Rel.,* **22** 4 (2019).
40. Kirillov A.A., Savelova E.P., Lecian O.M. *Eur. Phys. J. C* **81** 263 (2021).
41. De Falco, V., Battista, E., Capozziello, S. et al. *Eur. Phys. J. C* **81**, 157 (2021).
42. Khatsymovsky V. *Phys. Lett. B* **320** 234 (1994).
43. Bronnikov K. A.& Krechet V. G. *Phys. Rev. D* **99** 084051 (2019).
44. Bronnikov K. A., Bolokhov S. V., and Skvortsova M. V., *Int. J. Mod. Phys. D* **28**, 1941008 (2019).
45. E. Lifshitz, *J. Phys. (USSR)* **10**, 116–129 (1946).
46. Nicarstro F., et al. *Astrophys. J.* **629**, 700 (2005).
47. Tripp T.M., et al. *Astrophys. Journal. Suppl.*, **177**, 39 (2008).
48. Buote D.A., et al *Astrophys. J.,* **695**, 1351, (2009).
49. Samorodmitzky G., Taggy M.S. *Stable non-Gaussian random processes* - New York: Chapman & Hall, (1994).

Estimating the photometric redshifts of galaxies and QSOs using regression techniques in machine learning

A. Momtaz, M. H. Salimi and S. Shakeri*

*Department of Physics, Isfahan University of Technology,
Isfahan, 84156-8311, Iran*
*E-mail: s.shakeri@iut.ac.ir

Measuring distances of cosmological sources such as galaxies, stars and quasars plays an increasingly critical role in modern cosmology. Obtaining the optical spectrum and consequently calculating the redshift as a distance indicator could instantly classify these objects. As long as spectroscopic observations are not available for many galaxies and the process of measuring the redshift is time-consuming and infeasible for large samples, machine learning (ML) approaches could be applied to determine the redshifts of galaxies from different features including their photometric colors. In this paper, by using the flux magnitudes from the Sloan Digital Sky Survey (SDSS) catalog, we develop two ML regression algorithms (decision tree and random forest) for estimating the redshifts taking color indices as input features. We find that the random forest algorithm produces the optimum result for the redshift prediction, and it will be further improved when the dataset is limited to a subset with $z \leq 2$ giving the normalised standard deviation $\overline{\Delta Z}_{\text{norm}} = 0.005$ and the standard deviation $\sigma_{\Delta z} = 0.12$. This work shows great potential of using the ML approach to determine the photometric redshifts of distant sources.

Keywords: Spectroscopy; Photometry; Machine Learning; Random Forest; Decision Tree

1. Introduction

Spectroscopy is usually applied as a valuable technique to determine the redshift of extragalactic sources. However, its high wavelength resolution limits its accuracy, a problem that can only partially be solved with more observation time.[1]

In recent years, a growing number of studies have relied on less precise statistical but more efficient estimates of redshifts based on broadband photometry.[2–4] A lot of key projects for the upcoming survey telescopes will involve these photometric redshifts. The photometric redshift is a tool used by multiple fields of astronomy to estimate the distances between objects in the sky. Since the process of redshift estimation is of great importance in various endeavors such as astronomical transient events, galaxy clustering, the mass function of the galaxy and the weak-lensing approach through constraining the presence of Dark Energy, several methods have been developed to choose an optimum technique.[5] These methods include leveraging training sets,[6] utilizing template spectra for comparisons[7] and mostly template fitting methods.[8]

Additionally, for over a decade, cosmologists have used ML techniques based on neural networks and regression algorithms to determine photometric redshifts.[9] In an attempt to establish a quantitative approach towards the performance of Random

Forests, Carliles et al. 2010 concludes that in contrast to other regression techniques, Random Forest regression overcomes several vital weaknesses.[10] Random Forests algorithm as a non-parametric procedure does not use a statistical model to describe the underlying data. The performance of parametric methods depends on how well the model fits the underlying distribution of data.[11] However, with highly skewed noise distributions, the Random Forest still provides reliable estimate of the error distribution, and this behavior is backed up by strong theoretical support.[12]

In Hoyle et al. (2015), an analysis of feature importance selection applied to the photometric redshift estimation using the ML architecture decision trees was presented. Such an investigation in this regard remarked in five optical frequency bands known as u-g-r-i-z, the flux magnitudes available from the SDSS, as a determinative input feature that encodes the most information about the redshifts of galaxies or quasars.[13]

Over the last 20 years, the SDSS has made a map of the universe. SDSS measurements of the galaxies, quasars and intergalactic gas structure have contributed significantly to tests of the standard cosmological model that describes our understanding of the history and future of the universe. Data Release 16 of SDSS[14] includes infrared, extragalactic and integral field spectra for nearby galaxies. The survey has mapped 4846156 useful spectra, 2863635 of which are galaxies and 960678 are quasi-stellar objects or the so-called quasars.

In this paper, we focus on Data Release 16 of SDSS and design a decision tree and a random forest algorithm to obtain an accurate estimation of the redshifts and then investigated their evaluation procedures to obtain optimum algorithms. We create a dataset of color indices acting as an approximation for the spectrum and as our input features. A noteworthy aspect of this work is the effort put into incorporating more information than a simple point estimate of the redshift. We determine the uncertainty associated with redshift estimates and calculate a posterior distribution.[15]

The rest of the paper is organized as follows. In Sec. 2 we explain ML algorithms including decision trees and random forests. In Sec. 3 the last data release of SDSS, DR16, and our input features will be presented besides our ML methodology for training and learning. The analysis and results are presented in Sec. 4 where we apply optimizing process for Decision Tree and Random Forest algorithms and compare the results of these algorithms. Finally, we discuss our results and conclude in Sec. 5.

2. Machine Learning Algorithms

2.1. *Decision Trees*

A decision trees is a ML algorithm which is used for both classification and regression learning tasks.[16] Based on a set of input features, decision trees generates its corresponding output targets. This is accomplished by a series of single decisions, each representing a node or branching of the tree. Following the training data, the decision tree learning algorithm determines which decision should be made at each branch. Various metrics are employed by each algorithm in order to determine what is the best way to split the data (e.g. Gini impurity or information gain).

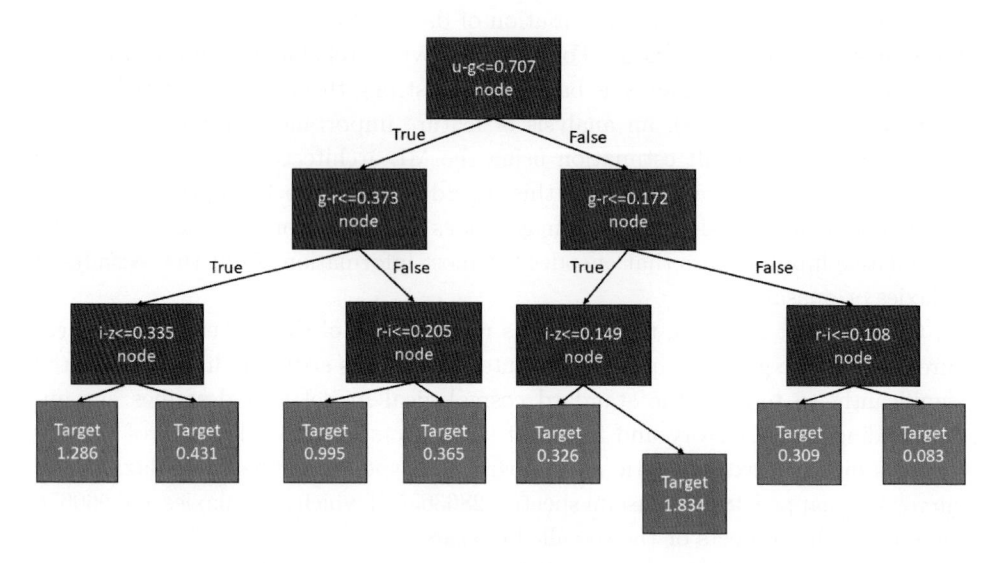

Fig. 1. Schematic of the decision tree algorithm.

The input of the calculated color indices into a series of decision nodes is shown above (Fig. 1), and the target redshift is calculated as output through the series of decision nodes. To implement ML, we will use Python's scikit-learn library. Using scikit-learn decision tree regression, a set of input features and target values are taken into account and then the model is constructed to adapt to new data.

2.1.1. *Important Hyperparameters of Decision Tree*

The most significant hyperparameter of Decision Trees is the max-depth. In all other cases, the nodes are expanded until all leaves contain less than min-samples-split samples, or until all leaves are pure. In the case of a continuous value, as it is in this study, the most commonly used criteria to determine split locations are Mean Square Error (MSE), Poisson deviance as well as Mean Absolute Error (MAE).

2.2. Random Forests

Random forests can be viewed as an ensemble of decision trees in which random subsamples of the input attributes are used to create each tree (Fig. 2).[17] In this case, the trees will only learn a portion of the input attribute pattern and it will be poor classifiers.

Additionally, the trees learn only a part of the data, so they cannot learn artificial structures or be influenced by correlated attributes the same way as a neural network can. As final output, they give an average result based on the trained trees, which indicates the probability of each object belonging to one of the specified categories. This method gathers an attractive package of advantages. For instance, the model resists overfitting and is robust against correlated input attributes. In most cases, Random Forest produces excellent results. Moreover, it is one of the most common algorithms, owing to its simplicity and versatility.

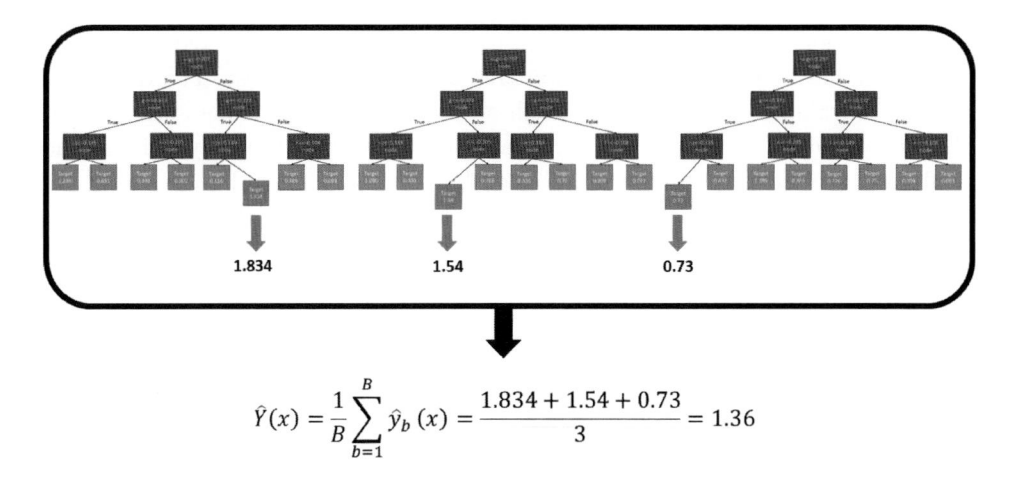

$$\hat{Y}(x) = \frac{1}{B}\sum_{b=1}^{B}\hat{y}_b(x) = \frac{1.834 + 1.54 + 0.73}{3} = 1.36$$

Fig. 2. Schematic of the random forest algorithm.

2.2.1. *Important Hyperparameters of Random Forest*

First and foremost, there is the n-estimators hyperparameter, which is essentially the number of trees the algorithms build before taking the maximum voting or calculating the average prediction. It is generally true that a higher number of trees leads to better estimation and helps to predict more accurately, but it can also slow down the calculation speed.

3. Data

In this study, SDSS Data Release 16[14] is used as the data source. Observations for the SDSS have been carried out from Apache Point Observatory (APO) since 1998 (using the 2.5m Sloan Foundation Telescope[18] and from Las Campanas Observatory (LCO) since 2017 (using the du Pont 2.5m Telescope).

The newest DR16 contains the final sets of spectra collected as part of the main eBOSS observing program. SDSS's DR16 survey, then, ends a twenty-year stretch of performing a large-scale survey of the universe's structure at redshifts. SDSS has produced the largest catalog of spectroscopic redshifts of galaxies compare to any other program over this time period. It is worth mentioning that DR16 provides spectra with usable redshifts for around 2.6 million unique galaxies. The photometric properties of around 100 million galaxies were also measured in this data set.

DR16 includes SDSS data products that are freely available through several channels. A large number of galaxy photometrically selected galaxies with spectroscopic redshifts are present in the SDSS that lend themselves well to the analysis presented in this paper to use as training, cross-validation and test samples.

3.1. *Input Features*

Using the color indices as our input features and the photometric redshift as the output, we have constructed a decision tree and a random forest. The data that we use for training are collected through accurate spectroscopic measurements of SDSS. These color indices have been created from flux magnitudes which are the total flux received in five frequency bands known as u-g-r-i-z (Fig. 3). Also, an astronomical color is derived from the difference in magnitudes of two filters, i.e. u - g. An object's color index provides an approximation to its spectrum, allowing it to be classified into various types.

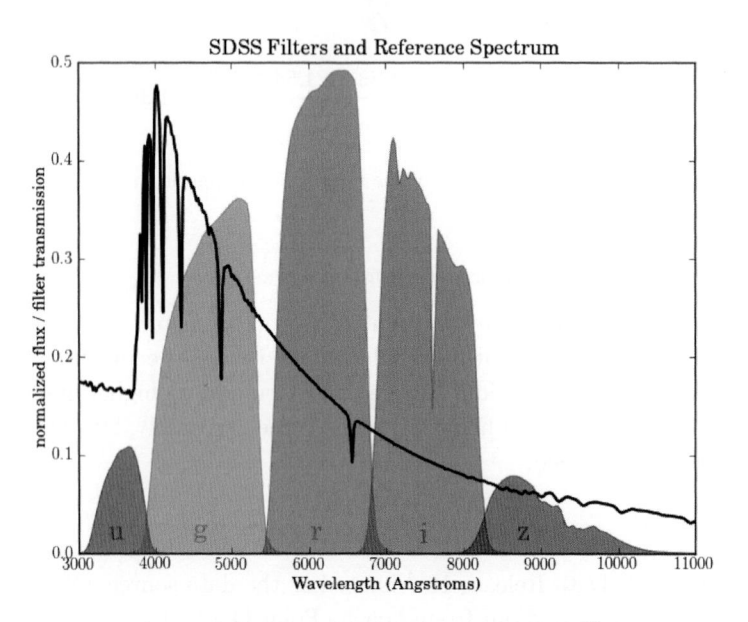

Fig. 3. SDSS filters and reference spectrum.[19]

We can get information about the physical processes taking place in distant astronomical sources by precise analysis of high-resolution spectra. Since the process of obtaining these spectra is very time-consuming and costly, astrophysicists usually observe objects through broadband filters and record them using the magnitude system. As an example, we can define the magnitude in the u-band filter above as follows:

$$u = m_{\text{ref}} - 2.5 \log 10 \left[\int_0^\infty F(\lambda) S(\lambda) d\lambda \right] \quad (1)$$

where $F(\lambda)$ is the star's flux at wavelength λ, $S(\lambda)$ is a sensitivity function describes the fraction of the star's flux that is detected at a specific wavelength and m_{ref} is apparent bolometric magnitude.

3.2. *Training and Learning*

Following conventional ML methodology, the galaxy catalog is then subdivided into training and testing samples, with portions of 80 and 20, respectively. For each architecture and hyperparameter set, the ML system is trained using a training sample. Testing the learned machine's generalization ability based on a test sample is necessary to determine whether it truly generalizes to new data sets. Furthermore, k-fold cross-validation allows us to test the accuracy of our model. Our model is trained k times, with each training test recording the accuracy. We train the model every time using a different combination of k-1 subsets, and we test it with the final kth subset. Then, the overall accuracy of the model is calculated by taking the average of the k accuracy measurements.

4. Analysis and Results

In the current section, we start to analyze the final results of our structured algorithms. First we make a contour map of the redshifts based on a combination of color indices (Fig. 4), the results indicate that relatively well-defined regions of

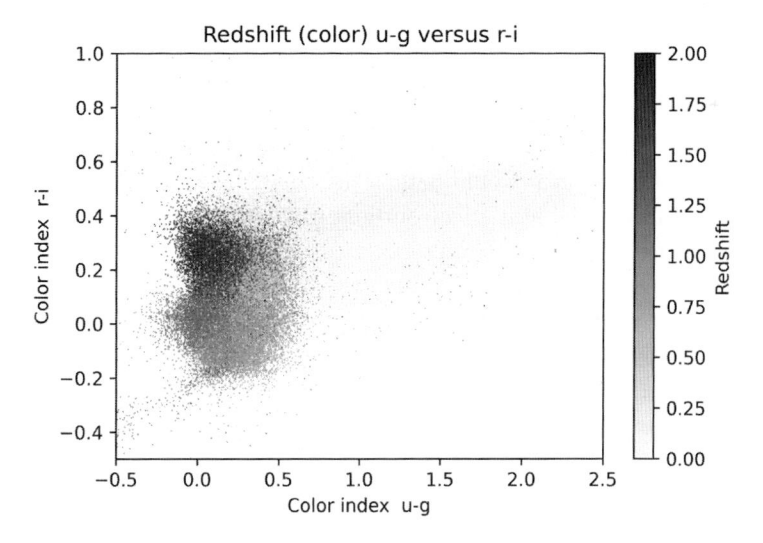

Fig. 4. Contour map of the redshifts based on a combination of color indices.

similar redshifts can be extracted and therefore the redshift of a new data point can be inferred from the color indices. So, this gesture underlines the fact that color indices are, indeed, appropriate input features for our ML algorithms.

In Fig. 5, the redshift distribution of galaxies and quasars are presented. In our dataset there are more galaxies in the dataset than quasars, and galaxies usually have lower redshifts.

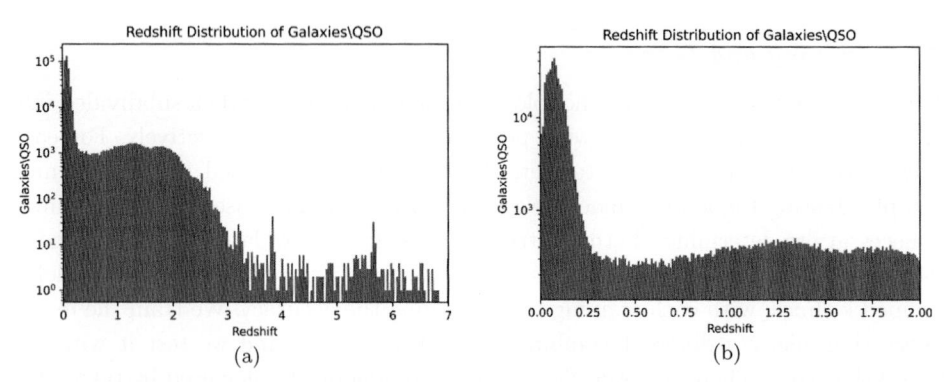

Fig. 5. Redshift distribution of Galaxies/QSOs. (a) Total range of the dataset. (b) limited range ($z \leq 2$) of the SDSS dataset.

We divide Our dataset into two ranges, i) contains all the measured redshifts ii) includes those below value 2. The reason behind this procedure is to achieve better performance of the algorithms, which will be discussed in detail in the following sections.

4.1. *Optimizing Process for Decision Tree*

There are some limitations for decision trees algorithm, including an over-fitting tendency. This means that it would potentially create a tree that is too complicated and does not address the statistical outliers in the data. In the process, general trends may not be accurately characterized.

Among the reasons for the over-fitting is the algorithm works by trying to optimize each node's decision locally. During our analysis, we will examine the impact of constraining the number of decision node rows (tree depth) on predictions. Various tree depths can be used to investigate whether the tree is over-fitting or not. We are particularly interested in comparing the algorithm performance on test data with its performance on training data (Fig. 6).

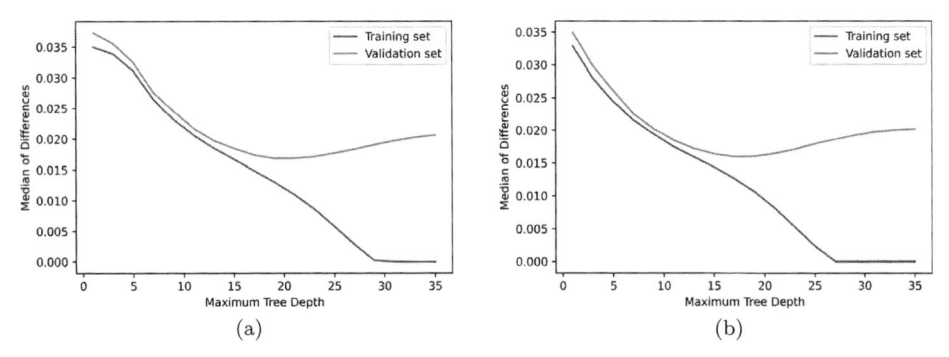

Fig. 6. Analysis of the maximum tree depth (a) Total range of the dataset. (b) limited range (z≤2) of the SDSS dataset.

4.2. *Optimizing Process for Random Forest*

Creating a parameter grid prior to fitting is the first step in optimizing the Random Forest algorithm. A new combination of features is selected on each iteration, especially the n-estimators parameter, which represents the number of trees. In our Random Forest algorithm, we see that 600 trees will give the best result, as measured by the median value of the residual of measured and predicted redshifts. By setting the number of trees parameter to 600, we investigate the optimum amount of each tree's depth as in our prior grid search in the algorithm.

4.3. *Illustrations of the Models Performance*

Once the maximum tree depths have been determined, the algorithms are ready to take on the two different sets of data extracted from DR 16. We have used 450000 of the catalog's data based on our system's performance. There were 400000 data under value 2 in the parts of the paper where calculations had been executed on the filtered dataset. Fig. 7 and Fig. 8 present the measured redshifts from the survey versus the algorithms predicted redshifts. The color bars indicate the density of the galaxies or quasars in the datasets. A straight line with an angle of 45 degrees illustrates the success of the algorithms where measured redshifts is equal to the predicted ones. The overall performance of each algorithm was evaluated using three metrics:[20] model accuracy, the Root Mean Square Error (RMSE), and the normalized standard deviation. The normalized standard deviation is defined by:

$$\Delta z(\text{norm}) \equiv \frac{z_{\text{spec}} - z_{\text{phot}}}{z_{\text{spec}} + 1} \qquad (2)$$

And, we calculate the standard deviation of the photometric redshifts from the spectroscopic redshift or namely the RMSE:

$$\sigma_{\Delta z} = \sqrt{\frac{1}{N}\sum_{i=1}^{N}\Delta z^2} \qquad (3)$$

Fig. 7 illustrates how the Decision Tree algorithm has performed on both subsets of the dataset. Each datum's predicted redshift is plotted as a function of its spectroscopically measured value. The left panels show the the results for the whole range of the redshift data, while the right panels limited to the results with redshifts below value 2. Moreover, the error distributions of the predicted redshifts appear under each graph. The mathematical criteria for each model's performance are provided in the corresponding tables, however, it can obviously be inferred from both of the diagrams that filtering the redshift to below 2 values has indeed enhanced the accuracy of results.

As the Table 1 shows, filtering data into lower redshifts leads to a significant improvement in the model's performance. The accuracy of the algorithm has increased by 15%, the median difference, the normalized error as well as the standard deviation were all decreased by corresponding amounts. The explanation which underlies this improvement could be the fact that by splitting the dataset, there are no more considerable biases in the values of target redshifts and the algorithm would not experience a scattered distribution of values in the training procedure. Thereby, there should be no excessive miscalculation or poor estimation in the testing mode.

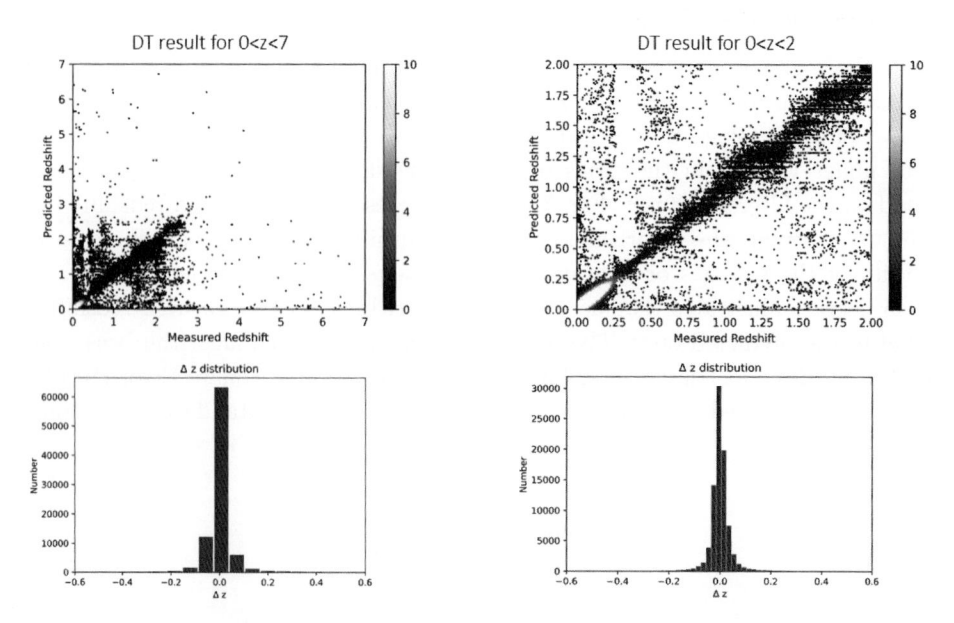

Fig. 7. The predictions of the Decision Tree algorithm for two ranges of redshifts in SDSS dataset.

Table 1. Analytical overview of statistical parameters for the Decision Tree algorithm for two ranges of redshifts $z\leq 7$ and $z\leq 2$.

Parameters	Decision Tree ($z\leq 7$)	Decision Tree ($z\leq 2$)
Accuracy	70.17%	85.26%
Max Depth	19	17
Median Difference	0.017	0.0156
$\overline{\Delta Z}_{\text{norm}}$	0.0135	0.005
$\sigma_{\Delta z}$	0.28	0.16

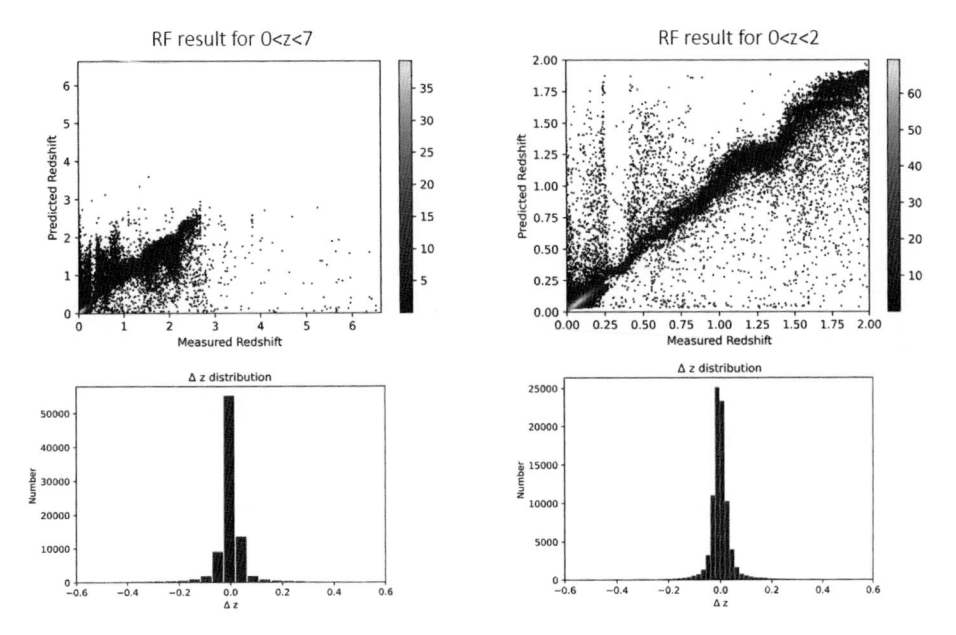

Fig. 8. The predictions of the Random Forest algorithm for two ranges in SDSS dataset.

Contemplating what was discussed in section 2.2, as the number of trees grow, the accuracy of the predicted value increase. Thus, it is expected that the Random Forests would have a better overall performance in terms of making more accurate predictions. As shown in Fig 8, both in the scattered plot and the distribution plot, the amount of precise estimations has increased. Since the color bar range indicates the density of data in the diagram and it includes a greater range of numbers than the Decision Tree algorithm. We conclude that the Random Forest algorithm has better accuracy. This fact is also presented in terms of statistical parameters showing the accuracy in Table 2 such as the standard deviation.

Table 2. Analytical overview of statistical parameters for the Random Forest algorithm for two ranges of redshifts $z\leq 7$ and $z\leq 2$.

Parameters	Random Forest ($z\leq 7$)	Random Forest ($z\leq 2$)
Accuracy	81.02%	91.00%
Max Depth	25	13
Number of Trees	600	600
Median Difference	0.0164	0.0154
$\overline{\Delta Z}_{norm}$	0.013	0.005
$\sigma_{\Delta z}$	0.23	0.12

5. Conclusion and Remarks

The current research addresses two leading ML regression algorithms namely the Decision Tree and the Random Forest, that were structured for estimating the redshifts of distant objects such as galaxies and quasars. Since there exist vital limitations in obtaining spectroscopic measurements, the photometric optical band data are widely investigated in this realm. This paper uses the 16 Data Release of the SDSS, where photometric colors are used as input features of the mentioned models. After developing the Decision tree and the Random Forest algorithms and evaluating the final results, it was concluded that the Random Forest algorithm will significantly perform better in this case (Table 3). The Random Forest algorithm leads to much better accuracy and marginally better standard deviation and median difference as seen in Table 3.

Another noteworthy improvement was filtering the dataset to redshifts below value 2. The significant effect of redshift splitting was illustrated in section 4.3 and we extensively discussed about all the possible reasons behind this effect.

Table 3. Comparison between statistical parameters of the Decision Tree and the Random forest algorithms for $z\leq 2$.

Parameters	Decision Tree ($z\leq 2$)	Random Forest ($z\leq 2$)
Accuracy	85.26%	91.00%
Median Difference	0.0156	0.0154
$\overline{\Delta Z}_{norm}$	0.005	0.005
$\sigma_{\Delta z}$	0.16	0.12

A few recent attempts for redshift estimation applying similar developed ML algorithms are addressed in Table 4. The crucial factor affecting their evaluations is the amount of data in the training sets. Remarkably, in this work taking 400000

Table 4. Comparison among results obtained using similar methodologies by different collaborations and our results in this work.

Refrence Articles	Data Release	Training Set	$\overline{\Delta Z}_{\text{norm}}$	ML Algorithm
Beck(2016)	12	1,976,978	5.84×10^{-5}	Local Linear Regression
Paul(2018)[1]	12	20,000	2×10^{-3}	Random-Forest
Baldeschi(2021)[12]	16	1,251,249	1×10^{-3}	Random-Forest
This work	16	320,000	5×10^{-3}	Random-Forest

data into consideration for the training set, we achieved nearly equivalent accuracy to the previous works.

Our results show the great potential of the ML methods for redshift estimation of distant sources using color index features. It is worth mentioning that applying ML methods is unavoidable when a large number of astrophysical data will be obtained from the next generation of sky surveys as the era of big data has started.

References

1. N. Paul, N. Virag and L. Shamir, A catalog of photometric redshift and the distribution of broad galaxy morphologies, *Galaxies* **6**, 1 (2018).
2. D. Wilson, H. Nayyeri, A. Cooray and B. Häußler, Photometric Redshift Estimation with Galaxy Morphology Using Self-organizing Maps, *The Astrophysical Journal* **888**, p. 83 (2020).
3. J. v. Vugt, Photometric Redshift Estimation of Distant Quasars (2016).
4. B. Mobasher, P. Capak, N. Z. Scoville, T. Dahlen, M. Salvato, H. Aussel, D. J. Thompson, R. Feldmann, L. Tasca, O. Lefevre, S. Lilly, C. M. Carollo, J. S. Kartaltepe, H. McCracken, J. Mould, A. Renzini, D. B. Sanders, P. L. Shopbell, Y. Taniguchi, M. Ajiki, Y. Shioya, T. Contini, M. Giavalisco, O. Ilbert, A. Iovino, V. Le Brun, V. Mainieri, M. Mignoli and M. Scodeggio, Photometric Redshifts of Galaxies in COSMOS, *The Astrophysical Journal Supplement Series* **172**, 117 (2007).
5. M. Salvato, O. Ilbert and B. Hoyle, The many flavours of photometric redshifts, *Nature Astronomy* **3**, 212 (2019).
6. A. Collister and O. Lahav, ANN z : Estimating Photometric Redshifts Using Artificial Neural Networks, *Publications of the Astronomical Society of the Pacific* **116**, 345 (2004).
7. N. Benitez, Bayesian Photometric Redshift Estimation, *The Astrophysical Journal* **536**, 571 (2000).
8. G. Bruzual and S. Charlot, Stellar population synthesis at the resolution of 2003, *Monthly Notices of the Royal Astronomical Society* **344**, 1000 (2003).
9. K. Zhang, D. J. Schlegel, B. H. Andrews, J. Comparat, C. Schäfer, J. A. Vazquez Mata, J.-P. Kneib and R. Yan, Machine-learning Classifiers for Intermediate Redshift Emission-line Galaxies, *The Astrophysical Journal* **883**, p. 63 (2019).
10. S. Carliles, T. Budavári, S. Heinis, C. Priebe and A. S. Szalay, Random forests for photometric redshifts, *Astrophysical Journal* **712**, 511 (2010).
11. S. Carliles, T. Budavári, S. Heinis, C. Priebe and A. Szalay, Photometric Redshift Estimation on SDSS Data Using Random Forests, **XXX**, 1 (2007).
12. A. Baldeschi, M. Stroh, R. Margutti, T. Laskar and A. Miller, Photometric redshift estimation of galaxies in the Pan-STARRS 3π survey- I. Methodology (2021).

13. B. Hoyle, M. Michael Rau, R. Zitlau, S. Seitz and J. Weller, Feature importance for machine learning redshifts applied to SDSS galaxies, *Monthly Notices of the Royal Astronomical Society* **449**, 1275 (2015).
14. R. Ahumada, C. A. Prieto, A. Almeida, F. Anders, S. F. Anderson, B. H. Andrews, B. Anguiano, R. Arcodia, E. Armengaud, M. Aubert, S. Avila, V. Avila-Reese, C. Badenes, C. Balland, K. Barger, J. K. Barrera-Ballesteros, S. Basu, J. Bautista, R. L. Beaton, T. C. Beers, B. I. T. Benavides, C. F. Bender, M. Bernardi, M. Bershady, F. Beutler, C. M. Bidin, J. Bird, D. Bizyaev, G. A. Blanc, M. R. Blanton, M. Boquien, J. Borissova, J. Bovy, W. N. Brandt, J. Brinkmann, J. R. Brownstein, K. Bundy, M. Bureau, A. Burgasser, E. Burtin, M. Cano-Díaz, R. Capasso, M. Cappellari, R. Carrera, S. Chabanier, W. Chaplin, M. Chapman, B. Cherinka, C. Chiappini, P. Doohyun Choi, S. D. Chojnowski, H. Chung, N. Clerc, D. Coffey, J. M. Comerford, J. Comparat, L. da Costa, M.-C. Cousinou, K. Covey, J. D. Crane, K. Cunha, G. d. S. Ilha, Y. S. Dai, S. B. Damsted, J. Darling, J. W. Davidson, R. Davies, K. Dawson, N. De, A. de la Macorra, N. De Lee, A. B. d. A. Queiroz, A. Deconto Machado, S. de la Torre, F. Dell'Agli, H. du Mas des Bourboux, A. M. Diamond-Stanic, S. Dillon, J. Donor, N. Drory, C. Duckworth, T. Dwelly, G. Ebelke, S. Eftekharzadeh, A. Davis Eigenbrot, Y. P. Elsworth, M. Eracleous, G. Erfanianfar, S. Escoffier, X. Fan, E. Farr, J. G. Fernández-Trincado, D. Feuillet, A. Finoguenov, P. Fofie, A. Fraser-McKelvie, P. M. Frinchaboy, S. Fromenteau, H. Fu, L. Galbany, R. A. Garcia, D. A. García-Hernández, L. A. G. Oehmichen, J. Ge, M. A. G. Maia, D. Geisler, J. Gelfand, J. Goddy, V. Gonzalez-Perez, K. Grabowski, P. Green, C. J. Grier, H. Guo, J. Guy, P. Harding, S. Hasselquist, A. J. Hawken, C. R. Hayes, F. Hearty, S. Hekker, D. W. Hogg, J. A. Holtzman, D. Horta, J. Hou, B.-C. Hsieh, D. Huber, J. A. S. Hunt, J. I. Chitham, J. Imig, M. Jaber, C. E. J. Angel, J. A. Johnson, A. M. Jones, H. Jönsson, E. Jullo, Y. Kim, K. Kinemuchi, C. C. Kirkpatrick IV, G. W. Kite, M. Klaene, J.-P. Kneib, J. A. Kollmeier, H. Kong, M. Kounkel, D. Krishnarao, I. Lacerna, T.-W. Lan, R. R. Lane, D. R. Law, J.-M. Le Goff, H. W. Leung, H. Lewis, C. Li, J. Lian, L. Lin, D. Long, P. Longa-Peña, B. Lundgren, B. W. Lyke, J. Ted Mackereth, C. L. MacLeod, S. R. Majewski, A. Manchado, C. Maraston, P. Martini, T. Masseron, K. L. Masters, S. Mathur, R. M. McDermid, A. Merloni, M. Merrifield, S. Mészáros, A. Miglio, D. Minniti, R. Minsley, T. Miyaji, F. G. Mohammad, B. Mosser, E.-M. Mueller, D. Muna, A. Muñoz-Gutiérrez, A. D. Myers, S. Nadathur, P. Nair, K. Nandra, J. C. do Nascimento, R. J. Nevin, J. A. Newman, D. L. Nidever, C. Nitschelm, P. Noterdaeme, J. E. O'Connell, M. D. Olmstead, D. Oravetz, A. Oravetz, Y. Osorio, Z. J. Pace, N. Padilla, N. Palanque-Delabrouille, P. A. Palicio, H.-A. Pan, K. Pan, J. Parker, R. Paviot, S. Peirani, K. P. Ramŕez, S. Penny, W. J. Percival, I. Perez-Fournon, I. Pérez-Ràfols, P. Petitjean, M. M. Pieri, M. Pinsonneault, V. J. Poovelil, J. T. Povick, A. Prakash, A. M. Price-Whelan, M. J. Raddick, A. Raichoor, A. Ray, S. B. Rembold, M. Rezaie, R. A. Riffel, R. Riffel, H.-W. Rix, A. C. Robin, A. Roman-Lopes, C. Román-Zúñiga, B. Rose, A. J. Ross, G. Rossi, K. Rowlands, K. H. R. Rubin, M. Salvato, A. G. Sánchez, L. Sánchez-Menguiano, J. R. Sánchez-Gallego, C. Sayres, A. Schaefer, R. P. Schiavon, J. S. Schimoia, E. Schlafly, D. Schlegel, D. P. Schneider, M. Schultheis, A. Schwope, H.-J. Seo, A. Serenelli, A. Shafieloo, S. J. Shamsi, Z. Shao, S. Shen, M. Shetrone, R. Shirley, V. S. Aguirre, J. D. Simon, M. F. Skrutskie, A. Slosar, R. Smethurst, R. Sobeck, B. C. Sodi, D. Souto, D. V. Stark, K. G. Stassun, M. Steinmetz, D. Stello, J. Stermer, T. Storchi-Bergmann, A. Streblyanska, G. S. Stringfellow, A. Stutz, G. Suárez, J. Sun, M. Taghizadeh-Popp, M. S. Talbot, J. Tayar, A. R. Thakar, R. Theriault, D. Thomas, Z. C. Thomas, J. Tinker, R. Tojeiro, H. H. Toledo, C. A. Tremonti, N. W. Troup, S. Tuttle, E. Unda-Sanzana,

M. Valentini, J. Vargas-González, M. Vargas-Magaña, J. A. Vázquez-Mata, M. Vivek, D. Wake, Y. Wang, B. A. Weaver, A.-M. Weijmans, V. Wild, J. C. Wilson, R. F. Wilson, N. Wolthuis, W. M. Wood-Vasey, R. Yan, M. Yang, C. Yèche, O. Zamora, P. Zarrouk, G. Zasowski, K. Zhang, C. Zhao, G. Zhao, Z. Zheng, Z. Zheng, G. Zhu and H. Zou, The 16th Data Release of the Sloan Digital Sky Surveys: First Release from the APOGEE-2 Southern Survey and Full Release of eBOSS Spectra, *The Astrophysical Journal Supplement Series* **249**, p. 3 (2020).
15. H. Oyaizu, M. Lima, C. E. Cunha, H. Lin and J. Frieman, Photometric Redshift Error Estimators, *The Astrophysical Journal* **689**, 709 (2008).
16. L. Breiman, J. Friedman, R. A. Olshen and C. J. Stone, *Classification and regression trees* (Chapman and Hall/CRC, 1984).
17. L. Breiman, Random Forests, *Machine Learning* **45**, 5 (2001).
18. J. E. Gunn, W. A. Siegmund, E. J. Mannery, R. E. Owen, C. L. Hull, R. F. Leger, L. N. Carey, G. R. Knapp, D. G. York, W. N. Boroski, S. M. Kent, R. H. Lupton, C. M. Rockosi, M. L. Evans, P. Waddell, J. E. Anderson, J. Annis, J. C. Barentine, L. M. Bartoszek, S. Bastian, S. B. Bracker, H. J. Brewington, C. I. Briegel, J. Brinkmann, Y. J. Brown, M. A. Carr, P. C. Czarapata, C. C. Drennan, T. Dombeck, G. R. Federwitz, B. A. Gillespie, C. Gonzales, S. U. Hansen, M. Harvanek, J. Hayes, W. Jordan, E. Kinney, M. Klaene, S. J. Kleinman, R. G. Kron, J. Kresinski, G. Lee, S. Limmongkol, C. W. Lindenmeyer, D. C. Long, C. L. Loomis, P. M. McGehee, P. M. Mantsch, E. H. Neilsen, Jr., R. M. Neswold, P. R. Newman, A. Nitta, J. Peoples, Jr., J. R. Pier, P. S. Prieto, A. Prosapio, C. Rivetta, D. P. Schneider, S. Snedden and S.-i. Wang, The 2.5 m Telescope of the Sloan Digital Sky Survey, *The Astronomical Journal* **131**, 2332 (2006).
19. Ž. Ivezić, A. Connolly, J. Vanderplas and A. Gray, *Statistics, Data Mining and Machine Learning in Astronomy* (Princeton University Press, 2014).
20. S. J. Curran, J. P. Moss and Y. C. Perrott, Qso photometric redshifts using machine learning and neural networks, *Monthly Notices of the Royal Astronomical Society* **503**, p. 2639–2650 (Feb 2021).

Deep learning in quasar physics

F. Rastegar Nia

Physics Department, Alzahra University Vanak, 1993891176, Tehran, Iran
ICRA and Dipartimento di Fisica, Università di Roma "La Sapienza", Piazzale Aldo Moro 5, I-00185 Roma, Italy
ICRANet, Piazza della Repubblica 10, I-65122 Pescara, Italy
E-mail: f.rastegarnia@alzahra.ac.ir

M. T. Mirtorabi

Physics Department, Alzahra University Vanak, 1993891176, Tehran, Iran
E-mail: torabi@alzahra.ac.ir

R. Moradi* and Y. Wang[†]

ICRANet, Piazza della Repubblica 10, Pescara,I-65122, Italy,
ICRA, Dipartimento di Fisica, Sapienza Universita' di Roma, Rome, I-00185, Italy
and INAF, Rome, 00136, Italy
* E-mail: ruffini@icra.it
* E-mail: rahim.moradi@icranet.org
[†] E-mail: yu.wang@icranet.org

A. Vafaei Sadr

Departement de Physique Theorique and Center for Astroparticle Physics,
University of Geneva
E-mail: Alireza.VafaeiSadr@unige.ch

In view of increasing data volume of existing and upcoming telescopes/detectors we here apply the 1–dimensional convolutional neural network (CNN) to estimate the redshift of (high-)redshifts quasars in Sloan Digital Sky Survey IV (SDSS-IV) quasar catalog from DR16 of eBOSS. Our CNN takes the flux of the quasars as an array and their redshift as labels. We here evidence that new structure of the network, and augmenting the training set, provide a high precision result in estimating the redshift of quasars.

Keywords: Quasar, Deep learning, CNN, SDSS

1. Introduction

Quasars are the most luminous active galactic nuclei(AGN) which are powered by accretion disk around supermassive black holes at centers of their host galaxies. Thanks to their high luminosity, they can be observed across the universe in wide range of redshift from z = 0 to z ∼ 7. Thus, quasars give us important information about the early universe, the structure formation and evolution.[1,2]

Nowadays, astronomy and astrophysics have been brought into the big data era through the construction and development of ground-based and space telescope. Since huge amount of data, ranging from gamma-ray, x-ray, ultraviolet, optical, infrared and radio bands of quasars is available in sky surveys, various challenges and opportunities are created for scientific discoveries.[3,6]

In recent years, machine learning (ML) and deep learning (DL) have been utilized in astronomy and astrophysics in order to deal with the big data surveys and as well extract the new physical understanding. The goal in ML and DL is to diagnose, by optimization, common characteristics and features in data.[10] These interesting branch of computer science have been used in estimating the physical parameters and classification of celestial objects; for example the morphological classification of galaxies,[15,16,20] estimation of photometric redshift,[12,25,33,34] classification of star/galaxy,[4,27,32] spectral classification of stars.[5,7,17,35]

This article is mainly dedicated to train a CNN to predict the redshift of Quasi-stellar radio source (quasars) or quasi stellar objects (QSO) in Sloan Digital Sky Survey IV (SDSS-IV) quasar catalog from Data Release 16 (DR16) of the extended Baryon Oscillation Spectroscopic Survey (eBOSS), which is the most comprehensive catalog of spectroscopically collected quasars to date.[26]

2. Dataset

In this paper, we exploit dataset from the quasar spectra obtained by the Sloan Digital Sky Survey-4(SDSS-4). They are provided by the Sixteenth Data Release (DR16) of SDSS extended Baryon Oscillation Spectroscopic Survey (eBOSS).[14] According to the technical details of eBOSS, namely the wavelength coverage in range of $361\text{nm} - 1014\text{nm}$ with the resolution $R = 2000$, where $R = \frac{\lambda}{\Delta\lambda}$, more than 700,000 quasar spectra have been detected in the redshift range $0 \leq z \leq 7.1$.

The distributions of detected quasars redshift in the DR16 catalog is shown in Fig. 1. As can be seen, the number of quasars reaches its maximum around $z \approx 2.5$; at earlier epochs i.e., higher redshifts, they are comparatively rare.

2.1. *Redshift*

The observed quasar spectra contain broad emission lines, often time-variable flux both in the continuum and in the emission lines and UV flux; see e.g.[11] The shift and deformation of the various lines and specific characteristic of different fluxes in the spectra of quasars, due to the cosmological redshift, makes quasars a proper tool to invest the deep learning method and extract the common features hidden in their spectra (flux).

In DR16Q catalog, redshifts obtained for quasars by different methods, such as principal component analysis (PCA) and QuasarNET are reported. In this work we use *"primary"* redshift or best redshift for quasars which has been selected from the available visual inspection redshifts,[8] or, alternatively, the SDSS automated pipeline redshift;, see[23,24] and references therein for more information. The best option is exploiting only the visual inspection redshifts which will be presented in the forthcoming papers.

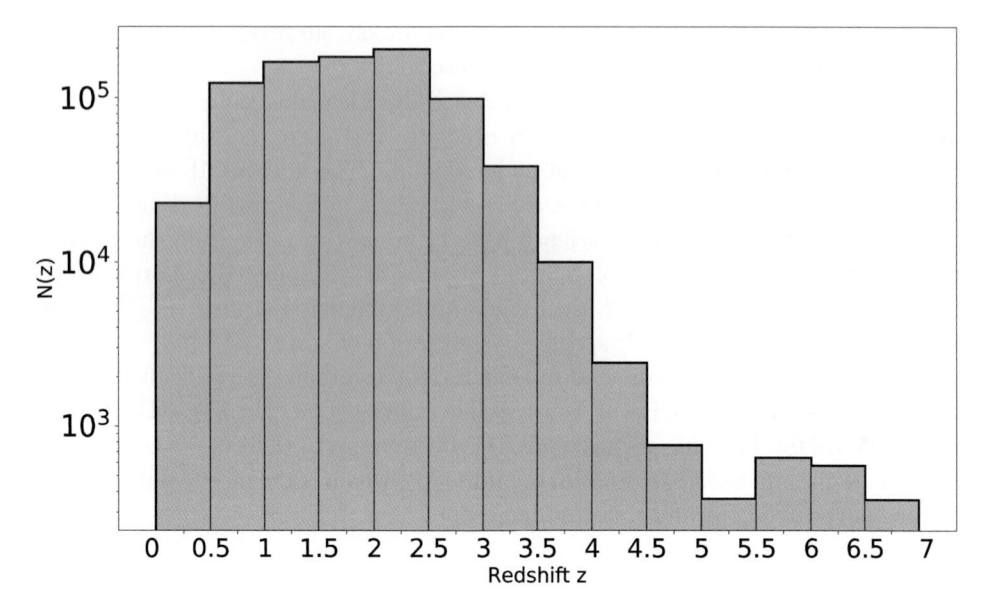

Fig. 1. The distributions of *"primary"* redshift of quasars in the DR16 catalog.

3. Convolutional neural network (CNN)

3.1. *CNN architecture*

Since the spectra of quasars are represented by flux versus the wavelength, namely 1+1 dimensional set of data, they can be considered as as time-series. For this reason, the neural network model in this work is designed to be a 1-dimensional CNN. It operates like a combination of some mathematical functions, which optimizes through several filters, and transforms the input data; here flux of quasars, to the output data, here redshift of quasars, by extracting the hidden features from the quasars' fluxes.

The physical information, such as redshift are hidden in the observed flux, and CNNs, as a regressor, are supposed to estimate the redshift through the training process. The CNN in the current work is a combination of convolutional and fully-connected layers. The convolutional layers are initialized with He Normal initializer.[22] If the model requires to access the non-linear modes in data he Rectified Linear Unit (ReLU) activation function is implemented.[36]

The filters in each convolutional layer scans each row (flux) and extract the prominent features from the raw input for the specific redshift. The feature-extraction layers have a repeating pattern of the convolutional layers whereas the pooling layers reduce the dimensions and concentrate only on the most prominent features. This process recognizes the non-linear correlation within the dataset. Finally, the fully-connected feed-forward layers connect and assign the extracted features to the output layer (redshift). All free parameters in the model change dynamically as the algorithm finds the best solution, achieved by the back-propagation learning algorithm.

Many free parameters, such as the number of layers, layer specifications, and their arrangement can be changed while one constructs a neural network model; known as model architecture. The architecture selection affects optimization and quality of the performance; this process is called hyperparameter optimization.[18] The hyper-parameter optimization process is necessary in order to ensure that neither underfits nor overfits of the training set happens.

In the hyper-parameter optimization process, the number and length of filters of convolutional layers, the number of nodes in fully-connected layers, and the kernel size of the Maxpooling layer are considered and finally the "Mean Squared Error" (MSE), as the loss function, is utilized in our CNN.

We also use Adam optimizer to optimize the loss function, which is an algorithm for the first-order gradient-based optimization of stochastic objective functions. We here set the learning rate as 0.0001 and the coefficients for computing the averages of gradient and its square as 0.5 and 0.9, the weight decay of L2 penalty is set as 0.[28, 29]

Figure 2 demonstrates the CNN pipeline of this work. It takes a quasar spectrum as a 1-dimensional array and predicts the redshift. We have tested different samples of training set, and the addition of more layers to this configuration does not enhance the prediction accuracy presented in this paper for different redshift intervals.

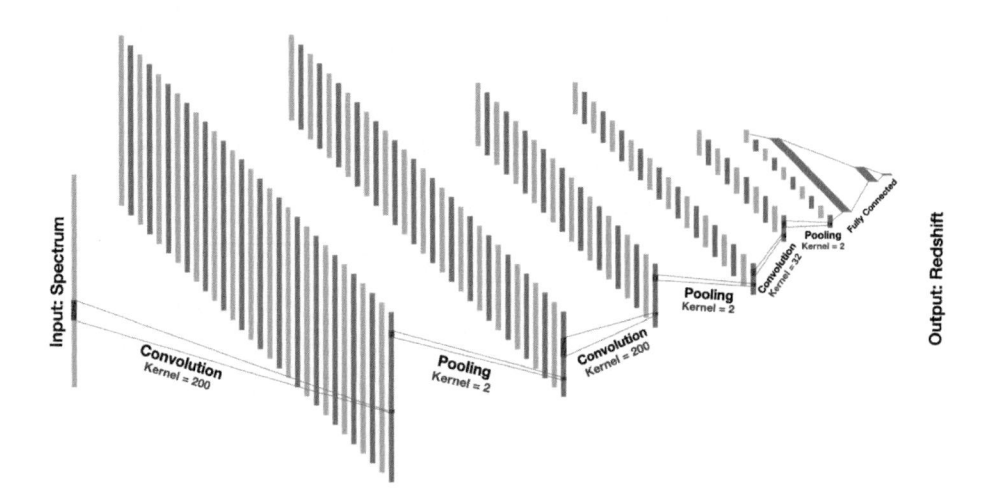

Fig. 2. Structure of 1-dimensional CNN developed in this work to learn higher-order features hidden in the input spectrum. The CNN goes through the spectrum via a convolutional layer of kernel size = 200, 200, 32, respectively in order to search for the global and local pattern. The fully connected layers output the redshift.

3.2. Pre-processing the data

Data pre–processing is crucial in two aspects: (1) to provide an understandable dataset for DL networks, and (2) to increase the speed and accuracy of processing. As the first step of the pr–eprocessing procedure in the present work, a two-dimensional matrix of the dataset is created. In the matrix each row represents the quasar flux and each column relates to a flux a certain wavelength. At the second step, the flux of every spectrum is normalized via the Zero-Mean Normalization method. Moreover, the normalized fluxes are stored in a Numpy array and applied as features dataset, their corresponding redshifts are collected for labels dataset as well.

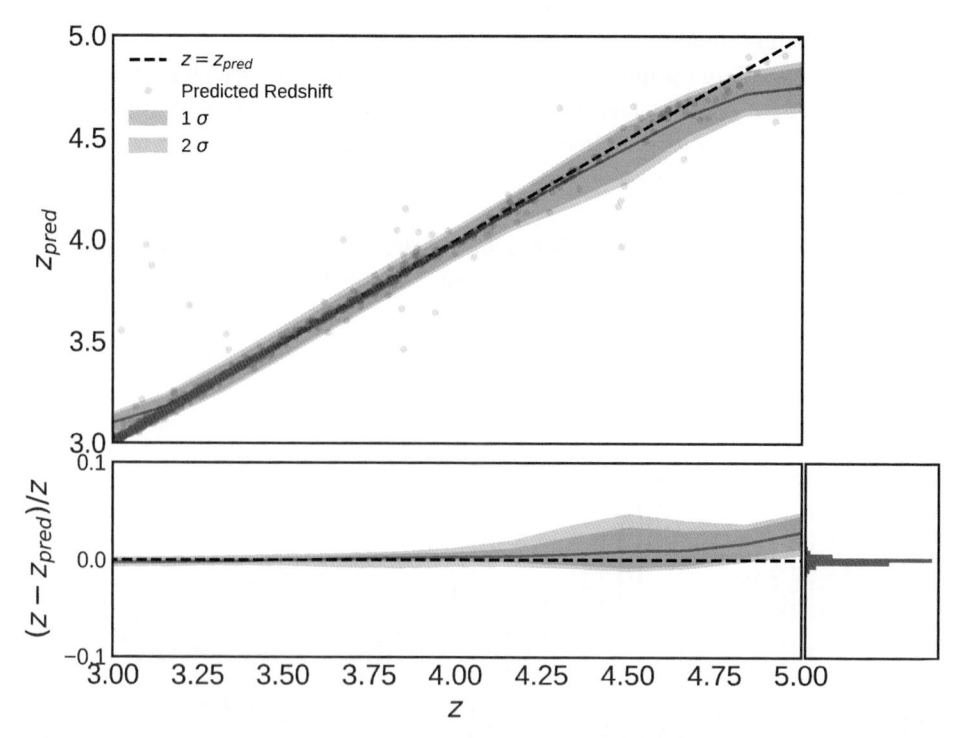

Fig. 3. Redshift predicted by our CNN for $3 \leq z \leq 5$. Top: The predicted redshift vs. the redshift reported in the DR catalog. Bottom: The relative error and their distribution. As it can be seen the distribution of relative error follows a Gaussian distribution with mean, $\mu = 0.0042$ and a standard deviation of $\sigma = 0.014$.

4. Prediction in the $3 \leq z \leq 5$ interval

As an example, we use the quasars in the $3 \leq z \leq 5$ interval as sources to test our CNN. In general, there are $51,100$ quasars in this interval, 75% of them, namely 38832 spectra are taken as the sample in order to train our CNN (training set) and

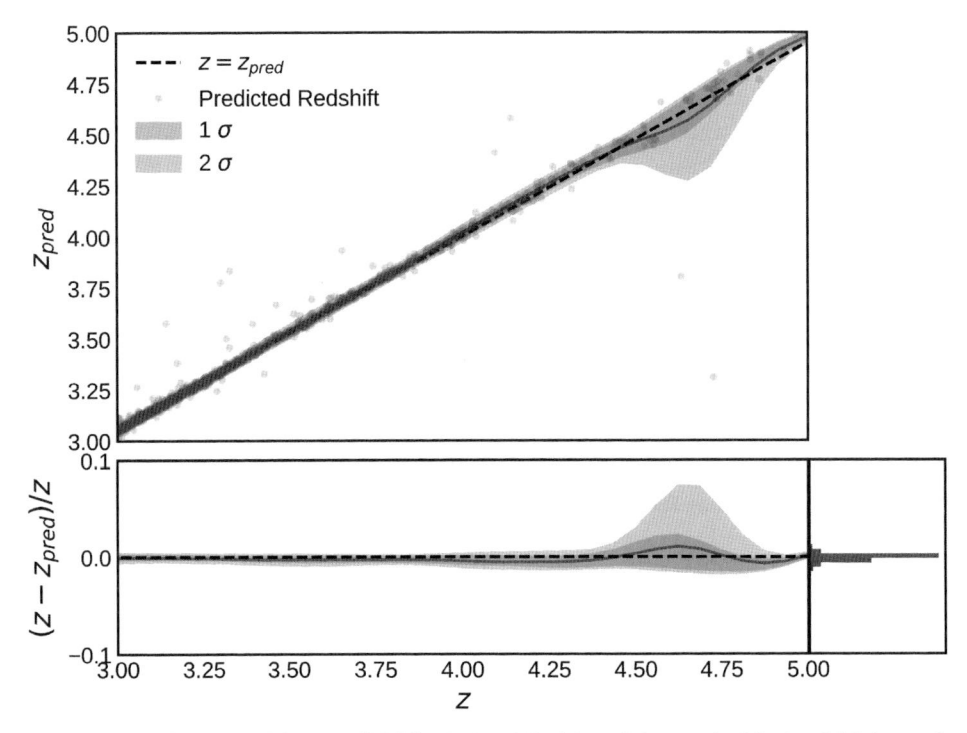

Fig. 4. Redshift predicted by our CNN for $3 \leq z \leq 5$ with training set in $2.9 \leq z \leq 5.2$ interval. Top: The predicted redshift vs. the redshift reported in the DR catalog. Bottom: The relative error and their distribution. The distribution of relative error follows a Gaussian distribution with mean, $\mu = 0.0038$ and a standard deviation of $\sigma = 0.012$.

25%, namely 12776 as sources to testify our CNN (test set). In the whole paper, the test set has not been used to train the CNN. Moreover, no limit on the S/N ratio of spectra is imposed.

The predicted redshift by our CNN for $3 \leq z \leq 5$ together with their relative errors distribution and the best fit is shown in Fig. 3. The distribution of relative error, RE,

$$\text{RE} \equiv \frac{z - z_{\text{pred}}}{z}, \qquad (1)$$

which z is the redshift reported by SDSS and z_{pred} is the redshift predicted by our CNN, follows a Gaussian distribution with mean, $\mu = 0.0042$ and a standard deviation of $\sigma = 0.014$. The method used for smoothing the scatterplot is locally weighted regression (LWR).[13]

As it can be seen in Fig. 3, the fit in the lower and upper edges of the prediction, namely $4.5 \lesssim z \leq 5$ and $3 \lesssim z \leq 3.1$ intervals, is not as significant as other time intervals.

This problem can be due to:

(1) the lack of data in $z < 3$ and $z > 5$ and consequently the failed LWR in the aforementioned intervals.
(2) the deficiency of training sample in $4.5 \lesssim z \leq 5$.

In order to solve the first issue, we extend our training set to $2.9 \leq z \leq 5.2$. By adding this extra data to the train set we make sure that there is no bias in the LWR fitting presented in Fig. 3 at its lower and upper part; see Fig. 4.

In order to accommodate the second issue and increase the number of spectra of the training set in $4.5 \lesssim z \leq 5$ we first convert the observed spectra in $4 \leq z \leq 4.5$ interval, where there are enough spectra to produce a reliable training set, into their cosmological rest-frame by dividing their wavelength by 1+z then we convert data set to $4.5 \leq z \leq 5$ by multiplying the wavelengths by a factor of 1+z+0.5.

Figure 5 represents the results when extra samples from $2.9 \leq z \leq 3$ and $5 \leq z \leq 5.2$ as well as the redshifted sample from $4 \leq z \leq 4.5$ to $4.5 \leq z \leq 5$ have been added to the original training set. The distribution of relative error follows a

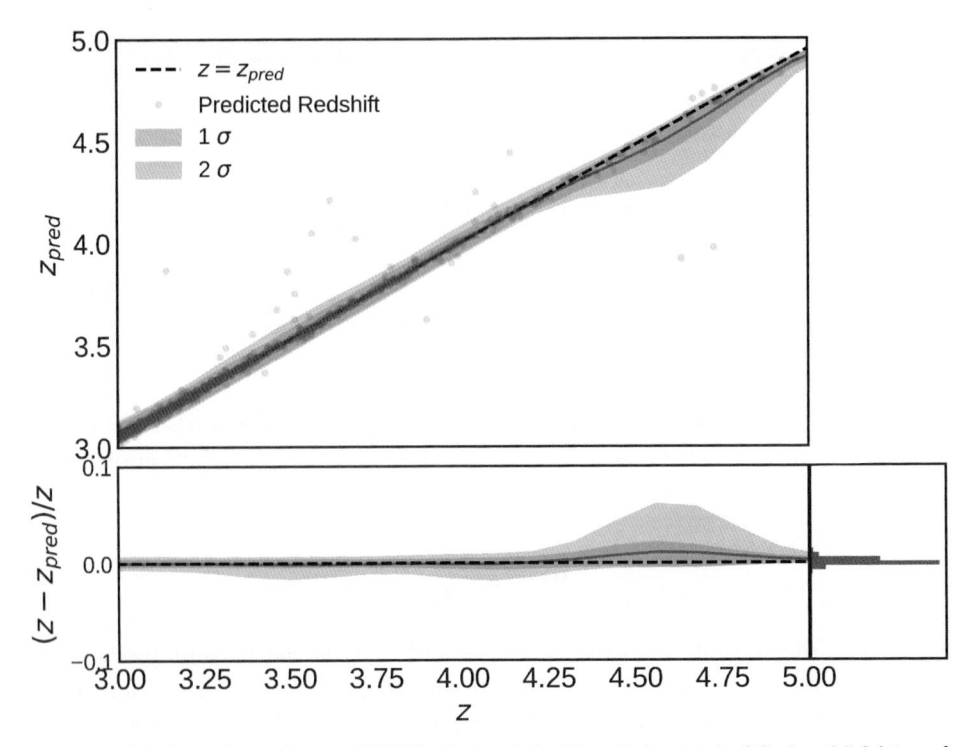

Fig. 5. Redshift predicted by our CNN for $3 \leq z \leq 5$ with training set in $2.9 \leq z \leq 5.2$ interval together with the converted observed spectra in $4 \leq z \leq 4.5$ interval into $4.5 \leq z \leq 5$. Top: The predicted redshift vs. the redshift reported in the DR catalog. Bottom: The relative error and its distribution which follows a Gaussian distribution with mean, $\mu = 0.0030$ and a standard deviation of $\sigma = 0.010$.

Gaussian distribution with mean, $\mu = 0.003$ and a standard deviation of $\sigma = 0.01$. The prediction is clearly improved in $4.5 \leq z \leq 5$ comparing to initial result shown in Fig. 3.

5. Conclusions

Deep learning, especially CNN[31, 37] is promising in the future Astrophysical studies. CNN can be utilized, owing to its several convolutional and fully connected layers to find the common deep hidden patterns in the spectrum, in provision for improving our astrophysical knowledge of distant objects. In this regard, we showed that exploiting a CNN leads to a statistically significant prediction of the redshift of quasars. We also showed that augmentation of dataset, which depends on the statistical and physical features of samples improves the prediction of redshift. Since CNN finds the physical characteristics of the spectra and these characteristics are deformed by the cosmological redshift the results presented here can be extended to the other energy bands like, X-ray, Infrared, UV, Gamma-ray and etc.

References

1. Nina Hernitschek et al 2016 ApJ 817 73, DOI: https://doi.org/10.3847/0004-637X/817/1/73.
2. A. Lupi, M. Volonteri, R. Decarli, S. Bovino, J. Silk and J. Bergeron, Mon. Not. Roy. Astron. Soc. **488** (2019) no.3, 4004-4022 doi:10.1093/mnras/stz1959 [arXiv:1901.02464 [astro-ph.GA]].
3. Allen, G., Andreoni, I., Bachelet, E., et al. 2019, arXiv preprint arXiv:1902.00522.
4. Bai, Y., Liu, J., Wang, S., & Yang, F. 2018, The Astronomical Journal, 157, 9.
5. Bailer-Jones, C. A., Irwin, M., & Von Hippel, T. 1998, Monthly Notices of the Royal Astronomical Society, 298, 361.
6. Ball, N. M., & Brunner, R. J. 2010, International Journal of Modern Physics D, 19, 1049.
7. Bialek, S., Fabbro, S., Venn, K. A., et al. 2019, arXiv preprint arXiv:1911.02602.
8. Bolton, A. S., Schlegel, D. J., Aubourg, É., et al. 2012, AJ, 144, 144, doi:10.1088/0004-6256/144/5/144.
9. Busca, N., & Balland, C. 2018, arXiv e-prints, arXiv:1808.09955.
10. Carleo, G., Cirac, I., Cranmer, K., et al. 2019, Rev. Mod. Phys., 91, 045002, doi:10.1103/RevModPhys.91.045002.
11. Carroll, B. W., & Ostlie, D. A. 1996, An Introduction to Modern Astrophysics.
12. Cavuoti, S., Brescia, M., Tortora, C., et al. 2015, Monthly Notices of the Royal Astronomical Society, 452, 3100.
13. Cleveland, W. S. 1979, Journal of the American Statistical Association, 74, 829, doi:10.1080/01621459.1979.10481038.
14. Dawson, K. S., Kneib, J.-P., Percival, W. J., et al. 2016, The Astronomical Journal, 151, 44.
15. De La Calleja, J., & Fuentes, O. 2004, Monthly Notices of the Royal Astronomical Society, 349, 87.
16. Dobrycheva, D., Vavilova, I., Melnyk, O., & Elyiv, A. 2017, arXiv preprint arXiv:1712.08955.

17. Fabbro, S., Venn, K., O'Briain, T., et al. 2018, Monthly Notices of the Royal Astronomical Society, 475, 2978.
18. Feurer, M., & Hutter, F. 2019, in Automated Machine Learning (Springer, Cham), 3–33.
19. Fiorentin, P. R., Bailer-Jones, C., Lee, Y. S., et al. 2007, Astronomy & Astrophysics, 467, 1373.
20. Gauci, A., Adami, K. Z., & Abela, J. 2010, arXiv preprint arXiv:1005.0390.
21. Glazebrook, K., Offer, A. R., & Deeley, K. 1998, The Astrophysical Journal, 492, 98.
22. He, K., Zhang, X., Ren, S., & Sun, J. 2015, in Proceedings of the IEEE international conference on computer vision, 1026–1034.
23. Hewett, P. C., & Wild, V. 2010, MNRAS, 405, 2302, doi:10.1111/j.1365-2966.2010.16648.x.
24. Higley, A. N., Lyke, B. W., Myers, A. D., et al. 2020, in American Astronomical Society Meeting Abstracts, Vol. 235, American Astronomical Society Meeting Abstracts #235, 219.03.
25. Hoyle, B. 2016, Astronomy and Computing, 16, 34.
26. Hutchinson, T. A., Bolton, A. S., Dawson, K. S., et al. 2016, AJ, 152, 205, doi:10.3847/0004-6256/152/6/205.
27. Kim, E. J., & Brunner, R. J. 2016, Monthly Notices of the Royal Astronomical Society, stw2672.
28. Kingma, D. P., & Ba, J. 2014, arXiv preprint arXiv:1412.6980.
29. LeCun, Y., Bottou, L., Bengio, Y., & Haffner, P. 1998, Proceedings of the IEEE, 86, 2278.
30. Li, X.-R., Pan, R.-Y., & Duan, F.-Q. 2017, Research in Astronomy and Astrophysics, 17, 036.
31. Liu, C.-L., Hsaio, W.-H., & Tu, Y.-C. 2018, IEEE Transactions on Industrial Electronics, 66, 4788.
32. Odewahn, S. C., Stockwell, E., Pennington, R., Humphreys, R. M., & Zumach, W. 1992, in Digitised Optical Sky Surveys (Springer), 215–224.
33. Pasquet-Itam, J., & Pasquet, J. 2018, A& A, 611, A97, doi:10.1051/0004-6361/201731106.
34. Sadeh, I., Abdalla, F. B., & Lahav, O. 2016, Publications of the Astronomical Society of the Pacific, 128, 104502.
35. Sharma, K., Kembhavi, A., Kembhavi, A., et al. 2020, Monthly Notices of the Royal Astronomical Society, 491, 2280.
36. Xu, B., Wang, N., Chen, T., & Li, M. 2015, arXiv preprint arXiv:1505.00853.
37. Xu, L., Ren, J. S., Liu, C., & Jia, J. 2014, Advances in neural information processing systems, 27, 1790.

Cosmological density field emulation and gravitational wave inference based on dimensionality reduction and supervised machine learning

Miguel Conceição

Instituto de Astrofísica e Ciências do Espaço,
Departamento de Física, Faculdade de Ciências, Universidade de Lisboa
Lisbon, 1749-016 Campo Grande, Portugal
E-mail: fc46798@alunos.fc.ul.pt

António da Silva

Instituto de Astrofísica e Ciências do Espaço,
Departamento de Física, Faculdade de Ciências, Universidade de Lisboa
Lisbon, 1749-016 Campo Grande, Portugal

Alberto Krone-Martins

Department of Informatics, University of California, Irvine
Irvine CA 92697, USA

Two major challenges in modern cosmology involve understanding the origin and growth of Cosmic structure and the progenitors of Gravitational Waves. Both scenarios currently require heavy computational resources to perform simulations and inference. In this work, we adopt simple Machine Learning methods to alleviate these requirements, to enable significantly faster sampling and inference. We show that using Dimensionality Reduction and simple Supervised Learning methods, it is possible to generate high-precision emulations of density fields given a set of parameters (such as the Dark Matter density parameter and redshift). Our method provides orders of magnitude improvement of CPU run times and much less computational resources when compared with N-Body simulations or more complex supervised learning approaches. We also show that it is possible to generate fast inference of gravitational wave parameters (such as the Chirp Mass) from Binary Black Hole systems using the same method. This method provides a promising approach to fast emulation and parameter inference to further explore in the context of upcoming large surveys like Euclid, LSST/Rubin, and LISA.

Keywords: N-body Simulations, Gravitational Waves, Supervised Machine Learning, Dimensionality Reduction, Emulation, Inference.

1. Introduction

Two main challenges in modern Cosmology involve understanding the origin and growth of Large Scale Structure (LSS) and the physics behind the progenitors of Gravitational Waves (GW). To study these phenomena, usual approaches rely on the generation of mock data for comparison with observations and consequent inference of parameters concerning the underlying preferred models.

Regarding Structure Formation, mock data is usually generated with N-body simulations, which are the most powerful method to study the non-linear evolution of large scale structure, within a huge variety of cosmological scenarios. With upcoming surveys like Euclid,[1] the urgency to generate large databases of these simulations for statistical analysis becomes even higher. One serious limitation is that simulations take large amounts of computational resources and time, making unfeasible their direct adoption in tasks that require the realization of multiple simulations and wide explorations of parameter spaces. To overcome these limitations, we propose the application of simple Machine Learning methods to generate high accuracy emulations of N-body density fields in a minimal amount of time, given a chosen set of cosmological parameters, more specifically the Dark Matter Density (Ω_{dm}) and redshift (z).

Similarly to the N-body case, current approaches for parameter inference from gravitational waveforms also rely on computationally heavy and sometimes model-dependent methods. With GW detectors like LIGO[2] and the upcoming LISA[3] mission there is also the urgency for the development of methods that can efficiently extract information from this type of data. Consequently, we aim at generalizing our proposed N-body approach to enable fast and accurate inferences of astrophysical parameters of the waveforms progenitors, namely, the Chirp Mass (M_{chirp}).

To achieve both goals we combine a simple data projection method called Principal Component Analysis (PCA)[4-6] with Supervised Machine Learning techniques, requiring only an initial dataset of N-body simulations and approximated waveforms. PCA enables us to take advantage of the redundancy intrinsic to the data by compressing the dimensional size of input features before providing them as an input to the Machine Learning methods, which learn the relationship between the compressed representation, i.e. the Principal Component coefficients, and the desired cosmological/astrophysical parameters for emulation/inference.

After convergence is achieved, we can use the models to infer or emulate previously unknown regions of the parameter space, which can be compared with ground truth examples not included in the training data, to gauge the performance of the methods. To test different approaches and discriminate which was more appropriate for our analysis we explored four different machine learning algorithms, Random Forest,[7] Extremely Randomized Trees,[8] Support Vector Machine[9] and Neural Networks.[10] Additionally, we also explore the possibility of using *Functional Principal Component Analysis* (FPCA) to perform the emulation of N-body density fields, a method that combines the capabilities of both the PCA and the Supervised Learning approach, providing better accuracy at the cost of higher computational memory.

2. Methodology

This Section presents the method that we developed and the approaches that we used to generate our training and test data sets. To ensure that our methods are effective even in infrastructures with limited resources, all work presented here was created, run, and tested on a regular desktop computer with an Intel Core i5-4460

(4 cores, 4 threads), with 16Gb RAM at 2400 Mhz, running the Linux Ubuntu 18.04LTS operating system, without discrete high-performance GPU cards.

The whole pipeline includes codes in different programming languages. These include `Fortran`, for generation the N-body simulations and power spectrum computation from 3-dimensional density volumes; `Python`,[11] to generate GW waveforms, noise models, and to compute density field bispectra; and, finally, the R programming language[12] for the new statistical learning pipeline that we propose. This also includes R libraries for dimensionality reduction, regression models and parameter estimation, that are written in `C`, `C++` and `Fortran`.

In the following Sections, we provide a detailed description of our pipelines.

2.1. Adopted Machine Learning Algorithms and Optimization

To build our pipeline, we tested four classical machine learning algorithms, Random Forest,[7] Extremely Randomized Trees,[8] Support Vector Machine[9] and Neural Networks.[10] Each algorithm is governed by a set of hyper-parameters that define the properties of the learning process and the structure of the model. Consequently, we optimized the combination of these hyper-parameters using three different optimization approaches, Grid-Search, Bootstrap and K-fold Cross-Validation, ultimately choosing the one which provided the best results.

For the Random Forest algorithm we used the `randomForest` package,[13] while optimizing the number of trees in the ensemble (`ntree`), the number of features tried at each split (`mtry`) and the minimum size of the terminal nodes (`nodesize`).

For the Extremely Randomized Trees, our implementation used the package `extraTrees` while optimizing the number of random cuts at each split (`numRandomCuts`) and similarly to the previous case, the number of trees in the ensemble and features tried at each split.

The Support Vector Machine models were built using the package e1078[14] and the hyper-parameters optimized were the kernel `kernel`, the margin/error `cost` and the amount of curvature allowed in the decision boundary of the Gaussian Radial Basis Function Kernel (`gamma`).

Finally, for the Neural Networks, our implementation used the package `nnet`,[15] and we optimized the number of perceptrons in the single layer (`size`) and the decay of the weights (`decay`).

For the particular case of Gravitational Wave parameter inference, since the Principal Components are used as independent variables, they were also optimized. Here we used a simple Grid-Search.

2.2. The N-body Emulation Pipeline

In the first half of our work, we attempted to estimate N-body dark matter density fields using our proposed compression-based machine learning methods.

We consider two scenarios. In the first scenario, we attempt to estimate the density fields considering just one cosmological parameter as the independent variable used to build the regression models, the Dark Matter density (Ω_{dm}). In the second scenario, we extend the pipeline to include the redshift (z) as a second cosmological variable and attempt to use both as independent variables to estimate the density field for different values of Ω_{dm} and at a continuous range of z.

2.2.1. Generation of the Training and Test Datasets

We generated the N-body simulations using a public version of the Hydra code,[16] which solves the Newtonian equations for a set of mass particles of Dark Matter. Every simulation has the same initial conditions, starting from the first snapshot at $z = 49$ until reaching $z = 0$, summing up to a total of 10 snapshots. We generated the fields for 160^3 particles of dark matter initially positioned on a regular cubic grid of comoving length $L = 100\ h^{-1}$Mpc on the side, and every snapshot contains positions and velocities for each one of them.

The cosmological model assumed was the Λ-CDM model with $\Omega_k = 0$, $\Omega_m = 1 - \Omega_\Lambda$, $\sigma_8 = 0.809$, and $h = 0.7$, where σ_8 the stardand deviation of density fluctuations when convoluted with a Kernel at a scale of $8\ h^{-1}$Mpc and h is the Hubble parameter (i.e. $h = H_0/100$).

After calculating the positions and velocities for each particle using the Hydra code, the data is compiled by another code called *darkdens* which calculates the densities of the particles using the *Smooth Particle Hydrodynamics* (SPH) formalism.[17] Finally, the data goes through yet another fundamental piece of code which computes the density field in 128^3 cubic voxels, in units of $10^{27}\ Kg\ m^{-3}$.

In the first scenario of emulation from a single free-parameter, as a demonstration of the validity of our method, it was enough to generate a small set of 24 simulations, setting one of them apart to evaluate the performance of the models. The 23 simulations in the training set were generated with Ω_m varying in the interval $\Omega_m \in [0.05, 0.6]$ with $\Delta\Omega_m = 0.025$, while our test simulation was generated with the density value from the Planck collaboration 2015,[18] corresponding to $\Omega_m = 0.309$.

For the scenario of multiple parameter (Ω, z) density field emulation, the training set we adopted in this work comprises 23 Ω_m density fields spanning four redshifts, $z = [0, 0.25, 0.75, 1]$, while $z = 0.5$ for $\Omega_m = 0.309$ was held for testing. Consequently, the final training dataset will consist of a total of 92 density cubes.

2.2.2. The Density Field Emulation

After creating the N-body simulations, we then proceed to load our training set into a matrix to perform dimensionality reduction using PCA, while forcing the data to be scaled and centered, and apply it to our training matrix in its logarithmic form. For that purpose we use the function `prcomp` from the package `stats`.

As a result of the PCA analysis, we have five objects. A vector containing the standard deviations of each Principal Component. Two vectors containing respectively the values used in the centring and scaling of our original data matrix. The matrix containing the *loadings* (in each column), holding the correlations between the original data and the PCs. And the scores matrix containing the PC scores, or in other words, our data projected in the principal directions. If we consider the loading and scores matrices to be given by **L** and **S**, the scale and centre vectors to be given by **s** and **c**, to obtain our original data representation the scores must be matrix multiplied by the loadings with a posterior sum of the centre vector and multiplication of the scaling one, yielding:

$$\boldsymbol{M_{orig}} = 10^{(\boldsymbol{SL^T s^T + c^T})} \tag{1}$$

Once we have our projected quantities, we use them to optimize and train the regression models. Since we aim to estimate the field itself, in the case of single free-parameter emulations the training is performed using the PCs as dependent variables and Ω_m's as independent ones. Once trained, the models are used to predict the new set of PCs for $\Omega_m = 0.309$ (or any other Ω_m), which can be de-projected into the final estimated cube. To achieve this, we created an iteration loop wherein each iteration our four different algorithms build a regression model accounting for that specific PC and the same set of Ω_m values.

To obtain the final PC predictions using these models, we rely on the function `predict` from the R package `stats`. This function accepts as inputs the regression model and the predictor variables, which in this case correspond to one of the four algorithms and $\Omega_m = 0.309$, respectively.

For the case of the two free-parameter regressions, it is just a matter of adding the redshift as a second independent variable, providing the correspondent training redshift vector to the supervised learning algorithms and the new test redshift (z=0.5) plus the trained models to the `predict` function. Keep in mind that in this case, we are training with 4 distinct redshifts, and thus 4 × 23 simulations, as mentioned in the previous section. After having the new PCs, the four final estimated cubes are obtained, by de-projecting them using Eq. 1.

2.2.3. *Testing the Models*

To test the emulation performance of our methods we need to define an appropriate metric for comparison against the ground-truth N-body simulation. Consequently we chose to use both the Power Spectrum and Bispectrum for this comparison.

The power spectrum corresponds to the Fourier Transform of the two-point correlation function defined by:

$$\xi(r,t) = \frac{V}{(2\pi)^3} \int \langle |\delta_k(\vec{k},t)|^2 \rangle e^{-i\vec{k}\cdot\vec{r}} d^3k \tag{2}$$

where V is the considered volume and $\delta_k(\vec{k},t)$ corresponds to the over-density field. Thus the power spectrum yields:

$$P(k,t) = \langle |\delta_k(\vec{k},t)|^2 \rangle = \frac{1}{V} \int \xi(r,t) e^{i\vec{k}\cdot\vec{r}} d^3r \tag{3}$$

this quantity gives a complete statistical description of a Gaussian Field. The Bispectrum corresponds to the Fourier Transform of the three-point correlation function and, as an higher order correlation function, it is sensitive to departures from Gaussianity. It is usually defined as B, yielding:

$$\langle \delta_{\vec{k}_1} \delta_{\vec{k}_3} \delta_{\vec{k}_3} \rangle = \delta_D(\vec{k}_1 + \vec{k}_2 + \vec{k}_3) B(k_1, k_2, k_3) \qquad (4)$$

where δ_D is the Kronecker delta function.

Since Dark Matter density contrast fields are considered to be well approximated by Gaussian Random Fields at the extreme of large scales (linear regime), and as we travel to smaller scales we begin to observe departures from Gaussianity (non-linear regime), this two quantities are quite appropriate to be used as testing metrics in the context of this work.

During the optimization process, each explored range and optimization scheme will provide us a different optimal model, in order to discriminate between the different models we compared their estimated outputs against our test simulation using the following quantity:

$$PSD_{RD} = \sum_{i=1}^{n} \left| 1 - \frac{y^i_{est}}{y^i_{sim}} \right| \qquad (5)$$

where $\mathbf{y_{est}}$ and $\mathbf{y_{sim}}$ are the power spectrum vector of our estimated field and the ground truth, respectively, n corresponds to the power spectrum vector size, y^i_{est} and y^i_{sim} are the ith power spectrum vector cell value for both the estimated and simulated vectors.

Consequently, to have an estimation as close to the ground truth as possible, we need this quantity as close to zero as possible, and thus, given a set of different optimal models, the best performing will be the one with a minimal PSD_{RD}.

2.2.4. *FPCA: An Alternative Approach*

In an attempt to increase the efficiency of our pipeline and explore less traditional approaches, we also demonstrated an application of *Functional Principal Component Analysis*, in the single free-parameter emulation context.

This method provides a continuous function relating the Principal Components with our desired free-parameter, thus combining the compression capabilities of PCA with the predictive usefulness of the Machine Learning methods, and consequently, enabling us to perform a "short-cut" in our pipeline by discarding the Supervised Machine Learning step. Here we adopt the R package `fda`[19] in a process divided into three steps, as follows.

In the first step we build a *Functional Data Object* from the training data. To do so we first need to specify the set of basis functions used to compute the FPCA. To follow our application of standard PCA, we defined 23 b-spline basis functions.

After having the basis functions, we use them to convert the training data (in logarithmic scaling) into the final *Functional Data Object* where the harmonics/FPCA's will be evaluated.

Once the harmonics are obtained, we apply them to compute the Principal Components (PCs) for $\Omega_{dm} = 0.309$, following the de-projection into the original density cube by multiplying each PC by each column of the scores matrix returned by the FPCA decomposition.

One important remark is that this method is highly expensive in terms of memory. Thus, we evaluated it in lower-resolution simulations of 64^3 density cells, instead of the 128^3 density cell simulations used in the previously other pipelines.

2.3. *The Gravitational Wave Inference Pipeline*

In this Section, we describe the methodology we adopted for the Gravitational Wave parameter inference. We demonstrate our implementation in Frequency Domain waveforms. To probe the generalization capabilities of our pipeline, all algorithms were trained in waveforms *without noise* but tested for Chirp Mass inferences in a dataset of waveforms *imbued with noise*, with decreasing S/N ratios.

In the following Subsections, we will be describing the process of waveform and noise generation, the GW parameter inference pipeline and finally, the performance evaluation of our pipeline.

2.3.1. *Generation of the Training and Test Datasets*

We generated a training set of 256 waveforms and a test set of 255 waveforms, varying the chirp mass in the ranges $M_{chirp} = [9.13; 25.80]\ M_\odot$ and $M_{chirp} = [9.19; 21.79]\ M_\odot$, respectively.

One crucial aspect of our work is that we tweak the S/N ratio by varying the distance to the source, consequently we generated 3 different test sets for the mentioned test Chirp Mass range, while only varying the distance parameter (eg. 1 Mpc, 100 Mpc and 1 Gpc).

Apart from the distance and masses, it is also necessary to provide high and low frequency cutoffs, the frequency resolution, and the frequency domain waveform approximator. To follow the LIGO detector parameters, the low and high frequency cutoffs were chosen to be, respectively, 10 Hz and 10kHz. Finally, we set the frequency resolution to $\Delta f = \frac{1}{16}$, and choose the *TaylorF2*[20] approximant to generate the simulated waveforms.

2.3.2. *Noise Generation and Data Pre-Processing*

To colour the waveforms with noise, we need to generate an analytical power spectral distribution (PSD) following the expectations for the Advanced Ligo detector. To do so, we use an analytical Gaussian Noise simulation, as implemented by the function `analytical.aLIGOZeroDetHighPower` from the package `pycbc.psd`. We set the length of the PSD (l_{PSD}), the frequency resolution ($\Delta f = \frac{1}{16}$) and the low-frequency cutoff ($f_{low} = 10\ Hz$).

The noise is then generated from the defined PSD using the `pycbc.noise` package and its `frequency_noise_from_psd` function. After obtaining the noise vector, we add it to the strain obtained as from the waveform generation.

Finally, we resize the simulated waves by cropping all the strain values for frequencies above 51 Hz, which corresponds to the limiting frequency domain of the shortest wave. Thus, each frequency domain waveform results into 656 data points.

2.3.3. The Inference Pipeline

Once we generate all waveforms, they are organized to form a training matrix composed of 256 instances and a test matrix with 255 instances, each corresponding to a matrix row. Similarly to the cosmological density fields case, the next step consists of performing dimensionality reduction. This data projection results into a compact representation, where each waveform is represented by 256 PCs.

In this case we are dealing with smaller matrices than in the N-body case. Thus the PCA projection step is significantly faster. However, as now a higher number of instances is considered (e.g 256 instead of 23), the final projection will result in a higher number of Principal Components.

After producing the compressed data representation, we proceed to the machine learning regressions. Different from the N-body emulation scenario, here we are not attempting to emulate waveforms, but we are instead attempting to infer parameters concerning those waveforms given their strain vectors.

Consequently, instead of using the PCs as dependent variables, now they are used as independent variables, while the chirp masses are the dependent variables for prediction. That implies a large simplification in our pipeline since we are not forced to build a regression model for every single PC.

Also, in this part of the work, we excluded the neural networks. Since in this scenario we have 256 dimensions/independent variables, as opposed to the N-body context where we have a maximum of 2 independent variables (e.g Ω_m and z), here the single-layer neural network is expected to highly under-perform.

After we train and optimize the models using the training set, they are used to infeer the parameters for the not previously seen waveforms. To do so we need to first project the test waveforms in the PC basis of the training set, were the same centering and scaling vectors as learnt from the training set are used, obtaining the PC vector for a specific waveform as:

$$\boldsymbol{PC_{new}} = \boldsymbol{L}^T \left(\frac{\boldsymbol{t_{wf}} - \boldsymbol{c}}{\boldsymbol{s}} \right) \qquad (6)$$

where, as in the Density fields case, $\boldsymbol{L}^T$ corresponds to the loadings (or rotation) matrix provided by the PCA, $\boldsymbol{s}$ the PCA scaling vector, $\boldsymbol{c}$ the PCA centering vector and $\boldsymbol{t_{WF}}$ to the test waveform vector for chirp mass inference.

After having our 255 inferred chirp masses we proceed to evaluate the algorithms.

2.3.4. Testing the Models

In this case of Chirp Mass inferences, since we are dealing with discrete instances represented by a real number, our choice for evaluation metric was the simple Root Mean Squared Error, given by:

$$RMSE = \sqrt{\sum_{i=1}^{n} \frac{(\hat{y}_i - y_i)^2}{n}} \qquad (7)$$

where $\hat{y}_i$ and y_i correspond, respectively, to the ith estimated and ground-truth chirp masses and n is the total number of instances.

Here, we use this metric to discriminate between the different models generated in the optimization process and also as the final evaluation measure, used to discriminate between the different algorithms explored in this approach.

3. Results

In this Section, we present the results of our work. We first show the results concerning the N-body dark density field estimations, and following that, the results regarding the GW parameter inference.

We present our final optimized regressions, and compare the performance of the algorithms against the ground-truth using the evaluation metrics described in the previous section.

3.1. N-body Density Fields

We begin by showing the results concerning our N-body Density Field Emulations.

First we present the results concerning our main pipeline, coupling PCA with the four supervised learning methods in the two emulation scenarios, with one and two free parameters. Lastly, we show the results regarding the FPCA emulations, implemented in the reduced size dataset.

3.1.1. Ω_{dm} Emulations

In Figure 1 we show the main results from the four supervised learning emulations. On the top panels, left-hand side we see the Power Spectra of our estimators against the ground-truth while on the right-hand side we see the Bispectra. The lower panels show the ratio between the spectra of the emulations and the ground-truth.

Regarding the Power Spectra, we achieved an accuracy within 99% throughout all of the k domain using the Single-Layered Neural Network, which was the best performing algorithm. This is impressive, because these results show that it is possible to attain very low errors even at extreme scales as $k \geq 2$ hMpc^{-1} and nearing $k \sim 0.3$ hMpc^{-1}, while using one of the most simple types of neural networks, a single-layer network. We note, however, that this is only possible because of the compression step that was adopted here.

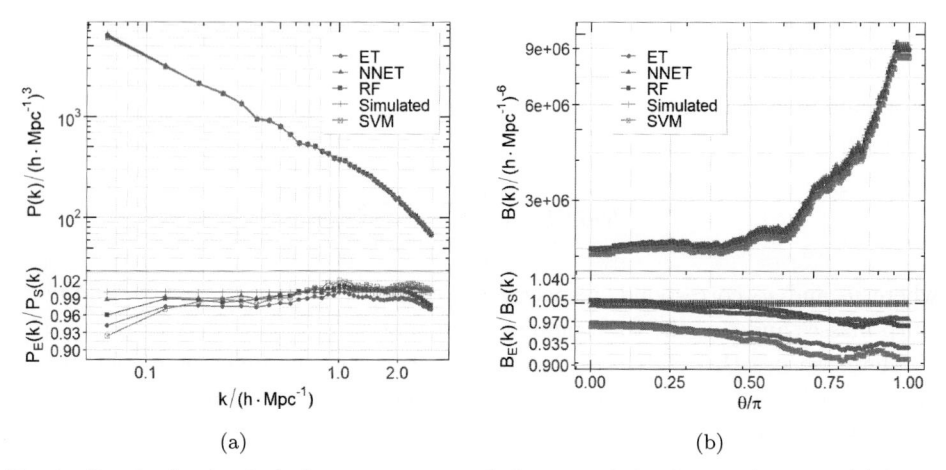

Fig. 1. Results for the single free-parameter emulation scenario implemented at z=0. (a) Power Spectrum Comparison. (b) Bispectrum Comparison.

Looking at the lower panel, it is possible to observe that generally, the algorithms seem to have a sharp decrease in their performance at the large scale extreme ($k \leq 0.2$ hMpc^{-1}), which can be attributed to the lack of independent modes in the training dataset.

On the opposing small scale extreme, we can also observe a slight decrease in performance, this time due to leakage of the Nyquist modes, as we approach the resolution limit of the simulations.

Regarding the Bispectra, we obtained an accuracy within 97% throughout all of the θ domain using the Neural Networks. Here we see Random Forest excelling at lower θ's ($\frac{\theta}{\pi} \leq 0.75$), but its accuracy eventually falls below 97% at the large θ extreme. The reason why we observe such an overall decrease in performance in the Bispectra case, compared to the Power Spectra can be attributed to the fact that the Bispectrum is non-linear in nature, giving a description of departures from Gaussianity, as opposed to the Power Spectrum. Since the Bispectrum deals with the non-linear aspects of the density fields, we should expect an higher challenge in reproducing it faithfully, since the non-linear features should be harder to compress via a simple PCA method and thus, later to predict via Supervised Learning. Non-linear compression methods would allow these results to be improved significantly.

3.1.2. (Ω_{dm}, z) Emulations

Figure 2 shows the results for the two-free parameter emulation scenario.

In the case of the two-free parameter emulation scenario we observe a decrease in the performance of the algorithms from the previous scenario. This can be expected, as now an increased dimensionality is faced. Also, the simple neural network is no

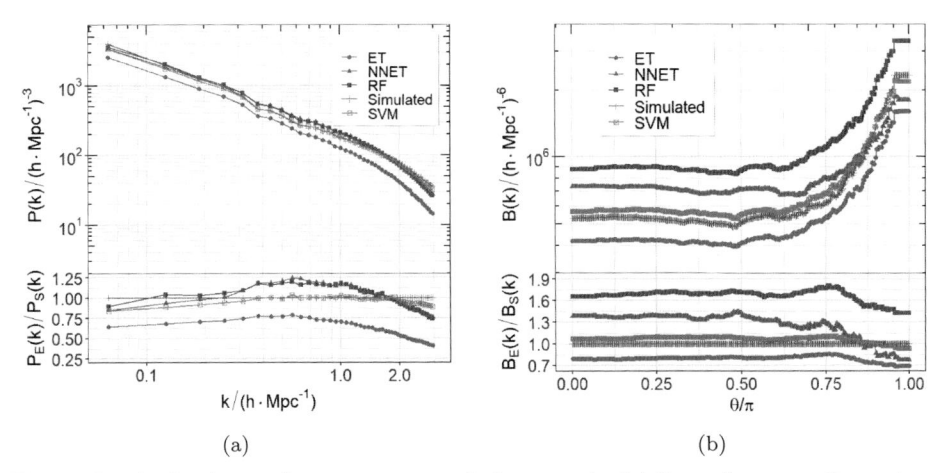

Fig. 2. Results for the two free-parameter emulation scenario. (a) Power Spectrum Comparison. (b) Bispectrum Comparison.

longer the best performing algorithm, and its adoption results in errors reaching 25% at around $k = 0.6$ hMpc^{-1}.

It is however remarkable how well the SVM method performed in this scenario. Here, the SVM achieves an accuracy of more than 95% for $0.3 \leq k \leq 2$ hMpc^{-1}, decreasing to about 90% at the low scale extreme and $\sim 85\%$ at the large scale one.

Finally, the observed decrease in overall accuracy between the previous scenario to the present, multidimensional one, can be explained due to the so-called *Curse of Dimensionality*. To reach similar performances compared to lower-dimensional cases, a required increase in the size of the training set can be exponential, when the number of dimensions in the feature space increases.

Regarding the Bispectrum, the results further indicate that SVMs are the best method among those studied in this work, since as we can see, even looking at higher order correlations it still out-performs the remaining algorithms. It is the only algorithm able to maintain an accuracy below 15% for the entire θ domain.

Finally, one additional interesting feature we see in this result, is the fact that the relation between the error and the θ domain seems to be inverted. While in previous, one dimensional case, the errors tend to increase for larger angles (corresponding to larger scales), here they tend to decrease. This could possibly be due to the increased size of our training dataset. By increasing the amount of full simulations in our training data we are effectively increasing the number of large scale modes, and consequently, improving the predictions of the algorithms at such scales.

3.1.3. *FPCA Results*

Finally, we close the N-body section by showing the results regarding our FPCA demonstration. The Power Spectra and Bispectra are shown in Figure 3,

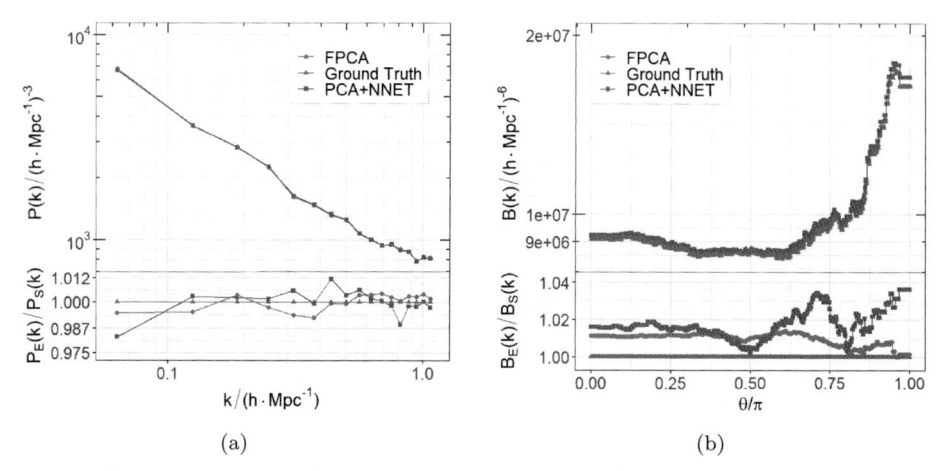

Fig. 3. FPCA emulation results at z=0. (a) Power Spectrum Results. (b) Bispectrum Results.

compared against an optimized Single-Layered Neural Network and the ground-truth simulation.

We can observe from Figure 3 that even when compared against the best performing algorithm of our previous results, FPCA seems to attain an slightly better performance, particularly at the large scale regime, indicating a strong capacity of the algorithm for generalization.

Additionally, FPCA seems to be more stable than the neural network, in the sense that we do not observe the frequent oscillations in the power ratio that we can observe in the neural network case. This could be due to the smoothing process of the b-spline basis functions that takes place within the FPCA.

Finally, one interesting thing to notice when looking at the error in terms of overestimation and underestimation of the power is the fact that the neural network and the FPCA seem to roughly exchange roles. When one underestimates, the other overestimates. This suggest that it would be possible to further improve the results by merging these two methods into an ensemble or a stacked generalization.[21] Since, roughly, their average results seem to overlap with the simulated Power Spectrum.

3.2. Gravitational Waves

Here we present the results from our Gravitational Wave inference pipeline. We show results concerning 255 Chirp Mass inferences from waveforms emitted at increasing distances and consequently, decreasing signal-to-noise ratios.

3.2.1. Frequency Domain Inferences

In Figure 4 we can see the results regarding inferences from waveforms emitted at 1 Mpc (left hand-side) and 100 Mpc (right hand-side). The top panels show our

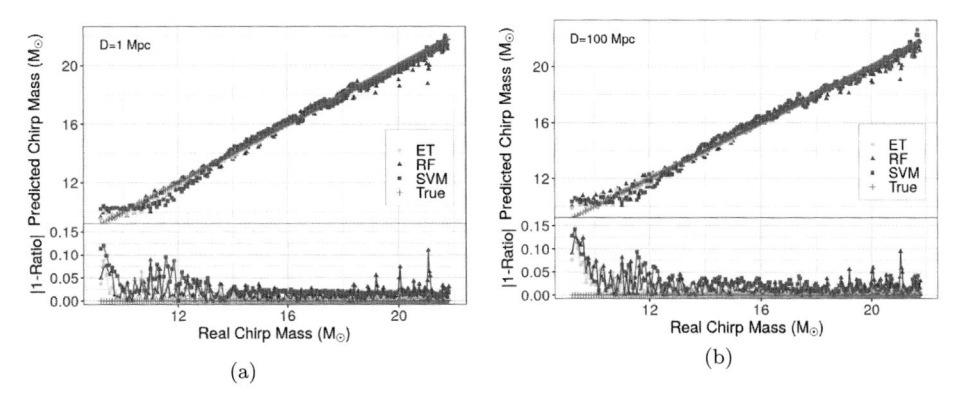

Fig. 4. Comparison between the estimated chirp masses and the ground truth in Frequency Domain. (a) For waveforms emitted at 1 Mpc (b) For waveforms emitted at 100 Mpc.

predictions against the ground-truth while the lower panels show a measure of the ratios.

These results show that up to 100 Mpc and for $M_{chirp} \geq 14$ we are able to obtain an accuracy within 98% using our best performing model which in this context was the Extremely Randomized Trees.

The Support Vector Machine also manages to obtain stable results throughout the mentioned domain, with an accuracy within 97%. On the other side, Random Forest was the worst performing algorithm, with its accuracy falling below 95%, even in this expected well behaved region of the Chirp Mass domain.

The large increase in error observed at the lower Chirp Mass extreme ($M_{chirp} < 14$) is a consequence of the fact that lower chirp masses result in lower amplitude Strains, which get highly diluted in the noise.

Turning our attention now to inferences in very low signal to noise ratio regimes, Figure 5 represent the results for inferences from waveforms emitted at much higher distances, at 1 Gpc.

Here we see a decrease in the quality of the results, with the previous best performing algorithm (Extremely Randomized Trees) having its accuracy falling to values close to 85% in the interval $14 \leq M_{chirp} \geq 16$ and to 90% for $16 \leq M_chirp \geq 20$.

We can also observe a shift in the "well behaved" domain, now $M_{chirp} > 16$, which is a natural consequence of increasing the distance to the progenitors of the waveforms, translating in a generalized decrease in the signal to noise ratio.

On the other side, the Support Vector Machine manages to excel compared to the other algorithms, achieving an accuracy $\sim 95\%$ for $M_{chirp} > 16$. The results from these simulated experiments reinforce the strong generalization capabilities of SVMs, and are particularly impressive considering that the algorithms were trained in a dataset of waveforms without noise while they are being tested on noisy ones. In part this is due to the data compression step, since by its very nature, it is also working as a denoising procedure.

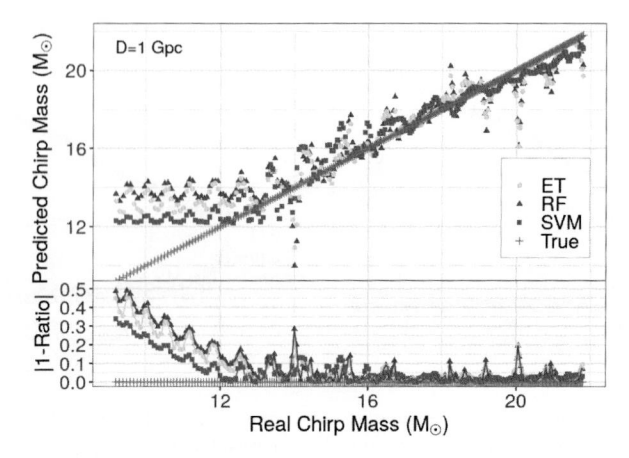

Fig. 5. Comparison between the estimated chirp masses and the ground truth in Frequency Domain for waveforms emitted at 1 Gpc.

4. Discussion

We showed that combining PCA with simple supervised learning methods allows fast and accurate estimation (regression) of cosmological density fields. We also demonstrated that the same method can be used, in the inverse way, to perform parameter inference, applied to the problem of GW source parameter determination.

Indeed, the fast increase in the demand for larger and more diverse sets of cosmological simulations, to study large-scale structure mechanisms and their dependence on Cosmology, demands fast and accurate methods to produce multiple realizations of density volumes. Our results show that our approach achieves this objective. On the other hand, our results demonstrate that our proposed method also provides a fast way of performing GW parameter inference without requiring additional prior assumptions on top of those that were already adopted to build the set of approximated waveforms.

Here we discuss the main results of our work. We comment on the relevance of our method for further developments in these fields, addressing its gains of performance and potential to explore other situations of interest. We also address the method's present constraints and discuss ways to mitigate them, proposing solutions for future implementation.

4.1. Efficiency

Here we focus on the efficiency of our method. In other words, we will discuss the amount of CPU time and computational resources required to produce a final result. We begin by showing the CPU run times for the N-body emulations, in both scenarios of single and two free-parameter emulation, and following that we show the CPU run times for the GW inference pipelines in both low and high signal to noise ratio regimes.

4.1.1. Cosmological Density Fields

In Table 1, we show the total time in order to perform the emulations. The first row regards the single free-parameter emulation scenario, where our best performing algorithm was the Neural Network (NNET), while the second row regards the two free-parameter emulation scenario, where the best performing algorithm was the Support Vector Machine (SVM).

Table 1. CPU run times for the N-body Emulation Case.

Emulation	PC Estimation	De-Projection	Total Emulation Time
Ω_{dm}	0.077 s	0.719 s	**0.796 s**
(Ω_{dm}, z)	0.082 s	4.380 s	**4.462 s**

We managed to achieve an high accuracy for the density field estimation, in a total of ~ 0.796 s for the one-dimensional case and ~ 4.462 s for the two-dimensional case. As a comparison, it takes ~ 84 min to perform an N-body simulation of the same scale. Our results, thus, correspond to an improvement of three orders of magnitude in the time required to generate the density field. Moreover, the computational resources required to implement our pipeline are far smaller than those required to perform the N-body simulations. Additionally, these emulations reproduced the real Power Spectra to less than a 1% (NNET in Figure 1 at $0.4 \leq k \leq 3$ and SVM in Figure 2 at $0.4 \leq k \leq 2$).

Finally, with respect to our work on Gravitational Wave inferences, we present the CPU running times of our pipeline in Table 2. The first row regards the high signal-to-noise ratio regime, where the best performing algorithm was the Extremely Randomized Trees (ET), while the second row regards the low signal-to-noise ratio regime, where the best performing algorithm was the Support Vector Machine (SVM).

Table 2. CPU run times for the GW Inference Case.

GW Inference (FD)	Projections into the PC Basis	Inferences	Total Time
D=1 Mpc	0.142 s	0.041 s	**0.182 s**
D=1 Gpc	0.252 s	0.004 s	**0.256 s**

Once again, we achieve a highly significant efficiency in inferring the Chirp Mass of the waveforms, obtain inference times down to 0.183 s for high signal-to-noise ratio regime. These results are particularly appealing, considering this is the time required to perform 255 simultaneous waveform projections and M_{chirp} inferences.

5. Conclusions

In this work, we presented a simple and computationally light methodology to enable fast sampling and inference of datasets in two gravity dominated contexts, Structure Formation and Gravitational Waves. To achieve that we implemented supervised Machine Learning methods coupled with Principal Component Analysis, on training datasets of full 3D N-body simulations and approximated Gravitational Waveforms.

In the context of structure formation, we provided contributions to the field using our methodology for fast and accurate emulations of full N-body dark matter density fields of 128^3 density cells in a box of 100 h^{-1} Mpc, given a choice of cosmological parameters. We applied four supervised Machine Learning Algorithms, Random Forest, Extremely Randomized Trees, Support Vector Machine and Neural Networks, in two different emulation scenarios. In the first scenario, we performed emulations solely based on the Dark Matter Density (Ω_{dm}) parameter. We managed to reproduce the Power Spectrum of the corresponding simulated field to a less than a 1% difference for $k > 0.3$ hMpc^{-1} in all redshifts, and reproducing the Bispectrum for all θ domain to less than a 3% difference for $z = 0$ and less than a 2% difference for the remaining redshifts, using the best-performing algorithm (Neural Networks). We additionally studied Functional Principal Component Analysis in the context of structure formation. We achieved even better results than the supervised methods for a reduced size dataset of simulations with 64^3 density cells, managing to reproduce the Power Spectrum and Bispectrum to less than a 2% and 5% difference from the ground truth, at all redshifts. In this scenario we trained our algorithms with 23 N-body simulations in the range $\Omega_{dm} = [0.05; 0.6]$ with $\Delta\Omega_{dm} = 0.025$, and tested the emulations for $\Omega_{dm} = 0.309$.

In the second scenario, we introduced an additional dimension, adding the redshift as free-parameter. Using the best-performing algorithm in this scenario (Support Vector Machine), we managed to reproduce the Power Spectrum to less than a 5% difference for $0.3 \leq k \leq 2$ hMpc^{-1} and the Bispectrum to less than a 15% difference in all θ domain. Here we trained the algorithms with simulations in the same Ω_{dm} range as in the first scenario, but in four distinct redshift snapshots ($z = 0$, $z = 0.25$, $z = 1$, $z = 10$), increasing the training dataset by a factor of four. We tested the emulations against an $\Omega_{dm} = 0.309$ simulation at redshift $z = 0.5$, although the emulator can be used for any value of Ω_{dm} and z.

We thus demonstrate that percent level accuracies can be reached using these emulators, and that moreover emulations can be performed in 0.796 s in the first scenario and in 4.462 s for the second scenario. This corresponds to an improvement of three orders of magnitude when compared to the time required to perform an N-body simulation of the same scale.

In the context of Gravitational Waves, we inverted the pipeline to perform inference of the Chirp Masses for a set of Frequency Domain simulated waveforms. We managed to achieve a high generalization capacity in our models by training them with 256 denoised waveforms, and testing on 255 waveforms imbued in theoretical LIGO detector noise, for three different datasets at decreasing signal-to-noise ratios. In this case we achieved differences in the inferences of around 2% for the higher signal-to-noise contexts and for $M_{chirp} > 14\ M_\odot$, while around 5% for lower signal-to-noise ratio contexts and for $M_{chirp} > 16\ M_\odot$. For both high and low signal-to-noise ratios, the parallel inference of 255 independent waveforms is performed in less than 0.3 seconds. The main success in these Gravitational Wave parameter inference results, however, reside in the generalization capabilities of our proposed methodology, since while it was trained on noise-free training sets, it was tested on highly noisy test sets.

Acknowledgments

The authors acknowledge the support of the Portuguese Fundação para a Ciência e a Tecnologia (FCT) for funding under the following Projects and Research Contracts with References: EXPL/FIS-AST/1368/2021, UID/FIS/00099/2019, CERN/FIS-PAR/0037/2019, PTDC/FIS-OUT/29048/2017, PTDC/FIS-AST/31546/2017, IF/01135/2015.

References

1. R. Laureijs et al., Euclid Definition Study Report, *arXiv e-prints*, p. arXiv:1110.3193 (October 2011).
2. LIGO Scientific Collaboration, Advanced LIGO, *Classical and Quantum Gravity* **32**, p. 074001 (April 2015).
3. P. Amaro-Seoane et al., Laser Interferometer Space Antenna, *arXiv e-prints*, p. arXiv:1702.00786 (February 2017).
4. K. P. F.R.S., Liii. on lines and planes of closest fit to systems of points in space, *Philosophical Magazine Series 1* **2**, 559.
5. H. Hotelling, Analysis of a complex of statistical variables into principal components., *Journal of Educational Psychology* **24**, 498 (1933).
6. I. Jolliffe and Springer-Verlag, *Principal Component Analysis*, 2 edn. (Springer, 2002).
7. L. Breiman, Random forests, *Machine Learning* **45**, 5 (10 2001).
8. P. Geurts, D. Ernst and L. Wehenkel, Extremely randomized trees, *Machine Learning* **63**, 3 (04 2006).
9. C. Cortes and V. Vapnik, Support-vector networks, *Machine Learning* **20**, 273 (09 1995).
10. W. McCulloch and W. Pitts, A logical calculus of the ideas immanent in nervous activity, *Bulletin of Mathematical Biology* **52**, 99 (1990).
11. G. Rossum V. and F. L. Drake, *Python 3 Reference Manual* (CreateSpace, Scotts Valley, CA, 2009).
12. R. C. Team, *R: A Language and Environment for Statistical Computing*. R Foundation for Statistical Computing, Vienna, Austria, (2021).

13. A. Liaw and M. Wiener, Classification and regression by randomforest, *R News* **2**, 18 (2002).
14. D. Meyer, E. Dimitriadou, K. Hornik, A. Weingessel and F. Leisch, *e1071: Misc Functions of the Department of Statistics, Probability Theory Group (Formerly: E1071), TU Wien*, (2021). R package version 1.7-8.
15. W. N. Venables and B. D. Ripley, *Modern Applied Statistics with S*, fourth edn. (Springer, New York, 2002).
16. P. A. T. H. M. P. Couchman and F. R. Pearce, Hydra: an adaptive-mesh implementation of p 3m-sph, *The Astrophysical Journal* **452**, p. 797 (1995).
17. L. B. Lucy, A numerical approach to the testing of the fission hypothesis, *Astronomical Journal* **82**, 1013 (1977).
18. Planck Collaboration, Planck 2015 results. XIII. Cosmological parameters, *Astronomy & Astrophysics* **594**, p. A13 (10 2016).
19. J. O. Ramsay, S. Graves and G. Hooker, *fda: Functional Data Analysis*, (2020). R package version 5.1.5.1.
20. F. Messina, R. Dudi, A. Nagar and S. Bernuzzi, Quasi-5.5PN TaylorF2 approximant for compact binaries: Point-mass phasing and impact on the tidal polarizability inference, *Physical Review D* **99**, p. 124051 (June 2019).
21. D. Wolpert, Stacked generalization, *Neural Networks* **5**, 241 (12 1992).

Unsupervised photometric detection of galaxy cluster candidates in large surveys

Ana Carvalho

Instituto de Astrofísica e Ciencias do Espaço,
Faculdade de Ciências, Universidade de Lisboa
Lisbon, 1749-016 Campo Grande, Portugal
E-mail: fc46443@alunos.fc.ul.pt

Alberto Krone-Martins

Department of Informatics, University of California, Irvine
Irvine CA 92697, USA

Antonio da Silva

Instituto de Astrofísica e Ciencias do Espaço,
Departamento de Física, Faculdade de Ciências, Universidade de Lisboa
Lisbon, 1749-016 Campo Grande, Portugal

Galaxy Clusters are essential to study galaxy evolution and are sensitive probes of cosmology and the dynamics of the Dark sector. Large galaxy surveys, such as Euclid, DES, LSST/Rubin will detect many new clusters. For example, the Euclid mission survey may reveal more than 6×10^4 clusters with S/N>3 up to $z \sim 2$, representing a whole new era for cluster cosmology. A large fraction of these clusters will be unknown high-redshift cluster candidates, lacking spectroscopic information. Thus, a major challenge for cluster detection is the identification of possible member galaxies from photometry alone, and ideally without strong assumptions of what a cluster is. Here we present the first results for the detection of galaxy clusters of a modified version of the UPMASK (Unsupervised Photometric Membership Assignment) method. The method, created to study star clusters, uses heuristics and statistical analysis to separate cluster candidate galaxies from other field galaxies without assuming cluster profiles or any strong theoretical cluster priors. We show that the method operates in a fully unsupervised way and it can even work with minimal amounts of astrometry and photometry information, using Euclid-like galaxy survey simulations. We then use Pan-STARRS data to assess the performance of the method to identify Planck clusters and present possible detections of optical counterparts for cluster candidates in the second PlanckSZ data release catalog. Finally, we compare our findings with other Planck cluster candidate follow-up efforts.

Keywords: Methods: data analysis, methods: statistical, galaxies: clusters: general.

1. Introduction

The distribution of galaxies in the Universe is not uniform. They permeate an immense cosmic web that has evolved from an initial density field, continuously sculpted by gravity and cosmological expansion, where galaxy groups and clusters emerge at the interceptions of filamentary structures. The study of these objects, their abundance, and spatial correlations provides unique ways to test cosmological models, including those featuring dark matter, dark energy, or modified gravity theories (see e.g. Refs. 1, 2). Regarding clusters, their use as cosmological probes in galaxy surveys critically depends on the definition of "cluster" and the separation of their member galaxies from other galaxies in the field. Spectroscopic information can significantly improve cluster identification, but present and near-future surveys lack spectroscopic information for a large fraction of detected objects. Additionally, most cluster identification methods adopt strong *a priori* models and explicitly search for the existence of a Red Sequence (see e.g. Ref. 3). Moreover, some of these *a priori* assumptions provide only the expected behavior of idealized systems, which are sometimes poor approximations to a more complex reality.

2. The method

UPMASK[4] is a method designed to study stellar clusters, that was successfully applied to discover multiple new objects of this type.[5,6] This method was created considering only the availability of minimal data, like photometry and astrometry. However it is also possible to use any other input feature that can help to discriminate objects. The method uses processes like the Principal Component Analysis[7] (PCA), clustering algorithms, Kernel Density Estimation[8,9] (KDE), data resampling, and an iterative process. In this proceeding we report our testings of UPMASK for a membership study in galaxy clusters. We also report on tests done with modified versions of the method (see Sec. 3), aiming at improving the processing speed of the original version, and looking towards the development of a future galaxy cluster search application for large datasets.

The method will firstly re-sample the measured data according to their error distributions and then apply PCA to the photometric parameters. It will cluster the data with k-means[10] in the space defined by the Principal Components. Each mathematical cluster is analyzed in the astrometric space with a KDE and then compared with the KDEs of a uniform random distribution. The method eliminates the KDEs compatible with those of a uniform distribution KDE and iterates. This way, UPMASK can discern clustered objects from field objects, by purifying the cluster data at each iteration. Finally, running this routine multiple times, UPMASK accounts for observational errors/uncertainties, and provides a score (equivalent to a frequentist membership probability) for each object in the dataset.

3. Modifying UPMASK

This method, in particular the KDE step, is computationally time-consuming. Thus, its application to large areas of the sky requires significant computational resources. We studied alternatives to replace the KDE step of the method. We have used tools such as the Voronoi tesselation, Anderson-Darling test and regression functions, as described next.

3.1. Voronoi selection procedure with Anderson-Darling Test

Here we apply a Voronoi[11] diagram to the K-means clusters in the astrometry space and then compare the polygon areas distributions of these objects with those obtained from a random uniform distribution. For an illustration of the method, we show in Fig. 1 the Voronoi Tesselations and the distribution of sky areas of the polygons of a random normal distribution and a random uniform distribution. Note that the first is naturally clustered at the center, whereas the latter shows a typical uniform distribution of points. The type of point distribution, therefore, affects the distribution of the areas of the Voronoi polygons. We have adopted a two-sample Anderson-Darling test[12] to perform the comparison between the resulting distributions of polygon areas. We use this test twice: testing the area distribution of the k-mean mathematical cluster against the area distribution of a random uniform realization, and testing the area distribution of random uniform realizations against each other – the later test has performed a maximum of 100 times to account for statistical fluctuations. Each test gives us a p-value that is used to discern between the two cases. A K-means group is classified as a clustered group if

$$p_{kmeans-uniform} \leq \langle p_{uniform-uniform} \rangle - T \times \sigma_{uniform-uniform} \qquad (1)$$

where $p_{kmeans-uniform}$ is the p-value of the Anderson-Darling test between the distribution of Voronoi areas of the k-means cluster and the distribution of areas of a random uniform realization, $p_{uniform-uniform}$ is the mean p-value of the Anderson-Darling test of two distributions of areas between 2 random uniform realizations, $\sigma_{uniform-uniform}$ is the standard deviation of p-values from the latter case and T is a threshold level. We have set $T = 3$ as default, but one can modify this parameter as desired. We improve the computational processing speed of this step by including a lookup table for quantities that can be pre-computed before running the method.

3.2. Voronoi selection procedure with simple statistic comparison

We have studied another modification, also using Voronoi diagrams. This alternative has a simple statistical comparison between tesselation area distributions instead of the Anderson-Darling Test. As in the previous section, Voronoi tessellation is performed on the K-means clustering points to compute the mean of the distribution of tessellation areas. The same thing is done for a set of random uniform realizations in identical conditions (same total area and number of points) and an average and standard deviation of polygon areas are also obtained. The K-means mathematical group is then assigned as an identified cluster if:

$$\langle N_{kmeans} \rangle > \langle N_{uniform} \rangle + T \times \sigma_{uniform} \qquad (2)$$

in which $\langle N_{kmeans} \rangle$ is the mean of the density of the polygons from the Voronoi Tesselation applied to the K-means group, $\langle N_{uniform} \rangle$ is the mean of all the uniform realizations average density of the polygons from the Voronoi Tesselation, $\sigma_{uniform}$

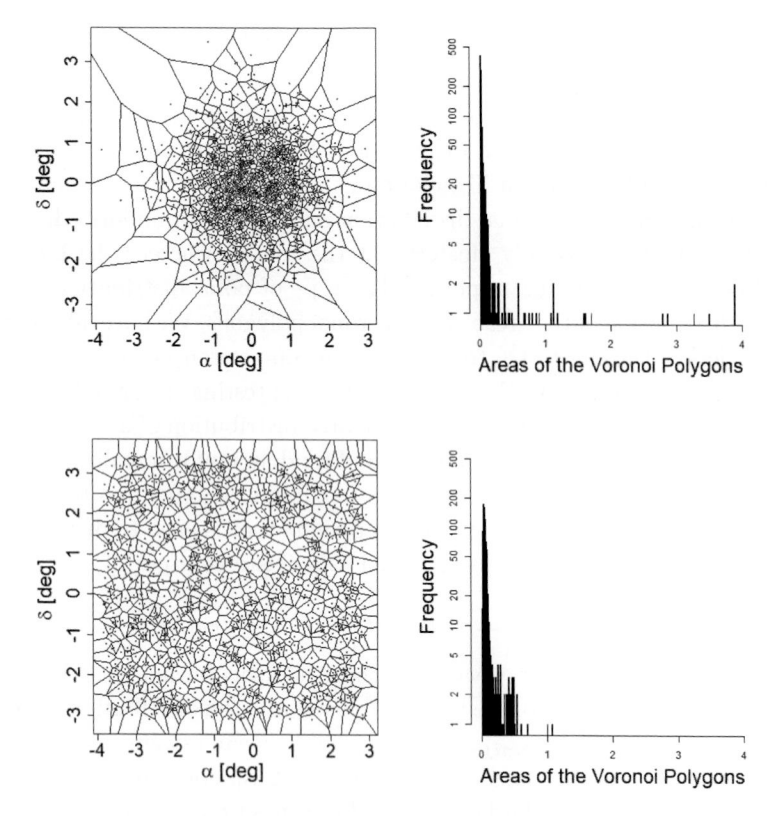

Fig. 1. Top: Left - Voronoi Tesselation (black lines) of a random normal distribution (red points). Right - Histogram of the distribution of polygon areas that resulted from the Voronoi Tesselation on the left. Bottom: Left - Voronoi Tesselation (black lines) of a random uniform distribution (red points). Right - Histogram of the distribution of polygon areas that resulted from the Voronoi Tesselation on the left.

is the standard deviation of all the uniform realizations average density of the polygons from the Voronoi Tesselation and T is a threshold level that can be adjusted by the user. As in the previous subsection, $T = 3$ is chosen to be the default case.

3.3. Grid selection procedure

Another approach to replace the KDE part in UPMASK is to create a new version of the method, implementing a "contingency table" as a very simplistic and discrete approximation of the KDE. This approach works as follows. Silverman's rule of thumb[13] is used to provide the width of grid divisions to distribute the K-means cluster points in the astrometry space. Then, a squared grid is generated and the number of points that fall inside each grid cell is counted. The counts are interpreted as a non-normalized frequency. Next, the method computes the distance between the maximum and the mean frequency, normalized to the standard deviation of the count distribution. This is then compared with the average of the same quantity for multiple random uniform realizations, using the same expression in the original UPMASK version (second equation in section 2 of Ref 4).

3.4. Grid selection procedure with fast thresholding

The computation of statistics for the random uniform distributions only depends on the number of points of the realizations and therefore does not depend directly on the input data. As such, and to reduce iteration times, we have applied regression methods to pre-compute a function that provides the threshold according to the number of K-means clustering points. This is obtained by performing 1000 random uniform realizations and computing threshold levels as a function of size as in subsection 3.3. The number, n, of considered points is in the range $1 - 1000$ and are more concentrated between $1 - 100$, motivated on one hand by the traditional galaxy cluster definition in which a cluster is expected to have more than 50 members and on the other hand by the fact that the data will be divided by the k-means into subsamples. The longer interval accounts for possible group samples that fall inside the 1–100 range. The generated threshold values are represented in Figure 2 and can be fitted by the following, two-branch, polynomial regression function:

$$f(x) = \begin{cases} a_0 + a_1 x + a_2 x^2 & n < 90 \\ b_0 + b_1 x + b_2 x^2 + b_3 x^3 + b_4 x^4 + b_5 x^5 + b_6 x^6 + b_7 x^7 & n \geq 90 \end{cases} \quad (3)$$

The function coefficient values are presented in Table 1. It is worth adding that the creation of this function and its points were generated outside the UPMASK method. As such, the kernel will simply use this function and it does not need to compute the values needed, improving the computational time.

Table 1. Fitting function coefficients of Eq. (3) for the Grid method.

a_0	1.149227	a_1	0.200402	a_2	-0.001189		
b_0	1.351×10	b_1	-7.293×10^{-2}	b_2	4.462×10^{-4}	b_3	-1.443×10^{-6}
b_4	2.529×10^{-9}	b_5	-2.422×10^{-12}	b_6	1.187×10^{-15}	b_7	-2.315×10^{-19}

3.5. KDE selection procedure with a fitting function

Following the same procedure and reasoning as in subsection 3.4, we have replaced the KDE random uniform part with a regression function created based on the KDE random uniform realization threshold output for the same range of n used in subsection 3.4. The generated threshold values are represented in Fig. 2, and can be fitted by the following regression function:

$$f(x) = \begin{cases} c_0 + c_1 x + c_2 x^2 + c_3 x^3 & n < 40 \\ d_0 + d_1 x + d_2 x^2 + d_3 x^3 & n \geq 40 \end{cases} \quad (4)$$

where the polynomial coefficients are listed in Table 2.

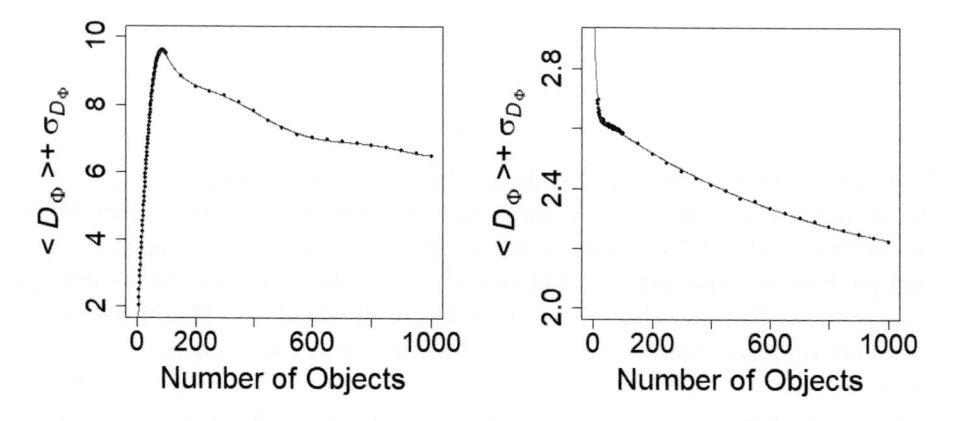

Fig. 2. Fitting function for the Grid (left) and KDE (right) method. In both cases, the red line corresponds to the first branch of the function and the blue line corresponds to the second branch.

Table 2. Fitting function coefficients of Eq. (4) for the KDE method.

c_0	3.0532634	c_1	-0.0381186	c_2	0.0011377	c_3	-0.0000115
d_0	2.648	d_1	-7.205×10^{-4}	d_2	3.781×10^{-7}	d_3	-7.897×10^{-11}

To validate UPMASK and all the proposed modifications of the method, we adopted state-of-the-art galaxy mock catalogues from N-body simulations. The simulated catalogue contains photometric information and is described in the following section. The study performed is presented in Sec. 5.

4. Data

In this section we describe the data that was used in this project. First, we applied UPMASK and its modifications (Refs Sec. 2 and Sec. 3) to simulated data, to validate and inspect their performance. Afterwards, we applied the method to real data, looking to re-identify the PLANCKSZ2 clusters from Pan-STARRS data.

4.1. Simulated data

We used simulated galaxy survey catalogues that contain estimated photometry for DES[14] and Euclid[15] bands to test the application of UPMASK and its modifications in the context of galaxy clusters. We used the MICE catalogue version 2,[16-20] obtained from the CosmoHub portal.[21,22] This data was obtained by selecting the most massive cluster that was present inside a one square degree area ($30.5° \leq \delta \leq 31.5°$, $0.5° \leq \alpha \leq 1.5°$) and its surrounding objects. The resulting subset contained a total of 8774 galaxies, 171 belonging to the most massive cluster that lies at $z = 1.09$. We selected the following catalogue entries: the DES[14] filters g, r, i, z, y, the Euclid[15] filters RIZ, Y, J and H, astrometry (α, δ), redshift, halo identifier and mass, and the galaxy identifier. In Sec. 5 we present the performance of UPMASK and its aforementioned modified versions using only this subset of galaxies and entries from the MICE catalogue.

4.2. Planck 2nd Sunyaev-Zel'dovich source catalogue

Many clusters that were detected via the Sunyaev-Zel'dovich (SZ) effect are still lacking optical counterparts as of the present time. After testing UPMASK and modifications with simulations, we search for the optical counterparts of Planck detected clusters. PLANCKSZ2 - Planck 2nd Sunyaev-Zel'dovich Source Catalogue[23] contains detections of galaxy clusters candidates, obtained during 29 months of observations. 1653 of the total objects in this catalogue, 1203 ($\approx$ 73%) are confirmed clusters. Here we use PLANCKSZ2 sources that were detected by the three detection methods in Ref. 23. We used the object identifier, the astrometric information, position errors and the integrated SZ intensity distortion, Y_{5R500}, from this catalogue. With this data we searched for galaxy clusters with UPMASK, in the PanSTARRS[24] catalogue as described below.

4.3. Pan-STARRS

As mentioned in the previous subsection, we decided to use the recent observations from the Pan-STARRS Panoramic Survey Telescope and Rapid Response System) survey[24] as the input to re-detect the PLANCKSZ2 galaxy cluster candidates. We used the second data release of the Pan-STARRS catalogue[25] published in 2019. Our method is as follows. Around each PLANCKSZ2 object, we extracted the following astrometric (α, δ) and photometric information: the mean PSF (Point Spread Function) magnitude of each filter (g - $486.6\,nm$, r - $621.5\,nm$, i - $754.5\,nm$, z - $867.9\,nm$ and y - $963.3\,nm$) and its standard deviation, and the mean Kron magnitude[26] of each filter and its standard deviation. We tailored the area queried for each PLANCKSZ2 catalogue entry using the sky coordinates and the position uncertainty – the latter used to determine the radius of the Pan-STARRS query. Thus we obtain multiple subsets, each containing the field that corresponds to the PLANCKSZ2 cluster coordinates. This catalogue contains mostly stars and galaxies, however, no flag is provided to discern between the two. To perform a simple separation, we adopted the difference between the PSF magnitude and the Kron magnitude of a filter (e.g. see Ref 27). To obtain a final galaxy catalogue we selected the objects that have a PSF-Kron magnitude > 0.05 in all of the selected filters. Finally, we applied UPMASK. We describe our findings in Sec. 6.

5. Validation of the method

This section is dedicated to a viability study of applying UPMASK to detect optical counterparts of galaxy clusters in photometric galaxy surveys. The validation process was carried out using state-of-the-art N-body simulations containing photometric and galaxy-dark-matter halo membership information that allows determining which galaxies are part of true cluster halos or are field galaxies. These simulations are described in Sec. 4. Below we present a detailed description of the tests and method yields for all versions of UPMASK under investigation, followed by a discussion of how the different modifications work and compare when varying method parameters.

5.1. *UPMASK and its modifications*

We applied the original UPMASK method as well as its modifications to the subset of simulated galaxies described in the previous section, using Euclid filters RIZ, Y, J, and H and also their respective colors, as well as the astrometry information. To compare performances between different method versions, we choose to set the number of runs equal to 10, $nruns = 10$, in all versions. This choice is a good compromise between having relatively short CPU running times and a fair membership frequentist probability, with a 10% resolution for all method versions. To perform a quantitative comparison, we compute the completeness and purity metrics as:

$$\text{Purity} = \frac{N_{UPMASK,cluster}}{N_{UPMASK,detec}}, \quad (5)$$

$$\text{Completeness} = \frac{N_{UPMASK,cluster}}{N_{cluster}}, \quad (6)$$

where $N_{UPMASK,cluster}$ is the number of known objects belonging to the cluster above a certain UPMASK probability threshold; $N_{cluster}$ is the number of known objects belonging to the simulated cluster and $N_{UPMASK,detec}$ is the number of objects above a certain UPMASK probability threshold. The results of this test are represented in Fig. 3, and their resulting CPU running times are shown in Table 3.

Table 3. CPU running times for the different UPMASK versions. The last column shows the relative CPU running time percentage of each version with respect to the original UPMASK method.

UPMASK Version	CPU running time (s)	%
KDE	274	100
KDE + Fitting Function	262	96
Voronoi + Anderson-Darling Test	190	69
Voronoi + Mean Comparison	148	54
Grid	303	110
Grid + Fitting Function	289	105

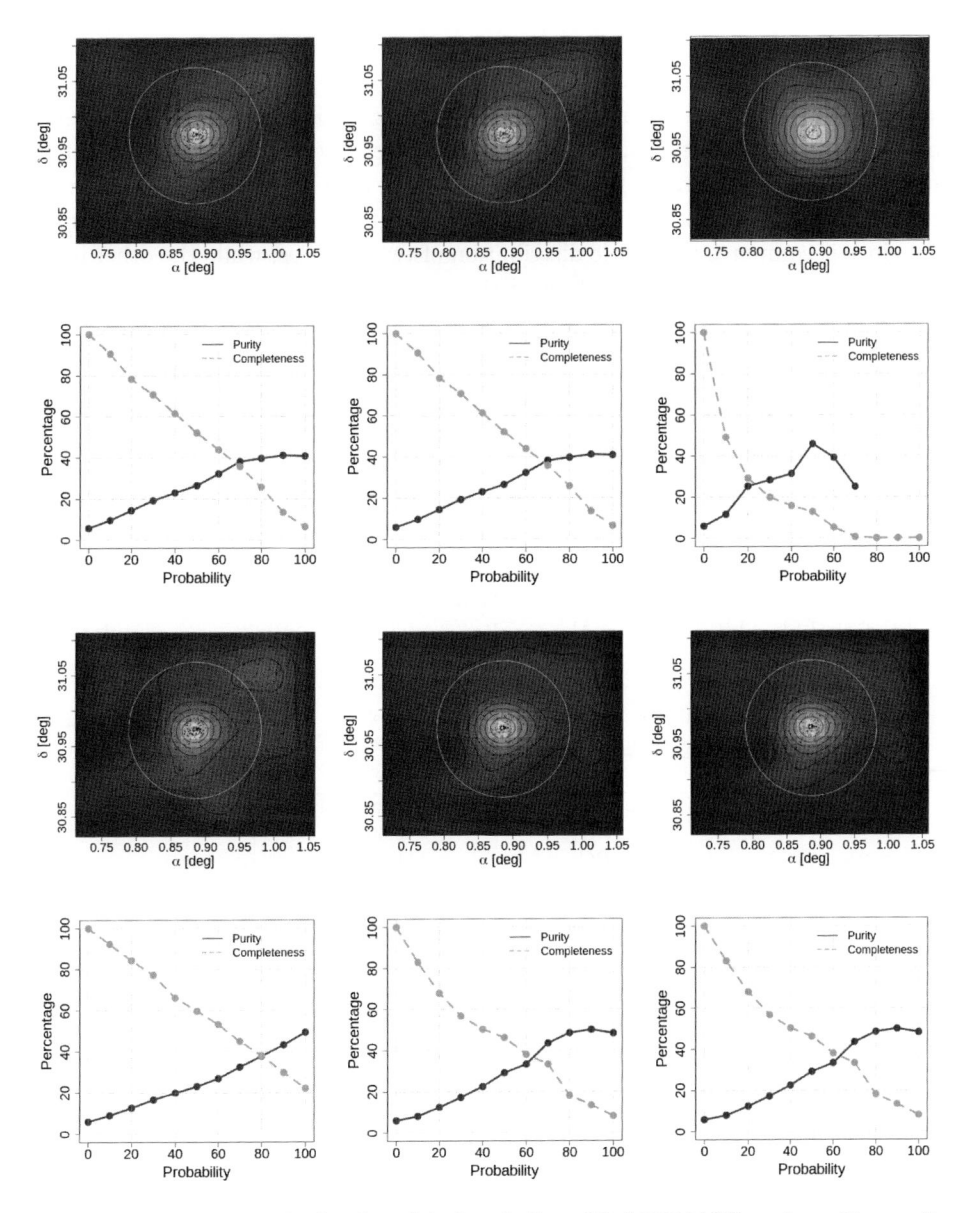

Fig. 3. The detection results for the original and all modified UPMASK versions. The results are displayed in groups of two rows, with each column corresponding to a version. The first and third rows show the density maps of UPMASK detected galaxies for the following versions: KDE, KDE + Fitting Function, Voronoi + Anderson-Darling Test, Voronoi + Mean Comparison, Grid, and Grid + Fitting Function. The color scale was set the same for all the field panels, with a color scheme where lower (higher) densities are in blue (yellow). The white circles indicate the cluster dark-matter halo radius. The second and fourth rows show the Completeness (green dashed) and Purity (blue solid) functions obtained from the unsupervised UPMASK classification, corresponding to the field above each case.

As expected when analyzing Fig. 3 and Table 3, the fitting function versions give the same results and improved in processing time, when comparing to their base UPMASK version. Voronoi+Anderson-Darling implementation is the one that improved the CPU time the most ($\sim 30\%$). However, the application of this version results in a less concentrated field (when comparing with KDE), as well as a more incomplete sample. This is due to the fact that the Anderson-Darling test is a stricter test since it compares the whole distribution of two samples, while the other implementations depend only on simple statistical calculations as the mean and standard deviation. When the Anderson-Darling test is replaced by a comparison of the mean of the Voronoi distributions. we were able to improve the completeness. On the other hand, the Grid implementation looks overall similar to the KDE version, although it results in a slightly purer sample when comparing to the latter. It is however unclear why the grid versions take more time to run than a KDE implementation, as the latter needs to perform more CPU-heavy tasks. We hypothesize that this difference is purely due to the implementation of the prototype code adopted here.

In the following subsections, we study the impact of the UPMASK parameters – number of Principal Components, number of objects per K-means cluster and threshold level T – have on the results, namely in the purity and completeness.

Table 4. Principal Components of the photometric information using simulated data (Sec. 4) and the Standard Deviation for each PC

Principal Component	Standard Deviation
PC_1	2.604481
PC_2	1.792770
PC_3	9.108574×10^{-1}
PC_4	3.631163×10^{-1}
PC_5	2.028331×10^{-1}
PC_6	4.036392×10^{-15}
PC_7	2.559386×10^{-15}
PC_8	2.356076×10^{-15}
PC_9	1.541463×10^{-15}
PC_{10}	1.157850×10^{-15}
PC_{11}	7.081957×10^{-16}

5.2. Dependency in the number of principal components

Here we show how the number of principal components affects the purity and completeness of the sample, as well as the UPMASK method run times. Principal components are ordered according to the variance of the original data projected on the PCA basis. Thus, by selecting the first few n principal components, one can grasp the most important information about the data. UPMASK calculates each PC from the provided photometry and colors. The standard deviation of each PC is shown in Table 4. This shows that the first five principal components are those that contribute the most to the data representation and all the others can be neglected. We have studied the case of using 2, 3, 4, or 5 PCs. For each of these scenarios, we show purity and completeness curves represented in Fig. 4, and the CPU run times in Table 5.

Table 5. CPU run time as a function of the number of Principal Components used in UPMASK.

Nº of Principal Components	2	3	4	5
Time (s)	1073	1193	1224	1249

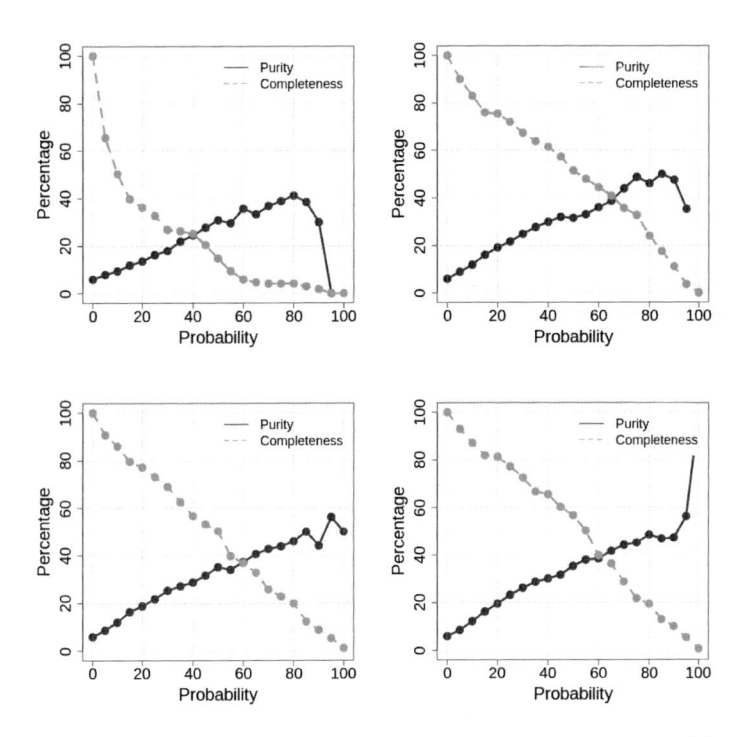

Fig. 4. Completeness (green dashed) and Purity (blue solid) of the unsupervised UPMASK classification (applied to the simulated data of Sec. 4) for different number of PCs being used in the method: 2 PCs (top left), 3 PCs (top right), 4 PCs (bottom left) and 5 PCs (bottom right).

Taking into account the completeness and purity in Fig. 4 as well as the computational time in Table 5, we have chosen to use the first 4 principal components for all of the applications below. The usage of 5 principal components includes more information, however, it is not significant when comparing with the study with 4 principal components. As such, it does not justify the additional run time.

5.3. Dependency on the number of k-means objects "N"

The next step is to test how the number of k-means objects "N" affect the results of the method, in all versions. We have performed this study for 20, 35, 50, 65, 80, 95, 110, 125, 140, 165, and 180 objects per K-means cluster. In Fig. 5 we show only some of the results, due to economy of space. For a complete grasp, we refer the reader to the appendix A of Ref 28.

Changing "N" impacts completeness and purity. Figure 5 shows that the completeness is increasing with the number of objects being clustered by k-means. On the other hand, the purity has the contrary behavior and decreases. This is because including more objects, these are not ignored by the method and the completeness will naturally increase. However, we are also contaminating more and as such, the purity is seen to be decreasing as expected.

5.4. Dependency on the threshold level "T"

Next, we study the impact of changing the threshold level T in UPMASK. This is a parameter that controls the detection limit comparison between the data and the uniform realization distributions. T can be adjusted in all method versions, except for those with thresholds provided by the fitting function procedures described earlier. We applied UPMASK and its modifications, testing different values for T, $T = \{0.5, 1, 1.5, 2, 2.5, 3\}$. The completeness and purity curves are shown in Fig. 6 for $T = \{0.5, 1.5, 3\}$. For complete results, we refer the reader to the Appendix A of Ref 28. From Fig. 6, we see a general behavior – a higher T leads to higher purity, but lower completeness. When increasing this value, the k-means cluster needs to achieve a higher threshold to be classified as a cluster. Thus, more groups will happen to be classified as following a uniform distribution and the completeness will decrease. On the other hand, k-means clusters that are without a doubt clustered, will be classified as such and kept in the UPMASK kernel.

Finally, the original implementation of the method seems to be a promising alternative for membership determination in galaxy clusters and cluster finding, as well as the newly implemented versions although there is room for accelerating UPMASK methodology, specially when making stronger assumptions about the cluster member distributions.[29]

6. Optical identification of Planck clusters with UPMASK

In this section, we apply UPMASK to search for optical counterparts of the PLANCKSZ2 cluster candidates in the Pan-STARRS catalogue. We are particularly interested in clusters not yet confirmed by other surveys. For each subset (which were obtained as described in Sec. 4) we applied UPMASK using the coordinates and the photometric data of each object. Taking into account the discussion in Sec. 5, here we used 4PCs. Some fields have a small number of objects after the star-galaxy separation, therefore we used 10 objects per k-means cluster for all the

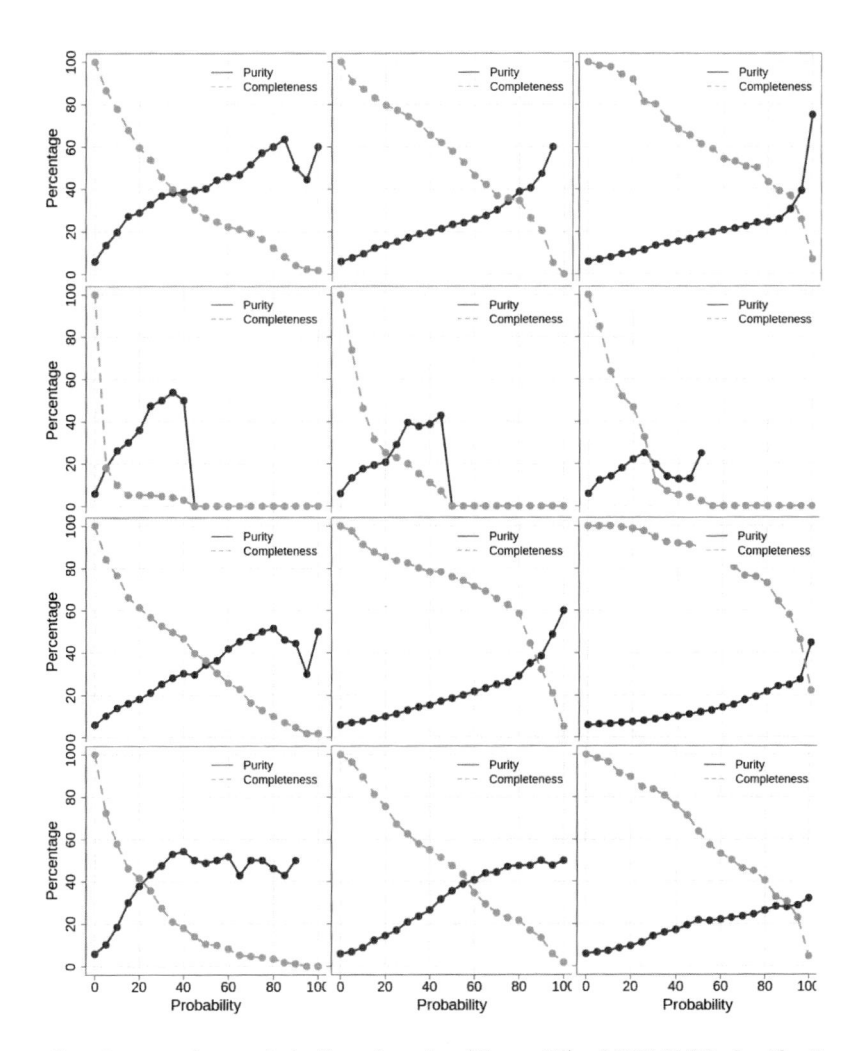

Fig. 5. Completeness (green dashed) and purity (blue solid) of UPMASK classification, applied to the simulated data of Sec. 4 for different N. We change this value along the lines ($N = \{20, 60, 140\}$), for the different methods. The lines are an application of the KDE version (original), Voronoi+Anderson-Darling, Voronoi+Mean and finally the Grid version.

fields. Since we are only interested in detect clusters with optical parameters, a resolution of 10% in the UPMASK score (frequentist probability) is a reasonable choice. The classification of a cluster is entirely up to the user of the method. Ours will depend on the number of objects each field has, above a certain probability. In Fig. 7 we show how this classification behaves when changing the cut in probability.

Thus, for the rest of this proceeding, we have chosen to classify a cluster as the field that has more than 10 members above 50% frequentist membership probability. In Fig. 8 we show the dependency of our findings with the redshift. The first plot shows the dependency of the measured SZ flux with the redshift. The figure

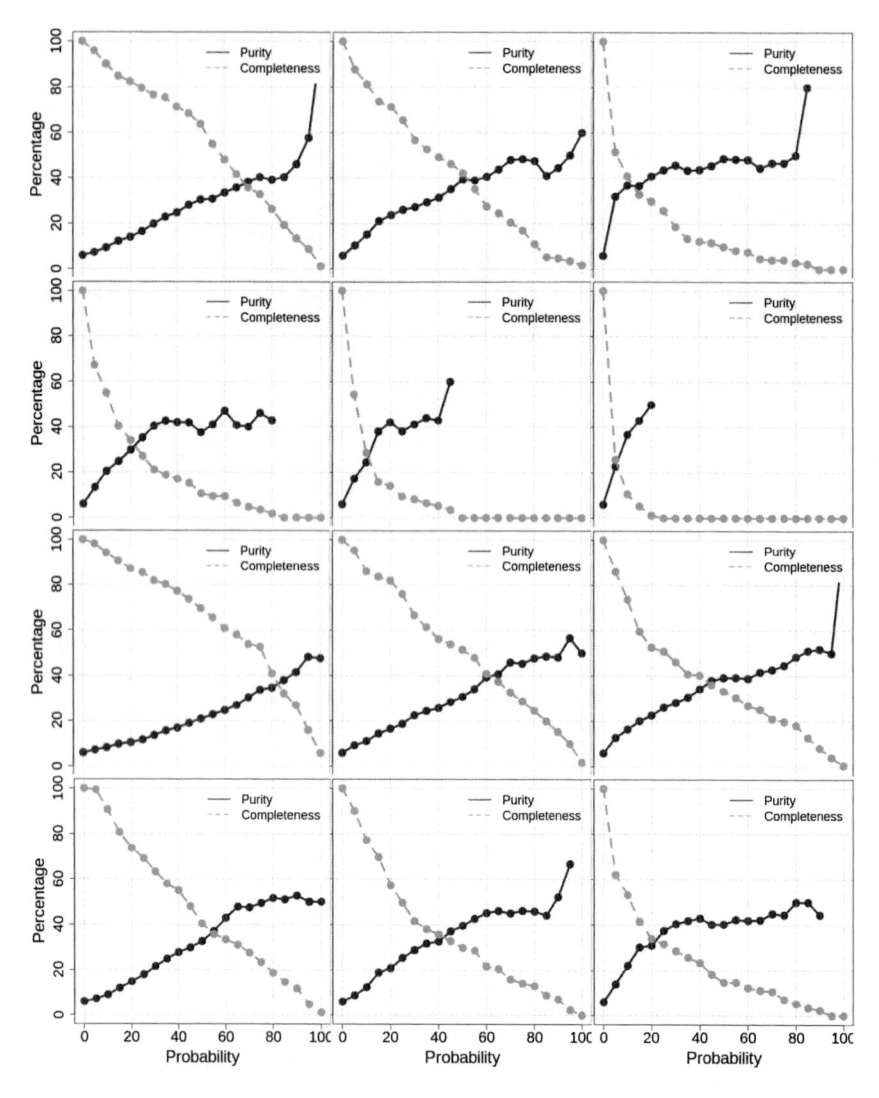

Fig. 6. Completeness (green dashed) and purity (blue solid) of UPMASK classification, applied to the simulated data of Sec. 4 for different T. We change this value along the lines ($T = \{0.5, 1.5, 3.0\}$), for the different methods. The lines are an application of the KDE version (original), Voronoi+Anderson-Darling, Voronoi+Mean and finally the Grid version.

shows three distributions: all PSZ2 sources (grey points), PSZ2 sources inside the Pan-STARRS sky-coverage (blue circles) and finally the UPMASK detections (blue dots). One can conclude that the detections do not seem to depend on the redshift (the dependency is only present due to the Planck selection function). In the second plot, we show the count dependency on the redshift for the same distributions described previously. Finally, the third plot shows the ratio of the detected objects over the total PSZ2 sources present in the Pan-STARRS sky coverage. This

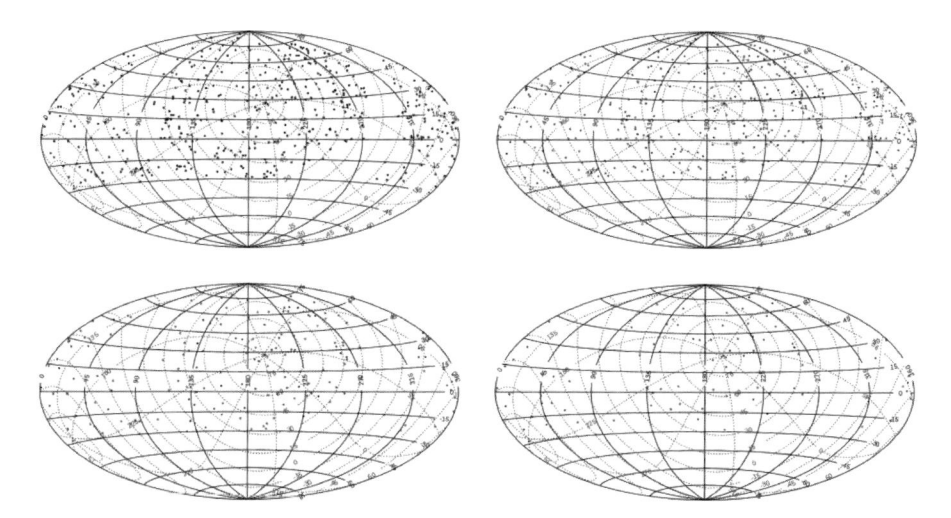

Fig. 7. Projection of the distribution of Planck Clusters in the sky detected by UPMASK for Clusters that have more than 10 objects with probability above of 50, 70, 90 and 100% (Left to right, top to bottom). Each point indicates one galaxy cluster from the PLANCKSZ2 catalogue. The red lines are the Galactic coordinate lines.

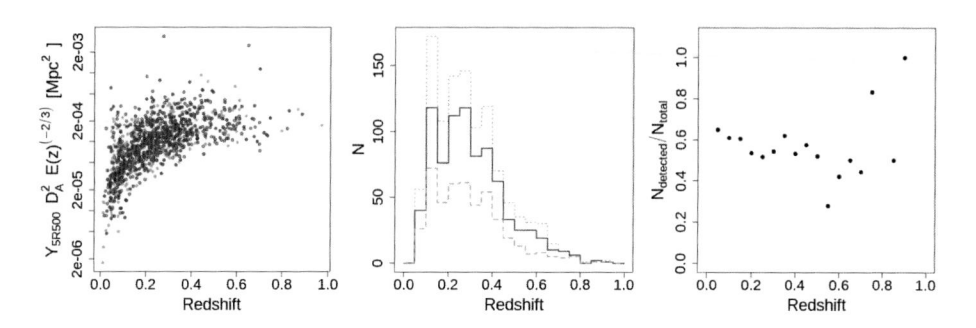

Fig. 8. Variation of PSZ2 sources properties with redshift. Left panel - Dependency of the measured Planck SZ flux with redshift. The grey points represent all the PSZ2 sources, the blue circles represent the PSZ2 sources that are included in the Pan-STARRS sky coverage and the blue points represent the sources that UPMASK detected (here, we established the detection criteria as the fields that contain more than 10 members above 50% membership probability. This detection criterion is the same in all panels of the figure). Center panel - Variation of PS2 source counts with redshift, for all sources (dotted grey), for sources included in the Pan-STARRS sky coverage (solid blue), and for the UPMASK detections (dashed green). Right panel - Fraction of the detected sources as a function redshift.

distribution shows a very weak dependency until redshift 0.5. Above this redshift, the ratio fluctuates significantly due to the small number of objects.

It is also particularly interesting to look for clusters in the PLANCKSZ2 survey catalogue that were not confirmed by an external counterpart at the moment of the

Table 6. Comparison table between the results of Refs 30 and 31 and UPMASK. The "True" and "False" fields are the unconfirmed PSZ2 sources that were found or not by the respective methods. The results are normalized to the total number of unconfirmed sources in the Pan-STARRS sky coverage.

	Streblyanska et al., Barahona et al. False	Streblyanska et al., Barahona et al. True
UPMASK False	36 (12%)	49 (16%)
UPMASK True	78 (26%)	138 (46%)

Table 7. Comparison table between the results of UPMASK and other authors (see Refs. 30–35). Here we used SIMBAD[36] to investigate which among the 216 UPMASK clusters had previous optical counterparts.

	Found (Other Authors)	Not Found (Other Authors)
UPMASK Found	67	149

release of the PLANCKSZ2 catalogue. Following the same classification, out of the 301 galaxy cluster candidates with no external validation, UPMASK was able to rediscover 72% (216) clusters with optical information. Furthermore, we have compared our results with other works in the literature (see Refs 30 and 31) in Table 6. The authors report that there are some spurious detections (ie, no obvious cluster observed in the photometric data) and therefore we have not included these detections in this table. The "False" and "True" fields refer to the fields that were not found in the list of PSZ2 sources without an optical counterpart, and those that are a clear detection, respectively. Overall we have a general accordance with the results from the aforementioned articles, while our method shows a more optimistic result (26% UPMASK clusters when compared with the "False" results). This optimistic behavior emerges naturally from the fact that UPMASK makes no assumptions about the cluster model, or requires direct redshift information from the galaxies in the data. However, more fortuitous detections might also be returned from the method in these conditions, and this should not be considered a drawback since any selected candidate still need to be spectroscopically confirmed. Here we were especially interested in the UPMASK candidates that were not previously confirmed by other authors, Refs. 30–35. In Table 7 we show that we found 67 cluster candidates in other recent efforts but without present optical confirmation. Fig. 9 shows an example of 4 of these detected clusters by UPMASK. Each panel is a KDE image with iso-contours obtained from the spatial distribution of galaxies that have membership probabilities $\geq 50\%$. Our forthcoming work will be dedicated to perform follow-up spectroscopy observations aiming to confirm or rule-out some of these new galaxy cluster candidates.

7. Conclusion

The study and characterization of galaxy clusters requires their detection and the identification of their member galaxies. In this proceeding, we modified and applied

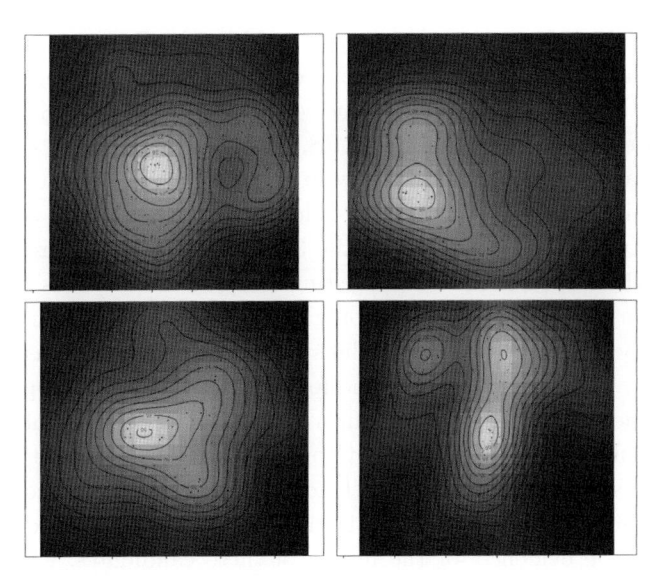

Fig. 9. Examples of UPMASK detections in Pan-STARRS fields around PSZ2 sources. The plots show a KDE image representation with iso-contours (color map: the brighter, the denser) of the most likely members (members with a probability above 50%)

UPMASK, a method originally designed to analyse stars in stellar clusters, to galaxy clusters. We show that the method is effective in this context, adopting only photometric and astrometric data as expected from upcoming surveys. Additionally, our study suggests that the performance of the method seems to be redshift independent.

In section Sec. 3 we describe the modifications proposed in this work: KDE+Fitting Function; Voronoi+Anderson-Darling test; Voronoi+Mean Comparison; Grid; Grid+Fitting Function. These modifications and the method itself were validated in Sec. 5, with simulated data from the MICE version 2 galaxy survey catalogue. In that same section we studied how the results behave with varying parameters, as the number of objects per K-means group, the number of Principal Components, and the threshold level. We conclude that the fastest modification is the Voronoi+Mean Comparison. On the other hand, the Grid implementation is the method that provided the highest improvement in purity. We also studied the optimal number of principal components to use. Overall, we were able to reduce dimensionality to 4 Principal Components. This number was chosen because additional components result in similar outcomes, with the penalty of increasing CPU time. Moreover, we have seen that using more objects per K-means cluster, results into higher completeness, while decreased purity. Also, when using a smaller threshold level, the completeness decreases, while the purity has an ascending behavior. In the end, we conclude that the UPMASK modifications and this parameter study shows that this is a very versatile tool for galaxy cluster cosmology, as the user can adjust the method and the parameters according to their goals: to use the method to quickly find galaxy cluster candidates or, to obtain membership probabilities.

In Sec. 6 we look for optical counterparts of Planck SZ clusters. We start with a list of candidates from the 2nd Sunyaev-Zel'dovich cluster catalogue (PSZ2) and the data from the Pan-STARRS catalogue collected from the Pan-STARRS survey. For each field obtained from Pan-STARRS, which corresponds to a certain PSZ2 candidate, we apply UPMASK. We show in this work (Fig. 8) that UPMASK can detect clusters independently of redshift. Additionally, we were also able to discover optical counterparts for about 72% of the 301 clusters without previous external validation. In the future, it can be interesting to apply the methods developed here to search for the new clusters directly from deep optical surveys, as the Rubin/Large Synoptic Survey Telescope and the Euclid space mission. For the cluster candidates detected in this work, we now plan to perform dedicated spectroscopic observation to determine their redshifts and to confirm or rule-out their physical existence.

Finally, thanks to the methods we developed here and to the adoption of the most modern optical surveys, we performed the detection of the optical counterparts for 67 galaxy cluster candidates previously identified by the ESA Planck space mission. This builds up the evidence for the reality of these candidates, which are at the backbones of the large-scale structure of the Universe.

Acknowledgments

AC acknowledges the support from the Portuguese Fundação para a Ciência e a Tecnologia (FCT) through the PhD Fellowship Ref: 2020.06644.BD. AKM acknowledges the support from FCT through the Portuguese Strategic Programme UID/FIS/00099/2019 for CENTRA and through the grant PTDC/FIS-AST/31546/2017. AdS acknowledges the support from FCT through the research contract No. IF/01135/2015 and Projects No. EXPL/FIS-AST/1368/2021, No. UID/FIS/04434/2020, No. CERN/FIS-PAR/0037/2019 and No. PTDC/FIS-OUT/29048/2017.

References

1. M. Roos, Astrophysical and Cosmological Probes of Dark Matter, *Journal of Modern Physics* **3**, 1152 (January 2012).
2. S. W. Allen, A. E. Evrard and A. B. Mantz, Cosmological Parameters from Observations of Galaxy Clusters, *Annual Review of Astronomy and Astrophysics* **49**, 409 (September 2011).
3. M. D. Gladders and H. K. C. Yee, A New Method For Galaxy Cluster Detection. I. The Algorithm, *The Astronomical Journal* **120**, 2148 (October 2000).
4. A. Krone-Martins and A. Moitinho, UPMASK: unsupervised photometric membership assignment in stellar clusters, *Astronomy and Astrophysics* **561**, p. A57 (January 2014).
5. T. Cantat-Gaudin, C. Jordi, A. Vallenari *et al.*, A Gaia DR2 view of the open cluster population in the Milky Way, *Astronomy and Astrophysics* **618**, p. A93 (October 2018).

6. T. Cantat-Gaudin, A. Krone-Martins, N. Sedaghat et al., Gaia DR2 unravels incompleteness of nearby cluster population: new open clusters in the direction of Perseus, *Astronomy and Astrophysics* **624**, p. A126 (April 2019).
7. H. Hotelling, Analysis of a complex of statistical variables into principal components., *Journal of Educational Psychology* **24**, 417 (1933).
8. E. Parzen, On estimation of a probability density function and mode, *Annals of Mathematical Statistics* **33**, 1065 (1962).
9. M. Rosenblatt, Remarks on some nonparametric estimates of a density function, *Annals of Mathematical Statistics* **27**, 832 (1956).
10. E. W. Forgy, Cluster analysis of multivariate data: efficiency versus interpretability of classifications, *Biometrics* **21**, 768 (1965).
11. G. Voronoi, Nouvelles applications des paramètres continus à la théorie des formes quadratiques. premier mémoire. sur quelques propriétés des formes quadratiques positives parfaites., *Journal für die reine und angewandte Mathematik (Crelles Journal)* **1908**, 97 (1908).
12. T. W. Anderson and D. Darling, Asymptotic theory of certain "goodness of fit" criteria based on stochastic processes, *Annals of Mathematical Statistics* **23**, 193 (1952).
13. B. W. Silverman, *Density Estimation for Statistics and Data Analysis* (Chapman & Hall, London, 1986).
14. K. Honscheid and D. L. DePoy, The Dark Energy Camera (DECam), *arXiv e-prints*, p. arXiv:0810.3600 (October 2008).
15. R. Laureijs, J. Amiaux, S. Arduini et al., Euclid Definition Study Report, *arXiv e-prints*, p. arXiv:1110.3193 (October 2011).
16. P. Fosalba, M. Crocce, E. Gaztañaga and F. J. Castander, The MICE grand challenge lightcone simulation – I. Dark matter clustering, *Monthly Notices of the Royal Astronomical Society* **448**, 2987 (03 2015).
17. M. Crocce, F. J. Castander, E. Gaztañaga et al., The MICE Grand Challenge lightcone simulation - II. Halo and galaxy catalogues, *Monthly Notices of the RAS* **453**, 1513 (October 2015).
18. P. Fosalba, E. Gaztañaga, F. J. Castander and M. Crocce, The MICE Grand Challenge light-cone simulation – III. Galaxy lensing mocks from all-sky lensing maps, *Monthly Notices of the Royal Astronomical Society* **447**, 1319 (12 2014).
19. J. Carretero, F. J. Castander, E. Gaztañaga et al., An algorithm to build mock galaxy catalogues using MICE simulations, *Monthly Notices of the RAS* **447**, 646 (February 2015).
20. K. Hoffmann, J. Bel, E. Gaztañaga et al., Measuring the growth of matter fluctuations with third-order galaxy correlations, *Monthly Notices of the RAS* **447**, 1724 (February 2015).
21. P. Tallada, J. Carretero, J. Casals et al., Cosmohub: Interactive exploration and distribution of astronomical data on hadoop, *Astronomy and Computing* **32**, p. 100391 (2020).
22. J. Carretero, P. Tallada, J. Casals et al., CosmoHub and SciPIC: Massive cosmological data analysis, distribution and generation using a Big Data platform, *PoS* **EPS-HEP2017**, p. 488 (2017).
23. Planck Collaboration, P. A. R. Ade, N. Aghanim et al., Planck 2015 results. XXVII. The second Planck catalogue of Sunyaev-Zeldovich sources, *Astronomy and Astrophysics* **594**, p. A27 (Sep 2016).
24. K. C. Chambers, E. A. Magnier, N. Metcalfe et al., The Pan-STARRS1 Surveys, *arXiv e-prints* , p. arXiv:1612.05560 (December 2016).

25. H. A. Flewelling, E. A. Magnier, K. C. Chambers et al., The Pan-STARRS1 Database and Data Products, *arXiv e-prints* , p. arXiv:1612.05243 (Dec 2016).
26. R. G. Kron, Photometry of a complete sample of faint galaxies., *Astrophysical Journal, Supplement* **43**, 305 (Jun 1980).
27. D. J. Farrow, S. Cole, N. Metcalfe et al., Pan-STARRS1: Galaxy clustering in the Small Area Survey 2, *Monthly Notices of the RAS* **437**, 748 (Jan 2014).
28. A. S. C. Carvalho, Exploration of unsupervised machine learning methods to study galaxy clustering (2019).
29. M. S. Pera, G. I. Perren, A. Moitinho et al., pyUPMASK: an improved unsupervised clustering algorithm, *Astronomy and Astrophysics* **650**, p. A109 (June 2021).
30. A. Streblyanska, A. Aguado-Barahona, A. Ferragamo et al., Optical validation and characterization of Planck PSZ2 sources at the Canary Islands observatories. I. First year of LP15 observations, *Astronomy and Astrophysics* **628**, p. A13 (Aug 2019).
31. A. Aguado-Barahona, R. Barrena, A. Streblyanska et al., Optical validation and characterization of Planck PSZ2 sources at the Canary Islands observatories. II. Second year of LP15 observations, *arXiv e-prints* , p. arXiv:1909.06235 (Sep 2019).
32. R. Barrena, A. Streblyanska, A. Ferragamo et al., Optical validation and characterization of Planck PSZ1 sources at the Canary Islands observatories. I. First year of ITP13 observations, *Astronomy and Astrophysics* **616**, p. A42 (August 2018).
33. S. Boada, J. P. Hughes, F. Menanteau et al., High Confidence Optical Confirmations among the High Signal-to-noise Planck Cluster Candidates, *The Astrophysical journal* **871**, p. 188 (Feb 2019).
34. A. Aguado-Barahona, R. Barrena, A. Streblyanska et al., Optical validation and characterization of Planck PSZ2 sources at the Canary Islands observatories. II. Second year of LP15 observations, *Astronomy and Astrophysics* **631**, p. A148 (November 2019).
35. H. Zohren, T. Schrabback, R. F. J. van der Burg et al., Optical follow-up study of 32 high-redshift galaxy cluster candidates from Planck with the William Herschel Telescope, *Monthly Notices of the RAS* **488**, 2523 (Sep 2019).
36. M. Wenger, F. Ochsenbein, D. Egret et al., The SIMBAD astronomical database. The CDS reference database for astronomical objects, *Astronomy and Astrophysics, Supplement* **143**, 9 (April 2000).

Time-dependent lepto-hadronic modeling of the emission processes in blazar jets

S. Gasparyan[1], D. Bégué[2,3] and N. Sahakyan[1,4,5]

[1] *ICRANet-Armenia, Marshall Baghramian Avenue 24a, Yerevan 0019, Armenia*
[2] *Department of Physics, Bar Ilan University, Ramat-Gan 52900, Israel*[*]
[3] *Max-Planck-Institut für extraterrestrische Physik, Giessenbachstrasse, D-85748 Garching, Germany*
[4] *ICRANet, P.zza della Repubblica 10, 65122 Pescara, Italy*
[5] *ICRA, Dipartimento di Fisica, Sapienza Universita' di Roma, P.le Aldo Moro 5, 00185 Rome, Italy*
[*] *E-mail: sargisgyan@gmail.com*

The recent associations of neutrino events with blazars (e.g. TXS 0506+056, 3HSP J095507.9+355101) provided a unique opportunity to study the possible physical connection between the multiwavelength electromagnetic and neutrino emissions. We present *SOPRANO*, a new conservative implicit kinetic code which follows the time evolution of the isotropic distribution functions of protons, neutrons and the secondaries produced in photo-pion and photo-pair interactions, alongside with the evolution of photon and electron/positron distribution functions. In the current work, we apply *SOPRANO* to model the broadband spectrum of TXS 0506+056, 3HSP J095507.9+355101 and 3C 279 blazars. It was possible to constrain main physical parameters within both a pure hadronic and lepto-hadronic scenarios.

Keywords: Radiation mechanisms; non-thermal–quasars; individual; TXS 0506+056, 3HSP J095507.9+355101 and 3C 279 – galaxies; jets – gamma-rays; galaxies

1. Introduction

In recent years, the discovery of very high energy neutrinos of astrophysical origin by the IceCube experiment[1–3] has opened a new window on very high energy sources such as gamma-ray bursts (hereafter GRBs), active galactic nuclei (AGNs) and tidal disruption events (TDEs). In 2017, the very high energy neutrino IceCube 170922A[4] and its further association (confidence level of 3.5σ) with the blazar TXS 0506+056[5] made clear that high energy protons, neutron and even possibly nucleons have an important role to play in the dynamics and the radiation of relativistic jets.[6–8]

In the forthcoming years, it is expected that many more crucial data will become available for high energy sources at all wavelengths, but more importantly at very high energy. For instance, the MAGIC collaboration recently reported the first observations of a GRB at energies above TeV with its observation of 190114C,[9] and several more are expected to be observed with CTA.[10,11] In addition, upgrades of existing neutrino facilities, with e.g. IceCube-Gen2,[12] as well as new experiments such as P-one,[13] KM3Net[14] and the Baikal-GVD,[15] will allow for increasingly more

---

[*]Current address.

sensitive searches of the origin of very high energy neutrinos.[16] Those experiments should also help to establish more firm coincidental observations of neutrino bursts with identified electromagnetic counterparts, thus allowing for models to be tested, constrained, challenged and eventually ruled out.

In order to understand observations and constrain models of emission able to explain very high energy neutrinos, it is necessary to perform self-consistent simulations of the time evolution of hadrons distribution functions, together with following the evolution of the photon and lepton distribution functions. This is a challenging task since 1- the number of distributions is much larger (from two to fourteen although some are trivial), 2- all equations describing the time evolution of particle distribution functions are coupled in a non-trivial (and non-linear) way by many complex processes that 3- have different time scales, requiring an implicit time discretization. The high number of distribution functions comes from the fact that we also wish to follow the cooling and emission of charged secondaries (pion and muons), preventing us from using semi-analytical expressions for the production rate of neutrinos, see $e.g.$[17]

Over the years, several groups have developed numerical models to estimate leptons, hadron and photon distribution functions in order to make predictions to explain observations, either under the steady state approximation[18–21] or for the fully time dependent equations either for leptons only[22] or adding protons.[23–28] In this paper, we present our approach to the problem: a modular code solving the time dependent isotropic kinetic equations which preserves the total energy of the system as well as the number of particles where needed. The code structure is modular such that processes can be added easily (or removed). It is also implicit so numerical stability is achieved at all time.

The paper is organised as follows. In Section 2, we detail the processes included in our numerical code and the associated kinetic equation. In Section 3, we provide elements of the numerical discretizations in energy and time. In Section 4 we present examples of the theoretical modelings obtained by *SOPRANO*. In particular, we model the spectra of TSX 0506+056, 3HSP J095507.9+355101 and of 3C 279. The conclusion follows.

2. *SOPRANO*: Simulator of Processes in Relativistic AstroNomical Objects

In its current version, the code evolves in time the isotropic kinetic equations for photons, electrons and positrons (considered as one species, see below), protons, neutrons, charged and neutral pions, muons, neutrino and anti-neutrino of all flavors. We summarize here all terms appearing in the kinetic equation for all particle species. For the cross-sections used in SOPRANO see.[29] In the photon distribution function, we assign $n_{\rm ph}$ to be the number of photons per unit volume per hertz. We further define $N_{\rm i}$ to be the number of particles of species i per unit volume per unit Lorentz factor of particle i. Here i can be all leptons and all hadrons. Then, we define N_{ν_i} the number of neutrinos of flavour i per units volume per GeV. Finally, for the sink and source terms we assign Q and S, respectively. The contribution of inverse Compton scattering is noted R_{IC} for the photons and is a cooling term for the leptons.

- *Photons* : they are created by synchrotron radiation from all charged particles, and by π_0 decay. They are absorbed by pair production and redistributed in energy by inverse Compton scattering. We neglect the absorption of photons in the photo-pion and photo-pair processes. The resulting kinetic equation takes the form

$$\frac{\partial n_{\text{ph}}}{\partial t} = -S_{\gamma\gamma \to e^+e^-} + Q_{\pi_0} + R_{\text{IC}} + \sum_i Q^i_{\text{synch}} \qquad (1)$$

- *Leptons* : electron and positrons are considered a single species. They are created by muon decay μ, by photo-pair production and photon pair production. The also undergo synchrotron cooling such that the final kinetic equation reads

$$\frac{\partial N_{e^\pm}}{\partial t} = Q_\mu + Q_{p\gamma \to e^+e^-} + Q_{\gamma\gamma \to e^+e^-} C_{\text{IC}} + C_{\text{synch}} \qquad (2)$$

- *Protons* : protons undergo cooling via synchrotron emission, Bethe-Heitler photo-pair production and via photo-pair production. They are produced by photo-pair interaction with neutron, and disappear for a fraction of photo-pair interaction. The kinetic equation takes the form

$$\frac{\partial N_p}{\partial t} = C_{p\gamma \to p\pi} + C_{p\gamma \to e^+e^-} + C_{\text{synch}} - S_{\gamma p \to n\pi} + Q_{\gamma n \to p\pi} \qquad (3)$$

- *Neutron* : Neutron are produced in photo-pion production and disappear in photo-pion interactions. The kinetic equation takes the form

$$\frac{\partial N_n}{\partial t} = -S_{n\gamma \to p\pi} + Q_{p\gamma \to n\pi} + C_{n\gamma \to n\pi} \qquad (4)$$

- *Charged pions* : π_+ and π_- are produced by photo-pair production. Then, they cool via synchrotron emission and decay. The kinetic equation for both species takes the form

$$\frac{\partial N_{\pi^\pm}}{\partial t} = Q_{p\gamma \to \pi} + Q_{n\gamma \to \pi} - S_\pi + C_{\text{synch}} \qquad (5)$$

We note that we solve the kinetic equation independently for both species, since the branching ratio in photo-pion production are different for negative and positive pions.
- *Neutral pions* : the π_0 kinetic equation is similar to that of charged pions but without synchrotron cooling.

- *Muons* : Muons are produced by the decay of charged pions. They are also cooled by the synchrotron process and they decay. Therefore, the kinetic equation is

$$\frac{\partial N_\mu}{\partial t} = Q_{\pi_\pm} - S_\mu + C_{\text{synch}} \qquad (6)$$

- *Neutrinos and anti-neutrinos:* neutrinos and anti-neutrinos are produced in the decay of pions and of muons. We consider all 2 flavours ζ

$$\frac{\partial N_{\nu,\zeta}}{\partial t} = Q_{\pi_\pm} + Q_\mu \qquad (7)$$

3. Numerical Discretization

The SOPRANO follows the evolution of distribution functions as a function of time under the following simplificative assumptions: i) space is infinite and homogeneous, ii) distribution functions are isotropic. For disretization, SOPRANO uses a flavour of finite volume approximation based on the discontinuous Galerkin method. This method fits nicely for solving integro-differential equations.

3.1. Energy discretization

In order to numerically solve the kinetic equations presented in Section 2, a numerical grid for the energy of all particles is introduced. The grid element are equally space in logarithmic of the energy.[a] The grid characteristics for each types of particle are given by Table 1. We use the approach of the discontinuous Galerkin method. On each energy cell I, we approximate the distribution function by a polynomial. In the current version we restraint to first order and consider the Legendre polynomial as basis function. Therefore, on each energy cell I, the distribution function is approximated by

$$N_i^I(x) = N_{i,0}^I L_0^I(x) \qquad (8)$$

where the first order Legendre polynomial on the energy cell I is

$$L_0^I = \frac{1}{\sqrt{x_{I+\frac{1}{2}} - x_{I-\frac{1}{2}}}} \equiv \frac{1}{\sqrt{||I||}} \qquad (9)$$

Here $x_{I\pm(1/2)}$ are the boundaries of energy cell I and where we introduced the additional notation $||I|| = (x_{I+1/2} - x_{I-1/2})$. An important properly of the Legendre polynomial is that

$$\int_I L_0^I dx = 1. \qquad (10)$$

---

[a]Note that our numerical method do not require to have a uniform grid. Because it is based on finite volume, we can refine the grid in one or several energy bands of interest. In this way, we can provide more detailed results in those specific bands, while the rest of the domain is coarse for faster numerical estimation.

Table 1. Characteristics of the numerical grids used by SOPRANO for the numerical models of this work. The cells are equally space in logarithmic scale.

Particle	Number of cells	Minimum energy	Maximum energy
Photons	150	$\nu = 10^{-2}$ Hz	$\nu = 10^{30}$ Hz
Leptons	130	$\gamma_{e\pm} = 1.2$	$\gamma_{e\pm} = 5 \times 10^{13}$
Hadrons	100	$\gamma_h = 1.2$	$\gamma_h = 10^{11}$
Neutrinos	100	$E_\nu = 10^{-3}$ GeV	$E_\nu = 10^{11}$ Gev

In the following we will use interchangeably $N_i^I \equiv N_{i,0}^I$. We seek the weak formulation of all kinetic equations presented below on all energy interval I. For this, we multiply both sides of the equation by L_0 and integrate over I. After simplification, we obtain a system of differential equations for all $N_{i,0}^I$. This specific discretization and the structure of the kinetic equation allows us to retrieve a numerical method which conserves energy and the number of particles when they are conserved.

3.2. *Temporal discretization*

Before discussing the temporal discretization, we note that the equation are non-linear in the distribution function for Compton scattering, pair production, photo-pion and photo-pair processes. We have decided to linearize the kinetic equation of photo-pion and photo-pair processes by assuming that the target photon-field is equal to the one at the previous time step, effectively making those process linear in the distribution function. For all leptonic processes,[b] we preserve the non-linearity of the kinetic equations and solve at each time step a non-linear system via Newton-Raphson iteration. The temporal evolution of the distribution function is performed with the implicit Euler.

The computation of one time step is done in the following form

(1) solve the linear kinetic equation for the protons since for photo-pion and photo-pair processes the photon distribution function is assumed to be known and given by its value at time t. The pairs created in the photo-pair processes are saved to be use as a source term in the leptonic computation.
(2) compute the decay and cooling (when required) of pions and muons. The pairs and photons created in the muon and pion decay are used as source terms in the leptonic computation.
(3) perform the fully implicit leptonic computation with the source term computed in the two previous steps.

4. Modeling of Blazar SEDs

The code *SOPRANO*, described in Section 2, is used to model the multiwavelength SEDs of TXS 0506+056, 3HSP J095507.9+355101 and 3C 279. Two of these sources,

---

[b]This is true for all process but synchrotron which is linear in the distribution function.

TXS 0506+056 and 3HSP J095507.9+355101, coincide in space and time with the IceCube 170922A[4] and IceCube 200107A[30] events, respectively. The other source, 3C 279, shows a prominent flare in the γ-ray band. In all modelings, the emission region assumed to be a sphere with a radius of R' which is moving with a bulk Lorentz factor of $\Gamma \sim \delta$, carries a magnetic field with an intensity of B' and a population of relativistic particles. The magnetic jet luminosity is defined as

$$L_B = \pi c R'^2 \delta^2 \frac{B'^2}{8\pi}, \qquad (11)$$

while for protons and electrons as follows:

$$L_p = \pi R'^2 \delta^2 m_p c^3 \int \gamma_p Q'_p(\gamma_p) \gamma_p, \qquad (12)$$

$$L_e = \pi R'^2 \delta^2 m_e c^3 \int \gamma_e Q'_e(\gamma_e) \, d\gamma_e, \qquad (13)$$

where c is the speed of light, m_p and m_e are the proton and electron masses, while Q'_p and Q'_e refer to proton and electron injection spectra, with the following forms:

$$Q'_p(\gamma_p) = Q'_{0,p} \gamma_p^{-\alpha_p} \qquad \gamma_p < \gamma_{p,\max}. \qquad (14)$$

$$Q'_e(\gamma_e) = \begin{cases} Q'_0 \gamma_e^{-\alpha_e} \exp\left(-\frac{\gamma_e}{\gamma_{e,\text{cut}}}\right) & \gamma_{e,\min} \leq \gamma_e \leq \gamma_{e,\max}, \\ 0 & \text{otherwise}, \end{cases} \qquad (15)$$

where $\gamma_{e,\min}$ is the minimum injection Lorentz factor. All primed quantities refer to the comoving frame. The distribution functions of protons and electrons evolve via cooling and via interaction with photons, producing different signatures in the broadband spectrum. Our aim is to identify those signatures and use them to constrain the emission mechanism within the framework of different scenarios. We also assume that the injection power-law indexes are such that $\alpha_e = \alpha_p$. Once injected in the emitting region, particles interact with the magnetic field and with the photons, producing secondary particles, which themselves interact, radiate and decay, shaping the broadband SED. The low energy component is interpreted as the synchrotron emission of the primary electrons while the HE component is modelled either within a pure hadronic model(hereafter HM) or a hybrid lepto-hadronic (hereafter hybrid) model e.g.[31,32] For the HM, the high energy peak on SED is formed due to the proton synchrotron emission, however in the hybrid model, the high energy peak is explained by leptonic processes and proton synchrotron emission is required to be subdominant. The proton content is obtained by maximizing the neutrino flux at PeV energies, which is constrained by the radiation from the secondaries produced by the Bethe-Heithler and photo-pion processes. Indeed, it has long been speculated that efficient neutrino production is associated with efficient Bethe-Heithler process, creating a population of HE pairs, which can over-shine the tight constraints in the X-ray band e.g., order of minutes.[33] The system of kinetic equations is evolved for one dynamical time scale $t'_{\rm dyn} \sim R'/c$ considering the magnetic field to be constant, and taking into account all relevant processes for particles interactions. Having estimated the model parameters of each blazar SEDs, the corresponding neutrino flux can be derived. The flux of muon neutrino, $F_{\nu_\mu}(E_{\nu_\mu})$, in all considered scenarios is shown by the light blue line in Figures 1-3. When available, the neutrino flux is compared with the limit imposed by the IceCube detector. This flux can be transformed to the expected observed number of neutrinos in the IceCube detector using its averaged effective area $A_{\rm eff}(E_\mu)$, which is mostly a function of the incident neutrino energy. For 3HSP J095507.9+355101 and 3C 279, the average area from[34] was considered, while for TXS 0506+056 we used the area released after the observation of IceCube-170922A.[c] The effective area increases with energy and reaches its maximal value for energies above several hundreds of PeV. The expected number of muon neutrinos and anti-neutrinos is computed through

$$N_{\nu_\mu + \bar\nu_\mu} = t_{\rm exp} \int_{E_{\rm min,\nu_\mu}}^{E_{\rm max,\nu_\mu}} F_{\nu_\mu}(E_{\nu_\mu})\, A_{\rm eff}(E_{\nu_\mu})\, dE_{\nu_\mu} \qquad (16)$$

where the minimum and maximum energy of the neutrinos are $E_{\rm min,\nu_\mu} = 100$ GeV and $E_{\rm max,\nu_\mu} = 10^9$ GeV, respectively, chosen to correspond the limits for the effective area. The expected number of neutrino events depends on the duration of the source activity, $t_{\rm exp}$, over which the neutrinos are emitted. The neutrino oscillation, within the quasi-two neutrino oscillation assumption, is taken into account by

$$N^{obs}_{\nu_\mu} = 0.575 N_{\nu_\mu} + 0.425 N_{\nu_e}, \qquad (17)$$

where $N^{obs}_{\nu_\mu}$ is the observable distribution of muon neutrinos, while, N_{ν_μ} and N_{ν_e} are the emitted muon and electron neutrino distributions.[35]

5. Results

The results of the SEDs modeling are shown in Fig. 1-3 with the Table 2 and 3.

TXS 0506+056: Two different periods are chosen for modelling: the single neutrino detection period,[4] and the historical neutrino flaring period.[5] The modeling results are shown in Figure 1 and Table 2. Panels a) and b) of Figure 1 represent the modeling of SED of the single neutrino event period, while panel c) and d) show flare for historical neutrino flare SED modelings. The multiwavelength data from[4] are modeled within a HM scenario in panel a). The corresponding model parameters are given in Table 2. The sum of all components, represented by the blue line in the top left panel of Figure 1, satisfactorily explains the observed data. The model overpredicts the radio data, but by taking into account the synchrotron self-absorption effect,[29] the model is in agreement with the data. The modeling parameters given in the first column of Table 1 are in the range of similar estimations for blazars in general and for TXS 0506+056 in particular. A Doppler factor $\delta = 20$ and a radius

---

[c]https://icecube.wisc.edu/science/data-releases/

$R' = 2.5 \times 10^{15}$ cm were used in our modeling. This is in agreement with the limits on the variability time of 10^5s presented in.[36] We note that when $\delta = 10$ or 15, the data can also be well reproduced by the model. The initial injection power-law index of the emitting electrons is $\alpha_e = 2.1$, a value that can be formed by shock accelerations, e.g.[37] Due to the high magnetic field, $B = 80$ G, electrons are in the fast cooling regime and their distribution function is a power-law with index $\alpha_e + 1$. The initial electron distribution extends up to $\gamma_{\text{cut}} = 2.4 \times 10^3$ (~ 1 GeV) which is representative of the acceleration and cooling time scales. Instead, protons cool less efficiently and they could be accelerated up to much higher energies, i.e. $\gamma_{\max} = 10^9$ (9.4×10^{17} eV), see.[29]

As an alternative model to HM or leptonic models, the hybrid model is also applied to the SED of TXS 0506+056, shown in panel b) of Figure 1. The model parameters are given in the second column of Table 2. The blue dashed lines represent the time evolution of the spectrum in selected numerical steps, which builds and forms the overall SED, represented by the solid blue line after one dynamical time scale. The synchrotron component peaking between 1-10 eV is up-scattered by the relativistic electrons to produce the HE and VHE component. In contrast to HM scenario, the magnetic field in the emitting region is $B = 0.57$G significantly lower, therefore, electrons with Lorentz factor $\gamma_{e,\min} = 10^3$ are not substantially cooled within one dynamical time scale. For this hybrid model, protons do not directly contribute to the observed SED, instead the contribution of secondary electron-positrons dominates in the X-ray band, which puts constraints on the proton luminosity and as a consequence the neutrino luminosity. For example, if one increases by 1.5 times the proton luminosity, the model would overshoot the X-ray data, as shown by the dotted-dashed blue line in panel b) of Figure 1.

Further the results of the SED modeling obtained during the historical neutrino flare of TXS 0506+056 is presented. Unfortunately, when 13 ± 5 neutrinos were observed between October 2014 and March 2015,[5] the multiwavelength coverage is scarce. Yet, the flux upper limit of $F < 9.12 \times 10^{-12}$ erg cm^{-2} s^{-1} derived from Swift BAT observations[38] introduces substantial difficulties for a one-zone modeling. Indeed, the predicted number of neutrino events cannot be matched to the IceCube observations[38] and[39] have shown that only few neutrino events could be detected under different optimistic considerations for the emitting region and for the target photon field (internal or external to the jet). Matching together the observed multiwavelength data and the neutrino data seems to require two zone models with more free parameters.[38,39]

To accommodate the X-ray limit and try to account for the neutrino flux during this flare, two different assumptions on the proton distribution function are made. On the one hand, radiation from the secondaries can be constrained to be dominant in the MeV band, in which there are no observational constraint. On the other hand, radiation from the secondaries could be dominant in the GeV band and produce the second HE hump. The SEDs of these two models are respectively shown in panels c) and d) of Figure 1, with data from.[39] Those two models lead to two very different sets of parameters for the emitting region, see column 3 and 4 of Table 2. The first model requires a large radius $R' = 10^{17}$cm and a slowly moving jet with Doppler factor $\delta = 10$, while the second model necessitates those parameters to be $R' = 10^{15}$cm and $\delta = 15$. The required magnetic field also significantly differs between these two models with $B = 35$G for the first model, to be compared to $B = 0.65$G for the second one. The first model tends to reproduce the neutrino flux, albeit produces the peak at lower energies. The second model puts the neutrino peak at larger energy, but is not able to reproduce the observed neutrino number. In both interpretations, it is clear that the upper limit in the X-ray band imposes strong constraints on the photon spectrum, which in turn limits the proton content in the jet. Considering larger proton luminosity would lead to over-estimate both the observed γ-ray flux and the X-ray upper limit.

Table 2. Parameter sets used for modeling the SEDs of TXS 0506+056, observed in 2017 and during the neutrino flare in 2014-2015. The electon, proton and magnetic luminosities are also given.

	TXS 0506+056: 2017		TXS 0506+056: 2014-2015	
	Hadronic	Lepto-hadronic	Hadronic	Lepto-hadronic
δ	20	20	15	10
$R/10^{15}$ cm	2.5	10	1	100
$B[G]$	80	0.57	35	0.65
$\gamma_{e,\min}$	100	1000	2×10^2	9×10^3
$\gamma_{e,\text{cut}}$	2.4×10^3	4.5×10^4	10^4	$=\gamma_{e,\max}$
$\gamma_{e,\max}$	3×10^4	6×10^4	8×10^4	8×10^4
α_e	2.1	2.0	2.0	2.0
$\alpha_p = \alpha_e$	2.1	2.0	2.0	2.0
$\gamma_{p,\min}$	1	1	1	1
$\gamma_{p,\max}$	10^9	10^6	2×10^8	1.2×10^5
L_e (erg s^{-1})	2.2×10^{44}	9.3×10^{44}	2.8×10^{44}	5.3×10^{44}
L_B (erg s^{-1})	6.0×10^{46}	4.9×10^{43}	10^{45}	1.6×10^{45}
L_p (erg s^{-1})	2.1×10^{47}	2.6×10^{50}	3.4×10^{47}	4.9×10^{52}

From the jet energetic perspective, the total jet luminosity in the case of TXS 0506+056, for the proton synchrotron model, shown on panel a) of Figure 1, is $L_{\text{tot}} = L_p + L_e + L_B = 2.7 \times 10^{47}$ erg s^{-1}, which exceeds by one order of magnitude the Eddington luminosity of $\simeq 4 \times 10^{46}$erg s^{-1} for a black hole mass of 3×10^8 $M_\odot$, as estimated for TXS 0506+056 using the absolute R-band magnitude.[40] This is in agreement with previous studies suggesting that in the case of proton synchrotron models or models producing a high neutrino flux, the required jet luminosity exceeds that of the Eddington limit.[41] Within the hybrid model, matching the neutrino flux with the neutrino event of TXS 0506+056, displayed on panel b) of Figure 1, requires the jet luminosity to be $\sim 10^{50}$ erg s^{-1}, significantly exceeding that of the Eddington luminosity. Although the Eddington luminosity is not a strict limit and super-Eddington luminosities were previously reported,[42] this value is extremely large. On the other hand, for the neutrino flare in 2014-2015, when assuming that

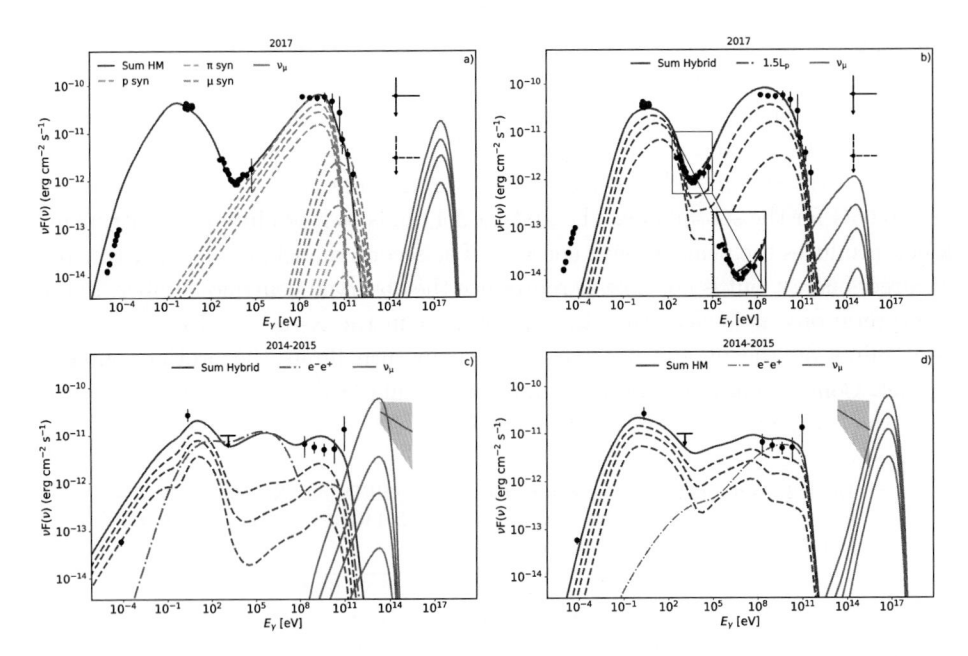

Fig. 1. The multiwavelength SED of TXS 0506+056 during the neutrino emission in 2017 (upper panels) and during the neutrino flare in 2014-2015 (lower panels) modeled within the hadronic and lepto-hadronic hybrid scenarios. The solid blue line in all plots represents the sum of all components which has been corrected for EBL absorption considering the model of.[43]

the emission from the secondary pairs solely dominates in the X-ray and γ-ray bands, an unrealistically high luminosity of $\sim 10^{52}$ erg s^{-1} is obtained. Indeed, matching the high neutrino flux with the large radius (10^{17} cm) imposed by the modeling in this case, requires a large protons density, hence the too large proton luminosity. In the alternative interpretation, when the emission from the secondary pairs dominates in the GeV band, a modest luminosity of 3.4×10^{47} erg s^{-1} is estimated.

The expected numbers of neutrinos during the 6 months flare of TXS 0506+056 are 0.43 and 0.23 for the hadronic and hybrid scenarios, respectively. During the 2014-2015 neutrino flare, our most optimistic models predict 3.0-3.3 neutrinos for a 6 months exposure time (note however that the IceCube observational window was ~ 110 days). Our results are in agreement with previous estimations for TXS 0506+056 and confirm that within a one-zone scenarios, 13 ± 5 events from the direction of TXS 0506+056 cannot be explained.[38,39]

3HSP J095507.9+355101: It is the first time that the jet of an extreme blazar is associated with a neutrino event,[30] straightening the assumption that the jets of this blazar type are potential sites for cosmic rays and even ultra-high energy cosmic ray acceleration.[44]

The SED of 3HSP J095507.9+355101 is shown in Figure 2, where the multiwavelength data are from.[45] Optical, UV and X-ray data were acquired on the 8th, 10th and 11th of January. However, since the data taken on the 8th and 11th of January seem to have the same flux and spectral shape,[46] we only model the data from the 8th. The lack of available multiwavelength data does not allow to constrain the low and high energy peaks, which hardens the estimation of the model free parameters. A hint of a 20 − 30 minutes variability has been found in the NICER and NuSTAR data, but only at the ∼ 3.5 σ level.[47] Therefore, the compactness of the emitting region cannot be constrained. In order to keep the generality, the SED of 3HSP J095507.9+355101 is modeled for two different parameter configurations. For the HM, we consider $R' = 3 \times 10^{14}$ cm and $\delta = 15$, while for the hybrid model we assume $R' \simeq 10^{16}$ cm and $\delta = 30$. The all estimated parameters are shown in Table 3.

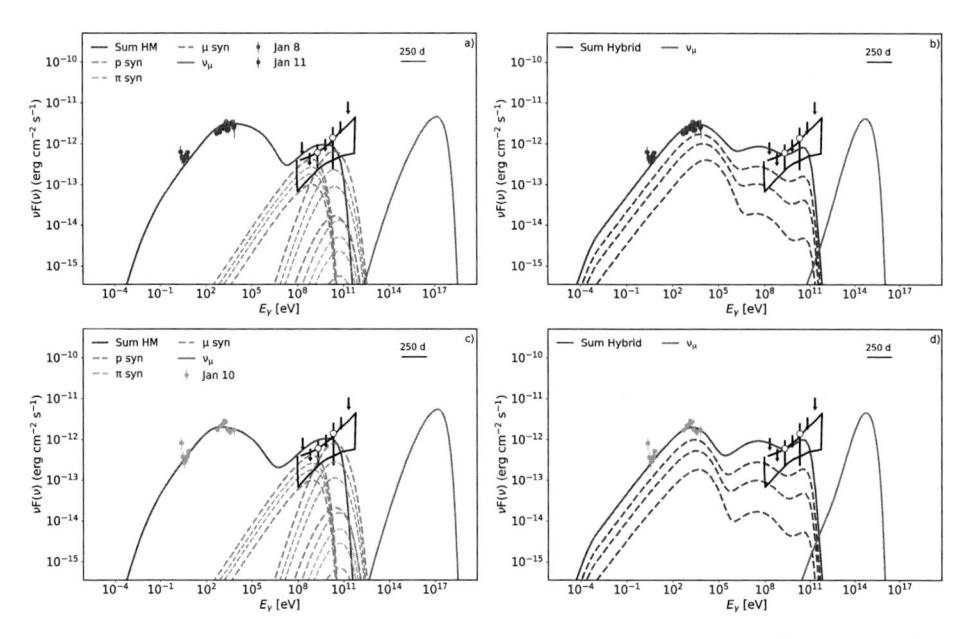

Fig. 2. The multiwavelength SEDs of 3HSP J095507.9+355101 on the the 8th and the 11th of January (panels a) and b) on the top raw) and on the 10th of January (panels c) and d) on the bottom raw). The data are taken from.[45,46] The observed spectrum including all processes is shown by the solid blue line. All models (solid blue lines) have been corrected for EBL absorption considering the model of.[43]

The estimated muon neutrino rate for 3HSP J095507.9+355101, is within $6 \times 10^{-4} - 4.8 \times 10^{-3}$ per day. This implies that under this rate of emission, the expected number of neutrinos to be detected by IceCube in a time corresponding to the duration of the flare is very low. Such low neutrino estimation was obtained also by the authors of,[46] where they concluded that in the most promising scenarios, there is a ∼ 1% to ∼ 3% to observe one neutrino over the time characteristic of the long-term emission of 3HSP J095507.9+355101 (years).

3C 279: The broadband emission from the powerful FSRQs 3C 279 at redshift $z = 0.536$ has characterized by high amplitude variability almost in all energy bands e.g., order of minutes,[48] and in particular in the HE γ-ray band, which present the fastest variability. On the 16th of June 2015, Fermi LAT observations showed that 3C 279 was in an exceptionally bright state. The flux increased up to 3.6×10^{-5} photon cm^{-2} s^{-1} with a flux doubling time on the order of 5 minutes.[49] IceCube performed a time-dependent neutrino signal search correlated with this γ-ray flare but no evidence for a signal was found.[50] We apply *SOPRANO* to model the SED of 3C 279 during its flare in the framework of the HM, when the second peak dominates by proton synchrotron emission. The parameters of our modeling are given in Table 3. Figure 3 shows the multiwavelength SED of 3C 279 taken from,[51] alongside with the results of our modeling. During the brightening, the X-ray emission of the source appears with a hard photon index < 1.50, smoothly connecting with the INTEGRAL data, described by a power-law with index 1.08.[51] In the HE γ-ray band, the spectrum presents a power-law with photon index 2.21 with a turn over.[52] We make the hypothesis that the HE component is produced from a single mechanism. In our modeling it is interpreted as proton synchrotron emission, represented by the red dashed lines in Figure 3. This interpretation requires that protons are accelerated up to $\gamma_{p,\text{max}} = 2.1 \times 10^8$, see Table 3.

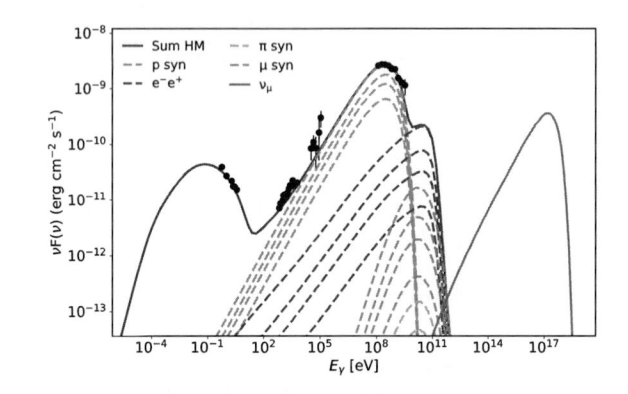

Fig. 3. The multiwavelength SED of 3C 279 during the exceptional flaring activity in 2015. The contribution of different particle emission is shown by dashed lines whereas the thick solid line represents the observed spectrum, corrected for EBL absorption considering the model of.[43]

The compactness of the emitting region implies a high efficiency for photo-pion and photo-pair interactions, which inject energetic secondary pairs. The contribution of these pairs dominates above ∼ 10 GeV and peak at ∼ 100 GeV, as can be seen by the blue dashed line in Figure 3. The synchrotron radiation of the primary electrons peaks at ∼ 0.1 eV and its HE tail accounts for the observed optical/UV data. These data constrain the cut-off energy to be relatively low, $\gamma_{e,\text{cut}} = 2.4 \times 10^2$, otherwise, for $B = 70$ G and $\delta = 55$, the synchrotron radiation would overshoot the observed flux in optical and UV bands. A similar hadronic modeling for this flare is presented in[51] and in.[53] The neutrino rate for the considered flaring period is as high as 0.15 per day is estimated. However, for a relatively short period of the source activity, from minutes to one day, no neutrino events in the IceCube detector are expected, in agreement with.[50]

Table 3. Parameters used to model the multiwavelength SEDs of 3HSP J095507.9+355101 and 3C 279. The electron, proton and magnetic luminosity is also displayed.

	3HSP J095507.9+355101				3C 279
	January 8th		January 10th		
	Hadronic	Lepto-hadronic	Hadronic	Lepto-hadronic	Hadronic
δ	15	30	15	30	55
$R/10^{15}$ cm	0.3	10	0.3	10	0.32
$B[G]$	45	0.11	45	0.08	70
$\gamma_{e,min}$	10^4	100	5×10^3	100	1
$\gamma_{e,cut}$	6×10^5	2×10^6	2×10^5	7×10^5	2.4×10^2
$\gamma_{e,max}$	9×10^5	6×10^6	5×10^5	6×10^6	4×10^2
α_e	1.9	2.0	1.9	2	1.8
$\alpha_p = \alpha_e$	1.9	2.0	1.9	2	1.8
$\gamma_{p,min}$	1	1	1	1	1
$\gamma_{p,max}$	9×10^8	10^6	9×10^8	10^6	2.1×10^8
L_e (erg s^{-1})	1.2×10^{44}	1.6×10^{44}	7.3×10^{43}	2.1×10^{44}	1.9×10^{44}
L_B (erg s^{-1})	1.5×10^{44}	4.1×10^{42}	1.5×10^{44}	2.2×10^{42}	5.7×10^{45}
L_p (erg s^{-1})	3.2×10^{46}	8.0×10^{50}	3.2×10^{46}	1.8×10^{51}	1.3×10^{49}

6. Conclusion

We have presented a new kinetic model of photo-hadronic and leptonic interactions aiming at studying the emission of optically thin (for Compton scattering) scenarios of relativistic sources (e.g., AGNs and GRBs). Our numerical solution of the kinetic equations for protons, neutrons, pions, muons, neutrinos, pairs, and photons conserves the total energy of the system as well as the number of particles where required. The code takes as an input the spectral injection rate of the particles (e.g., electrons and/or protons), and compute the time evolution of all relevant particles, including the secondaries, as they interact and cool, allowing the computation of the broadband emission spectrum at any given period. In this paper, we have applied *SOPRANO* to model the SEDs of three blazars, two of which are potentially associated to neutrino emission observed by IceCube. We have assumed different models for the production of the HE component and compute in all cases the expected number of muon neutrinos. The time-dependent nature of the code allowed to follow the evolution of all particles in one dynamical time scale and then assess the proton content in the jet by using the radiative spectrum of either secondaries or initial particles. This is necessary for the estimation of the expected number of neutrinos. Such time-dependent treatment of the particle evolution enabled us to constrain different scenarios of neutrino production by using the limits imposed by the observations in different bands.

References

1. IceCube Collaboration, Evidence for High-Energy Extraterrestrial Neutrinos at the IceCube Detector, *Science* **342**, p. 1242856 (November 2013).
2. M. G. Aartsen, et al., First Observation of PeV-Energy Neutrinos with IceCube, *Physical Review Letters* **111**, p. 021103 (July 2013).
3. M. G. Aartsen, et al., Characteristics of the Diffuse Astrophysical Electron and Tau Neutrino Flux with Six Years of IceCube High Energy Cascade Data, *Phys. Rev. Lett.* **125**, p. 121104 (Sep 2020).
4. IceCube Collaboration, et al., Multimessenger observations of a flaring blazar coincident with high-energy neutrino IceCube-170922A, *Science* **361**, p. eaat1378 (July 2018).
5. IceCube Collaboration, et al., Neutrino emission from the direction of the blazar TXS 0506+056 prior to the IceCube-170922A alert, *Science* **361**, 147 (July 2018).
6. M. C. Begelman, et al., Consequences of relativistic proton injection in active galactic nuclei, *The Astrophysical Journal* **362**, 38 (October 1990).
7. M. Sikora, et al., Radiation drag in relativistic active galactic nucleus jets, *Monthly Notices of the RAS* **280**, 781 (June 1996).
8. A. M. Atoyan and C. D. Dermer, Neutral Beams from Blazar Jets, *The Astrophysical Journal* **586**, 79 (Mar 2003).
9. MAGIC Collaboration, et al., Teraelectronvolt emission from the γ-ray burst GRB 190114C, *Nature* **575**, 455 (November 2019).
10. J. Kakuwa, et al., Prospects for detecting gamma-ray bursts at very high energies with the Cherenkov Telescope Array, *Monthly Notices of the RAS* **425**, 514 (September 2012).
11. Gilmore Rudy C., et al., IACT observations of gamma-ray bursts: prospects for the Cherenkov Telescope Array, *Experimental Astronomy* **35**, 413 (2013).
12. The IceCube-Gen2 Collaboration, et al., IceCube-Gen2: The Window to the Extreme Universe, *arXiv e-prints*, p. arXiv:2008.04323 (August 2020).
13. M. Agostini, et al., The Pacific Ocean Neutrino Experiment, *Nature Astronomy* **4**, 913 (September 2020).
14. S. Adrián-Martínez, et al., Letter of intent for KM3NeT 2.0, *Journal of Physics G Nuclear Physics* **43**, p. 084001 (August 2016).
15. C. Baikal-GVD, et al., Neutrino telescope in Lake Baikal: Present and Future, in *36th International Cosmic Ray Conference (ICRC2019)*, International Cosmic Ray Conference Vol. 36July 2019.
16. M. G. Aartsen, et al., Time-Integrated Neutrino Source Searches with 10 Years of IceCube Data, *Physical Review Letters* **124**, p. 051103 (February 2020).
17. S. Kelner and F. Aharonian, Energy spectra of gamma rays, electrons, and neutrinos produced at interactions of relativistic protons with low energy radiation, *Physical Review D* **78**, p. 034013 (2008).
18. K. Asano and S. Inoue, Prompt GeV-TeV Emission of Gamma-Ray Bursts Due to High-Energy Protons, Muons, and Electron-Positron Pairs, *The Astrophysical Journal* **671**, 645 (December 2007).
19. M. Böttcher, et al., Leptonic and Hadronic Modeling of Fermi-detected Blazars, *The Astrophysical Journal* **768**, p. 54 (May 2013).
20. M. Cerruti, et al., A hadronic origin for ultra-high-frequency-peaked BL Lac objects, *Monthly Notices of the RAS* **448**, 910 (March 2015).
21. A. Zech, et al., Expected signatures from hadronic emission processes in the TeV spectra of BL Lacertae objects, *Astronomy and Astrophysics* **602**, p. A25 (June 2017).

22. Y. G. Zheng, et al., A time-dependent particle acceleration and emission model: understanding particle spectral evolution and blazar flares, *Monthly Notices of the RAS* **499**, 1188 (October 2020).
23. A. Mastichiadis and J. G. Kirk, Self-consistent particle acceleration in active galactic nuclei., *Astronomy and Astrophysics* **295**, p. 613 (March 1995).
24. A. Pe'er and E. Waxman, Time-dependent Numerical Model for the Emission of Radiation from Relativistic Plasma, *The Astrophysical Journal* **628**, 857 (August 2005).
25. S. Dimitrakoudis, et al., The time-dependent one-zone hadronic model. First principles, *Astronomy and Astrophysics* **546**, p. A120 (October 2012).
26. C. Diltz, et al., Time Dependent Hadronic Modeling of Flat Spectrum Radio Quasars, *The Astrophysical Journal* **802**, p. 133 (April 2015).
27. S. Gao, et al., On the Direct Correlation between Gamma-Rays and PeV Neutrinos from Blazars, *The Astrophysical Journal* **843**, p. 109 (July 2017).
28. D. Kantzas, et al., A new lepto-hadronic model applied to the first simultaneous multiwavelength data set for Cygnus X-1, *Monthly Notices of the RAS* (October 2020).
29. S. Gasparyan, et al., Time-dependent lepto-hadronic modeling of the emission from blazar jets with SOPRANO: the case of TXS 0506+056, 3HSP J095507.9+355101 and 3C 279, *arXiv e-prints*, p. arXiv:2110.01549 (October 2021).
30. IceCube Collaboration, IceCube-200107A: IceCube observation of a high-energy neutrino candidate event, *GRB Coordinates Network* **26655**, p. 1 (January 2020).
31. M. Cerruti, et al., Leptohadronic single-zone models for the electromagnetic and neutrino emission of TXS 0506+056, *Monthly Notices of the RAS* **483**, L12 (February 2019).
32. S. Gao, et al., Modelling the coincident observation of a high-energy neutrino and a bright blazar flare, *Nature Astronomy* **3**, 88 (January 2019).
33. M. Petropoulou and A. Mastichiadis, Bethe-Heitler emission in BL Lacs: Filling the gap between X-rays and γ-rays, *Monthly Notices of the RAS* **447**, 36 (February 2015).
34. M. G. Aartsen, et al., Search for steady point-like sources in the astrophysical muon neutrino flux with 8 years of IceCube data, *European Physical Journal C* **79**, p. 234 (March 2019).
35. G. Fantini, et al., The formalism of neutrino oscillations: an introduction, *arXiv e-prints*, p. arXiv:1802.05781 (February 2018).
36. A. Keivani, et al., A Multimessenger Picture of the Flaring Blazar TXS 0506+056: Implications for High-energy Neutrino Emission and Cosmic-Ray Acceleration, *The Astrophysical Journal* **864**, p. 84 (September 2018).
37. R. Blandford and D. Eichler, Particle acceleration at astrophysical shocks: A theory of cosmic ray origin, *Physics Reports* **154**, 1 (October 1987).
38. A. Reimer, et al., Cascading Constraints from Neutrino-emitting Blazars: The Case of TXS 0506+056, *The Astrophysical Journal* **881**, p. 46 (August 2019).
39. X. Rodrigues, et al., Leptohadronic Blazar Models Applied to the 2014-2015 Flare of TXS 0506+056, *Astrophysical Journal, Letters* **874**, p. L29 (April 2019).
40. P. Padovani, et al., TXS 0506+056, the first cosmic neutrino source, is not a BL Lac, *Monthly Notices of the RAS* **484**, L104 (March 2019).
41. R. Xue, et al., On the Minimum Jet Power of TeV BL Lac Objects in the p-γ Model, *The Astrophysical Journal* **871**, p. 81 (January 2019).
42. Y.-F. Jiang, et al., Super-Eddington Accretion Disks around Supermassive Black Holes, *The Astrophysical Journal* **880**, p. 67 (August 2019).
43. A. Domínguez, et al., Extragalactic background light inferred from AEGIS galaxy-SED-type fractions, *Monthly Notices of the RAS* **410**, 2556 (February 2011).

44. P. Padovani, et al., Extreme blazars as counterparts of IceCube astrophysical neutrinos, *Monthly Notices of the RAS* **457**, 3582 (April 2016).
45. P. Giommi, et al., 3HSP J095507.9+355101: A flaring extreme blazar coincident in space and time with IceCube-200107A, *Astronomy and Astrophysics* **640**, p. L4 (August 2020).
46. M. Petropoulou, et al., Comprehensive Multimessenger Modeling of the Extreme Blazar 3HSP J095507.9+355101 and Predictions for IceCube, *The Astrophysical Journal* **899**, p. 113 (August 2020).
47. V. S. Paliya, et al., Multifrequency Observations of the Candidate Neutrino-emitting Blazar BZB J0955+3551, *The Astrophysical Journal* **902**, p. 29 (October 2020).
48. J. Aleksić, et al., MAGIC observations and multifrequency properties of the flat spectrum radio quasar 3C 279 in 2011, *Astronomy and Astrophysics* **567**, p. A41 (July 2014).
49. M. Ackermann, et al., Minute-timescale >100 MeV γ-Ray Variability during the Giant Outburst of Quasar 3C 279 Observed by Fermi-LAT in 2015 June, *Astrophysical Journal, Letters* **824**, p. L20 (June 2016).
50. R. Abbasi, et al., A Search for Time-dependent Astrophysical Neutrino Emission with IceCube Data from 2012 to 2017, *The Astrophysical Journal* **911**, p. 67 (April 2021).
51. E. Bottacini, et al., 3C 279 in Outburst in 2015 June: A Broadband SED Study Based on the INTEGRAL Detection, *The Astrophysical Journal* **832**, p. 17 (November 2016).
52. V. S. Paliya, Fermi-Large Area Telescope Observations of the Exceptional Gamma-Ray Flare from 3C 279 in 2015 June, *Astrophysical Journal, Letters* **808**, p. L48 (August 2015).
53. M. Petropoulou, et al., A hadronic minute-scale GeV flare from quasar 3C 279?, *Monthly Notices of the RAS* **467**, L16 (May 2017).

Multiwavelength study of high-redshift blazars

G. Harutyunyan and D. Israyelyan

ICRANet Armenia, Marshall Baghramian Avenue 24a, Yerevan 0019, Republic of Armenia

High-redshift blazars are among the most powerful objects in the Universe. The spectral and temporal properties of 33 distant blazars ($z > 2.5$) detected in the high-energy γ-ray band are discussed using *Fermi*-LAT and *Swift* Ultraviolet and Optical Telescope/X-ray Telescope (UVOT/XRT) data accumulated during 2008-2018. The properties of the jets of these blazar obtained by modeling the multiwavelength spectral energy distributions within a one-zone leptonic scenario are presented and discussed.

Keywords: Galaxies; active –Gamma rays; galaxies–radiation mechanisms; non-thermal.

1. Introduction

Blazars are a type of active galactic nuclei(AGN) which have relativistic jet that is directed towards to the Earth.[1] Blazars characteristic features are high degree of polarization, short and strong non-thermal emission variations both in time and amplitude. Based on the absence or presence of emission lines in their optical spectra blazars are divided in two large classes, namely FSRQs and BL Lacs.For FSRQs the equivalent width of emission line is >5 Å meanwhile BL Lacs have weak emission lines <5 Å.[1]

The spectral energy distribution (SED) of blazars has a double-peaked structure. Low energy peak, from radio to X-ray is due to synchrotron radiation of relativistic electrons. Instead, the high energy peak is most probably due to the Inverse Compton scattering of either synchrotron photons(Synchrotron-Self Compton(SSC)[2-4]) or photons field external to the jet (external Inverse Compton).[5-7] The external target fields can be photons of the accretion disc, broad-line region and dusty torus.

The dominant class of extragalactic γ-ray sources are blazars. During its ten year survey, Fermi-LAT has observed $\sim$ 5000 sources in γ-ray band from which more than 2863 are AGNs detected above the 5σ.[8] Only 33(1.18%) out of 2863 are distant blazars $z > 2.5$ (Table 1) from which 26 are FSRQs, 2 are BL Lacs and 5 are blazar candidate sources. Studying of these sources can shed light on some questions such as, cosmological evolution of blazars and black holes, evolution of relativistic jets across different cosmic epochs, accretion disc-jet connection, extragalactic Background Light density limit, etc.[9]

In this paper were investigated multiwavelength emissions from high red shift blazars($z > 2.5$) using data accumulated by *Fermi*-LAT and Swift telescopes.

Table 1. List of γ-ray emitting blazars at $z > 2.5$. The results of observation of distant blazars from August 4, 2008, to August 4, 2018 by Fermi-LAT are presented in the right part of the table.

Object	4FGL name	Class	RA	Dec	F_γ [1]	Photon index	TS	E_{max} [2]	Probability	z
GB 1508+5714	J1510.1+5702	FSRQ	227.54	57.04	0.76 ± 0.15	2.95 ± 0.15	63.50	8.76	0.8268	4.31
PKS 1351-018	J1354.3-0206	FSRQ	208.50	-2.11	1.11 ± 0.15	2.69 ± 0.09	98.49	1.30	0.7010	3.72
MG3 J163554+3629	J1635.6+3628	BCU	248.92	36.48	1.46 ± 0.27	2.84 ± 0.12	123.95	3.74	0.8413	3.65
NVSS J121915+365718	J1219.0+3653	BCU	184.77	36.89	0.22 ± 0.08	2.20 ± 0.14	40.56	2.67	0.8273	3.53
PKS 0335-122	J0337.8-1157	FSRQ	54.47	-11.96	0.72 ± 0.16	2.69 ± 0.13	49.47	10.19	0.9245	3.44
PKS 0537-286	J0539.9-2839	FSRQ	84.99	-28.66	4.38 ± 0.18	2.72 ± 0.03	1694.80	7.60	0.9619	3.10
TXS 0800+618	J0805.4+6147	FSRQ	121.36	61.80	2.23 ± 0.14	2.82 ± 0.05	475.17	4.83	0.8441	3.03
S4 1427+543	J1428.9+5406	FSRQ	217.23	54.11	0.59 ± 0.15	2.62 ± 0.14	67.10	10.26	0.7831	3.01
GB6 J0733+0456	J0733.8+0455	FSRQ	113.47	4.93	1.14 ± 0.15	2.39 ± 0.07	197.26	17.65	0.9854	3.01
B2 0743+25	J0746.4+2546	FSRQ	116.60	25.77	2.06 ± 0.19	2.87 ± 0.07	280.99	1.52	0.7449	2.99
PKS 0347-211	J0349.8-2103	FSRQ	57.47	-21.06	3.25 ± 0.15	2.47 ± 0.03	1372.81	5.83	0.9690	2.94
S4 1124+57	J1127.4+5648	FSRQ	171.87	56.80	0.96 ± 0.13	2.75 ± 0.09	147.30	7.09	0.8495	2.89
MRSS 291-081526	J2313.9-4501	BCU	348.49	-45.02	0.89 ± 0.20	2.80 ± 0.13	81.12	2.25	0.7550	2.88
PKS 0438-43	J0440.3-4333	FSRQ	70.09	-43.55	2.24 ± 0.20	2.60 ± 0.05	574.84	2.00	0.9225	2.85
S4 2015+65	J2015.4+6556	FSRQ	303.86	65.95	0.39 ± 0.15	2.37 ± 0.15	23.77	4.34	0.7257	2.84
87GB 214302.1+095227	J2145.5+1006	BL Lac	326.38	10.12	0.048 ± 0.014	1.71 ± 0.19	40.46	67.15	0.9874	2.83
MG2 J174803+3403	J1748.0+3403	FSRQ	267.01	34.06	0.97 ± 0.13	2.31 ± 0.07	284.21	31.63	0.9934	2.76
PKS 0834-20	J0836.5-2026	FSRQ	129.13	-20.45	1.93 ± 0.19	2.94 ± 0.08	171.15	1.15	0.5796	2.75
TXS 0222+185	J0224.9+1843	FSRQ	36.24	18.72	1.72 ± 0.22	3.05 ± 0.12	101.08	2.59	0.5327	2.69
OD 166	J0242.3+1102	FSRQ	40.59	11.05	1.94 ± 0.20	2.59 ± 0.06	252.83	6.91	0.8651	2.68
CRATES J233930+024420	J2339.6+0242	BCU	354.90	2.71	1.00 ± 0.21	2.58 ± 0.11	94.50	6.17	0.8537	2.66
TXS 0907+230	J0910.6+2247	FSRQ	137.67	22.80	1.17 ± 0.14	2.37 ± 0.06	262.58	5.38	0.9578	2.66
PMN J1441-1523	J1441.6-1522	FSRQ	220.41	-15.38	0.65 ± 0.23	2.32 ± 0.13	72.02	11.77	0.9535	2.64
CRATES J105433+392803	J1054.2+3926	BCU	163.56	39.44	0.27 ± 0.09	2.30 ± 0.16	34.05	4.79	0.9000	2.63
MG1 J154930+1708	J1549.6+1710	BL Lac	237.41	17.18	0.17 ± 0.08	2.01 ± 0.16	44.75	17.03	0.9759	2.62
TXS 1448+093	J1450.4+0910	FSRQ	222.62	9.18	0.76 ± 0.13	2.35 ± 0.08	130.24	10.58	0.9599	2.61
PMN J0226+0937	J0226.5+0938	FSRQ	36.63	9.63	0.48 ± 0.12	2.18 ± 0.10	96.49	56.42	0.9523	2.61
PKS 0451-28	J0453.1-2806	FSRQ	73.29	-28.11	5.83 ± 0.17	2.66 ± 0.02	3118.20	10.77	0.9815	2.56
B3 0908+416B	J0912.2+4127	FSRQ	138.06	41.46	1.51 ± 0.14	2.42 ± 0.05	539.57	12.10	0.9903	2.56
TXS 1616+517	J1618.0+5139	FSRQ	244.52	51.67	0.69 ± 0.13	2.68 ± 0.12	72.65	12.38	0.8408	2.56
B3 1624+414	J1625.7+4134	FSRQ	246.45	41.57	1.38 ± 0.14	2.49 ± 0.06	395.12	9.69	0.9787	2.55
B3 1343+451	J1345.5+4453c	FSRQ	206.39	44.88	15.01 ± 0.16	2.25 ± 0.008	34652.79	24.25	0.9994	2.53
PKS 2107-105	J2110.2-1021c	FSRQ	317.56	-10.36	0.88 ± 0.18	2.66 ± 0.13	53.29	5.46	0.6500	2.50

Note: [1] Integrated γ-ray flux in units of ×10^{-8} photon cm^{-2} s^{-1}.
Note: [2] Photon energy in GeV.

Table 2. Spectral parameters of the sources modeled with logparabola.

Object	F_γ [1]	α	β
PKS 1351-018	$(6.86 \pm 1.66) \times 10^{-9}$	2.20 ± 0.23	0.63 ± 0.23
PKS 0537-286	$(4.15 \pm 0.20) \times 10^{-8}$	2.66 ± 0.04	0.10 ± 0.03
TXS 0800+618	$(2.04 \pm 0.16) \times 10^{-8}$	2.67 ± 0.08	0.17 ± 0.06
B2 0743+25	$(1.72 \pm 0.23) \times 10^{-8}$	2.53 ± 0.14	0.40 ± 0.13
PKS 0347-211	$(2.69 \pm 0.17) \times 10^{-8}$	2.32 ± 0.05	0.19 ± 0.03
PKS 0438-43	$(1.15 \pm 0.23) \times 10^{-8}$	2.35 ± 0.12	0.48 ± 0.11
S4 2015+65	$(1.66 \pm 1.00) \times 10^{-9}$	2.42 ± 0.35	0.42 ± 0.31
PKS 0834-20	$(1.76 \pm 0.20) \times 10^{-8}$	2.62 ± 0.16	0.29 ± 0.13
OD 166	$(1.45 \pm 0.24) \times 10^{-8}$	2.43 ± 0.11	0.24 ± 0.08
TXS 0907+230	$(8.68 \pm 1.77) \times 10^{-8}$	2.28 ± 0.09	0.12 ± 0.06
PKS 0451-28	$(5.56 \pm 0.18) \times 10^{-8}$	2.56 ± 0.04	0.09 ± 0.02
B3 1343+451	$(1.41 \pm 0.02) \times 10^{-7}$	2.18 ± 0.01	0.07 ± 0.006

Note: [1] Integrated γ-ray flux in units of photon cm^{-2} s^{-1}.

2. Fermi LAT analysis

To investigate considered sources in the γ-ray band the data accumulated by *Fermi*-LAT were used. In the current paper, the 100 MeV to 500 GeV data from the region with 12° radius were downloaded and analysed. The data had been accumulated during ten years since launch of *Fermi*-LAT (4 August 2008 to 4 August 2018). *gtselect* and *gtmktime* tools were applied to select good time intervals when data were valid. The maximum zenith angle was 90° to avoid γ-rays which are due to Earth's limb. Events were binned into 16.9×16.9 ROI (region of interest) and 37 equal logarithmically spaced energy bins using *gtbin* tool. The model file of each source includes all the 4FGL sources falling within the ROI+5° region and it was generated using 4FGL-DR2 catalog which is the second release of 4FGL (based on ten years operation). For galactic and extragalactic diffuse emission components *gll_iem_v07* and *iso_P8R3_SOURCE_V2_v1* models were used. With the *gtlike* tool spectral analysis of considered sources using binned maximum likelihood method was performed. The spectral parameters of sources located within the ROI are set to free. Detection significance of the sources estimated using TS (Test Statistic)[10] which is defined as $TS = 2 \times (\log L_1 - \log L_0)$ where L_1 is the likelihood of the data with a point source at the given position and L_0 without the source. For each source the same γ-ray spectral model as in 4FGL catalog was used and additionally analysis was performed using power-law spectral model. SEDs of the sources were created by running *gtlike* for smaller energy intervals equal in logarithmic space. The γ-ray light curves were computed with *gtlike* tool applying unbinned likelihood analysis method which is suitable for shorter periods. The spectra of the considered source was modeled using a power-law which provide good results for small interval. The normalization and photon index of the chosen sources are free to vary except photon index of all sources which are lying within the ROI. For the fitting the events with energy 0.1-300 GeV were considered. To investigate γ-ray variability initially we calculated 30 day bins light curves for all the sources. There are statistically significant ($\geq 5\sigma$) sources in the sample which have flaring periods and for that periods the light curves with small bins such as day or week were calculated. For some powerful sources such as B3 1343+451, PKS 0537-286, PKS 0347-211, PKS 0451-28 additionally the adaptively binned method has been applied to generate the light curves. In this method time intervals are adapt to provide bins with constant flux uncertainty(with 15%) above the E_0 which is a powerful method to study flux variation in γ-ray band.[11–17]

3. Swift observations

In the current paper the data from the two of the instruments onboard Swift XRT[18] and UVOT[19] have been analysed. Although the primary scientific goal of the Swift telescope is the observation of GRBs,[20] also, due to its wide frequency coverage, it is suitable for studies of blazars. Except 4 sources from the Table 1 the rest of the sources at least once have been observed by Swift, some of them (e.g. B2 0743+25, PKS 0438-43, TXS 0222+185, TXS 1448+093, PMN J0226+0937, TXS 1616+517 and PKS 2107-105) had been observed more than ten times. The Swift XRT data analysis was available for twenty-two sources, and only twenty-six sources were detected in at least one of the optical-UV Swift-UVOT filters (see Table 3).

The Swift UVOT performs measurements at 6 wavelengths: UVW2 (188 nm), UVM2 (217 nm), UVW1 (251 nm), U (345 nm), B (439 nm), and V (544 nm). The photometry analysis of the sample was performed using the standard UVOT software distributed within the HEAsoft package (v6.25) and the calibration included in the CALDB (v.20170922). The source counts were extracted from a circular region with a 5″ radius around the source, while the background one is a region with 20″ radius not being contaminated with any signal from the nearby sources. If in the observation data from the different filters exists, the same models were used, after checking background region contamination by nearby sources. For converting source counts to magnitudes *uvotsource* tool and the conversion factors provided by[21] was used. The fluxes were corrected for extinction using the reddening coefficient $E(B-V)$ from the Infrared Science Archive[a].

In the X-ray band the Swift XRT data observed both in photon counting and window timing modes were used. The data were analyzed with the standard XRT-DAS tool distributed within the HEAsoft package (v6.25), applying standard procedures, filtering, and screening criteria. As a source region was selected a circular region with a 20-pixel (47″) centered on the coordinates of each source, while as a background region was selected an annulus, with the same center as the source region and inner and outer radii of 51 (120″) and 85 pixels (200″), respectively. For fitting the 0.3-10 kev X-ray spectrum was used XSPEC12.10.1 tool, adopting

---

[a]http://irsa.ipac.caltech.edu/applications/DUST/

Table 3. Summary of Swift-UVOT observations of the considered sources. For the sources, when several observations were available, the fluxes in each band are computed from the summed images. Averaged flux in each band is in units of erg cm^{-2} s^{-1}.

Object	V	B	U	W1	M2	W2
PKS 1351-108	–	–	$(4.54 \pm 2.53) \times 10^{-14}$	–	–	–
MG3 J163554 +3629	–	–	–	–	–	–
PKS 0537-286	$(3.78 \pm 5.86) \times 10^{-15}$	$(4.53 \pm 1.56) \times 10^{-14}$	$(6.93 \pm 2.72) \times 10^{-14}$	$(4.54 \pm 2.54) \times 10^{-14}$	$(6.84 \pm 0.75) \times 10^{-14}$	$(7.50 \pm 4.11) \times 10^{-14}$
TXS 0800+618	$(7.69 \pm 0.12) \times 10^{-15}$	–	$(3.54 \pm 0.42) \times 10^{-13}$	$(5.68 \pm 0.18) \times 10^{-13}$	–	$(4.61 \pm 0.55) \times 10^{-13}$
S4 1427+543	–	–	$(2.39 \pm 0.6) \times 10^{-13}$	–	–	$(6.58 \pm 0.13) \times 10^{-14}$
GB6 J0733+0456	–	$(2.52 \pm 2.03) \times 10^{-14}$	$(2.53 \pm 0.92) \times 10^{-13}$	$(9.40 \pm 0.25) \times 10^{-15}$	$(3.88 \pm 1.4) \times 10^{-14}$	$(1.50 \pm 0.02) \times 10^{-15}$
B2 0743+25	–	$(2.97 \pm 2.55) \times 10^{-14}$	$(3.39 \pm 0.59) \times 10^{-13}$	–	$(1.12 \pm 0.22) \times 10^{-13}$	$(4.76 \pm 0.76) \times 10^{-13}$
PKS 0347-211	–	$(4.92 \pm 0.82) \times 10^{-14}$	$(2.80 \pm 0.52) \times 10^{-13}$	–	$(1.69 \pm 0.5) \times 10^{-13}$	$(2.03 \pm 1.09) \times 10^{-13}$
S4 1124+57	$(1.16 \pm 0.85) \times 10^{-14}$	–	–	–	–	–
PKS 0438-43	$(7.90 \pm 0.1) \times 10^{-15}$	–	$(3.45 \pm 0.38) \times 10^{-13}$	–	–	$(8.02 \pm 0.69) \times 10^{-13}$
S4 2015+65	$(1.63 \pm 0.02) \times 10^{-15}$	–	–	$(6.91 \pm 0.33) \times 10^{-14}$	–	–
87 GB 214302.1 +095227	$(1.01 \pm 0.48) \times 10^{-13}$	$(2.49 \pm 0.36) \times 10^{-13}$	–	$(2.78 \pm 0.72) \times 10^{-13}$	$(3.49 \pm 0.63) \times 10^{-13}$	–
MG2 J174803 +3403	$(1.92 \pm 0.32) \times 10^{-13}$	$(2.53 \pm 0.25) \times 10^{-13}$	$(4.68 \pm 0.87) \times 10^{-13}$	$(2.40 \pm 0.33) \times 10^{-13}$	$(3.73 \pm 0.61) \times 10^{-13}$	$(3.20 \pm 1.52) \times 10^{-13}$
PKS 0834-20	–	–	$(7.82 \pm 0.54) \times 10^{-13}$	$(3.84 \pm 1.72) \times 10^{-14}$	$(2.39 \pm 0.36) \times 10^{-13}$	$(7.29 \pm 0.91) \times 10^{-13}$
TXS 0222+185	–	–	$(9.36 \pm 0.89) \times 10^{-13}$	–	$(8.18 \pm 1.11) \times 10^{-13}$	$(1.12 \pm 0.21) \times 10^{-12}$
OD 166	–	–	–	–	–	$(9.19 \pm 0.36) \times 10^{-14}$
TXS 0907+230	$(9.53 \pm 4.27) \times 10^{-14}$	$(9.66 \pm 3.17) \times 10^{-14}$	$(5.28 \pm 2.66) \times 10^{-13}$	$(8.77 \pm 3.31) \times 10^{-14}$	$(2.09 \pm 1.55) \times 10^{-13}$	–
PMN J1441-1523	–	–	$(6.33 \pm 4.81) \times 10^{-14}$	–	–	–
CRATES J05433 +392803	–	–	–	$(1.90 \pm 0.88) \times 10^{-16}$	–	–
TXS 1448+093	–	–	$(6.53 \pm 2.36) \times 10^{-14}$	$(4.39 \pm 1.53) \times 10^{-13}$	–	$(1.35 \pm 0.35) \times 10^{-13}$
PMN J0226+0937	$(9.95 \pm 4.17) \times 10^{-14}$	$(5.13 \pm 0.9) \times 10^{-13}$	$(1.22 \pm 0.06) \times 10^{-12}$	–	$(1.30 \pm 0.06) \times 10^{-12}$	$(1.26 \pm 0.08) \times 10^{-12}$
PKS 0451-28	–	$(9.52 \pm 1.21) \times 10^{-14}$	–	–	–	–
B3 0908+416B	$(3.45 \pm 0.11) \times 10^{-15}$	$(3.46 \pm 2.22) \times 10^{-14}$	$(2.08 \pm 0.66) \times 10^{-13}$	$(4.94 \pm 1.95) \times 10^{-14}$	$(6.87 \pm 1.91) \times 10^{-14}$	$(2.67 \pm 1.2) \times 10^{-13}$
TXS 1616+517	–	–	$(1.96 \pm 0.27) \times 10^{-13}$	–	–	$(1.25 \pm 0.34) \times 10^{-13}$
B3 1343+451	–	$(3.12 \pm 2.77) \times 10^{-14}$	$(4.54 \pm 0.55) \times 10^{-13}$	$(7.41 \pm 0.23) \times 10^{-15}$	$(2.52 \pm 0.29) \times 10^{-13}$	$(4.47 \pm 0.65) \times 10^{-13}$
PKS 2107-105	–	–	$(1.74 \pm 0.1) \times 10^{-12}$	–	–	$(1.44 \pm 0.13) \times 10^{-12}$

an absorbed power-law model with a neutral hydrogen column density fixed to its Galactic value in each direction.

As these sources are not observed with the Swift XRT instrument too long, for most of the sources the count rates were below 20, which would prevent spectral fitting, some cases several observations of the same source were merged if they were available for increasing the photon statistics. The merging was performed using the tool available from the UK Swift Science Data Center[b].[22] Again for the fitting of the 0.3-10 keV spectrum XSPEC was used, applying both the absorbed power-law and log-parabola models. Also, light curves have been generated for the investigation of the flux variation in each band.

4. Results of data analysis

In Table 1 the results of γ-ray data analysis(γ-ray flux, index, TS, etc.) obtained after power-law fitting are presented. Detection significance(TS) for all sources was TS > 34.05, only S4 2015+65 detected with TS=23.77. Also, fit with log-parabola spectral model was performed for sources which spectral model is log-parabola in 4FGL(Table 2). Results show that fluxes estimated using log-parabola spectral model are not much different from corresponding fluxes estimated from the power-law fitting. The results presented in Table 1 are shown in Fig. 1. The γ-ray photon index versus flux is shown in he upper left panel. The photon index estimated in the 0.1-500 GeV ranges from 1.71 to 3.05 with a mean of 2.54. The flux of considered sources ranges from 4.84×10^{-10} to $1.5 \times 10^{-7} photon\ cm^{-2}s^{-1}$. The two BL Lacs, 87 GB 214302.1+095227 and MG1 J154930+1708, have the lowest flux $(4.84 \pm 1.37) \times 10^{-10} photon\ cm^{-2}s^{-1}$ and $(1.66 \pm 0.79) \times 10^{-9} photon\ cm^{-2}s^{-1}$. The γ-ray flux of BCUs included in the sample ranges from 2.19×10^{-9} to $1.46 \times 10^{-8} photon\ cm^{-2}s^{-1}$ with Γ_γ within 2.20-2.84. The FSRQs occupy the region of high flux $\geq 3.89 \times 10^{-9} photon\ cm^{-2}s^{-1}$ with a mean $2.11 \times 10^{-8} photon\ cm^{-2}s^{-1}$. The highest γ-ray flux of $1.50 \times 10^{-7} photon\ cm^{-2}s^{-1}$ was observed from the bright FSRQ B3 1343+451. The luminosity of each source was computed using the observed flux(F_γ) and photon index(Γ_γ). In upper right panel is shown the distribution of the considered sources in Γ_γ-L_γ plane. The γ-ray luminosity of the considered sources ranges from $1.01 \times 10^{47} erg\ s^{-1}$ to $5.54 \times 10^{48} erg\ s^{-1}$. The lowest luminosity of $1.01 \times 10^{47} erg\ s^{-1}$ has been estimated for CRATES J105433+392803 which is of the same order with that of the two BL Lacs included in the sample $(1.42\pm0.98) \times 10^{47} erg\ s^{-1}$ for 87GB 214302.1+095227 and $(1.24\pm0.59) \times 10^{47} erg\ s^{-1}$ for MG1 J154930+1708. The luminosity of these BL Lacs corresponds to the highest end of the luminosity distribution of BL Lacs included in the fourth catalog of AGNs detected by *Fermi*-LAT.[23] The γ-ray luminosity of PKS 0347-211, PKS 0451-28, PKS 0537-286 and B3 1343+451 $\geq 10^{48} erg\ s^{-1}$. X-ray data analysis results (Table 3) show that flux ranges from $\simeq 5 \times 10^{-14} erg\ cm^{-2}s^{-1}$ to

---

[b]https://www.swift.ac.uk/user_objects/

$\simeq 10^{-14} erg\ cm^{-2} s^{-1}$, the highest flux of $(1.19 \pm 0.04) \times 10^{-11} erg\ cm^{-2} s^{-1}$ being observed for TXS 0222+185. In the lower left panel X-ray flux versus the photon index was plotted. Because of small number of detected counts flux and photon index were estimated with large uncertainties. X-ray photon indexes estimated for these sources is <2 which means that X-ray spectra has a rising shape. The hardest X-ray spectrum detected for B3 0908+416B with $\Gamma_x = 1.01 \pm 0.46$. PKS 0451-28, TXS 0222+185, PKS 0834-20, PKS 0537-286, TXS 0800+618, B2 0743+25 and PKS 0438-43 have a comparable high X-ray flux $\geq 2.13 \times 10^{-12} erg\ cm^{-2} s^{-1}$. In the lower right panel are compared γ-ray and X-ray fluxes. Sources which are bright in γ-ray band such as PKS 0537-286 and PKS 0451-28 appear to be,also a bright sources in X-ray band.

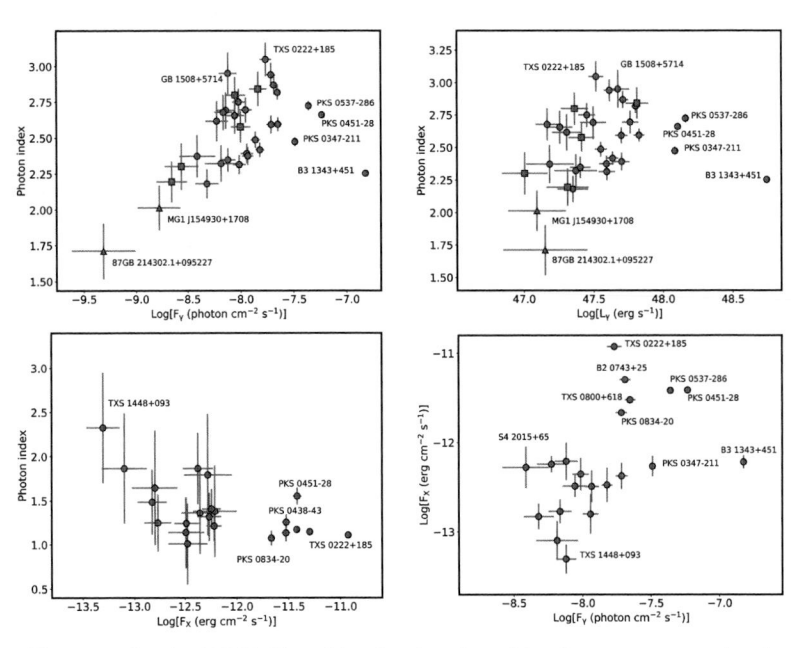

Fig. 1. The γ-ray flux (> 100 MeV) and luminosity of considered sources versus the photon index are shown in the upper panels. BL lacs, FSRQs and BCUs are shown with triangles, circles, and squares, respectively. *Lower left panel:* The X-ray flux (0.3 – 10 keV) versus the photon index. *Lower right panel:* Comparison of γ-ray and X-ray (if available) fluxes.

4.1. *Variability*

Multiple observations of some of these sources with the Swift telescope allow us to investigate their X-ray flux variability. After processing and analyzing data from each observation there were only eight objects with enough counts for constraining the flux and the photon index in a single observation. The results showed that the

X-ray emission from the considered sources was relatively constant except for PKS 0438-43, B2 0743+25, and TXS 0222+185.

The X-ray flux of TXS 0222+185 is mostly around $(0.96 - 1.1) \times 10^{-11}$ erg cm^{-2} s^{-1} which increased to $(1.62 \pm 0.13) \times 10^{-11}$ erg cm^{-2} s^{-1} and $(1.37 \pm 0.16) \times 10^{-11}$ erg cm^{-2} s^{-1} on 24 December 2014 and 31 July 2006, respectively. In case of PKS 0438-43, it was in a bright X-ray state on 15 December 2016 with a flux of $(1.09 \pm 0.16) \times 10^{-11}$ erg cm^{-2} s^{-1} as compared with the flux of $(1.30 \pm 0.31) \times 10^{-11}$ erg cm^{-2} s^{-1} in the quiescent state. Similarly, the X-ray flux of B2 0743+25 in the high state on 01 January 2006 was $(1.06 \pm 0.56) \times 10^{-11}$ erg cm^{-2} s^{-1}. The variation of the 0.3-10 keV X-ray flux of PKS 0438-43, B2 0743+25 and TXS 0222+185 is shown in Fig. 4. No variation of X-ray photon index was found, due to the large uncertainties in its estimation.

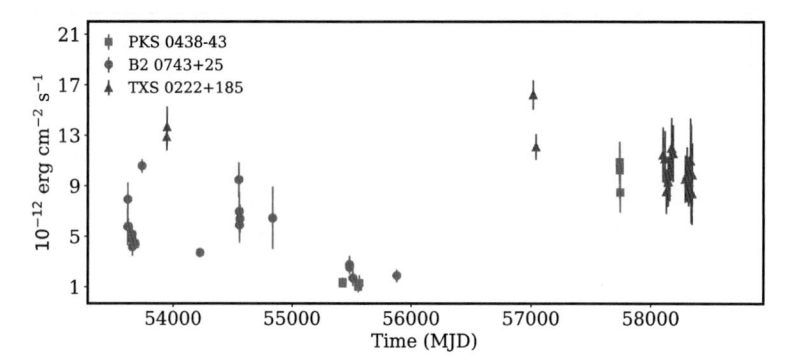

Fig. 2. The 0.3-10 keV X-ray fluxes of PKS 0438-43, B2 0743+25 and TXS 0222+185 measured by Swift-XRT.

A detailed investigation of γ-ray flux variation of the considered sources during the ten years was possible due to the continuous observation by *Fermi*-LAT. In some cases, when source detection significance is $< 10\sigma$, the data are not enough for variability searches in month scales, in these cases the variability has been checked for longer scales (6 to 12 months).[24] If the source detection significance is $> 37\sigma$, it is possible to use the adaptively binned intervals for computations. The adaptively binned light curves were possible to compute only for B3 1343+451, PKS 0451-28, PKS 0347-211 and PKS 0537-286, which are shown in Fig. 3. For the other sources included in Table 1 the variability on week and month scales are investigated.

The adaptively binned light curve of B3 1343+451, which is the brightest and the most variable source in the sample is shown in 3. During the bright γ-ray flaring periods: around MJD 55100, MJD 55890, MJD 56170, MJD 56640, and MJD 57060 the flux changes in sub-day scales. The width of 83 bins was shorter than 12 hours, which were observed during the flares around MJD 55890 (24 bins) and MJD 56170 (35 bins). There are about 200 bins with a width shorter than a day, and the

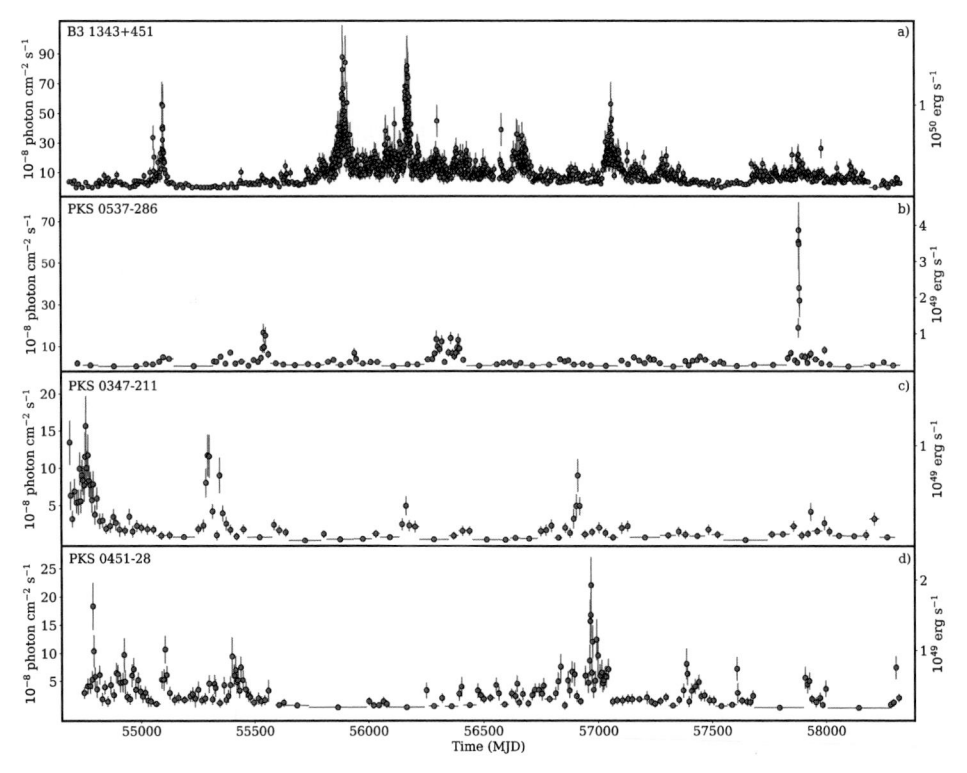

Fig. 3. γ-ray light curve of B3 1343+451, PKS 0537-286, PKS 0347-211, and PKS 0451-28 for the period from August 2008 to August 2018 calculated using adaptively-binned timescales.

minimum adaptively binned time width is 6.33 hours observed on MJD 56176.34 when the source flux was $(7.52\pm1.85)\times10^{-7}$ photon cm^{-2} s^{-1}. In the quiescent state, the γ-ray flux of the source is $\simeq (1-5)\times10^{-8}$ photon cm^{-2} s^{-1} with $\Gamma_\gamma = 2.48\pm0.29$ was observed on MJD 55891.7 with a detection significance of 9.1σ within a time bin having a width of 8.2 hours, which is 36.4 times higher than the γ-ray flux of the source in the quiescent state but the Γ_γ is within the uncertainties of the value given in Table 1. During the hardest γ-ray emission period, $\Gamma_\gamma = 1.45 \pm 0.21$ was detected on MJD 56432 with a significance of 7.2σ, which is unusual for this source.

PKS 0537-286 ($z = 3.10$) is the furthest source showing γ-ray flux variability in short time scales (Fig. 3b). The adaptive light curve showed variability in intra-day scales: 20.45, 15.96, and 18.90 hours. First about flaring activity of PKS 0537-286 was reported in[25] and the rapid γ-ray flux variations in.[24] γ-ray flux of PKS 0537-286 was increased from its 10 year average value, which was $(4.38 \pm 0.18)\times 10^{-8}$ photon cm^{-2} s^{-1}, on MJD 55528-55553, MJD 56264-56400 and MJD 57878.0-57883.4, with the maximum value of $(6.58\pm 1.35) \times 10^{-7}$ photon cm^{-2} s^{-1} observed on MJD 57879.2 with a detection significance of 10.57σ. But in this periods the Γ_γ

is not significantly different from its average value in Table 1, which means that the emission is dominated by the MeV photons.

In the case of PKS 0347-211 and PKS 0451-28 (Fig. 3c and d) the adaptively binned light curves show several periods of γ-ray brightening. For example, for PKS 0347-211 the shortest γ-ray flux increase time interval is 2.65 days, and for PKS 0451-28 it is 1.56 days. The light curves of both sources show multiple periods when γ-ray flux increased. For example, on MJD 54757.04 ± 2.71 the γ-ray flux of PKS 0347-211 was $(1.57 \pm 0.41) \times 10^{-7}$ photon cm^{-2} s^{-1}. In the case of PKS 0451-28, the peak γ-ray flux of $(2.20 \pm 0.50) \times 10^{-7}$ photon cm^{-2} s^{-1} was observed on MJD 56968.60 ± 0.79 with 9.64σ. During this period, Γ_γ was 2.06 ± 0.19.

For finding out whether the γ-ray emission of other sources is variable or not, a simple $\chi2$ test was performed;[26] the flux measured in each interval was fitted by a constant flux and the reduced $\chi2$ and the probability of the flux being constant are computed. The $\chi2$ fitting showed that the γ-ray emission variability of these sources varies from week to month scales. MG3 J163554+3629 at $z = 3.65$ is the most distant γ-ray flaring blazar; this source was reported to be in active state during May-July 2018: for example on July 7 2018 its daily averaged γ-ray flux peak value was $(6.4 \pm 1.15) \times 10^{-7}$ photon cm^{-2} s^{-1}.[27] During June-July 2018 this source was also bright and the maximum daily averaged γ-ray flux was observed $(1.18 \pm 0.23) \times 10^{-7}$ photon cm^{-2} s^{-1}.[27]

For the considered sources also investigated the γ-ray photon index evolution in time has been. This may reveal crucial information, because the photon index is defined by the processes responsible for particle acceleration and cooling and its changes are directly linked with the processes inside the jet. For the searching the photon index variation are used the γ-ray light curves produced in 30 and 7 days, in the case of B3 1343+451 3 day bins, and for escaping large uncertainties only those periods when the source detection was $TS > 25$ were considered, because adaptively binned light curves have narrow width, and photon indexes would be estimated with big uncertainties, which would would not allow to make definite conclusions. The $\chi2$ test shows that the photon index of B3 1343+451, PKS 0451-28, B3 0908+416B and TXS 0907+230 only varies in time and the evolution was shown in Fig. 4 where the horizontal line corresponds to the averaged photon index estimated in ten years (Table 1).

The most interesting photon index variability has B3 1343+451, there are 60 periods when $\Gamma_\gamma < 2.0$. The hardest spectrum of B3 1343+451 was observed on 58089.16 ± 1.5 with $\Gamma_\gamma = 1.73 \pm 0.24$, also it is interesting, that the γ-ray spectrum was hard in a brightly γ-ray flaring state on MJD 56172.16 ± 1.5 with 1.95 ± 0.07. In the 30-day binned light curve of PKS 0451-28 are observed $\Gamma_\gamma = 2.06 \pm 0.07$ and $\Gamma_\gamma = 2.17 \pm 0.15$ on MJD 56977.66 ± 15 and 58297.66 ± 15, respectively. In the case of B3 0908+416B we can see remarkable hardening on MJD 57517.66 ± 15 when the Γ_γ changed to 1.84 ± 0.25 compared to the average of 10 years 2.42 ± 0.05. And in the case of the most distant object where γ-ray spectrum hardening was

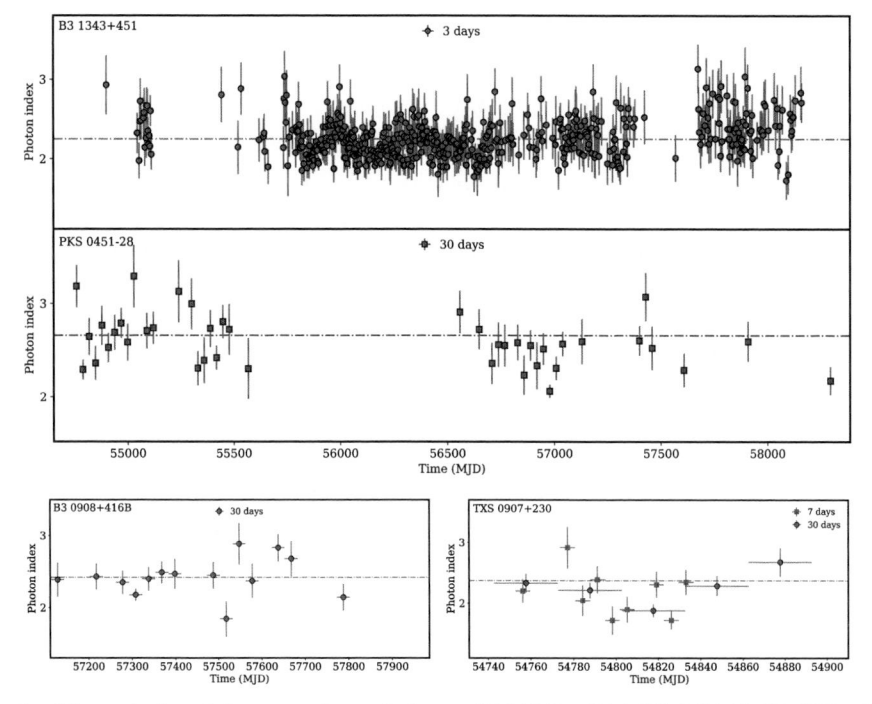

Fig. 4. The evolution of the γ-ray photon indexes of B3 1343+451, PKS 0451-28, B3 0908+416B and TXS 0907+230 in time.

observed is TXS 0907+230 with $z = 2.66$. It's 7 day γ-ray light curve shows that on MJD 54798.16 ± 3.5, 54805.16 ± 3.5 and 54826.16 ± 3.5 its γ-ray photon index appeared $\Gamma_\gamma = 1.72 \pm 0.23$, 1.90 ± 0.21 and 1.72 ± 0.15, respectively. Such a hard γ-ray spectrum is more typical for BL Lacs, but it has also been occasionally observed for the FSRQs during the flares.[12, 15, 28–31]

5. Theoretical modelling and results

The multiwavelength emission from blazars is due interaction of accelerated electrons[2–7] or protons[32–39] with magnetic and photon fields. The currently proposed models can not explain dynamical changes of the radiation and flares which are most likely caused by changes of radiating particles or the emission region.[40] Origin of flares can be investigated with contemporaneous multiwavelength data. From considered sources only for PKS 0438-43 and TXS 0800+618 are available contemporaneous Swift data. Our goal is to constrain the main physical parameters of distant blazars jets and because of lack of multiwavelength data in the modeling will be used only the averaged multiwavelength SEDs which presents the typical state of the source. To investigate broad band emission from considered sources we have used a one-zone leptonic model. The emission region is assumed to be a spherical blob with a radius of R which is filled with uniformly tangled magnetic field

B and with a homogeneous population of relativistic electrons. Non-thermal energy distribution of electrons is described by a power-law with exponential cut-off:

$$N(\gamma) \sim \gamma^{-\alpha} exp(-\gamma/\gamma_{cut}) \; \gamma > \gamma_{min}, \qquad (1)$$

where γ is the Lorentz factor of electrons in the blob rest frame and α is the power-law index which defines the properties of acceleration mechanism.[41–44] γ_{min} and γ_{cut} are the minimum and cut-off energy of the electron in the emission region correspondingly. γ_{cut} allows constraining the cooling process of the particles and the state of plasma in the jet.[29,45] In a simple one zone leptonic model emitting region parameters are the radius, Doppler factor($\Gamma=\delta$), and magnetic field. Magnetic field is a free parameter and its density is $B^2/4\pi$. In the modeling it is assumed that from radio to optical/UV emission is due to synchrotron emission of relativistic electrons, meanwhile high energy peak is due to the Inverse Compton scattering of both internal[2–4] or external[5–7] photons.

The previous studies show that high energy peak is well explained when assumed external photons for Inverse Compton scattering.[15,46–49] Depending on the position of emission region(blob) in the jet different photon field can be assumed.[50] In case of these sources it is assumed that emission region is outside of broad-line region(BLR) and in this position dominant photon field is the infrared emission from dusty torus.[51] IR radiation from dusty torus has a black body spectrum which luminosity is $L_{IR} = 0.6 L_{disc}$,[46] where L_{disc} is the accretion disc luminosity. Directly emission from accretion disk showing a UV excess in the SED and fitting of this excess allows us to estimate photons temperature and luminosity.[52] SEDs modeling results are shown in Table 3 and SEDs of sources for which were generated adaptively binned light curves are shown in Figure 4. The archival data from the Space Science Data Center are in gray, while the optical/UV, X-ray, and γ-ray data, obtained here, are shown in cyan, red, and blue, respectively. The radio data are not included in the SEDs fits, but are considered only as upper limits. The observed radio emission is assumed to originate from a different and extended region. The hard γ-ray emission spectra of B3 1343+451, PKS 0451-28 are in magenta, showing that the γ-ray flux increased and their spectra extend to higher energies.

The SEDs in Fig. 5 contain enough data from radio to HE γ-ray bands to shape both low and high energy peaks. The electron power-law index is defined by the X-ray data and depending on whether the SSC or EIC component is dominating in the X-ray band, different values for α are obtained. When the X-ray spectrum is hard and the SSC component is dominating, the energy distribution of the emitting electrons has a hard spectrum as well. For example for PKS 0537-286 $\alpha = 1.33 \pm 0.07$. The HE tails of both synchrotron and IC components are well defined by the optical/UV and γ-ray data, respectively, allowing precise estimation of $\gamma_{cut} = (1.01 - 15.73) \times 10^3$. γ_{cut} strongly depends on α and its highest values is $(15.73 \pm 1.60) \times 10^3$ which was estimated when $\alpha = 2.80 \pm 0.04$. Meanwhile, when $\alpha = 2.2 - 2.5$, the highest γ_{cut} is $(1.01 - 15.73) \times 10^3$ for B3 1343+451. The estimated Doppler factor is from $\delta = 10.00$ to $\delta = 27.42$ with a mean of $\delta = 19.09$ which is higher

Table 4. Parameters obtained from the modeling of multiwavelength SEDs. [1]: object name. [2]: Doppler factor. [3]: Slope of electron energy distribution. [4] and [5]: the Lorentz factors corresponding to the minimum and cutoff energy of the electron distribution. [6]: Magnetic field in units of G. [7] Radius of the emitting region in units of 10^{16} cm. [8] and [9]: Electron and magnetic field energy densities. [10]: accretion disk luminosity in units of 10^{46} erg s^{-1}. [11] and [12]: The power of the jet in the form of the relativistic electrons (L_e) and magnetic field (L_B) in units of 10^{45} erg s^{-1} and 10^{43} erg s^{-1}, respectively.

Sources [1]	δ [2]	α [3]	γ_{min} [4]	γ_{cut} [5]	B [6]	R [7]	U_e [8]	U_B [9]	L_d [10]	L_e [11]	L_B [12]
GB 1508+5714	15.72 ± 1.29	1.17 ± 0.07	26.90 ± 2.88	1.30 ± 0.10	0.19 ± 0.02	2.28	0.50	1.49	3.02	2.43	0.73
PKS 1351-018	20.47 ± 2.49	2.16 ± 0.11	2.68 ± 0.36	4.99 ± 0.71	0.20 ± 0.02	2.29	0.54	1.66	4.04	2.68	0.82
PKS 0537-286	11.50 ± 0.57	1.33 ± 0.07	15.70 ± 1.49	2.45 ± 0.16	0.28 ± 0.02	1.14	5.93	3.21	3.44	7.31	0.40
TXS 0800+618	14.04 ± 0.56	2.75 ± 0.04	13.98 ± 0.86	2.20 ± 0.02	0.26 ± 0.01	15.5	0.06	2.73	1.65	13.49	61.84
S4 1427+543	10.00 ± 0.37	2.04 ± 0.10	29.00 ± 2.55	2.79 ± 0.27	0.53 ± 0.04	1.90	0.63	10.02	1.83	2.14	3.75
GB6 J0733+0456	16.28 ± 1.36	2.80 ± 0.04	47.90 ± 3.42	15.73 ± 1.60	0.16 ± 0.03	2.98	0.12	6.22	3.40	0.98	5.20
PKS 0347-211	26.00 ± 1.02	2.79 ± 0.02	23.09 ± 1.12	2.62 ± 0.16	0.20 ± 0.01	8.15	0.03	1.61	1.99	1.72	10.08
B2 0743+25	10.02 ± 0.45	1.13 ± 0.19	7.66 ± 0.22	2.03 ± 0.08	0.36 ± 0.01	0.70	16.90	0.003	3.58	7.80	0.24
S4 1124+57	22.17 ± 1.37	2.78 ± 0.04	22.92 ± 1.45	1.28 ± 0.10	0.22 ± 0.01	5.15	0.14	1.95	1.69	3.39	4.87
PKS 0438-43	18.17 ± 1.29	2.78 ± 0.04	23.13 ± 1.54	7.19 ± 0.58	0.34 ± 0.02	5.42	0.12	4.52	3.91	3.33	12.52
S4 2015+65	17.85 ± 1.32	2.73 ± 0.05	20.63 ± 1.64	2.75 ± 0.29	0.46 ± 0.03	13.50	0.07	8.41	4.55	1.26	14.44
MG2 J174803+3403	24.50 ± 2.06	2.87 ± 0.06	14.67 ± 1.58	1.40 ± 0.49	1.45 ± 0.09	7.41	0.004	83.98	8.87	0.23	434.69
PKS 0834-20	27.42 ± 0.97	2.70 ± 0.06	20.57 ± 1.51	2.13 ± 0.18	0.37 ± 0.02	6.83	0.02	5.44	5.51	0.70	23.92
TXS 0222+185	10.03 ± 0.28	1.62 ± 0.05	19.56 ± 0.98	2.38 ± 0.10	0.35 ± 0.02	1.07	10.28	5.04	2.71	11.10	0.54
OD 166	19.02 ± 0.84	1.96 ± 0.04	2.58 ± 0.15	1.01 ± 0.03	1.15 ± 0.05	4.32	0.01	0.52	0.53	0.25	92.38
TXS 0907+230	21.66 ± 1.66	2.23 ± 0.11	20.26 ± 1.84	1.44 ± 0.10	0.31 ± 0.02	5.23	0.03	3.72	1.09	0.70	5.96
PMN J1441-1523	17.01 ± 1.50	2.19 ± 0.07	2.86 ± 0.29	3.31 ± 0.46	1.68 ± 0.14	1.47	0.07	112.38	0.17	0.14	22.85
TXS 1448+093	17.90 ± 1.13	1.52 ± 0.15	49.64 ± 5.82	0.84 ± 0.06	0.70 ± 0.05	7.96	0.003	19.44	0.56	0.17	115.93
PMN J0226+0937	25.02 ± 1.98	2.41 ± 0.04	5.37 ± 0.59	8.32 ± 0.62	1.74 ± 0.12	3.09	0.03	119.86	10.94	0.03	107.98
PKS 0451-28	26.14 ± 1.27	2.90 ± 0.28	21.93 ± 1.3*	2.19 ± 0.01	0.45 ± 0.03	5.90	0.11	8.01	7.20	3.59	26.32
B3 0908+416B	23.22 ± 1.72	1.31 ± 0.25	6.41 ± 0.72	1.11 ± 0.10	0.39 ± 0.03	1.76	0.09	6.10	0.43	0.26	1.78
TXS 1616+517	10.11 ± 0.31	2.09 ± 0.09	93.28 ± 4.15	4.34 ± 0.36	0.52 ± 0.02	3.59	0.06	10.79	0.35	0.70	13.11
B3 1343+451	26.55 ± 1.04	2.48 ± 0.04	16.49 ± 1.31	8.67 ± 0.48	0.10 ± 0.01	4.16	0.11	0.42	0.48	1.76	0.68
PKS 2107-105	27.32 ± 1.34	2.30 ± 0.06	7.45 ± 0.90	3.63 ± 0.39	0.67 ± 0.05	9.48	0.0006	17.73	8.30	0.05	150.16

Note: [1] Integrated γ-ray flux in units of $\times 10^{-8}$ photon cm^{-2} s^{-1}.
Note: [2] Photon energy in GeV.

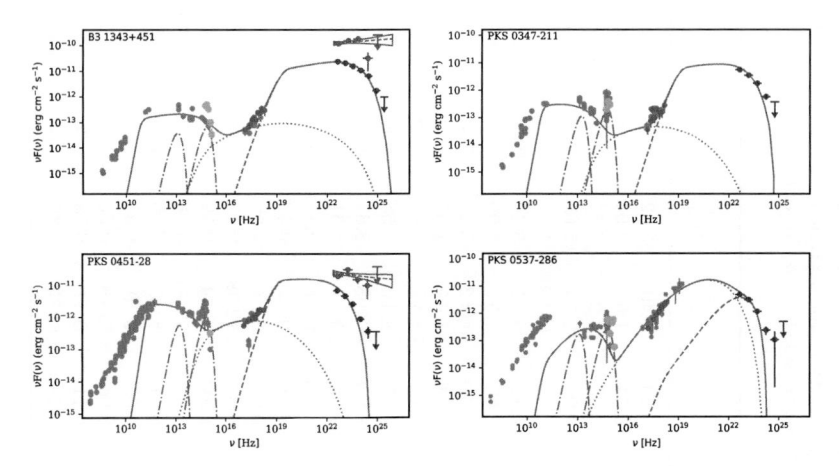

Fig. 5. The evolution of the γ-ray photon indexes of B3 1343+451, PKS 0347-211, PKS 0451-28, PKS 0537-286 in time.

than the average values estimated for FSRQs.[53,54] The emitting region size is within $R = (0.70-9.48) \times 10^{16}$ cm. Results obtained for R suggest that the multiwavelength emission is produced in the sub-parsec scale regions of the jet. Modeling results allow us to estimate energetics of the considered sources. For seventeen sources out of thirty three was possible to estimate discs luminosity assuming that disc has a black body spectrum. Estimations shows that $L_d \simeq (1.09 - 10.94) \times 10^{46}$ erg s^{-1} and highest value estimated for PMN J0226+0937 is $L_d \simeq 1.09 \times 10^{47}$ erg s^{-1}. Jet power was calculated as

$$L = \pi R^2 c \Gamma^2 U_i \qquad (2)$$

where U_i is electron or magnetic field energy density. Corresponding values from Table 4 show that $L_e \simeq (0.03 - 13.49) \times 10^{45}$ erg s^{-1} and $L_B \simeq (0.24 - 434.69) \times 10^{44}$ erg s^{-1}.

6. Summary

The main results after analysis of Fermi-LAT data, accumulated in 2008-2018 and Swift data, observed in fifteen years are summarized. The γ-ray photon index of all the considered sources is between 2.18-3.05 except for two BL Lacs. Swift XRT has detected significant X-ray emission only from FSRQs considered here and X-ray flux ranges from 5×10^{-14} erg cm^{-2} s^{-1} to 10^{-11} erg cm^{-2} s^{-1}. The γ-ray variability of the considered sources has shown emission on short and long time scales from sub day to month scales. During γ-ray flares the luminosity riches $(10^{49} - 10^{50})$ erg s^{-1}. The most luminous source in the sample is B3 1343+451 which luminosity during flare increases 36.4 times and corresponds to $L_\gamma = 1.5 \times 10^{50}$ erg s^{-1}. For SED modeling one zone leptonic model considering SSC of synchrotron and IC of dusty torus photons was used. Magnetic field ranges from $0.10-1.74$ G and Doppler factor is within $10.00-27.42$. Estimated black hole masses are within $(1.69-5.35) \times 10^9 M_\odot$.

References

1. C. M. Urry and P. Padovani, Unified Schemes for Radio-Loud Active Galactic Nuclei, *Publications of the ASP* **107**, p. 803 (September 1995).
2. G. Ghisellini, et al., Inhomogeneous synchrotron-self-Compton models and the problem of relativistic beaming of BL Lac objects, *Astronomy and Astrophysics* **146**, 204 (May 1985).
3. S. D. Bloom and A. P. Marscher, An Analysis of the Synchrotron Self-Compton Model for the Multi–Wave Band Spectra of Blazars, *The Astrophysical Journal* **461**, p. 657 (April 1996).
4. L. Maraschi, et al., A jet model for the gamma-ray emitting blazar 3C 279, *Astrophysical Journal, Letters* **397**, L5 (September 1992).
5. M. Błażejowski, et al., Comptonization of Infrared Radiation from Hot Dust by Relativistic Jets in Quasars, *The Astrophysical Journal* **545**, 107 (December 2000).
6. M. Sikora, et al., Comptonization of diffuse ambient radiation by a relativistic jet: The source of gamma rays from blazars?, *The Astrophysical Journal* **421**, 153 (January 1994).
7. G. Ghisellini and F. Tavecchio, Canonical high-power blazars, *Monthly Notices of the RAS* **397**, 985 (August 2009).
8. S. Abdollahi, et al., Fermi Large Area Telescope Fourth Source Catalog, *Astrophysical Journal, Supplement* **247**, p. 33 (March 2020).
9. M. Volonteri, Formation of supermassive black holes, **18**, 279 (July 2010).
10. J. R. Mattox, et al., The Likelihood Analysis of EGRET Data, *The Astrophysical Journal* **461**, p. 396 (April 1996).
11. B. Rani, et al., Constraining the location of rapid gamma-ray flares in the flat spectrum radio quasar 3C 273, *Astronomy and Astrophysics* **557**, p. A71 (Sep 2013).
12. N. Sahakyan and S. Gasparyan, High energy gamma-ray emission from PKS 1441+25, *Monthly Notices of the RAS* **470**, 2861 (September 2017).
13. N. Sahakyan, et al., Fermi-LAT observation of nonblazar AGNs, *Astronomy and Astrophysics* **614**, p. A6 (June 2018).
14. V. Baghmanyan, et al., Rapid Gamma-Ray Variability of NGC 1275, *The Astrophysical Journal* **848**, p. 111 (October 2017).
15. S. Gasparyan, et al., On the Multiwavelength Emission from CTA 102, *The Astrophysical Journal* **863**, p. 114 (August 2018).
16. M. S. Dutka, et al., Multiband Observations of the Quasar PKS 2326-502 during Active and Quiescent Gamma-Ray States in 2010-2012, *The Astrophysical Journal* **835**, p. 182 (February 2017).
17. D. Zargaryan, et al., Comparing 3C 120 jet emission at small and large scales, *Astronomy and Astrophysics* **608**, p. A37 (December 2017).
18. D. N. Burrows, et al., The Swift X-Ray Telescope, **120**, 165 (October 2005).
19. P. W. A. Roming, et al., The Swift Ultra-Violet/Optical Telescope, **120**, 95 (October 2005).
20. N. Gehrels, et al., The Swift Gamma-Ray Burst Mission, *The Astrophysical Journal* **611**, 1005 (August 2004).
21. T. S. Poole, et al., Photometric calibration of the Swift ultraviolet/optical telescope, *Monthly Notices of the RAS* **383**, 627 (January 2008).

22. P. A. Evans, et al., Methods and results of an automatic analysis of a complete sample of Swift-XRT observations of GRBs, *Monthly Notices of the RAS* **397**, 1177 (August 2009).
23. M. Ajello, et al., The Fourth Catalog of Active Galactic Nuclei Detected by the Fermi Large Area Telescope, *The Astrophysical Journal* **892**, p. 105 (April 2020).
24. S. Li, et al., Fast γ-Ray Variability in Blazars beyond Redshift 3, *The Astrophysical Journal* **853**, p. 159 (February 2018).
25. C. C. Cheung, Fermi LAT detection of a GeV flare from High-redshift Blazar PKS 0537-286, *The Astronomer's Telegram* **10356**, p. 1 (May 2017).
26. A. A. Abdo, et al., Gamma-ray Light Curves and Variability of Bright Fermi-detected Blazars, *The Astrophysical Journal* **722**, 520 (October 2010).
27. V. S. Paliya, et al., Fermi-LAT detection of high gamma-ray activity from the z=3.6 quasar NVSS J163547+362930, *The Astronomer's Telegram* **11847**, p. 1 (July 2018).
28. L. Pacciani, et al., Exploring the Blazar Zone in High-energy Flares of FSRQs, *The Astrophysical Journal* **790**, p. 45 (August 2014).
29. N. Sahakyan, Investigation of the γ-ray spectrum of CTA 102 during the exceptional flaring state in 2016-2017, *Astronomy and Astrophysics* **635**, p. A25 (March 2020).
30. V. S. Paliya, et al., Detection of a Gamma-Ray Flare from the High-redshift Blazar DA 193, *The Astrophysical Journal* **871**, p. 211 (February 2019).
31. R. Angioni, et al., The large gamma-ray flare of the flat-spectrum radio quasar PKS 0346-27, *Astronomy and Astrophysics* **627**, p. A140 (July 2019).
32. A. Dar and A. Laor, Hadronic Production of TeV Gamma-Ray Flares from Blazars, *Astrophysical Journal, Letters* **478**, L5 (March 1997).
33. J. H. Beall and W. Bednarek, On the Hadronic Beam Model for Gamma-Ray Production in Blazars, *The Astrophysical Journal* **510**, 188 (January 1999).
34. W. Bednarek and R. J. Protheroe, Gamma-rays from interactions of stars with active galactic nucleus jets, *Monthly Notices of the RAS* **287**, L9 (May 1997).
35. K. Mannheim, High-energy neutrinos from extragalactic jets, *Astroparticle Physics* **3**, 295 (May 1995).
36. K. Mannheim and P. L. Biermann, Photomeson production in active galactic nuclei, *Astronomy and Astrophysics* **221**, 211 (September 1989).
37. K. Mannheim, The proton blazar, *Astronomy and Astrophysics* **269**, 67 (March 1993).
38. A. Mücke and R. J. Protheroe, A proton synchrotron blazar model for flaring in Markarian 501, *Astroparticle Physics* **15**, 121 (March 2001).
39. A. Mücke, et al., BL Lac objects in the synchrotron proton blazar model, *Astroparticle Physics* **18**, 593 (March 2003).
40. A. Paggi, et al., Flaring Patterns in Blazars, *The Astrophysical Journal* **736**, p. 128 (August 2011).
41. J. G. Kirk and A. F. Heavens, Particle acceleration at oblique shock fronts, *Monthly Notices of the RAS* **239**, 995 (Aug 1989).
42. D. C. Ellison, et al., First-Order Fermi Particle Acceleration by Relativistic Shocks, *The Astrophysical Journal* **360**, p. 702 (Sep 1990).
43. E. J. Summerlin and M. G. Baring, Diffusive Acceleration of Particles at Oblique, Relativistic, Magnetohydrodynamic Shocks, *The Astrophysical Journal* **745**, p. 63 (Jan 2012).
44. L. O. Drury, REVIEW ARTICLE: An introduction to the theory of diffusive shock acceleration of energetic particles in tenuous plasmas, *Reports on Progress in Physics* **46**, 973 (Aug 1983).
45. M. G. Baring, et al., Probing acceleration and turbulence at relativistic shocks in blazar jets, *Monthly Notices of the RAS* **464**, 4875 (Feb 2017).

46. M. L. Ahnen, et al., Very High Energy γ-Rays from the Universe's Middle Age: Detection of the z = 0.940 Blazar PKS 1441+25 with MAGIC, *Astrophysical Journal, Letters* **815**, p. L23 (December 2015).
47. A. U. Abeysekara, et al., Gamma-Rays from the Quasar PKS 1441+25: Story of an Escape, *Astrophysical Journal, Letters* **815**, p. L22 (December 2015).
48. MAGIC Collaboration, et al., Detection of persistent VHE gamma-ray emission from PKS 1510-089 by the MAGIC telescopes during low states between 2012 and 2017, *Astronomy and Astrophysics* **619**, p. A159 (November 2018).
49. M. Hayashida, et al., Rapid Variability of Blazar 3C 279 during Flaring States in 2013-2014 with Joint Fermi-LAT, NuSTAR, Swift, and Ground-Based Multiwavelength Observations, *The Astrophysical Journal* **807**, p. 79 (July 2015).
50. M. Sikora, et al., Constraining Emission Models of Luminous Blazar Sources, *The Astrophysical Journal* **704**, 38 (October 2009).
51. M. Sikora, et al., On the Nature of MeV Blazars, *The Astrophysical Journal* **577**, 78 (September 2002).
52. G. Ghisellini, et al., Jet and accretion power in the most powerful Fermi blazars, *Monthly Notices of the RAS* **399**, 2041 (November 2009).
53. G. Ghisellini and F. Tavecchio, Fermi/LAT broad emission line blazars, *Monthly Notices of the RAS* **448**, 1060 (April 2015).
54. V. S. Paliya, et al., General Physical Properties of CGRaBS Blazars, *The Astrophysical Journal* **851**, p. 33 (December 2017).

Quantum gravity phenomenology from thermodynamics of spacetime

A. Alonso-Serrano

Max-Planck-Institut für Gravitationsphysik (Albert-Einstein-Institut)
Am Mühlenberg 1, 14476 Potsdam, Germany
E-mail: ana.alonso.serrano@aei.mpg.de

M. Liška

Institute of Theoretical Physics, Faculty of Mathematics and Physics, Charles University
V Holešovičkách 2, 180 00 Prague 8, Czech Republic,
Max-Planck-Institut für Gravitationsphysik (Albert-Einstein-Institut)
Am Mühlenberg 1, Potsdam, Germany
E-mail: liska.mk@seznam.cz

In this review, we discuss a derivation of effective low energy quantum gravitational dynamics from thermodynamics. The derivation is based on the formalism developed in semiclassical thermodynamics of spacetime that allows to obtain Einstein equations from the proportionality of entropy to the area. We first introduce the relevant ingredients of semiclassical thermodynamics of spacetime, paying special attention to the various concepts of entropy involved and their relations. We then extend the semiclassical formalism by considering low energy quantum gravity effects which imply a modified entropy formula with an additional term logarithmic in the area. Upon discussing the derivation of effective gravitational dynamics from this modified entropy, we comment on the most important features of our proposal. Moreover, we show its physical implications on a simple cosmological model and show that it suggests the replacement of the Big Bang singularity by a regular bounce.

Keywords: Quantum gravity phenomenology, Thermodynamics of spacetime

1. Introduction

The search for a consistent theory unifying gravity and quantum physics has been an important direction of research in the last decades. While promising candidates have been put forward, none of them presently provides a complete and consistent final theory. In the absence of a fully developed theoretical framework, quantum gravitational phenomenology offers a way to gain information about possible low energy dynamical effects of quantum gravity.[1–5] Phenomenological models concerning strong gravitational fields are mainly available for physics in the vicinity of classical singularities.[6–10] However, these models face limitations coming from the simplicity of the studied geometries and their results cannot be directly applied in more general settings. Motivated by overcoming these issues, the authors have employed thermodynamics of spacetime to study quantum gravitational phenomenology and propose effective equations of motion applicable in generic spacetimes.[11] As we will see, thermodynamic methods allow us to look for model-independent low energy phenomenological dynamics of quantum gravity without choosing any specific background spacetime. One can then particularise the resulting dynamics to any case of interest. Furthermore, the relevant thermodynamic predictions are common for most of the candidate theories of quantum gravity and can even be obtained by model independent considerations.

Thermodynamics of spacetime presents a useful tool for understanding gravitational dynamics. Following the seminal developments of black hole thermodynamics,[12–14] the framework has been extended both to more general spacetimes[15] and beyond general relativity.[16] A key step forward has been the derivation of Einstein equations from thermodynamics of local Rindler horizons.[17] The original approach has since been improved and generalised to work for different constructions of local horizons,[18–22] certain modified theories of gravity[20–26] and even to derive semiclassical gravitational equations of motion.[19, 21, 22]

Taking a step further, the authors have included quantum gravity effects on the thermodynamics of local causal horizons, obtaining equations governing low energy effective dynamics of quantum gravity.[11] To get sufficiently robust and general results, we concentrated on the leading order quantum correction to Bekenstein entropy, a term logarithmic in the horizon area. This is advantageous, since its presence is predicted by many different approaches to quantum gravity, including loop quantum gravity (LQG),[27, 28] string theory[29, 30] and AdS/CFT correspondence,[31] non-local effective field theory,[32] entanglement entropy calculations,[33] as well as model independent considerations based on generalised uncertainty principle (GUP) phenomenology[7] and analysis of statistical fluctuations.[34, 35] Thus, the effective dynamics we propose is relevant to most of the main approaches to quantum gravity.

While we are chiefly concerned with low energy quantum gravity effects, thermodynamics of spacetime provides interesting insights already on the semiclassical level. Furthermore, a complete understanding of the semiclassical regime is necessary to extend the thermodynamic formalism to the realm of quantum gravity. Therefore, we include a detailed review of the concepts considered in semiclassical thermodynamics of spacetime, especially various notions of entropy. Since derivations of gravitational dynamics rely on equilibrium conditions for local causal horizons which involve Bekenstein, entanglement and Clausius entropy, we further discuss to what extend are these entropies equivalent.

In the present work, we review the main features of our proposal, paying special attention to the various concepts of entropy involved as well as to the unimodular nature of the resulting gravitational dynamics.[36] Section 2 introduces the necessary entropy definitions and discusses their relations both in the semiclassical and low energy quantum gravity settings. In section 3, we first briefly recap derivation of the effective equations. Then we discuss their properties and illustrate their physical implications on a simple cosmological toy model (finding that the Big Bang singularity can be resolved). Lastly, section 4 sums up our results and presents possible directions for future research.

Throughout the paper, we work in four spacetime dimensions and use metric signature $(-,+,+,+)$. Definitions of the curvature-related quantities follow.[37] We use lower case Greek letters to denote abstract spacetime indices and lower case Latin letters for spatial indices with respect to a (local) Cartesian basis. Unless otherwise explicitly stated, we use the SI units.

2. Entropy in thermodynamics of spacetime

Thermodynamic derivations of gravitational dynamics are based on the observation that gravitational dynamic are encoded in the horizon area equilibrium condition for maximal entropy, $\delta S = 0$, if it holds for all local causal horizons. This condition sums together variations of entropy of the horizon, often interpreted in terms of entanglement (von Neumann) entropy due to quantum correlations across the horizon,[17,19,26] and of entropy of the matter. Since the latter is usually described in terms of thermodynamic Clausius entropy,[17,18] it is not obvious that one can combine both entropies to define a meaningful equilibrium condition (it has actually been suggested that this fails in the case of local Rindler wedges[38]). This combination requires that fluxes of Clausius and von Neumann entropy of matter across the horizon are equal with sufficient precission. In the following, we first introduce our implementation of local causal horizons: geodesic local causal diamonds (GLCD). Then we present the definitions of all the relevant entropies associated with GLCD's and review our previous argument for the interchangeability of Clausius and von Neumann entropy.[36]

2.1. *Geodesic local causal diamonds*

We begin by briefly introducing the construction and most important properties of GLCD's. More detailed description of GLCD's can be found, e.g. in.[39–42]

In an arbitrary spacetime point P choose any unit timelike vector $n(P)$. In every direction orthogonal to n send out of P geodesics of parameter length l. These form a spatial geodesic 3-ball, Σ_0, and the region causally determined by Σ_0 constitutes a GLCD (see figure 1). The boundary, $\mathcal{B}$, of Σ_0 is approximately a 2-sphere. Its area reads[19]

$$\mathcal{A} = 4\pi l^2 - \frac{4\pi}{9} l^4 G_{00}(P) + O(l^5), \quad (1)$$

where $G_{00} = G_{\mu\nu} n^\mu n^\nu$. The GLCD possesses an approximate (up to $O(l^3)$ curvature dependent terms) conformal Killing vector[19]

$$\zeta = C\left((l^2 - t^2 - r^2)\frac{\partial}{\partial t} - 2rt\frac{\partial}{\partial r} \right), \quad (2)$$

where C denotes an arbitrary normalisation constant. It has been argued that one can assign Hawking temperature to the GLCD's conformal horizon, $T_H = \hbar\kappa/2\pi k_B c$, where $\kappa = C/2l$ is the surface gravity corresponding to ζ.[19,42]

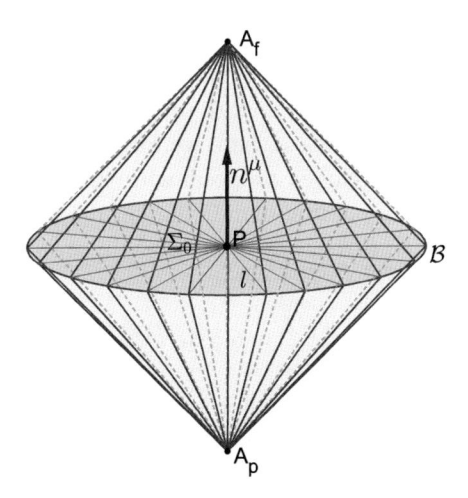

Fig. 1. A sketch of a GLCD with the origin in point P (the angular coordinate θ is suppressed). Σ_0 is a spatial geodesic ball of radius l (several of the geodesics forming it are depicted as grey lines), its boundary an approximate 2-sphere $\mathcal{B}$. Unit timelike vector n^μ is a normal of Σ_0. The tilted lines from the past apex A_p ($t = -l/c$) to the future apex A_f ($t = l/c$) represent the null geodesic generators of the GLCD boundary. The diamond's base Σ_0 is the spatial cross-section of both the future domain of dependence of A_p and the past domain of dependence of A_f at $t = 0$.

2.2. *Bekenstein entropy*

To derive the Einstein equations from thermodynamics of GLCD's (or, conversely, to interpret the first law of GLCD dynamics implied by Einstein equations in thermodynamic terms[42]), one must assume that entropy associated with its horizon obeys the Bekenstein formula[19,22]

$$S_{BH} = \frac{k_B \mathcal{A}}{4 l_P^2}, \qquad (3)$$

where $\mathcal{A}$ denotes the horizon area. However, it is far from clear to what types of horizons can one assign Bekenstein entropy. Since its interpretation in terms of quantum entanglement allows a natural extension of the Bekenstein formula to any causal horizon, it is often assumed in the context of thermodynamics of spacetime (although it was originally proposed in a different context[43,44]). To understand the entanglement interpretation of Bekenstein entropy, consider two causally separated spacetime regions. An observer in one region cannot measure vacuum fluctuations in the other one. Since the fluctuations are correlated between regions, some information is inaccessible to the observer and non-zero entanglement entropy appears. Its value is proportional to the area of causal horizon, $S_e = \eta \mathcal{A}$.[33,43,44] The proportionality constant η is infinite unless one introduces a cutoff. Then η becomes finite and depends on the cutoff length, the number and type of quantum fields considered in the theory and even on the position in spacetime.[26,33] To recover the Bekenstein entropy, a universal value $\eta = k_B/4l_P^2$ is necessary (see, e.g.[33,45] for discussions of feasibility and shortcomings of this assumption). Let us stress that the entanglement interpretation of Bekenstein entropy is in no way necessary to derive gravitational dynamics from thermodynamics. Any microscopic interpretation of black hole entropy which also applies to observer-dependent causal horizons would work just as well. Nevertheless, here we focus on the entanglement entropy as it is currently the most developed proposal with this property.

Beyond this semiclassical picture, many different models indicate that the leading order quantum gravity correction to Bekenstein entropy is a non-local term logarithmic in horizon area[7,9,27–35,46–49]

$$S = \frac{k_B \mathcal{A}}{4l_P^2} + k_B \mathcal{C} \ln\left(\frac{\mathcal{A}}{\mathcal{A}_0}\right), \qquad (4)$$

where $\mathcal{C}$ is a real number and $\mathcal{A}_0$ a constant with dimensions of area. The values of $\mathcal{C}$ and $\mathcal{A}_0$ are model dependent. Considering the entanglement entropy interpretation allows us to calculate modified entropy even for causal horizons in a flat spacetime.[33] Interestingly, a logarithmic term then appears for spherical horizons,[50] but not for planar ones[33] (due to different Euler characteristics). This is the reason we consider GLCD's rather than local Rindler wedges to find effective low energy dynamics of quantum gravity from thermodynamics[11] (for arguments against the Rindler wedges even in the semiclassical setting see, e.g.[20,38]).

While the presence of a logarithmic term seems to be a very general prediction of quantum gravity, the value and even the sign of $\mathcal{C}$ differ in various approaches. Generally speaking, two types of corrections to Bekenstein entropy have been studied in the literature. On one hand, microcanonical corrections appear due to more precise counting of the microstates at fixed horizon area, which reduces our uncertainty, leading to negative contribution to entropy. On the other hand, canonical corrections stem from thermal fluctuations at fixed temperature, which are an additional source of uncertainty increasing the entropy. As we discuss in section 3, the sign of $\mathcal{C}$ determines the physical implications of the modified dynamics we propose, allowing the avoidance of spacetime singularities only for $\mathcal{C} > 0$. Therefore, the presently unknown overall sign of $\mathcal{C}$ is crucial for the interpretation of our results.

2.3. *Clausius entropy of the matter*

Apart from Bekenstein entropy, derivation of gravitational dynamics from thermodynamics also requires a way to account for the entropy of matter. The simplest approach is to consider the thermodynamic Clausius entropy, $dS_C = \delta Q/T$. The heat flux δQ across an arbitrary timelike hypersurface Σ reads[18]

$$\delta Q = -\int_\Sigma T_{\mu\nu} V^\nu N^\mu d^3\Sigma, \qquad (5)$$

where V^ν and N^μ are timelike and spacelike unit normals of Σ. If V^ν corresponds to velocity of an eternal, uniformly accelerating observer with acceleration a, we can define the corresponding Unruh temperature, $T_U = \hbar a/2\pi k_B c$. This definition holds with sufficient precission even for observers with slowly varying acceleration or finite lifetime, as long as the proper length λ of the trajectory with an approximately constant acceleration is large enough, i.e. $\lambda \gg c^2/a$.[51] For the special case of uniformly accelerated observers travelling inside causal diamonds one also finds an equivalent result due to conformal mapping of a Rindler wedge to a causal diamond.[52,53] Therefore, as long as we consider a sufficiently large a, we can use the standard Unruh temperature together with the expression for heat flux to define Clausius entropy flux across a timelike hypersurface

$$S_C \equiv \frac{\delta Q}{T_U} = -\int_\Sigma \frac{2\pi k_B c}{\hbar a} T_{\mu\nu} V^\nu N^\mu \mathrm{d}^3\Sigma. \tag{6}$$

The timelike surface Σ coincides with the causal horizon perceived by the uniformly accelerating observer in the limit $a \to \infty$. Notably, this limit is well defined both for arbitrary causal horizons in flat spacetime and for sufficiently small horizons in curved spacetimes[18] (in that case, one simply considers Riemann normal coordinate expansion to the leading order). Before moving on to the special case of causal diamonds, several further remarks are in order. First, the definition of Clausius entropy flux across null surfaces is completely independent of gravitational dynamics or any requirements on symmetries of the spacetime. Second, the construction of the entropy is semiclassical as it explicitly depends on quantum field theory by invoking the Unruh effect. And, lastly, in contrast with the nature of Clausius entropy in non-relativistic thermodynamics, the entropy flux is manifestly observer dependent.[18]

For a GLCD, the resulting expression for Clausius entropy flux from $t = 0$ (geodesic ball Σ_0) to $t = l/c$ (future apex A_f) takes form[36]

$$\Delta S_C = \int_0^{l/c} \frac{2\pi k_B c}{\hbar} t \left(\int_{S(t)} T_{\mu\nu} k^\mu k^\nu \mathrm{d}^2\mathcal{A} \right) \mathrm{d}t + O\left(l^5\right), \tag{7}$$

where k^μ denotes the future pointing null normal to the GLCD's boundary. Performing the integration and some straightforward manipulations then yields

$$\Delta S_C = -\frac{8\pi^2 k_B l^4}{9\hbar c} \left(T_{00}(P) + \frac{1}{4} T(P) \right) + O\left(l^5\right), \tag{8}$$

where we explicitly stress that the energy momentum tensor is evaluated at the diamond's origin, P.

When one wishes to take into account low energy quantum gravity effects, defining the Clausius entropy flux becomes more complicated. The subtleties in its definition come from the need to consider the Unruh effect, which requires that the ground state of quantum fields is locally well approximated by Minkowski vacuum. This amounts to invoking Einstein equivalence principle:[26] "Fundamental non-gravitational test physics is not affected, locally and at any point of spacetime, by the presence of a gravitational field".[54] However, the status of the equivalence principle in the low energy quantum gravity regime is far from clear. For instance, possible violations of weak equivalence principle resulting from GUP phenomenology have been explored in a number of works with very different conclusions.[55–58]

A simple way to deal with possible influence of the equivalence principle violations on the Unruh effect is to consider heuristic modifications to Unruh temperature due to GUP, previously suggested in the literature.[59,60] All the proposals for modified Unruh temperature obey

$$T_{mod} = \frac{\hbar a \left(1 + \psi \frac{l_P^2}{c^4} a^2\right)}{2\pi k_B c} + O\left(\frac{l_P^4 a^5}{c^8}\right), \tag{9}$$

where ψ denotes a model dependent real number that is expected to be of the order of unity.[59,60] A similar prescription has also been earlier proposed for modified Hawking temperature.[7,9,33] To our best knowledge, these modifications to temperature have not been confirmed by any rigorous method. However, since GUP phenomenologically implements effects of a minimal resolvable length that arises in a number of approaches to quantum gravity,[1,2] the idea of modified Unruh temperature is worth considering. Hence, to incorporate leading order quantum gravity corrections in thermodynamics of spacetime, we need to show that the previously outlined construction of Clausius entropy flux works with this modified temperature. Note that the previous reasoning does not apply directly, since in the limit $a \to \infty$ correction terms in the modified temperature formula become dominant. Instead, one must consider acceleration much larger than c^2/l but much smaller than $c^2/\sqrt{\psi} l_P$ (this can be satisfied for $l \gg l_P$, i.e., whenever the GLCD is much larger than the Planck scale). The construction of Clausius entropy flux under this assumption has been carried out by the authors,[11] yielding

$$\Delta S_{C,mod} = -\left(1 - \psi \frac{l_P^2 a^2}{c^4}\right) \frac{2\pi k_B c}{\hbar} \int_0^{l/c} t \left(\int_{S(t)} T_{\mu\nu} k^\mu k^\nu d^2 \mathcal{A}\right) dt + O\left(l^5, \frac{l_P^4 a^4}{c^8}, \frac{1}{a^2}\right). \tag{10}$$

The only difference with respect to the semiclassical formula are the a-dependent sub-leading terms. We can recover it by setting $\psi = 0$ and then taking the limit $a \to \infty$. Let us note that while we assumed finite acceleration simply for mathematical convenience, the limit $a \lesssim c^2/\sqrt{\psi} l_P$ agrees quite well with the proposal of an upper limit to acceleration a_M set by quantum gravity effects, $a_M = c^2/l_P$.[61]

2.4. *Von Neumann entropy of the matter*

To be consistent with the entanglement interpretation of the entropy of GLCD's horizon, one should consider quantum von Neumann entropy of the matter rather than the thermodynamic Clausius one. For small variations from vacuum, this entropy can be obtained from the vacuum state density operator, $\rho = e^{-K/k_B T_\zeta}/Z$, where Z is the partition function, T_ζ denotes the previously defined temperature associated with conformal Killing vector ζ^μ and K is known as the modular Hamiltonian.[42] While variations of K can in general be non-local, for conformal fields they correspond to variations of the local matter Hamiltonian[42]

$$\delta H = \int_{\Sigma_0} \delta \langle T_{\mu\nu} \rangle \xi^\mu n^\nu d^2 \Omega dr, \tag{11}$$

where $n = \partial/\partial t$. Then, the variation of entropy reads

$$\delta S_m = \frac{1}{T}\delta K = \frac{2\pi k_B}{\hbar c}\frac{4\pi l^4}{15}\delta\langle T_{00}\rangle + O\left(l^5\right). \tag{12}$$

For non-conformal field theories with a UV fixed point, the von Neumann entropy variation is modified only by the presence of an additional l-dependent spacetime scalar, δX,[19,62,63]

$$\delta S_m = \frac{2\pi k_B}{\hbar c}\frac{4\pi l^4}{15}\left(\delta\langle T_{00}\rangle + \delta X\right). \tag{13}$$

In our study concerning the quantum gravity corrections, we have gone beyond the semiclassical case just by including modifications to the temperature[11] (in a future work we plan to analyse possible corrections to the modular Hamiltonian). Implementing the leading order quantum gravity modification to temperature gives rise to the following modified variation of matter von Neumann entropy

$$\delta S_{m,mod} = \frac{2\pi k_B c}{\hbar}\frac{4\pi}{15}l^4\left(\delta\langle T_{00}\rangle + \delta X\right)\left(1 - \psi l_P^2 \kappa^2\right) + O\left(l^5\right). \tag{14}$$

Note that for the particular case $\psi = 0$ we straightforwardly recover the semiclassical expression.

2.5. *Entropy equivalence*

Assuming the entanglement interpretation of Bekenstein entropy, the natural equilibrium condition for the GLCD involves von Neumann entropy of the matter. To consider the Clausius entropy instead, its equivalence with the von Neumann entropy is necessary. This condition requires that fluxes of Clausius and von Neumann entropy of matter across the horizon are equal with sufficient precision. Since the von Neumann entropy is defined for the geodesic ball Σ_0 corresponding to $t = 0$, the meaningful quantities to compare are time derivatives of both entropies evaluated at $t \ll l/c$ (at precisely $t = 0$ the entropy fluxes vanish). We start by considering conformal fields. For the time derivative Clausius entropy we have[36]

$$\frac{dS_C}{dt}(t) \approx -\frac{32\pi^2 k_B c}{3\hbar}tl^2 T_{00}, \tag{15}$$

while the time derivative of the von Neumann entropy reads[36]

$$\frac{dS_m}{dt} \approx -\frac{32\pi^2 k_B c}{3\hbar}tl^2 \delta\langle T_{00}\rangle. \tag{16}$$

Both expressions are indeed equivalent, making the use of Clausius entropy in thermodynamics of spacetime justified for conformal fields. Note that the argument in no way involves gravitational dynamics.

The situation becomes more complicated for non-conformal matter as the previously outlined approach cannot be directly applied to formulas for the von Neumann entropy.[62,63] Nevertheless, semiclassical gravitational dynamics derived from Clausius and von Neumann entropy are equivalent even in this case,[17,19,36] suggesting that both entropies are at least strongly related.

When low energy quantum gravity effects on the temperature are taken into account, we find for conformal fields

$$\frac{dS_C}{dt}(t) \approx -\frac{32\pi^2 k_B c}{3\hbar}\left(1 - \psi\frac{l_P^2}{c^4}a^2\right) tl^2 T_{00}, \quad (17)$$

and

$$\frac{dS_m}{dt} \approx -\frac{32\pi^2 k_B c}{3\hbar}\left(1 - \psi l_P^2 \kappa^2\right) tl^2 \delta\langle T_{00}\rangle. \quad (18)$$

Both formulas are equivalent only for a special value of the surface gravity, $\kappa = a/c^2$. Since we are not aware of any way to motivate a specific choice of κ, and a needs to be very large, $a \gg c^2/l$, we cannot say anything conclusive about the equivalence of both entropies. We will return to this question after we introduce the modified gravitational dynamics.

3. Effective low energy quantum gravity dynamics

Upon presenting the various notions of entropy involved, we proceed to discuss our proposal for the effective low energy quantum gravitational dynamics. Details of the derivation can be found in the original paper of the authors;[11] here we just briefly recall the main points. For the sake of comparison, we employed two different thermodynamic derivations. The first one, known as the physical process approach, keeps track of the Clausius entropy flux across the horizon and the corresponding changes in its Bekenstein entropy. Equilibrium condition for this process reads $\Delta S_{e,q} + \Delta S_C = 0$, where the Clausius entropy flux contribution, ΔS_C, was discussed in the previous section. The Bekenstein entropy part, $\Delta S_{e,q}$, can be evaluated from the formula for area of GLCD's boundary cross-section introduced in subsection 2.1. After a series of calculations (see[11] for details), we obtain the modified equations of motion

$$S_{\mu\nu} - \frac{Cl_P^2}{18\pi} S_{\mu\lambda} S^\lambda{}_\nu + \frac{Cl_P^2}{72\pi}\left(R_{\kappa\lambda}R^{\kappa\lambda} - \frac{1}{4}R^2\right)g_{\mu\nu} = \frac{8\pi G}{c^4}\left(T_{\mu\nu} - \frac{1}{4}T g_{\mu\nu}\right), \quad (19)$$

where $S_{\mu\nu} = R_{\mu\nu} - Rg_{\mu\nu}/4$ denotes the traceless part of Ricci tensor. The derivation works for GLCD's length scale l much larger than the Planck length but much smaller than the curvature length scale (square root of the inverse of the largest eigenvalue of the Riemann tensor).

The second method to derive the modified equations of motion starts from the entanglement equilibrium hypothesis: "When the geometry and quantum fields are simultaneously varied from maximal symmetry, the entanglement entropy in a small geodesic ball is maximal at fixed volume".[19] For a small variation from a maximally symmetric spacetime the hypothesis implies $\delta S_{e,q} + \delta S_m = 0$, where δS_m denotes the variation of matter von Neumann entropy. From here, calculations proceed similarly as for the physical process approach, yielding[11]

$$S_{\mu\nu} - \frac{\mathcal{C}l_{Pl}^2}{30\pi}S_{\mu\lambda}S^\lambda{}_\nu + \frac{\mathcal{C}l_{Pl}^2}{120\pi}\left(R_{\kappa\lambda}R^{\kappa\lambda} - \frac{1}{4}R^2\right)g_{\mu\nu} = \frac{8\pi G}{c^4}\left(\delta\langle T_{\mu\nu}\rangle - \frac{1}{4}\delta\langle T\rangle g_{\mu\nu}\right). \tag{20}$$

Notably, in neither derivation does the form of modified temperature affect the resulting equations. This is expected as definitions of both Hawking and Unruh temperature (even modified ones) are purely kinematic with no dependence on gravitational dynamics.[64] The correction terms are thus fully determined by the logarithmic contribution to Bekenstein entropy and they depend only on one presently unknown parameter, $\mathcal{C}$.

Comparing the results of both approaches, we can see that the equations have the same form, although coefficients in front of the terms quadratic in curvature differ. We can write both equations in a common form

$$S_{\mu\nu} - D l_P^2 S_{\mu\lambda} S^\lambda{}_\nu + \frac{D}{4}l_P^2\left(R_{\kappa\lambda}R^{\kappa\lambda} - \frac{1}{4}R^2\right)g_{\mu\nu} = \frac{8\pi G}{c^4}\left(\langle T_{\mu\nu}\rangle - \frac{1}{4}\langle T\rangle g_{\mu\nu}\right), \tag{21}$$

with $D = \mathcal{C}/18\pi$ for the physical process approach and $D = \mathcal{C}/30\pi$ for the entanglement equilibrium hypothesis one. In both cases, the coefficient D has the same sign and differs only by a factor $3/5$. The difference might be due to the details of the variation considered in the entanglement equilibrium hypothesis derivation, which is performed at fixed spatial volume.[11,19] Since, for modified theories of gravity, a more complicated quantity known as generalised volume needs to be held fixed instead,[21] finding the appropriate generalised volume in our case could account for the difference in D between both approaches. Alternatively, it might indicate a failure on the equivalence between Clausius and von Neumann entropy of the matter at this level (although, given the similarity of the results, both entropies would have to remain closely related).

Upon reviewing the two derivations of the modified equations of motion, we proceed to discus their properties (for a more detailed treatment, see[11]). First, note that while the value and even the sign of $\mathcal{C}$ is model dependent, any possible value can be viewed as being of the order of unity compared to the squared Planck length, $l_P^2 \approx 2.6 \times 10^{-70}\,\text{m}^2$. Therefore, the correction terms become relevant only when the curvature length scale nears the Planck length (although it needs to remain significantly larger than l_P, otherwise the assumptions of our derivation will break down).

As a second property, it is easy to check that the modified equations are traceless. Hence, they do not imply local energy-momentum conservation. If we want to assume it, we must impose divergence-free energy-momentum tensor, $\langle T_\mu{}^\nu\rangle_{;\nu} = 0$, as an additional condition. Satisfying it requires

$$\frac{1}{4}R_{;\mu} - Dl_P^2\left(S^{\lambda\nu}S_{\mu\lambda}\right)_{;\nu} + \frac{Dl_P^2}{2}\left(R^{\kappa\lambda}R_{\kappa\lambda;\mu} - \frac{1}{4}RR_{;\mu}\right) = -\frac{2\pi G}{c^4}\langle T\rangle_{;\mu}. \tag{22}$$

This condition does not have a general solution for T. Therefore, in general, the equations of motion cannot be recast in a form directly implying a divergence-free energy-momentum tensor. Nevertheless, the condition can be solved for spacetimes with a vanishing Weyl tensor. In that case, the cosmological constant, absent in the traceless equations of motion, appears as an arbitrary integration constant.

Third, while any terms containing higher than fourth derivatives of the metric or more than quadratic in curvature tensors are likely suppressed by higher powers of l_P, the higher derivative terms known from quadratic gravity should appear at the same order as the corrections we propose. They implicitly appear on the right hand side of modified equations in the quantum expectation value of the energy-momentum tensor.[65] In principle, one might also find higher derivative contributions to the left hand side by considering higher orders in the Riemann normal coordinate expansion of the metric. However, these corrections are ambiguous as they depend on shape deformations of the GLCD's horizon.[40] Without a physically motivated way to resolve these ambiguities, it is not possible to determine higher derivative terms contributing to the left hand side of the equations. Since these terms are anyway contained with undetermined coefficients on the right hand side, in the energy-momentum tensor expectation value, their omission on the left hand side does not change the resulting dynamics in any significant way.

Traceless equations of motion and the status of cosmological constant as an arbitrary integration constant both point out to the modified dynamics being a generalisation of unimodular gravity (or, more precisely, Weyl transverse gravity[66]). In fact, even the semiclassical gravitational dynamics derived from thermodynamics has more in common with unimodular gravity than general relativity.[25,36,67] We can partially understand the emergence of unimodular gravity from thermodynamics by noting that only the difference between entropy of two states is relevant for deriving the gravitational dynamics. In other words, vacuum contribution to matter entanglement entropy does not affect the conditions for thermodynamic equilibrium. Consequently, vacuum energy naturally does not couple to gravity, leading to the behaviour of the cosmological constant characteristic for unimodular gravity. Furthermore, thermodynamics of spacetime do not imply local energy-momentum conservation, which always needs to be postulated as an additional condition, again in agreement with unimodular gravity.

3.1. *Application to a cosmological toy model*

To illustrate the physical consequences of the modified dynamics, we examine a simple cosmological toy model, a homogeneous, isotropic, spatially flat universe filled with a perfect fluid with the equation of state $p = (\gamma - 1) c^2 \rho$ for some $\gamma \in [1, 2]$ (the limits correspond to dust and stiff matter, respectively). Due to previously noted unimodular character of the equations, we consider a unimodular form of the

Friedmann-Lemaître-Robertson-Walker (FLRW) metric

$$ds^2 = -\frac{c^2}{a(t)^6}dt^2 + a(t)^2\left(dr^2 + r^2 d\Omega^2\right), \qquad (23)$$

where $a(t)$ denotes the scale factor. Because of the symmetries of the metric, the modified equations of the motion yield only one non-trivial condition

$$\dot{H} - D\frac{l_P^2 \dot{H}^2}{c^2} = -4\pi\gamma G\rho, \qquad (24)$$

where $H = \dot{a}/a$ is the Hubble parameter and the dot denotes a time derivative. This condition corresponds to a modified Raychaudhuri equation, with a correction term, $-Dl_P^2 \dot{H}^2/c^2$, non-linear in second time derivatives of the scale factor. To simplify it, we assume that the Hubble parameter corresponds to its classical value H_0 up to $O(l_P^2)$ terms (validity of this assumption is extensively discussed in[11]),

$$H = H_0 + l_P^2 H_1 + O(l_P^4), \qquad (25)$$

and rewrite the modified Raychaudhuri equations in the following way

$$\dot{H} = -4\pi\gamma G\rho\left(1 - 4\pi D\gamma\frac{\rho}{\rho_P}\right), \qquad (26)$$

where $\rho_P = \sqrt{c^5/G^2\hbar}$ denotes the Planck density. If we further assume local energy-momentum conservation, we can integrate the modified Raychaudhuri equation to obtain the modified Friedmann equation

$$H^2 = \frac{8\pi G\rho}{3}\left(1 - \frac{2\pi D\gamma\rho}{\rho_P}\right) + \tilde{\Lambda}, \qquad (27)$$

where $\tilde{\Lambda}$ is an arbitrary integration constant corresponding to the cosmological term ($\tilde{\Lambda} = \Lambda c^2/3$). We see that the appearance of cosmological constant is indeed consistent with unimodular gravity.

Notably, for $D > 0$, our results correspond to the effective description of loop quantum cosmology (LQC).[68] Since effective dynamics of LQC replaces the Big Bang singularity by a non-singular quantum bounce, the same conclusion holds for our modified equations of motion assuming $D > 0$. The bounce corresponds to a critical density, $\rho_{crit} = \rho_P/2\pi D\gamma$. In other words, if the logarithmic correction to Bekenstein entropy of a GLCD is positive, the resulting modifications of the dynamics are already sufficient to remove the cosmological singularity. On the other hand, the case of $D < 0$ appears to not only preserve the singularity, but actually strengthen the gravitational attraction responsible for it. These preliminary results warrant a more detailed analysis of cosmological models and possible values for parameter D.

4. Discussion

In the present work we have first reviewed the issue of entropy equivalence in thermodynamics of spacetime. For conformal fields in the semiclassical regime, Clausius and von Neumann entropy turn out to be equivalent in the semiclassical regime independently of the gravitational dynamics, although a similar clear result is not available for non-conformal fields.

Then, we proceeded to review our proposal for a new phenomenological perspective on the effects of quantum gravity at low energies. The effective low energy quantum gravitational dynamics we have proposed is based on a single assumption: leading order quantum gravity correction to entropy associated with spherical local causal horizons is logarithmic in the horizon area. Since a number of conceptually different approaches predict such a logarithmic term (at the very least in the case of black hole entropy), our conclusions are fairly robust and relevant to many candidate theories of quantum gravity, e.g. LQG, string theory, AdS/CFT correspondence and GUP phenomenology.

Let us remark that the equations we found are a generalisation of the classical equations of motion of unimodular gravity and cannot even be restated as some generalised Einstein equations. This agrees with our previous results concerning the relation between thermodynamics of spacetime and unimodular gravity in the semiclassical setting. It does appear that the corrections we propose break the equivalence of unimodular gravity and general relativity that holds on the level of classical dynamics.

Our results also extend the semiclassical equivalence between Clausius and entanglement entropies. While they suggest a possible breaking of the exact equivalence on the quantum level, both entropies remain strongly related. Their precise relation should be analysed carefully in a future work. Importantly, a more systematic inclusion of quantum gravity effects on matter entropy will be necessary to completely resolve this issue.

Note that our approach still requires further development. First, issues of diffeomorphism invariance, equivalence principle and locality of the modified dynamics previously discussed by the authors[11] need to be addressed in greater detail. Moreover, the apparent breaking of local energy conservation requires a physically motivated explanation. Relating our proposal to other modified gravity theories might shed some light on all these questions. In particular, our effective equations of motion resemble the 4-dimensional version of Einstein-Gauss-Bonnet gravity[69,70] and non-local effective field theory of gravity.[71] The latter approach even leads to logarithmic term in Bekenstein entropy consistent with our assumptions.[32]

Another possible further development of our results lies in a careful inclusion of higher order Riemann normal coordinate corrections in the analysis in order to obtain higher derivative terms on the left hand side. Similarly, accounting for low energy quantum gravity effects on the entropy of matter might lead to interesting conclusions.

Furthermore, we have seen that the modified dynamics resolve the Big Bang singularity only if the logarithmic correction to entropy of a GLCD is positive, i.e., $D > 0$. To find which approaches to quantum gravity support this sign and what are the bounds on the magnitude of D they imply would help to constrain the physical implications of our proposal.

Lastly, the emergence of unimodular (Weyl transverse) gravity from thermodynamics needs to be better understood even in the semiclassical case. The first steps in this direction include developing rigorous formalism for thermodynamics of spacetime in the Weyl transverse gravity and connecting Weyl invariance of gravitational dynamics with properties of entropy. All these issues will be addressed in future works.

Acknowledgments

AA-S is supported by the ERC Advanced Grant No. 740209. ML is supported by the Charles University Grant Agency project GAUK 297721.

References

1. L. J. Garay, "Quantum gravity and minimum length," Int. J. Mod. Phys. A **10** (1995) 145 [gr-qc/9403008].
2. S. Hossenfelder, "Minimal Length Scale Scenarios for Quantum Gravity," Living Rev. Relativ. **16** (2013) 2 [gr-qc/1203.6191].
3. L. Smolin, "Four principles for quantum gravity," Fundam. Theor. Phys. **187** (2017) 427 [gr-qc/1610.01968].
4. S. Chakraborty, D. Kothawala and A. Pesci, "Raychaudhuri equation with zero point length," Phys. Lett. B **797** (2019) 134877 [gr-qc/1904.09053].
5. l. Buoninfante, G. Luciano, L. Petruzziello and F. Scardigli, "Bekenstein bound and uncertainty relations," [hep-th/2009.12530].
6. J. D. Bekenstein and V. F. Mukhanov, "Spectroscopy of the quantum black hole," Phys. Lett. B **360** (1995) 7 [gr-qc/9505012].
7. R. J. Adler, P. Chen and D. I. Santiago, "The Generalized Uncertainty Principle and Black Hole Remnants," Gen. Rel. Grav. **33** (2001) 2101 [gr-qc/0106080].
8. A. Awad and A. F. Ali, "Minimal Length, Friedmann Equations and Maximum Density," JHEP **06** (2014) 093 [gr-qc/1404.7825].
9. A. Alonso-Serrano, M. P. Dabrowski and H. Gohar, "Generalized uncertainty principle impact onto the black holes information flux and the sparsity of Hawking radiation," Phys. Rev. D **97** (2018) 044029 [gr-qc/1801.09660].
10. R. Casadio, "Quantum black holes and resolution of the singularity," [gr-qc/2103.00183].
11. A. Alonso-Serrano and M. Liška, "Quantum phenomenological gravitational dynamics: A general view from thermodynamics of spacetime," JHEP **2020** (2020) [gr-qc/2009.03826].
12. J. D. Bekenstein, "Black Holes and Entropy," Phys. Rev. D **7** (1973) 2333.
13. J. D. Bardeen, B. Carter and S. W. Hawking, "The Four Laws of Black Hole Mechanics," Commun. Math. Phys. **31** (1973) 161.
14. S. W. Hawking, "Particle Creation by Black Holes," Commun. Math. Phys. **43** (1975) 199.

15. T. Jacobson and R. Parentani, "Horizon Entropy," Found. Phys. **33** (2003) 323 [gr-qc/0302099].
16. R. M. Wald, "Black Hole Entropy is Noether Charge," Phys. Rev. D **48** (1993) 3427 [gr-qc/9307038].
17. T. Jacobson, "Thermodynamics of space-time: The Einstein equation of state," Phys. Rev. Lett. **75** (1995) 1260 [gr-qc/9504004].
18. V. Baccetti and M. Visser, "Clausius entropy for arbitrary bifurcate null surfaces," Class. Quant. Grav. **31** (2014) 035009 [gr-qc/1303.3185].
19. T. Jacobson, "Entanglement Equilibrium and the Einstein Equation," Phys. Rev. Lett. **116** (2016) 201101 [gr-qc/1505.04753].
20. M. Parikh and A. Svesko, "Einstein's Equations from the Stretched Future Light Cone," Phys. Rev. D **98** (2018) 026018 [hep-th/1712.08475].
21. P. Bueno, V. S. Min, A. J. Speranza and M. R. Visser, "Entanglement equilibrium for higher order gravity," Phys. Rev. D **95** (2017) 046003 [hep-th/1612.04374].
22. A. Svesko, "Equilibrium to Einstein: Entanglement, Thermodynamics, and Gravity," Phys. Rev. D **99** (2019) 086006 [hep-th/1810.12236].
23. R. Guedens, T. Jacobson and S. Sarkar, "Horizon entropy and higher curvature equations of state," Phys. Rev. D **85** (2012) 064017 [gr-qc/1112.6215].
24. C. Eling, R. Guedens and T. Jacobson "Non-equilibrium Thermodynamics of Spacetime," Phys. Rev. Lett. **96** (2006) 121301 [gr-qc/0602001].
25. T. Padmanabhan, "Thermodynamical Aspects of Gravity: New insights," Rep. Prog. Phys. **73** (2010) 046901 [gr-qc/0911.5004].
26. G. Chirco, S. Liberati, "Non-equilibrium Thermodynamics of Spacetime: the Role of Gravitational Dissipation," Phys. Rev. D **81** (2010) 024016 [gr-qc/0909.4194v1].
27. R. K. Kaul and P. Majumdar, "Logarithmic Correction to the Bekenstein-Hawking Entropy," Phys. Rev. Lett. **84** (2000) 5255 [gr-qc/0002040].
28. K. A. Meissner, "Black hole entropy in Loop Quantum Gravity," Class. Quant. Grav. **21** (2004) 5245 [gr-qc/0407052].
29. A. Sen, "Logarithmic Corrections to Schwarzschild and Other Non-extremal Black Hole Entropy in Different Dimensions," JHEP **04** (2013) 156 [hep-th/1205.0971].
30. S. Banerjee, R. K. Gupta, I. Mandal and A. Sen, "Logarithmic Corrections to N=4 and N=8 Black Hole Entropy: A One Loop Test of Quantum Gravity," JHEP **11** (2011) 143 [hep-th/1106.0080].
31. T. Faulkner, A. Lewkowycz and J. Maldacena, "Quantum corrections to holographic entanglement entropy," JHEP **2013** (2013) 074 [hep-th/1307.2892].
32. Y. Xiao and Y. Tian, [gr-qc/2104.14902].
33. S. Solodukhin, "Entanglement entropy of black holes," Living Rev. Rel. **14** (2011) 8 [hep-th/1104.3712].
34. S. Das, P. Majumdar and R. K. Bhaduri, "General Logarithmic Corrections to Black Hole Entropy," Class. Quant. Grav. **19** (2002) 2355 [hep-th/0111001].
35. G. Gourd and A. J. M. Medved, "Thermal Fluctuations and Black Hole Entropy," Class. Quant. Grav. **20** (2003) 3307 [gr-qc/0305018].
36. A. Alonso-Serrano and M. Liška, "New Perspective on thermodynamics of spacetime: The emergence of unimodular gravity and the equivalence of entropies," Phys. Rev. D **102** (2020) 104056 [gr-qc/2008.04805].
37. C. W. Misner, K. S. Thorne and J. A. Wheeler, "Gravitation," Princeton University Press, Princeton, NJ, U.S.A. (2017).
38. S. M. Carroll and G. N. Remmen, "What is the Entropy in Entropic Gravity?," Phys Rev D **93** (2016) 124052 [hep-th/1601.07558].

39. G. W. Gibbons and S. Solodukhin, "The Geometry of Small Causal Diamonds," Phys. Lett. B **649** (2007) 317 [hep-th/0703098].
40. T. Jacobson, J. M. M. Senovilla and A. J. Speranza, "Area deficits and the Bel-Robinson tensor," Class. Quant. Grav. **35** (2018) 085005 [gr-qc/1710.07379].
41. J. Wang, "Geometry of small causal diamonds," Phys. Rev. D **100** (2019) 064020 [gr-qc/1904.01034].
42. T. Jacobson and M. R. Visser, "Gravitational Thermodynamics of Causal Diamonds in (A)dS," SciPost Phys **7** (2019) 079 [hep-th/1812.01596].
43. L. Bombelli, R. K. Koul, J. Lee, R. D. Sorkin, "Quantum source of entropy for black holes," Phys. Rev. D **34** 373 (1986).
44. M. Srednicki, "Entropy and area," Phys. Rev. Lett. **71** (1993) 666 [hep-th/9303048v2].
45. T. Jacobson, "Black Hole Entropy and Induced Gravity," [gr-qc/9404039].
46. A. Davidson, "From Planck area to graph theory: Topologically distinct black hole microstates," Phys Rev D **100** (2019) 081502 [hep-th/1907.03090].
47. S. Hod, "High-Order Corrections to the Entropy and Area of Quantum Black Holes," Class. Quant. Grav. **21** (2004) L97 [hep-th/0405235].
48. A. J. M. Medved and E. C. Vagenas, "When conceptual worlds collide: The GUP and the BH entropy," Phys. Rev. D **70** (2004) 124021 [hep-th/0411022].
49. A. J. M. Medved, "A follow-up to 'Does Nature abhor a logarithm?' (and apparently she doesn't)," Class. Quant. Grav. **22** (2005) 5195 [gr-qc/0411065].
50. S. Solodukhin, "Entanglement entropy of round spheres," Phys. Lett. B **693** (2010) 605 [hep-th/1008.4314].
51. L. C. Barbado and M. Visser, "Unruh-DeWitt detector event rate for trajectories with time-dependent acceleration," Phys. Rev. D **86** (2012) 084011 [gr-qc/1207.5525].
52. P. Martinetti and C. Rovelli, "Diamonds's Temperature: Unruh effect for bounded trajectories and thermal time hypothesis," Class. Quant. Grav. **20** (2003) 4919-4932 [gr-qc/0212074].
53. M. Arzano, "Conformal quantum mechanics of causal diamonds," JHEP **2020** (2020) [gr-qc/2002.01836].
54. E. di Casola, S. Liberati, S. Sonego, "Nonequivalence of equivalence principles," Am. J. Phys. **83** (2015) 39 [gr-qc/1310.7426].
55. S. Ghosh, "Quantum Gravity Effects in Geodesic Motion and Predictions of Equivalence Principle Violation," Class. Quant. Grav. **31** (2014) 025025 [gr-qc/1303.1256].
56. V. M. Tkachuk, "Effect of the generalized uncertainty principle on Galilean and Lorentz transformations," Found. Phys. **46** (2016) 1666 [quant-ph/1310.6243].
57. S. Pramanik, "Implication of Geodesic Equation in Generalized Uncertainty Principle framework," Phys. Rev. D **90** (2014) 024023 [hep-th/1404.2567].
58. R. Casadio and F. Scardigli, "Generalized Uncertainty Principle, Classical Mechanics, and General Relativity," Phys. Lett. B **598** (2020) 135558 [gr-qc/2004.04076].
59. F. Scardigli, M. Blasone, G. Luciano and R. Casadio, "Modified Unruh effect from Generalized Uncertainty Principle," Eur. Phys. J. C **78** (2018) 728 [hep-th/1804.05282].
60. G. G. Luciano and L. Petruzziello, "GUP parameter from Maximal Acceleration," Eur. Phys. J. C **79** (2019) 283 [hep-th/1902.07059].
61. E. R. Caianiello, "Maximal acceleration as a consequence of Heisenberg's uncertainty relations," Lett. Nuovo Cimento **41** (1984) 370.
62. A. J. Speranza, "Entanglement entropy of excited states in conformal perturbation theory and the Einstein equation," JHEP **2016** (2016) [hep-th/1602.01380].
63. H. Casini, D. A. Galante, R. C. Myers, "Comments on Jacobson's "Entanglement equilibrium and the Einstein equation"," JHEP **2016** (2016) [hep-th/1601.00528].

64. M. Visser, "Essential and inessential features of Hawking radiation," Int. J. Mod. Phys. D **12** (2003) 649 [hep-th/0106111].
65. R. M. Wald, "Quantum field theory in curved spacetime and black hole thermodynamics," The University of Chicago Press, Chicago, IL, U.S.A. and London, U.K. (1994).
66. C. Barceló, L. J. Garay and R. Carballo-Rubio, "Absence of cosmological constant problem in special relativistic field theory of gravity," Ann. Phys. **398** (2018) 9 [gr-qc/1406.7713].
67. S. C. Tiwari, "Thermodynamics of Spacetime and Unimodular Relativity," (2006) [gr-qc/0612099].
68. A. Ashtekar and B. Gupt, "Generalized effective description of loop quantum cosmology," Phys. Rev. D **92** (2015) 084060 [gr-qc/1509.08899].
69. D. Glavan and C. Lin, "Einstein-Gauss-Bonnet gravity in 4-dimensional space-time," Phys. Rev. Lett. **124** (2019) 081301 [gr-qc/1905.03601].
70. J. Arrechea, A. Delhom and A. Jiménez-Cano, "Inconsistencies in four-dimensional Einstein-Gauss-Bonnet gravity," CPC **45** (2021) 013107 [gr-qc/2004.12998].
71. J. F. Donoghue, "General relativity as an effective field theory: The leading quantum corrections," Phys. Rev. D **50** (1994) 3784 [gr-qc/405057].

Gauge theory of gravity based on the correspondence between the 1st and the 2nd order formalisms

David Benisty

DAMTP, Centre for Mathematical Sciences, University of Cambridge, Wilberforce Road, Cambridge CB3 0WA, UK
Institute of Astronomy, University of Cambridge, Madingley Road, Cambridge, CB3 0HA, UK

A covariant canonical gauge theory of gravity free from torsion is studied. Using a metric conjugate momentum and a connection conjugate momentum, which takes the form of the Riemann tensor, a gauge theory of gravity is formulated, with form-invariant Hamiltonian. By the metric conjugate momenta, a correspondence between the Affine-Palatini formalism and the metric formalism is established. For, when the dynamical gravitational Hamiltonian $\tilde{H}_{Dyn}$ does not depend on the metric conjugate momenta, a metric compatibility is obtained from the equation of motions, and the equations of motion correspond to the solution is the metric formalism.

Keywords: Gauge-Theory; Gravity; Hamiltonian formulation.

1. Introduction

General Relativity is one of the well tested theories in physics, with many excellent predictions. A search of a rigorous derivation of General Relativity on the basis of the action principle and the requirement that the description of any system should be form-invariant under general space time transformations has been constructed in the framework of the Covariant Canonical Gauge theory of Gravity.

The Covariant Canonical Gauge theory of Gravity[1,2] is formulated within the framework of the covariant Hamiltonian formalism of classical field theories. The latter ensures by construction that the action principle is maintained in its form requiring all transformations of a given system to be canonical. The imposed requirement of invariance of the original action integral with respect to local transformations in curved space time is achieved by introducing additional degrees of freedom, the gauge fields. In the basis of the formulation there are two independent fields: the metric $g^{\alpha\beta}$, which contains the information about lengths and angles of the space time, and the connection $\gamma^\lambda_{\alpha\beta}$, which contains the information how a vector transforms under parallel displacement. In this formulation, these two fields are assumed to be independent dynamical quantities in the action and referred to as the Affine-Palatini formalism (or the 1st order formalism).

Using the structure of metric and the affine connection independently, with their conjugate momenta, yields a new formulation of gauge theories of gravity. In[1] the discussion was with the presence of torsion, and here we discuss about the formulation with no torsion from the beginning, that has a link between the metric affine and the metric formalism.[3]

2. A basic formulation

The Covariant Canonical Gauge theory of Gravity is a well defined formulation derived from the canonical transformation theory in the covariant Hamiltonian picture of classical field theories.[1] It identifies two independent fundamental fields, which form the basis for a description of gravity: the metric $g^{\alpha\beta}$ and the connection $\gamma^\lambda_{\alpha\beta}$. In the Hamiltonian description, any fundamental field has a conjugate momentum: the metric conjugate momentum is $\tilde{k}^{\alpha\lambda\beta}$ and the connection conjugate momentum is $\tilde{q}^{\alpha\xi\beta}_\eta$:

$$S = \int_R \left(\tilde{k}^{\alpha\lambda\beta} g_{\alpha\lambda,\beta} - \frac{1}{2}\tilde{q}^{\alpha\xi\beta}_\eta \gamma^\eta_{\alpha\xi,\beta} - \tilde{\mathcal{H}}_0 \right) d^4x \tag{1}$$

where the "tilde" sign denotes a tensor density, which multiplies the tensor with $\sqrt{-g}$. As the conjugate momentum components of the fields are the duals of the complete set of the derivatives of the field, the formulation is referred to as "covariant canonical". A closed description of the coupled dynamics of fields and space-time geometry has been derived in,[1] where the gauge formalism yields:

$$S = \int_R \left(\tilde{k}^{\alpha\lambda\beta} g_{\alpha\lambda;\beta} - \frac{1}{2}\tilde{q}^{\alpha\xi\beta}_\eta R^\eta_{\alpha\xi\beta} - \mathcal{H}(\tilde{q}, \tilde{k}, g) \right) d^4x \tag{2}$$

As a result of the gauge procedure, all partial derivatives of tensors in Eq. (1) reappear as covariant derivatives. The partial derivative of the (non-tensorial) connection changes into the tensor $R^\eta_{\alpha\xi\beta}$, which was shown to be the Riemann-Christoffel curvature tensor:

$$R^\eta_{\alpha\xi\beta} = \frac{\gamma^\eta_{\alpha\beta}}{x^\xi} - \frac{\gamma^\eta_{\alpha\xi}}{x^\beta} + \gamma^\tau_{\alpha\beta}\gamma^\eta_{\tau\xi} - \gamma^\tau_{\alpha\xi}\gamma^\eta_{\tau\beta}. \tag{3}$$

The "dynamics" Hamiltonian $\tilde{H}_{Dyn}$ — which is supposed to describe the dynamics of the free (uncoupled) gravitational field — is to be built from a combination of the metric conjugate momentum, the connection conjugate momentum, and the metric itself.

3. A correspondence between the 1st and the 2nd order formalism

In addition to the foundations of the gauge theory of gravity, it turned out that the part of the action: $\tilde{k}^{\alpha\beta\gamma}g_{\alpha\beta;\gamma}$, which contains the metric conjugate momentum, has a strong impact as a connector between the affine-Palatini formalism (or the 1st order formalism) and the metric formalism (or the 2nd order formalism):

$$\mathcal{L}(g,\gamma)_{1\,\text{order}} + k^{\alpha\beta\gamma}g_{\alpha\beta;\gamma} \Leftrightarrow \mathcal{L}(g)_{2\,\text{order}} \tag{4}$$

In the 1st order formalism, one assumes that there are two independent fields: the metric $g^{\mu\nu}$ and the connection $\gamma^\mu_{\alpha\beta}$. In contrast to that, in the 2nd order formalism the connection is assumed to be the Levi Civita or Christoffel symbol:

$$\gamma^\rho_{\mu\nu} = \begin{Bmatrix} \rho \\ \mu\nu \end{Bmatrix} = \frac{1}{2}g^{\rho\lambda}(g_{\lambda\mu,\nu} + g_{\lambda\nu,\mu} - g_{\mu\nu,\lambda}) \tag{5}$$

and appears in the action directly in this way. In general, only for Lovelock theories, which includes Einstein Hilbert action, both formulations will yield the same equations of motion and the connection will be in both cases the Christoffel symbol. In Ref.,[3] it was proved that for any general action which starts in the 1st order formalism in addition to the term $k^{\alpha\beta\gamma}g_{\alpha\beta;\gamma}$ the energy momentum tensor will be the same as it would be calculated in the 2nd order formalism. The main reason for that correspondence is the metric compatibility constraint. The variation with respect to $k^{\alpha\beta\gamma}$ gives the metricity condition:

$$g_{\alpha\beta;\gamma} = 0 \quad \Rightarrow \quad \gamma^\rho_{\mu\nu} = \left\{ \begin{matrix} \rho \\ \mu\nu \end{matrix} \right\}, \tag{6}$$

which cause the connection to be the Christoffel symbol. The variation with respect to the connection gives the tensors:

$$\frac{\delta}{\delta \gamma^\rho_{\mu\nu}} k^{\alpha\beta\gamma} g_{\alpha\beta;\gamma} = -k^{\alpha\mu\nu} g_{\rho\alpha} - k^{\alpha\nu\mu} g_{\rho\alpha} \tag{7}$$

with a symmetrization between the components μ and ν. The variation with respect to the metric is:

$$\frac{\delta}{\delta g_{\mu\nu}} k^{\alpha\beta\gamma} g_{\alpha\beta;\gamma} = -k^{\mu\nu\lambda}_{;\lambda}. \tag{8}$$

Because of the new contribution to the field equation $k^{\mu\nu\lambda}_{;\lambda}$, the complete field equation will contains additional terms which make the first order field equations to be equivalent to the field equation under the second order formalism. Indeed, isolating the tensor $k^{\mu\nu\lambda}$ and inserting it back into Eq. (8) gives the relation:

$$\frac{\partial \mathcal{L}(\kappa)}{\partial g_{\sigma\nu}} = \frac{1}{2} \nabla_\mu \left(g^{\rho\sigma} \frac{\partial \mathcal{L}(\kappa)}{\partial \gamma^\rho_{\mu\nu}} + g^{\rho\nu} \frac{\partial \mathcal{L}(\kappa)}{\partial \gamma^\rho_{\mu\sigma}} - g^{\rho\mu} \frac{\partial \mathcal{L}(\kappa)}{\partial \gamma^\rho_{\nu\sigma}} \right) \tag{9}$$

where $\mathcal{L}(\kappa) = k^{\alpha\beta\gamma} g_{\alpha\beta;\gamma}$. The terms in the right hand side represents the additional terms that appear in the second order formalism. One option for obtain the contributions into the field equation is to solve $k^{\alpha\beta\gamma}$. The direct way is by using this equation, that gives the new contributions for the second order formalism into the field equation, from the variation with respect to the connection $\gamma^\rho_{\mu\nu}$. An application for this correspondence is from the Covariant Canonical Gauge theory of gravity action (2).

4. Path to Gauge theories

From the correspondence between the 1st and the 2nd order formalisms theorem, we obtain a basic link between the dependence of the $\mathcal{H}_{\mathbf{Dyn}}$ with the metric conjugate momentum $\tilde{k}^{\alpha\beta\gamma}$ and the structure of the metric energy momentum tensor. In the first case, $\mathcal{H}_{\mathbf{Dyn}}$ does not depend on the metric conjugate momentum $\tilde{k}^{\alpha\beta\gamma}$. A variation with respect to the metric conjugate momentum $\tilde{k}^{\alpha\beta\gamma}$ gives the metric compatibility condition. According to the theorem (4) the gravitational energy momentum tensor is the same as the gravitational energy momentum tensor in the second order formalism. In the second case $\mathcal{H}_{\mathbf{Dyn}}$ does depend on the metric conjugate momentum $\tilde{k}^{\alpha\beta\gamma}$. A variation with respect to the metric conjugate momentum $\tilde{k}^{\alpha\beta\gamma}$ breaks the metric compatibility condition. This basic framework is not a special feature only for the Covariant Canonical Gauge Theory of Gravity, but leads to a fundamental correlation for many options of $\mathcal{H}_{Dyn}$.

In analogy to the definition of the metric energy-momentum tensor density of the given system Hamiltonian, the metric energy-momentum tensor density is being define as the variation of the $\tilde{\mathcal{L}}_m$ with respect to the metric:

$$T^{\mu\nu} = -\frac{2}{\sqrt{-g}}\frac{\partial \tilde{\mathcal{L}}_m}{\partial g_{\mu\nu}} \tag{10}$$

Therefore the complete action takes the form:

$$\tilde{\mathcal{L}} = \tilde{k}^{\alpha\beta\gamma}g_{\alpha\beta;\gamma} - \frac{1}{2}\tilde{q}_\lambda^{\alpha\beta\gamma}R^\lambda{}_{\alpha\beta\gamma} - \tilde{\mathcal{H}}_{\mathbf{dyn}}(\tilde{q},\tilde{k},g) + \tilde{\mathcal{L}}_m \tag{11}$$

The variation with respect to the metric conjugate momenta:

$$g_{\alpha\beta;\gamma} = \frac{\partial \tilde{H}_{\mathbf{Dyn}}}{\partial \tilde{k}^{\alpha\beta\gamma}} \tag{12}$$

which presents the existence of non-metricity if $\mathcal{H}_{Dyn}$ depends on $k^{\alpha\beta\gamma}$. The second variation is the variation with respect to the connection:

$$-\left(\tilde{k}^{\alpha\mu\nu} + \tilde{k}^{\alpha\nu\mu}\right)g_{\alpha\rho} = \frac{1}{2}\nabla_\beta\left(\tilde{q}_\rho^{\mu\beta\nu} + \tilde{q}_\rho^{\nu\beta\mu}\right), \tag{13}$$

which contracts the relation between the momenta of the metric and the connection. The third variation is with respect to the connection conjugate momentum $\tilde{q}_\sigma^{\mu\nu\rho}$, which gives:

$$\frac{\partial \tilde{H}_{\mathbf{Dyn}}}{\partial \tilde{q}_\sigma^{\mu\nu\rho}} = -\frac{1}{2}R^\sigma{}_{\mu\nu\rho} \tag{14}$$

If $\tilde{H}_{\mathbf{Dyn}}$ is not depend on $\tilde{q}$, the Riemann tensor will be zero. Therefore the contribution for the stress energy tensor comes from the Dynamical Hamiltonian and from the metric conjugate momenta:

$$T^{\mu\nu} = g^{\mu\nu}(k^{\alpha\beta\gamma}g_{\alpha\beta;\gamma} - \frac{1}{2}q_\lambda^{\alpha\beta\gamma}R^\lambda{}_{\alpha\beta\gamma}) - 2k^{\mu\nu\gamma}_{;\gamma} + \frac{2}{\sqrt{-g}}\frac{\partial \tilde{\mathcal{H}}_{\mathbf{Dyn}}}{\partial g_{\mu\nu}} \tag{15}$$

From the variation with respect the connection (13), the value of the momentum $\tilde{k}^{\alpha\beta\gamma}$. As an example, we consider a Dynamical Hamiltonian which has no dependence with the metric conjugate momentum.

5. Sample $\tilde{\mathcal{H}}_{\mathbf{dyn}}$ without breaking metricity

Our starting point is a dynamical Hamiltonian with the connection conjugate momentum up to the second order, without a dependence on the metric conjugate momentum:

$$\tilde{\mathcal{H}}_{\mathbf{dyn}} = \frac{1}{4g_1}\tilde{q}_\eta^{\alpha\epsilon\beta}q_\alpha^{\eta\tau\lambda}g_{\epsilon\tau}g_{\beta\lambda} - g_2\,\tilde{q}_\eta^{\alpha\tau\beta}g_{\alpha\beta}\delta_\tau^\eta + g_3\sqrt{-g} \tag{16}$$

This Hamiltonian was investigated in[4] under the original formalism for non-zero torsion (which is finally set to zero), and led to resolving the cosmological constant problem. In our case, assuming that there is no torsion, the formalism demands that the energy momentum tensor is covariantly conserved, as is supposed to be in the second order formalism.

The variation with respect to the metric conjugate momenta $\tilde{k}^{\alpha\beta\gamma}$ give the the metricity condition. The variation with respect to the connection conjugate momenta $\tilde{q}_\sigma^{\mu\nu\rho}$ gives

$$q_{\eta\alpha\epsilon\beta} = g_1 \left(R_{\eta\alpha\epsilon\beta} - \hat{R}_{\eta\alpha\epsilon\beta} \right) \tag{17}$$

where:

$$\hat{R}_{\eta\alpha\epsilon\beta} = g_2 \left(g_{\eta\epsilon} g_{\alpha\beta} - g_{\eta\beta} g_{\epsilon\alpha} \right) \tag{18}$$

refers to the ground state geometry of space-time which is the de Sitter (dS) or the anti-de Sitter (AdS) space-time for the positive or the negative sign of g_2, respectively. The last variation is with respect to the metric. In order to isolate the tensor $k^{\mu\nu\gamma}$ one can use the following process: First, we multiply by the metric $g^{\rho\sigma}$ and sum over the index σ:

$$-\tilde{k}^{\sigma\mu\nu} - \tilde{k}^{\sigma\nu\mu} = \frac{1}{2}\nabla_\alpha \left(\tilde{q}^{\sigma\mu\alpha\nu} + \tilde{q}^{\sigma\nu\alpha\mu} \right) \tag{19}$$

Switching the indices $\sigma \leftrightarrow \nu$ and the indices $\mu \leftrightarrow \nu$ gives a new combination of the $k^{\alpha\beta\gamma}$ tensor. By summing the Eqs. the isolated value gives:

$$-\tilde{k}^{\sigma\nu\mu} = \frac{1}{2}\nabla_\alpha \left(\tilde{q}^{\sigma\mu\alpha\nu} + \tilde{q}^{\nu\mu\alpha\sigma} \right) \tag{20}$$

Therefore, the contribution for the stress energy momentum comes from the covariant derivative of (20):

$$T^{\mu\nu} = -\frac{1}{2}g^{\mu\nu}q_\lambda^{\alpha\beta\gamma}R^\lambda_{\alpha\beta\gamma} + \nabla_\gamma\nabla_\alpha(q^{\mu\gamma\nu\alpha} + q^{\nu\gamma\mu\alpha}) + \frac{2}{\sqrt{-g}}\frac{\partial\tilde{\mathcal{H}}_{\text{Dyn}}}{\partial g_{\mu\nu}} \tag{21}$$

Plugging in the value of the tensor $q_{\alpha\beta\gamma\delta}$ from Eq. (17) gives the result:

$$T^{\mu\nu} = \frac{1}{8\pi G}G^{\mu\nu} + g^{\mu\nu}\Lambda$$
$$+g_1\left(R^{\mu\alpha\beta\gamma}R^\nu_{\alpha\beta\gamma} - \frac{1}{4}g^{\mu\nu}R^{\alpha\beta\gamma\delta}R_{\alpha\beta\gamma\delta} + (\nabla_\alpha\nabla_\beta + \nabla_\beta\nabla_\alpha)R^{\mu\alpha\nu\beta}\right) \tag{22}$$

where $G^{\mu\nu}$ is the Einstein tensor. The coupling constants relate to the physical quantities with the relations:

$$g_1 g_2 = \frac{1}{16\pi G}, \quad 6g_1 g_2^2 + g_3 = \frac{\Lambda}{8\pi G} \tag{23}$$

This stress energy momentum tensor is exactly the same metric energy momentum tensor if our starting point was the effective Lagrangian:

$$\mathcal{L} = g_1 R^{\alpha\beta\gamma\delta}R_{\alpha\beta\gamma\delta} - \frac{1}{16\pi G}(R - 2\Lambda) \tag{24}$$

and the stress energy momentum tensor is the same stress energy momentum tensor for this Lagrangian in the second order formalism. One from the big benefits of this formulation is common in many gauge theories of gravity,[5] where the starting point is with additional variables with no higher derivatives in the action, and the equations of motion are equivalent to actions with higher derivatives of metric. In this specific case, the starting point is with the quartic momentum q and at the end is equivalent to an action with quadratic Riemann term.

6. Discussion

In this paper we investigated the formulation of the covariant canonical gauge theory of gravity free from torsion. Diffeomorphisms appear as canonical transformations. A tensor field which plays the role of the canonical conjugate of the metric is introduced. It enforces the metricity condition provided that the "Dynamics" Hamiltonian does not depend on this field. The resulting theory has a direct correspondence with our recent work concerning the correspondence between the first order formalism and the second order formalism through the introduction of a Lagrange multiplier field which in this case corresponds with the field that is used to provide the metric with a canonically conjugate momentum. The procedure is exemplified by using a "Dynamics" Hamiltonian which consists of a quadratic term of the connection conjugate momentum. The effective stress energy momentum tensor that emerged from the canonical equations of motion were equivalent to Einstein Hilbert tensor in addition to quadratic term.[6] derives the complete combination for the quadratic theories of gravity with R^2 and $R_{\mu\nu}R^{\mu\nu}$.[7] derives inflation from fermios based on the Covariant Canonical Gauge theories of Gravity approach to spinors.[8]

References

1. J. Struckmeier, J. Muench, D. Vasak, J. Kirsch, M. Hanauske and H. Stoecker, *Phys. Rev. D* **95** (2017) 124048, arXiv:1704.07246 [gr-qc].
2. J. Struckmeier, J. Muench, P. Liebrich, M. Hanauske, J. Kirsch, D. Vasak, L. Satarov and H. Stoecker, *Int. J. Mod. Phys. E* **28** (2019) 1950007, arXiv:1711.10333 [gr-qc].
3. D. Benisty and E. I. Guendelman, *Phys. Rev. D* **98** (2018) 044023, arXiv:1805.09667 [gr-qc].
4. D. Vasak, J. Struckmeier, J. Kirsch and H. Stoecker (2 2018) arXiv:1802.07137 [gr-qc].
5. M. H. Lagraa, M. Lagraa and N. Touhami, *Class. Quant. Grav.* **34** (2017) 115010, arXiv:1606.06918 [gr-qc].
6. D. Benisty, E. I. Guendelman, D. Vasak, J. Struckmeier and H. Stoecker, *Phys. Rev. D* **98** (2018) 106021, arXiv:1809.10447 [gr-qc].
7. D. Benisty, E. I. Guendelman, E. N. Saridakis, H. Stoecker, J. Struckmeier and D. Vasak, *Phys. Rev. D* **100** (2019) 043523, arXiv:1905.03791 [gr-qc].
8. J. Struckmeier, D. Vasak, A. Redelbach, P. Liebrich and H. Stöcker (12 2018) arXiv:1812.09669 [gr-qc].

$U(1)$ local strings in hybrid metric-Palatini gravity

Tiberiu Harko

Astronomical Observatory, 19 Ciresilor Street, 400487 Cluj-Napoca, Romania
Faculty of Physics, Babes-Bolyai University, 1 Kogalniceanu Street, 400084 Cluj-Napoca, Romania
School of Physics, Sun Yat-Sen University, Xingang Road, 510275 Guangzhou, People's Republic of China

Francisco S. N. Lobo

Instituto de Astrofísica e Ciências do Espaço, Faculdade de Ciências da Universidade de Lisboa, Edifício C8, Campo Grande, P-1749-016 Lisbon, Portugal

Hilberto M. R. da Silva

Instituto de Astrofísica e Ciências do Espaço, Universidade do Porto, CAUP, Rua das Estrelas, PT4150-762 Porto, Portugal and Centro de Astrofísica da Universidade do Porto, Rua das Estrelas, PT4150-762 Porto, Portugal

In this work we made use of a general static cillindrically symmetric metric to find $U(1)$ local cosmic string solutions in the context of the hybrid metric-Palatini theory of gravity in it's scalar-tensor representation. After finding the dynamical equations for this particular case, we imposed boost invariance along t and z directions, which simplified the equations of motions, leaving only one single metric tensor component, $W^2(r)$. For an arbitrary potential $V(\phi)$, the solutions obtained can be put in a closed parametric form, with ϕ taken as a parameter. Several particular cases of the potential were studied, some yielding simple mathematical forms, others with only numerical solutions. In this way, we obtain a large class of novel stable stringlike solutions in the context of hybrid metric-Palatini gravity, in which the basic parameters, such as the scalar field, metric tensor components, and string tension, depend essentially on the initial values of the scalar field, and of its derivative, on the $r(0)$ circular axis.

Keywords: Cosmic Strings, Modified Gravity, hybrid metric-Palatini theory

1. Introduction

The recent observation of the accelerated expansion of the Universe[1] brought an identity crisis upon the standard theory of gravity, General Relativity. Albeit being a well established theory, with several important experimental confirmations, there is now a wide agreement that General Relativity may be, at the very least, an incomplete theory.[2] Not only due to the observations that demand the introduction of a Dark Sector to the energy budget of the Universe, but also due to theoretical difficulties, namely the existence of mathematical singularities and the non-quantization of the theory.[3] All of these issues paved the way to more general theories for gravitation, focusing on solving some of these problems, or at least to be used to falsify the theory. Lovelock's theorem[4] is a crucial roadmap to this quest, as it establishes the GR equations as the only possible solution (minus constant factors), if one assumes the same conditions Einstein followed when he proposed the theory. In order to produce a viable modified gravity theory, at least one of the assumptions must be broken.

The hybrid metric-Palatini theory was proposed by Capozzielo, Harko, Koivisto, Lobo and Olmo in 2011[5] in order to overcome the difficulties faced by $f(R)$ theories of gravity and successfully unifies the late-time cosmic acceleration period with the weak-field solar system dynamics without the need for chameleon mechanisms.[5] For a more in-depth review of the theory, we refer the reader to the review article.[6] In this theory, the connection is considered an independent dynamical variable, adding to the metric.

Cosmic strings are one of the possible topological defects formed after spontaneous symmetry breaking (SSB) during phase transitions in the history of the Universe. In fact, many grand unification theories (GUTs) postulate that the universe, as it cooled, underwent a series of phase transitions associated with SSB, meaning that at sufficiently high temperatures there was invariance under a more general group of symmetries. Each of these phase transitions may have left behind a network of topological defects, through the Kibble-Zurek mechanism. For a more in depth review of topological defects, we refer the reader to Ref. 7.

The type of strings to be considered in this work are local $U(1)$ cosmic strings, which are an extension of the global $U(1)$ strings to include gauge fields. Local strings differ from the global cosmic strings in what concerns the symmetry that is effective above the spontaneous breaking scale; in the case of local strings, the lagrangian remains invariant under local transformations of the type $\phi(x) \longrightarrow e^{i\alpha(x)}\phi(x)$.

The study of the properties and dynamics of cosmic strings in the context of modified theories of gravity is crucial in the advent of powerful observatories, such as LISA, as it may allow us to constrain both Modified Gravity theories and Grand Unified theories.

2. Hybrid metric-Palatini gravity

In this hybrid regime, the metric and Palatini approaches are combined, by adding a new term, $f(\mathcal{R})$ to the Einstein-Hilbert action:

$$S = \frac{1}{2\kappa^2} \int \sqrt{-g} \, d^4x \, [R + f(\mathcal{R}) + \mathcal{L}_m]. \tag{1}$$

where $\mathcal{R}$ is the Ricci-Palatini scalar, the geometrical analogous to the Ricci scalar, constructed in terms of an independent connection, $\hat{\Gamma}$:

$$\mathcal{R}_{\mu\nu} = \partial_\alpha \hat{\Gamma}^\alpha_{\mu\nu} - \partial_\nu \hat{\Gamma}^\alpha_{\mu\alpha} + \hat{\Gamma}^\alpha_{\alpha\beta}\hat{\Gamma}^\beta_{\mu\nu} - \hat{\Gamma}^\alpha_{\mu\beta}\hat{\Gamma}^\beta_{\alpha\nu}. \tag{2}$$

$$\mathcal{R} = g^{\mu\nu}\mathcal{R}_{\mu\nu} \tag{3}$$

In this theory we have two dynamical variables, the metric and the (independent) connection. And so, we apply variation calculations of the action with respect to both.

Varying (1) with respect to the metric, $g_{\mu\nu}$ we obtain

$$G_{\mu\nu} + \frac{df}{d\mathcal{R}}\mathcal{R}_{\mu\nu} - \frac{1}{2}f(\mathcal{R})g_{\mu\nu} = \kappa^2 T_{\mu\nu} \tag{4}$$

where $T_{\mu\nu}$ is the energy-momentum tensor defined, as usual, as:

$$T_{\mu\nu} \equiv -\frac{2}{\sqrt{-g}}\frac{\delta(\sqrt{-g}\mathcal{L}_m)}{\delta(g^{\mu\nu})} \tag{5}$$

When we perform the variation of the action (1) with respect to the independent connection, $\hat{\Gamma}$, the resulting equation is:

$$\hat{\nabla}_\alpha = \left(\sqrt{-g}\frac{df}{d\mathcal{R}}g^{\mu\nu}\right) \tag{6}$$

which has an interesting feature: if we consider a metric conformally related to $g_{\mu\nu}$ by a $\frac{df}{d\mathcal{R}}$ factor, $h_{\mu\nu} = \frac{df}{d\mathcal{R}}g_{\mu\nu}$, equation (6) implies that the independent connection $\hat{\Gamma}$ is the Levi-Civita connection of such metric.

One of the useful features of the hybrid metric-Palatini theory is that it admits a scalar-tensor representation, which simplifies the analysis of the dynamics of the theory.

Let's introduce an auxiliary field, A, so that the action (1) becomes

$$S = \frac{1}{2\kappa^2}\int \sqrt{-g}\, d^4x \left[\Omega_A R + f(A) + \frac{df}{dA}(\mathcal{R} - A) + \mathcal{L}_m\right]. \tag{7}$$

where the coupling constant Ω_A is introduced for generality. If we further define $\phi \equiv \frac{df}{dA}$ and $V(\phi) \equiv A\frac{df}{dA} - f(A)$, the action becomes:

$$S = \frac{1}{2\kappa^2}\int \sqrt{-g}\, d^4x \left[\Omega_A R + \phi\mathcal{R} - V(\phi) + \mathcal{L}_m\right]. \tag{8}$$

Since we now have three dynamical variables, the metric $g_{\mu\nu}$, the independent connection, $\hat{\Gamma}$ and the scalar field ϕ, we perform the variation of the action (8) with respect to each of the dynamical variables, resulting in the following equations of motion:

$$\Omega_A R_{\mu\nu} + \phi\mathcal{R}_{\mu\nu} - \frac{1}{2}(\Omega_A R + \phi\mathcal{R} - V(\phi))g_{\mu\nu} = \kappa^2 T_{\mu\nu} \tag{9}$$

$$\mathcal{R} - V_\phi = 0 \tag{10}$$

$$\hat{\nabla}_\alpha = \left(\sqrt{-g}\phi g_{\mu\nu}\right) \tag{11}$$

As we've seen before, the last equation implies that the independent connection is the Levi-Civita connection to a conformal related metric to $g_{\mu\nu}$: $h_{\mu\nu} = \phi g_{\mu\nu}$, allowing us to write the Ricci-Palatini tensor from the Ricci tensor and the conformal factor ϕ:

$$\mathcal{R}_{\mu\nu} = R_{\mu\nu} - \frac{1}{\phi}\left(\nabla_\mu \nabla_\nu \phi + \frac{1}{2}g_{\mu\nu}\Box\phi\right) + \frac{3}{2\phi^2}\partial_\mu\phi\partial_\nu\phi \qquad (12)$$

$$\mathcal{R} = R + \frac{3}{\phi}\Box\phi - \frac{3}{2\phi^2}\partial_\mu\phi\partial^\mu\phi \qquad (13)$$

where $\Box \equiv \nabla_\mu \nabla^\mu$ in the D'Alembert operator. Eq.(13) can be used to recast the action (8) into the following form:

$$S = \frac{1}{2\kappa^2}\int \sqrt{-g}\, d^4x \left[(\Omega_A + \phi)R + \frac{3}{2\phi}\partial_\mu\phi\partial^\mu\phi - V(\phi) + \mathcal{L}_m\right]. \qquad (14)$$

We can note now three different cases for the value of the coupling constant Ω_A, for $\Omega_A = 1$ we have the original hybrid threory, for $\Omega_A = 0$ we have the Palatini-$f(\mathcal{R})$ gravity and for $\Omega_A \to \infty$ we recover the metric-$f(R)$ theory.

Using eqs.(2) and (10), we can rewrite eq.(9) in the scalar-tensor representation for the original hybrid theory as:

$$(1+\phi)R_{\mu\nu} = \kappa^2\left(T_{\mu\nu} - \frac{1}{2}g_{\mu\nu}T\right) + \frac{1}{2}g_{\mu\nu}(V + \Box\phi) + \nabla_\mu\nabla_\nu\phi - \frac{3}{2\phi}\partial_\mu\phi\partial_\nu\phi \qquad (15)$$

In this equation we can conclude that the curvature of spacetime is due not only to the matter distribution, but also to the presence of the scalar field.

Taking the trace of equation (9) with $g^{\mu\nu}$, and using equation (10), we get

$$2V - \phi V_\phi = \kappa^2 T + \Omega_A R \qquad (16)$$

If we now rewrite eq. (16) using eqs. (13) and (10), we get an effective Klein-Gordon equation for the scalar field:

$$-\Box\phi + \frac{1}{2\phi}\partial_\mu\phi\partial^\mu\phi + \frac{\phi[2V - (1+\phi)V_\phi]}{3} = \frac{\phi\kappa^2}{3}T \qquad (17)$$

Which demonstrates that, unlike the purely Palatini case, the scalar field is dynamic and the theory is therefore not affected by the instabilities found in the Palatini gravity.[8]

3. Dynamical equations of local strings in Hybrid metric-palatini using Vilenkin's approximation

For the study of local $U(1)$ string in the context of the hybrid metric-Palatini gravity, we will start by defining the energy-momentum tensor of a straight, infinite cosmic string along the z-direction. Following Vilenkin's prescription,[9] one possible energy-momentum tensor is

$$T_r^r = T_t^t = -\sigma(r) \qquad (18)$$

where $\sigma(r)$ is the linear energy density of the string.

We consider a general cylindrically symmetric static metric

$$ds^2 = -e^{2(K-U)}dt^2 + e^{2(K-U)}dr^2 + e^{-2U}W^2 d\theta^2 + e^{2U}dz^2 \qquad (19)$$

Where t, r, θ and z denote the time, radial, angular and axial cylindrical coordinates respectively, and K, U and W are functions of r alone.

Inserting the metric (19) into the gravitational field equation (15) provides the following components

$$(1+\phi)\left(-U'^2 + K'\frac{W'}{W} - \frac{W''}{W}\right) = \phi'' - \frac{3}{4\phi}\phi'^2$$
$$-\left(K' - U' - \frac{W'}{W}\right)\phi' + \left(\kappa^2 \sigma + \frac{1}{2}V\right)e^{2(K-U)}, \qquad (20)$$

$$(1+\phi)\left(-U'^2 + K'\frac{W'}{W}\right) = -\frac{3}{4\phi}\phi'^2 - \left(K' - U' + \frac{W'}{W}\right)\phi' - \frac{1}{2}Ve^{2(K-U)}, \qquad (21)$$

$$(1+\phi)\left(U'^2 + K''\right) = -\phi'' + \frac{3}{4\phi}\phi'^2 - U'\phi' - \frac{1}{2}Ve^{2(K-U)}, \qquad (22)$$

$$(1+\phi)\left(U'^2 + K'' - 2U'' - 2U'\frac{W'}{W} + \frac{W''}{W}\right) = -\phi''$$
$$+\frac{3}{4\phi}\phi'^2 + \left(U' - \frac{W'}{W}\right)\phi' - \left(\kappa^2 \sigma + \frac{1}{2}V\right)e^{2(K-U)}. \qquad (23)$$

Additionally, we can use Eq. (17) to determine the effective Klein-Gordon equation for the scalar field ϕ:

$$e^{-2(K-U)}\left(-\phi'' - \frac{W'}{W}\phi' + \frac{\phi'^2}{2\phi}\right) + \frac{\phi}{3}[2V - (\phi+1)V_{,\phi}] \frac{2\phi \kappa^2 \sigma}{3} = 0. \qquad (24)$$

Since in this model the matter field couples minimally with curvature, it's possible to show that the energy conservation equation still holds, i.e.,

$$\nabla_\mu T^\mu{}_\nu = 0 \qquad (25)$$

which yields $K'\sigma = 0$, and apart from the trivial vacuum solution, $\sigma = 0$, this implies that $K' = 0$. Thus, we consider from now on that $e^K = 1$, so that Eqs. (20)–(23) simplify to the following relations

$$(1+\phi)\left(-U'^2 - \frac{W''}{W}\right) = \phi'' - \frac{3}{4\phi}\phi'^2 + \left(U' + \frac{W'}{W}\right)\phi'$$
$$+ \left(\kappa^2 \sigma + \frac{1}{2}V\right)e^{-2U}, \qquad (26)$$

$$(1+\phi)U'^2 = \frac{3}{4\phi}\phi'^2 + \left(-U' + \frac{W'}{W}\right)\phi' + \frac{1}{2}Ve^{-2U}, \qquad (27)$$

$$(1+\phi)U'^2 = -\phi'' + \frac{3}{4\phi}\phi'^2 - U'\phi' - \frac{1}{2}Ve^{-2U}, \qquad (28)$$

$$(1+\phi)\left(U'^2 - 2U'' - 2U'\frac{W'}{W} + \frac{W''}{W}\right) = -\phi'' + \frac{3}{4\phi}\phi'^2$$
$$+ \left(U' - \frac{W'}{W}\right)\phi' - \left(\kappa^2\sigma + \frac{1}{2}V\right)e^{-2U}, \qquad (29)$$

With the effective Klein-Gordon equation for the scalar field ϕ reducing to

$$e^{2U}\left(-\phi'' - \frac{W'}{W}\phi' + \frac{\phi'^2}{2\phi}\right) + \frac{\phi}{3}[2V - (\phi+1)V_{,\phi}] + \frac{2\phi\kappa^2\sigma}{3} = 0. \qquad (30)$$

If we further consider that local gauge strings preserve boost invariance along the t and z directions,[9] meaning, in this case, that $U = 0$, the gravitational field equations simplify considerably:

$$(1+\phi)\left(-\frac{W''}{W}\right) = \phi'' - \frac{3}{4\phi}\phi'^2 + \frac{W'}{W}\phi' + \kappa^2\sigma + \frac{1}{2}V, \qquad (31)$$

$$0 = \frac{3}{4\phi}\phi'^2 + \frac{W'}{W}\phi' + \frac{1}{2}V, \qquad (32)$$

$$0 = -\phi'' + \frac{3}{4\phi}\phi'^2 - \frac{1}{2}V, \qquad (33)$$

$$(1+\phi)\frac{W''}{W} = -\phi'' + \frac{3}{4\phi}\phi'^2 - \frac{W'}{W}\phi' - \kappa^2\sigma - \frac{1}{2}V. \qquad (34)$$

where we can see now that Eqs. (31) and (34) become redundant. Combining Eqs. (32) and (33) yields the following relation for the potential V:

$$V = -\phi'' - \frac{W'}{W}\phi', \qquad (35)$$

substituting into the Klein-Gordon equation (30), the latter reduces to:

$$V(3 + 2\phi) - V_\phi\phi(\phi + 1) + 2\kappa^2\sigma\phi + \frac{3\phi'^2}{2\phi} = 0. \qquad (36)$$

Additionally, we can further deduce:

$$\kappa^2\sigma = \frac{1}{W}[(1+\phi)W']', \qquad (37)$$

and

$$\frac{[(1+\phi)W]''}{W} = -(V + \kappa^2\sigma). \qquad (38)$$

An important physical parameter characterizing the cosmic string properties is the mass per unit length of the string, which is defined as

$$m(r) = \int_0^{2\pi} d\theta \int_0^{R_s} \sigma(r)W(r)dr$$
$$= 2\pi \int_0^{R_s} \sigma(r)W(r)dr, \qquad (39)$$

where R_s is the string radius.

The set of the previous equations allows us to write the gravitational equations of a cosmic string in hybrid metric-Palatini gravity in an exact(closed) form, with all the geometric and physical quantities expressed in a parametric form, in ϕ taken as the parameter.

By taking into account Eq. (33), the field equations (31) and (34) reduce to the form

$$(1+\phi)\frac{W''}{W} = -\frac{W'}{W}\phi' - \kappa^2\sigma. \tag{40}$$

3.1. *Parametric form of the dynamical equations*

From a mathematical point of view Equation (33) is independent of the metric tensor coefficient W and it represents a second order nonlinear differential equation. In order to solve it we first rescale the radial coordinate r according to the transformation $r = \beta\xi$. Hence Eq. (33) takes the form

$$\frac{d^2\phi}{d\xi^2} - \frac{3}{4\phi}\left(\frac{d\phi}{d\xi}\right)^2 + \frac{1}{2}\beta^2 V(\phi) = 0. \tag{41}$$

In order to solve Eq. (41) we introduce the transformations

$$\frac{d\phi}{d\xi} = u, \quad \frac{d^2\phi}{d\xi^2} = \frac{du}{d\xi} = \frac{du}{d\phi}\frac{d\phi}{d\xi} = u\frac{du}{d\phi} = \frac{1}{2}\frac{d}{d\phi}u^2, \tag{42}$$

and

$$u^2 = v, \tag{43}$$

respectively. Then Eq. (41) becomes a first order linear differential equation of the form

$$\frac{dv}{d\phi} - \frac{3}{2\phi}v + \beta^2 V(\phi) = 0, \tag{44}$$

with the general solution given by

$$v(\phi) = \phi^{3/2}\left[C - \beta^2 \int \phi^{-3/2}V(\phi)d\phi\right], \tag{45}$$

where C is an arbitrary constant of integration. We immediately obtain

$$u(\phi) = \phi^{3/4}\sqrt{\left[C - \beta^2 \int \phi^{-3/2}V(\phi)d\phi\right]}, \tag{46}$$

and

$$\xi + C_0 = \int \frac{\phi^{-3/4}d\phi}{\sqrt{\left[C - \beta^2 \int \phi^{-3/2}V(\phi)d\phi\right]}}, \tag{47}$$

respectively, where C_0 is an arbitrary constant of integration.

Equation (32) can be successively transformed as

$$\frac{1}{W}\frac{dW}{d\xi}\frac{d\phi}{d\xi} = -\frac{3}{4\phi}\left(\frac{d\phi}{d\xi}\right)^2 - \frac{\beta^2}{2}V(\phi), \qquad (48)$$

and

$$\frac{1}{W}\frac{dW}{d\phi} = -\frac{3}{4\phi} - \frac{\beta^2}{2}\frac{\phi^{-3/2}V(\phi)}{[C - \beta^2 \int \phi^{-3/2}V(\phi)d\phi]}$$
$$= -\frac{3}{4\phi} + \frac{1}{2}\frac{d}{d\phi}\ln\left[C - \beta^2 \int \phi^{-3/2}V(\phi)d\phi\right], \qquad (49)$$

yielding

$$W(\phi) = W_0 \phi^{-3/4}\sqrt{C - \beta^2 \int \phi^{-3/2}V(\phi)d\phi}, \qquad (50)$$

where W_0 is an arbitrary constant of integration.

As a last step we need to obtain the expression of σ. With the use of Eq. (32), then Eq. (40) can be rewritten as

$$(1+\phi)\frac{1}{W}\frac{d^2W}{d\xi^2} = \frac{3}{4\phi}\left(\frac{d\phi}{d\xi}\right)^2 + \frac{1}{2}\beta^2 V(\phi) - \beta^2\kappa^2\sigma. \qquad (51)$$

With the use of the mathematical identities

$$\frac{dW}{d\xi} = \frac{dW}{d\phi}\frac{d\phi}{d\xi} = \frac{dW}{d\phi}u, \qquad (52)$$

$$\frac{d^2W}{d\xi^2} = \frac{d^2W}{d\phi^2}v + \frac{1}{2}\frac{dW}{d\phi}\frac{dv}{d\phi}, \qquad (53)$$

Eq. (51) takes the form

$$(1+\phi)\left(\frac{1}{W}\frac{d^2W}{d\phi^2}v + \frac{1}{2}\frac{1}{W}\frac{dW}{d\phi}\frac{dv}{d\phi}\right) = \frac{3}{4\phi}v + \frac{1}{2}\beta^2 V(\phi) - \beta^2\kappa^2\sigma. \qquad (54)$$

Finally, after some simple calculations we obtain

$$\kappa^2\sigma(\phi) = \frac{1}{4\phi}\left\{\left[2\phi(\phi+1)V'(\phi) + 3\sqrt{\phi}\int\frac{V(\phi)}{\phi^{3/2}}d\phi\right. \right.$$
$$\left.\left. -2(2\phi+3)V(\phi)\right] - 3\left(C/\beta^2\right)\sqrt{\phi}\right\}. \qquad (55)$$

Equation (47), (50) and (55) give the complete solution of the field equations describing the geometry of a cosmic string in hybrid metric-Palatini gravity. The solution is obtained in a parametric form, with ϕ taken as a parameter. It also contains three arbitrary integration constants ξ_0, C, and W_0 which must be obtained from the initial or boundary conditions imposed on the cosmic string configuration.

As for the mass of the string, in the dimensionless variable ξ it can be obtained as

$$m(\xi) = 2\pi\beta \int_0^{\xi_s} \sigma(\xi)W(\xi)d\xi, \tag{56}$$

where $\xi_s = R_s/\beta$.

In order to study specific cosmic string solutions in the hybrid metric-Palatini framework, we need now to specify the form of the potential $V(\phi)$.

4. Solutions to the dynamical equations with specific potentials

In this section we will investigate the application of the set of parametric equations deduced on the previous section to different potential configurations, for a more complete set of possible potential configurations, we refer the reader to the original article Ref. 10.

4.1. Power law potential

The gravitational field equations describing a cosmic string in hybrid metric-Palatini gravity admit an exact solution, corresponding to the power law type scalar field potential $V(\phi) = V_0 \phi^{3/4}$. We rescale the radial coordinate r by imposing the condition $\beta^2 V_0 = 1$, which gives $r = \xi/\sqrt{V_0}$. With these choices from Eq. (47) we obtain explicitly the scalar field as a function of ξ, given by

$$\phi(\xi) = \frac{\left(\xi^2 \phi_0^{3/4} \pm 2\xi\phi_0' \pm 8\phi_0\right)^4}{4096\phi_0^3}, \tag{57}$$

where we have used the usual initial conditions $\phi(0) = \phi_0$ and $\phi'(0) = \phi_0'$, respectively. For the metric tensor component W we obtain

$$W(\xi) = \frac{W_0}{\left(\xi^2 \phi_0^{3/4} \pm 2\xi\phi_0' \pm 8\phi_0\right)^3 \sqrt{2\xi \pm 2\phi_0'/\phi_0^{3/4}}}. \tag{58}$$

where W_0 is an arbitrary constant of integration. On the string axis, i.e., $\xi = 0$, we obtain $W^2(0) = \pm W_0^2/524288\,\phi_0^{21/4}\phi_0'$. Since the metric tensor component W^2 must be positive for all $\xi \geq 0$, it follows that the physical solution for the string configuration is the one with the positive sign. Hence in the case of the $V(\phi) = V_0\phi^{3/4}$ potential, the solutions of the field equations describing a cosmic string in hybrid metric-Palatini gravity are

$$\phi(\xi) = \frac{\left(\xi^2 \phi_0^{3/4} + 2\xi\phi_0' + 8\phi_0\right)^4}{4096\phi_0^3},$$

$$W^2(\xi) = \frac{W_0^2}{\left(\xi^2 \phi_0^{3/4} + 2\xi\phi_0' + 8\phi_0\right)^6 \left(2\xi + 2\phi_0'/\phi_0^{3/4}\right)}, \tag{59}$$

respectively, with $W_0{}^2 = 524288\, W^2(0)\phi_0{}^{21/4}\phi_0'$, a condition that implies $\phi_0 > 0$ and $\phi_0' > 0$. For the string tension as a function of ϕ and ξ we obtain the expressions

$$\kappa^2 \sigma(\phi) = V_0 \frac{-6C - 5(\phi - 3)\sqrt[4]{\phi}}{8\sqrt{\phi}}, \tag{60}$$

and

$$\kappa^2 \sigma(\xi) = \frac{V_0 \phi_0^{3/4}}{\left(\xi^2 \phi_0^{3/4} + 2\xi\phi_0' + 8\phi_0\right)^2} \Bigg\{ -48C\phi_0^{3/4} - 5\left(\xi^2 \phi_0^{3/4} + 2\xi\phi_0' + 8\phi_0\right) \times \left[\frac{(\xi^2 \phi_0^{3/4} + 2\xi\phi_0' + 8\phi_0)^4}{4096\phi_0^3} - 3 \right] \Bigg\}, \tag{61}$$

respectively.

In this case, the scalar field is a monotonically increasing function of the radial distance from the string axis and tends to infinity for $\xi \to \infty$. On the other hand, the metric tensor component decreases monotonically from a finite value on the string axis to zero at infinity. For $\xi = 0$, the string tension takes the finite value

$$\sigma(0) = V_0 \left[-48C\phi_0^{3/4} - 40\left(\phi_0 - 3\right)\phi_0 \right] / 64\phi_0^{5/4} \tag{62}$$

while $\lim_{\xi \to \infty} \sigma(\xi) = -\infty$, indicating that σ is a monotonically decreasing function of the radial coordinate. In the first order of approximation we obtain for the mass of the string of radius ξ_s the expression

$$m = \frac{\pi \beta W_0 \xi_s}{8192 \phi_0^{33/8} \phi_0'^{3/2}} \Big\{ 6C\xi_s \phi_0^{7/4} + 15\xi_s \phi_0'{}^2 \left(C - 2\sqrt[4]{\phi_0} \right) - 4\phi_0 \phi_0' \left[6C + 5(\phi_0 - 3)\sqrt[4]{\phi_0} \right] + 5\xi_s (\phi_0 - 3)\phi_0^2 \Big\}. \tag{63}$$

In this approximation the mass monotonically increases with the string radius.

4.2. The Higgs-type potential

Next we consider the case where the scalar field potential is of the Higgs type, given by

$$V(\phi) = \pm \frac{\bar{\mu}^2}{2} \phi^2 + \frac{\nu}{4} \phi^4, \tag{64}$$

where $\bar{\mu}^2$ and ν are constants. In the following we will investigate only the case with $\bar{\mu}^2 < 0$, meaning we will adopt the minus sign in the definition of the potential. By following the standard approach in elementary particle physics, we assume that the constant $\bar{\mu}^2$ is related to the mass of the scalar field particle as $m_\phi^2 = 2\xi v^2 = 2\bar{\mu}^2$, where $v^2 = \bar{\mu}^2/\xi$ gives the minimum value of the potential. The Higgs self-coupling constant ν can be obtained, in the case of strong interactions, from the determination of the mass of the Higgs boson in laboratory experiments, and its

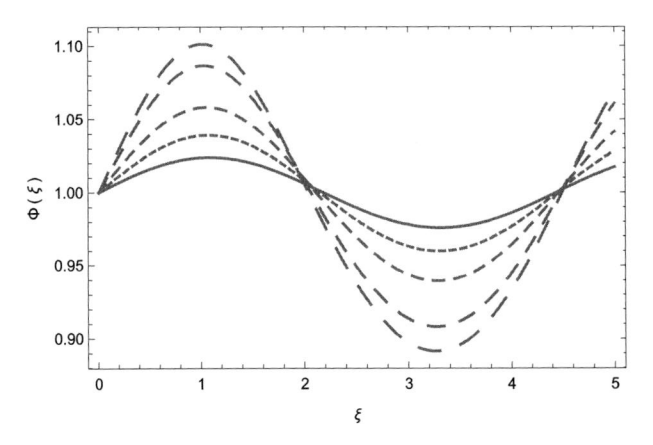

Fig. 1. Variation of the scalar field for the cosmic string configuration in the presence of a Higgs-type potential $V(\Phi) = -\Phi^2 + \Phi^4$ for $\Phi(0) = \Phi_0 = 1$, and for different values of Φ_0': $\Phi_0' = 0.034$ (solid curve), $\Phi_0' = 0.056$ (dotted curve), $\Phi_0' = 0.084$ (short dashed curve), $\Phi_0' = 0.126$ (dashed curve), and $\Phi_0' = 0.148$ (long dashed curve), respectively.

numerical value is of the order of $\nu \approx 1/8$.[11] By rescaling the radial coordinate and the scalar field according to

$$r = \sqrt{2\bar{\mu}}\xi, \qquad \phi = \frac{\Phi}{(\nu\bar{\mu})^{1/3}}, \qquad (65)$$

then Eq. (47) provides the profile of the scalar field in the following form

$$\frac{d^2\Phi}{d\xi^2} - \frac{3}{4\phi}\left(\frac{d\Phi}{d\xi}\right)^2 - \Phi^2 + \Phi^4 = 0. \qquad (66)$$

The general solution for this equation is given in a closed form by

$$\xi + C_0 = \int \frac{1}{\Phi^{3/4}\sqrt{C + \frac{2}{21}(7 - 3\Phi^2)\Phi^{3/2}}} d\Phi. \qquad (67)$$

However, this solution cannot be expressed in an analytical form in terms of known functions. In the first order approximation, we obtain

$$\xi + C_0 \approx \frac{4\sqrt[4]{\Phi}}{\sqrt{C}} - \frac{4\Phi^{7/4}}{21C^{3/2}} + O\left(\Phi^{9/4}\right), \qquad (68)$$

but this representation is not particularly useful from the point of view of concrete calculations.

The variation of the scalar field with Higgs potential supporting a string configuration in hybrid metric-Palatini gravity is represented in Fig. 1. There is a significant qualitative difference between this string model and the constant, simple power law or exponential potentials. Note that the scalar field for the Higgs-type potential shows a basically periodic structure, changing between successive maxima and minima. There are singularities in the field. Its behavior is strongly affected by the initial conditions on the string axis, and the field extends to infinity.

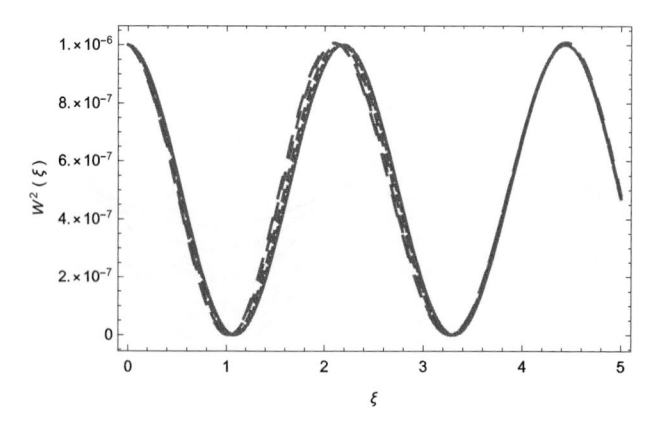

Fig. 2. Variation of the metric tensor component $W^2(\xi)$ of the cosmic string configuration in the presence of a Higgs type potential $V(\Phi) = -\Phi^2 + \Phi^4$ for $\Phi(0) = 1$, $W(0) = 10^{-3}$, and for different values of Φ'_0: $\Phi'_0 = 0.034$ (solid curve), $\Phi'_0 = 0.056$ (dotted curve), $\Phi'_0 = 0.084$ (short dashed curve), $\Phi'_0 = 0.126$ (dashed curve), and $\Phi'_0 = 0.148$ (long dashed curve), respectively.

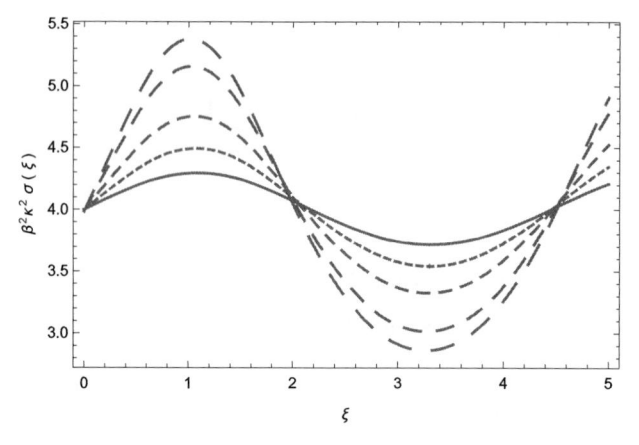

Fig. 3. Variation of the string tension $\kappa^2 \sigma(\xi)$ of the cosmic string configuration in the presence of a Higgs type potential $V(\Phi) = -\Phi^2 + \Phi^4$ for $\Phi(0) = 1$, $W(0) = 10^{-3}$, and for different values of Φ'_0: $\Phi'_0 = 0.034$ (solid curve), $\Phi'_0 = 0.056$ (dotted curve), $\Phi'_0 = 0.084$ (short dashed curve), $\Phi'_0 = 0.126$ (dashed curve), and $\Phi'_0 = 0.148$ (long dashed curve), respectively.

The variation of the metric tensor component $W^2(\xi)$ in the presence of a Higgs potential is represented in Fig. 2. The same oscillatory pattern can also be observed in the case of the metric tensor component W^2. However, there is a difference in the phase of these to quantities. When the field reaches its maximum at $\xi \approx 1$, the metric tends to zero, $W^2(1) \approx 0$. Then, while the scalar field decreases, the metric tensor increases, reaching its maximum at the minimum of the field, corresponding to $\xi \approx 2$. This pattern is repeated up to infinity.

The variation of the string tension with respect to the radial coordinate in the presence of the Higgs potential is depicted in Fig. 3. The variation of σ is in phase with that of the scalar field, and both quantities reach their maxima and minima at the same position. The string tension also has an oscillatory behaviour, which is a general property of all physical and geometrical parameters of the string configurations supported by scalar fields with a Higgs-type potential.

5. Conclusions

In this work we studied the existence and physical properties of cosmic strings in the context of the hybrid metric-Palatini gravity. The theory is an extension to General Relativity, combining both metric and Palatini formalism. A main success of the theory is the possibility to generate long-range forces that pass the classical local tests of gravity at the Solar System level, thus avoiding some problematic features of the standard $f(R)$ theories. Another interesting advantage of the theory is that it admits an equivalent scalar-tensor representation, simplifying greatly the dynamical equations. The type of strings studied in this work are local gauge strings, using an approximation to the Vilenkin-prescribed energy-momentum tensor and different potential configurations. For the case of the potential of the form $V = V_0 \phi^{3/4}$. The requirement of the positivity of the metric tensor for $r = 0$ imposes the condition that the metric tensor and the string tension are decreasing functions of r, since both ϕ_0 and ϕ_0' are required to be positive. In this case, the scalar field becomes singular at infinity. However, it is possible to construct finite string configurations: defining a string radius by introducing an effective cuttoff length, ξ_{co} for both the metric and the scalar field. This radius would allow us to get finite values for the scalar field, the metric tensor components and the string tension. For this type of potential the choice of ξ_{co} should be made based on empirical considerations, such as consistency with observational data. The case of the Higgs-type potential is quite different, since the string tension does not vanish for any value of the radial coordinate but it does reaches its minimum value at $\xi \approx 3.5$, where the scalar field is also at its minimum and $W^2(\xi)$ is singular and tends to zero. Another possible choice for the string radius could be $\xi \approx 1$, the first zero of the metric tensor component; in this case both the string tension and the scalar field are at their maxima. Or we could, as in the exponential potential, introduce a cutoff radius to be determined by confrontation with observations, matching the solution with the cosmological background or another GR string solution, thus achieving a well behaved structure throughout the radius of the string.

Acknowledgments

F. S. N. L. acknowledges support from the Fundação para a Ciência e a Tecnologia Scientific Employment Stimulus contract with reference CEECIND/04057/2017 and the research Grants No. UID/FIS/04434/2019 and No. PTDC/FIS-OUT/29048/2017.

References

1. A. G. Riess et al. [Supernova Search Team], "Observational evidence from supernovae for an accelerating universe and a cosmological constant," Astron. J. **116** (1998), 1009-1038 doi:10.1086/300499 [arXiv:astro-ph/9805201 [astro-ph]].
2. T. Clifton, P. G. Ferreira, A. Padilla and C. Skordis, "Modified Gravity and Cosmology," Phys. Rept. **513** (2012), 1-189 doi:10.1016/j.physrep.2012.01.001 [arXiv:1106.2476 [astro-ph.CO]].
3. R. Utiyama and B. S. DeWitt, "Renormalization of a classical gravitational field interacting with quantized matter fields," J. Math. Phys. **3** (1962), 608-618 doi:10.1063/1.1724264
4. D. Lovelock, J. Math. Phys. **12** (1971), 498-501 doi:10.1063/1.1665613
5. T. Harko, T. S. Koivisto, F. S. N. Lobo and G. J. Olmo, "Metric-Palatini gravity unifying local constraints and late-time cosmic acceleration," Phys. Rev. D **85** (2012), 084016 doi:10.1103/PhysRevD.85.084016 [arXiv:1110.1049 [gr-qc]].
6. T. Harko and F. S. N. Lobo, "Beyond Einstein's General Relativity: Hybrid metric-Palatini gravity and curvature-matter couplings," Int. J. Mod. Phys. D **29** (2020) no.13, 2030008 doi:10.1142/S0218271820300086 [arXiv:2007.15345 [gr-qc]].
7. A. Vilenkin and E. P. S. Shellard, "Cosmic Strings and Other Topological Defects,"
8. G. J. Olmo, "Palatini Approach to Modified Gravity: f(R) Theories and Beyond," Int. J. Mod. Phys. D **20** (2011), 413-462 doi:10.1142/S0218271811018925 [arXiv:1101.3864 [gr-qc]].
9. A. Vilenkin, "Gravitational Field of Vacuum Domain Walls and Strings," Phys. Rev. D **23** (1981), 852-857 doi:10.1103/PhysRevD.23.852
10. T. Harko, F. S. N. Lobo and H. M. R. da Silva, Phys. Rev. D **101** (2020) no.12, 124050 doi:10.1103/PhysRevD.101.124050 [arXiv:2003.09751 [gr-qc]].
11. G. Aad et al. [ATLAS and CMS], Phys. Rev. Lett. **114** (2015), 191803 doi:10.1103/PhysRevLett.114.191803 [arXiv:1503.07589 [hep-ex]].

Inflationary supersymmetric FRLW quantum cosmology

N.E. Martínez-Pérez* and C. Ramirez†

Facultad de Ciencias Físico-Matemíticas, Benemérita Universidad Autónoma de Puebla, Puebla, México P.O. Box 165, 72000
*E-mail: nephtali.martinezper@alumno.buap.mx
† E-mail: cramirez@fcfm.buap.mx

V.M. Vázquez-Báez

Facultad de Ingeniería, Benemérita Universidad Autónoma de Puebla, Puebla, México 72000
E-mail: manuel.vazquez@correo.buap.mx

We consider inflationary scenarios of the supersymmetric quantum cosmology of FRLW models with a scalar field. We use the superfield formalism with a superpotential for the scalar superfield. The probability amplitude solution of the supersymmetric Wheeler-DeWitt equation, gives a probability density from which we can compute mean trajectories that can be parametrized by the scalar. By suitable choices of the superpotential, the resulting evolutions of the scale factor correspond to consistent inflationary scenarios. We show the acceleration, the resulting e-folds and the horizon for several superpotentials.

Keywords: FRW metric; supersymmetry; quantum cosmology; inflation.

1. Introduction

We can think of the universe as originating from a homogeneous early phase, that lies presumably in the Planck scale, based on the numerous observations available nowadays from worldwide experiments and satellite missions which tell us about of the past convergnece of matter, the homogeneity and isotropy of the CMB, light elements abundance, the distribution and content of large scale structures, etc. To attack directly this early phase one would desire to be armed with a theory of the quantum spacetime, which we lack today. Nonetheless at classical level we have descriptions of the early universe with a FRLW metric, see e.g.,[1] which can be allowed to incorporate inhomogeneity perturbations of the metric and scalar fields, which upon quantization are believed to seed the structure we observe today.[2] However, this picture does not account for the very known problems we are confronted by the observations, such as the horizon problem, the homogeneity of the CMB and the flatness problem. The most accepted solution to these problems is inflation, see e.g.,[3] a mechanism that produces enough fluctuation growth as well as the suitable causal relations on the universe, from which, by means of a semiclassical quantum gravity treatment, one can obtain the seeds of structure at the ending of the homogeneous phase, making natural to think that the early homogenous phase should be treated by quantum mechanics. In this line of thought, quantum cosmology[4] gives a canonical quantization of cosmology, resulting in a time independent Schrödinger equation for the wave function of the universe, the Wheeler-deWitt equation. Given that the hamiltonian operator acting on the wave function vanishes, this is a timeless theory, but time can be reinstated in some way for the subsequent classical universe.[5-7]

In,[8] we are given a way to obtain a time, where a scalar field is chosen to be time, and a time dependent effective wave function is defined by the conditional probability of measuring a value of the scale factor for a given value of the scalar field, this allows to compute mean values (dependent on time) from the wave function. On the other hand, the knowledge of the fermionic and bosonic constituents of matter, as well as the required symmetry breaking, has led to the search and construction of unified theories, including fermions and bosons related and interacting in a non trivial way. Supersymmetry,[9] lies well in the category of such theories and it has given the way to supergravity and string theory. In this view, supersymmetric quantum cosmology[10-12] is a good option to study the early universe and attains its goals by the extension of spacetime diffeomorphisms to diffeomorphisms in a Grassmann, extended spacetime, called superspace. This supersymmetry-superspace has additional fermionic coordinates, and the fields become superfields, power expansions on the grassmann variables. Thus, supergravity is formulated as general relativity theory on a supermanifold.[9,18] There are several formulations for supersymmetric extensions of homogeneous models.[11,12] The type of formulation we consider here, is obtained by the extension of time general reparametrizations, to general reparametrizations on a "time superspace".[13,14] Another option is dimensional reduction which involves fields depending only on time, and the spatial coordinates are integrated out.[10] In the simple cases this system has exact solutions,[13-15] and the wave functions have several independent components. In[16] a semiclassical WKB analysis has been made, from which follow a classical hamiltonian, and the corresponding classical equations of motion, for the two relevant spinorial components of the wave function.

In this work we consider the supersymmetric quantum cosmology model of,[8] to explore inflationary scenarios. In sections 2 and 3, we review the supersymmetric model and its component formulation. In section 4 we review the quantization of the model from.[8] In section 5 we make a discussion of the problem of time. Following,[8] a time dependent, effective wave function, can be given. We obtain inflationary behavior from suitable exponential superpotentials, as shown in section 6. We illustrate the inflationary behavior for two types of decaying superpotentials. Finally, in section 7, we make a short discussion with some remarks and future work perspectives.

2. Supersymmetric FRLW model with a scalar field

We begin with a model consisting of a FRLW metric with a scalar field, a setting that can account for inflation, primordial matter generation and structure formation, and possibly dark energy, thus our model is

$$I = \frac{1}{\kappa^2} \int \left\{ -\frac{3}{c^2} N^{-1} a \dot{a}^2 + 3Nka - Na^3\Lambda + \kappa^2 a^3 \left[\frac{1}{2c^2} N^{-1} \dot{\phi}^2 - NV(\phi) \right] \right\} dt, \quad (1)$$

where $\kappa^2 = \frac{8\pi G}{c^4}$.

2.1. *Supersymmetric cosmology*

Supersymmetric cosmology can be obtained from one dimensional supergravity.[13] Here we review the derivation of the supersymmetric Wheeler-DeWitt equation following,[8,14] with several minor modifications. In particular we introduce SI dimensional constants into the action and the ensuing equations, and correct typos. In these works, we have formulated it as general relativity on supersymmetry-superspace, $t \to z^M = (t, \Theta, \bar{\Theta})$, where Θ and $\bar{\Theta}$ are anticommuting coordinates. Hence, under $z^M \to z'^M = z^M + \zeta^M(z)$, the superfields, see e.g.,[9,18] transform as $\delta_\zeta \Phi(z) = -\zeta^M(z) \partial_M \Phi(z)$, and their covariant derivatives are $\nabla_A \Phi = \nabla_A^M(z) \partial_M \Phi$. $\nabla_A^M(z)$ is the superspace vielbein, whose superdeterminant gives the invariant superdensity $\mathcal{E} = \mathrm{Sdet} \nabla_M{}^A$, $\delta_\zeta \mathcal{E} = (-1)^m \partial_M(\zeta^M \mathcal{E})$. For the supersymmetric extension of the FRLW metric, in the covariant Wess-Zumino gauge,[18] we have $\mathcal{E} = -e - \frac{i}{2}(\Theta \bar{\Psi} + \bar{\Theta} \Psi)$.[14] In this formulation, to the scale factor and the scalar field correspond real scalar superfields[9,13]:

$$\mathcal{A}(t, \Theta, \bar{\Theta}) = a(t) + \Theta \lambda(t) - \bar{\Theta} \bar{\lambda}(t) + \Theta \bar{\Theta} B(t), \quad (2)$$

$$\Phi(t, \Theta, \bar{\Theta}) = \phi(t) + \Theta \eta(t) - \bar{\Theta} \bar{\eta}(t) + \Theta \bar{\Theta} G(t). \quad (3)$$

Thus the superfield extension of the model (1), for $k = 0, 1$, is $I = I_G + I_M$, where I_G is the supergravity action and I_M is the matter term[8,13,21]

$$I_G = \frac{3}{\kappa^2} \int \mathcal{E} \left(\mathcal{A} \nabla_{\bar{\Theta}} \mathcal{A} \nabla_\Theta \mathcal{A} - \sqrt{k} \mathcal{A}^2 \right) d\Theta d\bar{\Theta} dt, \quad (4)$$

$$I_M = \int \mathcal{E} \mathcal{A}^3 \left[-\frac{1}{2} \nabla_{\bar{\Theta}} \Phi \nabla_\Theta \Phi + W(\Phi) \right] d\Theta d\bar{\Theta} dt. \quad (5)$$

W is the superpotential.

3. Component formulation

Upon component expansion of the superfields in (4) and (5), once we have performed the integration of the ferminic coordinates, we have[8]

$$L_G = \frac{1}{\kappa^2} \left[-\frac{3a}{c^2 e} \dot{a}^2 + \frac{3a}{ce} \dot{a} \left(\psi \lambda - \bar{\psi} \bar{\lambda} \right) + \frac{3i}{c} a \left(\lambda \dot{\bar{\lambda}} + \bar{\lambda} \dot{\lambda} \right) + eaB \left(6\sqrt{k} - 3B \right) \right.$$
$$\left. + e \left(6\sqrt{k} - 3B \right) \lambda \bar{\lambda} + ia \left(3\sqrt{k} - \sqrt{3} \Lambda a \right) \left(\bar{\psi} \bar{\lambda} + \psi \lambda \right) - \frac{3a}{2e} \lambda \bar{\lambda} \psi \bar{\psi} \right], \quad (6)$$

$$L_M = \frac{a^3}{2c^2e}\dot{\phi}^2 + \frac{a^3}{2ce}\dot{\phi}\left(\bar{\psi}\bar{\eta} - \psi\eta\right) + \frac{3ia^2}{2c}\dot{\phi}\left(\lambda\bar{\eta} + \bar{\lambda}\eta\right)$$
$$- \frac{ia^3}{2c}\left(\eta\dot{\bar{\eta}} + \bar{\eta}\dot{\eta}\right) - 3ea^2BW - ea^3GW' + \frac{ea^3}{2}G^2$$
$$- 6eaW\lambda\bar{\lambda} - ea^2\left(\frac{3B}{2} + aW''\right)\eta\bar{\eta} - \frac{3ia^2}{2}W\left(\psi\lambda + \bar{\psi}\bar{\lambda}\right) \quad (7)$$
$$+ 3ea^2\left(\frac{1}{2}G - W'\right)\left(\lambda\bar{\eta} - \bar{\lambda}\eta\right) - \frac{ia^3}{2}W'\left(\psi\eta + \bar{\psi}\bar{\eta}\right)$$
$$+ \frac{a^3}{4e}\eta\bar{\eta}\psi\bar{\psi} - 3ea\eta\bar{\eta}\lambda\bar{\lambda},$$

where $W \equiv W(\phi)$, $W' \equiv \partial_\phi W(\phi)$, and $W'' \equiv \partial_\phi^2 W(\phi)$. We note the presence of auxiliary fields B and G, whose equations of motion are purely algebraic and can be solved straigthforward, $B = \sqrt{k} - \frac{\lambda\bar{\lambda}}{2a} - \frac{a\kappa^2}{2}(W - \frac{1}{2}\eta\bar{\eta})$ and $G = W' + \frac{3}{2a}(\bar{\lambda}\eta - \lambda\bar{\eta})$.

Then, substituting the previous equations in (6) and (7), and making the redefinitions $\lambda \to a^{1/2}\lambda$, $\bar{\lambda} \to a^{1/2}\bar{\lambda}$, $\eta \to a^{3/2}\eta$, $\bar{\eta} \to a^{3/2}\bar{\eta}$, we end up with the following lagrangian

$$L_{Tot} = -\frac{3a\dot{a}^2}{c^2e\kappa^2} + \frac{a^3\dot{\phi}^2}{2c^2e} + \frac{3kea}{\kappa^2} + 3\sqrt{k}ea^2W + \frac{3e\kappa^2}{4}a^3W^2$$
$$- \frac{1}{2}a^3eW'^2 + \frac{3i}{c\kappa^2}\left(\lambda\dot{\bar{\lambda}} + \bar{\lambda}\dot{\lambda}\right) - \frac{i}{2c}\left(\eta\dot{\bar{\eta}} + \dot{\eta}\bar{\eta}\right) + \frac{3\sqrt{a}\dot{a}}{c\kappa^2 e}\left(\psi\lambda - \bar{\psi}\bar{\lambda}\right)$$
$$- \frac{a^{3/2}\dot{\phi}}{2ce}\left(\psi\eta - \bar{\psi}\bar{\eta}\right) + \frac{3i\dot{\phi}}{2c}\left(\lambda\bar{\eta} + \bar{\lambda}\eta\right) + 3e\left(\frac{\sqrt{k}}{\kappa^2 a} - \frac{3}{2}W\right)\lambda\bar{\lambda}$$
$$+ e\left(-\frac{3\sqrt{k}}{2a} + \frac{3\kappa^2}{4}W - W''\right)\eta\bar{\eta} + 3ia^{3/2}\left(\frac{\sqrt{k}}{\kappa^2 a} - \frac{1}{2}W\right)\left(\psi\lambda + \bar{\psi}\bar{\lambda}\right)$$
$$- \frac{ia^{3/2}}{2}W'\left(\psi\eta + \bar{\psi}\bar{\eta}\right) - \frac{3eW'}{2}\left(\lambda\bar{\eta} - \bar{\lambda}\eta\right) - \frac{3}{2e\kappa^2}\psi\bar{\psi}\lambda\bar{\lambda} + \frac{1}{4e}\psi\bar{\psi}\eta\bar{\eta}.$$

The conjugated momenta are $\pi_a = -\frac{6a\dot{a}}{c^2\kappa^2 e} + \frac{3\sqrt{a}}{c\kappa^2 e}\left(\psi\lambda - \bar{\psi}\bar{\lambda}\right)$, $\pi_\phi = \frac{a^3\dot{\phi}}{c^2 e} - \frac{a^{3/2}}{2ce}\left(\psi\eta - \bar{\psi}\bar{\eta}\right) + \frac{3i}{2c}\left(\lambda\bar{\eta} + \bar{\lambda}\eta\right)$, $\pi_\lambda = -\frac{3i}{c\kappa^2}\bar{\lambda}$, $\pi_{\bar{\lambda}} = -\frac{3i}{c\kappa^2}\lambda$, $\pi_\eta = \frac{i}{2c}\bar{\eta}$, $\pi_{\bar{\eta}} = \frac{i}{2c}\eta$. The Dirac Brackets are $\{a, \pi_a\} = \{\phi, \pi_\phi\} = 1$, $\{\lambda, \bar{\lambda}\}_+ = \frac{c\kappa^2}{6}$, $\{\eta, \bar{\eta}\}_+ = -c$, where $\{,\}_+$ are fermionic Dirac brackets. Therefore, the Hamiltonian is $H = NH_0 + \frac{1}{2}\psi S - \frac{1}{2}\bar{\psi}\bar{S}$, where the hamiltonian and supersymmetric constraints are

$$H_0 = -\frac{c^2\kappa^2\pi_a^2}{12a} + \frac{c^2\pi_\phi^2}{2a^3} - \frac{3ic\pi_\phi}{2a^3}\left(\lambda\bar{\eta} + \bar{\lambda}\eta\right) - \frac{3ak}{\kappa^2} + 3\sqrt{k}a^2W$$
$$- \frac{3\kappa^2}{4}a^3W^2 + \frac{1}{2}a^3W'^2 + \frac{9}{2}W\lambda\bar{\lambda} - \frac{3\kappa^2}{4}W\eta\bar{\eta} + \frac{3}{2}W'\left(\lambda\bar{\eta} - \bar{\lambda}\eta\right) \quad (8)$$
$$+ W''\eta\bar{\eta} - \frac{3\sqrt{k}}{\kappa^2 a}\lambda\bar{\lambda} + \frac{3\sqrt{k}}{2a}\eta\bar{\eta} - \frac{9\lambda\bar{\lambda}\eta\bar{\eta}}{4a^3}, \quad (9)$$

$$S = \frac{c\pi_a \lambda}{\sqrt{a}} + \frac{c\pi_\phi \eta}{a^{3/2}} - \frac{6i\sqrt{k}}{\kappa^2}\sqrt{a}\lambda + 3ia^{\frac{3}{2}}W\lambda + ia^{\frac{3}{2}}W'\eta + \frac{3i}{2}a^{-3/2}\lambda\eta\bar{\eta}, \qquad (10)$$

$$\bar{S} = \frac{c\pi_a \bar{\lambda}}{\sqrt{a}} + \frac{c\pi_\phi \bar{\eta}}{a^{3/2}} + \frac{6i\sqrt{k}}{\kappa^2}\sqrt{a}\bar{\lambda} - 3ia^{3/2}W\bar{\lambda} - ia^{3/2}W'\bar{\eta} - \frac{3i}{2a^{3/2}}\bar{\lambda}\eta\bar{\eta}, \qquad (11)$$

they satisfy the Dirac fermionic brackets

$$\{S, \bar{S}\}_+ = -2H_0, \qquad (12)$$

$$\{H_0, S\} = \{H_0, \bar{S}\} = 0. \qquad (13)$$

Further, the scalar potential in the hamiltonian H_0 is

$$V_S = \frac{3\sqrt{k}}{a}W - \frac{3\kappa^2}{4}W^2 + \frac{1}{2}W'^2. \qquad (14)$$

4. Quantization

There are several well known problems of the quantization of this system, which are address in.[19] In particular the time problem, a consequence of the invariance under time reparametrizations. It has been argued that time is an internal property that can be determined by a the choice of a clock.[5] On the other side, the observed universe is classical,[19] hence its description is given by mean values of the quantum operators. We further discuss the time problem in section 5.

We follow,[8,20] for the derivation of the Wheeler-DeWitt equation, which follows from the Hamiltonian constraint. In the supersymmetric case, the supercharges (10) and (11) give first order differential equations, from which the Hamiltonian constraint follows (12). For consistency it is required that the Hamiltonian is hermitian, hence the supercharges must satisfy $\bar{S} = S^\dagger$ and $S = \bar{S}^\dagger$. In fact, the constraints (9), (10), (11), and the algebra (12), (13) are symmetric under complex conjugation, with $\lambda^* = \bar{\lambda}$ and $\eta^* = \bar{\eta}$. As the momenta of the fermionic variables satisfy second class constraints, Dirac brackets must be implemented. It follows that the non-zero brackets are

$$[a, \pi_a] = [\phi, \pi_\phi] = i\hbar, \qquad \{\lambda, \bar{\lambda}\}_+ = \frac{4\pi}{3}l_p^2, \qquad \{\eta, \bar{\eta}\}_+ = -\hbar c. \qquad (15)$$

$l_p^2 = \frac{\hbar G}{c^3}$ is the Planck length. For the quantization, we redefine the fermionic degrees of freedom as $\lambda = \sqrt{\frac{\hbar c\kappa^2}{6}}\alpha$, $\bar{\lambda} = \sqrt{\frac{\hbar c\kappa^2}{6}}\bar{\alpha}$, $\eta = \sqrt{\hbar c}\beta$ and $\bar{\eta} = \sqrt{\hbar c}\bar{\beta}$. Hence the anticommutators are

$$\{\alpha, \bar{\alpha}\}_+ = 1, \qquad \{\beta, \bar{\beta}\}_+ = -1. \qquad (16)$$

as well as $\alpha^2 = \beta^2 = \bar{\alpha}^2 = \bar{\beta}^2 = 0$. The bosonic momenta are represented by derivatives, α and β are annihilation operators, and $\bar{\alpha}$ and $\bar{\beta}$ are creation operators. We fix the ordering ambiguities in the first and last terms of (10) and (11) by Weyl ordering, which for fermions is antisymmetric. Hence

$$\frac{1}{\sqrt{\hbar c}} S = \frac{c\kappa}{2\sqrt{6}} \left(a^{-\frac{1}{2}} \pi_a + \pi_a a^{-\frac{1}{2}} \right) \alpha + c a^{-\frac{3}{2}} \pi_\phi \beta + \frac{3i\kappa}{\sqrt{6}} a^{\frac{3}{2}} W \alpha$$
$$+ i a^{\frac{3}{2}} W' \beta - i \frac{\sqrt{6k}}{\kappa} a^{\frac{1}{2}} \alpha - \frac{i\sqrt{3}}{4\sqrt{2}} \hbar c \kappa a^{-\frac{3}{2}} \alpha [\bar{\beta}, \beta], \quad (17)$$

$$\frac{1}{\sqrt{\hbar c}} \bar{S} = \frac{c\kappa}{2\sqrt{6}} \left(a^{-\frac{1}{2}} \pi_a + \pi_a a^{-\frac{1}{2}} \right) \bar{\alpha} + c a^{-\frac{3}{2}} \pi_\phi \bar{\beta} - \frac{3i\kappa}{\sqrt{6}} a^{\frac{3}{2}} W \bar{\alpha}$$
$$- i a^{\frac{3}{2}} W' \bar{\beta} + i \frac{\sqrt{6k}}{\kappa} a^{\frac{1}{2}} \bar{\alpha} + \frac{i\sqrt{3}}{4\sqrt{2}} \hbar c \kappa a^{-\frac{3}{2}} \bar{\alpha} [\bar{\beta}, \beta]. \quad (18)$$

The anticommutator of these operators is $\{S, \bar{S}\}_+ = -2\hbar c H_0$, hence the quantum hamiltonian is[a]

$$H_0 = -\frac{c^2 \kappa^2}{24} \left(a^{-1} \pi_a^2 + \pi_a^2 a^{-1} \right) + \frac{c^2}{2} a^{-3} \pi_\phi^2 - \frac{\sqrt{k}}{4} \hbar c a^{-1} [\alpha, \bar{\alpha}]$$
$$- \frac{\sqrt{3}i}{2\sqrt{2}} \hbar c^2 \kappa a^{-3} \pi_\phi (\alpha \bar{\beta} + \bar{\alpha} \beta) + \frac{3\sqrt{k}}{4} \hbar c a^{-1} [\beta, \bar{\eta}]$$
$$- \frac{3k}{\kappa^2} a - \frac{3\kappa^2}{4} a^3 W^2 + 3\sqrt{k} a^2 W + \frac{1}{2} a^3 W'^2 \quad (19)$$
$$+ \frac{3}{8} \hbar c \kappa^2 W [\alpha, \bar{\alpha}] - \frac{3}{8} \hbar c \kappa^2 W [\beta, \bar{\beta}] + \frac{1}{2} \hbar c W'' [\beta, \bar{\beta}]$$
$$+ \frac{\sqrt{3}}{2\sqrt{2}} \hbar c \kappa W' (\alpha \bar{\beta} - \bar{\alpha} \beta) + \frac{3}{16} (\hbar c \kappa)^2 a^{-3} \left(\bar{\alpha} \alpha \beta \bar{\beta} + \alpha \bar{\alpha} \bar{\beta} \beta \right).$$

Thus, $\bar{S} = S^\dagger$, and H_0 is self-adjoint. The Hilbert space is generated from the vacuum state $|1\rangle$, which satisfies $\alpha |1\rangle = \beta |1\rangle = 0$. Hence, there are four orthogonal states

$$|1\rangle, \quad |2\rangle = \bar{\alpha} |1\rangle, \quad |3\rangle = \bar{\beta} |1\rangle \quad \text{and} \quad |4\rangle = \bar{\alpha} \bar{\beta} |1\rangle, \quad (20)$$

which have norms $\langle 2|2\rangle = \langle 1|1\rangle$, $\langle 3|3\rangle = -\langle 1|1\rangle$ and $\langle 4|4\rangle = -\langle 1|1\rangle$. Further, from the constraint equation $S|\Psi\rangle = 0$, we get, up to nonvanishing factors[8]

$$a \left(\partial_a - \frac{3}{\hbar} a^2 W + \frac{6\sqrt{k}}{\hbar c \kappa^2} a + \frac{1}{2} a^{-1} \right) \psi_2 - \frac{\sqrt{6}}{\kappa} \left(\partial_\phi - a^3 W' \right) \psi_3 = 0, \quad (21)$$

$$\left(\partial_a - \frac{3}{\hbar c} a^2 W + \frac{6\sqrt{k}}{\hbar c \kappa^2} a - a^{-1} \right) \psi_4 = 0 \quad \text{and} \quad \left(\partial_\phi - \frac{1}{\hbar c} a^3 W' \right) \psi_4 = 0, \quad (22)$$

---

[a]Note that the ordering differs from the one in[8]

while from $\bar{S}\Psi = 0$, we get

$$a\left(\partial_a + \frac{3}{\hbar c}a^2 W - \frac{6\sqrt{k}}{\hbar c \kappa^2}a + \frac{1}{2}a^{-1}\right)\psi_3 - \frac{\sqrt{6}}{\kappa}\left(\partial_\phi + a^3 W'\right)\psi_2 = 0, \quad (23)$$

$$\left(\partial_a + \frac{3}{\hbar c}a^2 W - \frac{6\sqrt{k}}{\hbar c \kappa^2}a - a^{-1}\right)\psi_1 = 0, \quad \text{and} \quad \left(\partial_\phi + \frac{1}{\hbar c}a^3 W'\right)\psi_1 = 0, \quad (24)$$

4.1. *Solutions*

Since the Wheeler-DeWitt equation is second order, its solutions require boundary conditions. However, in the supersymmetric theory the equations are first order (21)-(24), and have unique solutions, which can be fixed by the requirement of normalization.[8,17,20] The equations for ψ_1 and ψ_4 can be straightforwardly solved, yielding the, up to constant factors, unique solutions

$$\psi_1(a, \phi) = a \exp\left[-\frac{1}{\hbar c}\left(a^3 W(\phi) - \frac{3\sqrt{k}a^2}{\kappa^2}\right)\right], \quad (25)$$

$$\psi_4(a, \phi) = a \exp\left[\frac{1}{\hbar c}\left(a^3 W(\phi) - \frac{3\sqrt{k}a^2}{\kappa^2}\right)\right]. \quad (26)$$

Following[8,20] and the arguments stated there, we choose as the only physical solutions $|\Psi\rangle = C_1 \psi_1(a, \phi)|1\rangle + C_4 \psi_4(a, \phi)|4\rangle$, where the factors are arbitrary constants.

In the following, unless otherwise stated, we will consider $k = 0$, in this case we can write (25) and (26), together as

$$\Psi(a, \phi) = C a \exp\left[-\frac{1}{\hbar c}a^3 |W(\phi)|\right], \quad (27)$$

where the normalization constant is

$$|C|^2 = \frac{6}{c\hbar}\left\{\int_{-\infty}^{\infty} \frac{d\phi}{|W(\phi)|}\right\}^{-1}. \quad (28)$$

In[20] the corresponding expressions for $k = 1$ are given.

5. Time

A brief but comprehensive discussion of the problem of time in quantum cosmology is given in,[20] for the moment let us give some plausibility coments in the same line of thought. The wave function of a quantum system should give high probabilities on paths around classical trajectories in superspace.[19] Hence, it is possible to identify mean trajectories along regions around maxima of the wave function, and it should be possible to parameterize these trajectories, to give a time. Strictly speaking, measurements should give random values around these mean values. Therefore, this time would correspond itself to a sort of mean value. We consider the standard interpretation of quantum mechanics for the solutions of the Wheeler-DeWitt equation, i.e. the square module of the wave function is the probability density of measuring a certain three-geometry. Thus, the wave function must give probabilities for all possible three geometries of the universe.

In our case, the configuration space is given by the scale factor and the scalar field. If the probability density has crests, we could speak of "trajectories" in the (a, ϕ) plane. From (27) we see, that for ϕ constant, we have a bell curve for (27), with a maximum at $a_{\max}(\phi) = \left[\frac{c\hbar}{3W(\phi)}\right]^{1/3}$, and $\psi_{\max}(\phi) = \psi(a_{\max}, \phi) = e^{-1/3}a_{\max}(\phi)$. As an example, we set $W(\phi) = \phi^{-1}(e^{-\phi^2} + 1)$, with the probability density given in figure 2, and taking the scalar field to lie in $\phi \in [0, \infty)$, then the most probable value for the universe would be somewhere at $\phi \to \infty$; hence, the system is not localized. But, if the universe is at some value ϕ_0, it will be less probable to find it for $\phi < \phi_0$, and more probable to find it for $\phi > \phi_0$, around $a_{\max}(\phi)$, this behaviour suggest that the field ϕ can take the role of time,[6,8,20] as far as it is causal. This corresponds to the comoving gauge, where the scalar field is constant on the spacial slices.

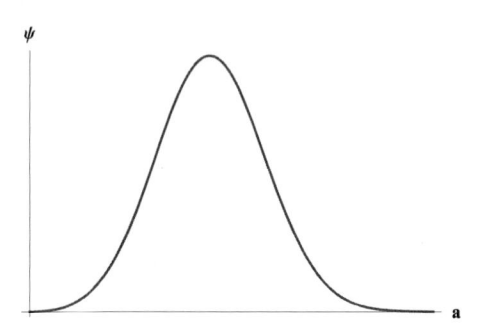

Fig. 1. Profile of $\psi(a, \phi)$, for ϕ constant.

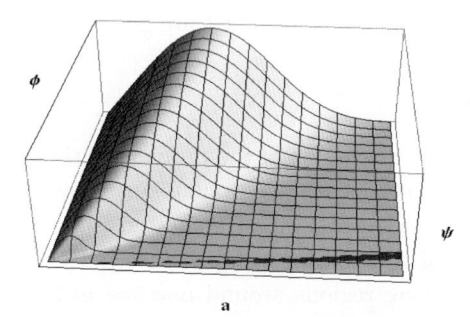

Fig. 2. Probability density for $W(\phi) = 1/\phi$.

Hence we set $\phi \to t$, with a probability amplitude[8]

$$\Psi(a,t) = \frac{1}{\sqrt{\int_0^\infty da \, |\psi(a,t)|^2}} \psi(a,t) = \sqrt{\frac{6|W(t)|}{\hbar c}} a \exp\left[-\frac{a^3|W(t)|}{\hbar c}\right], \quad (29)$$

normalized as $\int_0^\infty da \, |\Psi(a,t)|^2 = 1$, where the resulting probability density[8]

$$|\Psi(a,t)|^2 = \frac{|\psi(a,t)|^2}{\int_0^\infty da \, |\psi(a,t)|^2}, \quad (30)$$

is the conditional probability of the universe being at a and $t \sim \phi$, if the universe is at ϕ regardless of a. It satisfies a conservation equation as stated in.[8,20]

Since we do not have the possibility of recreating the universe in order to give a meaning to probabilities, what we can give a meaning is to mean values. Therefore, under the preceding ansatz, the classical setup arises from mean values with the probability amplitude (29), upon this line we get a time dependent scale factor

$$a(t) = \int_0^\infty a|\Psi(a,t)|^2 da = \Gamma(4/3) \left[\frac{\hbar c}{2|W(t)|}\right]^{1/3}. \quad (31)$$

with the standard deviations

$$(\Delta a)^2 = \left[\Gamma(5/3) - \Gamma(4/3)^2\right] \left[\frac{\hbar c}{2|W|}\right]^{2/3}, \quad (32)$$

and

$$(\Delta \pi_a)^2 = \hbar^2 \, \Gamma(1/3) \left[\frac{2|W|}{\hbar c}\right]^{2/3}, \quad (33)$$

from which follows the uncertainty relation holds

$$\Delta a \Delta \pi_a = \sqrt{\Gamma(1/3) \left[\Gamma(5/3) - \Gamma(4/3)^2\right]} \, \hbar \approx 0.53 \, \hbar. \quad (34)$$

6. Inflationary scenarios

In this section we will consider several superpotentials that lead to cosmological scenarios. The scalar field has real values, from $-\infty$ to ∞, and as mentioned in 4.1 and,[20] we require that the superpotential is a symmetric function and always positive. It is convenient to choose time beginning at $t = 0$. Hence, these superpotentials correspond to bouncing universes. With these settings, we are considering universes with a defined origin at t=0, described by homogeneous quantum cosmology from its very beginning. We will consider two types of superpotentials, depending on the initial conditions. The first type is suitable for $a(0) = 0$, hence $\lim_{t\to 0} W(t) = \infty$ (31), and the wave function (29) will vanish at $t = 0$, $\Psi(a,0) = 0$, similar to figure 1. Hence, the universe will arise for $t > 0$ from nothing. Otherwise, if $W(0)$ takes some finite value, then $a(0) = \Gamma(4/3) \left[\frac{\hbar c}{2|W(0)|}\right]^{1/3}$. We can obtain superpotentials of the first type by $W(\phi) \to \phi^{-2\alpha} W(\phi)$, with α a positive number.

From (31) we get

$$\ddot{a}(t) = \frac{a(t)}{9}\left[4\frac{\dot{W}^2(t)}{W^2(t)} - 3\frac{\ddot{W}(t)}{W(t)}\right]. \tag{35}$$

Hence the acceleration is positive if $\dot{W}^2(t) > \frac{3}{4}W(t)\ddot{W}(t)$. We consider inflation starting when the scale factor acceleration becomes positive, at $t = t_i$, until the exit when it becomes zero again $\ddot{a}(t_e) = 0$, with $N = \ln\frac{a(t_e)}{a(t_i)} = \frac{1}{3}\ln\frac{W(t_i)}{W(t_e)}$ e-folds. Note that in this way N is independent of the time parametrization.

The feasibility of inflation has an indicative in the Hubble horizon

$$(aH)^{-1} = -\frac{3 \times 2^{1/3}}{\Gamma(4/3)(c\hbar)^{1/3}} \frac{W(t)^{4/3}}{W'(t)}. \tag{36}$$

For simplicity, in the following we will consider an adimensional time $t \to \tau = t/t_p$, where $t_p = \sqrt{\hbar G/c^5}$ is the Planck time.

6.1. Superpotentials

We consider two types of superpotentials[20]

Gaussian superpotentials

$$W(\tau) = \frac{c^4 M_p^3}{\hbar^2}\tau^{-2\alpha}\left(e^{-\tau^2} + \lambda\right), \tag{37}$$

and Step superpotentials

$$W(\tau) = \frac{c^4 M_p^3}{\hbar^2}\tau^{-2\alpha}\left(\frac{1}{\tau^2 + \lambda} + 1\right), \tag{38}$$

where $M_p = \sqrt{\frac{\hbar c}{8\pi G}}$ is the reduced Planck mass, $\alpha \geq 0$, and λ is a positive constant. We consider representative cases which reproduce an inflationary period with $N \sim 60$ e-folds, evaluated considering the beginning and exit of inflation from the time interval where acceleration is positive, and a consistent Hubble horizon. As we will see, a very small λ is required for enough e-folds, and we set $\lambda = e^{-\nu}$. Regarding other parameters, as the tensor-scalar ratio, an estimate considering an effective one scalar FRLW cosmology leads to inconsistent results, a more precise evaluation is needed.

The general behaviour of the system under these superpotentials, (37) and (38), is as follows: the scale factor has an initial value $a(0) > 0$ with a very small positive acceleration for $\alpha = 0$, and $a(0) = 0$, with a vanishing acceleration for $\alpha \geq 1$. In order to see if there is a consistent inflation, we evaluate the values of the scale factor at $\tau = 0$, and the corresponding acceleration. If $a(0) > 0$, then inflation begins at the time $\tau = \tau_i$, when the acceleration becomes positive, until it becomes negative, at $\tau = \tau_f$. If the acceleration is positive already at $\tau = 0$, inflation begins right away. Further, if $a(0) = 0$ and $\ddot{a}(0) \geq 0$, and afterwards $\ddot{a} > 0$, then there will be exit, but there are infinite e-folds, unless we discard some initial period, for any reason. Otherwise, if $a(0) = 0$ and $\ddot{a}(0) < 0$, then inflation will begin as soon as the acceleration becomes positive, at $\tau = \tau_i$, and finish when acceleration becomes negative again, at $\tau = \tau_f$.

6.2. *Gaussian superpotentials*

The scale factor for (37) is

$$a(\tau) = \frac{\Gamma(4/3)\hbar\tau^{\alpha/3}}{2^{1/3}cM_p \left(e^{-\tau^2} + \lambda\right)^{1/3}}. \tag{39}$$

In the following, we will consider unities $c = 1$, $\hbar = 1$, and $\kappa = 1$. The acceleration vanishes around the value at which the superpotential (37) becomes nearly constant, at $e^{-\tau^2} \approx \lambda$, i.e. $\tau \approx \sqrt{\nu}$. Thus, for $\tau > \sqrt{\nu}$, the scale factor behaves as $a \gtrsim (\sqrt{\nu})^{\alpha/3}\lambda^{-1/3}$. Hence to have $a \lesssim 1$ for late times, it is convenient to rescale (39) by $\lambda^{1/3}$, such that

$$a(\tau) = \frac{\Gamma(4/3)\hbar\tau^{\alpha/3}}{2^{1/3}cM_p \left(\lambda^{-1}e^{-\tau^2} + 1\right)^{1/3}} \tag{40}$$

Therefore, for $\alpha = 0$, we have

$$a_0 = a(0) = \frac{\Gamma(4/3)\hbar}{2^{1/3}cM_p} \left(\frac{\lambda}{1+\lambda}\right)^{1/3} \approx \frac{\Gamma(4/3)\hbar\lambda^{1/3}}{2^{1/3}cM_p}, \tag{41}$$

with a positive acceleration

$$\ddot{a}(0) \approx \frac{2^{2/3}\Gamma(4/3)\hbar\lambda^{1/3}}{3cM_p}. \tag{42}$$

On the other side, for large times, $\tau > \sqrt{\nu}$, the gaussian in (37) can be neglected, and the scale factor is almost constant

$$a(\tau) \approx a_e = \frac{\Gamma(4/3)\hbar}{2^{1/3}cM_p}, \tag{43}$$

see figure 4. Thus, for $\alpha = 0$, the e-fold number satisfies

$$N \lesssim \ln\frac{a_e}{a_0} = -\frac{1}{3}\ln\lambda = \frac{\nu}{3}. \tag{44}$$

It turns out that a value $\lambda \sim 10^{-79}$ is necessary for ~ 60 e-folds. From (41), we see that there is a very small initial value $a(0) \sim 3 \times 10^{-27}$, with an initial velocity

$\dot{a}(0) = 0$. The initial acceleration is also very small $\ddot{a}(0) \sim 10^{-27}$, but inflation begins right away, until the acceleration slows and becomes negative at $\tau_f \approx 13.4$, see figure 3. We get $N = \ln \frac{a(\tau_f)}{a_0} \approx 60.1$, consistently with (44). A plot for the horizon is given in figure 5.

For $\alpha > 0$, $a(0) = 0$, and at early times, $\tau \ll 1$, the scale factor can be approximated by $a(\tau) \approx \frac{\Gamma(4/3)\hbar\lambda^{1/3}}{2^{1/3}cM_p}\tau^{\alpha/3}e^{\frac{\tau^2}{3}}$, and $\ddot{a}(\tau) \approx \frac{\Gamma(4/3)\kappa(c\hbar)^{1/2}\lambda^{1/3}}{9\times 2^{1/3}}[\alpha(\alpha-3)+2(2\alpha+3)\tau^2]\tau^{\alpha/3-2}$. The acceleration at late times is shown in figure 3 for $\alpha = 1, 2, 3$, for higher values it is similar. Further, for early times, we have: For $\alpha = 1, 2$, $\ddot{a}(0) = -\infty$, grows and becomes positive. For $\alpha = 3$, $\ddot{a}(0) = 0$, and then grows. For $\alpha = 4, 5$, $\ddot{a}(0) = \infty$, decreases almost to zero for $0 < \tau \lesssim 0.5$, and then grows again. For $\alpha = 6$, $\ddot{a}(0) = \frac{2^{2/3}\Gamma(4/3)\hbar}{cM_p} \sim 3 \times 10^{-27}$, and grows. Finally, the cases $\alpha > 6$ are similar to $\alpha = 3$.

For $\alpha = 1$ a meaningful e-fold number can be obtained. Namely, for $\lambda \sim 10^{-77}$, the acceleration becomes positive at $\tau_i \sim 0.4$, with $N = \ln a(\tau_f)/a(\tau_i) \sim 60.2$. For $\alpha = 2$, the initial acceleration is infinite; hence as $a(0) = 0$, N is unbounded. However, the initial acceleration is very quickly decreasing, see figure 11, and we could discard the initial, decelerating period, which presumably would require full quantum gravity. In this case, if we consider inflation starting at $\tau \sim 0.3$, where acceleration becomes practically zero and begins to grow, we get similar values as for $\alpha = 1$.

Thus, the previous three cases $\alpha = 0, 1, 2$, are consistent with inflation, see figures 3 and 4. Even if the previous results are alike, the event horizons, plotted in figure 5, are quite different. With the previous results, we can compute the effective matter density and pressure for a perfect fluid. It turns out that the resulting potential differs from the scalar potential following from the hamiltonian (14). Moreover, for the gaussian potential and $k = 0$, in the analysed cases, the fluid has phantom energy. The effective potentials for $k = 0$ and $k = 1$ are given in figures 6 and 7. Note that the second case seems to correspond to a tunneling.

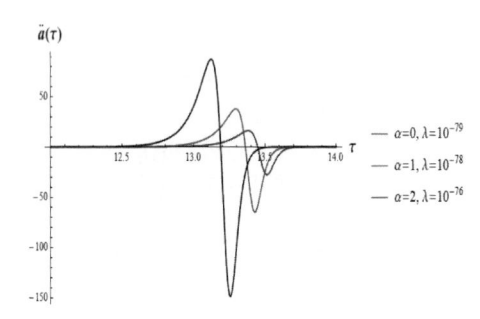

Fig. 3. Acceleration $\ddot{a}(\tau)$ for gaussian superpotentials.

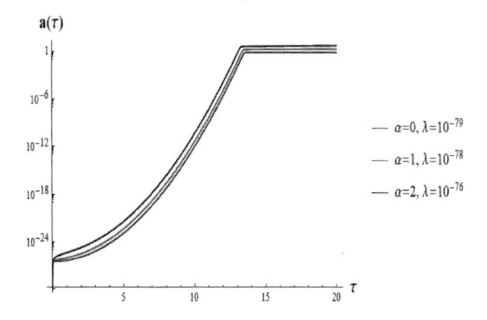

Fig. 4. Scale factor $a(\tau)$ for gaussian superpotentials, the graphics are logarithmic for clarity.

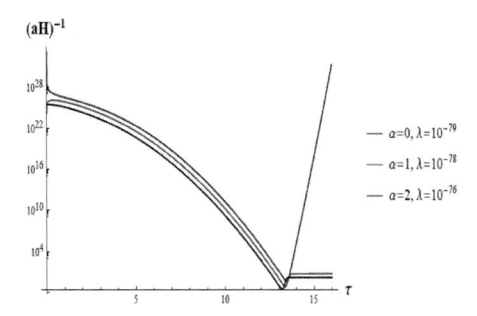

Fig. 5. Comoving Hubble radius $(aH)^{-1}$ for gaussian superpotentials, the graphics are logarithmic for clarity.

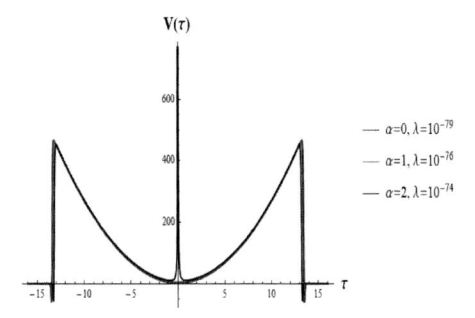

Fig. 6. Effective potentials from Friedmann equations, for $k=0$, for $k=1$, for $\alpha=1,2$ the potential becomes ∞ at $\tau=0$.

6.3. Step superpotentials

For the step superpotentials (38), we have

$$a(\tau) = \frac{\Gamma(4/3)\hbar\tau^{\alpha/3}}{2^{1/3}cM_p\left[(\tau^2+\lambda)^{-1}+1\right]^{1/3}} \quad (45)$$

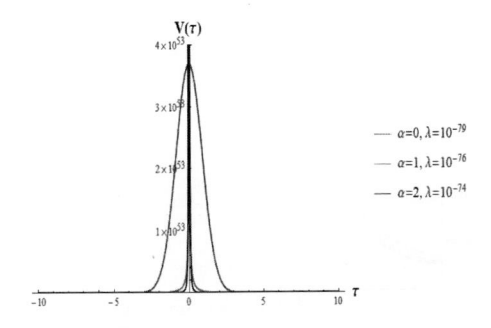

Fig. 7. Effective potentials from Friedmann equations, for $k = 1$, for $\alpha = 2$ the potential becomes ∞ at $\tau = 0$.

And the behaviour of the system is the same as for gaussian superpotentials, if $\alpha = 0$ the scale factor initial value is (41), and for large time values, $\tau \gg 1$, the scale factor tends to (43). Hence, the e-folds satisfy as well (44). The initial velocity and acceleration are zero, $\dot{a}(0) = 0$, $\ddot{a}(0) = 0$, and inflation begins from this moment, and ends at $\tau \approx 0.51$, when the acceleration becomes negative. For $N \sim 60$ a value $\lambda \sim 10^{-80}$ is required.

In the case $\alpha \geq 1$ the situation is also similar to the one of the preceding section, the initial values are practically the same. The acceleration initial behavior is similar, but after a short time the differences become notable, as can be seen from figures 11 and 12. We give also the corresponding profiles for the event horizons, shown in figures 5 and 10. For $\alpha = 1$, the 60 e-folds are reached for $\lambda \sim 10^{-53}$.

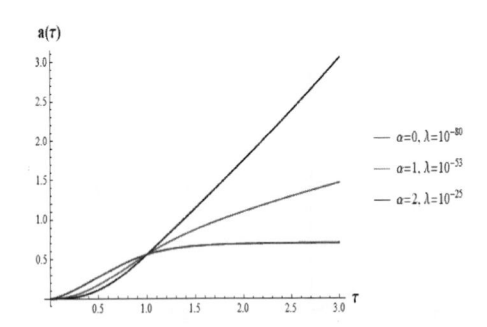

Fig. 8. Scale factor $a(\tau)$ for step superpotentials.

In this case the effective potentials, from the Friedmann equations, look qualitatively similar to the previous ones.

7. Discussion

Quantum cosmology gives a canonical quantization of general relativity in the Schrödinger picture. The invariance under time reparametrizations leads to the

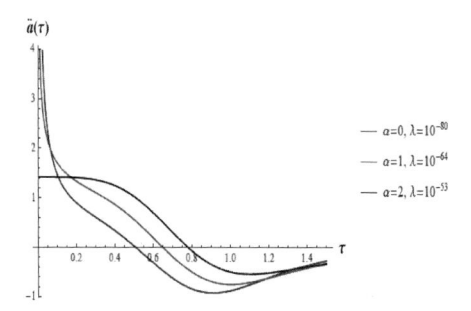

Fig. 9. Acceleration $\ddot{a}(\tau)$ for step superpotentials.

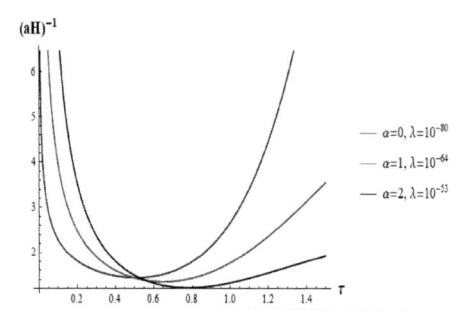

Fig. 10. Comoving Hubble radius $(aH)^{-1}$ for step superpotentials.

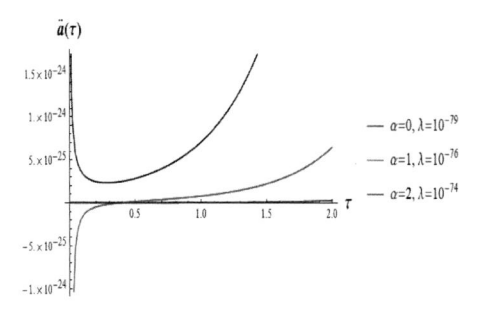

Fig. 11. Initial acceleration for gaussian superpotentials.

hamiltonian constraint that corresponds to a zero energy time independent Schrödinger equation, i.e. the Wheeler-DeWitt equation. There is no time dependent Schrödinger equation that generates a time dependence for the wave function. Thus, the wave function encodes the probability amplitudes for all possible configurations at any time. The observed universe is classical and has time, and classical physics should follow from quantum physics, hence a time evolution should follow from the

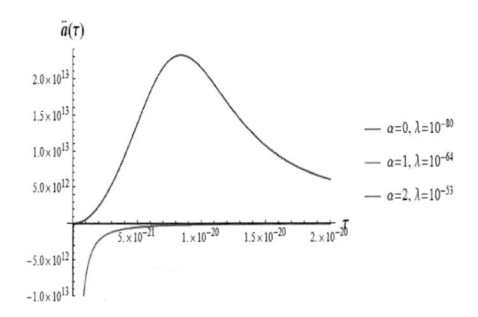

Fig. 12. Initial acceleration for step superpotentials.

quantum description. The Wheeler-DeWitt equation in the supersymmetric case is a system of first order equations, whose solutions are spinorial wave functions, see e.g.,[11,12] whose meaning has not been established. In general, there are only two nonvanishing components, see e.g.,[15] given by real exponentials with opposite exponent sign. Here we have considered a homogeneous theory with a minimally coupled scalar field. In this case, the solution of the supersymmetric Wheeler-DeWitt equation (21)-(24) has four components, two of them have analytic expressions (25),(26), and only one is physically consistent. As the equations are homogeneous and two components decouple, the other ones can be taken as trivial. The form of the solution, (27), suggests that in a certain gauge, time can be given by the scalar field and trajectories for the observables can be given by their mean values. We compute an evolution for the scale factor $a(t)$, and time reparametrizations can be performed. It remains the general question of how far can we get classical trajectories from a quantum state in this way.

We have considered several inflationary scenarios with this approach, with superpotentials (37) and (38). These superpotentials have a factor $\tau^{-2\alpha}$ that, for suitable values, gives a wave function that vanishes for $\tau = 0$ and produces a path of increasing probabilities, we can interpret this as giving the direction of time. The exit of inflation is implemented at the level of the superpotential through a constant $\lambda \sim e^{-3N}$, where N are the observationally required e-folds. Three cases were given in plots for each type of superpotential, figures 3-12. These results indicate that this kind of models could be realistic. The inclusion of inhomogeneous perturbations and the evolution of the fluctuations are part of future work. Further, more complex models, e.g. with several scalars could be considered, as in.[14]

Acknowledgments

We thank VIEP-BUAP, PRODEP-SEP and PROFEXCE-SEP for the support.

References

1. R. D'Inverno, *Introducing Einstein's Relativity* (Oxford University Press, Oxford, England, 1998).
2. V.F. Mukhanov and G.V. Chibisov, Quantum Fluctuations and a Nonsingular Universe, *JETP Lett.* **33** 532 (1981).
3. D. Baumann, *TASI Lectures on Inflation*, arXiv:0907.5424 [hep-th] (2012).
4. J. B. Hartle and S. W. Hawking, Wave function of the Universe, *Phys. Rev.* D **28** 2960 (1983).
5. K. V. Kuchař, Time and interpretations of quantum gravity, *Proceedings of the 4th Canadian Conference on General Relativity and Relativistic Astrophysics* edited by Kunstatter G, Vincent D and Williams J *Int. J. Mod. Phys* D20 3 (2011).
6. C. J. Isham, Canonical quantum gravity and the problem of time, *Proceeding of the NATO Advanced Study Institute "Recent Problems in Mathematical Physics"* arXiv:gr-qc/9210011 (1992).
7. E. Anderson, Problem of time in quantum gravity, *Ann. Phys.* **524** 12 757-786 (2012).
8. C. Ramírez and V.M. Vázquez-Báez, Quantum supersymmetric FRW cosmology with a scalar field, *Phys. Rev.* D **93** 043505 (2016).
9. J. Wess and J. Bagger, *Supersymmetry and Supergravity*, 2nd edn (Princeton University, Princeton, NJ, 1992).
10. A. Macías, O. Obregón and M. P. Ryan, Quantum cosmology: The supersymmetric square root, *Class. Quantum Grav.* **4** 1477 (1987).
11. P. D. D'Eath, *Supersymmetric quantum cosmology* (Cambridge University Press, Cambridge, England, 1996).
12. P. V. Moniz, *Quantum Cosmology - The Supersymmetric Perspective - Vol. 1: Fundamentals* (Springer, Berlin, Germany,2010).
    Moniz P V 2010 *Quantum Cosmology - The Supersymmetric Perspective - Vol. 2: Advanced Topics* (Springer, Berlin, Germany,2010).
13. O. Obregón, J.J. Rosales, J. Socorro and V. I. Tkach, Supersymmetry breaking and a normalizable wavefunction for the FRW ($k = 0$) cosmological model *Class. Quantum Grav.* **16** 2861 (1999).
14. G. García-Jiménez, C. Ramírez and V. Vázquez-Báez, Tachyon potentials from a supersymmetric FRW model *Phys. Rev.* D **89**, 043501 (2014).
15. O. Obregón and C. Ramírez, Dirac like formulation of quantum supersymmetric cosmology *Phys. Rev.* D **57** 1015 (1998).
16. C. Escamilla-Rivera, O. Obregon and L. A. Urena-Lopez, Supersymmetric classical cosmology *JCAP* **12**, 011 (2010).
17. C. Ramírez and V. M. Vázquez-Báez, Quantum cosmology of quadratic $f(R)$ theories with a FRW metric. *Adv. Math. Phys.* **2017** 1056514 (2017).
18. C. Ramírez, The realizations of local supersymmetry *Ann. Phys.* **186** 43 (1988).
19. J. J. Halliwell, Decoherence in quantum cosmology *Phys. Rev.* D **39** 2912 (1989).
20. N. E. Martínez-Pérez, C. Ramírez and V. Vázquez-Báez, arXiv:2104.12914v2 (2021).
21. O. Obregón, J. J. Rosales and V. I. Tkach, Superfield description of the FRW universe *Phys. Rev.* D **53** R1750 (1996).
22. M. Ryan, *Hamiltonian Cosmology* (Springer, Berlin, Germany, 1972).
23. V. I. Tkach, J. J. Rosales and O. Obregón, Supersymmetric action for Bianchi type models *Class. Quantum Grav.* **13** 2349 (1996).
24. A. Linde, Fast-Roll inflation *JHEP* **11** 052 (2001).
25. G. Felder, A. Frolov, L. Kofman and A. Linde, Cosmology with negative potentials *Phys. Rev.* D **66** 023507 (2002).

26. A. Csordás and R. Graham, Hartle-Hawking state in supersymmetric minisuperspace *Phys. Lett.* B **373** 51 (1996).
27. J. Bene and R. Graham, Supersymmetric homogeneous quantum cosmologies coupled to a scalar field *Phys. Rev.* D **49** 799 (1994).
28. B. S. DeWitt, Dynamical Theory in Curved Spaces. I. A Review of the Classical and Quantum Action Principles *Rev. Mod. Phys.* **29** 377 (1957).
    A. Vilenkin, Interpretation of the wave function of the Universe *Phys. Rev.* D **39** 1116 (1989).
29. H. García-Compeán, O. Obregón and C. Ramírez, Noncommutative Quantum Cosmology *Phys. Rev. Lett.* **88** 161301 (2002).
30. M. Bojowald, *Quantum Cosmology A fundamental Description of the Universe* (Springer, Berlin,Germany, 2011).
31. J. D. Brown and K. Kuchař, Dust as a standard of space and time in canonical quantum gravity *Phys. Rev.* D 51 5600 (1995).

Effective $f(R)$ actions for modified loop quantum cosmologies

Ana Rita Ribeiro

Instituto de Astrofísica e Ciências do Espaço, Faculdade de Ciências da Universidade de Lisboa, Edifício C8, Campo Grande, P-1749-016, Lisbon, Portugal
E-mail: anaritaribeiro95@hotmail.com

Daniele Vernieri

Department of Physics "E. Pancini", University of Naples "Federico II", Naples, Italy and INFN Sez. di Napoli, Compl. Univ. di Monte S. Angelo, Edificio G, Via Cinthia, I-80126, Naples, Italy
E-mail: daniele.vernieri@unina.it

Francisco S. N. Lobo

Instituto de Astrofísica e Ciências do Espaço, Faculdade de Ciências da Universidade de Lisboa, Edifício C8, Campo Grande, P-1749-016, Lisbon, Portugal and
Departamento de Física, Faculdade de Ciências, Universidade de Lisboa, Edifício C8, Campo Grande, PT1749-016 Lisbon, Portugal
E-mail: fslobo@fc.ul.pt

Although General Relativity (GR) is an extremely successful theory, at least for weak gravitational fields, it breaks down at very high energies. For example, extrapolating the expansion of the Universe backwards in time yields an infinite energy density, which is referred to as the initial singularity problem. Quantum Gravity is expected to provide a solution to this open question. In fact, one alternative scenario to the Big Bang, that avoids the singularity, is offered by Loop Quantum Cosmology (LQC), which predicts that the Universe undergoes a collapse to an expansion through a bounce. In this work we use metric f(R) gravity to reproduce the modified Friedmann equations, which have been obtained in the context of modified loop quantum cosmologies (mLQC). Using a order reduction method, we obtain covariant effective actions that lead to a bounce, for specific models of mLQC, considering a massless scalar field.

Keywords: Initial singularity, cyclic cosmology, loop quantum cosmology, $f(R)$ gravity, covariant order reduction.

1. Introduction

1.1. *Motivations: Loop quantum cosmology and its modifications*

A quantum theory of gravity is expected to provide insight on the behaviour of gravity at quantum scales,[1] and consequently in addressing fundamental open questions,[2] such as the initial singularity problem. Loop Quantum Gravity (LQG)[3–5] is one of the main candidates we have today. Indeed, through an effective Hamiltonian description, LQC, which is described as a symmetry-reduced model of LQG,[6] yields a modified Friedmann equation that dictates that the big bang singularity is replaced by a quantum bounce:[7–13]

$$H^2 = \frac{1}{3}\kappa\rho\left(1 - \frac{\rho}{\rho_c}\right),\qquad(1)$$

where $H \equiv \dot{a}/a$ is the Hubble function, given in terms of the scale factor $a(t)$, and $\rho_c = \sqrt{3}/(32\pi^2\gamma^3)$ is the critical energy density, where $\gamma \approx 0.2375$ is the Barbero–Immirzi parameter.[14] Throughout this work, we will be using the geometrized system of natural units in which $c = \hbar = G = 1$ and, accordingly, $\kappa \equiv 8\pi$. It is clear from Eq. (1) that the Universe behaves in a cyclic way and that the quantum bounce occurs at the critical density, when $H = 0$ and $\ddot{a} > 0$.

Nevertheless, the procedure used in LQC, to obtain the Hamiltonian constraint which then leads to Eq. (1), differs from the one used in the full theory of LQG. In LQC the Lorentzian and Euclidean terms are treated as proportional to each other, contrary to LQG, leading to different Hamiltonian constraints in the process of quantization.[9] One of the first attempts to construct a Hamiltonian constraint that is similar to the construction in LQG was undertaken in Ref. 15, in which Thiemann's regularization was used. Even so, there is still no systematic way of deriving LQC as a cosmological sector of LQG and different paths to obtain LQG-like Hamiltonians from LQC followed.[16–19] Given these quantization ambiguities in constructing the effective Hamiltonian constraint operator, in isotropic LQC, there is a need to understand how different quantization methods affect the physical predictions. More specifically, there are still great possibilities for the expanding universe to recollapse due to quantum gravity effects.

In this work, we focus on two specific modified loop quantum cosmology (mLQC) models,[15,20] which differ from standard LQC in the way the Lorentzian term in the Hamiltonian constraint is treated.[21]

1.2. *Modified loop quantum cosmology – I: mLQC-I*

This model was derived in Ref. 20, by treating the Lorentzian term in the Hamiltonian constraint separately and using Thiemann's regularization,[15] yielding a fundamental difference between LQC and mLQC-I, in that in the latter the evolution of the universe is described by two different branches, b_+ and b_-, which coincide at the bounce.

The modified Friedmann equation for the b_- branch takes the form[20,21]

$$H_-^2 = \frac{\kappa\rho}{3}\left(1 - \frac{\rho}{\rho_c^I}\right)\left[1 + \frac{\gamma^2\rho/\rho_c^I}{(\gamma^2+1)\left(1+\sqrt{1-\rho/\rho_c^I}\right)^2}\right],\qquad(2)$$

where $\rho_c^I \equiv \rho_c/[4(1+\gamma^2)]$ is the critical density at which the quantum bounce occurs. Notice how, for $\rho/\rho_c^I \ll 1$, the standard Friedmann equation $H^2 \approx \kappa\rho/3$ is recovered.

Concerning the b_+ branch, on the other hand, the modified Friedmann equation takes the form[20, 21]

$$H_+^2 = \frac{\kappa \alpha \rho_\Lambda}{3}\left(1 - \frac{\rho}{\rho_c^I}\right)\left[1 + \frac{\rho\left(1 - 2\gamma^2 + \sqrt{1 - \rho/\rho_c^I}\right)}{4\gamma^2 \rho_c^I \left(1 + \sqrt{1 - \rho/\rho_c^I}\right)}\right], \tag{3}$$

where $\alpha \equiv (1 - 5\gamma^2)/(\gamma^2 + 1)$, $\rho_\Lambda \equiv 3/[\kappa \alpha \lambda^2 (1 + \gamma^2)^2]$, and $\lambda^2 \equiv 4\sqrt{3}\pi\gamma$. The limit of Eq. (3) when $\rho/\rho_c \ll 1$, is given by $H^2 \approx 8\pi G_\alpha (\rho + \rho_\Lambda)/3$, where $G_\alpha := \alpha G$. Comparing with the standard Friedmann equation, this limit shows that quantum geometric effects are still present for low energy densities in the form of a modified Newtonian constant, G_α, and an emergent positive cosmological constant, ρ_Λ. If this branch lies in the post-bounce universe, in which we live, these pose phenomenological problems. It can be shown that the classical energy conservation law still holds in this modified model of LQC, concerning both branches.[20]

1.3. *Modified loop quantum cosmology – II: mLQC-II*

The second model that we consider in this work was derived by using Thiemann's regularization, similarly to the previous model, while also using the proportionality of between the Ashtekar's connection and the extrinsic curvature.[15, 22] In doing so, yields [15]

$$H^2 = \frac{2\kappa\rho}{3}\left(1 - \frac{\rho}{\rho_c^{II}}\right)\left[\frac{1 + 4\gamma^2\left(\gamma^2 + 1\right)\rho/\rho_c^{II}}{1 + 2\gamma^2\rho/\rho_c^{II} + \sqrt{1 + 4\gamma^2(1 + \gamma^2)\rho/\rho_c^{II}}}\right], \tag{4}$$

where the quantum bounce occurs at the critical density $\rho_c^{II} \equiv 4(\gamma^2 + 1)\rho_c$. Unlike in mLQC-I, the bounce in this model is perfectly symmetric, as in LQC. Similarly to the mLQC-I model, the dynamics in the Planck regime are less trivial and the classical limit is given by the usual Friedmann equation.[22] Moreover, the energy-momentum conservation law still holds without any change in the properties of the barotropic equation of state (EoS).

1.4. *Covariant order reduction*

The only covariant action that leads to second-order equations, under metric variation, is the Einstein–Hilbert (EH) action which leads to the usual Friedmann equation. In this work, we are interested in asking if the modified Friedmann Eqs. (2)–(4) can be obtained from different actions. An interesting analysis was considered in the Palatini approach of $f(R)$ gravity in Ref. 23, where R is the Ricci scalar and f some function of it. In this case, the modified Friedmann equation does not involve higher than second-order derivatives of the geometrical quantities and is just a function of the matter sources.[24]

In this work, however, we have used metric $f(R)$ gravity,[25–31] where the full field equations are of fourth-order. Given that our current theory of gravity is a second-order one, we have considered our chosen theory as an effective one, by applying the method of covariant order reduction, in which only the solutions that are perturbatively close to GR are considered as physical ones and the rest considered spurious.[32–34]

This technique has been applied within the context of bouncing cosmologies, for different modifications of GR. In Ref. 35, bouncing solutions in a modified Gauss–Bonnet gravity theory were explored, of the type $R + f(G)$, where G is the Gauss–Bonnet term.[35] This analysis was then extended in the context of $f(R, G)$ gravity.[36] The same approach has also been implemented in the context of $f(Q)$ symmetric teleparallel gravity theories, where Q is the non-metricity scalar.[37] Indeed, in all of these works, a covariant gravitational action, that leads to the quantum bounce observed in LQC, was found by demanding that the Friedmann equation derived within such gravity theories coincides with the one emerging from LQC.

2. Reduced equations in $f(R)$ gravity

In metric $f(R)$ gravity, the corresponding action is given by

$$S = \frac{1}{2\kappa} \int_V d^4x \sqrt{-g} f(R) + S_M(g_{\mu\nu}, \Psi), \tag{5}$$

where g is the determinant of the metric tensor $g_{\mu\nu}$, S_M is the matter action defined as $S_M = \int_V d^4x \sqrt{-g} \mathcal{L}_M(g_{\mu\nu}, \Psi)$, being $\mathcal{L}_M$ the matter Lagrangian density, in which matter is minimally coupled to the metric $g_{\mu\nu}$, and Ψ collectively denotes the matter fields. Without loss of generality, we parametrize the Lagrangian density $f(R)$ as the sum of the gravitational Lagrangian of GR and a deviation term, as follows

$$f(R) = R + 2\Lambda + \epsilon \varphi(R), \tag{6}$$

where Λ is the cosmological constant, ϵ is a dimensionless parameter, and $\epsilon\varphi(R)$ represents the deviation from GR. Substituting Eq. (6) in Eq. (5), and varying the action with respect to the metric, yields the following field equations

$$G_{\mu\nu} - g_{\mu\nu}\Lambda + \epsilon \left[-\frac{1}{2} g_{\mu\nu} \varphi(R) + \varphi'(R) R_{\mu\nu} - (\nabla_\mu \nabla_\nu - g_{\mu\nu} \Box) \varphi'(R) \right] = \kappa T_{\mu\nu}, \tag{7}$$

where the energy-momentum tensor $T_{\mu\nu}$ is defined as

$$T_{\mu\nu} = -\frac{2}{\sqrt{-g}} \frac{\delta(\sqrt{-g}\mathcal{L}_M)}{\delta g^{\mu\nu}}. \tag{8}$$

In simple terms, applying the order reduction technique to Eq. (7) amounts to replacing the Ricci scalar and the Ricci tensor, in the terms of order ϵ, by the expression we get for them, from the $\epsilon = 0$ version of the same equations. Thus, setting $\epsilon = 0$ in Eq. (7), yields the following

$$R^T_{\mu\nu} = \frac{1}{2} g_{\mu\nu}(R_T + 2\Lambda) + \kappa T_{\mu\nu}, \tag{9}$$

as the reduced expression of the Ricci tensor, where R_T is the order reduced Ricci scalar. Taking into account the trace of Eq. (9), the latter provides $R_T = -\kappa T - 4\Lambda$, and after substituting it into Eq. (9), we arrive at

$$R^T_{\mu\nu} = \kappa T_{\mu\nu} - \frac{1}{2}g_{\mu\nu}\kappa T - \Lambda g_{\mu\nu}. \qquad (10)$$

Replacing R and $R_{\mu\nu}$, in the ϵ-order terms in Eq. (7), with the expressions for R_T and $R^T_{\mu\nu}$ respectively, yields the reduced field equations

$$G_{\mu\nu} - g_{\mu\nu}\Lambda + \epsilon\left[-\frac{1}{2}g_{\mu\nu}\varphi(R_T) + \varphi'(R_T)\left(\kappa T_{\mu\nu} - \frac{1}{2}g_{\mu\nu}\kappa T - \Lambda g_{\mu\nu}\right)\right.$$
$$\left. - (\nabla_\mu\nabla_\nu - g_{\mu\nu}\Box)\varphi'(R_T)\right] = \kappa T_{\mu\nu}, \qquad (11)$$

which are valid for

$$|\epsilon\varphi(R)| \ll |R|. \qquad (12)$$

Throughout this work, we consider the FLRW metric with a $(-,+,+,+)$ signature, which in spherical coordinates is given by

$$ds^2 = -dt^2 + a(t)^2\left[\frac{dr^2}{1-kr^2} + r^2d\theta^2 + r^2\sin^2\theta d\phi^2\right], \qquad (13)$$

where $a(t)$ is the scale factor and k is the curvature of the universe. We assume a perfect fluid description for the content of the universe, given by the energy-momentum tensor, $T_{\mu\nu} = (\rho+p)U_\mu U_\nu + pg_{\mu\nu}$, where U^μ is the four-velocity field of an observer comoving with the fluid, defined in such a way that $U_\mu U^\mu = -1$, and $\rho = \rho(t)$ and $p = p(t)$ are the fluid's energy density and isotropic pressure, respectively.

Now, by taking into account a EoS $p = w\rho$, with $-1 \leq w \leq 1$, and taking into account Eq. (13), then Eq. (11) provides the following modified Friedmann equation in $f(R)$ gravity[38]

$$H^2 = \frac{1}{3}\kappa\rho - \frac{k}{a^2} - \frac{\Lambda}{3} - \frac{\epsilon}{3}\left[\frac{1}{2}(3w+1)\varphi'(R_T)\kappa\rho + \varphi'(R_T)\Lambda + \frac{1}{2}\varphi(R_T)\right.$$
$$\left. - \left(3\kappa\rho - \frac{9k}{a^2} - 3\Lambda\right)\varphi''(R_T)(1+w)(1-3w)\kappa\rho\right], \qquad (14)$$

where $\varphi_T = \varphi(R_T)$. It is clear that this equation is effectively a second-order one and that we recover the standard Friedmann equation for $\epsilon = 0$. With this result, we aim to find a function $\varphi(R_T)$, such that Eq. (14) is the same as some Friedmann equation with a modified source.

3. Strategy to obtain effective actions

Here, we describe the procedure for finding effective actions, which was used in Ref. 38, in order to determine an effective action for LQC. In this context, we consider a spatially flat universe ($k = 0$) with a zero cosmological constant ($\Lambda = 0$).

In order to be in agreement with the approach leading to Eq. (1), we consider a massless scalar field ($w = 1$) so that

$$R_T = -2\kappa\rho. \tag{15}$$

Taking these aspects into account, then Eq. (14) becomes

$$H^2 = \frac{1}{3}\kappa\rho - \frac{\epsilon}{3}\left[2\varphi'(R_T)\kappa\rho + \frac{1}{2}\varphi(R_T) + 12\kappa^2\rho^2\varphi''(R_T)\right], \tag{16}$$

In the following sections, our goal is to determine $\varphi(R_T)$ such that Eq. (16) is the same as the modified Friedmann Eqs. (2)–(4), considered in the modified loop quantum cosmologies. We conveniently write Eqs. (2)–(4) in a general way as

$$H^2 = \frac{1}{3}\kappa\rho + \Psi(\rho), \tag{17}$$

where $\Psi(\rho)$ depends on the model. Using Eq. (15) and comparing Eq. (17) with Eq. (16), the requirement is that $\varphi(R_T)$ satisfies

$$-\frac{\epsilon}{3}\left[\frac{1}{2}\varphi(R_T) - R_T\varphi'(R_T) + 3R_T^2\varphi''(R_T)\right] = \Psi(R_T). \tag{18}$$

In finding the deviation term $\varphi(R_T)$, a metric $f(R)$ action of the form

$$f(R) = R + \epsilon\varphi(R) \tag{19}$$

is found, that leads to the quantum bounce which characterizes the models we are considering.

4. Effective actions for modified loop quantum cosmology models

Independently of the model of LQC, the solution to the non-homogeneous Eq. (18) consists of the sum of the solution to the corresponding homogeneous equation and its particular solution, $\varphi(R_T) = \varphi_h(R_T) + \varphi_p(R_T)$. The homogeneous equation is a second order Cauchy–Euler equation, with a characteristic equation given by $m^2 - 4m/3 + 1/6 = 0$. Solving for m, we get two real roots, $m = \frac{1}{6}(4 \pm \sqrt{10})$, meaning that the solution to the homogeneous equation is given by

$$\varphi_h(R) = c_1 R^{\frac{1}{6}(4-\sqrt{10})} + c_2 R^{\frac{1}{6}(4+\sqrt{10})}. \tag{20}$$

This solution is not locally given by a convergent power series. For this reason, and also for the fact that $\varphi_h(R)$ does not contribute to the full Eq. (18), we set $c_1 = c_2 = 0$, without loss of generality.[38] As such, the solutions to Eq. (18) are simply given by the particular solution in question, i.e. $\varphi(R_T) = \varphi_p(R_T)$, depending on $\Psi(R_T)$.

4.1. Effective actions for mLQC-I

As described in the Introduction, mLQC-I is divided in two branches. As such, we consider each of them separately and find an effective action for both.

4.1.1. Effective action for the b_ branch

Considering Eq. (2) for the b_- branch, the definition for $\Psi(\rho)$ given by Eq. (17) and Eq. (15), $\Psi(R_T)$ is given by

$$\Psi(R_T) = -\frac{R_T^2}{12\rho_c^I \kappa} + \frac{R_T}{6}\left(1 + \frac{R_T}{2\kappa\rho_c^I}\right)\frac{\gamma^2 R_T/(2\kappa\rho_c^I)}{(\gamma^2+1)\left(1+\sqrt{1+R_T/(2\kappa\rho_c^I)}\right)^2}. \tag{21}$$

Therefore, in this case, Eq. (18) is given by

$$-\frac{\epsilon}{3}\left[\frac{1}{2}\varphi_T - R_T\varphi_T' + 3R_T^2\varphi_T''\right] = -\frac{R_T^2}{12\rho_c^I \kappa} + \frac{R_T}{6}\frac{\left(1+\frac{R_T}{2\kappa\rho_c^I}\right)\gamma^2 R_T/(2\kappa\rho_c^I)}{(\gamma^2+1)\left(1+\sqrt{1+R_T/(2\kappa\rho_c^I)}\right)^2}, \tag{22}$$

This equation was solved for $\varphi(R_T)$ using *Wolfram Mathematica*. Thus a metric $f(R)$ action, Eq. (19), was found which, when treated as an effective action, leads to the modified Friedmann Eq. (3). This effective action is given by

$$f(R) = R + \frac{1}{90(\gamma^2+1)}\left\{5\left(-72\gamma^2\kappa\rho_c^I + \frac{R^2}{\kappa\rho_c^I} + 54\gamma^2 R\right)\right.$$

$$+ \frac{18\gamma^2}{\sqrt{10}+10}\left[3\left(4\left(5-4\sqrt{10}\right)\kappa\rho_c^I + \left(\sqrt{10}+10\right)R\right)\right.$$

$${}_2F_1\left[-\frac{1}{2},\frac{1}{6}\left(-\sqrt{10}-4\right);\frac{1}{6}\left(2-\sqrt{10}\right);-\frac{R}{2\kappa\rho_c^I}\right]$$

$$+ 3\left(12\left(2\sqrt{10}+5\right)\kappa\rho_c^I + \left(\sqrt{10}+10\right)R\right)$$

$${}_2F_1\left[-\frac{1}{2},\frac{1}{6}\left(\sqrt{10}-4\right);\frac{1}{6}\left(\sqrt{10}+2\right);-\frac{R}{2\kappa\rho_c^I}\right]$$

$$+ (2\kappa\rho_c^I + R)\left(9\sqrt{10}\,{}_2F_1\left[\frac{1}{2},\frac{1}{6}\left(-\sqrt{10}-4\right);\frac{1}{6}\left(2-\sqrt{10}\right);-\frac{R}{2\kappa\rho_c^I}\right]\right.$$

$$\left.\left.-\left(11\sqrt{10}+20\right)\,{}_2F_1\left[\frac{1}{2},\frac{1}{6}\left(\sqrt{10}-4\right);\frac{1}{6}\left(\sqrt{10}+2\right);-\frac{R}{2\kappa\rho_c^I}\right]\right)\right]\right\}. \tag{23}$$

where we have dropped the subscript T since, to ϵ order, $f(R)$ and $f(R_T)$ are the same. This action contains hypergeometric functions, denoted by ${}_2F_1$, and its domain is given by $-2\kappa\rho_c^I \leq R$. Since it is only physically meaningful to consider $R \leq 0$, given Eq. (15), we have that our physical solution is defined for the range $-2\kappa\rho_c^I \leq R \leq 0$.

Using *Wolfram Mathematica*, a Taylor expansion of Eq. (23), about $R = 0$ and up to third order, was also determined and is given by

$$f(R) = R + \epsilon\varphi(R) = R + \frac{(4+3\gamma^2)R^2}{72(1+\gamma^2)\kappa\rho_c^I} + \frac{\gamma^2 R^3}{992(1+\gamma^2)(\kappa\rho_c^I)^2} + \cdots. \tag{24}$$

In order to visualize our solution, we provide two different plots in Fig. 1 regarding Eq. (23). In Fig. 1a we present the deviation terms of Eq. (23) and the deviation term of the effective action for LQC, given by $\epsilon\varphi(R) = R^2/(18\kappa\rho_c)$ according to Ref. 38. In Fig. 1b, we compare Eq. (23) with the effective $f(R)$ function for the case of LQC and the Lagrangian density of GR, with $\Lambda = 0$.

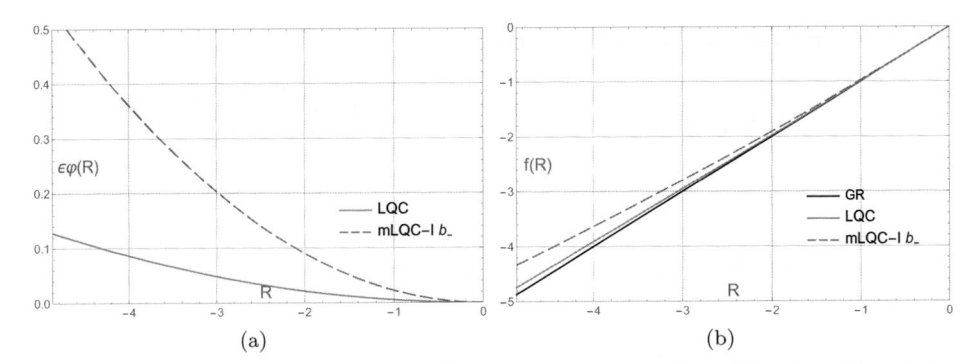

Fig. 1. Figure 1a presents the comparison between the deviation, from GR, of the effective Lagrangian for the case of LQC (solid blue line), given by $\epsilon\varphi(R) = R^2/(18\kappa\rho_c)$, and the deviation terms of Eq. (23), for the b_- branch of mLQC-I (dashed dark orange line), for $-2\kappa\rho_c^I \leq R \leq 0$. Although the deviation is higher for the case of the b_- branch of this modified model, both of them are dominated by the quadratic term. Figure 1b illustrates the differences between the Lagrangian density of GR (solid black line), with $\Lambda = 0$, and the effective $f(R)$ functions for the case of LQC (solid blue line) and Eq. (23), for the b_- branch of mLQC-I (dashed dark orange line), for the interval $-2\kappa\rho_c^I \leq R \leq 0$.

4.1.2. Effective action for the b_+ branch

Considering Eq. (2) for the b_+ branch, the definition for $\Psi(\rho)$ given by Eq. (17) and Eq. (15), $\Psi(R_T)$ is given by

$$\Psi(R_T) = \frac{R_T}{6} + \frac{1}{3}\alpha\kappa\rho_\Lambda\left(1 + \frac{R_T}{2\kappa\rho_c^I}\right)\left[1 - \frac{R_T\left(1 - 2\gamma^2 + \sqrt{1 + R_T/(2\kappa\rho_c^I)}\right)}{8\gamma^2\kappa\rho_c^I\left(1 + \sqrt{1 + R_T/(2\kappa\rho_c^I)}\right)}\right]. \quad (25)$$

Therefore, in this case, Eq. (18) becomes

$$-\frac{\epsilon}{3}\left[\frac{\varphi_T}{2} - R_T\varphi_T' + 3R_T^2\varphi_T''\right] = \frac{R_T}{6} + \frac{\alpha\kappa\rho_\Lambda}{3}\left[1 + \frac{R_T}{2\kappa\rho_c^I}\right]$$
$$\left[1 - \frac{R_T\left(1 - 2\gamma^2 + \sqrt{1 + \frac{R_T}{2\kappa\rho_c^I}}\right)}{8\gamma^2\kappa\rho_c^I\left(1 + \sqrt{1 + \frac{R_T}{2\kappa\rho_c^I}}\right)}\right], \quad (26)$$

As before, this equation was solved for $\varphi(R)$ using *Wolfram Mathematica*, and the corresponding effective action, that leads to the modified Friedmann Eq. (3), is given by

$$f(R) = R - \alpha\kappa\rho_\Lambda + R + \frac{\alpha\rho_\Lambda R \left(18\left(2\gamma^2 - 1\right)\kappa\rho_c^I + R\right)}{72\gamma^2 \kappa (\rho_c^I)^2}$$

$$+ \frac{\alpha\rho_\Lambda}{20\rho_c^I}\Bigg\{ -3\left[R - 2\left(\sqrt{10} - 2\right)\kappa\rho_c^I\right]$$

$${}_2F_1\left[-\frac{1}{2}, \frac{1}{6}\left(-\sqrt{10} - 4\right); \frac{1}{6}\left(2 - \sqrt{10}\right); -\frac{R}{2\kappa\rho_c^I}\right]$$

$$- 3\left(2\left(\sqrt{10} + 2\right)\kappa\rho_c^I + R\right) {}_2F_1\left[-\frac{1}{2}, \frac{1}{6}\left(\sqrt{10} - 4\right); \frac{1}{6}\left(\sqrt{10} + 2\right); -\frac{R}{2\kappa\rho_c^I}\right]$$

$$+ (2\kappa\rho_c^I + R)\Bigg(-\left(\sqrt{10} - 1\right) {}_2F_1\left[\frac{1}{2}, \frac{1}{6}\left(-\sqrt{10} - 4\right); \frac{1}{6}\left(2 - \sqrt{10}\right); -\frac{R}{2\kappa\rho_c^I}\right]$$

$$+ \left(\sqrt{10} + 1\right) {}_2F_1\left[\frac{1}{2}, \frac{1}{6}\left(\sqrt{10} - 4\right); \frac{1}{6}\left(\sqrt{10} + 2\right); -\frac{R}{2\kappa\rho_c^I}\right]\Bigg)\Bigg\}. \quad (27)$$

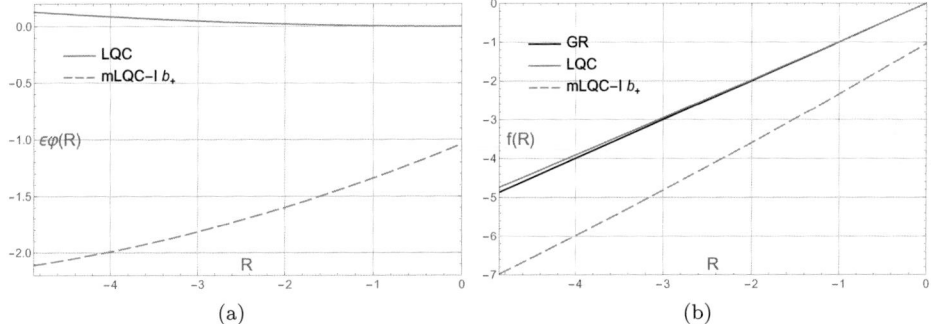

Fig. 2. Figure 2a. presents the comparison between the deviation, from GR, for the case of LQC (solid blue line), given by $\epsilon\varphi(R) = R^2/(18\kappa\rho_c)$, and the deviation terms of Eq. (27), for the b_+ branch of mLQC-I (dashed light orange line), for $-2\kappa\rho_c^I \leq R \leq 0$. Contrary to the previous case, for this branch the deviation is predominantly negative since it is dominated by the linear term. Figure 2b. illustrates the differences between the Lagrangian density of GR (solid black line), with $\Lambda = 0$, and the effective $f(R)$ functions for the case of LQC (solid blue line) and Eq. (27), for the b_+ branch of mLQC-I (dashed light orange line), for the interval $-2\kappa\rho_c^I \leq R \leq 0$.

For the same reasons as in the previous branch, the physical domain of this solution is also given by $-2\kappa\rho_c^I \leq R \leq 0$. The Taylor expansion of Eq. (27) up to third order, about $R = 0$, was computed using *Wolfram Mathematica*, resulting in

$$f(R) = -2\alpha\kappa\rho_\Lambda + \left(\frac{\alpha\left(5\gamma^2 - 1\right)\rho_\Lambda}{4\gamma^2 \rho_c^I} + 2\right)R + \frac{\alpha\left(4 - 3\gamma^2\right)\rho_\Lambda R^2}{288\gamma^2 \kappa (\rho_c^I)^2} + \frac{\alpha\rho_\Lambda R^3}{3968\kappa^2 (\rho_c^I)^3} + \dots . \quad (28)$$

We observe that, for this particular branch, $f(0) \neq 0$. We recall that ρ_Λ was interpreted as the energy density of an emergent positive cosmological constant in Ref. 20. Finally we provide similar plots for this branch, in Fig. 2.

4.2. *Effective action for mLQC-II*

We now consider the mLQC-II model, in which the modified Friedmann equation is given by Eq. (4). Considering the definition for $\Psi(\rho)$ given by Eq. (17) and Eq. (15), $\Psi(R_T)$ is given by

$$\Psi(R_T) = \frac{R_T}{6} - \frac{R_T\left(1 + R_T/(2\kappa\rho_c^{II})\right)\left(1 - 2\gamma^2\left(\gamma^2 + 1\right)R_T/(\kappa\rho_c^{II})\right)}{3\left(1 - \gamma^2 R_T/(\kappa\rho_c^{II}) + \sqrt{1 - 2\gamma^2\left(\gamma^2 + 1\right)R_T/(\kappa\rho_c^{II})}\right)}. \tag{29}$$

Therefore, in this case, Eq. (18) is given by

$$-\frac{\epsilon}{3}\left[\frac{1}{2}\varphi_T - R_T\varphi_T' + 3R_T^2\varphi_T''\right] = \frac{R_T}{6} - \frac{R_T\left(1 + \frac{R_T}{2\kappa\rho_c^{II}}\right)\left(1 - \frac{2\gamma^2(\gamma^2+1)R_T}{\kappa\rho_c^{II}}\right)}{3\left(1 - \frac{\gamma^2 R_T}{\kappa\rho_c^{II}} + \sqrt{1 - \frac{2\gamma^2(\gamma^2+1)R_T}{\kappa\rho_c^{II}}}\right)}. \tag{30}$$

This equation was solved for $\varphi(R)$ using *Wolfram Mathematica*. The corresponding metric $f(R)$ action which, when treated as an effective one, leads to the modified Friedmann Eq. (4) is given by

$$f(R) = R + \frac{1}{90\gamma^4}\left\{270\left(\gamma^4 + \gamma^2\right)R + 90\kappa\rho_c^{II} + \frac{20\left(\gamma^6 + \gamma^4\right)R^2}{\kappa\rho_c^{II}}\right.$$

$$+ 9\left[3\left(\left(\sqrt{10} - 2\right)\kappa\rho_c^{II} + 2\left(\gamma^4 + \gamma^2\right)R\right)\right.$$

$${}_2F_1\left[-\frac{1}{2},\frac{1}{6}\left(-\sqrt{10} - 4\right);\frac{1}{6}\left(2 - \sqrt{10}\right);\frac{2R\gamma^2\left(\gamma^2 + 1\right)}{\kappa\rho_c^{II}}\right]$$

$$+ \left(6\left(\gamma^4 + \gamma^2\right)R - 3\left(\sqrt{10} + 2\right)\kappa\rho_c^{II}\right)$$

$${}_2F_1\left[-\frac{1}{2},\frac{1}{6}\left(\sqrt{10} - 4\right);\frac{1}{6}\left(\sqrt{10} + 2\right);\frac{2R\gamma^2\left(\gamma^2 + 1\right)}{\kappa\rho_c^{II}}\right]$$

$$+ \left(2\left(\gamma^4 + \gamma^2\right)R - \kappa\rho_c^{II}\right)\left(\left(\sqrt{10} - 1\right)\right.$$

$${}_2F_1\left[\frac{1}{2},\frac{1}{6}\left(-\sqrt{10} - 4\right);\frac{1}{6}\left(2 - \sqrt{10}\right);\frac{2R\gamma^2\left(\gamma^2 + 1\right)}{\kappa\rho_c^{II}}\right]$$

$$\left.\left.- \left(\sqrt{10} + 1\right){}_2F_1\left[\frac{1}{2},\frac{1}{6}\left(\sqrt{10} - 4\right);\frac{1}{6}\left(\sqrt{10} + 2\right);\frac{2R\gamma^2\left(\gamma^2 + 1\right)}{\kappa\rho_c^{II}}\right]\right)\right]\right\}. \tag{31}$$

This solution also contains hypergeometric functions but, for this model, they present a different argument. According to this argument the domain of Eq. (31) is given by $R \leq \kappa\rho_c^{II}/\left(2\gamma^2(\gamma^2 + 1)\right)$. As such, since the Ricci scalar must be less or equal to zero for a massless sclar field scenario, in this case the solution only has physical meaning for the interval $R \leq 0$.

Using *Wolfram Mathematica*, a Taylor expansion of Eq. (31), about $R = 0$ and up to third order, was computed and is given by

$$f(R) = R + \frac{\left(-3\gamma^4 - 2\gamma^2 + 1\right) R^2}{18\kappa\rho_c^{II}} - \frac{\gamma^2 \left(\gamma^2 + 1\right)^3 R^3}{62(\kappa\rho_c^{II})^2} + \ldots, \qquad (32)$$

The solution for the mLQC-II model is depicted in Fig. 3. In Fig. 3a, we present the deviation terms of Eq. (31) and the deviation term of the effective action for LQC, given by $\epsilon\varphi(R) = R^2/(18\kappa\rho_c)$ according to Ref. 38. In Fig. 3b, we compare Eq. (31) with the effective $f(R)$ function for the case of LQC and the Lagrangian density of GR, with $\Lambda = 0$. As a summary, a combination of our results is presented in Fig. 4.

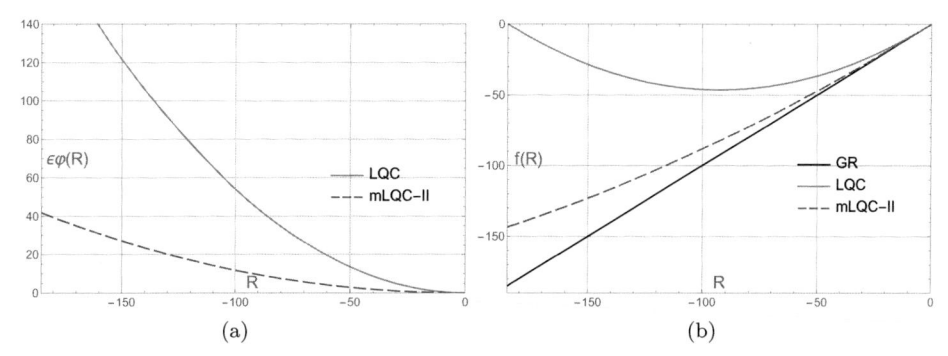

Fig. 3. Figure 3a. presents the comparison between the deviation, from GR, of the effective Lagrangian for the case of LQC (solid blue line), given by $\epsilon\varphi(R) = R^2/(18\kappa\rho_c)$, and the deviation terms of Eq. (31), for the case of mLQC-II (dashed pink line), for $-18\kappa\rho_c \leq R \leq 0$. Both of the deviations are dominated by the quadratic term. Figure 3b. illustrates the differences between the Lagrangian density of GR (solid black line), with $\Lambda = 0$, and the effective $f(R)$ functions, for the case of LQC (solid blue line), and Eq. (31), for mLQC-II (dashed pink line), for the interval $-18\kappa\rho_c \leq R \leq 0$.

5. Conclusions

In this work, we have addressed the initial singularity problem that is present in the ΛCDM model and considered a possible resolution to this question, as proposed by LQC, in which the Big Bang is replaced by a quantum bounce. Since this result comes from a different field in physics, it is relevant to ask if it is possible to replicate it in the framework of GR and its modifications. In this context we considered the class of metric $f(R)$ gravity. Motivated by Ref. 38, we have used the same procedure with two modifications of standard LQC, that also yield a quantum bounce, which are two attempts to bridge the gap between LQG and LQC, by means of similar treatments of the Hamiltonian constraint.

We have applied the covariant order reduction method to obtain a reduced version of the full field equations in $f(R)$ gravity. The corresponding modifed

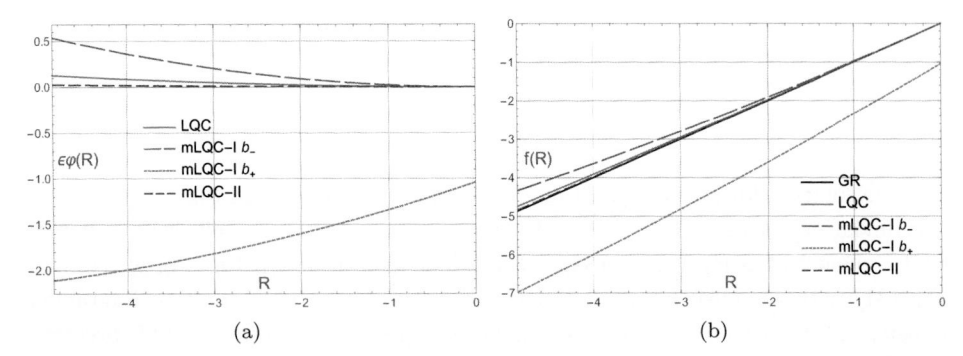

Fig. 4. Figure 4a. presents the comparison between the deviation, from GR, of the effective Lagrangian for the case of LQC (solid blue line), given by $\epsilon\varphi(R) = R^2/(18\kappa\rho_c)$, and the deviation terms of Eq. (23), for the b_- branch of mLQC-I (dashed dark orange line), Eq. (27), for the b_+ branch of mLQC-I (dashed light orange line) and Eq. (31), for mLQC-II (dashed pink line), for $-2\kappa\rho_c^I \leq R \leq 0$. Figure 4b. presents the differences between the Lagrangian density of GR (solid black line), with $\Lambda = 0$, and the effective $f(R)$ functions for the case of LQC (solid blue line), Eq. (23), for the b_- branch of mLQC-I (dashed dark orange line), Eq. (27), for the b_+ branch of mLQC-I (dashed light orange line) and Eq. (31), for mLQC-II (dashed pink line), for $-2\kappa\rho_c^I \leq R \leq 0$.

Friedmann equation depends on the $f(R)$ function, which we chose to parametrize as $f(R) = R + \epsilon\varphi(R)$. In this framework, we have determined functions $\varphi(R)$, such that Eqs. (2)–(4) are the same as Eq. (18). In other words, we have determined effective covariant $f(R)$ actions which lead to Eqs. (2)–(4). Moreover, these effective actions allow for a positive effective gravitational coupling constant and avoid the Dolgov–Kawasaki instability.[25] According to Eq. (12), the approximation that we use is valid for $|R| \ll \rho_c \sim l_p^{-2}$, therefore, breaking down at the bounce, since there $|R| \sim \rho_c \sim l_p^{-2}$. Thus, the argument that the effective Lagrangians deduced in this work yield Eqs. (2)–(4) is not quite a rigorous statement. However, our claim is that, at stages close enough to the bounce, the solutions found in this work may effectively, and correctly, describe the collapsing universe.

If a quantum theory of gravity is found, a proper description of the beginning of the Universe could eventually be reached. In this regard, the ΛCDM model is incomplete and, for this reason, there is motivation for attempting modifications of GR, in order to accommodate scenarios in which the Big Bang singularity is non-existent, such as the covariant effective actions determined in this work. In a forthcoming paper we will extend our analysis for mLQC-II to arbitrary values of w.

Acknowledgements

DV acknowledges support from the *Istituto Nazionale di Fisica Nucleare* (INFN) (*iniziativa specifica* TEONGRAV). FSNL acknowledges support from the Fundação para a Ciência e a Tecnologia (FCT) Scientific Employment Stimulus contract with reference CEECINST/00032/2018, and funding from the research grants

No. UID/FIS/04434/2020, No. PTDC/FIS-OUT/29048/2017 and No. CERN/FIS-PAR/0037/2019.

References

1. G. Amelino-Camelia, Quantum-Spacetime Phenomenology, *Living Rev. Rel.* **16**, p. 5 (2013).
2. S. Carlip, Quantum gravity: A Progress report, *Rept. Prog. Phys.* **64**, p. 885 (2001).
3. C. Rovelli, Loop quantum gravity, *Living Rev. Rel.* **1**, p. 1 (1998).
4. T. Thiemann, Modern canonical quantum general relativity (2001).
5. A. Ashtekar and J. Lewandowski, Background independent quantum gravity: A Status report, *Class. Quant. Grav.* **21**, p. R53 (2004).
6. M. Bojowald, Loop quantum cosmology, *Living Rev. Rel.* **8**, p. 11 (2005).
7. M. Bojowald, Absence of singularity in loop quantum cosmology, *Phys. Rev. Lett.* **86**, 5227 (2001).
8. A. Ashtekar, T. Pawlowski and P. Singh, Quantum Nature of the Big Bang: An Analytical and Numerical Investigation. I., *Phys. Rev. D* **73**, p. 124038 (2006).
9. A. Ashtekar, T. Pawlowski and P. Singh, Quantum Nature of the Big Bang: Improved dynamics, *Phys. Rev. D* **74**, p. 084003 (2006).
10. V. Taveras, Corrections to the Friedmann Equations from LQG for a Universe with a Free Scalar Field, *Phys. Rev. D* **78**, p. 064072 (2008).
11. K. Banerjee, G. Calcagni and M. Martin-Benito, Introduction to loop quantum cosmology, *SIGMA* **8**, p. 016 (2012).
12. J. De Haro and J. Amorós, Bouncing cosmologies via modified gravity in the ADM formalism: Application to Loop Quantum Cosmology, *Phys. Rev. D* **97**, p. 064014 (2018).
13. P. Singh, Loop cosmological dynamics and dualities with Randall-Sundrum braneworlds, *Phys. Rev. D* **73**, p. 063508 (2006).
14. K. A. Meissner, Black hole entropy in loop quantum gravity, *Class. Quant. Grav.* **21**, 5245 (2004).
15. J. Yang, Y. Ding and Y. Ma, Alternative quantization of the Hamiltonian in loop quantum cosmology II: Including the Lorentz term, *Phys. Lett. B* **682**, 1 (2009).
16. A. Dapor and K. Liegener, Cosmological Effective Hamiltonian from full Loop Quantum Gravity Dynamics, *Phys. Lett. B* **785**, 506 (2018).
17. A. Dapor and K. Liegener, Cosmological coherent state expectation values in loop quantum gravity I. Isotropic kinematics, *Class. Quant. Grav.* **35**, p. 135011 (2018).
18. E. Alesci, A. Barrau, G. Botta, K. Martineau and G. Stagno, Phenomenology of Quantum Reduced Loop Gravity in the isotropic cosmological sector, *Phys. Rev. D* **98**, p. 106022 (2018).
19. J. Bilski and A. Marcianò, Critical Insight into the Cosmological Sector of Loop Quantum Gravity, *Phys. Rev. D* **101**, p. 066026 (2020).
20. B.-F. Li, P. Singh and A. Wang, Towards Cosmological Dynamics from Loop Quantum Gravity, *Phys. Rev. D* **97**, p. 084029 (2018).
21. B.-F. Li, P. Singh and A. Wang, Genericness of pre-inflationary dynamics and probability of the desired slow-roll inflation in modified loop quantum cosmologies, *Phys. Rev. D* **100**, p. 063513 (2019).
22. B.-F. Li, P. Singh and A. Wang, Qualitative dynamics and inflationary attractors in loop cosmology, *Phys. Rev. D* **98**, p. 066016 (2018).
23. G. J. Olmo and P. Singh, Effective Action for Loop Quantum Cosmology a la Palatini, *JCAP* **01**, p. 030 (2009).

24. G. J. Olmo, Palatini Approach to Modified Gravity: f(R) Theories and Beyond, *Int. J. Mod. Phys. D* **20**, 413 (2011).
25. T. P. Sotiriou and V. Faraoni, f(R) Theories Of Gravity, *Rev. Mod. Phys.* **82**, 451 (2010).
26. F. S. N. Lobo, The Dark side of gravity: Modified theories of gravity (7 2008).
27. A. De Felice and S. Tsujikawa, f(R) theories, *Living Rev. Rel.* **13**, p. 3 (2010).
28. S. Nojiri and S. D. Odintsov, Unified cosmic history in modified gravity: from F(R) theory to Lorentz non-invariant models, *Phys. Rept.* **505**, 59 (2011).
29. T. Clifton, P. G. Ferreira, A. Padilla and C. Skordis, Modified Gravity and Cosmology, *Phys. Rept.* **513**, 1 (2012).
30. S. Capozziello and M. De Laurentis, Extended Theories of Gravity, *Phys. Rept.* **509**, 167 (2011).
31. T. Harko and F. S. N. Lobo, *Extensions of f(R) Gravity: Curvature-Matter Couplings and Hybrid Metric-Palatini Theory* (Cambridge University Press, 11 2018).
32. L. Bel and H. S. Zia, Regular reduction of relativistic theories of gravitation with a quadratic Lagrangian, *Phys. Rev. D* **32**, 3128 (1985).
33. J. Z. Simon, Higher Derivative Lagrangians, Nonlocality, Problems and Solutions, *Phys. Rev. D* **41**, p. 3720 (1990).
34. J. Z. Simon, No Starobinsky inflation from selfconsistent semiclassical gravity, *Phys. Rev. D* **45**, 1953 (1992).
35. I. Terrucha, D. Vernieri and J. P. S. Lemos, Covariant action for bouncing cosmologies in modified Gauss–Bonnet gravity, *Annals Phys.* **404**, 39 (2019).
36. B. J. Barros, E. M. Teixeira and D. Vernieri, Bouncing cosmology in $f(R,\mathcal{G})$ gravity by order reduction, *Annals Phys.* **419**, p. 168231 (2020).
37. F. Bajardi, D. Vernieri and S. Capozziello, Bouncing Cosmology in f(Q) Symmetric Teleparallel Gravity, *Eur. Phys. J. Plus* **135**, p. 912 (2020).
38. T. P. Sotiriou, Covariant Effective Action for Loop Quantum Cosmology from Order Reduction, *Phys. Rev. D* **79**, p. 044035 (2009).

Probing multiverse using gravitational wave observations

Moe Kukihara[*] and Kazuhiro Hayama[†]

Department of Applied Physics, Fukuoka University,
Fukuoka, 814-0180, Japan
[*] *E-mail: sd211003@cis.fukuoka-u.ac.jp*
[†] *E-mail: hayama@fukuoka-u.ac.jp*

From the theory of the multiverse cosmology, it is possible that our universe collides with other universes locally in its history, which may result in local changes of the curvature of the spacetime. In this paper, we propose a method to probe the multiverse using gravitational wave observations for the first time. Our method firstly makes triangles using two detected gravitational wave sources and the Sun, and then measures the curvature of the triangles. We use 11 gravitational wave sources detected by LIGO and Virgo during O1 and O2, and make 55 triangles by combining them to measure their curvature. The curvature is measured by comparing the distance between two gravitational wave sources estimated by the gravitational wave observations with the one obtained with assumption of a simple model of the cosmological evolution.

As a result, we found that, for 43 of 55 triangles, the distances estimated by the model are greater than the ones obtained by the gravitational wave observations. This indicates a negative curvature, which may be due to the simplification of the cosmological evolution. For the rest 12, the distances are not determined because of uncertainty of the parameters of the gravitational wave observations. Further gravitational wave observations and more sophisticated model of the cosmological evolution is essential to test the multiverse cosmology observationally.

Keywords: Gravitational wave observations, multiverse, spacetime geometry, cosmological evolution

1. Introduction

Since E. Hubble discovered the expansion of the universe in 1929,[1] it has been considered of the possibility that the beginning of the universe was a small point. G. Gamow proposed the Big Bang theory, from which the beginning of the universe was a fireball. The Big Bang theory was supported by observations such as the first observation of the cosmic microwave background radiation in 1965[2] and the discovery of temperature fluctuations originating in the early universe by the cosmic background radiation explorer COBE in 1989.[3] However, the Big Bang theory has problems such as the homogeneity and the flatness problem. Inflation theory proposed to solve these problems,[4–6] but inflation theory also has following problems: The average value of the vacuum energy density predicted by the field theory is $\rho_\Lambda \sim 10^{113}$ J/m^3, whereas the currently observed vacuum energy density is, $\rho_\Lambda \sim 10^{-9}$ J/m^3. There is a difference of about 120 digits in size between the theoretical value and the observed value.[7]

Multiverse cosmology may solve these problems. In the multiverse cosmology, each universe is allowed to have different vacuum energy density, and our universe happened to have current vacuum energy densities. Thus, in the multiverse cosmology, the formation of multiple universes is naturally predicted. It is possible that our universe collides with other universes locally and there is a local change of curvature at the collision surface.[8] The measurement of the curvature performed by the cosmic microwave background radiation observation satellite WMAP[9,10] showed that the curvature of the entire universe was flat. But there were uncertainties that the vortex-shaped polarization component were not discovered by CMB polarization observations, and therefore the determination of the curvature needs to be further refined in future observations.

In order to find whether there has been collisions between our universe and other universes in the past, There are studies that explore the temperature fluctuations that occur at the collisions surface. This temperature fluctuation appears as a ring pattern on the cosmic microwave background radiation. Several radio observations were conducted to see the properties,[11,12] and as a result, four sky areas were reported from the WMAP observations that were consistent with the ring patterns that appeared due to collision between the universes.[13,14] It should be noted that as the universe is expanded with time, the effects of collisions tend to be diluted as much as the structure of the initial universe.

In this paper, we proposed for the first time a method for probing the multiverse using gravitational wave observations, which is independent of radio wave observations performed so far.[15] Chapter 2 describes how to measure the local curvature of the universe, and Chapter 3 describes the results and discussion.

2. Measurement of the local curvatures of the universe

We will explain how we estimate local curvatures of the universe. The gravitational waves GW150914, GW151012, GW151226, GW170104, GW170608, GW170729, GW170809, GW170814, GW170817, GW170818, GW170823 were detected by the LIGO and Virgo observations.[16] Two of the 11 gravitational wave sources and the sun are used to form a triangle, and the distance between the two gravitational wave sources is estimated by gravitational wave observations. The distances are also estimated by simple assumption that the gravitational wave sources were born in the early universe and the distance between the two sources is the size of the flat universe. The local curvature of the universe was measured by comparing these values.

2.1. *Distance between gravitational waves by gravitational wave observations*

The sky locations of the almost all detected gravitational waves are highly uncertain. The summary plots in the paper B. P. Abbott, *et al.*[16] which show 50% and 90% credible area for the sky locations of detected gravitational wave events and most of the events have error regions with several hundred square degrees. But the error regions are estimated to be reduced in future observations. In this paper we regard the sky locations of the gravitational waves as the positions with the highest probabilities in the contours.

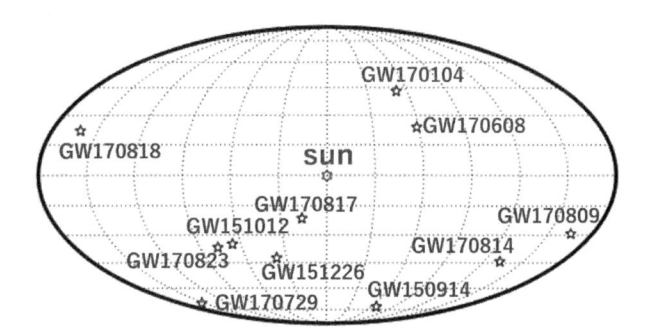

Fig. 1. Most probable sky locations of the detected gravitational waves in 2015-2017 in the Mollweide coordinates.[16]

index	combination	index	combination
area 1	GW150914,GW151012	area 29	GW170104,GW170729
area 2	GW150914,GW151226	area 30	GW170104,GW170809
area 3	GW150914,GW170104	area 31	GW170104,GW170814
area 4	GW150914,GW170608	area 32	GW170104,GW170817
area 5	GW150914,GW170729	area 33	GW170104,GW170818
area 6	GW150914,GW170809	area 34	GW170104,GW170823
area 7	GW150914,GW170814	area 35	GW170608,GW170729
area 8	GW150914,GW170817	area 36	GW170608,GW170809
area 9	GW150914,GW170818	area 37	GW170608,GW170814
area 10	GW150914,GW170823	area 38	GW170608,GW170817
area 11	GW151012,GW151226	area 39	GW170608,GW170818
area 12	GW151012,GW170104	area 40	GW170608,GW170823
area 13	GW151012,GW170608	area 41	GW170729,GW170809
area 14	GW151012,GW170729	area 42	GW170729,GW170814
area 15	GW151012,GW170809	area 43	GW170729,GW170817
area 16	GW151012,GW170814	area 44	GW170729,GW170818
area 17	GW151012,GW170817	area 45	GW170729,GW170823
area 18	GW151012,GW170818	area 46	GW170809,GW170814
area 19	GW151012,GW170823	area 47	GW170809,GW170817
area 20	GW151226,GW170104	area 48	GW170809,GW170818
area 21	GW151226,GW170608	area 49	GW170809,GW170823
area 22	GW151226,GW170729	area 50	GW170814,GW170817
area 23	GW151226,GW170809	area 51	GW170814,GW170818
area 24	GW151226,GW170814	area 52	GW170814,GW170823
area 25	GW151226,GW170817	area 53	GW170817,GW170818
area 26	GW151226,GW170818	area 54	GW170817,GW170823
area 27	GW151226,GW170823	area 55	GW170818,GW170823
area 28	GW170104,GW170608		

Fig. 2. 55 combinations of two gravitational sources for making triangles including the Sun.

Figure 1 shows the sky positions of the gravitational wave sources used here and the sun. we constructed triangles using the sun and two of the gravitational wave sources. The distances between the two gravitational wave sources were estimated using the estimated distances and sky locations of the gravitational wave sources in the triangle. Figure 2 shows 55 combinations of two gravitational sources for making triangles including the Sun.

2.2. *Distance between gravitational waves by a flat universe model*

We consider of the following four-dimensional metric that describes a uniform and isotropic expansion universe.

$$ds^2 = -c^2 dt^2 + a^2(t)\left[\frac{dr^2}{1-Kr^2} + r^2(d\theta^2 sin^2\theta d\phi^2)\right] \qquad (1)$$

c: speed of light, a(t): Scale factor at time t, r: Radius in 3D spherical coordinates, θ, ϕ: Declination in 3D spherical coordinates, K: constant

Using the natural unit system, the metric of the flat universe model is,

$$ds^2 = -dt^2 + a^2(t)[dr^2 + r^2(d\theta^2 + sin^2\theta d\phi^2)] \qquad (2)$$

When a gravitational wave with a redshift z is observed, the relation of the scale factor and z is as follows:

$$\frac{a(t)}{a(t_0)} = \frac{1}{1+z} \qquad (3)$$

Here, when we estimate the distance between two gravitational wave sources in the flat universe model, we put simple assumption that the gravitational wave sources occurred in the early universe and the evolution of the universe are not affected by gravity from other objects such as dark matter and galaxies.[17,18] z is the average of the redshifts of the two gravitational wave sources, and the distances between the two points are estimated to be the size of the universe at z. Hereafter we refer this as the simple universe model.

2.3. *Comparison of the estimated distances for 55 triangular areas*

Figure 3 shows the distances between the sources by gravitational wave observations and the distances between the sources by the simple universe model for each triangular area. The blue cross marks show the value distances estimated from the gravitational wave observations. The error bars reflect the uncertainties of the distances of the gravitational wave sources and the uncertainties of the sky locations of the gravitational wave sources. The red asterisks are the distances between the two gravitational wave sources in the simple universe model.

Figure 4 shows the curvature of each area. The curvature of each area was estimated by comparing the distances estimated by the two ways. If the two estimated

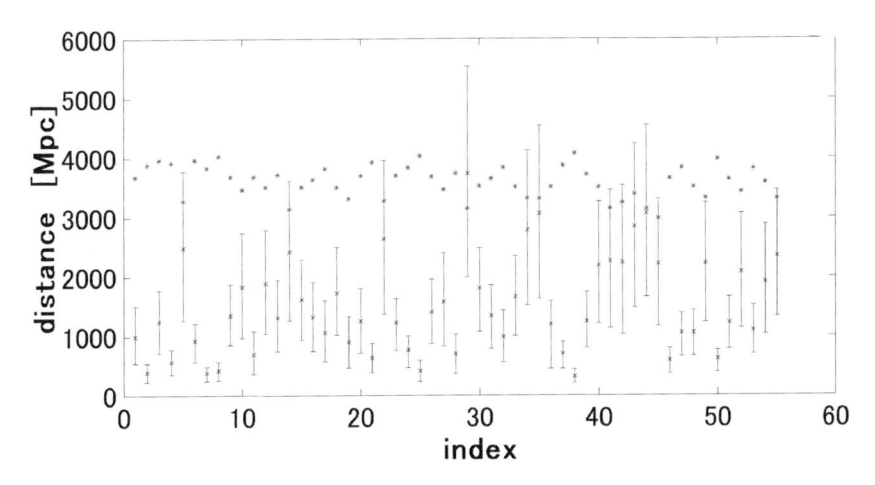

Fig. 3. Blue cross marks show the distances between gravitational wave sources estimated by the gravitational wave observations with uncertainty. Red asterisks show the distances calculated using a simple model of the cosmological evolution.

index	curvature	index	curvature
area 1	negative	area 29	Indistinguishable
area 2	negative	area 30	negative
area 3	negative	area 31	negative
area 4	negative	area 32	negative
area 5	Indistinguishable	area 33	negative
area 6	negative	area 34	Indistinguishable
area 7	negative	area 35	Indistinguishable
area 8	negative	area 36	negative
area 9	negative	area 37	negative
area 10	negative	area 38	negative
area 11	negative	area 39	negative
area 12	negative	area 40	negative
area 13	negative	area 41	Indistinguishable
area 14	Indistinguishable	area 42	Indistinguishable
area 15	negative	area 43	Indistinguishable
area 16	negative	area 44	Indistinguishable
area 17	negative	area 45	Indistinguishable
area 18	negative	area 46	negative
area 19	negative	area 47	negative
area 20	negative	area 48	negative
area 21	negative	area 49	negative
area 22	Indistinguishable	area 50	negative
area 23	negative	area 51	negative
area 24	negative	area 52	negative
area 25	negative	area 53	negative
area 26	negative	area 54	negative
area 27	negative	area 55	Indistinguishable
area 28	negative		

Fig. 4. Curvatures of the 55 triangles.

distances are equal each other, then the local curvature of the universe is zero. If the distance estimated by gravitational wave observations is larger than the distance estimated by the simple universe model, the positive curvature is suggested, and if smaller, the negative curvature is suggested.

In the 43 areas among 55 areas, the distances estimated by the simple universe model were larger than the distances estimated by gravitational wave observations, so negative curvatures were suggested. On the other hands area 5, area 14, area 22, area 29, area 34, area 35, area 41, area 42, area 43, area 44, area 45, area 55 in this 12 areas, the estimated distances estimated by the simple universe model were in the error bars of the distances estimated by gravitational wave observations, so the curvatures were not estimated from all at the gravitational wave observations.

3. Summary

In this study, we proposed for the first time a method to probe the multiverse cosmology using gravitational wave observations. We estimated the local curvatures of various areas in the universe by measuring the sums of the internal angles of the 55 triangles formed by the sun and the all combinations of 11 gravitational wave sources.

In the 43 areas among 55 areas, the distances estimated by the simple universe model were larger than the distances estimated by gravitational wave observations, so negative curvatures were suggested. This is due to the simplification of the universe model, and it is necessary to sophisticate the model of the universe by including the effects of other astronomical objects, dark matter, dark energy, and so on. On the other hands in the area 5, area 14, area 22, area 29, area 34, area 35, area 41, area 42, area 43, area 44, area 45, area 55 in this 12 areas, the distances estimated by the simple universe model were in the error bar of the distances estimated by gravitational wave observations, so the curvatures could not be estimated at the current gravitational wave observations. In the future, it will be important to reduce the error in order to limit the sign of the curvature.

Acknowledgments

This work was supported by JSPS KAKENHI Grant Number JP19K03896. This research has made use of data, software and/or web tools obtained from the Gravitational Wave Open Science Center (https://www.gw-openscience.org), a service of LIGO Laboratory, the LIGO Scientific Collaboration and the Virgo Collaboration. LIGO is funded by the U.S. National Science Foundation. Virgo is funded by the French Centre National de Recherche Scientifique (CNRS), the Italian Istituto Nazionaledella Fisica Nucleare (INFN) and the Dutch Nikhef, with contributions by Polish and Hungarian institutes.

References

1. E. Hubble, PNAS, **15**, 168-173 (1929).
2. A. A. Penzias, R. W. Willson, Astrophysical Journal, **142**, 419-421 (1965).
3. G. F. Smoot, *et al.*, Astrophysical Journal Letters, **396**, p.L1 (1992).
4. K. Sato, Physics Letters., **99**, 1, 66-70 (1981).
5. K. Sato, Monthly Notices of the Royal Astronomical Society, **195**, 467-479 (1981).
6. B. Einhorn Martin, K. Sato, Nuclear Physics B, **180**, 3, 385-404 (1981).
7. S. Weinberg, The cosmological constatnt problems, Red. Mod. Phys. **61**, 1 (1989).
8. A. Lue, G. Starkman, Physical Review D, **67**, 6, 064002 (2003).
9. A. Riess, *et al.*, Astrophys. J., **560**, 49 (2001).
10. D. N. Spergel, *et al.*, The Astrophysical Journal Supplement Series, **148**, 1, 175-194 (2003).
11. Spencer Chang, *et al.*, Journal of Cosmology and Astroparticle Physics, **32**, 4, 025 (2009).
12. M. Kleban, T. S. Levi, K. Sigurdson, Physical Review D, **87**, 4, 041301 (2013).
13. S. M. Feeney, *et al.*, Physical Review Letters, **107**, 7, 071301 (2011).
14. S. M. Feeney, *et al.*, Physical Review D, **84**, 4, 043507 (2011).
15. A. Gupta, D. Fox, B. S. Sathyaprakash and B. F. Schutz, The Astrophys. J., **886**, 1 (2019).
16. B. P. Abbott, *et al.*, Physical Review X, **9**, 3, 031040 (2019).
17. V. Bromm, N. Yoshida, C. McKee and L. Hernquist, Nature, **459**, 49 (2009).
18. V. Bromm and N. Yoshida, Annual Reviews of Astronomy and Astrophysics, **49**, 373 (2011).

Operator ordering ambiguity in observables of quantum cosmology

Harkirat Singh Sahota*

Kinjalk Lochan[†]

Department of Physical Sciences, Indian Institute of Science Education & Research (IISER) Mohali, Sector 81 SAS Nagar, Manauli PO 140306 Punjab India.
ph17078@iisermohali.ac.in, †kinjalk@iisermohali.ac.in

We discuss the status of observables and operator ordering ambiguity in the quantum cosmology model with Brown-Kuchař dust as the matter field. In order to study the dynamics of the FLRW universe, Hubble parameter and Ricci scalar are expressed as a function of phase space variables. As these functions exhibit operator ordering ambiguity, we write several Hermitian extensions corresponding to these observables. For the unitarily evolving semiclassical wave packet constructed in,[1] we have computed the expectation value of these observables, which shows that very early in the collapsing branch and very late in the expanding branch, the expectation values of the Hubble parameter and the Ricci scalar matches the classically obtained results irrespective of the operator ordering chosen. The expectation value of the Hubble parameter vanishes, and Ricci scalar attains an extremum at the point of classical singularity for all orderings, showing a robust singularity resolution. The signature of the operator ordering ambiguity is most pronounced at the classical singularity. For Weyl ordering, the expectation value of the Ricci scalar becomes negative for certain parameter values. We have computed the expectation value of other curvature invariants as well, which follows the trend.

Keywords: FLRW Model, Wheeler-DeWitt equation, Operator ordering ambiguity, Quantum Cosmology, Brown-Kuchař dust

1. Introduction

Any consistent quantization scheme for gravity must address the longstanding issues that plague the theory, like observables in quantum gravity or operator ordering ambiguity. In this work we will address the issue of operator ordering ambiguity in the observables of quantum gravity, in the context of flat FLRW model with Brown-Kuchař dust.[2]

General relativity is an example of singular systems, which has diffeomorphisms and time reparametrizations as gauge freedom.[3] A consistent (Dirac) observable in the general relativity must be invariant under diffeomorphisms and time reparametrizations. Now the systems with time reparametrization symmetry are tricky to handle, as the Hamiltonian of such systems itself is a constraint. Which would means that physical observables in the theory would be frozen in time or are constant of motion. To circumvent this issue, a possible resolution is proposed by Kuchař,[4] a phase space function does not need to have weakly vanishing Poisson bracket with Hamiltonian constraint to be an observable of general relativity.

The special objects which have vanishing Poisson bracket with Hamiltonian constraint are called a perennials.

Upon quantization, one would ideally like to obtain a self-adjoint extension of all the relevant observables appearing in the theory and study their spectral properties. But if one is interested in the expectation value of the operators in a wave packet, Hermiticity of the operator is sufficient to ensure the reality of the expectation value. For that reason we will concern ourselves with the Hermitian extensions of the observables and their expectation value for the wave packets constructed in the quantum model.

In this analysis, we will follow Kuchař's prescription[4] of observables in the quantum gravity models. For the FLRW model we will write the Hermitian extension of the operators that correspond to the Hubble parameter and the curvature invariants. We will find the expectation value of these operators and show the robustness of the singularity resolution claimed in the aforementioned quantum cosmology model. Apart from that, we will also address the operator ordering ambiguity in these observables and discuss at what stage this ambiguity will play a role.

2. FLRW Model with Brown-Kuchař Dust

We will start with the canonical formulation of the flat FLRW model coupled to Brown-Kuchař dust. We will first write the Hamiltonian constraint for this system and then write the phase space expression for the observables we are interested in.

The line element and the Ricci scalar for a homogeneous and isotropic flat FLRW spacetime is

$$ds^2 = -\mathcal{N}^2(t)dt^2 + a^2(t)d\mathbf{x}^2, \tag{1}$$

$$\mathcal{R} = \frac{6}{\mathcal{N}^2}\left[-\frac{\dot{\mathcal{N}}\dot{a}}{\mathcal{N}a} + \frac{\ddot{a}}{a} + \left(\frac{\dot{a}}{a}\right)^2\right], \tag{2}$$

where $a(\tau)$ is the scale factor and $\mathcal{N}$ is the lapse function. The action for this model with Brown-Kuchař dust[2,5] written in ADM form is,

$$S = S_G + S_m = \int \left(p\dot{a} + p_\tau \dot{\tau} - \mathcal{N}(H^G + H^D)\right) dt. \tag{3}$$

The Hamiltonian constraint for this model is given by,

$$\mathsf{H} = H^G + H^D = -\frac{\kappa^2}{6V_0}\frac{p_a^2}{2a} + p_\tau \approx 0. \tag{4}$$

In the further analysis, we will choose $\kappa^2 = 6V_0$. The solution of the Friedmann's equations with dust as matter is $a(t) \propto t^{2/3}$. The dust proper time τ and the coordinate time t are related as $\dot{\tau} = 1 \implies \tau(t) = t + $const. This model exhibits curvature singularity and has two disjointed solutions, representing a universe expanding from a Big Bang singularity and a universe collapsing to a Big Crunch singularity.

2.1. *Hubble Parameter and Ricci Scalar*

We are interested in the canonical expression for the Hubble parameter and the Ricci scalar. Using defining equation for the momentum conjugate to scale factor and the Hamilton's equations of motion, we get

$$\dot{a} = -\frac{p_a \mathcal{N}}{a}, \tag{5}$$

$$\ddot{a} = -\frac{p_a \dot{\mathcal{N}}}{a} - \frac{p_a^2 \mathcal{N}^2}{2a^3}. \tag{6}$$

Since we are working in comoving gauge $\mathcal{N} = 1$, the Hubble parameter takes the form

$$\mathbb{H} = \frac{\dot{a}}{a} = -a^{-2} p_a. \tag{7}$$

From (2), (5) and (6), the Ricci scalar is given by,

$$\mathcal{R} = \frac{3 p_a^2}{a^4}. \tag{8}$$

Classically for dust as matter source, the Ricci scalar is $\mathcal{R} = 4/3t^2$. The flat FLRW model with dust as matter has curvature singularity at $t = 0$ when $a \sim t^{2/3} \to 0$ and $\mathcal{R} \to \infty$.

2.2. *Riemann and Kretschmann Scalar*

Riemann Scalar for this model is

$$\mathcal{R}ie = R_{\mu\nu} R^{\mu\nu} = 9 \frac{(\dot{a}\dot{\mathcal{N}} - \mathcal{N}\ddot{a})^2}{a^2 \mathcal{N}^6} + 3 \frac{(a\mathcal{N}\ddot{a} - a\dot{a}\dot{\mathcal{N}} + 2\mathcal{N}\dot{a}^2)^2}{a^4 \mathcal{N}^6} = \frac{3 p_a^4}{a^8}. \tag{9}$$

Kretschmann Scalar for this model is,

$$K = R_{\mu\nu\alpha\beta} R^{\mu\nu\alpha\beta} = 12 \left(\frac{(\dot{a}\dot{\mathcal{N}} - \mathcal{N}\ddot{a})^2}{\mathcal{N}^6 a^2} + \frac{\dot{a}^4}{a^4 \mathcal{N}^4} \right) = \frac{15 p_a^4}{a^8} = 5\mathcal{R}ie. \tag{10}$$

Classically for dust as matter, Riemann and Kretschmann scalar takes the form $\mathcal{R}ie = 16/27t^4$, and $K = 80/27t^4$. These curvature invariants also diverge at $t = 0$.

3. Quantum Cosmology

Quantization of this system is done by implementation of the constraint $\mathsf{H} \approx 0$ as supplementary condition on wave functions. Brown-Kuchař dust appears as natural clock for the quantum theory and we are essentially working with dust proper time. Wheeler Dewitt equation for this model takes the form of Schrödinger equation,

$$i \frac{\partial \Psi(R, \tau)}{\partial \tau} = \hat{H} \Psi(a, \tau), \tag{11}$$

$$\hat{H} = \hbar^2 a^{-1+p+q} \frac{d}{da} a^{-p} \frac{d}{da} a^{-q}. \tag{12}$$

Since the Hamiltonian is a product of non-commuting variables, therefore, it does not have a unique quantum counterpart and the model exhibits operator ordering ambiguity. The parameters p and q represent our freedom to choose operator ordering. The eigenvalue of Hamiltonian can be interpreted as Misner-Sharp mass which on-shell is related to the energy of the dust[a]. The self-adjoint extensions of Hamiltonian (12) are discussed in.[1]

To make the momentum operator $\hat{P}$ Hermitian on the real half line $\mathbb{R}^+$, we choose measure a^2 and the momentum operator that is symmetric with this measure $\hat{p}_a = -ia^{-1}\partial_a a$. Therefore, to accommodate hermiticity of the momentum, we have to impose the constraint $1 - p - 2q = 2$ or $p + 2q = -1$ on operator ordering parameters. Using this constraint, we can eliminate one of these parameters. It is shown in,[6] the expectation values of a general observables in a general wave packet constructed in this model is independent of parameter q and it appears as a free parameter in the model. Therefore, the above constraint does not put any restriction on the physical content of the theory. The detailed discussion about the Hermiticity and the self-adjointness of momentum operator on real half-line can be found in.[6] The positive energy stationary states with this choice are,

$$\phi_E^1(a) = \frac{2}{\sqrt{3}} E^{\frac{1}{4}} J_{\frac{2|q|}{3}}\left(\frac{2}{3}\sqrt{2E}a^{\frac{3}{2}}\right). \tag{13}$$

Which form an orthogonal set under the scalar product we have chosen, thus making them suitable for the construction of wave packet. From the positive energy modes, a unitarily evolving wave packet is constructed by choosing a normalized Poisson-like distribution

$$\psi(R,\tau) = \int_0^\infty d\sqrt{E}\,\phi_E^1(R)e^{iE\tau}A(\sqrt{E}), \tag{14}$$

$$A(\sqrt{E}) = \frac{\sqrt{2}\lambda^{\frac{1}{2}(\kappa+1)}}{\sqrt{\Gamma(\kappa+1)}}\sqrt{E}^{\kappa+\frac{1}{2}}e^{-\frac{\lambda}{2}E}, \tag{15}$$

where $\kappa \geq 0$ and $\lambda > 0$ are real parameters with κ being dimensionless and λ has dimensions of length or inverse of energy. For this choice of distribution, expectation value of the Hamiltonian is inversely proportional to λ. With this distribution and constraint $\kappa = 2|q|/3$, the wave packet takes the form,

$$\psi(a,\tau) = \sqrt{3}\frac{a^{|q|}}{\sqrt{\Gamma(\frac{2}{3}|q|+1)}}\left(\frac{\frac{\sqrt{2\lambda}}{3}}{\frac{\lambda}{2}-i\tau}\right)^{\frac{2}{3}|q|+1} e^{-\frac{2a^3}{9\left(\frac{\lambda}{2}-i\tau\right)}}. \tag{16}$$

Taking this constraint on the parameter makes the distribution a function of the operator ordering parameter. We can not be sure if the dependency of an observable

---

[a]Misner-Sharpe mass for spherically symmetric system $ds^2 = g_{ab}(z)dz^a dz^b + R^2(z)d\Omega^2$ is $M_{MS} = R(z)\left(1 - g^{ab}\partial_a R(z)\partial_b R(z)\right)/2$. For the case of FLRW mode, Misner-Sharp mass is $M_{MS} = a\dot{a}^2 r^3/2 = (4\pi r^3/3)\rho a^3 G$. The gravitational Hamiltonian is given by $H = -(3V/8\pi G)a\dot{a}^2 = -V\rho a^3$, since ρa^3 is a constant of motion and the Hamiltonian represents energy associated with the dust.

on parameter q is coming from the its dependence on the shape of the distribution or is it a genuine artifact of the operator ordering ambiguity. The signature of this parameter on the observables is discussed in[6] and we are not interested in operator ordering ambiguity in the Hamiltonian operator here. We are interested in the operator ordering ambiguity in the observables of this theory. It is shown in,[1] this model avoids singularity following DeWitt's criteria and in the current context, it represents a bouncing cosmology model.

4. Observables

In this analysis, we will follow Kuchař's proposal,[4,7,8] the observables in a time reparametrization invariant systems need not to commute with Hamiltonian constraint. Moreover in the quantum domain, we will require the Hermitian extension of operators to ensure the reality of expectation value of these observables. We will write the Hermitian extension of phase space functions that we are interested in and compute their expectation values in the wave packet (16).

4.1. Hubble Parameter

Corresponding to the canonical form of the Hubble parameter (7), several operator orderings for which the Hubble parameter is Hermitian can be written as,

$$F.O.1 \to \hat{\mathbb{H}}_1 = -a^{-1}\hat{p}_a a^{-1}, \tag{17}$$

$$F.O.2 \to \hat{\mathbb{H}}_2 = -\frac{1}{2}\left(a^{n-2}\hat{p}_a a^{-n} + a^{-n}\hat{p}_a a^{n-2}\right), \tag{18}$$

$$\hat{\mathbb{H}}_1 \psi = \hat{\mathbb{H}}_2 \psi = i\, a^{-2}\frac{\partial \psi}{\partial a} = \hat{\mathbb{H}}. \tag{19}$$

To ensure the Hermiticity of the operator, the boundary term $i[\psi^*\chi]_0^\infty$ has to vanish. It is achieved by the wavefunctions that vanishes when $a \to 0$ or $a \to \infty$. For the wave packets (16), it is the case provided $q \neq 0$.

The expectation value of the Hubble parameter for the wave packet (16) is,

$$\bar{\mathbb{H}}_1 = \langle \psi|\hat{\mathbb{H}}_1|\psi\rangle = i \int_0^\infty \psi^*(a,\tau)\frac{\partial \psi(a,\tau)}{\partial a}\, da = \frac{8\tau}{3(\lambda^2 + 4\tau^2)}. \tag{20}$$

In the large τ limit, i.e. $\tau^2 \gg \lambda^2$, we recovers the classical value of Hubble parameter for the flat FLRW model with dust as matter.

$$\bar{\mathbb{H}}|_{\lambda \to 0} = \frac{2}{3\tau}. \tag{21}$$

The expectation value of the Hubble parameter is plotted in Fig. 1.

The Hubble parameter $\bar{\mathbb{H}}$ has global maximum at $\tau = \lambda/2$ and global minimum at $\tau = -\lambda/2$. At the point of classical singularity the Hubble parameter vanishes thus signifying a robust singularity resolution.

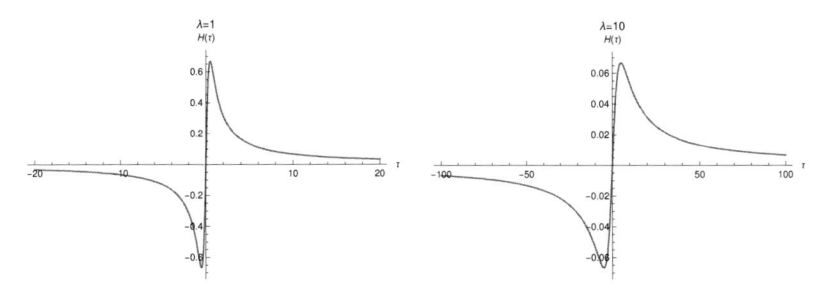

Fig. 1. Expectation value of the Hubble Parameter for different λ values.

4.2. Ricci Scalar

We will write general operator orderings that will make the operator corresponding to the phase space function given in Eq. (8) Hermitian with the given measure. There are two choices, normal symmetric operator ordering and Weyl ordering.

$$\hat{\mathcal{R}}_1 = 3a^{-j}\hat{p}_a a^{2j-4}\hat{p}_a a^{-j}, \tag{22}$$

$$\hat{\mathcal{R}}_2 = -\frac{3}{2}\left(a^{-j}\hat{p}_a a^{-k}\hat{p}_a a^{j+k-4} + a^{j+k-4}\hat{p}_a a^{-k}\hat{p}_a a^{-j}\right). \tag{23}$$

Here j and k are parameters that encapsulate the operator ordering ambiguity and describe our freedom in choosing operator ordering corresponding to the Ricci scalar.

For the operators to be Hermitian, the boundary term

$$-3\left[a^{-2}\left(\psi^*\frac{\partial \chi}{\partial a} - \frac{\partial \psi^*}{\partial a}\chi\right)\right]_0^\infty = 0 \tag{24}$$

has to be satisfied. For the case of the wave packet (16), the boundary term vanishes when $q > 3/2$. The expectation value of the Ricci scalar for this wave packet is,

$$\bar{\mathcal{R}}_1 = \frac{16\left(\lambda^2(3|q| + 2(j-4)(j-1)) + 4|q|(2|q|-3)\tau^2\right)}{3|q|(2|q|-3)\left(\lambda^2 + 4\tau^2\right)^2}, \tag{25}$$

$$\bar{\mathcal{R}}_2 = \frac{16\left(\lambda^2(3|q| - 2j(j+k-4) + 5k - 12) + 4|q|(2|q|-3)\tau^2\right)}{3|q|(2|q|-3)\left(\lambda^2 + 4\tau^2\right)^2}. \tag{26}$$

We see, the expectation value is well behaved regular function in the domain of parameters that ensure the Hermiticity. Again for large $|\tau|$ i.e. $\tau^2 >> \lambda^2$, we recover the classical expression for the Ricci scalar irrespective of the operator ordering chosen,

$$\bar{\mathcal{R}} = \frac{4}{3\tau^2}. \tag{27}$$

For the limit $q \gg j, k$ there is no signature of the operator ordering parameters j and k in the expectation value of the Ricci scalar.

$$\bar{\mathcal{R}}_1 = \bar{\mathcal{R}}_2 = \frac{16\left(3|q|\lambda^2 + 4|q|(2|q|-3)\tau^2\right)}{3|q|(2|q|-3)\left(\lambda^2+4\tau^2\right)^2}. \tag{28}$$

The Ricci scalar in this regime has local minima at $\tau = 0$ and global maxima at $\tau = \pm\lambda/2$. Surprisingly in the large q regime, the Ricci scalar has maxima at the dust proper time, where the Hubble parameter has extrema.

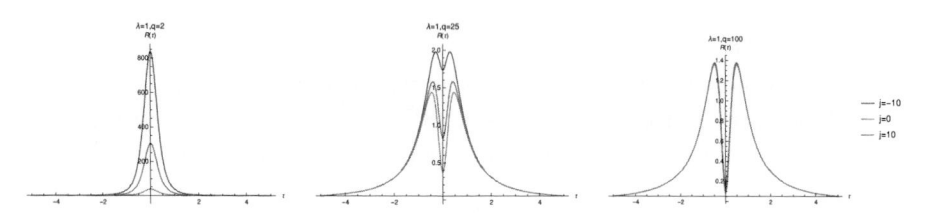

Fig. 2. Expectation value of the Ricci scalar $\bar{\mathcal{R}}_1$ for different operator orderings.

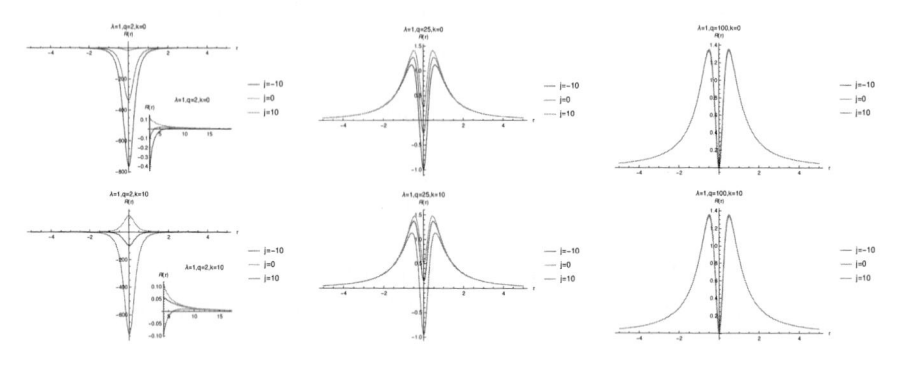

Fig. 3. Expectation value of Ricci scalar with Weyl ordering $\bar{\mathcal{R}}_2$ for different operator ordering parameters.

We have plotted the Ricci scalar for normal operator ordering in Fig. 2 and for the Weyl ordering in Fig 3. We see that the signature of the operator ordering parameters is most pronounced at the point of classical singularity i.e. at $\tau = 0$. Moreover, as we keep on increasing parameter q, the expectation value of the Ricci scalar for different operator ordering keeps on merging and for very large q, there is no signature of the operator ordering parameters. For the case of Weyl ordered Ricci scalar, the expectation value of the operator has negative values for certain parameter range.

4.3. *Riemann and Kretschmann Scalar*

Since the Kretschmann scalar is proportional to the Riemann scalar, we will write the Hermitian extensions of one of them, say, Kretschmann scalar and find the expectation value of the operator with given wave packet (16).

$$F.O.1 \rightarrow \hat{K}_1 = 15a^{-4}\hat{p}_a^4 a^{-4}, \tag{29}$$

$$F.O.2 \rightarrow \hat{K}_2 = 15\hat{p}_a^2 a^{-8} \hat{p}_a^2, \tag{30}$$

$$F.O.3 \rightarrow \hat{K}_3 = \frac{15}{2}\left(\hat{p}_a^4 a^{-8} + a^{-8}\hat{p}_a^4\right), \tag{31}$$

$$F.O.4 \rightarrow \hat{K}_4 = \frac{15}{2}\left(a^{-2}\hat{p}_a^4 a^{-6} + a^{-6}\hat{p}_a^4 a^{-2}\right). \tag{32}$$

The boundary term which needs to vanish for the Hermiticity of these operators is,

$$\left[a^{-6}(\psi^*\chi''' - \psi'^*\chi'' + \psi''^*\chi' - \psi'''^*\chi - 6a^{-1}(\psi^*\chi'' \right.$$
$$\left. -\psi''^*\chi) + 30a^{-2}(\psi^*\chi' - \psi'^*\chi))\right]_0^\infty = 0 \implies |q| > \frac{9}{2} \tag{33}$$

The expectation value of the Kretschamann scalar for various operator orderings is,

$$\bar{K}_1(\tau) = \frac{1280(\lambda^2 + 4\tau^2)^{-4}}{27|q|(2|q| - 9)(2|q| - 3)} \bigg(8(2|q| - 9)(9|q| - 20)\lambda^2\tau^2 + 3(9|q| - 40)\lambda^4$$
$$+ 16|q|(2|q| - 9)(2|q| - 3)\tau^4 \bigg), \tag{34}$$

$$\bar{K}_2(\tau) = \frac{1280\left(\lambda^2 + 4\tau^2\right)^{-4}}{27|q|(2|q| - 9)(2|q| - 3)(|q| - 3)} \bigg(3(|q|(9|q| + 29) + 504)\lambda^4 + 8(|q| - 3)$$
$$(2|q| - 9)(9|q| + 28)\lambda^2\tau^2 + 16(|q| - 3)|q|(2|q| - 9)(2|q| - 3)\tau^4 \bigg), \tag{35}$$

$$\bar{K}_3(\tau) = \frac{1280\left(\lambda^2 + 4\tau^2\right)^{-4}}{27(|q| - 3)|q|(2|q| - 9)(2|q| - 3)} \bigg(3(|q|(9|q| - 259) + 1272)\lambda^4 + 8(|q| - 3)$$
$$(2|q| - 9)(9|q| - 116)\lambda^2\tau^2 + 16(|q| - 3)|q|(2|q| - 9)(2|q| - 3)\tau^4 \bigg), \tag{36}$$

$$\bar{K}_4(\tau) = \frac{1280\left(\lambda^2 + 4\tau^2\right)^{-4}}{27(|q| - 3)|q|(2|q| - 9)(2|q| - 3)} \bigg(3(|q| - 8)(9|q| - 43)\lambda^4 + 8(|q| - 3)$$
$$(2|q| - 9)(9|q| - 44)\lambda^2\tau^2 + 16(|q| - 3)|q|(2|q| - 9)(2|q| - 3)\tau^4 \bigg). \tag{37}$$

Again, the expectation value of these observables is a well behaved regular function in the domain of parameters that ensures the Hermiticity of this observable. Classical expression is recovered irrespective of the operator ordering chosen i.e., when $\tau^2 >> \lambda^2$, $\bar{K} = 80/27\tau^4$.

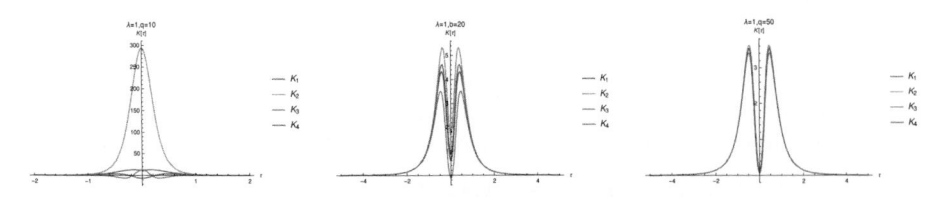

Fig. 4. Expectation value of Kretschmann scalar for various operator orderings.

We have plotted the expectation value of the Kretschmann scalar for different operator orderings. Here as well, we can see the signature of operator ordering is most pronounced at the point of classical singularity and Weyl ordered operator attains negative values for certain parameter range. Thus, the Kretschmann scalar also shows the features that are observed in the case of the Ricci scalar.

5. Discussion and Conclusion

We have studied the operator ordering ambiguity in the observables of a quantum model of cosmology with Brown-Kuchař dust as the matter source. The quantum model is singularity-free following DeWitt's criteria and it is shown that the expectation value of the scale factor is regular function with non-zero minima at the point of classical singularity and it follows classical trajectory, far away from the singularity. Thus, the quantum model represents a bouncing cosmological model which mimics classical behavior away from singularity.

We have studied the dynamics of the quantum FLRW model via the observables of the theory, Hubble parameter and curvature invariants. After writing the phase space functions for these observables, we have constructed the Hermitian extension of these observables. As these functions exhibit operator ordering ambiguity, there exists infinite many Hermitian extensions. For unitarily evolving wave packet, we have computed the expectation value of these observables. Very early in the collapsing phase and late in the expanding phase, these expectation values mimic the classical behavior irrespective of the operator ordering chosen. At the point of classical singularity, expectation value of the Hubble parameter vanishes and the Ricci scalar attains an extremum for all operator orderings, thus showing a robust singularity resolution.

This extremum value of the Ricci scalar is sensitive to the operator ordering parameters and the signature of these parameters is most pronounced at the point of singularity. The expectation value of the Ricci scalar is insensitive to this parameter away from singularity. Furthermore, in the large q regime, there is no signature of operator ordering parameter and the two maxima of Ricci scalar are at the time where the extrema of the Hubble parameter are located. For certain parameter range, the expectation value of the Weyl ordered Ricci scalar attains negative values. These features are present for the case of other curvature invariants as well.

Acknowledgments

HSS would like to acknowledge the financial support from University Grants Commission, Government of India, in the form of Junior Research Fellowship (UGC-CSIR JRF/Dec- 2016/503905). Research of KL is partially supported by the Startup Research Grant of SERB, Government of India (SRG/2019/002202).

References

1. C. Kiefer and T. Schmitz, Singularity avoidance for collapsing quantum dust in the Lemaître-Tolman-Bondi model, *Physical Review D* **99**, p. 126010 (June 2019).
2. J. D. Brown and K. V. Kuchar, Dust as a Standard of Space and Time in Canonical Quantum Gravity, *Physical Review D* **51**, 5600 (May 1995).
3. C. Kiefer, *Quantum gravity*International series of monographs on physics, no. 155 in International series of monographs on physics, third edition edn. (Oxford University Press, Oxford, 2012).
4. K. Kuchař, Canonical Quantum Gravity, *arXiv:gr-qc/9304012* (April 1993).
5. H. Maeda, Unitary evolution of the quantum universe with a Brown-Kuchar dust, *Classical and Quantum Gravity* **32**, p. 235023 (December 2015).
6. H. S. Sahota and K. Lochan, Infrared signatures of quantum bounce in collapsing geometry, *arXiv:2110.06247 [gr-qc]* (Oct 2021).
7. J. Barbour and B. Z. Foster, Constraints and gauge transformations: Dirac's theorem is not always valid *arXiv:0808.1223 [gr-qc]* (Aug 2008).
8. M. Bojowald, P. A. Höhn and A. Tsobanjan, Effective approach to the problem of time: General features and examples, *Physical Review D* **83** (Jun 2011).

Decoupled quark stars in self-interacting Brans-Dicke gravity

M. Sharif* and Amal Majid

Department of Mathematics, University of the Punjab,
Quaid-e-Azam Campus, Lahore-54590, Pakistan.
*E-mail: msharif.math@pu.edu.pk
www.pu.edu.pk

In this paper, we generate an anisotropic solution for a static sphere filled with quark matter in the framework of self-interacting Brans-Dicke theory. For this purpose, we add an anisotropic source in the seed distribution and decouple the field equations through deformation in the radial metric function. As a result of this transformation, the field equations are disintegrated into two systems which separately include the effects of isotropic and anisotropic sources. The system related to the additional source is solved via the MIT bag model equation of state. We consider Tolman V spacetime to formulate a solution for the isotropic sector which is extended to the anisotropic domain via decoupling technique. The junction conditions at the boundary determine the unknown parameters in terms of mass and radius of the spherical object. We investigate the viability and stability of the constructed strange star model in the presence of massive scalar field corresponding to the strange star candidate PSR J1614-2230. It is concluded that the anisotropic extension is well-behaved as it fulfills the necessary requirements of a physically acceptable model.

Keywords: Brans-Dicke theory; Quark star; Gravitational decoupling.

1. Introduction

Astronomical systems (such as stellar structures, galaxies and planets) are scattered throughout the universe in the form of a cosmic web. These self-gravitating objects contain significant clues regarding the history and structure of the vast universe. Strange quark stars intriguing cosmic objects that are smaller than neutron stars and possess extremely dense cores. Researchers believe that the enormous release of radiation and energy in extremely luminous supernovae can be explained through quark stars.[1] A model that adequately describes the interactions of quarks at high density levels is still under investigation. However, in the absence of the best fit, researchers have used MIT bag model equation of state (EoS) to examine different properties of strange quark stars.[2] The statistical data obtained from GW170817[3] and GW190425[4] was used to predict the compactness and mass of quark stars. These predictions match the estimates made via the MIT bag model which strengthens the choice of this EoS. Bhar[5] used the MIT bag model to compute a solution representing strange stars in the background of Krori and Barua spacetime. The bag model has also been used to investigate the stability of quark stars by introducing radial perturbations.[6] Deb et al.[7] adopted the EoS to construct a charged stellar structure.

The task of obtaining well-behaved spacetimes corresponding to realistic models is difficult due to the non-linearity of field equations. Recently, Ovalle simplified the extraction of solutions by proposing the gravitational decoupling approach via minimal geometric deformation (MGD).[8] In this scheme, an extra source is successively added to a seed distribution (vacuum or isotropic) to incorporate intricate features of physical systems. The degree of freedom in the field equations is reduced by splitting the field equations into two arrays via a linear transformation in the radial metric function. These sets exclusively include the effects of seed and additional gravitational sources. Moreover, no energy is transferred between the two matter distributions as they are individually conserved. The respective solutions of these systems are combined to formulate a new solution. An extension of this technique has also been proposed which induces transformations in temporal as well as radial metric functions.[9]

The efficient technique of gravitational decoupling has successfully been employed to generate anisotropic solutions from well-known ansatz. The anisotropic extensions of Tolman IV have been obtained in braneworld[10] as well as general relativity (GR)[11] via MGD scheme. Isotropic configurations corresponding to Durgapal-Fuloria,[12] Krori-Barua,[13] Heintzmann[14] and Schwarzschild[15] interior solutions have been decoupled to evaluate their corresponding anisotropic versions. Contreras[16,17] deformed the metric component of (2+1)- dimensional spacetime to decouple the field equations with a cosmological constant. Singh et al.[18] derived an anisotropic spacetime by incorporating the embedding class-one condition in the decoupling approach. Hensh and Stuchlik[19] constructed an anisotropic counterpart of Tolman VII by the method of gravitational decoupling. Sharif and Ama-Tul-Mughani[20] implemented the MGD scheme to extend charged solutions to anisotropic domain in a cloud of strings. Anisotropic cosmological solutions have also been obtained by applying the MGD technique to FLRW as well as Kantowski-Sachs spacetimes.[21] Recently, Contreras et al.[22] studied axially symmetric black holes and showed that gravitational decoupling can be adopted beyond spherical symmetry.

The general theory of relativity is modified to incorporate the effects of cosmic expansion. In this regard, the family of scalar-tensor theories has gained attention. Brans-Dicke (BD) theory (a prototype of scalar-tensor theories) includes a spacetime varying scalar field $\vartheta = \frac{1}{G}$. (G is Newton's gravitational constant) along with the metric tensor to describe the effects of gravitational field.[23] A BD coupling parameter (ω_{BD}) couples the matter distribution and the massless scalar field. Different values of the tunable coupling parameter explain different cosmological scenarios. However, a conflict occurs when large values of ω_{BD} in the weak-field limit[24] do not coincide with the small values required to describe the inflationary era.[25] In order to remove the discrepancy, a potential function $V(\varsigma)$ is introduced which allots a mass to the scalar field (ς). This modification leads to self-interacting BD (SBD) theory[26] which admits all values of the coupling parameter greater than $-3/2$ for $m_\varsigma > 2 \times 10^{-25} GeV$ (m_ς denotes mass of the scalar field).[27] Recently,

MIT bag model was employed to examine the behavior of strange quark stars in the presence of a massive scalar field.[28] Some well-behaved solutions in SBD gravity as well as modified theories have been computed through gravitational decoupling technique.[29]

In this paper, we formulate two anisotropic strange star models by implementing MGD scheme on isotropic distributions in the context of SBD gravity. For this purpose, we adopt Tolman V ansatz and use the MIT bag model to investigate the viability and stability of the constructed structures. We evaluate the field equations under the effect of the additional source in section **2**. In section **3**, we deform the radial metric function to split the field equations. The anisotropic extension is checked for viability and stability in section **4**. In section **5**, the main results are discussed.

2. Self-interacting Brans-Dicke Theory

The SBD gravity is described by the action

$$S = \int \sqrt{-g}(\mathcal{R}\varsigma - \frac{\omega_{BD}}{\varsigma}\nabla^\gamma \nabla_\gamma \varsigma - V(\varsigma) + L_m + \sigma L_\Theta)d^4x, \tag{1}$$

where relativistic units have been used. Here, $\mathcal{R}$ and L_m denote the Ricci scalar and matter lagrangian whereas $g = |g_{\gamma\delta}|$. The contribution of the anisotropic source (Θ) via the lagrangian L_Θ is controlled by the decoupling parameter σ. The additional gravitational source can be categorized as a scalar, vector or tensor field. The field and wave equations derived from the action (1) are written as

$$G_{\gamma\delta} = T_{\gamma\delta}^{(\text{eff})} = \frac{1}{\varsigma}(T_{\gamma\delta}^{(m)} + \sigma\Theta_{\gamma\delta} + T_{\gamma\delta}^\varsigma), \tag{2}$$

$$\Box\varsigma = \frac{T^{(m)} + \Theta}{3 + 2\omega_{BD}} + \frac{1}{3 + 2\omega_{BD}}(\varsigma\frac{dV(\varsigma)}{d\varsigma} - 2V(\varsigma)), \tag{3}$$

where $\Box\varsigma = \frac{1}{\sqrt{-g}}(\sqrt{-g}g^{\gamma\delta}\varsigma_{,\gamma})_{,\delta}$, $T^{(m)} = g^{\gamma\delta}T_{\gamma\delta}^{(m)}$ and $\Theta = g^{\gamma\delta}\Theta_{\gamma\delta}$. We consider an isotropic seed source whose energy-momentum tensor has the form

$$T_{\gamma\delta}^{(m)} = \rho u_\gamma u_\delta + p(u_\gamma u_\delta - g_{\gamma\delta}), \tag{4}$$

where p, u_γ and ρ represent pressure, four-velocity and energy density, respectively. The influence of massive scalar field on the physical aspects of static sphere are governed by the following energy-momentum tensor

$$T_{\gamma\delta}^\varsigma = \varsigma_{,\gamma;\delta} - g_{\gamma\delta}\Box\varsigma + \frac{\omega_{BD}}{\varsigma}(\varsigma_{,\gamma}\varsigma_{,\delta} - \frac{g_{\gamma\delta}\varsigma_{,\alpha}\varsigma^{,\alpha}}{2}) - \frac{V(\varsigma)g_{\gamma\delta}}{2}. \tag{5}$$

The anisotropic extension is obtained by describing the internal geometry of the static sphere as

$$ds^2 = e^{\phi(r)}dt^2 - e^{\psi(r)}dr^2 - r^2 d\theta^2 - r^2\sin^2\theta d\varphi^2. \tag{6}$$

The field equations, formulated in the presence of the anisotropic source, are expressed as

$$\frac{1}{r^2} - e^{-\psi}\left(\frac{1}{r^2} - \frac{\psi'}{r}\right) = \frac{1}{\varsigma}(\rho + \sigma\Theta_0^0 + T_0^{0\varsigma}), \tag{7}$$

$$-\frac{1}{r^2} + e^{-\psi}\left(\frac{1}{r^2} + \frac{\phi'}{r}\right) = \frac{1}{\varsigma}(p - \sigma\Theta_1^1 - T_1^{1\varsigma}), \tag{8}$$

$$\frac{e^{-\psi}}{4}\left(2\phi'' + \phi'^2 - \psi'\phi' + 2\frac{\phi' - \psi'}{r}\right) = \frac{1}{\varsigma}(p - \sigma\Theta_2^2 - T_2^{2\varsigma}), \tag{9}$$

where

$$T_0^{0\varsigma} = e^{-\psi}\left[\varsigma'' + \left(\frac{2}{r} - \frac{\psi'}{2}\right)\varsigma' + \frac{\omega_{BD}}{2\varsigma}\varsigma'^2 - e^{\psi}\frac{V(\varsigma)}{2}\right],$$

$$T_1^{1\varsigma} = e^{-\psi}\left[\left(\frac{2}{r} + \frac{\phi'}{2}\right)\varsigma' - \frac{\omega_{BD}}{2\varsigma}\varsigma'^2 - e^{\psi}\frac{V(\varsigma)}{2})\right],$$

$$T_2^{2\varsigma} = e^{-\psi}\left[\varsigma'' + \left(\frac{1}{r} - \frac{\psi'}{2} + \frac{\phi'}{2}\right)\varsigma' + \frac{\omega_{BD}}{2\varsigma}\varsigma'^2 - e^{\psi}\frac{V(\varsigma)}{2}\right].$$

Here differentiation with respect to the radial coordinate is denoted by $'$. Moreover, the wave equation (3), containing information about the evolution of the massive scalar field, takes the form

$$\Box\varsigma = -e^{-\psi}\left[\left(\frac{2}{r} - \frac{\psi'}{2} + \frac{\phi'}{2}\right)\varsigma' + \varsigma''\right]$$

$$= \frac{1}{3 + 2\omega_{BD}}\left[T^{(m)} + \Theta + \left(\varsigma\frac{dV(\varsigma)}{d\varsigma} - 2V(\varsigma)\right)\right]. \tag{10}$$

The system of field equations (7)-(9) correspond to an anisotropic fluid distribution for $\Theta_1^1 \neq \Theta_2^2$.

3. Gravitational Decoupling

Currently, the system (7)-(9) involves unknown metric potentials, state determinants, massive scalar field and anisotropic source. Thus, we require additional constraints to reduce the degrees of freedom and close the system. In this regard, the MGD technique is an efficient method for decoupling the complex field equations into simpler sets by transforming the radial metric component as

$$e^{-\psi(r)} \mapsto \lambda(r) + \sigma\nu(r), \tag{11}$$

where $\nu(r)$ is the deformation function that governs the translation in the radial metric component. The temporal metric potential is not transformed and remains unchanged. It must be noted that the linear mapping does not affect the spherical geometry of the structure. Plugging the transformation in Eqs. (7)–(9) and setting

$\sigma = 0$ yields the first set as

$$\rho = -\frac{1}{2r^2\varsigma(r)}[r^2\omega\lambda(r)\varsigma'^2(r) - r^2\varsigma(r)V(\varsigma) + r\varsigma(r)(r\lambda'(r)\varsigma'(r) + 2r\lambda(r)\varsigma''(r) + 4\lambda(r)\varsigma'(r)) + 2\varsigma^2(r)(r\lambda'(r) + \lambda(r) - 1)], \quad (12)$$

$$p = \frac{1}{r^2}[\varsigma(r)(r\lambda(r)\phi'(r) + \lambda(r) - 1)] + \frac{1}{2r\varsigma(r)}[\lambda(r)\varsigma'(r)(\varsigma(r)(r\phi'(r) + 4) - r\omega_{BD}\varsigma'(r))] - \frac{V(\varsigma)}{2}, \quad (13)$$

$$p = \frac{1}{4r\varsigma(r)}[\varsigma(r)\lambda'(r)(\varsigma(r)(r\phi'(r) + 2) + 2r\varsigma'(r)) + \lambda(r)(2\varsigma(r)\varsigma'(r) \\ \times ((r\phi'(r) + 2) + 2r\varsigma''(r)) + \varsigma^2(r)(2r\phi''(r) + r\phi'^2(r) + 2\phi'(r)) \\ + 2r\omega_{BD}\varsigma'^2(r)) - 2r\varsigma(r)V(\varsigma)]. \quad (14)$$

The above system corresponds to the perfect fluid configuration exclusively as the anisotropic effects are excluded. The isotropic source observes the following conservation equation

$$T_1^{1'(\mathrm{eff})} - \frac{\phi'(r)}{2}(T_0^{0(\mathrm{eff})} - T_1^{1(\mathrm{eff})}) = 0. \quad (15)$$

The second set, encompassing the terms related to the additional source, is expressed as

$$\Theta_0^0 = \frac{-1}{2r^2\varsigma(r)}[r\varsigma(r)\nu'(r)(r\varsigma'(r) + 2\varsigma(r)) + \nu(r)(r^2\omega_{BD}\varsigma'^2(r) + 2r\varsigma(r) \\ \times (r\varsigma''(r) + 2\varsigma'(r)) + 2\varsigma^2(r))], \quad (16)$$

$$\Theta_1^1 = \frac{-1}{2r^2\varsigma(r)}[\nu(r)(-r^2\omega_{BD}\varsigma'(r)^2 + r\varsigma(r)(r\phi'(r) + 4)\varsigma'(r) + 2\varsigma^2(r) \\ \times (r\phi'(r) + 1))], \quad (17)$$

$$\Theta_2^2 = \frac{-1}{4\varsigma(r)}[2\varsigma(r)(r\nu'(r)\varsigma'(r) + \nu(r)((r\phi'(r) + 2)\varsigma'(r) + 2r\varsigma''(r))) \\ + \varsigma^2(r)(\nu'(r)(r\phi'(r) + 2) + \nu(r)(2r\phi''(r) + r\phi'^2(r) + 2\phi'(r))) \\ + 2r\omega_{BD}\nu(r)\varsigma'^2(r)]. \quad (18)$$

The energy and momentum of the anisotropic source is conserved as

$$\Theta_1^{1'(\mathrm{eff})} - \frac{\phi'(r)}{2}(\Theta_0^{0(\mathrm{eff})} - \Theta_1^{1(\mathrm{eff})}) - \frac{2}{r}(\Theta_2^{2(\mathrm{eff})} - \Theta_1^{1(\mathrm{eff})}) = 0, \quad (19)$$

where
$$\Theta_0^{0(\text{eff})} = \frac{1}{\varsigma}\left(\Theta_0^0 + \frac{1}{2}\nu'(r)\varsigma'(r) + \nu(r)\varsigma''(r) + \frac{\omega_{BD}\nu(r)\varsigma'^2(r)}{2\varsigma(r)} + \frac{2\nu(r)\varsigma'(r)}{r}\right),$$

$$\Theta_1^{1(\text{eff})} = \frac{1}{\varsigma}\left(\Theta_1^1 + \frac{1}{2}\nu(r)\phi'(r)\varsigma'(r) - \frac{\omega_{BD}\nu(r)\varsigma'^2(r)}{2\varsigma(r)} + \frac{2\nu(r)\varsigma'(r)}{r}\right),$$

$$\Theta_2^{2(\text{eff})} = \frac{1}{\varsigma}\left(\Theta_2^2 + \frac{1}{2}\nu'(r)\varsigma'(r) + \frac{1}{2}\nu(r)\phi'(r)\varsigma'(r) + \nu(r)\varsigma''(r)\right.$$
$$\left. + \frac{\omega_{BD}\nu(r)\varsigma'^2(r)}{2\varsigma(r)} + \frac{\nu(r)\varsigma'(r)}{r}\right).$$

The MGD scheme restricts the exchange of matter or energy between the two sources (seed and additional) by conserving them individually. As a consequence of disintegrating the field equations via MGD, the two systems can be solved separately. A well-behaved isotropic spacetime can specify the system (12)-(14) which minimizes the degrees of freedom as the second system contains the deformation function and components of $\Theta_{\gamma\delta}$ as undetermined variables only. In the next section, we attain a solution for the anisotropic setup by assuming a well-known ansatz along with an additional constraint.

4. Anisotropic Solution

Tolman V ansatz (one of the eight solutions proposed by Tolman) describes a spherical structure with infinite density and pressure at the center.[30] Zubair and Azmat[31] evaluated the anisotropic counterpart of Tolman V via the MGD method. Recently, Jasim et al.[32] employed this spherical solution to study charged strange stars. Tolman V spacetime is defined as

$$ds^2 = B^2 r^{2n} dt^2 - \left(\frac{1+2n-n^2}{1-(1+2n-n^2)\left(\frac{r}{F}\right)^W}\right) dr^2 - r^2 d\theta^2 - r^2 \sin^2\theta d\varphi^2, \quad (20)$$

where n, F and B are unknown constants with $W = \frac{2(1+2n-n^2)}{1+n}$. We set $\lambda = \frac{1+2n-n^2}{1-(1+2n-n^2)\left(\frac{r}{F}\right)^W}$ and determine the isotropic sector via the above spacetime. For this purpose, we evaluate the unknown parameters through the continuity of first and second fundamental forms at the junction (Σ) of interior and exterior geometries. The exterior of a static uncharged celestial object is defined via Schwarzschild metric given as

$$ds^2 = \frac{r-2M}{r} dt^2 - \frac{r}{r-2M} dr^2 - r^2 d\theta^2 - r^2 \sin^2\theta d\varphi^2, \quad (21)$$

where M is the total mass of the compact structure. The boundary conditions at $r = R$ (R is the radius of compact object)

$$(g_{\gamma\delta}^-)_\Sigma = (g_{\gamma\delta}^+)_\Sigma, \quad (p_r)_\Sigma = 0,$$
$$(\varsigma^-(r))_\Sigma = (\varsigma^+(r))_\Sigma, \quad (\varsigma'^-(r))_\Sigma = (\varsigma'^+(r))_\Sigma.$$

are utilized to determine the constants as

$$B = \frac{\sqrt{M}R^{\frac{R}{4M-2R}}}{\sqrt{-\frac{M}{2M-R}}}, \tag{22}$$

$$n = \frac{M}{R-2M}, \tag{23}$$

$$W = -\frac{2(M^2 + 2MR - R^2)}{2M^2 - 3MR + R^2}, \tag{24}$$

$$F = R\left(\frac{M^2(R-2M)}{R(-M^2 - 2MR + R^2)}\right)^{-\frac{1}{W}} \tag{25}$$

$$\omega_{BD} = \frac{2M-R}{8M^2((n-2)n-1)}\bigg(-((n-2)n-1)(2M-R)\left(\frac{R}{F}\right)^W (m_\varsigma R$$
$$\times (2M-R) - 4) - 4m_\varsigma M^2 R + 4m_\varsigma MR^2 - m_\varsigma R^3 + 8Mn^3$$
$$- 24Mn^2 + 8Mn + 16M - 8n^3 R + 12n^2 R + 16nR\bigg). \tag{26}$$

Here, the corresponding scalar field has been calculated by following the technique in.[33]

The energy density and pressure of the anisotropic analogue of Tolman V are expressed as

$$\rho = \frac{-1}{2r^2\varsigma}\bigg(r\varsigma\left(r\varsigma'\left(\sigma\nu'(r) + \frac{\varsigma_1}{r}\right) + 2\sigma\nu(r)\left(r\varsigma'' + 2\varsigma'\right) + 2\varsigma_2\left(r\varsigma''\right.\right.$$
$$+ 2\varsigma')) + 2\varsigma^2(\sigma r\nu'(r) + \sigma\nu(r) + \varsigma_1 + \varsigma_2 - 1) + r^2\omega_{BD}\varsigma'^2(\sigma\nu(r)$$
$$+ \varsigma_2) - r^2\varsigma V(\varsigma)\bigg), \tag{27}$$

$$p_r = \frac{\varsigma}{r^2}\left(\nu(r)(\sigma + 2\sigma n) + \varsigma_2(2n+1) - 1\right) + \frac{\varsigma'\left(2(n+2)\varsigma - r\omega_{BD}\varsigma'\right)}{2r\varsigma}$$
$$\times (\sigma\nu(r) + \varsigma_2) - \frac{V(\varsigma)}{2}, \tag{28}$$

$$p_\perp = \frac{\varsigma}{2r^2}\bigg(\sigma(n+1)r\nu'(r) + 2\sigma n^2\nu(r) + \frac{1}{\varsigma_3^2}((n-2)n-1)\left(2n - n^2 + 1\right)$$
$$\times (2n^2 - (n+1)W)\left(\frac{r}{F}\right)^W - 2n^2\bigg) + (\sigma\nu(r) + \varsigma_2)\left(\frac{\varsigma'}{2}\right.$$
$$\times \left(\frac{\sigma\nu'(r) + \frac{\varsigma_1}{r}}{\sigma\nu(r) + \varsigma_2} + \frac{2n}{r} + \frac{2}{r}\right) + \varsigma'' + \frac{\omega_{BD}\varsigma'^2}{2\varsigma}\bigg) - \frac{V(\varsigma)}{2}, \tag{29}$$

where $\varsigma_1 = \frac{(n^2-2n-1)^2 W\left(\frac{r}{F}\right)^W{}^2}{\varsigma_3}$, $\varsigma_2 = \frac{-n^2+2n+1}{\varsigma_3}$ and $\varsigma_3 = \left((n^2 - 2n - 1)\left(\frac{r}{F}\right)^W + 1\right)$ with anisotropy $\Delta = p_\perp - p_r$. The matter variables are completely specified if the deformation function is known. For this purpose, a constraint on the deformation function or appropriate EoS is applied to the anisotropic structure.

In this work, we develop an anisotropic model for strange quark stars by implementing the MIT bag model. It is hypothesized that the core of a quark star is composed of three flavors of quarks: up (u), strange (s), and down (d). We assume that the quarks are massless and non-interacting in nature. According to the bag model, the pressure and density of quark matter read

$$p_r = \sum_f p^f - \mathcal{B}, \quad \rho = \sum_f \rho^f + \mathcal{B}, \quad f = u, d, s, \tag{30}$$

where p^f and ρ^f correspond to the pressure and density of each flavor, respectively. Kapusta[34] formulated the EoS for strange quark matter through the relation $\rho^f = 3p^f$ as

$$3p_r = \rho - 4\mathcal{B}. \tag{31}$$

Utilizing Eqs.(27) and (28) in the bag model, we obtain the following differential equation

$$(\sigma r \nu'(r) \varsigma' + \sigma \nu(r)\left(2(3n+8)\varsigma' + 2r\varsigma''\right) + 2\zeta_2 r\varsigma'' + \zeta_1 \varsigma' + 6n\zeta_2 \varsigma'$$
$$+ 16\zeta_2 \varsigma' - 4rV(\varsigma) + 8r\mathcal{B}) + \frac{2\varsigma}{r}\left(\sigma r \nu'(r) + \sigma(6n+4)\nu(r) + \zeta_1\right.$$
$$+(6n+4)\zeta_2 - 4) - 2r^2 \omega_{BD} \varsigma'^2 \left(\sigma \nu(r) + \zeta_2\right) = 0, \tag{32}$$

which is numerically solved along with the wave equation subject to central conditions ($\varsigma(0) = 0.2$, $\varsigma'(0) = 0$ and $\nu(0) = \nu_c$) for $V(\varsigma) = \frac{1}{2}m_\varsigma^2 \varsigma^2$.

In SBD gravity, the values of coupling parameter greater than $-3/2$ are allowed for $m_\varsigma > 10^{-4}$ (in dimensionless units). Therefore, the wave equation is solved numerically for $m_\varsigma = 0.001$. Furthermore, the constants B, F, n remain unchanged for the anisotropic sphere whereas ω_{BD} is an undetermined free parameter. Thus, we choose the value of ω_{BD} as given in Eq.(26). The constants are computed by utilizing the observed mass and radii of three quark star candidates (PSR J1614-2230, Her X1 and 4U 1608-52) for $\sigma = 0.2$, 0.9 and $\mathcal{B} = 60 MeV/fm^3$. The values of ω_{BD} and ν_c for the considered stars are given in Table 1. It is noted that ω_{BD} attains values greater than $-3/2$ for all stellar candidates. The physical properties of the anisotropic stellar model are examined in the next section.

Table 1. Values of different parameters corresponding for $m_\varsigma = 0.001$ and $\mathcal{B} = 60 MeV/fm^3$.

	PSR J1614-2230	Her X-1	4U 1608-52
$M (M_\odot)$	1.97	0.88	1.74
$R (km)$	13	7.7	9.3
ω_{BD}	9.750	15.353	6.593
$\nu_c (\sigma = 0.2)$	-5.1	-3.6	-6.8

4.0.1. Physical Features of Anisotropic Model

The metric potentials of a well-behaved solution are positive and increase monotonically.[35] The state parameters must observe a monotonically decreasing behavior away from the center. The graphical representations of Eqs.(27)-(29) in Figure 1 reveals that the strange star model has maximum density and radial/tangential pressures in the core. Furthermore, radial pressure is zero at the surface for the considered stellar objects. It is observed from the plots of anisotropy that $p_\perp > p_r$ for 4U 1608-52 whereas anisotropy related to the remaining stars is negative, i.e., $p_\perp < p_r$. It is worthwhile to mention here that the GR analog exhibits similar behavior.[31]

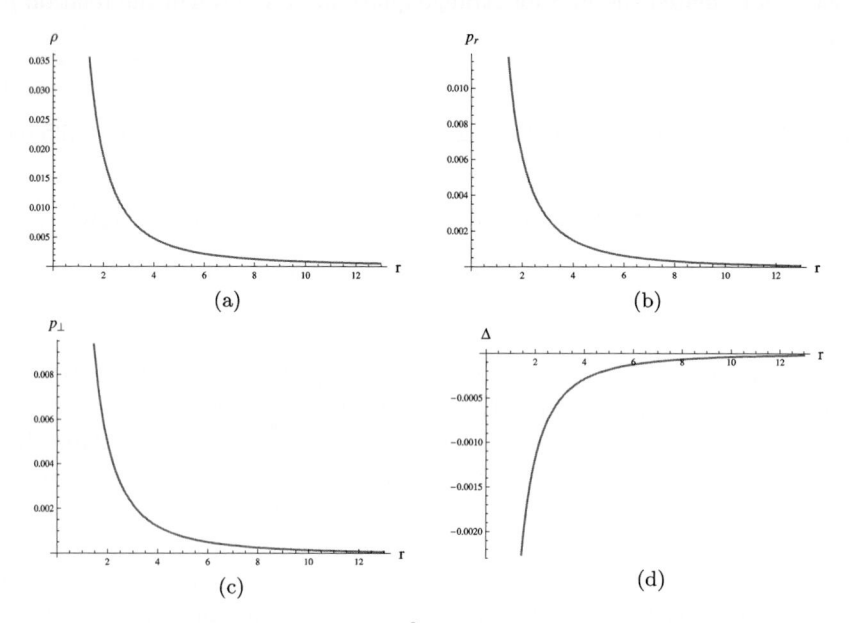

Fig. 1. Plots of (a) ρ, (b) p_r, (c) $p_\perp$ (in km^{-2}) and (d) Δ of anisotropic Tolman V solution for $\sigma = 0.2$.

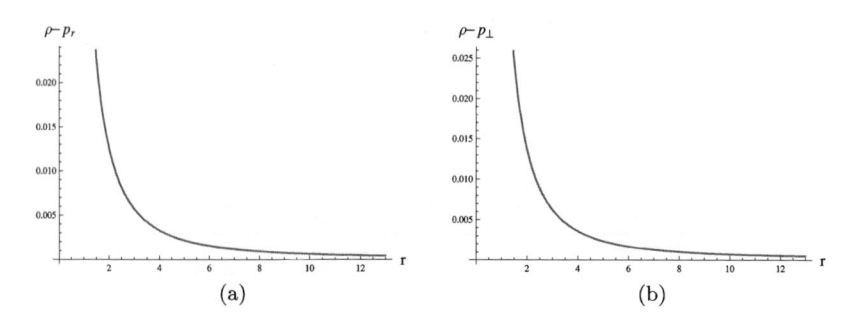

Fig. 2. (a), (b) DEC for extended Tolman V solution for $\sigma = 0.2$.

As the interior of compact stellar structures consists of normal matter, therefore the energy-momentum tensor describing the internal configuration must obey the four energy bounds[36]

null energy condition: $\rho + p_r \geq 0, \quad \rho + p_\perp \geq 0,$

weak energy condition: $\rho \geq 0, \quad \rho + p_r \geq 0, \quad \rho + p_\perp \geq 0,$

strong energy condition: $\rho + p_r + 2p_\perp \geq 0,$

dominant energy condition: $\rho - p_r \geq 0, \quad \rho - p_\perp \geq 0.$

The first three conditions require that energy density and pressure components remain positive throughout the setup. As the matter variables presented in Figure 1 fulfil this criterion, the anisotropic Tolman V is consistent with null, weak and strong energy constraints. Figure 2 indicates that the decoupled model obeys the fourth condition as well. Thus, the constructed model represents a viable quark star.

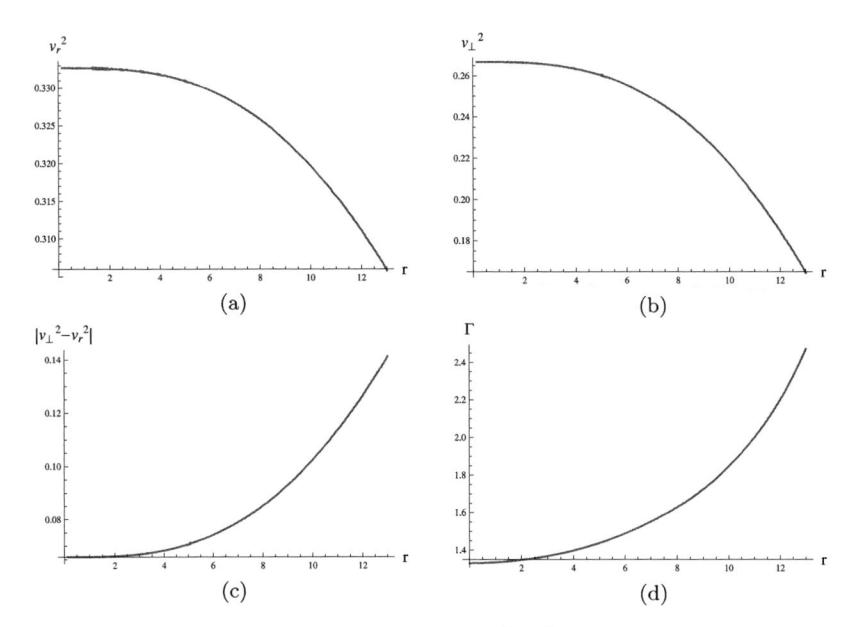

Fig. 3. Plots of (a)radial/(b) tangential velocities, (c) $|v_\perp^2 - v_r^2|$ and (d) adiabatic index of extended Tolman V solution for $\sigma = 0.2$.

The extended version of Tolman V solution is stable if it complies with the causality condition which states that velocity of light always exceeds the rate at which sound travels, i.e., $0 < v_\perp^2 < 1$ and $0 < v_r^2 < 1$ ($v_\perp^2 = \frac{dp_\perp}{d\rho}$ and $v_r^2 = \frac{dp_r}{d\rho}$ represent transverse and radial components of sound, respectively). It must be noted that the propagation of sound waves changes with a change in the medium. Figure 3 depicts that the extended solution is consistent with the causality criterion for higher as well as lower values of decoupling parameter. In order to inspect the anisotropic system for potential stability, we implement Herrera's cracking criterion. According to this approach, if a disturbance in the equilibrium of the system leads to radial forces of different signs, the configuration cracks. The condition $0 < |v_\perp^2 - v_r^2| < 1$ ensures that no cracking appears within the compact sphere. This condition holds true for the current setup as shown in Figure 3.

If a stellar model obeys a stiff EoS, it is compact and difficult to compress as pressure increases greatly in response to a small change in density. Adiabatic index measures the stiffness of the EoS as

$$\Gamma = \frac{p_r + \rho}{p_r}\frac{dp_r}{d\rho} = \frac{p_r + \rho}{p_r}v_r^2.$$

The value of adiabatic index greater than $4/3$ corresponds to a stiff matter distribution.[37] The adiabatic index for $\sigma = 0.2$ is displayed in Figure 3. The generated extension of Tolman V observes the required restraint under the influence of massive scalar field.

5. Conclusions

In this work, we have extended a known isotropic solution to the anisotropic domain through the method of gravitational decoupling. Anisotropy has been induced in the isotropic matter configuration by means of an additional source. The two sources (seed and additional) have been decoupled through a linear transformation of the radial metric component. As a consequence, we have obtained two systems of differential equations. The first system includes the effects of the seed distribution only while the influence of the additional source is restricted to the second set. We have considered Tolman V spacetime to represent the first array. The system related to the anisotropic source has been solved by imposing MIT bag model on state variables of the anisotropic solution. We have numerically evaluated the wave equation for $V(\varsigma) = \frac{1}{2}m_\varsigma^2\varsigma^2$, $m_\varsigma = 0.001$ and $\sigma = 0.2$. Finally, the physical behavior of the extended model has been examined for $\mathcal{B} = 60 MeV/fm^3$ through energy constraints as well as causality and cracking approaches for the star PSR J1614-2230.

The graphical analysis has shown that the state parameters observe a monotonically decreasing trend towards the surface and attain the maximum value at $r = 0$. Moreover, the anisotropy corresponding to PSR J1614-2230 is negative. Thus, radial pressure is more than the transverse component indicating a presence of attractive force within the spherical object. The extended model is composed of viable normal matter as it is consistent with the energy conditions. We have established that the constructed setup is stable as radial/tangential components of speed agree with causality and cracking criteria. The adiabatic parameter is greater than $4/3$ which indicates that the static model holds itself against inward gravitational pull for the considered values of the parameters. Thus, the strange star structure formulated via decoupling is physically realistic and stable in the presence of a massive scalar field. It is interesting to mention here that all the obtained results reduce to GR for $\varsigma = $ constant and $\omega_{BD} \to \infty$.

References

1. E. O. P. Ofek, et al., SN 2006gy: An extremely luminous supernova in the galaxy NGC 1260, *Astrophys. J.* **659**, L13 (2007); R. Ouyed, D. Leahy and P. Jaikumar, P., Predictions for signatures of the quark-nova in superluminous supernovae, arXiv:0911.5424.
2. G. H. Bordbar and A. R. Peivand, Computation of the structure of a magnetized strange quark star, *Res. Astron. Astrophys.* **11**, 851 (2011).
3. B. P. Abbott et al., GW170817: Observation of gravitational waves from a binary neutron star inspiral, *Phys. Rev. Lett.* **119**, 161101 (2017).
4. The LIGO Scientific Collaboration, the Virgo Collaboration, B. P. Abbott et al., GW190425: Observation of a compact binary coalescence with total mass $3.4 M_\odot$, *Astrophys. J. Lett.* **892**, L3 (2020).
5. P. Bhar, A new hybrid star model in Krori-Barua spacetime, *Astrophys. Space Sci.* **357**, 46 (2015).
6. J. D. V. Arbañil and M. Malheiro, Stability of charged strange quark stars, *AIP Conf. Proc.* **1693**, 030007 (2015).
7. D. Deb, Anisotropic strange stars in the Einstein–Maxwell spacetime, *Eur. Phys. J. C* **78**, 465 (2018).
8. J. Ovalle, Searching exact solutions for compact stars in braneworld: A conjecture, *Mod. Phys. Lett. A* **23** 3247 (2008).
9. J. Ovalle, Decoupling gravitational sources in general relativity: The extended case, *Phys. Lett. B* **788**, 213 (2019).
10. J. Ovalle and F. Linares, Tolman IV solution in the Randall-Sundrum braneworld, *Phys. Rev. D* **88**, 104026 (2013).
11. J. Ovalle et al., Anisotropic solutions by gravitational decoupling, *Eur. Phys. J. C* **78**, 122 (2018).
12. L. Gabbanelli, A. Rincon and C. Rubio, Gravitational decoupled anisotropies in compact stars, *Eur. Phys. J. C* **78**, 370 (2018).
13. M. Sharif and S. Sadiq, Gravitational decoupled charged anisotropic spherical solutions, *Eur. Phys. J. C* **78**, 410 (2018).
14. M. Estrada and F. Tello-Ortiz, A new family of analytical anisotropic solutions by gravitational decoupling, *Eur. Phys. J. C* **133**, 453 (2018).
15. L. Gabbanelli et al., A causal Schwarzschild-de Sitter interior solution by gravitational decoupling, *Eur. Phys. J. C* **79**, 486 (2019).
16. E. Contreras, Gravitational decoupling in 2+1-dimensional spacetimes with cosmological term, *Class. Quantum Grav.* **36**, 095004 (2019).
17. E. Contreras and P. Bargueño, Extended Gravitational Decoupling in 2+1 Dimensional Spacetimes, *Class. Quantum Grav.* **36**, 215009 (2019).
18. K. N. Singh et al., Minimally deformed anisotropic model of class one space-time by gravitational decoupling, *Eur. Phys. J. C* **79**, 851 (2019).
19. S. Hensh and Z. Stuchlik, Anisotropic Tolman VII solution by gravitational decoupling, *Eur. Phys. J. C* **79**, 834 (2019).
20. M. Sharif and Q. Ama-Tul-Mughani, Study of (1+2)-dimensional charged string cloud with minimal geometric deformation, *Int. J. Geom. Methods Mod. Phys.* **16**, 1950187 (2019); Gravitational Decoupled Solutions of Axial String Cosmology *Mod. Phys. Lett. A* **35**, 2050091 (2020).
21. F. X. L. Cedeño and E. Contreras, Gravitational decoupling in cosmology, *Phys. Dark Universe* **28**, 100543 (2020).
22. E. Contreras, J. Ovalle and R. Casadio, Gravitational decoupling for axially symmetric systems and rotating black holes, *Phys. Rev. D* **103**, 044020 (2021).

23. C. Brans and R. H. Dicke, Mach's principle and a relativistic theory of gravitation, *Phys. Rev.* **124**, 3 (1961).
24. C. M. Will, The confrontation between general relativity and experiment, *Living Rev. Rel.* **4**, 4 (2001).
25. E. J. Weinberg, Some problems with extended inflation, *Phys. Rev. D* **40**, 3950 (1989).
26. J. Khoury and A. Weltman, Chameleon Cosmology, *Phys. Rev. D* **69**, 044026 (2004).
27. L. Perivolaropoulos, PPN parameter γ and solar system constraints of massive brans-dicke theories, *Phys. Rev. D* **81**, 047501 (2010).
28. M. Sharif, and A. Majid, Anisotropic strange stars through embedding technique in massive Brans–Dicke gravity, *Eur. Phys. J. Plus* **135**, 558 (2020); Quark stars in massive Brans–Dicke gravity with tolman–kuchowicz spacetime, *Universe* **6**, 8 (2020).
29. M. Sharif and S. Saba, Gravitational decoupled anisotropic solutions in $f(\mathcal{G})$ gravity, *Eur. Phys. J. C* **78**, 921 (2018); M. Sharif and A. Waseem, Anisotropic spherical solutions by gravitational decoupling in $f(\mathcal{R})$ gravity, *Ann. Phys.* **405**, 14 (2019); M. Sharif and A. Majid, Anisotropic compact stars in self-interacting Brans-Dicke gravity, *Astrophys. Space Sci.* **365**, 42 (2020); Decoupled anisotropic spheres in self-interacting Brans-Dicke gravity, *Chin. J. Phys.* **68**, 406 (2020); Extended gravitational decoupled solutions in self-interacting Brans–Dicke theory, *Phys. Dark Universe* **30**, 100610 (2020).
30. R. C. Tolman, Static solutions of einstein's field equations for spheres of fluid, *Phys. Rev.* **55**, 364 (1939).
31. M. Zubair and H. Azmat, Anisotropic Tolman V solution by minimal gravitational decoupling approach, *Ann. Phys.* **420**, 168248 (2020).
32. M. K. Jasim et al., Charged strange stellar model describing by Tolman V metric, *Results Phys.* **20**, 103648 (2021).
33. W. F. Bruckman and E. Kazes, Properties of the solutions of cold ultradense configurations in the Brans-Dicke theory, *Phys. Rev. D* **16**, 2 (1977).
34. J. Kapusta, *Finite-Temperature Field Theory* (Cambridge University Press, Cambridge, 1994).
35. K. Lake, All static spherically symmetric perfect-fluid solutions of einstein's equations, *Phys. Rev. D* **67**, 104015 (2003).
36. Y. Fujii and K. Maeda, *The Scalar-Tensor Theory of Gravitation* (Cambridge University Press, Cambridge, 2003).
37. H. Heintzmann and W. Hillebrandt, Neutron Stars with an Anisotropic Equation of State: Mass, Redshift and Stability, *Astron. Astrophys.* **24**, 51 (1975).

Big-bounce in projectively invariant Nieh-Yan models: The Bianchi I case

Flavio Bombacigno

Departament de Física Teòrica and IFIC, Centro Mixto Universitat de València - CSIC, Universitat de València, Burjassot 46100, València, Spain
E-mail: flavio.bombacigno@ext.uv.es

Simon Boudet

Dipartimento di Fisica, Università di Trento,
Via Sommarive 14, I-38123 Povo (TN), Italy
and
Trento Institute for Fundamental Physics and Applications (TIFPA)-INFN,
Via Sommarive 14, I-38123 Povo (TN), Italy
E-mail: simon.boudet@unitn.it

Gonzalo J. Olmo

Departament de Física Teòrica and IFIC, Centro Mixto Universitat de València - CSIC, Universitat de València, Burjassot 46100, València, Spain
E-mail:gonzalo.olmo@uv.es

Giovanni Montani

Physics Department, "Sapienza" University of Rome,
P.le Aldo Moro 5, 00185 (Roma), Italy
and
ENEA, Fusion and Nuclear Safety Department,
C. R. Frascati, Via E. Fermi 45, 00044 Frascati (Roma), Italy
E-mail: giovanni.montani@enea.it

We show that the Nieh-Yan topological invariant breaks projective symmetry and loses its topological character in presence of non vanishing nonmetricity. The notion of the Nieh-Yan topological invariant is then extended to the generic metric-affine case, defining a generalized Nieh-Yan term, which allows to recover topologicity and projective invariance, independently. As a concrete example a class of modified theories of gravity is considered and its dynamical properties are investigated in a cosmological setting. In particular, bouncing cosmological solutions in Bianchi I models are derived. Finite time singularities affecting these solutions are analysed, showing that the geodesic completeness and the regular behavior of scalar perturbations in these space-times are not spoiled.

Keywords: Nieh-Yan, metric-affine, Bianchi I, big-bounce

1. Introduction

The theory of General Relativity (GR)[1,2] relies on the geometric interpretation of the gravitational field, described in terms of a metric tensor and a connection on a pseudo-Riemannian manifold. Both GR and many alternative theories of gravity are based on a metric formulation, in which the connection is given by the symmetric and metric compatible Levi-Civita connection, which is completely determined by the metric and its derivatives. An alternative formulation for geometric theories of gravity consists in adopting the metric-affine paradigm, in which the metric tensor and the connection are considered as independent variables. In this approach, symmetry and metric compatibility of the connection are not imposed a priori, resulting in the presence of torsion and nonmetricity, respectively. Well known examples of metric-affine theories are Ricci based gravity,[3,4] Palatini $f(R)$ theory,[5] quadratic gravity,[6] Born-Infeld-type models,[7] general teleparallel models,[8] generalized hybrid metric-Palatini gravity[9–13] and metric-affine extension of higher order theories.[14–17]

The metric-affine approach plays a crucial role also in one of the current attempts to quantize gravity, i.e. loop quantum gravity (LQG),[18,19] where GR is reformulated in terms of a gauge $SU(2)$ connection (Ashtekar-Barbero-Immirzi connection) and its conjugate momentum, the densitized triad.[20–23] This formulation, indeed, can be derived[24] by including an additional contribution to the first order (Palatini) action of GR, namely the Nieh-Yan (NY) topological invariant[25,26] (the Holst term[27] can be used as well). The NY term was discovered in the context of Riemann-Cartan theory (where nonmetricity is set to zero) and its main property is topologicity: it reduces to a boundary term without affecting the field equations at all. This additional term is driven by the so called Immirzi parameter β,[28,29] which concurs in the definition of the Ashtekar variables and is related to a quantization ambiguity.[30] Attempts to address this issue led to the proposal of considering the Immirzi parameter as a new fundamental field,[31–33] an idea that has been later developed within several different contexts.[31,33,33–40,40–46] The promotion of such constant parameter to a dynamical field is usually pursued "by hand", substituting $\beta \to \beta(x)$ in the Lagrangian and possibly adding a potential term $V(\beta)$.

More recently, beside LQG the NY term has been studied in the context of teleparallel gravity[47] and in condensed matter physics.[48–51]

Another important property we will focus on, is projective invariance,[52,53] which has recently been shown to be of crucial importance in metric-affine theories since the breaking of this symmetry can give rise to dynamical instabilities.[54] In this regard, we want to stress that the NY term breaks this symmetry. This feature has always been neglected in literature and a revision of previous formulations seems necessary. Moreover, as will be shown in the following, the topological character of the NY term is also lost when nonmetricity is included.

The approach followed in this note is grounded on the choice of recovering these features from the very beginning in the action, without imposing any restriction on the affine connection. After a formal discussion, we will implement the gravitational model in a cosmological setting. In particular, we investigate Bianchi I models,[55–57] focusing our attention on the emergence of a classical bouncing cosmology.[42,58–64]

2. The role of nonmetricity in the Nieh-Yan term

In Einstein-Cartan theory the NY term[25,26] is explicitly defined as

$$NY \equiv \frac{1}{2}\varepsilon^{\mu\nu\rho\sigma}\left(\frac{1}{2}T^{\lambda}{}_{\mu\nu}T_{\lambda\rho\sigma} - R_{\mu\nu\rho\sigma}\right), \tag{1}$$

where

$$R^{\rho}{}_{\mu\sigma\nu} = \partial_{\sigma}\Gamma^{\rho}{}_{\mu\nu} - \partial_{\nu}\Gamma^{\rho}{}_{\mu\sigma} + \Gamma^{\rho}{}_{\tau\sigma}\Gamma^{\tau}{}_{\mu\nu} - \Gamma^{\rho}{}_{\tau\nu}\Gamma^{\tau}{}_{\mu\sigma}, \tag{2}$$

is the Riemann tensor built with the independent connection and

$$T^{\mu}{}_{\nu\rho} = \Gamma^{\mu}{}_{\nu\rho} - \Gamma^{\mu}{}_{\rho\nu} \tag{3}$$

is the torsion tensor. The starting point of our discussion is the observation that for a non-vanishing nonmetricity tensor $Q_{\mu\nu\rho} = -\nabla_{\mu}g_{\nu\rho}$, the NY term (1) is spoilt of its topological character. Indeed, extracting the nonriemmanian part of the Riemann tensor leads to[65]

$$NY = -\frac{1}{2}\bar{\nabla}\cdot S - \frac{1}{2}\varepsilon^{\mu\nu\rho\sigma}T^{\lambda}{}_{\mu\nu}Q_{\rho\sigma\lambda}, \tag{4}$$

where $\bar{\nabla}_{\mu}$ is built with the Levi-Civita connection $\bar{\Gamma}^{\mu}{}_{\nu\rho}$ and

$$S_{\mu} \equiv \varepsilon_{\mu\nu\rho\sigma}T^{\nu\rho\sigma}. \tag{5}$$

Therefore, when $Q_{\rho\mu\nu} \neq 0$, the Nieh-Yan term does not simply reduce to the divergence of a vector, and the appearance of nonmetricity spoils the topologicity. Let us now consider the behavior of (1) under projective transformations of the connection, namely

$$\tilde{\Gamma}^{\rho}{}_{\mu\nu} = \Gamma^{\rho}{}_{\mu\nu} + \delta^{\rho}{}_{\mu}\xi_{\nu}, \tag{6}$$

It can easily be shown that (1) is also not invariant under projective transformations, since

$$\frac{1}{4}\varepsilon^{\mu\nu\rho\sigma}\tilde{T}^{\lambda}{}_{\mu\nu}\tilde{T}_{\lambda\rho\sigma} - \frac{1}{4}\varepsilon^{\mu\nu\rho\sigma}T^{\lambda}{}_{\mu\nu}T_{\lambda\rho\sigma} = -S_{\mu}\xi^{\mu}. \tag{7}$$

Now, by looking at (4), we point out that a newly topological Nieh-Yan term can be recovered by simply setting

$$NY^{*} \equiv NY + \frac{1}{2}\varepsilon^{\mu\nu\rho\sigma}T^{\lambda}{}_{\mu\nu}Q_{\rho\sigma\lambda}. \tag{8}$$

We note that projective invariance is now enclosed as well, since

$$\frac{1}{2}\varepsilon^{\mu\nu\rho\sigma}\tilde{T}^{\lambda}{}_{\mu\nu}\tilde{Q}_{\rho\sigma\lambda} - \frac{1}{2}\varepsilon^{\mu\nu\rho\sigma}T^{\lambda}{}_{\mu\nu}Q_{\rho\sigma\lambda} = +S_{\mu}\xi^{\mu}, \tag{9}$$

which exactly cancels out (7). We stress, however, that projective invariance is not strictly related to topologicity, and suitable generalizations of (2) breaking up only with the latter can be actually formulated. Let us consider, for instance, the following modified Nieh-Yan term

$$NY_{gen} \equiv \frac{1}{2}\varepsilon^{\mu\nu\rho\sigma}\left(\frac{\lambda_{1}}{2}T^{\lambda}{}_{\mu\nu}T_{\lambda\rho\sigma} + \lambda_{2}\,T^{\lambda}{}_{\mu\nu}Q_{\rho\sigma\lambda} - R_{\mu\nu\rho\sigma}\right), \tag{10}$$

where we introduced the real parameters λ_1, λ_2. In this case the term (10) transforms under a projective transformation as

$$NY_{gen} \to NY_{gen} - (\lambda_1 - \lambda_2)\xi^\mu S_\mu, \qquad (11)$$

so that by setting $\lambda_1 = \lambda_2$ we can recover again projective invariance, despite topologicity being in general violated if $\lambda_1 = \lambda_2 \neq 1$, since

$$NY_{gen} = -\frac{1}{2}\bar{\nabla}\cdot S + \frac{(\lambda_1 - 1)}{4}\varepsilon^{\mu\nu\rho\sigma}T^\lambda{}_{\mu\nu}T_{\lambda\rho\sigma} + \frac{(\lambda_2 - 1)}{2}\varepsilon^{\mu\nu\rho\sigma}T^\lambda{}_{\mu\nu}Q_{\rho\sigma\lambda}. \qquad (12)$$

In the following, we will consider the general form (10), which by a suitable choice of the parameters $\lambda_{1,2}$ can reproduce all known actions usually studied in literature, as the Holst ($\lambda_1 = \lambda_2 = 0$) or the standard Nieh-Yan (4) ($\lambda_1 = 1$, $\lambda_2 = 0$) terms.

3. Generalized Nieh-Yan models

As a specific gravitational model featuring the generalized NY term we consider an action defined by a general function of two arguments, the Ricci scalar and the generalized NY term (10):

$$S_g = \frac{1}{2\kappa}\int d^4x\sqrt{-g}\,F(R, NY_{gen}), \qquad (13)$$

Now, performing the transformation to the Jordan frame leads to the scalar tensor representation

$$S_g = \frac{1}{2\kappa}\int d^4x\sqrt{-g}\,(\phi R + \beta NY_{gen} - W(\phi, \beta)), \qquad (14)$$

with $\phi \equiv \frac{\partial F}{\partial R}$, $\beta \equiv \frac{\partial F}{\partial NY_{gen}}$ and $W \equiv \phi R(\phi, \beta) + \beta NY_{gen}(\phi, \beta) - F(\phi, \beta)$.

The scalar field β can be identified with the Immirzi field, which acquires in this way a dynamical character without the need of introducing this feature by hand in the action. Moreover, this formulation offers a viable mechanism to produce an interaction term $W(\phi, \beta)$ as well. Now, the field equation for the connection are obtained varying (14) with respect to $\Gamma^\mu{}_{\nu\rho}$. For the full set of equations the reader may cosnult,[65] while here we are interest in the following contraction

$$\delta^\lambda_\nu \frac{\delta S_g}{\delta \Gamma^\lambda{}_{\nu\mu}} = 0 \qquad (15)$$

which leads to

$$(\lambda_1 - \lambda_2)S^\mu = 0. \qquad (16)$$

This implies that the features of the solutions depend on the parameters λ_1 and λ_2, and when projective invariance is broken ($\lambda_1 \neq \lambda_2$) one is compelled to set $S_\mu = 0$. In this case, (10) can be re-expressed as

$$NY_{gen} = -\frac{1}{2}\bar{\nabla}\cdot S - \frac{(1 - \lambda_1)}{3}S^\mu T^\rho{}_{\mu\rho} - \frac{(1 - \lambda_2)}{2}S^\mu Q^\rho{}_{\mu\rho}, \qquad (17)$$

implying that the generalized Nieh-Yan term (10) is identically vanishing on half-shell. In other words, terms violating projective invariance are harmless along the dynamics. This can be further appreciated deriving the effective scalar tensor action stemming from (14), when the solutions of the full set of connection field equations are plugged in it. Explicit calculations (see[65] for details) lead to

$$S = \frac{1}{2\kappa} \int d^4x \sqrt{-g} \left(\phi \bar{R} + \frac{3}{2\phi} \bar{\nabla}_\mu \phi \bar{\nabla}^\mu \phi - W(\phi, \beta) \right), \tag{18}$$

where $\bar{R}$ is the Ricci scalar of the Levi-Clvita connection. This resembles the form of a Palatini $f(R)$ theory, with a potential depending on the Immirzi field as well. The equation for the latter, i.e.

$$\frac{\partial W(\phi, \beta)}{\partial \beta} = 0, \tag{19}$$

fixes its form in terms of the remaining scalar field: $\beta = \beta(\phi)$. Then, using the trace of the metric field equations, variation of (18) with respect to ϕ results in the usual structural equation featuring Palatini $f(R)$ theories,[5] i.e.

$$\left[2W(\phi, \beta) - \phi \frac{\partial W(\phi, \beta)}{\partial \phi} \right]_{\beta=\beta(\phi)} = \kappa T, \tag{20}$$

where T is the trace of the stress energy tensor of matter. This implies that the dynamics of the scalaron ϕ is frozen as well, and completely determined by T. Conditions (19) and (20) then guarantee that the scalar fields ϕ, β are not propagating degrees of freedom, and reduce to constants in vacuum, where the theory is stable and the breaking of projective invariance does not lead to ghost instabilities, in contrast to.[54]

If $\lambda_1 = \lambda_2 \equiv \lambda$, instead, the projective invariance of the model can be used to get rid of one vector degree of freedom, which can be set to zero properly choosing the vector ξ_μ. A convenient choice consists in setting $\xi_\mu = -\frac{1}{2} Q^\rho{}_{\mu\rho}$, which allows to deal only with torsion in the connection field equations. The effective action stemming from (14) then reads (see[65])

$$S = \frac{1}{2\kappa} \int d^4x \sqrt{-g} \left(\phi \bar{R} + \frac{3}{2\phi} \bar{\nabla}_\mu \phi \bar{\nabla}^\mu \phi - \frac{3\phi}{2} \frac{1}{\phi^{2\lambda} + (1-\lambda)^2 \psi^2} \bar{\nabla}_\mu \psi \bar{\nabla}^\mu \psi - V(\phi, \psi) \right), \tag{21}$$

where we used the transformation $\psi \equiv \beta \phi^{\lambda-1}$ and redefined the potential as $V(\phi, \psi) = W(\phi, \psi \phi^{1-\lambda})$. In general, the Immirzi field is expected to be a well-behaved dynamical degree of freedom, since in the Einstein frame action, defined by the conformal rescaling $\tilde{g}_{\mu\nu} = \phi g_{\mu\nu}$, the kinetic term for the Immirzi field takes the form

$$-\frac{3}{2} \frac{\tilde{g}^{\mu\nu} \nabla_\mu \psi \nabla_\nu \psi}{\phi^{2\lambda} + (1-\lambda)^2 \psi^2}. \tag{22}$$

Since $\phi^{2\lambda} + (1-\lambda)^2 \psi^2 > 0$ for every value of ϕ, ψ and λ, (22) has always the correct sign and no ghost instability arise.[66]

Let us end this section with a remark on how previous results with vanishing nonmetricity can properly be recovered. In particular, the Riemann-Cartan structure of[32,33,36,37,46,67–69] can be replicated by inserting in (13) the condition of vanishing nonmetricity with a Lagrange multiplier, i.e. adding to the Lagrangian a term $l^{\rho\mu\nu}Q_{\rho\mu\nu}$, with $l^{\rho\mu\nu} = l^{\rho\nu\mu}$. Then, results of[32,33,36,37,46,67–69] are simply obtained by setting $\lambda_1 = 1$. The fact that the usual Einstein-Cartan NY invariant and related models are recovered in this way, supports the correctness of our generalization of the NY term, with respect to other possible generalizations.

4. Big bounce in Bianchi I cosmology

In this section we consider dynamical models, i.e. those described by (21), which are characterized by a dynamical Immirzi field and look for cosmological solutions in Bianchi I spacetimes. In particular, we will be interested in obtaining solutions characterized by a bouncing behavior for the universe volume, thanks to which the big bang singularity is regularized in favour of a big bounce scenario.

Let us start from the equations of motion for the metric and scalar fields which are given by

$$\bar{G}_{\mu\nu} = \frac{\kappa}{\phi}T_{\mu\nu} + \frac{1}{\phi}\left(\bar{\nabla}_\mu\bar{\nabla}_\nu - g_{\mu\nu}\bar{\Box}\right)\phi - \frac{3}{2\phi^2}\bar{\nabla}_\mu\phi\bar{\nabla}_\nu\phi + \frac{3}{2}\frac{\bar{\nabla}_\mu\psi\bar{\nabla}_\nu\psi}{\phi^{2\lambda}+(1-\lambda)^2\psi^2}$$
$$+ \frac{1}{2}g_{\mu\nu}\left(\frac{3(\bar{\nabla}\phi)^2}{2\phi^2} - \frac{3}{2}\frac{(\bar{\nabla}\psi)^2}{\phi^{2\lambda}+(1-\lambda)^2\psi^2} - \frac{V(\phi,\psi)}{\phi}\right), \quad (23)$$

$$2V(\phi,\psi) - \phi\frac{\partial V(\phi,\psi)}{\partial\phi} + \frac{3\lambda\phi^{2\lambda+1}}{(\phi^{2\lambda}+(1-\lambda)^2\psi^2)^2}(\bar{\nabla}\psi)^2 = \kappa T, \quad (24)$$

$$\bar{\Box}\psi - \frac{(1-\lambda)^2\psi}{\phi^{2\lambda}+(1-\lambda)^2\psi^2}(\bar{\nabla}\psi)^2 + \left(1 - \frac{2\lambda\phi^{2\lambda}}{\phi^{2\lambda}+(1-\lambda)^2\psi^2}\right)\bar{\nabla}_\mu\ln\phi\bar{\nabla}^\mu\psi = \frac{\partial V(\phi,\psi)}{3\partial\psi}. \quad (25)$$

As will be shown, cosmological solutions can be found for projective invariant models ($\lambda = 1$), and restricting to potentials of the form $V(\phi,\psi) = V(\phi)$. To this end, we consider the metric for a Bianchi I flat spacetime, i.e.

$$ds^2 = -dt^2 + a(t)^2 dx^2 + b(t)^2 dy^2 + c(t)^2 dz^2, \quad (26)$$

which represents a homogeneous but anisotropic spacetime, with three different scale factors $a(t), b(t), c(t)$. We include matter in the form of a perfect fluid with stress energy tensor

$$T_{\mu\nu} = \mathrm{diag}(\rho, a^2 p, b^2 p, c^2 p), \quad (27)$$

where ρ is the energy density and p the pressure. Assuming the equation of state $p = w\rho$, conservation of the stress energy tensor implies

$$\rho(t) = \frac{\mu^2}{(abc)^{w+1}}, \quad (28)$$

where μ^2 is a constant. Now, considering a Starobinsky quadratic potential[70]

$$V(\phi) = \frac{1}{\alpha}\left(\frac{\phi-1}{2}\right)^2, \qquad (29)$$

it can be shown that the equations for the scalar fields yield[a]

$$\dot\psi = \frac{k_0\phi}{v}, \qquad \phi = \frac{v^2 f(v)}{6\alpha k_0^2 + v^2}, \qquad (30)$$

in terms of the volume-like variable $v \equiv abc$ and the function $f(v) \equiv 1 - 2\alpha\kappa(3w-1)\rho(v)$, while k_0 is an integration constant. Regarding the metric field equations, lengthy computations[65] allow to rewrite the tt component in the form of a modified Friedmann equation:

$$H^2 \equiv \left(\frac{\dot v}{3v}\right)^2 = \frac{\frac{\kappa}{3}\left(\frac{\mu_I^2}{v^2} + \frac{\rho}{\phi} + \frac{\mu_{AN}^2}{\phi^2 v^2}\right) + \frac{V(\phi)}{6\phi}}{\left(1 + \frac{3v}{2}\frac{d}{dv}\ln\phi\right)^2}, \qquad (31)$$

where μ_A^2 and μ_I^2 are constants, representing the anisotropy density parameter and the energy density parameter of the Immirzi field, respectively. We note that the r.h.s is a rational function of the volume alone.

In the following we will take into account dust and radiation as matter contributions, specified by the choices $w = 0$, $\mu = \mu_D$ and $w = 1/3$, $\mu = \mu_R$ in (28), respectively. Then, bouncing solutions can be derived for $\alpha < 0$ integrating Eq. (31) for $v(t)$, which then yields the scalar fields behavior via (30).

4.1. Vacuum case

It is convenient to first focus on the vacuum case, where $f(v) = 1$ and $\mu_D = \mu_R = 0$. In this case we found the big bounce in the volume variable depicted in Fig. 1, where also the behavior of each scale factor is shown. We note that the volume is affected by a future finite-time *singularity*[71,72] where the Hubble function diverges, while the scale factors are always finite and nonvanishing. Such singular points will be carefully investigated in the next section studying the geodesic completeness and scalar perturbations across them. Here we just note that, in general, quantum effects of particle creation[73–76] can produce additional effective terms in the Friedman equation, able to regularize singularities of the Hubble function.

Finally, the scalar fields behaviour is shown in Fig. 2 where the field ϕ asymptotically reaches unity as $t \to \infty$, while the Immirzi field relaxes to a constant Immirzi parameter.

4.2. Radiation and dust

The above analysis can be extended to the non vacuum case, including the energy density of radiation and dust. A first difference concerns the late time region, since

---

[a]A dot denotes derivatives with respect to time.

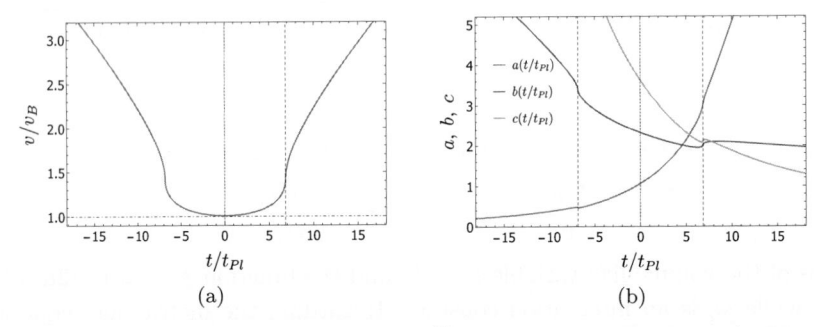

Fig. 1. Numerical solutions for $\alpha = -5/3$, $\mu_I = \sqrt{3}$, $\mu_A = 0.2\mu_I$ as a function of t/t_{Pl}. Dotted and dashed lines represent where bounce and future time singularity happen, respectively. The bounce is centered at the origin of time for convenience, and the values of the parameters are chosen in order to yield graphs that display features in a clear fashion. (a) Universe volume normalised to v_B. (b) Scale factors.

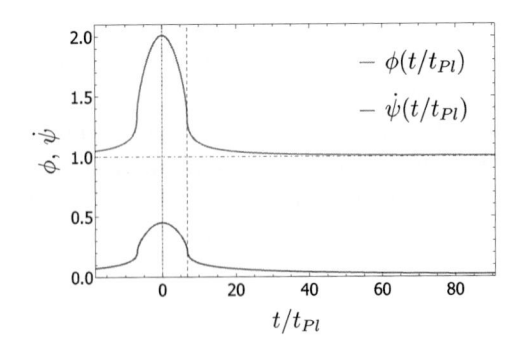

Fig. 2. Scalaron ϕ and Immirzi field derivative $\dot\psi$ for $\alpha = -5/3$, $\mu_I = \sqrt{3}$, $\mu_A = 0.2\mu_I$ as a function of t/t_{Pl}.

both radiation and dust are able to provide an isotropization mechanism for the universe, as is apparent studying the anisotropy degree

$$A(t) = \frac{(H_A^2 + H_B^2 + H_C^2)}{3H^2} - 1, \qquad (32)$$

whose behavior is shown in Fig. 3. Regarding the universe in its early phase, instead, two different scenarios may occur, depending on the value of the parameter α. If $\bar\alpha < \alpha < 0$, where $\bar\alpha = -2\mu_I^2/\mu_D^4$, the solutions are qualitatively equivalent to the vacuum case. If $\bar\alpha > \alpha$, instead, we still obtain a bouncing behavior for the volume (See Fig. 4), which however is now devoid of singularities. However, now the scale factors either diverge or vanish at some critical time t_c.

5. Physical implications of curvature divergences

As described in the previous section there are two classes of solutions, characterized by a singularity in the Hubble function and non vanishing and finite scale factors

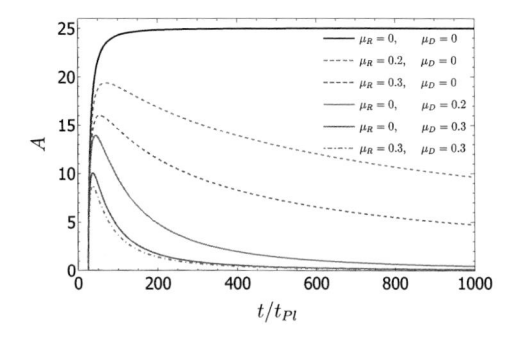

Fig. 3. Asymptotic behavior of the anisotropy degree A as a function of t/t_{Pl} after the finite time singularity for various values of μ_R, μ_D and $\alpha = -5/3$, $\mu_I = \sqrt{3}$, $\mu_A = 0.2\mu_I$.

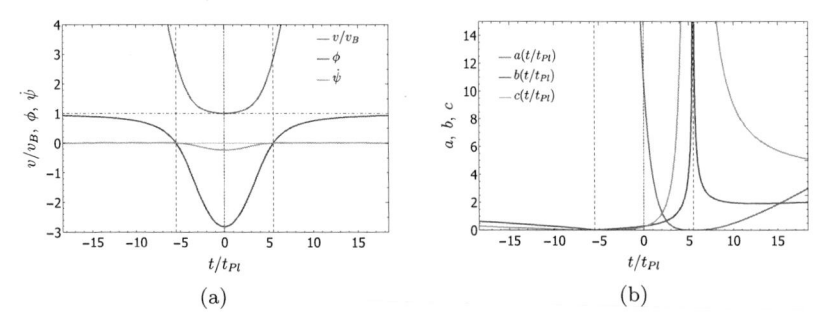

Fig. 4. Numerical solutions as a function of t/t_{Pl} for $\mu_I = 0.057$, $\mu_A = 2.4$, $\mu_D = 0.365$, $\mu_R = 1.56$ and $\alpha = -8.42 < \bar{\alpha}$. The dashed lines represent where the scalaron vanishes. (a) Volume normalised to v_B, ϕ and derivative of the Immirzi field. (b) Scale factors.

(Fig. 1) or with regular Hubble function but vanishing or divergent scale factors (Fig. 4). In this section we will analyse such singularities studying the behavior of null geodesics and of scalar perturbations near the critical time t_c, at which the singularity is located.

Regarding null geodesics with tangent vector $u^\alpha = dx^\alpha/ds$, it can be shown that they admit a first integral of the form[77,78]

$$x' = \frac{k_a}{a^2}, \quad y' = \frac{k_b}{b^2}, \quad z' = \frac{k_c}{c^2}, \quad t' = \left(\frac{k_a^2}{a^2} + \frac{k_b^2}{b^2} + \frac{k_c^2}{c^2}\right)^{1/2} + C_0, \quad (33)$$

where prime denotes derivative with respect to the affine parameter s and k_a, k_b, k_c and C_0 are integration constants. It follows that if $a(t)$, $b(t)$, and $c(t)$ are continuous and non-vanishing, as in Fig. 1, the tangent vector to the geodesics will be unique and well defined. Therefore, such cases are geodesically complete, a result that holds both in the anisotropic and in the isotropic case.[79]

In the other class of solutions (Fig. 4), instead, we see that the volume remains finite despite the vanishing/divergence of some scale factors. The divergence of individual scale factors does not affect the geodesics, but the vanishing of some of them may spoil the continuity and lead to the impossibility of a unique extension across t_c. Indeed, let us consider the case in which one scale factor vanishes at some affine parameter s_c. In particular, suppose that

$$a(s) = a_0(s - s_c)^\gamma, \tag{34}$$

with $\gamma > 0$. Then, integrating the relevant equations yields

$$x(s) = x_c + \frac{k_a(s - s_c)^{1-2\gamma}}{a_0^2(1 - 2\gamma)}, \tag{35}$$

$$t(s) = t_c + C_0(s - s_c) + \frac{k_a(s - s_c)^{1-\gamma}}{a_0(1 - \gamma)}, \tag{36}$$

which are smooth if $0 < \gamma < 1/2$ and $0 < \gamma < 1$, respectively. Note that if $1/2 < \gamma < 1$, then $x(s) \xrightarrow{s \to s_c} \pm\infty$, which would imply reaching infinity in finite coordinate time. Conversely, if $0 < \gamma < 1/2$, then the geodesic path will span the range $\{t, x\} \in (-\infty, \infty)$, and the geodesics would be complete, despite the vanishing of some scale factors. However, this result is dependent on how rapidly the zero is reached, i.e. we have to determine the value of γ relative to the solutions in question. The results are shown in Fig. 5 and prove that the solution approaches zero too rapidly, corresponding to a value of γ larger than $1/2$. We are thus forced to conclude that the example shown in Fig. 4 does represent a geodesically incomplete space-time.

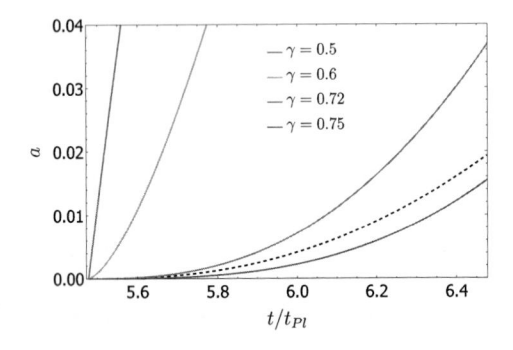

Fig. 5. Outcomes of null geodesics test for $\alpha < \bar{\alpha}$. Scale factor $a(s(t))$ for different values of γ. The dashed-black line represent the numerical solution $a(t)$ reported in Fig. 4.

We now turn the attention to the behavior of scalar field perturbations. For a scalar mode given by $\sigma_{\vec{k}}(t, \vec{x}) = \Theta(t)e^{i\vec{k}\cdot\vec{x}}$, one finds[65] an equation of the form

$$\ddot{\Theta} + h(v)\frac{\dot{v}}{v}\dot{\Theta} + \left(\frac{k_x^2}{a^2} + \frac{k_y^2}{b^2} + \frac{k_z^2}{c^2}\right)\Theta = 0, \tag{37}$$

where $h(v)$ represents some regular function of the volume v and $\vec{k} = (k_x, k_y, k_z)$ represents a set of constants. From this expression, we see that scalar modes are sensible to the presence of the individual scale factors $a, b,$ and c, and of the Hubble function $H = \dot{v}/3v$. If the scalar factors do not vanish anywhere, then any potential problems should come only from the term involving the Hubble function, which diverges in t_c. In particular, in vacuum one finds[65] the following approximate solution near the singularity

$$\Theta(t) \approx \Theta_c + \frac{\dot{\Theta}_c}{2\tilde{h}_c^2} e^{\mp 2\tilde{h}_c |t-t_c|^{1/2}} \left(1 \pm 2\tilde{h}_c |t-t_c|^{1/2}\right), \tag{38}$$

with $\Theta_c, \dot{\Theta}_c, \tilde{h}_c$ constants, from which we see that scalar field perturbations remain bounded around t_c despite the divergence in the Hubble function. A similar result holds in presence of dust and radiation, since

$$\Theta \approx \Theta_c - \frac{\dot{\Theta}_c}{32\tilde{h}_c^4} e^{\mp 4\tilde{h}_c |t-t_c|^{1/4}} \left(3 \pm 12\tilde{h}_c |t-t_c|^{1/4} \right.$$
$$\left. + 24\tilde{h}_c^2 |t-t_c|^{1/2} \pm 32\tilde{h}_c^3 |t-t_c|^{3/4}\right), \tag{39}$$

which is easy to see to be again bounded. On the other hand, for a regular Hubble function but vanishing scale factors, equation (37) describes a harmonic oscillator with a time dependent frequency,

$$\ddot{\Theta}(t) + \frac{k_x^2}{a^2(t)} \Theta(t) \approx 0, \tag{40}$$

which diverges as $a(t) \to 0$. Therefore, for the values of $a(t)$ obtained numerically in the previous section neither geodesics nor scalar perturbations are well behaved.

6. Conclusion

We proposed a generalization of the Nieh-Yan term to metric-affine gravity, by including an additional term featuring nonmetricity and inserting two parameters (λ_1, λ_2), which allow to recover the projective invariance and the topological character, otherwise lost in presence of nonmetricity. In particular, projective invariance can be independently obtained by setting $\lambda_1 = \lambda_2 = \lambda$, whereas topologicity is only guaranteed for $\lambda = 1$.

As an explicit example, we considered a model with Lagrangian $F(R, NY_{gen})$, which re-expressed in the Jordan frame features two scalar fields. We identified these scalar degrees as the $f(R)$-like scalaron ϕ and the Immirzi field β and showed that the latter acquires dynamical character and a potential term in a more natural way than in previous treatments, where these features are introduced by hand in the action. Depending on the values of λ_1 and λ_2, we found two different scalar tensor theories. Models with $\lambda_1 \neq \lambda_2$, are non-dynamical, and the scalar fields are frozen to constant values in vacuum. In the projective invariant case ($\lambda_1 = \lambda_2$), instead, the theory is endowed with one additional dynamical degree of freedom, the Immirzi field, while the field ϕ is algebraically related to the latter via a modified structural equation.

Then, we considered in more detail the dynamical models, looking for cosmological solutions in Bianchi I spacetimes. We found numerical solutions in which the big bang singularity is replaced by a big bounce scenario, in which the universe volume undergoes a contraction up to a minimum value and then bounces back, re-expanding in another branch. The scalaron and the Immirzi field reach a maximum during the bounce and relax to constant values at later times, where the standard LQG picture, with $\phi = 1$ and a constant Immirzi parameter $\beta = \beta_0$, is recovered. Moreover, the inclusion of dust and radiation turns out to provide an isotropization mechanism at late times, a feature that is absent in the vacuum case.

Such solutions are characterized by future finite time singularities after the bounce, either in the Hubble function or in the individual scale factors. In the former case, we showed that null geodesics are still well behaved and scalar perturbations bounded, which allows us to conclude that the solution is physically acceptable. In the latter case, instead, the study of null geodesics shows that they cannot be extended across the singular point, where also scalar perturbations grow in time, leading us to regard such solutions as unphysical.

References

1. Wald R. M., *General Relativity* (University of Chicago Press, 1984).
2. T. K. S. W. J. A. Misner C. W. and K. D.I., *Gravitation* (Princeton University Press, 2017).
3. V. I. Afonso, G. J. Olmo and D. Rubiera-Garcia, Mapping Ricci-based theories of gravity into general relativity, *Phys. Rev. D* **97**, p. 021503 (2018).
4. V. I. Afonso, G. J. Olmo, E. Orazi and D. Rubiera-Garcia, Correspondence between modified gravity and general relativity with scalar fields, *Phys. Rev. D* **99**, p. 044040 (2019).
5. G. J. Olmo, PALATINI APPROACH TO MODIFIED GRAVITY: f(R) THEORIES AND BEYOND, *International Journal of Modern Physics D* **20**, 413 (2011).
6. F. S. N. Lobo, G. J. Olmo and D. Rubiera-Garcia, Semiclassical geons as solitonic black hole remnants, *JCAP* **07**, p. 011 (2013).
7. J. Beltran Jimenez, L. Heisenberg, G. J. Olmo and D. Rubiera-Garcia, Born–Infeld inspired modifications of gravity, *Phys. Rept.* **727**, 1 (2018).
8. J. Beltrán Jiménez, L. Heisenberg, D. Iosifidis, A. Jiménez-Cano and T. S. Koivisto, General teleparallel quadratic gravity, *Physics Letters B* **805**, p. 135422 (2020).
9. J. a. L. Rosa, F. S. N. Lobo and G. J. Olmo, Weak-field regime of the generalized hybrid metric-Palatini gravity (4 2021).
10. T. Harko, T. S. Koivisto, F. S. N. Lobo and G. J. Olmo, Metric-Palatini gravity unifying local constraints and late-time cosmic acceleration, *Phys. Rev. D* **85**, p. 084016 (2012).
11. S. Capozziello, T. Harko, T. S. Koivisto, F. S. N. Lobo and G. J. Olmo, Hybrid metric-Palatini gravity, *Universe* **1**, 199 (2015).
12. F. Bombacigno, F. Moretti and G. Montani, Scalar modes in extended hybrid metric-Palatini gravity: weak field phenomenology, *Phys. Rev. D* **100**, p. 124036 (2019).
13. K. A. Bronnikov, Spherically symmetric black holes and wormholes in hybrid metric-Palatini gravity, *Grav. Cosmol.* **25**, 331 (2019).

14. M. Borunda, B. Janssen and M. Bastero-Gil, Palatini versus metric formulation in higher curvature gravity, *JCAP* **11**, p. 008 (2008).
15. B. Janssen, A. Jiménez-Cano and J. A. Orejuela, A non-trivial connection for the metric-affine Gauss-Bonnet theory in $D=4$, *Phys. Lett. B* **795**, 42 (2019).
16. B. Janssen and A. Jiménez-Cano, On the topological character of metric-affine Lovelock Lagrangians in critical dimensions, *Phys. Lett. B* **798**, p. 134996 (2019).
17. R. Percacci and E. Sezgin, New class of ghost- and tachyon-free metric affine gravities, *Phys. Rev. D* **101**, p. 084040 (2020).
18. C. Rovelli, *Quantum Gravity* (Cambridge University Press, Cambridge, England, 2004).
19. T. Thiemann, *Modern Canonical Quantum General Relativity* (Cambridge University Press, Cambridge, England, 2007).
20. A. Ashtekar, New Variables for Classical and Quantum Gravity, *Phys. Rev. Lett.* **57**, 2244 (nov 1986).
21. A. Ashtekar, New Hamiltonian formulation of general relativity, *Physical Review D* **36**, 1587 (sep 1987).
22. A. Ashtekar, J. D. Romano and R. S. Tate, New variables for gravity: Inclusion of matter, *Physical Review D* **40**, 2572 (oct 1989).
23. A. Ashtekar and C. J. Isham, Representations of the holonomy algebras of gravity and nonAbelian gauge theories, *Classical and Quantum Gravity* **9**, 1433 (jun 1992).
24. G. Date, R. K. Kaul and S. Sengupta, Topological interpretation of Barbero-Immirzi parameter, *Phys. Rev. D* **79**, p. 44008 (feb 2009).
25. H. T. Nieh and M. L. Yan, An identity in Riemann–Cartan geometry, *Journal of Mathematical Physics* **23**, 373 (1982).
26. H. T. Nieh, A TORSIONAL TOPOLOGICAL INVARIANT, *International Journal of Modern Physics A* **22**, 5237 (2007).
27. S. Holst, Barbero's Hamiltonian derived from a generalized Hilbert-Palatini action, *Phys. Rev. D* **53**, 5966 (may 1996).
28. G. Immirzi, Real and complex connections for canonical gravity, *Class. Quant. Grav.* **14**, L177 (1997).
29. G. Immirzi, Real and complex connections for canonical gravity, *Classical and Quantum Gravity* **14**, L177 (oct 1997).
30. C. Rovelli and T. Thiemann, The Immirzi parameter in quantum general relativity, *Phys. Rev. D* **57**, 1009 (1998).
31. V. Taveras and N. Yunes, Barbero-Immirzi parameter as a scalar field: K-inflation from loop quantum gravity?, *Phys. Rev. D* **78**, p. 64070 (sep 2008).
32. G. Calcagni and S. Mercuri, Barbero-Immirzi field in canonical formalism of pure gravity, *Phys. Rev. D* **79**, p. 84004 (apr 2009).
33. F. Bombacigno, F. Cianfrani and G. Montani, Big-bounce cosmology in the presence of Immirzi field, *Phys. Rev. D* **94**, p. 64021 (sep 2016).
34. O. J. Veraguth and C. H. Wang, Immirzi parameter without Immirzi ambiguity: Conformal loop quantization of scalar-tensor gravity, *Physical Review D* **96**, p. 084011 (oct 2017).
35. C. H. Wang and D. P. Rodrigues, Closing the gaps in quantum space and time: Conformally augmented gauge structure of gravitation, *Physical Review D* **98**, p. 124041 (dec 2018).
36. F. Bombacigno and G. Montani, Implications of the Holst term in a f(R) theory with torsion, *Phys. Rev. D* **99**, p. 64016 (mar 2019).
37. F. Bombacigno and G. Montani, f(R) gravity with torsion and the Immirzi field: Signature for gravitational wave detection, *Phys. Rev. D* **97**, p. 124066 (jun 2018).

38. C. H.-T. Wang and M. Stankiewicz, Quantization of time and the big bang via scale-invariant loop gravity, *Physics Letters B* **800**, p. 135106 (jan 2020).
39. D. Iosifidis and L. Ravera, Parity Violating Metric-Affine Gravity Theories (9 2020).
40. F. Bombacigno, S. Boudet and G. Montani, Generalized ashtekar variables for palatini f(r) models, *Nuclear Physics B* **963**, p. 115281 (2021).
41. M. Långvik, J.-M. Ojanperä, S. Raatikainen and S. Räsänen, Higgs inflation with the Holst and the Nieh–Yan term, *Phys. Rev. D* **103**, p. 083514 (2021).
42. F. Bombacigno and G. Montani, Big bounce cosmology for Palatini R^2 gravity with a Nieh-Yan term, *The European Physical Journal C* **79**, p. 405 (may 2019).
43. S. Boudet, F. Bombacigno, G. Montani and M. Rinaldi, Superentropic black hole with immirzi hair, *Phys. Rev. D* **103**, p. 084034 (Apr 2021).
44. M. Lattanzi and S. Mercuri, A solution of the strong cp problem via the peccei-quinn mechanism through the nieh-yan modified gravity and cosmological implications, *Phys. Rev. D* **81**, p. 125015 (Jun 2010).
45. O. Castillo-Felisola, C. Corral, S. Kovalenko, I. Schmidt and V. E. Lyubovitskij, Axions in gravity with torsion, *Phys. Rev. D* **91**, p. 085017 (Apr 2015).
46. S. Mercuri, Peccei-Quinn Mechanism in Gravity and the Nature of the Barbero-Immirzi Parameter, *Phys. Rev. Lett.* **103**, p. 81302 (aug 2009).
47. M. Li, H. Rao and D. Zhao, A simple parity violating gravity model without ghost instability, *Journal of Cosmology and Astroparticle Physics* **2020**, 023 (nov 2020).
48. J. Nissinen and G. E. Volovik, Thermal nieh-yan anomaly in weyl superfluids, *Phys. Rev. Research* **2**, p. 033269 (Aug 2020).
49. J. Nissinen and G. E. Volovik, On Thermal Nieh-Yan Anomaly in Topological Weyl Materials, *JETP Letters* **110**, 789 (2019).
50. Z.-M. Huang, B. Han and M. Stone, Nieh-yan anomaly: Torsional landau levels, central charge, and anomalous thermal hall effect, *Phys. Rev. B* **101**, p. 125201 (Mar 2020).
51. C.-X. Liu, Phonon helicity and nieh-yan anomaly in the kramers-weyl semimetals of chiral crystals (2021).
52. V. I. Afonso, C. Bejarano, J. Beltran Jimenez, G. J. Olmo and E. Orazi, The trivial role of torsion in projective invariant theories of gravity with non-minimally coupled matter fields, *Class. Quant. Grav.* **34**, p. 235003 (2017).
53. D. Iosifidis, Linear Transformations on Affine-Connections, *Class. Quant. Grav.* **37**, p. 085010 (2020).
54. J. Beltrán Jiménez and A. Delhom, Ghosts in metric-affine higher order curvature gravity, *The European Physical Journal C* **79**, p. 656 (2019).
55. G. Montani, M. V. Battisti, R. Benini and G. Imponente, *Primordial cosmology* (World Scientific, Singapore, 2009).
56. A. Corichi and P. Singh, A Geometric perspective on singularity resolution and uniqueness in loop quantum cosmology, *Phys. Rev. D* **80**, p. 044024 (2009).
57. A. Y. Kamenshchik, E. O. Pozdeeva, A. A. Starobinsky, A. Tronconi, G. Venturi and S. Y. Vernov, Induced gravity, and minimally and conformally coupled scalar fields in Bianchi-I cosmological models, *Phys. Rev. D* **97**, p. 023536 (2018).
58. G. Montani and R. Chiovoloni, A Scenario for a Singularity-free Generic Cosmological Solution (3 2021).
59. G. Montani, A. Marchi and R. Moriconi, Bianchi I model as a prototype for a cyclical Universe, *Phys. Lett. B* **777**, 191 (2018).
60. F. Cianfrani, A. Marchini and G. Montani, The picture of the Bianchi I model via gauge fixing in Loop Quantum Gravity, *EPL* **99**, p. 10003 (2012).
61. R. Moriconi and G. Montani, Behavior of the Universe anisotropy in a big-bounce cosmology, *Phys. Rev. D* **95**, p. 123533 (2017).

62. E. Giovannetti, G. Montani and S. Schiattarella, Semiclassical and quantum features of the Bianchi I cosmology in the polymer representation (5 2021).
63. C. Barragan and G. J. Olmo, Isotropic and Anisotropic Bouncing Cosmologies in Palatini Gravity, *Phys. Rev. D* **82**, p. 084015 (2010).
64. C. Barragan, G. J. Olmo and H. Sanchis-Alepuz, Bouncing Cosmologies in Palatini f(R) Gravity, *Phys. Rev. D* **80**, p. 024016 (2009).
65. F. Bombacigno, S. Boudet, G. J. Olmo and G. Montani, Big bounce and future time singularity resolution in bianchi i cosmologies: The projective invariant nieh-yan case, *Phys. Rev. D* **103**, p. 124031 (Jun 2021).
66. G. J. Olmo, Post-Newtonian constraints on f(R) cosmologies in metric and Palatini formalism, *Phys. Rev. D* **72**, p. 083505 (2005).
67. S. Mercuri, Fermions in the Ashtekar-Barbero connection formalism for arbitrary values of the Immirzi parameter, *Phys. Rev. D* **73**, p. 84016 (apr 2006).
68. S. Mercuri, From the Einstein-Cartan to the Ashtekar-Barbero canonical constraints, passing through the Nieh-Yan functional, *Physical Review D - Particles, Fields, Gravitation and Cosmology* **77**, p. 024036 (jan 2008).
69. S. Mercuri and V. Taveras, Interaction of the Barbero-Immirzi field with matter and pseudoscalar perturbations, *Phys. Rev. D* **80**, p. 104007 (nov 2009).
70. A. Starobinsky, A new type of isotropic cosmological models without singularity, *Physics Letters B* **91**, 99 (1980).
71. S. Nojiri, S. D. Odintsov and S. Tsujikawa, Properties of singularities in (phantom) dark energy universe, *Phys. Rev. D* **71**, p. 063004 (2005).
72. S. D. Odintsov and V. K. Oikonomou, Dynamical Systems Perspective of Cosmological Finite-time Singularities in $f(R)$ Gravity and Interacting Multifluid Cosmology, *Phys. Rev. D* **98**, p. 024013 (2018).
73. G. Montani, Influence of the particles creation on the flat and negative curved FLRW universes, *Class. Quant. Grav.* **18**, 193 (2001).
74. K. Dimopoulos, Is the Big Rip unreachable?, *Phys. Lett. B* **785**, 132 (2018).
75. L. H. Ford, Gravitational Particle Creation and Inflation, *Phys. Rev. D* **35**, p. 2955 (1987).
76. F. Contreras, N. Cruz, E. Elizalde, E. González and S. Odintsov, Linking little rip cosmologies with regular early universes, *Phys. Rev. D* **98**, p. 123520 (2018).
77. P. Singh, Curvature invariants, geodesics and the strength of singularities in Bianchi-I loop quantum cosmology, *Phys. Rev. D* **85**, p. 104011 (2012).
78. K. Nomura and D. Yoshida, Past extendibility and initial singularity in Friedmann-Lemaître-Robertson-Walker and Bianchi I spacetimes (5 2021).
79. J. Beltran Jimenez, R. Lazkoz, D. Saez-Gomez and V. Salzano, Observational constraints on cosmological future singularities, *Eur. Phys. J. C* **76**, p. 631 (2016).

Late time cosmology with derivatives of matter Lagrangian

Shahab Shahidi

School of Physics, Damghan University, Damghan, 36716-41167, Iran
E-mail: s.shahidi@du.ac.ir

A class of modified gravity theories with higher order derivative terms of a function of the matter Lagrangian $f(L_m)$ is considered. We will consider the Newtonian limit of the theory and show that the model predicts the standard Poisson equation for a massive test particle due to the higher order nature of the derivative matter coupling. Generally the energy momentum tensor is not conserved, leading to the fifth force similar to $f(R,T)$ theories. We will however show that in the FRW background the energy-momentum tensor is conserved. Cosmological implications of this model with different functions of the matter Lagrangian f will be investigated in details and we will show that current observational data can be satisfied. Evolution of the matter density perturbation in the longitudinal gauge is also considered for dust matter sources and we will show that the observational data can be satisfied in this model.

Keywords: Modified gravity, Late time cosmology.

1. Introduction

The accelerated expansion of the universe is one of the most interesting findings of modern cosmology which is confirmed by observations.[1] Our first and standard treatment to explain this expansion is to introduce a cosmological constant Λ to the standard Einstein Hilbert action so that the Lagrangian of the gravitational theory becomes

$$\mathcal{L} = \sqrt{-g}(R - 2\Lambda + L_m), \tag{1}$$

where R is the Ricci scalar and L_m is the matter Lagrangian. Together with cold dark matter which takes care of local celestial motions, this theory could explain almost all of current observations and is well-known as the ΛCDM model for cosmology. However, the standard ΛCDM model suffers from some phenomenological and also observational issues such as the cosmological constant problem,[2] the Hubble and σ_8 tensions,[3] etc. In fact there are many attempts to explain these problems in the context of ΛCDM model. For example in,[4] the authors have tried to explain why the σ_8 tension is not a problem at all.

One of the solutions to all of the aforementioned problems is to dismiss the cosmological constant in the Lagrangian and search for a new method to describe the dynamics of accelerated universe at late times. This can be done by introducing extra degrees of freedom to the theory such as scalar-tensor[5] or vector-tensor theories,[6] or by generalizing the gravitational action itself, such as $f(R)$ gravity theories[7] or massive gravity theories.[8] Another interesting idea among these modified gravity theories, is to introduce some non-standard couplings between gravity and matter fields. These theories include minimal couplings such as energy-momentum powered gravity[9] or non-minimal couplings such as $f(R,T)$ theories and their generalizations.[10] In figure (1) we have summarized the most important generalizations of gravitational action. The general property in non standard matter coupling theories is that the energy-momentum tensor is no longer conserved. This implies that we have a fraction of matter creation from geometry in these classes of theories which could be tested by observations.

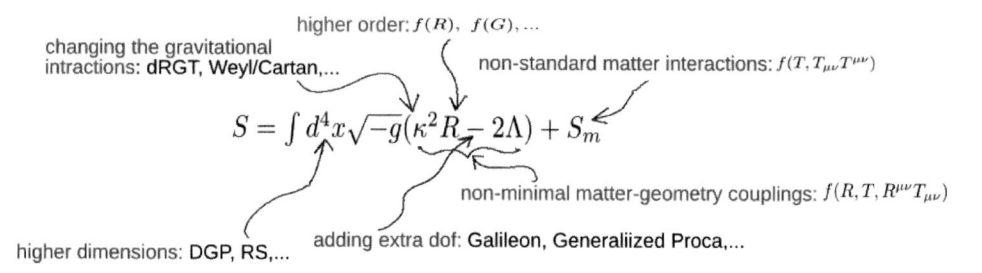

Fig. 1. Summary of modified gravity theories from the Einstein-Hilbert action.

2. The model

In this paper we introduce a new method to generalize the coupling between matter and geometry. Let us consider the evolution of the non-relativistic matter energy density with respect to the redshift z which is plotted in figure (2). One can see from this figure that the matter density is nearly flat around $z \approx 0$. This implies that the derivatives of matter density is nearly constant around present time which can mimic the cosmological constant (CC). This brings the idea that maybe derivatives of the

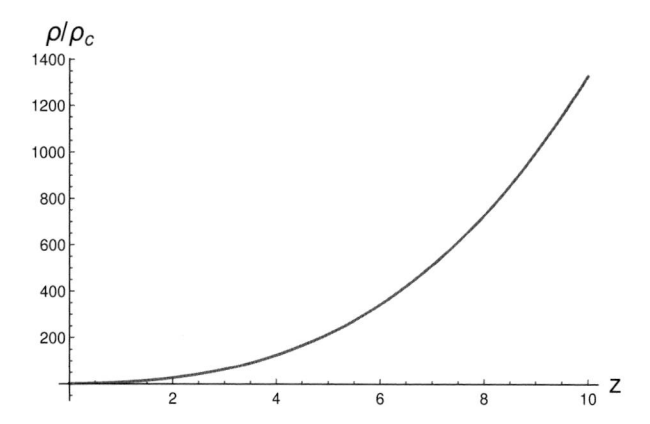

Fig. 2. The evolution of the pressure-less energy density as a function of redshift z.

matter density or matter Lagrangian could play the role of CC and be responsible for late time accelerated expansion of the universe. To explore this possibility, let us consider the action functional[11]

$$S = \int d^4x \sqrt{-g} \left[\kappa^2(R - 2\Lambda) + \alpha \nabla_\mu f \nabla^\mu f \right] + S_m, \qquad (2)$$

where $f = f(L_m)$ is an arbitrary function of the matter Lagrangian with mass dimension 1 and α is a dimensionless constant. It should be noted that the function f is a scalar field. As a result, one can consider the α-term in the action, as a canonical kinetic term for f. So, the theory (2) is a scalar tensor theory (or a simplest class of Galileon theory) where the scalar field is substituted by an energy-density valued scalar field. As we will see in the following, this rich structure allows us to explain the late time accelerated expansion of the universe. We should also note that the theory (2) is different from the so-called $f(R, L_m)$ gravity theories,[10] since in $f(R, L_m)$ theories, we have non-minimal couplings between matter and geometry but here we have a minimal derivative interaction of the matter Lagrangian.

In order to obtain the equation of motion of this model, note that the definition of the energy-momentum tensor is given by

$$T_{\mu\nu} = -\frac{2}{\sqrt{-g}} \frac{\delta(\sqrt{-g} L_m)}{\delta g^{\mu\nu}}, \qquad (3)$$

which implies that

$$\delta L_m = \frac{1}{2}(L_m g_{\mu\nu} - T_{\mu\nu})\delta g^{\mu\nu}. \qquad (4)$$

As a result, one can obtain the equation of motion of the derivative matter coupling (DMC) model (2) as

$$\kappa^2(G_{\mu\nu} + \Lambda g_{\mu\nu}) + \alpha f' \Box f (T_{\mu\nu} - g_{\mu\nu} L_m)$$
$$+ \alpha \left(\nabla_\mu f \nabla_\nu f - \frac{1}{2} g_{\mu\nu} \nabla_\alpha f \nabla^\alpha f \right) = \frac{1}{2} T_{\mu\nu}, \qquad (5)$$

Here, prime denotes derivative with respect to the argument. As we mentioned above, the term proportional to the coupling constant α is the second Galileon equation of motion for the scalar field f.

The general behavior of the coupled matter-geometry theories is that the energy-momentum tensor is no longer conserved. In our model, one can easily obtain

$$\nabla^\mu T_{\mu\nu} = 2(T_{\mu\nu} - L_m g_{\mu\nu}) \nabla^\mu \text{Log}[1 - \alpha f' \Box f]. \qquad (6)$$

One can see that in the case $\alpha = 0$, the energy-momentum tensor becomes conserved. Here, we have to note an important property of the model. Let us assume that the matter content of the universe could be explained by a perfect fluid with Lagrangian $L_m = -\rho$ and energy-momentum tensor

$$T_{\mu\nu} = (\rho + p)u_\mu u_\nu + p g_{\mu\nu}. \qquad (7)$$

In this case, the non-conservation of the energy-momentum tensor becomes

$$\nabla^\mu T_{\mu\nu} = -2(\rho+p)h_{\mu\nu}\nabla^\mu \text{Log}\big[1-\alpha f' \Box f\big]. \tag{8}$$

where $h_{\mu\nu} = u_\mu u_\nu + g_{\mu\nu}$ is the projection tensor. On top of FRW space-time, the right hand side of the conservation equation (8) vanishes and we recover the conservation of the energy-momentum tensor in our model. This is however a new feature in the context of matter-geometry coupling theories.

3. Newtonian limit

Let us first consider the geodesics of the DMC model. We assume that the cosmological constant could be ignored in the low energy limit. One can easily prove that the conservation of the energy-momentum tensor (8) for a perfect fluid results in the geodesic equation of the form

$$\frac{d^2 x^\lambda}{ds^2} + \Gamma^\lambda_{\mu\nu} u^\mu u^\nu = f^\lambda, \tag{9}$$

where

$$f^\lambda = -2h^{\lambda\nu}\nabla_\nu \log\big[1-\alpha f'\Box f\big] - \frac{h^{\lambda\nu}\nabla_\nu p}{\rho+p}, \tag{10}$$

where the new vector field f^μ represents an extra force inserted to the particles moving in the geodesic lines. This will imply that a test particle move along a non-geodesic path. This is actually a general behavior of theories with matter-geometry coupling. In the low energy limit of the theory the metric takes the form

$$ds^2 = -(1+2\Phi(\vec{x}))dt^2 + (1-2\Phi(\vec{x}))d\vec{x}^2, \tag{11}$$

where Φ is the Newtonian potential. In this limit, only the (00) component of the energy-momentum tensor, namely ρ, is non-vanishing. If we assume that the function f in the Lagrangian is a smooth funciton and could be expanded as a power series in ρ, one obtains

$$f = \sum_{i=0} \alpha_i \rho^i.$$

As one can see from the field equation (5), f appears with at least two derivatives. As a result the derivative matter coupling terms could not contribute in the linear Newtonian approximation. We then recover the standard Poisson equation as

$$\vec{\nabla}^2 \Phi(\vec{x}) = 4\pi G \rho(\vec{x}). \tag{12}$$

One should note that this result is in contrast to the general discussion on the form of Poisson equation in matter-geometry coupling theories,[12] since in that work the coupling is assumed to have a linear contribution to the field equations.

4. Cosmology

In this section, we consider the cosmological implications of the DMC model. Let us assume that the universe can be explained by a spatially flat FRW space-time with line element

$$ds^2 = a^2(t)(-dt^2 + dx^2 + dy^2 + dz^2), \tag{13}$$

where we have chosen the conformal time t with scale factor a. From the field equation (5), one can obtain the Friedmann and Raychaudhuri equations as

$$6\kappa^2 H^2 = a^2\rho - \alpha f'^2 \dot{\rho}^2 + 2\kappa^2 a^2 \Lambda, \tag{14}$$

and

$$\begin{aligned}
-4\kappa^2 \dot{H} - 2\kappa^2 H^2 &= pa^2 - 2\kappa^2 a^2 \Lambda \\
&\quad + 2\alpha f'(\rho + p)(f'' \dot{\rho}^2 - f'\ddot{\rho}) \\
&\quad - 4\alpha H(\rho + p)f'^2 \dot{\rho} - 2\alpha f'^2 \dot{\rho}^2.
\end{aligned} \tag{15}$$

In this paper, we will consider a power-law case for the function f as $f = \gamma(-L_m/\rho_c)^n$. Defining the following dimensionless parameters as

$$H = H_0 h, \quad \bar{\rho}_m = \frac{\rho_m}{\rho_c}, \quad \bar{\rho}_r = \frac{\rho_r}{\rho_c}, \quad \Omega_{\Lambda 0} = \frac{\Lambda}{3H_0^2},$$

$$r \equiv \bar{\rho}_m + \bar{\rho}_r, \quad \rho_c = 6\kappa^2 H_0^2, \quad \beta = \frac{\gamma^2 \alpha}{6\kappa^2}, \tag{16}$$

where H_0 is the current value of the Hubble parameter and ρ_c is the critical density, the Friedmann equation reduces to

$$h^2 = a^2(r + \Omega_{\Lambda 0}) + \frac{1}{9}\beta r^{2(n-1)} \dot{r}^2. \tag{17}$$

We note that the matter sources on top of FRW universe is conserved. As a result, we obtain

$$\bar{\rho}_m = \frac{\Omega_{m0}}{a^3}, \quad \bar{\rho}_r = \frac{\Omega_{r0}}{a^4}.$$

Transforming to the redshift coordinate, defined as

$$1 + z = \frac{1}{a},$$

and using the above equations, one obtains the dimensionless Hubble parameter as

$$(1+z)^2 h^2 = \frac{(1+z)^3 \Omega_{m0} + \Omega_{\Lambda 0}}{1 + \beta(1+z)^{6n} \Omega_{m0}^{2n}}. \tag{18}$$

We should note that the dimensionless Hubble parameter h has a property $h(z = 0) = 1$. In the following, we will consider two different cases, corresponding to the vanishing CC and non-vanishing CC. In the case of vanishing CC, one obtains from the constraint $h(0) = 1$

$$\beta = (\Omega_{m0} - 1)\Omega_{m0}^{-2n}.$$

In the case of non-vanishing CC, one obtains

$$\Omega_{\Lambda 0} = 1 - \Omega_{m0} + \beta \Omega_{m0}^{2n}.$$

In order to obtain the best estimate on the model parameters, H_0, Ω_{m0}, n and β, we will obtain the best fit values of these parameters by confronting the model with observational data on the Hubble parameter in the redshift range $(0,2)$.[13] In order to do this, we use the maximum likelihood analysis of the model based on the data on H_0. The likelihood function in the case of n independent data points can be defined as

$$L = L_0 e^{-\chi^2/2}, \qquad (19)$$

where L_0 is the normalization constant, and χ^2 is

$$\chi^2 = \sum_i \left(\frac{O_i - T_i}{\sigma_i}\right)^2, \qquad (20)$$

where i indicates the number of data, O_i are the observational values, T_i are the theoretical values and σ_i are the observational errors associated with the ith data. In the present model we have

$$L = L_0 \exp\left[-\frac{1}{2}\sum_i \left(\frac{O_i - H_0 T_i}{\sigma_i}\right)^2\right]. \qquad (21)$$

By maximizing the likelihood function, one can find the best fit values of the parameters. In the presence of the CC, one obtains

$$H_0 = 65.91^{+3.23}_{-3.45},$$
$$\Omega_{m0} = 0.41^{+0.11}_{-0.08},$$
$$\beta = 0.004^{+0.003}_{-0.002}, \qquad (22)$$

where the $\pm$ values are the 1σ confidence intervals. In this case, the CC parameter $\Omega_{\Lambda 0}$ could be obtained as

$$\Omega_{\Lambda 0} = 0.59. \qquad (23)$$

In figure (3), we have plotted the triangle diagram for this case. It should be noted that the parameter values for the Hubble parameter H_0 is in agreement with the ΛCDM model, indicating that the present model could not make the Hubble tension any better. We can see from the estimate (22) that the matter density Ω_0 is more than the ΛCDM value by 10 percent. Also, the CC abundance of the universe reduces up to 10 percent in this model. This in fact shows that the CC could be partially substituted by a simple derivative matter coupling. In fact, more complicated couplings could alleviate the contribution of the CC to the accelerated expansion of the universe even more.[11]

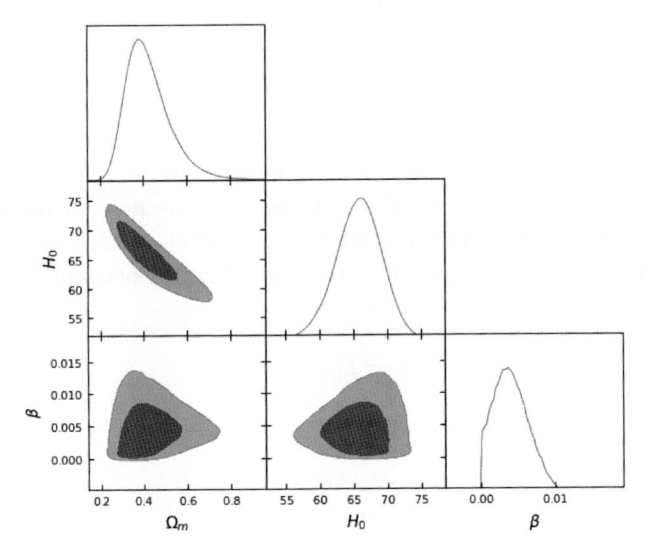

Fig. 3. The triangle diagram corresponding to 1σ intervals of the model paratmer in the case of non-vanishing CC.

Let us now consider the case of vanishing CC. In this case, all the accelerated expansion of the universe should be fully addressed by derivatives of the matter Lagrangian. The maximum likelihood analysis in this case gives

$$H_0 = 69.32^{+3.85}_{-4.82},$$
$$\Omega_{m0} = 0.29^{+0.07}_{-0.09},$$
$$n = -0.21^{+0.11}_{-0.15}. \qquad (24)$$

In this case on obtains $\beta = -0.42$. In figure (4), we have plotted the triangle diagram for this case. Also, in figure (5), we have depicted the evolution of the Hubble and deceleration parameters for the best fit values of the parameters. One can see from the figures that the DMC model satisfies the observational data. In fact the Hubble parameter is a little larger than the ΛCDM value for redshifts bigger that $z \approx 0.5$. This implies that the DMC model predicts smaller universe respect to the ΛCDM model. Also, the transition from deceleration to acceleration phase is occurred later than ΛCDM model, which indicates that the universe remains in dust dominated universe more than the ΛCDM model. However, the late time observations is fully addressed in this model, thanks to the presence of derivative of matter Lagrangian.

5. Dynamical system analysis

In order to see whether the DMC model could explain the cosmic history of the universe well or not, let us consider the dynamical system analysis of the model.

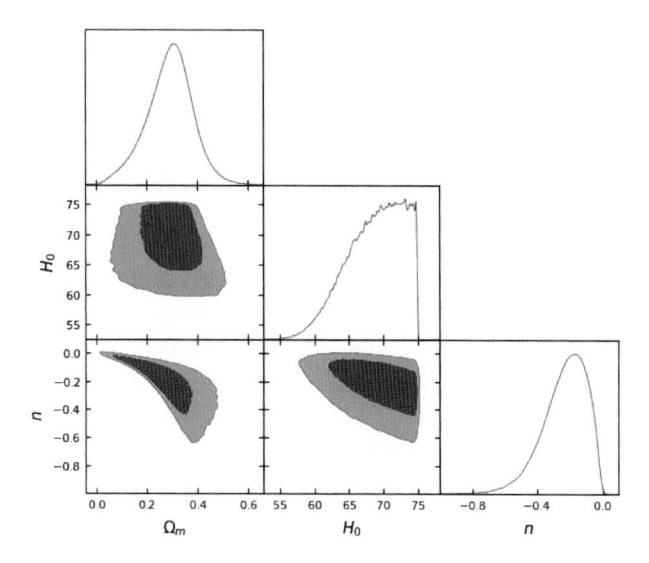

Fig. 4. The triangle diagram corresponding to 1σ intervals of the model paratmer in the case of vanishing CC.

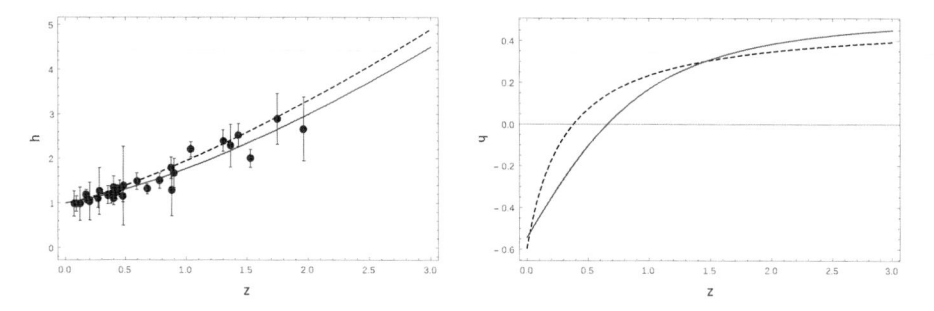

Fig. 5. The evolution of the Hubble (left) and deceleration (right) parameters as a function of redshift z for the best fit values of model parameters. The red solid line indicates the ΛCDM curve. Also, the error bars are the observational values together with their errors.[13]

We define the dynamical variables as

$$\Omega_m = \frac{\bar{\Omega}_m a^2}{h^2}, \quad \Omega_r = \frac{\bar{\Omega}_r a^2}{h^2}, \quad \Omega_h = \frac{h^2}{a^2}, \quad \Omega_\Lambda = \frac{\Omega_{\Lambda 0} a^2}{h^2}. \tag{25}$$

In the case of vanishing CC, one obtains from the Friedmann equation

$$\Omega_h = \left[\sqrt{\frac{1-\Omega_m-\Omega_r}{-\beta}} \frac{3}{(\Omega_m+\Omega_r)^{n-1}(3\Omega_m+4\Omega_r)}\right]^{\frac{1}{n}}. \tag{26}$$

In this case, we have two dynamical degrees of freedom. Also, in the case of non-vanishing CC, one obtains

$$\Omega_\Lambda = 1 - \Omega_m - \Omega_r$$
$$+ \frac{1}{9}\beta\Omega_h^{2n}(\Omega_m + \Omega_r)^{2(n-1)}(3\Omega_m + 4\Omega_r)^2, \qquad (27)$$

indicating that the model has three dynamical degrees of freedom. In figure (6), we have plotted the evolution of the dust and radiation abundances and dark energy abundance defined as $\Omega_{dark} \equiv 1 - \Omega_m - \Omega_r$, as a function of $N \equiv \ln a$. The dashed lines represent the behavior of the abundances in ΛCDM model, the dotted lines indicating the DMC model with CC and the solid lines indicate the DMC model with vanishing CC. One can see from this figure, that both cases could fully describe the history of the universe as in the ΛCDM model.

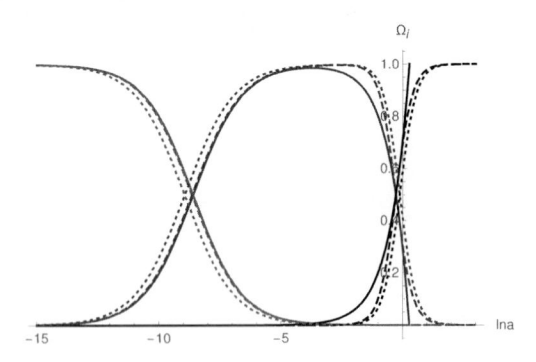

Fig. 6. The evolution of the dust (blue), radiation (red) and dark energy (black) abundances in ΛCDM model (dahsed), DMC model with CC (dotted) and DMC model with vanishing CC (solid).

In the case of vanishing CC, we have two fixed points corresponding to the radiation and dust dominated universe. In table (1), we have summarized these two fixed points. The stream plot of the evolution of the dynamical system could be seen in figure (7). In this case, there is no stable fixed point corresponds to the de Sitter acceleration of the universe. However, we have a stable manifold passing through the origin. As we get closer to the origin, the effective parameter of state of the model takes negative and larger values $w_{eff} < 0$ and we have more acceleration. In figure (7), we have plotted the $w_{eff} = -1$ curve as a solid line, indicating the

Table 1. The fixed points together with their properties for the DMC model without CC.

	(Ω_m, Ω_r)	Type	w_{eff}	Status
R	$(0,1)$	Radiation	$1/3$	unstable
M	$(1,0)$	matter	0	saddle

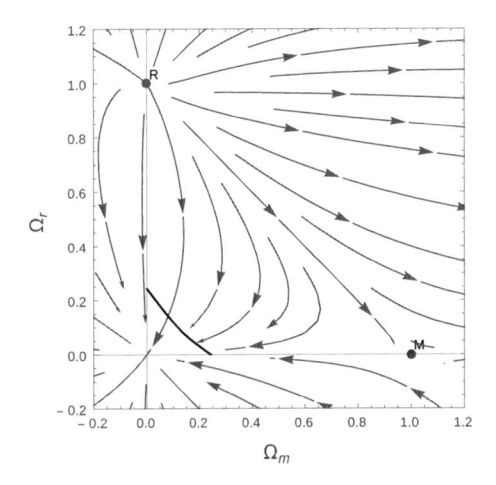

Fig. 7. The phase portrait of the dynamical system of the DMC model in the case of vanishing CC. The fixed points can also be seen in the figure. The black solid line indicates the line of de Sitter expansion.

de Sitter expansion. In figure (6), one can see that the dark energy abundance blows up at $N \approx 0$, indicating the aforementioned property of the model in this case. As a result, in this case, the universe could begin from an unstable radiation dominated fixed point, fall into the saddle dust dominated point and end at some accelerated expanding phase.

In the case of non-vanishing CC, we have three fixed points as we have summarized in table (2). In this case, we have all the standard fixed points of the ΛCDM model. However, as one can see from the table, the stable de Sitter fixed point is in fact a fixed line, passing through the origin. We have plotted the $\Omega_h = 0$ plane of the phase space in figure (8). In this case, the history of the universe is the same as the standard ΛCDM model. This can also be seen in figure (6).

Table 2. The fixed points together with their properties for the DMC model with CC.

	$(\Omega_m, \Omega_r, \Omega_h)$	Type	ω_{eff}	Status
R	$(0, 1, 0)$	Radiation	$1/3$	unstable
M	$(1, 0, 0)$	matter	0	saddle
Λ	$(0, 0, x)$	de Sitter	-1	stable

6. Conclusion

In this paper, we have considered a new possibility in the class of matter-geometry coupled theories namely, adding derivative interactions of the matter Lagrangian. We have used an arbitrary function f of the matter Lagrangian L_m which is a scalar

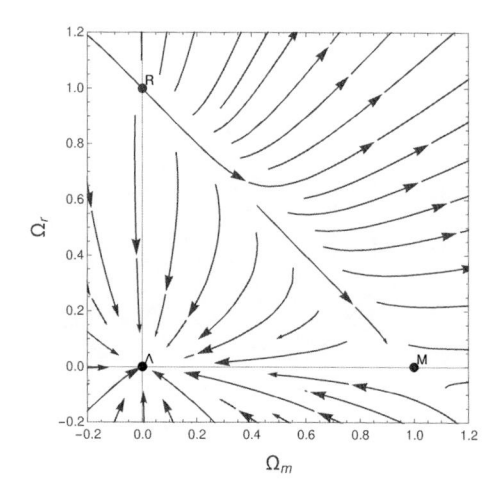

Fig. 8. The phase portrait of the dynamical system of the DMC model in the case of non-vanishing CC. The fixed points can also be seen in the figure.

field in nature, and add a canonical kinetic term of f to the action. In fact more general Galileon interactions could also be added to the theory which makes the late time behavior more reliable.

The cosmological implications of the theory in the case of vanishing and non-vanishing CC was studied in detail and we have found that CC could in part or fully be substituted by derivatives of matter Lagrangian. In the case of vanishing CC however, the cosmic history of the universe does not have a stable de Sitter fixed point and we need some higher order Galileon invariants to make the theory reliable. This was done in.[11]

In summary, we have shown in this paper that derivatives of matter Lagrangian could be considered more seriously as a reliable modified gravity theory for late times.

References

1. A. G. Riess et al., Astron. J. 116 (1998) 1009, arXiv:astro-ph/9805201; S. Perlmutter et al., Astrophys. J. 517(1999) 565, arXiv:astro-ph/9812133.
2. S. Weinberg, Rev. Mod. Phys. 61 (1989) 1; L. Lombriser, arXiv:1901.08588 [gr-qc].
3. Di Valentino, O. Mena, S. Pan, L. Visinelli, W. Yang, A. Melchiorri, D. F. Mota, A. G. Riess, J. Silk, arXiv:2103.01183 [astro-ph.CO].
4. R. C. Nunes and S. Vagnozzi, Mon. Not. Roy. Astron. Soc. 505 (2021) 5427.
5. I. Quiros, Int. J. Mod. Phys. D 28 (2019) 1930012; T. Kobayashi, Rept. Prog. Phys. 82 (2019) 086901; C. Deffayet, D. A Steer, Class. Quantum Grav. 30 (2013) 214006.
6. R. Kimura, A. Naruko, D. Yoshida, JCAP 01 (2017) 002; L. Heisenberg, JCAP 05 (2014) 015; L. Heisenberg, R. Kase, S. Tsujikawa, Phys. Lett. B 760 (2016) 617; Z. Haghani, T. Harko, H. R. Sepangi, S. Shahidi, Eur. Phys. J. C 77 (2017) 137; S. Shahidi, EPJC 79 (2019) 448; S. Shahidi, Phys. Rev. D 98 (2018) 084004; A. Amado, Z. Haghani, A. Mohammadi, S. Shahidi, Phys. Lett. B 772 (2017) 141.

7. T. Clifton, P. G. Ferreira, A. Padilla, C. Skordis, Physics Reports 513 (2012) 1; K. Koyama, Rept. Prog. Phys. 79 (2016) 046902; S. Nojiri, S. Odintsov, Int. J. Geom. Methods in Mod. Phys. 04 (2007) 115.
8. C. de Rham, Living Rev. Relativity 17 (2014), 7; K. Hinterbichler, Rev. Mod. Phys. 84 (2012) 671.
9. M. Roshan and f. Shojai, Phys. Rev. D 94 (2016) 044002; , J. D. Barrow and C. Board, Phys. Rev. D 96 (2017) 123517; O. Akarsu, N. Katirci and S. Kumar, Phys. Rev. D 97 (2018) 024011.
10. T. Harko, F. S. N. Lobo, S. Nojiri and S. D. Odintsov, Phys. Rev. D 84, 024020 (2011); T. Harko and F. S. N. Lobo, Eur. Phys. J. C 70, 373 (2010); S. D. Odintsov and D. Saez-Gomez, Phys. Lett. B 725 (2013) 437; O. Bertolami, C.G. Boehmer, T. Harko, f.S.N. Lobo, Phys. Rev. D 75 (2007) 104016; Z. Haghani, T. Harko, f.S.N. Lobo, H.R. Sepangi, S. Shahidi, Phys. Rev. D 88 (2013) 044023.
11. Z. Haghani, S. Shahidi, PDU (2020) 100683; Z. Haghani, S. Shahidi, EPJ plus 135 (2020) 509.
12. B. T. P. Sotiriou and V. Faraoni, Rev. Mod. Phys. 82 (2010) 451.
13. H. Boumaza and K. Nouicer, Phys. Rev. D 100 (2019) 124047.

On the semiclassical and quantum picture of the Bianchi I polymer dynamics

E. Giovannetti*

Department of Physics, La Sapienza University of Rome, Rome, Italy
*Speaker. E-mail: eleonora.giovannetti@uniroma1.it

G. Montani

Department of Physics, La Sapienza University of Rome, Rome, Italy
Fusion and Nuclear Safety Department, ENEA, Frascati (RM), Italy

S. Schiattarella

Department of Physics, La Sapienza University of Rome, Rome, Italy

We analyze the Bianchi I cosmology in the presence of a massless scalar field and describe its dynamics via a semiclassical and quantum polymer approach. We investigate the morphology of the emerging Big Bounce by adopting three different sets of configurational variables: the natural Ashtekar connections, the Universe volume plus two anisotropy coordinates and a set of anisotropic volume-like coordinates (the latter two sets of variables would coincide in the case of an isotropic Universe). In the semiclassical analysis we demonstrate that the Big Bounce emerges in the dynamics for all the three sets of variables. Moreover, when the Universe volume itself is considered as a configurational variable, we have derived the polymer-modified Friedmann equation and demonstrated that the Big Bounce has a universal nature, *i.e.* the total critical energy density has a maximum value fixed by fundamental constants and the Immirzi parameter only. From a pure quantum point of view, we investigate the Bianchi I dynamics only in terms of the Ashtekar connections. In particular, we apply the Arnowitt–Deser–Misner (ADM) reduction of the variational principle and then we quantize the system. We study the resulting Schrödinger dynamics, stressing that the wave packet peak behavior over time singles out common features with the semiclassical trajectories.

Keywords: Polymer Quantum Mechanics; Polymer Cosmology; Bianchi I Universe; Ashtekar variables.

1. INTRODUCTION

The emergence of a Big Bounce in the quantum dynamics of the isotropic Universe is one of the most relevant result achieved in Loop Quantum Cosmology (LQC) as a phenomenological implication of Loop Quantum Gravity (LQG)[1,2] when applied to the cosmological sector.[3–9] Although, many criticisms have been expressed towards the LQC framework, especially regarding the lack of a real quantum description of the Big Bounce properties, the unclear equivalence between the so-called improved scheme with the original LQC formulation in the Ashtekar variables and the process through which the symmetry reduction is performed in order to properly derive LQC as the cosmological sector of LQG.[10] In this context, Polymer Quantum Mechanics (PQM)[11,12] represents a convenient mathematical instrument through which deeply analyze bouncing cosmologies, since it is able to reproduce LQC results at least at an effective level and without entering the issues of LQG and LQC. In this work we apply PQM to the Bianchi I model in the presence of a massless scalar field and we explore both its semiclassical and quantum dynamics in different sets of configurational variables,[12] in particular the natural Ashtekar connections and two different sets of volume-like variables (the anisotropic volume-like coordinates and the Universe volume itself plus two anisotropies), following the LQC formulation in.[13,14]

The paper is structured as follows. In Sec. 2 the theory of PQM is introduced, while the original part of the paper is developed in Secs. 3–5. In particular, in Secs. 3 and 4 it is solved the semiclassical polymer dynamics of the Bianchi I model in the Ashtekar variables and in the two sets of volume-like variables respectively, then in Sec. 5 a full quantum treatment in the Ashtekar variables is developed using a Scrödinger-like formalism. Finally, in Sec. 6 some concluding remarks are commented.

2. POLYMER QUANTUM MECHANICS

PQM is a non-equivalent representation of quantum mechanics with respect to the standard Schrödinger one[12] and is based on the assumption that one or more variables of the phase space are discretized.

Firstly, we consider a set of abstract kets $|\mu\rangle$ with $\mu \in \mathbb{R}$ with the inner product $\langle \mu | \nu \rangle = \delta_{\mu\nu}$, where $\delta_{\mu\nu}$ is a Kronecker delta. This procedure defines the non-separable Hilbert space H_{poly} where two fundamental operators can be introduced: the *label* operator $\hat{\epsilon}$, whose action on the kets is given by $\hat{\epsilon}|\mu\rangle = \mu|\mu\rangle$, and the *shift* operator $\hat{s}(\lambda)$ ($\lambda \in \mathbb{R}$), where $\hat{s}(\lambda) = |\mu + \lambda\rangle$. The action of $\hat{s}(\lambda)$ is discontinuous since the kets are orthonormal $\forall \lambda$. In this sense, the set of kets indexed by μ is said to be discrete.

Now, we consider a one-dimensional system identified by the coordinates (q, p) and we suppose that the coordinate q has a discrete character. In the p-polarization the wave function writes as ($\hbar = 1$) $\psi_\mu(p) = \langle p|\mu\rangle = e^{ip\mu}$, the action of the operator $\hat{q}$ is differential and in particular coincident with the label operator. Its eigenvalues are precisely the μ parameters and constitute a discrete set. On the other hand, in this polarization the shift operator acts in a multiplicative way as

$$\hat{s}(\lambda)\psi_\mu(p) = e^{i\lambda p}e^{i\mu p} = \psi_{(\mu+\lambda)}(p). \tag{1}$$

As already mentioned, its action is discontinuous; therefore, we must conclude that the operator $\hat{p}$ does not exist since it is not possible to obtain a discontinuous operator from the exponentiation of a Hermitian one. Similar conclusions are reached by analyzing the structure of the q-polarization. Indeed, defining the variable q as discrete implies the non-existence of the operator $\hat{p}$, which must be regularized in order to deal with a well-defined dynamics. In order to overcome this issue, we introduce a regular graph $\gamma_{\mu_0} = \{q \in \mathbb{R} \,|\, q = n\mu_0, \forall n \in \mathbb{Z}\}$, *i.e.* a numerable set of equidistant points whose spacing is given by the scale μ_0, and we restrict the action of the shift operator $e^{i\lambda p}$ by imposing $\lambda = n\mu_0$ in order to remain in the lattice. Its action is well-defined, so we use it to approximate any function of p in the following way:

$$p \approx \frac{1}{\mu_0} \sin(\mu_0 p) = \frac{1}{2i\mu_0} \left(e^{i\mu_0 p} - e^{-i\mu_0 p} \right). \tag{2}$$

We notice that this approximation is good for $\mu_0 p \ll 1$. Under this hypothesis, the action of the regularized $\hat{p}$ operator is

$$\hat{p}_{\mu_0} |\mu_n\rangle = -\frac{i}{2\mu_0} (|\mu_{n+1}\rangle - |\mu_{n-1}\rangle). \tag{3}$$

In the original part of the paper we will apply this picture to the configurational variables describing the Bianchi I cosmology. The interest we have in using a representation of quantum mechanics characterized by a discrete configurational variable relies in investigating cut-off effects on geometrical quantities and hence on the cosmological dynamics.

3. SEMICLASSICAL POLYMER DYNAMICS OF THE BIANCHI I MODEL IN THE ASHTEKAR VARIABLES

In this section we firstly investigate the semiclassical polymer dynamics of the Bianchi I model in terms of the Ashtekar variables. The phase space is six-dimensional and it is expressed through the canonical couple (c_i, p_j), which link with the scale factors a_i and their velocities is

$$p_i = |\epsilon_{ijk} a_j a_k| \text{sign}(a_i), \quad c_i = \gamma \dot{a}_i, \tag{4}$$

with $i = 1, 2, 3$ and $\{c_i, p_j\} = \kappa \gamma \delta_{ij}$. In order to implement the polymer paradigm, we proceed by imposing the polymer substitution for the Ashtekar connections

$$c_i \to \frac{1}{\mu_i} \sin(\mu_i c_i), \tag{5}$$

so the polymer Hamiltonian constraint with a massless scalar field takes the form

$$\mathcal{H}_{poly} = -\frac{1}{\kappa \gamma^2 V} \sum_{i \neq j} \frac{\sin(\mu_i c_i) p_i \sin(\mu_j c_j) p_j}{\mu_i \mu_j} + \frac{p_\phi^2}{2V} = 0, \tag{6}$$

where $i, j = 1, 2, 3$ and $V = \sqrt{p_1 p_2 p_3}$. This way, we have chosen to define the variables p_i on three independent polymer lattices (with spacing μ_i respectively) due to their geometrical character. We also choose ϕ as the internal time, so N is fixed by the gauge $N = \frac{\sqrt{p_1 p_2 p_3}}{p_\phi}$, so that the equations of motion in the polymer representation are:

$$\begin{cases} \dfrac{dp_i}{d\phi} = -\dfrac{p_i \cos(\mu_i c_i)}{\gamma p_\phi} \left[\dfrac{p_j}{\mu_j} \sin(\mu_j c_j) + \dfrac{p_k}{\mu_k} \sin(\mu_k c_k) \right] \\ \dfrac{dc_i}{d\phi} = \dfrac{\sin(\mu_i c_i)}{\gamma \mu_i p_\phi} \left[\dfrac{p_j}{\mu_j} \sin(\mu_j c_j) + \dfrac{p_k}{\mu_k} \sin(\mu_k c_k) \right] \end{cases} \tag{7}$$

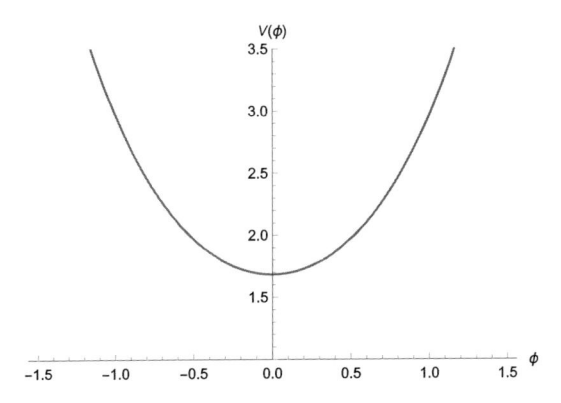

Fig. 1. Polymer trajectory of the Universe volume $V = \sqrt{p_1 p_2 p_3}$ in function of time ϕ: the Big Bounce replaces the initial singularity of the Bianchi I model.

for $i, j, k = 1, 2, 3$, $i \neq j \neq k$. By identifying proper constants of motion, the equations in (7) can be decoupled and the system can be analytically solved. In particular, in Fig. 1 it is shown the behavior of the Universe volume $V(\phi) = \sqrt{p_1(\phi) p_2(\phi) p_3(\phi)}$ as function of ϕ. The resulting trajectory highlights that a semiclassical Big Bounce replaces the classical Big Bang in the polymer framework.

4. SEMICLASSICAL POLYMER DYNAMICS OF THE BIANCHI I MODEL IN THE VOLUME-LIKE VARIABLES

In this section we study the dynamics of the Bianchi I Universe for a new choice of variables. In particular, the anisotropic character of the Bianchi I model leads to the possibility of considering two different sets of volume-like variables, that coincide in the case of the isotropic model.

4.1. *Analysis in the anisotropic volume-like variables:* (V_1, V_2, V_3)

Firstly, we consider three equivalent generalized coordinates which correspond to the proper Universe volume in the isotropic limit only:[14]

$$V_i = \text{sign}(p_i)|p_i|^{\frac{3}{2}}, \qquad \eta_i = \frac{2c_i}{3\sqrt{|p_i|}}, \qquad (8)$$

where η_i for $i = 1, 2, 3$ are the conjugate momenta and the new symplectic structure for the system is characterized by the Poisson brackets $\{\eta_i, V_j\} = \kappa\gamma\delta_{ij}$.

After that the canonical transformation has been performed, we obtain the polymer Hamiltonian constraint in the new variables by using the polymer substitution for the momenta η_i, since the variables V_i live on the corresponding polymer lattices. It reads as

$$\mathcal{H}_{poly} = -\frac{9}{4\kappa\gamma^2 V} \sum_{i \neq j} \frac{V_i \sin(\mu_i \eta_i) V_j \sin(\mu_j \eta_j)}{\mu_i \mu_j} + \frac{p_\phi^2}{2V} = 0, \qquad (9)$$

where $i,j = 1,2,3$ and $V = (V_1 V_2 V_3)^{\frac{1}{3}}$. Analogously, we impose $N = \frac{V}{p_\phi}$ due to the choice of ϕ as relational time, so the Hamilton equations describing the dynamics are

$$\begin{cases} \dfrac{dV_i}{d\phi} = -\dfrac{9 V_i \cos(\mu_i \eta_i)}{4\gamma p_\phi} \left[\dfrac{V_j}{\mu_j} \sin(\mu_j \eta_j) + \dfrac{V_k}{\mu_k} \sin(\mu_k \eta_k) \right] \\ \dfrac{d\eta_i}{d\phi} = \dfrac{9 \sin(\mu_i \eta_i)}{4\gamma \mu_1 p_\phi} \left[\dfrac{V_j}{\mu_j} \sin(\mu_j \eta_j) + \dfrac{V_k}{\mu_k} \sin(\mu_k \eta_k) \right] \end{cases} \quad (10)$$

for $i \neq j \neq k$. In analogy with the previous treatment, we can identify proper constants of motion that decouple the system (10) along the three directions.

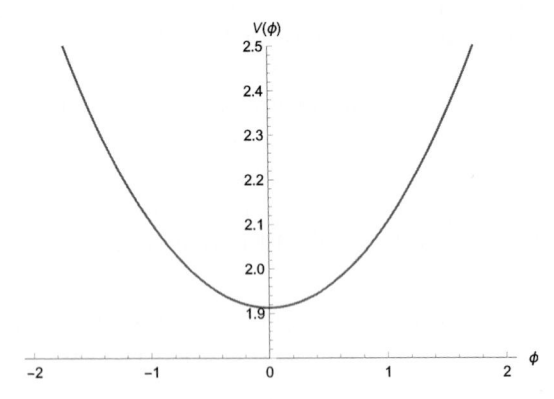

Fig. 2. Semiclassical polymer trajectory of the Universe volume $V = (V_1 V_2 V_3)^{1/3}$ as function of ϕ.

By taking general initial conditions according to (9), analytical solutions for the anisotropic volume coordinates can be gained. In particular, the Universe volume as function of ϕ reads as $V(\phi) = (V_1(\phi) V_2(\phi) V_3(\phi))^{1/3}$ and its behavior is shown in Fig. 2. The Big Bounce clearly appears as a polymer regularization effect instead of the classical Big Bang.

4.2. *Analysis in the volume variables:* $(v, \lambda_1, \lambda_2)$

In the new set of volume variables $(\lambda_i = \text{sign}(p_i)\sqrt{|p_i|},\ v = \lambda_1 \lambda_2 \lambda_3)$ the Universe volume itself v is considered and $\eta_{1,2} = 2\sqrt{p_{1,2}} c_{1,2}$, $\eta_3 = 2\sqrt{\frac{p_3}{p_1 p_2}} c_3$ are the conjugate momenta. The Poisson brackets are conserved ($\{\eta_i, \lambda_j\} = \kappa \gamma \delta_{ij}$ for $i \neq j$, $i,j = 1,2$ and $\{\eta_3, v\} = \kappa \gamma$) and the semiclassical polymer Hamiltonian takes the form

$$\mathcal{H}_{poly} = -\frac{1}{4\kappa\gamma^2 V} \left(\sum_{i=1,2} \frac{\lambda_i \sin(\mu_i \eta_i) v \sin(\mu_3 \eta_3)}{\mu_i \mu_3} + \frac{\lambda_1 \sin(\mu_1 \eta_1) \lambda_2 \sin(\mu_2 \eta_2)}{\mu_1 \mu_2} \right) + \frac{p_\phi^2}{2V} = 0,$$
(11)

where the canonical transformation has been performed before the implementation of the semiclassical polymer paradigm on the variables η_i, as in the previous subsection. Analogously, we derive the Hamilton equations for the couple of variables (v, η_3)

$$\begin{cases} \dfrac{dv}{d\phi} = -\dfrac{v\cos(\mu_3\eta_3)}{4\gamma p_\phi}\left[\dfrac{\lambda_1}{\mu_1}\sin(\mu_1\eta_1) + \dfrac{\lambda_2}{\mu_2}\sin(\mu_2\eta_2)\right] \\ \dfrac{d\eta_3}{d\phi} = \dfrac{\sin(\mu_3\eta_3)}{4\gamma\mu_3 p_\phi}\left[\dfrac{\lambda_1}{\mu_1}\sin(\mu_1\eta_1) + \dfrac{\lambda_2}{\mu_2}\sin(\mu_2\eta_2)\right] \end{cases} \quad (12)$$

and also for the conjugate variables (λ_1, η_1), (λ_2, η_2)

$$\begin{cases} \dfrac{d\lambda_i}{d\phi} = -\dfrac{\lambda_i\cos(\mu_i\eta_i)}{4\gamma p_\phi}\left[\dfrac{v}{\mu_3}\sin(\mu_3\eta_3) + \dfrac{\lambda_j}{\mu_j}\sin(\mu_j\eta_j)\right] \\ \dfrac{d\eta_i}{d\phi} = \dfrac{\sin(\mu_i\eta_i)}{4\gamma\mu_i p_\phi}\left[\dfrac{v}{\mu_3}\sin(\mu_3\eta_3) + \dfrac{\lambda_j}{\mu_j}\sin(\mu_j\eta_j)\right] \end{cases} \quad (13)$$

where we have used $N = \frac{V}{p_\phi}$ in order to derive the dynamics of the model in function of the relational time ϕ.

Once fixed the initial conditions on the variables (λ_1, η_1), (λ_2, η_2), (v, η_3) according to (11), we can solve this system analytically since the 3D-motion is decoupled in three one-dimensional trajectories, thanks to the use of constants of motion analogous to those ones of the previous cases. In particular, the analytical solution for the Universe volume $v(\phi)$ clearly resembles a bouncing behavior, as shown in Fig. 3. Also, by choosing a particular shape for these constants of motion, we find the following convenient form for the polymer-modified Friedmann equation of the Bianchi I model in the proper volume variables:

$$H^2 = \frac{\kappa}{54}\frac{p_\phi^2 + \bar{\mathcal{K}}^2}{v^2}\left[1 - \frac{4\kappa\gamma^2\mu^2}{3}\left(\frac{p_\phi^2 + \bar{\mathcal{K}}^2}{2v^2}\right)\right], \quad \bar{\mathcal{K}} = \frac{\mathcal{K}}{\sqrt{2\kappa\gamma^2}}, \quad (14)$$

where we have fixed $\mu_1 = \mu_2 = \mu_3 = \mu$ without loss of generality. In (14), the additional term $\bar{\mathcal{K}}^2/2v^2$ reasonably mimics the energy-like contribution of the

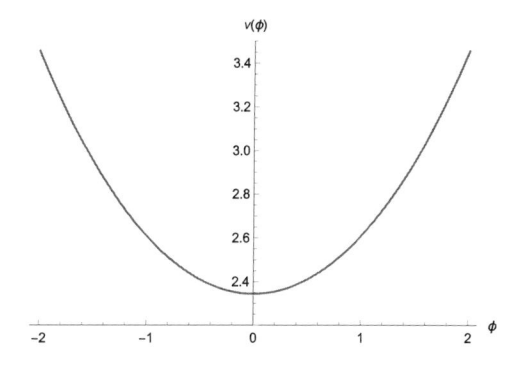

Fig. 3. Semiclassical polymer trajectory of the Universe volume $v(\phi)$.

anisotropies to the total energy density ($\mathcal{K}$ is an arbitrary constant) and the total critical energy density results to be

$$\rho_{crit}^{tot} = \frac{3}{4\kappa\gamma^2\mu^2}, \qquad (15)$$

so it has universal features since it is independent from the initial conditions on the motion. By concluding, thanks to equation (14) we have inferred the physical properties of the critical point, showing that taking the Universe volume itself as a configurational variable makes the Big Bounce acquire universal physical properties.

5. QUANTUM ANALYSIS

The purpose of this section is studying the Bianchi I model in the Ashtekar variables at a quantum level by applying the Dirac quantization. Firstly, we perform an ADM reduction of the variational principle at a semiclassical level in order to deal with a Schrödinger-like formalism. More specifically, after choosing the scalar field ϕ as the temporal parameter, we derive the ADM-Hamiltonian by solving the scalar constraint (6) with respect to the momentum associated to the scalar field:

$$p_\phi \equiv \mathcal{H}_{ADM} = \sqrt{\Theta}, \qquad \Theta = \frac{2}{\kappa\gamma^2}\sum_{i\neq j}\frac{\sin(\mu_i c_i)p_i \sin(\mu_j c_j)p_j}{\mu_i\mu_j}, \qquad (16)$$

where $i, j = 1, 2, 3$. We choose the positive root in order to guarantee the positive character of the lapse function (see Sec. 3). Now we promote the ADM-Hamiltonian to a quantum operator, obtaining the following Schrödinger-like equation:

$$-i\partial_\phi\Psi = \sqrt{\hat{\Theta}}\Psi, \qquad \sqrt{\hat{\Theta}} = \left[\frac{2}{\kappa^2\gamma^2}\left(\partial_{x_1}\partial_{x_2} + \partial_{x_1}\partial_{x_3} + \partial_{x_2}\partial_{x_3}\right)\right]^{1/2}, \qquad (17)$$

where we have used the substitution $x_i = \ln\left[\tan\left(\frac{\mu c_i}{2}\right)\right] + \bar{x}_i$. The associated probability density is $\mathcal{P}(\vec{x}, \phi) = \Psi^*(\vec{x}, \phi)\Psi(\vec{x}, \phi)$, where

$$\Psi(\vec{x}, \phi) = \int_{-\infty}^{\infty} dk_1\, dk_2\, dk_3 \prod_{i=1}^{3} \exp\left[-\frac{(k_i - \mu_{k_i})^2}{2\sigma_{k_i}^2}\right]$$

$$\times e^{i(k_1 x_1 + k_2 x_2 + k_3 x_3 + \sqrt{2|k_1 k_2 + k_1 k_3 + k_2 k_3|}\phi)}. \qquad (18)$$

Now we can analyze the quantum dynamics of (18) by following the peak of the probability density $\mathcal{P}$ over time, in order to verify the consistency between the information carried by the quantum wave packet of the Bianchi I model and the semiclassical solutions provided in Sec. 3 when the Ashtekar variables are considered. In Fig. 4 some different sections of the probability density $\mathcal{P}$ at different values of ϕ are shown. As we can see, their spreading behavior over time is evident, as well as their gaussian-like shape. Also, in Fig. 5 the position of the peaks of $\mathcal{P}$ are represented by the red dots and have also been fitted by means of a linear interpolation. The resulting fitting functions are represented by the red dashed straight lines, while the semiclassical trajectories by the continuous straight ones. In particular,

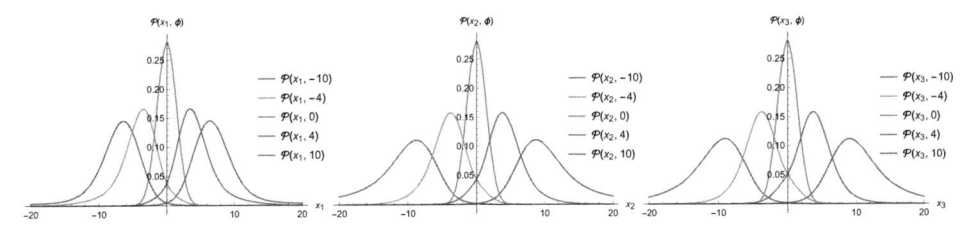

Fig. 4. The normalized sections $\mathcal{P}(x_i, \phi)$ are shown in sequence for $i = 1, 2, 3$ respectively at different times (here $\mu_{k_1} = \mu_{k_2} = \mu_{k_3} = 0, \sigma_{k_1} = \sigma_{k_2} = \sigma_{k_3} = 1/2$). Their spreading behavior over time is evident together with the gaussian-like shape.

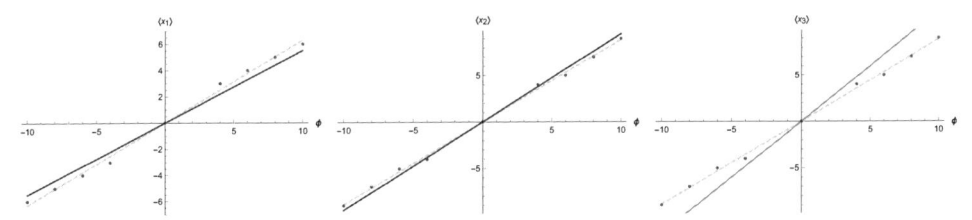

Fig. 5. The three pictures show the position of the peaks of $\mathcal{P}(x_i, \phi)$ for $i = 1, 2, 3$ respectively in function of time ϕ (red dots). The resulting fitting functions (red dashed straight lines) overlap the semiclassical trajectories (continuous lines) with a confidence level of three standard deviations.

the slope of the fitting straight lines is consistent with the semiclassical one with a confidence level of three standard deviations for all the three coordinates. Therefore, we conclude that there is a good correspondence between the quantum behavior of the Universe wave function and the solutions of the semiclassical dynamics.

6. CONCLUDING REMARKS

In this paper we analyzed the polymer semiclassical and quantum dynamics of the Bianchi I model with a massless scalar field in the Ashtekar variables and in two sets of volume-like ones. In the polymer semiclassical analysis we obtained a bouncing behavior in all the three sets of variables. Also, a polymer-modified Friedmann equation of the Bianchi I model has been derived when the Universe volume itself is considered as a configurational variable. This way, the proper expression of the total critical energy density has been provided, giving a complete picture of the Big Bounce and showing its universal features, *i.e.* its dependence from fundamental constants and parameters only. Finally, by performing an ADM reduction of the variational problem, we passed to a Schrödinger-like formalism and then we implemented the canonical quantization in the Ashtekar variables. In particular, the study of the probability density behavior has outlined a good correspondence between the dynamics of the quantum Universe wave packet and the corresponding semiclassical trajectories. In conclusion, due to the role of the Bianchi I model in constructing the general cosmological solution, this study acquires a great relevance in order to understand the properties of the primordial Universe.

References

1. C. Rovelli and F. Vidotto, *Covariant Loop Quantum Gravity: an Elementary Introduction to Quantum Gravity and Spinfoam Theory* (Cambridge University Press, 2014).
2. F. Cianfrani, O. M. Lecian, M. Lulli and G. Montani, *Canonical Quantum Gravity* (World Scientific, 2014).
3. A. Ashtekar, M. Bojowald, J. Lewandowski et al., Mathematical Structure of Loop Quantum Cosmology, *Advances in Theoretical and Mathematical Physics* **7** (2003).
4. A. Ashtekar, Gravity and the Quantum, *New Journal of Physics* **7** (2005).
5. A. Ashtekar, T. Pawlowski and P. Singh, Quantum nature of the big bang: An analytical and numerical investigation, *Physical Review D* **73** (Jun 2006).
6. A. Ashtekar, T. Pawlowski and P. Singh, Quantum nature of the big bang: Improved dynamics, *Physical Review D* **74** (Oct 2006).
7. A. Ashtekar, A. Corichi and P. Singh, Robustness of key features of Loop Quantum Cosmology, *Physical Review D* **77** (Jan 2008).
8. A. Ashtekar and P. Singh, Loop Quantum Cosmology: a Status Report, *Classical and Quantum Gravity* **28** (2011).
9. M. Bojowald, Loop Quantum Cosmology, *Living Reviews in Relativity* **11** (2008).
10. M. Bojowald, Critical evaluation of common claims in loop quantum cosmology, *Universe* **6**, p. 36 (Feb 2020).
11. A. Ashtekar, Polymer geometry at Planck scale and quantum Einstein equations, *International Journal of Modern Physics D* **05**, p. 629–648 (Dec 1996).
12. J. A. Z. Alejandro Corichi, Tatjana Vukasinac, Polymer Quantum Mechanics and its Continuum Limit, *Phys.Rev.* (2007).
13. A. Ashtekar and E. Wilson-Ewing, Loop Quantum Cosmology of Bianchi type I models, *Physical Review D* **79** (2009).
14. L. Szulc, Loop Quantum Cosmology of Diagonal Bianchi type I model: Simplifications and Scaling Problems, *Physical Review D* **78** (2008).

Quantum corrections to the Bianchi II transition under local rotational invariance

Sara F. Uria* and David Brizuela[†]

Fisika Saila, Universidad del País Vasco/Euskal Herriko Unibertsitatea, Barrio Sarriena s/n, 48940 Leioa, Spain
*E-mail: sara.fernandezu@ehu.eus
[†] E-mail: david.brizuela@ehu.eus

Ana Alonso-Serrano

Max-Planck-Institut für Gravitationsphysik, Am Mühlenberg 1, 14476 Potsdam, Germany
E-mail: ana.alonso.serrano@aei.mpg.de

A quantum state in a Bianchi II model is studied as it approaches the cosmological singularity, by means of the evolution of its moments. Classically this system presents a transition between two Bianchi I models. This phenomenon is described by a very specific and well-known transition law, which is derived based on the conservation of certain physical quantities. In the quantum theory fluctuations, as well as higher-order quantum moments, of the different variables arise. Consequently, these constants of motion are modified and hence also the transition rule. We focus on the so-called locally rotationally symmetric and vacuum case, as a first step towards a more complete study. Indeed, the future goal of this research line is to generalize this analysis to the Bianchi IX spacetime, which can be seen as a succession of Bianchi II models. Ultimately, these results will shed light on the role played by quantum effects in the BKL conjecture.

Keywords: Bianchi II; local rotational symmetry (LRS); quantum Bianchi spacetime; Bianchi transition.

1. Introduction

Close to a spacelike singularity, it is conjectured that the classical dynamics of any universe follows a chaotic behavior, according to Belinski-Khalatnikov-Lifshitz (BKL).[1] In this scenario, the dynamics of each point is decoupled from the rest and can be described by a Bianchi IX spacetime, which can be understood as a succession of Bianchi II models.[1] This model is much easier to analyze than the full Bianchi IX dynamics, and therefore provides a good first step to study the full BKL scenario. More precisely, as it was described in Misner's seminal work,[2] in the Bianchi II model the system undergoes a single transition between two Bianchi I models. However, close to the singularity quantum effects are expected to become relevant, and thus, in the present work we will analyze how they modify this classical transition.

2. Classical Model

A Bianchi II model is a type of spatially homogeneous but anisotropic four-dimensional spacetime. If we follow the usual 3+1 decomposition in order to describe the model canonically, the vacuum Hamiltonian constraint of this system is found to be

$$\mathcal{C} = \frac{1}{2}e^{-3\alpha}\left(-p_\alpha^2 + p_-^2 + p_+^2\right) + e^{\alpha - 8\beta_+} = 0, \quad (1)$$

where α describes the spatial volume and $\beta_\pm$ are the shape parameters that encode the spatial anisotropy of the spacetime. These are the so-called Misner variables and p_α and $p_\pm$ are their corresponding conjugate momenta. If α is chosen as the internal time, the physical Hamiltonian of the system takes the subsequent form:

$$H := -p_\alpha = \left(p_+^2 + p_-^2 + 2e^{4\alpha - 8\beta_+}\right)^{1/2}. \quad (2)$$

This is the most general vacuum description but, in order to further simplify the problem, we will remove one of the shape parameters by imposing $\beta_- = 0 = p_-$, which is known as the *locally rotationally symmetric* (LRS) case. Consequently, the Hamiltonian (2) is reduced to:

$$H = \left(p^2 + 2e^{4\alpha - 8\beta}\right)^{1/2}, \quad (3)$$

where, for compactness, $\beta := \beta_+$ and $p := p_+$ have been defined.

This model presents a singularity, even in the particular LRS case, precisely when $\alpha \to -\infty$. Hence, we will be interested in studying the evolution towards this limit. For this purpose, the first step is to obtain the equations of motion:

$$\dot{\beta} = \frac{p}{H}, \quad (4)$$

$$\dot{p} = \frac{8}{H}e^{4\alpha - 8\beta}, \quad (5)$$

where the dot represents the derivative with respect to the internal time α. From (4)-(5) we note that, when the exponential term $e^{4\alpha - 8\beta}$ is negligible, the equations of motion can easily be solved. Under such an assumption, p would be a constant of motion and, in this sense, the system would follow a free dynamics, whereas the shape-parameter β would be a linear function of α:

$$\beta = \text{sign}(p)\alpha + c, \quad (6)$$

with an integration constant c. During this period the system is equivalent to a LRS vacuum Bianchi I –or Kasner– solution. This Kasner regime is completely characterized by the values of the constants of motion p and c. As illustrated in Fig. 1 and Fig. 2, if we begin the evolution towards the singularity in one of these regimes, with $p > 0$ and at large values of α, the shape parameter β follows the linear behavior as given in (6) until the exponential term $e^{4\alpha - 8\beta}$ ceases to be negligible. At that point, a transition happens and the system enters in another Kasner regime.

In order to study this transition, a useful procedure is to exploit the conserved quantities of the system. The mentioned constants of motions are found to be the following:

$$R_1 := 2H - p, \quad (7)$$

$$R_2 := e^{2(\alpha+\beta)}(H - p). \quad (8)$$

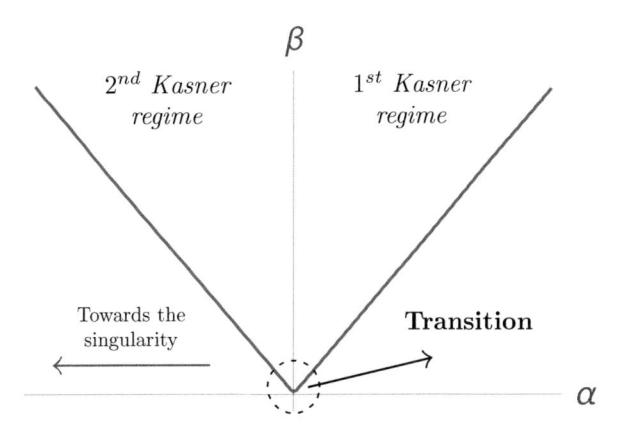

Fig. 1. Classical evolution of the variable β with respect to α, where $p > 0$ for large values of α and β.

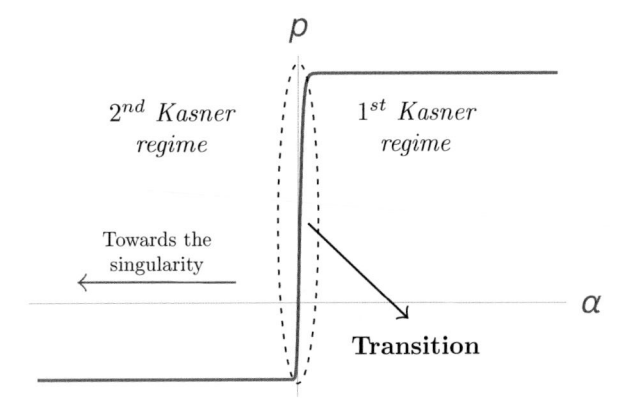

Fig. 2. Classical evolution of the variable p with respect to α, where $p > 0$ for large values of α and β.

If we evaluate these quantities in the initial and final states and equate them, we obtain a system of two equations, which relate the parameters of the first Kasner epoch $(\bar{c}, \bar{p})$ with those of the second one $(\tilde{c}, \tilde{p})$. Thus, after solving it we obtain the law that describes the transition between the two Kasner regimes, namely:

$$\tilde{p} = -\frac{1}{3}\bar{p}, \tag{9}$$

$$\tilde{c} = -3\bar{c} - \frac{1}{2}\ln\left(\frac{2}{3}\bar{p}^3\right). \tag{10}$$

3. Quantum Transition Rules

Once that we have provided a canonical description of the classical model, we are ready to develop the quantum analysis. The quantum dynamics is governed by the following Hamiltonian operator, which is defined from the classical one and chosen to be Weyl-ordered, that is, with a totally symmetric ordering of the basic operators:

$$\hat{H}(\hat{p}, \hat{\beta}) = \left(\hat{p}^2 + 2e^{4\alpha - 8\hat{\beta}}\right)^{1/2}_{\text{Weyl}}. \tag{11}$$

Then, instead of studying the evolution of the wave function itself, we follow a formalism developed for quantum cosmology and quantum mechanics in general, which is based on the moment decomposition of the wave function.[4] Thus, according to this formalism, the system is fully described by the expectation values of the basic variables,

$$\beta := \langle \hat{\beta} \rangle, \quad p = \langle \hat{p} \rangle, \tag{12}$$

as well as the following infinite set of quantum moments:

$$\Delta(\beta^i p^j) := \langle (\hat{\beta} - \beta)^i (\hat{p} - p)^j \rangle_{\text{Weyl}} \quad (i, j \in \mathbb{N}). \tag{13}$$

The sum of the indices $i + j$ will be referred as the order of the corresponding moment. The evolution of these variables is ruled by a quantum effective Hamiltonian H_Q, that is defined as the expectation value of $\hat{H}$. By performing a Taylor expansion around the expectation values of $\hat{\beta}$ and $\hat{p}$, it can be written as the following infinite series:

$$H_Q = \langle \hat{H}(\hat{p}, \hat{\beta}) \rangle \tag{14}$$

$$= H(\beta, p) + \sum_{i+j=2}^{\infty} \frac{1}{i! j!} \frac{\partial^{i+j} H(\beta, p)}{\partial \beta^i \partial p^j} \Delta(\beta^i p^j),$$

where $H(\beta, p)$ is the classical Hamiltonian (3). This effective Hamiltonian H_Q encodes the complete dynamical information of the system. Indeed, the equations of motion for the variables of the system –β, p and $\Delta(\beta^i p^j)$– are obtained by computing their Poisson brackets with H_Q:

$$\frac{d\beta}{d\alpha} = \{\beta, H_Q\} = \frac{\partial H_Q}{\partial p}, \tag{15}$$

$$\frac{dp}{d\alpha} = \{p, H_Q\} = -\frac{\partial H_Q}{\partial \beta}, \tag{16}$$

$$\frac{d\Delta(\beta^i p^j)}{d\alpha} = \{\Delta(\beta^i p^j), H_Q\} \tag{17}$$

$$= \sum_{m,n=0}^{+\infty} \frac{1}{m! n!} \frac{\partial^{m+n} H(\beta, p)}{\partial \beta^m \partial p^n} \{\Delta(\beta^i p^j), \Delta(\beta^m p^n)\},$$

where the Poisson brackets between expectation values are defined in the usual way in terms of the commutator, that is, $\{\langle \hat{A} \rangle, \langle \hat{B} \rangle\} := -i\langle [\hat{A}, \hat{B}] \rangle / \hbar$. Let us emphasize that this evolution of the variables is completely equivalent to that given by the Schrödinger picture in terms of the wave function.

We observe that the classical Hamiltonian H defined in (3) is not polynomial, which means that the series in (14) is indeed infinite and it is not truncated at certain order. Thus, the equations of motion (15)-(17) form an infinite system of coupled equations. Therefore, in order to study and compute the dynamics explicitly, a cut-off must be introduced. That is, we will consider all the moments of order higher than a certain value N to be vanishing:

$$\Delta(\beta^i p^j) \approx 0 \text{ for } i+j > N. \qquad (18)$$

In fact, such a truncation corresponds to considering a semiclassical regime, where the quantum state is peaked on a classical trajectory and hence the high-order moments are negligible.

However, even if we apply a cut-off, instead of solving the coupled system of equations for any value of α, we will focus on the so-called Kasner regimes, as we have done in the classical analysis. During these periods, the equations of motion take the form

$$\frac{d\beta}{d\alpha} \approx \text{sign}(p), \quad \frac{dp}{d\alpha} \approx 0, \quad \frac{d\Delta(\beta^i p^j)}{d\alpha} \approx 0, \qquad (19)$$

which are immediate to solve:

$$\beta \approx \text{sign}(p)\alpha + c, \qquad (20)$$

$$p \approx const., \qquad (21)$$

$$\Delta(\beta^i p^j) \approx const., \qquad (22)$$

with an integration constant c. Comparing these results with the classical ones, we observe that the behavior of p and β in these states remains identical in the quantum analysis. Moreover, the moments hold a constant value. In summary, the parameters that characterize each quantum Kasner epoch will be, as in the classical case, the constants c and p, along with the infinite constant set of moments $\Delta(\beta^i p^j)$. Then, in order to analyze the transition between two of these quantum Kasner regimes, we will once again exploit the constants of motion. In this quantum scenario, the conserved quantities are found to be the expectation values $\langle \hat{R}_1 \rangle$ and $\langle \hat{R}_2 \rangle$, where $\hat{R}_1$ and $\hat{R}_2$ are the operator counterpart of the classical conserved quantities (7) and (8). In fact, any of the following combinations is also a constant of motion:

$$\langle \hat{R}_i^n \hat{R}_j^m \rangle = const., \text{ for } m, n \in \mathbb{N} \text{ and } i, j \in \{1, 2\}. \qquad (23)$$

Nonetheless, as a technical subtlety, it must be mentioned that the choice of ordering of these operators is far from trivial: one must find the proper ordering so that they are conserved. Furthermore, at higher orders in moments, there may appear some terms that go with some explicit powers of $\hbar$. A more detailed discussion about these issues can be found in.[3]

Based on the classical results, we will consider that we have an initial Kasner regime characterized by the parameters $(\bar{c}, \bar{p}, \overline{\Delta(\beta^i p^j)})$ and that, as we approach the singularity, another such regime is reached described by the parameters $(\widetilde{c}, \widetilde{p}, \widetilde{\Delta(\beta^i p^j)})$. Hence, if we evaluate the constants of motion in these two states and equate them, we obtain a system of algebraic equations that relate the different parameters. After solving this system, we get the quantum transition law, which takes the following form:

$$\widetilde{p} = -\frac{1}{3}\bar{p}, \tag{24}$$

$$\widetilde{c} = -3\bar{c} - \frac{1}{2}\ln\left(\frac{2\bar{p}^2}{3}\right) + \sum_{n=2}^{N} \frac{(-1)^n}{n\bar{p}^n} \overline{\Delta(p^n)}, \tag{25}$$

$$\widetilde{\Delta(\beta^m p^n)} = \sum_{l=0}^{N-(m+n)} \sum_{k=0}^{m} \frac{a_{mnkl}}{\bar{p}^{m+l-k}} \overline{\Delta(\beta^k p^{m+n+l-k})} \tag{26}$$

$$+ \sum_{r=2}^{N-2} \sum_{k=0}^{m-1} \sum_{l=l_{min}}^{l_{max}} \frac{b_{mnklr}}{\bar{p}^{m+r+l-k}} \overline{\Delta(p^r)}\, \overline{\Delta(\beta^k p^{m+n+l-k})} + \sum_{k=1}^{\lfloor N/4 \rfloor} \frac{c_{mnk}}{\bar{p}^{2k-n}} \hbar^{2k},$$

where N denotes the order of the truncation. On the one hand, as can be seen from (24), the transition law for p remains identical as the classical one. However, we do obtain some quantum corrections for the transition law of β, as can be seen by comparing (10) with (25). Nevertheless, as expected, if all the moments are set to zero we recover the classical transition law. On the other hand, the transition law for the moments can be written in the compact form (26), with certain numerical coefficients a_{mnkl}, b_{mnklr} and c_{mnk}. Up to fifth order in moments, we have obtained the explicit expression of these coefficients and we refer the reader to[3] for the detailed expressions. If we analyze this formula in detail, we observe that it is linear in all of the moments except for some quadratic terms that contain pure moments of p. Moreover, regardless of the order of the truncation, there is a strong dependence on the index m of the shape parameter β of the corresponding moment. In particular, this index determines which initial moments will directly affect the value of a given final moment. For instance, the value of $\widetilde{\Delta(p^n)}$ (which corresponds to $m = 0$) only depends on the initial pure p-moments $\overline{\Delta(p^n)}$. Nevertheless, the value of $\widetilde{\Delta(\beta p^n)}$, that is $m = 1$, depends not only on pure p-moments, but also on $\overline{\Delta(\beta p^n)}$. In general, the value of the final moment $\widetilde{\Delta(\beta^m p^n)}$ will depend on the initial moments $\overline{\Delta(\beta^j p^i)}$ with $j \leq m$.

4. Quantum Dynamics

Once we have studied the asymptotic characteristics of this model in the Kasner regimes, we complete it by performing a numerical analysis to examine in detail its dynamical evolution. For this purpose, we have chosen an initial Gaussian state, namely

$$\overline{\Delta(\beta^{2m}p^{2n})} = 2^{-2(m+n)}\hbar^{2m}\sigma^{2(n-m)}\frac{(2m)!(2n)!}{m!n!}, \qquad (27)$$

for $\forall m, n \in \mathbb{N}$, and vanishing otherwise. As expected, the numerical study shows that starting from high values of α and evolving towards lower ones, the system follows the Kasner dynamics until it undergoes a transition, which happens near $\alpha = 0$. This transition takes place in a very small period of time and then the system reaches its final equilibrium value –the final Kasner regime– very quickly.

Regarding the evolution of the expectation values p and β, we remark that they remain almost identical as in the classical case, that is, as depicted in Fig. 1 and Fig. 2. In fact, only in a very close zoom into the transition (near $\alpha = 0$) we can appreciate a slight modification in their evolution: quantum effects slightly increase the value of p and β during the transition.

Moreover, the evolution of the moments show that during the initial Kasner regime they hold a constant value, at certain point they begin to perform strong oscillations and then quickly relax to their final constant value, which characterizes the coherent state during the final Kasner regime. The precise dynamics of the moments are quite complicate but, if we look into the transition in more detail, some general features can be detected. For instance, we remark that the higher the index of p, the earlier the moments reach their final equilibrium value. Furthermore, we observe that the lower the order of a given moment, the sooner it starts to oscillate and with a larger amplitude, which is in agreement with the semiclassical hierarchy of moments we are assuming. More specifically, at each given order the pure fluctuations of p show the biggest amplitudes. In addition, moments with at least one odd index, $i.e.$, the initially vanishing ones, present more oscillations.

It is particularly interesting to observe that the moments that were vanishing in the initial Kasner epoch –due to the choice of the Gaussian state– are not vanishing in the final one, due to the mentioned oscillations. This is indeed an expected outcome according to the transition laws (26). However, it means that even when we choose an initial state where there are no correlations between β and p, the transition will generate correlations for the final state. In particular, all the initial vanishing moments are activated in a similar way: as they approach the transition they experience an excitation and start to grow exponentially, until they begin to oscillate.

5. Conclusions

In summary, we have described the quantum LRS Bianchi II model making use of a decomposition of the wave function into its infinite set of moments. For the classical case, we have obtained the explicit constants of motion for the full dynamics, and thus we have completely integrated the equations of motion. For the quantum case, making use of the conserved quantities (23), we have been able to obtain the exact quantum transition law for every variable (24)-(26) up to fifth-order in moments. Furthermore, by performing a numerical analysis of the model, we have studied the dynamical part of the evolution. In particular we have focused on the region where the transition takes place, and we have derived some general features of the behavior of the different variables. The follow-up of this work is to remove the LRS symmetry and to study the most general Bianchi II model. Then, the next step will be to extend the analysis to the full Bianchi IX model, and ultimately, to obtain the quantum corrections to the BKL transitions.

Acknowledgments

SFU acknowledges financial support from an FPU fellowship of the Spanish Ministry of Universities. AA-S is supported by the ERC Advanced Grant No. 740209. This work is funded by Projects FIS2017-85076-P and PID2020-118159GB-C44 (MICINN/AEI/FEDER, UE), and by Basque Government Grant No. IT956-16.

References

1. V. A. Belinskii, I. M. Khalatnikov and E. M. Lifschitz, A general solution of the Einstein equations with a time singularity, *Adv. Phys.* **13**, 639 (1982).
2. C. W. Misner, Mixmaster Universe, *Phys. Rev. Lett.* **22**,1071 (1969).
3. A. Alonso-Serrano, D. Brizuela and S. F. Uria, Quantum Kasner transition in a locally rotationally symmetric Bianchi II universe, *Phys. Rev. D* **104**, 024006 (2021).
4. M. Bojowald and A. Skirzewski, Effective equations of motion for quantum system, *Rev. Math. Phys.* **18**, 713 (2006).

The hypercomplex medium as storage of physical equations

Alexander P. Yefremov

Institute of Gravitation and Cosmology, RUDN University,
6 Miklukho-Maklay Street, Moscow, 117198 Russian Federation,
E-mail: efremov-ap@rudn.ru
www.rudn.ru

Using the quaternion framework (Q-math), we show that the specific mathematical equations born in "quaternion medium" in physical units become known physical laws. In particular, it is shown how one can discover immanently hidden "geometric physical laws": Cartesian frames, equations of electrodynamics, Q-vector formulation of the relativity theory. One can also find the linked logical chain between laws of quantum, classical, and relativistic mechanics.

Keywords: Hypercomplex numbers; Quaternions; Fundamental equations.

1. Introduction: Hypercomplex Numbers

We draw attention to the mathematics of hypercomplex (HC) numbers, which, by analogy with differential geometry so fruitful for modern physics, can serve as an exceptionally rich environment. The HC math set comprises, first of all, four "good" algebras of real, complex, quaternion (Q) and octonion numbers; the Frobenius-Hurwitz theorem states that these are the fundamental division algebras admitting the identities of squares (Table 1).

Table 1. Classical "good" HC algebras

Algebra of numbers	Symbol	Number of units (real, imaginary)	Coefficients at units	Multiplication	Division, identity of squares
Real	R	$2^0 = 1$ (1, 0)	real	commutative, associative	+
Complex	C	$2^1 = 2$ (1, 1)	real	commutative, associative	+
Quaternion	Q, H	$2^2 = 4$ (1, 3)	real	non-commut., associative	+
Octonion	O	$2^3 = 8$ (1, 7)	real	non-commut., non-assoc.	+

"Close in spirit" algebras of "not good" HC numbers: double (perplex, split-complex), dual, biquaternion numbers (all having zero dividers) must be also mentioned here because their units can be structured similarly to the units of "good" numbers.

These sets of HC numbers, together with their adjacent domains (spinor elements and related groups), deserve to be considered not only as suitable or helpful mathematical instruments but also as an environment in which physical laws (once discovered empirically or heuristically) turn out to be immanently contained.

Without loss of generality here we make an accent on the still associative but non-commutative algebra of quaternion (Q-) numbers. Nonetheless, under the term "Q-math set" we imply the Q-numbers, biquaternion (BQ) numbers, specific Q-spinor set, and relevant invariance groups. Due to Heaviside and Gibbs with their palliative vector algebra, the Q-math set was unfairly abandoned in XX century though rarely emerging just as an exotic math tool (see e.g. Ref. 1). However, firstly incidental findings and later systematic investigations demonstrated that the Q-set contains many geometric images and equations closely related to fundamental physics. Here is a brief review of the revealed Q-math – physical coincidences.

2. First Physical Findings in Q-Math

Discovered by W.R.Hamilton in 1843, Q-numbers are built on one real scalar unit 1 (normally omitted in formulas), and three non-commuting imaginary vector units $\mathbf{i}, \mathbf{j}, \mathbf{k} \equiv \mathbf{q}_n$; coefficients at the units a, b_n are real

$$q = a + b_1 i + b_2 j + b_3 k \equiv a + b_n \mathbf{q}_n. \tag{1}$$

The multiplication law for the units has the form

$$\mathbf{q}_k \mathbf{q}_n = -\delta_{kn} + \varepsilon_{knj} \mathbf{q}_j, \quad 1 \cdot \mathbf{q}_n = \mathbf{q}_n \cdot 1, \tag{2}$$

$\delta_{kn}, \varepsilon_{knj}$ are 3D Kronecker and Levi-Civita tensors, index summation rule is implied. This algebra appeared to be near as "good" as that of complex numbers. With the definition of conjugation $\bar{q} = a - b_n \mathbf{q}_n$ a Q-number may be endowed the norm $\|q\| \equiv q\bar{q} = \bar{q}q = a^2 + b_n b_n$, then the algebra admits division $(q_2/q_1)_{left} = \bar{q}_1 q_2 / \|q_1\|$ (right and left as multiplication) and comprises the identity of four squares $\|q_1 q_2\| = \|q_1\| \|q_2\|$.

2.1. *Cartesian frame*

Hamilton was the first to realize that Q-imaginary units automatically behave like three vectors initializing an orthogonal frame which was empirically postulated by Descartes two hundred years before; in fact, this observation appeared to be the first Q-math – Physics coincidence. However, the scalar unit until recently had no clear geometric image (see below).

2.2. *Electrodynamics*

The next finding occurs a century later. Nearly abandoned quaternions (due to the predominance of the "vector algebra"), nonetheless had their faithful supporters. One of them Rudolf Fueter considered ways to build a theory of functions of quaternion variables. In 1937 he published a series of papers (e.g., Ref. 2) where a Cauchi-Riemann-type differentiability condition

$$d_u \mathbf{F} \equiv \left(\frac{i}{c} \frac{\partial}{dt} - \mathbf{q}_n \frac{\partial}{dx_n} \right) \mathbf{F} = 0 \tag{3}$$

for a vector BQ-function $\mathbf{F}(u) = (H_k + iE_k)\mathbf{q}_k$ of a BQ-variable $u = -ict + x_n\mathbf{q}_n$ was postulated. It was a great surprise to reveal that Eq. (3) written in the form of "imaginary" and "real" parts (in the C-algebra sense)

$$d_u\mathbf{F} = \underbrace{\frac{i}{c}\frac{\partial H_k}{\partial t}\mathbf{q}_k - i\frac{\partial E_k}{\partial x_k} + \frac{\partial E_k}{\partial x_n}\varepsilon_{knj}\mathbf{q}_j}_{\text{"imaginary" part}} + \underbrace{\frac{1}{c}\frac{\partial E_k}{\partial t}\mathbf{q}_k + \frac{\partial H_k}{\partial x_k} - \frac{\partial H_k}{\partial x_n}\varepsilon_{knj}\mathbf{q}_j}_{\text{"real" part}}$$

eventually (in the Q-algebra sense) decays into four real equations which exactly coincide with the vacuum Maxwell equations of electrodynamics.

2.3. Pauli basis for Q-algebra

Here we must recall one more event concerning Q-math non-directly, but very important. In 1927 Pauli suggested his mechanical equation for a charged quantum particle in an exterior magnetic field. To describe spin-magnetic field interaction he heuristically introduced three traceless 2 × 2-matrices with determinants equal to -1. Later analysis showed that these matrices multiplied by $-i$ together with the unit 2 × 2-matrix form a set of Q-units identically obeying the product rule (2)

$$1 = \begin{pmatrix} 1 & 0 \\ 0 & 1 \end{pmatrix}, \quad \mathbf{q}_1 = -i\begin{pmatrix} 0 & 1 \\ 1 & 0 \end{pmatrix}, \quad \mathbf{q}_2 = -i\begin{pmatrix} 0 & -i \\ i & 0 \end{pmatrix}, \quad \mathbf{q}_3 = -i\begin{pmatrix} 1 & 0 \\ 0 & -1 \end{pmatrix}. \quad (4)$$

It is important to note that representation (4) is the simplest one but not unique.

3. Form-Invariance of Q-Multiplication and Q-Spaces

Within the last three decades, the interest in Q-math has grown greatly; in current databases, one finds hundreds of relevant pure math investigations as well as Q-number links with physics (see e.g. Ref. 3). The first natural aspect of this research concerns the stability of the multiplication law (Eq. (2)) under changers of the imaginary (vector) Q-units $\mathbf{q}_n$, i.e., under changes of the geometry of the Q-frames. A simple analysis shows[4] that Eq. (2) keeps its form under transformations of the vector Q-units by the vector group SO(3,C) or by 1 : 2 isomorphic to it the spinor (reflection) group SL(2,C)

$$\mathbf{q}_{n'} = O_{n'm}\mathbf{q}_m \to O \in SO(3,C); \quad \mathbf{q}_{n'} = U\mathbf{q}_n U^{-1} \to U \in SL(2,C). \quad (5)$$

In general case each group has 6 independent parameters, implying natural isomorphism with the Lorentz group. Three real parameters just rotate the frame in the 3D space; three imaginary parameters perform respective hyperbolic rotations (though specific since only the 3D frame's vectors are involved).

The Q-units derivatives by the parameters Φ_ξ can be defined as

$$d\mathbf{q}_k(\Phi_\xi) = \omega_{\xi\,kn}\mathbf{q}_n\,d\Phi_\xi, \quad (6)$$

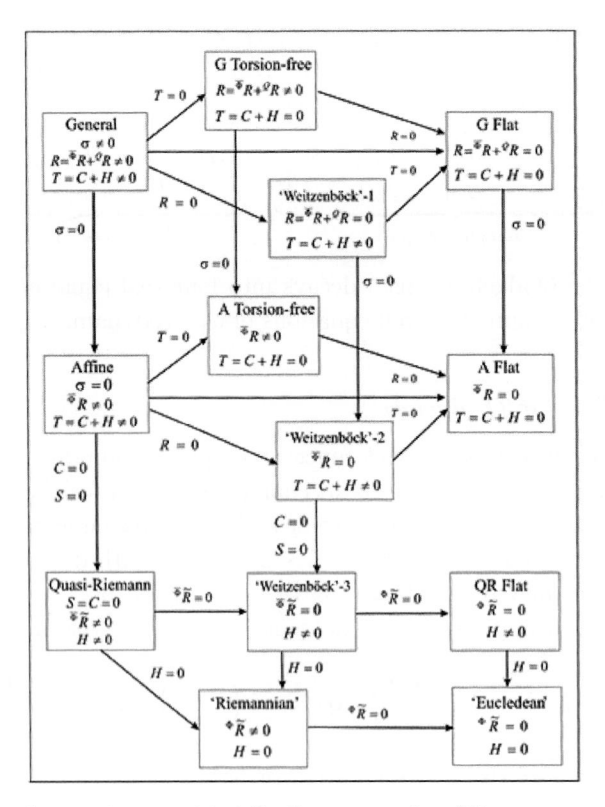

Fig. 1. Q-space of general type with full affine connection (Riemann + contortion + non-metricity) and full Q-connection (proper + Q-nonmetricity) generates at least 13 variants of different Q-spaces.

with $\omega_{\xi\,kn}$ being some coefficients skew in vector indices. If the parameters are functions of space-time coordinates x^α, then the Q-unit derivatives acquire the form

$$\frac{d\mathbf{q}_k}{dx^\alpha} = \frac{d\Phi_\xi}{dx^\alpha} \omega_{\xi\,kn} \mathbf{q}_n \equiv \Omega_{\alpha kn} \mathbf{q}_n; \qquad (7)$$

$\Omega_{\alpha kn}$ can be associated with a connection of a specific vector space each point of which is an initial point of a Q-frame. This additional geometric property can be endowed to any space-time (e.g., already curved), thus making it a Q-enriched differential manifold with supplementary components of affine connection (therefore, curvature).[5]

For instance, apart from "standard" Riemann, Cartan, and non-metricity terms, the Q-space geometry can include respective proper Q-connection (giving zero curvature), Q-torsion, and Q-non-metricity. This gives a greatly wider scheme of the space geometry classification, hence greater possibilities to formulate generalized versions of relativistic theories of gravity comprising models with distributed polarized sources (Fig. 1).

4. Equations of Mechanics in Quaternion Frames

4.1. *Representation of Newton's dynamic equation in rotating Q-frames*

For real parameters $\Phi_\xi(t)$ of the subgroup $SO(3,R) \in SO(3,C)$ dependent only on time provide one gets a special type of the Q-connection components which in this case are physically equivalent to angular velocities of the Q-frame space rotations $\Omega_{kn} \equiv \dot{\Phi}_\xi \omega_{\xi\,kn}$. Together with the Q-vector form-invariance conditions $\mathbf{r} \equiv x_{\tilde{k}}\mathbf{q}_{\tilde{k}} = x_n\mathbf{q}_n$, $\mathbf{f} \equiv f_{\tilde{k}}\mathbf{q}_{\tilde{k}} = f_n\mathbf{q}_n$ (specific force), this helps to rewrite "inertial" Newton's dynamic equation $\frac{d^2}{dt^2}(x_{\tilde{k}}\mathbf{q}_{\tilde{k}}) = f_{\tilde{k}}\mathbf{q}_{\tilde{k}}$ in an arbitrarily rotating Q-frame $\mathbf{q}_n(t)$

$$\ddot{\mathbf{r}} = \mathbf{f}. \tag{8}$$

The Q-vector components of Eq. (8) are

$$\ddot{x}_k + 2\dot{x}_n\Omega_{nk} + x_n\dot{\Omega}_{nk} + x_n\Omega_{nm}\Omega_{mk} = f_k; \tag{9}$$

its form in the traditional vector notations is

$$\ddot{\mathbf{r}} + 2[\mathbf{\Omega} \times \mathbf{v}] + [\dot{\mathbf{\Omega}} \times \mathbf{r}] + [\mathbf{\Omega} \times [\mathbf{r} \times \mathbf{\Omega}]] = \mathbf{f}.$$

Equation (8) fits for any arbitrarily complex rotations of the reference system; in particular, it describes very well the dynamics of bodies observed from the so-called chasing frames.[4]

4.2. *BQ-vector version of the theory of relativity*

Full group $SO(3,C)$ preserve form-invariance of the following "time + space" BQ-vector

$$dz = (idt\,e_k + dx_k)\mathbf{q}_k, \quad e_k e_k = 1, \quad e_k dx_k = 0, \tag{10}$$

which can be regarded as a specific "quaternion square root" from the space-time interval of special relativity $dz^2 = dt^2 - dr^2$. This gives a chance to build a specific BQ-vector relativity theory (Fig. 2), with the basic correlation given by Eq. (10) and the generalized "rotational equation"

$$\Sigma' = O\Sigma, \quad \Sigma \equiv \{\mathbf{q}_k\}, \quad O \in SO(3,C);$$

this "rotational relativity" gives all effects of Einstein's Special Relativity, but a different model of the universe, which in this case is (3+3)D. However, the most suitable (and fruitful) theory is for solving problems with non-inertial frames, directly giving solutions for the so-called hyperbolic motion, Thomas precession, linear relativistic oscillator, and relativistic shift of planets' satellites.[6,7] As well, this theory straightly admits a format of Newton-type dynamic equation for relativistic particles.[8]

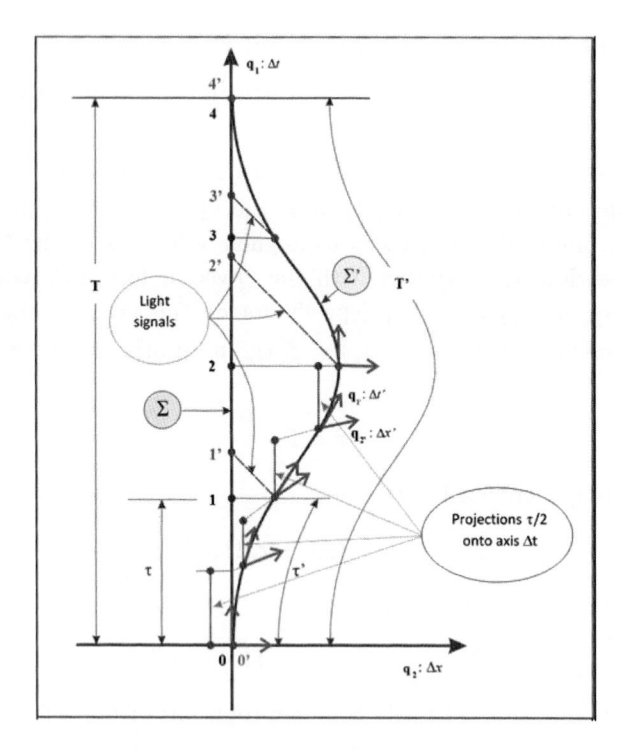

Fig. 2. Minkowski diagram for relativistic harmonic oscillator (1 cycle).

5. Q-Math Version of Pregeometry and a Matrix Image of the Complex Number

In search for the nature of quantum physics, J. A. Wheeler heuristically suggested a concept of pregeometry which "breaks loose all mention of geometry and distance".[9]

5.1. *Spectral theorem and fractal surface "under 3D Q-geometry"*

Within Q-math this concept of pregeometry can be in a way associated with a specific fractal surface (with dimensionality 1/2), being a type of subspace of 3D geometric space generated by Q-triad $\mathbf{q}_n$ (Fig. 3).

An area of the fractal surface (2D-cell) is formed by two vectors, a dyad, which originates as a bi-orthogonal basis of vectors $\{\psi^+, \psi^-\}$ and convectors $\{\varphi^+, \varphi^-\}$ within the framework of the spectral theorem since vector Q-units can be represented as simple non-degenerate matrices. In particular, the fractal dyad vectors may appear as right and left eigenvectors of one vector Q-unit. Unexpectedly it turned out that all four quaternion units are, in fact, structured, since they can be built from only one set of a Q-unit's eigenvectors (and co-vectors) as bilinear tensor products

$$\mathbf{q}_1 = -i(\psi^+\varphi^+ + \psi^-\varphi^-), \quad \mathbf{q}_2 = \psi^+\varphi^- - \psi^-\varphi^+,$$
$$\mathbf{q}_3 = i(\psi^+\varphi^+ - \psi^-\varphi^-); \quad 1 = \psi^+\varphi^+ + \psi^-\varphi^-. \tag{11}$$

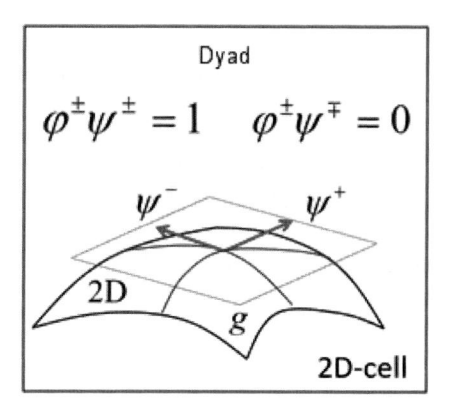

Fig. 3. A fractal surface domain.

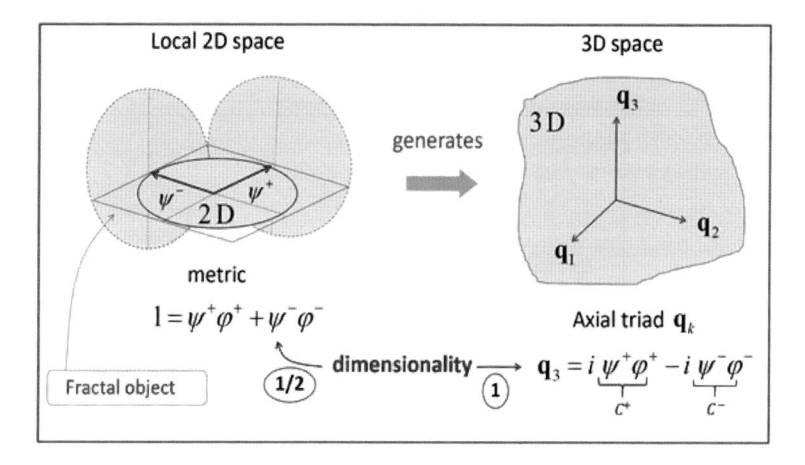

Fig. 4. Elements of a fractal surface generate volume of 3D space.

The first three equalities of Eq. (11) state that a domain of the 3D space formed by axial vector Q-triad $\mathbf{q}_n$ is a composed structure whose elements are vectors $\{\psi^+, \psi^-\}$ and convectors $\{\varphi^+, \varphi^-\}$ forming a local area of the fractal surface. Thus, the local volume of three-dimensional space associated with the triad of unit quaternionic axial vectors is, in fact, a derived geometric object, the true elements of which are two vectors (co-vectors) of the fractal dyad. It is possible to say that an invisible 2D fractal space (a pre-geometric surface) generates a 3D geometric space (Fig. 4).

In its turn, the last equality of Eq. (11) demonstrates that the scalar unit, in this case, the unit diagonal 2×2-matrix (in Cartesian components)

$$\psi^{+(A)}\psi^{+}{}_{(B)} + \psi^{-(A)}\psi^{-}{}_{(B)} = \delta^A_B$$

$$\Rightarrow \begin{pmatrix} 0 \\ 1 \end{pmatrix}(0\ 1) + \begin{pmatrix} 1 \\ 0 \end{pmatrix}(1\ 0) = \begin{pmatrix} 0 & 0 \\ 0 & 1 \end{pmatrix} + \begin{pmatrix} 1 & 0 \\ 0 & 0 \end{pmatrix} = \begin{pmatrix} 1 & 0 \\ 0 & 1 \end{pmatrix} = 1,$$

is nothing but metric tensor of the fractal surface; thus, the scalar unit may be said to acquire its not geometric but pregeometric meaning.

Another significant observation in this context is that it is precisely due to the structural decomposition of Q-units in Eq. (11) that the law of multiplication of the Q-algebra keeps its form under $SL(2, C)$ transformations. In this case, each dyad vector (co-vector) is subject to a direct $\psi' = U\psi$ (inverse $\varphi' = \varphi U^{-1}$) transformation of this group or its subgroup.

5.2. *Conic-gearing model of the complex number*

One of the pure math consequences of the existence of the Q-unit's structure is the appearance of an original matrix model of the complex number previously imaged on the complex plane or the Riemann sphere.[10]

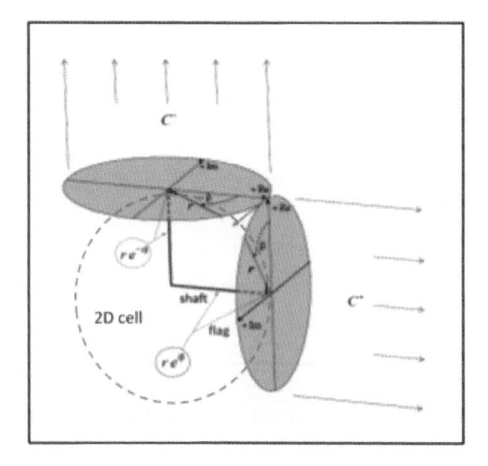

Fig. 5. C-number as a conic-gearing couple on a 2D-cell.

Indeed, if only two units are in the game (e.g., 1, $\mathbf{q}_3$), then any complex number can be represented as $z = x + iy \equiv x \cdot 1 + y \cdot \mathbf{q}_3$, $a, b \in R$; this number belongs to the C-algebra commutative in multiplication. Applying to the units the decomposition

in Eq. (11) one gets
$$z = (x+iy)\psi^+\varphi^+ + (x-iy)\psi^-\varphi^-.$$
This number can be rewritten in the polar coordinates
$$z = r\left(e^{i\beta}C^+ + e^{-i\beta}C^-\right), \qquad (12)$$
here $C^\pm \equiv \psi^\pm \varphi^\pm$ are the projectors, idempotent, and mutually orthogonal matrices. Equation (12) has a clear geometric image. It models a type of conic-gearing couple, one gear orthogonal to another touching in a point (Fig. 5). Each gear has the shaft equal to r; a rotation of one gear by angle β forces another one to rotate by the angle $-\beta$. This picture conformally changes with the change of the number's modulus. Besides, its projectors C^+ and C^- determine the same orthogonal directions as the dyad vectors ψ^+ and ψ^-, so, in a way this model can be used to visualize the behavior of a 2D-cell under variations of the phase angle. Below we use it in this sense.

6. "General Theory of Particle Mechanics"

6.1. *Q-algebra stability under transformations of the fractal structure*

The next question to answer is which transformations of a fractal surface leave the algebra validity. The simplest mapping is a multiplication of the initially constant dyad by an arbitrary complex number
$$\Psi^+ = \lambda\psi^+, \quad \Psi^- = \lambda^*\psi^-; \quad \lambda \equiv \sigma e^{i\alpha} \qquad (13)$$
thus, introducing the phase change α and the 2D-cell's conformal stretching factor σ (Fig. 6). Under mapping (13) new 3D vectors (and the scalar too) built according to the pattern (11) lose their property of unity, e.g., $\Psi^+\Phi^+ + \Psi^-\Phi^- = \lambda\lambda^*(\psi^+\varphi^+ + \psi^-\varphi^-) \neq 1$.

To cure the algebra, we, first, assume that the mapping parameters are functions of a scalar θ and coordinates ξ_n of an abstract math phase $\alpha(\theta,\xi)$, $\sigma(\theta,\xi)$, then define a normalizing integral over a volume of the space
$$f(\theta) \equiv \int_V \lambda\lambda^*\, d^3\xi = 1, \qquad (14)$$
and finely, renormalize new vectors and the scalar, e.g., as $1' = f(\theta)(\psi^+\varphi^+ + \psi^-\varphi^-) = 1$. Further on, we demand that this normalization last "forever" (in the sense of parameter θ)
$$\partial_\theta \int_{V_\xi} \lambda\lambda^* dV_\xi = 0; \qquad (15)$$
this gives a differential condition of the algebra stability (a continuity-type equation)
$$\partial_\theta(\lambda\lambda^*) + \nabla(\lambda\lambda^*\mathbf{k}) = 0; \qquad (16)$$
with $\mathbf{k}$ being a 3D vector. We can choose this vector arbitrarily.

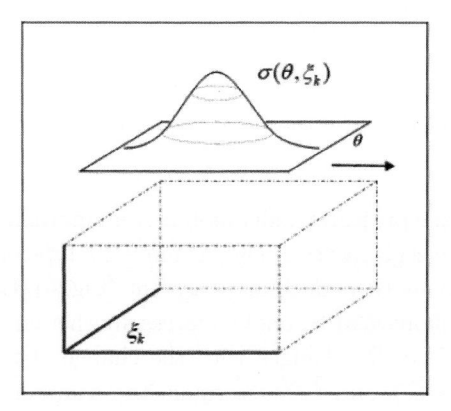

Fig. 6. σ-factor over an abstract space.

6.2. Quantum mechanics

If the free vector indicates the direction of the phase increase (behaves as a propagator) $k_n = \partial_n \alpha$, then the algebra stability condition given by Eq. (16) fractalizes and acquires the form

$$\left[\partial_\theta - \frac{i}{2}\left(\partial_n \partial_n - 2W\right)\right]\lambda = 0, \tag{17}$$

where W is an arbitrary scalar function. All magnitudes and operators entering Eq. (17) are pure mathematical (abstract), hence, measured in no units. It is natural to introduce micro-world units' standards, e.g., the Compton length $\varepsilon \equiv \hbar/(mc)$ and respective time $\tau \equiv \hbar/(mc^2)$. Then the abstract coordinates and scalar parameter are transformed as $\xi_n \to x_n/\varepsilon$, $\theta \to t/\tau$ and the fractal algebra stability condition in Eq. (17) takes the precise form of the Schrodinger equation

$$\left(i\hbar \partial_t + \frac{\hbar^2}{2m}\nabla^2 - U(x_n, t)\right)\lambda = 0 \tag{18}$$

the free function acquiring the meaning of the potential energy $U \equiv mc^2 W$.

In a more complex case, the propagator can depend also on a vector field $k_n = \partial_n \alpha + A_n$, this requires the use of the matrix dyad (e.g., of positive parity φ, ψ) and the Clifford-type metric $g_{mn} \equiv (\mathbf{p}_m \mathbf{p}_n + \mathbf{p}_n \mathbf{p}_m)/2$, $\mathbf{p}_k \equiv i\mathbf{q}_k$. Then the continuity-type stability condition takes the form $\partial_\theta(\varphi\psi) + g_{mn}\partial_m[\varphi\psi(\partial_n\alpha + A_n)] = 0$, while its fractal mathematical version is

$$\left[i\partial_\theta - \frac{1}{2}(-i\partial_k + A_k)(-i\partial_k + A_k) - \frac{1}{2}\mathbf{p}_k B_k - W\right]\psi = 0, \quad B_n \equiv \varepsilon_{kmn}\partial_k A_m; \tag{19}$$

written in physical units (on the base of the micro-world units' standards) Eq. (19) becomes exactly the Pauli equation for quantum-mechanical charged particle in the exterior magnetic field.[11] Thus, investigation of fractal pregeometry helps to deduce the basic quantum mechanical equations purely out of mathematical considerations.

6.3. Non-static solution for H-atom

The suggested approach hints to look for non-standard solutions to the quantum mechanical equation. As an example, we mention a non-static solution for the hydrogen atom where instead of Schrodinger's static ansatz for the wave function $\lambda = \sigma(r)e^{-\alpha(t)}$ a stationary function is assumed: $\lambda = \sigma(r,t)e^{i(k\varphi-\omega t)}$, with the same Coulomb potential $U = q^2/r$. In this case, the quantization follows from the normalization condition (so that no special cutting of a series is needed), while the result of the quantization precisely gives formulas of the Bohr H-atom heuristic model $m\Omega_n r_n^2 = n\hbar$, $\Omega_n = 2\omega/n = mq^4/(2n^2\hbar^3)$. In this stationary solution, the electron is not a point; its density is harmonically distributed along a circular orbit, and this configuration revolves around the nucleus with a constant angular velocity.[12]

6.4. From quantum to analytical mechanics

Decomposition of the math Schrodinger equation (Eq. (17)) into real and imaginary parts leads to a couple of the Bohm-type equations,[13] the first one providing conservation of the conformal factor $\partial_\theta \sigma + \partial_k \sigma \, \partial_k \alpha + \sigma \partial_k \partial_k \alpha = 0$, the second (more complicated) dealing with the "phase dynamics"

$$\partial_\theta \alpha + \frac{1}{2}(\partial_n \alpha)(\partial_n \alpha) + W_{\text{ex}} + W_{\text{int}} - \frac{1}{2}\partial_n\partial_n\sigma/\sigma = 0. \qquad (20)$$

Separation functions of Eq. (20) into fast (σ, W_{int}) and slow ones (α, W_{ex}) gives a Helmholtz-type equation for the interior distribution of the σ-factor "density" onto the 2D-cell surface, while the "slow" equation

$$\partial_\theta \alpha + \frac{1}{2}(\partial_n \alpha)(\partial_n \alpha) + W_{\text{ex}} = 0 \qquad (21)$$

in the physical units and under assumption $S = \alpha \hbar$ takes the exact form of the Hamilton-Jacobi equation of the analytical mechanics

$$\partial_t S + \frac{(\partial_n S)(\partial_n S)}{2m} + U_{\text{ex}} = 0, \quad U_{\text{ex}} = mc^2 W_{\text{ex}}. \qquad (22)$$

Thus, the classical action function can be shown directly linked to the fractal 2D-cell's phase measured in values of Planck constant. Then, using evident math steps, we automatically arrive at the Lagrangian format (kinematic energy minus potential energy) heuristically handpicked for the Newtonian dynamics.[14] In this approach, an elementary object of mechanics, a particle, turns out to have two images (Fig. 7), a fractal one – a 2D-cell loaded with a fractal mass density and oscillating within its real and complex sectors, and a geometric one – a point-like massive particle rotating about one 3D-axis with the angular velocity twice greater in modulus than the angular frequency of the 2D-cell's oscillation.

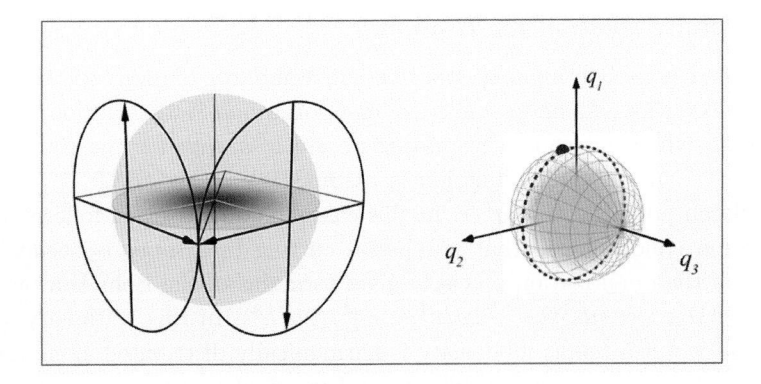

Fig. 7. Particle's 2D and 3D models.

6.5. *From analytical to relativistic mechanics*

The last model leads to an original derivation of the action function for the classical relativistic particle. We consider a point-like object of the characteristic size ε (length standard) moving in 3D space with velocity u and rotating about one axis with angular velocity Ω (twice as great as its 2D-cell analog's oscillation frequency), see Fig. 8.

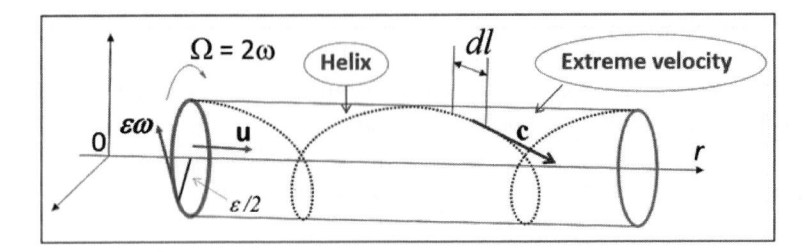

Fig. 8. Derivation of the action function for a relativistic particle.

A bordering point of this object, hence, depicts in the space a helix line; the only assumption for this model is that the velocity modulus of the bordering point is always equal to the fundamental velocity c. We compute a square of the helix' line element

$$dl^2 = c^2 dt^2 = \varepsilon^2 d\alpha^2 + u^2 dt^2$$

and find from here the phase change for the time interval $[t_1, t_2]$

$$\alpha = \pm \frac{c}{\varepsilon} \int_{t_1}^{t_2} \sqrt{1 - \frac{u^2}{c^2}}\, dt, \qquad (23)$$

the signs indicate the right or left helicity. Choosing the sign minus (left helicity) and taking into account the correlation $\alpha = S/\hbar$ we rewrite Eq. (23) in the physical units to obtain

$$S = \alpha \hbar = -mc^2 \int_{t_1}^{t_2} \sqrt{1 - \frac{u^2}{c^2}}\, dt, \qquad (24)$$

which precisely coincides with the mechanical action of the relativistic particle (previously introduced heuristically). It can be shown that reduction of Eq. (24) (written in differential form) to the non-relativistic case automatically establishes relations between classical and quantum quantities, thus linking the free particle 2D model as a De Broglie wave, the particle's rest energy linked to the permanent oscillation of the 2D cell.

6.6. *The map of the general theory of particle mechanics*

Thus, a profound investigation of the Q-math environment helps to distinguish in it a series of pure mathematical equations similar in the form to those merging from the physical experiment or found by great researchers "in a flash of a genius". Written in proper physical units these equations become the undisputed laws of quantum, classical and relativistic mechanics. The logical chain of this "general theory of particle mechanics" can be represented in the form of the following schematic map (see Fig. 9).

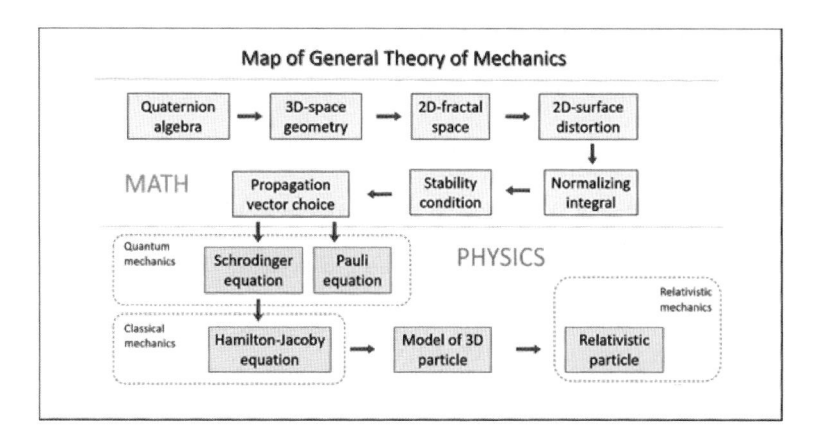

Fig. 9. Map of general theory of mechanics.

7. Conclusion and Perspectives

We demonstrated that the specific mathematical equations born in "quaternion medium" in physical units become known physical laws; briefly we remind the results. Q-math environment comprises 3D geometric and 2D pre-geometric (fractal) domains. In the geometric domain, one discovers immanently hidden "geometric physical laws": Cartesian frames, equations of electrodynamics, Q-vector version of the relativity theory ("Rotational Relativity") giving the same effects as the special relativity. In the fractal domain, one finds the linked logical chain laws of quantum mechanics, classical mechanics, and relativistic mechanics. These coincidences are hardly incidental; moreover, they suggest new ways to move the theory ahead.

Among possible directions, one can pay attention to the following (at least three) aspects. (i) Coupling affine differential manifold with the rotational relativity gives a chance to build a new type of Q-vector gravity. (ii) Such a gravity model is known to be naturally split into spinor-type structures[15] which can reconcile relativistic gravity with quantum physics. (iii) Gauge fields, in particular, electromagnetic and Yang-Mills potentials seem to be promising objects to investigate their geometric and fractal structures within Q-math medium approaches.

References

1. P. Rastall, Quaternions in relativity, *Rev. Mod. Phys.* **36**, 820 (1964).
2. R. Fueter Über die analytische Darstellung der regulären Funktionen einer Quaternionenvariablen. *Commentarii Mathematici Helvetici* **8**, 371 (1935).
3. A. Gsponer and J.-P. Hurni, *Quaternions in mathematical physics (2): analytical bibliography* (Independent Sci. Research Inst. Oxford, OX4 4YS, England, 2005), arXiv:math-ph/0510059.
4. A. P. Yefremov, Physical theories in hypercomplex geometric description, *Int J. Geom. Methods Mod. Phys.* **11**, 1450062 (2014).
5. A. P. Yefremov, Vector quaternionic spaces: geometry and classification, *Grav. Cosmol.* **9**, 319 (2003).
6. A. P. Yefremov, Six-Dimensional rotational relativity, *Acta Phys. Hung.* **11**, 147 (2000).
7. A. P. Yefremov, Quaternion model of relativity: solutions for non-inertial motions and new effects, *Adv. Sci. Lett.* **1**, 179 (2008).
8. A. P. Yefremov, Newton-type dynamics in quaternion model of relativity, *Adv. Sci. Lett.* **2**, 81 (2009).
9. J. A. Wheeler, Pregeometry: motivations and prospects, in *Quantum theory and gravitation*, ed. A. R. Marlow (Academic Press, New York, 1980).
10. A. P. Yefremov, The conic-gearing image of a complex number and a spinor-born surface geometry, *Grav. Cosmol.* **17**, 1 (2011).
11. A. P. Yefremov, The fractal structure of space entails origin of Pauli's equation, *Grav. Cosmol.* **25**, 305 (2019).
12. A. P. Yefremov, Bohr-Schrödinger hydrogen truce, *Quantum Matter* **6**, 510 (2014).
13. D. Bohm, A suggested interpretation of the quantum theory in terms of hidden variables. I, *Phys. Rev.* **85**, 166 (1952).
14. A. P. Yefremov, General theory of particle mechanics arising from a fractal surface, *Grav. Cosmol.* **21**, 19 (2015).
15. A. P. Yefremov, Theory of relativity in quaternion spinors, *Grav. Cosmol.* **22**, 97 (2016).

The Maxwell-Bopp-Landé-Thomas-Podolsky-Einstein system for a static point source

Érik Amorim

Department Mathematik, Universität zu Köln,
Cologne, Germany
E-mail: edeamori@math.uni-koeln.de

We discuss the existence of a static, spherically symmetric spacetime that is the solution of the Einstein field equations coupled with an electric field obeying the equations of electromagnetism of Maxwell-Bopp-Landé-Thomas-Podolsky for a static point charge. Contrary to what happens with the Reissner-Weyl-Nordström spacetime, the electric field energy is finite, just as for this same theory on a background flat spacetime.

Keywords: Bopp-Podolsky, Field self-energy

1. Introduction

The problem of the *self-force* in electrodynamics consists of finding an expression for the force that the electromagnetic field generated by a charged point particle exerts on the particle itself. The possibility to write well-posed classical systems of equations for the joint evolution of electromagnetic (EM) fields and their sources, without resorting to *ad hoc* field averaging or bare mass renormalization at point charges, requires working with laws of electromagnetism such that the energy-momentum density of the electromagnetic field generated by charged particles is locally integrable, which is not the case for the usual Maxwell equations. There are generalized EM theories that were proposed specifically to address this problem, one of them being the so-called *Bopp-Podolsky* theory, which we will call **Bopp-Landé-Thomas-Podolsky** or **BLTP** theory. Using this theory, Kiessling and Tahvildar-Zadeh[1] have recently shown how to formulate a well-posed system for the joint evolution of point particles and their EM fields in *flat-space*, that is, the Minkowski spacetime of Special Relativity. Local integrability of the field energy-momentum at the location of the particles is essential in their work, hence why it is important to work with generalizations of the usual Maxwell equations. But the non-linearities in the Einstein field equations pose serious obstacles to generalizing this study to the theory of General Relativity.

The present work is a small first step towards extending this framework to General Relativity. It reports on a recent result by the author from his PhD thesis (Ref. 2) concerning the existence of a finite-energy solution to the Einstein equations for the spacetime of a single, static point charge whose electric field obeys the equations in Bopp-Podolsky theory.

2. Problem description

The usual Maxwell equations or **Maxwell-Maxwell system** for the EM fields $\boldsymbol{E},\boldsymbol{B},\boldsymbol{D},\boldsymbol{H}$ of a static point particle of charge Q sitting at position $\boldsymbol{x}=\boldsymbol{0}$ in flat-space consists of the **pre-metric Maxwell equations**

$$\begin{cases} \nabla \cdot \boldsymbol{B} = 0 \\ \nabla \times \boldsymbol{E} + \dfrac{1}{c}\dfrac{\partial \boldsymbol{B}}{\partial t} = 0 \end{cases}, \quad \begin{cases} \nabla \cdot \boldsymbol{D} = 4\pi Q \delta_0 \\ \nabla \times \boldsymbol{H} - \dfrac{1}{c}\dfrac{\partial \boldsymbol{D}}{\partial t} = 0 \end{cases}, \tag{1}$$

where δ_0 is the Dirac Delta, together with the **Maxwell vacuum law**, which specifies $\boldsymbol{D} = \boldsymbol{E}$ and $\boldsymbol{H} = \boldsymbol{B}$. Upon solving this system, one finds $\boldsymbol{B} = \boldsymbol{H} = \boldsymbol{0}$ and

$$\boldsymbol{D}(\boldsymbol{r}) = \boldsymbol{E}(\boldsymbol{r}) = -\varphi'(r)\boldsymbol{e_r} = \frac{Q}{r^2}\boldsymbol{e_r},$$

for $r = \|(x,y,z)\| = \|\boldsymbol{r}\|$ and $\boldsymbol{e_r} = r^{-1}\boldsymbol{r}$, and where the *electric potential* φ is the so-called *Coulomb potential*

$$\varphi(r) = \frac{Q}{r}.$$

But plugging these fields into the standard integral formula for the electric field energy (set $\varkappa^{-2} = 0$ in (4) and (5) ahead) produces an integral that diverges at the location $\boldsymbol{x} = \boldsymbol{0}$ of the point charge.

In the 1940's, a modification of the above system was proposed. We call it the **Maxwell-BLTP system**, in honor of its original proponents Bopp,[3] Landé and Thomas,[4] and Podolsky.[5] The pre-metric equations (1) remain the same, but the **BLTP vacuum law** stipulates a modified relation between the electric and magnetic fields:

$$\begin{cases} \boldsymbol{D} = \boldsymbol{E} - \varkappa^{-2}\Box \boldsymbol{E} \\ \boldsymbol{H} = \boldsymbol{B} - \varkappa^{-2}\Box \boldsymbol{B} \end{cases} \tag{2}$$

where $\Box = -c^{-2}\partial_t + \Delta$ is the wave operator and $\varkappa > 0$ is a postulated large parameter of Nature with dimension of inverse length. Note that $\varkappa = \infty$ recovers the Maxwell-Maxwell system. The solution of (1) and (2) has $\boldsymbol{B} = \boldsymbol{H} = \boldsymbol{0}$ and

$$\boldsymbol{D}(\boldsymbol{r}) = \frac{Q}{r^2}\boldsymbol{e_r}, \quad \boldsymbol{E}(\boldsymbol{r}) = -\varphi'(r)\boldsymbol{e_r},$$

for the electric potential being

$$\varphi(r) = \frac{Q(1 - e^{-\varkappa r})}{r}. \tag{3}$$

We remark that φ is continuous at $r = 0$ and everywhere bounded. The exponential term in it is a small correction to the Coulomb potential for large values of r, while also ensuring that $\varphi(r)$ remains bounded for small r. The field energy density, which in this static case works out to be

$$\varepsilon_{\text{BLTP}} = \frac{1}{8\pi}\left(\boldsymbol{E} \cdot \boldsymbol{D} - \frac{1}{2}(|\boldsymbol{E}|^2 - \varkappa^{-2}(\nabla \cdot \boldsymbol{E})^2)\right), \tag{4}$$

yields a finite value for the total field energy $\mathcal{E}$ when integrated:

$$\mathcal{E} := \int_{\mathbb{R}^3} \varepsilon_{\text{BLTP}} \, dV = \frac{Q\varphi(0)}{2} = \frac{Q^2 \varkappa}{2} \ . \tag{5}$$

Now suppose we "switch on gravity," that is, we seek solutions of the Einstein field equations of General Relativity for a static, spherically symmetric spacetime with a naked timelike singularity representing a single point charge at rest. The underlying manifold is $\mathbb{R}^4$ minus a line, with a global spherical coordinate system (ct, r, θ, ϕ). This universe is devoid of matter away from the particle, but the latter generates electromagnetic fields that can be calculated at any point and contribute to the stress-energy tensor $T_{\mu\nu}$, which is the source term in the Einstein equations. In the case of EM theories arising from a Lagrangian, which is the case for both the Maxwell-Maxwell and Maxwell-BLTP theories, one calculates $T_{\mu\nu}$ via the standard procedure of considering variations of the matter action with respect to the metric. A globally defined electric potential $\varphi(r)$ satisfying $\lim_{r\to\infty} \varphi(r) = 0$ enters this long calculation and must be considered an unknown of the system. We refer the reader to Ref. 2 for the details. The other two unknowns of the problem appear in the metric, which can be written in the general form

$$ds^2 = -c^2 \frac{\psi(r)}{\zeta(r)} dt^2 + \zeta(r) dr^2 + r^2 (d\theta^2 + \sin^2\theta \, d\phi^2) \ ,$$

where r is the area-radius coordinate and $\psi(r), \zeta(r)$ are unknown. In order for the spacetime to be asymptotically flat away from the singularity, we look for solutions satisfying

$$\lim_{r\to\infty} \psi(r) = \lim_{r\to\infty} \zeta(r) = 1 \ . \tag{6}$$

In place of φ, we will consider as the third unknown of the problem the function

$$w(r) := \frac{r^2 \varphi'(r)}{\psi(r)} + Q \ . \tag{7}$$

One can think of w as measuring how much the electric potential deviates from the Coulomb potential. Physically meaningful solutions should satisfy

$$\lim_{r\to\infty} w(r) = 0 \tag{8}$$

so that the laws of EM away from the point charge become the usual Maxwell laws.

Using the Lagrangian of the Maxwell-Maxwell theory in the above framework, it is well-known that the solution of the Einstein equations is the *Reissner-Weyl-Nordström solution*, which we abbreviate as **RWN solution**:

$$\psi^{(\text{RWN})}(r) = 1 \ , \quad \zeta_M^{(\text{RWN})}(r) = \left(1 - \frac{2GM}{c^2 r} + \frac{GQ^2}{c^4 r^2}\right)^{-1} , \quad w^{(\text{RWN})}(r) = 0 \ ,$$

with G being the gravitational constant and M a free parameter that turns out to be the *ADM mass* of the spacetime. However, just like in flat-space, it can be calculated from the stress-energy tensor that the electric field energy integral (set

$\varkappa^{-2} = 0$ in (11) ahead) diverges around the singularity. This means that the field self-energy of the particle is infinite.

Using instead the Lagrangian of the Maxwell-BLTP theory, the Einstein equations reduce to the **Maxwell-BLTP-Einstein system**. In units where $c = Q = \varkappa = 1$, it reads

$$\begin{cases} \psi' = -\dfrac{\varepsilon\psi}{r^3}(w')^2 , \\[2mm] \zeta' = \dfrac{\zeta(1-\zeta)}{r} + \dfrac{\varepsilon}{r^3}\left(\zeta^2 - \zeta^2 w^2 - (w')^2 \zeta\right) , \\[2mm] w'' = \left(\dfrac{3-\zeta}{r} + \dfrac{\varepsilon\zeta}{r^3}(1-w^2)\right) w' + \zeta w . \end{cases} \qquad (9)$$

where the dimensionless parameter ε takes the role of Newton's G, that is, it stands for $\varepsilon := GQ^2\varkappa^2/c^4$. Even if $\varkappa$ is as large as physically reasonable — the inverse of the Planck length, — we find that ε is of order 10^{-20} for Q being the charge of an electron. Therefore it makes sense to study the solutions of system (9) as a perturbation of those corresponding to the $\varepsilon = 0$ case, which we call the **flat-space solution**:

$$\psi^{(\text{flat})}(r) = 1 , \quad \zeta^{(\text{flat})}(r) = 1 , \quad w^{(\text{flat})}(r) = (1+r)e^{-r} , \qquad (10)$$

where $w^{(\text{flat})}$ was obtained from (7) and (3). The integral for the electric field energy, reinstating the constants $c, Q, \varkappa$, can be calculated to be

$$\mathcal{E} = \frac{1}{2}\int_0^\infty \frac{\psi}{r^2}\left(Q^2 - w^2 - \frac{1}{\varkappa^2}\cdot\frac{(w')^2}{\zeta}\right) dr \qquad (11)$$

(performed on any constant-time hypersurface).

The goal of this work is to prove that a finite-energy solution to system (9) exists and to study the nature of its singularity at $r = 0$. For the lack of a better name, the ensuing spacetime will be referred to as the **M-BLTP spacetime**.

Remark 2.1. For any value of $\varkappa \leq \infty$, the RWN solution (2) also solves the version of system (9) with the constants $c, G, \varkappa$ reintroduced, but it is an undesirable solution because of the divergence of the energy integral. A recent result by Cuzinatto[6] et al. shows that RWN is in fact the only physically meaningful exterior solution of this system in case the spacetime contains a black hole — that is, if the coordinate system is only valid on a domain of the form $r \in (r_0, \infty)$ for $r_0 > 0$. So it is remarkable that another solution can exist if the domain is taken to be $r \in (0, \infty)$, as it is for us.

3. Main result

The main theorem proved in Ref. 2 can be paraphrased as follows:

Theorem 3.1. There exists $\varepsilon_* \in (0,1)$ such that, for all $\varepsilon \in [0, \varepsilon_*]$, the Maxwell-BLTP-Einstein system (9) of a static point charge admits a solution $(\psi_\varepsilon, \zeta_\varepsilon, w_\varepsilon)$ for $r \in (0, \infty)$ satisfying the asymptotic properties (6), (8) and the condition $\mathcal{E} < \infty$, where $\mathcal{E}$ is given in (11). Furthermore, the behavior of the solution for large r is

$$\psi_\varepsilon(r) = 1 + O(e^{-r}), \quad \zeta_\varepsilon(r) = \zeta_M^{(\text{RWN})}(r) + O(e^{-r}), \quad w_\varepsilon(r) = O(e^{-r}),$$

and that for small r is

$$\psi_\varepsilon(r) = O(e^{-Y\varepsilon}), \quad \zeta_\varepsilon(r) = X + O(r^2), \quad w_\varepsilon(r) = 1 + O(r^2),$$

where the parameters M, X, Y are determined by ε, with $X \in [1, 1.1)$ and $Y \in (0.9, 1]$. Additionally, pointwise at any $r > 0$, we have

$$\lim_{\varepsilon \to 0} (\psi_\varepsilon(r), \zeta_\varepsilon(r), w_\varepsilon(r)) = (\psi^{(\text{flat})}(r), \zeta^{(\text{flat})}(r), w^{(\text{flat})}(r)). \tag{12}$$

We give an outline of the proof:

- First it is shown that, for any fixed $r_0 > 0$, a family of solutions exists on $[r_0, \infty)$ satisfying the asymptotic conditions (6), (8) as long as $\varepsilon > 0$ is small enough. This family is parametrized by (and continuous in) two arbitrary real parameters μ and α, the first one being related to the ADM mass. The method consists of writing the solution as a power series in ε starting from the $\varepsilon = 0$ flat-space solution, and then employing a novel technique for estimating the growth of the coefficients in order to get a lower bound for the radius of convergence. Also note that conditions (6), (8) already imply the finiteness of the energy integral (11) away from $r = 0$.
- Next a suitable rewriting of the system is found that casts its study, for small r, as a first-order, 4-dimensional autonomous dynamical system around a hyperbolic equilibrium point P. The 2-dimensional unstable manifold $\mathcal{W}$ of P is analytic and consists of a continuous 1-parameter family (we call σ the parameter) of solutions which, in the original variables, corresponds to solutions satisfying the condition

$$\lim_{r \to 0} \frac{\psi(r)(w(r) - 1)}{r^2} \in \mathbb{R}. \tag{13}$$

  This is proven to imply $\mathcal{E} < \infty$. More than that, it also implies $\mathcal{E} = Q\varphi(0)/2$, as in flat-space. The estimation technique mentioned above, this time adapted for power series in two real variables, enables the computation of points in $\mathcal{W}$ to arbitrarily small error.
- With the above work, we can construct, in a suitable 4-dimensional space $\{(x, y, z, r)\}$, a 3-dimensional hypersurface $\mathcal{Z}$ corresponding to solutions satisfying the desirable asymptotic conditions for large r, and a 2-dimensional surface $\mathcal{W}$ corresponding to solutions satisfying sufficient asymptotic conditions for small r to guarantee a finite $\mathcal{E}$. To complete the proof, one needs to show that $\mathcal{W}$ and $\mathcal{Z}$ intersect. To this end we consider the 3-dimensional

hypersurface $r = r_0$ of (x, y, z, r)-space. Intersected with it, $\mathcal{W}$ becomes a continuous curve $\mathcal{W}_0$ and $\mathcal{Z}$ becomes a continuous surface $\mathcal{Z}_0$. By looking at the x, y, z coordinates of points on $\mathcal{W}_0$ and $\mathcal{Z}_0$ as continuous functions of their parameters σ, μ, α, and by considering that a point intersection exists when $\varepsilon = 0$, the *Poincaré-Miranda theorem* can be applied to ensure that this point intersection still exists for small $\varepsilon > 0$. It corresponds to one solution over $r \in (0, \infty)$ for the chosen value of ε.

4. Properties of the solution

We conclude by analyzing some important properties of the M-BLTP spacetime and reporting on current work in progress related to recent results in the same vein.

4.1. *Bare mass*

There is another well-known modification of the Maxwell-Maxwell equations which also deals with the problem of infinite field energy-momentum of a point particle in flat-space. Originally proposed by Born,[7] it is part of what nowadays is commonly called *Born-Infeld electrodynamics*. It was then first observed by Hoffmann[8] that, under this formulation of EM, the singularity of the static, spherically symmetric spacetime of a resting point charge is milder than that of the RWN spacetime, in the sense that the blowup of certain curvature scalars at $r = 0$ is less severe in it. In Ref. 9, a class of electrostatic, spherically symmetric spacetimes that generalize that of Hoffmann is studied in much the same way as we did here for the BLTP laws. We call these *Hoffmann spacetimes*. An important quantity considered in that work is the so-called *mass-function* $m(r)$, which is defined by its relation to the second metric coefficient:

$$\zeta(r) = \left(1 - \frac{2Gm(r)}{c^2 r}\right)^{-1}. \tag{14}$$

The ADM mass is given by $m(\infty) := \lim_{r \to \infty} m(r)$, while the number $m(0) := \lim_{r \to 0} m(r)$ is called the **bare mass** of the spacetime. It is observed that $m(0) \in (-\infty, 0)$ for the class of Hoffmann spacetimes, and that this finite, negative bare mass contributes to the electric field energy to provide the entire mass/energy content of the spacetime:

$$\mathcal{E} = c^2(m(\infty) - m(0)).$$

But the methods of that work are fundamentally distinct from ours. The metric coefficients of the Hoffmann spacetimes can be explicitly solved by quadrature, partly due to the helpful fact that they satisfy $g_{tt} g_{rr} = -1$. This is not the case for the M-BLTP spacetime, turning even the question of existence of a solution into a completely different and more challenging task for us. Nevertheless, one can prove that the curvature blowup of the M-BLTP spacetime is just as mild as that of the

Hoffmann spacetimes, but, contrary to the latter, the following relation holds in the former:
$$\mathcal{E} > c^2(m(\infty) - m(0)) \,.$$
This suggests that $m(0)$ doesn't have a simple interpretation in the M-BLTP spacetime as a bare mass located at the point charge.

4.2. Equations of motion

In Ref. 10, a weak form of the twice-contracted second Bianchi identity for static, spherically symmetric spacetimes with a "singularity worldline" is studied. Sufficient conditions for it to hold are found for when $\psi \equiv 1$ and $m(0) < 0$. Considering how the classical Bianchi identities imply the local conservation laws $\nabla_\mu T^{\mu\nu} = 0$ (equations of motion of the matter/fields), the importance of this work to the scope of our project is that it provides a rigorous formulation of an equation of motion for a spacetime singularity, such as a point charge in the way that it is modeled in our spacetime. However, we find that the M-BLTP spacetime satisfies $\psi(r) > 1$ and $m(0) = 0$, which means that this work would not be directly applicable to study the motion of point-charge-singularities in GR under the BLTP laws of electromagnetism. More work in this topic will be needed when considering spacetimes containing two or more point charges that obey the BLTP laws.

4.3. Further solutions

Our existence proof obtains a solution whose ADM mass parameter $M = m(\infty)$ is determined by the value of ε. Physically it should be the case that M can be chosen *a priori*, independently from ε, so that point charges of arbitrary mass can be modeled. So the question arises whether we are missing more solutions to system (9). One point where our existence proof has potentially missed other solutions is clear: we have imposed condition (13), which is sufficient but not necessary for a finite energy. It also turns out that this condition implies $m(0) = 0$, but, considering what happens in the Hoffmann spacetimes, it is not unreasonable to expect that other solutions with $m(0) < 0$ and a finite energy might exist. If this turns out to be true, then, in the proof outline above, the curve $\mathcal{W}_0$ corresponding to suitable solutions for small r could potentially be turned into a surface with parameters σ and $m(0)$, which would intersect the surface $\mathcal{Z}_0$ in more than just one point. That is, one would expect a whole 1-parameter family of solutions over $r \in (0, \infty)$, allowing for a free parameter such as M. This is currently being studied by the author.

Acknowledgments

The author would like to thank his PhD advisors Michael Kiessling and Shadi Tahvildar-Zadeh for all the valuable discussions throughout his course of studies at Rutgers University and for the opportunity to present this work during the 16th Marcel Grossmann Meeting.

References

1. M. Kiessling and S. Tahvildar-Zadeh, The Einstein–Infeld–Hoffmann legacy in mathematical relativity I: The classical motion of charged point particles, *International Journal of Modern Physics D* **28** (2019).
2. E. Amorim, Two Problems in Mathematical Physics, PhD Thesis, Rutgers University (NJ, USA, 2021), https://doi.org/doi:10.7282/t3-czsg-4t42.
3. F. Bopp, Eine lineare Theorie des Elektrons, *Annalen Phys.* **430** (1940).
4. A. Landé and L. H. Thomas, Finite self-energies in radiation theory. Part II, *Phys. Rev.* **60** (1941).
5. B. Podolsky, A generalized electrodynamics. Part I: Non-quantum, *Phys. Rev.* **62** (1942).
6. R. R. Cuzinatto, C. A. M. de Melo, L. G. Medeiros, B. M. Pimentel, P. J. Pompeia, Bopp–Podolsky black holes and the no-hair theorem, *Eur. Phys. J. C* **78** (2018).
7. M. Born, Modified field equations with a finite radius of the electron, *Nature* **132** (1933).
8. B. Hoffmann, Gravitational and electromagnetic mass in the Born-Infeld electrodynamics, *Phys. Rev.* **47** (1935).
9. S. Tahvildar-Zadeh, On the static spacetime of a single point charge, *Rev. Math. Phys.* **23** (2011).
10. A. Burtscher, M. Kiessling, S. Tahvildar-Zadeh, Weak second Bianchi identity for spacetimes with timelike singularities, preprint (2021), https://arxiv.org/abs/1901.00813.

On recent developments in the theory of relativistic dissipative fluids

V. Hoang

Department of Mathematics, University of Texas at San Antonio,
One UTSA Circle
San Antonio, Texas 78249 (USA)
E-mail: duynguyenvu.hoang@utsa.edu

I give an overview about recent results on the well-posedness and breakdown of solutions for relativistic fluid equations.

Keywords: Relativistic dissipation, fluids, quark-gluon plasma, neutron star merger, causality, blowup of solutions

1. Relativistic fluids and heavy-ion collisions

The study of the quark-gluon plasma is provides a window into fundamental physics 10^{-6} seconds after the big bang.[1] On Earth, this state of matter is produced in collisions between heavy nuclei at relativistic speeds, creating a strongly interacting mixture of quarks and gluons. Current state-of-the art modeling of the quark-gluon plasma[1] is based on relativistic fluid equations, showing that the plasma behaves very much like an expanding liquid drop. Dissipative effects[1-3] have to be taken into account to make theoretical predictions match experimental data. Dissipative effects may also be relevant for the study of neutron star mergers.[4]

In Einstein's theory of relativity, a Lorentzian manifold (M, g) is taken as a model for spacetime. M can be thought of as the set of all events in the universe, characterized by *where and when* they happen. For simplicity consider a flat spacetime $M = \mathbb{R}^4 = \{x^\alpha := (x^0, \ldots, x^3)\}$, where $x^0 = ct$ is the time coordinate and c the speed of light. The Minkowski metric $g = \text{diag}(-1, 1, 1, 1)$ describes distances of events between one another. We use standard tensor notation throughout (repeated greek indices summed from 0 to 3, latin indices from 1 to 3). For a textbook introduction, see Refs. 5–7.

The basic fields in a relativistic fluid description are (e, n, u^α), where the total energy density e, the particle number density n and the four-velocity $u^\alpha = \frac{1}{\sqrt{1-|\vec{v}|^2/c^2}}\left(1, \frac{\vec{v}}{c}\right)$ all depend on x^α. The four-velocity replaces the ordinary three-dimensional velocity $\vec{v}$ of a fluid and is a time-like vector satisfying $g_{\mu\nu}u^\mu u^\nu = -1$. We first review the perfect fluid equations:

$$\text{relativistic Euler/momentum equation: } (e+p)\dot{u}^\beta = -(g^{\beta\alpha} + u^\beta u^\alpha)\nabla_\alpha p$$
$$\text{conservation of energy: } \dot{e} + (e+p)\nabla_\alpha u^\alpha = 0$$
$$\text{conservation of particle number: } \nabla_\alpha(nu^\alpha) = 0$$
$$\text{equation of state/pressure equation: } p = p(e, n)$$

(1)

where a dot $\dot{f} = u^\alpha \nabla_\alpha f$ denotes the relativistic material derivative. The momentum equation is analogous to Newton's second law $m \cdot a = F$, as $(e+p)$ corresponds to relativistic mass density, $a^\beta := u^\alpha \nabla_\alpha u^\beta = \dot{u}^\beta$ is the acceleration and the gradient of the pressure is a force. Additionally the projection operator $h^{\beta\alpha} := g^{\beta\alpha} + u^\beta u^\alpha$ appears in the relativistic version. In the formal limit $c \to \infty$, the velocity field $\vec{v}$ will satisfy the non-relativistic Euler equation for perfect fluids with rest mass density ρ

$$\rho \left(\partial_t v^i + v^j \partial_j v^i \right) = -g^{ij} \partial_j p. \qquad (2)$$

The usual way to derive the fluid equations (1) is to define the energy momentum tensor

$$T^{\mu\nu} = (e+p) u^\mu u^\nu + p g^{\mu\nu} \qquad (3)$$

and to postulate the conservation of energy and momentum $\nabla_\mu T^{\mu\nu} = 0$. This formulation goes back to the work of Einstein and Schwarzschild.[8,9] The first and second equation of (1) are equivalent to $\nabla_\mu T^{\mu\nu} = 0$. While the relativistic Euler equations are a rich source of mathematical problems, they constitute a highly idealized description of a fluid. A physically more complete description includes dissipative processes such as viscosity, diffusion and heat conduction.

To model dissipative effects of viscosity and heat conduction, the energy-momentum tensor is extended to

$$T^{\mu\nu} = (e+p+\Pi) u^\mu u^\nu + (p+\Pi) g^{\mu\nu} + \pi^{\mu\nu} + q^\mu u^\nu + q^\nu u^\mu, \qquad (4)$$

where q^ν is the heat-flux vector, Π the bulk viscosity, and $\pi^{\mu\nu}$ the tensor of shear viscosity. These quantities satisfy the orthogonality and symmetry constraints

$$q^\nu u_\nu = 0, \quad \pi^{\mu\nu} u_\mu = 0, \quad \pi^{\mu\nu} = \pi^{\nu\mu}, \quad \pi^{\mu\nu} g_{\mu\nu} = 0. \qquad (5)$$

The equations of motion that result from conservation of energy, momentum and particle number are now

$$\begin{aligned}
\text{momentum: } & (e+p+\Pi) \dot{u}_\mu + h_\mu^\nu \nabla_\nu (p+\Pi) + h_\mu^\alpha \nabla_\nu \pi_\alpha^\nu \\
& + h_{\nu\mu} \dot{q}^\nu + (\nabla_\nu u_\mu + \nabla_\alpha u^\alpha h_{\mu\nu}) q^\nu = 0 \\
\text{energy: } & \dot{e} + (e+p+\Pi) \nabla_\mu u^\mu + q_\mu \dot{u}^\mu + \nabla_\mu q^\mu + \pi^{\mu\nu} \sigma_{\mu\nu} = 0 \\
\text{particles: } & \nabla_\alpha (n u^\alpha) = 0 \\
\text{equation of state: } & p = p(e, n)
\end{aligned} \qquad (6)$$

To complete the system, additional dynamical equations for $(\Pi, q^\nu, \pi^{\mu\nu})$ have to be postulated. A large body of literature (see Ref. 7 and references therein) has been devoted to finding suitable dynamical equations for these quantities.

For a fluid with a single species of particles, i.e. excluding mixtures and chemical reactions, these evolution equations in the Israel-Stewart model take the form

$$\tau_0 \dot{\Pi} + \Pi + \zeta \nabla_\alpha u^\alpha + \left[\frac{1}{2} \zeta T \nabla_\alpha \left(\frac{\tau_0}{\zeta T} u^\alpha\right) \Pi\right] = 0$$

$$\tau_1 h_\nu^\lambda \dot{q}_\lambda + q_\nu = -\kappa T (h_\nu^\lambda \nabla_\lambda \ln T + a_\nu) - \left[\frac{1}{2} \kappa T^2 \nabla_\alpha \left(\frac{\tau_1}{\kappa T^2} u^\alpha\right) q_\nu\right] \quad (7)$$

$$\tau_2 h_\mu^\alpha h_\nu^\beta \dot{\pi}_{\alpha\beta} + \pi_{\mu\nu} = -2\eta \sigma_{\mu\nu} - \left[\frac{1}{2} \eta T \nabla_\gamma \left(\frac{\tau_2}{\eta T} u^\gamma\right) \pi_{\mu\nu}\right]$$

The appearance of the relaxation times $\tau_0, \tau_1, \tau_2 > 0$ is crucial for the stability and well-posedness of the model. The physical meaning of variables and various transport coefficients is as follows:

- Π bulk viscous pressure (isotropic force from fluid element shrinking/expanding).
- $\pi^{\mu\nu}$ shear viscous stresses (anisotropic force from transverse fluid layer movement).
- $p = p(e, n)$ hydrostatic pressure (isotropic gas pressure)
- e total energy density (rest energy density + internal energy density)
- n particle density (measures particles per volume)
- T absolute temperature
- $\zeta > 0, \eta > 0$ bulk/shear viscosity coefficient
- $\kappa > 0$ heat conductivity coefficient $\tau_0, \tau_1, \tau_2 > 0$ characteristic relaxation times for $\Pi, q^\nu, \pi^{\mu\nu}$
- $\sigma_{\mu\nu}$ kinematic shear tensor $\sigma_{\mu\nu} = h_\mu^\alpha h_\nu^\beta \frac{1}{2}(\nabla_\beta u_\alpha + \nabla_\alpha u_\beta)$, distortion of fluid element

I will refer to the set of equations (6), (7) as the full Israel-Stewart (IS) model. To see the mathematical structure of the equations (7) more clearly, the *truncated IS model*[7] (p. 302) is introduced. In (7) the divergence-type terms are dropped, leading to

$$\tau_0 \dot{\Pi} + \Pi = -\zeta \nabla_\alpha u^\alpha,$$
$$\tau_1 h_\nu^\lambda \dot{q}_\lambda + q_\nu = -\kappa T (h_\nu^\lambda \nabla_\lambda \ln T + a_\nu), \quad (8)$$
$$\tau_2 h_\mu^\alpha h_\nu^\beta \dot{\pi}_{\alpha\beta} + \pi_{\mu\nu} = -2\eta \sigma_{\mu\nu}$$

A formal non-relativistic limit $c \to \infty$, $\tau_i \to 0$ of (6), (8) recovers the classical compressible Navier-Stokes equations.[7] The equations (7) can be derived using a systematic procedure starting from the second law to thermodynamics (entropy production) (see Ref. 7). The full IS model can also be motivated by considerations from kinetic theory, which aims to derive macroscopic fluid equations by a moment expansion process (see Refs. 10–14).

The first dissipative relativistic fluid theories were formulated by Eckart[15] and Landau-Lifshitz.[16] These models are more direct covariant analogues of the non-relativistic Navier-Stokes equations. Consequently the equations of motion have a *parabolic character* and information can propagate at infinite speed, violating the most basic requirement of relativity.[17] In addition, the Eckart model can exhibit catastrophic instabilities.[18–20] As a reaction to these undesired properties, the IS model was developed in Refs. 21–25, with an initial contribution by Müller.[26] Partial differential operators with the property of finite speed of propagation are called *hyperbolic*[27] and the IS model is conjectured to have the even stronger property of *causality*. Causality requires both finite speed of propagation and that changes in initial data propagate at sub-light speeds, i.e. that the values of $(e, n, \Pi, u^\mu, q^\nu, \pi^{\mu\nu})$ at any point (t_0, x_0) depend only on the initial data given on the domain of dependence, i.e. inside the past-directed light cone.

The following heuristic argument illustrates why (7) should lead to finite speed of propagation: Consider the following modification of Fourier's law of heat conduction

$$\tau_0 \partial_t \vec{q} + \vec{q} = -\kappa \nabla T \tag{9}$$

with $\vec{q}(t, \cdot) : \mathbb{R}^3 \to \mathbb{R}^3$ being the three-dimensional heat flux. Assuming that the temperature T is proportional to the internal energy of the fluid and using conservation of energy leads to

$$\tau_0 \partial_t^2 T + \partial_t T - \kappa \Delta T = 0, \tag{10}$$

a generalized form of the heat equation, which is recovered upon setting $\tau_0 = 0$. (10) for $\tau_0 > 0$ is the telegraph equation[28] which has finite speed of propagation. The idea is therefore that the presence of relaxation times τ_i in (7) will have a similar effect and guarantee finite speed of propagation.

2. Local-wellposedness

The local well-posedness problems for the full and truncated systems (6),(7) (or (6), (8)) is still open. In Ref. 29, local-wellposedness and causality was shown for a related system used in heavy-ion collisions:

$$\begin{aligned}
u^\alpha \nabla_\alpha e + (e + P + \Pi) \nabla_\alpha u^\alpha + \pi^\alpha_\mu \nabla_\alpha u^\mu &= 0, \\
(e + P + \Pi) u^\beta \nabla_\beta u_\alpha + c_s^2 h_\alpha^\beta \nabla_\beta e + h_\alpha^\beta \nabla_\beta \Pi + h_\alpha^\beta \nabla_\mu \pi_\beta^\mu &= 0, \\
\tau_\Pi u^\mu \nabla_\mu \Pi + \Pi &= -\zeta \nabla_\mu u^\mu - \delta_{\Pi\Pi} \Pi \nabla_\mu u^\mu - \lambda_{\Pi\pi} \pi^{\mu\nu} \sigma_{\mu\nu}, \\
\tau_\pi h^{\mu\nu}_{\alpha\beta} u^\lambda \nabla_\lambda \pi^{\alpha\beta} + \pi^{\mu\nu} &= -2\eta \sigma^{\mu\nu} - \delta_{\pi\pi} \pi^{\mu\nu} \nabla_\alpha u^\alpha - \tau_{\pi\pi} \pi^{\langle\mu}_\alpha \sigma^{\nu\rangle\alpha} - \lambda_{\pi\Pi} \Pi \sigma^{\mu\nu},
\end{aligned} \tag{11}$$

which introduces new relaxation times and system coefficients $\tau_\pi, \lambda_{\pi\Pi}, \ldots$ etc. This system contains shear/bulk viscosity but no heat conduction. The equations for shear and bulk viscosity differ somewhat from the Israel-Stewart model, but follow the same general idea of introducing a relaxation mechanism.

Theorem 2.1. *Consider the Cauchy problem for equations (11) in Minkowski space, with initial data $\mathring{\Psi} = (\mathring{e}, \mathring{u}^\nu, \mathring{\Pi}, \mathring{\pi}^{\mu\nu})$ given on $\{t = 0\}$. There is an open set of inital data satisfying the constraints and that $\mathring{\Psi} \in \mathcal{G}^\delta(\{t = 0\})$, where $1 \leq \delta < 20/19$. Then, there exist a $T > 0$ and a unique $\Psi = (e, u^\nu, \Pi, \pi^{\mu\nu})$ defined on $[0, T) \times \mathbb{R}^3$*

such that Ψ is a solution in $[0,T) \times \mathbb{R}^3$ and $\Psi = \mathring{\Psi}$ on $\{t=0\}$. Moreover, the solution Ψ is causal (i.e. domain of influence of initial data is contained in forward light-cones).

The set of admissible initial data is physically reasonable and can be described by a set of inequalities involving ε, Π and the eigenvalues of π_ν^μ. The notation $\mathcal{G}^\delta(\{t=0\})$ refers to a Gevrey-type space, and we refer to Ref. 29 for more details.

3. Breakdown of solutions

Solutions to nonlinear partial differential equations may have a finite lifespan, the most elementary example being Burgers' equation.[30] For suitable C^∞ initial data, solutions develop a shock, i.e. a singularity in the first derivative after a finite time. A deeper question can also be asked: What precisely happens at breakdown time? Do derivatives or the fields themselves become infinite? For perfect relativistic fluids there exists a well-developed theory that proves shock formation[31–33] giving a detailed picture of the quantities that actually blow up. These results are very deep and rely on hidden geometric-analytic structures in the perfect fluid equations, which allow their formulation as quasilinear second-order covariant wave equations. It is a hard unsolved problem how to generalize these delicate hidden structures to dissipative fluids. Considering the available mathematical technology, asking for a detailed description of the singularity in the dissipative case seems to be out of reach for now. The investigation of these matters is clearly in its beginning stages, and in Ref.[34] we establish a first blowup result for a viscous dissipative fluid with only bulk viscosity (no shear viscosity or heat conduction). The basic ideas are based on the work by Sideris[35] and for relativistic fluids based on Guo-Tahvildar-Zadeh,[36] who developed a robust technique to show breakdown of smooth solutions for compressible fluids using the fundamental conservation $\nabla_\mu T^{\mu\nu} = 0$. Novel aspects of this method continue being discovered.[34,37] At the core of this technique lies a type of virial identity involving the second moment of the energy density, from which differential inequalities are derived, leading to the blowup via a contradiction argument.

Theorem 3.1. *Consider the viscous equations with bulk viscosity (without shear viscosity) with given smooth constitutive functions p, ζ, τ_0. Assume that*

$$\mathcal{C} := \int_0^\infty \frac{1}{n} \sup_{\rho \geq 0} \frac{\zeta(\rho,n)}{\tau_0(\rho,n)} \, dn < \infty$$

and make further (mild) technical assumptions of the equation of state $p = p(e,n)$. There exists a smooth initial data $(\mathring{\rho}, \mathring{n}, \mathring{\Pi}, \mathring{u})$ with large velocities such that the local smooth solution breaks down in finite time.

A detailed discussion of the model and the assumptions on equations of state and bulk viscosity can be found in Ref. 34. The viscous case requires novel estimates for Π. From its evolution, we have $\dot{\Pi} \sim \nabla_\alpha u^\alpha$, but the quantity $\nabla_\alpha u^\alpha$ is very hard to control in a non-constructive blowup proof. Instead, we use a hidden structure in the equations, namely an auxiliary transport equation in ρ, n, Π allowing us to get estimates for Π.

4. Conclusion

Including dissipation into models of relativistic fluids is necessary for a complete macroscopic description, as effects such as viscosity and heat conduction are ubiquitous in nature. Investigating dissipative effects in relativity has a long history, yet there is a gap in knowledge considering many fundamental questions about existence, uniqueness, blowup and decay properties of solutions. First breakthroughs have been made but many important problems remain open, for example to show well-posedness and singularity formation for the Israel-Stewart model (6), (7).

References

1. W. Busza, K. Rajagopal and W. van der Schee, Heavy ion collisions: The big picture and the big questions, *Annual Review of Nuclear and Particle Science* **68**, p. 339–376 (2018).
2. U. Heinz and R. Snellings, Collective flow and viscosity in relativistic heavy-ion collisions, *Ann. Rev. Nucl. Part. Sci.* **63**, 123 (2013).
3. The 2015 Nuclear Science Advisory Committee, *Reaching for the Horizon. The 2015 Long Range Plan for Nuclear Science* (US Department of Energy and the National Science Foundation, 2015), https://science.energy.gov/~/media/np/nsac/pdf/2015LRP/2015_LRPNS_091815.pdf.
4. M. G. Alford, L. Bovard, M. Hanauske, L. Rezzolla and K. Schwenzer, Viscous dissipation and heat conduction in binary neutron-star mergers, *Phys. Rev. Lett.* **120**, p. 041101 (2018).
5. L. P. Hughston and K. P. Tod, *An introduction to general relativity* (Cambridge University Press, 2006).
6. E. Poisson and C. M. Will, *Gravity: Newtonian, post-Newtonian, relativistic* (Cambridge University Press, 2014).
7. L. Rezzolla and O. Zanotti, *Relativistic hydrodynamics* (Oxford University Press, New York, 2013).
8. A. Einstein, The formal foundation of the general theory of relativity, *Sitzungsber. Preuss. Akad. Wiss. Berlin (Math. Phys.)* **1914**, 1030 (1914).
9. K. Schwarzschild, On the gravitational field of a sphere of incompressible fluid according to Einstein's theory, *Sitzungsber. Preuss. Akad. Wiss. Berlin (Math. Phys.)* **1916**, 424 (1916).
10. S. Bhattacharyya, V. E. Hubeny, S. Minwalla and M. Rangamani, Nonlinear fluid dynamics from gravity, *JHEP* **02**, p. 045 (2008).
11. M. P. Heller, A. Kurkela, M. Spalinski and V. Svensson, Hydrodynamization in kinetic theory: Transient modes and the gradient expansion, *Phys. Rev.* **D97**, p. 091503 (2018).
12. R. Baier, P. Romatschke, D. T. Son, A. O. Starinets and M. A. Stephanov, Relativistic viscous hydrodynamics, conformal invariance, and holography, *JHEP* **04**, p. 100 (2008).

13. G. S. Denicol and J. Noronha, Divergence of the Chapman-Enskog expansion in relativistic kinetic theory (2016), https://arxiv.org/abs/1608.07869.
14. G. S. Denicol, H. Niemi, E. Molnar and D. H. Rischke, Derivation of transient relativistic fluid dynamics from the Boltzmann equation, *Phys. Rev.* **D85**, p. 114047 (2012), [Erratum: Phys. Rev.D91,no.3,039902(2015)].
15. C. Eckart, The thermodynamics of irreversible processes III. Relativistic theory of the simple fluid, *Physical Review* **58**, 919 (1940).
16. L. D. Landau and E. M. Lifshitz, *Fluid Mechanics - Volume 6 (Course of Theoretical Physics)*, second edn. (Butterworth-Heinemann, 1987).
17. W. A. Hiscock and L. Lindblom, Linear plane waves in dissipative relativistic fluids, *Phys. Rev. D* **35** (1987).
18. W. A. Hiscock and L. Lindblom, Stability and causality in dissipative relativistic fluids, *Annals of Physics* **151**, 466 (1983).
19. W. A. Hiscock and L. Lindblom, Generic instabilities in first-order dissipative fluid theories, *Phys. Rev. D* **31**, 725 (1985).
20. W. A. Hiscock and L. Lindblom, Nonlinear pathologies in relativistic heat-conducting fluid theories, *Physics Letters A* **131**, 509 (1988).
21. W. Israel, Nonstationary irreversible thermodynamics: A causal relativistic theory, *Ann. Phys.* **100**, 310 (1976).
22. W. Israel and J. M. Stewart, Thermodynamics of nonstationary and transient effects in a relativistic gas, *Phys. Lett. A* **58**, 213 (1976).
23. J. M. Stewart, On transient relativistic thermodynamics and kinetic theory, *Proc. R. Soc. London, Ser. A* **357**, 59 (oct 1977).
24. W. Israel and J. M. Stewart, On transient relativistic thermodynamics and kinetic theory. II, *Proc. R. Soc. London, Ser. A* **365**, 43 (feb 1979).
25. W. Israel and J. M. Stewart, Transient relativistic thermodynamics and kinetic theory, *Ann. Phys.* **118**, 341 (1979).
26. I. Mueller, Zum Paradox der Wärmeleitungstheorie, *Zeit. fur Phys* **198**, 329 (1967).
27. P. D. Lax, *Hyperbolic partial differential equations* (Courant Institute of Mathematical Sciences, 2006).
28. G. B. Nagy, O. E. Ortiz and O. A. Reula, The behavior of hyperbolic heat equations' solutions near their parabolic limits, *Journal of Mathematical Physics* **35**, p. 4334–4356 (1994).
29. F. S. Bemfica, M. M. Disconzi, V. Hoang, J. Noronha and M. Radosz, Nonlinear constraints on relativistic fluids far from equilibrium, *Physical Review Letters* **126**, p. 222301 (2021), https://journals.aps.org/prl/abstract/10.1103/PhysRevLett.126.222301.
30. L. C. Evans, *Partial differential equations*, Graduate Studies in Mathematics, Vol. 19, second edn. (American Mathematical Society, Providence, RI, 2010).
31. D. Christodoulou, The Euler equations of compressible fluid flow, *Bull. Amer. Math. Soc. (NS)* **44**, 581 (2007).
32. J. Speck, *Shock formation in small-data solutions to 3D quasilinear wave equations*, Mathematical Surveys and Monographs, Vol. 214 (American Mathematical Society, Providence, RI, 2016).
33. M. M. Disconzi and J. Speck, The Relativistic Euler Equations: Remarkable Null Structures and Regularity Properties, *Ann. Henri Poincaré* **20**, 2173 (2019).
34. M. Disconzi, V. Hoang and M.Radosz, Breakdown of smooth solutions to the Müller-Israel-Stewart equations of relativistic viscous fluids https://arxiv.org/abs/2008.03841.

35. T. C. Sideris, Formation of singularities in three-dimensional compressible fluids, *Communications in Mathematical Physics* **101**, p. 475–485 (1985).
36. Y. Guo and A. S. Tahvildar-Zadeh, Formation of singularities in relativistic fluid dynamics and in spherically symmetric plasma dynamics, *Nonlinear Partial Differential Equations* **238**, p. 151–161 (1999).
37. Z. Jin and Y. Zhou, Formation of finite-time singularities for nonlinear hyperbolic systems with small initial disturbances, *Journal of Mathematical Physics* **61**, p. 071510 (2020).

Adiabatic solutions in general relativity as null geodesics on the space of boundary diffeomorphisms

Emine Şeyma Kutluk

Physics Department, Middle East Technical University,
Ankara, 06800, Turkey
E-mail: ekutluk@metu.edu.tr
www.metu.edu.tr

We use Weinberg's trick for adiabatic modes, in a Manton approximation for general relativity on manifolds with spatial boundary. This results in a description of the slow-time dependent solutions as null geodesics on the space of boundary diffeomorphisms, with respect to a metric we prove to be composed solely of the boundary data. We show how the solutions in the bulk space is determined with the constraints of general relativity.

To give our description a larger perspective, we furthermore identify our resulting Lagrangian as a generalized version of the covariantized Lagrangian for continuum mechanics. We study the cases of 3+1 and 2+1 dimensions and show for the solutions we propose, the Hamiltonian constraint becomes the real homogeneous Monge-Ampere equation in the special case of two spatial dimensions.

Keywords: Adiabatic Solutions; Large Gauge Symmetries; Manton Approximation; Soft Modes; Moduli Space; Geometric Continuum Mechanics

1. Introduction and Summary

Asymptotic symmetries and soft theorems has been a topic that drew much attention in the last decade. Starting from 2013, Strominger have shown[1–3] that soft theorems arise as Ward identities of asymptotic space-time and/or gauge symmetries. Since then many new versions of soft theorems have been suggested.

Independently of this line of research, in quantum cosmology people have been studying similar Ward identities.[4–6] These studies heavily relies on Weinberg's argument for the existence of adiabatic modes on a generic cosmological background.[7]

We use a similar argument for general relativity in a Manton approximation.[8,9] Manton approximation tells one slow time trajectories on the space of static and minimum energy solutions, called the vacua, are good approximate solutions. In our approach we take the vacua to be gauge transformations of a reference metric; then introduce the time dependency in a way that the resulting trajectory is no longer a redundant gauge transformation-as was the case in Weinberg's argument. We study what becomes of the Lagrangian and the equations of motion for these trajectories, and see

- Lagrangian solely depends on the quantities on the boundary of spatial slices,
- constraints of general relativity serves to determine the bulk metric from its boundary values,

- solutions are geodesics on the space of vacua, which are further required to be null due to the Hamiltonian constraint.

Trajectories on diffeomorphism groups were previously used to describe the motion of ideal fluids[10] (see also Ref. 11), where they are described as geodesics with respect to a metric. We covariantize this description,[9] and show that our aforementioned solutions correspond to a specific choice of a generalized metric.

As particular examples we study solutions produced from a flat metric on 3-dimensional ball and also general two dimensional enclosed surface. We show how Hamiltonian constraint enforces coupling of two independent towers in the former and how it reduces down to homogeneous-real Monge Ampere equation in the latter case.

2. A Manton Approximation for General Relativity

2.1. *Setup*

We start by reviewing the Manton approximation[12] (see also Refs. 13, 14). Let us have a set of fields $\phi^I(t, x)$, on a spacetime described by the coordinates (t, x). Let us describe our system with a *natural* action

$$S = \int \left(\frac{1}{2} g_{IJ}(\phi) \dot{\phi}^I \dot{\phi}^J - V(\phi) \right) dV^{d+1} \tag{1}$$

where dV^{d+1}, with a slight abuse of notation, denotes the Riemannian volume form for a metric on the $d+1$ dimensional space-time manifold. Let us consider the configuration space, i.e. the space of static fields, called $\mathcal{F}$.

Assume that the potential have a continuous set of minima called $\mathcal{E}$; more specifically, in the configuration space let there be a submanifold such that

$$(\partial_I V)(\varphi^I) = 0 \quad \text{where} \quad \varphi^I \in \mathcal{E}. \tag{2}$$

Note that these static fields are solutions to equations of motion for the type of theory we are considering, since the equation of motion is given by

$$g_{IK} \left(\ddot{\phi}^I + \Gamma^I_{MJ} \dot{\phi}^M \dot{\phi}^J \right) = -\partial_K V. \tag{3}$$

Now the metric g_{IJ} will induce a metric on $\mathcal{E}$. The Manton approximation tells us that a *geodesic* on $\mathcal{E}$ with respect to this metric, that is slow in time, is a good approximate solution and the motion off $\mathcal{E}$ can be ignored.

Now we want to apply this procedure to general relativity. For this we need a Lagrangian for general relativity that is of the natural form. This can be achieved by considering a spacetime manifold in the form of $\mathbb{R} \times M$ with the ADM action, and then choosing Gaussian normal coordinates (GNC) where $g_{00} = -1, g_{0i} = 0$. Then, renaming the spatial part of the metric as $h_{ij} = g_{ij}$ the action we have is

$$S = \frac{1}{2} \int g_h(\dot{h}_{ij}, \dot{h}_{kl}) \, dt - \int V[h] \, dt \tag{4}$$

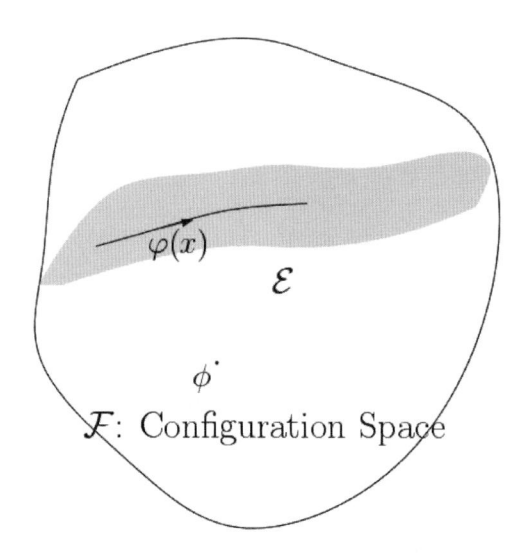

Fig. 1. Configuration space and the space of minima

where

$$g_h(\delta_1 h, \delta_2 h) = \frac{1}{2} \int_M \left(h^{ik} h^{jl} - h^{ij} h^{kl} \right) \delta_1 h_{ij} \delta_2 h_{kl} \, dV^d \,, \tag{5}$$

$$V[h] = -\int_M R(h) \, dV^d \,. \tag{6}$$

Here dV^d is the Riemannian volume form and $R(h)$ Ricci scalar for $h.g_h$ will be the metric on the configuration space. Note that since g_{00}, g_{0i}, generally known as lapse and shift, are Lagrange multipliers which we have fixed; constraints of GR

$$\nabla^i \left(\dot{h}_{ij} - h^{kl} \dot{h}_{kl} h_{ij} \right) = 0 \,, \tag{7}$$

$$R(h) + \frac{1}{2} h^{ij} h^{kl} \dot{h}_{i[j} \dot{h}_{k]l} = 0 \,, \tag{8}$$

needs to be imposed externally from now on.

To implement the Manton approximation, we now need to identify the set of static solutions that extremize the theory. Note that the potential is not bounded from below, so there will be no minimal energy. However it will have an extrema:

$$\delta V|_{\bar{h}} = 0 \rightarrow \quad R_{ij}(\bar{h}) = 0 \,. \tag{9}$$

So the Ricci flat metrics $\bar{h}$ and their gauge transformations will compose the space of static set of extrema of the action. For our investigation we focus on a single reference metric and its gauge transformations, i.e. we define the static extrema $\mathcal{E}$ to be composed of metrics

$$h = \psi \cdot \bar{h} \,, \tag{10}$$

i.e. a Ricci flat metric and its gauge transformations. Remember we have chosen a gauge, thus the remaining gauge transformations are not full set of diffeomorphisms. They turn out to be two sets that can be written as

$$\psi_\chi = \left(0, \chi^i(x)\right),\tag{11}$$

$$\psi_\alpha = \left(\alpha(x), \partial_j \alpha(x) \int_0^t h^{ij}(t', x) dt'\right).\tag{12}$$

First of these are simply the spatial diffeomorphisms, whereas the second type are a form of local boost- they are the transformations that take a choice of "initial" hypersurface to another one when choosing GNC, see Ref. 14 for more details. Local boosts are field-dependent transformations, and thus they do not form a proper algebra- reflecting the fact that constraints of general relativity do not form a proper algebra.[a] Moreover they are not static as what a Manton description tells a vacuum ought to be. Because of these reasons we restrict our attention to spatial diffeomorphisms and define $\mathcal{E}$ as the space of metrics produced by spatial gauge transformations of the flat metric.

So we take $\mathcal{E}$ to be the set of spatial metrics that are -spatial- gauge transformations of a spatial reference metric, i.e.

$$h = \phi^* \bar{h}.\tag{13}$$

Written in a coordinate basis this reads as

$$h_{ij}^z(x) = \frac{\partial \phi^k(x, z)}{\partial x^i} \frac{\partial \phi^m(x, z)}{\partial x^j} \bar{h}_{km}\tag{14}$$

where z parametrizes the gauge transformations. The dynamics is then described as a motion on this space:

$$h_{ij}^z(x, t) = \frac{\partial \phi^k(x, z(t))}{\partial x^i} \frac{\partial \phi^m(x, z(t))}{\partial x^j} \bar{h}_{km},\tag{15}$$

or

$$h(t) = \phi_t^* \bar{h}.\tag{16}$$

Note here the "trickiness": Once we introduce the time dependency this way, what we are doing is not a coordinate/gauge transformation in the full spacetime.

Let us illustrate this with a simple example in 3+1 dimensions. Take reference spatial metric to be the flat metric $\bar{h}_{ij} = \delta_{ij}$. Consider the transformations

$$\phi_t^i = a(t) x^i.\tag{17}$$

For these transformations our ansatz will produce the spacetime metric

$$ds^2 = -dt^2 + a^2(t)(dx^2 + dy^2 + dz^2).\tag{18}$$

---

[a] Commutators of constraints of general relativity gives what is called an algebroid, see Ref. 15 and Ref. 16 for further discussion.

This illustrates very clearly that our ansatz gives us physically new solutions, for this case the spatially flat FRW spacetime.[b]

2.2. *Motion as a Geodesic on the Space of Boundary Diffeomorphisms*

In the last subsection we have proposed solutions to Einstein equations in GNC where

$$h(t) = \phi_t^* \bar{h} . \tag{19}$$

Now we would like to check whether these solve the Einstein equations or if they should satisfy further conditions. Note that our free variable is the diffeomorphism $\phi(t,x)$ here. We start by first checking the constraint equations that we have started imposing externally after we have eliminated the Lagrange multipliers. First we observe for our solutions Eq. (19) we have

$$\dot{h}_{ij} = \nabla_i \xi_j + \nabla_j \xi_i \quad \text{where} \quad \xi^i := \dot{\phi}^k \frac{\partial x^i}{\partial \phi^k} \quad \text{so that} \quad K_{ij} = \nabla_{(i} \xi_{j)} . \tag{20}$$

Here ∇ is the covariant derivative belonging to h. Using this and the fact $R_{ij}(h) = R_{ij}(\bar{h}) = 0$, momentum constraint becomes

$$\mathcal{P}_j(\xi) = \nabla^i \nabla_{[i} \xi_{j]} = 0 , \tag{21}$$

whereas Hamiltonian constraint is

$$\mathcal{H}(\xi) = (\nabla_i \xi^i)^2 - \nabla_{(i} \xi_{j)} \nabla^i \xi^j = 0 . \tag{22}$$

Furthermore the dynamics will be determined with the reduced Lagrangian, where one plugs Eq. (19) in Eq. (4). For our solutions the potential is zero whereas the kinetic term is the length of $\dot{h}$ with respect to the metric

$$g_h(\delta_1 h, \delta_2 h) = \frac{1}{2} \int_M \left(\nabla_{(i} \xi_{1j)} \nabla^i \xi_2^j - (\nabla_i \xi_1^i)(\nabla_i \xi_2^i) \right) dV^d . \tag{23}$$

This is the metric Eq. (5) on the configuration space pulled back to the space of vacua. As we have noted, solutions to the dynamical equation of the above action will be geodesics on the space of vacua with respect to this metric. Then we see *Hamiltonian constraint restricts these geodesics to be null.*

Now note that each spatial slice is diffeomorphic to the reference slice, so everything can be re-expressed in coordinates where the spatial metric is equal to reference metric i.e. defining

$$\sigma := \phi_{t*} \xi \tag{24}$$

---

[b]This will not solve vacuum Einstein equations, but this is not relevant for the point made here.

constraint equations and the metric on the vacua space can be rewritten as

$$\mathcal{P}_j(\sigma) = \bar{\nabla}^i \bar{\nabla}_{[i}\sigma_{j]} = 0 , \tag{25}$$

$$\mathcal{H}(\sigma) = (\bar{\nabla}_i \sigma^i)^2 - \bar{\nabla}_{(i}\sigma_{j)}\bar{\nabla}^i \sigma^j = 0 , \tag{26}$$

$$g_h(\delta_1 h, \delta_2 h) = \frac{1}{2} \int_M \left(\bar{\nabla}_{(i}\sigma_{1j)} \bar{\nabla}^i \sigma_2^j - (\bar{\nabla}_i \sigma_1^i)(\bar{\nabla}_i \sigma_2^i) \right) dV^d(\bar{h}). \tag{27}$$

We will use this coordinate frame for ease of calculation. Note that coordinate transformation to this frame will be different for each spatial slice.

Now we proceed to showing that the metric on the space of vacua, Eq. (27), is composed of the boundary data. For this we would like to decompose things into parts tangent and normal to the boundary ∂M, so we simply write everything in the basis $\{n, e^a\}$ where n is the unique normalized vector field orthogonal to ∂M and e^a is a orthogonal basis tangent to ∂M.[c] Now if one uses the momentum constraint Eq. (25) within Eq. (27), and assume vector field σ to be boundary preserving i.e.

$$n_i \sigma^i \big|_{\partial M} = 0 , \tag{28}$$

one can see that

$$g_h(\sigma_{(1)}, \sigma_{(2)}) = \oint_{\partial M} \left(\sigma_{(1)}^a D^\perp \sigma_a^{(2)} - \mathcal{K}_{ab} \sigma_{(1)}^a \sigma_{(2)}^b \right) dV^{d-1}(\bar{k}) \tag{29}$$

where $\mathcal{K}$ is the extrinsic curvature of ∂M in M, σ^a is the part of σ^i that is tangential to ∂M, $\bar{k}$ is the induced metric on the boundary and we have defined a normal derivative

$$D^\perp \chi^a \equiv n^i \partial_i \chi^a + \Gamma^a_b \chi^b \quad \text{where} \quad \Gamma^b_a = n^i e^b_j \bar{\nabla}_i e^j_a . \tag{30}$$

Note that

- $D^\perp$ is $\bar{k}$-compatible.
- For a basis where $[n, e_a] = 0$ one has $\Gamma^a_b = K^a_b$.

Looking back at the metric Eq. (29) we see that it is completely composed of the boundary data, except the term with the normal derivative. Remember that σ still need to satisfy the constraint equations Eq. (25) and Eq. (26) in the bulk. If we can show given a vector field on the boundary, there exist a solution to these equations with unique normal derivative $D^\perp \sigma$ on the boundary, we can say we have reduced our action to boundary data. Let us examine these equations and their solutions.

We will start with the momentum constraint: Using the theory of differential forms on manifolds with boundary, especially the *Hodge-Morrey-Friedrichs decomposition* following theorem can be proven.[8]

---

[c]We take this to be true also slightly off the ∂M.

Theorem 2.1. *On a homologically trivial manifold with boundary, given a boundary vector field ζ^a, there exists a vector field σ such that*

$$P(\sigma) = 0, \quad n_i \sigma^i \big|_{\partial M} = 0, \quad \sigma^a = \zeta^a \tag{31}$$

and unique up to the gradients of scalars that vanish on the boundary. More specifically σ can be written as

$$\sigma = (d\alpha + *d * \beta)^\sharp \quad \text{where} \quad n\beta = 0 . \tag{32}$$

This is true in arbitrary dimensions, and in 3d it takes the form of the Helmholtz theorem. We conjecture that the arbitrariness in α will be fixed by the Hamiltonian constraint, though we were not able to prove this; please see Ref. 8 for more details.

However to show that the metric on the space of vacua is solely determined by boundary data one will not need to show this. This is because for the exact part where arbitrariness lies, one can show

$$D^\perp \partial_a \alpha \big|_{\partial M} = -\mathcal{K}_a^b \partial_b \alpha . \tag{33}$$

With this, we have shown that the metric on the space of vacua is solely composed of the data on the spatial boundary.

Because of this conclusion, we can consider this metric as an inner product on the space of boundary vector fields now:

$$g_h(\sigma_1, \sigma_2) = \langle \zeta_{(1)}, \zeta_{(2)} \rangle_h \tag{34}$$

$$\equiv \oint_{\partial M} \left(\zeta_{(1)}^a D^\perp \zeta_a^{(2)} - \mathcal{K}_{ab} \zeta_{(1)}^a \zeta_{(2)}^b \right) dV^{d-1}(\bar{k}) . \tag{35}$$

We conclude this section by noting that the space of vacua now can be described as

$$\mathcal{V} \cong \frac{\text{Diff}(\partial M)}{\text{biso}(\bar{h})} . \tag{36}$$

We quotient by boundary preserving isometries of the reference metric since these will disappear in g_h, see the original expression Eq. (23). This quotient can be performed precisely because of our conjecture that for a given arbitrary boundary diffeomorphism there exists a unique solution to constraint equations implies $\text{Diff}(\partial M) \cong \text{BDiff}_C(M)$, boundary preserving diffeomorphisms of M that satisfies constraint equations.

One can show that $\mathcal{V}$ is a (pseudo-)Riemannian homogeneous space: i.e. the metric $g_{\bar{h}}$ we have defined is $\text{Diff}(\partial M)$ invariant. This metric will have a mixed signature. Indeed one can see $\langle,\rangle$ is zero for boundary vector fields such that

$$D^\perp \zeta^a - \mathcal{K}_b^a \zeta^b = \mathbb{D}\zeta = 0 . \tag{37}$$

i.e. if $\zeta \in \ker \mathbb{D}$. One can show that isometries are necessarily in $\ker \mathbb{D}$. If the reverse is not also true the metric will be degenerate on the space of vacua.

3. Geometric Continuum Mechanics Interpretation

The idea of describing motion as a trajectory on a diffeomorphism group is well-known in studies of "ideal continuum motion",[11] which are generalizations of Arnold's work on putting motion of an incompressible-ideal fluid in the Lagrangian and Hamiltonian framework.[10] In the following we summarize a covariantized generalization of ideal continuum motion of Ref. 11, as presented in Ref. 9. Later on we will see how our formalism of previous section fits within this generalization.

Consider a manifold M with a flow $\phi(x,t)$ on it. Derivative with respect to t, at $t=0$ of this flow is a vector field on M. What about at other times? At other times hardship arises since $\dot\phi(x,t) := \partial_t \phi(x,t)$ is the velocity at the point $\phi(x,t)$, not x. However one can define

$$\chi(x;t) := \dot\phi(y,t)\Big|_{y=\phi^{-1}(x;t)}, \tag{38}$$

then $\chi(x;t)$ will be a proper vector field. Now assume there exists a metric g on this manifold M, and consider the action

$$S = \frac{1}{2} \int_I \int_M g(\chi, \mathbb{D}\chi) dV_g \, dt \tag{39}$$

for some interval I of t, where dV_g is the Riemannian volume form for the metric g and $\mathbb{D} : \mathfrak{X}(M) \to \mathfrak{X}(M)$ is a self-adjoint, positive definite operator. We want to find the equation of motion for this action. Since the operator $\mathbb{D}$ is self-adjoint

$$\delta S = \int_I \int_M g(\delta\chi, \mathbb{D}\chi) dV_g \, dt. \tag{40}$$

Now let us find $\delta\chi$ in terms of $\delta\phi$. We see

$$\delta\chi^i(x;t) = \delta^i \dot\phi(y;t) - \partial_j \dot\phi(y;t) \partial_k \left(\phi^{-1}\right)^j \delta\Phi^k(x;t) \tag{41}$$

where we set $y = \phi^{-1}(x;t)$ and defined

$$\delta\Phi^i(z;t) = \delta\phi^j\left(\phi^{-1}(z;t);t\right). \tag{42}$$

With further modifications we get

$$\delta\chi(x;t) = \partial_t \delta\Phi(x;t) + \mathcal{L}_\chi \delta\Phi, \tag{43}$$

so that

$$\delta S = \int_I \int_M g\left(\partial_t \delta\Phi + \mathcal{L}_\chi \delta\Phi, \mathbb{D}\chi\right) dV_g dt. \tag{44}$$

To get variational principle working we should integrate by parts to collect all the operators to one side. For this we note

$$\int_M g\left(\mathcal{L}_\chi \eta, \alpha\right) dV_g = \int_M \alpha_i \left(\chi^j \nabla_j \eta^i - \eta^j \nabla_j \chi^i\right) dV_g, \tag{45}$$

$$= \int_{\partial M} \alpha_i \eta^i \chi^\perp - \int_M \eta^i \left(\nabla_j \alpha_i \chi^j + \alpha_i \nabla_j \chi^j + \alpha_j \nabla_i \chi^j\right) dV_g, \tag{46}$$

where ∇ is the unique metric compatible and torsion free connection for g. We will assume M to have no boundary so that the first term drops. Defining $\mathcal{L}_\chi^\dagger$ as

$$\int_M g(\mathcal{L}_\chi \eta, \alpha)\, dV_g = \int_M g\left(\eta, \mathcal{L}_\chi^\dagger \alpha\right) dV_g \tag{47}$$

we see that

$$\mathcal{L}_\chi^\dagger \alpha = -\left(\nabla \cdot \chi\, \alpha + \mathcal{L}_\chi \alpha + \alpha \lrcorner \mathcal{L}_\chi g\right), \tag{48}$$

where $\mathcal{L}_\chi g_{ij} = 2\nabla_{(i}\chi_{j)}$ and $(\alpha \lrcorner \omega)_j := \alpha^i \omega_{ij}$. Using this then, we see that the equation of motion becomes

$$\left(\partial_t - \mathcal{L}_\chi^\dagger\right) \mathbb{D}\chi = 0. \tag{49}$$

Writing down explicitly $\mathcal{L}^\dagger$ and expressing in a basis we get

$$(\partial_t + \zeta^b \nabla_b)\mathbb{D}\zeta^a + (\nabla^a \zeta_b + \delta^a_b \nabla_c \zeta^c)\mathbb{D}\zeta^b = 0. \tag{50}$$

One can retrieve some classic examples for certain choices of $\mathbb{D}$:

- $\mathbb{D} = \mathrm{id}$ gives Euler's equation for the free motion of an incompressible fluid.
- $\mathbb{D} = \mathrm{id} - \nabla^2$ gives Camassa-Holm equation for shallow water waves.

As it can be easily identified we get the system of previous subsection for the choice of $\mathbb{D} = D^\perp - \mathcal{K}^a_b$.

4. Some Results in 3+1 and 2+1 Dimensions

Having described our solutions as null geodesics on the space of boundary diffeomorphisms we now proceed to studying some specific examples.

4.1. On Round Ball

We start by considering the case where we take Euclidean 3d ball with round boundary as reference. Let us first look at the momentum constraint. Expressed in vector calculus form it turns out to be

$$\vec{\nabla} \times \vec{\nabla} \times \vec{\sigma} = 0. \tag{51}$$

Solution to this in spherical coordinates will be

$$\vec{\sigma} = a_{\ell m} r^\ell \vec{r} \times \vec{\nabla} Y_{\ell m}(\theta, \varphi) + \vec{\nabla}\left(f_{\ell m}(r) Y_{\ell m}(\theta, \varphi)\right). \tag{52}$$

Note that this satisfies our theorem: σ is composed of parts that are exact and coexact with zero normal on the boundary. We conjectured that the exact part should be fixed by the Hamiltonian constraint. However we were not able to solve it even for this simple case.

Plugging in the solution, we get for the metric on the space of vacua

$$g(\sigma^{(1)}, \sigma^{(2)}) = R^3 \sum_{\ell,m} \ell(\ell+1)\left((\ell-1)a^{(1)}_{\ell m} a^{(2)}_{\ell m} - 2f^{(1)}_{\ell m}(R) f^{(2)}_{\ell m}(R)\right). \tag{53}$$

Notice that even though we do not know $f_{\ell m}(r)$ in the bulk, indeed its bulk value does not appear in the metric, as we have proposed. Moreover Hamiltonian equations forces $g(\sigma, \sigma) = 0$, thus we see that single towers of $a_{\ell m}$ or $f_{\ell m}$ cannot be solutions, there has to be mixing.

On the boundary our solutions have the form

$$\sigma^a = \epsilon^{ab} \partial_b \tau + \bar{k}^{ab} \partial_b \kappa \ . \tag{54}$$

Note that this is basically the Hodge decomposition of a one form on S^2, thus our solution space is set of all diffeomorphisms on S^2. Except the isotropy group: boundary preserving isometries of $\bar{h}_{ij} = \delta_{ij}$, these will be rotations. For this case the isotropy group will be equal to $\ker \mathbb{D}$ since

$$\ker \mathbb{D} = \{\sigma^a \,|a_{\ell m} = 0 \; \ell > 1, f_{\ell m}(R) = 0 \; \forall \ell, m\} = \{\sigma^a = \sum_m a_{1m} \, R\vec{R} \times \vec{\nabla} Y_{1m}\} \ . \tag{55}$$

Thus our physical vacua space is

$$\mathcal{V} = \text{Diff}(S^2)/\text{SO}(3) \tag{56}$$

and our metric on this is non-degenerate.

4.2. *Case of 2 Dimensions*

Since we were not able to solve the Hamiltonian constraint to find solutions in the bulk, we now check if things simplify in $2+1$ dimensions. We will consider a flat reference metric with an arbitrary boundary, and then focus on some specific choices for the boundary. In two spatial bulk dimensions momentum equation gets solved when

$$\vec{\sigma} = c \frac{\partial}{\partial \theta} + \vec{\nabla} \alpha \tag{57}$$

where c and α is arbitrary. Hamiltonian equation then becomes

$$(\partial_x \partial_y \alpha)^2 - \partial_x^2 \alpha \partial_y^2 \alpha = 0 \ , \tag{58}$$

the well-known *homogeneous real Monge-Ampere equation (HRMA)*.[17] Most generalized solution to this is known in a parametric form, together with some family of explicit solutions. However we find that these mostly do not survive the boundary preservingness condition we impose for simple choices of the boundary.

Let us first consider some specific examples and start with the case of a round boundary, where $r = R$. The boundary preservingness condition become

$$\partial_r \alpha|_{r=R} = 0 \ . \tag{59}$$

We find no solution that satisfy this condition. Indeed looking at the metric we see

$$g(\chi, \chi) = -\frac{2}{R^2} \int \partial_\theta \alpha(R, \theta) \partial_\theta \alpha(R, \theta) d\theta \ . \tag{60}$$

Remember that the metric is derived from the Hamiltonian condition, and thus since it cannot be made to be zero for a non trivial α, there exists no non-trivial solution to this problem. (Note that the coexact part is an isometry and will be quotiented out.)

Next simplest example is the case of an elliptic boundary. We consider an ellipse that is written as

$$r = \frac{\rho}{2} \frac{\sinh(2\Upsilon)}{\sqrt{\cosh^2 \Upsilon - \cos^2 \varphi}}, \tag{61}$$

where Υ and ρ are parameters of the ellipse. In this case the boundary preservingness condition is

$$\partial_u \alpha|_{\partial M} = -\frac{\rho^2 c}{4} \sin(2v) \tag{62}$$

where u, v are elliptic coordinates such that

$$x = \rho \cosh u \cos v, \tag{63}$$
$$y = \rho \sinh u \sin v. \tag{64}$$

For this case we find a solution to the HRMA equation

$$\alpha(x, y) = -\frac{\rho^2 c}{2 \cosh \Upsilon} \operatorname{sgn}(x) \, y \, F\left(\frac{y}{x}\right), \tag{65}$$

where F is a hypergeometric function. However this solution has a singularity at the origin. We note here that the HRMA equation is pseudo-elliptic; its elliptic version where the right hand side is positive is more studied and results on existence exists, see e.g. Ref. 18. Because of this we think this type of singularity may not be a surprise in this case. We note that this singularity will be transferred to the resulting metric. We leave further investigation of whether a sensible solution can be obtained from this to the future.

5. Conclusions

In this note we summarized the results of Refs. 8, 9 where using Manton approximation we have proposed some adiabatic solutions of GR produced from diffeomorphisms. We have concluded that an adiabatic solution to GR can be described as a geodesic on the space of vacua

$$\mathcal{V} \sim \operatorname{Diff}(\partial M)/\operatorname{biso}(\bar{h}) \tag{66}$$

that are null with respect to the metric

$$\langle \zeta^1, \zeta^2 \rangle = \int_{\partial M} \zeta_a^1 \mathbb{D} \zeta_2^a \tag{67}$$

that is solely composed of the data on the boundary of spatial slices. We remind that along the way we have used the conjecture that the Hamiltonian constraint solves for the exact part uniquely. We argued $\mathcal{V}$ is a "pseudo"-Riemannian homogeneous space with respect to this metric. The metric has mixed but constant signature, and is degenerate if $\ker \mathbb{D} \neq \text{biso}(\bar{h})$. We showed our formulation is akin to examples in continuum mechanics in which choice of $\mathbb{D}$ is different.

For the specific example of 3 spatial dimensions with round boundary; we explicitly saw our theorems to be holding, we found our vector field only up to exact parts since Hamiltonian equation seems hard to solve. However we saw any non-trivial solution of it has to have both exact and coexact parts. We also have realized $\ker \mathbb{D} = \text{biso}(\bar{h})$ for this case. In 2 spatial dimensions things got easier in solving the Hamiltonian constraint, since it becomes the Monge-Ampere equation whose solutions are known. For round boundary we found that there exists no non-trivial solution for the vector field in the bulk that is boundary preserving, and for elliptic boundary we were only able to find a solutions that is singular at the origin.

We conclude with a quick overview of the remaining issues. First of all let us list some technical questions still to be worked out:

(1) Does Hamiltonian equation completely fixes the exact part?
(2) Is $\ker \mathbb{D} = \text{biso}(\bar{h})$?
(3) For 2d case can HRMA be solved for some boundary?

Note that only after we complete solve the bulk vector field, we can construct first σ in the bulk of each spatial slice, then we can construct ξ by making the proper transformation for each slice, and only after that one can find $h_{ij}(x,t)$ and the full space-time metric for the adiabatic solutions we propose.

Analysis thus far might be suggesting the set of solutions we propose do not survive for vacuum Einstein equations, so next logical step is to perform the analysis for Einstein equations with matter, for example with a cosmological constant. Similarly one can also consider non-compact spatial slices with some fall-off conditions at infinities and study the infrared effects. This type of study would link our work to the studies in asymptotic symmetries and soft theorems and shed a different light to the subject.

Acknowledgments

This article summarizes and slightly expands the works in Refs. 8, 9, 14 which was produced in collaboration with Dieter Van den Bleeken and Ali Seraj. I am supported by Research Fund of the Middle East Technical University, Project Number DOSAP-B-105-2021-10763.

References

1. A. Strominger, Asymptotic Symmetries of Yang-Mills Theory, *JHEP* **07**, p. 151 (2014).
2. T. He, V. Lysov, P. Mitra and A. Strominger, BMS supertranslations and Weinberg's soft graviton theorem, *JHEP* **05**, p. 151 (2015).
3. T. He, P. Mitra, A. P. Porfyriadis and A. Strominger, New Symmetries of Massless QED, *JHEP* **10**, p. 112 (2014).
4. P. Creminelli, J. Noreña and M. Simonović, Conformal consistency relations for single-field inflation, *Journal of Cosmology and Astroparticle Physics* **2012**, p. 052–052 (Jul 2012).
5. K. Hinterbichler, L. Hui and J. Khoury, An infinite set of ward identities for adiabatic modes in cosmology, *Journal of Cosmology and Astroparticle Physics* **2014**, p. 039–039 (Jan 2014).
6. M. Mirbabayi and M. Simonović, Weinberg Soft Theorems from Weinberg Adiabatic Modes (2 2016).
7. S. Weinberg, Adiabatic modes in cosmology, *Physical Review D* **67** (Jun 2003).
8. E. S. Kutluk, A. Seraj and D. Van Den Bleeken, Strolling along gravitational vacua, *JHEP* **01**, p. 184 (2020).
9. E. S. Kutluk and D. V. d. Bleeken, Geodesic motion on the group of boundary diffeomorphisms from Einstein's equations (6 2021).
10. V. Arnold, Sur la géométrie différentielle des groupes de lie de dimension infinie et ses applications à l'hydrodynamique des fluides parfaits, *Annales de l'Institut Fourier* **16**, 319 (1966).
11. D. Holm, T. Schmah and C. Stoica, *Geometric Mechanics and Symmetry: From Finite to Infinite Dimensions* 01 2009.
12. N. Manton and P. Sutcliffe, *Topological Solitons* (Cambridge University Press, 2004).
13. D. M. A. Stuart, Analysis of the adiabatic limit for solitons in classical field theory, *Proc. Roy. Soc. Lond. A* **463**, 2753 (2007).
14. E. Şeyma Kutluk, Adiabatic solutions in general relativity and boundary symmetries (2021).
15. C. Isham and K. Kuchar, Representations of spacetime diffeomorphisms. i. canonical parametrized field theories, *Annals of Physics* **164**, 288 (1985).
16. M. Bojowald, Symmetries of spacetime, *International Journal of Modern Physics D* **25**, p. 1644007 (Oct 2016).
17. V. F. Zaitsev and A. D. Polyanin, *Handbook of Nonlinear Partial Differential Equations: Exact Solutions, Methods, and Problems* (Chapman and Hall/CRC, 2012).
18. N. Trudinger and X.-J. Wang, The monge-ampère equation and its applications, *Handbook of Geometric Analysis* **7** (01 2008).

The point spectrum of the Dirac Hamiltonian on the zero-gravity Kerr-Newman spacetime

M. Kiessling, E. Ling, and A. S. Tahvildar-Zadeh

*Math Department, Rutgers University,
New Brunswick, New Jersey 08854, USA*

In this short paper, we review the Dirac equation on the zero-gravity Kerr-Newman spacetime. Our main objective is to provide a correspondence between the classification of the bound states for the zGKN spectrum and the usual hydrogenic states $1s_{1/2}$, $2s_{1/2}$, etc. of the Hydrogen atom.

Keywords: Kerr-Newman, Dirac, Hamiltonian, Hydrogen, Point spectrum.

1. The purpose of this paper

The zero-gravity Kerr-Newman (zGKN) spacetime has been studied extensively.[8,9,13] In reference 9 it was shown that the discrete spectrum of the Dirac Hamiltonian on zGKN is nonempty. In an upcoming paper[10] we classify the discrete spectrum and show that the spectrum is indexed by three integers. See Theorem 2.1 below. It was conjectured[8,9] that the discrete spectrum of the Dirac Hamiltonian on zGKN should converge to the Bohr-Sommerfeld spectrum of the usual Hydrogen problem on Minkowski spacetime with a Coulomb potential in the limit as the ring radius of zGKN approaches 0. This problem remains open but a first step in solving this problem is to determine which states in the zGKN spectrum should correspond to which states in the usual hydrogenic spectrum. For example, which states should correspond to $1s_{1/2}$, $2s_{1/2}$, $2p_{1/2}$, etc.? The purpose of this paper is to provide this correspondence.

2. The zGKN spacetime

2.1. The zGKN spacetime and the Dirac equation

The zero-gravity Kerr-Newman (zGKN) spacetime[8] is obtained by formally taking Newton's gravitational constant $G \to 0$ in the Kerr-Newman spacetime. In Boyer-Lindquist coordinates, the resulting spacetime has line element

$$ds_{\mathbf{g}}^2 = c^2 dt^2 - (r^2 + a^2)\sin^2\theta d\varphi^2 - \frac{r^2 + a^2 \cos^2\theta}{r^2 + a^2}\big(dr^2 + (r^2+a^2)d\theta^2\big). \quad (1)$$

The zGKN spacetime is static and its orthogonal slices have the topology of two copies of $\mathbb{R}^3$ glued along a disc in the $z = 0$ plane; this topology is known as the

Zipoy topology.[18] Specifically the spacetime manifold is given by $\mathbb{R} \times \Sigma$ where

$$\Sigma = \{(r, \theta, \varphi) \mid r \in \mathbb{R},\, \theta \in [0, \pi],\, \varphi \in [0, 2\pi)\} \setminus R \qquad (2)$$

where R denotes the ring $R = \{r = 0, \theta = \pi/2, \varphi \in [0, 2\pi)\}$.

The electromagnetic fields on the Kerr-Newman spacetime $\mathbf{F}_{KN} = d\mathbf{A}_{KN}$ do not depend on Newton's gravitational constant and so they survive the $G \to 0$ limit. Hence the zGKN spacetime comes already decorated with the same electromagnetic fields. The four-potential reads

$$\mathbf{A}_{KN} = -\frac{r}{r^2 + a^2 \cos^2 \theta} \left(Q dt - \frac{Qa}{c} \sin^2 \theta \, d\varphi \right). \qquad (3)$$

The field $\mathbf{F}$ is thus singular on the same ring $\{r = 0, \theta = \pi/2, \varphi \in [0, 2\pi)\}$ as the metric; for r very large and positive it exhibits an electric monopole of strength Q and a magnetic dipole moment of strength Qa, while for r very negative it exhibits an electric monopole of strength $-Q$ and a magnetic dipole moment of strength $-Qa$.

Equipped with the Kerr-Newman electromagnetic fields, one can interpret the ring bounding the disc as an elementary particle. With this interpretation, it is natural to consider the Dirac equation

$$\tilde{\gamma}^\mu \left(-i\hbar \nabla_\mu + eA_\mu \right) \Psi + mc^2 \Psi = 0, \qquad (4)$$

on the zGKN spacetime and compare its spectral properties to that of the usual Hydrogen problem (i.e. the Dirac equation on Minkowski spacetime with a Coulomb potential centered at the origin in $\mathbb{R}^3$ within the Born-Oppenheimer approximation).

In equation (4), m is the mass of an electron, $-e$ is its fundamental charge, and A_μ is the 1-form electromagnetic potential for $\mathbf{F}_{KN}$ related via $F_{\mu\nu} = \partial_\mu A_\nu - \partial_\nu A_\mu$. The Dirac matrices $(\tilde{\gamma}^\mu)_{\mu=0}^3$ satisfy $\tilde{\gamma}^\mu \tilde{\gamma}^\nu + \tilde{\gamma}^\nu \tilde{\gamma}^\mu = 2g^{\mu\nu}$, with $g^{\mu\nu}$ the (inverse) metric coefficients of the zGKN metric.

At this point, one should recognize that if one takes the limit $a \to 0$, then (1) becomes the Minkowski metric, (3) becomes the usual Coulomb potential of a charge Q located at the origin, and (4) becomes the usual Dirac equation on Minkowski spacetime. These statements hold only formally as there are issues with the domain of the Dirac Hamiltonian when trying to make these limits precise. In particular, note that the domain of the r coordinate is $\mathbb{R}$ in zGKN while it's just $(0, \infty)$ for Minkowski spacetime. Nevertheless, the $a \to 0$ limit approach of the usual Hydrogen problem suggests a tantalizing mathematical problem.

2.2. Separation of variables

Using Cartan's frame method[1] with a frame well-adapted to oblate spheroidal coordinates, Chandrasekhar,[3,4] Page,[12] and Toop[16] transformed the Dirac equation (4) into an equation for a bispinor that allows a clear separation of the t, r, θ, and φ derivatives. The same transformation works for zGKN as well.[9] By introducing an explicit diagonal matrix $\mathfrak{D} = \mathfrak{D}(r,\theta,\varphi)$ and defining $\hat{\Psi} = \mathfrak{D}^{-1}\Psi$, the Dirac equation becomes

$$(\hat{R} + \hat{A})\hat{\Psi} = 0, \tag{5}$$

where $\hat{R}$ and $\hat{A}$ are given by (with $\hbar = c = 1$ units from now on)

$$\hat{R} := \begin{pmatrix} imr & 0 & D_- - ieQ\frac{r}{\varpi} & 0 \\ 0 & imr & 0 & D_+ - ieQ\frac{r}{\varpi} \\ D_+ - ieQ\frac{r}{\varpi} & 0 & imr & 0 \\ 0 & D_- - ieQ\frac{r}{\varpi} & 0 & imr \end{pmatrix}, \tag{6}$$

$$\hat{A} := \begin{pmatrix} -ma\cos\theta & 0 & 0 & -L_- \\ 0 & -ma\cos\theta & -L_+ & 0 \\ 0 & L_- & ma\cos\theta & 0 \\ L_+ & 0 & 0 & ma\cos\theta \end{pmatrix}, \tag{7}$$

where

$$D_\pm := \pm\varpi\partial_r + \left(\varpi\partial_t + \frac{a}{\varpi}\partial_\varphi\right), \qquad L_\pm := \partial_\theta \pm i\left(a\sin\theta\,\partial_t + \csc\theta\,\partial_\varphi\right), \tag{8}$$

and

$$\varpi := \sqrt{r^2 + a^2}.$$

Once a solution $\hat{\Psi}$ to (5) is found, the bispinor $\Psi := \mathfrak{D}\hat{\Psi}$ solves the original Dirac equation (4). The explicit form of $\mathfrak{D}$ can be found in reference 9, but it's not needed for this paper.

Separation of variables is now achieved with the Ansatz that a solution $\hat{\Psi}$ of (5) is of the form

$$\hat{\Psi} = e^{-i(Et - \kappa\varphi)} \begin{pmatrix} R_1 S_1 \\ R_2 S_2 \\ R_2 S_1 \\ R_1 S_2 \end{pmatrix}, \tag{9}$$

with E a yet to be found energy eigenvalue of the Dirac hamiltonian, $\kappa \in \mathbb{Z} + \frac{1}{2}$, and with R_k being complex-valued functions of r alone, and S_k being real-valued functions of θ alone. Let

$$\vec{R} := \begin{pmatrix} R_1 \\ R_2 \end{pmatrix}, \qquad \vec{S} := \begin{pmatrix} S_1 \\ S_2 \end{pmatrix}. \tag{10}$$

Plugging the Chandrasekhar Ansatz (9) into (5) one easily finds that there must be $\lambda \in \mathbb{C}$ such that

$$T_{rad}\vec{R} = E\vec{R}, \tag{11}$$

$$T_{ang}\vec{S} = \lambda\vec{S}, \tag{12}$$

where

$$T_{rad} := \begin{pmatrix} d_- & m\frac{r}{\varpi} - i\frac{\lambda}{\varpi} \\ m\frac{r}{\varpi} + i\frac{\lambda}{\varpi} & -d_+ \end{pmatrix} \qquad (13)$$

$$T_{ang} := \begin{pmatrix} ma\cos\theta & l_- \\ -l_+ & -ma\cos\theta \end{pmatrix} \qquad (14)$$

The operators $d_\pm$ and $l_\pm$ are ordinary differential operators in r and θ respectively, with coefficients that depend on the unknown E, and parameters a, κ, and eQ:

$$d_\pm := -i\frac{d}{dr} \pm \frac{-a\kappa + eQr}{\varpi^2} \qquad (15)$$

$$l_\pm := \frac{d}{d\theta} \pm (aE\sin\theta - \kappa\csc\theta). \qquad (16)$$

2.3. *The coupled spectral problems for T_{rad} and T_{ang}*

The angular operator T_{ang} in (12) is easily seen to be essentially self-adjoint on $(C_c^\infty((0,\pi),\sin\theta d\theta))^2 \subset (L^2((0,\pi),\sin\theta d\theta))^2$, and its self-adjoint extension (also denoted T_{ang}) has a purely discrete spectrum $\lambda = \lambda_n(am, aE, \kappa) \in \mathbb{R}$, $n \in \mathbb{Z}\setminus 0$ (see references 2, 14).

With $\lambda \in \mathbb{R}$ it then follows that the radial operator T_{rad} is essentially self-adjoint on $(C_c^\infty(\mathbb{R}, dr))^2 \subset (L^2(\mathbb{R}, dr))^2$; its self-adjoint extension will also be denoted T_{rad}. Moreover, we can take $R_1 = R_2^*$ without loss of generality.[a] Thus, we can set

$$R_1 = \frac{1}{\sqrt{2}}(u - iv), \qquad R_2 = \frac{1}{\sqrt{2}}(u + iv) \qquad (17)$$

for real funcions u and v. This brings the radial system (11) into the following standard (Hamiltonian) form

$$(H_{rad} - E)\begin{pmatrix} u \\ v \end{pmatrix} = \begin{pmatrix} 0 \\ 0 \end{pmatrix}, \qquad (18)$$

where

$$H_{rad} := \begin{pmatrix} m\frac{r}{\varpi} + \frac{\gamma r + a\kappa}{\varpi^2} & -\partial_r + \frac{\lambda}{\varpi} \\ \partial_r + \frac{\lambda}{\varpi} & -m\frac{r}{\varpi} + \frac{\gamma r + a\kappa}{\varpi^2} \end{pmatrix}, \qquad (19)$$

and

$$\gamma := -eQ < 0. \qquad (20)$$

Equation (19) should be compared with equation (7.105) in reference 15. Specifically, note that as $a \to 0$, H_{rad} approaches the radial Hamiltonian of the usual Hydrogen problem on Minkowski spacetime with a Coulomb potential.

---

[a]This follows by multiplying the rows of equation (11) by either R_1^* and R_2^* and adding the equations to conclude that $|R_1| = |R_2|$. Therefore $R_1 = Re^{i\phi_1}$ and $R_2 = Re^{i\phi_2}$. Again, by multiplying by conjugates, one can show that $\frac{d}{dr}(R_1/R_2^*) = 0$ which implies $\frac{d}{dr}(\phi_1 + \phi_2) = 0$.

Using techniques of Weidmann[17] it is straightforward to show that the essential spectrum of H_{rad} consists of values $E \in (-\infty, 1] \cup [1, \infty)$, and its interior is purely absolutely continuous; see reference 9. The remaining task is to characterize the discrete spectrum in the gap, i.e. the eigenvalues $E \in (-1, 1)$. In reference 9 it was shown that the spectrum is symmetric about 0, hence it suffices to consider $E > 0$.

2.4. *The Prüfer transformed system*

Following reference 9, we transform the equations (18) and (12) for the four unknowns (u, v) and (S_1, S_2) by defining four new unknowns (R, Ω) and (S, Θ) via the Prüfer transform

$$u = \sqrt{2}R\cos\frac{\Omega}{2}, \quad v = \sqrt{2}R\sin\frac{\Omega}{2}, \quad S_1 = S\cos\frac{\Theta}{2}, \quad S_2 = S\sin\frac{\Theta}{2}. \tag{21}$$

Thus

$$R = \frac{1}{2}\sqrt{u^2 + v^2}, \quad \Omega = 2\tan^{-1}\frac{v}{u}, \quad S = \sqrt{S_1^2 + S_2^2}, \quad \Theta = 2\tan^{-1}\frac{S_2}{S_1}. \tag{22}$$

As a result, $R_1 = Re^{-i\Omega/2}$ and $R_2 = Re^{i\Omega/2}$. Hence $\hat{\Psi}$ can be re-expressed in terms of the Prüfer variables as

$$\hat{\Psi}(t, r, \theta, \varphi) = R(r)S(\theta)e^{-i(Et-\kappa\varphi)} \begin{pmatrix} \cos(\Theta(\theta)/2)e^{-i\Omega(r)/2} \\ \sin(\Theta(\theta)/2)e^{i\Omega(r)/2} \\ \cos(\Theta(\theta)/2)e^{i\Omega(r)/2} \\ \sin(\Theta(\theta)/2)e^{-i\Omega(r)/2} \end{pmatrix}, \tag{23}$$

and we obtain the following equations for the new unknowns, first

$$\frac{d}{dr}\Omega = 2\frac{mr}{\varpi}\cos\Omega + 2\frac{\lambda}{\varpi}\sin\Omega + 2\frac{a\kappa + \gamma r}{\varpi^2} - 2E, \tag{24}$$

$$\frac{d}{dr}\ln R = \frac{mr}{\varpi}\sin\Omega - \frac{\lambda}{\varpi}\cos\Omega, \tag{25}$$

and second,

$$\frac{d}{d\theta}\Theta = -2ma\cos\theta\cos\Theta + 2\left(aE\sin\theta - \frac{\kappa}{\sin\theta}\right)\sin\Theta + 2\lambda, \tag{26}$$

$$\frac{d}{d\theta}\ln S = -ma\cos\theta\sin\Theta - \left(aE\sin\theta - \frac{\kappa}{\sin\theta}\right)\cos\Theta. \tag{27}$$

Note that the Ω-equation (24) is decoupled from R, and the Θ-equation (26) is decoupled from S. Thus the pair (24), (26) can be solved together independently of equations (25), (27), which in turn can be integrated subsequently by direct quadrature.

We can further simplify the analysis of these systems and reduce the number of parameters involved by noting that by defining the constants $a' = ma$, $E' = E/m$, and changing to the variable $r' = mr$, we eliminate m from the system. Henceforth we therefore set $m = 1$.

2.5. Transformation onto a coupled dynamical system on cylinders

Equations (24) and (26) exhibit the independent and the dependent variables explicitly. It is more convenient to transform them to a parametrically coupled pair of autonomous two-dimensional dynamical systems, by introducing a new independent variable τ, as follows.

Equation (26) can be written as a smooth dynamical system in the (θ, Θ) plane by introducing τ such that $\frac{d\theta}{d\tau} = \sin\theta$. Then, with dot representing differentiation in τ, we have,

$$\begin{cases} \dot\theta = \sin\theta \\ \dot\Theta = -2a\sin\theta\cos\theta\cos\Theta + 2aE\sin^2\theta\sin\Theta - 2\kappa\sin\Theta + 2\lambda\sin\theta \end{cases} \quad (28)$$

Identifying the line $\Theta = \pi$ with $\Theta = -\pi$, this becomes a dynamical system on a closed finite cylinder $\mathcal{C}_1 := [0, \pi] \times \mathbb{S}^1$. The only equilibrium points of the flow are on the two circular boundaries: Two on the left boundary: $S^- = (0, 0)$, $N^- = (0, \pi)$; two on the right: $S^+ = (\pi, -\pi)$ and $N^+ = (\pi, 0)$.

For $\kappa > 0$, the linearization of the flow at the equilibrium points reveals that S^- and S^+ are hyperbolic saddle points (with eigenvalues $\{1, -2\kappa\}$ and $\{-1, 2\kappa\}$ respectively), while N^- is a source node (with eigenvalues 1 and 2κ) and N^+ is a sink node (with eigenvalues -1 and -2κ). The situation with $\kappa < 0$ is entirely analogous, with the two critical points on each boundary switching their roles.

Similarly, the Ω equation (24) can be rewritten as a smooth dynamical system on a cylinder, in this case by setting $\tau := \frac{r}{a}$ as new independent variable, as well as introducing a new dependent variable

$$\xi := \tan^{-1}\frac{r}{a} = \tan^{-1}\tau \quad (29)$$

Then, with dot again representing differentiation in τ, (24) is equivalent to

$$\begin{cases} \dot\xi = \cos^2\xi \\ \dot\Omega = 2a\sin\xi\cos\Omega + 2\lambda\cos\xi\sin\Omega + 2\gamma\sin\xi\cos\xi + 2\kappa\cos^2\xi - 2aE \end{cases} \quad (30)$$

Once again, identifying $\Omega = -\pi$ with $\Omega = \pi$ turns this into a smooth flow on the closed finite cylinder $\mathcal{C}_2 := [-\frac{\pi}{2}, \frac{\pi}{2}] \times \mathbb{S}^1$. The only equilibrium points of the flow are on the two circular boundaries. For $E \in (0, 1)$ there are two equilibria on each: $S_E^- = (-\frac{\pi}{2}, -\pi + \cos^{-1}E)$ and $N_E^- = (-\frac{\pi}{2}, \pi - \cos^{-1}E)$ on the left boundary, and $S_E^+ = (\frac{\pi}{2}, -\cos^{-1}E)$ and $N_E^+ = (\frac{\pi}{2}, \cos^{-1}E)$ on the right boundary. $S_E^\pm$ are non-hyperbolic (degenerate) saddle-nodes, with eigenvalues 0 and $\pm 2a\sqrt{1-E^2}$, while N_E^- is a degenerate source-node and N_E^+ a degenerate sink-node (see Theorem 2.19(iii) in reference 6).

In reference 9, it was shown that E is an energy eigenvalue of the Dirac Hamiltonian and the corresponding Ψ is a bound state if and only if there exists a $\lambda \in \mathbb{R}$ such that each of the two dynamical systems above possesses a *saddles connector*, i.e. an orbit on $\mathcal{C}_1$ connecting the two saddle-nodes S^- and S^+ in the Θ-system (28) and an orbit on $\mathcal{C}_2$ connecting the two saddle-nodes S_E^- and S_E^+ in the Ω-system (30).

Given a dynamical system on a cylinder, there corresponds an integer known as the *winding number* which describes how many times an orbit in the dynamical system winds around the cylinder before terminating at an equilibrium point. See reference 9 and the upcoming paper 10. For the Ω system, saddles connectors with different winding numbers correspond to different energy values (with energy increasing as the winding number increases). In reference 9 it was shown that a bound state Ψ exists corresponding to winding number $N_\Theta = 0$ for the Θ system and winding number $N_\Omega = 0$ for the Ω system (and $\kappa = \frac{1}{2}$). In the upcoming paper 10, we improve on this result by fully classifying the spectrum. Specifically, we prove the following theorem.

Theorem 2.1. *Set $a_{\max} = 1 - \frac{1}{\sqrt{2}}$ and $\gamma_{\min} = -\frac{1}{2}$. Fix $a \in (0, a_{\max})$, $\gamma \in (\gamma_{\min}, 0)$, and $\kappa \in \mathbb{Z} + \frac{1}{2}$. Assume Ψ is of the form (23) constructed from solutions of (24)–(27).*

- *Suppose $N_\Theta \geq 0$ is an integer. For all integers $N_\Omega \geq 0$, there is a bound state Ψ such that the Θ system and Ω system have winding numbers N_Θ and N_Ω, respectively. There are no bound states with $N_\Omega \leq -1$.*
- *Suppose $N_\Theta \leq -1$ is an integer. For all integers $N_\Omega \geq 1$, there is a bound state Ψ such that the Θ system and Ω system have winding numbers N_Θ and N_Ω, respectively. There are no bound states with $N_\Omega \leq 0$.*

Our conditions on a and γ are used to ensure that there are no bound states with $N_\Omega \leq -1$ for $N_\Theta \geq 0$ and no bound states with $N_\Omega \leq 0$ for $N_\Theta \leq -1$, which, as we will see in the next section, occurs in an analogous way for the familiar hydrogenic Dirac operator on a Minkowski background with a Coulomb potential.

When restoring units and mass m, we have $a_{\max} = (1 - \frac{1}{\sqrt{2}})\frac{\hbar}{mc}$ and $\gamma_{\min} = -\frac{1}{2}\hbar c$. If, with the hydrogenic problem in mind, we set $\gamma = -Ze^2$, then $\gamma \in (\gamma_{\min}, 0)$ implies $\frac{Ze^2}{\hbar c} < \frac{1}{2}$, that is, $Z < \frac{137.036}{2}$. Now let's compare these conditions with the conditions on Z for the familiar hydrogenic Dirac operator on a Minkowski background with a Coulomb potential, for which essential self-adjointness breaks down for $Z > 118$. For the Dirac operator on zGKN, there is no condition for essential self-adjointness.[9] So our conditions are probably not optimal.

3. Relating the zGKN bound states to the usual hydrogenic states

In this section we relate the zGKN bound states found in Theorem 2.1 to the usual hydrogenic states of the Dirac problem on Minkowski spacetime with a Coulomb potential. The main objective is to relate the winding numbers which appear in Theorem 2.1 to the usual spectroscopic notation $n\ell_j$ of hydrogenic states.

3.1. *The correspondence between winding numbers and the usual spectroscopic notation of hydrogenic states*

Based on the above results, for fixed a and γ, the discrete spectrum of our Dirac Hamiltonian is indexed by *three* integers: N_Ω, N_Θ, and 2κ. By contrast, the energy spectrum of special relativistic Hydrogen, i.e., the Dirac Hamiltonian for a point-like electron in ordinary Minkowski space interacting with a Coulomb point charge at the origin, is indexed by *two* integers only, namely the main (or Bohr's) quantum number, often denoted by n, and the spin-orbit quantum number[b], i.e., the set of eigenvalues of the spin-orbit operator $K = \beta(2\mathbf{S} \cdot \mathbf{L} + 1)$.

In the limit $a \to 0$, the angular Hamiltonian (14), takes the simple form

$$\mathfrak{a}_\kappa := \lim_{a \to 0} T_{ang} = i\sigma_2 \partial_\theta + \frac{\kappa}{\sin\theta}\sigma_1. \tag{31}$$

From reference 2, if λ is an eigenvalue of T_{ang}, then $k := \lim_{a \to 0} \lambda$ is an eigenvalue of $\mathfrak{a}_\kappa$, also the limit defining k exists since λ is analytic in a. Note that $\mathfrak{a}_\kappa$ is independent of E unlike T_{ang}.

In the limit $a \to 0$, the formal limit of the radial Hamiltonian (19) coincides with the radial Hamiltonian arising in the special relativistic Hydrogen problem (e.g. see reference 15, eq. (7.105)):

$$\mathfrak{h}_k := \lim_{a \to 0} H_{rad} = \begin{pmatrix} m + \dfrac{\gamma}{r} & -\partial_r + \dfrac{k}{r} \\ \partial_r + \dfrac{k}{r} & -m + \dfrac{\gamma}{r} \end{pmatrix}. \tag{32}$$

Therefore k can be identified with the *spin-orbit coupling*.

The spectrum of $\mathfrak{a}_\kappa$ is completely understood.[2] In particular, for all half-integers $\kappa \in \mathbb{Z} + \frac{1}{2}$, the operator $\mathfrak{a}_\kappa$ is essentially self-adjoint and has a discrete spectrum indexed by a nonzero integer which we call N:

$$k = -\operatorname{sgn}(N)\left(|N| + |\kappa| - \frac{1}{2}\right), \tag{33}$$

as well as a complete set of eigenvectors $\vec{S}_{N,\kappa}$ that are explicitly known and can be expressed in terms of Jacobi polynomials.

$$\vec{S}_{N,\kappa}(\theta) := \sin^{\kappa+\frac{1}{2}}\theta \begin{pmatrix} -\sqrt{\cot\frac{\theta}{2}}\, P_{|N|-1}^{\kappa-\frac{1}{2},\kappa+\frac{1}{2}}(\cos\theta) \\ \operatorname{sgn}(N)\sqrt{\tan\frac{\theta}{2}}\, P_{|N|-1}^{\kappa+\frac{1}{2},\kappa-\frac{1}{2}}(\cos\theta) \end{pmatrix}. \tag{34}$$

Note that the above holds for $\kappa > 0$. To find the eigenvectors for $\kappa < 0$, recognize that if $\vec{S}$ is an eigenvector of $\mathfrak{a}_\kappa$, then $i\sigma_2 \vec{S}$ is an eigenvector of $\mathfrak{a}_{-\kappa}$.

---

[b]The spin-orbit quantum number is called κ_j in reference;[15] it should not be confused with our κ, which is the eigenvalue of the z-component of angular momentum, for which Thaller uses the notation m_j.

From the above and the definition of Θ it follows that the saddles connectors of the Θ-system that correspond to the eigenvectors of the angular Hamiltonian are given explicitly by the formula

$$\Theta_{N,\kappa}(\theta) = -\text{sgn}(N) \left\{ 2\tan^{-1}\left(\frac{P_{|N|-1}^{|\kappa|+\frac{1}{2},|\kappa|-\frac{1}{2}}(\cos\theta)}{P_{|N|-1}^{|\kappa|-\frac{1}{2},|\kappa|+\frac{1}{2}}(\cos\theta)} \tan\frac{\theta}{2} \right) - \pi\chi_{\kappa<0} \right\}. \quad (35)$$

Here the branch of $\tan^{-1}$ needs to be chosen in such a way that $\Theta_{N,\kappa}$ is continuous on $[0, \pi]$.

The above formula implies that we can fix the initial value of the saddles connectors to be

$$\Theta_{N,\kappa}(0) = \begin{cases} 0 & \kappa > 0 \\ \text{sgn}(N)\pi & \kappa < 0. \end{cases} \quad (36)$$

and that for the final value of those connectors, we need

$$\Theta_{N,\kappa}(\pi) = \begin{cases} -\text{sgn}(N)\pi & \kappa > 0 \\ 0 & \kappa < 0 \end{cases} \quad [\text{mod}\, 2\pi] \quad (37)$$

in agreement with what we have already observed about the boundary values of the saddles connectors for the Θ-system (28).

Furthermore, from the properties of Jacobi polynomials, it follows that for $\Theta_{N,\kappa}$ to be a continuous function of θ on $[0, \pi]$, we need

$$\Theta_{N,\kappa}(\pi) = -2\pi\,\text{sgn}(N)(|N|-1) + \begin{cases} -\text{sgn}(N)\pi & \kappa > 0 \\ 0 & \kappa < 0 \end{cases} \quad (38)$$

Thus we establish a correspondence between the integer N and the winding number N_Θ of the Θ-saddles connectors in the case $a = 0$.

$$N_\Theta \sim \begin{cases} N-1 & N \geq 1 \\ N & N \leq -1, \end{cases} \quad (39)$$

where '$\sim$' simply means a correspondence.

From the relationship (33) between the eigenvalue k and the number N it follows that instead of N we can equally well label the angular eigenstates by the integer k, in which case

$$N = -\text{sgn}(k)\left(|k| - |\kappa| + \frac{1}{2}\right). \quad (40)$$

We now turn our attention to the radial Hamiltonian $\mathfrak{h}_k = \lim_{a \to 0} H_{rad}$. This operator is closely related to the radial Hamiltonian h_k of the special-relativistic Hydrogen problem, as formulated by Dirac:[5]

$$h_k = -i\sigma_2 \partial_r + m\sigma_3 + \frac{k}{r}\sigma_1 + \frac{\gamma}{r}I_{2\times 2}. \quad (41)$$

The only difference between h_k and $\mathfrak{h}_k$ is their domains: Since H_{rad} is defined on the double-sheeted Sommerfeld space, this is inherited by its $a \to 0$ limit $\mathfrak{h}_k$, which is still defined on two copies of Minkowski space glued together along a timelike line. In particular the r variable in $\mathfrak{h}_k$ has the range $(-\infty, \infty)$. By contrast, the r variable in h_k goes from 0 to ∞. The eigenvalue problem for h_k was shown to be exactly solvable by Gordon,[7] who proved the discrete spectrum to coincide exactly with the Bohr-Sommerfeld spectrum, and found explicit formulas for the eigenfunctions in terms of generalized Laguerre polynomials.

Consider first the restriction of $\mathfrak{h}_k$ to functions supported in the sheet $r > 0$. As described in detail in section 7.4 of Thaller's book,[15] this operator, for all $k \in \mathbb{Z}\setminus\{0\}$, is essentially self-adjoint on $C_c^\infty((0, \infty))$, has a discrete spectrum in $(0, 1)$ and a complete set of eigenvectors, if $-\sqrt{3}/2 < \gamma < 0$. The discrete spectrum is indexed by two integers, $n \geq 1$ and $k = -n, \ldots, -1, 1, \ldots, n-1$. Let $M := n - |k|$. Then we have

$$E_{M,k} = \frac{m}{\sqrt{1 + \left(\frac{\gamma^2}{M+\sqrt{k^2-\gamma^2}}\right)^2}} \tag{42}$$

Note that the case $k > 0$ and $M = 0$ is excluded.

Gordon[7] computed the corresponding eigenfunctions in terms of generalized Laguerre polynomials: Let (ϕ_1, ϕ_2) be defined by

$$u = \sqrt{1 + E_{M,k}}(\phi_1 + \phi_2), \qquad v = \sqrt{1 - E_{M,k}}(\phi_1 - \phi_2) \tag{43}$$

where (u, v) is an eigenfunction of $\mathfrak{h}_k$ with eigenvalue $E_{M,k}$ (and we have set $m = 1$). Then, using the abbreviations

$$\rho := \sqrt{k^2 - \gamma^2}, \qquad \eta := \sqrt{1 - E_{M,k}^2} \tag{44}$$

we have that for all nonnegative integers M and real constants c_1, c_2 such that

$$\mu := \frac{c_1}{c_2} = \frac{M}{k + \frac{\gamma}{\eta}}. \tag{45}$$

we have

$$\phi_1(r) = c_1 e^{-\eta r} r^\rho F(-M+1, 2\rho+1, 2\eta r) \tag{46}$$
$$\phi_2(r) = c_2 e^{-\eta r} r^\rho F(-M, 2\rho+1, 2\eta r) \tag{47}$$

where F denotes Gauss's *confluent hypergeometric function*

$$F(\alpha, \beta, x) = 1 + \frac{\alpha}{1!\beta}x + \frac{\alpha(\alpha+1)}{2!\beta(\beta+1)}x^2 + \ldots \tag{48}$$

Note that when α is a negative integer, the above series terminates, and F is a polynomial of degree $-\alpha$, which (up to a numerical factor) is the generalized Laguerre polynomial $L_{-\alpha}^{(\beta-1)}(x)$.

Accordingly, since $\Omega = 2\tan^{-1}\frac{v}{u}$, the corresponding solution to the $a \to 0$ limit of the Ω-equation (24) will be

$$\Omega(r) = 2\tan^{-1}\left(\sqrt{\frac{1-E}{1+E}} \frac{\mu F(-M+1, 2\rho+1, 2\eta r) - F(-M, 2\rho+1, 2\eta r)}{\mu F(-M+1, 2\rho+1, 2\eta r) + F(-M, 2\rho+1, 2\eta r)}\right) \tag{49}$$

The values of Ω at $r = 0$ and $r = \infty$ can thus be calculated (modulo 2π):

$$\Omega(0) = 2\tan^{-1}\left(\sqrt{\frac{1-E}{1+E}}\frac{\mu-1}{\mu+1}\right) = \sin^{-1}\left(\frac{-\gamma}{k}\right) \tag{50}$$

$$\Omega(\infty) = -2\tan^{-1}\left(\sqrt{\frac{1-E}{1+E}}\right) = -\cos^{-1} E \tag{51}$$

which is in agreement with the analysis of the equilibrium points of the corresponding dynamical system. We choose our principal branch of $\sin^{-1}$ depending on the sign of k:

$$\Omega(0) = \begin{cases} \sin^{-1}\left(\frac{-\gamma}{k}\right) & \text{if } k < 0. \\ -\pi - \sin^{-1}\left(\frac{-\gamma}{k}\right) & \text{if } k > 0 \end{cases} \tag{52}$$

On the other hand, from the properties of Laguerre polynomials, it follows that the denominator of the rational function in (49) has M zeros in $[0, \infty)$ when $k < 0$ and $M - 1$ zeros when $k > 0$ (note that this explains why $k \leq n - 1$). Thus in order for Ω to be a continuous function of r, the branch of $\tan^{-1}$ needs to be chosen such that -2π gets added to the value every time r crosses one of those poles, which implies that

$$\Omega(\infty) = -2\pi M - \cos^{-1} E \tag{53}$$

which holds for both $k < 0$ and $k > 0$ (this is why we chose $\Omega(0) = -\pi - \sin^{-1}\left(\frac{-\gamma}{k}\right)$ for $k > 0$). Thus we establish the following correspondence between the integer M and the winding number N_Ω for the Ω-saddles connectors in the case $a = 0$.

$$N_\Omega \sim M. \tag{54}$$

Now consider the case $a > 0$ (i.e. the Dirac Hamiltonian on zGKN). The bound states are indexed by three integers N_Θ, N_Ω, and 2κ appearing in Theorem 2.1. Using (54) and (39), we can define a correspondence between the integers $N_\Theta, N_\Omega, 2\kappa$ and the usual spectroscopic notation $n\ell_j$ of hydrogenic states. Given N_Θ and N_Ω, define N and M via

$$N := \begin{cases} N_\Theta + 1 & N_\Theta \geq 0 \\ N_\Theta & N_\Theta \leq -1, \end{cases} \quad \text{and} \quad M := N_\Omega. \tag{55}$$

Then n, ℓ, and j appearing in $n\ell_j$ are given by

$$k := -N - \text{sgn}(N)\left(|\kappa| - \frac{1}{2}\right) \tag{56}$$

$$n := M + |k| \tag{57}$$

$$j := |k| - \frac{1}{2} \tag{58}$$

$$\ell := j + \text{sgn}(k)\frac{1}{2} \tag{59}$$

$$m_j := \kappa. \tag{60}$$

This establishes the desired correspondence between the winding numbers appearing in Theorem 2.1 and the usual spectroscopic notation $n\ell_j$ of hydrogenic states. For example, suppose we ask: which state in zGKN corresponds to $2p_{1/2}$ with $m_{1/2} = -\frac{1}{2}$? Well $\ell = 1$ implies $1 = \frac{1}{2} + \text{sgn}(k)\frac{1}{2}$. Therefore k is positive and so $j = \frac{1}{2}$ implies $k = 1$. Therefore $N = -1$ implies $N_\Theta = -1$. Lastly, $n = 2$ implies $M = 1$ and so $N_\Omega = 1$. Thus the state $2p_{1/2}$ with $m_{1/2} = -\frac{1}{2}$ corresponds to $N_\Theta = -1$, $N_\Omega = 1$, and $\kappa = -\frac{1}{2}$.

3.2. *Breaking degeneracies*

It is well known that the energy levels of the special-relativistic Hydrogen Hamiltonian are independent of m_j, the eigenvalue of the z-component of total angular momentum, while the eigenstates of it do depend on m_j. As a result, all energy levels are degenerate in that case, i.e. have multiplicity at least two. In the case of our Hamiltonian H_{rad}, this degeneracy is broken by the appearance of $a\kappa$ in equation (19). This yields a hyperfine-like splitting of the spectral lines, which in the standard setting is thought of as being a consequence of the nucleus having a magnetic dipole moment. In our setting, it can be thought of as following from the nonzero $d\varphi$ term in equation (3) which produces a magnetic dipole moment.

In addition to the above symmetry-related degeneracy, Dirac's original model for special-relativistic Hydrogen also has *accidental* degeneracies; the energy eigenvalues do not depend on the *sign* of the spin-orbit quantum number k, only on its magnitude, while the eigenstates do depend on the sign of k. The celebrated experiment of Lamb[11] showed that this degeneracy is only in Dirac's model, not in nature, i.e., the measured energy levels of orbitals corresponding to k and $-k$ are slightly different. This difference is known as the *Lamb shift*. In our model, these accidental degeneracies are also broken producing a small but observable Lamb shift-like effect.

Recall that hyperfine splitting and the Lamb shift are calculated using perturbative techniques. It is important to note that our model does not use perturbation theory to calculate energy differences.

In the upcoming paper,[10] we will report on numerical results of the zGKN spectrum showing the breaking of these degeneracies for various values of a.

References

1. D. R. Brill and J. M. Cohen, *Cartan frames and the general relativistic Dirac equation*, J. Math. Phys. **7** (1966).
2. D. Batic, H. Schmid, and M. Winklmeier, *On the eigenvalues of the Chandrasekhar-Page angular equation*, J. Math. Phys. **46** (2005).
3. S. Chandrasekhar, *The solution of Dirac's equation in Kerr geometry*. Proc. Roy. Soc. London Ser. A **349** (1976).
4. S. Chandrasekhar, *Errata: The solution of Dirac's equation in Kerr geometry*. Proc. Roy. Soc. London Ser. A **350** (1976).
5. P. A. M. Dirac, *The quantum theory of the electron I*. Proc. Roy. Soc. London Ser. A **117** (1928).

6. F. Dumortier, J. Llibre, and J. C. Artés, *Qualitative theory of planar differential systems*, Universitext, Springer-Verlag, Berlin, (2006).
7. W. Gordon, *Die Energieniveaus der Wassenstoffatoms nach der Diracschen Quantentheorie des Elektrons*, Z.
8. M.K.-H. Kiessling and A. S. Tahvildar-Zadeh, *A novel quantum-mechanical interpretation of the Dirac equation*, J. Phys. A. **49** (2016).
9. M.K.-H. Kiessling and A. S. Tahvildar-Zadeh, *The Dirac point electron in zero-gravity Kerr-Newman spacetime*, J. Math. Phys. **56** (2015).
10. M.K.-H. Kiessling, E. Ling, and A. S. Tahvildar-Zadeh, *On the discrete Dirac spectrum of a point electron in the zero-gravity Kerr-Newman spacetime*, in preparation.
11. W. E. Lamb, *Fine structure of the hydrogen atom*, Nobel Lecture. (1955)
12. D. Page, *Dirac equation around a charged, rotation black hole*, Phys. Rev. D **14** (1976).
13. A. S. Tahvildar-Zadeh, *On a zero-gravity limit of the Kerr-Newman spacetimes and their electromagnetic fields*, J. Math. Phys. **56** (2015).
14. K. G. Suffern, E. D. Fackerell, and C.M. Cosgrove, *Eigenvalues of the Chanrasekhar-Page angular functions*, J. Math. Phys. **24** (1983).
15. B. Thaller, *The Dirac Equation*. Springer-Verlag, Berlin, (1992).
16. N. Toop, *The Thermal Radiation of Electrons from a Charged Spinning Black Hole in a Cosmological background* (DAMTP, Cambridge, 1976).
17. J. Weidmann, *Absolut stetiges Spektrum bei Sturm-Liouville-Operatoren und Systemen*. Math. Z. **180** (1982).
18. D. M. Zipoy, *Topology of Some Spheroidal Metrics*. J. Math. Phys. **7** (1996).

Causal fermion systems: Classical gravity and beyond

Felix Finster

Fakultät für Mathematik, Universität Regensburg, D-93040 Regensburg, Germany
E-mail: finster@ur.de
www.mathematik.ur.de/Mat1

In this short review, we explain how and in which sense the causal action principle for causal fermion systems gives rise to classical gravity and the Einstein equations. Moreover, methods are presented for going beyond classical gravity, with applications to a positive mass theorem for static causal fermion systems, a connection between area change and matter flux and the construction of a quantum state.

Keywords: Causal fermion system, causal action principle, globally hyperbolic spacetimes, Einstein equations, surface layer integrals.

1. Introduction

The theory of *causal fermion systems* is a recent approach to fundamental physics (see a few basics in Section 2, the reviews,[8,10] the textbooks[7,14] or the website[1]). In this approach, spacetime and all objects therein are described by a measure ρ on a set $\mathcal{F}$ of linear operators on a Hilbert space $(\mathcal{H}, \langle .|.\rangle_\mathcal{H})$. The physical equations are formulated via the so-called *causal action principle*, a nonlinear variational principle where an action $\mathcal{S}$ is minimized under variations of the measure ρ.

The purpose of this survey article is to report on the present status of the theory with regards to the gravitational interaction. It has been shown that, in a well-defined limiting case, the so-called *continuum limit*, the causal action principles gives classical gravity and the Einstein equations, with the gravitational coupling constant determined by the regularization scale. Without taking the continuum limit, the causal action principle describes a novel gravitational theory which is presently under investigation. We here give a survey on different approaches towards unraveling the structure and the properties of this gravitational theory.

The paper is structured as follows. After giving the necessary background on causal fermion systems (Section 2), we explain how and in which sense classical gravity and the Einstein equations are obtained in the continuum limit (Section 3). In Section 4 we report on the approaches for going beyond classical gravity. After a few comments on the intrinsic geometric structures of a causal fermion system (Section 4.1), we introduce surface layer integrals as the main object for the subsequent analysis (Section 4.2). We finally report on a positive mass theorem for static causal fermion systems (Section 4.3), a relation between area change and matter flux (Section 4.4) and the construction of a quantum state (Section 4.5).

2. A Brief Introduction to Causal Fermion Systems

This section provides the necessary abstract background on causal fermion systems.

2.1. Causal Fermion Systems and the Causal Action Principle

We begin with the general definitions.

Definition 2.1. (causal fermion systems) *Given a separable complex Hilbert space $\mathcal{H}$ with scalar product $\langle .|.\rangle_{\mathcal{H}}$ and a parameter $n \in \mathbb{N}$ (the spin dimension), we let $\mathcal{F} \subset L(\mathcal{H})$ be the set of all symmetric operators on $\mathcal{H}$ of finite rank, which (counting multiplicities) have at most n positive and at most n negative eigenvalues. On $\mathcal{F}$ we are given a positive measure ρ (defined on a σ-algebra of subsets of $\mathcal{F}$). We refer to $(\mathcal{H}, \mathcal{F}, \rho)$ as a causal fermion system.*

A causal fermion system describes a spacetime together with all structures and objects therein. In order to single out the physically admissible causal fermion systems, one must formulate physical equations. To this end, we impose that the measure ρ should be a minimizer of the causal action principle, which we now introduce. For any $x, y \in \mathcal{F}$, the product xy is an operator of rank at most $2n$. However, in general it is no longer symmetric because $(xy)^* = yx$, and this is different from xy unless x and y commute. As a consequence, the eigenvalues of the operator xy are in general complex. We denote the non-trivial eigenvalues counting algebraic multiplicities by $\lambda_1^{xy}, \ldots, \lambda_{2n}^{xy} \in \mathbb{C}$ (more specifically, denoting the rank of xy by $k \leq 2n$, we choose $\lambda_1^{xy}, \ldots, \lambda_k^{xy}$ as all the non-zero eigenvalues and set $\lambda_{k+1}^{xy}, \ldots, \lambda_{2n}^{xy} = 0$). We introduce the Lagrangian and the causal action by

$$\text{Lagrangian:} \qquad \mathcal{L}(x,y) = \frac{1}{4n} \sum_{i,j=1}^{2n} \left(|\lambda_i^{xy}| - |\lambda_j^{xy}| \right)^2 \qquad (1)$$

$$\text{causal action:} \qquad \mathcal{S}(\rho) = \iint_{\mathcal{F} \times \mathcal{F}} \mathcal{L}(x,y) \, d\rho(x) \, d\rho(y) \,. \qquad (2)$$

The *causal action principle* is to minimize $\mathcal{S}$ by varying the measure ρ under the following constraints,

$$\text{volume constraint:} \qquad \rho(\mathcal{F}) = \text{const} \qquad (3)$$

$$\text{trace constraint:} \qquad \int_{\mathcal{F}} \operatorname{tr}(x) \, d\rho(x) = \text{const} \qquad (4)$$

$$\text{boundedness constraint:} \qquad \iint_{\mathcal{F} \times \mathcal{F}} |xy|^2 \, d\rho(x) \, d\rho(y) \leq C \,, \qquad (5)$$

where C is a given parameter, tr denotes the trace of a linear operator on $\mathcal{H}$, and the absolute value of xy is the so-called spectral weight,

$$|xy| := \sum_{j=1}^{2n} |\lambda_j^{xy}| \,.$$

This variational principle is mathematically well-posed if $\mathcal{H}$ is finite-dimensional. For the existence theory and the analysis of general properties of minimizing measures we refer to[3,5] or [14, Chapter 12]. In the existence theory one varies in the class of regular Borel measures (with respect to the topology on L($\mathcal{H}$) induced by the operator norm), and the minimizing measure is again in this class. With this in mind, here we always assume that

ρ is a regular Borel measure.

2.2. Spacetime and Causal Structure

Let ρ be a *minimizing* measure. *Spacetime* is defined as the support of this measure,

$$M := \operatorname{supp} \rho \subset \mathcal{F}.$$

Thus the spacetime points are symmetric linear operators on $\mathcal{H}$. On M we consider the topology induced by $\mathcal{F}$ (generated by the operator norm on L($\mathcal{H}$)). Moreover, the measure $\rho|_M$ restricted to M gives a volume measure on spacetime. This gives spacetime the structure of a *topological measure space*.

The operators in M contain a lot of information which, if interpreted correctly, gives rise to spacetime structures like causal and metric structures, spinors and interacting fields (for details see [7, Chapter 1]). All the resulting objects are *inherent* in the sense that we only use information already encoded in the causal fermion system. Here we restrict attention to those structures needed in what follows. We begin with the following notion of causality:

Definition 2.2. (causal structure) *For any $x, y \in \mathcal{F}$, we again denote the non-trivial eigenvalues of the operator product xy (again counting algebraic multiplicities) by $\lambda_1^{xy}, \ldots, \lambda_{2n}^{xy}$. The points x and y are called* spacelike *separated if all the λ_j^{xy} have the same absolute value. They are said to be* timelike *separated if the λ_j^{xy} are all real and do not all have the same absolute value. In all other cases (i.e. if the λ_j^{xy} are not all real and do not all have the same absolute value), the points x and y are said to be* lightlike *separated.*

Restricting the causal structure of $\mathcal{F}$ to M, we get causal relations in spacetime.

The Lagrangian (1) is compatible with the above notion of causality in the following sense. Suppose that two points $x, y \in M$ are spacelike separated. Then the eigenvalues λ_i^{xy} all have the same absolute value. As a consequence, the Lagrangian (1) vanishes. Thus pairs of points with spacelike separation do not enter the action. This can be seen in analogy to the usual notion of causality where points with spacelike separation cannot influence each other. This is the reason for the notion "causal" in *causal* fermion system and *causal* action principle.

Moreover, a causal fermion system distinguishes a *direction of time*. To this end, we let π_x be the orthogonal projection in $\mathcal{H}$ on the subspace $x(\mathcal{H}) \subset \mathcal{H}$ and introduce the functional

$$\mathcal{C} : M \times M \to \mathbb{R}, \qquad \mathcal{C}(x,y) := i \operatorname{tr} \left(y \, x \, \pi_y \, \pi_x - x \, y \, \pi_x \, \pi_y \right).$$

Obviously, this functional is anti-symmetric in its two arguments, making it possible to introduce the notions

$$\begin{cases} y \text{ lies in the } \textit{future} \text{ of } x & \text{if } \mathcal{C}(x,y) > 0 \\ y \text{ lies in the } \textit{past} \text{ of } x & \text{if } \mathcal{C}(x,y) < 0 \,. \end{cases}$$

2.3. The Euler-Lagrange Equations

A minimizer of a causal variational principle satisfies the following *Euler-Lagrange (EL) equations*. For a suitable value of the parameter $\mathfrak{s} > 0$, the function $\ell : \mathcal{F} \to \mathbb{R}_0^+$ defined by

$$\ell(x) := \int_M \mathcal{L}_\kappa(x,y)\, d\rho(y) - \mathfrak{s} \tag{6}$$

is minimal and vanishes on spacetime $M := \operatorname{supp} \rho$,

$$\ell|_M \equiv \inf_{\mathcal{F}} \ell = 0 \,. \tag{7}$$

Here the κ-*Lagrangian* $\mathcal{L}_\kappa$ is defined by

$$\mathcal{L}_\kappa : \mathcal{F} \times \mathcal{F} \to \mathbb{R}, \qquad \mathcal{L}_\kappa(x,y) := \mathcal{L}(x,y) + \kappa\, |xy|^2 \tag{8}$$

with a non-negative parameter κ, which can be thought of as the Lagrange parameter corresponding to the boundedness constraint. Likewise, the parameter $\mathfrak{s} \geq 0$ in (6) is the Lagrange parameter corresponding to the volume constraint. For the derivation and further details we refer to [16, Section 2] or [14, Chapter 7].

2.4. Spinors and Physical Wave Functions

A causal fermion system also gives rise to spinorial wave functions in spacetime, as we now explain. For every $x \in \mathcal{F}$ we define the *spin space* S_x by $S_x = x(\mathcal{H})$; it is a subspace of $\mathcal{H}$ of dimension at most $2n$. It is endowed with the *spin inner product* $\prec.|.\succ_x$ defined by

$$\prec u|v \succ_x = -\langle u|xv \rangle_\mathcal{H} \qquad (\text{for all } u,v \in S_x) \,. \tag{9}$$

A *wave function* ψ is defined as a function which to every $x \in M$ associates a vector of the corresponding spin space,

$$\psi : M \to \mathcal{H} \quad \text{with} \quad \psi(x) \in S_x M \quad \text{for all } x \in M \,.$$

It is an important observation that every vector $u \in \mathcal{H}$ of the Hilbert space gives rise to a unique wave function denoted by ψ^u. It is obtained by projecting the vector u to the corresponding spin spaces,

$$\psi^u : M \to \mathcal{H}, \qquad \psi^u(x) := \pi_x u \in S_x M \,. \tag{10}$$

We refer to ψ^u as the *physical wave function* of the vector $u \in \mathcal{H}$. Choosing an orthonormal basis (e_i) of $\mathcal{H}$, we obtain a whole family of physical wave functions (ψ^{e_i}).

This ensemble of wave functions is crucial for the understanding of what a causal fermion systems is about. In fact, all spacetime structures (like for example the causal structure in Definition 2.2) can be recovered from this ensemble. Moreover, one can construct concrete examples of causal fermion systems by choosing the physical wave functions more specifically as the quantum mechanical wave functions in a classical Lorentzian spacetime. In the next section we explain this construction in more detail.

3. The Limiting Case of Classical Gravity

In this section we outline how and in which sense the causal action principle gives rise to classical gravity. For more details we refer to[7] and the review article.[8]

3.1. *Describing a Lorentzian Spacetime by a Causal Fermion System*

We now explain how a classical curved spacetime is described by a causal fermion system. Our starting point is Lorentzian spin geometry. Thus we let $(\mathcal{M}, g)$ be a smooth, globally hyperbolic, time-oriented Lorentzian spin manifold of dimension four. For the signature of the metric we use the convention $(+, -, -, -)$. We denote the corresponding spinor bundle by $S\mathcal{M}$. Its fibers $S_x\mathcal{M}$ (with $x \in \mathcal{M}$) are endowed with an inner product $\prec.|.\succ_x$ of signature $(2, 2)$. Clifford multiplication is described by a mapping γ which satisfies the anti-commutation relations,

$$\gamma : T_x\mathcal{M} \to \mathrm{L}(S_x\mathcal{M}) \quad \text{with} \quad \gamma(u)\,\gamma(v) + \gamma(v)\,\gamma(u) = 2\,g(u,v)\,\mathbb{1}_{S_x(\mathcal{M})}\,.$$

We also write Clifford multiplication in components with the Dirac matrices γ^j. The metric connections on the tangent bundle and the spinor bundle are denoted by ∇. The sections of the spinor bundle are also referred to as wave functions.

We denote the smooth sections of the spinor bundle by $C^\infty(\mathcal{M}, S\mathcal{M})$. The Dirac operator $\mathcal{D}$ is defined by

$$\mathcal{D} := i\gamma^j \nabla_j \,:\, C^\infty(\mathcal{M}, S\mathcal{M}) \to C^\infty(\mathcal{M}, S\mathcal{M})\,.$$

Given a real parameter $m \in \mathbb{R}$ (the *mass*), the Dirac equation reads

$$(\mathcal{D} - m)\,\psi = 0\,.$$

We mainly consider solutions in the class $C^\infty_{\mathrm{sc}}(\mathcal{M}, S\mathcal{M})$ of smooth sections with spatially compact support (i.e. wave functions whose restriction to any Cauchy surface is compact). On such solutions, one has the scalar product

$$(\psi|\phi)_m = 2\pi \int_\mathcal{N} \prec\!\psi\,|\,\gamma(\nu)\,\phi\!\succ_x d\mu_\mathcal{N}(x)\,,$$

where $\mathcal{N}$ denotes any Cauchy surface and ν its future-directed normal (due to current conservation, the scalar product is in fact independent of the choice of $\mathcal{N}$; for details see [20, Section 2]). Forming the completion gives the Hilbert space $(\mathcal{H}_m, (.|.)_m)$.

Next, we choose a closed subspace $\mathcal{H} \subset \mathcal{H}_m$ of the solution space of the Dirac equation. The induced scalar product on $\mathcal{H}$ is denoted by $\langle.|.\rangle_{\mathcal{H}}$. There is the technical difficulty that the wave functions in $\mathcal{H}$ are in general not continuous, making it impossible to evaluate them pointwise. For this reason, we need to introduce an *ultraviolet regularization* on the length scale ε, described mathematically by a linear

$$\text{regularization operator} \quad \mathfrak{R}_\varepsilon \,:\, \mathcal{H} \to C^0(\mathcal{M}, S\mathcal{M}) \,.$$

In the simplest case, the regularization can be realized by a convolution on a Cauchy surface or in spacetime (for details see [20, Section 4] or [7, Section §1.1.2]). For us, the regularization is not merely a technical tool, but it realizes the concept that we want to change the geometric structures on the microscopic scale. With this in mind, we always consider the regularized quantities as those having mathematical and physical significance. Different choices of regularization operators realize different microscopic spacetime structures.

Evaluating the regularization operator at a spacetime point $x \in \mathcal{M}$ gives the *regularized wave evaluation operator* $\Psi^\varepsilon(x)$,

$$\Psi^\varepsilon(x) = \mathfrak{R}_\varepsilon(x) \,:\, \mathcal{H} \to S_x\mathcal{M} \,. \tag{11}$$

We also take its adjoint (with respect to the Hilbert space scalar product $\langle.|.\rangle_{\mathcal{H}}$ and the spin inner product $\prec.|.\succ_x$),

$$\left(\Psi^\varepsilon(x)\right)^* \,:\, S_x\mathcal{M} \to \mathcal{H} \,.$$

Multiplying $\Psi^\varepsilon(x)$ by its adjoint gives the operator

$$F^\varepsilon(x) := -\left(\Psi^\varepsilon(x)\right)^* \Psi^\varepsilon(x) \,:\, \mathcal{H} \to \mathcal{H} \,, \tag{12}$$

referred to as the *local correlation operator* at the spacetime point x. The local correlation operator is also characterized by the relation

$$(\psi \,|\, F^\varepsilon(x)\,\phi) = -\prec(\mathfrak{R}_\varepsilon\psi)(x)|(\mathfrak{R}_\varepsilon\phi)(x)\succ_x \quad \text{for all } \psi, \phi \in \mathcal{H} \,. \tag{13}$$

Taking into account that the inner product on the Dirac spinors at x has signature $(2,2)$, it is a symmetric operator on $\mathcal{H}$ of rank at most four, which (counting multiplicities) has at most two positive and at most two negative eigenvalues. Varying the spacetime point, we obtain a mapping

$$F^\varepsilon \,:\, \mathcal{M} \to \mathcal{F} \subset \mathrm{L}(\mathcal{H}) \,,$$

where $\mathcal{F}$ denotes all symmetric operators of rank at most four with at most two positive and at most two negative eigenvalues. Finally, we introduce the measure ρ on $\mathcal{F}$ by taking the push-forward of the volume measure on $\mathcal{M}$ under the mapping F^ε,

$$\rho := (F^\varepsilon)_* \mu_{\mathcal{M}} \tag{14}$$

(thus $\rho(\Omega) := \mu_{\mathcal{M}}((F^\varepsilon)^{-1}(\Omega))$). The resulting structure $(\mathcal{H}, \mathcal{F}, \rho)$ is a causal fermion system of spin dimension two.

We conclude with a few comments on the significance of this construction. We first point out that the construction uses all the structures of Lorentzian spin geometry as well as the properties of the Dirac wave functions in $\mathcal{H}$. We thus obtain a *very specific class of examples* of causal fermion systems describing classical spacetimes. In general, the measure ρ defined by (14) will not be a minimizer of the causal action principle. But it is an approximate minimizer if the Einstein equations are satisfied. Before making this point precise in the next section (Section 3.2), we now explain the physical picture behind the Dirac wave functions in $\mathcal{H}$. These wave functions have the interpretation as being those Dirac wave functions which are realized in the physical system under consideration. If we describe for example a system of one electron, then the wave function of the electron is contained in $\mathcal{H}$. Moreover, $\mathcal{H}$ includes all the wave functions which form the so-called Dirac sea (for an explanation of this point see for example[6]). All the Dirac wave functions in $\mathcal{H}$ can be identified with the ensemble of *physical wave functions* of the causal fermion system as introduced in (10). This "identification" is made mathematically precise by also identifying the objects of Lorentzian spin geometry with corresponding inherent objects of the causal fermion system (for details see [14, Section 1.2]). The name causal *fermion* system is motivated by the fact that Dirac particles are fermions. According to (13), the local correlation operator $F^\varepsilon(p)$ describes densities and correlations of the physical wave functions at the spacetime point p. Working exclusively with the local correlation operators and the corresponding push-forward measure ρ means in particular that the geometric structures are encoded in and must be retrieved from the physical wave functions. Since the physical wave functions describe the distribution of matter in spacetime, one can summarize this concept by saying that *matter encodes geometry.*

3.2. *Classical Gravity in the Continuum Limit*

The construction of the causal fermion system in the previous section involved the Lorentzian metric g. But this Lorentzian metric did not need to satisfy the Einstein equation. Instead of postulating the Einstein equations, our strategy is to *derive* these equations from the causal action principle. To this end, we need to evaluate the EL equations (6) for the causal fermion system $(\mathcal{H}, \mathcal{F}, \rho)$ constructed in the previous section in the limit $\varepsilon \searrow 0$ when the ultraviolet regularization is removed. This analysis, referred to as the *continuum limit*, is carried out in detail in [7, Chapter 4]. Before giving a brief outline of how this analysis works, we state the main result in the context of gravitational fields: The EL equations (6) are satisfied asymptotically for small $\varepsilon > 0$ only if the Lorentzian metric satisfies the Einstein equations, up to possible higher order corrections in curvature (which scale in powers of $(\delta^2 \operatorname{Riem})$, where δ is the Planck length and Riem is the curvature tensor), i.e. (see [7, Theorems 4.9.3 and 5.4.4])

$$R_{jk} - \frac{1}{2} R\, g_{jk} + \Lambda\, g_{jk} = G\, T_{jk} + \mathcal{O}\!\left(\delta^4 \operatorname{Riem}^2\right). \tag{15}$$

Moreover, it is shown that the gravitational coupling constant G is determined by the length scale of the microscopic spacetime structures and has the scaling

$$G \sim \delta^2 \ .$$

The cosmological constant Λ, however, is not determined by our method. In order to avoid confusion, we finally note that we carefully distinguish the Planck length δ from the regularization length ε. The reason is that, although it seems natural to assume that these length scales coincide, this does not necessarily need to be the case. In fact, the are indications that ε should be chosen even much smaller than δ (for a detailed discussion of the length scales see for example [4, Appendix A]).

We now briefly explain the general procedure in the analysis of the continuum limit. Given a causal fermion system $(\mathcal{H}, \mathcal{F}, \rho)$ describing a globally hyperbolic spacetime $(\mathcal{M}, g)$ (as constructed in Section 3.1), our task is to evaluate the EL equations (7). The first step is to compute the eigenvalues $\lambda_1^{xy}, \ldots, \lambda_{2n}^{xy}$ of the operator product $F^\varepsilon(x) F^\varepsilon(y)$ for given $x, y \in \mathcal{M}$. Using (12) together with the fact that the non-zero eigenvalues of a matrix product as well as the corresponding algebraic multiplicities do not change when the matrices are cyclically commuted, one can just as well compute the eigenvalues of the *closed chain* A_{xy} defined by

$$A_{xy} := P^\varepsilon(x, y) P^\varepsilon(y, x) \ : \ S_x \mathcal{M} \to S_x \mathcal{M} \ , \tag{16}$$

where the *regularized kernel of the fermionic projector* $P^\varepsilon(x, y)$ is defined by

$$P^\varepsilon(x, y) = -\Psi^\varepsilon(x) \big(\Psi^\varepsilon(y)\big)^* \ : \ S_y \mathcal{M} \to S_x \mathcal{M} \ .$$

In this way, it suffices to compute the eigenvalues of a linear endomorphism of $S_x M$, which can be represented by a 4 × 4-matrix. Moreover, the regularized kernel of the fermionic projector can be analyzed explicitly using the *regularized Hadamard expansion*. In general terms, $P^\varepsilon(x, y)$ is a smooth function which in the limit $\varepsilon \searrow 0$ converges to a distribution which has singularities on the lightcone (i.e. for lightlike separation of x and y). As a consequence, the pointwise product in (16) is ill-defined in this limit. In the continuum limit analysis, one deals with this issue by studying the Lagrangian and other composite expressions in $P^\varepsilon(x, y)$ asymptotically for small $\varepsilon > 0$. Evaluating the resulting expressions in the EL equations (7), one gets equations involving the gravitational field and the Dirac wave functions. In models containing neutrinos, these equations imply the Einstein equations (15).

The detailed computations can be found in,[7] where the continuum limit analysis is carried out in Minkowski space. In this context, the Hadamard expansion is referred to as the *light cone expansion*. The reader interested in the general construction of the regularized Hadamard expansion in curved spacetime is referred to.[18]

4. Going Beyond Classical Gravity

The above derivation of the Einstein equations in the continuum limit has two disadvantages. First, it is rather technical and thus does not give a good intuitive understanding of the underlying mechanisms. Second and more importantly, the Einstein equations are obtained only for the special class of examples of causal fermion systems constructed in Section 3.1 and hold only in the continuum limit. But the methods do not give an insight into the geometric meaning of the EL equations (7) for general causal fermion systems describing more general "quantum" spacetimes. This raises the following question:

$$\text{Given a general causal fermion system } (\mathcal{H}, \mathcal{F}, \rho), \text{ how do the EL equations (7) relate matter to the geometry of spacetime?} \tag{17}$$

For a general causal fermion system, we cannot work with tensor fields, making it impossible to formulate the Einstein equations or modifications thereof. Therefore, we need to go beyond the mathematical setting of Lorentzian geometry. In the next sections, we explain step by step how this can be done and mention a few results.

4.1. *A Lorentzian Quantum Geometry*

In[9] it was shown that a causal fermion system gives rise to geometric structures in spacetime. The general strategy for obtaining these geometric structures is as follows. Given two spacetime points $x, y \in M$, the corresponding spin space S_x and S_y (see Section 2.4) are subspaces of the underlying Hilbert space $\mathcal{H}$. Denoting the orthogonal projection to the spin spaces S_x again by

$$\pi_x : \mathcal{H} \to S_x \,,$$

the *kernel of the fermionic projector* is introduced by

$$P(x,y) = \pi_x y|_{S_y} : S_y \to S_x \,.$$

Being an operator from one spin space to another, it gives relations between the spacetime points. In other words, the kernel of the fermionic projector induces additional structures in spacetime. One important structure is the *spin connection* $D_{x,y}$, being a unitary mapping between the spin spaces,

$$D_{x,y} : S_y M \to S_x M \quad \text{unitary} \tag{18}$$

(unitary with respect to the spin inner product (9)). A first idea for construction $D_{x,y}$ is to take a polar decomposition of $P(x,y)$. This idea needs to be refined in order to also obtain a metric connection and to arrange that the different connections are compatible. Here for brevity we omit the details and refer to[9] or the review.[8] In general terms, it turns out that there is a canonical spin connection (18), provided that the operators x and y satisfy certain conditions, which are subsumed in the notion that the spacetime points be *spin-connectable*. *Curvature* $\mathfrak{R}$ can be defined as the holonomy of the spin connection. Thus, in the simplest case, for three points $x, y, z \in M$ which are mutually spin-connectable, one sets

$$\mathfrak{R}(x,y,z) = D_{x,y}\, D_{y,z}\, D_{z,x} : S_x M \to S_x M \,.$$

In[9] also the correspondence to Lorentzian spin geometry is established, in the sense that for causal fermion systems describing a globally hyperbolic Lorentzian manifold (as constructed in Section 3.1) and taking a suitable limit $\varepsilon \searrow 0$, the spin connection (18) goes over to the spinorial Levi-Civita connection of the Lorentzian manifold.

While these structures give a good understanding of the geometry of a causal fermion system, so far they have not been fruitful for unraveling the form of the gravitational interaction as described by the causal action principle. The basic problem is that the EL equations (7) cannot be formulated in terms of these geometric structures. In other words, it does not seem possible to rewrite the causal action principle as a geometric variational principle involving $D_{x,y}$ and $\mathfrak{R}$. With this in mind, we now move on to other structures which again have a geometric meaning, but harmonize better with the EL equations (7).

4.2. *Surface Layer Integrals*

Coming back to our question (17), we follow another path for getting a connection between the geometric structures and the EL equations (7). This method is inspired by the fact that the effects of gravity can also be captured by considering the volume and area of surfaces in spacetime, and by analyzing how this area changes under flows of the surfaces. Typical examples for this connection are Huisken's isoperimetric mass (see for example[22]) and Jacobson's connection between area change and matter flux.[4] Thinking along these lines, the first obvious question is how a surface integral can be defined in the setting of causal fermion systems. Once this question has been answered, one can analyze the area of families of surfaces and make the above analogies more precise.

As a typical example, suppose we want to define the analog of an integral over a Cauchy surface $\mathcal{N}$ in a globally hyperbolic spacetime, i.e. symbolically

$$\int_{\mathcal{N}} (\cdots)\, d\mu_{\mathcal{N}}(x)\,, \tag{19}$$

where $d\mu_{\mathcal{N}}$ is the induced volume measure on $\mathcal{N}$. Here one can think of $(\cdots)$ as a density like for example the inner product $\nu_i J^i$ of a current vector field with the future-directed normal ν. In the setting of causal fermion system, surface integrals like (19) are undefined. Instead, one considers so-called *surface layer integrals*. In general terms, a surface layer integral is a double integral of the form

$$\int_{\Omega} \left(\int_{M\setminus\Omega} (\cdots)\, \mathcal{L}_\kappa(x,y)\, d\rho(y) \right) d\rho(x)\,, \tag{20}$$

where one variable is integrated over a subset $\Omega \subset M$, and the other variable is integrated over the complement of Ω. Here $(\cdots)$ is the analog of the corresponding factor in (19), but now having the mathematical structure of being a differential operator acting on the Lagrangian.

In order to explain the basic concept, let us assume for a moment that the Lagrangian is of *short range* in the following sense. We let $d \in C^0(M \times M, \mathbb{R}_0^+)$ be a suitably chosen distance function on M. Then the assumption of short range can be quantified by demanding that $\mathcal{L}_\kappa$ should vanish on distances larger than l, i.e.

$$d(x,y) > l \quad \Longrightarrow \quad \mathcal{L}_\kappa(x,y) = 0 \,. \tag{21}$$

Under this assumption, the surface layer integral (20) only involves pairs (x,y) of distance at most l, where x lies in Ω, whereas y lies in the complement $M \setminus \Omega$. As a consequence, the integral only involves points in a layer around the boundary of Ω of width l, i.e.

$$x, y \in B_l(\partial \Omega) \,.$$

Therefore, a double integral of the form (20) can be regarded as an approximation of a surface integral on the length scale l, as shown in Figure 1. In most applications, the Lagrangian is *not* of short range in the strict sense (21). But it decays on the Compton scale $l \sim 1/m$ (where m denotes again the mass of the Dirac particles), so that the qualitative picture in Figure 1 still applies.

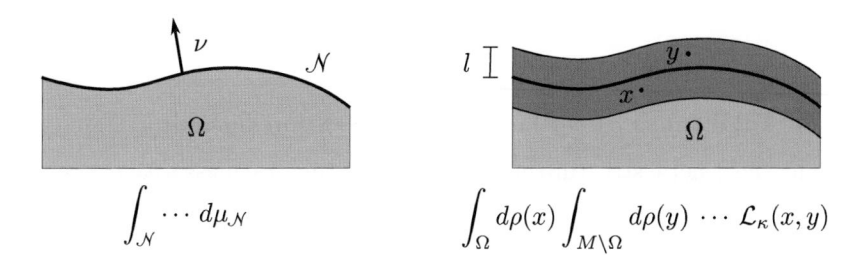

Fig. 1. A surface integral and a corresponding surface layer integral.

Surface layer integrals were first introduce in[15] in the context of Noether-like theorems. The analysis of this paper revealed that, in contrast to the geometric structures in Section 4.1, the structure of a surface layer integral does fit nicely to the EL equations (7), giving rise to very useful conservation laws. This connection was analyzed further and more systematically in.[16,17] Moreover, in[11] another variant of a surface layer integral was introduced, which will be importance for what follows. This new surface layer integral can be regarded as a generalization or "nonlinear version" of (20), as can be understood as follows. The differential operator $(\cdots)$ in the integrand can be regarded as describing first or second variations of the measure ρ. Instead of considering variations of ρ, we now consider an additional measure $\tilde{\rho}$ which can be thought of as a finite perturbation of the measure ρ. Consequently, we also have two spacetimes

$$M := \operatorname{supp} \rho \quad \text{and} \quad \tilde{M} := \operatorname{supp} \tilde{\rho} \,.$$

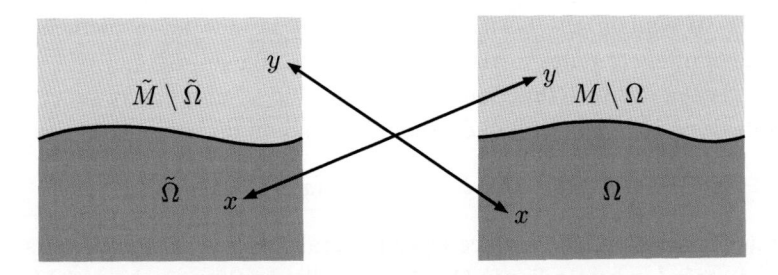

Fig. 2. The nonlinear surface layer integral.

Choosing two compact subsets $\Omega \subset M$ and $\tilde{\Omega} \subset \tilde{M}$ of the corresponding spacetimes, we form the *nonlinear surface layer integral* by

$$\gamma^{\tilde{\Omega},\Omega}(\tilde{\rho},\rho) := \int_{\tilde{\Omega}} d\tilde{\rho}(x) \int_{M\setminus\Omega} d\rho(y)\, \mathcal{L}_\kappa(x,y) - \int_{\Omega} d\rho(x) \int_{\tilde{M}\setminus\tilde{\Omega}} d\tilde{\rho}(y)\, \mathcal{L}_\kappa(x,y)\,. \quad (22)$$

Note that one argument of the Lagrangian is in M, whereas the other is in $\tilde{M}$. Moreover, one argument lies inside the set Ω respectively $\tilde{\Omega}$, whereas the other argument lies outside this set. In this way, the nonlinear surface layer integral "compares" the two spacetimes near the boundaries of Ω and $\tilde{\Omega}$, as is illustrated in Figure 2.

4.3. *The Total Mass of a Static Causal Fermion System*

Combining the general structure of Huisken's isoperimetric mass with the concept of a surface layer integral, the question arises whether notions like the total mass and total energy can be introduced for a class of causal fermion systems which generalize asymptotically flat Lorentzian manifolds. This question has been answered in the affirmative in[19] in the static setting. We now outline a few constructions and results of this paper.

Static causal fermion systems are introduced as usual by demanding a one-parameter group of symmetries:

Definition 4.1. Let $(\mathcal{U}_t)_{t\in\mathbb{R}}$ be a strongly continuous one-parameter group of unitary transformations on the Hilbert space $\mathcal{H}$ (i.e. s-$\lim_{t'\to t} \mathcal{U}_{t'} = \mathcal{U}_t$ and $\mathcal{U}_t \mathcal{U}_{t'} = \mathcal{U}_{t+t'}$). The causal fermion system $(\mathcal{H},\mathcal{F},\rho)$ is **static with respect to** $(\mathcal{U}_t)_{t\in\mathbb{R}}$ if it has the following properties:

(i) Spacetime $M := \operatorname{supp}\rho \subset \mathcal{F}$ is a topological product,

$$M = \mathbb{R} \times N\,.$$

We write a spacetime point $x \in M$ as $x = (t,\mathbf{x})$ with $t \in \mathbb{R}$ and $\mathbf{x} \in N$.

(ii) The one-parameter group $(\mathcal{U}_t)_{t\in\mathbb{R}}$ leaves the measure ρ invariant, i.e.

$$\rho(\mathcal{U}_t\,\Omega\,\mathcal{U}_t^{-1}) = \rho(\Omega) \qquad \text{for all } \rho\text{-measurable } \Omega \subset \mathcal{F}\,.$$

Moreover,
$$\mathcal{U}_{t'}(t, \mathbf{x}) \mathcal{U}_{t'}^{-1} = (t + t', \mathbf{x}).$$

As a consequence of (ii), the measure ρ has the product form
$$d\rho = dt\, d\mu,$$
where μ is a measure on $\mathcal{G} := \mathfrak{G} = \mathfrak{F}^{\mathrm{reg}}/\mathbb{R}$.

Restricting attention to static causal fermion systems and varying within the class of measures which are invariant under the action of a given one-parameter group $(\mathcal{U}_t)_{t \in \mathbb{R}}$, one obtains a corresponding *static causal action principle*, where one minimizes the static action
$$\mathcal{S}_{\mathrm{static}}(\mu) = \int_{\mathcal{G}} d\mu(\mathbf{x}) \int_{\mathcal{G}} d\mu(\mathbf{y})\, \mathcal{L}_{\mathrm{static}}(\mathbf{x}, \mathbf{y})$$
under variations of the measure μ on $\mathcal{G}$, keeping the total volume $\mu(\mathcal{G})$ fixed (*volume constraint*). The static Lagrangian is obtained by integrating one argument of the κ-Lagrangian (8) over time,
$$\mathcal{L}_{\mathrm{static}}(\mathbf{x}, \mathbf{y}) := \int_{-\infty}^{\infty} \mathcal{L}_{\kappa}\big((0, \mathbf{x}), (t, \mathbf{y})\big)\, dt.$$

The *total mass* $\mathfrak{M}$ of a static causal fermion system described by the measure $\tilde{\mu}$ is defined by comparing $\tilde{\mu}$ asymptotically near infinity with a measure μ describing the vacuum. To this end, one exhausts the supports N and $\tilde{N}$ of these measures by sequences of compact subsets $(\Omega_n)_{n \in \mathbb{N}}$ and $(\tilde{\Omega}_n)_{n \in \mathbb{N}}$, respectively, and takes the limit of a nonlinear surface layer integral of structure similar to (22),
$$\mathfrak{M}(\tilde{\mu}, \mu) = \lim_{\Omega_n \nearrow N,\, \tilde{\Omega}_n \nearrow \tilde{N} \text{ with } \mu(\Omega_n) = \tilde{\mu}(\tilde{\Omega}_n) < \infty}$$
$$\times \left(\int_{\tilde{\Omega}_n} d\tilde{\mu}(\mathbf{x}) \int_{N \setminus \Omega_n} d\mu(\mathbf{y})\, \mathcal{L}_{\mathrm{static}}(\mathbf{x}, \mathbf{y}) - \int_{\Omega_n} d\mu(\mathbf{x}) \int_{\tilde{N} \setminus \tilde{\Omega}_n} d\tilde{\mu}(\mathbf{y})\, \mathcal{L}_{\mathrm{static}}(\mathbf{x}, \mathbf{y}) \right). \quad (23)$$

In order for this expression to be well-defined, one needs to assume that the spacetimes are *asymptotically flat* (for brevity, we do not give the precise definition, which can be found in [19, Definition 1.5]). As a consequence of the EL equations, the mass does not depend on the choice of the exhaustions, except that the volume condition $\mu(\Omega_n) = \tilde{\mu}(\tilde{\Omega}_n)$ must hold. Moreover, a *positive mass theorem* is proved which states that the total mass $\mathfrak{M}(\tilde{\mu}, \mu)$ is non-negative if a suitable *local energy condition* holds (for details see [19, Definition 1.8 and Theorem 1.9]).

The correspondence to the classical positive mass theorem (see for example[23]) is established by showing that for a static causal fermion systems describing the Schwarzschild spacetime (constructed again as explained in Section 3.1), the total mass $\mathfrak{M}(\tilde{\mu}, \mu)$ coincides (up to an irrelevant prefactor) with the ADM mass[2] (see [19, Theorem 1.10]). For brevity, we cannot enter the proof and the detailed constructions. But we make one remark which will be important in connection with the construction of the quantum state in Section 4.5: When comparing causal fermion systems describing the Schwarzschild spacetime and Minkowski space, one needs to take into account that the resulting causal fermion systems are defined on two different Hilbert spaces, namely a Hilbert space $\tilde{\mathcal{H}}$ formed of Dirac solutions in Schwarzschild and a Hilbert space $\mathcal{H}$ formed of Dirac solutions in Minkowski space. Before we can make sense of the nonlinear surface layer integral (23), these Hilbert spaces must be identified by a unitary transformation V,

$$V : \mathcal{H} \to \tilde{\mathcal{H}}. \qquad (24)$$

This identification is *not* canonical but leaves us with the freedom of choosing a unitary transformation. Therefore, in order to make sense of (23), one must prove that the total mass is independent of the choice of the unitary transformation V (for details see [19, Section 4.3]).

4.4. *Connection Between Area Change and Matter Flux*

In 1995, Ted Jacobson gave a derivation of the Einstein equations from thermodynamic principles.[21] At the heart of his argument is the formula

$$\frac{d}{d\tau} A(S_\tau) = c\, F(S_\tau) \qquad (25)$$

which states that the area change of a family of two-surfaces S_τ propagating along a null Killing direction is proportional to the matter flux $F(S_\tau)$ across these surfaces (with c a universal constant). In,[4] this formula is derived in the setting of causal fermion systems from the EL equations (7) (without referring to thermodynamics). This result gives an alternative derivation of the Einstein equations from the causal action principle (again with an undetermined cosmological constant). Compared to the continuum limit analysis described in Section 3.2, this alternative derivation has the advantage that it is more conceptual and thus gives a more direct understanding of why and how the Einstein equations arise. Moreover, the procedure in[4] has the benefit that it does not rely on tensor calculus. Therefore, it goes beyond Lorentzian geometry and applies to more general "quantum" spacetimes.

We now explain the general procedure and a few constructions from.[4] The first question is how to define the area A of a two-dimensional surface S in the setting of causal fermion systems. It is most convenient to describe $S \subset M$ as

$$S = \partial\Omega \cap \partial V,$$

where Ω can be thought of as being the past of a Cauchy surface, and V describing a spacetime cylinder. This description has the advantage that the resulting surface layer integrals are well-defined even in situations when spacetime is singular or discrete, in which case the boundaries $\partial\Omega$ and ∂V are no longer a sensible concept. The most natural way of introducing a surface layer integral localized in a neighborhood of S is a double integral of the form

$$\int_{\Omega \cap V} \left(\int_{M \setminus (\Omega \cup V)} (\cdots)\, \mathcal{L}_\kappa(x,y)\, d\rho(y) \right) d\rho(x) \qquad (26)$$

(where $(\cdots)$ stands again for a differential operator acting on the Lagrangian). If the Lagrangian has short range, we only get contributions to this surface layer integral if both x and y are close to the two-dimensional surface S (see the left of Figure 3).

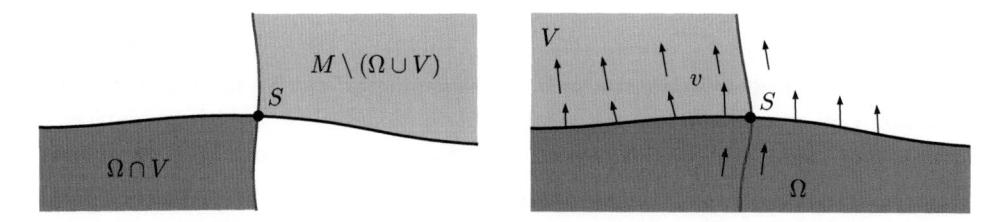

Fig. 3. Two-dimensional surface layer integrals.

The disadvantage of this method is that, similar as explained in Section 4.1 for the structures of the Lorentzian quantum geometry and the EL equations, the surface layer integral (26) does not fit together with the notion of matter flux. Therefore, it is preferable to define the two-dimensional area as follows. We need to assume that M has a smooth manifold structure, and that the measure ρ is absolutely continuous and smooth with respect to the Lebesgue measure in every chart (x, U) of M, i.e.

$$d\rho = h(x)\, d^4x \qquad \text{with } h \in C^\infty(U, \mathbb{R}^+)\,. \tag{27}$$

Also assuming that the boundaries of Ω and V are smooth, we can choose a smooth vector field v which is transverse to the hypersurface $\partial\Omega$ and tangential to ∂V (see the right of Figure 3). Under these additional assumptions, one can introduce an integration measure $d\mu$ on the hypersurface $\partial\Omega$ by

$$d\mu(v, x) = h\, \epsilon_{ijkl}\, v^i\, dx^j dx^k dx^l\,,$$

where ϵ_{ijkl} is the totally anti-symmetric Levi-Civita symbol (normalized by $\epsilon_{0123} = 1$). Now we can define the two-dimensional area by

$$A := \int_{\partial\Omega \cap V} d\mu(v, x) \int_{M\setminus V} d\rho(y)\, \mathcal{L}_\kappa(x, y)\,. \tag{28}$$

We next describe a symmetry by a notion of a Killing field. This notion will also give rise to a notion of matter flux.

Definition 4.2. A vector field u on M is called **Killing field** of the causal fermion system if the following conditions hold:

(i) The divergence of u vanishes, i.e.

$$\frac{1}{h} \partial_j (h\, u^j) = 0$$

(where h is again the weight function in (27)).

(ii) The directional derivative of the Lagrangian is small in the sense that

$$\left(D_{1,u} + D_{2,u}\right)\mathcal{L}_\kappa(x,y) \lesssim \frac{m^4}{\varepsilon^4\,\delta^4} \tag{29}$$

(where again ε is the regularization length, and δ is the Planck length).

The reason why the right side in (29) is non-zero is that the derivative of the Lagrangian involves contributions from both the geometry and the matter fields. The condition (29) means that the geometric contributions vanish (which are typically much larger). The fact that the matter contribution remains makes it possible to define the matter flux by

$$F(S) := \int_{\partial\Omega \cap V} d\mu(v,x) \int_{M\setminus V} d\rho(y) \left(D_{1,u} + D_{2,u}\right)\mathcal{L}_\kappa(x,y)\,, \tag{30}$$

where we assume that the Killing field u is tangential to Ω (see Figure 4). In the limiting case of lightlike propagation, the vector fields u and v coincide, making it possible to recover the matter flux (30) as the derivative of the area (28) in the direction of the Killing field u. This gives the desired relation (25).

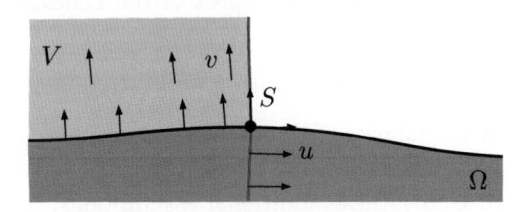

Fig. 4. Matter flux through S.

4.5. *The Quantum State of a Causal Fermion System*

We finally give an outlook on quantum field theory and quantum gravity. So far, the connection to quantum field theory has been established only for causal fermion systems describing Minkowski space.[11,12] But most of the methods apply just as well to more general causal fermion systems describing curved spacetimes. Moreover, one should keep in mind that in a causal fermion system, all the bosonic interactions are described in a unified way with the same mathematical structures, giving hope that methods developed for the electromagnetic interaction in Minkowski space can be adapted to the gravitational field. But, as is usually the case in mathematics, the connections and analogies are rather subtle and need to be explored carefully and in depth. We plan to do so in the near future.

Coming back to causal fermion systems describing Minkowski space, in[12] a *quantum state* ω^t of a causal fermion system $(\tilde{\mathcal{H}}, \tilde{\mathcal{F}}, \tilde{\rho})$, which describes an interacting spacetime, is constructed. Here by a "quantum state" we mean a positive linear functional on the $*$-algebra of observables $\mathcal{A}$, i.e.

$$\omega^t : \mathcal{A} \to \mathbb{C} \quad \text{complex linear} \quad \text{and} \quad \omega^t(A^*A) \geq 0 \quad \text{for all } A \in \mathcal{A}.$$

The observables are formed of linearized solutions of the EL equations. The general idea for constructing the quantum state is to compare $(\tilde{\mathcal{H}}, \tilde{\mathcal{F}}, \rho)$ at time t with a causal fermion system $(\mathcal{H}, \mathcal{F}, \rho)$ describing the vacuum. Similar to the procedure for the total mass (23), the "comparison" is again performed with a nonlinear surface layer integral (22), but now with $\tilde{\Omega}$ and Ω chosen as the past of the respective Cauchy surfaces (similar as shown in Figure 2). The unitary freedom in identifying the Hilbert spaces already mentioned in the connection of the positive mass theorem in (24) is now taken care of by integrating over a group $\mathcal{G}$ of unitary operators. This leads to a formula for the quantum state of the symbolic form

$$\omega^t(A) := \frac{1}{Z^t(\beta, \tilde{\rho})} \int_{\mathcal{G}} (\cdots) \, e^{\beta \gamma^t(\tilde{\rho}, \mathcal{U}\rho)} \, d\mu_{\mathcal{G}}(\mathcal{U}), \tag{31}$$

where $Z^t(\beta, \tilde{\rho})$ is the partition function defined by

$$Z^t(\beta, \tilde{\rho}) := \int_{\mathcal{G}} e^{\beta \gamma^t(\tilde{\rho}, \mathcal{U}\rho)} \, d\mu_{\mathcal{G}}(\mathcal{U}),$$

and β is a real parameter. The factor $(\cdots)$ in (31) consists of a product of surface layer integrals formed of the linearized solutions contained in the observable A (for details see [12, Section 4]).

The significance of this construction is that it becomes possible to describe the interacting causal fermion system in the familiar language of quantum field theory. Consequently, also the dynamics as described by the EL equations (7) can be rewritten as a time evolution of the state ω^t. The detailed form of the resulting quantum dynamics is presently under investigation.[13]

Acknowledgments

I would like to thank Michael Kiessling and Shadi Tahvildar-Zadeh for the kind invitation to the Marcel Grossmann Meeting. I am grateful to Christoph Krpoun for helpful comments on the manuscript.

References

1. *Link to web platform on causal fermion systems: www.causal-fermion-system.com.*
2. R. Arnowitt, S. Deser, and C.W. Misner, *Energy and the criteria for radiation in general relativity*, Phys. Rev. (2) **118** (1960), 1100–1104.
3. Y. Bernard and F. Finster, *On the structure of minimizers of causal variational principles in the non-compact and equivariant settings*, arXiv:1205.0403 [math-ph], Adv. Calc. Var. **7** (2014), no. 1, 27–57.
4. E. Curiel, F. Finster, and J.M. Isidro, *Two-dimensional area and matter flux in the theory of causal fermion systems*, arXiv:1910.06161 [math-ph], Internat. J. Modern Phys. D **29** (2020), 2050098.

5. F. Finster, *Causal variational principles on measure spaces*, arXiv:0811.2666 [math-ph], J. Reine Angew. Math. **646** (2010), 141–194.
6. _____, *A formulation of quantum field theory realizing a sea of interacting Dirac particles*, arXiv:0911.2102 [hep-th], Lett. Math. Phys. **97** (2011), no. 2, 165–183.
7. _____, *The Continuum Limit of Causal Fermion Systems*, arXiv:1605.04742 [math-ph], Fundamental Theories of Physics, vol. 186, Springer, 2016.
8. _____, *Causal fermion systems: A primer for Lorentzian geometers*, arXiv:1709.04781 [math-ph], J. Phys.: Conf. Ser. **968** (2018), 012004.
9. F. Finster and A. Grotz, *A Lorentzian quantum geometry*, arXiv:1107.2026 [math-ph], Adv. Theor. Math. Phys. **16** (2012), no. 4, 1197–1290.
10. F. Finster and M. Jokel, *Causal fermion systems: An elementary introduction to physical ideas and mathematical concepts*, arXiv:1908.08451 [math-ph], Progress and Visions in Quantum Theory in View of Gravity (F. Finster, D. Giulini, J. Kleiner, and J. Tolksdorf, eds.), Birkhäuser Verlag, Basel, 2020, pp. 63–92.
11. F. Finster and N. Kamran, *Complex structures on jet spaces and bosonic Fock space dynamics for causal variational principles*, arXiv:1808.03177 [math-ph], Pure Appl. Math. Q. **17** (2021), no. 1, 55–140.
12. _____, *Fermionic Fock spaces and quantum states for causal fermion systems*, arXiv:2101.10793 [math-ph], Ann. Henri Poincaré **23** (2022), no. 4, 1359–1398.
13. F. Finster, N. Kamran, and M. Reintjes, *The quantum dynamics of a causal fermion system: Holographic mixing and bosonic loop diagrams*, in preparation.
14. F. Finster, S. Kindermann, and J.-H. Treude, *An Introductory Course on Causal Fermion Systems*, in preparation, www.causal-fermion-system.com/intro-public.pdf.
15. F. Finster and J. Kleiner, *Noether-like theorems for causal variational principles*, arXiv:1506.09076 [math-ph], Calc. Var. Partial Differential Equations **55:35** (2016), no. 2, 41.
16. _____, *A Hamiltonian formulation of causal variational principles*, arXiv:1612.07192 [math-ph], Calc. Var. Partial Differential Equations **56:73** (2017), no. 3, 33.
17. _____, *A class of conserved surface layer integrals for causal variational principles*, arXiv:1801.08715 [math-ph], Calc. Var. Partial Differential Equations **58:38** (2019), no. 1, 34.
18. F. Finster and M. Kraus, *The regularized Hadamard expansion*, arXiv:1708.04447 [math-ph], J. Math. Anal. Appl. **491** (2020), no. 2, 124340.
19. F. Finster and A. Platzer, *A positive mass theorem for static causal fermion systems*, arXiv:1912.12995 [math-ph], Adv. Theor. Math. Phys. **25** (2021), no. 7, 1735–1818.
20. F. Finster and M. Reintjes, *A non-perturbative construction of the fermionic projector on globally hyperbolic manifolds I – Space-times of finite lifetime*, arXiv:1301.5420 [math-ph], Adv. Theor. Math. Phys. **19** (2015), no. 4, 761–803.
21. T. Jacobson, *Thermodynamics of spacetime: The Einstein equation of state*, Phys. Rev. Lett. **75** (1995), 1260–1263.
22. J.L. Jauregui and D.A. Lee, *Lower semicontinuity of mass under C^0 convergence and Huisken's isoperimetric mass*, arXiv:1602.00732 [math.DG], J. Reine Angew. Math. **756** (2019), 227–257.
23. R. Schoen and S.-T. Yau, *On the proof of the positive mass conjecture in general relativity*, Commun. Math. Phys. **65** (1979), no. 1, 45–76.

Newman-Penrose-Debye formalism for fields of various spins in pp-wave backgrounds

Aleksandr Kulitskii

Faculty of Physics, Lomomosov Moscow State University,
Moscow, Russia
E-mail: av.kulitskiy@yandex.ru

Elena Yu Melkumova

Faculty of Physics, Lomomosov Moscow State University,
Moscow, +74992492878, Russia
E-mail: EYM@srdlan.npi.msu.su

Using Newman-Penrose formalism in tetrad and spinor forms, we perform separation of variables in the wave equations for massless fields of various spins s=1/2, 1, 3/2, 2 on the background of exact plane-fronted gravitational wave metrics. Then, applying Wald's method of conjugate operators, we derive equations for Debye potentials and we find the back-projection operators expressing multicomponent fields in terms of these potentials. For shock wave backgrounds, as a special case of the non-vacuum pp-waves, the exact solutions for Debye potentials are constructed explicitly. The possibilities of generalization to the case of massive fields are discussed, in particular, construction of exact solutions of the Dirac and Proca equations. These results can be used in various supergravity problems on the pp-wave backgrounds, including holographic applications.

Keywords: PP-waves, Newman-Penrose formalism, Debye potentials, shock waves

1. Introduction

Wave equations for fields of different spins in curved space have been extensively studied since the early 1970s. Solutions describing propagation of fields on curved backgrounds are in demand in various contexts including the problem of radiation, supergravity and superstrings theories. Generically, considering fields of higher spins in curved space-time, difficulties arise with splitting the systems of coupled equations into separate ones for certain combinations of the field components. Two efficient methods to do this are known. The first is the application of the Newman-Penrose (NP) formalism,[1] in which the intrinsic symmetries of the massless field equations with respect to the Lorentz group are conveniently incorporated. The second efficient tool is the method of Debye potentials,[2] which allows to reconstruct the multicomponent fields in terms of solutions of some scalar equations. Debye potentials are complex functions which incorporate two degree of freedom of the massless field of any spin.

Formalism of Debye potentials was suggested in gravity theory in the works by Cohen[3] and Kegeles[4] and then effectively used by Chrzanowksi[5] in Kerr spacetime of type D, according to the Petrov classification,[6] in combination with the Teukolsky equation.[7] In the Kerr metric Debye representations were found for electromagnetic field and gravitational perturbations. Later, formalism of Debye potentials was discussed in detail for Rarita-Schwinger spin 3/2 field by Torres del Castilho.[8]

In this work we apply the Newman-Penrose-Debye formalism to the case of metrics of type N. More specifically, we consider the case of pp-wave metrics, which have numerous applications both in astrophysics and in various theoretical aspects, including supergravity and holography.

2. PP-waves

These metrics were introduced by Brinkmann[9] in 1925 and later interpreted as representing the plane-fronted gravitational waves (pp-waves). They are exact solutions of Einstein's equations of the following form

$$ds^2 = dudv - H(u,\zeta,\bar\zeta)dudu - d\zeta d\bar\zeta, \qquad (1)$$

where $\zeta = x + iy$ is a complex transverse coordinate, H is arbitrary nonlinear real profile function of $\zeta, \bar\zeta$, which specifies the nature of the wave. The determinant $g = 1/16$ is coordinate-independent. The scalar curvature turns out to be zero. For $H = 0$ the metric is Minkowski. These metrics describe plane waves with parallel rays belonging to the class of solutions that admits isotropic nonexpanding congruences without shear and twist, as well as the existence of an isotropic Killing vector.

A natural choice of the null tetrad basis for them is

$$\mathbf{l} = \sqrt{2}\partial_v, \qquad \mathbf{n} = \sqrt{2}(\partial_u + H\partial_v), \qquad \mathbf{m} = \sqrt{2}\partial_\zeta, \qquad \bar{\mathbf{m}} = \sqrt{2}\partial_{\bar\zeta}. \qquad (2)$$

We will also use the NP covariant derivatives along the null tetrad vectors:

$$D = l^\mu \nabla_\mu, \qquad \Delta = n^\mu \nabla_\mu, \qquad \delta = m^\mu \nabla_\mu, \qquad \bar\delta = \bar m^\mu \nabla_\mu \qquad (3)$$

and satisfying, in the case of a plane wave metrics, the following commutation relations

$$[\Delta, D] = 0, \qquad [\delta, D] = 0, \qquad [\delta, \Delta] = -\bar\nu D, \qquad [\bar\delta, \delta] = 0. \qquad (4)$$

The nonzero tetrad projections of the traceless part of the Ricci tensor, the Weyl scalar, and the only nonzero spin coefficient ν are

$$\Phi_{22} = \frac{1}{2} n^\alpha n^\beta R_{\alpha\beta} = -H_{,\zeta\bar\zeta}, \qquad \nu = -\bar m^\mu \delta n_\mu = -H_{,\bar\zeta},$$

$$\Psi_4 = -n^\alpha \bar m^\beta n^\sigma \bar m^\tau C_{\alpha\beta\sigma\tau} = -H_{,\bar\zeta\bar\zeta}, \qquad \Lambda = \frac{1}{24} R = 0, \qquad (5)$$

where $C_{\alpha\beta\sigma\tau}$ is the Weyl tensor. In the vacuum case, the gravitational field equations $\Phi_{22} = 0$ reduce to the two-dimensional Laplace equation

$$H_{,\zeta\bar\zeta} = 0.$$

The d'Alembert operator for the massless scalar field $\Box = \nabla_\mu \nabla^\mu$ reads:

$$\Box \equiv \frac{1}{\sqrt{|g|}} \partial_\mu \left(\sqrt{|g|} g^{\mu\nu} \partial_\nu \right) = 2(D\Delta - \delta\bar\delta). \qquad (6)$$

3. Debye potentials

Here we briefly recall the Wald's procedure[10] for constructing a solution of the field equations of higher spins, which we then apply to the metrics of plane waves. Consider some multicomponent field f (tensor or spinor) satisfying the field equation $\mathcal{E}(f) = 0$, where $\mathcal{E}$ is an appropriate matrix linear differential operator. This is generically a non-quadratic matrix $n \times m$ taking the m-component field into the column of n differential equation. To solve this system of equations one has to disentangle it, which in general is not possible in the closed form. However, it can be possible to decouple a separate equation (or several equations) for some combination φ of the components of the initial field f by the action of another linear partial differential operator $\mathcal{T}$, defining a scalar $\varphi = \mathcal{T}(f)$. Then one can define a pair of linear operators $\mathcal{S}$ and $\mathcal{O}$ such, that

$$\mathcal{S}\mathcal{E}(f) = \mathcal{O}\mathcal{T}(f) = \mathcal{O}(\varphi).$$

The problem of finding such operators is facilitated if one knows the source terms in the inhomogeneous equations both for an initial multicomponent field $\mathcal{E}(f) = J$, and in the decoupled scalar equation $O(\varphi) = \mathcal{S}(J)$. The number of decoupled equations depends on the number of principal null direction of the metric.

The final step is the construction of the adjoint operator $\mathcal{S}^\dagger$ with respect to a suitably defined functional scalar product such that, in the matrix form,

$$\int \phi^{A_n} M_{A_n B_m} \psi^{B_m} = \int \psi^{B_n} M^\dagger_{B_n A_m} \phi^{A_m},$$

where the indices A_n, B_m take n and m values respectively and the integration measure is supressed. Note that complex conjugation is not used.

Now it can be verified that the solution of the homogeneous field equation $\mathcal{E}(f) = 0$ will be guaranteed if

$$f = \mathcal{S}^\dagger \psi, \qquad\qquad \mathcal{O}^\dagger \psi = 0. \qquad (7)$$

The last equation is the Debye potential equation, the relevant operator is therefore the adjoint to one used in the equation for a decoupled scalar. It there are several such decoupled equations (e.g. two in type D metrics), one will have two different representations for the initial multicomponent field which are usually related by some tetrad transformation. In type N case the Debye potential is unique.

The complex Debye representation for for real-valued massless fields reflects the existence of two independent polarizations, which can be obtained as the real and imaginary parts of the complex f in the Debye form.

In what follows we apply this procedure to the pp-wave background with the only one nonzero spin coefficient ν. Clearly, the adjoint to the product of two operators will be the product of the adjoints to each of them in reverse order. So to construct an adjoint of some polynomial product it will suffice to know the adjoint to basic operators. The adjoint NP differential operators will read

$$D^\dagger = -D, \qquad \Delta^\dagger = -\Delta, \qquad \delta^\dagger = -\delta, \qquad \bar\delta^\dagger = -\bar\delta. \qquad (8)$$

4. Maxwell field

Maxwell's equations in the Newman-Penrose formalism are written in terms of the projections of the electromagnetic field tensor onto the bivector constructed of null tetrad as follows:

$$\Phi_0 = F_{lm}, \qquad 2\Phi_1 = (F_{ln} + F_{m\bar{m}}), \qquad \Phi_2 = F_{\bar{m}n}. \qquad (9)$$

A sourceless decoupled equation for the scalar Φ_0 in the case of vacuum pp-waves was obtained in the Refs.[11] and.[12] According to above procedure, we have to construct the source term to this equation. For this, one should act with an appropriate NP differential operators on the first pair of the system of equations and exclude the variable Φ_1 from them using the commutation relations. This gives

$$\Box \Phi_0 = 2\pi J_0, \qquad J_0 = 2\left[\delta J_l - D J_m\right]. \qquad (10)$$

Since metrics of type N have only one principal null direction (contrary to the type D, where there are two), the NP component Φ_0 will be the only one for which the decoupling can be made. Further, having written down both adjoint operators, one can easily construct a solution for vector A^μ, satisfying the Lorentz gauge condition, in terms of the Debye potential:

$$A^\mu = \left[\bar{m}^\mu D - l^\mu \bar{\delta}\right]\psi, \qquad \Box \psi = 0. \qquad (11)$$

It is easy to see that the contraction of the Ricci tensor with the expression for the vector potential gives zero; therefore, the solution is valid also for the non-vacuum pp-waves.

5. Weyl field

For the Weyl equations of spin 1/2, one uses the two-component spinor version of the NP formalism. In this case, we will no longer deal with a tetrad, but with a spinor dyad. The massless spin 1/2 equation has the following form:

$$\nabla^A{}_{B'}\chi_A = 0. \qquad (12)$$

Writing this in components and carrying out transformations similar those for the vector field, we obtain the decoupled equation with the source term:

$$\Box \chi_0 = N_0, \qquad N_0 = 2\left[D j_{1'} - \delta j_{0'}\right], \qquad (13)$$

where the spinor source is denoted as $j_{A'}$. Then performing the conjugation, we construct a solution in terms of the Debye potential, which, in turn, satisfies the d'Alembert equation:

$$\chi_0 = -D\psi, \qquad \chi_1 = -\bar{\delta}\psi, \qquad \Box \psi = 0. \qquad (14)$$

6. Rarita-Schwinger field

The spin 3/2 field is described by the Rarita-Schwinger equation for the spinor-vector ψ_μ, which satisfies the equations

$$\gamma^\mu(\nabla_\mu\psi_\nu - \nabla_\nu\psi_\mu) = 0, \qquad \gamma^\rho\psi_\rho = 0. \qquad (15)$$

This system is consistent only in the case of the vacuum metrics, the non-vacuum case refers to the supergravity context.

The field of an arbitrary spin s in the two-component spinor formalism is described by a totally symmetric spinor of valence 2s satisfying the equation of motion

$$\nabla^{AB'}\phi_{AB...C} = 0.$$

If $s \geqslant 3/2$ the Buchdahl consistency constraint[13]

$$\Psi^{ABC}{}_{(D}\phi_{EF...)ABC} = 0$$

must be satisfyed, where Ψ_{SABC} denotes the Weyl spinor. But there exists also an alternative approach, developed in the work,[8] where the consistency constraint is satisfied automatically. This method can be easily adapted to the case of the pp-wave backgrounds.

In the spinor equivalent of the Eq. (15)

$$\nabla_{AB'}\psi^A{}_{CD'} - \nabla_{CD'}\psi^A{}_{AB'} = 0, \qquad (16)$$

one has to pass from field $\psi^A{}_{CD'}$ to the symmetric rank three spinor arriving at the modified equations of motion

$$\nabla^{AB'}\phi_{ABC} = \Psi^S{}_{ABC}\psi^A{}_S{}^{B'}, \qquad \phi^A{}_{BC} \equiv \nabla_{(B|R'|}\psi^A{}_{C)}{}^{R'}.$$

We write down the complete system of equations with the sources for the symmetric spinor field ϕ_{ABC} in the component form, applicable to the type N metrics:

$$\bar{\delta}\phi_{000} - D\phi_{100} = \delta J_{0'0'0} - DJ_{1'0'0}; \qquad \Delta\phi_{000} - \delta\phi_{100} = \delta J_{0'1'0} - DJ_{1'1'0};$$

$$\bar{\delta}\phi_{100} - D\phi_{110} = \frac{1}{2}[\Delta J_{0'0'0} + \delta J_{0'0'1} - \bar{\delta}J_{0'1'0} - DJ_{1'0'1}];$$

$$\Delta\phi_{100} - \delta\phi_{110} - \nu\phi_{000} = \frac{1}{2}[\Delta J_{1'0'0} + \delta J_{0'1'1} - \bar{\delta}J_{1'1'0} - DJ_{1'1'1} - \bar{\nu}J_{0'0'0}];$$

$$\bar{\delta}\phi_{110} - D\phi_{111} = \Psi_4\psi_{000'} + \Delta J_{0'0'1} - \frac{1}{2}\bar{\delta}(J_{1'0'1} + J_{0'1'1}) - \nu J_{0'0'0};$$

$$\Delta\phi_{110} - \delta\phi_{111} - 2\nu\phi_{100} = \Psi_4\psi_{001'} - \bar{\delta}J_{1'1'1} + \frac{1}{2}\Delta(J_{0'1'1} + J_{1'0'1}) - \bar{\nu}J_{0'0'1} - \nu J_{1'0'0}.$$
$$(17)$$

One can exclude the component ϕ_{100} from the first pair of equations, obtaining the decoupled equation for ϕ_{000} with the source term:

$$\Box\phi_{000} = K_0, \qquad K_0 = 2[D\delta(J_{0'1'0} + J_{1'0'0}) - D^2 J_{1'1'0} - \delta^2 J_{0'0'0}]. \qquad (18)$$

Using this, one can further represent a spin-vector in terms of the Debye potential as follows:

$$\psi_\mu = \begin{pmatrix} \bar{m}_\mu D\bar{\delta} - l_\mu \bar{\delta}^2 \\ l_\mu D\bar{\delta} - \bar{m}_\mu D^2 \end{pmatrix} \psi, \qquad \Box \psi = 0. \qquad (19)$$

The resulting expression satisfies the system (15). Note that the equation for the Debye potential is the same for the vector field, the Weyl field and, as we will see in the next section, also for the tensor field.

7. Gravitational perturbations

Starting with the Einstein's equations and expanding the metric on the background

$$g_{\mu\nu} = g_{\mu\nu}^{(0)} + h_{\mu\nu},$$

one derives the Lichnerowitz equation for the spin 2 field in curved space-time:[14]

$$\nabla^\alpha \nabla_\alpha \psi_{\mu\nu} + 2R^\sigma{}_\mu{}^\tau{}_\nu{}^{(0)} \psi_{\sigma\tau} - 2R^\sigma{}_{(\nu}{}^{(0)} \psi_{\mu)\sigma} = 0, \qquad \nabla_\mu \psi^{\mu\nu} = 0, \qquad (20)$$

where

$$\psi_{\mu\nu} = h_{\mu\nu} - \frac{1}{2} g_{\mu\nu} h, \quad h = g^{\mu\nu} h_{\mu\nu}, \quad \psi = g^{\mu\nu} \psi_{\mu\nu}.$$

In the case of non-vacuum background, the additional gauge fixing condition $\psi = 0$ should be imposed.

To apply the NP formalism, similar splitting has to be performed in the null tetrad vectors, spin coefficients, Weyl scalars and Ricci tensor deviators, equipping the first order perturbations with an index one. The complete set of gravitational perturbation equations in the Newman-Penrose formalism is obtained by linearizing the Bianchi identities. We present here two equations from the resulting system, which are relevant for pp-waves:

$$\bar{\delta}\Psi_0^{(1)} - D\Psi_1^{(1)} = 4\pi \left[\delta T_{ll}^{(1)} - DT_{lm}^{(1)} \right], \qquad \Delta \Psi_0^{(1)} - \delta \Psi_1^{(1)} = 4\pi \left[\delta T_{lm}^{(1)} - DT_{mm}^{(1)} \right]. \qquad (21)$$

After some manipulations using the perturbed Ricci identities in the NP formalism, we obtain the decoupled equation for the perturbation of Ψ_0 with the corresponding source term:

$$\Box \Psi_0^{(1)} = 4\pi T_0^{(1)}, \qquad T_0^{(1)} = 2\left[2D\delta T_{lm}^{(1)} - D^2 T_{mm}^{(1)} - \delta^2 T_{ll}^{(1)} \right]. \qquad (22)$$

Then using the conjugate operator we can write down the solution in terms of the Debye potential:

$$\psi^{\mu\nu} = \left[2l^{(\mu}\bar{m}^{\nu)}\bar{\delta}D - \bar{m}^\mu \bar{m}^\nu D^2 - l^\mu l^\nu \bar{\delta}^2 \right] \psi, \qquad \Box \psi = 0. \qquad (23)$$

This expression satisfies the Lichnerowitz equation with the gauge condition (20).

As in the case of the vector field, this construction will be also valid for the non-vacuum pp-waves. This can be easily verified by the direct substitution.

8. Shock wave backgrounds

An important subclass of pp-waves is generated via boosting the black hole metrics to an infinite-momentum frame. The line element of the resulting metrics (parametrized by the real transverse coordinates x_i $i = 1, 2$) reads

$$ds^2 = \delta(u)f(\mathrm{x})du^2 + dudv - dx_i^2. \tag{24}$$

This is an exact solution of the Einstein equations representing the gravitational shock wave. When $u \neq 0$, the space-time is flat, but for $u = 0$ it has a delta-like singularity. But the field equations on such a background are still meaningful due to lack of singularities in the metric determinant. The function $f(\mathrm{x})$ describes the gravitational wave profile. In particular, for the case of the boosted Schwarzschild solution (the Aichelburg-Sexl metric[15])

$$f(\mathrm{x}) = -8p_m \ln \rho, \quad \rho = \sqrt{x_1^2 + x_2^2},$$

where p_m denotes the energy of shock wave. For the case of a boosted Einstein-Maxwell-dilaton solution[16]

$$f(\mathrm{x}) = -8p_m \ln \rho + \frac{(3-4a^2)}{(1-a^2)}\frac{\pi p_e}{\rho},$$

whetre a - the dilaton coupling constant, p_e - the electric charge. For boosted Taub-NUT[17]

$$f(\mathrm{x}) = -8p_n \tan^{-1}\frac{x_1}{x_2},$$

where p_n is the NUT charge. Also known in the literature are the boosted Kerr-Newman solution,[18] the boosted Schwarzschild-anti-de Sitter[19] space and some other metrics.

Here we present the solution of the massive Klein-Gordon equation on the background of the singular shock-wave metrics:

$$(\Box + m^2)\phi = 2(D\Delta - \delta\bar{\delta})\psi + m\psi = \left(4\partial_u\partial_v + 4\kappa\,\delta(u)f(\mathrm{x})\partial_v^2 - \partial_i^2 + m^2\right)\phi = 0. \tag{25}$$

In spite of presence of the singularity, there exists an exact solution of this equation containing the Heaviside function discontinuity only:

$$\phi = \int \exp[i\,\mathcal{W}]\,d\mathcal{G}, \qquad d\mathcal{G} = \frac{d\boldsymbol{q}}{(2\pi)^2}\,d\boldsymbol{x},$$

$$\mathcal{W} = -\frac{k_v}{2}[v - \kappa\,\theta(u)f(\mathrm{x}')] - \frac{(\boldsymbol{k}-\boldsymbol{q})^2+m^2}{2k_v}u + \boldsymbol{k}\boldsymbol{x} + \boldsymbol{q}(\boldsymbol{x}'-\boldsymbol{x}), \tag{26}$$

where we have introduced the notation $\boldsymbol{k} = (k_{x_1}, k_{x_2})$, $\boldsymbol{q} = (q_{x_1}, q_{x_2})$, $\boldsymbol{x} = (x_1, x_2)$ for the two-dimensional transverse vectors. If we put the mass equal to zero, then we obtain the solution of the equation for the Debye potential.

9. Massive field with spin $\frac{1}{2}$

Now consider other massive fields, starting from the spin 1/2. In the two-component notation, the Dirac bispinor equation $i\gamma^\mu \nabla_\mu \psi - \mu \psi = 0$ with $\psi = (\xi^A, \eta_{A'})$, splits into two equations

$$\nabla_{AB'}\xi^A - i\mu \eta_{B'} = 0, \qquad \nabla^{AB'}\eta_{B'} - i\mu \xi^A = 0. \qquad (27)$$

Their solution in the case of shock-wave backgrounds is a generalization of the previously obtained expression (14) for the massless field and can be written in the following form

$$\eta_{1'} = 2\int \big([k_{x_1} - q_{x_1}] + i[k_{x_2} - q_{x_2}] - \mu\big) \exp[i\,\mathcal{W}]\, d\mathcal{G}, \quad \eta_{0'} = -\int k_v \exp[i\,\mathcal{W}]\, d\mathcal{G},$$

$$\xi^0 = 2\int \big([k_{x_1} - q_{x_1}] - i[k_{x_2} - q_{x_2}] + \mu\big) \exp[i\,\mathcal{W}]\, d\mathcal{G}, \quad \xi^1 = \int k_v \exp[i\,\mathcal{W}]\, d\mathcal{G}, \qquad (28)$$

where $\mathcal{W}$ defined in (26).

10. Proca equation

For the massive spin-1 field the gauge invariance of Maxwell's field is broken by the mass term. Instead of the gauge fixing condition, we deal with the Lorentz-like dynamical constraint, so we have two equations:

$$\nabla_\mu F^{\mu\nu} + m^2 A^\nu = 0, \qquad \nabla_\mu A^\mu = 0. \qquad (29)$$

The massive vector field is no longer transverse, possessing three physical degrees of freedom. The first two polarizations in the case of shock wave background are realized by modified expressions with Debye potentials (the real and imaginary parts of the solution):

$$A^\mu_{(1,2)} = \int \mathcal{K}^\mu_{(1,2)} \exp[i\,\mathcal{W}]\, d\mathcal{G}, \quad \mathcal{K}^\mu_{(1,2)} = \big\{0, 2[k_{x_1} - q_{x_1}] - 2i[k_{x_2} - q_{x_2}], k_v, -ik_v\big\}. \qquad (30)$$

For the third polarization we solve the dynamical constraint acting by the covariant derivative on the massive scalar field, obtaining

$$A^\mu_{(3)} = \int \mathcal{K}^\mu_{(3)} \exp[i\,\mathcal{W}]\, d\mathcal{G} + c.c,$$

$$\mathcal{K}^\mu_{(3)} = \left\{k_v, \frac{(-q)^2 - m^2}{k_v} + k_v \delta(u) f(x), k_{x_1} - q_{x_1}, k_{x_1} - q_{x_1}\right\}. \qquad (31)$$

It can be seen that this expression satisfies the constraint indeed. But this expression gives us only one additional polarization, because of real multipliers in front of the exponent. Therefore the complete solution of the Proca equation in AS metric is a sum $A^\mu = A^\mu_{(1,2)} + A^\mu_{(3)}$. To write down the solution for massless electromagnetic field, it is sufficient to set the mass to zero.

11. Conclusions

This work is devoted to some novel applications of the Newman-Penrose formalism and the method of Debye potentials. Previously this technique was successfully used to construct solutions of equations for massless fields of different spins on the background of vacuum black hole solutions of Petrov type D. Here it was applied to solutions of type N. Unlike the case D, where the metric has two principal null directions and, accordingly, two decoupled equations for NP projections can be derived, in the metrics of type N only one decoupled equation exists. Namely, one can decouple the χ_0-equation for the Weyl field, the ϕ_{000}-equation for the Rarita-Schwinger field, and the equations for perturbations of Φ_0 and Ψ_0 of the vector and tensor fields respectively. It is still enough to construct the Debye representation for the solutions obtaining the universal equation for the Debye potential for all spins. We also managed to generalize our construction to the case of massive fields on the background of shock-wave metrics. Our formulas can be used for quantization in shock wave backgrounds and in some holographic applications.

Acknowledgments

The work was supported by the Russian Foundation for Basic Research on the project 20-52-18012, and the Scientific and Educational School of Moscow State University "Fundamental and Applied Space Research".

References

1. E. Newman and R. Penrose, "An Approach to gravitational radiation by a method of spin coefficients," J. Math. Phys. **3** (1962), 566-578.
2. P. Debye, Ann. Phys. (Leipz.) **30**, 57 (1909).
3. J. M. Cohen and L. S. Kegeles, "Electromagnetic fields in curved spaces - A constructive procedure," Phys. Rev. D **10** (1974), 1070-1084.
4. L. S. Kegeles and J. M. Cohen, "Constructive procedure for perturbations of spacetimes," Phys. Rev. D **19** (1979), 1641-1664.
5. P. L. Chrzanowski, "Vector Potential and Metric Perturbations of a Rotating Black Hole," Phys. Rev. D **11** (1975), 2042-2062.
6. A. Z. Petrov, "The Classification of Spaces Defining Gravitational Fields," Gen. Relativ. Gravit. **32** 1665-1685 (2000).
7. S. A. Teukolsky, "Perturbations of a rotating black hole. 1. Fundamental equations for gravitational electromagnetic and neutrino field perturbations," Astrophys. J. **185** (1973), 635-647.
8. G. F. Torres Del Castillo, "Debye Potentials for Rarita-schwinger Fields in Curved Space-times," J. Math. Phys. **30** (1989), 1323-1328.
9. H. W. Brinkmann, "Einstein spapces which are mapped conformally on each other," Math. Ann. **94** (1925) 119.
10. R. M. Wald, "Construction of Solutions of Gravitational, Electromagnetic, Or Other Perturbation Equations from Solutions of Decoupled Equations," Phys. Rev. Lett. 41 (1978) 203.
11. C. Sanchez-Trujillo and G. F. Torres del Castillo, "Petrov type N space-times admitting a Killing spinor," Revista Mexicana de Fisica **36** (Suppl1) (1990) 167-171.

12. K. Duztas and I. Semiz, "The decoupling problem of the Proca equation; and treatment of Dirac, Maxwell and Proca fields on the resulting pp-wave spacetimes," Gen. Rel. Grav. **48** (2016) no.7, 99.
13. H. A. Buchdahl, "On the compatibility of relativistic wave equations for particles of higher spin in the presence of a gravitational field," Nuovo Cim. **10** (1958) 96.
14. A. Lichnerowicz, in *"Relativity, Groups and Topology"*, edited by C. DeWitt and B. DeWitt (Gordon and Breach Science Publishers, Inc., New York, 1964), p. 827.
15. P. C. Aichelburg and R. U. Sexl, "On the Gravitational field of a massless particle," Gen. Rel. Grav. **2** (1971), 303.
16. R. G. Cai, J. Y. Ji and K. S. Soh, "Ultrarelativistic limits of boosted dilaton black holes," Nucl. Phys. B **528** (1998), 265-282.
17. R. Argurio, F. Dehouck and L. Houart, "Boosting Taub-NUT to a BPS NUT-wave," JHEP **01** (2009), 045.
18. C. O. Lousto and N. G. Sanchez, "The Ultrarelativistic limit of the boosted Kerr-Newman geometry and the scattering of spin 1/2 particles," Nucl. Phys. B **383** (1992), 377-394.
19. J. Podolsky and J. B. Griffiths, "Impulsive gravitational waves generated by null particles in de Sitter and anti-de Sitter backgrounds," Phys. Rev. D **56** (1997), 4756-4767.

Gravitational geometric phase

Banibrata Mukhopadhyay

Department of Physics, Indian Institute of Science, Bangalore 560012, India
E-mail: bm@iisc.ac.in

Tanuman Ghosh

Raman Research Institute, Bangalore, 560080, India
E-mail: tanuman@rri.res.in

Soumya Kanti Ganguly

Ongil Private Limited, Tidel Park, Rajiv Gandhi IT Expressway, Chennai 600113, India
E-mail: soumya09ganguly@gmail.com

We show that spinors propagating in curved gravitational background acquire an interaction with spacetime curvature, which leads to a quantum mechanical geometric effect. This is similar to what happens in the case of magnetic fields, known as Pancharatnam-Berry phase. As the magnetic and gravitational fields have certain similar properties, e.g. both contribute to curvature, this result is not difficult to understand. Interestingly, while spacetime around a rotating black hole offers Aharonov-Bohm and Pancharatnam-Berry both kinds of geometric effect, a static spacetime offers only the latter. In the bath of primordial black holes, such gravity induced effects could easily be measured due to their smaller radius.

Keywords: Geometric phase; Dirac equation; semi-classical theory; classical black holes; field theory; curved spacetime.

1. Introduction

In recent works,[1,2] we showed that spinors propagating in a curved background acquire a geometric phase (GP) similar to the case of GP in electromagnetic field. The study of GP in electromagnetic field has been widely explored. Two most important notions of GPs are: Aharonov-Bohm (AB) effect[3] and Pancharatnam-Berry (PB)[4,5] phase. AB effect and PB phase occur in two different physical scenarios. In presence of a varying magnetic field, PB phase is acquired by a spinor, whereas AB effect can be acquired even without a varying field. In fact, AB effect is one of the signature properties of magnetic potential influencing a particle's quantum state. These effects/phases in case of electromagnetic fields originate from the effective curvature of magnetic potential and field in the (flat) Minkowski spacetime. We showed[2] that in a curved spacetime, a spinor in the vicinity of a gravitating body can acquire similar geometric phases which originate from the effective curvature of the spacetime itself.

Analogous effects for gravitational and magnetic fields are well known. Some of the examples are: curvature generated in both scenarios; electromagnetic radiation from accelerated charge and gravitational radiation from accelerated mass (only quadrupolar in nature), both propagating with the speed of light; energy splitting of spin-half particles in presence of both fields.[6,7] With the continuation of these analogous results, it is expected that the quantum effects, which generate the GPs in case of magnetic field, similarly should be present in case of gravitational field. Some studies have already explored these effects in local coordinates.[1,7,8] There are many astrophysical and cosmological phenomena like baryogenesis, neutrino emissions from supernovae and active galactic nuclei (AGNs), neutrino oscillation, neutrino dominated accretion disks, Fermi degenerate gas in compact objects, etc., where study of spinor propagation and evolution is crucial to understand the physical nature of these phenomena.[9-16]

When it comes to the study of gravity with quantum mechanics and understand various effects of quantum systems in curved spacetime, semi-classical formalism is a very effective tool to perform such study. In fact, there are plenty of available works in the literatures which have explored the dynamics of spinors in curved spacetime. These have been done with the Lagrangian[9,17] and Hamiltonian[6,18] formalisms. It is also well known fact that in the Hamiltonian formalism, the Dirac Hamiltonian of a spinor in curved spacetime has a non-hermiticity and uniqueness problem. Different authors tried to implement different approaches to address these issues.[6,18-22] Non-hermitian biorthogonal quantum mechanics[23] provides tool for solving the non-hermiticity issue of Dirac Hamiltonian. One approach is to define a relativistically invariant scalar product (Parker scalar product)[6,18] and use that scalar product to define the expectation values of all operators. In case of curved spacetime, this scalar product is different from the standard flat spacetime scalar product because of the presence of curved spacetime metric and vierbeins. The other approach is known as $\eta-$ representation or pseudo-Hermitian approach,[21,22] where the Hamiltonian and eigenstates of the particle are modified by the metric and vierbeins in such a way that effectively one can use the standard flat scalar product to define all the operators in the Hilbert space. In fact, these two approaches are shown to be equivalent.[21,22]

In this work, we explore the Dirac Hamiltonian in curved spacetime background, especially in Kerr and Schwarzschild geometries, using the pseudo-Hermitian approach or the η-representation and explore the possibilities of appearance of GPs in spinors traversing in curved spacetime. In section 2, we recapitulate the quantum mechanics in η-representation. Then in section 3, we derive the Dirac Hamiltonian in the Kerr geometry and further derive its non-relativistic counterpart for slowly moving particles around a weakly rotating black hole and its analogy with that in electromagnetic fields in section 4. In section 5, we find GPs in curved spacetime. Finally, in section 6, we summarize our findings.

2. Quantum Mechanics in the η-Representation

We briefly discuss the quantum mechanics in η-representation.[21,22,24,25] If an operator η satisfies the relation

$$\rho = \eta^\dagger \eta, \qquad (1)$$

where ρ is an invertible operator which assures the relation to be satisfied as

$$\rho H \rho^{-1} = H^\dagger, \qquad (2)$$

then the Hamiltonian in η-representation turns out to be

$$H_\eta = \eta H \eta^{-1} = H_\eta^\dagger. \qquad (3)$$

The relation between the wave functions in the η–representation and in the standard representation is given by

$$\Psi = \eta \psi, \qquad (4)$$

where these two wave functions satisfy the following wave equations:

$$i\frac{\partial \psi}{\partial t} = H\psi, \qquad (5)$$

$$i\frac{\partial \Psi}{\partial t} = H_\eta \Psi. \qquad (6)$$

As we mentioned above, the Parker scalar product,[6,18] which is a modification of standard scalar product, in Hilbert space is defined as

$$(\phi, \psi)_\rho = \int d^3x (\phi^\dagger \rho \psi), \qquad (7)$$

whereas in the pseudo-Hermitian approach, the scalar product takes the standard form of flat space scalar product since the Hamiltonian and the wave functions are already modified there, which is

$$(\Phi, \Psi) = \int (\Phi^\dagger \Psi) d^3x. \qquad (8)$$

We can easily verify that

$$(\phi, \psi)_\rho = (\Phi, \Psi). \qquad (9)$$

3. Dirac Hamiltonian in the Kerr and Schwarzschild Metrices

We use the convention of natural unit system with $\hbar = G = c = 1$ and metric signature of $(+, -, -, -)$.

We can start from the Dirac equation in curved spacetime which is,

$$(i\gamma^\mu D_\mu - m)\psi(x) = 0. \qquad (10)$$

where the covariant derivative $D_\mu = \partial_\mu + \Gamma_\mu$. Here Γ_μ is the spinorial affine connection.[6,18] m is the mass of the Dirac particle, ψ is the four-component column bispinor. γ^μ are the Dirac matrices in curved spacetime which satisfies the relation

$$\gamma^\alpha \gamma^\beta + \gamma^\beta \gamma^\alpha = 2g^{\alpha\beta} I_4, \tag{11}$$

where I_4 is the 4×4 identity matrix and $g^{\alpha\beta}$ is the contravariant metric tensor of curved spacetime. The adjoint spinor is defined as $\bar\psi = \psi^\dagger \gamma^0$.

The gamma matrices in curved spacetime, also known as global gamma matrices (γ^α), are related to the local flat spacetime gamma matrices (γ^a) by the relation

$$\gamma^\alpha = e^\alpha_a \gamma^a, \tag{12}$$

where e^α_a-s are the tetrads defined by

$$g_{\mu\nu} = e^a_\mu e^b_\nu \eta_{ab}. \tag{13}$$

We then derive the global Dirac Hamiltonian operator from equation (10), which is

$$H = -i\Gamma_t - i(g^{tt})^{-1} \gamma^t \left[\gamma^r (\partial_r + \Gamma_r) \right. \\ \left. + \gamma^\theta (\partial_\theta + \Gamma_\theta) + \gamma^\phi (\partial_\phi + \Gamma_\phi) \right] + (g^{tt})^{-1} \gamma^t m. \tag{14}$$

This Hamiltonian is self-adjoint under the Parker scalar product given in equation (7). Nevertheless, our purpose is to find the Dirac Hamiltonian in η-representation which will be useful for working in standard flat Hilbert space. We choose astrophysically important metrices to work with and hence we shall find the Dirac Hamiltonian in η-representation for the Kerr metric, which reduces to the Schwarzschild metric when the Kerr parameter $a = 0$.

3.1. Kerr metric

The Kerr metric in the Boyer-Lindquist coordinates is

$$ds^2 = \left(1 - \frac{2Mr}{\rho^2}\right) dt^2 + \frac{4Mra \sin^2\theta}{\rho^2} dt d\phi - \frac{\rho^2}{\Delta} dr^2 \\ - \rho^2 d\theta^2 - \left[(r^2 + a^2) \sin^2\theta + \frac{2Mra^2 \sin^4\theta}{\rho^2} \right] d\phi^2, \tag{15}$$

where $\rho^2 = r^2 + a^2 \cos^2\theta$, $\Delta = r^2 - 2Mr + a^2$, M is the mass of black hole and a is the Kerr parameter (angular momentum per unit mass of the black hole). We choose the Schwinger gauge of tetrad,[26-28] given by

$$e^t_0 = \sqrt{g^{tt}}, \quad e^r_1 = \frac{\sqrt{\Delta}}{\rho}, \quad e^\theta_2 = \frac{1}{\rho}, \\ e^\phi_3 = \frac{1}{\sin\theta \sqrt{\Delta} \sqrt{g^{tt}}}, \quad e^\phi_0 = \frac{2Mar}{\rho^2 \Delta \sqrt{g^{tt}}}. \tag{16}$$

The Dirac Hamiltonian in the η-formalism in Kerr metric then turns out to be[29]

$$H_\eta = \frac{m}{\sqrt{g^{tt}}}\gamma^0 - i\frac{\sqrt{\Delta}}{\rho\sqrt{g^{tt}}}\left(\frac{\partial}{\partial r} + \frac{1}{r}\right)\gamma^0\gamma^1$$
$$- i\frac{1}{\rho\sqrt{g^{tt}}}\left(\frac{\partial}{\partial\theta} + \frac{1}{2}\cot\theta\right)\gamma^0\gamma^2 - i\frac{1}{g^{tt}\sqrt{\Delta}\sin\theta}\frac{\partial}{\partial\phi}\gamma^0\gamma^3$$
$$- i\frac{2Mar}{g^{tt}\rho^2\Delta}\frac{\partial}{\partial\phi} - i\frac{1}{2}\frac{\partial}{\partial r}\left(\frac{\sqrt{\Delta}}{\rho\sqrt{g^{tt}}}\right)\gamma^0\gamma^1 - i\frac{1}{2}\frac{\partial}{\partial\theta}\left(\frac{1}{\rho\sqrt{g^{tt}}}\right)\gamma^0\gamma^2$$
$$+ i\frac{\sqrt{g^{tt}}\Delta Ma\sin\theta}{2\rho}\left(\frac{\partial}{\partial r}\left(\frac{r}{g^{tt}\rho^2\Delta}\right)\right)\gamma^3\gamma^1$$
$$+ \frac{1}{\sqrt{\Delta}}\frac{\partial}{\partial\theta}\left(\frac{r}{g^{tt}\rho^2\Delta}\right)\gamma^3\gamma^2\bigg). \tag{17}$$

We can write this Hamiltonian as

$$H_\eta = (\sqrt{g^{tt}})^{-1}\left[\gamma^0 m + \gamma^0\gamma^j(p_j - iA_j) + i\gamma^0\gamma^j\gamma^5 k_j + e_0^\phi p_\phi\right], \tag{18}$$

where $A_1 = \frac{\sqrt{\Delta}}{\rho r} + \frac{\sqrt{g^{tt}}}{2}\frac{\partial}{\partial r}\left(\frac{\sqrt{\Delta}}{\rho\sqrt{g^{tt}}}\right)$, $A_2 = \frac{\cot\theta}{2\rho} + \frac{\sqrt{g^{tt}}}{2}\frac{\partial}{\partial\theta}\left(\frac{1}{\rho\sqrt{g^{tt}}}\right)$ and $A_3 = 0$; $k_1 = \frac{ig^{tt}Ma\sqrt{\Delta}\sin\theta}{2\rho}\frac{\partial}{\partial\theta}\left(\frac{r}{g^{tt}\rho^2\Delta}\right)$, $k_2 = -\frac{ig^{tt}Ma\Delta\sin\theta}{2\rho}\frac{\partial}{\partial r}\left(\frac{r}{g^{tt}\rho^2\Delta}\right)$ and $k_3 = 0$. Here we use the fact that $\gamma^3\gamma^2$ and $\gamma^3\gamma^1$ can be respectively written as $i\gamma^0\gamma^1\gamma^5$ and $-i\gamma^0\gamma^2\gamma^5$.

Now using the relations $H_\eta = i\frac{\partial}{\partial t} = p_t$ and $\partial_0 = e_0^t\partial_t + e_0^\phi\partial_\phi$, we rearrange the equation (18) to

$$\left[p_0 - \gamma^0\{m + \gamma^j(p_j - iA_j) + i\gamma^j\gamma^5 k_j\}\right]\Psi = 0, \tag{19}$$

where we use the tetrad transformation relation between global and local 4-momenta as

$$p_j = e_j^\mu p_\mu, \tag{20}$$

where Greek indices represent global coordinates (t, r, θ, ϕ) and roman indices represent flat coordinates $(0, 1, 2, 3)$.

Now we need to identify the terms in these equations with the analogy of magnetic field scenario which we discussed in section 1. A_js are analogous to the magnetic vector potential and k_js are "pseudo-vector" potential, which in this case of Kerr metric appears due to the chirality in the system owing to the rotation of spacetime.

If we put $a = 0$, the equations in the Kerr metric reduce to those in the Schwarzschild metric. The Hamiltonian then turns out to be

$$H_\eta = (\sqrt{g^{tt}})^{-1}\left[\gamma^0 m + \gamma^0\gamma^j(p_j - iA_j^s)\right], \tag{21}$$

where $A_1^s = \frac{1}{r}\sqrt{1 - \frac{2M}{r}} + \frac{\sqrt{g^{tt}}}{2}\frac{\partial}{\partial r}\left(\frac{\sqrt{1-\frac{2M}{r}}}{\sqrt{g^{tt}}}\right)$, $A_2^s = \frac{\cot\theta}{2r}$ and $A_3^s = 0$.

We can also rearrange the Hamiltonian for $a = 0$ to write the Dirac equation in a compact form as

$$[p_0 - \gamma^0\{m + \gamma^j(p_j - iA_j^s)\}]\Psi = 0. \tag{22}$$

Here A_j^ss are the "gravito-magnetic potential" in the Schwarzschild geometry similar to the A_js in Kerr metric.

4. Nonrelativistic Approximation of Dirac Hamiltonian

In the standard Dirac representation, we write the Dirac equation in Kerr metric from equation (19) as

$$\begin{pmatrix} -p_0 + i\vec{\sigma} \cdot \vec{k} + m & \vec{\sigma} \cdot \vec{\Pi}_A \\ \vec{\sigma} \cdot \vec{\Pi}_A & -p_0 + i\vec{\sigma} \cdot \vec{k} - m \end{pmatrix} \Psi = 0, \tag{23}$$

where

$$\vec{k} = (k_1, k_2, 0),$$
$$\vec{\Pi}_A = \vec{p} - i\vec{A}. \tag{24}$$

Following the standard process of deriving the non-relativistic limit of the Hamiltonian (see reference 30) we can write the coupled equations as

$$(\vec{\sigma} \cdot \vec{\Pi}_A)\Psi_B = (E - i\vec{\sigma} \cdot \vec{k} - m)\Psi_A, \tag{25a}$$

$$(\vec{\sigma} \cdot \vec{\Pi}_A)\Psi_A = (E - i\vec{\sigma} \cdot \vec{k} + m)\Psi_B. \tag{25b}$$

where E is the energy eigenvalue, Ψ_A and Ψ_B are the two components of wavefunction Ψ and we take into account the fact that $\vec{A}$ and $\vec{k}$ are time-independent.

We now assume slowly rotating spacetime and non-relativistic particles such that the particle velocity $v \ll c$, hence

$$E \sim m, \quad |\vec{k}| \ll m \tag{26}$$

and define the non-relativistic particle energy,

$$E^{NR} = E - m. \tag{27}$$

It can easily be derived that by keeping only leading order terms by combining equations (25a) and (25b), we obtain

$$\frac{1}{2m}(\vec{\sigma} \cdot \vec{\Pi}_A)(\vec{\sigma} \cdot \vec{\Pi}_A)\Psi_A = (E^{NR} - i\vec{\sigma} \cdot \vec{k})\Psi_A, \tag{28}$$

which can be further written as

$$\left[\frac{\Pi^2}{2m} + \sigma \cdot (i\vec{k} - \frac{i}{2m}\vec{B}_g)\right]\Psi_A = E^{NR}\Psi_A, \tag{29}$$

where $\vec{B}_g = \vec{\nabla} \times \vec{A}$ is the effective "gravito-magnetic field" and $\vec{A}$ is "gravito-magnetic potential". This implies that

$$H^{NR}\Psi_A = \left[\frac{\Pi^2}{2m} + \vec{\sigma} \cdot \vec{B}_g^{kerr}\right]\Psi_A, \tag{30}$$

where $\vec{B}_g^{kerr} = (i\vec{k} - \frac{i}{2m}\vec{B}_g)$ which involves both field analogue term and potential analogue term.

Similarly for $a = 0$ (Schwarzschild) case, we can find that

$$H^{sNR}\Psi_A = \left[\frac{\Pi^{s2}}{2m} + \vec{\sigma}\cdot\vec{B}_g^{sch}\right]\Psi_A, \tag{31}$$

where $\vec{B}_g^{sch} = -\frac{i}{2m}\vec{B}_g^s$ where $\vec{B}_g^s = \vec{\nabla}\times\vec{A}^s$.

Note importantly that $\vec{B}_g^{kerr}$ involves the field ($\vec{B}_g$) and potential ($\vec{k}$) both, whereas $\vec{B}_g^{sch}$ involves only field.

4.1. *Analogy with electromagnetism*

In the presence of electromagnetic field, the Dirac equation is given by

$$[i\gamma^\mu(\partial_\mu - ieA_\mu) - m]\psi = 0, \tag{32}$$

where e is the electric charge and A_μ is the electromagnetic covariant 4-vector potential. For the non-trivial solution for ψ, the energies/Hamiltonians of the spin-up and spin-down particles are given by

$$(H + eA_0)^2 = (\hat{p} - e\vec{A})^2 + m^2 + e\vec{\sigma}\cdot\vec{B}, \tag{33}$$

where A_0 is the temporal component of A_μ which is basically the Coulomb potential and $\hat{p}$ is the quantum mechanical momentum operator $-i\nabla$. In the non-relativistic limit, equation (33) reduces to[1]

$$H = -eA_0 \pm \left[\frac{(\hat{p}-e\vec{A})^2}{2m} + m + \frac{e\vec{\sigma}\cdot\vec{B}}{2m}\right]. \tag{34}$$

Clearly equation (34) is very similar to equation (31) and, hence, whatever effects have been proposed for electromagnetism, the same are expected to suffice for gravitation.

Apart from the split due to the positive and negative energy solutions, clearly there is an additional split in the respective energy levels in equations (31) and (34). This is basically the Zeeman-splitting (or Zeeman-like for gravitation) governed by the term with Pauli's spin matrix, in the up- and down-spinors for the positive and negative energy spinors induced by magnetic/gravitational fields, whether we choose relativistic or non-relativistic regimes.

5. Geometric Phase

To find the geometric effects, we construct Poincaré sphere by $\vec{B}_g^{kerr}$. Essentially, the interaction between the spinor and the gravitational background comes from the interaction Hamiltonian of

$$H_{int} = \vec{\sigma}\cdot\vec{B}, \tag{35}$$

where $\vec{B} = \vec{B}_g^{kerr}$. We can write this Hamiltonian as

$$H_{int} = |\vec{B}| \begin{pmatrix} \cos\zeta & \sin\zeta \exp(-i\xi) \\ \sin\zeta \exp(+i\xi) & -\cos\zeta \end{pmatrix}, \tag{36}$$

where ζ and ξ are the latitude and azimuthal angles of spherical polar coordinates respectively of the parameter space constructed by the vector $\vec{B}$. Here ρ is the radial coordinate in this system.

Now, using the standard definition of phase (Φ_B) and connection ($\vec{A}_B$) (see reference 2 for details) we find that the connection is

$$\vec{A}_B = \frac{(1 - \cos\zeta)}{2\rho \sin\zeta} \hat{\xi}, \tag{37}$$

and the phase is

$$\Phi_B = \frac{\tilde{\xi}}{2}(1 - \cos\zeta) = \frac{\Omega}{2}, \tag{38}$$

where $\tilde{\xi}$ is the total integrated azimuthal coordinate and Ω is the integrated solid angle.

Thus the GP in curved spacetime around Kerr (and Schwarzschild) geometry takes the similar form as revealed in the case of magnetic field but the angle coordinates and phases are fixed by the spacetime geometry. It is important to note that in the Kerr metric case, the GP is a combination of AB effect which appears due to the potential like term $\vec{k}$ and PB phase which appears due to the field like term $\vec{\nabla} \times \vec{A}$. In case of Schwarzschild metric however only PB contributes to the GP.

5.1. *Possible measurement*

Previous studies[31,32] have proven the relevance of semi-classical effects in gravitational background for massive particles. In this paper, we have shown that origin of GPs in spinors traversing in curved spacetime is theoretically possible. However, the question remains that how effectively these effects can be measured. For that, we need to estimate some of the length scales of the systems. Usually, quantum effects become prominent when length scale (l) of the system becomes comparable to or less than the de-Broglie wavelength of the particle $\lambda = \hbar/p$, where p is the momentum. In the case of gravity, this l is typically the radius of the gravitational body. We find that although the appearance of GPs is theoretically possible in all conditions, it may be detected only in selective cases like, e.g. primordial black holes (see reference 2 for details). The qualitative reason is simple. Larger the size of the gravitating body, smaller the field $\vec{B}$ (or $\vec{A}$ or $\vec{k} \sim 1/r$) is and thus smaller the geometric effects are. Hence, for smaller black holes these effects are prominent, but not for astrophysical black holes.

6. Summary

It is found that the Dirac particles interacting with spacetime curvature give rise to effective spin-orbit coupling which eventually manifests geometric phases/effects: Aharonov-Bohm (AB) effect and Pancharatnam-Berry (PB) phase. AB term originates from the spin of the background geometry which is responsible for the chirality in the system and this effect goes off when black hole spin becomes zero. PB phase appears in the Kerr metric as well as in spherically symmetric static spacetime like Schwarzschild geometry. Although theoretically these effects can appear in all cases, detection of such semi-classical effects is observationally possible, at least for non-relativistic particles, in a scenario where a nonrelativistic massive particle moves around a primordial black hole. Future mission by *Fermi* satellite can prove the existence of primordial black holes by detecting small interference pattern within gamma-ray bursts. Although the results of this work are outcome for a special case of nonrelativistic particles and weakly rotating black holes, it is expected that a covariant formalism will provide similar results in a general gravitational background from the analogy of covariant formalism of study of GPs in magnetic fields.[33]

References

1. B. Mukhopadhyay and S. K. Ganguly, *Universe*, **6(10)**, 160 (2020), arXiv:1802.10377 [gr-qc]
2. T. Ghosh and B. Mukhopadhyay, *IJMPD*, **30**, 12 (2021), arXiv:2010.05945 [gr-qc]
3. Y. Aharonov and D. Bohm, *Phys. Rev.*, **115**, 485 (1959)
4. S. Pancharatnam, *Proceedings of the Indian Academy of Sciences-Section A*, **Vol. 44** (Springer, 1956) pp. 398–417
5. M. V. Berry, *Proc. Roy. Soc. Lon. A*, **392**, 45 (1984)
6. L. Parker, *Phys. Rev. D*, **22**, 1922 (1980)
7. B. Mukhopadhyay, *Exploring the Universe: From Near Space to Extra-Galactic*, **Vol. 53**, edited by B. Mukhopadhyay and S. Sasmal (2018) p. 3
8. K. Dixit, J. Naikoo, B. Mukhopadhyay, and S. Banerjee, *Phys. Rev. D*, **100**, 055021 (2019), arXiv:1903.05664 [hep-ph]
9. B. Mukhopadhyay, *MPLA*, **20**, 2145 (2005), arXiv:astro-ph/0505460 [astro-ph]
10. B. Mukhopadhyay, *Class. Quantum Grav.*, **24**, 1433 (2007), arXiv:gr-qc/0702062 [gr-qc]
11. V. Alan Kostelecký and M. Mewes, *Phys. Rev. D*, **69**, 016005 (2004), arXiv:hep-ph/0309025 [hep-ph]
12. D. Píriz, M. Roy, and J. Wudka, *Phys. Rev. D*, **54**, 1587 (1996), arXiv:hep-ph/9604403 [hep-ph]
13. W.-X. Chen and A. M. Beloborodov, *Astrophys. J.* **657**, 383 (2007), arXiv:astro-ph/0607145 [astro-ph]
14. C. Y. Cardall, M. Prakash, and J. M. Lattimer, *Astrophys. J.*, **554**, 322 (2001), arXiv:astro-ph/0011148 [astro-ph]
15. U. Das and B. Mukhopadhyay, *JCAP*, **06**, 050, arXiv:1404.7627 [astro-ph.SR]
16. G. B. Cook, S. L. Shapiro, and S. A. Teukolsky, *Astrophys. J.*, **424**, 823 (1994)
17. J. Schwinger *Particles, sources and fields*, *Vol. 1*, Redwood City, California (Addison-Wesley Publishing Company, INC. 1973)
18. X. Huang and L. Parker, *Phys. Rev. D*, **79**, 024020 (2009)

19. Y. N. Obukhov, *Phys. Rev. Lett.*, **86**, 192 (2001)
20. Y. N. Obukhov, A. J. Silenko, and O. V. Teryaev, *Phys. Rev. D*, **80**, 064044 (2009)
21. M. V. Gorbatenko and V. P. Neznamov, *Phys. Rev. D*, **82**, 104056 (2010)
22. M. V. Gorbatenko and V. P. Neznamov, *Phys. Rev. D*, **83**, 105002 (2011)
23. D. C. Brody, *J. Phys. A: Math. and Th.*, **47**, 035305 (2013)
24. C. M. Bender, D. C. Brody, and H. F. Jones, *Phys. Rev. Lett.*, **89**, 270401 (2002)
25. A. Mostafazadeh, *J. Math. Phys.*, **43**, 205 (2002), arXiv:math-ph/0107001 [math-ph]
26. J. Schwinger, *Phys. Rev.*, **130**, 800 (1963)
27. M. V. Gorbatenko and V. P. Neznamov, *A Modified Method for Deriving Self-Conjugate Dirac Hamiltonians in Arbitrary Gravitational Fields and Its Application to Centrally and Axially Symmetric Gravitational Fields*, 2011, arXiv:1107.0844 [gr-qc]
28. V. P. Neznamov and V. E. Shemarulin, *Gravitation and Cosmology*, **24**, 129 (2018), arXiv:1806.03835 [gr-qc]
29. M. V. Gorbatenko and V. P. Neznamov, *Annalen der Physik*, **526**, 491 (2014), https://onlinelibrary.wiley.com/doi/pdf/10.1002/andp.201400035
30. J. Sakurai, *Advanced Quantum Mechanics*, Always learning (Pearson Education, Incorporated, 1967)
31. Y. Wu, and G. Meng, *Chinese Phys. Lett.*, **12**, 193 (1995)
32. R. Colella, A. W. Overhauser, and S. A. Werner, *Phys. Rev. Lett.*, **34**, 1472 (1975)
33. M. Stone, V. Dwivedi, and T. Zhou, *Phys. Rev. D*, **91**, 025004 (2015)

Retarded potentials and radiation in odd dimensions

D. V. Gal'tsov[*] and M. Khlopunov[*,†]

[*]*Faculty of Physics, Lomonosov Moscow State University,
Moscow, 119899, Russia*
[†]*Institute of Theoretical and Mathematical Physics, Lomonosov Moscow State University,
Moscow 119991, Russia*
E-mail: [*] galtsov@phys.msu.ru, [†] khlopunov.mi14@physics.msu.ru

Free massless fields of any spin in flat D-dimensional spacetime propagate at the speed of light. But the retarded fields produced by the corresponding point-like moving sources share this property only for even D. Since the Green's functions of the d'Alembert equation are localized on the light cone in even-dimensional spacetime, but not in odd dimensions, extraction of the emitted part of the retarded field in odd D requires some care. We consider the wave equations for spins 0, 1, and 2 in five-dimensional spacetime and analyze the fall-off conditions for the retarded fields at large distances. It is shown that the farthest part of the field contains a component propagating at the speed of light, while the non-derivative terms propagate with all velocities up to that of light. The generated radiation will contain a radiation tail corresponding to the complete prehistory of the source's motion preceding the retarded moment of time. We also demonstrate that dividing the Green's function into a part localized on the light cone and another part that is not zero inside the light cone gives separately the divergent terms in the Coulomb field of a point source. Their sum, however, is finite and corresponds to the usual power-law behaviour.

Keywords: Extra dimensions, radiation, scalar field, electromagnetic field, gravitational waves

1. Introduction

The recent interest in the theory of radiation in spacetime dimensions other than four is mostly related to the development of the theories with extra dimensions of spacetime. While the superstring theory, pretending to the status of fundamental theory, predicts the existence of extra dimensions, there is a number of phenomenological multi-dimensional gravity theories[1–4] solving some problems of elementary particles physics and cosmology. However, the characteristics of extra dimensions, such as their number, geometry and size, vary widely from one theory to another.

The actively developing gravitational-wave astronomy is the one of the most promising tools to probe the extra dimensions. So, the first constraints on the characteristics of extra dimensions have already been obtained by use of the GW170817/GRB170817A event data.[5–7] The possibility of using the future gravitational-wave observatories, such as LISA, to constrain the extra dimensions on cosmological scales has also been discussed.[8,9] Also, it is worth to note the recent advances in the constraining extra dimensions by the photograph of the supermassive black hole M87* shadow.[10,11]

However, in most of the literature, only the radiation in even-dimensional spacetimes is considered,[12–16] while the odd dimensions have been mainly discussed in the context of radiation reaction force.[17–20] It is mostly due to the Huygens principle violation in odd dimensions known since the classical works of Hadamard, Courant and Hilbert, Ivanenko and Sokolov.[21–23] In any dimensions, the signal from the instant flash of the source reaches an observer in the interval of time required for it to propagate at the speed of light. However, in odd dimensions, the endless tail signal decaying with time is observed after that, which is not the case in even dimensions. Mathematically, the Huygens principle violation consists in odd-dimensional retarded Green's functions being localised not only on the light cone, as they are in even dimensions, but also inside it. As a result, the retarded fields in odd dimensions propagate in space with all velocities up to that of light. However, free massless fields propagate exactly at the speed of light in any dimensions. Therefore, there is the apparent mismatch as the radiation being the free field far from the source is determined by its retarded field.

In this paper, we demonstrate that despite the Huygens principle violation in odd dimensions the radiation can be computed by the integration of the energy-momentum flux in the wave zone. We use the Rohrlich-Teitelboim radiation definition[24–26] (see, also,[27–29]) based on the Lorentz-invariant decomposition of the on-shell energy-momentum tensor. Considering the radiation of spin-0, spin-1 and spin-2 fields in five spacetime dimensions we show that the emitted part of the field energy-momentum propagates in space exactly at the speed of light, while it depends on the entire history of the source motion preceding the retarded time, in contrast with the four-dimensional theory.

The paper is organised as follows. In second section we consider the scalar radiation from the point charge in five spacetime dimensions. We briefly recall the recurrent relation for the odd-dimensional retarded Green's functions and the Rohrlich-Teitelboim approach to radiation. Based on the latter, we compute the emitted part of the on-shell energy-momentum tensor. In Sec. 3, we consider the analogous problem for the five-dimensional electromagnetic field. Section 4 is devoted to the calculation of the gravitational radiation from the point particle moving along an arbitrary world line in five dimensions. In the last section we briefly discuss our results.

2. Scalar radiation in five dimensions

Action of the massless scalar field $\varphi(x)$ interacting with the massive point particle moving along an arbitrary world line $z^\mu(\tau)$ in the five-dimensional Minkowski spacetime is written as

$$S = \frac{1}{4\pi^2} \int d^{4+1}x \, \partial^\mu \varphi(x) \partial_\mu \varphi(x) - \int d\tau \sqrt{\dot{z}^\alpha \dot{z}_\alpha}(m + g\varphi(z)), \quad \dot{z}^\mu = \frac{dz^\mu}{d\tau}, \quad (1)$$

where m is the particle's mass, g its scalar charge, and Minkowski metric is $\eta_{\mu\nu} = \text{diag}(1,-1,-1,-1,-1)$. We assume that particle's motion is governed by the external forces and is not affected by the radiation of scalar field, so here the world line variables are non-dynamical.

The action (1) leads to the scalar field equation of motion in form

$$\Box \varphi(x) = -2\pi^2 j(x), \tag{2}$$

$$j(x) = g \int d\tau \sqrt{\dot{z}^\alpha \dot{z}_\alpha} \delta^{(4+1)}(x-z), \tag{3}$$

where $j(x)$ is the scalar current, and $\Box = \partial^\mu \partial_\mu$ is the d'Alembert operator on the five-dimensional Minkowski space. To determine the radiation energy-momentum flux carried by the scalar field, we use its canonical energy-momentum tensor

$$T_{\mu\nu}(x) = \frac{1}{2\pi^2}\left(\partial_\mu\varphi\partial_\nu\varphi - \frac{1}{2}\eta_{\mu\nu}\partial^\alpha\varphi\partial_\alpha\varphi\right). \tag{4}$$

The retarded solution of the Eq. (2) is given as

$$\varphi(x) = -2\pi^2 \int d^{4+1}x'\, j(x') G_{\text{ret}}^{4+1}(x-x'), \tag{5}$$

where $G_{\text{ret}}^{4+1}(x)$ is the retarded Green's function of the five-dimensional d'Alembert equation. It is defined by the equation

$$\Box G_{\text{ret}}^{4+1}(x) = \delta^{(4+1)}(x), \tag{6}$$

$$G_{\text{ret}}^{4+1}(x) = 0,\ x^0 < 0. \tag{7}$$

In the odd-dimensional Minkowski spacetimes, retarded Green's functions are determined by the following recurrent relation[23] (see, also,[30])

$$G_{\text{ret}}^{2\nu+1}(x) = \frac{(-1)^{\nu-1}}{(2\pi)^\nu} \frac{d^{\nu-1}}{(rdr)^{\nu-1}} \frac{\theta(t)\,\theta(t^2-r^2)}{\sqrt{t^2-r^2}},\ \nu \in \mathbb{N}, \tag{8}$$

where $t = x^0$ and $r = |\mathbf{x}|$. Considering the expression under derivatives in Eq. (8) as a product of separate distributions and taking into that $d\theta(x)/dx = \delta(x)$, we find the five-dimensional retarded Green's function as

$$G_{\text{ret}}^{4+1}(x) = \frac{\theta(t)}{2\pi^2}\left[\frac{\delta(t^2-r^2)}{(t^2-r^2)^{1/2}} - \frac{1}{2}\frac{\theta(t^2-r^2)}{(t^2-r^2)^{3/2}}\right]. \tag{9}$$

As discussed above, it is localised not only on the light cone, but also inside it, leading to the propagation of the retarded field in space with all velocities up to that of light. Also, retarded field depends on the entire history of the source's motion preceding the retarded time and is given by the sum of separately divergent on the light cone $t^2 - r^2 = 0$ terms. However, one can show that the divergences contained in each of the terms in Eq. (9) mutually cancel out and the resulting field is finite.

2.1. Field of a static charge

Let us consider the case of static particle, to demonstrate the absence of divergences in the retarded field. In our calculations, we will use the "finite lifetime" trick to show the cancellation of divergences between the two terms.

We assume that the particle is at the origin and it is "switched on" for a finite interval of the proper time $a < \tau < b$, where $a < 0$ and $b > 0$ for concreteness. For this interval its world line has the form $z^\mu = [\tau, 0, 0, 0, 0]$. Then, by use of Eqs. (5), (3) and (9) the scalar field is written as

$$\varphi(x) = \frac{g}{2} \int_a^b d\tau \left[\frac{\theta(t - \tau - r - \epsilon)}{[(t - \tau)^2 - r^2]^{3/2}} - \frac{\delta(t - \tau - r - \epsilon)}{r[(t - \tau)^2 - r^2]^{1/2}} \right], \tag{10}$$

where we introduced the regularising parameter $\epsilon \to +0$ into the delta and Heaviside functions to shift the divergences from the light cone. Preforming the integration we obtain

$$\varphi(x) = \frac{g}{2} \begin{cases} 0, \ t < a + r, \\ -\dfrac{t - a}{r^2[(t - a)^2 - r^2]^{1/2}}, \ a + r \leq t < b + r, \\ \dfrac{t - b}{r^2[(t - b)^2 - r^2]^{1/2}} - \dfrac{t - a}{r^2[(t - a)^2 - r^2]^{1/2}}, \ t \geq b + r. \end{cases} \tag{11}$$

In the limit of eternal particle, we arrive at the finite Coulomb-like field

$$\lim_{a,b \to \pm\infty} \varphi(x) = -\frac{g}{2r^2}, \tag{12}$$

with the power-law behaviour corresponding to the increased dimensionality of space. Similar cancellation of divergences has been shown to take place, also, for the moving particle.[30]

2.2. The Rohrlich-Teitelboim radiation definition

The structure of the odd-dimensional Green's functions (8) makes the extraction of the emitted part of the retarded field in a standard manner non-trivial and requires a more sophisticated approach.

Such an approach was suggested by Rohrlich[24,25] and Teitelboim[26] (see, also,[27–29]). It is based on the use of certain covariantly defined quantities, so we briefly recall their definitions. Let us consider the point particle moving along the world line $z^\mu(\tau)$ with velocity $v^\mu = dz^\mu/d\tau$ in the D-dimensional spacetime. The observation point coordinates are denoted as x^μ. Assume the observation point to be a top of the light cone in the past and denote the intersection point of this light cone with the particle's world line as $z^\mu(\hat{\tau}) \equiv \hat{z}^\mu$. The corresponding moment of proper time $\hat{\tau}$ is called the retarded proper time and is defined by equation

$$(x^\mu - \hat{z}^\mu)^2 = 0, \ x^0 \geq \hat{z}^0. \tag{13}$$

Further, all the hatted quantities correspond to that moment. Then, we introduce three spacetime vectors: a lightlike vector $\hat{X}^\mu = x^\mu - \hat{z}^\mu$ directed from the retarded point of the world line to the observation point, a spacelike vector $\hat{u}^\mu$ orthogonal to the particle's velocity at the retarded moment of proper time, and a lightlike vector $\hat{c}^\mu = \hat{u}^\mu + \hat{v}^\mu$ aligned with the vector $\hat{X}^\mu$. Introduced vectors have the following properties

$$\hat{X}^2 = 0, \quad (\hat{u}\hat{v}) = 0, \quad \hat{u}^2 = -\hat{v}^2 = -1, \quad \hat{c}^2 = 0, \tag{14}$$

where $(\hat{u}\hat{v}) \equiv \hat{u}^\alpha \hat{v}_\alpha$. Using these vectors we, also, introduce the Lorentz-invariant distance $\hat{\rho}$ being the scalar product of two spacetime vectors

$$\hat{\rho} \equiv (\hat{v}\hat{X}), \quad \hat{X}^\mu = \hat{\rho}\hat{c}^\mu. \tag{15}$$

It is equal to the spatial distance in the Lorentz frame comoving with the particle at the retarded proper time. If the particle moves inside the compact region of space, then the Lorentz-invariant distance $\hat{\rho}$ is equivalent to the spatial distance

$$\hat{\rho} \xrightarrow{r \gg |\hat{z}|} r. \tag{16}$$

In accordance with the Rohrlich-Teitelboim approach, it is the Lorentz-invariant distance $\hat{\rho}$ that is used in the long-range expansion of tensors and definition of the wave zone.

In the Rohrlich-Teitelboim approach, the radiation is determined by the most long-range part of the on-shell energy-momentum tensor expansion in the inverse powers of the Lorentz-invariant distance $\hat{\rho}$. In D dimensions, the retarded field's on-shell energy-momentum tensor is expanded as[12, 16, 26–29]

$$T^{\mu\nu} = T^{\mu\nu}_{\text{Coul}} + T^{\mu\nu}_{\text{mix}} + T^{\mu\nu}_{\text{rad}} \tag{17}$$

$$T^{\mu\nu}_{\text{Coul}} \sim \frac{A^{\mu\nu}}{\hat{\rho}^{2D-4}}, \quad T^{\mu\nu}_{\text{mix}} \sim \frac{B^{\mu\nu}}{\hat{\rho}^{2D-5}} + \ldots + \frac{C^{\mu\nu}}{\hat{\rho}^{D-1}}, \quad T^{\mu\nu}_{\text{rad}} \sim \frac{D^{\mu\nu}}{\hat{\rho}^{D-2}}. \tag{18}$$

Here, the first term $T^{\mu\nu}_{\text{Coul}}$ is the energy-momentum tensor of the deformed Coulomb-like part of the retarded field. The second one is the mixed part, which consists of more than one term for $D > 4$ and is absent in $D = 3$. The most long-range part $T^{\mu\nu}_{\text{rad}}$ of the on-shell energy-momentum tensor expansion has the properties allowing to associate it with the radiation energy-momentum:

- It is separately conserved $\partial_\mu T^{\mu\nu}_{\text{rad}} = 0$, corresponding to its dynamical independence from the other parts;
- It is proportional to the direct product of two null vectors $T^{\mu\nu}_{\text{rad}} \sim \hat{c}^\mu \hat{c}^\nu$, corresponding to its propagation exactly with the speed of light $\hat{c}_\mu T^{\mu\nu}_{\text{rad}} = 0$;
- It falls down as $T^{\mu\nu}_{\text{rad}} \sim 1/r^{D-2}$ and gives positive definite energy-momentum flux through the distant $(D-2)$-dimensional sphere of area $\sim r^{D-2}$.

Therefore, the radiation power in D-dimensions can be computed as the energy flux associated with $T^{\mu\nu}_{\text{rad}}$ through the distant $(D-2)$-dimensional sphere of radius r

$$W_D = \int T^{0i}_{\text{rad}} n^i r^{D-2} d\Omega_{D-2}; \quad i = \overline{1, D-1}, \tag{19}$$

where $n^i = x^i/r$ is the unit spacelike vector in the direction of observation, and $d\Omega_{D-2}$ is the angular element on the $(D-2)$-dimensional sphere. This structure holds in both even and odd dimensions with the only difference that in odd dimensions the emitted part of the energy-momentum tensor depends on the entire history of the particle's motion preceding the retarded proper time $\hat{\tau}$.

Note that, usually, the energy-momentum tensor is just the bilinear form of the field derivatives, as, e.g., in Eq. (4). Then, one can define the emitted part of the retarded field derivative, by analogy with that of the energy-momentum tensor,

$$(\partial_\mu \Phi)^{\text{rad}} \sim 1/\hat{\rho}^{D/2-1}. \tag{20}$$

This definition is valid in the cases of scalar and electromagnetic fields and linearised gravity considered below.

2.3. Emitted part of the scalar field

Now we turn to the calculation of the emitted part of the retarded scalar field derivative. The computations below are similar to that in,[30] where we have considered the scalar synchrotron radiation in three and five spacetime dimensions.

Using the Eq. (5) together with Eqs. (9) and (3) we obtain the retarded scalar field of the moving particle as

$$\varphi(x) = -g \int d\tau\, \theta(X^0(\tau)) \left[\frac{\delta(X^2(\tau))}{(X^2(\tau))^{1/2}} - \frac{1}{2} \frac{\theta(X^2(\tau))}{(X^2(\tau))^{3/2}} \right], \tag{21}$$

where we introduced the vector $X^\mu(\tau) = x^\mu - z^\mu(\tau)$. In what follows, we omit its dependence on the proper time for brevity.

Its derivative is found to have the form

$$\partial_\mu \varphi(x) = -2g \int d\tau\, \theta(X^0) \left[\frac{3}{4} \frac{\theta(X^2)}{(X^2)^{5/2}} + \frac{\delta'(X^2)}{(X^2)^{1/2}} - \frac{\delta(X^2)}{(X^2)^{3/2}} \right] X_\mu, \tag{22}$$

where $\delta'(x) = d\delta(x)/dx$. Integrating by parts the term containing derivative of delta function by use of the relation

$$\frac{dX^2}{d\tau} = -2(vX), \tag{23}$$

we obtain the scalar field derivative in form

$$\partial_\mu \varphi(x) = -g \int d\tau\, \theta(X^0) \left[\frac{3}{2} \frac{\theta(X^2)}{(X^2)^{5/2}} X_\mu - \frac{\delta(X^2)}{(X^2)^{3/2}} X_\mu - \frac{\delta(X^2)}{(vX)^2(X^2)^{1/2}} \left[(aX) - 1 \right] X_\mu - \frac{\delta(X^2)}{(vX)(X^2)^{1/2}} v_\mu \right], \tag{24}$$

where we introduced the acceleration vector $a^\mu = d^2 z^\mu / d\tau^2$.

To obtain its emitted part, we extract the leading $\hat{\rho}$-asymptotic of the Eq. (24). We transform the products of delta and Heaviside functions by use of the relation for the delta function of complex argument

$$\theta(X^0)\delta(X^2) = \frac{\delta(\tau - \hat{\tau})}{2\hat{\rho}}. \tag{25}$$

We, also, rewrite the vector X^μ in terms of the Lorentz-invariant distance

$$X^\mu = Z^\mu + \hat{\rho}\hat{c}^\mu, \quad Z^\mu = \hat{z}^\mu - z^\mu. \tag{26}$$

Then, by use of Eqs. (25) and (26) we arrive at the emitted part of the scalar field derivative in form

$$(\partial_\mu \varphi(x))^{\text{rad}} = -\frac{g\hat{c}_\mu}{2^{5/2}\hat{\rho}^{3/2}} \int_{-\infty}^{\hat{\tau}} d\tau \left[\frac{3}{2}\frac{1}{(Z\hat{c})^{5/2}} - \frac{\delta(\tau - \hat{\tau})}{(Z\hat{c})^{3/2}} - \frac{2(a\hat{c})\delta(\tau - \hat{\tau})}{(v\hat{c})^2(Z\hat{c})^{1/2}}\right], \tag{27}$$

where we have taken into account that up to the leading order $X^2 \sim 2\hat{\rho}(Z\hat{c})$ and $(vX) \sim \hat{\rho}(v\hat{c})$. Note that each integral in the Eq. (27) diverges on the upper integration limit $\tau \to \hat{\tau}$, as $(Z\hat{c}) \to (\hat{v}\hat{c})(\hat{\tau} - \tau) = (\hat{\tau} - \tau)$. However, one can show that the last two terms of the integrand do not carry physical information concerning the field in the wave zone and just eliminate the divergences contained in the first one. To do this, we introduce the regularising parameter $\epsilon \to +0$ into the argument of delta function and perform integration by use of it, obtaining the divergent result

$$\int_{-\infty}^{\hat{\tau}} d\tau \frac{\delta(\tau - \hat{\tau} + \epsilon)}{(Z\hat{c})^{3/2}} = \frac{1}{\epsilon^{3/2}}, \tag{28}$$

which can be rewritten as

$$\frac{1}{\epsilon^{3/2}} = \frac{3}{2}\int_{-\infty}^{\hat{\tau}-\epsilon} \frac{d\tau}{(\hat{\tau} - \tau)^{3/2}}. \tag{29}$$

By analogy, the second term with the delta function transforms to

$$\int_{-\infty}^{\hat{\tau}} d\tau \frac{(a\hat{c})\delta(\tau - \hat{\tau})}{(v\hat{c})^2(Z\hat{c})^{1/2}} = \frac{1}{2}\int_{-\infty}^{\hat{\tau}-\epsilon} d\tau \frac{(\hat{a}\hat{c})}{(\hat{\tau} - \tau)^{3/2}}. \tag{30}$$

Then, omitting the regularising parameter in the upper integration limit we find the emitted part of the scalar field derivative as

$$(\partial_\mu \varphi(x))^{\text{rad}} = -\frac{g\hat{c}_\mu}{2^{5/2}\hat{\rho}^{3/2}} \int_{-\infty}^{\hat{\tau}} d\tau \left[\frac{3}{2}\frac{1}{(Z\hat{c})^{5/2}} - \frac{3}{2}\frac{1}{(\hat{\tau} - \tau)^{5/2}} - \frac{(\hat{a}\hat{c})}{(\hat{\tau} - \tau)^{3/2}}\right]. \tag{31}$$

In practice, calculating the radiation from the particle moving along some trajectory one needs to make the convergence of the integral in Eq. (31) explicit. To achieve it, one has to reintroduce the regularising parameter $\epsilon \to +0$ into the upper integration limit and perform some transformation of the first term in the integrand: usually, it is the integrations by parts, which extract the divergences from it and cancel them out by use of the remaining two integrals. The above structure of the emitted part of the field holds in any odd spacetime dimensions.[30]

Substituting the emitted part of the scalar field derivative into the Eq. (4) we find the radiated part of the energy-momentum tensor

$$T_{\mu\nu}^{\text{rad}}(x) = \frac{g^2 \hat{c}_\mu \hat{c}_\nu}{64\pi^2 \hat{\rho}^3} \mathcal{A}^2(x), \tag{32}$$

$$\mathcal{A}(x) = \int_{-\infty}^{\hat{\tau}} d\tau \left[\frac{3}{2}\frac{1}{(Z\hat{c})^{5/2}} - \frac{3}{2}\frac{1}{(\hat{\tau} - \tau)^{5/2}} - \frac{(\hat{a}\hat{c})}{(\hat{\tau} - \tau)^{3/2}}\right]. \tag{33}$$

In accordance with the Rohrlich-Teitelboim approach, it is proportional to the direct product of two null vectors $\hat{c}_\mu \hat{c}_\nu$ corresponding to the propagation of this part of field's energy-momentum exactly with the speed of light. Also, as was discussed above, the emitted part of the energy-momentum tensor depends on the entire history of the source's motion preceding the retarded proper time $\hat{\tau}$, as well as the radiation power determined by it.

3. Electromagnetic radiation in five dimensions

Having found the emitted part of the five-dimensional scalar field and the corresponding radiation energy-momentum tensor, let us now briefly discuss the electromagnetic and gravitational radiation in five dimensions. We start with the former.

3.1. *The setup*

Action of the electromagnetic field $A_\mu(x)$ interacting with the massive point particle moving along an arbitrary world line $z^\mu(\tau)$ in five dimensions is analogous to that of the scalar field (1) and has the form

$$S = -\frac{1}{8\pi^2} \int d^{4+1}x \, F^{\mu\nu} F_{\mu\nu} - e \int d\tau \, \dot{z}^\mu A_\mu(z), \quad F_{\mu\nu} = \partial_\mu A_\nu - \partial_\nu A_\mu, \quad (34)$$

where e is particle's electric charge. Here, we omit the particle's kinetic term in the action, given that its motion is completely governed by the external forces and, thus, the world line variables are non-dynamical.

The action (34) yields the standard equation of motion of the electromagnetic field

$$\Box A^\mu(x) = 2\pi^2 j^\mu(x), \quad (35)$$

$$j^\mu(x) = e \int d\tau \, \dot{z}^\mu \delta^{(4+1)}(x-z). \quad (36)$$

where we imposed on the field the Lorentz gauge condition to fix its gauge symmetry

$$\partial_\mu A^\mu = 0. \quad (37)$$

Note that this condition requires the current to be conserved

$$\partial_\mu j^\mu = 0, \quad (38)$$

and it is, when the observation point is off the world line, as can be easily seen from the Eq. (36).

To determine the energy flux carried by the electromagnetic radiation we use symmetric energy-momentum tensor of the electromagnetic field

$$\Theta_{\mu\nu} = \frac{1}{2\pi^2}\left[F_\mu{}^\alpha F_{\alpha\nu} + \frac{1}{4}\eta_{\mu\nu} F_{\alpha\beta} F^{\alpha\beta}\right]. \quad (39)$$

By analogy with that of the scalar field, it is the bilinear functional of the field derivatives $\Theta \sim \partial A \partial A$ and, thus, admits defining the emitted part of the electromagnetic field derivative.

3.2. Emitted part of the electromagnetic field

By use of the Eqs. (36) and (9) we obtain the retarded electromagnetic field of the point charge in form

$$A_\mu(x) = e \int d\tau\, \dot{z}_\mu\, \theta(X^0) \left[\frac{\delta(X^2)}{(X^2)^{1/2}} - \frac{1}{2} \frac{\theta(X^2)}{(X^2)^{3/2}} \right]. \tag{40}$$

We calculate its derivative using the relation (23)

$$\partial_\nu A_\mu(x) = e \int d\tau\, \theta(X^0) \left[\frac{3}{2} \frac{\theta(X^2)}{(X^2)^{5/2}} v_\mu X_\nu - \frac{\delta(X^2)}{(X^2)^{3/2}} v_\mu X_\nu - \right.$$
$$\left. - \frac{\delta(X^2)}{(vX)^2(X^2)^{1/2}}[(aX) - 1]v_\mu X_\nu + \frac{\delta(X^2)}{(vX)(X^2)^{1/2}}[a_\mu X_\nu - v_\mu v_\nu] \right]. \tag{41}$$

Using the relations (25) and (26), and transforming the terms with delta functions by analogy with the Eqs. (28–30) we obtain the emitted part of the retarded electromagnetic field as the long-range part of its derivative with respect to the Lorentz-invariant distance

$$(\partial_\nu A_\mu)^{\mathrm{rad}} = \frac{e\hat{c}_\nu}{2^{5/2}\hat{\rho}^{3/2}} \int_{-\infty}^{\hat{\tau}} d\tau \left[\frac{3}{2} \frac{v_\mu}{(Z\hat{c})^{5/2}} - \frac{3}{2} \frac{\hat{v}_\mu}{(\hat{\tau} - \tau)^{5/2}} - \frac{(\hat{a}\hat{c})\hat{v}_\mu - \hat{a}_\mu}{(\hat{\tau} - \tau)^{3/2}} \right]. \tag{42}$$

By analogy with the scalar field, in Eq. (42) all the physical information concerning the electromagnetic field in the wave zone is contained in the first term of the integrand, while the remaining ones just subtract the divergences contained in it at the upper integration limit.

Substituting the Eq. (42) into the symmetric energy-momentum tensor (39) we arrive at the five-dimensional electromagnetic radiation energy-momentum tensor

$$\Theta_{\mu\nu}^{\mathrm{rad}} = -\frac{e^2 \hat{c}_\mu \hat{c}_\nu}{64\pi^2 \hat{\rho}^3} \mathcal{A}_\alpha^2(x), \tag{43}$$

$$\mathcal{A}_\alpha(x) = \int_{-\infty}^{\hat{\tau}} d\tau \left[\frac{3}{2} \frac{v_\alpha}{(Z\hat{c})^{5/2}} - \frac{3}{2} \frac{\hat{v}_\alpha}{(\hat{\tau} - \tau)^{5/2}} - \frac{(\hat{a}\hat{c})\hat{v}_\alpha - \hat{a}_\alpha}{(\hat{\tau} - \tau)^{3/2}} \right]. \tag{44}$$

The obtained tensor structure of the radiated part of the energy-momentum tensor corresponds to the propagation of the associated energy flux exactly with the speed of light. Also, by analogy with the scalar field (32), it depends on the history of charge's motion preceding the retarded proper time.

4. Five-dimensional gravitational radiation

Now we turn to the calculation of the gravitational radiation produced by the point particles. If interaction between them is also gravitational, the problem is not described by the linearized approximation, and the quadratic terms in expansion of the Einstein tensor are required to take into account the contribution of field stresses to radiation.[32] If the dominant forces are non-gravitational, the corresponding field stresses are also required, making the calculation rather difficult. Here we calculate only the local contribution of particles themselves, so the result is incomplete. We give it just to reveal difference with the scalar and electromagnetic cases and to show how to deal with polarisations.

4.1. *The setup*

We start with the generally covariant Einstein-Hilbert action for the five-dimensional gravity interacting with massive point particle and some external field governing its motion

$$S = \frac{1}{2\kappa_5} \int d^{4+1}x \sqrt{-g} R - m \int d\tau \sqrt{g_{\alpha\beta}(z)\dot{z}^\alpha \dot{z}^\beta} + S_F, \qquad (45)$$

where κ_5 is the five-dimensional gravitational constant, g is the determinant of metric tensor, and S_F is the action for the external field moving point particle.

We linearise the Einstein's equation over the background Minkowski metric

$$g_{\mu\nu}(x) = \eta_{\mu\nu} + h_{\mu\nu}(x), \quad |h_{\mu\nu}| \ll 1. \qquad (46)$$

Introducing the reduced metric perturbations

$$\bar{h}_{\mu\nu} = h_{\mu\nu} - \frac{1}{2}\eta_{\mu\nu} h, \quad h = \eta^{\alpha\beta} h_{\alpha\beta}, \qquad (47)$$

we arrive at the linearised Einstein equation

$$\Box \bar{h}_{\mu\nu}(x) = 2\kappa_5 \left(T^P_{\mu\nu}(x) + T^F_{\mu\nu}(x) \right), \qquad (48)$$

$$T^P_{\mu\nu}(x) = m \int d\tau \, \dot{z}_\mu \dot{z}_\nu \, \delta^{(5)}(x-z), \quad T^F_{\mu\nu}(x) = -\frac{2}{\sqrt{-g}} \frac{\delta S_F}{\delta g^{\mu\nu}} \bigg|_{g=\eta} \qquad (49)$$

where $T^P_{\mu\nu}(x)$ is the energy-momentum of point particle moving on the flat Minkowski background and interacting with some external field, which energy-momentum tensor is given by $T^F_{\mu\nu}(x)$. To obtain the Eq. (48) we, also, imposed the Lorentz gauge condition on the metric perturbations

$$\partial^\mu \bar{h}_{\mu\nu} = 0, \qquad (50)$$

to fix the gauge symmetry of the system. Such a condition requires the particle's and external field's energy momentum-tensors to be jointly conserved

$$\partial^\mu \left(T^P_{\mu\nu} + T^F_{\mu\nu} \right) = 0, \qquad (51)$$

which is assumed to be valid on-shell.

To determine the energy-momentum flux carried by the gravitational radiation we use the effective energy-momentum tensor of metric perturbations, by analogy with,[31]

$$t_{\mu\nu} = \frac{1}{4\kappa_5} \langle \partial_\mu \bar{h}^{TT}_{ij} \partial_\nu \bar{h}^{TT}_{ij} \rangle, \quad \bar{h}^{TT}_{ij}(x) = \Lambda_{ij,kl}(\mathbf{n}) \bar{h}_{kl}(x), \qquad (52)$$

$$\Lambda_{ij,kl}(\mathbf{n}) = P_{ik} P_{jl} - \frac{1}{3} P_{ij} P_{kl}, \quad P_{ij} = \delta_{ij} - n_i n_j, \quad n^i = \frac{x^i}{r}, \qquad (53)$$

where we assume the particle's motion to be periodic, and $\langle\ldots\rangle$ is the averaging over the period. Here, we turned into the transverse-traceless gauge by the contraction of metric perturbations (52) with the projector (53) defined by analogy with.[31] Note that differentiation of the projector would increase the fall-off asymptotic of the field, so its derivative can be neglected when one computes the emitted part of the gravitational field in the transverse-traceless gauge.

4.2. *Emitted part of the gravitational field (incomplete)*

Using the Eqs. (9) and (49) we find the retarded gravitational field of the point particle as

$$\bar{h}^{\text{P}}_{\mu\nu}(x) = \frac{m\kappa_5}{\pi^2} \int d\tau\, \dot{z}_\mu \dot{z}_\nu\, \theta(X^0) \left[\frac{\delta(X^2)}{(X^2)^{1/2}} - \frac{1}{2} \frac{\theta(X^2)}{(X^2)^{3/2}} \right]. \tag{54}$$

We compute its derivative integrating by parts by use of the relation (23) arriving at

$$\partial_\alpha \bar{h}^{\text{P}}_{\mu\nu} = \frac{m\kappa_5}{\pi^2} \int d\tau\, \theta(X^0) \left[\frac{3}{2} \frac{\theta(X^2)}{(X^2)^{5/2}} v_\mu v_\nu X_\alpha - \frac{\delta(X^2)}{(X^2)^{3/2}} v_\mu v_\nu X_\alpha - \right.$$
$$\left. - \frac{\delta(X^2)}{(vX)^2 (X^2)^{1/2}} [(aX) - 1] v_\mu v_\nu X_\alpha + \frac{\delta(X^2)}{(vX)(X^2)^{1/2}} [2a_{(\mu} v_{\nu)} X_\alpha - v_\mu v_\nu v_\alpha] \right], \tag{55}$$

where $a^\mu = d^2 z^\mu / d\tau^2$ is the acceleration vector, and we define the symmetrisation over two indices as $A_{(\mu} B_{\nu)} = (A_\mu B_\nu + A_\nu B_\mu)/2$.

Extracting the long-range part of the gravitational field derivative by use of the relations (25) and (26) and transforming the terms with delta functions by analogy with Eqs. (28–30) we obtain the emitted part of the gravitational field as

$$\left(\partial_\alpha \bar{h}^{\text{P}}_{\mu\nu}\right)^{\text{rad}} = \frac{m\kappa_5 \hat{c}_\alpha}{2^{5/2} \pi^2 \hat{\rho}^{3/2}} \int_{-\infty}^{\hat{\tau}} d\tau \left[\frac{3}{2} \frac{v_\mu v_\nu}{(Z\hat{c})^{5/2}} - \frac{3}{2} \frac{\hat{v}_\mu \hat{v}_\nu}{(\hat{\tau} - \tau)^{5/2}} - \frac{(\hat{a}\hat{c})\hat{v}_\mu \hat{v}_\nu - 2\hat{a}_{(\mu}\hat{v}_{\nu)}}{(\hat{\tau} - \tau)^{3/2}} \right]. \tag{56}$$

By analogy with the scalar (31) and electromagnetic (42) fields, it consists of one integral determining the properties of the gravitational field in the wave zone and two integral being counter-terms eliminating the divergences from the first one.

Substituting the obtained expression for the emitted part of the retarded gravitational field (56) into the Eq. (52) we find the energy-momentum tensor of gravitational radiation generated by the point particle

$$\left(t^{\text{P}}_{\mu\nu}\right)^{\text{rad}} = \frac{m^2 \kappa_5 \hat{c}_\mu \hat{c}_\nu}{128 \pi^4 \hat{\rho}^3} \mathcal{A}^{\text{TT}}_{ij}(x) \mathcal{A}^{\text{TT}}_{ij}(x), \quad \mathcal{A}^{\text{TT}}_{ij}(x) \equiv \Lambda_{ij,kl}(\mathbf{n}) \mathcal{A}_{kl}(x), \tag{57}$$

$$\mathcal{A}_{ij}(x) = \int_{-\infty}^{\hat{\tau}} d\tau \left[\frac{3}{2} \frac{v_i v_j}{(Z\hat{c})^{5/2}} - \frac{3}{2} \frac{\hat{v}_i \hat{v}_j}{(\hat{\tau} - \tau)^{5/2}} - \frac{(\hat{a}\hat{c})\hat{v}_i \hat{v}_j - 2\hat{a}_{(i}\hat{v}_{j)}}{(\hat{\tau} - \tau)^{3/2}} \right]. \tag{58}$$

As in the cases of scalar (32) and electromagnetic (43) radiation, the emitted part of the gravitational field energy-momentum tensor has the tensor structure corresponding to the propagation of the associated energy-momentum flux exactly at the speed of light and depends on the entire history of the particle's motion preceding the retarded proper time $\hat{\tau}$.

5. Conclusions

In this short article, we have demonstrated that despite the Huygens principle violation in odd spacetime dimensions, radiation can be computed by the integration of the energy-momentum flux in the wave zone. However, it requires the Lorentz-invariant modification of the radiation and wave zone definitions, in accordance with the Rohrlich-Teitelboim approach. Also, due to the Huygens principle violation, the emitted part of the field depends on the history of the source's motion preceding the retarded proper time, in contrast with even dimensions, where properties of radiation at given moment of time are determined only by the state of the source at the retarded time. Another feature of the odd dimensions is that the retarded field is given by the sum of separately divergent integrals. Nevertheless, these divergence mutually cancel out and the resulting field is finite.

Based on the Rohrlich-Teitelboim approach, we have considered the radiation of the scalar, electromagnetic and gravitational fields by point particle in five dimensions. We computed the emitted parts of the fields' energy-momentum tensors. The obtained expressions have the tensor structures corresponding to the propagation of the radiated energy-momentum in space exactly with the speed of light. Also, they are given by the sum of separately divergent integrals over the history of particle's motion, one of which carries all the physical information concerning the field in the wave zone, while the remaining ones are just the counter-terms subtracting the divergences from the former. To make the convergence of the resulting tensor explicit, one has to integrate the first term by parts.

In our previous work,[30] we have considered the scalar synchrotron radiation in three and five dimensions. The results were checked by the calculation of the spectral decompositions of the radiation power, which are indifferent to the dimensionality of the spacetime. Based on this, we assume that the obtained similar expressions for the emitted parts of the electromagnetic and gravitational fields should, also, be valid.

Acknowledgements

The work of M. Kh. was supported by the "BASIS" Foundation Grant No. 20-2-10-8-1. The work of D.G. was supported by the Russian Foundation for Basic Research on the project 20-52-18012, and the Scientific and Educational School of Moscow State University "Fundamental and Applied Space Research".

References

1. N. Arkani-Hamed, S. Dimopoulos and G. R. Dvali, The Hierarchy problem and new dimensions at a millimeter, *Phys. Lett. B* **429**, 263 (1998).

2. L. Randall and R. Sundrum, A Large mass hierarchy from a small extra dimension, *Phys. Rev. Lett.* **83**, 3370 (1999).
3. L. Randall and R. Sundrum, An Alternative to compactification, *Phys. Rev. Lett.* **83**, 4690 (1999).
4. G. R. Dvali, G. Gabadadze and M. Porrati, 4D gravity on a brane in 5D Minkowski space, *Phys. Lett. B* **485**, 208 (2000).
5. L. Visinelli, N. Bolis and S. Vagnozzi, Brane-world extra dimensions in light of GW170817, *Phys. Rev. D* **97**, no.6, 064039 (2018).
6. K. Pardo, M. Fishbach, D. E. Holz and D. N. Spergel, Limits on the number of spacetime dimensions from GW170817, *JCAP* **07**, 048 (2018).
7. K. Chakravarti, S. Chakraborty, K. S. Phukon, S. Bose and S. SenGupta, Constraining extra-spatial dimensions with observations of GW170817, *Class. Quant. Grav.* **37**, no.10, 105004 (2020).
8. C. Deffayet and K. Menou, Probing Gravity with Spacetime Sirens, *Astrophys. J. Lett.* **668**, L143 (2007).
9. M. Corman, C. Escamilla-Rivera and M. A. Hendry, Constraining extra dimensions on cosmological scales with LISA future gravitational wave siren data, *JCAP* **02**, 005 (2021).
10. S. Vagnozzi and L. Visinelli, Hunting for extra dimensions in the shadow of M87*, *Phys. Rev. D* **100**, no.2, 024020 (2019).
11. I. Banerjee, S. Chakraborty and S. SenGupta, Silhouette of M87*: A New Window to Peek into the World of Hidden Dimensions, *Phys. Rev. D* **101**, no.4, 041301 (2020).
12. B. P. Kosyakov, Exact solutions of classical electrodynamics and the Yang-Mills-Wong theory in even-dimensional space-time, *Theor. Math. Phys.* **119**, 493 (1999).
13. V. Cardoso, M. Cavaglia and J. Q. Guo, Gravitational Larmor formula in higher dimensions, *Phys. Rev. D* **75**, 084020 (2007).
14. V. Cardoso, O. J. C. Dias and J. P. S. Lemos, Gravitational radiation in D-dimensional space-times, *Phys. Rev. D* **67**, 064026 (2003).
15. A. Mironov and A. Morozov, Radiation beyond four space-time dimensions, *Theor. Math. Phys.* **156**, 1209 (2008).
16. B. P. Kosyakov, Electromagnetic radiation in even-dimensional spacetimes, *Int. J. Mod. Phys. A* **23**, 4695 (2008).
17. D. V. Galtsov, Radiation reaction in various dimensions, *Phys. Rev. D* **66**, 025016 (2002).
18. P. O. Kazinski, S. L. Lyakhovich and A. A. Sharapov, Radiation reaction and renormalization in classical electrodynamics of point particle in any dimension, *Phys. Rev. D* **66**, 025017 (2002).
19. Y. Yaremko, Self-force in 2+1 electrodynamics, *J. Phys. A* **40**, 13161 (2007).
20. E. Shuryak, H. U. Yee and I. Zahed, Self-force and synchrotron radiation in odd space-time dimensions, *Phys. Rev. D* **85**, 104007 (2012).
21. J. Hadamard, *Lectures on Cauchy's Problem in Linear Partial Differential Equations* (Dover Publications, New York, 2014).
22. R. Courant and D. Hilbert, *Methods of Mathematical Physics: Partial Differential Equations*, Wiley Classics Library (Wiley, New York, 2008).
23. D. Ivanenko and A. Sokolov, *Sov. Phys. Dokl.* **36**, 37 (1940); *Classical Field Theory* (State Publishing House of Technical and Theoretical Literature, Moscow, 1951) (in Russian) [*Klassische Feldtheorie* (Akademie-Verlag, Berlin, 1953)].
24. F. Rohrlich, The definition of electromagnetic radiation, *Nuovo Cim* **21**, 811 (1961).
25. F. Rohrlich, *Classical Charged Particles* (World Scientific, Singapore, 2007).

26. C. Teitelboim, Splitting of the maxwell tensor - radiation reaction without advanced fields, *Phys. Rev. D* **1**, 1572 (1970) [erratum: *Phys. Rev. D* **2**, 1763 (1970)].
27. D. V. Gal'tsov and P. Spirin, Radiation reaction reexamined: Bound momentum and Schott term, *Grav. Cosmol.* **12**, 1 (2006).
28. B. P. Kosyakov, Radiation in electrodynamics and in Yang-Mills theory, *Sov. Phys. Usp.* **35**, 135 (1992).
29. P. A. Spirin, Massless field emission in the space-time of extra dimensions, *Grav. Cosmol.* **15**, 82 (2009).
30. D. V. Gal'tsov and M. Khlopunov, Synchrotron radiation in odd dimensions, *Phys. Rev. D* **101**, no.8, 084054 (2020).
31. M. Maggiore, *Gravitational Waves: Volume 1: Theory and Experiments*, Gravitational Waves (OUP, Oxford, 2008).
32. S. Weinberg, *Gravitation and Cosmology*, (Wiley, New York, 1972).

Wave propagation in the anti-deSitter optical metric

D. García-Peláez

Universidad Autónoma Metropolitana Azcapotzalco,
Avenida San Pablo Xalpa 180, Azcapotzalco, Reynosa Tamaulipas, 02200 Ciudad de México,
México

Universidad Panamericana,
Tecoyotitla 366. Col. Ex Hacienda Guadalupe Chimalistac, 01050 México D.F., México
E-mail: dgarciap@up.edu.mx

C. S. López-Monsalvo

Conacyt-Universidad Autónoma Metropolitana Azcapotzalco,
Avenida San Pablo Xalpa 180, Azcapotzalco, Reynosa Tamaulipas, 02200 Ciudad de México,
México
E-mail: cslopezmo@conacyt.mx

In this work, we use the fact that kinematics of light propagation in a *non-dispersive medium* associated with a bi-metric spacetime is expressed by means of a 1-parameter family of contact transformations. We present a general technique to find such transformations and explore some explicit examples for Minkowski and anti-deSitter spacetimes geometries.

Keywords: Contact geometry; Wave propagation; Anti-deSitter.

1. Introduction

Soon after the advent of general relativity, it was observed that the gravitational field *bends* the path followed by a light ray. This was confirmed by Eddington after noticing that the apparent position of the stars are shifted from their expected position in the sky when observed during a solar eclipse. This *bending* phenomenon is analogous to the deviation of light rays while traveling in a medium whose refractive index changes from one place to the other. In this sense, it was shown that a class of optical media can be modeled by means of a metric tensor encoding its electromagnetic properties (Refs. 1–3). Furthermore, this analogy has evolved into the very active field of transformation optics, where the techniques and tools of differential geometry – that have been insightful in gravitational physics – have found its way into the more applied area of material science (Refs. 4–7). In addition, this has also been used in modeling analogue gravitational spacetimes such as black holes and cosmological solutions (Refs. 8–11).

Fermat's principle poses a well known problem in the calculus of variations. In the non-relativistic setting – where the notion of time is *absolute* and *universal* – it states that light travels between two given *spatial* locations following a path minimizing a time functional. Such a perspective is clearly untenable in the context of General Relativity, where it is commonly replaced by the assumption that the path taken by light in traveling from one location to another corresponds to a null geodesic. However, albeit it remains a variational problem, its precise formulation is far more elaborate (see Theorem 7.3.1 in Ref. 12).

Similarly (cf. Theorem 7.1.2 in Ref.12), Huygens' principle is centered in the idea of light emissions being instantaneous for different observers at each instant in time (Ref. 13). In this way, light emission is described by well localized wavefronts, as they travel through three dimensional space. In the relativistic setting, the electromagnetic field on a precise event on spacetime should depend only on initial conditions originated its past null cone (Ref. 14). This has led to explore different wave phenomena where Huygens' principle is not fulfilled, most of which are due to dissipation processes where the wave distribution has not converging tails. As a consequence, the wavefronts cannot be located in exactly at a point of spacetime. With the Hadamard conjecture, this phenomenon has been related to the dimensions and curvature of spacetime (Refs. 15, 16).

One of the simplest and of most interesting curved spacetimes for theoretical physicists, is the anti-deSitter spacetime (AdS). This spacetime model has a very deep relationship with hyperbolic geometry, where its boundary at spacelike infinity leads to have strange peculiar like closed timelike curves and achornal surfaces (Refs. 17, 18). Nevertheless, AdS has gained more interest in recent years, as it has showed its value in topics like the *holographic principle*, the ground state of gauged supergravity theories and its central role in high energy physics in the correspondence with the Conformal Field Theory (AdS/CFT).

In this work, we use the fact that an optical medium can be represented by a Riemannian manifold $(\mathcal{B}, g)$ where $\mathcal{B}$ is considered to be the physical space and g the optical spatial metric. The geodesic flow in its unitary tangent bundle can be represented by a contact transformation acting on its space of contact elements. This fact, allows us to describe the wavefront evolution in an optical medium solely in terms of the contact transformation and to reconstruct the geodesic flow from the Reeb vector field. This provides us with a way to construct wavefronts in optical media without directly solving the wave equation. Particularly, we use this powerful tool to reconstruct wave propagation, along with with its corresponding light rays in a $(2+1)$-dimensional AdS spacetime.

This manuscript is structured as follows. In section 2 we give the mathematical formalism to construct the technique. In section 3 we use this technique to reconstruct wavefronts and ray lights in a $(2+1)$-dimensional anti-deSitter spacetime. We find explicitly the 1-parameter family of contact transformations and solve numerically to reconstruct the wave propagation in optical media with interfaces of different refractive index.

2. Mathematical background

In this work, an optical medium will be a Riemannian manifold $(\mathcal{B}, g)$ submersed in a bi-metric Lorentzian spacetime $(M, g_0, \tilde{g})$. Where g_0 is the spacetime metric, used to low and rise index, the metric $\tilde{g}$ is the optical metric introduced by Gordon (Ref. 1), from which the effective speed of light in a medium can be read off. The manifold $\mathcal{B}$ along with his metric g, is called *the material manifold*, The metric g can be decomposed in terms of the material manifold Riemannian metric and an observer's four velocity.

The cotangent bundle of the material manifold carries a natural symplectic structure, endowed by a non-degenerated closed 2-form ω. In this sense, the Liouville's vector filed, which preserves the symplectic 2-form in terms of its Lie derivative, defines a 1-form $\lambda \in T^*(T^*\mathcal{B})$ which generates the symplectic structure. As defined by Perlick (see Definition 5.1.1 and Proposition 5.1.1 in Ref. 12) the punctured cotangent bundle $PT^*\mathcal{B}$, corresponds to a *ray-optical structure* $\mathcal{N}$. Using the inclusion map from this ray-optical structure to the cotangent bundle, the 1-form λ induces a contact 1-form η, where the pair $(\mathcal{N}, \mathcal{D})$ is a contact manifold, known as the *space of contact elements* or the *contact bundle* of $\mathcal{B}$.

Let us use the defintion of a *wave front* centered at the point $b \in \mathcal{B}$ as the hypersurface (Ref. 19)

$$F_b(t) = \{b_i \in \mathcal{B} \,|\, \gamma(0) = b, \gamma(t) = b_i\} \tag{1}$$

where γ is a geodesic on $(\mathcal{B}, g)$. For every point in the wave front, the contact element of $\mathcal{B}$ associated to that point is tangent to the wave front. If we consider a geodesic flow on the unitary tangent bundle of $\mathcal{B}$, there exists a unique contact element, which is perpendicular to. So the Reeb vector filed, associated to the contact 1-form of the ray-optical structure is dual to the geodesic flow in the unitary tangent bundle of $\mathcal{B}$. The Reeb vector field is also, the infinitesimal generator of a family of 1-parameter strict contact transformations $\phi_t : \mathcal{N} \to \mathcal{N}$, which preserves the contact form and thus the contact elements on $\mathcal{B}$, which are tangent to the wave fronts. In this sense, the family of transformations ϕ_t can evolve the geodesic flow preserving the wave fronts in each point.

The method is to solve the Reeb's vector field flow, associated to contact 1-form in the ray-optical structure to reconstruct numerically from it, the wave fronts and the ray lights propagating in an optical medium. When interfaces are present between media with different refractive index, no further adaptions are needed for the technique to reconstruct wave fronts and light rays while refracted. If this technique is used in a Minkowski spacetime geometry, Snell's law can be deduced and total inner reflection is obtained when the source of light is settle to refract to another medium with smaller refractive index.

3. Wave propagation in (2 + 1)-dimensional anti-deSitter spacetime

If we consider now a (2+1)-dimensional anti-deSitter spacetime with spatial optical metric given by (Ref. 7)

$$g = \left(\frac{n}{y}\right)^2 \sum_{i=1}^{2} dx^i \otimes dx^i. \qquad (2)$$

we find the associated 1-parameter family of strict contact transformations, generated by the Reeb's flow, for which we obtained

$$\phi_t = \left[x = \frac{(x\sin\varphi + y\cos\varphi - x)e^{\frac{2t}{n}} - x\sin\varphi - y\cos\varphi - x}{(\sin\varphi - 1)e^{\frac{2t}{n}} - \sin\varphi - 1}, \right. \qquad (3)$$

$$y = -\frac{2ye^{\frac{t}{n}}}{(\sin\varphi - 1)e^{\frac{2t}{n}} - \sin\varphi - 1},$$

$$\left. \varphi = \arctan\left(-\frac{(-\sin\varphi + 1)e^{\frac{2t}{n}} - \sin\varphi - 1}{2e^{\frac{t}{n}}\cos\varphi}\right). \right]$$

With this transformation, it is possible to observe that the projection of the flows corresponds to semi-circles centered in the x-axis, as expected by the hyperbolic geometry associated to the anti-deSitter spacetime. For interfaces between media with different refractive index, refraction can be observed and no total inner reflection is observed when projected to the Poincaré disc. As it is known, the AdS spacetime is nos globally hyperbolic, so it admits closed timelike curves and achronal surfaces can be observed where light rays are closer to the infinity circle boundary of the disc. It is also observed that light rays can intersect more than one time the same wave front (figure 1 Ref. 20).

4. Final remarks

The fact that geodesic flows can be written in terms of a 1-parameter family of contact transformations, allows us to reconstruct trajectories and wavefronts of light while propagating through an optical medium, just from the Reeb flow. With this technique, we recreate the wave fronts as they propagate in an optical medium with interfaces of different refractive index in a (2 + 1)-dimensional Minkowski spacetime and (2+1)-dimensional anti-deSitter spacetime. In the first example, we could reproduce Snell's law of refraction and the total inner reflexion phenomenon. In the second example, we observe refraction when mapped to the Poincaré disc. No inner total reflection was observed when the light source is in a medium with larger refractive index. Achronal surfaces can be observed in this configuration, as light rays closer to the circle boundary intersects more than once the same wavefront.

The formalism, is robust enough to deal with interfaces without further adaptations. This technique can be used to recreate wave propagation in analogue gravitational spacetimes, such as Schwarzschild's blackholes, or to study interface between

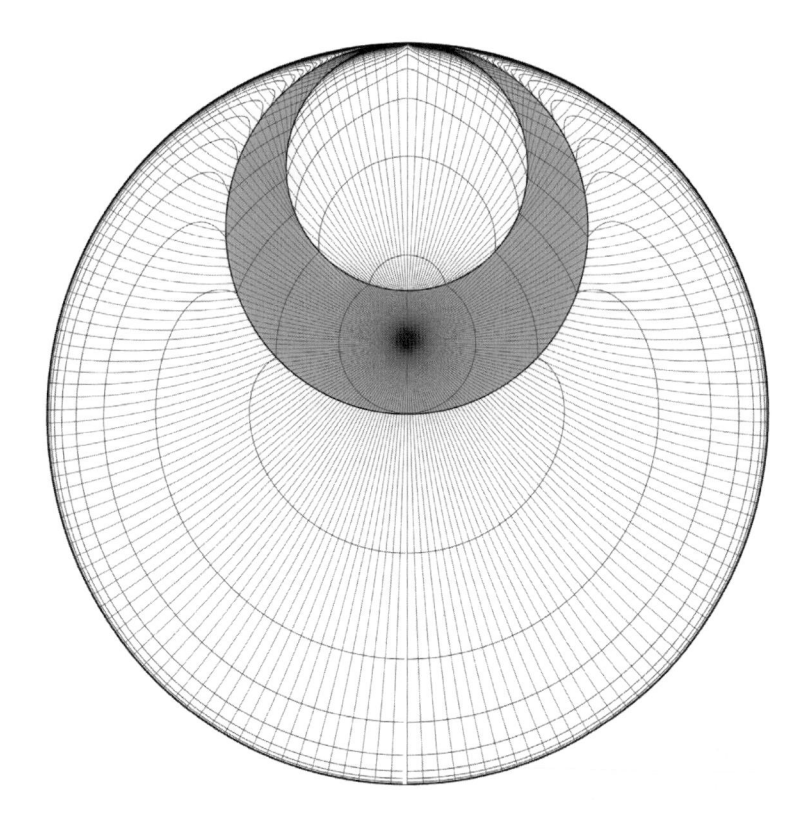

Fig. 1. Light rays and wavefronts emitted by a source of light refracting through a horizontal interface mapped to the Poincaré disc. The refractive index in the darker layer (where the light source is settled) is larger than the one in the whiter space.

vacuum and plasma. In recent years, this type of techniques can be important in the development of metamaterials, which can mimic some spacetime properties impossible to find in nature.

Acknowledgments

DGP was funded by a CONACYT Scholarship with CVU 425313.

References

1. W. Gordon, Zur lichtfortpflanzung nach der relativitätstheorie, *Annalen der Physik* **377**, 421 (1923).
2. F. de Felice, On the gravitational field acting as an optical medium, *General Relativity and Gravitation* **2**, 347 (1971).
3. J. Ehlers, F. A. Pirani and A. Schild, Republication of: The geometry of free fall and light propagation, *General Relativity and Gravitation* **44**, 1587 (2012).
4. J. B. Pendry, D. Schurig and D. R. Smith, Controlling electromagnetic fields, *science* **312**, 1780 (2006).

5. U. Leonhardt and T. G. Philbin, General relativity in electrical engineering, *New Journal of Physics* **8**, p. 247 (2006).
6. H. Chen, C. T. Chan and P. Sheng, Transformation optics and metamaterials, *Nature materials* **9**, 387 (2010).
7. C. Lopez-Monsalvo, D. Garcia-Pelaez, A. Rubio-Ponce and R. Escarela-Perez, The geometry of induced electromagnetic fields in moving media, *Annals of Physics* **420**, p. 168270 (2020).
8. H. Chen, S. Tao, J. Bělín, J. Courtial and R.-X. Miao, Transformation cosmology, *Phys. Rev. A* **102**, p. 023528 (Aug 2020).
9. S. Schuster and M. Visser, Electromagnetic analogue space-times, analytically and algebraically, *Classical and Quantum Gravity* (2019).
10. D. Faccio, F. Belgiorno, S. Cacciatori, V. Gorini, S. Liberati and U. Moschella, *Analogue gravity phenomenology: analogue spacetimes and horizons, from theory to experiment* (Springer, 2013).
11. S. Schuster and M. Visser, Bespoke analogue space-times: Meta-material mimics, *General Relativity and Gravitation* **50**, 1 (2018).
12. V. Perlick, *Ray optics, Fermat's principle, and applications to general relativity* (Springer Science & Business Media, 2000).
13. Y. Y. Berest and A. P. Veselov, Huygens' principle and integrability, *Russian Mathematical Surveys* **49**, 5 (1994).
14. A. I. Harte, Tails of plane wave spacetimes: Wave-wave scattering in general relativity, *Physical Review D* **88**, p. 084059 (2013).
15. R. McLenaghan, An explicit determination of the empty space-times on which the wave equation satisfies huygens' principle, in *Mathematical Proceedings of the Cambridge Philosophical Society*, (1)1969.
16. T. W. Noonan, Huygens' principle in conformally flat spacetimes, *Classical and Quantum Gravity* **12**, p. 1087 (1995).
17. G. W. Gibbons, Anti-de-sitter spacetime and its uses, in *Mathematical and quantum aspects of relativity and cosmology*, (Springer, 2000) pp. 102–142.
18. U. Moschella, The de sitter and anti-de sitter sightseeing tour, in *Einstein, 1905–2005*, (Springer, 2006) pp. 120–133.
19. H. Geiges, *An Introduction to Contact Topology* (Cambridge University Press, 2008).
20. D. García-Peláez, C. López-Monsalvo and A. R. Ponce, The duality of fermat and huygens principles through contact transformations, *arXiv preprint arXiv:2108.06044* (2021).

New approaches to constrained dynamics and Hamilton-Jacobi procedures in general relativity

D. Salisbury

Physics Department, Austin College,
Sherman, Texas 75090, USA
E-mail: dsalisbury@austincollege.edu
www.austincollege.edu

J. Renn and K. Sundermeyer

Max Planck Institute for the History of Science, Boltzmannstrasse 22,
14195 Berlin, Germany

Élie Cartan's invariant integral formalism is extended to gauge field theory, including general relativity. This constitutes an alternative procedure that is equivalent to the Rosenfeld, Bergmann, Dirac algorithm. Also a new derivation of the generator of diffeomorphism-induced canonical transformations is given that proceed's from the Poincaré-Cartan form. In addition, a Hamilton-Jacobi formalism is developed for constructing explicit phase space functions in general relativity that are invariant under the full four-dimensional diffeomorphism group. These identify equivalence classes of classical solutions of Einstein's equations. Each member is dependent on intrinsic spatial coordinates and also undergoes non-trivial evolution in intrinsic time. The intrinsic coordinates are determined by the spacetime geometry in terms of Weyl scalars. The implications of this analysis for an eventual quantum theory of gravity are profound.

Keywords: General relativity; Hamilton-Jacobi formalism.

1. Introduction

We have found some new profound implications of Élie Cartan's theory, as presented in his 1922 work, Ref. 1. We show how his invariant integral program can be extended to gauge field theories, including general relativity. Our procedure in fact constitutes a new approach to constrained Hamiltonian dynamics that is equivalent to the Rosenfeld-Bergmann-Dirac procedure. Secondly, we show that the Poincaré-Cartan form that arises in this context can be utilized to deduce the generator of diffeomorphism-induced canonical transformations that have previously been derived using group theoretical arguments. We show how the required metric field dependence of the diffeomorphism-induced transformation group comes into play. Finally, employing the related symplectic form, we undertake canonical transformations to intrinsic spacetime coordinates, thus isolating the true gravitational degrees of freedom in a formalism in which all objects are invariant under the action of the full four-dimensional diffeomorphism group. The following is a summary of some results. Full details will appear in Ref. 2.

2. Cartan invariant integral — extension to gauge field theory

In 1922 Élie Cartan, Ref. 1, introduced an alternative approach to the classical dynamics of a configuration variable $q^i(t)$ in which he demanded that a certain closed integral evaluated at a fixed time t be independent of the chosen time.[a] He proposed that one consider a tube of trajectories parameterized by s with the property that as s ranges varies over its full range one returns to the original trajectory. Thus he demanded that the integral I over s, employing the parameterized set $q^i(t(s); s)$, $v^j(t(s); s)$, $t(s)$, be independent of t where

$$\begin{aligned} I &= \oint ds \left(\frac{\partial L}{\partial v^i} \frac{\partial q^i}{\partial s} \bigg|_{t(s)} - \left(\frac{\partial L}{\partial v^i} v^i - L \right) \frac{dt}{ds} \right) \\ &=: \oint \left(\frac{\partial L}{\partial v^i} dq^i - \left(\frac{\partial L}{\partial v^i} v^i - L \right) dt \right) \end{aligned} \quad (1)$$

We consider the free relativistic particle as a first example of an extension of this procedure to a gauge model. In this case the required invariant integral is

$$I_p = \oint \left(N^{-1} v_\mu dq^\mu - \frac{1}{2} \left(N^{-1} v^2 + Nm^2 \right) dt \right). \quad (2)$$

We require that its variation vanish under independent δ variations. Integrating by parts over the closed interval we get

$$\delta I_p = \oint \left[\left(-N^{-2} \delta N v_\mu + N^{-1} \delta v_\mu \right) dq^\mu + \left(\frac{1}{2} N^{-2} \delta N v^2 - N^{-1} v_\mu \delta v^\mu \right. \right. \\ \left. \left. \frac{1}{2} \delta N m^2 \right) dt - \left(\frac{1}{2} N^{-2} dN v^2 - N^{-1} v_\mu dv^\mu - \frac{1}{2} dN m^2 \right) \delta t \right] = 0. \quad (3)$$

The required vanishing coefficient of δv^μ yields $v^\mu = \frac{dq^\mu}{dt} := \dot{q}^\mu$. Similarly, the vanishing coefficient for δN, gives $N = m^{-1} \left(-\dot{q}^2 \right)^{1/2}$. The result for δt is redundant, yielding $-m^2 \dot{N} = N^{-1} \dot{q} \cdot \ddot{q}$. Finally, the coefficient of δq^μ yields the reparameterization covariant equation of motion $\frac{d}{dt} \left(N^{-1} \dot{q}^\mu \right) = 0$.

It is especially instructive to undertake a Legendre transformation, but with the understanding that the analogues of the velocities that we represent as v^μ and N_v represent independent functions. Thus $\pi = \frac{\partial L_p}{\partial N_v} = 0$ is a primary constraint. The required invariant integral becomes

$$I_p = \oint \left[p_\mu dq^\mu + \pi dN - \left(\frac{N}{2} \left(p^2 + m^2 \right) + \pi N_v \right) dt \right], \quad (4)$$

---

[a] A translation into English by D. H. Delphenich, Ref. 3, is available.

resulting in

$$dI_p = \oint \left[\delta p_\mu (dq^\mu - Np^\mu dt) - \delta q^\mu dp_\mu + \delta N \left(-d\pi - \frac{1}{2}(p^2 + m^2)dt \right) \right.$$
$$+ \delta \pi \left(dN - \dot{N} dt \right) + \delta t \left(\left(\frac{1}{2}(p^2 + m^2) \right) dN + Np^\mu \delta p_\mu + \delta \pi \dot{N} + \pi \delta \dot{N} \right)$$
$$\left. + \delta \dot{N} \pi dt \right] = 0. \qquad (5)$$

The required vanishing of the first and second coefficients result in $\frac{dq^\mu}{dt} = Np^\mu$ and $\frac{dp^\mu}{dt} = 0$. The third term yields the secondary constraint $p^2 + m^2 = 0$, and the forth $N_v = \frac{dN}{dt}$. The remaining terms are redundant.

One can in fact carry out a similar variation with an analogous general relativistic invariant integral, namely

$$I_{ADM} = \oint d^3x \left[p^{ab} dg_{ab} + P_\mu dN^\mu - \mathcal{H}_{ADM} dt - P_\mu N_v^\mu dt \right], \qquad (6)$$

where the Arnowittt-Deser-Misner (ADM) Hamiltonian

$$\mathcal{H}_{ADM} = \frac{N}{\sqrt{^3g}} \left(p_{ab} p^{ab} - (p^a{}_a)^2 - N\sqrt{^3g}\,^3R - 2N^a p^b{}_{a|b} \right), \qquad (7)$$

is derived from the ADM Lagrangian

$$\mathcal{L}_{ADM} = \left(^3g\right)^{1/2} N \left(^3R + K_{ab} K^{ab} - K^2 \right), \qquad (8)$$

with $K_{ab} = \frac{1}{2N} \left(v_{ab} - N_{a|b} - N_{b|a} \right)$. Note that the v_{ab} are assumed to be independent spacetime functions. This Lagrangian is independent of the analogue velocity N_v^μ and there is therefore a primary constraint $P_\mu = 0$. The independent variations of g_{ab}, K_{ab}, N^μ, and N_v^μ yields the correct secondary constraints and the correct Einstein Hamiltonian equations. Details are given in Ref. 2. These two systems are examples of a general new invariant integral approach to constrained Hamiltonian dynamics, equivalent to the Rosenfeld-Bergmann-Dirac prodedure.

3. Derivation of diffeomorphism generator

In the free relattivistic particle model take ds in the Poincaré-Cartan increment to correspond to the change in solutions that results from an infinitesimal reparameterization $t' = t - ds\epsilon(t)$. Represent the change in the variables as $\bar{d}q^\mu = ds\dot{q}^\mu \epsilon$ and $\bar{d}N = ds(\dot{\epsilon}N + \epsilon \dot{N})$, recognizing that N transforms as a scalar density under the reparamterization. (These are actually the Lie derivatives with respect to ϵ.)

Now use the identity which is the statement that the particle Lagrangian transforms as a scalar density under reparameterizations to deduce the existence of a vanishing Noether charge C_p:

$$\frac{dC_p}{dt} = \frac{d}{dt} \left[\frac{N\epsilon}{2} (p^2 + m^2) + \pi \left(\dot{N}\epsilon + N\dot{\epsilon} \right) \right] = 0. \qquad (9)$$

But since this depends on $\dot{N}$ this is clearly not projectable under the Legendre transformation to the particle co-tangent space. We must assume a variable-dependent reparameterizations $\epsilon(t) = N^{-1}\xi(t)$ to get Legendre-projectable reparameterizations. The general proof for the required dependence is given in.[4] In this case we have

$$\begin{aligned}C_p &= \frac{\xi}{2}(p^2 + m^2) + \pi\left(\dot{N}\epsilon + N\dot{\epsilon}\right) \\ &= \frac{\xi}{2}(p^2 + m^2) + \pi\left(\dot{N}N^{-1}\xi - NN^{-2}\dot{N}\xi + \dot{\xi}\right) \\ &= \frac{\xi}{2}(p^2 + m^2) + \pi\dot{\xi}.\end{aligned} \qquad (10)$$

This is the phase space generator of the N-dependent reparameterizations.

It is shown in Ref. 2 that the analogous substitution into the ADM vanishing Noether charge yields the Pons-Salisbury-Shepley generator $\mathcal{C}_{PSS}$, Ref. 4, of diffeomorphism-induced general coordinate transformations $\epsilon^\mu(x) = \left(N^{-1}\xi^0(x), -N^{-1}N^a\xi^0(x) + \xi^a(x)\right)$,

$$\begin{aligned}\mathcal{C}_{PSS} &= P_\mu\dot{\xi}^\mu + \mathcal{H}_\mu\xi^\mu + P_0(\xi^0 - N^a\xi^0_{,a} + N_{,a}\xi^a) \\ &+ P_a(N_{,b}e^{ab}\xi^0_{,b} - N\xi^0_{,b}e^{ab} + N_{,a}\xi^a + N^a_{,b}\xi^b - N^b\xi^a_{,b}).\end{aligned} \qquad (11)$$

4. Intrinsic coordinates and diffeomophism invariants

The non-vanishing contributions to the integrand in Cartan's invariant integral are of course now recognized as the symplectic potential one-form. Perhaps less fully appreciated is the fact that Cartan justified canonical transformations to new phase space coordinates through the recognition that exact differential generator did not contribute to the invariant integral. We examine first what we believe is novel new approach to the introduction of a proper time parameterization of the relativistic free particle. This is an example of a choice of intrinsic time. As proved in general in Ref. 5 the chosen intrinsic canonical coordinate must transform as a scalar under general coordinate transformations - in this case, reparamterizations.

Thus we now choose as the intrinsic particle time evolution variable the scalar $T = -mq^0/p_0$. This is the proper time. Then we perform a canonical transformation in the Poincaré-Cartan increment such that

$$p_0 dq^0 = PdT + \frac{\partial G}{\partial q^0} dq^0 + \frac{\partial G}{\partial T} dT. \qquad (12)$$

The required non-trivial generator is

$$G = -\frac{m}{2T}(q^0)^2 - mT + mT\ln(T), \qquad (13)$$

with the resulting canonical conjugate

$$P = -m\ln\left(-\frac{mq^0}{p_0}\right) - \frac{p_0^2}{2m}. \qquad (14)$$

It is important to recognize that the system is still reparameterization covariant – and now with a new generator

$$C_p = \xi \left[-P - m \ln(T) + \frac{1}{2} \left(p^a p_a + m^2 \right) \right] + \pi \dot{\xi} \quad (15)$$

But we can now make a proper time gauge choice by setting the evolution parameter equal to the intrinsic variable T, i.e., set $t = T$. And given particle solutions in any parameterization the gauge generator can be employed to transform to solutions satisfying the gauge condition. The remaining canonical variables are invariants under reparameterizations. The general procedure is described in Ref. 5.

We can indeed, in principle, carry out a similar procedure in general relativity. Choose appropriate spacetime scalars $X^\mu \left(g_{ab}, p^{cd} \right)$, constructed with the use of Weyl scalars, as intrinsic spacetime coordinates. An initial effort in this direction is described in Refs. 6 and 7. Fuller details with corrections and revisions will appear in Ref. 2. Perform canonical transformations in the non-vanishing portion of the Poincaré-Cartan increment so that the non-vanishing contribution becomes

$$dI_{ADM} = \int d^3x \, p^{ab} dg_{ab}$$

$$= \int d^3x \left(\pi_\mu dX^\mu + p^A dg_A + \frac{\delta G}{\delta g_{ab}} dg_{ab} + \frac{\delta G}{\delta \alpha_A} d\alpha_A + \frac{\delta G}{\delta X^\mu} dX^\mu \right). \quad (16)$$

Now make the gauge choices $x^\mu = X^\mu \left(g_{ab}, p^{cd} \right)$. The diffeomorphism generator C_{PSS} can be employed to explicitly display the corresponding diffeomorphism invariants, as shown in Ref. 5.

5. Quantum outlook

The results that we describe here were largely inspired by the work of Peter G. Bergmann and his associates. An extensive analysis of the work of his school and the conflicts that arose with the geometrical dynamical approach advocated by the John A. Wheeler can be found in Ref. 8. Of particular relevance is work performed by Bergmann in collaboration with Arthur Komar, analyzed in detail in Ref. 9. A revision and further elaboration is in preparation. The fundamental disagreement with the conventional geometrodynamical approach is in the treatment of the full four-dimensional diffeomorphism invariance. The classical approach we describe here works exclusively with the $2 \times \infty^3$ invariant fundamental gravitational degrees of freedom. It remains to be seen how these invariants may be employed in an eventual quantum theory of gravity. Work is now underway. A central challenge is to find a scheme that takes into account the abundance of physically distinct gauge choices, each of which leads to a distinct classical intrinsic time evolution.

References

1. E. Cartan, *Leçons sur les Invariants Intégraux* (Librairie Scientifique A. Hermann et Fils, 1922).

2. D. Salisbury, J. Renn and K. Sundermeyer, Rediscovering cartan, *in preparation* (2021).
3. E. Cartan, *Lessons on Integral Invariants* (Hermann, 1922).
4. J. Pons, D. Salisbury and L. Shepley, Gauge transformations in the Lagrangian and Hamiltonian formalisms of generally covariant theories, *Physical Review D* **55**, 658 (1997).
5. J. Pons, D. Salisbury and K. Sundermeyer, Revisiting observables in generally covariant theories in light of gauge fixing methods, *Physical Review D* **80**, 084015 (2009).
6. D. Salisbury, J. Renn and K. Sundermeyer, Restoration of four-dimensional diffeomorphism covariance in canonical general relativity: An intrinsic Hamilton-Jacobi approach, *International Journal of Modern Physics A* **31**, 1650014 (2016).
7. D. Salisbury, J. Renn and K. Sundermeyer, Erratum. Restoration of four-dimensional diffeomorphism covariance in canonical general relativity: An intrinsic Hamilton Jacobi approach, *International Journal of Modern Physics A* **33**, p. 1892001 (2018).
8. D. Salisbury, Toward a quantum theory of gravity: Syracuse 1949-1962, in *The Renaissance of General Relativity in Context*, eds. A. Blum, R. Lalli and J. Renn (Birkhäuser, 2020) pp. 221–255.
9. D. Salisbury, Observables and Hamilton-Jacobi approaches to general relativity. I. Early history, *arXiv:2106.10774[gr-qc]* (2021).

Orientability of space from electromagnetic quantum fluctuations

N. A. Lemos

Instituto de Física, Universidade Federal Fluminense, Av. Litorânea, S/N, 24210-340 Niterói – RJ, Brazil
E-mail: nivaldolemos@id.uff.br

M. J. Rebouças

Centro Brasileiro de Pesquisas Físicas, Rua Dr. Xavier Sigaud 150, 22290-180 Rio de Janeiro – RJ, Brazil
E-mail: reboucas.marcelo@gmail.com

Whether the 3−space where we live is a globally orientable manifold M_3, and whether the local laws of physics require that M_3 be equipped with a canonical orientation, are among the important unsettled questions in cosmology and quantum field theory. It is often assumed that a test for spatial orientability requires a global journey across the whole 3−space to check for orientation-reversing closed paths. Since such a global expedition is not feasible, physically motivated theoretical arguments are usually offered to support the choice of canonical time orientation for the 4−dimensional spacetime manifold, and space orientation for 3−space. One can certainly take advantage of such theoretical arguments to support these assumptions on orientability, but the ultimate answer should rely on cosmological observations or local experiments, or can come from a topological fundamental theory of physics. In a recent paper we have argued that it is potentially possible to locally access the the 3−space orientability of Minkowski empty spacetime through physical effects involving point-like 'charged' objects under vacuum quantum electromagnetic fluctuations. More specifically, we have studied the stochastic motions of a charged particle and an electric dipole subjected to these fluctuations in Minkowski spacetime, with either an orientable or a non-orientable 3−space topology, and derived analytical expressions for a statistical orientability indicator in these two flat topologically inequivalent manifolds. For the charged particle, we have shown that it is possible to distinguish the two topologies by contrasting the evolution of their respective indicators. For the point electric dipole we have found that a characteristic inversion pattern exhibited by the curves of the orientability indicator is a signature of non-orientability, making it possible to locally probe the orientability of Minkowski 3−space in itself. Here to shed some additional light on the spatial orientability, we briefly review these results, and also discuss some of its features and consequences. The reviewed results might be seen as opening the way to a conceivable experiment involving quantum vacuum electromagnetic fluctuations to look into the spatial orientability of Minkowski empty spacetime.

Keywords: Spatial topology of Minkowski spacetime; Orientability of Minkowsk space; Quantum fluctuations of electromagnetic field; Motion of changed particle and electric dipole under electromagnetic fluctuations

1. Introduction

In the framework of general relativity the Universe is described as a four-dimensional differentiable manifold locally endowed with a spatially homogeneous and isotropic

Friedmann–Lemaître–Robertson–Walker (FLRW) metric. Geometry is a local attribute that brings about intrinsic curvature, whereas topology is a global feature of a manifold related, for example, to compactness and orientability. The FLRW spatial geometry constrains but does not specify the topology of the spatial sections, M_3, of the space-time manifold, which we assume to be of the form $\mathcal{M}_4 = \mathbb{R} \times M_3$. In the FLRW description of the Universe, two diverse sets of fundamental questions are related to, first, the 3−geometry; second, to the topology of spatial sections M_3. Regarding the latter, at the cosmological level it is expected that one should be able to detect the spatial topology through cosmic microwave background radiation (CMB) or (and) stochastic primordial gravitational waves.[1,2] However, so far, direct searches for a nontrivial topology of M_3, using CMB data from Wilkinson Microwave Anisotropy Probe (WMAP) and Planck collaborations, have found no convincing evidence of nontrivial topology below the radius of the last scattering surface.[3-9] This absence of evidences does not exclude the possibility of a FLRW universe with a detectable nontrivial spatial topology.[10-12]

It is well-known that the topological properties of a manifold antecede its geometrical features and the differential tensor structure with which the physical theories are formulated. Thus, it is relevant to determine whether, how and to what extent physical results depend upon or are somehow affected by a nontrivial topology. Since the net role played by the spatial topology is more properly examined in static space-times, the dynamical degrees of freedom of which are frozen, here we focus on the static Minkowski space-time, whose spatial geometry is Euclidean. However, rather than the general topology of the spatial sections M_3 of Minkowski space-time, in this work we investigate its topological property called *orientability*, which is related to the existence of orientation-reversing closed paths on the spatial section M_3. Questions as to whether the 3−space of Minkowski space-time, which is the standard arena of quantum field theory, is necessarily an orientable manifold, or to what extent the known *laws of physics require a canonical spatial orientation* are among the underlying primary concerns of this work.

To be more precise regarding the setting of the present work, let us first briefly provide some mathematical results. The spatial section M_3 of the Minkowski space-time manifold $\mathcal{M}_4 = \mathbb{R} \times M_3$ is usually taken to be the simply-connected Euclidean space $\mathbb{E}^3$, but it is known mathematical result that it can also be any one of the possible 17 topologically distinct quotient manifolds $M_3 = \mathbb{E}^3/\Gamma$, where Γ is a discrete group of isometries or holonomies acting freely on the covering space $\mathbb{E}^3$.[a] The action of Γ tiles the covering manifold $\mathbb{E}^3$ into identical cells which are copies of what is known as fundamental domain (FD) fundamental cell or polyhedron (FC or FP). So, the multiple-connectedness gives rise to periodic conditions (repeated cells) in the simply-connected covering manifold $\mathbb{E}^3$ that are defined by the action

---

[a]For recent accounts on the classification of three-dimensional Euclidean spaces the reader is referred to Refs. 13 –18.

of the group Γ on $\mathbb{E}^3$. Different groups Γ give rise to different periodicities on the covering manifold $\mathbb{E}^3$, which in turn define different Euclidean spatial topologies M_3 for Minkowski spacetime. These mathematical results make it explicit that besides the simply-connected $\mathbb{E}^3$ there is a variety of topological possibilities (17 classes) for the spatial section of Minkowski spacetime. The potential consequences of multiple-connectedness for physics come about when, for example, one takes into account that in a manifold with periodic boundary conditions only certain modes of fields can exist. In this way, a nontrivial topology may leave its signature on the expectation values of local physical quantities.[19] So, for example, the energy density for a scalar field in Minkowski space-time with nontrivial spatial section is shifted from the corresponding result for the Minkowski space-time with trivial spatial topology. This is the Casimir effect of topological origin.[20–25]

Regarding orientability, the central issue of this work, three important points should be emphasized. First, we mention that it is widely assumed, implicitly or explicitly, that a four-dimensional manifold $\mathcal{M}_4 = \mathbb{R} \times M_3$ that models the physical world is spacetime orientable and, additionally, that it is separately time and space orientable. Second, eight out of the above-mentioned 17 quotient flat 3–manifolds are non-orientable.[13–18] A non-orientable 3–space is then a concrete mathematical possibility among the quotient manifolds $M_3 = \mathbb{E}^3/\Gamma$, and it comes about when the holonomy group Γ contains at least a flip or reflexion as one of its elements. Finally, it is generally assumed that, being a global property, the 3–space orientability cannot be tested locally. In this way, to disclose the spatial orientability of our physical world one would have to make trips along some specific closed paths around 3–space to check, for example, whether one returns with left- and right-hand sides exchanged.

Since such a global journey across the whole 3–space is not feasible one might think that spatial orientability cannot be probed. In this way, one would have either to answer the orientability question through cosmological observations or local experiments. Hence, assuming that spatial orientability is a falsifiable property of 3–space, a question that arises is whether spatial orientability can be subjected to local tests. Our main goal in this work is to present a way to tackle this question. To this end, we have investigated[26] stochastic motions of a charge particle and an electric dipole under vacuum quantum fluctuations of the electromagnetic field in Minkowski spacetime with two inequivalent spatial topologies, namely the non-orientable *slab with flip* and the orientable *slab*, which are often denoted by the symbols E_{17} and E_{16}, respectively.[17,18] Manifolds endowed with these topologies turned out to be appropriate to identify orientability or non-orientability signatures through the stochastic motions of point-like particles in Minkowski spacetime. In the next section, to shed some additional light on spatial orientability, we briefly review the most significant results of our article, Ref. 26, and discuss some of their consequences.

2. Main results and their interpretation

The general idea underlying our work is to perform a comparative study of the time evolution of physical systems in Minkowski spacetime with orientable and non-orientable spatial sections. To this end, the physical systems chosen are a point charged particle and a point electric dipole under vacuum quantum electromagnetic fluctuations. We shall describe the results for the dipole only because they are more significant — see Ref. 26 for the point charge case.

2.1. *The setting and the physical system*

We begin by recalling that simply-connected spacetime manifolds are necessarily orientable. On the other hand, the product of two manifolds is simply-connected if and only if the factors are. Thus, the space-orientability of Minkowski spacetime manifold $\mathcal{M}_4 = \mathbb{R} \times M_3$ reduces to orientability of the 3–space M_3. In this paper, we shall consider the topologically nontrivial spaces E_{16} and E_{17}. The slab space E_{16} is constructed by tessellating $\mathbb{E}^3$ by equidistant parallel planes, so it has only one compact dimension associated with a direction perpendicular to those planes. Taking the x-direction as compact, one has that, with $n_x \in \mathbb{Z}$ and $a > 0$, points (x, y, z) and $(x + n_x a, y, z)$ are identified in the case of the slab space E_{16}. The slab space with flip E_{17} involves an additional inversion of a direction orthogonal to the compact direction, that is, one direction in the tessellating planes is flipped as one moves from one plane to the next. Letting the flip be in the y-direction, the identification of points (x, y, z) and $(x + n_x a, (-1)^{n_x} y, z)$ defines the E_{17} topology. The slab space E_{16} is orientable whereas the slab space with flip E_{17} is non-orientable.

We consider a nonrelativistic point electric dipole with mass m and electric dipole moment $\mathbf{p}$ which is locally subject to vacuum fluctuations of the electric field $\mathbf{E}(\mathbf{x}, t)$ in a topologically nontrivial spacetime manifold equipped with the Minkowski metric $\eta_{\mu\nu} = \mathrm{diag}(+1, -1, -1, -1)$. The spatial section is usually taken to be $\mathbb{E}^3$, but here we take for M_3 either E_{16} or E_{17}.

Locally, the nonrelativistic motion of the dipole is determined by the equation of motion

$$m\frac{d\mathbf{v}}{dt} = \mathbf{p} \cdot \boldsymbol{\nabla} \mathbf{E}(\mathbf{x}, t), \tag{1}$$

where $\mathbf{v}$ is the dipole's velocity and $\mathbf{x}$ its position at time t. We assume that on the time scales of interest the dipole practically does not move, that is, it has a negligible displacement, so we can ignore the time dependence of $\mathbf{x}$. Thus, the dipole's position $\mathbf{x}$ is taken as constant in what follows.[27,28] Assuming the dipole is initially at rest, integration of Eq. (1) yields

$$\mathbf{v}(\mathbf{x}, t) = \frac{1}{m} p_j \int_0^t \partial_j \mathbf{E}(\mathbf{x}, t') \, dt' \tag{2}$$

with $\partial_j = \partial/\partial x_j$ and summation over repeated indices implied.

The mean squared speed in each of the three independent directions $i = x, y, z$ is given by

$$\left\langle \Delta v_i^2 \right\rangle = \frac{p_j p_k}{m^2} \int_0^t \int_0^t \left\langle (\partial_j E_i(\mathbf{x}, t'))(\partial_k E_i(\mathbf{x}, t'')) \right\rangle dt' dt'', \qquad (3)$$

which can be conveniently rewritten as

$$\left\langle \Delta v_i^2 \right\rangle = \lim_{\mathbf{x}' \to \mathbf{x}} \frac{p_j p_k}{m^2} \int_0^t \int_0^t \partial_j \partial_k' \left\langle E_i(\mathbf{x}, t') E_i(\mathbf{x}', t'') \right\rangle dt' dt'' \qquad (4)$$

where $\partial_k' = \partial/\partial x_k'$ and there is no summation over i. Following Yu and Ford,[27] we assume that the electric field is a sum of classical $\mathbf{E}_c$ and quantum $\mathbf{E}_q$ parts. Because $\mathbf{E}_c$ is not subject to quantum fluctuations and $\langle \mathbf{E}_q \rangle = 0$, the two-point function $\langle E_i(\mathbf{x}, t) E_i(\mathbf{x}', t') \rangle$ in equation (4) involves only the quantum part of the electric field.[27]

In Minkowski spacetime with a topologically nontrivial spatial section, the spatial separation r^2 that enters the electric field correlation functions takes a different form that captures the periodic boundary conditions imposed on the covering space $\mathbb{E}^3$ by the covering group Γ, which characterize the spatial topology. In consonance with Ref. 22, the spatial separations for E_{16} and E_{17} are

$$E_{16}: \quad r^2 = (x - x' - n_x a)^2 + (y - y')^2 + (z - z')^2, \qquad (5)$$

$$E_{17}: \quad r^2 = (x - x' - n_x a)^2 + (y - (-1)^{n_x} y')^2 + (z - z')^2. \qquad (6)$$

2.2. *Orientability indicator*

The orientability indicator that we will consider is defined by replacing the electric field correlation functions in Eq. (4) by their renormalized counterparts.[26] For a dipole oriented along the y-axis the dipole moment is $\mathbf{p} = (0, p, 0)$ and we have

$$^{(y)}I_{v_i^2}^{E_{17}}(\mathbf{x}, t) = \lim_{\mathbf{x}' \to \mathbf{x}} \frac{p^2}{m^2} \int_0^t \int_0^t \partial_y \partial_{y'} \left\langle E_i(\mathbf{x}, t') E_i(\mathbf{x}', t'') \right\rangle_{ren}^{E_{17}} dt' dt'', \qquad (7)$$

where the left superscript within parentheses indicates the dipole's orientation.

The renormalized correlation functions are given by[26]

$$\left\langle E_i(\mathbf{x}, t) E_i(\mathbf{x}', t') \right\rangle_{ren} = \frac{\partial}{\partial x_i} \frac{\partial}{\partial x_i'} D_{ren}(\mathbf{x}, t; \mathbf{x}', t') - \frac{\partial}{\partial t} \frac{\partial}{\partial t'} D_{ren}(\mathbf{x}, t; \mathbf{x}', t') \qquad (8)$$

where

$$D_{ren}(\mathbf{x}, t; \mathbf{x}', t') = \sum_{n_x = -\infty}^{\infty}{}' \frac{1}{4\pi^2 (\Delta t^2 - r^2)} \qquad (9)$$

in which $\sum'$ indicates that the Minkowski contribution term $n_x = 0$ is excluded from the summation, $\Delta t = t - t'$, and the spatial separation for E_{17} is given by Eq. (6). The Hadamard function $D(\mathbf{x}, t; \mathbf{x}', t')$ for the multiply-connected space is defined by including the term with $n_x = 0$ in the summation (9). Thus, $D_{ren} = D - D_0$, where D_0 is the Hadamard function for the simply-connected space.

Before presenting the results for some components of the orientability indicator (7), we point out that from equations (4) and (7)–(9) a general definition of the orientability indicator reads

$$I_{v_i^2}^{MC} = \langle \Delta v_i^2 \rangle^{MC} - \langle \Delta v_i^2 \rangle^{SC}, \qquad (10)$$

where $\langle \Delta v_i^2 \rangle$ is the mean square velocity dispersion, and the superscripts MC and SC stand for multiply- and simply-connected manifolds, respectively. The right-hand side of (10) is defined by first taking the difference of the two terms with $\mathbf{x}' \neq \mathbf{x}$ and then setting $\mathbf{x}' = \mathbf{x}$.

The components of the orientability indicator for the dipole in E_{17} are[26]

$$^{(y)}I_{v_x^2}^{E_{17}}(\mathbf{x}, t) = -\frac{4p^2}{\pi^2 m^2} \sum_{n_x=-\infty}^{\infty}{}' (-1)^{n_x} \left\{ 2I_1 + 3(r^2 - r_x^2 + 6r_y^2)I_2 + 24(r^2 - r_x^2)r_y^2 I_3 \right\}, \qquad (11)$$

$$^{(y)}I_{v_y^2}^{E_{17}}(\mathbf{x}, t) = -\frac{2p^2}{\pi^2 m^2} \sum_{n_x=-\infty}^{\infty}{}' (-1)^{n_x} \left\{ (5 - 3(-1)^{n_x})I_1 \right.$$
$$\left. + 6[r^2 + (7 - 6(-1)^{n_x})r_y^2]I_2 + 48[r^2 - (-1)^{n_x}r_y^2]r_y^2 I_3 \right\} \qquad (12)$$

and

$$^{(y)}I_{v_z^2}^{E_{17}}(\mathbf{x}, t) = -\frac{4p^2}{\pi^2 m^2} \sum_{n_x=-\infty}^{\infty}{}' (-1)^{n_x} \left\{ 2I_1 + 3(r^2 + 6r_y^2)I_2 + 24 r^2 r_y^2 I_3 \right\}, \qquad (13)$$

where, with $\Delta t = t' - t''$,

$$I_1 = \int_0^t \int_0^t \frac{dt'\, dt''}{(\Delta t^2 - r^2)^3} = \frac{t}{16}\left[\frac{4t}{r^4(t^2 - r^2)} + \frac{3}{r^5}\ln\frac{(r-t)^2}{(r+t)^2}\right], \qquad (14)$$

$$I_2 = \int_0^t \int_0^t \frac{dt'\, dt''}{(\Delta t^2 - r^2)^4} = \frac{1}{6r}\frac{\partial I_1}{\partial r} = \frac{t}{96}\left[\frac{4t(9r^2 - 7t^2)}{r^6(t^2 - r^2)^2} - \frac{15}{r^7}\ln\frac{(r-t)^2}{(r+t)^2}\right], \qquad (15)$$

$$I_3 = \int_0^t \int_0^t \frac{dt'\, dt''}{(\Delta t^2 - r^2)^5} = \frac{1}{8r}\frac{\partial I_2}{\partial r}$$
$$= \frac{t}{768}\left[\frac{4t(57t^4 - 136r^2t^2 + 87r^4)}{r^8(t^2 - r^2)^3} + \frac{105}{r^9}\ln\frac{(r-t)^2}{(r+t)^2}\right]. \qquad (16)$$

In Eqs. (11) to (16) one must put

$$r = \sqrt{n_x^2 a^2 + 2(1 - (-1)^{n_x})y^2},$$
$$r_x^2 = n_x^2 a^2, \qquad r_y^2 = 2(1 - (-1)^{n_x})y^2. \qquad (17)$$

For the slab space E_{16} the components of the dipole orientability indicator are obtained from those for E_{17} by setting $r_x^2 = r^2, r_y = 0$, and replacing $(-1)^{n_x}$ by 1 everywhere. Therefore, we have

$$^{(y)}I_{v_x^2}^{E_{16}}(\mathbf{x},t) = -\frac{8p^2}{\pi^2 m^2} \sum_{n_x=-\infty}^{\infty}{}' I_1, \qquad (18)$$

$$^{(y)}I_{v_y^2}^{E_{16}}(\mathbf{x},t) = -\frac{4p^2}{\pi^2 m^2} \sum_{n_x=-\infty}^{\infty}{}' (I_1 + 3r^2 I_2), \qquad (19)$$

$$^{(y)}I_{v_z^2}^{E_{16}}(\mathbf{x},t) = -\frac{4p^2}{\pi^2 m^2} \sum_{n_x=-\infty}^{\infty}{}' (2I_1 + 3r^2 I_2), \qquad (20)$$

in which $r = |n_x|a$.

2.3. *Analysis of the results*

Since equations (11)–(13) and (18)–(20) are too complicated to allow a straightforward interpretation, we plot figures for the components of the orientability indicator. Figures 1 and 2 arise from Eqs. (11)–(13) as well as (18)–(20), with the topological length $a = 1$ and $n_x \neq 0$ ranging from -50 to 50. In both figures the solid lines stand for the orientability indicator curves for the dipole in Minkowski spacetime

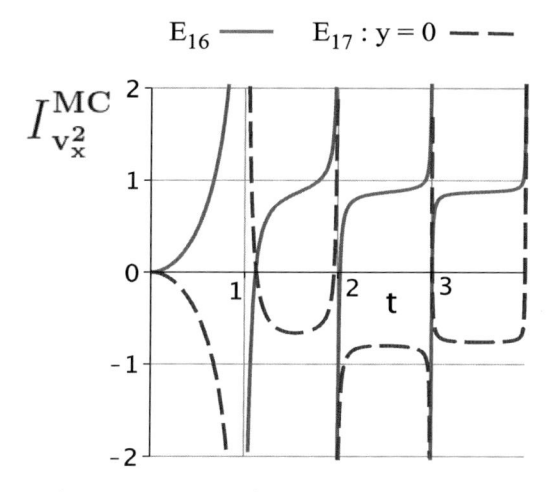

Fig. 1. Time evolution of the x-component of the orientability indicator in units of p^2/m^2 for a point electric dipole oriented in the flip y-direction in Minkowski spacetime with orientable E_{16} and non-orientable E_{17} spatial topologies, both with compact length $a = 1$. The solid and dashed lines stand, respectively, for the indicator curves for a dipole in 3–space with E_{16} and E_{17} topologies. For the globally inhomogeneous topology E_{17} the dipole is at $P_0 = (x, 0, z)$, thus freezing out the topological inhomogeneity. Both orientability indicator curves show a periodicity, but the curve for E_{17} exhibits a different kind of periodicity characterized by a distinctive inversion pattern. Non-orientability is responsible for this pattern of successive inversions, which is absent in the indicator curve for the orientable E_{16}.

E_{16} —— $E_{17} : y = 0$ — —

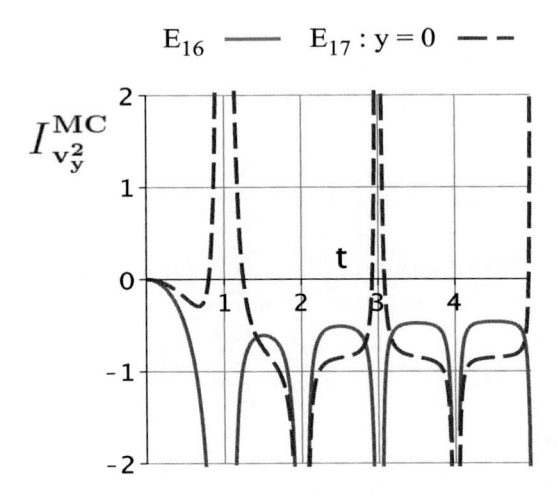

$I^{MC}_{v_y^2}$

Fig. 2. Time evolution of the y-component of the orientability indicator for a point electric dipole oriented in the y-direction under the same conditions as those of Fig. 1. The orientability indicator curve for E_{17} also displays a characteristic inversion pattern but which is different from the one for the x-component shown in Fig. 1. For the y-component of the orientability indicator the signature of non-orientability can be recognized in the pattern of successive upward and downward "horns" formed by the dashed curve.

with E_{16} orientable spatial topology, whereas the dashed lines represent orientability indicator curves for the dipole located at $P_0 = (x, 0, z)$ in a 3–space with E_{17} non-orientable topology.

In the case of the x-component, the time evolution curves of the orientability indicator for E_{16} and E_{17}, shown in Fig. 1, present a common periodicity but with distinguishable patterns. The orientability indicator curve for E_{17} displays a distinctive sort of periodicity characterized by an inversion pattern. Non-orientability gives rise to this pattern of consecutive inversions, which is not present for the orientable E_{16}.

The differences become more striking when one considers the y-component of the orientability indicator, shown in Fig. 2. The non-orientability of E_{17} is disclosed by an inversion pattern whose structure is more striking than the one for the x-component. The orientability indicator curves for E_{17} form a pattern of alternating upward and downward "horns", making the non-orientability of E_{17} unmistakably identifiable. The z-component of the indicator behaves the same way.[26]

The characteristic inversion pattern exhibited by the dipole indicator curves makes it possible to identify the non-orientability of E_{17} in itself, without having to make a comparison with the indicator curves for its orientable counterpart, which is necessary in the point charge case.[26]

This discussion suggests that it may be possible to unveil a presumed spatial non-orientability by local means, namely by the stochastic motions of charged objects caused by quantum electromagnetic vacuum fluctuations. If the motion of a point electric dipole is taken as probe, non-orientability can be intrinsically discerned by the inversion pattern of the dipole's orientability indicator curves.

3. Concluding remarks

In general relativity and quantum field theory spacetime is modeled as a differentiable manifold, which is a topological space equipped with a differential structure. It is usually assumed that the spacetime manifold is orientable and, additionally, that it is separately time and space orientable. The theoretical arguments usually offered to assume orientability combine the space-and-time universality of local physical experiments with physically well-defined (thermodynamically, for example) local arrow of time, violation of charge conjugation and parity (CP violation) and CPT invariance.[42–44] One can certainly use such reasonings in support of the standard assumptions on the global structure of spacetime.[b] Nevertheless, it is reasonable to expect that the ultimate answer to questions regarding the orientability of spacetime should rely on cosmological observations or local experiments, or might come from a fundamental theory of physics.

In the physics at daily and even astrophysical length and time scales, we do not find any sign or hint of non-orientability. This being true, the remaining open question is whether the physically well-defined local orientations can be extended continuously to cosmological and/or microscopic scales.

At the cosmological scale, one would think at first sight that to disclose spatial orientability one would have to make a trip around the whole 3−space to check for orientation-reversing paths. Since such a global journey across the Universe is not feasible one might think that spatial orientability cannot be probed globally. However, a determination of the spatial topology through the so-called circles in the sky,[47] for example, would bring out as a bonus an answer to the 3−space orientability problem at the cosmological scale.

We have addressed the question as to whether electromagnetic quantum vacuum fluctuations can be used to bring out the spatial orientability of Minkowski spacetime. We have found that there exists a characteristic inversion pattern exhibited by the orientability indicator curves for a dipole in the case of E_{17}, signaling that the non-orientability of E_{17} might be identified per se. The inversion pattern of the orientability indicator curves for the dipole is a signature of the reflection holonomy, and ought to be present in the orientability indicator curves for the dipole in all remaining seven non-orientable topologies with flip, namely the four Klein spaces (E_7 to E_{10}) and those in the chimney-with-flip class (E_{13} to E_{15}).

Observation of physical phenomena and controlled experiments are essential to our understanding of nature. Our results indicate that it might be possible to locally unveil spatial non-orientability through stochastic motions of point-like objects

---

[b]See Ref. 45 for a dissenting point of view, and also the related Ref. 46.

under electromagnetic quantum vacuum fluctuations. The present paper may be seen as a hint of a possible way to locally probe the spatial orientability of Minkowski spacetime.

Acknowledgements

M.J. Rebouças acknowledges the support of FAPERJ under a *CNE E-26/202.864/2017* grant, and thanks CNPq for the grant *306104/2017-2* under which this work was carried out. We also thank A.F.F. Teixeira and C.H.G. Bessa for fruitful discussions.

References

1. G.F.R. Ellis, Gen. Rel. Grav. **2**, 7 (1971); M. Lachièze-Rey and J.P. Luminet, Phys. Rep. **254**, 135 (1995); G.D. Starkman, Class. Quantum Grav. **15**, 2529 (1998); J. Levin, Phys. Rep. **365**, 251 (2002); M.J. Rebouças and G.I. Gomero, Braz. J. Phys. **34**, 1358 (2004); M.J. Rebouças, A Brief Introduction to Cosmic Topology, in *Proc. XIth Brazilian School of Cosmology and Gravitation*, eds. M. Novello and S.E. Perez Bergliaffa (Americal Institute of Physics, Melville, NY, 2005) AIP Conference Proceedings vol. **782**, p 188, also: arXiv:astro-ph/0504365; J.P. Luminet, Universe 2016, 2(1), 1.
2. M.J. Rebouças, *Detecting cosmic topology with primordial gravitational waves*, in preparation (2022).
3. P.A.R. Ade *et al.* (Planck Collaboration 2013), Astron. Astrophys. **571**, A26 (2014).
4. P.A.R. Ade *et al.* (Planck Collaboration 2015), Astron. Astrophys. **594**, A18 (2016).
5. N.J. Cornish, D.N. Spergel, G.D. Starkman and E. Komatsu, Phys. Rev. Lett. **92**, 201302 (2004).
6. J.S. Key, N.J. Cornish, D.N. Spergel, and G D. Starkman, Phys. Rev. D **75**, 084034 (2007).
7. P. Bielewicz and A.J. Banday, M.N.R.A.S. **412**, 2104 (2011).
8. P.M. Vaudrevange, G.D. Starkman, N.J. Cornish, and D.N. Spergel, Phys. Rev. D **86**, 083526 (2012).
9. R. Aurich and S. Lustig, M.N.R.A.S. **433**, 2517 (2013).
10. A. Bernui, C.P. Novaes, T.S. Pereira, G.D. Starkman, arXiv:1809.05924 [astro-ph.CO].
11. R. Aurich, T. Buchert, M.J. France, and F. Steiner, arXiv:2106.13205 [astro-ph.CO].
12. G. Gomero, B. Mota, and M.J. Rebouças, Phys. Rev. D **94**, 043501 (2016).
13. J.A. Wolf, *Spaces of Constant Curvature* (McGraw-Hill, New York, 1967).
14. W.P. Thurston, *Three-Dimensional Geometry and Topology. Vol.1*, Edited by Silvio Levy (Princeton University Press, Princeton, 1997).
15. C. Adams and J. Shapiro, American Scientist **89**, 443 (2001).
16. B. Cipra, *What's Happening in the Mathematical Sciences* (American Mathematical Society, Providence, RI, 2002).
17. A. Riazuelo, J. Weeks, J.P. Uzan, R. Lehoucq, and J.P. Luminet, Phys. Rev. D **69**, 103518 (2004).
18. H. Fujii and Y. Yoshii, Astron. Astrophys. **529**, A121 (2011).
19. C.H.G. Bessa and M.J. Rebouças, Class. Quantum Grav. **37**, 125006 (2020).
20. B.S. DeWitt, C.F. Hart and C.J. Isham, Physica **96A**, 197 (1979).
21. J.S. Dowker and R. Critchley, J. Phys. A **9**, 535 (1976).

22. P.M. Sutter and T. Tanaka, Phys. Rev. D **74**, 024023 (2006).
23. M.P. Lima and D. Muller, Class. Quant. Grav. **24**, 897 (2007).
24. D. Muller, H.V. Fagundes, and R. Opher, Phys. Rev. D **66**, 083507 (2002).
25. D. Muller, H.V. Fagundes, and R. Opher, Phys. Rev. D **63**, 123508 (2001).
26. N. A. Lemos and M. J. Rebouças, Eur. Phys. J. C **81**, 618 (2021).
27. H. Yu and L.H. Ford, Phys. Rev. **D 70**, 065009 (2004); 062501 (2009).
28. V.A. De Lorenci, C.C.H. Ribeiro, and M. M. Silva, Phys. Rev. D **94**, 105017 (2016).
29. M. Seriu and C.H. Wu, Phys. Rev. A **77**, 022107 (2008).
30. G. Gour and L. Sriramkumar, Found. Phys. **29**, 1917 (1999).
31. M. T. Jaekel and S. Reynaud, Quant. Opt. **4**, 39 (1992).
32. J.R. Weeks, *The Shape of Space*, 3rd ed. (CRC Press, Boca Raton, FL, 2020).
33. N.D. Birrel and P.C.W. Davies, *Quantum Fields in Curved Space* (Cambridge University Press, Cambridge, 1982).
34. J. Chen and H.W. Yu, Chin. Phys. Lett. **37**, 2362 (2004).
35. R. Lehoucq, M. Lachièze-Rey & J.-P. Luminet, *Astron. Astrophys.* **313**, 339 (1996).
36. G.I. Gomero, M.J. Rebouças, and A.F.F. Teixeira, Class. Quantum Grav. **18**, 1885 (2001).
37. G.I. Gomero, A.F.F. Teixeira, M.J. Rebouças, and A. Bernui, Int. J. Mod. Phys. D **11**, 869 (2002).
38. M.J. Rebouças Int. J. Mod. Phys. D **9** 561 (2000).
39. L.S Brown and G.J. Maclay, Phys. Rev. **184**, 1272 (1969).
40. V.A. De Lorenci, and C.C.H. Ribeiro, JHEP **1904**, 072 (2019).
41. O. Boada, A. Celi, J. Rodríguez-Laguna, J. Latorre, M. Lewenstein, New J. Phys. **17**, 045007 (2015).
42. Ya.B. Zeldovich and I.D. Novikov, JETP Letters **6**, 236 (1967).
43. S.W. Hawking and G.F.R. Ellis, *The Large Scale Structure of Space-Time* (Cambridge University Press, Cambridge, 1973).
44. R. Geroch and G.T. Horowitz, *Global structure of spacetimes* in General relativity: An Einstein centenary survey, pp. 212-293, Eds. S. Hawking and W. Israel (Cambridge University Press, Cambridge, 1979).
45. M. Hadley, Testing the Orientability of Time. Preprints 2018, 2018040240.
46. M. Hadley, Class. Quantum Grav. **19**, 4565 (2002).
47. N.J. Cornish, D. Spergel, and G. Starkman, Class. Quantum Grav. **15**, 2657 (1998).

Essential self-adjointness of Dirac operators under the influence of general-relativistic gravity

Michael K.-H. Kiessling

Mathematics Department, Rutgers University,
Piscataway, NJ, 08854, USA
E-mail: miki@math.rutgers.edu

A. Shadi Tahvildar-Zadeh

Mathematics Department, Rutgers University,
Piscataway, NJ, 08854, USA
E-mail: shadit@math.rutgers.edu

Ebru Toprak

Mathematics Department, Yale University,
New Haven, CT, 06520, USA
E-mail: ebru.toprak@yale.edu

Physical reasoning gives expressions for the hamiltonian of a system of quantum-mechanical particles. These hamiltonians are often differential operators that are symmetric in a densely-defined domain. However, to study the dynamics of the unitary group corresponding to a hamiltonian, it is required that the hamiltonian be self-adjoint or essentially self-adjoint. This study analyzes the effect of the static non-linear electromagnetic-vacuum spacetime of a point nucleus on the self-adjointness and the spectrum of the general–relativistic Dirac hamiltonian for a test electron.

Keywords: Dirac hamiltonian, Reissner–Weyl–Nordström spacetime, self-adjointness

1. Introduction

In non-relativistic physics, whether Newtonian mechanics or quantum mechanics, the gravitational and the electrical attraction between a point electron and a point nucleus obey the same mathematical law and only their coupling strengths differ. Indeed, as the gravitational force is too small compared to the electrical force, it is common to ignore its effect in calculations of realistic hydrogenic spectra.

By contrast, if one models gravity the Newtonian way in the special-relativistic setting, the situation is more subtle. While Coulomb and Newton potential still have the same mathematical form, differing only in their coupling constants, they appear paired up with different Dirac matrices in the Dirac hamiltonian, viz.[a]

$$H := -i\alpha \cdot \nabla + \left(m - \frac{GmM}{r}\right)\beta - \frac{Qe}{r}$$

---

[a] In this note we take $c = \hbar = 1$.

where the hermitian matrices α_j satisfy $\alpha_j\alpha_k + \alpha_k\alpha_j = 2\delta_{jk}1_{\mathbb{C}^4}$, $0 \leq j,k \leq 3$, with $\alpha_0 = \beta$. Here, (m,e) are the mass and charge of the electron and (M,Q) are the mass and charge of the nucleus. It is known, see [6], that H is essentially self-adjoint if and only if

$$Q^2e^2 - G^2m^2M^2 \leq \frac{3}{4}.$$

The self-adjoint extension has $\sigma_{ess}(H) = (-\infty, -m] \cup [m, \infty)$ with $\sigma_{ac}(H) = \sigma_{ess}(H)$ and $\sigma_{sc}(H) = \emptyset$. One can conclude that Newtonian gravity interaction has no significant effect on realistic hydrogenic spectra also in otherwise relativistic settings, as $G^2M^2m^2$ is an exceedingly tiny number[b] compared to Q^2e^2. For instance, one has $\frac{Gmm_p}{e^2} \approx 4.5 \cdot 10^{-40}$, where m_p is the mass of the proton.

On the other hand, the relative contributions of gravitation and electricity to the atomic spectra might be dramatically different, if one considers relativistic gravity. Einstein's gravity refines Newton's law of universal gravitation by providing a unified description of gravity as a geometric property of space and time, and it is formulated by Einstein's field equations. Coupling Einstein's field equations to Maxwell's electromagnetic field equations, we obtain the Einstein-Maxwell system of PDE's

$$\mathbf{R}_{\mu\nu} - \frac{1}{2}R\mathbf{g}_{\mu\nu} = \frac{8\pi G}{c^4}\mathbf{T}_{\mu\nu} \qquad (1)$$

$$d\mathbf{F} = 0, \quad d\mathbf{M} = 0, \qquad (2)$$

which describes the geometry of a spacetime endowed with an electromagnetic field. Here, $\mathbf{R}$ is the Ricci curvature tensor, R is the scalar curvature of the metric $\mathbf{g}$, $\mathbf{F}$ is the Faraday tensor and $\mathbf{M}$ is the Maxwell tensor. Furthermore, $\mathbf{T}$ is the electromagnetic energy-momentum-stress tensor associated to $\mathbf{F}$. In order to measure the electrical and gravitational effects on the Dirac spectrum in the relativistic settings, one needs to analyze the relativistic Dirac equation

$$\gamma^\mu(-i\nabla_\mu + eA_\mu)\psi + mI_{4\times 4}\psi = 0 \qquad (3)$$

in a background that is a solution to (1), (2). Here, ∇_μ is the covariant derivative and A_μ is the electromagnetic 4-potential. In a curved spacetime, $\beta = \gamma^0$, $\beta\alpha^k = \gamma^k$ are related to the metric tensor by $\gamma^\mu\gamma^\nu + \gamma^\nu\gamma^\mu = 2g^{\mu\nu}I_{4\times 4}$. Tahvildar-Zadeh[5] showed the following: spherically symmetric, static, asymptotically flat solutions to (1), (2) that are topologically identical to $\mathbb{R}^{1,3}$ minus a timelike line, are covered by a single global chart and have a metric whose line element in spherical coordinates $(t, r, \theta, \phi) \in \mathbb{R} \times \mathbb{R}_+ \times [0, \pi] \times [0, 2\pi)$ reads

$$ds^2 = -f^2(r)dt^2 + f^{-2}(r)dr^2 + r^2(d\theta^2 + \sin^2\theta d\phi^2) \qquad (4)$$

$$f^2(r) = 1 - 2G\frac{m(r)}{r}, \quad m(r) = M - \mathcal{E}(r). \qquad (5)$$

---

[b]Gravity could be significant for those nuclei satisfying $GM^2 > Q^2$, with mass M and electric charge Q, however, this inequality is not reachable for known nuclei.

Here r is the so-called area radius of a spherical orbit,[c] $m(r)$ is the radial mass function, and $\mathcal{E}(r)$ is the electrostatic field energy outside a ball of surface area $4\pi r^2$. Moreover, M is the ADM mass.

There are well-known examples of such solutions. In particular, $\mathcal{E}(r) = 0$ gives the Schwarzschild metric, and $\mathcal{E}(r) = \frac{Q^2}{2r}$ gives the Reissner–Weyl–Nordström (RWN) metric. In [2], Cohen and Powers considered the relativistic Dirac equation in the RWN spacetime. Note that the structure of the RWN spacetimes depends on the ratio of $\frac{Q^2}{GM^2}$. If $\frac{Q^2}{GM^2} \leq 1$, then $f^2(r)$ has zeros given by

$$r_\pm = GM\left(1 \pm \sqrt{1 - \frac{Q^2}{GM^2}}\right). \tag{6}$$

Also, in this case, the RWN spacetime features a dynamical black hole region in $r_- < r < r_+$.[d] Otherwise, $f^2(r)$ is always positive, and the manifold has a naked singularity at $r = 0$. In [2], it was obtained that in the naked singularity sector, the Dirac hamiltonian $\mathcal{H}$ associated with the relativistic Dirac equation is not essentially self-adjoint.

The RWN spacetime of a nucleus has some undesirable features.[7] It has a very strong curvature singularity at its center associated with a negative infinite bare mass, arising from $\mathcal{E}(r)$. In fact, the electrostatic energy density is not integrable about $r = 0$, whereas the system has finite ADM mass, interpreted as the total energy of the spacetime. In Section 2 we answer the question whether a more mildly singular $f^2(r)$, which is compatible with (4), suffices to guarantee an essentially self-adjoint $\mathcal{H}$ for a test electron.

In RWN settings, we say that $f^2(r)$ yields a *subextremal* black hole if $r_- < r_+$; and $f^2(r)$ yields an *extremal* black hole if $r_- = r_+ =: r_0$. In [2], Cohen and Powers also investigated (3) in the static region outside the event horizon of a subextremal (and extremal) RWN black hole, i.e. when $r \geq r_+$. They found that $\mathcal{H}$ is essentially self-adjoint, that its self-adjoint extension has essential spectrum equal to the real line, without a gap, and that it has no eigenvalues at all. Thus, the electron is expected to be swallowed by the black hole unless it escapes to ∞. Therefore, the absence of bound states of an electron outside of the event horizon of a RWN black hole is not a surprising result. In Section 3 we complement this study by considering the static region inside the Cauchy horizon of the subextremal RWN black hole spacetime, i.e., when $0 \leq r \leq r_-$, respectively inside the event horizon of the extremal RWN black hole spacetime, i.e., when $0 \leq r \leq r_0$.

---

[c]Every point in the stipulated spacetime is an element of a unique orbit under a Killing vector flow corresponding to the $SO(3)$ symmetry, and this orbit is a scaled copy of $\mathbb{S}^2$ with area $4\pi r^2$, defining $r > 0$.

[d]Note that $r = r_+$ and $r = r_-$ are the boundaries of the dynamical region and not themselves dynamical. In particular, in the extremal black hole case, there is no dynamical part of the spacetime.

2. Electrostatic spacetimes with negative bare mass and no horizon

Due to the spherical symmetry and static character of the spacetimes, the Dirac operator $\mathcal{H}$ of a test electron in the curved space whose line element ds^2 is given by (4) separates in the spherical coordinates and their default spin frame.[2] More precisely, we study the family of radial Dirac operators H_k, $k \in \mathbb{Z}\backslash\{0\}$, with

$$H_k := \begin{bmatrix} f(r) - e\phi(r) & \frac{k}{r}f(r) - f^2(r)\partial_r \\ \frac{k}{r}f(r) + f^2(r)\partial_r & -f(r) - e\phi(r) \end{bmatrix}, \qquad (7)$$

acting on $g(r) := (g_1(r), g_2(r))^T$, with a weighted L^2 norm given by

$$\|g\|^2 := \int_0^\infty \frac{1}{f^2(r)}\Big(|g_1(r)|^2 + |g_2(r)|^2\Big)dr. \qquad (8)$$

Recall that we want to consider $f^2(r)$ having singularity at zero that is milder than the RWN spacetime has. For this purpose, we make the following assumptions on $m(r)$:

- $m(r)$ is continuous for $r > 0$;
- $m(r)/r < 1/2G$;
- $m(r) \sim -C_\alpha r^{-\alpha}$ as $r \searrow 0$, where $\alpha \geq 0$ and $C_\alpha > 0$;
- $m(r) \to M > 0$ as $r \to \infty$.

Our first two assumptions on $m(r)$ are equivalent to ruling out black holes in spacetimes with the line element (4). So our spacetimes feature a charged naked singularity. By the third and fourth assumptions on $m(r)$, the naked singularity has a negative *bare mass* ($\lim_{r\downarrow 0} m(r)$), which is finite only for $\alpha = 0$, in which case $m(0) = -C_0$.

The function $\phi(r)$ is the potential of the electrostatic field generated by the nucleus, and we have $\mathcal{E}(r) = \frac{1}{2}\int_r^\infty |\phi'(s)|^2 s^2 ds$. We also assume

- $\phi(r)$ is continuously differentiable;
- $\phi(r) \sim Ze/r$ as $r \to \infty$;
- $\phi(r) \sim C''_\beta + C'_\beta r^{-\beta}$ as $r \searrow 0$, with $\beta \leq 1$.

Before we give the main theorem, we need to define the unitary operator U. Let $r(x)$ be the solution to the differential equation

$$\frac{d}{dx}r(x) = f^2(r(x)) \qquad (9)$$

subject to the conditions that $r(x) \to 0^+$ as $x \to 0^+$. We now define U as

$$(Ug_i)(x) = g_i(r(x))f(r(x))^{1/2} \qquad (10)$$

for (g_1, g_2) in the subspace induced by the norm (8). Let also $\widetilde{H}_k = UH_kU^{-1}$. Then, we have the following theorem. Interested readers can find the details of the proof in [3].

Theorem 2.1. *Under the stated assumptions on $m(r)$ and $\phi(r)$ the operator $\widetilde{H}_k$, and, therefore H_k, for $k \in \mathbb{Z}\setminus\{0\}$, has uncountably many self-adjoint extensions. The extensions are given by $\widetilde{H}_{k:\theta} = \widetilde{H}_k|_{D_\theta}$ where*

$$D_\theta = \left\{(f_1, f_2) \in D(\widetilde{H}_k^*); \ f_1(0) = -f_2(0)\tan\theta, \ -\frac{\pi}{2} \leq \theta \leq \frac{\pi}{2}\right\}.$$

Moreover, for each θ

   (a) *The essential spectrum $\sigma_{ess}(\widetilde{H}_{k:\theta}) = (-\infty, -m] \cup [m, \infty)$;*
   (b) *$\widetilde{H}_{k:\theta}$ has purely absolutely continuous spectrum in $(-\infty, -m) \cup (m, \infty)$;*
   (c) *the singular continuous spectrum $\sigma_{sc}(\widetilde{H}_{k:\theta}) = \emptyset$.*

Note that this theorem concludes that a milder singularity with strictly negative bare mass than that of RWN does not yield an essentially self-adjoint H_k. On the contrary, it appears that the self-adjointness might require a stronger singularity such as when $\beta > \frac{\alpha+3}{2}$. However, these values of α and β do not match with the asymptotics of the mass functions for the electrostatic spacetimes in (4).

It turns out that there is a way to restore the essential self-adjointness of the Dirac operator, namely by including a sufficiently large anomalous magnetic moment of the electron. This has been carried out in the naked RWN geometry in [1].

Assuming a nonzero anomalous magnetic moment, the radial partial-wave Dirac operator is given by

$$H_{\mu_a,k} := H_k + \begin{bmatrix} 0 & -\mu_a\phi'(r)f(r) \\ -\mu_a\phi'(r)f(r) & 0 \end{bmatrix}. \tag{11}$$

Regarding $H_{\mu_a,k}$, we have the following theorem:

Theorem 2.2. *Let $m(r)$ be as in the Theorem 3.1 with $\alpha \geq 0$ and $\phi(r) = C_\beta'' + C_\beta' r^{-\beta} + O_1(r^{\frac{3}{2}-\beta})$ for $\beta \leq 1$, where $f \in O_k(g)$ indicates $\frac{d^j}{dr^j}f = O(\frac{d^j}{dr^j}g)$ for $j = 0, 1, ..k$. Then the operator $H_{\mu_a,k}$ is essentially self-adjoint if either $\beta > \frac{1+\alpha}{2}$, or $\beta = \frac{1+\alpha}{2}$ and $|\mu_a| \geq \frac{2+\alpha}{1+\alpha}\sqrt{2GC_\alpha}/|C_\beta'|$. On the other hand, if $\beta < \frac{1+\alpha}{2}$, then $H_{\mu_a,k}$ has multiple self-adjoint extension.*

An important consequence of this theorem is the fact that the Dirac operator in the Hoffmann spacetime is not self-adjoint unless $m(0) = 0$; in the negative bare mass case the anomalous magnetic moment cannot restore essential self-adjointness. Recall, the electric potential in the Hoffmann spacetime is given as

$$\phi(r) = Q\int_r^\infty \zeta'\left(\frac{Q^2}{2s^4}\right)\frac{ds}{s^2}, \ \zeta(\mu) = \sqrt{1+2\mu} - 1.$$

3. Point nucleus as singularity in static interior of black hole spacetime

Recall that in the RWN spacetime, the line element $f^2(r)$ in (4) arises as

$$f^2(r) = 1 - 2\frac{GM}{r} + \frac{GQ^2}{r^2} = \frac{1}{r^2}(r - r_-)(r - r_+) \tag{12}$$

where r_- and r_+ are given as in (6). We consider the operators H_k given in (7) when $0 \leq r \leq r_-$. Note that, in the extremal case, we have $r_- = r_+ = r_0$.

As in the previous section, we define $\widetilde{H}_k = U H_k U^{-1}$, where U is defined as in (10). We use (12) in the change of variable (9), with $x = 0$ when $r = 0$, which for the subextremal sector yields

$$x = r + \frac{r_+^2}{r_+ - r_-} \ln\left(1 - \frac{r}{r_+}\right) - \frac{r_-^2}{r_+ - r_-} \ln\left(1 - \frac{r}{r_-}\right); \qquad r < r_-; \tag{13}$$

in the extremal limit $r_- \nearrow r_0$ & $r_+ \searrow r_0$ this becomes

$$x = r_0 \left[\frac{1}{1 - \frac{r}{r_0}} + 2\ln\left(1 - \frac{r}{r_0}\right) - \left(1 - \frac{r}{r_0}\right) \right], \qquad r < r_0. \tag{14}$$

It is clear from (13) and (14), one has $r - r_- \sim e^{-ax}$ as $x \to \infty$ in the subextremal case, whereas $r - r_0 \sim x^{-1}$ as $x \to \infty$ in the extremal case. This difference between the asymptotics result in differences in the spectrum of the corresponding Dirac operators, see [4] for more details. We have,

Theorem 3.1. *The operator $\widetilde{H}_k$ has uncountably many self-adjoint extensions for both the subextremal and the extremal black hole sector. The extensions are given by $\widetilde{H}_{k:\theta} = \widetilde{H}_k|_{D_\theta}$ where*

$$D_\theta = \left\{ (f_1, f_2) \in D(\widetilde{H}_k^*); \quad f_1(0) = -f_2(0)\tan\theta, \quad -\frac{\pi}{2} \leq \theta \leq \frac{\pi}{2} \right\}.$$

Moreover for each θ,

(a) *The essential spectrum $\sigma_{ess}(\widetilde{H}_{k:\theta}) = \mathbb{R}$ in both subextremal and the extremal case.*

(b) *$\widetilde{H}_{k:\theta}$ has absolutely continuous spectrum in $\mathbb{R}$ in both subextremal and the extremal case. Moreover, $\widetilde{H}_{k:\theta}$ has no eigenvalue in the subextremal case.*

(c) *The singular continuous spectrum $\sigma_{sc}(\widetilde{H}_{k:\theta}) = \emptyset$ in both subextremal and the extremal case.*

In the extremal case the only possible eigenvalue is $-\frac{Q}{r_0}$, and whether it is an eigenvalue or not is not determined in this study. However, we believe that the answer should depend on the values of Q and r_0.

Similar to our previous section, we also considered the effect of an anomalous magnetic moment. Consider (11) with $\phi(r) = Q/r$. We have

Theorem 3.2. *In both the subextremal and the extremal case, the operator $H_{\mu_a,k}$ is essentially self-adjoint iff $|\mu_a| \geq \frac{3}{2}\sqrt{G}$. Moreover, in both subextremal and extremal cases, the self-adjoint operators have $\sigma_{ess}(H_{\mu_a,k}) = \sigma_{ac}(H_{\mu_a,k}) = \mathbb{R}$, $\sigma_{sc}(H_{\mu_a,k}) = \emptyset$, and $\sigma_p(H_{\mu_a,k}) = \emptyset$.*

References

1. Belgiorno, F., Martellini, M., and Baldicchi, M., *Naked Reissner–Nordström singularities and the anomalous magnetic moment of the electron field*, Phys. Rev. D **62**:084014, (2000).
2. Cohen, J.M. and Powers, R.T., *The general-relativistic hydrogen atom*, Commun. Math. Phys. **86**:96–86 (1982).
3. Kiessling, M.K.-H., Tahvildar-Zadeh, A.S., and Toprak, E., *On general-relativistic hydrogen and hydrogenic ions*, J. Math. Phys. 61, 092303 (2020).
4. Kiessling, M.K.-H., Tahvildar-Zadeh, A.S., and Toprak, E., *On the Dirac operator for a test electron in a Reissner–Weyl–Nordström black hole spacetime*, General Relativity and Gravitation (2021), 53 (1).
5. Tahvildar-Zadeh, A.S., *On the static spacetime of a single point charge*, Rev. Math. Phys. **23**:309–346 (2011).
6. Thaller, B., *The Dirac equation*, Springer, Berlin – Heidelberg (1992).
7. Weyl, H., *Space, Time, Matter*, 4th. ed., Dover (1952).

Relic magnetic wormholes as possible source of toroidal magnetic fields in galaxies

A. A. Kirillov* and E. P. Savelova

Department of Mathematical Modeling, Bauman Moscow State Technical University, Moscow, 105005, Russian Federation
E-mail: kirillov@bmstu.ru

We present the hypothesis that some of ring galaxies were formed by relic magnetic torus - shaped wormholes. In the primordial plasma before the recombination magnetic fields of wormholes trap baryons whose energy is smaller than a threshold energy. They work as the Maxwell's demons collecting baryons from the nearest (horizon size) region and thus forming clumps of baryonic matter which have the same torus-like shapes as wormhole throats. Such clumps may serve as seeds for the formation of ring galaxies and smaller objects having the ring form. Upon the recombination torus-like clumps may decay and merge. Unlike galaxies, such objects may contain less or even no dark matter in halos. However, the most stringent feature of such objects is the presence of a large - scale toroidal magnetic field. We show that there are threshold values of magnetic fields which give the upper and lower boundary values for the baryon clumps in such protogalaxies.

Keywords: Wormholes; cosmic rays; ring galaxies; galactic magnetic fields.

1. Introduction

One of challenges of modern astrophysics is to finding possible traces of relic wormholes. It is expected that relic cosmological wormholes were created from virtual wormholes on quantum stage, or during the inflationary period of evolution of the Universe. Virtual wormholes exist at Planckian scales and they represent the most natural objects to compose spacetime foam picture.[1,2] Their existence is straightforwardly predicted by lattice quantum gravity models, e.g., see Refs.[3-6] and references therein.

Spherically symmetric relic wormholes are highly instable and collapse very rapidly. To be stable they require the presence of exotic matter at throats or an essential modification of general relativity.[7,8] This means that all primordial spherical wormholes have collapsed long ago and at present they cannot probably be distinguished from black holes. However less symmetric configurations can be made stable without exotic matter or any modification of GR. First rigorous example was presented in Ref.[9] It was demonstrated that in the open Friedmann model a stable wormhole can be obtained simply by the factorization of space over a discrete subgroup of the group of motions of space. To illustrate such a factorization one may consider flat plane in which one of coordinates, say x, becomes periodic $x = R\varphi/(2\pi)$ with the angle $0 < \varphi < 2\pi$. Then the space becomes a cylinder with the radius R. In the open model (on space of a constant negative curvature) any parallel geodesics ($\varphi = 0$ and $\varphi = 2\pi$) diverge and the distance between them changes $R(\ell)$, where ℓ is a parameter along the geodesic line. Therefore, if we move along the geodesic line from the point where the distance is the shortest R_{min}, the space opens out $R \to \infty$ and becomes unrestricted.[10] Here the wormhole configuration coincides with a cylinder on which the metric is specified to produce a constant negative curvature. The simplest 3D wormhole obtained by the factorization has also the topology of a cylinder, while its throat has the topology of the 2D- torus.[9, 10] In flat space such a configuration corresponds to a wormhole whose throat has the shape of a doughnut. Such wormholes are not static but expand in agreement with the expansion rate of the Universe. It can be considered as having been frozen into space and, therefore, they are static in the co-moving coordinates. It is important that the factorization allows to get an arbitrary number of such wormholes in space.

In flat space the torus - like wormholes become dynamical objects and evolve.[9] Whether they are static, expand, or collapse, depends on surrounding matter and peculiar motions of throats. The shape of throats of such wormholes resembles a doughnut and is characterized by two radii R_w and r_w. In the limit $R_w \gg r_w$ it can be approximately described by the cylindrical (axial) configuration. It turns out that static and stationary cylindrical wormhole solutions do exist and it was found that asymptotically flat wormhole configurations do not require exotic matter violating the weak energy condition.[11, 12] This shows that such objects, as doughnut - shaped wormholes, have all chances to be observed in astrophysical systems. We point out that the investigation of the evolution of doughnut-shaped wormholes in flat space is a rather complex problem.

The possibility to directly observe wormholes attracts the more increasing attention, e.g., see Refs.[13-15] At first glance the most promising are collective effects produced by a distribution of wormholes in space. However, our previous investigation have shown that observational effects of a distribution of wormholes are very well hidden under analogous effects produced by ordinary matter e.g., see Refs.[16, 17] The only exclusion may be the noise (stochastic background) produced by the scattering of emitted by binaries gravitational waves on wormholes.[18]

In general a single wormhole produces much less noticeable effects (lensing, cosmic ray scattering, etc.). However, wormholes may possess non-trivial magnetic fields as vacuum solutions. In this case possible imprints of wormholes in the present picture of the Universe may be rather considerable. In particular, when such a magnetic wormhole gets close to a galaxy, it starts to work as an accelerator of charged particles[10, 19] which is capable of explaining the origin of high-energy cosmic-ray particles.[20] The idea that the observed cosmic rays require magnetic fields for their creation was first suggested by Fermi.[21] In voids a relic magnetic wormhole works simply as a generator of synchrotron radiation and can be detected via the magnetic field.[22, 23] The primordial magnetic fields[24] in turn may form small-scale non-linear clumps of baryonic matter[25, 26] and as it was recently discussed in Ref.[27] they may allow to solve the existing Hubble tension. In other words, magnetic wormholes should leave a clear imprint on the sky. In particular, relic magnetic wormholes may play also the key role in formation of ring type baryonic structures, analogous to the ring galaxies without involving dark matter.[28] Moreover, such wormholes may also form ring - type structures even in the present epoch which may explain the origin of the recently found unexpected class of astronomical ring-type objects.[29]

2. Vacuum magnetic fields of wormholes

Nontrivial topology of space which contains a static wormhole allows us to get additional nontrivial solutions of static vacuum Maxwell equations.[30] This means that already in the absence of real sources (charged particles, electric currents) space may possess nontrivial quasi-static magnetic and electric fields. The physical mechanism is rather clear, during the quantum period of the Universe when the wormhole forms, it may capture some portion of closed magnetic or electric lines. Such lines cannot simply leave the wormhole. Electric fields perform work and decay very rapidly in the primordial plasma. Magnetic fields do not perform work and may survive till the present days. For exact solutions which involve magnetic fields and wormholes see e.g.,[31, 32]

In this section for the sake of simplicity we assume that sufficiently far from the wormhole entrances the space is flat. Generalization to the curved spacetime and consideration of magnetic fields in the Friedmann model can be found, e.g., in.[33] Consider first the simplest genus $n = 0$ wormhole. Then the space-time metric can be taken as

$$dl^2 = c^2 dt^2 - h^2(r)\left(dx^2 + dy^2 + dz^2\right). \quad (1)$$

We shall use the Ellis–Bronnikov massless wormhole[34, 35] when the scale function is simply $h = 1 + \frac{R^2}{r^2}$. This model of a wormhole possesses two asymptotic Euclidean spaces E_+ as $r \gg R$ and E_- as $r \ll R$. In the region $r \ll R$ the transformation $\tilde{r} = R^2/r$ reduces the above metric to the standard Euclidean form. The Maxwell equations for magnetic field take the standard form

$$rot\mathbf{B} = div\mathbf{B} = 0, \quad (2)$$

where $B_i = \varepsilon_{ijk} F^{jk}$. These equations possess a nontrivial solution in the form

$$\mathbf{B} = -\frac{Q}{r^2 h}\mathbf{n} \quad (3)$$

with an arbitrary constant value Q, where $\mathbf{n} = \mathbf{r}/r$ is the unit vector. Indeed, vacuum magnetic field can be expressed via the magnetic scalar potential $\mathbf{B} = -\nabla \phi$ which obeys the equation

$$\Delta \phi = 0. \quad (4)$$

In the spherically symmetric case this equation reduces to
$$\frac{1}{r^2 h^3}\partial_r r^2 h \partial_r \phi = 0 \tag{5}$$
and has the solution as
$$\phi = \int_0^r \frac{Q}{r^2 h} dr + \phi_0. \tag{6}$$
This defines the magnetic field
$$\mathbf{B} = -\nabla \phi = -\frac{Q}{r^2 h}\nabla r = -\frac{Q}{r^2 h}\mathbf{n}. \tag{7}$$
This solution works for any spherically symmetric wormhole with an arbitrary scale function $h(r)$ in (1).

In the region E_+ ($r \gg R$) it describes the field of the magnetic charge Q homogeneously distributed over the sphere $r = R$ (Coulomb law). In the region E_- ($r \ll R$) the transformation $\tilde{r} = R^2/r$ interchanges the inner and outer regions of the sphere $r = R$ and we get the same field with the magnetic charge $-Q$.

In the case when both entrances are in the same space this transforms to the dipole field. Let the positions of the two spheres are $\mathbf{x}_+$ and $\mathbf{x}_-$ then the field can be taken as ($h_\pm = h(r_\pm) \sim 1$ as $r_\pm = |\mathbf{x} - \mathbf{x}_\pm| \gg R$)
$$\mathbf{B}(\mathbf{x}) = \frac{Q(\mathbf{x} - \mathbf{x}_+)}{h_+ |\mathbf{x} - \mathbf{x}_+|^3} - \frac{Q(\mathbf{x} - \mathbf{x}_-)}{h_- |\mathbf{x} - \mathbf{x}_-|^3}. \tag{8}$$

Consider now the genus $n = 1$ wormhole. In the flat space such a wormhole can be constructed by means of cutting two solid tori and gluing along their surfaces. In this case we have two different new kinds of solutions. First is obtained by placing an arbitrary magnetic charge density $\rho(x)$ in the internal region of one torus and the opposite density $-\rho(x)$ in the internal region of the second torus. Then we solve the system
$$rot\mathbf{B} = 0, \quad div\mathbf{B} = 4\pi\rho. \tag{9}$$
Recall that internal regions of tori correspond to fictitious points, while $\rho(x) = 0$ as x lies outside the tori. Therefore, such a system coincides exactly with (2). In this case the exact form of the magnetic field is rather complicated. However averaging over orientations of the tori we restore the spherical symmetry of the wormhole and get exactly the same solution as (8). In this sense for the sake of simplicity we may always restrict to the spherically symmetric wormholes (i.e., consider $n = 0$ wormhole as the first order approximation).

Solutions of the second kind can be obtained by placing an arbitrary current density $\mathbf{j}(x)$ within the surface of torus/throat and solving the system
$$rot\mathbf{B} = \frac{4\pi}{c}\mathbf{j}, \quad div\mathbf{B} = 0. \tag{10}$$
Again here the non-vanishing current density corresponds only to fictitious points, while in physical regions of space such a system represents the same system (2).

The system (10) corresponds to the field generated by an electric loop which produces the toroidal magnetic field. Such solutions cannot be reduced to the spherically symmetric case, since upon the averaging over orientations of the loop the field vanishes.

In conclusion of this section we point out that the new two classes of vacuum solutions reflect the topological non-triviality of space. Indeed, according to the Stocks theorem the system (2) implies $\oint \mathbf{B}d\mathbf{l} = 0$ for any loop which can be pulled to a point. In the case of a non-trivial topology of space there appear new classes of loops Γ_a which cannot be contracted to a point and, therefore, to fix the unique solution we have to fix additional boundary data $\oint_{\Gamma_a} \mathbf{B}d\mathbf{l} = C_a$. In general $C_a \neq 0$. In the case of genus $n = 0$ wormhole there is only one such a non-trivial loop which goes through the wormhole throat. In the case of genus $n = 1$ wormhole we have already two such loops, one goes through the throat (it corresponds to the system (9)) and one additional crosses the torus (the system (10)).

3. Wormhole as an accelerator

In galaxies charged particles undergo an acceleration when interacting with galactic radiation. For definiteness we shall speak of electrons. Indeed, by means of the Compton scattering photons transmit part of their momentum to electrons. Upon the scattering the momentum obtained by the electron from the incident photon is

$$\Delta \mathbf{p} = \mathbf{p}' - \mathbf{p} = \frac{h\nu}{c}\left(\mathbf{n} - \frac{\nu'}{\nu}\mathbf{n}'\right) \tag{11}$$

where $\mathbf{n}$ and $\mathbf{n}'$ are the direction of the photon before and after scattering and

$$\frac{\nu'}{\nu} = \frac{\left(1 - \frac{c}{E}\mathbf{pn}\right)}{\left(1 + \frac{h\nu}{E}\left(1 - \mathbf{nn}'\right) - \frac{c}{E}\mathbf{pn}'\right)}. \tag{12}$$

Upon averaging over possible orientations of $\mathbf{n}'$ we get for the average momentum transmitted from the incident photon

$$\Delta \mathbf{p} = \frac{1}{c}\beta_\nu(\mathbf{p})h\nu\mathbf{n}. \tag{13}$$

Here the spectral coefficient $\beta_\nu(\mathbf{p}) = 1 - \left\langle \frac{\nu'}{\nu}\mathbf{nn}' \right\rangle$ is given by

$$\beta_\nu(\mathbf{p}) = 1 - \frac{1}{4\pi}\int \left(\frac{\nu'}{\nu}\mathbf{nn}'\right) d\Omega', \tag{14}$$

where $\frac{\nu'}{\nu}$ is determined by (12). In the case when $\mathbf{p} = p\mathbf{n}$, it reduces to the form

$$\beta_\nu = 1 + \frac{1}{2x}\left[2 - \left(1 + \frac{1}{x}\right)\ln(1 + 2x)\right],$$

where $x = (h\nu + cp)(E + cp)/m^2c^4$. Now multiplying (13) on the number density of photons with the frequency ν and on the cross section we get the spectral force which accelerates the electron in the form

$$\mathbf{f}_\nu = \frac{\Delta \mathbf{p}}{\Delta t} = c\sigma_T N_\nu \frac{1}{c}\beta_\nu(p) h\nu \mathbf{n} = \frac{\sigma_T \beta_\nu(p)}{c}\mathbf{P}_\nu \qquad (15)$$

where $\mathbf{P}_\nu$ is the spectral component of the Poynting vector $\mathbf{P}_\nu = \frac{c}{4\pi}\mathbf{E}_\nu \times \mathbf{B}_\nu$ and σ_T is the Thomson cross section. The total force is given by $\mathbf{F} = \int \mathbf{f}_\nu d\nu$.

It is important that the force is determined by the Poynting's vector $\mathbf{P}_\nu$. In a quite (quasi-stationary or steady state) galaxy both the Poynting's vector and the force have the potential character, i.e., they can be presented as $\mathbf{P}_\nu = -\nabla\Psi_\nu$. Non-stationary processes in active galactic nuclei may produce some additional acceleration, e.g., the stochastic Fermi acceleration, etc., which we do not discus here. For the quasi-stationary galaxy the Poynting's theorem gives the discontinuity equation

$$div\mathbf{P}_\nu = \ell_\nu \qquad (16)$$

where $\ell_\nu(x)$ is the spectral density of sources of radiation (stars, hot gas, dust, etc.) or the radiative capability of a unite volume in the galaxy. If the topology is simple, then sufficiently far from the galaxy we get

$$\mathbf{P}_\nu = \frac{M_\nu}{4\pi r^2}\mathbf{l}, \qquad (17)$$

where $\mathbf{l} = \mathbf{r}/r$, $\mathbf{r}$ is the distance from the center of the galaxy, and M_ν is the total spectral energy emitted by the galaxy in the unit time. Observations show that the intergalactic medium possesses a magnetic field.[22,23] Therefore, the electron may have a closed trajectory. It is easy to verify that the total energy obtained by the electron from the galactic radiation during the cycle is exactly zero, i.e., $\oint \mathbf{f}_\nu d\mathbf{l} \equiv 0$. This means that in the case when topology is simple, the only possible mechanism of the electron acceleration relates to high-energy non-stationary processes (jets, shock waves, supernovae explosions, active galactic nuclei, etc.).

The situation changes when the galaxy is accompanied with a wormhole. In the presence of the wormhole the Poynting's field also admits non-trivial solutions of (16). For the sake of simplicity we consider the spherically symmetric (genus $n = 0$) wormhole. For a more general wormhole the rough picture remains the same, at least from the qualitative standpoint. We point out that the genus $n \geq 1$ wormholes are more preferred from the astrophysical standpoint, since they may work as accelerators even in the case when a wormhole is not traversable (e.g., when the length of the trajectories which go through the throat are too big).

Indeed, the scattering of the radiation on the wormhole (e.g., see[16,17]) produces an additional field in the dipole form

$$\delta\mathbf{P}_\nu = \frac{\delta M_\nu}{4\pi r_-^2}\mathbf{n}_- - \frac{\delta M_\nu}{4\pi r_+^2}\mathbf{n}_+ \qquad (18)$$

where $\mathbf{n}_\pm = \mathbf{r}_\pm/r_\pm$, $\mathbf{r}_\pm = \mathbf{r} - \mathbf{x}_\pm$, $\mathbf{x}_\pm$ are positions of the wormhole entrances (we assume that $r_+ \ll r_-$), $\delta M_\nu \simeq \frac{M_\nu \pi R^2}{4\pi r_+^2}$ is the portion of the spectral energy absorbed by the closest entrance into the wormhole throat and R is the radius of the throat. If the wormhole possesses a magnetic field in the form (8), it forms a magnetic trap for the electron, while the Poynting's vector field $\delta \mathbf{P}_\nu$ in form (18) forms the accelerating force which acts exactly along the magnetic lines. On every cycle the electron will gain the energy from radiation $A = \int A_\nu d\nu > 0$, where $A_\nu = \oint \delta \mathbf{f}_\nu \mathbf{dl}$, whose exact value depends on the length of the trajectory of the electron and on all the rest parameters of the wormhole (distance to the galaxy, throat size, etc.). Some part of this energy will be spent on the synchrotron radiation of electrons and, therefore, there is a competition between the acceleration produced by the galactic radiation and loss of energy on the reradiation. The reradiation can be accounted for by adding the standard force of the radiation friction.

4. Magnetic wormholes as baryon traps

Consider a single wormhole whose throat has the shape of a torus (the genus - 1 wormhole by the classification suggested in Ref.[10]). In the presence of such a wormhole Maxwell's equations possess two additional classes of non-trivial vacuum solutions. Indeed, according to the Stocks theorem the system of vacuum Maxwell equations implies $\oint \mathbf{B} \mathbf{dl} = 0$ for any loop which can be pulled to a point (where $\mathbf{B}$ is the magnetic field). In the case of a non-trivial topology of space[a] there appear new classes of loops Γ_a which cannot be contracted to a point and, therefore, to fix the unique solution we have to fix additional boundary data $\oint_{\Gamma_a} \mathbf{B} \mathbf{dl} = \frac{4\pi}{c} I_a$ and in general $I_a \neq 0$. The constants I_a depend only on time and they can be viewed as fictitious currents[b] which intersect the loops Γ_a. In the case of genus $n = 0$ (spherical) wormhole there is only one such a non-trivial loop which goes through the wormhole throat. In the case of genus $n = 1$ wormhole (doughnut - shaped throat) we have already two such loops, one goes through the throat and one additional goes through the hole in the center of the doughnut and surrounds the throat.

The first class produces the magnetic field of a wormhole which can be described by magnetic poles placed in two different entrances into the throat. The two entrances have opposite magnetic poles. If the distance between the entrances is big enough the resulting field is very weak and when crossing such a field high-energy charged particles only slightly change the direction of propagation. The field can be strong only very close to the throat entrances. However, since charged particles can

---

[a]The simplest scheme to get a general genus - n wormhole can be described as follows. We take a couple of equal spheres with n handles in space, remove the internal regions (insides of the spheres), and glue along their surfaces (the so-called Hegor diagrams). If we take two simple spheres without handles the resulting space corresponds to a spherical wormhole (throat is the sphere). The sphere with a handle is the torus. A couple of toruses corresponds to the doughnut shaped wormhole, etc.
[b]We point out that the currents are fictitious, for from the point of view of the Hegor diagrams they take place in inner regions of spheres which are removed, i.e., in fictitious regions.

freely propagate along the field lines (which are roughly orthogonal to entrances), the particles captured by the field are distributed in the whole region between the entrances. Such fields have the long-range character and can be used to explain the origin of long-correlated magnetic fields in voids[22,23] and, more generally, of primordial magnetic fields.[24]

The situation changes when the wormhole possesses also the field of the second class. The second class corresponds to the field produced by a single loop of a current (the loop of the corresponding fictitious current goes inside of the surface of the doughnut). In this case the field lines of force repeat the shape of the entrance (the shape of a doughnut) which roughly corresponds to the fields observed in spiral galaxies.[36-38] It is necessary to point out that the magnetic fields in the galaxies cannot exactly repeat the shape of a doughnut. There are a number of well-known processes in galaxies which naturally lead to the generation of galactic magnetic fields[37] and the actual field does not reduce to such a simple model. It is known that the pitch angle (between the toroidal field and radial one) is usually between 4 and 17 degrees.

The most strong field is close to the entrance and particles captured by the field remain always near the entrance. In the primordial plasma before the recombination such a wormhole traps all baryons[c] propagating near it and thus forms a primeval structure of a galaxy (a protogalaxy). Such a scheme works only for wormholes which possess sufficiently strong magnetic fields, since high-energy baryons cannot be captured by the wormhole. The mean energy of baryons is determined by the temperature which depends on the redshift. The intensity of the magnetic field also depends on the redshift. While baryons are relativistic particles the threshold value of the fictitious (or equivalent) current does not depend on time.

Indeed, only particles below the threshold energy are captured by the wormhole magnetic field[10] which is given by

$$E = 3kT < E_{th} = eBR_w,$$

where e is the electron charge and R_w is the biggest radius of the doughnut - shaped throat of the wormhole. The energy of relativistic baryons behaves with the redshift as $T = T_\gamma(1+z)$, where T_γ is the present day temperature of CMB radiation. The intensity of the magnetic field can be estimated by the value in the hole of the doughnut. We take it as

$$B = \frac{\kappa I}{cR_w},$$

where $\kappa = 2\pi$ in the center of the doughnut hole, while close to the throat (surface of the doughnut), where the field reaches the maximum value, in the approximation $r_w/R_w \ll 1$ we get the estimate $\kappa \simeq 2R_w/r_w$. The field depends on the parameter I

---

[c]We present here estimates for baryons only, since leptons are much lighter than baryons and in the primordial plasma leptons simply follow baryons (bounded by the Coulomb potential).

(which is the fictitious or equivalent current) and the big radius R_w of the doughnut which also depends on the redshift as $R_w = R_0/(1+z)$.

The constant I behaves with the redshift as $I = I_0(1+z)$. Indeed the invariant characteristics is the number of magnetic lines captured by the throat (which go through the internal hole of the doughnut). This gives $\int_S \mathbf{B} d\mathbf{s} = const = \Phi$, where S an arbitrary surface whose boundary contour γ (dual to Γ) lays on the surface of the throat and cannot be contracted to a point, so that all magnetic lines intersect S only once. Taking the minimal surface S we find $\Phi \sim \frac{2\pi^2}{c} R_w I$ which gives the behavior $I \sim 1/R_w \sim 1/a$, where $a = a_0/(1+z)$ is the scale factor of the Universe. We point out that the same dependence on the redshift z follows from the fact that the energy density of the magnetic field $\rho_B \sim B^2/4\pi$ decreases with the scale factor as $\rho_B \sim 1/a^4$. This gives the threshold value for the equivalent current which defines the intensity of the magnetic field as

$$I_0 > I_{th} = \frac{ce}{\kappa r_\gamma} \sim \frac{3.2}{\kappa} \times 10^{-5} A, \tag{19}$$

where $r_\gamma = \frac{e^2}{3kT_\gamma}$. It is convenient to express r_γ as follows $r_\gamma = r_p(1+z_r)$, where $r_p = \frac{e^2}{m_p c^2}$ is the classical radius of the proton and $1+z_r = \frac{m_p c^2}{3kT_\gamma} \sim 10^{12}$ is the redshift at which baryons become relativistic particles. It is curious that the threshold value I_{th} is extremely small. It does not depend on the absolute size of the wormhole (which is given by the big radius R_w) but only on the ratio of the wormhole radii $\kappa = 2R_w/r_w$. All wormholes with the present day values $I_0 > I_{th}$ strongly interact with baryons. We may say that they are frozen into baryons and, therefore, peculiar motions of baryons repeat peculiar motions of such wormholes. Wormholes with smaller magnetic fields $I_0 < I_{th}$ slightly interact with baryons and can be considered as free objects. They may participate in independent from baryons motions. As we shall see on the early stage of the evolution of the Universe, before the recombination, they cannot capture baryons and therefore do not form an enhancement in the baryon density. On latter stages upon reheating they may capture charged particles and form cosmic rays and compact sources of synchrotron radiation. The relativistic stage for baryons finishes at the redshift z_r upon which (e.g., for $z < z_r$) baryons become non-relativistic and the above consideration brakes.

At redshifts $z_r > z > z_{rec}$ baryons are non-relativistic, while upon the recombination z_{rec} baryons form neutral Hydrogen atoms and do not interact with magnetic fields of all wormholes. They again start to interact with wormholes only at the epoch of re-ionization when first stars have fired.

On the stage $z_r > z > z_{rec}$ for every particular wormhole it is possible to define the critical redshift z_0 when it captures baryons (for $z > z_0$). The critical value z_0 can be estimated as follows. The mean energy of baryons is $m_p V^2/2 = 3kT/2$ with $T = T_\gamma(1+z)$. Then the critical redshift can be found from the inequality $r_B = \frac{V}{\omega_B} = \frac{V m_p c}{eB} < r_d$, where r_B and ω_B are Larmor radius and frequency respectively for protons, while r_d denotes the width of the baryon cloud around the wormhole throat. The width r_d should be smaller, than the proton diffusion length and it defines the critical value of the magnetic field. This gives

$$B = \frac{\kappa I}{cR_w} > \frac{m_p c}{er_d}\sqrt{\frac{3kT}{m_p}},$$

or equivalently

$$I_0(1+z) > \frac{\alpha e}{\kappa r_p}\sqrt{\frac{3kT}{m_p}} = \alpha I_{th}(1+z_r)\sqrt{\frac{(1+z)}{(1+z_r)}},$$

where the ratio $\alpha = \frac{R_w}{r_d} \gg 1$. This defines the critical redshift z_0 at which the wormhole starts to trap baryons as

$$(1+z) > (1+z_0) = \alpha^2 \frac{I_{th}^2}{I_0^2}(1+z_r).$$

The relation between z_0 and I_0 can be rewritten as

$$I_0^2 = \frac{(1+z_r)}{(1+z_0)}\alpha^2 I_{th}^2. \qquad (20)$$

When $z_0 = z_r$ we get $I_0 = \alpha I_{th}$ and if we take $\alpha = 1$, this will give the absolute threshold of the field. We point out that the value $\alpha = 1$ may have sense only for sufficiently small wormholes with the radius $R_w \lesssim 10^{-5} R_{gal}$, e.g., see estimates in the next section. At redshifts $z > z_r$ we get into the epoch where baryons are relativistic particles and wormholes with $I_0 < I_{th}$ do not bound baryons at all. There is one more critical value I_{rec} which corresponds to $z_0 = z_{rec}$.

$$I_{rec}^2 = \alpha^2 I_{th}^2 \frac{(1+z_r)}{(1+z_{rec})} \gg I_{th}^2. \qquad (21)$$

All fields with $I_0 > I_{rec}$ are strong enough to capture baryons during the whole evolution $z > z_{rec}$.

5. The number of baryons in traps

The efficiency of wormhole traps can be described by the number of baryons collected. The number of baryons collected around magnetic wormholes depends on the proton diffusion length $\ell(z)$, the big radius a wormhole throat $R_w(z)$, and the radius of the baryon cloud $r_{cl}(z) \ll R_w$. For estimates one may use $r_{cl} \sim r_w$. This number can be estimated as the increase of the effective volume of the torus-shaped throat

$$\Delta N = <n_b> (V(R_w + \ell, r_{cl} + \ell) - V(R_w, r_{cl})),$$

where $<n_b>$ is the mean density of baryons and $V = 2\pi^2 R_w r_{cl}^2$ is the throat volume. We define the parameter $\delta_b = \Delta N/(V <n_b>)$ which depends on the position in space. Close to wormhole throats $\delta_b > 0$, while sufficiently far from the wormhole $\delta_b < 0$ since baryons from those regions have captured by the wormhole.

The value $<\delta_b^2> = b$, where brackets define the averaging over the space, relates to the baryon clumping factor $b = (<n_b^2> - <n_b>^2)/<n_b>^2$, e.g.,[25,26]

In the case $\ell(z) \ll r_{cl}(z)$ we get

$$\delta_b(z) \sim \frac{\ell(z)}{R_w(z)} + \frac{2\ell(z)}{r_{cl}(z)} \ll 1. \tag{22}$$

In the intermediate case $r_{cl}(z) \ll \ell(z) \ll R_w(z)$ we find the estimate

$$\delta_b(z) \sim \frac{\ell^2(z)}{r_{cl}^2(z)}\left(1 + \frac{\ell(z)}{R_w(z)}\right) \gg 1. \tag{23}$$

And in the case $\ell(z) \gg R_w(z)$ the estimate has the order

$$\delta_b(z) \sim \frac{\ell^3(z)}{R_w(z) r_{cl}^2(z)} \gg 1. \tag{24}$$

On the stage $z > z_r$ protons are relativistic particles, plasma is degenerate, and the length of the proton propagation can be estimated by the value of the horizon size $\ell(z) \sim l_h = c/H(z)$. At the redshift $z = z_r$ it is extremely small and has the order $\ell(z_r) \sim (7 \div 8) \times 10^{-15} pc$. Consider a wormhole throat with the big radius $R_w(0) \sim 15 kpc$ which corresponds to a galaxy size,[41] while the radius of the baryon cloud has the order $r_{cl} \sim 0.2 R_w$. Then we find $R_w(z_r) \sim 15 \times 10^{-9} pc \gg \ell(z_r)$ and from (22) we get $\delta_b(z_r) \sim (0.5 \div 0.6) \times 10^{-5}$. Such a value is too small to form a galaxy without additional means (e.g., a dark matter clump).

At the recombination $z_{rec} = 1100$ the proton diffusion length has the co-moving value of the order $\ell(z_{rec}) \sim 0.4 \div 1 pc$, while $R_w(z_{rec}) \sim 13.6 pc$ and we still may consider $\ell(z_{rec}) \ll R_w$ and $\ell \lesssim r_{cl}$. Therefore we again may use (22) and find $\delta_b(z) \sim 0.32 \div 0.8$. Such a big value shows that the respective protogalaxy forms immediately after the recombination and it is already in the non-linear regime. We should expect that wormholes with such strong clumps of baryons depart the Hubble expansion very soon and form rather small objects. Smaller wormholes form too strong inhomogeneities before recombination and probably collapse to blackholes. We point out that this may give a new mechanism of blackhole formation with huge masses.

Galaxies are observed up to $z \simeq 11$ (e.g., the most distant GN-z11 is observed at $z = 11.09$[39]). Therefore, to be consistent with the present day size of a typical ring galaxy the wormhole radius should be at least two orders bigger $R_w(0) \lesssim 1 Mpc$, which gives already $R_w(z_{rec}) \lesssim 900 pc$ and $\delta_b(z_{rec}) \sim 4,8 \times 10^{-3}$. Such a clump departs the Hubble expansion already at $z \sim 100$ and gives a ring of the order $R \sim 10 Kpc$.

6. Conclusions

In conclusion we point out two important facts. First one is that the wormholes whose size $R(z_{rec})$ exceeds the value $\ell(z_{rec})$ more than on the factor 10^3 do not form a sufficient enhancement in the baryon number density and, therefore, cannot form ring galaxies. They however may form ring-type structures in the future, e.g. see the recently reported findings of unexpected class of astronomical ring-type objects in.[29]

The second fact is that upon the recombination $z < z_{rec}$ the doughnut-shaped wormholes do not interact with baryons and evolve. Therefore, they may leave the ring clump formed. They either expand or collapse forming a magnetized black hole in the middle. If the wormhole collapses, it should also draw some portion of the baryon clump and form a bulge in the center of the ring. In this case it may form the ideal symmetric structure similar to the Hoag's object. Additional rotational perturbations of clumps may however lead to irregular structures. If the wormhole expands further, the center part of the ring remains to be empty. We may expect that in such a case the mean value of the magnetic field within the ring retains. We recall that different active processes in galaxies generate magnetic fields which in general have a turbulent character. Therefore, by the measuring the mean flow of the magnetic field in a ring galaxy one may at least estimate the present day value of the big radius $R = \frac{\kappa I}{cB}$ of such a wormhole and estimate its present day position. This may be used in the direct search for wormhole traces in the Universe.

At first glance the most direct indication on the possible role of relic magnetic wormholes in the formation of some ring galaxies should be the discrepancy between the observed amount of dark matter in such galaxies and the predictions of the standard theory.[40,42,43] However there exist some extensions of general relativity which are capable of reproducing dark matter effects in galaxies without dark matter particles, e.g., see[44,45] and references therein. Therefore, we think that the only rigorous indication on the presence of relic magnetic wormholes should be large-scale toroidal magnetic fields.

References

1. Hawking, S.W. *Nucl. Phys. B* **114**, 349 (1978).
2. Savelova, E.P. *Grav. Cosmol.* **21**, 48–56 (2015).
3. Knizhnik V., Polyakov A., Zamolodchikov A. *Mod. Phys. Lett. A*, **3**, p. 819 (1988).
4. Kawai H., Kawamoto N., Mogami T., Watabiki Y. Phys. Lett. B, **306**, pp. 19–26 (1993).
5. Ambjorn, J. Jurkiewicz, and R. Loll, *Phys. Rev. Lett.* **95** 17 (2005).
6. Ambjorn J. et al, *Eur. Phys. J. C* **81**:708 (2021).
7. Amendola, et al. *Living Rev. Relativ.* **21** 2 (2018).
8. Harko, T.; Lobo, F. *Extensions of f (R) Gravity: Curvature-Matter Couplings and Hybrid Metric-Palatini Theory*, Cambridge Monographs on Mathematical Physics; Cambridge University Press: Cambridge, UK, (2018).
9. Kirillov A.A. & Savelova E.P., *Int. J. Mod. Phys. D* **25**, 1650075 (2016).
10. Kirillov A.A. & Savelova E.P., *Eur. Phys. J. C* **80** 45 (2020).
11. Bronnikov K.A., Krechet V.G., and Lemos J.P.S., *Phys. Rev. D* **87** 084060 (2013).
12. Bronnikov K.A.& Krechet V.G., *Phys. Rev. D* **99** 084051 (2019).
13. Shaikh, R. et al., *Phys. Lett. B* **789** 270 (2019).
14. Shaikh, R., Banerjee, P., Paul, S., and Sarkar, T., *JCAP* 1907, 028 (2019).

15. Safonova, M., Torres, D. F., and Romero, G. E., *Phys. Rev. D* **65** 023001 (2002).
16. Kirillov A.A. & Savelova E.P., *Universe* **4** 35 (2018).
17. Kirillov A.A. & Savelova E.P., *Astr. Sp. Sc.* **364** 1 (2019).
18. Kirillov A.A., Savelova E.P., Lecian O.M., *Eur. Phys. J. C* **81**: 263 (2021).
19. Kirillov A.A., Savelova E.P., *Int J Mod Phys A,* **35** 2040026 (2020).
20. DAMPE Collaboration, *Nature* **552** 24475 (2017).
21. Fermi, E.: *Phys. Rev.* **75**, 1169 (1949).
22. Neronov, A.; Vovk, I., Science **328** 73(2010).
23. Takahashi, K.; Mori, M.; Ichiki, K.; Inoue, S.; Takami, H., *Astrophys. J. Lett.* **771** L42 (2013).
24. Subramanian K., *Rep. Prog. Phys.* **79** 076901 (2016).
25. Jedamzik, K. & Abel, T., *JCAP*, 1310, 050 (2013).
26. Jedamzik, K. & Saveliev, A., *Phys. Rev. Lett.* **123** 021301 (2019).
27. Jedamzik, K. & Pogosian, L., Relieving the Hubble tension with primordial magnetic fields, arXive: 2004.09487 (2020).
28. Kirillov A.A. & Savelova E.P., *Eur. Phys. J. C* **80** 810 (2020).
29. Norris, R. P. et al., Unexpected Circular Radio Objects at High Galactic Latitude, *Publications of the Astronomical Society of Australia,* **38** E003 (2021).
30. Eguchi, T., Gilkey, P.B., Hanson, A., *Phys. Rep.* **66**(6) 213-393 (1980).
31. Arellano A. V. B., Lobo, F.S.N., *Class. Quant. Grav.* **23** 5811 (2006).
32. Bronnikov K. A., *Int. J. Mod. Phys. D* **27** 1841005 (2018).
33. Subramanian K., *Rep. Prog. Phys.* **79**, 076901 (2016).
34. Bronnikov K. A., *Acta Physica Polonica A* **4** 251 (1973).
35. Ellis H. G., *J. Math. Phys.* **14** 104 (1973).
36. Jones, T. J. et al. *The Astrophysical Journal Letters* **870** L9 (2019).
37. Beck, R., *Astron Astrophys Rev.* **24**: 4 (2016).
38. Moss D., Mikhailov E., Sokoloff D., Silchenko O., Horellou C., Beck R. *Astron. Astrophys.* **592** A44 (2016).
39. Oesch, P. A. et al. *Astrophys. J.* **819** 129 (2016).
40. White, S. & Rees, M. *Mon. Not. R. Astron. Soc.* **183** 341 (1978).
41. Yuan, T. et al. *Nature Astronomy Letters.* (2020). https://doi.org/10.1038/ s41550-020-1102-7.
42. Steinmetz, M. & Navarro, J. F. *New Astronomy* **7** 155 (2002).
43. Persic M., Salucci P., Stel F., *Mon. Not. Roy. Astron. Soc.* **281** 27 (1996).
44. Kirillov, A. A. and D. Turaev, *Mon. Not. Roy. Astron. Soc.* **371** L31 (2006).
45. Kirillov A. A., *Phys. Lett. B,* **632** 453 (2006).

Wormhole geometries induced by action-dependent Lagrangian theories

Ismael Ayuso*, Francisco S. N. Lobo† and José P. Mimoso‡

Instituto de Astrofísica e Ciências do Espaço, Faculdade de Ciências da Universidade de Lisboa,
Edifício C8, Campo Grande,
Lisbon, P-1749-016, Portugal
* E-mail: iayuso@fc.ul.pt
† E-mail: fslobo@fc.ul.pt
‡ E-mail: jpmimoso@fc.ul.pt

In this work, we explore wormhole geometries in a recently proposed modified gravity theory arising from a non-conservative gravitational theory, tentatively denoted action-dependent Lagrangian theories. The generalized gravitational field equation essentially depends on a background four-vector λ^μ, that plays the role of a coupling parameter associated with the dependence of the gravitational Lagrangian upon the action, and may generically depend on the spacetime coordinates. Considering wormhole configurations, by using "Buchdahl coordinates", we find that the four-vector is given by $\lambda_\mu = (0, 0, \lambda_\theta, 0)$, and that the spacetime geometry is severely restricted by the condition $g_{tt} g_{uu} = -1$, where u is the radial coordinate. We find a plethora of specific asymptotically flat, symmetric and asymmetric, solutions with power law choices for the function λ, by generalizing the Ellis-Bronnikov solutions and the recently proposed black bounce geometries, amongst others. We show that these compact objects possess a far richer geometrical structure than their general relativistic counterparts.

Keywords: General relativity, alternative theories of gravity; wormhole; action-dependent Lagrangian theories; energy conditions.

1. Introduction

A key ingredient in traversable wormhole geometries is the flaring-out condition,[1,2] which in General Relativity (GR) entails the violation of the null energy condition (NEC). The latter is defined as $T_{\mu\nu} k^\mu k^\nu \geq 0$, for *any* null vector k^μ,[3,4] and matter violating the NEC has been denoted as *exotic matter*. However, it has been shown that these violations may be minimized using several procedures, such as the cut-and-paste techniques in the thin-shell formalism, where the exotic matter is concentrated at the junction interface.[5–14] In fact, the problem is improved with evolving traversable wormholes, where it has been demonstrated that these time-dependent geometries may satisfy the energy conditions in arbitrary finite intervals of time,[15,16] and recently specific dynamical four-dimensional solutions were presented that satisfy the null and weak energy conditions everywhere and everywhen.[17,18] In fact, modified theories of gravity is an interesting avenue of research to explore traversable wormholes, where these compact objects possess a richer geometrical structure than their general relativistic counterparts. In this context, it has been shown that the NEC can be satisfied for normal matter threading the wormhole throat, where it is the higher order curvature terms that sustain the wormhole.[19–27]

In this work, we will be interested in studying wormhole geometries in a recently proposed modified gravity theory arising from a non-conservative gravitational theory, tentatively denoted action-dependent Lagrangian theories.[28] The latter are obtained through an action principle for action-dependent Lagrangians by generalizing the Herglotz variational problem[29,30] for several independent variables. The novel feature when comparing with previous implementations of dissipative effects in gravity is the possible arising of such phenomena from a least action principle, so they are of a purely geometric nature. Applications to this model have also been explored, namely, in cosmology,[31] braneworld gravity,[32] cosmic string configurations,[33] the late-time cosmic accelerated expansion and large scale structure,[34] and static spherically symmetric stellar solutions,[35] amongst others.

The complete set of field equations considered in this action-dependent Lagrangian theory[28] is based on the following total Lagrangian

$$\mathcal{L} = \mathcal{L}_g + \mathcal{L}_m = (R - \lambda_\mu s^\mu) + \mathcal{L}_m, \tag{1}$$

where the Einstein-Hilbert Lagrangian is extended with the geometrical sector dealing with the additional dissipative term $\lambda_\mu s^\mu$ while $\mathcal{L}_m$ is the Lagrangian of the matter fields. In general, the background four-vector λ^μ depends on the spacetime coordinates, however it can be assumed to be constant. The field s^μ is an action-density field which disappears after the variation of the action such that the modification to the GR counterpart is given by the four-vector λ^μ only. Note that λ^μ may be considered a background four-vector, that plays the role of a coupling parameter associated with the dependence of the gravitational Lagrangian upon the action. In the majority of the works considered above it is assumed to be constant, however, in a more general scenario, one may assume it to be a coordinate-dependent four-vector.

Thus, the field equations are given by

$$G_{\mu\nu} + Z_{\mu\nu} = \kappa^2 T_{\mu\nu}, \tag{2}$$

where we have defined $\kappa^2 = 8\pi$, $G_{\mu\nu}$ is the Einstein tensor, and for notational simplicity, we have defined $Z_{\mu\nu}$ as

$$Z_{\mu\nu} = K_{\mu\nu} - \frac{1}{2} g_{\mu\nu} K. \tag{3}$$

The symmetric geometric structure $K_{\mu\nu}$ is defined as

$$K_{\mu\nu} = \lambda_\alpha \Gamma^\alpha_{\mu\nu} - \frac{1}{2}(\lambda_\mu \Gamma^\alpha_{\nu\alpha} + \lambda_\nu \Gamma^\alpha_{\mu\alpha}), \tag{4}$$

which is constructed from the particular combination of the four-vector λ_μ and the Christofell symbols

$$\Gamma^\alpha_{\mu\nu} = \frac{g^{\alpha\beta}}{2} (g_{\beta\mu,\nu} + g_{\beta\nu,\mu} - g_{\mu\nu,\beta}). \tag{5}$$

The quantity $K_{\mu\nu}$ (and its trace K) represents the geometric structure behind the dissipative nature of the theory. Note that the limit of a vanishing λ_μ restores the dissipationless feature of GR.

Thus, motivated by the existence of static spherically-symmetric compact objects analysed in,[35] we extend this analysis to the context of wormhole physics. This work is outlined in the following manner: In Sec. 2, we present the most general restrictions on static and spherically symmetric wormhole geometries imposed by the geometrical structure of the action-dependent Lagrangian theory. In Sec. 3, we consider a plethora of specific solutions of action-dependent Lagrangian induced wormhole geometries. Finally, in Sec. 4, we summarize our results and conclude.

2. General restrictions on wormhole geometries

Consider the general static and spherically symmetric metric given by

$$ds^2 = -f(u)dt^2 + g(u)du^2 + R^2(u)d\Omega^2, \tag{6}$$

where $d\Omega^2 = d\theta^2 + \sin^2\theta d\phi^2$ is the linear element of the unit sphere, and the metric functions $f(u)$, $g(u)$ and $R(u)$ are functions of the radial coordinate u. The coordinate choices used in metric (6) are often called "Buchdahl coordinates".[36–38] Note that one possesses a freedom in choosing the radial coordinate, consequently allowing one to fix the form of one of the metric functions $f(u)$, $g(u)$ or $R(u)$, which will be considered below. Here the radial coordinate lies in the range $u \in (-\infty, +\infty)$, so that two asymptotically flat regions exist, i.e., $u \to \pm\infty$, and are connected by the throat. The function $R(u)$ possesses a global positive minimum at the wormhole throat $u = u_0$, which one can set at $u_0 = 0$, without a loss of generality. Thus, the wormhole throat is defined as $R_0 = \min\{R(u)\} = R(0)$.

In order to avoid event horizons and singularities throughout the spacetime, one imposes that the metric functions $f(u)$ and $g(u)$ are positive and regular everywhere. Taking into account these restrictions, namely, the necessary conditions for the minimum of the function imposes the flaring-out conditions, which are given by

$$R'_0 = 0, \qquad R''_0 > 0. \tag{7}$$

In this work, we consider an anisotropic distribution of matter threading the wormhole described by the following stress-energy tensor $T_{\mu\nu}$

$$T_{\mu\nu} = (\rho + p_t)U_\mu U_\nu + p_t\, g_{\mu\nu} + (p_r - p_t)\chi_\mu \chi_\nu, \tag{8}$$

where U^μ is the four-velocity, χ^μ is the unit spacelike vector in the radial direction, i.e., $\chi^\mu = g^{-1/2}(u)\delta^\mu_u$; $\rho(u)$ is the energy density, $p_r(u)$ is the radial pressure measured in the direction of χ^μ, and $p_t(u)$ is the transverse pressure measured in the orthogonal direction to χ^μ.

Now, rather than write out the full gravitational field equations (2) for the metric (6), we note that the only non-zero components of the Einstein and the stress-energy tensor are the diagonal terms, so that the non-diagonal part of the additional tensor $Z_{\mu\nu}$, defined by Eq. (3), also provides additional information on the geometrical structure of the solutions of the theory, namely, that $Z_{\mu\nu} = 0$ for $\mu \neq \nu$. More specifically, the non-diagonal components of the symmetric tensor $Z_{\mu\nu}$ places restrictions on the form of the four-vector λ_μ.

The independent components of the tensor $Z^\mu_\nu = K^\mu_\nu - \frac{1}{2}\delta^\mu_\nu K$ are given by

$$Z^u_t = -\frac{\lambda_t[fg'R - g(f'R - 4fR')]}{4fg^2 R}, \quad Z^u_u = \frac{\lambda_\theta}{R^2}\cot\theta, \tag{9}$$

$$Z^u_\theta = -\frac{\lambda_\theta(fg)'}{4fg^2} - \frac{\lambda_u}{2g}\cot\theta, \quad Z^u_\phi = -\frac{\lambda_\phi(fg)'}{4fg^2}, \tag{10}$$

$$Z^\theta_\theta = Z^\phi_\phi = \frac{\lambda_u(Rf' + 2fR')}{2fgR}, \tag{11}$$

$$Z^\theta_\phi = \frac{\lambda_\phi}{2R^2}\cot\theta, \quad Z^\theta_t = -\frac{\lambda_t}{2R^2}\cot\theta, \tag{12}$$

$$Z^t_t = \frac{2\lambda_u R'}{gR} + \frac{\lambda_\theta}{R^2}\cot\theta, \quad Z^t_\phi = 0. \tag{13}$$

From $Z^\theta_\phi = Z^\theta_t = 0$, one readily extracts the restrictions $\lambda_\phi = \lambda_t = 0$. Taking into account the assumption of the static and spherical symmetric character of the spacetime, the field equations should only depend on the radial coordinate, so that from the diagonal Z^u_u component, one readily verifies that $\lambda_\theta \propto (\cot\theta)^{-1}$, or more specifically $\lambda_\theta = \lambda(u)/(\cot\theta)$ (one may consider the simple case $\lambda(u) = \lambda_0 = \mathrm{const}$). Note that if one were to consider $\lambda_\theta = 0$, then the condition $Z^u_\theta = 0$ would impose that $\lambda_u = 0$, taking us trivially back to GR. Analogously, in order for Z^t_t to only depend on the radial coordinate, from $Z^u_\theta = 0$ this imposes that $\lambda_u = 0$ and consequently places a further constraint on the metric functions, namely, $(fg)' = 0$.

Thus, the additional information on the geometrical structure of the theory, which imposes that the non-diagonal components of the symmetric tensor $Z_{\mu\nu}$ vanish, imposes the following condition on the four-vector λ_μ:

$$\lambda_\mu = \left(0, 0, \frac{\lambda(u)}{\cot\theta}, 0\right), \tag{14}$$

and the additional geometric tensor Z^μ_ν takes the diagonal form $Z^\mu_\nu = (\lambda(u)/R^2)\mathrm{diag}(1,1,0,0)$. Furthermore, from the constraint on the metric functions $(fg)' = 0$, we can consider, without a loss of generality, the following choice:

$$g(u) = f^{-1}(u) = A(u). \tag{15}$$

3. Specific solutions of action-dependent Lagrangian induced wormhole geometries

The analysis outlined in the previous section imposes that the static and spherical symmetric configuration (6) in the theory (1), can be written as

$$ds^2 = -A(u)dt^2 + A^{-1}(u)du^2 + R^2(u)d\Omega^2, \tag{16}$$

where as before the wormhole throat is defined as $R_0 = \min\{R(u)\} = R(0)$, and in order to avoid event horizons and singularities throughout the spacetime, one imposes that the function $A(u)$ is positive and regular everywhere. These restrictions imposes the flaring-out conditions, translated by Eq. (7).

As the metric function $A(u)$ is positive and regular for $\forall u$, it is useful to analyse its derivatives at the throat $u = 0$. In particular, the sign of A_0'' determines the type of extrema of $A(u)$, i.e., it is a minimum if $A_0'' > 0$ and a maximum if $A_0'' < 0$. This implies that the maximum (minimum) of $A(u)$ corresponds to a maximum (minimum) of the gravitational potential, so that in the vicinity of a maximum (minimum) the gravitational force is repulsive (attractive). Thus, the wormhole throat possesses a repulsive or an attractive nature that depends on the sign of A_0''.

Now, taking into account the modified Einstein equation (2), the spacetime metric (16) and the stress-energy tensor (8), the gravitational field equations are finally given by:

$$8\pi\rho = -\frac{2ARR'' + AR'^2 + A'RR' - 1}{R^2} - \frac{\lambda(u)}{R^2}, \tag{17}$$

$$8\pi p_r = \frac{AR'^2 + A'RR' - 1}{R^2} + \frac{\lambda(u)}{R^2}, \tag{18}$$

$$8\pi p_t = \frac{A''R + 2AR'' + 2A'R'}{2R}. \tag{19}$$

Adding Eqs. (17) and (18), yields the following relation

$$R''|_{R_0} = -\frac{4\pi R}{A}(\rho + p_r)|_{R_0}, \tag{20}$$

and using the condition at the throat $R_0'' > 0$, one verifies that in these specific action-dependent Lagrangian theories the NEC is generically violated at the throat, i.e., $(\rho + p_r)|_{R_0} < 0$.

Taking into account the field equations (17)–(19), one has three independent equations with six unknown functions of the radial coordinate u, namely, $\rho(u)$, $p_r(u)$, $p_t(u)$, $A(u)$, $R(u)$ and $\lambda(u)$. There are several strategies that one may now follow. More specifically, one may consider specific choices for the components of the stress-energy tensor, and then solve the field equations to determine the metric functions and $\lambda(u)$; one may also take into account a plausible stress-energy tensor profile by imposing equations of state $p_r = p_r(\rho)$ and $p_t = p_t(\rho)$, and close the system by adequately choosing the energy density, or any of the metric functions. In alternative to this approach, one may use the reverse philosophy usually adopted in wormhole physics by simple choosing specific choices for the metric functions and $\lambda(u)$, and through the field equations determine the stress-energy profile responsible for sustaining the wormhole geometry. In the following section, we will adopt several strategies outlined above, and a mixture thereof, to obtain specific exact solutions of wormhole spacetimes induced by these action-dependent Lagrangian theories.

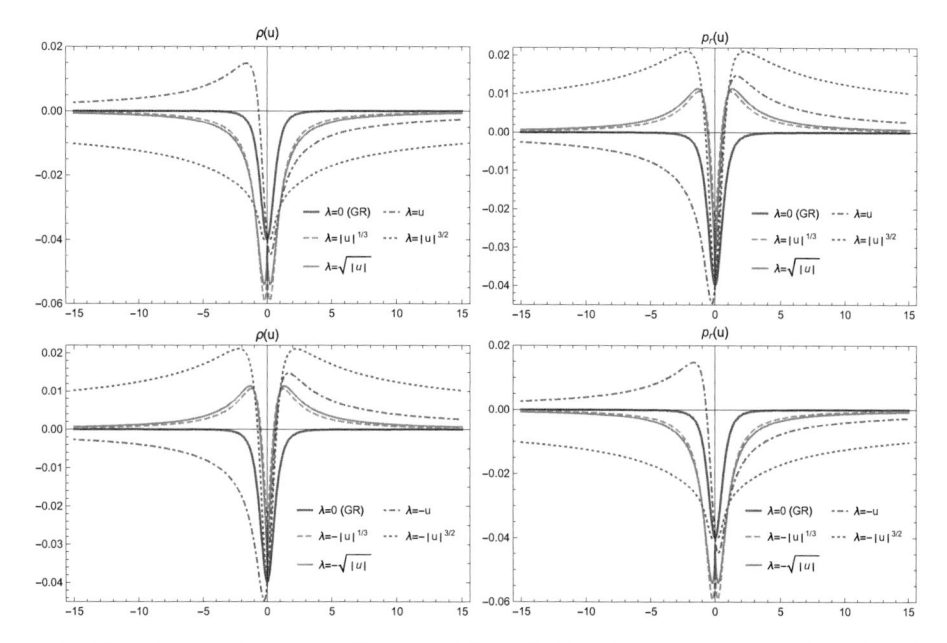

Fig. 1. The plots depict the specific case of the Ellis-Bronnikov wormhole configuration with $a = 1$, for convenience, and for different choices of the function $\lambda(u)$. Depending on the sign of $\lambda(u)$, one obtains a plethora of specific symmetric or asymmetric solutions. Note that for $\lambda(u) \sim \pm u$, one obtains asymmetric solutions, where the energy density is negative at the throat and in the positive (negative) branch of u, but becomes positive in the negative (positive) branch; the radial pressure exhibits the inverse qualitative behavior. We refer the reader to the text for more details.

3.1. *Specific wormhole solutions: Ellis-Bronnikov solution*

Using an appropriate parametrization, we can present a solution by taking into account the reverse philosophy of solving the modified field equations, as follows[39]

$$R(u) = e^{-\alpha(u)}\sqrt{u^2 + a^2}, \qquad A(u) = e^{2\alpha(u)}, \qquad (21)$$

with the factor $\alpha(u)$ defined as

$$\alpha(u) = \left(\frac{m}{a}\right)\arctan\left(\frac{u}{a}\right), \qquad (22)$$

where m and a are two free parameters. Thus, the spacetime metric is given by

$$ds^2 = -e^{2\alpha}dt^2 + e^{-2\alpha}\left[du^2 + (u^2 + a^2)d\Omega^2\right]. \qquad (23)$$

Following the previous definition of the wormhole throat, which is situated at $u_0 = 0$, we readily obtain $R'(0) = -m/a$, so that the condition $R'(0) = 0$ imposes $m = 0$. Note that these conditions imply that the solution reduces to the well-known Ellis-Bronnikov wormhole spacetime.[40–42] This does indeed simplify the analysis below, such that $\alpha(u) = 0$, $A(u) = 1$, and

$$R''(u_0) = \frac{1}{|a|} > 0 \qquad (24)$$

In addition to this, Eqs. (17)–(19) yield the following stress-energy profile:

$$\rho(u) = -\frac{(a^2 + u^2)\lambda(u) + a^2}{8\pi(a^2 + u^2)^2}, \qquad (25)$$

$$p_r(u) = \frac{(a^2 + u^2)\lambda(u) - a^2}{8\pi(a^2 + u^2)^2}, \qquad (26)$$

$$p_t(u) = \frac{a^2}{8\pi(a^2 + u^2)^2}. \qquad (27)$$

For the specific case of $\lambda = 0$, where the four-vector λ^μ vanishes, this solution simply reduces to the general relativistic Ellis-Bronnikov stress-energy components. However, for the general case, one still needs to impose one more condition to close the system, and in the following we consider specific choices for the function $\lambda(u)$. Equations (25)–(26) yield the following relation:

$$\rho(u) + p_r(u) = -\frac{a^2}{4\pi(a^2 + u^2)^2}, \qquad (28)$$

which states that the NEC is violated throughout the entire spacetime, and is independent of the function $\lambda(u)$.

We are only interested in asymptotically flat solutions, so that taking into account the limit of Eq. (25), one finds

$$\lim_{u \to \infty} \rho(u) \sim -\lim_{u \to \infty} \frac{\lambda(u)}{u^2}. \qquad (29)$$

For instance, assuming a power law solution for $\lambda(u) \sim u^\alpha$, the asymptotic flatness condition imposes that $\alpha < 2$, and from the regularity of the stress-energy components we have $\alpha \geq 0$, so that the parameter lies in the range $0 \leq \alpha < 2$. One may perform a similar analysis with the radial pressure $p_r(u)$, but with a change in the sign for the limit. Note that the tangential pressure, $p_t(u)$, is independent of $\lambda(u)$, possesses a maximum value at the throat, $p_t(u=0) = (8\pi a^2)^{-1}$, and tends to zero with increasing u.

Several choices for the function $\lambda(u)$ are depicted in Fig. 1. Depending on the sign of $\lambda(u)$, one obtains a plethora of specific symmetric or asymmetric solutions. More specifically, for the case of $\lambda(u) \sim \pm u$, one obtains asymmetric solutions where the energy density is negative at the throat and in the positive (negative) branch of u, but becomes positive in the negative (positive) branch, while the radial pressure possesses the inverse qualitative behavior, as is transparent from Fig. 1. Thus, it is possible to alleviate the negative energy densities needed to thread this wormhole configurations, relative to GR. The wormhole solutions obtained with $\lambda \neq 0$ possess a richer structure that their general relativistic counterparts.

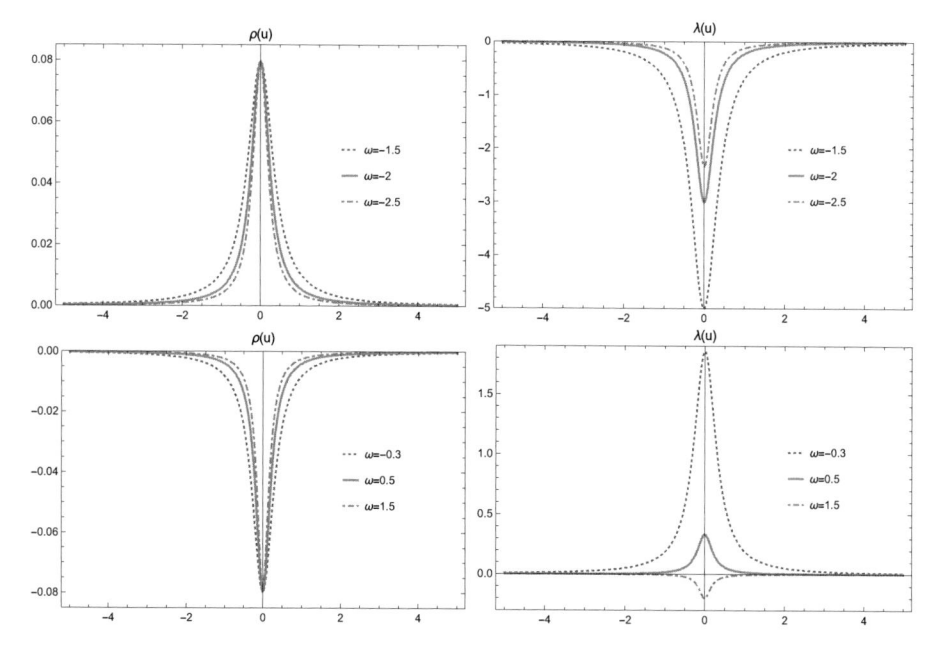

Fig. 2. Results for the specific stress-energy profile given by (30) and (31) with $a^2 = -1/(4\pi\rho_0(1+\omega))$ and $\alpha = 2$. The upper plots are for the case $\rho_0 = 1$ ($\omega < -1$), and the lower plots for $\rho_0 = -1$ ($\omega > -1$).

3.2. Specific stress-energy profile

We now consider the strategy of specifying the profile of the energy density and radial pressure given by:

$$\rho(u) = \rho_0 \left(\frac{a^2}{a^2 + u^2}\right)^\alpha, \tag{30}$$

$$p_r(u) = p_0 \left(\frac{a^2}{a^2 + u^2}\right)^\alpha, \tag{31}$$

with $\alpha > 0$, so that both components tend to zero at spatial infinity. In addition to this, we close the system by considering the specific choice for the metric function

$$R(u) = \sqrt{a^2 + u^2}. \tag{32}$$

Note that Eqs. (30) and (31) can be written as $p_r = \omega\rho$, with $\omega = p_0/\rho_0$. Thus, this case is formally equivalent to choosing Eq. (32), one of Eqs. (30) or (31), and the equation of state $p_r(u) = \omega\rho(u)$.

The gravitational field equations (17)–(19) provide the following solutions:

$$A(u) = -4\pi a^2 \rho_0 (\omega + 1) \left(\frac{a^2}{a^2 + u^2}\right)^{\alpha-2}, \tag{33}$$

$$\lambda(u) = 1 + 4\pi\rho_0 \left[2a^2\omega - (2\alpha - 5)u^2(\omega + 1)\right] \left(\frac{a^2}{a^2 + u^2}\right)^{\alpha-1}. \tag{34}$$

As before, we impose the asymptotic flatness condition, namely,

$$\lim_{u \to \pm\infty} A(u) \to 1, \qquad (35)$$

and taking into account that $A(u)$ should be positive and regular $\forall u$, implies the following two stringent restrictions:

$$\alpha = 2, \quad \text{and} \quad 4\pi a^2 \rho_0(1+w) = -1, \qquad (36)$$

where the second condition imposes:

$$\rho_0(1+w) < 0. \qquad (37)$$

This implies two specific cases: (i) $\rho_0 > 0$ and $w < -1$, so that taking into account the equation of state $w = p_0/\rho_0$, implies a negative radial pressure at the throat; or (ii) $\rho_0 < 0$ and $w > -1$, so that $p_0 > 0$ for $-1 < w < 0$, and $p_0 < 0$ for $w > 0$. Specific cases are depicted in Fig. 2. Relative to the analysis at the throat, note that the wormhole conditions are satisfied, namely, $R'(u_0) = 0$ and $R''(0) = 1/|a| > 0$. In addition to this, for the imposition of the asymptotic flatness condition, namely, $\alpha = 2$, we readily obtain $A(u) = 1$, so that $A'(u_0) = A''(u_0) = 0$.

3.3. Black bounce solutions

Recently, a number of novel regular "black-bounce" spacetimes were explored.[43,44] These are specific geometries where the "area radius" always remains non-zero, thereby leading to a "throat" that is either timelike (corresponding to a traversable wormhole), spacelike (corresponding to a "bounce" into a future universe), or null (corresponding to a "one-way wormhole"). The regularity, the energy conditions, and the causal structure of these models were analysed in detail in Refs.[43,44] The main results are several new geometries with two or more horizons, with the possibility of an extremal case. Motivated by these novel solutions, in this subsection we shall analyse specific generalized "black-bounce" wormhole geometries induced by action-dependent Lagrangian theories.

3.3.1. Simpson–Visser black-bounce spacetime

In this section, we consider a specific black bounce geometry, which we denote as the Simpson-Visser solution.[13,43,44] Consider the following parameters, which were presented in Ref.[43]:

$$R(u) = \sqrt{u^2 + a^2}, \qquad A(u) = 1 - \frac{2m}{\sqrt{u^2 + a^2}}. \qquad (38)$$

Note that the Schwarzschild solution is recovered, if we take the limit $a \to 0$.

This spacetime possesses several interesting properties.[43] First, for $a > 0$ the geometry is everywhere regular, which can verified as $R(u)$ is never zero, and is regular, as is $A(u)$. Now, one has several cases, for instance: (i) if $0 < a < 2m$, two horizons exist, namely, $u_{\pm} = \pm\sqrt{(2m)^2 - a^2}$, where u_+ is positive and u_- is

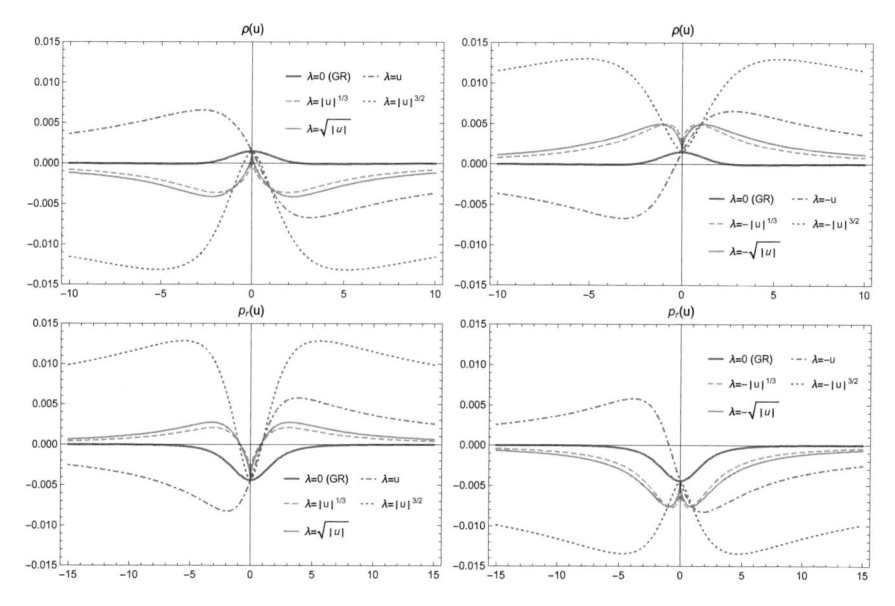

Fig. 3. The plots depict the Simpson-Visser black bounce solution, for the specific choices $m = 1$, $a = 3$. Note that one may obtain wormhole configurations with an entirely positive energy density throughout the spacetime, for negative values of the function $\lambda(u)$; and positive radial pressures in the negative branch of the u-axis. As before, it is transparent from the plots that these compact objects possess a richer geometrical structure than their general relativistic counterparts. See the text for more details.

negative. This solution corresponds to a regular black hole spacetime, where the core consists of a bounce located at $u = 0$; (ii) if $a = 2m$, a wormhole exists with a throat located at $u = 0$. This is an extremal null throat, which can only be crossed from one region to another, so that the wormhole is only one-way traversable; (iii) finally, if $a > 2m$, a two-way traversable wormhole exists, that possesses a timelike throat located at $u = 0$. Thus, only the case (c) for $a > 2m$ interests us here. We refer the reader to Refs.[43,44] for specific details.

Taking into account the choices for the metric functions (38), the field equations (17)–(19) provide the following stress-energy profile:

$$\rho(u)_{SV} = -\frac{1}{8\pi} \left[\frac{a^2 \left(\sqrt{a^2 + u^2} - 4m\right)}{(a^2 + u^2)^{5/2}} + \frac{\lambda(u)}{a^2 + u^2} \right], \tag{39}$$

$$p_r(u)_{SV} = \frac{(a^2 + u^2)\lambda(u) - a^2}{8\pi (a^2 + u^2)^2}, \tag{40}$$

$$p_t(u)_{SV} = \frac{a^2 \left(\sqrt{a^2 + u^2} - m\right)}{8\pi (a^2 + u^2)^{5/2}}, \tag{41}$$

respectively. The asymptotic limits of the energy density and the radial pressure are given by:

$$\lim_{u \to \pm\infty} \rho(u)_{SV} \sim -\lim_{u \to \pm\infty} p_r(u)_{SV} \sim -\lim_{u \to \pm\infty} \frac{\lambda(u)}{a^2 + u^2}. \tag{42}$$

As before, if we assume a power law for $\lambda(u) \sim u^\alpha$, the asymptotic flatness condition and the regularity of the stress-energy components, as before, imposes that $0 \leq \alpha < 2$; note that the tangential pressure $p_t(u) \to 0$ for $u \to \pm\infty$, and possesses a maximum at the wormhole throat, i.e., $p_t(u=0) = (a-m)/(8\pi a^3)$, and is positive throughout the spacetime as we are only considering the condition $a > 2m$.

Several choices for the function are depicted in Fig. 3. Depending on the sign of $\lambda(u)$, one obtains a plethora of specific symmetric or asymmetric solutions. Note that these compact objects possess a richer geometrical structure than their general relativistic counterparts. It is transparent from Fig. 3 that one may obtain wormhole configurations with an entirely positive energy density throughout the spacetime, for negative values of the function $\lambda(u)$; for instance, for the latter it is also possible to obtain positive radial pressures in the negative branch of the u-axis. However, the NEC is always violated at the wormhole throat.

3.3.2. Black bounce II

Another black bounce spacetime that exhibits interesting properties, is given by the following specific metric functions:[44]

$$R(u) = \sqrt{u^2 + a^2}, \qquad A(u) = 1 - \frac{2mu^2}{(u^2 + a^2)^{3/2}}. \tag{43}$$

Note that by solving for the roots of the function $A(u) = 0$, we have: i) for $a < a_{\text{ext}} = 4m/(3\sqrt{3})$, there are four real solutions, which are symmetrical to each other, namely, $(r_+, r_C, -r_C, -r_+)$, (where u_+ corresponds to the event horizon and u_C to a Cauchy horizon); ii) for $a = a_{\text{ext}}$, we have two real solutions $(u_+, -u_+)$; iii) and for $a > a_{\text{ext}}$, no real value exists. We refer the reader to[44] for more details. Thus, in order to have a traversable wormhole solution, where only the case of $A(u) > 0$ is satisfied, only the specific case for $a > a_{\text{ext}}$ interests us here.

For this case, the gravitational field equations (17)–(19) yield the stress-energy profile, given by the following relations:

$$\rho(u) = -\frac{1}{8\pi} \left[\frac{a^2 \left(a^2 + u^2\right)^{3/2} - 8ma^2 u^2}{(a^2 + u^2)^{7/2}} + \frac{\lambda(u)}{a^2 + u^2} \right], \tag{44}$$

$$p_r(u) = \frac{1}{8\pi} \left[-\frac{a^2 \left(a^2 + u^2\right)^{3/2} + 4ma^2 u^2}{(a^2 + u^2)^{7/2}} + \frac{\lambda(u)}{a^2 + u^2} \right], \tag{45}$$

$$p_t(u) = \frac{a^2 u^2 \left(\sqrt{a^2 + u^2} + 5m\right) + a^4 \left(\sqrt{a^2 + u^2} - 2m\right)}{8\pi (a^2 + u^2)^{7/2}}, \tag{46}$$

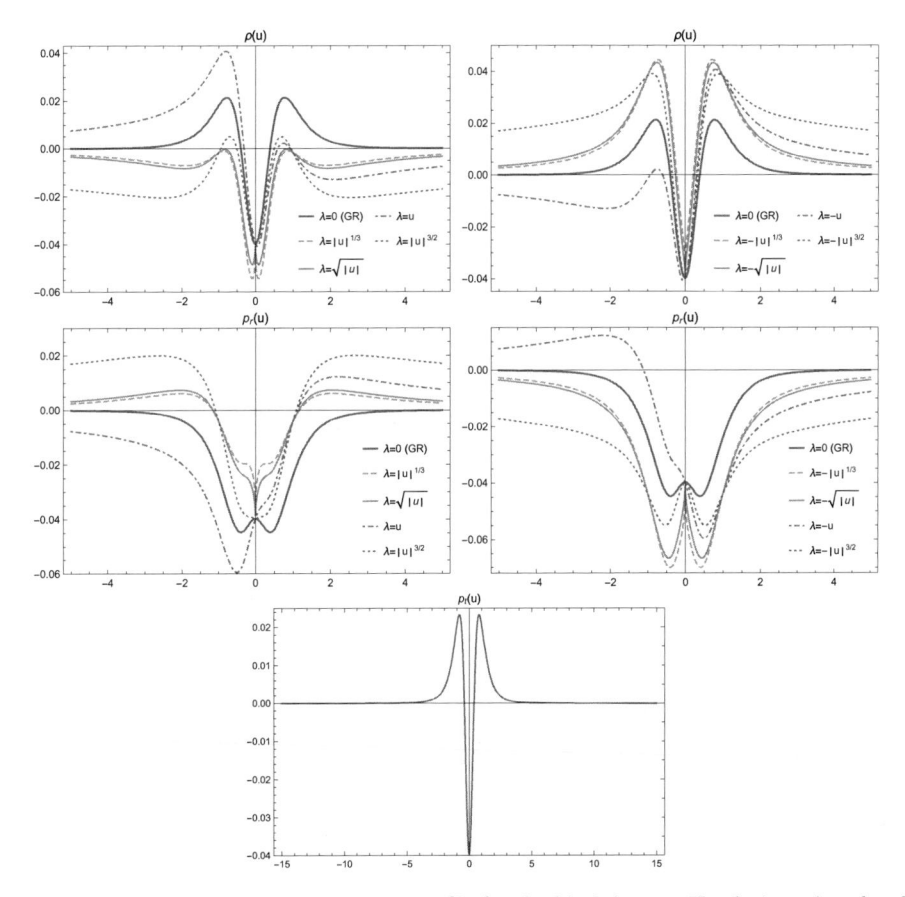

Fig. 4. The plots depict the stress-energy profile for the black bounce II solution, given by the metric function (43), where for numerical convenience we have assumed the following choices for the parameters: $m = 1, a = 1$. Recall that the parameters are restricted by the condition $a > 4m/(3\sqrt{3})$. As before these wormhole configurations possess a far richer internal structure than their general relativistic counterparts, and depending on the sign of $\lambda(u)$, specific symmetric or asymmetric solutions are obtained. However, here the tangential pressure at the wormhole throat, $p_t(u = 0) = (a - 2m)/(8\pi a^3)$, takes negative values for the parameter range $4m/(3\sqrt{3}) < a < 2m$, and positive values for $a > 2m$. We refer the reader to the text for more details.

respectively, which are depicted in Fig. 4 for specific choices of the model parameters.

Assume, once again, a power law for $\lambda(u) \sim u^\alpha$, we have that $0 \leq \alpha < 2$ by the asymptotic flatness condition and the regularity of the stress-energy components, as before. As before these wormhole geometries induced by action-dependent Lagrangian theories possesses a far richer internal structure than their general relativistic counterparts, and depending on the sign of $\lambda(u)$, specific symmetric or asymmetric solutions are obtained. We refer the reader to Fig. 4 for a qualitative behaviour of the stress-energy profile; recall that taking into account the parameter range, we consider the condition $a > 4m/(3\sqrt{3})$. Here the tangential pressure at the wormhole throat is given by $p_t(u=0) = (a-2m)/(8\pi a^3)$, and takes negative values for $4m/(3\sqrt{3}) < a < 2m$, possessing a minimum at the throat, and positive values for $a > 2m$; note that $p_t(u) \to 0$ for $u \to \pm\infty$.

3.3.3. *Black bounce III*

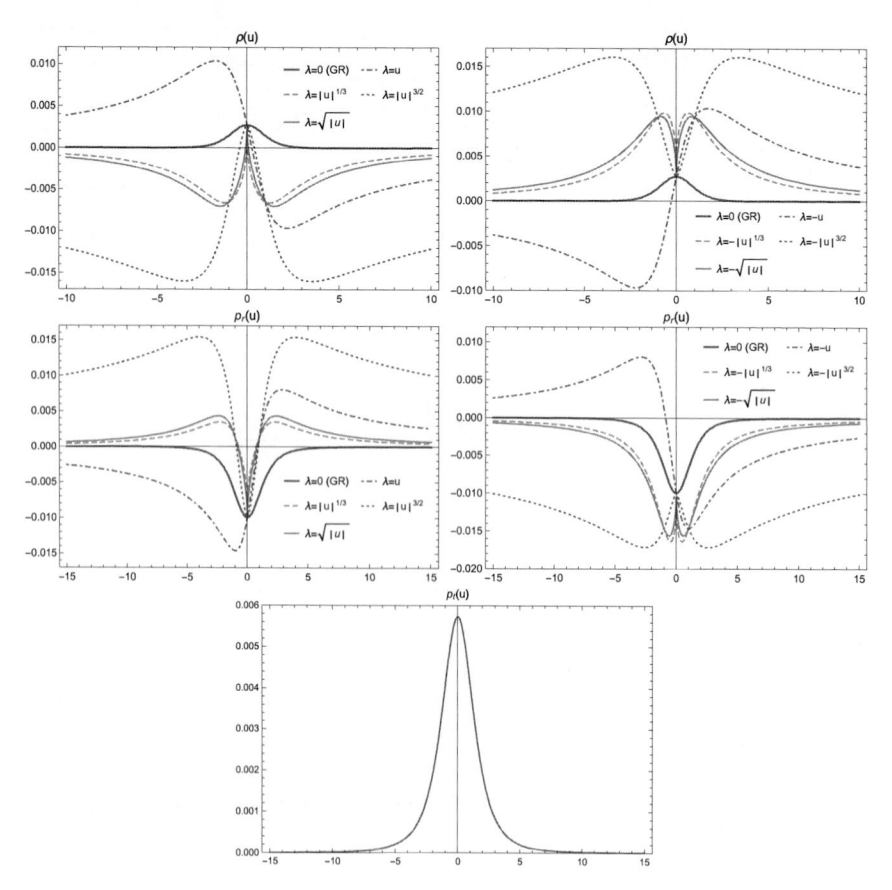

Fig. 5. The plots depict the stress-energy profile for the black bounce III solution, given by the functions (47) and (49), for the case $n = 1$, where $a > a_{\text{ext}}$, so that there are no event horizons. We have chosen the following values for the parameters: $m = 1$ and $a = 2$. Note that for these solutions, the negative energy densities are improved, and one may also obtain positive radial pressures for positive values of the function $\lambda(u)$. See the text for more details.

Finally, we consider another black bounce solution explored in,[44] that also exhibits interesting properties, given by

$$R(u) = \sqrt{u^2 + a^2}. \tag{47}$$

and the mass function:
$$M(u) = m\left(\frac{R(u)}{u}\right)\left(\frac{2}{\pi}\right)^n \arctan^n\left(\frac{u}{a}\right), \qquad (48)$$

so that the metric function $A(u)$ is given by
$$A(u) = 1 - \frac{2M(u)}{R(u)} = 1 - \frac{2m}{u}\left(\frac{2}{\pi}\right)^n \arctan^n\left(\frac{u}{a}\right). \qquad (49)$$

In the limit $(a, n) \to 0$ we regain the Schwarzschild solution. However, one can fix n and regulate the presence of horizons by adjusting a. For instance, consider $n = 1$, where the extreme case is given by $a_{\text{ext}} = 4m/\pi$.[44]

The causal structure, for the specific case of $n = 1$, is given by: (i) for $a > a_{\text{ext}}$, this corresponds to the traditional two-way traversable wormhole; (ii) for $a = a_{\text{ext}}$, we have a one-way wormhole geometry with an extremal null throat; (iii) for $a < a_{\text{ext}}$, we have one horizon located in each universe, where one may propagate through this event horizon, located at $u = u_+$ in order to reach the spacelike "bounce" hypersurface at $u = 0$, before "bouncing" into a future version of our own universe. We refer the interested reader to Ref.[44] for more details. Thus, we are only interested in the case $a > a_{\text{ext}}$, for $n = 1$, where there are no event horizons.

Taking into account the metric functions (47) and (49), the gravitational field equations (17)–(19) provide the following stress-energy components:

$$\rho(u) = -\frac{1}{8\pi}\left\{\frac{a^2}{(a^2+u^2)^2}\left[1 - \frac{2m}{ua}\left(\frac{2}{\pi}\right)^n\left(\arctan\left(\frac{u}{a}\right)\right)^{n-1}\left(a\arctan\left(\frac{u}{a}\right)+nu\right)\right]\right.$$
$$\left.+\frac{\lambda(u)}{a^2+u^2}\right\}, \qquad (50)$$

$$p_r(u) = \frac{1}{8\pi}\left\{\frac{2ma}{u(a^2+u^2)^2}\left(\frac{2}{\pi}\right)^n\left(\arctan\left(\frac{u}{a}\right)\right)^{n-1}\left[a\arctan\left(\frac{u}{a}\right)-nu\right]\right.$$
$$\left.+\frac{(a^2+u^2)\lambda(u)-a^2}{(a^2+u^2)^2}\right\}, \qquad (51)$$

$$p_t(u) = \frac{a^2}{8\pi(a^2+u^2)^2}\left\{1 - \frac{m}{au^3}\left(\frac{2}{\pi}\right)^n\left(\arctan\left(\frac{u}{a}\right)\right)^{n-2}\right.$$
$$\times\left[2\left(a^3+2au^2\right)\left(\arctan\left(\frac{u}{a}\right)\right)^2\right.$$
$$\left.\left.- 2nu\left(a^2+u^2\right)\arctan\left(\frac{u}{a}\right)+a(n-1)nu^2\right]\right\}. \qquad (52)$$

respectively. Here, we will only consider, for simplicity, the specific case of $n = 1$ and $a > a_{\text{ext}}$.

If we consider, as before, a power law for $\lambda(u) \sim u^\alpha$, the asymptotic flatness and regularity conditions impose $0 \leq \alpha < 2$. Once again, one obtains a wide variety of solutions, both symmetric and asymmetric, which are depicted in Fig. 5. The advantage of these solutions consists essentially in that they ameliorate the negative energy densities for negative values of the function $\lambda(u)$. However, positive values of the function $\lambda(u)$ allow positive radial pressures as is transparent in Fig. 5. The tangential pressure tends to zero at spatial infinity, i.e., $p_t(u) \to 0$ for $u \to \pm\infty$, and possesses a maximum at the throat, as depicted in Fig. 5.

4. Conclusions

In this work, we have explored wormhole geometries in the recently proposed action-dependent Lagrangian theories,[28] that are obtained through an action principle for action-dependent Lagrangians by generalizing the Herglotz variational problem for several independent variables. An interesting feature of these theories as compared with previous implementations of dissipative effects in gravity is the possible arising of such phenomena from a least action principle, so they are of a purely geometric nature. It was shown that the generalized gravitational field equation essentially depends on a background four-vector λ^μ, that plays the role of a coupling parameter associated with the dependence of the gravitational Lagrangian upon the action, and may generically depend on the spacetime coordinates. In the context of wormhole configurations, we have used the "Buchdahl coordinates", and found that the four-vector is given generically by $\lambda_\mu = (0, 0, \lambda_\theta(u, \theta), 0)$. In addition to this restriction the spacetime geometry is also severely constrained by the condition $g_{tt}g_{uu} = -1$, where u is the radial coordinate.

More specifically, we have shown that the field equations (17)–(19), impose a system of three independent equations with six unknown functions of the radial coordinate u, namely, $\rho(u)$, $p_r(u)$, $p_t(u)$, $A(u)$, $R(u)$ and $\lambda(u)$. Thus, one possesses several strategies to solve the system of equations. For instance, one may consider a plausible stress-energy tensor profile by imposing equations of state $p_r = p_r(\rho)$ and $p_t = p_t(\rho)$, and close the system by adequately choosing the energy density, or a specific metric function. However, one may also adopt the reverse philosophy approach usually used in wormhole physics by simple choosing specific choices for the metric functions and $\lambda(u)$, and through the field equations determine the stress-energy profile responsible for sustaining the wormhole geometry. Here, we have found a plethora of specific asymptotically flat, symmetric and asymmetric, solutions with power law choices for the function λ, for instance, by generalizing the Ellis-Bronnikov solutions and the recently proposed black bounce geometries, amongst other solutions. We have shown that these compact objects possess a far richer geometrical structure than their general relativistic counterparts. It would be interesting to investigate time-dependent spacetimes as outlined in[17,18] in order to explore the energy conditions, and work along these lines is presently underway.

Acknowledgments

IA is funded by the Fundação para a Ciência e a Tecnologia (FCT, Portugal) grant No. PD/BD/114435/2016 under the IDPASC PhD Program. FSNL acknowledges support from the FCT Scientific Employment Stimulus contract with reference CEECIND/04057/2017. The authors also acknowledge funding from FCT Projects No. UID/FIS/04434/2020, No. CERN/FIS-PAR/0037/2019 and No. PTDC/FIS-OUT/29048/2017.

References

1. M. S. Morris and K. S. Thorne, "Wormholes in space-time and their use for interstellar travel: A tool for teaching general relativity," Am. J. Phys. **56**, 395 (1988).
2. M. S. Morris, K. S. Thorne and U. Yurtsever, "Wormholes, Time Machines, and the Weak Energy Condition," Phys. Rev. Lett. **61**, 1446 (1988).
3. M. Visser, "Lorentzian wormholes: From Einstein to Hawking," Woodbury, USA: AIP (1995).
4. F. S. N. Lobo, "Wormholes, Warp Drives and Energy Conditions", Fundam. Theor. Phys. **189**, pp. (2017), (formerly Lecture Notes in Physics), Springer Nature Switzerland AG.
5. M. Visser, "Traversable wormholes from surgically modified Schwarzschild spacetimes", Nucl. Phys. B **328** (1989) 203 [arXiv:0809.0927 [gr-qc]].
6. M. Visser, "Traversable wormholes: Some simple examples", Phys. Rev. D **39** (1989) 3182 [arXiv:0809.0907 [gr-qc]].
7. E. Poisson and M. Visser, "Thin shell wormholes: Linearization stability", Phys. Rev. D **52**, 7318 (1995) [arXiv:gr-qc/9506083].
8. F. S. N. Lobo and P. Crawford, "Linearized stability analysis of thin shell wormholes with a cosmological constant," Class. Quant. Grav. **21** (2004), 391-404 [arXiv:gr-qc/0311002 [gr-qc]].
9. F. S. N. Lobo, "Energy conditions, traversable wormholes and dust shells," Gen. Rel. Grav. **37** (2005), 2023-2038 [arXiv:gr-qc/0410087 [gr-qc]].
10. F. S. N. Lobo and P. Crawford, "Stability analysis of dynamic thin shells," Class. Quant. Grav. **22** (2005), 4869-4886 [arXiv:gr-qc/0507063 [gr-qc]].
11. N. Montelongo-García, F. S. N. Lobo and M. Visser, "Generic spherically symmetric dynamic thin-shell traversable wormholes in standard general relativity", Phys. Rev. D **86** (2012) 044026 [arXiv:1112.2057 [gr-qc]].
12. M. Bouhmadi-López, F. S. N. Lobo and P. Martín-Moruno, "Wormholes minimally violating the null energy condition," JCAP **11** (2014), 007 [arXiv:1407.7758 [gr-qc]].
13. F. S. N. Lobo, A. Simpson and M. Visser, "Dynamic thin-shell black-bounce traversable wormholes," Phys. Rev. D **101** (2020) no.12, 124035 [arXiv:2003.09419 [gr-qc]].
14. T. Berry, F. S. N. Lobo, A. Simpson and M. Visser, "Thin-shell traversable wormhole crafted from a regular black hole with asymptotically Minkowski core," Phys. Rev. D **102** (2020) no.6, 064054 [arXiv:2008.07046 [gr-qc]].
15. S. Kar, "Evolving wormholes and the weak energy condition," Phys. Rev. D **49**, 862-865 (1994).
16. S. Kar and D. Sahdev, "Evolving Lorentzian wormholes," Phys. Rev. D **53**, 722 (1996) [arXiv:gr-qc/9506094 [gr-qc]].
17. M. Kord Zangeneh, F. S. N. Lobo and H. Moradpour, "Evolving traversable wormholes satisfying the energy conditions in the presence of pole dark energy," [arXiv:2008.04013 [gr-qc]].
18. M. Kord Zangeneh and F. S. N. Lobo, "Dynamic wormhole geometries in hybrid metric-Palatini gravity," [arXiv:2011.01745 [gr-qc]].

19. F. S. N. Lobo, "General class of wormhole geometries in conformal Weyl gravity", Class. Quant. Grav. **25**, 175006 (2008) [arXiv:0801.4401 [gr-qc]].
20. F. S. N. Lobo, M. A. Oliveira, "Wormhole geometries in $f(R)$ modified theories of gravity", Phys. Rev. **D80**, 104012 (2009) [arXiv:0909.5539 [gr-qc]].
21. N. Montelongo-García, F. S. N. Lobo, "Wormhole geometries supported by a nonminimal curvature-matter coupling", Phys. Rev. **D82**, 104018 (2010) [arXiv:1007.3040 [gr-qc]].
22. N. Montelongo-García, F. S. N. Lobo, "Nonminimal curvature-matter coupled wormholes with matter satisfying the null energy condition", Class. Quant. Grav. **28**, 085018 (2011) [arXiv:1012.2443 [gr-qc]].
23. C. G. Boehmer, T. Harko and F. S. N. Lobo, "Wormhole geometries in modified teleparralel gravity and the energy conditions", Phys. Rev. D **85** (2012) 044033 [arXiv:1110.5756 [gr-qc]].
24. T. Harko, F. S. N. Lobo, M. K. Mak and S. V. Sushkov, "Modified-gravity wormholes without exotic matter", Phys. Rev. D **87** (2013) no.6, 067504 [arXiv:1301.6878 [gr-qc]].
25. M. R. Mehdizadeh, M. Kord Zangeneh and F. S. N. Lobo, "Einstein-Gauss-Bonnet traversable wormholes satisfying the weak energy condition", Phys. Rev. D **91**, no. 8, 084004 (2015) [arXiv:1501.04773 [gr-qc]].
26. M. Kord Zangeneh, F. S. N. Lobo and M. H. Dehghani, "Traversable wormholes satisfying the weak energy condition in third-order Lovelock gravity", Phys. Rev. D **92**, no. 12, 124049 (2015) [arXiv:1510.07089 [gr-qc]].
27. J. L. Rosa, J. P. S. Lemos and F. S. N. Lobo, "Wormholes in generalized hybrid metric-Palatini gravity obeying the matter null energy condition everywhere," Phys. Rev. D **98**, no. 6, 064054 (2018) [arXiv:1808.08975 [gr-qc]].
28. M. J. Lazo, J. Paiva, J. T. S. Amaral and G. S. F. Frederico, "Action principle for action-dependent Lagrangians toward nonconservative gravity: Accelerating universe without dark energy," Phys. Rev. D **95** (2017) no. 10, 101501 [arXiv:1705.04604 [gr-qc]].
29. G. Herglotz, Berührungstransformationen, Lectures at the University of Götingen, Göttingen, (1930).
30. R. B. Guenther, C. M. Guenther and J. A. Gottsch, The Herglotz Lectures on Contact Transformations and Hamiltonian Systems, Lecture Notes in Nonlinear Analysis, Vol. 1, Juliusz Schauder Center for Nonlinear Studies, Nicholas Copernicus University, Torún, (1996).
31. J. C. Fabris, H. Velten, T. R. P. Caramês, M. J. Lazo and G. S. F. Frederico, "Cosmology from a new nonconservative gravity," Int. J. Mod. Phys. D **27** (2018) no.06, 1841006 [arXiv:1711.06206 [gr-qc]].
32. J. C. Fabris, T. R. P. Caramês and J. M. Hoff Da Silva, "Braneworld gravity within non-conservative gravitational theory," Eur. Phys. J. C **78** (2018) no.5, 402 [arXiv:1804.01072 [gr-qc]].
33. E. A. F. Bragança, T. R. P. Caramês, J. C. Fabris and A. d. Santos, "Some effects of non-conservative gravity on cosmic string configurations", Eur. Phys. J. C **79** (2019) no.2, 162 [arXiv:1808.01653 [gr-qc]].
34. T. R. P. Caramês, H. Velten, J. C. Fabris and M. J. Lazo, "Dark energy with zero pressure: Accelerated expansion and large scale structure in action-dependent Lagrangian theories," Phys. Rev. D **98** (2018) no. 10, 103501 [arXiv:1808.02798 [gr-qc]].
35. J. C. Fabris, H. Velten and A. Wojnar, "Existence of static spherically-symmetric objects in action-dependent Lagrangian theories," Phys. Rev. D **99** (2019) no.12, 124031 [arXiv:1903.12193 [gr-qc]].
36. M. R. Finch and J. E. F. Skea, "A review of the relativistic static fluid sphere", 1998, unpublished.

37. P. Boonserm and M. Visser, "Buchdahl-like transformations for perfect fluid spheres", Int. J. Mod. Phys. D **17** (2008), 135–163 [arXiv:0707.0146 [gr-qc]].
38. P. Boonserm and M. Visser, "Buchdahl-like transformations in general relativity", Thai Journal of Mathematics **5 # 2** (2007) 209–223.
39. S. V. Sushkov and R. Korolev, "Scalar wormholes with nonminimal derivative coupling," Class. Quant. Grav. **29** (2012), 085008 [arXiv:1111.3415 [gr-qc]].
40. H. G. Ellis, "Ether flow through a drainhole: A particle model in general relativity," *J. Math. Phys.* **14**, 104 (1973).
41. H. G. Ellis, "The evolving, flowless drain hole: a nongravitating particle model in general relativity theory," *Gen. Rel. Grav.* **10**, 105-123 (1979).
42. K. A. Bronnikov, "Scalar-tensor theory and scalar charge," *Acta Phys. Pol. B* **4**, 251 (1973).
43. A. Simpson and M. Visser, "Black-bounce to traversable wormhole," JCAP **02** (2019), 042 [arXiv:1812.07114 [gr-qc]].
44. F. S. N. Lobo, M. E. Rodrigues, M. V. d. S. Silva, A. Simpson and M. Visser, "Novel black-bounce geometries," [arXiv:2009.12057 [gr-qc]].

Gravitational lensing by wormholes in binary systems

S. Pietroni

Dipartimento di Fisica "E.R. Caianiello", Università di Salerno, Via Giovanni Paolo II 132, I-84084 Fisciano, Italy
Istituto Nazionale di Fisica Nucleare, Sezione di Napoli, Via Cintia, 80126, Napoli, Italy
E-mail: spietroni@unisa.it

We investigate binary lenses with $1/r^n$ potentials in the asymmetric case with two lenses with different indexes n and m. These kinds of potentials have been widely used in several contexts, ranging from galaxies with halos described by different power laws to lensing by wormholes or exotic matter.

Keywords: Gravitational lensing; black holes; wormholes; galaxies

1. Introduction

Space-time is curved by the presence of massive bodies and this curvature influences the motion of the bodies themselves: this leads to a geometry in constant evolution. One of the consequences is that even light, supposed to be massless, bends its trajectory while passing close to a massive body.[1]

Gravitational lensing is an important tool in astrophysics and in cosmology widely used to study both populations of compact objects (including exoplanets, black holes and other stellar remnants) , and extended objects, such as galaxies, clusters of galaxies and large-scale structures . Since most of the mysteries of our Universe do not show up in observations based on electromagnetic interactions, gravitational lensing is more and more employed to study the dark side of the Universe, including dark matter, dark energy, and any kind of exotic matter (such as wormholes) conjectured by theorists.[2]

2. Lensing by Wormholes

The metric of the Ellis wormhole falls down asymptotically as $1/r^2$ and its deflection angle goes as the inverse square of the impact parameter $1/u^2$.

Metrics falling as $1/r^n$ were investigated also by Kitamura et al.[3] who found out that the deflection angle falls down with the same exponent as the metric, $\hat{\alpha} \sim 1/u^n$ with $n > 1$, and that a demagnification of the total lensed images could appear at $\beta > \frac{2}{n+1}$ (in units of θ_E, the Einstein radius, and under a large-n approximation, β is the source position). This demagnification effect may be evidence of an Ellis wormhole and it might be used for hunting the search for exotic matter. Particular attention was posed on the study of caustics of $1/r^n$ binary lenses by Bozza and Melchiorre in Ref.[4]

The implications for the energy-momentum tensor supporting this kind of metrics falling as $1/r^n$ were investigated by Bozza and Postiglione,[5] we remind that $0 < n < 1$ may describe galactic halos, $n > 1$ would be the signature of a violation of the weak energy condition and so the existence of exotic matter, $n = 2$ correspond to the Ellis wormhole; n is the ratio between tangential and radial pressure, $n = -2p_t/p_r$.

3. The Lens Equation, Critical Curves and Caustics

In a binary system composed by two lenses (binary lenses, A and B), the lens equation can be written as follows

$$\vec{\beta} = \vec{\theta} - \frac{\vec{\theta} - \vec{\theta_A}}{|\vec{\theta} - \vec{\theta_A}|^{n+1}} - \gamma^{m+1} \frac{\vec{\theta} - \vec{\theta_B}}{|\vec{\theta} - \vec{\theta_B}|^{m+1}}, \qquad (1)$$

where $\gamma = \theta_{E,B}/\theta_{E,A}$ is the "strength ratio".

The lens equation allows us to find images, given the source position and a lens configuration.

The number of images formed at a given source β depends on the source position and these regions with a different number of images are delimited by caustics.

The condition $J(z) = 0$ (the Jacobian determinant of the lens map) defines the critical curves on the lens plane; and by applying the lens map on critical points we find the corresponding points on the source plane, which form the caustics. When a source crosses a caustic, a new pair of images is created on the corresponding point in the critical curve.

4. Cases and Topology Regimes

We investigated 3 cases: the equal-strength binary with $\gamma = 1$, the unequal-strength binary with $\gamma = \sqrt{0.1}$ (the bigger lens is the standard one with fixed $n = 1$), and the reversed unequal-strength binary with $\gamma = \sqrt{0.1}$ (the standard lens is the smaller one).

For the standard binary Schwarzschild lens in the equal-strength case, we know that three topologies exist:

- close separation, for $s < s_{CI}$;
- intermediate separation, for $s_{CI} < s < s_{IW}$;
- wide separation, for $s > s_{IW}$;

and the two transitions are $s_{CI} = 1$ and $s_{IW} = 2\sqrt{2}$ in our units.

The three topologies exist for any value of m and n.

Our model contains 4 parameters: the indexes of the two potentials n, m, the separation between the two lenses s, and the ratio of the two Einstein radii γ.

5. Critical Curves and Caustics: Wide, Intermediate and Close Separations

Here we show the equal-strength case with $\gamma = 1$, the full research can be found in: *Bozza V., Pietroni S., Melchiorre C., Universe 2020, 6(8), 106*.[6]

The red curve is for the standard Schwarzschild case $n = m = 1$, we keep $n = 1$ for the first lens and we see what happens when m varies in the second lens

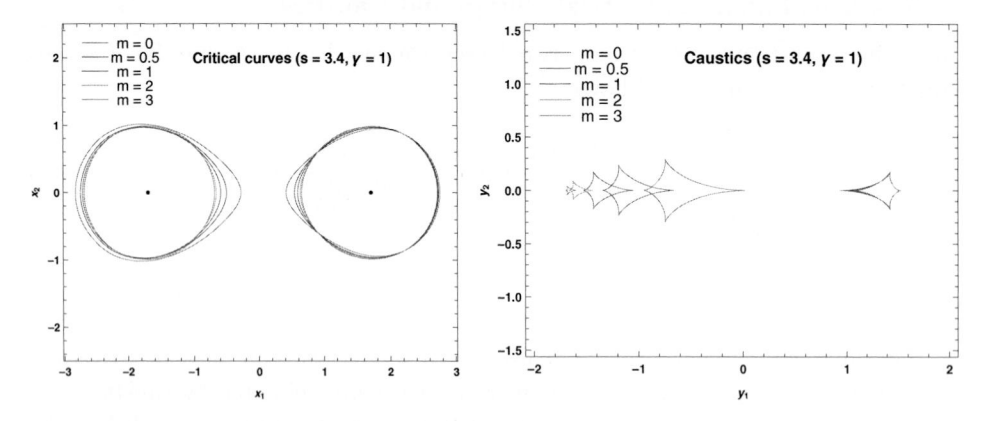

Fig. 1. Critical curves and caustics in the equal-strength binary, wide separation with fixed $n = 1$ and variable m: $m = 0$ is the singular isothermal sphere already investigated by Shin and Evans, $m = 0.5$ is the galactic halo, $m = 2$ is the Ellis wormhole and $m = 3$ is for exotic matter.

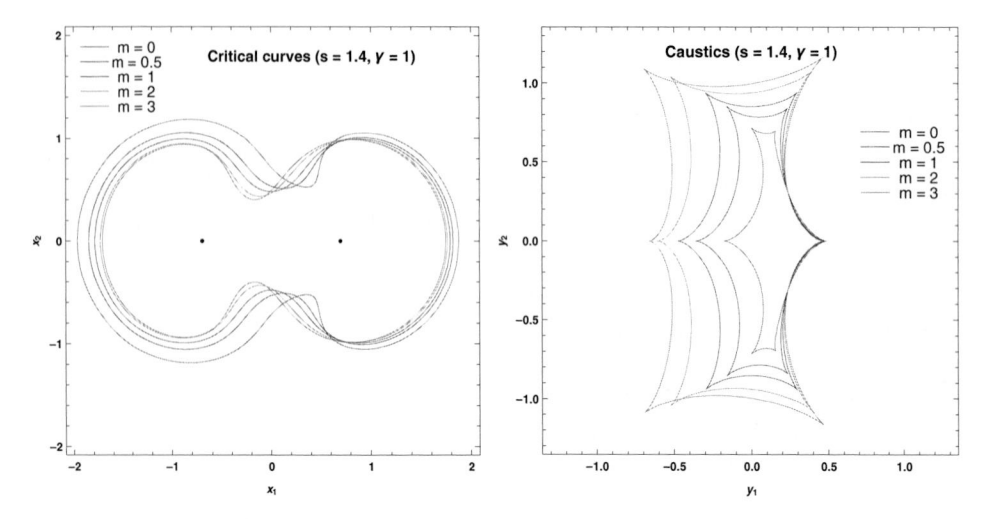

Fig. 2. Critical curves and caustics in the equal-strength binary, intermediate separation with fixed $n = 1$ and variable m. The red curve is for the standard Schwarzschild case $n = m = 1$.

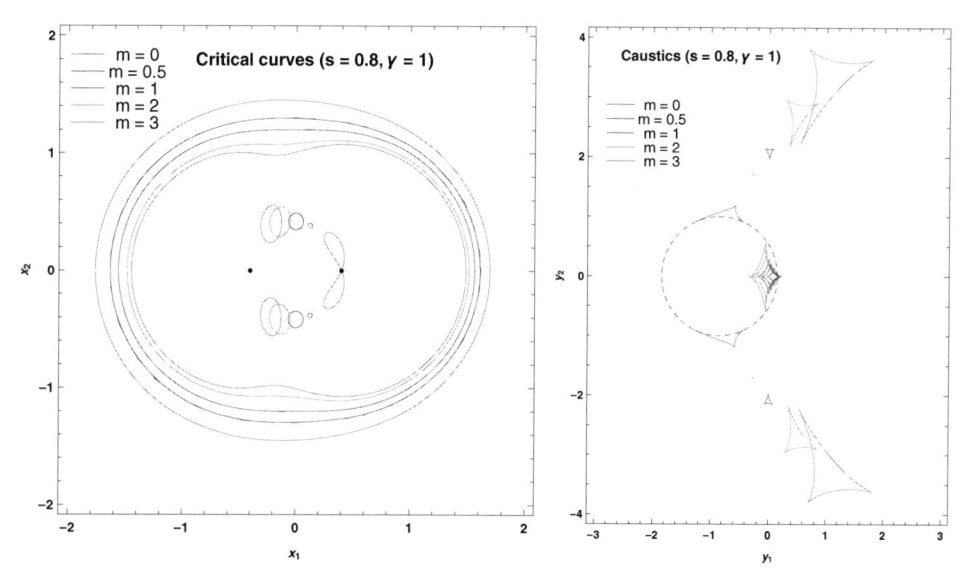

Fig. 3. Critical curves and caustics in the equal-strength binary, close separation with fixed $n = 1$ and variable m. The red curve is for the standard Schwarzschild case $n = m = 1$. Dashed magenta circle indicates the pseudocaustic for $m = 0$.

6. The Elliptic Umbilic and the Extremely Unequal-Strength Ratio Limit

In the range $0 \leq m < 1$ an *elliptic umbilic catastrophe* exists in the close separation. The value of s at which the catastrophe happens is

$$s_{euc} = \left(\frac{1-mn}{m+1}\right)^{\frac{1}{n+1}} \sqrt{1 + \frac{\gamma^2(m+1)^{\frac{2}{n+1}}}{(n+1)^{\frac{2}{m+1}}(1-mn)^{\frac{2(m-n)}{(m+1)(n+1)}}}}. \qquad (2)$$

Fig. 4. The elliptic umbilic catastrophe for $n = 2$, $m = 0.25$. The separation at which the catastrophe occurs is $s_{euc} = 0.774$.

For any n, m, γ we found the boundaries for s_{CI}, given only numerically, and the analytical expression for s_{IW}.

The caustic evolution in the extreme limit $\theta_{E,B} \ll \theta_{E,A}$, in the case of two Schwarzschild objects ($n = m = 1$), is the so-called "planetary" limit. For the caustics of the perturbing object in the wide case we have an extension of the caustics in the parallel and in the vertical direction:

$$\Delta \zeta_{\parallel,wide} = 2(n+1) \frac{\gamma}{s^{\frac{m(n+1)}{m+1}} (s^{n+1} - 1)^{\frac{1}{m+1}}} \tag{3}$$

$$\Delta \zeta_{\perp,wide} = 2(n+1) \frac{\gamma}{s^{\frac{m(n+1)}{m+1}} (s^{n+1} + n)^{\frac{1}{m+1}}}. \tag{4}$$

7. Conclusions

These mixed binary lenses are important from the astrophysical point of view in the investigation of pairs of galaxies with different halos ($n, m < 1$), in the opening of a new channel in the search for wormholes when they appear in a non-isolated environment ($n = 1$, $m = 2$), in the case in which one object is made up of exotic matter and the other one is a normal star ($n \geq 2$, $m = 1$).

References

1. Einstein, *Entwurf einer verallgemeinerten Relativitätstheorie und eine Theorie der Gravitation* (Leipzig, Berlin: Teubner, 1913).
2. V. Bozza, *Gravitational Lensing by Black Holes* (Gen. Rel. and Grav., 2010).
3. K. A. H. Kitamura, T.; Nakajima, *Demagnifying gravitational lenses toward hunting a clue of exotic matter and energyr* (Phys. Rev. D, 2013).
4. C. M. Bozza, V., *Gravitational Lensing by Black Holes Caustics of $1/r^n$ binary gravitational lenses: from galactic haloes to exotic matter* (JCAP, 2016).
5. P. A. Bozza, V., *Gravitational Lensing by Black Holes Alternatives to Schwarzschild in the weak field limit of General Relativity.* (JCAP, 2015).
6. M. C. Bozza V., Pietroni S., *Caustics in gravitational lensing by mixed binary systems* (Universe, 2020).

Hyper-fast positive energy warp drives

E. W. Lentz

Pacific Northwest National Laboratory, Richland, WA 99354 USA
E-mail: erik.lentz@pnnl.gov

Solitons in space–time capable of transporting time-like observers at superluminal speeds have long been tied to violations of the weak, strong, and dominant energy conditions of general relativity. This trend was recently broken by a new approach that identified soliton solutions capable of superluminal travel while being sourced by purely positive energy densities. This is the first example of hyper-fast solitons satisfying the weak energy condition, reopening the discussion of superluminal mechanisms rooted in conventional physics. This article summarizes the recent finding and its context in the literature. Remaining challenges to autonomous superluminal travel, such as the dominant energy condition, horizons, and the identification of a creation mechanism are also discussed.

Keywords: Warp Drive; Energy Conditions; Weak Energy Condition; Superluminal Travel.

1. Introduction

One of the most prominent critiques of superluminal travel within Einstein's general relativity (GR) is that any geometry that facilitates such travel must be largely sourced by a form of negative energy density.[1–18] Other concerns include the immense (magnitude) energy requirements to create a soliton, the difficulty associated with constructing a soliton from a nearly flat spacetime up to the superluminal phase, where the transported central observers become surrounded by a horizon, and the equal difficulties of driving the superluminal phase back the nearly flat spacetime.

There has been a recent uptick in interest regarding warp drives due to a set of papers made available in 2020 and 2021 claiming the construction of solutions that do not require sources with negative energy density,[19–22] obeying the weak energy condition (WEC). These increasingly physical warp drives were the focus of a mini-session at the 16th Marcel Grossmann meeting that covered the history of warp drive research in academia, the recent positive energy warp drive research papers, and two articles regarding their reception.[23,24] This article will concern only the paper written by the author,[19] summarizing its findings and discussing its standing in the literature. Mathematical notation will largely follow that of the original paper.

2. Natário Class Spacetimes

The class of relativistic spacetime metrics describing warp drive geometries in the literature are decomposed according to "3+1" Arnowitt-Deser-Misner (ADM) formalism[25]

$$ds^2 = -\left(N^2 - N^i N_i\right) dt^2 - 2N_i dx^i dt + h_{ij} dx^i dx^j, \tag{1}$$

where the time coordinate t stratifies spacetime into space-like hypersurfaces, the space metric components h_{ij} evaluated at t provide the intrinsic geometry of that hypersurface, and the similarly-evaluated shift vector components N^i at t provide the coordinate three-velocity of the hypersurface's normal. The time-like unit normal one-form is therefore proportional to the coordinate time element $\mathbf{n}^* = N dt$, and the unit normal vector $\mathbf{n}$ to the hypersurface has components

$$n^\nu = \left(\frac{1}{N}, \frac{N^i}{N}\right). \tag{2}$$

For simplicity, we will use natural units $G = c = 1$.

The majority of previous warp drive papers including Lentz 2021[19] set the lapse function N to unity and the hypersurface metric to be flat under Cartesian coordinates $h_{ij} = \delta_{ij}$. The non-flat geometry is therefore encoded in the three-component shift vector, N_i. The class of spacetimes described in this way have been coined as "Natário spacetimes".[20, 23, 24]

The projection of the Einstein equation onto the hypersurface normal gives the Hamiltonian constraint of a Natário spacetime

$$G^{\mu\nu} n_\mu n_\nu = 8\pi T^{\mu\nu} n_\mu n_\nu, \tag{3}$$

with the projected stress-energy being referred to as the Eulerian energy density

$$T^{\mu\nu} n_\mu n_\nu = T^{00} = E. \tag{4}$$

The geometric side of this energy constraint equation can be expressed in terms of the extrinsic curvature's trace $K = K_i^i$ and its quadratic hypersurface scalar $K_j^i K_i^j$

$$8\pi E = \frac{1}{2}\left(-K_j^i K_i^j + K^2\right). \tag{5}$$

The combination of extrinsic curvatures expanded in terms of the shift vector components take the form

$$K^2 - K_j^i K_i^j = 2\partial_x N_x \partial_y N_y + 2\partial_x N_x \partial_z N_z + 2\partial_z N_z \partial_y N_y$$
$$- \frac{1}{2}(\partial_x N_y + \partial_y N_x)^2 - \frac{1}{2}(\partial_x N_z + \partial_z N_x)^2 - \frac{1}{2}(\partial_z N_y + \partial_y N_z)^2. \tag{6}$$

The warp drive solution of Alcubierre[1] set the precedent for WEC violation by requiring negative Eulerian energy throughout. Specifically, utilizing only a single component of the shift vector in the direction of motion, here taken to be along the positive z-axis, produces the renowned toroid of negative energy density about the soliton bubble of N_z, here displayed in Cartesian coordinates,

$$E_{\text{Alc}} = \frac{-1}{32\pi}\left((\partial_x N_z)^2 + (\partial_y N_z)^2\right). \tag{7}$$

The expansionless ($K = -1/2(\partial_x N_x + \partial_y N_y + \partial_z N_z) = 0$) elliptic relation of Natário 2002[11] restricted the energy form to the negative definite square of the extrinsic curvature

$$E_{\text{Nat}} = \frac{-1}{16\pi} K_j^i K_i^j. \tag{8}$$

Parabolic and hyperbolic relations remained to be explored at the start of 2020.

3. Positive Energy Warp Drives

The soliton geometry of Lentz 2021[19] distinguishes itself from the previous literature in that it satisfies the WEC, even when moving at superluminal speeds. The WEC states that the energy of a spacetime is nowhere negative for any time-like observer. Mathematically, this means that for any time-like vector field X, the projection with the stress-energy tensor T must be non-negative

$$X_\mu T^{\mu\nu} X_\nu \geq 0. \tag{9}$$

The positive-energy soliton was identified through the construction of a set of rules sufficient to define geometries with everywhere non-negative energy. A brief presentation of the rules is given below.

Recall the expansion of the Hamiltonian constraint of Eqn. 6. Observe that the last three elements of the above expression are negative definite, while the first three are of indeterminant type. These first three terms provide opportunity for the Eulerian energy density function to be non-negative under particular configurations, so long as they are everywhere dominate over the first three terms. The next steps focus on such configurations.

The first rule is to reduce the 3D shift vector field to a single potential function, a real-valued function ϕ with spatial gradient relating the shift vector components

$$N_i = \partial_i \phi, \tag{10}$$

satisfying a linear wave equation over the spatial coordinates

$$\partial_x^2 \phi + \partial_y^2 \phi - \frac{2}{v_h^2} \partial_z^2 \phi = \rho, \tag{11}$$

where $v_h/\sqrt{2}$ is the dimensionless wave front 'speed' on the hypersurface, and ρ is the wave equation source function, not to be confused with mass or energy density. This step provides nearly all the structure needed to find the first example positive energy drives.

Two more simplifications are used to set sufficient rules for positive Eulerian energy. The energy functional is reduced to a two-coordinate form (z, x) by restricting ρ and ϕ to be parameterized in the (x, y) plane by the l_1 norm $s = |x| + |y|$,

$$E = \frac{1}{16\pi} \left(2\partial_z^2 \phi \left(\rho + \frac{2}{v_h^2} \partial_z^2 \phi \right) - 4 \left(\partial_z \partial_x \phi \right)^2 \right), \tag{12}$$

which can be bounded from below by

$$16\pi E \geq 2\rho \times \partial_z^2 \phi$$
$$= \rho \times \frac{1}{2v_h} \int_{-\infty}^{\infty} dx' \partial_r \rho(r, |x'| + |y|)|_{r=z-|\Delta x|/v_h}, \qquad (13)$$

where the Green's expressions for the shift vector is used in the last expression. From the lower bound expression, the last rule is formed to ensure the Eulerian energy density is everywhere non-negative: the energy function will be non-negative for configurations such that the local source density and the z-component source density gradient integrated along the intersecting 'past' wave trajectories are of the same sign. In other words, the two factors in Expr. 13 must have the same sign.

It is from this sequence of rules that the Eulerian energy can be constrained to be non-negative. Demonstrating the fullness of the WEC takes several additional steps to understand the contributions of the Eulerian momentum and stress components, and is covered in detail in the original publication,[19] but are omitted here in the interest of space. The rules invoked are not strictly necessary to positive-energy warp drives. The solution space of physical warp drives is expected to be much larger and more diverse.

The shift vector of the positive-energy soliton created in Lentz 2021[19] is given in Fig. 1. The soliton moves along the positive z axis at a speed set by the value of the shift vector at the origin of the co-moving coordinate coordinates in Fig. 1, which may be given arbitrary positive value. The transport logistics of the solitons are then similar to that of the Alcubierre solution. The solitons are constructed to contain a central region with minimal tidal forces, where proper time coincides with asymptotic coordinate time, and any Eulerian observer – which in this case is free falling and whose velocity matches the shift vector – within the central region would remain stationary with respect to the soliton. This is the region where a spacecraft would be placed.

The total energy requirements of the positive-energy solitons closely follow that of Pfenning & Ford 1997[3] as applied to the Alcubierre solution

$$E_{tot} = \int E\sqrt{-g}d^3x. \qquad (14)$$

For solitons where the radial extent of the central region R is much larger than the thickness of the energy-density laden boundary shell w ($w \ll R$), the energy is estimated to be

$$E_{tot} \sim Cv_s^2 \frac{R^2}{w} \qquad (15)$$

where C is a form factor typically of order unity. The required energy for a positive-energy soliton with central region mean radius $R = 100$ m and average source thickness along the z-axis $w = 1$ m approaches a mass equivalent of $E_{tot} \sim$ (few) $\times 10^{-1} M_\odot v_s^2$, which is of the same magnitude as the estimate of an Alcubierre solution of the same dimensions.

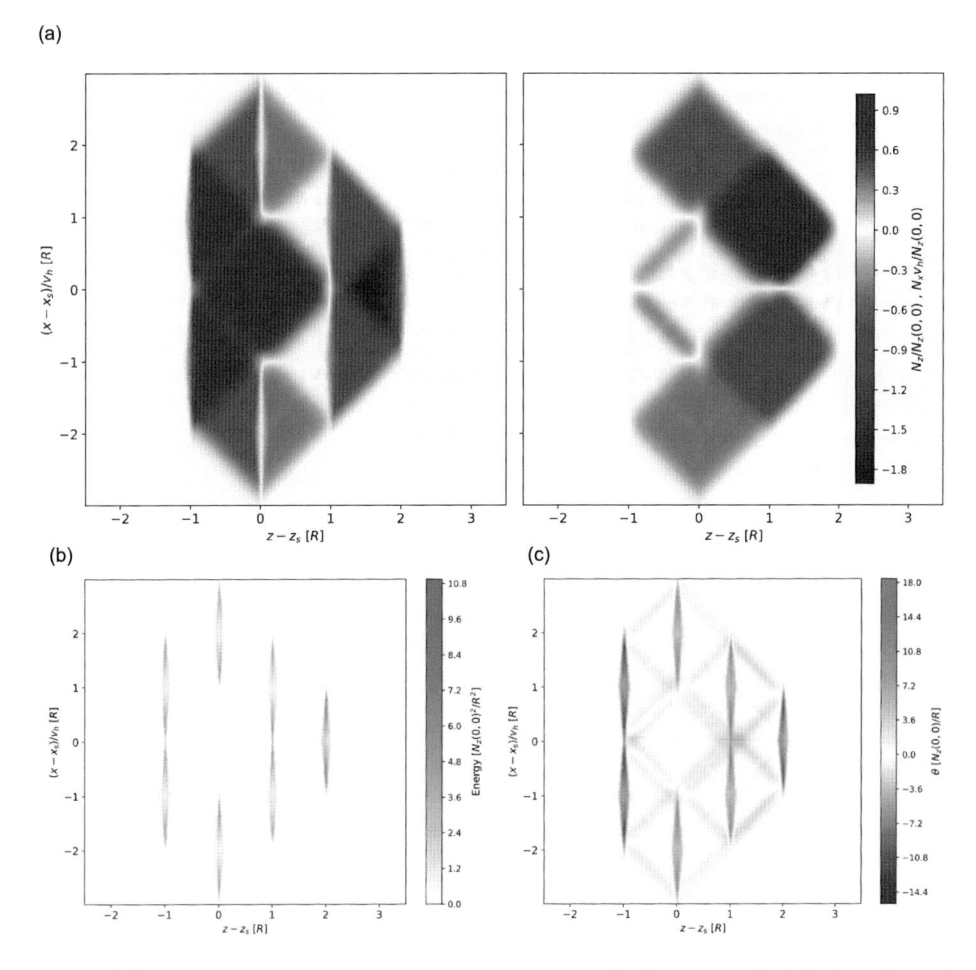

Fig. 1. (a) Projection of the shift vector components N_z (left) and N_x (right) along $(x, 0, z)$. Propagation direction of the soliton is from left to right along the z-axis. The multi-compartment structure is a distinct departure from the single top-hat soliton found in Alcubierre 1994[1] and Natário 2002.[11] Total integrated shift in each direction is 0. Note that the shift vector components are normalized with respect to the value of N_z a the co-moving origin. (b) Projection of the local energy density. The energy density is dominated by those regions containing hyperbolic source ρ, but also extends weakly to the boundaries of the wavefronts. The energy density is everywhere positive for Eulerian observers. (c) Projection of the local volume expansion factor θ. Positive and negative expansion factor are largely associated with negative and positive hyperbolic sources respectively. Non-zero expansion factor also exist in the spaces in-between hyperbolic sources along the hyperbolic wavefronts. Total integrated expansion factor is 0. These plots are taken from Lentz 2021.[19]

4. Addressing the Literature

The findings of Lentz 2021[19] run against the common wisdom of the warp drive literature to that point and the proofs set forth in Olum 1999[6] and Lobo & Crawford

2003[13] stating that any superluminal spacetime must violate the WEC via violations of the null energy condition (NEC). The proofs are both based on an analysis of the Raychaudhuri equation for null geodesics, confined to spacetimes with only a single fastest (superluminal) causal path between two space-like 2-surfaces. The pre-conditions of these proofs are very local in nature and appear analogous to collapsing the interior of a warp drive soliton to a point in order to produce a single fastest causal path. The solitons of the early literature, such as Alcubierre 1994[1] and Natário 2002,[11] have simple structures and can survive this limit. The example positive energy warp drive of Lentz 2021[19] cannot undergo this limit without being destroyed. This drive therefore does not meet the pre-conditions of the proofs and exists outside their scope, implying that the proofs are not applicable.

Several warp drive papers have addressed the findings of Lentz 2021[19] since an early manuscript of it was made publicly available.[20,22,23,23,26] Of particular note, the papers of[23,24] have made several assertions claiming that the solution of Lentz 2021[19] cannot satisfy the WEC. Follow-up correspondence with the authors as well as discussion captured at the recent Marcel Grossmann meeting have demonstrated that these papers did not adequately analyze the contents of Lentz 2021.[19] To summarize the discussions, Santiago et al.[23,24] argue that the Eulerian energy density of a soliton in a Natário class spacetime can be written as the sum of a total divergence and a negative definite term

$$E = \frac{1}{16\pi} \left(\partial_i \left(N_i \partial_j N_j - N_j \partial_j N_i \right) - \frac{1}{2} \omega_i \omega_i \right), \quad (16)$$

where $\omega_i = \epsilon_{ijk} \partial_k N_j$ is the shift vector vorticity. The divergence term is then argued to produce zero net energy if the warp drive is finite in size due to an application of the divergence theorem on the hypersurface where the integral's volume boundary is extended towards infinity where the divergence kernel quickly vanishes, implying that the total Eulerian energy of a Natário spacetime is non-positive. This argument does not hold in the case of Lentz 2021[19] as the Eulerian energy density of the example positive energy soliton is smooth save for the boundaries $x = 0$ and $y = 0$ where stress-energy sources are only continuous, while a requirement of the divergence theorem is that the total divergence be at least first order smooth everywhere. The integral volume boundary therefore cannot be separated from the soliton and instead must be applied in a patchwork,[27] with some boundaries running adjacent to the 2-surfaces $x = 0$ and $y = 0$, where the divergence kernel is non-vanishing. Expansion beyond Natário class of spacetimes may smooth the geometry and sources of positive energy warp drives further.

5. Further Challenges and Future Prospects

There are still numerous challenges between the current state of physical warp drive research and a functioning prototype. I list here several of the more near-term challenges and give my perspective as to how research in these areas may be approached.

The most glaring challenge is the astronomical energy cost of even a modest warp drive, currently measured in solar masses where kilograms is closer to the threshold of human technology. Extreme energy savings is going to be necessary – tens of orders of magnitude – to bring the energy required for a warp drive down to a level that can be tested in a laboratory setting let alone be considered a viable transportation technology.

There exist numerous techniques for reducing the energy requirements of the Alcubierre solution, several of which have been very successful in reducing the (magnitude) energy requirements of the system in excess of thirty orders of magnitude.[7,10,16,18,28] Unfortunately, each one of these methods in their presented forms require negative energies themselves. One possible approach to uncovering significant energy savings is to modify one of these existing techniques to obey the WEC.

If the required energy can be sufficiently reduced, the next hurdle to approach is modeling the full life cycle of a physical warp drive (creation, acceleration, inertial motion, deceleration, and diffusion). Every previous publication in the field of warp drives has either assumed inertial motion (constant velocity) or has produced an accelerating/decelerating drive that violates the law of covariant conservation of stress-energy-momentum

$$\nabla \cdot \mathbf{T} = \mathbf{0}, \tag{17}$$

that accompanies the Einstein equation. Deriving mechanisms for creation and acceleration is crucial to any experimental test.

The last hurdle I will mention is the full characterization of the sourcing fields, whether it be a plasma or other state of matter and energy. As stated by Matt Visser in the Q&A of my talk, the specification of the drive geometry only is an incomplete description of the full solution. Stress-energy sources must be specified to close the system. In the hypothetical plasma of Lentz 2021,[19] the stress-energy governing equations include the Maxwell equations for the electric and magnetic fields, the equations of motion for each species of matter, and various constituent equations governing the state of the Einstein-Maxwell-matter system. The total system is expected to be far too complex to provide analytical solutions, requiring numerical simulation as the primary means to specify each field of a soliton at any point in its life cycle.

References

1. M. Alcubierre, The warp drive: hyper-fast travel within general relativity, *Classical and Quantum Gravity* **11**, L73 (May 1994).
2. A. E. Everett, Warp drive and causality, *Phys. Rev. D* **53**, 7365 (Jun 1996).
3. M. J. Pfenning and L. H. Ford, The unphysical nature of 'warp drive', *Classical and Quantum Gravity* **14**, 1743 (Jul 1997).
4. W. A. Hiscock, Quantum effects in the alcubierre warp-drive spacetime, *Classical and Quantum Gravity* **14**, L183 (Nov 1997).
5. S. V. Krasnikov, Hyperfast travel in general relativity, *Phys. Rev. D* **57**, 4760 (Apr 1998).

6. K. D. Olum, Superluminal travel requires negative energies, *Phys. Rev. Lett.* **81**, 3567 (Oct 1998).
7. C. V. D. Broeck, A 'warp drive' with more reasonable total energy requirements, *Classical and Quantum Gravity* **16**, 3973 (Nov 1999).
8. M. G. Millis, NASA breakthrough propulsion physics program, *Acta Astronautica* **44**, 175 (1999), Missions to the Outer Solar System and Beyond.
9. M. Visser, B. Bassett and S. Liberati, Superluminal censorship, *Nuclear Physics B - Proceedings Supplements* **88**, 267 (2000).
10. F. Loup, D. Waite and J. Halerewicz, E., Reduced Total Energy Requirements for a Modified Alcubierre Warp Drive Spacetime, *arXiv e-prints*, p. arXiv:grqc/0107097 (July 2001).
11. J. Natário, Warp drive with zero expansion, *Classical and Quantum Gravity* **19**, 1157 (Mar 2002).
12. C. Gauthier, P. Gravel and J. Melanson, New Lower Bounds for Warp Drive Energy, *International Journal of Modern Physics A* **17**, p. 2761 (January 2002).
13. F. Lobo and P. Crawford, *Weak Energy Condition Violation and Superluminal Travel*, in *Current Trends in Relativistic Astrophysics*, eds. L. Fernández-Jambrina and L. M. González-Romero 2003, p. 277.
14. F. S. N. Lobo and M. Visser, Fundamental limitations on 'warp drive' spacetimes, *Classical and Quantum Gravity* **21**, 5871 (Nov 2004).
15. F. S. N. Lobo, Exotic solutions in General Relativity: Traversable wormholes and 'warp drive' spacetimes, *Classical and Quantum Gravity Research*, 1 (October 2008).
16. R. K. Obousy and G. Cleaver, Warp Drive - A New Approach, *Journal of the British Interplanetary Society* **61**, 364 (January 2008).
17. S. Finazzi, S. Liberati and C. Barceló, Semiclassical instability of dynamical warp drives, *Phys. Rev. D* **79**, p. 124017 (Jun 2009).
18. H. White, Warp Field Mechanics 101, *Journal of the British Interplanetary Society* **66**, 242 (January 2013).
19. E. W. Lentz, Breaking the warp barrier: hyper-fast solitons in einstein–maxwell-plasma theory, *Classical and Quantum Gravity* **38**, p. 075015 (Mar 2021).
20. A. Bobrick and G. Martire, Introducing physical warp drives, *Classical and Quantum Gravity* **38**, p. 105009 (Apr 2021).
21. O. L. Santos-Pereira, E. M. C. Abreu and M. B. Ribeiro, Fluid dynamics in the warp drive spacetime geometry, *The European Physical Journal C* **81** (Feb 2021).
22. S. D. B. Fell and L. Heisenberg, Positive energy warp drive from hidden geometric structures, *Classical and Quantum Gravity* **38**, p. 155020 (Jul 2021).
23. J. Santiago, S. Schuster and M. Visser, Generic warp drives violate the null energy condition, *arXiv e-prints*, p. arXiv:2105.03079 (May 2021).
24. J. Santiago, S. Schuster and M. Visser, Tractor Beams, Pressor Beams and Stressor Beams in General Relativity, *Universe* **7**, p. 271 (July 2021).
25. R. Arnowitt, S. Deser and C. W. Misner, Dynamical structure and definition of energy in general relativity, *Phys. Rev.* **116**, 1322 (Dec 1959).
26. O. L. Santos-Pereira, E. M. C. Abreu and M. B. Ribeiro, Perfect fluid warp drive solutions with the cosmological constant, *The European Physical Journal Plus* **136** (Sep 2021).
27. T. Dray and C. Hellaby, The patchwork divergence theorem, *Journal of Mathematical Physics* **35**, p. 5922–5929 (Nov 1994).
28. S. Krasnikov, Quantum inequalities do not forbid spacetime shortcuts, *Phys. Rev. D* **67**, p. 104013 (May 2003).

From black-bounce to traversable wormhole, and beyond

Alex Simpson

School of Mathematics and Statistics, Victoria University of Wellington, PO Box 600, Wellington 6140, New Zealand
E-mail: alex.simpson@sms.vuw.ac.nz

Key results from the literature pertaining to a class of nonsingular black hole mimickers are explored. The family of candidate spacetimes is for now labelled the 'black-bounce' family, stemming from the original so-called 'Simpson–Visser' spacetime in static spherical symmetry. All model geometries are analysed through the lens of standard general relativity, are globally free from curvature singularities, pass all weak-field observational tests, and smoothly interpolate between regular black holes and traversable wormholes. The discourse is segregated along geometrical lines, with candidate spacetimes each belonging to one of: static spherical symmetry, spherical symmetry with dynamics, and stationary axisymmetry.

Keywords: Black-bounce, regular black hole, traversable wormhole, Simpson–Visser, Vaidya, thin-shell, black hole mimic.

1. Introduction

In classical general relativity (GR), solutions to the Einstein equations representing black holes typically contain curvature singularities at their cores. These singularities occur at a distance scale that only a complete theory of quantum gravity could adequately describe. In the absence of such a theory, or at least in the absence of one that has any phenomenological verification, one desirable approach is to appeal to the recent advances made in observational and gravitational wave astronomy. In view of the propagation of gravitational waves emanating from an astrophysical source being directly observed in the recent LIGO/VIRGO merger events,[1,2] it is well-motivated to explore mathematically tractable candidate spacetimes, which are curvature-singularity-free alternatives to classical black holes, through the lens of standard GR. The community hopes that LIGO/VIRGO (or more likely LISA[3]) will eventually be able to provide phenomenological evidence that allows us to delineate between specific candidate spacetimes based on their astrophysical accuracy. Theoretical physicists would then have experimentally informed clues as to which modifications to the Einstein equations are most desirable in working towards a so-called 'theory of everything' (or, indeed, whether an entirely different framework is required). Discussion regarding the extraction of astrophysical observables for nonsingular sample spacetimes in several frameworks can be found in references 4–14.

One such family of candidate geometries which models alternatives to classical black holes is the family of 'black-bounce' spacetimes.[15–20] All of these black hole mimickers are globally free from curvature singularities, pass all weak-field observational tests of standard GR, and belong either to the class of regular black holes or traversable wormholes. By 'regular black hole', one means in the sense of Bardeen,[21] with regularity defined *via* enforcing global finiteness on nonzero curvature tensor components and Riemann curvature invariants. Regular black holes have a well-established lineage in the historical literature.[21–27] By 'traversable wormhole', one means in the sense of Morris and Thorne;[28] a horizon-free geometry with a centralised throat connecting two asymptotically Minkowski regions of spacetime and satisfying the 'flare-out' condition for the area function: $A''(r_{throat}) > 0$. Various intriguing wormhole spacetimes have been developed and explored in references 28–31.

For exposition, it is prudent to separate the discourse surrounding the family of black-bounce spacetimes along geometrical lines. Broadly speaking, there are three relevant geometrical categories: static spherical symmetry, spherical symmetry with dynamics, and stationary axisymmetry (this also *somewhat* follows the chronological development of the literature). Unless otherwise stated, all candidate spacetimes discussed have metric signature $(-, +, +, +)$ outside any would-be horizons.

2. Static spherical symmetry

2.1. *Simpson–Visser*

The so-called 'Simpson–Visser' (SV) spacetime, initially presented in reference 15, is represented by the line element

$$ds^2 = -\left(1 - \frac{2m}{\sqrt{r^2 + \ell^2}}\right) dt^2 + \frac{dr^2}{\left(1 - \frac{2m}{\sqrt{r^2+\ell^2}}\right)} + (r^2 + \ell^2) \, d\Omega_2^2 \,. \tag{1}$$

It should be noted that the parameter 'ℓ' was in fact labelled 'a' in the original article.[15] This minor alteration is performed for consistency with the remainder of the discourse herein, as when in the axisymmetric environment of § 4, it is prudent to use ℓ in order to avoid confusion with the spin parameter from Kerr spacetime, a.

The original motivation for the construction of the metric specified by Eq. (1) was to minimally modify the Schwarzschild solution in common curvature coordinates such that the resulting candidate spacetime was globally nonsingular. It was considered that the most straightforward way to achieve this was to introduce a new scalar parameter to the line element in a tightly controlled manner; this is ℓ in Eq. (1). By minimally modifying Schwarzschild, it was hoped the result would have a high degree of mathematical tractability. When viewed as a modification of Schwarzschild, there are the following two alterations:

- $m \mapsto m(r) = \frac{mr}{\sqrt{r^2+\ell^2}}$;
- The coefficient of $d\Omega_2^2$ is modified from $r^2 \to r^2 + \ell^2$.

Analysis of the nonzero curvature tensor components and Riemann curvature invariants concludes that for $|\ell| > 0$, the resulting candidate spacetime is globally regular. It was also noticed that Eq. (1) has very neat limiting behaviour. In the limit as $m \to 0$, one obtains

$$ds^2 = -dt^2 + dr^2 + \left(r^2 + \ell^2\right) d\Omega_2^2 \,. \tag{2}$$

This is precisely the two-way traversable wormhole solution as presented in Morris and Thorne's aforementioned seminal paper[28] (and arguably the most straightforward of all traversable wormhole geometries). In the limit as $\ell \to 0$, Eq. (1) becomes the Schwarzschild solution in the usual curvature coordinates. The newly introduced scalar parameter ℓ can hence be viewed as quantifying the extent of the deviation away from Schwarzschild, and it invokes a rich, ℓ-dependent horizon structure. The causal structure is characterised by

$$r_H = \sqrt{(2m)^2 - \ell^2} \,, \tag{3}$$

and the candidate spacetime neatly interpolates between the following qualitatively different geometries:

- $\ell = 0$ corresponds to the Schwarzschild black hole;
- $|\ell| \in (0, 2m)$ corresponds to a regular black hole in the sense of Bardeen;
- $|\ell| = 2m$ corresponds to a one-way wormhole with an extremal null throat;
- $|\ell| > 2m$ corresponds to a two-way traversable wormhole geometry in the canonical sense of Morris and Thorne.

The Carter–Penrose diagrams for the two lesser known cases are worth closer examination; this is when $|\ell| \in (0, 2m)$ (see Fig. 1), and when $|\ell| = 2m$ (see Fig. 2).

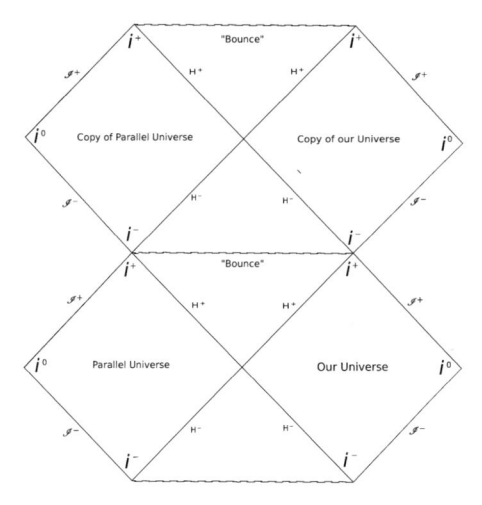

Fig. 1. Carter–Penrose diagram for the maximally extended spacetime when $|\ell| \in (0, 2m)$. In this example one 'bounces' through the $r = 0$ hypersurface in each black hole region into a future copy of the universe *ad infinitum*.

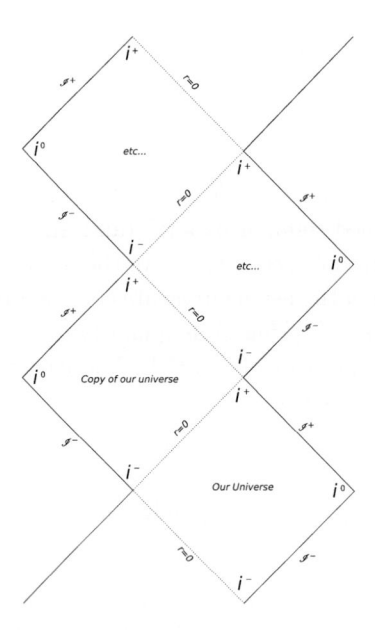

Fig. 2. Carter–Penrose diagram for the maximally extended spacetime in the case when $|\ell| = 2m$. In this example one has a one-way wormhole geometry with an extremal null throat.

Analysing the satisfaction/violation of the standard point-wise energy conditions of GR, one concludes that when $|\ell| > 0$, the radial 'null energy condition' (NEC) is manifestly violated in the region $\sqrt{r^2 + \ell^2} > 2m$. This is *outside* any would-be horizons. In the context of static spherical symmetry, this is sufficient to conclude that all of the standard point-wise energy conditions shall be similarly violated. If horizons are present, then the geometry has surface gravity

$$\kappa = \frac{\sqrt{(2m)^2 - \ell^2}}{8m^2} = \kappa_{Sch.}\sqrt{1 - \frac{\ell^2}{(2m)^2}}, \qquad (4)$$

and hence associated Hawking temperature

$$T_H = \frac{\hbar\sqrt{(2m)^2 - \ell^2}}{16\pi\, k_B\, m^2} = T_{H,Sch.}\sqrt{1 - \frac{\ell^2}{(2m)^2}}. \qquad (5)$$

SV spacetime is amenable to the extraction of astrophysical observables, and the coordinate locations of the photon sphere for null orbits and the ISCO for timelike orbits are straightforward, given by

$$r_\gamma = \sqrt{(3m)^2 - \ell^2}\,; \qquad r_{ISCO} = \sqrt{(6m)^2 - \ell^2}\,. \qquad (6)$$

Further research analysing SV spacetime has been performed in a plethora of other papers; please see reference 32 for details. These analyses include discussion of the quasi-normal modes and associated ringdown,[33,34] calculations pertaining to shadows and gravitational lensing effects,[35–40] as well as discourse surrounding precession phenomena.[41]

2.2. Black-bounce Reissner–Nordström

The extension of SV spacetime which represents the black-bounce analog to Reissner–Nordström (RN) spacetime was constructed and analysed in reference 20. There is a simple regularisation procedure which can be applied to any spherically symmetric or axisymmetric geometry in possession of a curvature singularity at $r = 0$ in the standard (t, r, θ, ϕ) curvature coordinates. The procedure outputs a candidate geometry which is globally nonsingular, and maintains the manifest symmetries. It is as follows:

- Leave the object dr in the line element undisturbed;
- Whenever the metric components $g_{\mu\nu}$ have an explicit r-dependence, replace the r-coordinate with $\sqrt{r^2 + \ell^2}$, where ℓ is some length scale, performing the same holistic role as the ℓ parameter in SV spacetime (such parameters are often identified with the Planck scale; $\ell \sim m_p$).

It should be emphasised that this procedure is *not* a coordinate transformation. Application of this procedure to the usual RN spacetime in standard curvature coordinates yields the following line element, the 'black-bounce Reissner–Nordström' (bbRN) spacetime:

$$ds^2 = -\left(1 - \frac{2m}{\sqrt{r^2 + \ell^2}} + \frac{Q^2}{r^2 + \ell^2}\right) dt^2 + \frac{dr^2}{1 - \frac{2m}{\sqrt{r^2+\ell^2}} + \frac{Q^2}{r^2+\ell^2}} + (r^2 + \ell^2) d\Omega_2^2. \quad (7)$$

For $|\ell| > 0$, this spacetime neatly interpolates between nonsingular electrovac black holes and traversable wormholes in standard GR, depending on the value of the charge parameter Q and the 'bounce' parameter ℓ. When compared with standard RN spacetime, the domain for the r coordinate is extended from $r \in [0, +\infty)$ to $r \in (-\infty, +\infty)$. The presence of the additional charge term invokes a richer causal structure than that of SV spacetime. Horizons are characterised by

$$r_H = S_1 \sqrt{(m + S_2 \sqrt{m^2 - Q^2})^2 - \ell^2}. \quad (8)$$

Here $S_1 = S_2 = \pm 1$, with S_1 fixing which universe one is in, and S_2 determining whether it is an outer ($S_2 = +1$) or inner ($S_2 = -1$) horizon. There are several qualitatively different geometries:

- $|Q| > m$: There are no horizons, and the geometry models a two-way traversable wormhole in the sense of Morris and Thorne;
- $|Q| \leq m$ but $|\ell| > m \pm \sqrt{m^2 - Q^2}$: first the inner, and then the outer horizons vanish, leaving a traversable wormhole;
- $|Q| = m$ and $|\ell| \leq m$: one finds extremal horizons at $r_H = \pm\sqrt{m^2 - \ell^2}$;
- $|Q| \leq m$ and $|\ell| < m - \sqrt{m^2 - Q^2}$: one observes the 'standard' causal structure of both an inner and outer horizon present in each universe.

If horizons are present, the surface gravity of the outer horizon is given by

$$\kappa = \frac{\sqrt{(m+\sqrt{m^2-Q^2})^2-\ell^2}\sqrt{m^2-Q^2}}{(m+\sqrt{m^2-Q^2})^3} = \kappa_{\text{RN}}\sqrt{\frac{r_H^2}{r_H^2+\ell^2}}. \qquad (9)$$

The following astrophysical observables are amenable to extraction; firstly the location of the photon sphere

$$r_\gamma = \sqrt{\frac{m}{2}(9m+3\sqrt{9m^2-8Q^2})-2Q^2-\ell^2}, \qquad (10)$$

and also the location of the ISCO for timelike particles

$$r_{ISCO} = \frac{\sqrt{9m^4Q^4-6m^2Q^2(A^2+2Am^2+4m^4)+(A^2+2Am^2+4m^4)^2-A^2\ell^2m^2}}{mA},$$

$$A = \left[2m^2Q^4+m^2(\pm B-9m^2)Q^2+8m^6\right]^{\frac{1}{3}}, \quad B = \sqrt{4Q^4-9m^2Q^2+5m^4}. \qquad (11)$$

In standard GR, the stress-energy tensor takes the following form outside the outer horizon (or inside the inner horizon):

$$\frac{1}{8\pi}G^{\hat{\mu}}{}_{\hat{\nu}} = T^{\hat{\mu}}{}_{\hat{\nu}} = [T_{\text{bb}}]^{\hat{\mu}}{}_{\hat{\nu}} + [T_Q]^{\hat{\mu}}{}_{\hat{\nu}} = \text{diag}(-\rho, p_r, p_t, p_t), \qquad (12)$$

whilst in between the two horizons one has

$$\frac{1}{8\pi}G^{\hat{\mu}}{}_{\hat{\nu}} = T^{\hat{\mu}}{}_{\hat{\nu}} = [T_{\text{bb}}]^{\hat{\mu}}{}_{\hat{\nu}} + [T_Q]^{\hat{\mu}}{}_{\hat{\nu}} = \text{diag}(p_r, -\rho, p_t, p_t), \qquad (13)$$

where $[T_{\text{bb}}]^{\hat{\mu}}{}_{\hat{\nu}}$ is the gravitational stress-energy tensor (identical to that of SV spacetime), and $[T_Q]^{\hat{\mu}}{}_{\hat{\nu}}$ is the charge-dependent contribution, corresponding to the electromagnetic stress-energy tensor. Isolating the charge-dependent components, it is straightforward to make the following decomposition

$$[T_Q]^{\hat{\mu}}{}_{\hat{\nu}} = \frac{Q^2 r^2}{8\pi(r^2+\ell^2)^3}\left[\text{diag}(-1,-1,1,1)+\text{diag}(\frac{2\ell^2}{r^2},0,0,0)\right]$$

$$= [T_{\text{Maxwell}}]^{\hat{\mu}}{}_{\hat{\nu}} + \Xi V^{\hat{\mu}}V_{\hat{\nu}}, \qquad (14)$$

where $[T_{\text{Maxwell}}]^{\hat{\mu}}{}_{\hat{\nu}}$ is the usual stress-energy associated with standard Maxwell electromagnetism, and $\Xi V^{\hat{\mu}}V_{\hat{\nu}}$ is interpreted as the stress-energy of "charged dust", with $V^{\hat{\mu}}$ being the normalised time-translation Killing vector. The density of the charged dust, Ξ, is given by

$$\Xi = -\frac{1}{4\pi}\frac{Q^2\ell^2}{(r^2+\ell^2)^3}, \qquad (15)$$

while the electric field strength is determined via

$$[T_Q]^{\hat{t}}{}_{\hat{t}} = -\rho_{\text{em}} = [T_{\text{Maxwell}}]^{\hat{t}}{}_{\hat{t}} - \Xi = -\frac{1}{8\pi}E^2 - \Xi;$$

$$\implies E = \frac{Qr}{(r^2+\ell^2)^{\frac{3}{2}}} = E_{\text{RN}}\left[\frac{r^3}{(r^2+\ell^2)^{\frac{3}{2}}}\right], \qquad (16)$$

where E_{RN} is the electric field strength for a usual RN black hole. The electromagnetic potential is readily obtained *via* integration of Eq. (16),

$$A_\mu = (\Phi_{\text{em}}(r), 0, 0, 0) = -\frac{Q}{\sqrt{r^2 + \ell^2}}(1, 0, 0, 0), \quad (17)$$

which is simply the RN electromagnetic potential under the mapping $r \to \sqrt{r^2 + \ell^2}$. All told, one has:

$$[T_Q]^{\hat\mu}{}_{\hat\nu} = \frac{1}{4\pi}\left[-F^{\hat\mu}{}_{\hat\alpha} F^{\hat\alpha}{}_{\hat\nu} - \frac{1}{4}\delta^{\hat\mu}{}_{\hat\nu} F^2\right] - \frac{1}{4\pi}\frac{Q^2 \ell^2}{(r^2 + \ell^2)^3} V^{\hat\mu} V_{\hat\nu},$$

$$\text{with} \quad F_{\hat\mu\hat\nu} = \nabla_{\hat\mu} A_{\hat\nu} - \nabla_{\hat\nu} A_{\hat\mu}. \quad (18)$$

Consequently, in standard GR the bbRN spacetime possesses stress-energy components which are interpreted as everywhere-SV in the gravitational sector, coupled to standard Maxwell's electromagnetism in the presence of charged dust in the electromagnetic sector.

2.3. *Generalised extensions to Simpson–Visser*

Further extensions to the SV line element in the context of static spherical symmetry were explored in reference 16, with some useful general theorems also being presented. The first of these theorems is general to all static spacetimes, and is concerned with expediting the 'usual' test for curvature-regularity; examination of the finiteness of all nonzero components of the Riemann curvature tensor in an orthonormal basis. It is as follows, with the proof provided in reference 16:

Theorem 2.1. *For any static spacetime, in the strictly static region, the Kretschmann scalar is positive semi-definite, being a sum of squares which involves all of the nonzero components $R^{\hat\mu\hat\nu}{}_{\hat\alpha\hat\beta}$. Then if this scalar is finite, all of the orthonormal components of the Riemann curvature tensor must also be finite. Consequently, for static candidate spacetimes, confirmation of the global finiteness of the Kretschmann scalar is sufficient to conclude as to curvature-regularity in the sense of Bardeen.*

It is by now well-known that the most general static spherically symmetric line element can always locally be put into the following form, typically known as "Buchdahl" coordinates[42–46] (for § 2.3 only, the metric signature $(+,-,-,-)$ is adopted outside horizons for consistency with the discourse in reference 16)

$$ds^2 = f(r)\, dt^2 - \frac{dr^2}{f(r)} - \Sigma^2(r)\, d\Omega_2^2. \quad (19)$$

Now constrained to Buchdahl coordinates, it is straightforward to establish the following list of sufficient conditions for curvature regularity in the sense of Bardeen (note these constraints exist as an independent result from Theorem 2.1; which of the techniques is preferable/applicable should be determined from context):

- $\Sigma(r) \neq 0$ globally;
- $\Sigma'(r)$ and $\Sigma''(r)$ must be globally finite;
- $f(r)$, $f'(r)$, and $f''(r)$ must be globally finite.

With respect to Buchdahl coordinates, another theorem was presented in reference 16. Concerning satisfaction/violation of the standard point-wise energy conditions of GR, it states:

Theorem 2.2. *For any static anisotropic fluid sphere with line element as in Eq. (19), all of the standard point-wise energy conditions are violated whenever $f(r) \neq 0$, $\Sigma(r) > 0$, and $\Sigma''(r) > 0$.*

In the same article,[16] further decomposition of Eq. (19) via $f(r) = 1 - 2M(r)/\Sigma(r)$ was performed to allow for a two-parameter extension of SV spacetime. One fixes

$$\Sigma(r) = \sqrt{r^2 + \ell^2}\,, \qquad M(r) = \frac{mr^k\sqrt{r^2+\ell^2}}{(r^{2n}+\ell^{2n})^{\frac{k+1}{2n}}}\,, \qquad (20)$$

with the form for $M(r)$ mathematically inspired by the Fan–Wang mass function for regular black holes.[27] The resulting class of geometries has the following properties:

- SV spacetime is recovered *via* fixing $n = 1, k = 0$;
- $\forall\, n, k \in \mathbb{Z}^+$, Schwarzschild in the usual curvature coordinates is recovered as $\ell \to 0$;
- Enforcing $|\ell| > 0$, $\forall\, n, k \in \mathbb{Z}^+$ the candidate geometry is globally regular.

Several models of interest possessing vibrant causal structures can be explored using Eq. (20), each corresponding to various fixed values of both n and k. All models in some fashion smoothly interpolate between regular black holes and traversable wormholes. Several other model geometries were also explored in reference 16, *via* certain modifications to the $M(r)$ present in Eq. (20), all within the geometric context of static spherical symmetry in Buchdahl coordinates.

3. Spherical symmetry with dynamics

3.1. *Vaidya black-bounce*

The SV metric was elevated to the regime of dynamical spherical symmetry in reference 17. One first rewrites the line element from Eq. (1) in Eddington–Finkelstein coordinates, before playing a Vaidya-like 'trick' by allowing the mass parameter m to be a function of the null time coordinate w. The resulting candidate spacetime is given by the following line element

$$\mathrm{d}s^2 = -\left(1 - \frac{2m(w)}{\sqrt{r^2+\ell^2}}\right)\mathrm{d}w^2 - (\pm 2\,\mathrm{d}w\mathrm{d}r) + (r^2+\ell^2)\,\mathrm{d}\Omega_2^2\,, \qquad (21)$$

where $w = \{u, v\}$ denotes the *outgoing/ingoing* null time coordinate, representing *retarded/advanced* time respectively. In the limit as $m(w) \to m$, SV spacetime is recovered (in Eddington–Finkelstein coordinates). Introducing dynamics in this specific manner allows for one to discuss simple phenomenological models of an evolving regular black hole/traversable wormhole geometry, either *via* net accretion or net evaporation, whilst still keeping the discourse mathematically tractable. Analysis of the radial null curves yields a dynamical horizon location

$$r_H(w) = \pm\sqrt{[2m(w)]^2 - \ell^2} \ . \tag{22}$$

While this permits analysis of numerous phenomenological models, the most qualitatively interesting are:

- Increasing $m(v)$ crossing the $\ell/2$ limit describing the conversion of a traversable wormhole into a regular black hole *via* the accretion of null dust. This qualitative scenario is depicted in Fig. 3;
- Decreasing $m(u)$ crossing the $\ell/2$ limit describes the evaporation of a regular black hole leaving a traversable wormhole remnant. The causal structure is depicted in Fig. 4. This phenomena is causally equivalent to a regular black hole transmuting into a traversable wormhole *via* the accretion of phantom energy (though mathematically this scenario would instead correspond to increasing $m(v)$ crossing the $\ell/2$ limit).

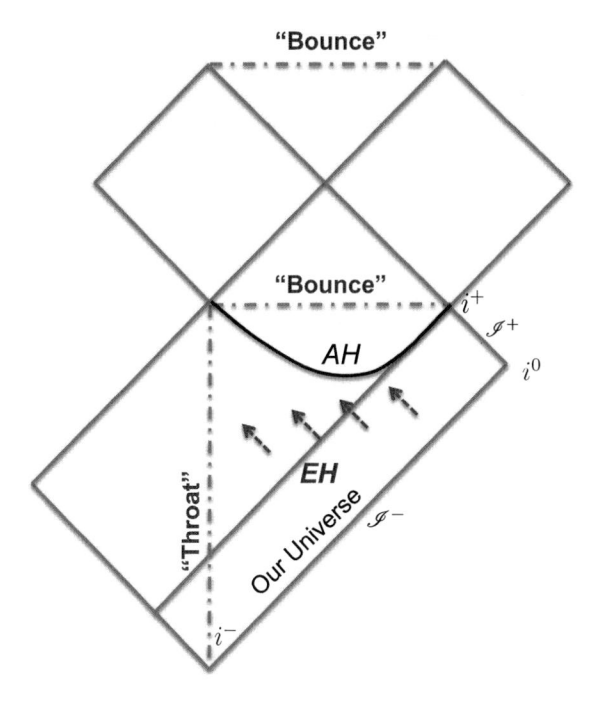

Fig. 3. Carter–Penrose diagram for a wormhole to black-bounce transition *via* accretion of null dust.

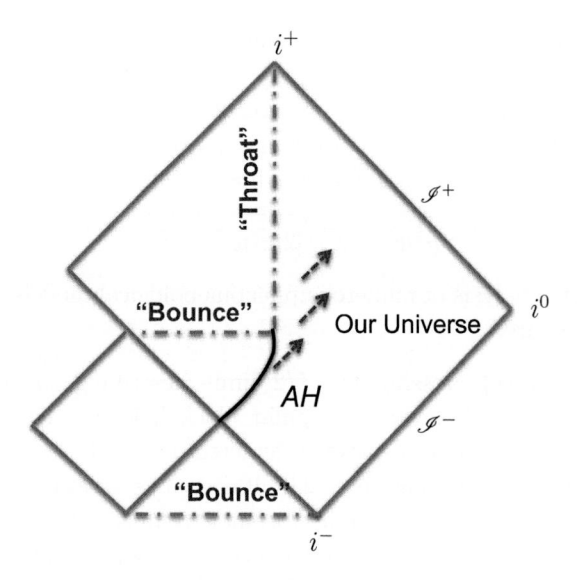

Fig. 4. Carter–Penrose diagram for a black-bounce to wormhole transition due to the emission of positive energy. This is essentially the back reaction of the Hawking evaporation for a semi-classical regular black hole; in this case leaving a wormhole remnant.

General discussion concerning evaporation/accretion models involving both regular black holes and traversable wormholes can be found in references 47–54. It is worth emphasising that one is able to classically describe the transmutation of a wormhole into a regular black hole, or *vice versa*, only because the curvature-regularity of the black hole implies there is no topology change.

In what has become a typical result for nonsingular black hole mimickers in standard GR, the candidate spacetime is found to be in global violation of the NEC. For the 'Vaidya black-bounce' spacetime, the existence of the radial null vector $k^\mu = (0, 1, 0, 0)$ implies that one has

$$T_{\mu\nu}k^\mu k^\nu \propto G_{\mu\nu}k^\mu k^\nu = -\frac{2\ell^2}{(r^2 + \ell^2)^2} < 0 \,. \tag{23}$$

For a full analysis of the nonzero curvature tensor components and Riemann curvature invariants for the Vaidya black-bounce geometry, as well as a more detailed discussion surrounding energy condition satisfaction/violation and various phenomenological models, please see reference 17.

3.2. *Thin-shell black-bounce traversable wormhole*

A thin-shell traversable wormhole variant of SV spacetime was constructed and analysed in reference 18. The thin-shell surgery is performed *via* a 'cut and paste' procedure which has its mathematical roots in the Darmois–Israel formalism.[55] Physically, the geometrodynamics are kept as close to standard GR as possible *via* examination of the Lanczos equations (please see references 56–58 for details pertaining to thin-shell surgery).

In the thin-shell construction,[18] one analyses both the stability and the evolution of an SV thin-shell traversable wormhole under linearized radial perturbation of the throat. The 'bounce' parameter ℓ induces a nonzero flux term arising from the conservation identity due to the second contracted Gauss–Codazzi–Mainardi equation. Consequently, enforcing a nonzero ℓ leads to an additional constraint on the stability analysis. Several qualitative examples from the parameter space are explored, and the viable stability regions in each case are readily extracted.

4. Stationary axisymmetry

4.1. *Black-bounce Kerr–Newman*

The first entry from the family of 'black-bounce' spacetimes belonging to the geometrical regime of stationary axisymmetry was constructed and explored by Liberati *et al.* in reference 19. This spacetime was constructed *via* application of the Newman–Janis procedure to standard SV spacetime, and acts as the black-bounce analog to Kerr spacetime. Given that in any real, astrophysical setting, one shall have both rotation and the condition that $|Q|/m \ll 1$, this is the most astrophysically relevant member of the family of black-bounce spacetimes. The black-bounce analog to Kerr–Newman spacetime was then discovered in reference 20; this was obtained *via* application of the regularisation procedure outlined in § 2.2, applied to the Kerr–Newman geometry in standard Boyer–Lindquist (BL) coordinates. The line element is given by

$$ds^2 = -\frac{\Delta}{\rho^2}(a\sin^2\theta\, d\phi - dt)^2 + \frac{\sin^2\theta}{\rho^2}[(r^2+\ell^2+a^2)\,d\phi - a\,dt]^2 + \frac{\rho^2}{\Delta}dr^2 + \rho^2\, d\theta^2 , \quad (24)$$

with the usual Kerr quantities modified to be

$$\rho^2 = r^2 + \ell^2 + a^2\cos^2\theta , \qquad \Delta = r^2 + \ell^2 + a^2 - 2m\sqrt{r^2+\ell^2} + Q^2 . \quad (25)$$

In the astrophysically relevant limit as $Q \to 0$, the Kerr-analog explored in reference 19 is recovered precisely. For specifics pertaining to 'black-bounce Kerr' (bbK), please consult reference 19. Generally speaking, if one takes the $Q \to 0$ limit for the relevant results obtained for the 'black-bounce Kerr–Newman' (bbKN) spacetime (Eq. (24)), the analogous result for bbK is recovered precisely. In the limit as the spin parameter $a \to 0$, bbKN reduces to the bbRN geometry from § 2.2.

One can see, somewhat trivially, that the natural domains for the angular and temporal coordinates are unaffected when comparing Eq. (24) with standard Kerr–Newman spacetime in BL coordinates. In contrast, the domain for the radial coordinate extends from $r \in [0, +\infty)$ to $r \in (-\infty, +\infty)$, in exactly the same fashion as was seen for bbRN spacetime in § 2.2. Examination of the Riemann curvature invariants and orthonormal Riemann tensor components reveals that they are globally finite when $|\ell| > 0$, hence the geometry is free from curvature singularities. Consequently, bbKN qualitatively interpolates between charged rotating regular black holes and charged rotating traversable wormholes. Both the Ricci and Einstein tensors are diagonal in an orthonormal basis.

The causal structure is nontrivial, with horizons characterised by the roots of Δ. This gives the following horizon location(s):

$$r_H = S_1\sqrt{(m + S_2\sqrt{m^2 - Q^2 - a^2})^2 - \ell^2} \,. \tag{26}$$

As it was in § 2.2, $S_1 = S_2 = \pm 1$, with S_1 fixing which universe one is in, and S_2 determining whether it is an outer ($S_2 = +1$) or inner ($S_2 = -1$) horizon. The qualitatively different possible causal structures are the same as explored in § 2.2, with the quantitative aspects slightly shifted due to the presence of the spin parameter a. Notably, in the standard Kerr–Newman geometry in BL coordinates one demands $Q^2 + a^2 \leq m^2$ in order to avoid naked singularities. In the case for bbKN, arbitrary values of both spin and charge may be considered, as in the absence of any horizons one has a traversable wormhole geometry with a rotating throat. Therefore, if one uses bbKN to model astrophysical objects, the weak cosmic censorship conjecture is trivially satisfied.

If horizons are present, their surface gravity is given by

$$\kappa_{S_2} = \frac{1}{2}\frac{d}{dr}\left(\frac{\Delta}{r^2 + \ell^2 + a^2}\right)\bigg|_{r=r_H} = \kappa_{S_2}^{KN}\sqrt{\frac{r_H^2}{r_H^2 + \ell^2}} \,, \tag{27}$$

where S_2 fixes whether one is describing the surface gravity of an outer or inner horizon. The ergosurface is characterised by $g_{tt} = 0$, giving

$$r_{erg} = S_1\sqrt{(m + S_2\sqrt{m^2 - Q^2 - a^2\cos^2\theta})^2 - \ell^2} \,. \tag{28}$$

An informative result pertaining to circular orbits in the equatorial plane for the bbKN spacetime is as follows: if standard Kerr–Newman in BL coordinates has an equatorial circular orbit at $r_{KN,0}$, then bbKN possesses an analogous equatorial circular orbit at coordinate location $r_0 = \sqrt{r_{KN,0}^2 - \ell^2}$, provided that $r_{KN,0}^2 \geq \ell^2$.

The candidate spacetime possesses a nontrivial Killing tensor; upon definition of the objects

$$l^\mu = \left(\frac{r^2 + \ell^2 + a^2}{\Delta}, 1, 0, \frac{a}{\Delta}\right) \,, \text{ and } n^\mu = \frac{1}{2\rho^2}(r^2 + \ell^2 + a^2, -\Delta, 0, a) \,, \tag{29}$$

one finds that the following is a Killing tensor, i.e., $K_{(\mu\nu;\lambda)} = 0$:

$$K_{\mu\nu} = \rho^2(l_\mu n_\nu + l_\nu n_\mu) + (r^2 + \ell^2)g_{\mu\nu} \,. \tag{30}$$

In this context, the objects l^μ and n^μ are a pair of geodesic null vectors belonging to a generalised Kinnersley tetrad (see reference 19 for details). The Killing tensor from Eq. (30) has diagonal matrix representation. The existence of a nontrivial Killing tensor directly implies the existence of a generalised Carter constant $\mathcal{C}$, and together with the conserved quantities arising from the temporal and azimuthal

Killing vectors (energy and angular momentum per unit mass), as well as the conserved quantity arising from the metric itself (which is a *trivial* Killing tensor), this gives four constants of the motion. This, in principle, means that the geodesics governing the motion of test particles are integrable on the bbKN spacetime. It should be noted that the resulting integral formulae may or may not be analytic.

In reference 59, a refinement was made to Proposition 1.3 from reference 60. It should also be noted that this result is implicitly present in reference 61. The result is best summarised by the following theorem:

Theorem 4.1. *Let $(\mathcal{M}, g_{\mu\nu})$ be a Lorentzian manifold in possession of a non-trivial Killing tensor $K_{\mu\nu}$. Then upon definition of the Carter operator as: $\mathcal{K}\Phi = \nabla_\mu(K^{\mu\nu}\nabla_\nu\Phi)$, and the D'Alembertian scalar wave operator as: $\Box\Phi = \nabla_\mu(g^{\mu\nu}\nabla_\nu\Phi)$, there is the following result:*

$$[\mathcal{K}, \Box]\Phi = \frac{2}{3}(\nabla_\mu[R, K]^\mu{}_\nu)\nabla^\nu\Phi . \tag{31}$$

A sufficient condition for this operator commutator to vanish is therefore the commutativity of the Ricci and Killing tensors via matrix multiplication; $R^\mu{}_\alpha K^\alpha{}_\nu = K^\mu{}_\alpha R^\alpha{}_\nu \Longrightarrow [R, K]^\mu{}_\nu = 0$. Hence for any candidate spacetime with a nontrivial Killing tensor, commutativity of the Ricci and Killing tensors via matrix multiplication is sufficient to conclude that the massive minimally coupled Klein–Gordon equation is separable on the candidate geometry.

In view of Theorem 4.1, given that both the Ricci and nontrivial Killing tensors for the bbKN geometry have a diagonal matrix representation, one may conclude that the scalar wave equation is separable on bbKN spacetime.

Given the existence of a nontrivial Killing tensor, it is natural to ponder the existence of the full 'Killing tower'[62] in bbKN spacetime. One finds a 'would-be' Killing–Yano tensor, of the form

$$f_{\mu\nu} = \begin{pmatrix} 0 & -a\cos\theta & 0 & 0 \\ a\cos\theta & 0 & 0 & -a^2\cos\theta\sin^2\theta \\ 0 & 0 & 0 & 0 \\ 0 & a^2\cos\theta\sin^2\theta & 0 & 0 \end{pmatrix}$$

$$+ \sqrt{r^2+\ell^2}\sin\theta \begin{pmatrix} 0 & 0 & a & 0 \\ 0 & 0 & 0 & 0 \\ -a & 0 & 0 & (r^2+\ell^2+a^2) \\ 0 & 0 & -(r^2+\ell^2+a^2) & 0 \end{pmatrix} . \tag{32}$$

It is not difficult to verify that $f_{\mu\alpha}f^\alpha{}_\nu = K_{\mu\nu}$, and as such this is a genuine 'square root' of the Killing tensor, however it fails to be a genuine Killing–Yano tensor because $f_{\mu(\nu;\alpha)} \neq 0$. It is a known result that a candidate spacetime only possesses a closed conformal Killing–Yano tensor if the spacetime is of Petrov type D.[62] However, it was proven by Liberati *et al.* in reference 19 that the bbK spacetime is Petrov type I, and it is a direct implication of this proof that the bbKN spacetime is also not algebraically special. Consequently, it is an expected result that one can not find a genuine Killing–Yano tensor on bbKN spacetime.

Now coupling the geometry to the Einstein equations of standard GR, the fact that the Einstein tensor is diagonal in an orthonormal basis proves that the stress-energy tensor for bbKN spacetime is Hawking–Ellis type I.[63–66] The radial NEC is violated in view of

$$\varepsilon + p_r = -\frac{\ell^2 \Delta}{8\pi \rho^6}, \tag{33}$$

where ε and p_r are energy density and radial pressure respectively.

The stress-energy tensor can be decomposed into gravitational and electromagnetic contributions (similar to bbRN spacetime in § 2.2):

$$\frac{1}{8\pi} G^{\hat{\mu}}{}_{\hat{\nu}} = T^{\hat{\mu}}{}_{\hat{\nu}} = [T_{\text{bbK}}]^{\hat{\mu}}{}_{\hat{\nu}} + [T_Q]^{\hat{\mu}}{}_{\hat{\nu}}, \tag{34}$$

where

$$[T_Q]^{\hat{\mu}}{}_{\hat{\nu}} = \frac{1}{8\pi} \frac{Q^2(\rho^2 - \ell^2)}{\rho^6} \left[\text{diag}(-1, -1, 1, 1) + \frac{2\ell^2}{\rho^2 - \ell^2} \text{diag}(1, 0, 0, 0) \right]. \tag{35}$$

When comparing Eq. (35) directly with the charge-dependent contribution to the stress-energy from bbRN spacetime, one simply makes the substitutions

$$\frac{Q^2 r^2}{(r^2 + \ell^2)^3} \longleftrightarrow \frac{Q^2(\rho^2 - \ell^2)}{\rho^6} \quad \text{and} \quad \frac{2\ell^2}{r^2} \longleftrightarrow \frac{2\ell^2}{\rho^2 - \ell^2}. \tag{36}$$

Structurally, the first term in Eq. (35) is of the form of the Maxwell stress-energy tensor. The second term appears to be structurally of the form of charged dust. However, the interpretation of the stress-energy is far less straightforward than the somewhat similar picture present in bbRN spacetime (§ 2.2). If one performs the substitution $r \to \sqrt{r^2 + \ell^2}$ to the electromagnetic potential from Kerr–Newman spacetime, one finds

$$A_{\hat{\mu}} = -\frac{Q\sqrt{r^2 + \ell^2}}{\sqrt{\rho^2 |\Delta|}} (1, 0, 0, 0), \tag{37}$$

giving the following for the electromagnetic field strength tensor $F_{\hat{\mu}\hat{\nu}}$:

$$F_{\hat{t}\hat{r}} = -F_{\hat{r}\hat{t}} = -\frac{Q}{\rho^4} \sqrt{\frac{r^2}{r^2 + \ell^2}} (r^2 + \ell^2 - a^2 \cos^2 \theta), \tag{38}$$

$$F_{\hat{\theta}\hat{\phi}} = -F_{\hat{\phi}\hat{\theta}} = \frac{2aQ \cos \theta \sqrt{r^2 + \ell^2}}{\rho^4}. \tag{39}$$

Immediately it is clear that $F_{[\hat{\mu}\hat{\nu},\hat{\sigma}]} = 0$. For the inhomogeneous Maxwell equation, defining $z = \sqrt{r^2 + \ell^2}$, one has

$$\nabla^{\hat{\mu}} F_{\hat{\mu}\hat{\nu}} = J_{\hat{\nu}} = \frac{Q\ell^2}{\rho^7 z} \left(-\frac{\Delta(\rho^4 + 2\rho^2 z^2 - 4z^4)}{z^2 \sqrt{|\Delta|}}, 0, 0, 2a \sin \theta \left(\rho^2 - 2z^2 \right) \right). \tag{40}$$

Interpreting this as an effective electromagnetic source, one has $E_{\hat{r}} = F_{\hat{t}\hat{r}}$ and $B_{\hat{r}} = F_{\hat{\theta}\hat{\phi}}$, giving

$$[T_{\text{Maxwell}}]^{\hat{\mu}}{}_{\hat{\nu}} = \frac{E_{\hat{r}}^2 + B_{\hat{r}}^2}{8\pi} \text{diag}(-1,-1,1,1) , \qquad (41)$$

with

$$E_{\hat{r}}^2 + B_{\hat{r}}^2 = \frac{Q^2}{\rho^4} \frac{r^2}{r^2+\ell^2} + \frac{4Q^2\ell^2 a^2 \cos^2\theta}{\rho^8} . \qquad (42)$$

Comparison with Eq. (35) reveals that a more subtle interpretation of the electromagnetic stress-energy than standard Maxwell's is required. Presented herein are two alternatives.

Nonlinear electrodynamics One can decompose the electromagnetic stress-energy tensor as follows

$$[T_Q]^{\hat{\mu}}{}_{\hat{\nu}} = \mathcal{A}\,[T_{\text{Maxwell}}]^{\hat{\mu}}{}_{\hat{\nu}} + \Xi\, V^{\hat{\mu}} V_{\hat{\nu}} . \qquad (43)$$

The $\Xi V^{\hat{\mu}} V_{\hat{\nu}}$ term is once again appropriate to interpret as charged dust. Comparing Eq's. (41) and (43) allows one to solve for the multiplicative factor $\mathcal{A}$:

$$\mathcal{A} = \frac{Q^2(\rho^2-\ell^2)}{\rho^6(E_{\hat{r}}^2+B_{\hat{r}}^2)} = 1 - a^2\ell^2 \frac{\cos^2\theta[4(r^2+\ell^2)-\rho^2]}{\rho^4 r^2 + 4a^2\ell^2\cos^2\theta(r^2+\ell^2)} . \qquad (44)$$

It is clear that in both the limit as $\ell \to 0$ (Kerr–Newman), and the limit as $a \to 0$ (bbRN), $\mathcal{A} \to 1$, recovering standard Maxwell's as expected. The fact that $\mathcal{A}$ is independent of the charge Q indicates it is appropriate to interpret this term through the lens of nonlinear electrodynamics (NLED), where generally one has $[T_{\text{NLED}}]^{\hat{\mu}}{}_{\hat{\nu}} \propto [T_{\text{Maxwell}}]^{\hat{\mu}}{}_{\hat{\nu}}$. NLED in the context of regular black holes is prevalent throughout the literature.[22, 67–73] In the large distance limit one has

$$\mathcal{A} = 1 - \frac{3\ell^2 a^2 \cos^2\theta}{r^4} + \mathcal{O}(r^{-6}) , \qquad (45)$$

indicating that standard Maxwell's + charged dust is a safe approximation as $r \to +\infty$. Conversely, for small r one has

$$\mathcal{A} = \frac{\ell^2 + a^2 \cos\theta^2}{4\ell^2} + \mathcal{O}(r^2) , \qquad (46)$$

which allows one to interpret a rescaling of the Maxwell stress-energy deep in the core of the black-bounce. This holistic picture is common in NLED.

Anisotropic fluid One can instead ask that

$$[T_Q]_{\hat{\mu}\hat{\nu}} - [T_{\text{Maxwell}}]_{\hat{\mu}\hat{\nu}} = \text{diag}(\varepsilon_f, -p_f, p_f, p_f), \qquad (47)$$

which would imply that (recall $z = \sqrt{r^2+\ell^2}$)

$$\varepsilon_f = \frac{Q^2\ell^2}{z^2\rho^8}\left(4z^4 - 7z^2\rho^2 + \rho^4\right), \quad p_f = \frac{Q^2\ell^2}{z^2\rho^8}\left(4z^4 - 5z^2\rho^2 + \rho^4\right). \qquad (48)$$

Consequently, $[T_Q]^{\hat{\mu}}{}_{\hat{\nu}}$ can be interpreted as standard Maxwell's in the presence of an anisotropic fluid. The anisotropic fluid can then be written as

$$\varepsilon_f V_{\hat{\mu}} V_{\hat{\nu}} + \frac{p_f}{3}\left(g_{\hat{\mu}\hat{\nu}} + V_{\hat{\mu}} V_{\hat{\nu}}\right) + \pi_{\hat{\mu}\hat{\nu}}, \tag{49}$$

with $V^{\hat{\mu}} = (1,0,0,0)$ being the velocity of the fluid, and

$$\pi_{\hat{\mu}\hat{\nu}} = \frac{2p_f}{3}\text{diag}\,(0,-2,1,1) \tag{50}$$

being the (traceless) anisotropic shear.[63]

5. Discussion

The family of black-bounce spacetimes contains many different candidate geometries which smoothly interpolate between regular black holes and traversable wormholes in standard GR, both with and without rotation, both with and without electrical charge, and both with and without dynamics. The high degree of mathematical tractability of the black-bounce spacetimes means that all models are amenable to the straightforward extraction of astrophysical observables, which *may* be falsifiable/verifiable by the experimental community.

Future research options abound. Given the knowledge of Klein–Gordon separability on bbKN spacetime, one should also test for Maxwell separability on the bbKN spacetime. The knowledge of Klein–Gordon separability already implies that bbKN is amenable to a standard spin zero quasi-normal modes analysis, and if Maxwell's equations also separate then this would extend to a spin one analysis. Further investigation into the spin two axial and polar modes may eventually lead to a measurable ringdown signal able to be captured by LIGO/VIRGO (or LISA) and compared with the analogous signal from Kerr-like mergers. Alternative lines of inquiry for future research could involve attempting to provide a physical mechanism for the bounce, or possibly discovering precisely which mathematical modifications to the Einstein equations would be required such that SV is the unique solution in static spherical symmetry in the new framework.

Acknowledgements

AS was supported by a Victoria University of Wellington PhD scholarship, and was also indirectly supported by the Marsden Fund, *via* a grant administered by the Royal Society of New Zealand.

AS would also like to acknowledge the following list of authors, all of whom have contributed in meaningful ways towards the development of the family of black-bounce spacetimes: Matt Visser, Prado Martín–Moruno, Francisco S. N. Lobo, Manuel E. Rodrigues, Marcos V. d. S. Silva, Stefano Liberati, Edgardo Franzin, and Jacopo Mazza.

References

1. See https://www.ligo.caltech.edu/page/detection-companion-papers for a collection of detection papers from LIGO.
   See also https://pnp.ligo.org/ppcomm/Papers.html for a complete list of publications from the LIGO Scientific Collaboration and Virgo Collaboration.
2. See, for example, wikipedia.org/List_of_gravitational_wave_observations for a list of current (May 2020) gravitational wave observations.
3. E. Barausse, E. Berti, T. Hertog, S. A. Hughes, P. Jetzer, P. Pani, T. P. Sotiriou, N. Tamanini, H. Witek and K. Yagi, et al., "Prospects for Fundamental Physics with LISA", Gen. Rel. Grav. **52** (2020) no. 8, 81, doi:10.1007/s10714-020-02691-1, [arXiv:2001.09793 [gr-qc]].
4. E. F. Eiroa and C. M. Sendra, "Gravitational lensing by a regular black hole", Class. Quant. Grav. **28** (2011), 085008, doi:10.1088/0264-9381/28/8/085008, [arXiv:1011.2455 [gr-qc]].
5. A. Flachi and J. P. S. Lemos, "Quasinormal modes of regular black holes", Phys. Rev. D **87** (2013) no. 2, 024034, doi:10.1103/PhysRevD.87.024034, [arXiv:1211.6212 [gr-qc]].
6. A. Abdujabbarov, M. Amir, B. Ahmedov and S. G. Ghosh, "Shadow of rotating regular black holes", Phys. Rev. D **93** (2016) no. 10, 104004, doi:10.1103/PhysRevD.93.104004, [arXiv:1604.03809 [gr-qc]].
7. R. Carballo-Rubio, F. Di Filippo, S. Liberati, C. Pacilio and M. Visser, "On the viability of regular black holes", JHEP **07** (2018), 023, doi:10.1007/JHEP07(2018)023, [arXiv:1805.02675 [gr-qc]].
8. R. Carballo-Rubio, F. Di Filippo, S. Liberati and M. Visser, "Opening the Pandora's box at the core of black holes", Class. Quant. Grav. **37** (2020) no. 14, 14, doi:10.1088/1361-6382/ab8141, [arXiv:1908.03261 [gr-qc]].
9. R. Carballo-Rubio, F. Di Filippo, S. Liberati and M. Visser, "Geodesically complete black holes", Phys. Rev. D **101** (2020), 084047, doi:10.1103/PhysRevD.101.084047, [arXiv:1911.11200 [gr-qc]].
10. T. Berry, A. Simpson and M. Visser, "Photon spheres, ISCOs, and OSCOs: Astrophysical observables for regular black holes with asymptotically Minkowski cores", Universe **7** (2020) no. 1, 2, doi:10.3390/universe7010002, [arXiv:2008.13308 [gr-qc]].
11. R. Carballo-Rubio, F. Di Filippo and S. Liberati, "Hearts of Darkness: the inside out probing of black holes", IJMPD (in press), [arXiv:2106.01530 [gr-qc]].
12. K. A. Bronnikov, R. A. Konoplya and T. D. Pappas, "General parametrization of wormhole spacetimes and its application to shadows and quasinormal modes", Phys. Rev. D **103** (2021) no. 12, 124062, doi:10.1103/PhysRevD.103.124062, [arXiv:2102.10679 [gr-qc]].
13. M. S. Churilova, R. A. Konoplya, Z. Stuchlik and A. Zhidenko, "Wormholes without exotic matter: quasinormal modes, echoes and shadows", [arXiv:2107.05977 [gr-qc]].
14. A. Simpson, "Ringing of the regular black hole with asymptotically Minkowski core", [arXiv:2109.11878 [gr-qc]].
15. A. Simpson and M. Visser, "Black-bounce to traversable wormhole", JCAP **02** (2019), 042, doi:10.1088/1475-7516/2019/02/042 [arXiv:1812.07114 [gr-qc]].
16. F. S. N. Lobo, M. E. Rodrigues, M. V. d. S. Silva, A. Simpson and M. Visser, "Novel black-bounce spacetimes: wormholes, regularity, energy conditions, and causal structure", Phys. Rev. D **103** (2021) no. 8, 084052, doi:10.1103/PhysRevD.103.084052, [arXiv:2009.12057 [gr-qc]].

17. A. Simpson, P. Martín-Moruno and M. Visser, "Vaidya spacetimes, black-bounces, and traversable wormholes", Class. Quant. Grav. **36** (2019) no. 14, 145007, doi:10.1088/1361-6382/ab28a5, [arXiv:1902.04232 [gr-qc]].
18. F. S. N. Lobo, A. Simpson and M. Visser, "Dynamic thin-shell black-bounce traversable wormholes", Phys. Rev. D **101** (2020) no. 12, 124035, doi:10.1103/PhysRevD.101.124035, [arXiv:2003.09419 [gr-qc]].
19. J. Mazza, E. Franzin and S. Liberati, "A novel family of rotating black hole mimickers", JCAP **04** (2021), 082, doi:10.1088/1475-7516/2021/04/082, [arXiv:2102.01105 [gr-qc]].
20. E. Franzin, S. Liberati, J. Mazza, A. Simpson and M. Visser, "Charged black-bounce spacetimes", JCAP **07** (2021), 036, doi:10.1088/1475-7516/2021/07/036, [arXiv:2104.11376 [gr-qc]].
21. J. M. Bardeen, "Non-singular general relativistic gravitational collapse", Abstracts of the 5th international conference on gravitation and the theory of relativity (GR5), eds. V. A. Fock *et al.* (Tbilisi University Press, Tblisi, Georgia, former USSR, 1968), pages 174—175.
22. E. Ayon-Beato and A. Garcia, "The Bardeen model as a nonlinear magnetic monopole", Phys. Lett. B **493** (2000), 149–152, doi:10.1016/S0370-2693(00)01125-4, [arXiv:gr-qc/0009077 [gr-qc]].
23. S. A. Hayward, "Formation and evaporation of regular black holes", Phys. Rev. Lett. **96** (2006), 031103, doi:10.1103/PhysRevLett.96.031103, [arXiv:gr-qc/0506126 [gr-qc]].
24. C. Bambi and L. Modesto, "Rotating regular black holes", Phys. Lett. B **721** (2013), 329–334, doi:10.1016/j.physletb.2013.03.025, [arXiv:1302.6075 [gr-qc]].
25. V. P. Frolov, "Information loss problem and a 'black hole' model with a closed apparent horizon", JHEP **05** (2014), 049, doi:10.1007/JHEP05(2014)049, [arXiv:1402.5446 [hep-th]].
26. J. C. S. Neves and A. Saa, "Regular rotating black holes and the weak energy condition", Phys. Lett. B **734** (2014), 44–48, doi:10.1016/j.physletb.2014.05.026, [arXiv:1402.2694 [gr-qc]].
27. Z. Y. Fan and X. Wang, "Construction of Regular Black Holes in General Relativity", Phys. Rev. D **94** (2016) no. 12, 124027, doi:10.1103/PhysRevD.94.124027, [arXiv:1610.02636 [gr-qc]].
28. M. S. Morris and K. S. Thorne, "Wormholes in space-time and their use for interstellar travel: A tool for teaching general relativity", Am. J. Phys. **56** (1988), 395–412, doi:10.1119/1.15620.
29. M. S. Morris, K. S. Thorne and U. Yurtsever, "Wormholes, Time Machines, and the Weak Energy Condition", Phys. Rev. Lett. **61** (1988), 1446–1449, doi:10.1103/PhysRevLett.61.1446.
30. M. Visser, "Traversable wormholes: Some simple examples", Phys. Rev. D **39** (1989), 3182–3184, doi:10.1103/PhysRevD.39.3182, [arXiv:0809.0907 [gr-qc]].
31. M. Visser, "Traversable wormholes from surgically modified Schwarzschild spacetimes", Nucl. Phys. B **328** (1989), 203–212, doi:10.1016/0550-3213(89)90100-4, [arXiv:0809.0927 [gr-qc]].
32. See inspirehep.net for a full list of pre-published and published papers citing reference 15.
33. K. A. Bronnikov and R. A. Konoplya, "Echoes in brane worlds: ringing at a black hole–wormhole transition", Phys. Rev. D **101** (2020) no. 6, 064004, doi:10.1103/PhysRevD.101.064004, [arXiv:1912.05315 [gr-qc]].
34. M. S. Churilova and Z. Stuchlik, "Ringing of the regular black-hole/wormhole transition", Class. Quant. Grav. **37** (2020) no. 7, 075014, doi:10.1088/1361-6382/ab7717, [arXiv:1911.11823 [gr-qc]].

35. S. U. Islam, J. Kumar and S. G. Ghosh, "Strong gravitational lensing by rotating Simpson–Visser black holes", [arXiv:2104.00696 [gr-qc]].
36. N. Tsukamoto, "Gravitational lensing by two photon spheres in a black-bounce spacetime in strong deflection limits", Phys. Rev. D **104** (2021) no. 6, 064022, doi:10.1103/PhysRevD.104.064022, [arXiv:2105.14336 [gr-qc]].
37. M. Guerrero, G. J. Olmo, D. Rubiera-Garcia and D. S. C. Gómez, "Shadows and optical appearance of black bounces illuminated by a thin accretion disk", JCAP **08** (2021), 036, doi:10.1088/1475-7516/2021/08/036, [arXiv:2105.15073 [gr-qc]].
38. H. C. D. Lima, Junior., L. C. B. Crispino, P. V. P. Cunha and C. A. R. Herdeiro, "Can different black holes cast the same shadow?", Phys. Rev. D **103** (2021) no. 8, 084040, doi:10.1103/PhysRevD.103.084040, [arXiv:2102.07034 [gr-qc]].
39. N. Tsukamoto, "Gravitational lensing in the Simpson-Visser black-bounce spacetime in a strong deflection limit", Phys. Rev. D **103** (2021) no. 2, 024033, doi:10.1103/PhysRevD.103.024033, [arXiv:2011.03932 [gr-qc]].
40. J. R. Nascimento, A. Y. Petrov, P. J. Porfirio and A. R. Soares, "Gravitational lensing in black-bounce spacetimes", Phys. Rev. D **102** (2020) no. 4, 044021, doi:10.1103/PhysRevD.102.044021, [arXiv:2005.13096 [gr-qc]].
41. T. Y. Zhou and Y. Xie, "Precessing and periodic motions around a black-bounce/traversable wormhole", Eur. Phys. J. C **80** (2020) no. 11, 1070, doi:10.1140/epjc/s10052-020-08661-w.
42. M. S. R. Delgaty and K. Lake, "Physical acceptability of isolated, static, spherically symmetric, perfect fluid solutions of Einstein's equations", Comput. Phys. Commun. **115** (1998), 395–415, doi:10.1016/S0010-4655(98)00130-1, [arXiv:gr-qc/9809013 [gr-qc]].
43. M. R. Finch and J. E. F. Skea, "A review of the relativistic static fluid sphere", 1998, unpublished.
44. P. Boonserm and M. Visser, "Buchdahl-like transformations for perfect fluid spheres", Int. J. Mod. Phys. D **17** (2008), 135–163, doi:10.1142/S0218271808011912, [arXiv:0707.0146 [gr-qc]].
45. P. Boonserm and M. Visser, "Buchdahl-like transformations in general relativity", Thai Journal of Mathematics **5** #**2** (2007) 209–223.
46. İ. Semiz, "On the (non)genericity of the Kiselev spacetime", doi:10.1088/2633-1357/aba1f5, [arXiv:2001.06310 [gr-qc]].
47. E. Babichev, V. Dokuchaev and Y. Eroshenko, "Black hole mass decreasing due to phantom energy accretion", Phys. Rev. Lett. **93** (2004), 021102, doi:10.1103/PhysRevLett.93.021102, [arXiv:gr-qc/0402089 [gr-qc]].
48. E. Babichev, V. Dokuchaev and Y. Eroshenko, "Dark energy cosmology with generalized linear equation of state", Class. Quant. Grav. **22** (2005), 143–154, doi:10.1088/0264-9381/22/1/010, [arXiv:astro-ph/0407190 [astro-ph]].
49. P. Martín-Moruno, J. A. J. Madrid and P. F. González-Díaz, "Will black holes eventually engulf the universe?", Phys. Lett. B **640** (2006), 117–120, doi:10.1016/j.physletb.2006.07.067, [arXiv:astro-ph/0603761 [astro-ph]].
50. P. F. González-Díaz and P. Martín-Moruno, "Wormholes in the accelerating universe", doi:10.1142/9789812834300_0358, [arXiv:0704.1731 [astro-ph]].
51. P. Martín-Moruno, "On the formalism of dark energy accretion onto black- and worm-holes", Phys. Lett. B **659** (2008), 40–44, doi:10.1016/j.physletb.2007.10.083, [arXiv:0709.4410 [astro-ph]].
52. J. A. J. Madrid and P. Martín-Moruno, "On accretion of dark energy onto black- and worm-holes", (2010), [arXiv:1004.1428 [astro-ph.CO]].

53. F. S. N. Lobo, J. Martinez-Asencio, G. J. Olmo and D. Rubiera-Garcia, "Planck scale physics and topology change through an exactly solvable model", Phys. Lett. B **731** (2014), 163–167, doi:10.1016/j.physletb.2014.02.038, [arXiv:1311.5712 [hep-th]].
54. S. Chakrabarti and S. Kar, "Wormhole geometry from gravitational collapse", Phys. Rev. D **104** (2021) no. 2, 024071, doi:10.1103/PhysRevD.104.024071, [arXiv:2106.14761 [gr-qc]].
55. W. Israel, "Singular hypersurfaces and thin shells in general relativity", Nuovo Cim. B **44S10** (1966), 1 [erratum: Nuovo Cim. B **48** (1967), 463], doi:10.1007/BF02710419.
56. M. Visser, "Traversable wormholes from surgically modified Schwarzschild spacetimes", Nucl. Phys. B **328** (1989), 203–212, doi:10.1016/0550-3213(89)90100-4, [arXiv:0809.0927 [gr-qc]].
57. E. Poisson and M. Visser, "Thin shell wormholes: Linearization stability", Phys. Rev. D **52** (1995), 7318–7321, doi:10.1103/PhysRevD.52.7318, [arXiv:gr-qc/9506083 [gr-qc]].
58. M. Visser, "Lorentzian wormholes: From Einstein to Hawking".
59. J. Baines, T. Berry, A. Simpson and M. Visser, "Killing tensor and Carter constant for Painleve-Gullstrand form of Lense-Thirring spacetime", [arXiv:2110.01814 [gr-qc]].
60. E. Giorgi, "The Carter tensor and the physical-space analysis in perturbations of Kerr-Newman spacetime", [arXiv:2105.14379 [gr-qc]].
61. S. Benenti, C. Chanu, and G. Rastelli, "Remarks on the connection between the additive separation of the Hamilton–Jacobi equation and the multiplicative separation of the Schrödinger equation. I. The completeness and Robertson conditions", Journal of Mathematical Physics, **43** (2002) no. 11, 5183–5222, American Institute of Physics, doi:10.1063/1.1506180.
62. V. Frolov, P. Krtous and D. Kubiznak, "Black holes, hidden symmetries, and complete integrability", Living Rev. Rel. **20** (2017) no. 1, 6, doi:10.1007/s41114-017-0009-9, [arXiv:1705.05482 [gr-qc]].
63. S. W. Hawking and G. F. R. Ellis, "The Large Scale Structure of Space-Time", doi:10.1017/CBO9780511524646.
64. P. Martín-Moruno and M. Visser, "Generalized Rainich conditions, generalized stress-energy conditions, and the Hawking-Ellis classification", Class. Quant. Grav. **34** (2017) no. 22, 225014, doi:10.1088/1361-6382/aa9039, [arXiv:1707.04172 [gr-qc]].
65. P. Martín-Moruno and M. Visser, "Essential core of the Hawking–Ellis types", Class. Quant. Grav. **35** (2018) no. 12, 125003, doi:10.1088/1361-6382/aac147, [arXiv:1802.00865 [gr-qc]].
66. P. Martín-Moruno and M. Visser, "Hawking-Ellis classification of stress-energy tensors: Test fields versus backreaction", Phys. Rev. D **103** (2021) no. 12, 124003, doi:10.1103/PhysRevD.103.124003, [arXiv:2102.13551 [gr-qc]].
67. K. A. Bronnikov, "Regular magnetic black holes and monopoles from nonlinear electrodynamics", Phys. Rev. D **63** (2001), 044005, doi:10.1103/PhysRevD.63.044005, [arXiv:gr-qc/0006014 [gr-qc]].
68. E. Ayon-Beato and A. Garcia, "Four parametric regular black hole solution", Gen. Rel. Grav. **37** (2005), 635, doi:10.1007/s10714-005-0050-y, [arXiv:hep-th/0403229 [hep-th]].
69. F. S. N. Lobo and A. V. B. Arellano, "Gravastars supported by nonlinear electrodynamics", Class. Quant. Grav. **24** (2007), 1069–1088, doi:10.1088/0264-9381/24/5/004, [arXiv:gr-qc/0611083 [gr-qc]].
70. S. V. Bolokhov, K. A. Bronnikov and M. V. Skvortsova, "Magnetic black universes and wormholes with a phantom scalar", Class. Quant. Grav. **29** (2012), 245006, doi:10.1088/0264-9381/29/24/245006, [arXiv:1208.4619 [gr-qc]].

71. L. Balart and E. C. Vagenas, "Regular black holes with a nonlinear electrodynamics source", Phys. Rev. D **90** (2014) no. 12, 124045, doi:10.1103/PhysRevD.90.124045, [arXiv:1408.0306 [gr-qc]].
72. K. A. Bronnikov, "Nonlinear electrodynamics, regular black holes and wormholes", Int. J. Mod. Phys. D **27** (2018) no. 06, 1841005, doi:10.1142/S0218271818410055, [arXiv:1711.00087 [gr-qc]].
73. M. E. Rodrigues and M. V. d. Silva, "Bardeen Regular Black Hole With an Electric Source", JCAP **06** (2018), 025, doi:10.1088/1475-7516/2018/06/025, [arXiv:1802.05095 [gr-qc]].

Tractor beams, pressor beams, and stressor beams within the context of general relativity

Matt Visser* and Jessica Santiago†

School of Mathematics and Statistics, Victoria University of Wellington,
PO Box 600, Wellington 6140, New Zealand
* E-mail: matt.visser@sms.vuw.ac.nz
† E-mail: jessica.santiago@sms.vuw.ac.nz

Sebastian Schuster

Institute of Theoretical Physics, Faculty of Mathematics and Physics, Charles University,
V Holešovičkách 2, 180 00 Prague 8, Czech Republic
E-mail: sebastian.schuster@utf.mff.cuni.cz

Both traversable wormholes and warp drives, concepts originally developed within the context of science fiction, have now (for some 30 odd years) been studied, debated, and carefully analyzed within the framework of general relativity. An overarching theme of the general relativistic analysis is unavoidable violations of the classical point-wise energy conditions. Another science fiction trope, now over 80 years old, is the tractor beam and/or pressor beam. We shall discuss how to formulate both tractor beams and/or pressor beams, and a variant to be called a stressor beam, within the context of reverse engineering the spacetime metric. (While such reverse engineering is certainly well beyond our civilization's current capabilities, we shall be more interested in asking what an arbitrarily advanced civilization might be able to accomplish.) We shall see that tractor beams and/or pressor beams can be formulated by suitably modifying the notion of warp drives, and that, as for wormholes and warp drives, violations of the classical point-wise energy conditions are utterly unavoidable.

Keywords: Traversable wormholes; warp drives; tractor/pressor/stressor beams

1. Introduction

Traversable wormholes have now been extensively studied for some 33 years.[1–19] The general theoretical framework has been to precisely define, and then reverse engineer, a physically interesting spacetime metric, using the Einstein equations to determine what matter sources some arbitrarily advanced civilization might need to employ in order to generate such interesting spacetime geometries. Perhaps the key feature of reverse engineering is that adopting this point of view reduces the problem of solving the Einstein equations to a relatively simple exercise in differentiation, instead of the much harder problem of integrating the underlying nonlinear PDEs.

A key feature of traversable wormhole spacetimes, at least within the usual context of standard general relativity, is the utterly unavoidable violation of the classical energy conditions.[1–19]

Even if one moves beyond the framework of standard general relativity there are unavoidable purely geometric constraints, violations of both the null convergence condition and also violations of the timelike convergence condition, that place very strong constraints on any "effective" stress-energy tensor that one might use as a source to generate the spacetime.[9]

Similarly, "warp drives" have now been extensively studied for some 27 years.[20-31] As is the case for traversable wormholes once one defines a suitable class of warp field spacetimes it is easy to see that reverse engineering the spacetime metric, at least within the context of standard general relativity, quite unavoidably leads to significant violations of the classical energy conditions.[20-31] Again, even when stepping outside the framework of standard general relativity there are still unavoidable but purely geometric constraints, violations of the null convergence condition and violations of the timelike convergence condition, that place very strong constraints on any "effective" stress-energy tensor.[20-31] (There have recently been several misguided counterclaims regarding these issues which we shall address more fully below, see references 32, 33, 34. For somewhat related but distinct analyses, with somewhat different flaws, see also the discussion in references 35, 36, 37, 38, and in reference 39.)

Much more recently, the last 6 months have seen the current authors reformulate yet another science fiction trope, tractor beams, pressor beams, and stressor beams, within the framework of general relativity.[40] Again we resort to reverse engineering, and again the classical energy conditions are violated.[40] Even if one steps outside the framework of standard general relativity there are still purely geometric constraints, violations of the null convergence condition, and also violations of the timelike convergence condition, that make the underlying physics "exotic" in some purely technical sense.[40]

Of course, in all of these cases one must first precisely define what one means by a traversable wormhole, or a warp drive, or a tractor/pressor/stressor beam. One also needs to carefully assess the extent to which the energy conditions (or more geometrically, the null and timelike convergence conditions) are to be taken as truly fundamental physics.[9,31,40,41]

2. Energy conditions — generalities

It should be emphasized that the energy conditions are not fundamental physics.[41] The energy conditions are instead warning flags: They tell you "here be unusual physics". Violations of the energy conditions are not an absolute prohibition; but they are an indication that one should think very carefully about the underlying physics.

For instance:

- Observational cosmology (either in the current epoch of the accelerating universe, or during the epoch of cosmological inflation) violates the strong energy condition (SEC).[42,43]
- Speculative theoretical cosmologies (asymptotically AdS spacetimes) with a negative cosmological constant violate the weak energy condition (WEC).
- Gravitational vacuum polarization (in the test field limit) can violate all the energy conditions, null, weak, strong, and dominant (NEC, WEC, SEC, and DEC).[44–48]
- Hawking radiation violates all the energy conditions (NEC, WEC, SEC, and DEC).[9]
- Quantum scale anomalies (trace anomalies) violate even the averaged null energy condition (ANEC).[49]

But these known energy condition violating scenarios do not necessarily imply that it is possible to concentrate energy condition violating physics in a sufficiently small region to enable "interesting" effects — such as wormholes, warp drives, and the tractor/pressor/stressor beams.[9,13,16] However, in view of these known energy condition violating scenarios, neither would the necessity of energy condition violations necessarily prohibit "interesting" physics.[50–69]

We emphasise that to verify that the energy conditions are *satisfied*:

- One needs to check *all* relevant "observers" — both *all* physical timelike observers, and in the null limit, *all* null tangent vectors.
- One needs at least *some* information concerning *all* of the stress-energy components.

In contrast, to demonstrate the energy conditions are *violated*:

- It is sufficient to check that *one* timelike observer, (or *one* null curve), violates the energy conditions.
- It is sufficient to check that *some* combination of stress-energy components violates the energy conditions.

3. Generic warp metric and tractor/pressor/stressor metric

A sufficiently generic spacetime metric, (suitable for investigating both warp drives and tractor/pressor/stressor beams), is to consider:[20–31]

$$ds^2 = -dt^2 + \delta_{ij} \left(dx^i - v^i(t,\vec{x})\,dt\right) \left(dx^j - v^j(t,\vec{x})\,dt\right). \tag{1}$$

This class of metrics has the properties that it is:

- Spatially flat.
- Unit lapse.
- The gradients of the flow vector $v^i(t, \vec{x})$ must satisfy suitable asymptotic fall-off conditions.
    - (Otherwise you do not have a localized warp-field.)
    - (You do not want to accelerate the entire universe.)

    In particular, the spacetime must be asymptotically flat.
- Three special cases are commonly considered:
    - Alcubierre: $\vec{v}(t, \vec{x}) = v(t, z)\,\hat{z}$.
    - Zero-expansion: $\nabla \cdot \vec{v}(t, \vec{x}) = 0$.
    - Zero-vorticity: $\nabla \times \vec{v}(t, \vec{x}) = 0$.
- For tractor/pressor/stressor beam spacetimes one will add extra conditions, such as cylindrical symmetry, and simplify the form of the flow vector $\vec{v}(t, \vec{x})$ by introducing suitable "envelope" and "profile" functions.
- Further generalizations are in principle possible, but very quickly become calculationally intractable.

To start specific computations it is convenient to first pick a co-tetrad:[31, 40]

- Take the timelike leg to be:
$$(e^{\hat{0}})_a = (1; 0, 0, 0)_a = n_a. \qquad (2)$$
- Take the spatial co-triad to be:
$$(e^{\hat{1}})_a = (-v_x; 1, 0, 0)_a, \quad (e^{\hat{2}})_a = (-v_y; 0, 1, 0)_a, \quad (e^{\hat{3}})_a = (-v_z; 0, 0, 1)_a. \qquad (3)$$

This *choice* serves to keep computations more-or-less tractable.

The corresponding tetrad is then fixed:[31, 40]

- The timelike leg is:
$$(e_{\hat{0}})^a = (1; v^x, v^y, v^z)^a = n^a. \qquad (4)$$
- The spatial triad is:
$$(e_{\hat{1}})^a = (0; 1, 0, 0)^a, \quad (e_{\hat{2}})^a = (0; 0, 1, 0)^a, \quad (e_{\hat{3}})^a = (0; 0, 0, 1)^a. \qquad (5)$$

With this choice of tetrad the orthonormal components of the extrinsic curvature are now particularly simple:[31, 40]

$$K_{\hat{a}\hat{b}} = \begin{bmatrix} 0 & 0 \\ \hline 0 & K_{ij} \end{bmatrix}, \qquad (6)$$

where

$$K_{ij} = v_{(i,j)}. \qquad (7)$$

(Effectively one can just quietly drop the hats from covariant spatial components of any tensor in this tetrad basis.[31,40])

Brute force computation now yields two easy results, and one somewhat messier result.[31,40]

- Easy (Gauss–Coddazzi):

$$G_{nn} = \frac{1}{2}\left(K^2 - \text{tr}(K^2)\right), \tag{8}$$

$$G_{ni} = K_{ij,j} - K_{,i}. \tag{9}$$

- Somewhat messier (specialization of ADM formalism):

$$G_{ij} = \mathcal{L}_n K_{ij} + KK_{ij} - 2(K^2)_{ij} - \left(\mathcal{L}_n K + \frac{1}{2}K^2 + \frac{1}{2}\text{tr}(K^2)\right)\delta_{ij}. \tag{10}$$

In order to claim that the energy conditions are satisfied (or claim that the null and timelike convergence conditions are satisfied) one would need to compute and analyze *all* the components of the Einstein tensor. (This is one specific place, there are others, at which the claims made in references 32, 33, 34 simply fail. See reference 31 for an extensive discussion of these issues. The analyses of references 35, 36, 37, 38, and reference 39 exhibit somewhat different pathologies; once the Einstein equations are fully solved, many of those specific examples are actually Riemann flat.)

Standard general relativity (the Einstein equations) now yields the stress-energy:

- Eulerian energy density:

$$\rho = \frac{G_{nn}}{8\pi} = \frac{1}{16\pi}\left\{\nabla \cdot \{\vec{v}K - (\vec{v}\cdot\nabla)\vec{v}\} - \frac{1}{2}(\vec{\omega}\cdot\vec{\omega})\right\}. \tag{11}$$

Note: (comoving density) = (3-divergence) + (negative semidefinite term).

- Eulerian flux:

$$f_i = \frac{G_{ni}}{8\pi} = \frac{1}{8\pi}(K_{ij,j} - K_{,i}) = \frac{1}{16\pi}(\nabla \times (\nabla \times \vec{v}))_i. \tag{12}$$

Note: curl of a curl. (So this can sometimes be set to zero.)

- Eulerian spatial stresses

$$T_{ij} = \frac{G_{ij}}{8\pi} = \frac{1}{8\pi}\left(\mathcal{L}_n K_{ij} + KK_{ij} - 2(K^2)_{ij} - \left(\mathcal{L}_n K + \frac{1}{2}K^2 + \frac{1}{2}\text{tr}(K^2)\right)\delta_{ij}\right). \tag{13}$$

The Eulerian density and Eulerian flux are easy, the Eulerian spatial stresses are more complicated. A key quantity of interest is the average pressure:

$$\bar{p} = \frac{1}{3}T_{ij}\delta^{ij} = \frac{1}{24\pi}\left(-2\mathcal{L}_n K - \frac{1}{2}K^2 - \frac{3}{2}\text{tr}(K^2)\right). \tag{14}$$

This can also be written as:
$$\bar{p} = \frac{1}{3} T_{ij}\,\delta^{ij} = -\frac{1}{24\pi}\left(2\nabla_a(Kn^a) - \frac{3}{2}K^2 + \frac{3}{2}\mathrm{tr}(K^2)\right). \tag{15}$$

Equivalently:
$$\bar{p} = \rho - \frac{1}{12\pi}\nabla_a(Kn^a). \tag{16}$$

Furthermore, consider the two combinations:
$$\rho + 3\bar{p} = -\frac{1}{4\pi}\left(\mathcal{L}_n K + \mathrm{tr}(K^2)\right), \tag{17}$$

$$\rho + \bar{p} = \frac{1}{24\pi}\left(-2\mathcal{L}_n K + K^2 - 3\,\mathrm{tr}(K^2)\right). \tag{18}$$

These two quantities are relevant to investigating violations of the SEC and NEC, respectively.[31]

4. Forces: Tractor/pressor/stressor beams

For tractor/pressor/stressor beam spacetimes we now make a specific, concrete choice for the form of the generic warp metric. Let us consider a beam pointed in the $\hat{z}$ direction, and specialize the flow vector to be of the form:

$$v_x(t,x,y,z) = k(t,z)\,x\,h(x^2+y^2),$$
$$v_y(t,x,y,z) = k(t,z)\,y\,h(x^2+y^2),$$
$$v_z(t,x,y,z) = v(t,z)\,f(x^2+y^2).$$

Note the introduction of two envelope functions, $k(t,z)$ and $v(t,z)$; and two profile functions, $h(x^2+y^2)$ and $f(x^2+y^2)$. Note that for simplicity we have also imposed cylindrical symmetry (in Cartesian coordinates).

Now consider the forces such a tractor/pressor/stressor beam spacetime would exert on a target with cross-section $\mathbb{S}$ that is at time t placed at position z.

$$F(t,z) = \pm \int_{\mathbb{S}} T_{zz}(t,x,y,z)\,dx\,dy. \tag{19}$$

There are two special cases to consider depending on whether the beam is wide or narrow compared to the cross-sectional area $A(\mathbb{S})$ of the tatget.

- Narrow beam:
$$F(t,z) = \pm \int_{\mathbb{R}^2} T_{zz}(t,x,y,z)\,dx\,dy. \tag{20}$$

- Wide beam:
$$F(t,z) = \pm T_{zz}(t,0,0,z)\,A(\mathbb{S}). \tag{21}$$

Let us now calculate, setting $u = x^2 + y^2$ for conciseness.

- Narrow beam:

$$F(t,z) = -\frac{1}{2}v(t,z)^2 \int_0^\infty u[f'(u)]^2 du$$
$$+ \frac{1}{8} \int_0^\infty u \left[v(t,z)f'(u) + \frac{1}{2}\partial_z k(t,z)h(u) \right]^2 du.$$

This is of indefinite sign, depending delicately on the envelope functions and profile functions, potentially allowing either tractor/pressor behaviour.

- Wide beam:

$$F(t,z) = -\frac{h(0)}{8\pi} \left\{ 2f(0)\, v(t,z) \partial_z k(t,z) + 2\, \partial_t k(t,z) + 3h(0)\, k(t,z)^2 \right\} A(\mathbb{S}). \tag{22}$$

This is of indefinite sign, depending delicately on the envelope functions, potentially allowing either tractor/pressor behaviour.

There are very many special cases to study, depending on one's choice of envelope and profile functions. See reference 40 for extensive details and discussion.

	Generic Natário	Modified Alcubierre	Zero Expansion	Zero Vorticity
envelope $k(t,z)$		0	$-\partial_z v$	Φ
envelope $v(t,z)$		v	v	$\partial_z \Phi$
profile $h(u)$		0	h	$2f'$
profile $f(u)$		f	$2(h + uh')$	f

One can easily tune the resulting forces in a wide variety of ways. In particular we can define a *stressor* beam to be one where the *net* force is zero, but forces alternate between attractive and repulsive as one moves across the cross section of the target, thereby stressing the target in a (in principle) controllable manner.

5. Energy conditions — specifics

In this context, all of the classical point-wise energy conditions are violated. The arguments are fully generic to tractor/pressor/stressor beam spacetimes, and, with suitable subsidiary conditions, apply also to warp drive configurations. (In the warp drive context, many special cases have been well known for over 20 years.)

Generically for either tractor/pressor/stressor or warp drive configurations we have:

$$\rho = (\text{3-divergence}) - \frac{1}{32\pi} (\vec{\omega} \cdot \vec{\omega}). \tag{23}$$

Then for all tractor/pressor/stressor beams (where by construction all fields fall off sufficiently rapidly at spatial infinity):

$$\int \rho \, \mathrm{d}^3 x = -\frac{1}{32\pi} \int (\vec{\omega} \cdot \vec{\omega}) \, \mathrm{d}^3 x \leq 0. \tag{24}$$

This kills off the WEC for all tractor/pressor/stressor beams. For warp drives one must sometimes be more careful, see the Appendix, and to prove or disprove the WEC one must check both the Eulerian energy density ρ and the NEC ($\rho + \bar{p} \geq 0$).

Generic to either tractor/pressor/stressor or warp drive configurations we have:

$$\bar{p} = \rho - \frac{1}{12\pi} \nabla_a (K n^a). \tag{25}$$

$$\int \bar{p} \, \mathrm{d}^3 x = \int \rho \, \mathrm{d}^3 x - \frac{1}{12\pi} \int \partial_t K \, \mathrm{d}^3 x. \tag{26}$$

$$\int (\rho + \bar{p}) \, \mathrm{d}^3 x = -\frac{1}{16\pi} \int (\vec{\omega} \cdot \vec{\omega}) \, \mathrm{d}^3 x - \frac{1}{12\pi} \int \partial_t K \, \mathrm{d}^3 x. \tag{27}$$

For any tractor/pressor/stressor/beam configuration (and for any suitably localized warp bubble):

$$\int (\rho + \bar{p}) \, \mathrm{d}^3 x = -\frac{1}{16\pi} \int (\vec{\omega} \cdot \vec{\omega}) \, \mathrm{d}^3 x - \frac{1}{12\pi} \partial_t \int K \, \mathrm{d}^3 x. \tag{28}$$

Furthermore, for any tractor/pressor/stressor/beam configuration (and for any suitably localized warp bubble) we also have:

$$\int K \, \mathrm{d}^3 x = 0. \tag{29}$$

Therefore, for any tractor/pressor/stressor/beam configuration (and for any suitably localized warp bubble) we conclude:

$$\int (\rho + \bar{p}) \, \mathrm{d}^4 x = -\frac{1}{16\pi} (\vec{\omega} \cdot \vec{\omega}) \, \mathrm{d}^4 x \leq 0. \tag{30}$$

This kills off the NEC.

That is, all of the classical point-wise energy conditions are violated. This certainly holds for any tractor/pressor/stressor/beam configuration, and for any suitably localized warp bubble, will also work for warp drive spacetimes. An example of a more delocalized warp bubble is considered in the Appendix.

6. Conclusions

- Traversable wormholes, warp drives, and tractor/pressor/stressor beams can all usefully be "reverse engineered", debated, analyzed, and studied within the framework of standard general relativity.
- Reverse engineering a specified interesting spacetime reduces the task of solving the Einstein equations to a relatively straightforward exercise of differentiation, rather than the more complicated task of integration.

- Traversable wormholes, warp drives, and tractor/pressor/stressor beams all violate all of the standard point-wise energy conditions.
- Even in various modified theories of gravity, wormholes, warp drives, and tractor/pressor/stressor beams violate the null convergence condition and timelike convergence condition.
- Violation of the classical energy conditions is not an absolute prohibition on "interesting" physics — it is merely an invitation to think very carefully about the underlying physics.

Appendix A. Falloff conditions at spatial infinity

For tractor/pressor/stressor beams suitable falloff conditions at spatial infinity are inherent to the definition, and utterly automatic. Similarly, for Alcubierre warp drives and zero-expansion warp drives suitable falloff conditions at spatial infinity are also inherent to the definition and utterly automatic. For zero vorticity warp drives one must be just a little more careful.

As an example, consider the general framework

$$ds^2 = -dt^2 + \delta_{ij}\left(dx^i - v^i(t,\vec{x})\,dt\right)\left(dx^j - v^j(t,\vec{x})\,dt\right), \tag{A.1}$$

and for one's warp field take the specific case

$$v^i(t,\vec{x}) = -\sqrt{\frac{2m}{r}}\,\hat{r}^i + v^i_\infty(t). \tag{A.2}$$

This corresponds to a warp bubble, centred at the origin, in a coordinate system that is moving with the warp bubble. The presence of the warp velocity term, $v^i_\infty(t)$, is essential, since otherwise the warp bubble is not moving with respect to spatial infinity, (the "fixed stars"), which would make the warp field trivial.

For the specific warp field (A.2) it is easy to calculate

$$K = \boldsymbol{\nabla}\cdot\vec{v} = -\frac{3}{2}\frac{\sqrt{2m}}{r^{3/2}}, \tag{A.3}$$

and see that this is independent of the warp velocity $v^i_\infty(t)$.

Then for the Eulerian energy density and flux one has the particularly simple results:

$$\rho = 0; \quad \text{and} \quad \vec{f} = 0. \tag{A.4}$$

This does *not* mean that the WEC is satisfied since one still has to check $\rho + \bar{p}$.

Specifically, in this particular warp field we have

$$\rho + \bar{p} = \bar{p} = -\frac{1}{12\pi}\nabla_a(K\,n^a) = -\frac{1}{12\pi}\boldsymbol{\nabla}\cdot(K\,\vec{v}(t,\vec{x})). \tag{A.5}$$

That is

$$\rho + \bar{p} = -\frac{1}{12\pi}\boldsymbol{\nabla}\cdot\left(\frac{3}{2}\frac{2m}{r^2}\hat{r} + K\vec{v}_\infty\right) = -\frac{1}{12\pi}\vec{v}_\infty(t)\cdot\boldsymbol{\nabla}K. \tag{A.6}$$

Finally

$$\rho + \bar{p} = -\frac{3}{16\pi} \frac{\sqrt{2m}}{r^{5/2}} \, \vec{v}_\infty(t) \cdot \hat{r}. \qquad (A.7)$$

But the factor $\vec{v}_\infty(t) \cdot \hat{r}$ explictly changes sign depending on whether one is "in front of" or "behind" the warp bubble. Thus this warp bubble explicitly violates the NEC, and so violates the WEC as well — this is a specific and explicit example of why merely checking the non-negativity of the Eulerian density is simply insufficient for checking the WEC.

More generally, note that an *asymptotic* version of this argument will still apply to any warp field that is asymptotically of the form (A.2):

$$v^i(t, \vec{x}) = -\sqrt{\frac{2m}{r}} \, \{1 + o(1/r)\} \, \hat{r}^i + v^i_\infty(t). \qquad (A.8)$$

This now applies to any warp bubble that asymptotes to Schwarzschild spacetime at large distances.

Acknowledgments

MV was directly supported by the Marsden Fund, via a grant administered by the Royal Society of New Zealand.

JS acknowledges indirect financial support via the Marsden fund, administered by the Royal Society of New Zealand.

SS acknowledges support from both the technical and administrative staff at the Charles University, and specific financial support via OP RDE project number CZ.02.2.69/0.0/0.0/18_053/0016976 (International mobility of research).

References

1. M. S. Morris and K. S. Thorne, "Wormholes in space-time and their use for interstellar travel: A tool for teaching general relativity", Am. J. Phys. **56** (1988), 395-412 doi:10.1119/1.15620.
2. M. S. Morris, K. S. Thorne and U. Yurtsever, "Wormholes, Time Machines, and the Weak Energy Condition", Phys. Rev. Lett. **61** (1988), 1446-1449 doi:10.1103/PhysRevLett.61.1446.
3. M. Visser, "Traversable wormholes: Some simple examples", Phys. Rev. D **39** (1989), 3182-3184 doi:10.1103/PhysRevD.39.3182 [arXiv:0809.0907 [gr-qc]].
4. M. Visser, "Traversable wormholes from surgically modified Schwarzschild spacetimes", Nucl. Phys. B **328** (1989), 203-212 doi:10.1016/0550-3213(89)90100-4 [arXiv:0809.0927 [gr-qc]].
5. T. A. Roman, "Inflating Lorentzian wormholes", Phys. Rev. D **47** (1993), 1370-1379 doi:10.1103/PhysRevD.47.1370 [arXiv:gr-qc/9211012 [gr-qc]].
6. J. G. Cramer, R. L. Forward, M. S. Morris, M. Visser, G. Benford and G. A. Landis, "Natural wormholes as gravitational lenses", Phys. Rev. D **51** (1995), 3117-3120 doi:10.1103/PhysRevD.51.3117 [arXiv:astro-ph/9409051 [astro-ph]].
7. S. Kar, "Evolving wormholes and the weak energy condition", Phys. Rev. D **49** (1994), 862-865 doi:10.1103/PhysRevD.49.862.

8. S. Kar and D. Sahdev, "Restricted class of traversable wormholes with traceless matter", Phys. Rev. D **52** (1995), 2030-2035 doi:10.1103/PhysRevD.52.2030.
9. M. Visser, "Lorentzian wormholes: From Einstein to Hawking", (AIP Press, now Springer, New York, 1995).
10. L. H. Ford and T. A. Roman, "Quantum field theory constrains traversable wormhole geometries", Phys. Rev. D **53** (1996), 5496-5507 doi:10.1103/PhysRevD.53.5496 [arXiv:gr-qc/9510071 [gr-qc]].
11. E. Teo, "Rotating traversable wormholes", Phys. Rev. D **58** (1998), 024014 doi:10.1103/PhysRevD.58.024014 [arXiv:gr-qc/9803098 [gr-qc]].
12. S. A. Hayward, "Dynamic wormholes", Int. J. Mod. Phys. D **8** (1999), 373-382 doi:10.1142/S0218271899000286 [arXiv:gr-qc/9805019 [gr-qc]].
13. M. Visser, S. Kar and N. Dadhich, "Traversable wormholes with arbitrarily small energy condition violations", Phys. Rev. Lett. **90** (2003), 201102 doi:10.1103/PhysRevLett.90.201102 [arXiv:gr-qc/0301003 [gr-qc]].
14. J. P. S. Lemos, F. S. N. Lobo and S. Quinet de Oliveira, "Morris-Thorne wormholes with a cosmological constant", Phys. Rev. D **68** (2003), 064004 doi:10.1103/PhysRevD.68.064004 [arXiv:gr-qc/0302049 [gr-qc]].
15. T. A. Roman, "Some thoughts on energy conditions and wormholes", doi:10.1142/9789812704030_0236 [arXiv:gr-qc/0409090 [gr-qc]].
16. S. Kar, N. Dadhich and M. Visser, "Quantifying energy condition violations in traversable wormholes", Pramana **63** (2004), 859-864 doi:10.1007/BF02705207 [arXiv:gr-qc/0405103 [gr-qc]].
17. T. Muller, "Exact geometric optics in a Morris-Thorne wormhole spacetime", Phys. Rev. D **77** (2008), 044043 doi:10.1103/PhysRevD.77.044043.
18. S. A. Hayward, "Wormhole dynamics in spherical symmetry", Phys. Rev. D **79** (2009), 124001 doi:10.1103/PhysRevD.79.124001 [arXiv:0903.5438 [gr-qc]].
19. O. James, E. von Tunzelmann, P. Franklin and K. S. Thorne, "Visualizing Interstellar's Wormhole", Am. J. Phys. **83** (2015), 486 doi:10.1119/1.4916949 [arXiv:1502.03809 [gr-qc]].
20. M. Alcubierre, "The Warp drive: Hyperfast travel within general relativity", Class. Quant. Grav. **11** (1994), L73-L77 doi:10.1088/0264-9381/11/5/001 [arXiv:gr-qc/0009013 [gr-qc]].
21. R. J. Low, "Speed limits in general relativity", Class. Quant. Grav. **16** (1999), 543-549 doi:10.1088/0264-9381/16/2/016 [arXiv:gr-qc/9812067 [gr-qc]].
22. C. Clark, W. A. Hiscock and S. L. Larson, "Null geodesics in the Alcubierre warp drive space-time: The View from the bridge", Class. Quant. Grav. **16** (1999), 3965-3972 doi:10.1088/0264-9381/16/12/313 [arXiv:gr-qc/9907019 [gr-qc]].
23. F. Lobo and P. Crawford, "Weak energy condition violation and superluminal travel", Lect. Notes Phys. **617** (2003), 277-291 [arXiv:gr-qc/0204038 [gr-qc]].
24. F. S. N. Lobo and M. Visser, "Fundamental limitations on 'warp drive' spacetimes", Class. Quant. Grav. **21** (2004), 5871-5892 doi:10.1088/0264-9381/21/24/011 [arXiv:gr-qc/0406083 [gr-qc]].
25. F. S. N. Lobo and M. Visser, "Linearized warp drive and the energy conditions", [arXiv:gr-qc/0412065 [gr-qc]].
26. F. S. N. Lobo, "Exotic solutions in General Relativity: Traversable wormholes and 'warp drive' spacetimes", [arXiv:0710.4474 [gr-qc]].
27. S. Finazzi, S. Liberati and C. Barceló, "Semiclassical instability of dynamical warp drives", Phys. Rev. D **79** (2009), 124017 doi:10.1103/PhysRevD.79.124017 [arXiv:0904.0141 [gr-qc]].

28. B. K. Tippett and D. Tsang, "The Blue Box White Paper", [arXiv:1310.7983 [physics.pop-ph]].
29. M. Alcubierre and F. S. N. Lobo, "Wormholes, Warp Drives and Energy Conditions", Fundam. Theor. Phys. **189** (2017), pp. 1–279 doi:10.1007/978-3-319-55182-1 [arXiv:2103.05610 [gr-qc]].
30. M. Alcubierre and F. S. N. Lobo, "Warp Drive Basics", Fundam. Theor. Phys. **189** (2017), 257–279 doi:10.1007/978-3-319-55182-1_11.
31. J. Santiago, S. Schuster and M. Visser, "Generic warp drives violate the null energy condition", [arXiv:2105.03079 [gr-qc]].
32. E. W. Lentz, "Breaking the warp barrier: hyper-fast solitons in Einstein–Maxwell-plasma theory", Class. Quant. Grav. **38** (2021) no.7, 075015 doi:10.1088/1361-6382/abe692 [arXiv:2006.07125 [gr-qc]].
33. A. Bobrick and G. Martire, "Introducing Physical Warp Drives", Class. Quant. Grav. **38** (2021) no.10, 105009 doi:10.1088/1361-6382/abdf6e [arXiv:2102.06824 [gr-qc]].
34. S. D. B. Fell and L. Heisenberg, "Positive energy warp drive from hidden geometric structures", Class. Quant. Grav. **38** (2021) no.15, 155020 doi:10.1088/1361-6382/ac0e47 [arXiv:2104.06488 [gr-qc]].
35. O. L. Santos-Pereira, E. M. C. Abreu and M. B. Ribeiro, "Dust content solutions for the Alcubierre warp drive spacetime", Eur. Phys. J. C **80** (2020) no.8, 786 doi:10.1140/epjc/s10052-020-8355-2 [arXiv:2008.06560 [gr-qc]].
36. O. L. Santos-Pereira, E. M. C. Abreu and M. B. Ribeiro, "Fluid dynamics in the warp drive spacetime geometry", Eur. Phys. J. C **81** (2021) no.2, 133 doi:10.1140/epjc/s10052-021-08921-3 [arXiv:2101.11467 [gr-qc]].
37. O. L. Santos-Pereira, E. M. C. Abreu and M. B. Ribeiro, "Charged dust solutions for the warp drive spacetime", Gen. Rel. Grav. **53** (2021) no.2, 23 doi:10.1007/s10714-021-02799-y [arXiv:2102.05119 [gr-qc]].
38. O. L. Santos-Pereira, E. M. C. Abreu and M. B. Ribeiro, "Perfect fluid warp drive solutions with the cosmological constant," Eur. Phys. J. Plus **136** (2021) no.9, 902 doi:10.1140/epjp/s13360-021-01899-7 [arXiv:2108.10960 [gr-qc]].
39. W. Béatrix-Drouhet, "Exotic Fluids Matching the Stress-Energy Tensor of Alcubierre Warp Drive Spacetimes", [arXiv:2012.09941 [gr-qc]].
40. J. Santiago, S. Schuster and M. Visser, "Tractor beams, pressor beams, and stressor beams in general relativity", Universe **7** (2021) no.8, 271 doi:10.3390/universe7080271 [arXiv:2106.05002 [gr-qc]].
41. C. Barceló and M. Visser, "Twilight for the energy conditions?", Int. J. Mod. Phys. D **11** (2002), 1553-1560 doi:10.1142/S0218271802002888 [arXiv:gr-qc/0205066 [gr-qc]].
42. M. Visser, "General relativistic energy conditions: The Hubble expansion in the epoch of galaxy formation", Phys. Rev. D **56** (1997), 7578-7587 doi:10.1103/PhysRevD.56.7578 [arXiv:gr-qc/9705070 [gr-qc]].
43. M. Visser and C. Barceló, "Energy conditions and their cosmological implications", doi:10.1142/9789812792129_0014 [arXiv:gr-qc/0001099 [gr-qc]].
44. M. Visser, "Gravitational vacuum polarization. 1: Energy conditions in the Hartle-Hawking vacuum", Phys. Rev. D **54** (1996), 5103-5115 doi:10.1103/PhysRevD.54.5103 [arXiv:gr-qc/9604007 [gr-qc]].
45. M. Visser, "Gravitational vacuum polarization. 2: Energy conditions in the Boulware vacuum", Phys. Rev. D **54** (1996), 5116-5122 doi:10.1103/PhysRevD.54.5116 [arXiv:gr-qc/9604008 [gr-qc]].
46. M. Visser, "Gravitational vacuum polarization. 3: Energy conditions in the (1+1) Schwarzschild space-time", Phys. Rev. D **54** (1996), 5123-5128 doi:10.1103/PhysRevD.54.5123 [arXiv:gr-qc/9604009 [gr-qc]].

47. M. Visser, "Gravitational vacuum polarization. 4: Energy conditions in the Unruh vacuum", Phys. Rev. D **56** (1997), 936-952 doi:10.1103/PhysRevD.56.936 [arXiv:gr-qc/9703001 [gr-qc]].
48. M. Visser, "Gravitational vacuum polarization", MG8: 8th Marcel Grossmann Meeting, Jerusalem, July 1997, [arXiv:gr-qc/9710034 [gr-qc]].
49. M. Visser, "Scale anomalies imply violation of the averaged null energy condition", Phys. Lett. B **349** (1995), 443-447 doi:10.1016/0370-2693(95)00303-3 [arXiv:gr-qc/9409043 [gr-qc]].
50. V. Baccetti, P. Martín-Moruno and M. Visser, "Null Energy Condition violations in bimetric gravity", JHEP **08** (2012), 148 doi:10.1007/JHEP08(2012)148 [arXiv:1206.3814 [gr-qc]].
51. P. Martín-Moruno and M. Visser, "Semiclassical energy conditions for quantum vacuum states", JHEP **09** (2013), 050 doi:10.1007/JHEP09(2013)050 [arXiv:1306.2076 [gr-qc]].
52. P. Martín-Moruno and M. Visser, "Classical and quantum flux energy conditions for quantum vacuum states", Phys. Rev. D **88** (2013) no.6, 061701 doi:10.1103/PhysRevD.88.061701 [arXiv:1305.1993 [gr-qc]].
53. D. Hochberg, C. Molina-París and M. Visser, "Tolman wormholes violate the strong energy condition", Phys. Rev. D **59** (1999), 044011 doi:10.1103/PhysRevD.59.044011 [arXiv:gr-qc/9810029 [gr-qc]].
54. P. Martín-Moruno and M. Visser, "Classical and semi-classical energy conditions", Fundam. Theor. Phys. **189** (2017), 193-213 doi:10.1007/978-3-319-55182-1_9 [arXiv:1702.05915 [gr-qc]].
55. M. Visser, B. Bassett and S. Liberati, "Perturbative superluminal censorship and the null energy condition", AIP Conf. Proc. **493** (1999) no.1, 301-305 doi:10.1063/1.1301601 [arXiv:gr-qc/9908023 [gr-qc]].
56. P. Martín-Moruno and M. Visser, "Semi-classical and nonlinear energy conditions", doi:10.1142/9789813226609_0126 [arXiv:1510.00158 [gr-qc]].
57. J. Friedman, M. S. Morris, I. D. Novikov, F. Echeverria, G. Klinkhammer, K. S. Thorne and U. Yurtsever, "Cauchy problem in space-times with closed timelike curves", Phys. Rev. D **42** (1990), 1915-1930 doi:10.1103/PhysRevD.42.1915.
58. S. W. Hawking, "The Chronology protection conjecture", Phys. Rev. D **46** (1992), 603-611 doi:10.1103/PhysRevD.46.603.
59. S. W. Kim and K. S. Thorne, "Do vacuum fluctuations prevent the creation of closed timelike curves?", Phys. Rev. D **43** (1991), 3929-3947 doi:10.1103/PhysRevD.43.3929.
60. F. Echeverria, G. Klinkhammer and K. S. Thorne, "Billiard balls in wormhole space-times with closed timelike curves: Classical theory", Phys. Rev. D **44** (1991), 1077-1099 doi:10.1103/PhysRevD.44.1077.
61. M. Visser, "From wormhole to time machine: Comments on Hawking's chronology protection conjecture", Phys. Rev. D **47** (1993), 554-565 doi:10.1103/PhysRevD.47.554 [arXiv:hep-th/9202090 [hep-th]].
62. M. Visser, "Hawking's chronology protection conjecture: Singularity structure of the quantum stress energy tensor", Nucl. Phys. B **416** (1994), 895-906 doi:10.1016/0550-3213(94)90560-6 [arXiv:hep-th/9303023 [hep-th]].
63. B. S. Kay, M. J. Radzikowski and R. M. Wald, "Quantum field theory on space-times with a compactly generated Cauchy horizon", Commun. Math. Phys. **183** (1997), 533-556 doi:10.1007/s002200050042 [arXiv:gr-qc/9603012 [gr-qc]].
64. S. Krasnikov, "Quantum field theory and time machines", Phys. Rev. D **59** (1999), 024010 doi:10.1103/PhysRevD.59.024010 [arXiv:gr-qc/9802008 [gr-qc]].

65. M. Visser, "The Quantum physics of chronology protection", [arXiv:gr-qc/0204022 [gr-qc]].
66. J. L. Friedman, K. Schleich and D. M. Witt, "Topological censorship", Phys. Rev. Lett. **71** (1993), 1486-1489 [erratum: Phys. Rev. Lett. **75** (1995), 1872] doi:10.1103/PhysRevLett.71.1486 [arXiv:gr-qc/9305017 [gr-qc]].
67. T. Jacobson and S. Venkataramani, "Topology of event horizons and topological censorship", Class. Quant. Grav. **12** (1995), 1055-1062 doi:10.1088/0264-9381/12/4/012 [arXiv:gr-qc/9410023 [gr-qc]].
68. G. J. Galloway, K. Schleich, D. M. Witt and E. Woolgar, "Topological censorship and higher genus black holes", Phys. Rev. D **60** (1999), 104039 doi:10.1103/PhysRevD.60.104039 [arXiv:gr-qc/9902061 [gr-qc]].
69. J. L. Friedman and A. Higuchi, "Topological censorship and chronology protection", Annalen Phys. **15** (2006), 109-128 doi:10.1002/andp.200510172 [arXiv:0801.0735 [gr-qc]].

A singularity theorem for evaporating black holes

E.-A. Kontou* and B. Freivogel

ITFA and GRAPPA, Universiteit van Amsterdam
Science Park 904, Amsterdam, the Netherlands
*E-mail: e.a.kontou@uva.nl

D. Krommydas

Instituut-Lorentz, Universiteit Leiden
P.O. Box 9506, 2300 RA Leiden, The Netherlands

The classical singularity theorems of General Relativity rely on energy conditions that are easily violated by quantum fields. Here, we provide motivation for an energy condition obeyed in semiclassical gravity: the smeared null energy condition (SNEC), a proposed bound on the weighted average of the null energy along a finite portion of a null geodesic. Using SNEC as an assumption we proceed to prove a singularity theorem. This theorem extends the Penrose singularity theorem to semiclassical gravity and has interesting applications to evaporating black holes.

Keywords: Quantum fields, gravity, energy conditions, quantum inequalities, singularities

1. Introduction

The classical or pointwise energy conditions are bounds on components of the stress-energy tensor and were introduced early on in the history of general relativity. Their purpose is to encode properties of what is considered "reasonable" matter, and predict the evolution of gravitational systems in a model-independent way.

The energy condition of interest in this work is the null energy condition (NEC). The NEC states that the stress-energy tensor contracted with two null vectors is non-negative everywhere. Using the Einstein Equation, we get the geometric form of the NEC or the null convergence condition. Using a perfect fluid stress-energy tensor, we can give a physical interpretation of the NEC: the sum of energy density and pressure cannot be negative. The three forms are summarized in Table 1.

Table 1. The different forms of the NEC. Here ℓ^μ is a null vector.

Physical form	Geometric form	Perfect fluid
$T_{\mu\nu}\ell^\mu\ell^\nu \geq 0$	$R_{\mu\nu}\ell^\mu\ell^\nu \geq 0$	$\rho + P \geq 0$

---

*Presenting author.

The NEC is obeyed by minimally coupled scalar fields but as with all pointwise energy conditions, it is violated by quantum fields.[1] Ford[2] was the first to introduce *quantum energy inequalities* (QEIs), restrictions on the possible magnitude and duration of any negative energy densities within a quantum field theory.

QEIs have since been derived for flat and curved spacetimes, bosonic and fermionic fields (see Ref. 3 and 4 for recent reviews). Those bounds are for averages over timelike curves or worldvolumes. As an example, the renormalized null energy of the quantum massless minimally coupled scalar field in Minkowski spacetime averaged over a smooth timelike curve γ obeys the following QEI[5]

$$\int dt \langle :T_{\mu\nu}:\ell^\mu \ell^\nu \rangle_\omega f^2(t) \geq -\frac{(v^\mu \ell_\mu)}{12\pi^2} \int dt f''(t)^2, \tag{1}$$

for all Hadamard states ω and any smooth, real-valued compactly supported function f. Here v^μ is the timelike vector tangent to γ. For f a normalized Gaussian with zero mean and t_0 variance the right hand side of (1) becomes

$$\int dt \langle :T_{\mu\nu}:\ell^\mu \ell^\nu \rangle_\omega f^2(t) \geq -\frac{(v^\mu \ell_\mu)}{64\pi^2 t_0^4}. \tag{2}$$

Then we can see the physical interpretation of the QEI: the longer the timescale t_0, the less negative null energy is allowed.

Important classical relativity results such as the Penrose singularity theorem[6] have the NEC in their hypotheses. If one wants to apply such theorems in a semiclassical setting it is necessary to replace the pointwise energy condition with a condition obeyed by quantum fields, namely a QEI. As the Penrose theorem proves null geodesic incompleteness, the relevant QEI would be a null averaged one.

The purpose of this contribution is to motivate a null QEI, the smeared null energy condition (SNEC) and use it to prove a semiclassical singularity theorem for null geodesic incompleteness. This theorem is applicable to the case of evaporating black holes. We begin with a description of the challenges to develop a null QEI and motivation for SNEC in Sec. 2. In Sec. 3 we state the singularity theorem of Ref. 7 and show that SNEC can be used as an assumption. In Sec. 4 we apply the theorem to a toy model of evaporating black holes. We conclude in Sec. 5 with a summary and discussion of future work.

2. Null quantum energy inequalities

2.1. *The Fewster-Roman counterexample*

In the expression of Eq. (1) the renormalized null energy is averaged over a timelike curve. A similar expression integrated over a null geodesic has been derived two-dimensions. In particular, Fewster and Hollands[8] showed that

$$\int_{-\infty}^{+\infty} f(\lambda) \langle :T_{\mu\nu}:\ell^\mu \ell^\nu \rangle_\omega \geq -\frac{c}{48\pi} \int_{-\infty}^{+\infty} \frac{(f')^2}{f} d\lambda, \tag{3}$$

holds for a class of interacting quantum fields, namely the unitary, positive energy conformal field theories (CFTs) with stress-energy tensor in Minkowski spacetime. Here c is the central charge of the theory. We recently generalized that result for a large class of curved backgrounds.[9]

The situation is different in more than two dimensions. Fewster and Roman[5] showed using an explicit construction, that the renormalized null energy averaged over a null geodesic is unbounded from below for the massless minimally coupled scalar field. So there are no null QEIs in four-dimensional Minkowski space.

Their construction was a sequence of vacuum-plus-two-particle states. Then they allowed the three-momenta of excited modes to become increasingly parallel to the spatial part of the null vector ℓ^μ. As the three momenta grows, the lower bound of the inequality diverges to negative infinity.

2.2. The smeared null energy condition

To overcome the problem encountered by Fewster and Roman, Freivogel and Krommydas proposed the smeared null energy condition (SNEC).[10] The main concept behind it is that in quantum filed theory there often exists an ultraviolet cutoff $\ell_{\rm UV}$. It was shown[9,10] that the existence of a cutoff restricts the three momenta of the excited modes in the Fewster-Roman counterexample, leading to a finite lower bound.

The SNEC can be written as

$$\int_{-\infty}^{+\infty} d\lambda g^2(\lambda) \langle T_{kk}(x^\mu(\lambda)) \rangle \geq -\frac{4B}{G_N} \int_{-\infty}^{+\infty} d\lambda \left(g'(\lambda)\right)^2, \qquad (4)$$

where $x^\mu(\lambda)$ is a null geodesic, $g(\lambda)$ is a differentiable 'smearing function' that controls the region where the null energy is averaged, B is a constant and G_N is the Newton constant. In four-dimensional field theory we can write

$$NG_N \lesssim \ell_{\rm UV}^2, \qquad (5)$$

where N is the number of fields. This relationship means the SNEC provides a finite lower bound even for a large number of fields. This is particularly useful for applications where the negative energy arises from multiple fields with small negative energy fluctuations (see e.g. 11).

To have B be an order one number, we need to saturate that inequality. This is the case for the induced gravity proof of 12 where they derived $B = 1/32\pi$. However, it is reasonable to consider a $B \ll 1$ since (5) is typically not saturated in controlled constructions.

SNEC has been proven to hold for free fields on Minkowski spacetime.[9,13] The proof utilizes the fact that free field theory factorizes on the lightsheet in a collection of two-dimensional CFTs. For each of those CFTs the two-dimensional null QEI of Eq. (3) holds leading to a proof for the higher dimensional theory.

2.3. The double smeared null energy condition

It is unclear if the proof of SNEC described in the previous subsection can be generalized to curved spacetimes and interacting fields. Additionally, the bound diverges fro $\ell_{UV} \to 0$, with the ultraviolet cutoff depending on the theory.

Those disadvantages of SNEC led to the proposal of a different bound, the double smeared null energy condition (DSNEC). The idea is to average the renormalized null energy density in both null directions, denote $+$ and $-$. Schematically the DSNEC can be written as

$$\int d^2x^{\pm} g^2(x^+, x^-) \langle :T_{--}: \rangle_\omega \geq -\frac{\mathcal{N}}{\delta_+ \delta_-^3}, \qquad (6)$$

where $\mathcal{N}$ depends on the number of fields and the smearing function, and $\delta_\pm$ is the smearing length in each of the null directions.

For a massless scalar in Minkowski the DSNEC can be explicitly written as

$$\int d^2x^{\pm} g^2(x^+, x^-) \langle :T_{--}: \rangle_\omega \geq -A \left[\int dx^+ (g''_+(x^+))^2 \right]^{1/4} \left[\int dx^- (g''_-(x^-))^2 \right]^{3/4}, \qquad (7)$$

where A is a number and we assumed that the smearing function factorizes as $g^2 = g_+(x^+)^2 g_-(x^-)^2$.

The DSNEC was motivated in 13 and its rigorous proof will appear in future work.[14] The proof of DSNEC can straightforwardly generalized for curved spacetimes as it is derived from a general QEI valid in spacetimes with curvature.[15] It includes no theory dependent cutoff and the smearing in each direction can be controlled. However, it is still unclear if the DSNEC can be used to prove singularity theorems. The main obstacle is that the usual proofs of those theorems require bounds on single geodesics.

3. The singularity theorem

3.1. The Penrose singularity theorem

In general relativity a spacetime is singular if it possesses at least one incomplete and inextendible geodesic. This definition does not give us information about the nature of the singularity (e.g. if curvature scalars diverge) but it allowed for the first model-independent theorems, the singularity theorems of Penrose[6] and Hawking.[16]

Most singularity theorems have the same three types of hypotheses: the energy condition, the initial or boundary condition and the causality condition. In the case of the Penrose theorem the energy condition is the NEC or more accurately the geometric form of the NEC, the null convergence condition. The boundary condition is the existence of a trapped surface, a co-dimension two spacelike submanifold which has two null normals with negative expansions. Equivalently, a trapped surface has negative null normal curvature everywhere. Finally, the causality condition is the existence of a non-compact Cauchy hypersurface. The conclusion is that the spacetime is future null geodesically incomplete.

Schematically, singularity theorems work in the following way: the initial condition establishes the convergence of a congruence of geodesics. The energy condition guarantees that the convergence will continue and a focal point will form. Finally, the causality condition does not allow the formation of focal points leading to a contradiction that proves the geodesic incompleteness.

3.2. *Singularity theorems with weaker conditions*

As quantum fields violate all pointwise energy conditions, a semiclassical singularity theorem is required to have a weaker energy condition. Examples of singularity theorems with such conditions include Refs. 17, 18 and 19 but none of them address the case of a condition obeyed by quantum fields. First Ref. 20 proved singularity theorems with energy conditions inspired by QEIs. Ref. 7 proved singularity theorems with similar conditions using index form methods. Utilizing these results Ref. 21 proved the first semiclassical singularity theorem for timelike geodesic incompleteness. Here we follow Ref. 21 theorem for null geodesic incompleteness.

To state the theorem we first need to fix a parametrization of the affine parameter of the null geodesic. For a manifold M let P be submanifold of co-dimension 2 with mean normal curvature vector field $H^\mu = H\hat{H}^\mu$ where $\hat{H}^\mu$ is a future-pointing timelike unit vector. Then let γ be a future-directed null geodesic emanating normally from P. Then $\hat{H}_\mu$ is extended by parallel transporting along γ. Now we can choose an affine parameter λ on γ, such that $\hat{H}_\mu d\gamma^\mu/d\lambda = 1$. Now we can state the energy condition from 7

$$\int_0^\ell g(\lambda)^2 R_{\mu\nu}\ell^\mu \ell^\nu d\lambda \geq -Q_m(\gamma)\|g^{(m)}\|^2 - Q_0(\gamma)\|g\|^2, \tag{8}$$

where Q_m and Q_0 are unknown constants dependent on the choice of γ and m a positive integer. The notation $\|\cdot\|$ denotes the L^2 norm.

The bound required by the singularity theorem is a geometric assumption, while SNEC is an assumption on the renormalized stress-energy tensor. Classically, the Einstein equation connects curvature to the stress-energy tensor. Semiclassically, the semiclassical Einstein equation (SEE) equates the expectation value of the stress-energy tensor with the classical Einstein tensor

$$8\pi G_N \langle T_{\mu\nu}\rangle_\omega = G_{\mu\nu}. \tag{9}$$

Using the SEE the bound of Eq. (4) can be written as

$$\int_{-\infty}^\infty g(\lambda)^2 R_{kk} d\lambda \geq -32\pi B \|g'(\lambda)\|^2. \tag{10}$$

Then this is a bound of the form of Eq. (8) with $m = 1$, $Q_1 = 32\pi B$ and $Q_0 = 0$. Using the SEE assumes that we have a self-consistent solution, which includes a state ω and a metric $g_{\mu\nu}$.

In addition to the energy condition the theorem of Ref. 7 has an assumption on the pointwise null energy density for a finite affine parameter. In particular, there are two scenarios to describe all possible initial conditions: in scenario 1, initially the NEC is satisfied for an affine length ℓ_0, short compared to the one for the formation of a focal point ℓ. In scenario 2 this requirement is dropped and instead conditions are imposed on the null contracted Ricci tensor for small negative values of the affine parameter. Here we focus on scenario 2.

We first extend γ to $\gamma : [-\ell_0, \ell] \to M$ and assume that Eq. (10) holds on the extended geodesic. Then we define $\rho_{\max} = \max_{[-\ell_0, 0]} \rho$ and we can use Lemma 4.7 of Ref. 7 with $m = 1$, $Q_0 = 0$, $A_1 = 1/3$, $B_1 = C_1 = 1$. If we additionally assume that $\rho_{\max} < 0$ we have

Lemma 3.1. *For ρ satisfying Eq. (10) on $[-\ell_0, \ell]$ if*

$$-2H \geq \frac{Q_1 + 2}{\ell} + \frac{Q_1}{\ell_0} + \frac{1}{3}\rho_{\max}\ell_0, \tag{11}$$

then there is a focal point to P along γ in $[0, \ell]$.

Negative null energy in $[-\ell_0, 0]$ region leads to smaller required initial contraction because this negative energy must be over-compensated by positive energy. This effect has been studied and it is known as "quantum interest".[22]

4. Application to evaporating black holes

Penrose proved the first singularity theorem which applies to a classical black hole spacetime. However, this theorem cannot be applied in an evaporating black hole spacetime, where the NEC is violated. Here we apply Lemma 3.1 in a toy model of an evaporating black hole spacetime.

First, we assume that the metric is approximated by Schwarzschild geometry near the classical horizon

$$ds^2 = \left(\frac{R_s}{r} - 1\right) dt^2 - \left(\frac{R_s}{r} - 1\right)^{-1} dr^2 + r^2 d\Omega^2, \tag{12}$$

where R_s is the Schwarzschild radius. We focus on spherically symmetric hypersurfaces P, so that the hypersurface is defined by Schwarzschild coordinates (t_p, r_p) where the mean normal curvature vector field is purely in the r direction.

Inside the horizon, the mean normal curvature H of our surfaces P is given by[23]

$$H(r_P) = -\frac{1}{r_P}\sqrt{\frac{R_s}{r_P} - 1}. \tag{13}$$

Since we assumed $\rho_{\max} < 0$ we can drop the last term of Eq. (11)

$$H < -\frac{Q_1}{2\ell} - \frac{1}{\ell} - \frac{Q_1}{2\ell_0}. \tag{14}$$

H depends on two parameters, the maximum affine parameter for the formation of the singularity ℓ and the length of the affine parameter that the NEC is violated ℓ_0.

We define the dimensionless parameter x

$$R_s - r_P \equiv x R_s, \qquad 0 < x < 1, \tag{15}$$

and y by demanding that the affine distance ℓ is a coordinate distance yR_s. We can consider the case that $y \to \infty$ meaning we have no information about the location of the singularity.

The idea is that if the mean normal curvature of the hypersurfaces P is smaller than the one required by Lemma 3.1 we have a singularity. So we equate the expressions (13) and (14) to find the location of the first hypersurface inside the horizon for which we can apply the Lemma. We want P to be as close to the classical horizon as possible. The setup is shown in Fig. 1.

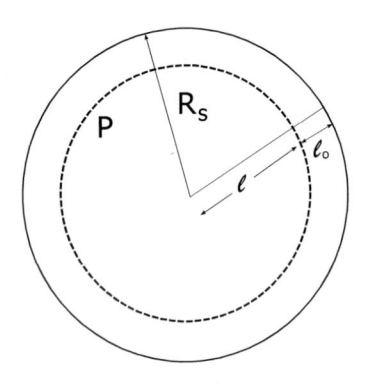

Fig. 1. Schematic representation of a Schwarzschild black hole and the parameters. The dashed circle is constant r and t hypersurface P. Distance ℓ_0 is from the point where the NEC starts being violated, and distance ℓ is from P to the singularity (pictured here at $r = 0$).

A plot of x for different values of y is shown in Fig. 2 for two different values of Q_1. The Ref. 12 value of $B = 1/32\pi$ translates to $Q_1 = 1$. Using this value for Q_1, we find that the minimum x is $1/3$. As discussed earlier, there is also strong motivation to use a value of $B \ll 1$ and so $Q_1 \ll 1$. For small Q_1, we have a singularity theorem for spheres P with

$$R_s - r_P \gtrsim R_s \frac{Q_1}{2} \qquad \text{for } Q_1 \ll 1. \tag{16}$$

5. Conclusions

In this work we provided motivation for both the smeared null energy condition (SNEC) and the double smeared null energy condition (DSNEC). We proved a semiclassical singularity theorem using SNEC and applied this theorem to establish that spacetimes that approximate the Schwarzschild solution near the horizon must contain a singularity.

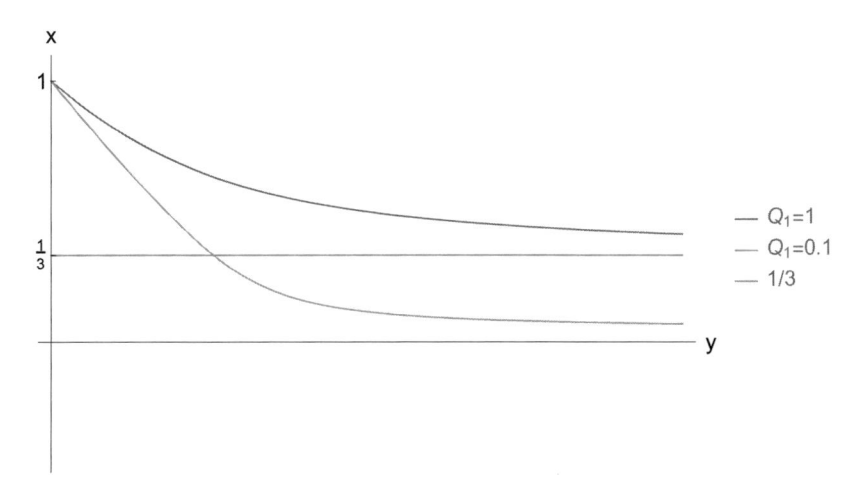

Fig. 2. Required value of x to have a singularity for different values y. For $Q_1 = 0.1$ the minimum value is much smaller compared to $Q_1 = 1$.

As the version of SNEC we use for the singularity theorem has only been proven for Minkowski spacetime, an important future direction is a theorem with a condition that incorporates curvature. There are different ways to approach that. One is to attempt to prove SNEC for spacetimes with curvature. Another is to use the new bound of DSNEC instead. This would require novel concepts as the current singularity theorem proofs are for bounds on single geodesics.

Acknowledgments

BF and E-AK are supported by the ERC Consolidator Grant QUANTIVIOL. This work is part of the Δ ITP consortium, a program of the NWO that is funded by the Dutch Ministry of Education, Culture and Science (OCW).

References

1. H. Epstein, V. Glaser and A. Jaffe, Nonpositivity of energy density in Quantized field theories, *Nuovo Cim.* **36**, p. 1016 (1965).
2. L. Ford, Quantum Coherence Effects and the Second Law of Thermodynamics, *Proc. Roy. Soc. Lond. A* **364**, 227 (1978).
3. E.-A. Kontou and K. Sanders, Energy conditions in general relativity and quantum field theory, *Class. Quant. Grav.* **37**, p. 193001 (2020).
4. C. J. Fewster, *Quantum Energy Inequalities*, in *Wormholes, Warp Drives and Energy Conditions*, ed. F. S. N. Lobo (Springer International Publishing, Cham, 2017), Cham, pp. 215–254.
5. C. J. Fewster and T. A. Roman, Null energy conditions in quantum field theory, *Phys. Rev.* **D67**, p. 044003 (2003), [Erratum: Phys. Rev.D80,069903(2009)].
6. R. Penrose, Gravitational collapse and space-time singularities, *Phys. Rev. Lett.* **14**, 57 (1965).

7. C. J. Fewster and E.-A. Kontou, A new derivation of singularity theorems with weakened energy hypotheses, *Class. Quant. Grav.* **37**, p. 065010 (2020).
8. C. J. Fewster and S. Hollands, Quantum energy inequalities in two-dimensional conformal field theory, *Rev. Math. Phys.* **17**, p. 577 (2005).
9. B. Freivogel, E.-A. Kontou and D. Krommydas, The Return of the Singularities: Applications of the Smeared Null Energy Condition (12 2020).
10. B. Freivogel and D. Krommydas, The Smeared Null Energy Condition, *JHEP* **12**, p. 067 (2018).
11. J. Maldacena, A. Milekhin and F. Popov, Traversable wormholes in four dimensions (7 2018).
12. S. Leichenauer and A. Levine, Upper and Lower Bounds on the Integrated Null Energy in Gravity, *JHEP* **01**, p. 133 (2019).
13. J. R. Fliss and B. Freivogel, Semi-local Bounds on Null Energy in QFT (8 2021).
14. F. B. Fliss, Jackson R. and E.-A. Kontou, In preparation. (2021).
15. C. J. Fewster and C. J. Smith, Absolute quantum energy inequalities in curved spacetime, *Annales Henri Poincare* **9**, 425 (2008).
16. S. W. Hawking, The Occurrence of singularities in cosmology, *Proc. Roy. Soc. Lond.* **A294**, 511 (1966).
17. F. J. Tipler, Energy conditions and spacetime singularities, *Phys. Rev.* **D17**, 2521 (1978).
18. C. Chicone and P. Ehrlich, Line integration of Ricci curvature and conjugate points in Lorentzian and Riemannian manifolds, *Manuscripta Math.* **31**, 297 (1980).
19. A. Borde, Geodesic focusing, energy conditions and singularities, *Class. Quant. Grav.* **4**, 343 (1987).
20. C. J. Fewster and G. J. Galloway, Singularity theorems from weakened energy conditions, *Class. Quant. Grav.* **28**, p. 125009 (2011).
21. C. J. Fewster and E.-A. Kontou, A semiclassical singularity theorem (8 2021).
22. L. Ford and T. A. Roman, The Quantum interest conjecture, *Phys. Rev.* **D 60**, p. 104018 (1999).
23. T. Pilkington, A. Melanson, J. Fitzgerald and I. Booth, Trapped and marginally trapped surfaces in Weyl-distorted Schwarzschild solutions, *Class. Quant. Grav.* **28**, p. 125018 (2011).

Circularly symmetric thin-shell wormholes in F(R) gravity with (2+1)-dimensions

Cecilia Bejarano*, Ernesto F. Eiroa† and Griselda Figueroa-Aguirre‡

Instituto de Astronomía y Física del Espacio (IAFE, CONICET-UBA),
Casilla de Correo 67, Sucursal 28, 1428, Buenos Aires, Argentina
* E-mail: cbejarano@iafe.uba.ar
† E-mail: eiroa@iafe.uba.ar
‡ E-mail: gfigueroa@iafe.uba.ar

Within the framework of $F(R)$ theories of gravity with (2+1)-dimensions and constant scalar curvature R, we construct a family of thin-shell wormholes with circular symmetry and we analyze the stability of the static configurations under radial perturbations. We show an example of asymptotically anti-de Sitter thin-shell wormholes with charge, finding that stable configurations with normal matter are possible for a suitable range of the parameters.

Keywords: Wormholes; F(R) gravity; Thin shells.

1. Introduction

One of the main goals of alternative theories of gravity is focused on dealing with some fundamental issues in the current cosmological picture, from the early-time inflation scenario to the late-time cosmic accelerated expansion. Basically, the intention is to modify the geometrical side of the gravitational field equations without adding any unknown matter-energy content. Certainly, any alternative approach also intends to provide a geometrical explanation for the spacetime singularities as well as a cornerstone for a quantum version of gravity theory. There is a plethora of different modified gravity models. In particular, $F(R)$ gravity[1-3] is one of the most straightforward modifications to General Relativity (GR), since the Einstein-Hilbert action is replaced by

$$S = \frac{1}{2\kappa} \int d^4x \sqrt{|g|} \left(F(R) + \mathcal{L}_m \right), \tag{1}$$

with $\kappa = 8\pi$ and R the scalar curvature (we adopt units such that $c = G = 1$, with c the speed of light and G the gravitational constant). In the metric formalism, in which the metric tensor is the only dynamical variable to perform the variation of the action, the field equations read

$$F'(R)R_{\mu\nu} - \frac{g_{\mu\nu}}{2}F(R) - \nabla_\mu \nabla_\nu F'(R) + g_{\mu\nu} \nabla_\rho \nabla^\rho F'(R) = \kappa T_{\mu\nu}, \tag{2}$$

where ∇ is the covariant derivative and $T_{\mu\nu}$ is the energy-momentum tensor.

The junction formalism[4-7] in (3+1)-dimensions has been applied within $F(R)$ gravity, for instance, to study thin layers of matter surrounding vacuum (namely, bubbles)[8,9] and black holes.[9,10] Bubbles made of a pure double layer in quadratic

$F(R)$ have been also studied a few years ago.[11] Recently, thin-shell wormholes in $F(R)$ gravity have been explored.[12-16] In this work, we present charged thin-shell wormholes in $(2+1)$-dimensional $F(R)$ gravity with and we analyze the stability of the static solutions under radial perturbations.

2. Junction conditions

The cut-and-paste formalism is commonly used to construct some wormhole geometries. It is based on the junction conditions of the corresponding theory, which allows to match different solutions across a hypersurface Σ. For convenience, we adopt the usual notation that the jump of any quantity Υ across Σ is $[\Upsilon] \equiv (\Upsilon^2 - \Upsilon^1)|_\Sigma$.

2.1. *General relativity*

In GR, the junction conditions are expressed in the Darmois-Israel formalism,[4,5] which can be sketched as follows:

- Two manifolds $\mathcal{M}_1$ and $\mathcal{M}_2$ are glued at a hypersurface Σ to obtain a geodesically complete manifold $\mathcal{M} = \mathcal{M}_1 \cup \mathcal{M}_2$.
- The first fundamental form (the induced metric) at Σ is

$$h_{ij}^{1,2} = g_{\mu\nu}^{1,2} \frac{\partial X_{1,2}^\mu}{\partial \xi^i} \frac{\partial X_{1,2}^\nu}{\partial \xi^j}\bigg|_\Sigma, \qquad (3)$$

where $X_{1,2}^\mu$ are, respectively, the coordinates that describe $\mathcal{M}_{1,2}$, and ξ^a are the intrinsic local coordinates at the hypersurface, hence $X_{1,2}^\mu = X_{1,2}^\mu(\xi^a)$.
- The second fundamental form (the extrinsic curvature) at Σ is given by

$$K_{ij}^{1,2} = -n_\gamma^{1,2}\left(\frac{\partial^2 X_{1,2}^\gamma}{\partial \xi^i \partial \xi^j} + \Gamma_{\alpha\beta}^\gamma \frac{\partial X_{1,2}^\alpha}{\partial \xi^i}\frac{\partial X_{1,2}^\beta}{\partial \xi^j}\right)\bigg|_\Sigma, \qquad (4)$$

with $n_\gamma^{1,2}$ the unit normal ($n^\gamma n_\gamma = 1$) pointing from $\mathcal{M}_1$ to $\mathcal{M}_2$.
- The matching between $\mathcal{M}_1$ and $\mathcal{M}_2$ at Σ, should fulfill the so-called junction conditions:
  - The line element should be continuous across Σ:

$$[h_{\mu\nu}] = 0. \qquad (5)$$

  - The field equations at Σ (Lanczos equations) reduce to

$$\kappa S_{\mu\nu} = -[K_{\mu\nu}] - h_{\mu\nu} K^\gamma{}_\gamma, \qquad n^\mu S_{\mu\nu} = 0 \qquad (6)$$

where $S_{\mu\nu}$ is the energy-momentum tensor at the gluing hypersurface.

The hypersurface Σ is called a *boundary surface* if $S_{\mu\nu} = 0$, or a *thin shell* of matter if $S_{\mu\nu} \neq 0$.

2.2. $F(R)$ gravity

The formalism for the junction conditions in $F(R)$ gravity was developed in recent years.[6,7] In this theory, there are two separate cases to take into account:

- General (non-quadratic) case: $F'''(R) \neq 0$
    - At the matching hypersurface Σ, the following continuity relations should be satisfied
    $$[h_{\mu\nu}] = 0, \quad [K^\mu{}_\mu] = 0, \quad [R] = 0, \tag{7}$$
    - The field equations at Σ result
    $$\kappa S_{\mu\nu} = -F'(R)[K_{\mu\nu}] + F''(R)[n^\rho \nabla_\rho R]h_{\mu\nu}, \quad n^\mu S_{\mu\nu} = 0. \tag{8}$$

- Quadratic case: $F'''(R) = 0$
    - There is one less restriction in this case, so that the discontinuity of R at Σ is allowed
    $$[h_{\mu\nu}] = 0, \quad [K^\mu{}_\mu] = 0. \tag{9}$$
    - If we write $F(R) = \alpha R^2 + R - 2\Lambda$, the field equations at Σ read
    $$\kappa S_{\mu\nu} = -[K_{\mu\nu}] + 2\alpha([n^\gamma \nabla_\gamma R]h_{\mu\nu} - [RK_{\mu\nu}]), \quad n^\mu S_{\mu\nu} = 0. \tag{10}$$
    - In order to guarantee a divergence-free energy-momentum tensor (locally conservation) at Σ, it is necessary to add the following extra contributions[17,18]
        * The external energy flux vector:
        $$\kappa \mathcal{T}_\mu = -2\alpha \nabla_\mu[R], \quad n^\mu \mathcal{T}_\mu = 0,$$
        * The external scalar pressure/tension:
        $$\kappa \mathcal{T} = 2\alpha[R]K^\gamma{}_\gamma,$$
        * The double layer contribution:
        $$\kappa \mathcal{T}_{\mu\nu} = \nabla_\gamma \left(2\alpha[R]h_{\mu\nu}n^\gamma \delta^\Sigma\right),$$
        with δ^Σ the Dirac delta on Σ (which is analogous to the dipole distributions in classical electrodynamics). It is easy to verify that all these contributions vanish if the scalar curvature is continuous at Σ.

The constraint $[K^\mu{}_\mu] = 0$ of $F(R)$ gravity, which is not present in GR, has important consequences, as we shall see in the next sections.

3. Charged solutions with constant curvature

$F(R)$ gravity coupled to a nonlinear electromagnetic field is described in (2+1)-dimensions by the action[19]

$$S = \frac{1}{2\kappa} \int d^3x \sqrt{|g|}(F(R) + (-\mathcal{F}_{\mu\nu}\mathcal{F}^{\mu\nu})^s), \qquad (11)$$

where s is a positive parameter ($s \neq 1/2$) and $\mathcal{F}_{\mu\nu} = \partial_\mu A_\nu - \partial_\nu A_\mu$ is the electromagnetic tensor. The corresponding energy-momentum tensor becomes traceless for $s = 3/4$, so this value is adopted in what follows.

The dynamical equations given by Eq. (2) for the gravitational sector are completed with the electromagnetic field part

$$\partial_\mu \left(\sqrt{-g} F^{\mu\nu} (-F_{\alpha\beta} F^{\alpha\beta})^{-1/4} \right) = 0. \qquad (12)$$

For constant $R = R_0$, the spherically symmetric geometry[19]

$$ds^2 = -A(r)dt^2 + A(r)^{-1}dr^2 + r^2 d\theta^2, \qquad (13)$$

with

$$A(r) = -M - \frac{(2\mathcal{Q}^2)^{3/4}}{2F'(R_0)r} - \frac{R_0 r^2}{6}, \qquad (14)$$

is solution of the theory represented by the action (11), where $R_0 = 6\Lambda_{eff}$ can be thought in terms of an effective cosmological constant, M is the mass and $\mathcal{Q}$ is the charge. Notice that this spacetime is asymptotically anti-de Sitter for $R_0 < 0$. The vacuum static BTZ geometry of GR is obtained if $\mathcal{Q} = 0$, so it is also a solution in $F(R)$ gravity. We can define an effective charge with its sign determined by the sign of $F'(R_0)$

$$Z \equiv \frac{(2\mathcal{Q}^2)^{3/4}}{2F'(R_0)}. \qquad (15)$$

The different values of Z establish the horizon structure of the geometry given by Eq. (14).

In the next Section, we use this spacetime to construct thin-shell wormholes by applying the junction formalism in $F(R)$ gravity, and we study the stability of the static configurations by following the standard potential approach.[20]

4. Wormhole geometry: Construction and stability

We proceed to build a class of thin-shell wormholes by cutting the outer parts of the spherically symmetric spacetimes with metrics of the form

$$ds_{1,2}^2 = -A_{1,2}(r)dt_{1,2}^2 + A_{1,2}(r)^{-1}dr^2 + r^2 d\theta^2, \qquad (16)$$

and glueing them on the circle Σ defined by $G(r) = r - a = 0$. In this way, we create the manifold $\mathcal{M} = \mathcal{M}_1 \cup \mathcal{M}_2$, where the regions at the sides of Σ are given by $\mathcal{M}_{1,2} = \{X^\alpha = (t_{1,2}, r, \theta)/r \geqslant a\}$ and with the metrics $A_{1,2}$, respectively. The only angular coordinate is $0 \leq \theta \leq 2\pi$ and the circle length $2\pi r$ is minimal at Σ, so $\mathcal{M}$ represents a wormhole connecting two regions with a throat of radius a, i.e. the flare-out condition is satisfied there. In order to obtain a traversable wormhole, the radius a is taken large enough to remove the presence of possible event horizons and singularities in both original manifolds. We take $\xi^i = (\tau, \theta)$ as the coordinates on Σ, being τ the proper time. The radius of Σ is taken as a function of time, i.e. $a = a(\tau)$, in order to analyze the stability of the static shells. The proper time should coincide at both sides of Σ, so that $dt_{1,2}/d\tau = \sqrt{A_{1,2}(a) + \dot{a}^2}/A_{1,2}(a)$, with the overdot representing $da/d\tau$ (the free signs are fixed provided that the times $t_{1,2}$ and τ all run into the future).

In the orthonormal basis $\{e_{\hat{\tau}} = e_\tau, e_{\hat{\theta}} = a^{-1} e_\theta\}$, at the hypersurface Σ, the first fundamental form results

$$h_{\hat{i}\hat{j}}^{1,2} = \text{diag}(-1, 1), \tag{17}$$

and the non-null components of the second fundamental form for static configurations are

$$K_{\hat{\tau}\hat{\tau}}^{1,2} = \pm \frac{A'_{1,2}(a_0)}{2\sqrt{A_{1,2}(a_0)}}, \tag{18}$$

$$K_{\hat{\theta}\hat{\theta}}^{1,2} = \mp \frac{1}{a_0} \sqrt{A_{1,2}(a_0)}, \tag{19}$$

where the prime represents derivative with respect to r. In our construction, the equation $[h_{\hat{i}\hat{j}}] = 0$ is automatically satisfied, while the condition $[K^{\hat{i}}{}_{\hat{i}}] = 0$ gives the following relation

$$\frac{A'_2(a_0)}{2\sqrt{A_2(a_0)}} + \frac{A'_1(a_0)}{2\sqrt{A_1(a_0)}} + \frac{1}{a_0}\left(\sqrt{A_1(a_0)} + \sqrt{A_2(a_0)}\right) = 0, \tag{20}$$

that should be always fulfilled by the throat radius a_0.

We can obtain the dynamics of the thin shell from the time dependent version of $[K^{\hat{i}}{}_{\hat{i}}] = 0$, which takes the form

$$\frac{2\ddot{a} + A'_2(a)}{2\sqrt{A_2(a) + \dot{a}^2}} + \frac{2\ddot{a} + A'_1(a)}{2\sqrt{A_1(a) + \dot{a}^2}} + \frac{1}{a}\left(\sqrt{A_1(a) + \dot{a}^2} + \sqrt{A_2(a) + \dot{a}^2}\right) = 0. \tag{21}$$

Then, we can analyze the stability of the configuration by rewriting this dynamical equation of the throat in terms of the potential

$$\dot{a}^2 = -V(a), \tag{22}$$

where

$$V(a) = -\frac{a^2 (A_1(a) - A_2(a))^2}{4a_0^2 \left(\sqrt{A_1(a_0)} + \sqrt{A_2(a_0)}\right)^2} - \frac{a_0^2 \left(\sqrt{A_1(a_0)} + \sqrt{A_2(a_0)}\right)^2}{4a^2}$$

$$+ \frac{A_1(a) + A_2(a)}{2}. \tag{23}$$

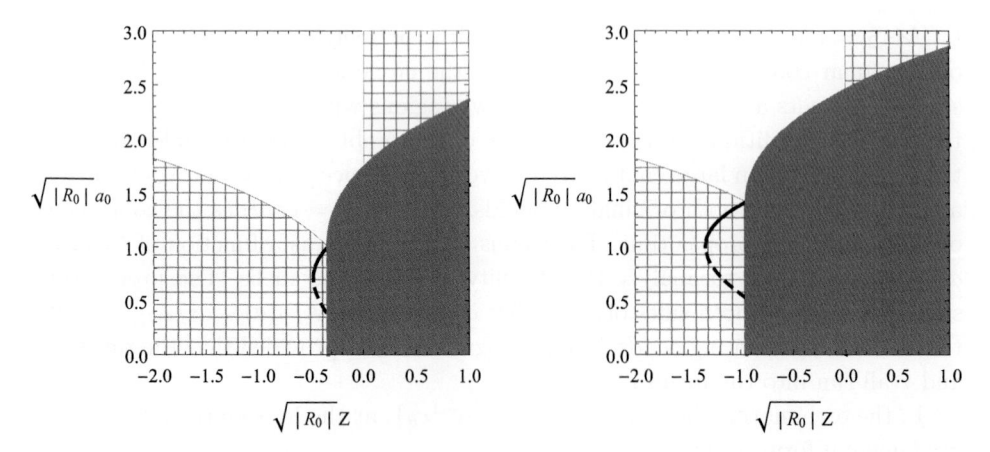

Fig. 1. Wormholes in general $F(R)$ gravity symmetric across the throat. Solid lines represent stable solutions while dashed ones unstable solutions. Meshed zones represent matter satisfying WEC. Grey zones have no physical meaning. Left plot: $M = 0.5$; right one: $M = 1$.

It is straightforward to see that $V(a_0) = 0$ and $V'(a_0) = 0$. Then, the static solutions are stable under radial perturbations when $V''(a_0) > 0$, otherwise they are unstable.

In the following examples, we adopt for our construction the charged solution with constant scalar curvatue introduced in the previous section, so the metric functions read

$$A_i(r) = -M_i - \frac{(2\mathcal{Q}_i^2)^{3/4}}{2F'(R_i)r} - \frac{R_i r^2}{6}, \quad i = 1, 2 \qquad (24)$$

where R_i, M_i, and $\mathcal{Q}_i$ are the values of the different parameters in each region $\mathcal{M}_i$.

4.1. Wormholes in general $F(R)$ with $[R] = 0$

In the first example, we adopt a symmetric construction across the throat, i.e. $R_1 = R_2 = R_0$, $M_1 = M_2 = M$, and $\mathcal{Q}_1 = \mathcal{Q}_2 = \mathcal{Q}$ so that $A_1(r) = A_2(r) = A(r)$. The throat radius a_0 should fulfill Eq. (20). Then, from Eq. (8), by using that in the orthonormal basis $S_{\hat{i}\hat{j}} = \text{diag}(\sigma_0, p_0)$, we get the surface energy density and the pressure for the static solutions

$$\sigma_0 = \frac{F'(R_0)}{\kappa} \frac{A'(a_0)}{\sqrt{A(a_0)}}, \qquad (25)$$

$$p_0 = -2\frac{F'(R_0)}{a_0 \kappa}\sqrt{A(a_0)}. \qquad (26)$$

If $\sigma_0 \geq 0$ and $\sigma_0 + p_0 \geq 0$, we say that the matter at the throat is normal, because it satisfies the weak energy condition (WEC), otherwise it is exotic. By using Eq. (20), we can see that the matter should satisfy the equation of state $\sigma_0 - 2p_0 = 0$.

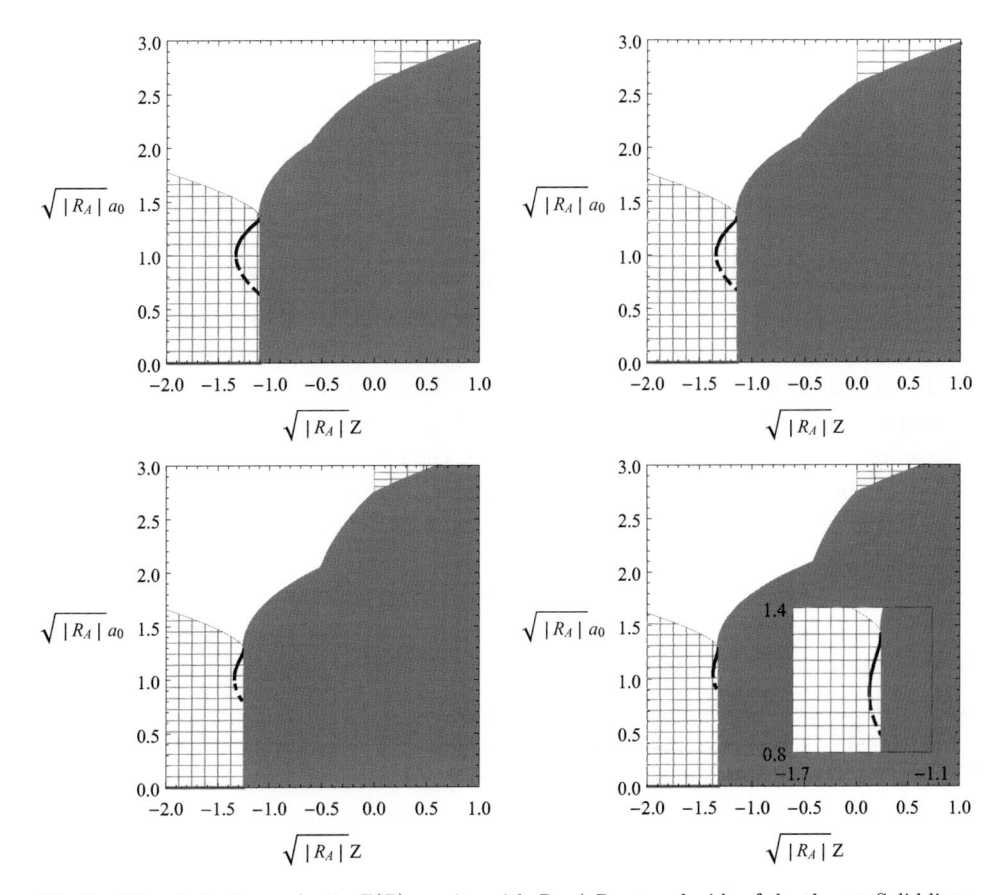

Fig. 2. Wormholes in quadratic $F(R)$ gravity with $R_1 \neq R_2$ at each side of the throat. Solid lines represent stable solutions while dashed ones unstable solutions. Meshed zones represent matter satisfying WEC. Grey zones have no physical meaning. For all plots: $M = 1$, $R_A = (R_1 + R_2)/2$. Upper row: $R_1 = 0.9R_A$ and $R_2 = 1.1R_A$; lower row: $R_1 = 0.8R_A$ and $R_2 = 1.2R_A$. Left column: $\alpha R_A = -0.1$ for $Z > 0$ and $\alpha R_A = -0.9$ for $Z < 0$; right column: $\alpha R_A = -0.2$ for $Z > 0$ and $\alpha R_A = -0.8$ for $Z < 0$.

From Fig. 1, we see that there are two solutions constituted of normal matter for a short range of $\sqrt{|R_0|}Z$ with $Z < 0$. Hence it requires the presence of ghost fields, i.e. $F'(R_0) < 0$. The solution with the largest radius is stable while the other one is unstable under radial perturbations. The qualitative behavior of the solutions is not affected by the different values of M which only represent a change of scale.

4.2. Wormholes in quadratic $F(R)$ with $[R] \neq 0$

In the second example, we adopt $M_1 = M_2 = M$, and $\mathcal{Q}_1 = \mathcal{Q}_2 = \mathcal{Q}$ but $R_1 \neq R_2$, so we are restricted to quadratic $F(R)$ gravity. The throat radius a_0 should satisfy Eq. (20). From Eq. (10) the energy density and pressure at the throat in the static configuration are

$$\sigma_0 = \frac{1+2\alpha R_2}{\kappa}\left(\frac{A_2'(a_0)}{2\sqrt{A_2(a_0)}}\right) + \frac{1+2\alpha R_1}{\kappa}\left(\frac{A_1'(a_0)}{2\sqrt{A_1(a_0)}}\right), \quad (27)$$

$$p_0 = -\frac{1+2\alpha R_2}{\kappa}\left(\frac{\sqrt{A_2(a_0)}}{a_0}\right) - \frac{1+2\alpha R_1}{\kappa}\left(\frac{\sqrt{A_1(a_0)}}{a_0}\right). \quad (28)$$

In this case, there exists an external scalar pressure/tension $\mathcal{T}_0$ that satisfies the equation of state $\sigma_0 - p_0 = \mathcal{T}_0$ which results by using Eq. (20). The other extra contributions are: $\mathcal{T}_\mu^{(0)} = 0$ and $\mathcal{T}_{\mu\nu}^{(0)} \propto (2\alpha[R]/\kappa)h_{\mu\nu}$.

From Fig. 2, we see that there are two solutions made of normal matter for a short range of $\sqrt{|R_A|}Z$ with $R_A = (R_1+R_2)/2$; since $Z<0$, ghost fields appear. The solution with the largest radius is stable; the other is unstable. The larger the difference between R_1 and R_2, the smaller the range of $\sqrt{|R_A|}Z$ where solutions exist. The same qualitative behaviour is obtained when α decreases. As in the previous example, the different values of M does not affect the qualitative behavior of the solutions and it only represents a change of scale.

5. Summary

We have constructed a family of circularly symmetric thin-shell wormholes in (2+1)-dimensional $F(R)$ gravity with constant scalar curvature R at each side of the throat. We have studied their stability under perturbations preserving the symmetry. The junction conditions in $F(R)$ gravity are more restrictive than in GR. In fact, the extra condition $[K^\mu{}_\mu] = 0$ forces the type of equation of state: for general $F(R)$, it should be $\sigma_0 - 2p_0 = 0$, while for quadratic $F(R)$, it results $\sigma_0 - 2p_0 = \mathcal{T}_0$. We have analyzed two examples: (i) symmetric wormholes ($R_1 = R_2 = R_0$; $M_1 = M_2 = M$; $\mathcal{Q}_1 = \mathcal{Q}_2 = \mathcal{Q}$) across the throat in general $F(R)$ and (ii) wormholes asymmetric in the scalar curvature ($R_1 \neq R_2$; $M_1 = M_2 = M$ and $\mathcal{Q}_1 = \mathcal{Q}_2 = \mathcal{Q}$) only in quadratic $F(R)$. In both cases, we have found two solutions made of normal matter (i.e., satisfying WEC) for a range of values with the effective charge $Z<0$. However, for these solution the presence of ghost fields is always required since $Z<0$ implies $F'(R_0)<0$. We have found that the solution with the larger radius is stable while the other is unstable. The qualitative behavior of the solutions is not altered by M, resulting only in a change of scale. In particular, for quadratic $F(R)$ as long as the difference between the constant (negative) scalar curvatures R_1 and R_2 grows, the range of the squared charge $\mathcal{Q}^2$ where stable solutions exist becomes smaller; similar behavior can be observed when α decreases. Another example and more references can be found in our recently published work.[20]

Acknowledgments

This work has been supported by CONICET and Universidad de Buenos Aires. C. B. thanks the partial support of the John Templeton Foundation.

References

1. T. P. Sotiriou and V. Faraoni, F(R) theories of gravity, *Rev. Mod. Phys.* **82**, 451 (2010).
2. A. De Felice and S. Tsujikawa, F(R) theories, *Living Rev. Relativ.* **13**, 3 (2010).
3. S. Nojiri, S. D. Odintsov, and V. K. Oikonomou, Modified gravity theories on a nutshell: Inflation, bounce and late-time evolution, *Phys. Rep.* **692**, 1 (2017).
4. G. Darmois, Mémorial des Sciences Mathématiques, Fascicule XXV, Chap. V (Gauthier-Villars, Paris, 1927).
5. W. Israel, Singular hypersurfaces and thin shells in general relativity, *Il Nuovo Cimento B* **44**, 1 (1966); **48**, 463 (E) (1967).
6. N. Deruelle, M. Sasaki, and Y. Sendouda, Junction conditions in F(R) theories of gravity, *Prog. Theor. Phys.* **119**, 237 (2008).
7. J. M. M. Senovilla, Junction conditions for F(R) gravity and their consequences, *Phys. Rev. D.* **88**, 064015 (2013).
8. E. F. Eiroa and G. Figueroa-Aguirre, Spherical thin shells in F(R) gravity: construction and stability, *Eur. Phys. J. C* **78**, 54 (2018).
9. E. F. Eiroa and G. Figueroa-Aguirre, Thin shells in F(R) gravity with non-constant scalar curvature, *Eur. Phys. J. Plus* **135**, 774 (2020).
10. E. F. Eiroa and G. Figueroa-Aguirre, Thin shells surrounding black holes in F(R) gravity, *Eur. Phys. J. C* **79**, 171 (2019).
11. E. F. Eiroa, G. Figueroa-Aguirre, and J. M. M. Senovilla, Pure double-layer bubbles in quadratic F(R) gravity, *Phys. Rev. D* **95**, 124021 (2017).
12. E. F. Eiroa and G. Figueroa-Aguirre, Thin-shell wormholes with charge in F(R) gravity, *Eur. Phys. J. C* **76**, 132 (2016).
13. E. F. Eiroa and G. Figueroa-Aguirre, Thin-shell wormholes with a double layer in quadratic F(R) gravity, *Phys. Rev. D* **94**, 044016 (2016).
14. M. Zaeem-ul-Haq Bhatti, A. Anwar, S. Ashraf, Construction of thin shell wormholes from metric F(R) gravity, *Mod. Phys. Lett. A* **32**, 1750111 (2017).
15. S. Habib Mazharimousavi, A note on thin-shell wormholes with charge in F(R)-gravity, *Eur. Phys. J. C* **78**, 612 (2018).
16. S. Habib Mazharimousavi, M. Halilsoy, K. Kianfar, Thin-shell wormholes in F(R)-gravity coupled with nonlinear electrodynamics, *Eur. Phys. J. Plus* **135**, 440 (2020).
17. J. M. M. Senovilla, Gravitational double layers, *Class. Quant. Grav.* **31**, 072002 (2014).
18. B. Reina, J. M .M. Senovilla, and R. Vera, Junction conditions in quadratic gravity: thin shells and double layers, *Class. Quant. Grav.* **33**, 105008 (2016).
19. S. H. Hendi, B. Eslam Panah, and R. Saffari, Exact solutions of three-dimensional black holes: Einstein gravity versus F(R) gravity, *Int. J. Mod. Phys. D* **23**, 1450088 (2014).
20. C. Bejarano, E. F. Eiroa, and G. Figueroa-Aguirre, Thin-shell wormholes in (2+1)-dimensional F(R) theories, *Eur. Phys. J. C* **81**, 668 (2021).

Warp drive dynamic solutions considering different fluid sources

Osvaldo L. Santos-Pereira[1,*], Everton M. C. Abreu[2,3,4,†] and Marcelo B. Ribeiro[1,4,‡]

[1] *Physics Institute, Universidade Federal do Rio de Janeiro, Rio de Janeiro, Brazil,*
[2] *Physics Department, Universidade Federal Rural do Rio de Janeiro, Seropédica, Brazil,*
[3] *Physics Department, Universidade Federal de Juiz de Fora, Juiz de Fora, Brazil*
[4] *Applied Physics Graduate Program, Physics Institute, Universidade Federal do Rio de Janeiro, Rio de Janeiro, Brazil*
*E-mails: * olsp@if.ufrj.br, † evertonabreu@ufrrj.br, ‡ mbr@if.ufrj.br*

Alcubierre proposed in 1994 that the well known special relativistic limitation that particles cannot travel with velocities bigger than the light speed can be bypassed when such trips are considered globally within specific general relativistic frameworks. Although initial results indicated this scenario as being unphysical, since it would seem to require negative mass-energy density, recent theoretical analyses suggest that such an unphysical situation may not always be necessarily true. In this paper, we present solutions of the Einstein equations using the original Alcubierre warp drive metric endowed with various matter-energy sources, namely dust, perfect fluid, anisotropic fluid, and perfect fluid within a cosmological constant spacetime. A connection of some of these solutions featuring shock waves described by the Burgers equation is also shown.

Keywords: Warp drive solutions, perfect fluid, anisotropic fluid, shock waves, electromagnetic field, cosmological constant

1. Introduction

Alcubierre[1] advanced a model based on a specific general relativistic spacetime geometry in which massive particles can travel at superluminal speeds if they are located inside a specially designed spacetime distortion. The physics of this possible propulsion method, named as *warp drive* (WD) after science fiction literature, consists of a special spacetime metric forming a spacetime distortion, called *warp bubble*, such that it generates an expansion behind the distortion and a contraction in front of it. That makes it possible for a massive particle to be in a local sub-luminal speed inside the bubble, as required by special relativity, whereas outside the particle is propelled at superluminal speeds. Therefore, employing of this spacetime distortion a massive particle travels between two points in spacetime with apparent time less than the time a light particle with zero mass would require to travel between the same two points.

The WD metric, as originally proposed by Alcubierre, is based on a general metric that uses the 3+1 formalism.[2,3] It consists of a boost in the direction of one of the spatial coordinates, described by the shift vector, a function of spacetime coordinates and the product of two functions, the velocity of the center of the warp bubble and the shape function that controls the shape of the bubble. Although

Alcubierre did not solve the Einstein equations with his proposed spacetime geometry, he gave an example of a shape function in the form of a hat function.[1] One of the main caveats of the Alcubierre WD spacetime is the requirement of negative mass-energy density and the violation of the dominant and weak energy conditions.

Ford and Roman[4] derived quantum inequalities for free massless quantized scalar fields, electromagnetic fields, and massive scalar fields in four-dimensional Minkowski spacetime and concluded that these constraints have the form of an uncertainty principle limitation on the magnitude and duration of negative mass-energy densities and that the exotic solutions of Einstein equations such as wormholes and WD would have significant limitations in their viability. Pfenning and Ford[5] followed this last work and calculated the upper bound limits necessary for the WD viability, concluding then that the energy required to create a warp bubble is ten orders of magnitude greater than the total mass of the entire visible universe, also negative.

Krasnikov[6] approached the hyperfast interstellar travel problem in general relativity by discussing the possibility of whether or not a mass particle can reach a remote point in spacetime and return sooner than a photon would. Krasnikov argued that it is not possible for a mass particle to win this race under reasonable assumptions for globally hyperbolic spacetimes. He discussed in detail the specific spacetime topologies, but with the constraint that tachyons would be a requirement for superluminal travel to occur. He conjectured a spacetime modification device that can be used to make superluminal travel possible without tachyons. Such spacetime was named as *Krasnikov tube* by Everet and Roman,[7] and they generalized the metric proposed by Krasnikov by hypothesizing a tube along the path of the particle connecting Earth to a distant star.

The Krasnikov metric cannot shorten the time for a one-way trip from Earth to a distant star, but it can make the time for a round trip arbitrarily short for clocks on Earth. However, the Everet and Roman[7] extension of the Krasnikov metric has the property that inside the tube the spacetime is flat and the lightcones are opened in such a way that they allow the superluminal travel in one direction. They also mentioned that even though the Krasnikov tube does not involve closed timelike curves it is possible to construct a time machine with a system of two non-overlapping tubes, and demonstrated that the Krasnikov tube also requires thin layers of negative energy density and large total negative energies.

Lobo and Crawford[8] discussed the Krasnikov metric in detail, addressed the violation of the weak energy condition and the viability of superluminal travel. These authors concluded that with the imposition of the weak energy condition the Olum theorem[9] prohibits superluminal travel and pointed out the necessity of further research on spacetimes with closed timelike curves and the need for a precise definition of superluminal travel. They argued that one can construct metrics that allow superluminal travel but are flat Minkowski spacetimes. The quantum inequalities, brought from quantum field theory,[7] were also discussed. Van de Broeck[10] showed how a minor modification of the Alcubierre WD geometry can reduce the total energy required for the creation of a warp bubble. He presented a modification of the original WD metric where the total negative mass would be of the order of just a few solar masses.

Natário[11] proposed a new version of the WD theory with zero expansion and questioned the effects that occur in the WD in opposition to his newly proposed metric, namely, the zero expansion Natário WD metric. Natário discussed the nature of the WD spacetime symmetries with a series of propositions and corollaries such as the proof that the WD spacetime is flat whenever the tangent vector to the Cauchy surfaces is a Killing vector field for the Euclidean metric despite being time-dependent and as a particular case. In addition, it is also flat wherever the tangent vector is spatially constant. He also showed that nonflat WD spacetime violate both the *weak energy condition* (WEC) and the *strong energy condition* (SEC), as well as that the WD metric can be obtained from the Natário metric by a particular choice of coordinates. The spherical coordinates were the choice of charts for the zero expansion of the Natário WD spacetime.

Lobo and Visser[12] pointed out that the WD theory is an example of reverse engineering of the solutions of the Einstein equations where one defines a specific spacetime metric and then one finds the matter distribution responsible for the respective geometry. These authors verified that the class of WD spacetimes necessarily violate the classical energy conditions even for low warp bubble velocity. Hence, this is the case of a geometric choice and not of superluminal properties. They proposed a more realistic WD by applying linearized gravity to the weak WD with nonrelativistic warp bubble velocities and argued that for the Alcubierre WD and its version proposed by Natário[11] the center of the bubble must be massless. They found that even for low velocities the negative energy stored in the warp fields must be a significant fraction of the particle's mass at the center of the warp bubble.

White[13,14] described how a warp field interferometer could be implemented at the Advanced Propulsion Physics Laboratory with the help of the original[1] WD ideias. He also pointed out that the expansion behind the warp bubble and contraction in front of it is due to the nature of the WD functions, and that the distortion of spacetime may be interpreted as a kind of Doppler effect or stress and strain on spacetime. Lee and Cleaver[15] argued that external radiation might affect the WD, and that the warp field interferometer proposed by White[13,14] could not detect spacetime distortions. Mattingly et al.[16] discussed curvature invariants in the Natário WD.

Bobrick and Martire[17] proposed a general WD spacetime that encloses all WD definitions removing any alleged issues with the original Alcubierre WD. They presented a general subluminal model with spherical symmetry and positive energy solutions that satisfies the quantum energy inequalities such that it reduces two orders of magnitude the WD requirement for negative energy density. They claimed that any type of WD, including the original one, is a place of regular or exotic material moving in inertial form with a certain speed.

Lentz[18] claimed that the original warp bubble proposed by Alcubierre[1] can be physically interpreted as hyper-fast gravitational solitons and presented the first solution for superluminal solitons in general relativity satisfying the WEC and the momentum conditions for conventional sources of stress, like energy and momentum, that do not require large amounts of negative energy. The basis for his work is to assume that the shift vector components obey a kind of wave equation giving rise to a positive energy geometry. Fell and Heisenberg[19] also addressed the WD as gravitational solitons and shed light on the Eulerian energies and their relation to the WEC, raising the possibility for superluminal spacetimes with viable amounts of energy density.

Quarra[20] established that within the scope of general relativity certain gravitational waveforms can result in geodesics that arrive at distant points earlier than light signals in flat spacetime, and presented an example waveform that can be used to manifest superluminal behavior.

Santiago et al.[21] claimed that generic WD metrics violate the *null energy conditions* (NEC) and discussed how Eulerian observers are privileged, meaning that these observers may perceive positive energy densities causing the impression of viable WD. They also argue that for the WD to become a possibility it would require that all timelike observers observe positive energy densities. They stated that any WD spacetime will unavoidably violate the energy conditions. In a subsequent work[22] they claimed that exotic spacetimes, such as the WD one will always violate energy conditions. They also provided other examples of such spacetimes relating them to wormholes, tractor beams and stress beams.

For a detailed discussion on the basics of WD theory, the reader is referred to Alcubierre and Lobo.[23] For a nice exposition on WD theory one is referred to the lecture notes of the course given by Shoshany.[24] It is particularly noteworthy the recent results concerning the possibility of WD features in negative energy density distribution of an experimental Casimir cavity,[25] results that open the striking possibility of ingenious experimental avenues on how to create the WD phenomena in a laboratory environment.

In this work, we present a summary of the results we have recently obtained when solving the Einstein equations with the assumption of simple fluid distributions embedded in the original Alcubierre WD spacetime geometry. New results such as the vacuum solutions connecting the WD to shock waves via the Burgers equation are presented.[26] We used the perfect fluid energy-momentum tensor[27] (EMT) which disclosed new exact solutions of the Einstein equations. We also demonstrated that starting with simple forms of mass and energy sources, vacuum solutions for the WD spacetime arise when we impose that the WEC is trivially satisfied by a choice of gauge on the shift vector and the spacetime coordinates.[27] Further results of the Alcubierre WD metric endowed with a charged dust EMT that considers an electromagnetic tensor in curved spacetime with the cosmological constant are mentioned.[28] Finally, adding the cosmological constant to the Einstein equations coupled with the Alcubierre WD spacetime having perfect fluid as a source has the effect of leading the energy density to possibly becoming positive depending on both the value and sign of the cosmological constant.[29]

The paper is organized as follows. Section 2 reviews very brief the Alcubierre WD metric. Section 3 depicts the perfect and anisotropic fluid cases[27] and Section 4 discusses the relationship between the WD spacetime, vacuum solutions, and shock waves described by the Burgers equations.[26] Section 5 presents a discussion on the role of the cosmological constant in the Einstein equation solutions for the WD spacetime.[29] Section 6 presents the conclusions.

2. The Alcubierre Warp Drive Spacetime Metric

Alcubierre originally used[1] the Arnowitt-Deser-Misner (ADM) approach of general relativity,[2,3] a formalism where the spacetime is described by a foliation of space-like hypersurfaces of constant time coordinate. The general form of the WD metric in this formalism is described by the following equation,

$$ds^2 = -d\tau^2 = g_{\alpha\beta} dx^\alpha dx^\beta$$
$$= -\left(\alpha^2 - \beta_i \beta^i\right) dt^2 + 2\beta_i \, dx^i \, dt + \gamma_{ij} \, dx^i \, dx^j , \quad (1)$$

where $d\tau$ is the lapse of proper time, α is the lapse function, β^i is the space-like shift vector, and γ_{ij} is the spatial metric for the hypersurfaces. The Greek indices range from 0 to 3, whereas the Latin ones indicate the space-like hypersurfaces and range from 1 to 3. The lapse function α and the shift vector β^i are functions to be determined, γ_{ij} is a positive-definite metric on each of the space-like hypersurfaces, for all values of time, a feature that makes the spacetime globally hyperbolic. The lapse function $d\tau$ is a measure of proper time between two adjacent hypersurfaces by observers moving along the normal direction to the hypersurfaces (Eulerian observers). The shift vector is a tangent vector to the hypersurfaces that relates the spatial coordinate systems on different hypersurfaces.

Alcubierre assumed the following ad hoc particular choices for the parameters of the general ADM metric,[1]

$$\alpha = 1, \quad (2)$$
$$\beta^1 = -v_s(t) f\left[r_s(t)\right], \quad (3)$$
$$\beta^2 = \beta^3 = 0, \quad (4)$$
$$\gamma_{ij} = \delta_{ij}. \quad (5)$$

Rewriting Eq. (1) with these definitions yields the *Alcubierre WD spacetime metric* below,

$$ds^2 = -\left(1 - \beta^2\right) dt^2 - \beta \, dx \, dt + dx^2 + dy^2 + dz^2. \quad (6)$$

3. Einstein Equations Solutions for Simple Fluids

We to find solutions to the Einstein equations with the Alcubierre WD metric as the underlying geometry by coupling simple matter-energy distributions, namely the dust of particles, the perfect fluid and the anisotropic fluid with off-diagonal metric terms to see if those EMTs could lead to a viable WD bubble.

Starting with incoherent fluid, or dust, vacuum solutions of the Einstein equations for the WD metric (6) were recovered, which led to the connection of the WD with shock waves via Burgers equation.[26] Vacuum solutions mean that all the energy conditions are trivially satisfied, but the possibility of vacuum shock waves that could physically represent warp bubbles indicated that other known matter-energy distributions could result in more complex solutions of Einstein equations. Under this perception we proposed two other energy-momentum tensors, the perfect and "parametrized" fluids, where the latter is, in fact, an anisotropic fluid with heat flux.[27]

The EMT for an anisotropic and dissipative fluid may be written by the following equation,

$$T^{\alpha\beta} = \mu u^\alpha u^\beta + p h^{\alpha\beta} + u^\alpha q^\beta + u^\beta q^\alpha + \pi^{\alpha\beta}, \tag{7}$$

where

$$h_{\alpha\beta} = g_{\alpha\beta} + u_a u_b \tag{8}$$

projects tensors onto hypersurfaces orthogonal to u^α, μ is the matter density, p is the fluid static pressure, q^α is the heat flux vector and $\pi^{\alpha\beta}$ is the viscous shear tensor. The world lines of the fluid elements are the integral curves of the four-velocity vector u^α. The heat flux vector and the viscous shear tensor are transverse to the world lines, that is,

$$q_a u^a = 0, \quad \text{and} \quad \pi_{ab} u^b = 0. \tag{9}$$

For simplicity we depicted the EMT of the anisotropic fluid in the following matrix form,

$$T_{\alpha\sigma} = \begin{pmatrix} \mu + \beta^2 p & -\beta D & 0 & 0 \\ -\beta D & A & 0 & 0 \\ 0 & 0 & B & 0 \\ 0 & 0 & 0 & C \end{pmatrix}, \tag{10}$$

where p, A, B and C are anisotropic static pressures, D is the momentum density parameter that represents the heat flux for this fluid, and μ is the particles' matter density. Notice that if we choose all pressures and momentum density as being equal to the static pressure p we recover the perfect fluid form shown below,

$$T_{\alpha\sigma} = \begin{pmatrix} \mu + \beta^2 p & -\beta p & 0 & 0 \\ -\beta p & p & 0 & 0 \\ 0 & 0 & p & 0 \\ 0 & 0 & 0 & p \end{pmatrix}. \tag{11}$$

The EMT for a perfect fluid can be written in terms of the tensor notation as follows,

$$T_{\alpha\beta} = (\mu + p)\, u_\alpha u_\beta + p\, g_{\alpha\beta}, \tag{12}$$

where μ is the matter density, p is the fluid static pressure, $g_{\alpha\beta}$ is the metric tensor and u_α is the 4-velocity of an observer inside the fluid. Perfect fluids have no shear stress, rotation, heat conduction or viscosity. To recover the EMT for dust of particles, we have to choose the static fluid pressure to be zero, and the matrix form for the dust is given by the following equation,

$$T_{\alpha\sigma} = \begin{pmatrix} \mu & 0 & 0 & 0 \\ 0 & 0 & 0 & 0 \\ 0 & 0 & 0 & 0 \\ 0 & 0 & 0 & 0 \end{pmatrix}, \tag{13}$$

which can be written in tensor notation as follows,

$$T_{\alpha\beta} = \mu\, u_\alpha u_\beta, \tag{14}$$

where μ is the matter density represented by a scalar function of the spacetime coordinates, and u^α are the observers 4-velocity components.

Table 1 lists the solutions of the Einstein equations for the anisotropic fluid defined by Eq. (10),[27] where the two solutions subsets 1b and 2b are considered unphysical because the resulting EMT leads to the anisotropic static pressures A and D equal to zero, whereas $B = C$. The energy density in the T_{00} component of the EMT is equal to zero, resulting in the following equation of state relating the matter density μ, the shift vector β and the static pressure p,

$$\mu = -\beta^2 p. \tag{15}$$

We must point out that we made a notational change on the shift vector definition β^1 so that it has the negative sign of the original parameter defined by Alcubierre,[1] yielding the shift vector β used in here as being given as below,

$$\beta = -\beta^1 = v_s(t) f[r_s(t)]. \tag{16}$$

Finally, one should also notice that solutions 1b and 2b brought about the following Burgers equation in dissipative form,

$$\frac{\partial}{\partial x}\left[\frac{\partial \beta}{\partial t} + \frac{1}{2}\frac{\partial}{\partial x}(\beta^2)\right] = -64\pi B. \tag{17}$$

Table 1. WD solutions of the Einstein equations with anisotropic fluid as source.

Case	Conditions	Results
1) $\dfrac{\partial \beta}{\partial z} = 0$	1a) $\dfrac{\partial \beta}{\partial x} = 0$	$\mu = \beta^2(2D - A - p) + \dfrac{A}{3}$ $\beta = \beta(t, y)$ $B = -C = \dfrac{A}{3}$ $\left(\dfrac{\partial \beta}{\partial y}\right)^2 = 32\pi C,$ $\dfrac{\partial^2 \beta}{\partial y^2} = 16\pi \beta(A - D)$
	1b) $\dfrac{\partial \beta}{\partial y} = 0$	$\mu = -\beta^2 p$ $\beta = \beta(t, x)$ $B = C$ $A = D = 0$ $\dfrac{\partial}{\partial x}\left[\dfrac{\partial \beta}{\partial t} + \dfrac{1}{2}\dfrac{\partial}{\partial x}(\beta^2)\right] = -64\pi B$ $\to$ solution *dismissed* as unphysical
2) $\dfrac{\partial \beta}{\partial y} = 0$	2a) $\dfrac{\partial \beta}{\partial x} = 0$	$\mu = \beta^2(2D - A - p) + \dfrac{A}{3}$ $\beta = \beta(t, z)$ $B = -C = \dfrac{A}{3}$ $\left(\dfrac{\partial \beta}{\partial z}\right)^2 = 32\pi C$ $\dfrac{\partial^2 \beta}{\partial z^2} = 16\pi \beta(A - D)$
	2b) $\dfrac{\partial \beta}{\partial z} = 0$	$\mu = -\beta^2 p$ $\beta = \beta(t, x)$ $B = C$ $A = D = 0$ $\dfrac{\partial}{\partial x}\left[\dfrac{\partial \beta}{\partial t} + \dfrac{1}{2}\dfrac{\partial}{\partial x}(\beta^2)\right] = -64\pi B$ $\to$ solution *dismissed* as unphysical

Perfect fluid solutions have equations of state given by the expression below,[30]

$$p = p(\mu) = (\gamma - 1)\mu , \qquad (18)$$

where $\gamma =$ is a constant which for ordinary fluids can be approximated by $1 \leq \gamma \leq 2$. The incoherent matter, or dust, corresponds to $\gamma = 1$, and radiation corresponds to $\gamma = \frac{4}{3}$. For solutions 1b and 2b in Table 1 it is clear that γ is a function of the shift vector given by the following equation,

$$\gamma = 1 - \frac{1}{\beta^2} . \qquad (19)$$

Notice that since the shift vector is a function of the warp velocity and it is also the regulating function, we are facing a problem with a discontinuity when $\beta = 0$ since outside the warp bubble the regulating function approaches to zero, but inside the warp bubble $f(r_s) = 1$. So Eq. (19) takes the following form,

$$\gamma = 1 - \frac{1}{v_s^2}, \qquad (20)$$

where $v_s = v_s(t)$ is the warp bubble velocity. Solutions 1a and 2a shown in Table 1 are very similar, except that for solution 1a the shift vector is a function of spacetime coordinates (t, y), whereas solution 2a is a function of (t, z) coordinates. However, in both of these cases, the shift vector may be a complex-valued function depending on the values of the static pressure C. For these solutions the equations of state relating the matter density μ and the fluid pressures are identical and given by the following expression,

$$\mu = \beta^2(2D - A - p) + \frac{A}{3} . \qquad (21)$$

The perfect fluid solutions listed in Table 2 are a special case of the anisotropic fluid if we chose all pressures to be equal to p. Table 3 presents the special dust case $(p = 0)$, which leads to vacuum.

4. Warp Drive and Shock Waves

In previous studies[26, 27] it was found an intrinsic relationship between the WD concept and shock waves via the Burgers equation arising from vacuum solutions of Einstein equations for the Alcubierre WD metric. Such a result may mean that the warp bubble could be interpreted as shock waves in vacuum. In other words, the Burgers equation can be seen as a vacuum solution of Einstein equations connecting the Alcubierre WD metric to shock waves.

In the case of the anisotropic fluid, we considered as unphysical the solution which led to a Burgers equation (17) because the parameter values resulted in an EMT with only two static pressures (diagonal terms) and no energy density. Nevertheless, for the perfect fluid and dust EMTs we found the Burgers equation

Table 2. WD solutions of the Einstein equations with perfect fluid as source.

Case	Condition	Results
1) $\dfrac{\partial \beta}{\partial z} = 0$	1a) $\dfrac{\partial \beta}{\partial x} = 0$	$p = 3\mu$ $\beta = \beta(y,t)$ $\dfrac{\partial \beta}{\partial y} = \pm\sqrt{-32\pi\mu}$
	1b) $\dfrac{\partial \beta}{\partial y} = 0$	$p = 3\mu = 0$ $\beta = \beta(x,t)$ $\dfrac{\partial \beta}{\partial t} + \dfrac{1}{2}\dfrac{\partial}{\partial x}(\beta^2) = h(t)$
2) $\dfrac{\partial \beta}{\partial y} = 0$	2a) $\dfrac{\partial \beta}{\partial x} = 0$	$p = 3\mu$ $\beta = \beta(z,t)$ $\dfrac{\partial \beta}{\partial z} = \pm\sqrt{-32\pi\mu}$ $\dfrac{\partial \beta}{\partial z} = \pm\sqrt{\pm 96\pi\mu}$
	2b) $\dfrac{\partial \beta}{\partial z} = 0$	$p = 3\mu = 0$ $\beta = \beta(x,t)$ $\dfrac{\partial \beta}{\partial t} + \dfrac{1}{2}\dfrac{\partial}{\partial x}(\beta^2) = h(t)$

Table 3. WD solutions of the Einstein equations with dust source (leads to vacuum).

Case	Consequence	Results
1) $\dfrac{\partial \beta}{\partial z} = 0$	$\dfrac{\partial \beta}{\partial y} = 0$	$\mu = 0$ $\beta = \beta(t,x)$ $\dfrac{\partial \beta}{\partial t} + \dfrac{1}{2}\dfrac{\partial}{\partial x}(\beta^2) = h(t)$
2) $\dfrac{\partial \beta}{\partial y} = 0$	$\dfrac{\partial \beta}{\partial z} = 0$	$\mu = 0$ $\beta = \beta(t,x)$ $\dfrac{\partial \beta}{\partial t} + \dfrac{1}{2}\dfrac{\partial}{\partial x}(\beta^2) = h(t)$

in its viscous form describing a dissipative system with the right-hand side being a function of time coordinate only, according to the expression below,

$$\frac{\partial \beta}{\partial t} + \frac{1}{2}\frac{\partial}{\partial x}(\beta^2) = h(t) \ . \tag{22}$$

Here $h = h(t)$ is an arbitrary function to be determined by the boundary conditions. If $h(t) = 0$ Eq. (22) takes its homogeneous form describing a conservative system known as inviscid Burgers equation.

The Burgers or Bateman-Burgers, equation is a well-known partial differential equation that models several physical systems such as gas dynamics, traffic flows, and even stock market, since, for the latter application, it is connected to the symmetries of the Black-Scholes equation. Its most notorious system description is, however, the phenomena arising from conservation laws and formation of shock waves, that is, discontinuities that appears after a finite time and then propagates in a regularly. The physics behind the field solutions of the Burgers equation can be seen as a current density.

The WD is depicted by the shift vector $\beta = v_s(t) f(r_s)$, where v_s is the bubble velocity, $f(r_s)$ is the regulating function of the warp bubble shape and the inviscid Burgers in Eq. (22) can be interpreted and representing a conservation law for this current density. Analyzing each term of Eq. (22), the first one on the l.h.s., $\partial \beta / \partial t$ can be interpreted as a force per unit mass, i.e., the time derivative of momentum. The second term on the l.h.s., $\frac{1}{2} \partial (\beta^2) / \partial x$, can be interpreted as the divergence of the total energy, which is entirely kinetic. Physically the result can be understood by considering the WD metric as conservation of both energy and momentum in the direction of the wave propagation. Calculating the divergence of the parametrized, or anisotropic, perfect fluid energy-momentum tensor, and demanding that it should be zero, one arrives at the following system,[27]

$$-\frac{\partial \beta}{\partial x}(D+\mu) - \frac{\partial \mu}{\partial t} - \beta \left[\frac{\partial D}{\partial x} + \frac{\partial \mu}{\partial x} + \frac{\partial \beta}{\partial t}(2p + A - 3D)\right]$$
$$+ \beta^2 \left[\frac{\partial D}{\partial t} - \frac{\partial p}{\partial t} + 3\frac{\partial \beta}{\partial x}(D-p)\right] + \beta^3 \left(\frac{\partial D}{\partial x} - \frac{\partial p}{\partial x}\right) = 0, \quad (23)$$

$$\frac{\partial A}{\partial x} + \frac{\partial \beta}{\partial t}(D-A) + \beta \left[3\frac{\partial \beta}{\partial x}(D-A) + \frac{\partial D}{\partial t} - \frac{\partial A}{\partial t}\right]$$
$$+ \beta^2 \left(\frac{\partial D}{\partial x} - \frac{\partial A}{\partial x}\right) = 0, \quad (24)$$

$$\frac{\partial B}{\partial y} + \beta \frac{\partial \beta}{\partial y}(D-A) = 0, \quad (25)$$

$$\frac{\partial C}{\partial z} + \beta \frac{\partial \beta}{\partial z}(D-A) = 0. \quad (26)$$

The perfect fluid zero divergence is recovered by letting

$$p = A = B = C = D, \quad (27)$$

hence, Eqs. (23) to (26) become,

$$-\frac{\partial \mu}{\partial t} - \beta\left(\frac{\partial p}{\partial x} + \frac{\partial \mu}{\partial x}\right) = 0, \quad (28)$$

$$\frac{\partial p}{\partial x} = \frac{\partial p}{\partial y} = \frac{\partial p}{\partial z} = 0, \quad (29)$$

which means that the static pressure p of the perfect fluid does not depend on the spatial coordinates, and Eq. (28) reduces to the expression below,

$$\frac{\partial \mu}{\partial t} + \beta \frac{\partial \mu}{\partial x} = 0, \quad (30)$$

which is a continuity equation, μ is the fluid density, and β is the flow velocity vector field. Notice that for constant density the fluid has an incompressible flow. Therefore, all partial derivatives of β in terms of the spatial coordinates vanish, and the flow velocity vector field has zero divergence, this being a classical fluid dynamics scenario. The local bubble volume expansion rate is zero, and the WD metric becomes the Minkowski metric in this scenario.

If we want to find these results for the dust of particles as a particular case, we can see that the partial time derivative of the matter-density is zero and we have

$$\mu \frac{\partial \beta}{\partial x} = 0, \quad (31)$$

which is immediately satisfied since the matter density is zero for the dust EMT and the Einstein equations solution for the WD is the vacuum one. This is also true for the sets of solutions 1b and 2b found for the perfect fluid, as shown in Table 2. This result for the vacuum solutions of the Einstein equations with the WD metric as a background suggests that the necessary energy to create the associate shock wave is purely geometrical. It is interesting evidence that the WD metric can be understood as a spacetime motion equivalent to a shock wave moving in a fluid, where spacetime itself plays the role of the fluid.

Considering all these results one can speculate about vacuum energy, quantum fluctuations and dark matter as fuel for the feasibility of the warp bubble, but one has to overcome possible difficulties caused by the event horizon of the bubble that would require particles with imaginary mass like tachyons.[31]

5. The Cosmological Constant

Bearing in mind the results above led to the next step of adding the cosmological constant in the Einstein equation to seek solutions for Alcubierre WD spacetime geometry.[29] The motivation came from Eq. (19) in the original Alcubierre work,[1] which was obtained by applying the WEC considering Eulerian observers, contracting the EMT and writing the final expression $G_{\mu\nu} = \kappa T_{\mu\nu}$ in the Einstein equation, whose result reads as follows,

$$T^{\mu\nu} u_\mu u_\nu = \alpha^2 T^{00} = G^{00} = -\frac{v_s^2 \rho^2}{4r_s^2}\left(\frac{df}{dr_s}\right)^2. \quad (32)$$

Here u^μ and u_μ are respectively the contravariant and covariant components of the four-vector velocity of the Eulerian observers given by

$$u^\mu = \frac{1}{\alpha}(1, \beta^1, \beta^2, \beta^3) \ , \quad u_\mu = -(\alpha, 0, 0, 0) \,, \tag{33}$$

where α is the lapse time between the constant hypersurfaces of the ADM-formalism and β^i are the three-components of the shift vector $\boldsymbol{\beta}$. Using the original parameters from the 3+1-formalism, its general metric and the chosen chart of coordinates we can write Eq. (32) as below,

$$T_{\alpha\beta} u^\alpha u^\beta = -\frac{1}{4}\left[\left(\frac{\partial \beta}{\partial y}\right)^2 + \left(\frac{\partial \beta}{\partial z}\right)^2\right]. \tag{34}$$

The above expression is clearly a non-positive term everywhere, violating the WEC in a nontrivial way. We then showed that if we begin with simple energy and momentum sources and impose Eq. (34) to be as identically zero we arrive at vacuum solutions for the WD spacetime.[26,27] However, if we include the cosmological constant in the Einstein equations the expression (34) is changed, yielding,

$$T_{\alpha\beta} u^\alpha u^\beta = \Lambda - \frac{1}{4}\left[\left(\frac{\partial \beta}{\partial y}\right)^2 + \left(\frac{\partial \beta}{\partial z}\right)^2\right]. \tag{35}$$

For positive and large enough values of the cosmological constant, it may be possible to construct a WD that does not violate the WEC, because the original negative mass-energy density necessary to create the warp bubble could become positive.

The solutions for the WD metric which include the cosmological constant in the Einstein equations[29] are presented in Table 4. Cases 1b and 2b are just the vacuum solutions connecting the WD spacetime to shock waves via the Burgers equations, and they also require a vanishing cosmological constant, since both the static fluid pressure (p) and the matter density (μ) also vanish. The other two solutions subsets 1a and 2a are also similar to the equally labeled ones in Table 2, but now they include the cosmological constant and the solutions are no longer required to be complex if the following conditions are satisfied,

$$\Lambda - 8\pi\mu \geq 0 \,, \tag{36}$$

$$\Lambda - 8\pi p \geq 0 \,. \tag{37}$$

Taking all these results into account imply that creating a warp bubble for superluminal travel of massive particles seem to require more complex forms of matter than the dust for stable solutions, and that the requirement of negative mass-energy may not be as strict as originally thought for superluminal spacetime travel with warp speeds. The shift vector in the direction of the warp bubble movement creates a coupling in Einstein equations that requires the off-diagonal source terms in the energy-momentum tensor that represent momentum densities.

Previous authors investigated the WD theory from the geometrical point of view[6,7,10–12] and came up with other types of WD mechnics, but it now seems clear that it is also necessary to consider both the energy and momentum tensors to propose a superluminal propelling system in the WD theory.

Table 4. WD solutions of the Einstein equations with Λ and perfect fluid.

Case	Condition	Results
1) $\frac{\partial \beta}{\partial z} = 0$	1a) $\frac{\partial \beta}{\partial x} = 0$	$\Lambda = 6\pi \left(\mu - \frac{p}{3}\right)$ $\beta = \beta(y, t)$ $\frac{\partial \beta}{\partial y} = \pm\sqrt{4(\Lambda - 8\pi\mu)}$ $\frac{\partial \beta}{\partial y} = \pm\sqrt{\frac{4}{3}(\Lambda - 8\pi p)}$ $\beta\frac{\partial \mu}{\partial x} + \frac{\partial \mu}{\partial t} = 0$ (null divergence)
	1b) $\frac{\partial \beta}{\partial y} = 0$	$\Lambda = 8\pi\mu = 8\pi p = 0$ $\beta = \beta(x, t)$ $\frac{\partial \beta}{\partial t} + \frac{1}{2}\frac{\partial}{\partial x}(\beta^2) = h(t)$ Null divergence is trivially satisfied This is the solution found in Ref.[26]
2) $\frac{\partial \beta}{\partial y} = 0$	2a) $\frac{\partial \beta}{\partial x} = 0$	$\Lambda = 6\pi \left(\mu - \frac{p}{3}\right)$ $\beta = \beta(y, t)$ $\frac{\partial \beta}{\partial z} = \pm\sqrt{4(\Lambda - 8\pi\mu)}$ $\frac{\partial \beta}{\partial z} = \pm\sqrt{\frac{4}{3}(\Lambda - 8\pi p)}$ $\beta\frac{\partial \mu}{\partial x} + \frac{\partial \mu}{\partial t} = 0$ (null divergence)
	2b) $\frac{\partial \beta}{\partial z} = 0$	$\Lambda = 8\pi\mu = 8\pi p = 0$ $\beta = \beta(x, t)$ $\frac{\partial \beta}{\partial t} + \frac{1}{2}\frac{\partial}{\partial x}(\beta^2) = h(t)$ Null divergence is trivially satisfied This is the solution found in Ref.[26]

6. Conclusions

In this work, we described new exact solutions of the Einstein equations endowed with the Alcubierre warp drive (WD) spacetime geometry having simple energy-momentum tensor (EMT) distributions of matter and energy. The incoherent matter, or dust, the simplest fluid source EMT used with the WD metric, led to vacuum solutions and the weak energy condition being satisfied with null energy density. In addition, we showed that the dynamics of the vacuum WD spacetime are governed by the Burgers equation, which links the WD bubble to shock waves.[26] Both the perfect fluid EMT and an anisotropic fluid recover the Burgers equation as vacuum solutions, but some of these new sets of solutions were considered unphysical, and others showed that the shift vector can be a complex-valued function.[27] The Einstein equations with the cosmological constant were used with the WD metric having the perfect fluid as the source, whose results showed that if the cosmological constant is big enough it would be possible to attain positive energy density for the WD spacetime.[29] This result is in line with recent research activity in WD theory by other authors, who provide examples of different WD spacetimes geometries,[17-19] which suggests that it may be possible to create warp bubbles with positive energy densities.

References

1. M. Alcubierre, *The warp drive: hyper-fast travel within general relativity*. Class. Quant. Grav. 11 (1994) L73, arXiv:gr-qc/0009013.
2. R. Arnowitt, S. Deser and C.W. Misner. *Dynamical Structure and Definition of Energy in General Relativity*, Phys. Rev. 116 (1959) 1322.
3. R. Arnowitt, S. Deser and C.W. Misner. *The Dynamics of General Relativity. Gravitation: An introduction to current research*, L. Witten, (ed.), Wiley, NY, 1962. Reprinted in arXiv:gr-qc/0405109.
4. L.H. Ford and T.A. Roman, *Quantum Field Theory Constrains Traversable Wormhole Geometries*, Phys. Rev. D 53 (1996) 5496, arXiv:gr-qc/9510071.
5. M.J. Pfenning and L.H. Ford *The unphysical nature of Warp Drive*, Class. Quant. Grav. 14 (1997) 1743, arXiv:gr-qc/9702026.
6. S.V. Krasnikov *Hyperfast Interstellar Travel in General Relativity*, Phys. Rev. D 57 (1998) 4760, arXiv:gr-qc/9511068.
7. A. Everett and T.A. Roman, *A Superluminal Subway: The Krasnikov Tube*, Phys. Rev. D 56 (1997) 2100, arXiv:gr-qc/9702049.
8. F.S.N. Lobo and P. Crawford, *Weak Energy Condition Violation and Superluminal Travel*, Lect. Notes Phys. 617 (2003) 277, arXiv:gr-qc/0204038.
9. K. Olum, *Superluminal travel requires negative energy density*, Phys. Rev. Lett, 81 (1998) 3567, arXiv:gr-qc/9805003.
10. C. Van Den Broeck, *A warp drive with more reasonable total energy*, Class. Quant. Grav. 16 (1999) 3973, arXiv:gr-qc/9905084.
11. J. Natário, *Warp Drive With Zero Expansion*, Class. Quant. Grav. 19 (2002) 1157, arXiv:gr-qc/0110086.
12. F.S.N. Lobo and M. Visser, *Linearized warp drive and the energy conditions*, arXiv:gr-qc/0412065.

13. H.G. White, *A Discussion of Space-Time Metric Engineering*, Gen. Relat. Grav. 35 (2003) 2025.
14. H.G. White, *Warp Field Mechanics 101*, J. Brit. Interplanetary Society 66 (2011) 242.
15. J. Lee and G. Cleaver, *Effects of External Radiation on an Alcubierre Warp Bubble*, Physics Essays 29 (2016) 201.
16. B. Mattingly, A. Kar, M. Gorban, W. Julius, C. Watson, M.D. Ali, A. Baas, C. Elmore, J. Lee, B. Shakerin, E. Davis, and G. Cleaver, *Curvature Invariants for the Accelerating Natário Warp Drive*, Particles 3 (2020) 642, arXiv:2008.03366.
17. A. Bobrick and G. Martire, *Introducing physical warp drives*, Class. Quant. Grav. 38 (2021) 105009, arXiv:2102.06824.
18. E.W. Lentz, *Breaking the warp barrier: Hyper-fast solitons in Einstein-Maxwell-plasma Theory*, Class. Quant. Grav. 38 (2021) 075015, arXiv:2006.07125.
19. S.D.B. Fell and L. Heisenberg, *Positive energy warp drive from hidden geometric structures*, Class. Quant. Grav. 38 (2021) 155020, arXiv:2104.06488.
20. C.J. Quarra, *Creating spacetime shortcuts with gravitational waveforms*, arXiv:1602.01439.
21. J. Santiago, S. Schuster and M. Visser, *Generic warp drives violate the null energy condition*, arXiv:2105.03079.
22. J. Santiago, S. Schuster and M. Visser, *Tractor beams, pressor beams and stressor beams in General Relativity*, Universe 7 (2021) 271, arXiv:2106.05002.
23. M. Alcubierre and F.S.N. Lobo, *Wormholes, Warp Drives and Energy Conditions*, Fundam. Theor. Phys. 189 (2017) 279, arXiv:2103.05610.
24. B. Shoshany, *Lectures on Faster-than-Light Travel and Time Travel*, SciPost Phys. Lect. Notes, 10 (2019), arXiv:1907.04178.
25. H. White, J. Vera, A. Han. A.R. Bruccoleri and J. MacArthur, Eur. Phys. J. C 81 (2021) 677.
26. O.L. Santos-Pereira, E.M.C. Abreu and M.B. Ribeiro, *Dust content content solutions for the Alcubierre warp drive spacetime*, Eur. Phys. J. C 80 (2020) 786, arXiv:2008.06560.
27. O.L. Santos-Pereira, E.M.C. Abreu and M.B. Ribeiro, *Fluid dynamics in the warp drive spacetime geometry*, Eur. Phys. J. C 81 (2021) 133, arXiv:2101.11467.
28. O.L. Santos-Pereira, E.M.C. Abreu and M.B. Ribeiro, *Charged dust solutions for the warp drive spacetime*, Gen. Relat. Gravit. 53 (2021) 23, arXiv:2102.05119.
29. O.L. Santos-Pereira, E.M.C. Abreu and M.B. Ribeiro, *Perfect fluid warp drive solutions with the cosmological constant*, Eur. Phys. J. Plus 136 (2021) 902, arXiv:2108.10960.
30. G.F.R. Ellis and H. van Elst, *Cosmological Models*, (Cargése Lectures 1998), NATO Adv. Study Inst. Ser. C. Math. Phys. Sci. 541 (1999) 1, arXiv:gr-qc/9812046.
31. M. Alcubierre, talk at the 16th Marcel Grossmann Meeting: AT3-Wormholes, Energy Conditions and Time Machines (7 July 2021). Available at https://youtu.be/NqN1c-2fv8Y?t=784.

Symmetries and geometry of spacetime: Towards a new paradigm

Francisco Cabral[1]

Instituto de Astrofísica e Ciências do Espaço, Faculdade de Ciências da Universidade de Lisboa, Campo Grande, P-1749-016 Lisbon, Portugal
[1] *Email:ftcabral@fc.ul.pt*

Francisco S. N. Lobo[2]

Instituto de Astrofísica e Ciências do Espaço, Faculdade de Ciências da Universidade de Lisboa, Campo Grande, P-1749-016 Lisbon, Portugal
[2] *Email:fslobo@fc.ul.pt*

Diego Rubiera-Garcia[3]

Departamento de Física Teórica and IPARCOS, Universidad Complutense de Madrid, E-28040 Madrid, Spain
[3] *Email:drubiera@ucm.es*

In this work the geometrical methods and symmetry principles in gravitation are explored motivating a new perspective into the spacetime paradigm. The effects of post-Riemann spacetime geometries with torsion are briefly studied in applications to fundamental fermionic and bosonic fields, cosmology and gravitational waves. The physical implications and related phenomenological considerations are addressed, and the fundamental ideas related to spacetime physics, motivated by geometrical methods and symmetry principles, are also briefly discussed in the context of the possible routes towards a new spacetime paradigm in gravitation and unified field theories

Keywords: Riemann-Cartan spacetime, torsion, fermionic systems, gravitational waves

1. Introduction

The success of Einstein's General Theory of Relativity (GR) to describe the gravitational interaction is quite remarkable. GR has passed all tests performed so far: Solar System observations and binary pulsars,[1] stellar orbits around the central galactic black hole,[2] gravitational waves (GWs) from coalescing compact objects (black holes and neutron stars),[3-6] or the indirect observation of the black hole horizon with the Event Horizon Telescope,[7] among others. At the same time, GR provides us with the observationally valid framework for the standard cosmological paradigm when supplemented with the (cold) dark matter and dark energy hypothesis.[8]

Soon after GR theory, Weyl (1918) introduced the notion of gauge transformations, in an attempt to unify gravity and electromagnetism.[9] By extending the Local Lorentz group to include scale transformations (dilatations) he was led to assume what we call a Riemann-Weyl spacetime geometry, a post-Riemann geometry with (the trace-vector part of) non-metricity beyond curvature. The theory was then abandoned and Weyl (1929) clarified that the electromagnetic field is intimately related to local internal symmetries, under the U(1) group that act on the 4-spinor fields of charged matter.[10] In the mid 1950's Yang (1954) and Mills (1954)[11] further explored the notion of gauge symmetries in field theories going beyond the $U(1)$ group to include non-abelian Lie groups ($SU(2)$), in order to address nuclear physics, while Utiyama (1956)[12] extended the gauge principle to all semi-simple Lie groups including the Lorentz group. The gauge principle is based on the localization of the rigid, global symmetry group of a field theory, introducing a new interaction described by the gauge potential. The latter is a compensating field that makes it possible for the matter Lagrangian to be locally invariant under the symmetry group and is included in the covariant derivative of the theory. There is a clear geometrical interpretation of the gauge potential as the connection of the fiber bundle, which is the manifold obtained from the base spacetime manifold and the set of all fibers. These are attached at each spacetime point and are the (vector, tensor or spinor) spaces of representation of the local symmetries. In the geometrical interpretation, the imposition of local symmetries implies that the geometry of the fiber bundle is non-Euclidean, and the gauge field strengths are the curvatures of such a manifold.

The gauge formulation of gravity was resumed through the works of Kibble (1961)[13] and Sciama[14] (1964), who gauged the (rigid) Poincaré group of Minkowski spacetime symmetries. This can be viewed as the starting point of a self-consistent gauge theory of gravity. They arrived at what is now known as a Riemann-Cartan (RC) geometry, and to the corresponding Einstein-Cartan-Sciama-Kibble (ECSK) gravity, with non-vanishing torsion and curvature. This is a natural extension of GR, which is able to successfully incorporate the intrinsic spin of fermions as a source of gravity, while passing all weak-field limit tests. The theory has no free parameters but introduces a new scale given by Cartan's density, which yields many relevant applications in cosmology and astrophysics.[15–23] The ECSK is the simplest of all Poincaré gauge theories of gravity (PGTG) in RC spacetime. Beyond the Poincaré group we have, for instance, the Weyl and the conformal groups, which live on a subset of a general metric-affine geometry, with non-vanishing curvature, torsion and non-metricity (for a detailed analysis and reviews on several topics of the gauge approach to gravity see the remarkable works in[24–26]). *By extending the gauge symmetry group of gravity, one is naturally led to extend the spacetime geometry paradigm as well.*

Just as quantum field theories of the standard model are gauge theories with (local) internal symmetries, similarly, classical theories of gravity can indeed be formulated as gauge theories, leading to non-Euclidean geometries. Therefore, the gauge principle (with its geometrical methods) is a convenient formalism in order to address the possible avenues towards unified field theories of matter, gravity and spacetime geometry. The spacetime paradigm changes when we extend the gauge group of gravity and the history of Physics have shown that changing the fundamental ideas about space and time is at the basis of major breakthroughs. Gauge methods in gravity and post-Riemann geometries deserve further developments with potential applications in astrophysical and cosmological scenarios with very strong gravitational fields. Above all, they are a vital part of the effort to understand the nature of spacetime and gravitation.

In this paper we review the fundamental geometrical objects and its relation to spacetime symmetries in the gauge formulation of gravity, and consider specific applications. We will consider the structure of gauge theories of gravity and have a special focus on PGTG, in particular we will consider some of its predictions and implications including interactions with fermions and bosons, cosmological and gravitational wave applications.

2. The gauge approach to gravity

The gauge approach to the gravitational interaction is based on the localization of the global (rigid) spacetime symmetries of the matter field Lagrangian, under a certain group of spacetime coordinate transformations. In this procedure, the gauge potentials, the field strengths and the Noether currents are clearly identified. The gauge potentials are then interpreted as the geometrical degrees of freedom representing the gravitational interaction, while the corresponding field strengths correspond to well identified objects from differential geometry such as curvature, torsion or non-metricity. The Noether currents associated to the spacetime symmetries represent the sources of the gravitational field and provide also valuable information on the physical properties of matter that couple to gravity, clarifying the appropriate test matter for the probing of spacetime geometry. One of the main lessons from the gauge approach to gravity is the fact that the requirement of local, non-rigid symmetries in a matter field theory under spacetime transformations, leads naturally to non-rigid spacetime geometries, meaning general non-Euclidean geometries with curvature, torsion and non-metricity.

2.1. *From symmetries to spacetime geometry*

The gauge approach to gravity broadens our study of the deep relation between symmetry principles (group theory) and geometrical methods. In this framework, the Metric-Affine Gravity (MAG) formalism,[27] where the metric and the affine connection are both independent degrees of freedom, becomes clearly formulated. In fact, the MAG approach includes a general (metric-affine) geometry with curvature, torsion and non-metricity, that arises naturally from the localization (gauging) of the Affine group A(4,$\Re$) and taking into consideration also a metric structure (although the metric structure can be considered not to be "fundamental" in the so-called premetric approaches to field theories).

The Affine group A(4,$\Re$) is the (semi-direct) product of the group of 4-translations T(4) with the "General Linear group" GL(4,$\Re$). The gauge potentials

of T(4) are the vector valued 1-form tetrads (or covector frames)
$$\theta^a = \theta^a{}_\mu dx^\mu, \tag{1}$$
where $\{dx^0, dx^1, dx^2, dx^3\}$ is the holonomic co-vector frame basis, with the vector valued 2-form torsion as the field strength
$$T^a = D\theta^a = d\theta^a + \Gamma^a{}_b \wedge \theta^b, \tag{2}$$
while the gauge potentials of GL(4,$\Re$) are the 2-tensor valued linear connection 1-form fields
$$\Gamma^a{}_b = \Gamma^a{}_{b\mu} dx^\mu, \tag{3}$$
and the corresponding field strength is the curvature, 2-tensor valued 2-form, given by
$$R^a{}_b = d\Gamma^a{}_b + \Gamma^a{}_c \wedge \Gamma^c{}_b. \tag{4}$$
In these expressions D is the (gauge) covariant exterior derivative, d is the exterior derivative, a kind of curl operator that raises the degree of any p-form, $\wedge$ is the wedge product. The torsion 2-form has $4 \times 6 = 24$ independent components
$$T^a{}_{\mu\nu} = 2\partial_{[\mu}\theta^a{}_{\nu]} + 2\Gamma^a{}_{c[\mu}\theta^c{}_{\nu]}, \tag{5}$$
while the curvature 2-form has $16 \times 6 = 96$ independent components
$$R^a{}_{b\mu\nu} = 2\partial_{[\mu}\Gamma^a{}_{b|\nu]} + 2\Gamma^a{}_{c[\mu}\Gamma^c{}_{b|\nu]}. \tag{6}$$
The presence of the linear connection, which is the gauge potential associated to curvature, in the last term of the expression for the torsion in (2) is of high importance in the context of the Poincaré gauge gravity and MAG, as will be discussed. In MAG the Noether currents (the sources of gravity) are the canonical energy-momentum (related to T(4)) and the hyper-momentum (related to GL(4,$\Re$)) which includes a spin part s_{ab}, a term related to dilatations and another connected to shear type of "deformations" $\bar{\Delta}_{ab}$. The hypermomentum can then be decomposed according to
$$\Delta_{ab} = s_{ab} + \frac{1}{4}g_{ab}\Delta^c{}_c + \bar{\Delta}_{ab}, \tag{7}$$
including the spin $s_{ab} = -s_{ba}$, the dilatation $\Delta^c{}_c$, and the shear $\bar{\Delta}_{ab}$ currents. The Noether currents are not only the fundamental sources of gravity in MAG, but also represent the physical properties of the appropriate test matter to probe the spacetime geometry.

We can also introduce the Lorentzian metric as the (0,2) tensor $g = g_{ab}\theta^a \otimes \theta^b$, where $a, b = 0, 1, 2, 3$ are anholonomic indices, which is the metric (with constant components) of the tangent space, while the spacetime metric $g_{\mu\nu}$ gives the inner products $g(u,v) = g_{\alpha\beta}u^\alpha v^\beta = u_\alpha v^\alpha$ and is given by $g_{\mu\nu} = \theta^a{}_\mu \theta^a{}_\nu g_{ab}$. Therefore, the spacetime metric can be seen as the deformation of the Lorentzian (tangent space) metric according to $g_{\mu\nu} = \Omega^{ab}{}_{\mu\nu} g_{ab}$, with $\Omega^{ab}{}_{\mu\nu} \equiv \theta^a{}_\mu \theta^a{}_\nu$ being a deformation tensor.

Besides the linear co-frame (tetrads) and the linear connection, the 0-form metric g_{ab} can then be introduced as a kind of potential and the corresponding field strength is the tensor valued 1-form $Q_{ab} = Q_{ab\mu} dx^\mu$, given by

$$Q_{ab} = Dg_{ab} = dg_{ab} + \Gamma^c{}_a \wedge g_{cb} + \Gamma^c{}_b \wedge g_{ac} = 2\Gamma_{(ab)}, \qquad (8)$$

with $10 \times 4 = 40$ independent components $Q_{ab\mu}$. This field strength corresponds to the non-metricity tensor valued 1-form and one concludes that if the connection is non-Lorentzian ($\Gamma^{ab} \neq -\Gamma^{ba}$), then the non-metricity is non-vanishing. The linear connection 1-form can be decomposed according to

$$\Gamma_{ab} = \tilde{\Gamma}_{ab} + N_{ab} = \tilde{\Gamma}_{ab} + N_{[ab]} + \frac{1}{2} Q_{ab}, \qquad (9)$$

where $\tilde{\Gamma}_{ab}$ is the Levi-Civita part of the connection and $N^a{}_b$ is the so-called distortion 1-form characterizing the post-Riemannian geometries. In particular, one finds that $Q_{ab} = 2N_{(ab)}$ and $T^a = N^a{}_b \wedge \theta^b$. In the most general case, the connection is non-Lorentzian (which implies the presence of non-metricity in the spacetime geometry) and is linked to gauge symmetry groups that extend the Poincaré group, leading therefore to the breaking of Lorentz invariance and to the physics beyond the standard model. If one restricts the symmetry group to the case of PGTG, then the linear connection is Lorentzian (a spin connection) and the hypermomentum is restricted to the spin current. Therefore the presence of non-metricity is related to the breaking of Lorentz invariance, non-Lorentzian connections and hypermomentum with non-trivial currents beyond the spin part.

2.2. Metric-Affine gravity revisited

Let us now summarize the fundamental structures of spacetime and their relation to symmetry groups. We have the fundamental 1-forms, the linear co-frame θ^a and the linear connection $\Gamma^a{}_b$, which are the potentials for the 4-dimensional translations $T(4)$ and the general linear $GL(4, \Re)$ groups, respectively. The corresponding field strengths correspond to well known objects from differential geometry, namely, the torsion $T^a = D\theta^a = d\theta^a + \Gamma^a{}_b \wedge \theta^b$ and curvature $R^a{}_b = d\Gamma^a{}_b + \Gamma^a{}_c \wedge \Gamma^c{}_b$ 2-forms, respectively. The metric is introduced as the 0-form potential with the corresponding field strength being the non-metricity 1-form $Q_{ab} = Dg_{ab}$. The linear frame establishes a link between the (symmetries on the) local tangent fibers and the spacetime manifold, while the linear connection can be viewed as a guidance field reflecting the inertial character for matter fields propagating on the spacetime manifold. Finally, the metric allows the determination of spatial and temporal distances and angles. The spacetime geometry with all these structures is called a *metric-affine geometry*, with non-vanishing torsion, curvature and non-metricity, and its fundamental local group of spacetime symmetries is the affine group $A(4, \Re) = T(4) \rtimes GL(4, \Re)$. As one can see from the expressions for the field strengths, torsion and curvature, in (2) and (4), respectively, the connection potential also enters in the expression for the field strength of the co-frame potential. This term is unavoidably present and is due to the semi-direct product[a] structure of the Poincaré group (or the affine group) and, therefore, curvature and torsion are somehow intertwined.

In the self-consistent metric-affine formalism, the gravitational interaction is described as a gauge theory of the affine group $A(4, \Re)$, together with the assumption of a metric, with the potentials (θ^a, Γ^{ab}) coupled to the corresponding Noether currents $(\tau^a, \Delta^a{}_b)$. The latter are the vector-valued canonical energy-momentum $\tau^a = \delta\mathcal{L}_{mat}/\delta\theta_a$ and the tensor-valued hypermomentum $\Delta^a{}_b = \delta\mathcal{L}_{mat}/\delta\Gamma_a{}^b$ 3-form currents[b], respectively, while the metric g_{ab} couples to the symmetric (Hilbert) energy momentum $T_{ab} = 2\delta\mathcal{L}_{mat}/\delta g^{ab}$.

A truly independent connection in MAG can be written as

$$\Gamma^{ab} = \Gamma^{[ab]} + \frac{1}{4}g^{ab}\Gamma^c{}_c + \left(\Gamma^{(ab)} - \frac{1}{4}g^{ab}\Gamma^c{}_c\right), \tag{10}$$

including the Lorentzian piece $\Gamma^{[ab]}$, the trace part $\frac{1}{4}g^{ab}\Gamma^c{}_c$ and the shear part $\Gamma^{(ab)} - \frac{1}{4}g^{ab}\Gamma^c{}_c$. The Lorentzian connection couples to the spin current and the trace and shear parts couple to the dilatation and shear currents, respectively. As previously said it is the non-Lorentzian part of the connection that imply the non-vanishing of non-metricity, therefore, the dilatation and shear hypermomentum currents are intimately related to the non-metricity of metric affine spacetime geometry.

The variational principle is applied to the action of this theory (including the gravitational part and the matter Lagrangian) by varying it with respect to the gauge potentials of the affine group, (θ^a, Γ^{ab}). This leads to two sets of dynamical equations, while a third set of equations is obtained by varying the action with respect to the metric potential g_{ab}. At the end, the dynamics is described only via two sets of equations, since the gravitational equation obtained by varying with respect to the metric potential or the one obtained by variation with respect to the translational potential can be dropped out, as long as the other gravitational equation derived from variation with respect to the linear connection is fulfilled (for details we recommend the reader to see[25]). This procedure and the fundamental quantities and relations here exposed summarizes the basics of the MAG formalism.

---

[a]The semi direct product implies that the generators of $T(4)$ and $GL(4, \Re)$ (or $SO(1,3)$) do not commute.

[b]These currents can be represented as 1-forms or as 3-forms. In fact, in the gauge approach to gravity they emerge naturally from Noether equations as 3-forms, being natural objects for integration over volumes. As 1-forms one can write $\tau^a = \tau^a{}_\mu dx^\mu$ and $\Delta^a{}_b = \Delta^a{}_{b\mu} dx^\mu$.

2.3. *Poincaré gauge theories and its extensions*

The description of the gravitational interaction as a gauge theory opens the door for its inclusion in unifying gauge field theories. Indeed, the analogies with gauge Yang-Mills theories can be easily established, (see[28]). Particularly relevant is of course the PGTG that constitutes a valid and quite promising class of models for an appropriate description of classical gravity including post-Einstein strong gravity predictions. The PGTG arises from restricting the symmetry group to the Poincaré group $P(1,3) = T(4) \rtimes SO(1,3)$, and this leads directly to RC spacetime geometry. If only the translational part is taken as symmetry group, one gets the translational gauge theories (TGTG) that include non-vanishing torsion but zero curvature and non-metricity, while both Weyl(-Cartan) gauge gravity (WGTG) and conformal gauge gravity (CGTG) include curvature, torsion and non-metricity. For the 15-parametric conformal group $C(1,3)$ a generalization of Kibble's gauge procedure is required, since although locally $C(1,3)$ is isomorphic to $SO(2,4)$ its realization in M_4 (Minkowski spacetime) is non-linear.[29] The PGTG can further be extended into the de Sitter or anti-de Sitter (A)dS gauge theories of gravity by localizing the $SO(1,4)$ or $SO(2,3)$ groups, respectively. Another important class of extensions requires going beyond the Lie algebra (by considering also anticommutators), in order to arrive at the super-Poincaré group[30] proper supersymmetry (SUSY) transformations between fermions and bosons. The gauging of these (and other) super-algebras lead directly supergravity (SUGRA), that need to take into account post-Riemannian spacetime geometries.

In PGTG the tetrads and the spin connection 1-forms are the gauge potentials, associated with translations, $T(4)$, and Lorentz rotations, $SO(1,3)$, respectively. Torsion and the curvature 2-forms are the respective field strengths. There are 6 generators in the Lorentz group with the corresponding potentials ($\Gamma^{ab} = -\Gamma^{ba}$) and 6 Noether (spin) currents ($s^{ab} = -s^{ba}$). Analogously, there are 4 generators in the group of spacetime translations, which entail 4 gauge potentials θ^a and 4 conserved Noether (canonical energy-momentum) currents τ^a. By constructing the gravitational Lagrangian with the curvature and torsion invariants, the potentials are coupled to the Noether currents via $24 + 16 = 40$ second order field equations. Let us briefly summarize the PGTG formalism. We consider a physical system, represented by the matter fields Lagrangian $\mathcal{L}_m = \mathcal{L}_m(g_{ab}, \theta^c, D\Psi)$. The covariant derivative with respect to the Riemann-Cartan connection $D\Psi$ allows the Lagrangian to be invariant under local Poincaré spacetime transformations. The canonical energy-momentum tensor density (equivalent to the dynamical tetrad energy-momentum density $\tau_a \equiv \delta\mathcal{L}_m/\delta\theta^a$) and the canonical spin density (equivalent to the dynamical spin density $s_{ab} \equiv \delta\mathcal{L}_m/\delta\Gamma^{ab}$) couple to the gravitational potentials, acting as sources of gravity and obey generalized conservation equations. The gravity sector in the action is constructed with the gauge-invariant gravitational field strengths in the kinetic part associated with the dynamics of the gravitational degrees of freedom. The total Lagrangian density thus reads

$$\mathcal{L} = \mathcal{L}_G(g_{ab}, \theta^a, T^a, R^{ab}) + \mathcal{L}_m(g_{ab}, \theta^a, D\Psi) \;. \tag{11}$$

By varying this action with respect to the gauge fields of gravity (θ^a, Γ^{ab}) and the matter fields Ψ, we get the corresponding field equations.

2.4. *Applications in PGTG*

Without going into details we will briefly mention here some results from simple applications of PGTG, namely in the case of the ECSK theory with fermions and $(s = 1)$ bosons and some of its extensions. The reader can find details in the references.[31–33]

2.4.1. *Einstein-Cartan-Dirac-Maxwell dynamics*

Considering in the ECSK action

$$S_{\rm EC} = \frac{1}{2\kappa^2}\int d^4x \sqrt{-g} R(\Gamma) + \int d^4x \sqrt{-g}\, \mathcal{L}_m \tag{12}$$

the matter Lagrangian

$$\mathcal{L}_m = \mathcal{L}_{\rm D} + \mathcal{L}_{\rm M} + j^\mu A_\mu, \tag{13}$$

where $\mathcal{L}_{\rm D}$ and $\mathcal{L}_m$ are the Lagrangians for a Dirac spinor field and a bosonic $(s=1)$ field minimaly coupled to the spacetime torsion, respectively, and the Ricci scalar is computed from the connection of RC spacetime geometry, the full dynamics for the matter and geometrical degrees of freedom can be derived. This results in the non-linear dynamics in the matter sector with both the non-linearities and non-minimal couplings between fermions and bosons induced by torsion, and in the generalized Einstein and Cartan equations for the metric and torsion/contorsion variables. For example, varying the Dirac Lagrangian minimally coupled to torsion[c] (in these expressions all tilde quantities correspond to the case of pseudo-Riemann geometry)

$$\mathcal{L}_{\rm Dirac} = \tilde{\mathcal{L}}_{\rm Dirac} + \frac{i\hbar}{4} K_{\alpha\beta\mu} \bar\psi \gamma^{[\mu}\gamma^{\alpha}\gamma^{\beta]}\psi, \tag{14}$$

and the bosonic Lagrangian minimally coupled to torsion,

$$\mathcal{L}_{\rm Max} = \tilde{\mathcal{L}}_{\rm Max} + \lambda\left(K^{\lambda[\mu\nu]}K^{\gamma}_{\;[\mu\nu]}A_\gamma + K^{\lambda[\mu\nu]}\tilde F_{\mu\nu}\right) A_\lambda, \tag{15}$$

with respect to the corresponding spinor and vector fields, and substituting the torsion as a function of the matter fields (Cartan equations), one obtains the generalized Dirac and Maxwell dynamics

$$i\hbar\gamma^\mu \tilde D_\mu \psi + (q\gamma^\mu A_\mu - m)\psi = f(A)(\bar\psi\gamma^\nu\gamma^5\psi)\gamma_\nu\gamma^5\psi + \alpha^\lambda_{\;\alpha}(A)(\bar\psi\gamma^\alpha\gamma^5\psi)\gamma_\lambda\gamma^5\psi$$
$$+ \beta^\lambda(A,\tilde F)\gamma_\lambda\gamma^5\psi \;, \tag{16}$$

---

[c]We consider the torsion tensor as $T^\lambda_{\;\alpha\beta} \equiv \Gamma^\lambda_{[\alpha\beta]}$ and the contortion given by $K^\lambda_{\;\mu\nu} \equiv T^\lambda_{\;\mu\nu} - 2T_{(\mu\;\nu)}^{\;\;\lambda} = T^\lambda_{\;\mu\nu} + 2T_{(\mu\nu)}^{\;\;\;\lambda}$.

and
$$\tilde{\nabla}_\mu \tilde{F}^{\mu\nu} = \lambda^{-1}(j^\nu + J^\nu),\qquad(17)$$

where
$$J^\nu \equiv \frac{\partial \mathcal{L}_M^{corr}}{\partial A_\nu} - \tilde{\nabla}_\mu\left(\frac{\partial \mathcal{L}_M^{corr}}{\partial(\tilde{\nabla}_\mu A_\nu)}\right),$$

with $\mathcal{L}_M^{corr}$ the correction term to the usual Maxwell Lagrangian in (15), and we have defined

$$f(A) \equiv \frac{3\kappa^2 \hbar^2}{8} + \frac{\lambda \kappa^4 \hbar^2}{4} A^2,$$
$$\alpha^{\sigma\varepsilon}(A) \equiv -\lambda \kappa^4 \hbar^2 A^\sigma A^\varepsilon,$$
$$\beta^\lambda(A, \tilde{F}) \equiv -\frac{\lambda \kappa^2 \hbar}{2} \epsilon^{\lambda\alpha\beta\gamma} A_{[\alpha} \tilde{F}_{\beta\gamma]}.\qquad(18)$$

Due to the presence of the cubic terms, this Dirac equation changes under the actions of C (charge conjugation) transformations, resulting in a different dynamics for anti-fermions. This dynamics breaks the U(1) symmetry explicitly and might be relevant in the very early Universe. These non-linear dynamics in the matter fields can be simplified for cases where certain approximations are valid as in cosmological applications for homogeneous fields and random spin distributions.

2.4.2. Cosmological applications

The application of this theory, the Einstein-Cartan-Dirac model coupled to ($s = 1$) bosons with explicit $U(1)$ symmetry breaking, to homogeneous and isotropic cosmologies leads to the dynamics of the scale factor given by the generalized Einstein equations (assuming the FLRW metric and isotropic pressure)

$$\left(\frac{\dot{a}}{a}\right)^2 = \frac{\kappa^2}{3}(\rho + \rho^{corr}) - \frac{k}{a^2},\qquad(19)$$

$$\frac{\ddot{a}}{a} = -\frac{\kappa^2}{6}[3(p + p^{corr}) + (\rho + \rho^{corr})],\qquad(20)$$

where dots over functions represent time derivatives. Effective densities can be defined $\rho^{\text{eff}} = \rho + \rho^{\text{corr}}$, with the corrections to GR, $\rho^{\text{corr}} = \rho^s + \rho^{s-A} + \rho^A$, corresponding to the spin-spin interaction energy, the non-minimal interactions between fermionic spin and the bosonic four-potential, and self-interactions in the bosonic sector, respectively and the same apply to the pressure contributions. Different families of solutions can be derived for the dynamics of the scale factor including cyclic models with early bounce, early acceleration, deceleration and late-bounce, and also cases with early bounce, early acceleration, deceleration and late-time acceleration. Some of these are illustrated in the figures 1 and 2.

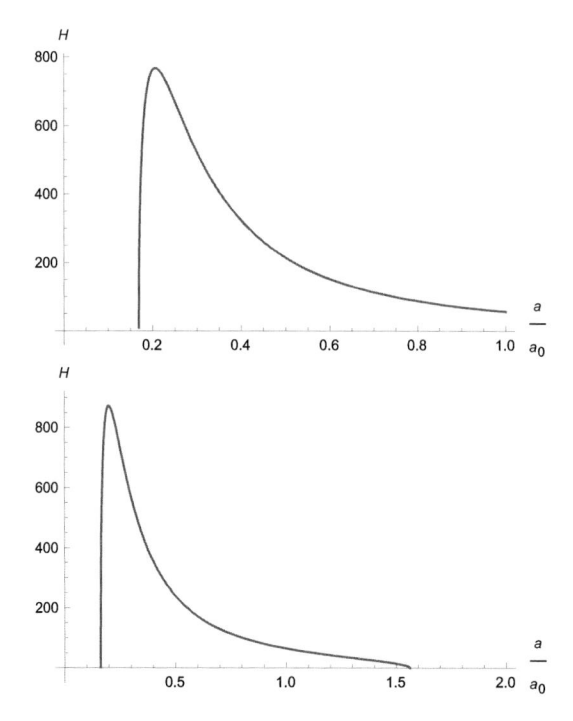

Fig. 1. Evolution of the Hubble parameter $H(a)$ with the scale factor a/a_0 for the ECDM model without (ECSK model, top) and with (bottom) the non-minimal couplings in the matter fields induced by torsion. These corrections to the effective energy density $\rho^{s-A} \sim \rho^s f(A) \sim a^b$ give raise to late-time effects, whereas $\rho^s \sim -\kappa^2 \tilde{s}^2$ is the spin-spin interaction term that is responsible for the non-singular behaviour in the early Universe. The plot on the bottom shows a typical solution with a future bounce, a non-singular behaviour at the minimum of the scale factor, and a period of early accelerated expansion.

2.4.3. *Gravitational waves in Riemann-Cartan spacetime*

By considering the quadratic models in PGTG, where the Lagrangian is quadratic in the curvature and torsion, one obtains two sets of field equations for the metric and the contorsion, (or equivalently for the tetrads and the spin connection), where both fields are dynamically coupled and propagate in vacuum. Gravitational waves with torsion modes coupled to the metric modes are then expected and the possibility of measuring these effects with GW astronomy is a relevant open question.

In cosmological backgrounds, one possible parametrization for GW, encompassing a wide class of metric theories of gravity, is provided in the following wave equation

$$h''_{ij} + (2+\nu)\mathcal{H}h'_{ij} + (c_g^2 k^2 + m_g^2 a^2)h_{ij} = \tilde{\Pi}_{ij}. \qquad (21)$$

In this equation the parameters (ν, c_g, m_g) and the source term represent deviations from GR and the derivatives are taken with respect to conformal time. The parameter ν represents an additional "friction" term, affecting the decay induced by the

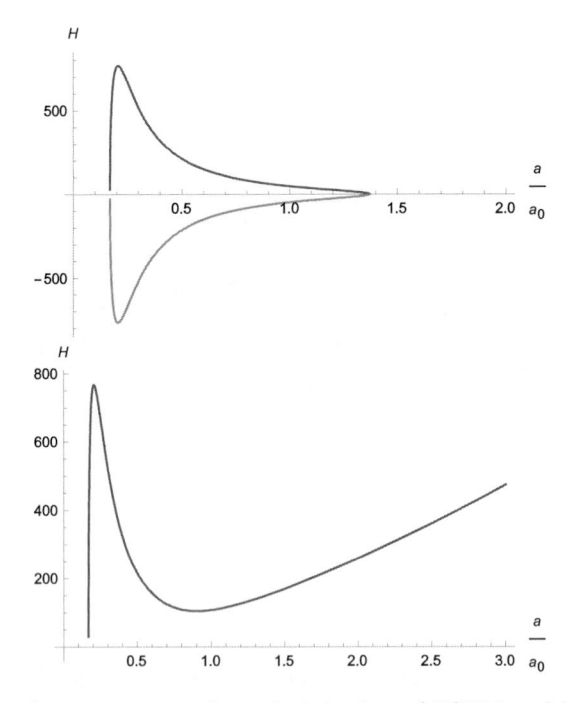

Fig. 2. On the top figure we can see the cyclic behaviour of ECDM model explicitly, with the two branches in $H(a) = \pm\sqrt{\rho^{\text{eff}}(a) - k/a^2}$ smoothly joined together at the bounces. A period of early accelerated expansion is followed by decelerated expansion, bounce and accelerated contraction, decelerated contraction and again the bounce at the minimum of the scale factor, with the repetition of the cosmological cycle. On the bottom we have the relevant case where a late-time accelerated phase is also present.

cosmological expansion. The effect of a propagation speed different than the speed of light is represented by c_g, while m_g stands for an effective mass for the graviton ($s = 2$) field. In GR $\nu = 0$, $c_g = 1$ and $m_g = 0$ and the right-hand side of (21) is equal to zero. The tensor $\tilde{\Pi}_{ij}$ represents an extra "source" term due to additional propagating tensor fields.

In the PGTG, the situation is generalized to include in the dynamics another set of equations. Through the variational principle, the two sets of field equations corresponding to the dynamics of the two gravitational potentials $(\theta^a_\mu, \Gamma^a_{b\nu})$, can also be expressed in terms of the equivalent set of dynamical variables $(g_{\alpha,\beta}, K^\alpha_{\mu\nu})$. Since in quadratic PGTG models the torsion in general propagates, the contorsion is an extra propagating tensor field with respect to GR and therefore, the wave equation for the metric in the first-order perturbation theory in cosmological backgrounds will have a term as $\tilde{\Pi}_{ij}$ in (21) due to the propagating torsion (or contorsion) tensor degrees of freedom.

One simple approach for the study of GW with torsion modes is to consider the linear perturbation theory in RC spacetime. The background spacetime in general is assumed to have the following metric and connection $(\mathring{g}_{\mu\nu}, \mathring{\Gamma}^\alpha_{\lambda\beta})$. The perturbed quantities are

$$g_{\mu\nu} = \mathring{g}_{\mu\nu} + h_{\mu\nu}, \quad \Gamma^{\alpha}{}_{\lambda\beta} = \mathring{\Gamma}^{\alpha}{}_{\lambda\beta} + \gamma^{\alpha}{}_{\lambda\beta}, \qquad (22)$$

where the perturbations $h_{\mu\nu} \equiv \delta g_{\mu\nu}$ and $\gamma^{\alpha}{}_{\lambda\beta} \equiv \delta\Gamma^{\alpha}{}_{\lambda\beta}$, are assumed to be small. The RC connection is given by $\Gamma^{\alpha}{}_{\beta\nu} = \tilde{\Gamma}^{\alpha}{}_{\beta\nu} + K^{\alpha}{}_{\beta\nu}$, expression also valid at the background level. It can be shown that the perturbation in the connection includes a perturbation in contorsion and another part related to the background metric and metric perturbation. In summary, the relevant quantities in this perturbative approach can be chosen to be

$$g_{\mu\nu} = \mathring{g}_{\mu\nu} + h_{\mu\nu}, \quad K^{\alpha}{}_{\lambda\beta} = \mathring{K}^{\alpha}{}_{\lambda\beta} + \kappa^{\alpha}{}_{\lambda\beta}. \qquad (23)$$

From this the generalized curvature tensor, Ricci tensor and Ricci scalar of the linearly perturbed RC spacetime geometry are given by

$$R^{\alpha}{}_{\beta\mu\nu} = \tilde{R}^{\alpha}{}_{\beta\mu\nu} + 2\tilde{\nabla}_{[\mu}\mathring{K}^{\alpha}{}_{\beta|\nu]} + 2\tilde{\nabla}_{[\mu}\kappa^{\alpha}{}_{\beta|\nu]} + \mathring{K}^{\alpha}{}_{\lambda\mu}\mathring{K}^{\lambda}{}_{\beta\nu} - \mathring{K}^{\alpha}{}_{\lambda\nu}\mathring{K}^{\lambda}{}_{\beta\mu}$$
$$+\mathring{K}^{\alpha}{}_{\lambda\mu}\kappa^{\lambda}{}_{\beta\nu} - \mathring{K}^{\alpha}{}_{\lambda\nu}\kappa^{\lambda}{}_{\beta\mu} + \kappa^{\alpha}{}_{\lambda\mu}\mathring{K}^{\lambda}{}_{\beta\nu} - \kappa^{\alpha}{}_{\lambda\nu}\mathring{K}^{\lambda}{}_{\beta\mu}, \qquad (24)$$

$$R_{\beta\nu} = \tilde{R}_{\beta\nu} + 2\tilde{\nabla}_{[\alpha}\mathring{K}^{\alpha}{}_{\beta|\nu]} + 2\tilde{\nabla}_{[\alpha}\kappa^{\alpha}{}_{\beta|\nu]} + \mathring{K}^{\alpha}{}_{\lambda\alpha}\mathring{K}^{\lambda}{}_{\beta\nu} - \mathring{K}^{\alpha}{}_{\lambda\nu}\mathring{K}^{\lambda}{}_{\beta\alpha}$$
$$+\mathring{K}^{\alpha}{}_{\lambda\alpha}\kappa^{\lambda}{}_{\beta\nu} - \mathring{K}^{\alpha}{}_{\lambda\nu}\kappa^{\lambda}{}_{\beta\alpha} + \kappa^{\alpha}{}_{\lambda\alpha}\mathring{K}^{\lambda}{}_{\beta\nu} - \kappa^{\alpha}{}_{\lambda\nu}\mathring{K}^{\lambda}{}_{\beta\alpha}, \qquad (25)$$

and

$$R = \tilde{R} - 2\tilde{\nabla}^{\lambda}\mathring{K}^{\alpha}{}_{\lambda\alpha} - 2\tilde{\nabla}^{\lambda}\kappa^{\alpha}{}_{\lambda\alpha} + g^{\beta\nu}(\mathring{K}^{\alpha}{}_{\lambda\alpha}\mathring{K}^{\lambda}{}_{\beta\nu} - \mathring{K}^{\alpha}{}_{\lambda\nu}\mathring{K}^{\lambda}{}_{\beta\alpha})$$
$$+g^{\beta\nu}(\mathring{K}^{\alpha}{}_{\lambda\alpha}\kappa^{\lambda}{}_{\beta\nu} - \mathring{K}^{\alpha}{}_{\lambda\nu}\kappa^{\lambda}{}_{\beta\alpha}) + g^{\beta\nu}(\kappa^{\alpha}{}_{\lambda\alpha}\mathring{K}^{\lambda}{}_{\beta\nu} - \kappa^{\alpha}{}_{\lambda\nu}\mathring{K}^{\lambda}{}_{\beta\alpha}), \qquad (26)$$

respectively.

For a torsionless background and at first order in the metric and connection perturbations, we get

$$R^{\alpha}{}_{\beta\mu\nu} = \tilde{R}^{\alpha}{}_{\beta\mu\nu} + 2\tilde{\tilde{\nabla}}_{[\mu}\kappa^{\alpha}{}_{\beta|\nu]} \qquad (27)$$

$$R_{\beta\nu} = \tilde{R}_{\beta\nu} + 2\tilde{\tilde{\nabla}}_{[\alpha}\kappa^{\alpha}{}_{\beta|\nu]}, \qquad (28)$$

and

$$R = \tilde{R} - 2\tilde{\tilde{\nabla}}^{\lambda}\kappa^{\alpha}{}_{\lambda\alpha}, \qquad (29)$$

respectively. These quantities are useful to derive the GW equations for PGTG in the linear perturbation framework. As an example and without going into details, by choosing the quadratic model given by[26]

$$\mathcal{L} = \frac{1}{2\kappa^2}\left(R - 2\alpha T^{\alpha}{}_{\mu\nu}T_{\alpha}{}^{\mu\nu}\right) - \frac{1}{8\lambda}R^{\alpha\beta}{}_{\mu\nu}R_{\alpha\beta}{}^{\mu\nu} + \mathcal{L}_m, \qquad (30)$$

where α and λ are free parameters, one can derive the following coupled wave equations

$$\frac{l_0^2}{2}\left(\Box\partial_{(\alpha}\bar{h}_{\beta)}{}^{\mu} + 2\partial_\nu\partial^{[\mu}\kappa_{\alpha\beta}{}^{\nu]}\right) + 3\eta^{\mu\nu}\kappa_{[\alpha\beta\nu]} + \delta^\mu_{[\alpha}\kappa_{\beta]} = 0, \tag{31}$$

$$-\Box\bar{h}_{ij} = 2\Lambda^{TT}_{ij}, \tag{32}$$

with $\kappa_\beta \equiv \kappa_{\beta\alpha}{}^\alpha$, $\Box \equiv \partial^\alpha\partial_\alpha$, we choose $\alpha = 1$ and define $l_0 \equiv \kappa^2/\lambda$, $\bar{h}_{ij}$ is the metric perturbation in the TT Lorentz gauge, $\eta^{\mu\nu}$ is the Minkowski metric, δ^μ_α is the Kronecker symbol and

$$\Lambda_{\mu\nu} \equiv \partial_{(\nu}\kappa_{\mu)} - \eta_{\mu\nu}\partial_\lambda\kappa^\lambda. \tag{33}$$

In principle one can apply Greens functions methods to get

$$\bar{h}_{ij}(t,\vec{x}) \sim \int d^3y\, \frac{\Lambda^{TT}_{ij}(t_R,\vec{y})}{|\vec{x}-\vec{y}|}. \tag{34}$$

This reinforces the notion that metric and torsion perturbations can be interconvertible. Moreover, the equation (32) can be used to replace in (31) to obtain a second order partial diferential equation for the torsion modes

$$\frac{l_0^2}{2}\left(-2\partial_{(\alpha}\Lambda_{\beta)}{}^{\mu} + 2\partial_\nu\partial^{[\mu}\kappa_{\alpha\beta}{}^{\nu]}\right) + 3\eta^{\mu\nu}\kappa_{[\alpha\beta\nu]} + \delta^\mu_{[\alpha}\kappa_{\beta]} = 0, \tag{35}$$

with all quantities calculated in the TT gauge. Now, taking into account the RC curvature tensor in (24) for a RC background and in (27) for a torsionless background (to first order), respectively, one expects generalizations to the geodesic deviation equations. This implies a generalization to the GR effects of the propagating GW in test-masses. For example, in Minkowski backgrounds, useful to compute the weak, linearised GW effects in detectors, we have

$$R_{\alpha\beta\mu\nu} = \tilde{R}_{\alpha\beta\mu\nu} + 2\partial_{[\mu}\kappa_{\alpha\beta|\nu]}, \tag{36}$$

and using the TT gauge, the non-zero components of the Riemann part of the RC curvature are given by

$$\tilde{R}_{i0j0} = -\frac{1}{2}\ddot{h}_{ij}. \tag{37}$$

If we take the corresponig components in (36),

$$R_{i\beta j\nu} = -\frac{1}{2}\ddot{h}_{ij}\delta^0_\beta\delta^0_\nu + 2\partial_{[j}\kappa_{i\beta|\nu]}, \tag{38}$$

where δ^0_β are defined as Kronecker symbols, and we see explicit extra terms due to the presence of the propagating contorsion perturbation.

The FRWL torsionless background geometry can be taken to illustrate the effects of torsion GW modes propagating over cosmological distances. For simplicity the spatially flat FRWL metric background can be taken. In a more general approach the perturbed versions of the field equations would be computed over a RC backgroud geometry with a FRWL metric and a background contorion obeying the cosmological principle. Notice also that in curved backgrounds, terms such as $\mathring{R}^2$, $\mathring{R}\kappa$ and $\mathring{R}\mathring{\nabla}\kappa$ would also apear in the field equations, therefore, a far more richer phenomenology is expected than the one derived from a flat, Minkowski, torsionless background. In principle, it should be possible to obtain a set of two wave equations in cosmological backgrounds, similar to and generalizing the expression in (21). From such equations, the general beyond-GR effects can be recognized in the amplitudes, dispersion relation and due to the presence of extra degrees of freedom (for example contorsion d.o.f.). Then these direct consequences can be applied for the general expressions for the GW forms (in the weak source limit) due to binaries, in order to encompass the effects of a propagation over cosmological distances. We will not perform such procedure here, but emphasize the relevance of it in order to search for signatures of propagating torsion modes in the GW signals.

3. Probing post-Riemann geometries

It is known that torsion can give rise to precession effects in systems with intrinsic spin, for example, elementary particles such as the electron, or baryons such as the neutron.[34–36] Moreover, as we will see, torsion effects on the dynamics and energy levels of spinors are expected. Also, the spin-spin contact interactions of the ECSK theory, or the propagating spin-spin interactions mediated by gravitational gauge ($s = 0, 1, 2$) bosons of quadratic PGTG might be tested/constrained in laboratory experiments and cosmological GW probes.

Regarding non-metricity, the gauge approach to gravity clearly shows that the hypermomentum currents, such as the dilatations or the shear currents, couple to the trace and shear parts of the connection (10), respectively and therefore to non-metricity. If torsion can be measured by the spin precession of test matter with intrinsic spin, then the non-metricity of spacetime can be measured by pulsations (mass quadrupole excitations) of test matter with (non-trivial) hypermomentum currents. In order to be "sensitive" to non-Riemann geometries, test matter should carry dilatation, shear, or spin currents, whether macroscopic or at the level of fundamental fields/particles. From the gauge approach to gravity one conclusion is very clear: if matter has neither (intrinsic) spin, nor dilatation/shear currents, then it follows the Riemannian (extremal length) geodesics, regardless of the geometry of spacetime or of the form of the Lagrangian in metric-affine geometry.

3.1. *Effects on fundamental fermionic systems*

From the Dirac Lagrangian of a fermion minimally coupled to the background RC geometry, one can predict torsion effects on the energy levels of quantum systems.[37] Similarly, if non-minimal couplings between the torsion trace vector and Dirac axial vector and/or between torsion axial vector and Dirac vector are present, then the parity symmetry is broken and the corresponding energy level corrections due to torsion will contain the signatures of those parity breaking interactions. Therefore, tests with advanced spectrographs might be able to probe torsion effects on quantum systems. Without going into details, we present here some simple results concerning predicted effects on the energy levels of fermionic spinors coupled to background torsion quantities, for cases of minimal and non-minimal couplings (including parity breaking effects).[37]

For the minimal coupling case, which can be expressed by the Lagrangian

$$\mathcal{L}_{\text{Dirac}} = \tilde{\mathcal{L}}_{\text{Dirac}} + 3\check{T}^\lambda \check{s}_\lambda, \tag{39}$$

where

$$\check{s}^\lambda \equiv \frac{\hbar}{2}\bar{\psi}\gamma^\lambda\gamma^5\psi \tag{40}$$

is the Dirac axial spin vector current and

$$\check{T}^\lambda \equiv \frac{1}{6}\epsilon^{\lambda\alpha\beta\gamma}T_{\alpha\beta\gamma} \tag{41}$$

is the axial vector part of torsion, we obtain the Dirac equation,

$$i\hbar\gamma^\mu \tilde{D}_\mu\psi - m\psi = -\frac{3\hbar}{2}\check{T}^\lambda\gamma_\lambda\gamma^5\psi, \tag{42}$$

for spinors. From this, energy level corrections due to torsion can be derived, depending on the alignment or anti-alignment between the spin and the spacetime torsion. For a constant background torsion $\check{T}^3$, the two corresponding energy levels are

$$E^2 = p^2 + \left(m \mp \frac{3\hbar}{2}\check{T}^3\right)^2, \tag{43}$$

for the spin down/up states, respectively.

Let us denote by $m_{\check{T}}$ the mass correction due to the spin-torsion interaction, and consider the two possible energy levels E_1 and E_2, with $E_2 > E_1$. Then in the reference frame of the particle, the corresponding energy transition is given by

$$h\nu = \frac{1}{2}m_{\check{T}} = \frac{3\hbar}{4}\check{T}. \tag{44}$$

Reinserting the speed of light in vacuum, we get

$$\nu = \frac{3c}{8\pi}\check{T}. \tag{45}$$

If we consider, for instance, $\check{T} \sim 10^{-16}m^{-1}$, then we end up with the prediction of a transition in the $\nu \sim$nHz regime. In the case of a spherically symmetric torsion, using perturbation theory to first order, where

$$E \simeq E_{(0)} + <\psi_{(0)}|\hat{U}_{torsion-spin}|\psi_{(0)}>, \tag{46}$$

and $\psi_{(0)}$ are the eigen states of the unperturbed Hamiltonian associated to the eigen value $E_{(0)}$, we get a similar result with

$$\nu = \frac{\delta E}{h} = \frac{3E_{(0)}}{\pi}F(r), \tag{47}$$

where $F(r)$ represents a geometrical term coming from the integration of the background spherical torsion over some volume.

To include parity breaking terms in the model we also consider the couplings $T \cdot a$ and $\check{T} \cdot j$ in the Lagrangian

$$\mathcal{L}_{\text{fermions}} = \tilde{\mathcal{L}}_{\text{Dirac}} + (\alpha_1 T + \beta_2 \check{T}) \cdot j + (\alpha_2 \check{T} + \beta_1 T) \cdot a. \tag{48}$$

The terms $\beta_1 T^\lambda a_\lambda$ and $\beta_2 \check{T}^\mu j_\mu$ break the parity invariance. Here j and a represent the Dirac vector and axial vectors, respectively, and T is the trace torsion vector. The corresponding extended Dirac equation is given by

$$i\hbar \gamma^\mu \tilde{D}_\mu \psi - m\psi = -\left(\alpha_1 T^\lambda + \beta_2 \check{T}^\lambda\right)\gamma_\lambda \psi - \left(\alpha_2 \check{T}^\lambda + \beta_1 T^\lambda\right)\gamma_\lambda \gamma^5 \psi. \tag{49}$$

In this case, and considering constant torsion quantities, and using the definitions

$$t^\nu \equiv \alpha_1 T^\nu + \beta_2 \check{T}^\nu, \qquad \tau^\lambda \equiv \alpha_2 \check{T}^\lambda + \beta_1 T^\lambda, \tag{50}$$

and taking $t^\mu = (0, t^1, t^2, t^3)$, and $\tau^\mu = (0, 0, 0, \tau)$, for simplicity, we obtain the following energy level corrections $E_2^2 = p_{\text{eff}}^2 + (m+\tau)^2$ and $E_1^2 = p_{\text{eff}}^2 + (m-\tau)^2$, corresponding to the energy transition

$$h\nu = E_2 - E_1 = \frac{4m\tau}{E_1 + E_2}, \tag{51}$$

which in the reference frame of the particle reads

$$h\nu = \frac{4m\tau}{\left[\vec{t}^2 + (m+\tau)^2\right]^{1/2} + \left[\vec{t}^2 + (m-\tau)^2\right]^{1/2}}, \tag{52}$$

and $p_{\text{eff}}^2 \equiv (p_1 + t^1)^2 + (p_2 + t^2)^2 + (p_3 + t^3)^2$. The parity symmetry breaking is one of the conditions usually considered in order to explain some early Universe particle physics that can provide a matter/anti-matter asymmetry. The torsion of the RC spacetime can induce parity breaking effects in the fermionic sector via the non-minimal couplings explored here. These effects include the prediction of well-defined frequencies that a free fermion can absorb or emit in order to make transitions between the predicted two energy levels that arise depending on the spin orientation with respect to external torsion quantities. The signature of parity breaking (chirality) might also be present in the radiated field itself, in the form of polarized light, and these type of parity-breaking spin-torsion interactions might be probed in the very early Universe with GW astronomy, where the signatures of chirality in the GW signals in principle require non-planar detectors and analysis with 3-point correlation functions.

4. Open questions and concluding remarks

In special and general relativity theories the metric is fundamental, providing the relevant spacetime geometry. In special relativity the metric provides a fixed background, while in GR it is described by a tensor field theory being one of the fundamental dynamical fields together with the matter fields. In its essence GR is a background independent theory, where the metric (the local geometry) has to be derived by solving the Einstein field equations, for each particular physical/astrophysical scenario. It is the fundamental geometrical field, solution to the Einstein gravity equations, from which all the aspects of pseudo-Riemannian geometry can be derived. It is therefore natural that due to epistemological historical reasons the metric has gained a fundamental importance in gravity and in the description of physical fields propagating in some spacetime geometry.

In spite of this, developments of geometrical methods in field theories led to the notion that the spacetime metric is no longer to be considered as a fundamental field. One can say that both the pre-metric foundations of electrodynamics and the gauge approach to gravity point in the same direction. The pre-metric approach to electrodynamics as expressed in differential forms give completely general, coordinate-free covariant inhomogeneous and homogeneous equations from charge conservation and magnetic flux conservation respectively. No metric is involved and therefore, electrodynamics is not linked to Minkowski spacetime at a fundamental level. Moreover, the spacetime metric up to a conformal factor, and therefore, the conformal-causal spacetime structure, can be derived from local and linear electrodynamics.[38] The resulting lightcone or causal-electromagnetic structure is a conformal geometry with local conformal symmetries associated to the lightcone at each spacetime point. The group of conformal transformations preserve the light-cone (causal) structure but the metric can change, with the set of all conformally related metrics associated to the local light-cone representing different equally valid metrics. There isn't a specific metric which is more fundamental or that can be considered to be more "physical" than the others. Moreover, in such geometry, under the assumption of locality, the parallel transport of a light cone from a given point to a neighbouring point gives rise to a deformation of the local causal/light-cone structure according to the non-metricity tensor. And since, as we saw, the tensor-valued non-metricity 1-form is linked to the existence of a non-Lorentzian linear connection, from a gauge point of view, this alone inevitably leads to Lorentz symmetry breaking. Therefore, on one hand, and in spite of the historical reasons relating Maxwell's theory with special relativity and Minkowski spacetime, electrodynamics is fundamentally connected to the conformal geometrical structure and the conformal group, and not to Minkowski spacetime, nor the Poincaré or Lorentz group. On the other hand, the notion of local symmetries, the basis of gauge theories, as applied to spacetime leads to gravitational theories with post-Riemann geometries, and non-metricity is directly related to non-Lorentzian connections, i.e, to Lorentz symmetry breaking. *If both the gauge theories of gravity and the premetric formulation of electrodynamics (with its spacetime constitutive relations) are jointly analysed, then we are led to consider that the conformal structure is more fundamental than the metric, post-Riemann geometries with non-metricity and to conformal gauge theories of gravity. Symmetry breaking mechanisms are plausible scenarios for bringing both gravity and electrodynamics into the phenomenological regime of Poincaré symmetries and related spacetime paradigm.* It should be mentioned that the analogies between Yang-Mills fields and gauge theories of gravity in the exterior calculus of forms, clearly show that gravitational dynamics can also be described in a pre-metric way, just as electrodynamics, and its the gravitational spacetime constitutive relations that bring the conformal causal structure.

The exploration of the gauge theories of gravity, including its connection to spacetime symmetries and post-Riemann geometries, can lead to a vast number of predictions relevant for relativistic astrophysics, cosmology and GWs and also to interesting avenues towards unified gauge field theories. Moreover the connection between the gauge formalism, the Lagrangian and Hamiltonian formalisms, the pre-metric foundations, the constitutive relations (between the field strengths and its conjugate momenta, the excitations) and the causal structure of spacetime, might also contribute towards relevant non-perturbative, background-independent methods for quantum field theory and quantum gravity. The gauge approach can clarify which gravitational geometrical degrees of freedom should be taken as canonical conjugate variables for quantization. In its turn, this can relax the traditional emphasis that is usually put into the metric degrees of freedom, for historical reasons, within attempts at reconciling GR (or more general metric theories) with quantum theory.

The gauge theories of gravity are built upon a self-consistent approach that clarifies the fundamental connection between spacetime symmetries and spacetime geometries. In this context, the metric-affine formalism is clearly formulated within general spacetime geometries with curvature, torsion and non-metricity. In this work, the geometrical methods and symmetry principles in gravitation were explored motivating a new perspective into the spacetime paradigm. The effects of post-Riemann spacetime geometries with torsion were briefly exemplified in applications to fundamental fermionic and bosonic fields, cosmology and gravitational waves. Besides the brief exposition on some phenomenological considerations within PGTG, the fundamental ideas related to spacetime physics, motivated by geometrical methods and symmetry principles, have been discussed in the context of the possible routes towards a new spacetime paradigm in gravitation and unified field theories.

Acknowledgments

FC acknowledges the support by Fundação para a Ciência e a Tecnologia (FCT, Portugal) through the grant No. PD/BD/128017/2016 and the project PTDC/FIS-OUT/29048/2017. FSNL acknowledges support from the FCT Scientific Employment Stimulus contract with reference CEECIND/04057/2017. DRG is funded by the *Atracción de Talento Investigador* programme of the Comunidad de Madrid (Spain) No. 2018-T1/TIC-10431, and acknowledges further support from the Ministerio de Ciencia, Innovación y Universidades (Spain) project No. PID2019-108485GB-I00/AEI/10.13039/501100011033. The authors also acknowledge funding from the FCT projects No.UID/FIS/04434/2019 and also the organizers of the MG16 conference for the opportunity to share this research.

References

1. C. M. Will, "The Confrontation between General Relativity and Experiment," Living Rev. Rel. **17** (2014) 4 [arXiv:1403.7377 [gr-qc]].
2. A. Hees, T. Do, A. M. Ghez, G. D. Martinez, S. Naoz, E. E. Becklin, A. Boehle, S. Chappell, D. Chu and A. Dehghanfar, et al. "Testing General Relativity with stellar orbits around the supermassive black hole in our Galactic center," Phys. Rev. Lett. **118** (2017) 211101 [arXiv:1705.07902 [astro-ph.GA]].
3. B. P. Abbott et al. [LIGO Scientific and Virgo Collaborations], "Observation of Gravitational Waves from a Binary Black Hole Merger," Phys. Rev. Lett. **116** (2016), 061102 [arXiv:1602.03837 [gr-qc]].
4. B. P. Abbott et al. [LIGO Scientific and Virgo], "GW170814: A Three-Detector Observation of Gravitational Waves from a Binary Black Hole Coalescence," Phys. Rev. Lett. **119** (2017) no. 14, 141101 [arXiv:1709.09660 [gr-qc]].
5. B. P. Abbott et al. "GW170817: Observation of Gravitational Waves from a Binary Neutron Star Inspiral," Phys. Rev. Lett. **119**, 161101 (2017).
6. B. P. Abbott et al. [LIGO Scientific and Virgo], "Tests of general relativity with GW150914," Phys. Rev. Lett. **116** (2016) no. 22, 221101 [erratum: Phys. Rev. Lett. **121** (2018) no. 12, 129902] [arXiv:1602.03841 [gr-qc]].
7. K. Akiyama et al. [Event Horizon Telescope], "First M87 Event Horizon Telescope Results. I. The Shadow of the Supermassive Black Hole," Astrophys. J. **875** (2019) L1 doi:10.3847/2041-8213/ab0ec7 [arXiv:1906.11238 [astro-ph.GA]].
8. P. Bull, Y. Akrami, J. Adamek, T. Baker, E. Bellini, J. Beltran Jimenez, E. Bentivegna, S. Camera, S. Clesse and J. H. Davis, et al. "Beyond ΛCDM: Problems, solutions, and the road ahead", Phys. Dark Univ. **12** (2016) 56.
9. H. Weyl, "A New Extension of Relativity Theory," Annalen Phys. **59** (1919) 101.
10. H. Weyl, "Gravitation and the electron", Proc. Nat. Acad. Sci. **15** (1929) 323.
11. C. N. Yang and R. L. Mills, "Conservation of Isotopic Spin and Isotopic Gauge Invariance," Phys. Rev. **96** (1954) 191.
12. R. Utiyama, "Invariant theoretical interpretation of interaction," Phys. Rev. **101** (1956) 1597.
13. T. W. B. Kibble, "Lorentz invariance and the gravitational field," J. Math. Phys. **2** (1961) 212.
14. D. W. Sciama, "The Physical structure of general relativity," Rev. Mod. Phys. **36** (1964), 463. [Erratum: Rev. Mod. Phys. **36** (1964) 1103].
15. C. G. Boehmer and J. Burnett, "Dark spinors with torsion in cosmology," Phys. Rev. D **78** (2008) 104001 [arXiv:0809.0469 [gr-qc]].
16. "Nonsingular, big-bounce cosmology from spinor-torsion coupling", Phys. Rev. D **85** (2012) 107502 [arXiv:1111.4595 [gr-qc]].
17. N. J. Poplawski, "Big bounce from spin and torsion", Gen. Rel. Grav. **44** (2012) 1007 [arXiv:1105.6127 [astro-ph.CO]].
18. B. Vakili and S. Jalalzadeh, "Signature transition in Einstein-Cartan cosmology," Phys. Lett. B **726** (2013), 28-32 [arXiv:1308.2877 [gr-qc]].
19. K. A. Bronnikov and A. M. Galiakhmetov, "Wormholes and black universes without phantom fields in Einstein-Cartan theory," Phys. Rev. D **94** (2016) no. 12, 124006 [arXiv:1607.07791 [gr-qc]].

20. A. N. Ivanov and M. Wellenzohn, "Einstein–cartan Gravity with Torsion Field Serving as an Origin for the Cosmological Constant or Dark Energy Density," Astrophys. J. **829** (2016) no. 1, 47 [arXiv:1607.01128 [gr-qc]].
21. J. A. R. Cembranos, J. Gigante Valcarcel and F. J. Maldonado Torralba, "Singularities and n-dimensional black holes in torsion theories," JCAP **1704**, 021 (2017) [arXiv:1609.07814 [gr-qc]].
22. J. A. R. Cembranos and J. Gigante Valcarcel, "Extended Reissner–Nordström solutions sourced by dynamical torsion," Phys. Lett. B **779** (2018), 143-150 [arXiv:1708.00374 [gr-qc]].
23. G. Unger and N. Popławski, "Big bounce and closed universe from spin and torsion," Astrophys. J. **870** (2019) no. 2, 78 [arXiv:1808.08327 [gr-qc]].
24. M. Blagojevic and F. W. Hehl, "Gauge Theories of Gravitation,", Imperial College Press, London, April, 2013. arXiv:1210.3775 [gr-qc].
25. M. Blagojević, "Gravitation and Gauge symmetries" Institute of Physics Publishing, 2002.
26. V. N. Ponomarev, A. O. Barvinsky, Y. N. Obukhov, "Gauge approach and quantization methods in gravity theory" Nauka, 2017.
27. F. W. Hehl, J. D. McCrea, E. W. Mielke and Y. Ne'eman, "Metric affine gauge theory of gravity: Field equations, Noether identities, world spinors, and breaking of dilation invariance," Phys. Rept. **258** (1995) 1 [arXiv:gr-qc/9402012 [gr-qc]].
28. F. Cabral, F. S. N. Lobo and D. Rubiera-Garcia, "Fundamental Symmetries and Spacetime Geometries in Gauge Theories of Gravity: Prospects for Unified Field Theories," Universe **6** (2020), 238 [arXiv:2012.06356 [gr-qc]].
29. E. A. Lord and P. Goswami, "Gauging the conformal group," Pramana **25** (1985) 635.
30. N. Berkovits, "SuperPoincaré invariant superstring field theory," Nucl. Phys. B **450** (1995) 90 [Erratum: Nucl. Phys. B **459** (1996) 439] [arXiv:hep-th/9503099].
31. F. Cabral, F. S. N. Lobo and D. Rubiera-Garcia, "Einstein-Cartan-Dirac gravity with U(1) symmetry breaking," Eur. Phys. J. C **79**, 1023 (2019).
32. F. Cabral, F. S. N. Lobo and D. Rubiera-Garcia, "Cosmological bounces, cyclic universes, and effective cosmological constant in Einstein-Cartan-Dirac-Maxwell theory," Phys. Rev. D **102** (2020) no. 8, 083509 [arXiv:2003.07463 [gr-qc]].
33. F. Cabral, F. S. N. Lobo and D. Rubiera-Garcia, "The cosmological principle in theories with torsion: The case of Einstein-Cartan-Dirac-Maxwell gravity," JCAP **10** (2020), 057 [arXiv:2004.13693 [gr-qc]].
34. H. Rumpf, "Quasiclassical limit of the Dirac equation and the equivalence principle in the Riemann-Cartan geometry," NATO Sci. Ser. B **58** (1980) 93.
35. J. Audretsch, "Dirac Electron in Space-times With Torsion: Spinor Propagation, Spin Precession, and Nongeodesic Orbits," Phys. Rev. D **24** (1981) 1470.
36. J. Nitsch and F. W. Hehl, "Translational Gauge Theory of Gravity: Postnewtonian Approximation and Spin Precession," Phys. Lett. B **90** (1980) 98.
37. F. Cabral, F. S. N. Lobo, D. Rubiera-Garcia, "Imprints from a Riemann-Cartan space-time on the energy levels of Dirac spinors", Class. Quant. Grav. **38** (2021) 19 [arXiv:2102.02048 [gr-qc]].
38. F. W. Hehl and Y. N. Obukhov, "Spacetime metric from local and linear electrodynamics: A New axiomatic scheme," Lect. Notes Phys. **702** (2006) 163 [arXiv:gr-qc/0508024].

Thermodynamics of scalar-tensor gravity: A new approach

Valerio Faraoni

Dept. of Physics & Astronomy, Bishop's University
Sherbrooke, Québec, Canada J1M 1Z7
E-mail: vfaraoni@ubishops.ca

We propose a new approach to the thermodynamics of scalar-tensor gravity and its possible "diffusion" toward general relativity, previously regarded as an equilibrium state in spacetime thermodynamics. The main idea is describing scalar-tensor gravity as an effective dissipative fluid and applying Eckart's first order thermodynamics to it. This gives explicit effective quantities: heat current density, "temperature of gravity", viscosity coefficients, entropy density, plus an equation describing the "diffusion" to Einstein gravity. These quantities, otherwise missing in spacetime thermodynamics, pop out with minimal assumptions.

Keywords: Scalar-tensor gravity, temperature of gravity theories, limit to general relativity.

1. Introduction

The thermodynamics of spacetime proposal became the subject of great interest when Jacobson derived the Einstein equation as an equilibrium equation of state from the thermodynamical properties of vacuum[1] and, later, the field equation of (metric) $f(R)$ gravity was obtained in a non-equilibrium thermodynamical setting.[2] These works have generated a large literature and suggest that general relativity (GR) could be a sort of lowest energy state of gravity, while alternative theories of gravity correspond to excited states. Indeed, modifying gravity with respect to GR introduces extra degrees of freedom in addition to the usual massless spin two field of GR. Therefore, theories containing GR as a limit correspond to excitations of these extra degrees of freedom, which are quiescent or absent in GR. Ultimately, if modified gravity is an excited state of GR, one should quantify the distance of an excited state from the GR "ground state" and identify some order parameter and equations describing the relaxation of gravity to GR. This order parameter, a sort of "temperature of gravity theories", is a crucial piece missing from this picture. Here we restrict ourselves to scalar-tensor[3,4] and $f(R)$ gravity (the latter is a subclass of the former[5–7]) and we identify a possible "temperature of gravity" candidate. The identification should be made in some relativistic thermodynamical context. Here we start from a very simple fact: the field equations of scalar-tensor gravity can be rewritten as effective Einstein equations by grouping the terms generated by the extra scalar field in the right hand side and noticing that they assume the form of the stress-energy tensor of an *imperfect* effective fluid. Next, we ask ourseleves what we know about dissipative fluids. The simplest description of dissipation and heat flux in GR is given by Eckart's first order thermodynamics.[8] This theory is notoriously plagued by non-causality and instabilities but is still widely used as an approximation. By describing scalar-tensor gravity as an effective imperfect fluid and using the constitutive equations of Eckart's theory (which are minimal assumptions and could be imposed in different models as well), we identify a "temperature of gravity" in the space of scalar-tensor theories,[3,4] which contain GR as the zero temperature limit.[9]

Let us recall the basics of scalar-tensor gravity, the prototypical alternative to Einstein's GR. The Jordan frame action is[a][3]

$$S_{\rm ST} = \frac{1}{16\pi} \int d^4x \sqrt{-g} \left[\phi R - \frac{\omega(\phi)}{\phi} \nabla^c \phi \nabla_c \phi - V(\phi) \right] + S^{(m)}, \quad (1)$$

where $\phi > 0$ is the Brans-Dicke scalar (approximately equivalent to the inverse of the effective gravitational coupling strength), $\omega(\phi)$ is the "Brans-Dicke coupling", $V(\phi)$ is a scalar field potential, and $S^{(m)}$ is the matter action. Varying (1) produces the field equations

$$R_{ab} - \frac{1}{2} g_{ab} R = \frac{8\pi}{\phi} T_{ab}^{(m)} + \frac{\omega}{\phi^2} \left(\nabla_a \phi \nabla_b \phi - \frac{1}{2} g_{ab} \nabla_c \phi \nabla^c \phi \right) + \frac{1}{\phi} \left(\nabla_a \nabla_b \phi - g_{ab} \Box \phi \right)$$
$$- \frac{V}{2\phi} g_{ab}, \quad (2)$$

$$\Box \phi = \frac{1}{2\omega + 3} \left(\frac{8\pi g^{ab} T_{ab}^{(m)}}{\phi} + \phi \frac{dV}{d\phi} - 2V - \frac{d\omega}{d\phi} \nabla^c \phi \nabla_c \phi \right), \quad (3)$$

where $T_{ab}^{(m)}$ is the matter stress-energy tensor.

2. The temperature of scalar-tensor gravity

An effective fluid description of the field equations (2) has been proposed in[11] for non-minimally coupled scalar fields and in[12] for general scalar-tensor gravity, and completed in Ref. 13. The fluid 4-velocity is

$$u^a = \frac{\nabla^a \phi}{\sqrt{-\nabla^e \phi \nabla_e \phi}} \quad (4)$$

when the gradient $\nabla^c \phi$ is timelike. The $3+1$ splitting of spacetime into the 3-space "seen" by the comoving observers of the fluid and their time direction u^a follows, with $h_{ab} \equiv g_{ab} + u_a u_b$ and $h_{ab} u^a = h_{ab} u^b = 0$, $h^a{}_b h^b{}_c = h^a{}_c$. The fluid 4-acceleration is

$$\dot{u}_a = (-\nabla^e \phi \nabla_e \phi)^{-2} \nabla^b \phi \left[(-\nabla^e \phi \nabla_e \phi) \nabla_a \nabla_b \phi + \nabla^c \phi \nabla_b \nabla_c \phi \nabla_a \phi \right], \quad (5)$$

---
[a]We follow the notation of Ref. 10, using units in which Newton's constant and the speed of light are unity.

and the effective stress-energy tensor of the Brans-Dicke-like field

$$8\pi T_{ab}^{(\phi)} = \frac{\omega}{\phi^2}\left(\nabla_a\phi\nabla_b\phi - \frac{1}{2}g_{ab}\nabla^c\phi\nabla_c\phi\right) + \frac{1}{\phi}\left(\nabla_a\nabla_b\phi - g_{ab}\Box\phi\right) - \frac{V}{2\phi}g_{ab} \quad (6)$$

can be written as the imperfect fluid stress-energy tensor

$$T_{ab} = \rho u_a u_b + q_a u_b + q_b u_a + \Pi_{ab}, \quad (7)$$

where[12,13]

$$\rho = T_{ab}u^a u^b, \quad q_a = -T_{cd}u^c h_a{}^d, \quad \Pi_{ab} \equiv P h_{ab} + \pi_{ab} = T_{cd} h_a{}^c h_b{}^d, \quad (8)$$

$$P = \frac{1}{3}g^{ab}\Pi_{ab} = \frac{1}{3}h^{ab}T_{ab}, \quad \pi_{ab} = \Pi_{ab} - P h_{ab}, \quad (9)$$

are, respectively, the effective energy density, heat flux density, stress tensor, isotropic pressure, and anisotropic stresses in the comoving frame, while $q_c u^c = \Pi_{ab}u^b = \pi_{ab}u^b = \Pi_{ab}u^a = \pi_{ab}u^a = \pi^a{}_a = 0$. These comoving frame fluid quantities read[12,13]

$$8\pi\rho^{(\phi)} = -\frac{\omega}{2\phi^2}\nabla^e\phi\nabla_e\phi + \frac{V}{2\phi} + \frac{1}{\phi}\left(\Box\phi - \frac{\nabla^a\phi\nabla^b\phi\nabla_a\nabla_b\phi}{\nabla^e\phi\nabla_e\phi}\right), \quad (10)$$

$$8\pi q_a^{(\phi)} = \frac{\nabla^c\phi\nabla^d\phi}{\phi(-\nabla^e\phi\nabla_e\phi)^{3/2}}\left(\nabla_d\phi\nabla_c\nabla_a\phi - \nabla_a\phi\nabla_c\nabla_d\phi\right), \quad (11)$$

$$8\pi\Pi_{ab}^{(\phi)} = \left(-\frac{\omega}{2\phi^2}\nabla^c\phi\nabla_c\phi - \frac{\Box\phi}{\phi} - \frac{V}{2\phi}\right)h_{ab} + \frac{1}{\phi}h_a{}^c h_b{}^d \nabla_c\nabla_d\phi, \quad (12)$$

$$8\pi P^{(\phi)} = -\frac{\omega}{2\phi^2}\nabla^e\phi\nabla_e\phi - \frac{V}{2\phi} - \frac{1}{3\phi}\left(2\Box\phi + \frac{\nabla^a\phi\nabla^b\phi\nabla_b\nabla_a\phi}{\nabla^e\phi\nabla_e\phi}\right), \quad (13)$$

$$8\pi\pi_{ab}^{(\phi)} = \frac{1}{\phi\nabla^e\phi\nabla_e\phi}\left[\frac{1}{3}\left(\nabla_a\phi\nabla_b\phi - g_{ab}\nabla^c\phi\nabla_c\phi\right)\left(\Box\phi - \frac{\nabla^c\phi\nabla^d\phi\nabla_d\nabla_c\phi}{\nabla^e\phi\nabla_e\phi}\right)\right.$$
$$\left. + \nabla^d\phi\left(\nabla_d\phi\nabla_a\nabla_b\phi - \nabla_b\phi\nabla_a\nabla_d\phi - \nabla_a\phi\nabla_d\nabla_b\phi + \frac{\nabla_a\phi\nabla_b\phi\nabla^c\phi\nabla_c\nabla_d\phi}{\nabla^e\phi\nabla_e\phi}\right)\right]. \quad (14)$$

The comparison of Eqs. (11) and (5) yields

$$q_a^{(\phi)} = -\frac{\sqrt{-\nabla^c\phi\nabla_c\phi}}{8\pi\phi}\dot{u}_a, \quad (15)$$

which brings us to our main point. The relation (15) has a physical consequence in Eckart's first order thermodynamics,[8] in which the heat flux density is related to the temperature $\mathcal{T}$ by the generalized Fourier law (a constitutive relation)[8]

$$q_a = -K\left(h_{ab}\nabla^b\mathcal{T} + \mathcal{T}\dot{u}_a\right), \quad (16)$$

where K is the thermal conductivity. Comparing Eqs. (15) and (16) leads to the result that, in the comoving frame, the spatial temperature gradient vanishes and the heat flow is caused solely by the inertia of energy (the acceleration term in (16)). The positive-definite temperature of the effective fluid is[9,13]

$$\mathcal{T} = \frac{\sqrt{-\nabla^c \phi \nabla_c \phi}}{8\pi K \phi}. \tag{17}$$

According to Eq. (17) GR, which is the limit $\phi =$ const. of scalar-tensor gravity,[3,4] corresponds to zero temperature $\mathcal{T}$, while in scalar-tensor spacetimes the scalar degree of freedom ϕ is excited and $\mathcal{T} > 0$.[9] The "temperature of gravity" is higher when the gravitational coupling $G_{\text{eff}} \sim \phi^{-1}$ is larger. In the space of scalar-tensor theories, gravity (viewed as a dissipative system) left to itself can "diffuse" toward GR, as described in.[9] Let us confront this idea with examples from gravitational physics.

3. Examples

3.1. $f(R)$ gravity

Metric $f(R)$ gravity (see[5–7] for reviews) is the most popular alternative to Einstein theory to explain the current acceleration of the universe without invoking an *ad hoc* dark energy. This theory is equivalent to an $\omega = 0$ Brans-Dicke theory with dynamical[b] scalar field $\phi = f'(R)$ and potential $V(\phi) = \phi R - f(R)\big|_{R=R(\phi)}$,[5–7] hence

$$\mathcal{T} = \frac{f''(R)\sqrt{-\nabla^c R \nabla_c R}}{8\pi K f'(R)}. \tag{18}$$

In order for the graviton to carry positive energy, it must be $f'(R) > 0$, while $f''(R) > 0$ is required for stability,[14] which guarantees that $K\mathcal{T} \geq 0$. This inequality is saturated by GR which, with $f(R) = R - 2\Lambda$, corresponds to $\mathcal{T} = 0$. It is significant that the requirement $\mathcal{T} > 0$ corresponds to local stability.

3.2. *Friedmann-Lemaître-Robertson-Walker universes*

In Friedmann-Lemaître-Robertson-Walker (FLRW) universes, spatial isotropy implies that the spatial heat flux of the effective fluid vanishes. For the same reason, the spatial temperature gradient $h_{ab}\nabla^b \mathcal{T} = 0$, while $\dot{a}_c \neq 0$ (in general, the ϕ-fluid does not obey the dust equation of state). Then, Eq. (16) implies that FLRW universes have "gravity temperature" $\mathcal{T} = 0$ in the comoving frame, whether they are solutions of scalar-tensor gravity or GR. Equivalently, in any FLRW space the imperfect effective fluid reduces to a perfect one for which heat flux and anisotropic

---

[b]In the Palatini version of $f(R)$ gravity, instead, ϕ is not dynamical and this theory is not an excitation of GR (cf.[23]).

stresses vanish identically (this property is valid also for Lovelock and $f(R,\mathcal{G})$ theories, where $\mathcal{G} \equiv R^2 - 4R_{ab}R^{ab} + R_{abcd}R^{abcd}$ is the Gauss-Bonnet term, in arbitrary dimension[15]). This conclusion goes against the idea (see, e.g., Ref.[16]) that an attractor mechanism to GR operates in scalar-tensor cosmology. The situation of FLRW and Bianchi cosmologies with regard to the temperature of gravity is under examination and will be reported elsewhere.

3.3. *Vacuum, asymptotically flat, stationary black holes*

It is well known since an early theorem by Hawking that vacuum, asymptotically flat black holes in Brans-Dicke gravity are the same as in GR,[17] a result later generalized to scalar-tensor theories[18,19] provided that $V(\phi)$ has a minimum for the scalar ϕ to sit in stable equilibrium (the exceptions are maverick solutions with ϕ diverging on the horizon, e.g.,[20]). The key ingredient of Hawking's theorem consists of proving that ϕ is constant outside the horizon, in which case the theory reduces to GR in that region, corresponding to zero "theory temperature" $\mathcal{T}$. The interpretation is that these extreme objects "freeze" the extra dynamical degrees of freedom outside their horizons. Then, the no-hair theorems state that the GR black holes are the states of "lowest temperature" in the space of scalar-tensor black holes.

3.4. *Stealth scalar fields*

Clearly, Minkowski spacetime should correspond to zero temperature and, indeed, it is a constant ϕ solution of the field equations (2) and (3). However, Minkowski spaces with non-gravitating stealth scalar fields are also solutions of scalar-tensor gravity (e.g.,[21,22]). For example, the Ayon-Beato stealth solution $g_{ab} = \eta_{ab}$, $\phi = a_1 x^\mu x_\mu + p_\mu x^\mu + a_2$ (where $a_{1,2}$ and p_μ are constants)[21] correspond to "theory temperature"

$$\mathcal{T} = \frac{\sqrt{4a_1(\phi - a_2) + p_\alpha p^\alpha}}{8\pi K \phi}. \tag{19}$$

This interpretation makes sense where $\phi > 0$ and $a_1(\phi - a_2) + p_\mu p^\mu/4 > 0$. Even though the stress-energy tensor of the effective imperfect fluid disappears, the scalar degree of freedom is excited and the temperature of gravity is non-zero.

In another stealth solution due to Robinson,[22] $V \equiv 0$, $\omega = $ const., the geometry is Minkowskian, and the scalar is the wave

$$\phi = \begin{cases} \phi_0\, e^{c_1 u + c_2} & \text{if } \omega = -1, \\ \phi_0\,(c_1 u + c_1)^{\frac{1}{\omega+1}} & \text{if } \omega \neq -1, \end{cases} \tag{20}$$

where u is the retarded time and $c_{1,2}$ are constants. In this case, a massless wave-like excitation of the scalar degree of freedom with $\nabla_c \phi \nabla^c \phi = 0$ gives $\mathcal{T} = 0$. A ϕ-wave as a dissipative system was regarded as a problem in[23] because classical gravitational theories are time-reversal invariant, but this state cannot decay, therefore this is not a truly dissipative system.

4. Conclusions

We have introduced a candidate to the role of "temperature of gravity" $\mathcal{T}$ using the effective imperfect fluid description of scalar-tensor gravity and Eckart's thermodynamics.[9,13] In this picture, the approach to GR is a diffusion-like process. Altough our proposal is intriguing at first sight, a deeper analysis is needed before it can be taken seriously. The specific examples discussed (plus those in[9]) corroborate the proposed Eq. (17), but our proposal remains preliminary. In any case, ultimately it will suffer from the same limitations of Eckart's theory. Nevertheless, the explicit expression of the "temperature of gravity" in the wide class of scalar-tensor theories (the prototypical alternative to GR, containing the $f(R)$ subclass extremely popular in cosmology) provides a working scheme to investigate the relaxation to GR.

Alternative approaches are possible: one can trade temperature with chemical potential, assigning to the effective ϕ-fluid zero temperature and entropy but nonzero chemical potential as done, e.g., in.[24] These approaches and a more detailed analysis of our proposal for $\mathcal{T}$ are under study and will be reported elsewhere.

Acknowledgments

I am grateful to Andrea Giusti and Jeremy Côté, who contributed to parts of the research presented here. This work is supported by the Natural Sciences & Engineering Research Council of Canada (Grant No. 2016-03803) and by Bishop's University.

References

1. T. Jacobson, Phys. Rev. Lett. **75**, 1260 (1995).
2. C. Eling, R. Guedens, and T. Jacobson, Phys. Rev. Lett. **96**, 121301 (2006).
3. C. Brans and R.H. Dicke, Phys. Rev. **124**, 925 (1961).
4. P.G. Bergmann, Int. J. Theor. Phys. **1**, 25 (1968); R.V. Wagoner, Phys. Rev. D **1**, 3209 (1970); K. Nordvedt, Astrophys. J. **161**, 1059 (1970).
5. T.P. Sotiriou and V. Faraoni, Rev. Mod. Phys. **82**, 451 (2010).
6. A. De Felice and S. Tsujikawa, Living Rev. Relativ. **13**, 3 (2010).
7. S. Nojiri and S.D. Odintsov, Phys. Rept. **505**, 59 (2011).
8. C. Eckart, Phys. Rev. **58**, 919 (1940).
9. V. Faraoni and A. Giusti, Phys. Rev. D **103**, no.12, L121501 (2021).
10. R.M. Wald, *General Relativity* (Chicago University Press, Chicago, 1987).
11. M.S. Madsen, Class. Quantum Grav. **5**, 627 (1988).
12. L.O. Pimentel, Class. Quantum Grav. **6**, L263 (1989).
13. V. Faraoni and J. Coté, Phys. Rev. D **98**, 084019 (2018).
14. V. Faraoni, Phys. Rev. D **74**, 104017 (2006).
15. M. Gurses and Y. Heydarzade, Eur. Phys. J. C **80**, 1061 (2020).
16. T. Damour and K. Nordtvedt, Phys. Rev. Lett. **70**, 2217 (1993).
17. S.W. Hawking, Commun. Math. Phys. **25**, 167 (1972).
18. J.D. Bekenstein, 1996, in *Second International A.D. Sahkarov Conference on Physics*, Moscow, 20-23 May 1996, edited by I.M. Dremin and A.M. Semikhatov (World Scientific, Singapore), p. 21 (arXiv:9605059 [gr-qc]).

19. T.P. Sotiriou and V. Faraoni, Phys. Rev. Lett. **108**, 081103 (2012).
20. N.M. Bocharova, K.A. Bronnikov, and V.N. Melnikov, Vestn. Mosk. Univ. Fiz. Astron. **6**, 706 (1970); J.D. Bekenstein, Ann. Phys. (N.Y.) **82**, 535 (1974).
21. E. Ayon-Beato, C. Martinez, R. Troncoso, and J. Zanelli, Phys. Rev. D **71**, 104037 (2005).
22. D.C. Robinson, Gen. Relativ. Gravit. **38**, 153 (2006).
23. G. Chirco, C. Eling, and S. Liberati, Phys. Rev. D **83**, 024032 (2011).
24. O. Pujolas, I. Sawicki, and A. Vikman, J. High Energy Phys. **1111**, 156 (2011); R. Akhoury, C. Gauthier, and A. Vikman, J. High Energy Phys. **0903**, 082 (2009).

Two body dynamics in a quadratic modification of general relativity

Soham Bhattacharyya

Max Planck Institute for Gravitational Physics (Albert Einstein Institute)
Leibniz Universität Hannover

It is shown in this study that deviations from the Einstein-Hilbert action at the quadratic level using a proper analyses and suitable dynamical variables lead to a tiny modification to the post Newtonian equations of motion, and non-GR like behavior at very short length scales.

Keywords: Modifed gravity; two-body dynamics; post-Newtonism formalism.

1. Introduction

General theory of Relativity (GR) is a field theory, one of the first of its kind, that is classified under classical physics. The validity of the theory ranges from solar system length scales to cosmological length scales. It has passed most of its predictions with flying colors, starting from the extra perihelion precession of Mercury in the inner solar system,[1] to gravitational lensing,[2] to the generation of gravitational waves (GW),[3–8] and finally to the existence of objects called black holes (BH).[9]

One of the first calculations that tested the predictive power of GR was the perihelion precession of Mercury, which is to say that GR gave predictions of all the possible orbital dynamics that was possible to be observed in the early 20th century, and its predictive power remains the same to this date. GR predicted that the *gravitational force* will not always be inverse squared of the distance from the source, and that at shorter length scales, the behavior changes. To be precise, a perturbative treatment of GR, also known as the post Newtonian (PN) formalism,[10–16] reveals that a series of shorter (than inverse squared) ranged velocity dependent forces can have a prominent effect on the dynamics of two objects trapped in their mutual gravitational field (like the Sun and Mercury system). Hence, the universality of Newtonian gravity stops being universal when one goes beyond the *Newtonian bubble*, broadly speaking.

However, an uncomfortable question pops up when one considers the PN forces of GR, and keeps on continuing the PN series to shorter and shorter length scales. Or when one considers the collapse of a self-gravitating mass of fluid at the extreme scenario. At every point along the collapse, the gravitational force, including the PN forces, are attractive in nature. Hence, if the fermionic pressure, or the force that makes matter solid, is unable to balance the increasingly powerful (but shorter ranged) forces of gravity, a singularity may occur. This is because in the tug of war of all the forces present in one or multiple gravitating systems, gravity seems to win in some extreme conditions. Such conditions can occur in ultra dense self gravitating systems like the end stages of a star collapsing under its own gravity. If there is no other force that can stop the unyielding pull of gravity, matter eventually collapses fully in on itself. But long before such a full collapse, or singularity, can happen, a special surface forms around the eventual singularity. Such a surface is known as the event horizon, or the surface the forms the termination of all *events* in the Universe that lies outside of the surface. Here *event* refers to the special relativistic notation of space-time events, which are, in the sense of mathematical modelling, points in a four dimensional object known as the manifold, which in turn refers to the complete past, present, and future of the Universe that is being modelled.

However, the universality of attraction of gravity may not be the case when one goes beyond the Einstein-Hilbert (EH) action, referred to as GR in literature. In order to demonstrate that, a quadratic deviation to the EH action is considered, which is a subclass of post-Einsteinian theories known as $f(R)$ theories of gravity.[17,18] Such theories are characterized by an extra massive scalar degree of freedom,[19–21] in addition to the two massless tensor degrees of freedom.

A PN treatment of the densitized field equations of a quadratic extension to GR will be performed in this study that resembles the Landau-Lifshitz formulation of GR. It will be shown that the equations of motion have a rather good limit to GR (almost indistinguishable in fact), and only deviates from the predictions of GR at very high energy scales (where energy scales refer to really large velocities and very high spatial curvatures combined).

Geometrized units, $c = G = 1$ will be used in this study unless explicitly mentioned otherwise. The notations of[22] will be followed except a few changes in variable and index labeling. The mostly minus sign convention will be followed for the metric, that is $(+, -, -, -)$.

2. Layout

2.1. *The densitized formulation of GR*

The gothic metric/Landau-Lifshitz/densitized formulation of GR may be motivated from a particular observation regarding the structure of the second-most condensed form of the Einstein field equations in its covariant form (or the canonical form), that is

$$R_{\mu\nu} - \frac{1}{2} g_{\mu\nu} R \propto T_{\mu\nu} \tag{1}$$

where the first tensor quantity on the LHS of the above is the Ricci tensor, and the scalar multiplied to the metric tensor in the second term of the LHS is the contraction of the Ricci tensor with the metric, known as the Ricci scalar. The RHS is the classical matter energy-momentum-stress density tensor, which contains certain information (although non-exhaustive) about the content that is separate from the space-time. One notices that the net content of the RHS of (1) is essentially a trace reversed form of the Ricci tensor. Trace reversal implies that the trace of the new tensor that was introduced in the beginning of the 20th century has a trace that is negative of the trace of the Ricci tensor, and is known as the Einstein tensor, which leads to the most condensed form of the field equations of GR, or

$$G_{\mu\nu} \propto T_{\mu\nu} \qquad (2)$$

where all components of the tensor $G_{\mu\nu}$ has a one-to-one relationship with all of the corresponding components of the matter energy-momentum-stress density tensor. However, the cost of condensation is the loss of information and usability. As it is, Eq. (2) does not tell one about how planets and stars move and how GWs are radiated. To be able to predict such phenomenon mathematically, one needs to 'dirty their hands'.

In classical GR, $T_{\mu\nu}$ can contain fluids (serving as a model for stars, dust, etc.), or it can contain the energy-momentum-stress density equivalent of electromagnetic fields and charges. The Ricci tensor/scalar are obtained from geometric principles governing the nature of surfaces, volumes, and higher dimensional generalization; which are in turn obtained by contracting the tensor quantity that serves as the model for the space-time 'fabric'[a], or the Riemann tensor $R_{\mu\sigma\rho\nu}$. The Riemann tensor in GR is a function of the metric and its derivatives (till second). It has certain symmetries that are given as follows

$$R_{\mu\sigma(\nu\rho)} = R_{(\mu\sigma)\nu\rho} = 0 \qquad (3)$$
$$R_{\mu[\sigma\nu\rho]} = 0 \qquad (4)$$
$$R_{\mu\rho\nu\sigma} = R_{\nu\sigma\mu\rho} \qquad (5)$$
$$R_{\mu\rho[\nu\sigma;\alpha]} = 0. \qquad (6)$$

The first, third of the identities, that is Eqs. (3) and (5), are called skew and interchange symmetries respectively. Whereas Eqs. (4) and (6) are known as the first and second Bianchi identities respectively. The second Bianchi identity is particularly useful since it leads to the following identity on the Einstein tensor $G_{\mu\nu}$

$$\nabla^\mu G_{\mu\nu} = 0, \qquad (7)$$

where $\nabla^\mu \equiv g^{\mu\rho} \nabla_\rho$ is the index-raised covariant derivative associated with the metric $g_{\alpha\beta}$. The above, combined with the proportionality condition (2), lead to the following

$$\nabla^\mu T_{\mu\nu} = 0 \qquad (8)$$

which is a covariant conservation law on the classical matter (or electromagnetic fields) energy-momentum-stress density tensor, and using which equation of motion of classical matter itself can be deduced. Hence the famous saying by J.A. Wheeler

---

[a] Although the term fabric is used, it is put under quotation to differentiate from an actual material object, which is something that the physics community thought of as 'Aether' before the famous Michelson-Morley experiment. In conventional notion, material or fabric can be torn or broken; however, a similar 'tearing' of space-time is something that does not seem to happen. Hence one must take the concept of 'fabric' with a pinch of salt.

about Eq. (2): *Spacetime tells matter how move; matter tells spacetime how to curve,* is incomplete without throwing in Eq. (8) into the fold.

With the above motivations one can define a new tensor given by[23–25]

$$\mathfrak{g}^{\mu\nu} = \sqrt{-g}\, g^{\mu\nu} \qquad (9)$$

which utilizes the contravariant metric, or the 'dual' of the covariant metric, whose components actually define the space-time structure. Now the point of taking the dual is to simplify the equations that need to be solved, by replacing the problem at hand with another problem which relates to the original problem via transformation and/or reparametrizations. One also notices the presence of the determinant of the metric tensor through $\sqrt{-g}$ multiplying $g^{\mu\nu}$. Under the transformation (9), Eq. (1) or (2) can be framed as a slightly less condensed (but more useful) form given as follows

$$\frac{1}{2(-g)} \partial_{\alpha\beta} H^{\mu\alpha\nu\beta} - 8\pi t^{\mu\nu}_{LL} = 8\pi T^{\mu\nu}_m \qquad (10)$$

$$H^{\mu\alpha\nu\beta} = \mathfrak{g}^{\alpha\beta}\mathfrak{g}^{\mu\nu} - \mathfrak{g}^{\alpha\nu}\mathfrak{g}^{\beta\mu} \qquad (11)$$

$$16\pi(-g) t^{\alpha\beta}_{LL} = \partial_\alpha \mathfrak{g}^{\mu\nu} \partial_\beta \mathfrak{g}^{\alpha\beta} - \frac{1}{4}\mathfrak{g}^{\alpha\beta}\mathfrak{g}_{\gamma\varsigma}\mathfrak{g}_{\theta\iota}\mathfrak{g}^{\mu\nu}\partial_\alpha \mathfrak{g}^{\gamma\theta}\partial_\beta \mathfrak{g}^{\varsigma\iota}$$
$$+\frac{1}{2}\mathfrak{g}_{\gamma\varsigma}\mathfrak{g}_{\theta\iota}\mathfrak{g}^{\mu\alpha}\mathfrak{g}^{\nu\beta}\partial_\alpha \mathfrak{g}^{\gamma\theta}\partial_\beta \mathfrak{g}^{\varsigma\iota} + \frac{1}{8}\mathfrak{g}^{\alpha\beta}\mathfrak{g}_{\gamma\varsigma}\mathfrak{g}_{\theta\iota}\mathfrak{g}^{\mu\nu}\partial_\alpha \mathfrak{g}^{\gamma\varsigma}\partial_\beta \mathfrak{g}^{\theta\iota}$$
$$-\frac{1}{4}\mathfrak{g}_{\gamma\varsigma}\mathfrak{g}_{\theta\iota}\mathfrak{g}^{\mu\alpha}\mathfrak{g}^{\nu\beta}\partial_\alpha \mathfrak{g}^{\gamma\varsigma}\partial_\beta \mathfrak{g}^{\theta\iota} - \partial_\alpha \mathfrak{g}^{\mu\alpha}\partial_\beta \mathfrak{g}^{\nu\beta} + \mathfrak{g}^{\alpha\beta}\mathfrak{g}_{\gamma\varsigma}\partial_\alpha \mathfrak{g}^{\mu\gamma}\partial_\beta \mathfrak{g}^{\nu\varsigma}$$
$$+\frac{1}{2}\mathfrak{g}_{\alpha\beta}\mathfrak{g}^{\mu\nu}\partial_\gamma \mathfrak{g}^{\beta\varsigma}\partial_\varsigma \mathfrak{g}^{\alpha\gamma} - \mathfrak{g}_{\beta\gamma}\mathfrak{g}^{\nu\alpha}\partial_\alpha \mathfrak{g}^{\gamma\varsigma}\partial_\varsigma \mathfrak{g}^{\mu\beta} - \mathfrak{g}_{\beta\gamma}\mathfrak{g}^{\mu\alpha}\partial_\alpha \mathfrak{g}^{\gamma\varsigma}\partial_\varsigma \mathfrak{g}^{\nu\beta}. \qquad (12)$$

The definition of the Landau-Lifshitz pseudo-tensor $t^{\mu\nu}_{LL}$ deviates slightly from the usual definition found in literature since all the metrics that are used to raise or lower the indices have been transformed into the gothic metric. The covariant gothic metric is defined as

$$\mathfrak{g}_{\mu\nu} = \frac{g_{\mu\nu}}{\sqrt{-g}}. \qquad (13)$$

One notices that the rank 4 tensor $H^{\mu\alpha\nu\beta}$ has the same symmetries as the Riemann tensor, and is proportional to the Riemann tensor corresponding to the maximally symmetric Riemann tensor. The maximally symmetric Riemann tensor is a solution of the field equations of GR when the space-time is homogeneous and isotropic everywhere. Deviation from such a space-time with the maximum number of symmetries is marked by the appearance of a coordinate or a gauge dependent tensor (or a pseudo-tensor) $t^{\mu\nu}_{LL}$, also known as the Landau-Lifshitz energy-momentum-stress density pseudo-tensor. $t^{\mu\nu}_{LL}$ is a quantification of the energy, momentum, and stress that is inherent in the space-time, and leads to a solutions that are less symmetric than the completely homogeneous and isotropic space-time one started off with. Such solutions are perturbative in nature and formed the early basis for the Post-Newtonian formalism in GR.[10–16] The perturbation is defined about the Minkowski space-time as

$$\mathfrak{h}^{\mu\nu} = \eta^{\mu\nu} - \mathfrak{g}^{\mu\nu}. \qquad (14)$$

The above tensor is projected on a Cartesian coordinate frame of a freely falling observer by choosing the following gauge condition

$$\partial_\mu \mathfrak{h}^{\mu\nu} = 0 \tag{15}$$

which not only simplifies the field equations but also puts it in a form that offers a more intimate insight into the nature of space-time and its relationship to classical matter. They are given by the following

$$\Box \mathfrak{h}^{\mu\nu} = -16\pi \Lambda^{\mu\nu} \tag{16}$$

$$\Lambda^{\mu\nu} = \Theta^{\mu\nu} + \partial_{\alpha\beta} \chi^{\mu\nu\alpha\beta} \tag{17}$$

$$\Theta^{\mu\nu} = (-g)(T^{\mu\nu} + t_{LL}^{\mu\nu} - t_H^{\mu\nu}) \tag{18}$$

$$\chi^{\mu\nu\alpha\beta} = \frac{1}{16\pi}\left(\mathfrak{h}^{\alpha\nu}\mathfrak{h}^{\beta\mu} - \mathfrak{h}^{\alpha\beta}\mathfrak{h}^{\mu\nu}\right) \tag{19}$$

where a proportionality constant of 16π has now been used, which is the case when one uses geometrized units ($G = c = 1$). The rank 4 tensor $\chi^{\mu\alpha\nu\beta}$ with Riemann symmetry, being a total derivative term, can be turned into a boundary term using Gauss's law, and can be discarded as the source of the wave equation (16) when a particular choice of the Green's function is made for the flat-space Laplacian/wave operator $\Box$. One immediately notices that the dynamical variable now follows the well studied massless wave equation, which has standard solutions. It is also to be noted that if one chooses the effective energy-momentum-stress density tensor to be the sum of both the matter and the pseudo part, the dynamical variable has a one-to-one relationship with the matter density. The Landau-Lifshitz or the gothic metric formalism is hence often called as the densitized formalism, as it allows the introduction of a variable that can be taken as the space-time density itself, in contrast to the regular metric tensor which has a very complicated relationship with the energy-momentum-stress density tensor. The covariant conservation identity in Eq. (8) in this 'reduced' formalism, when added to the Landau-Lifshitz pseudo-tensor, along with the harmonic gauge condition (15), reduces to the following

$$\partial_\nu \Lambda^{\mu\nu} = 0. \tag{20}$$

Now to come back to the motivation for mentioning trace-reversal at the beginning of the section; one may choose to study perturbative GR by simply linearizing the metric tensor about the Minkowski space-time itself, that is

$$g^{\mu\nu} = \eta^{\mu\nu} - h^{\mu\nu} \tag{21}$$

At the linear order the gothic metric perturbation and the metric perturbation are related as follows (using Jacobi's identity)

$$\mathfrak{h}^{\mu\nu} = h^{\mu\nu} - \frac{1}{2}\eta^{\mu\nu} h \tag{22}$$

$$\mathfrak{h} = -h \tag{23}$$

where h and $\mathfrak{h}$ are the trace of the metric perturbation and the gothic metric perturbation respectively. Eq. (22) is used as a standard textbook solution for modeling the propagation of gravitational waves in empty space-times. Multiplying $\sqrt{-g}$ to the dual of the metric tensor is also similar to the multiplication of the same factor to the Ricci scalar (other than making the volume element covariant) to make the Einstein-Hilbert Lagrangian density, which has the same dimensions as any other matter Lagrangian density which may appear at the action level along with the Einstein-Hilbert Lagrangian density, that is

$$S = \int_M \sqrt{-g}\, d^4x \left(\frac{R}{16\pi} + \mathcal{L}_{matter} + \mathcal{L}_{electromagnetism} + \cdots \right) \quad (24)$$

2.2. The densitized formulation of $f(R)$ theories of gravity

Like any other field theory, the class of theories known as $f(R)$ theories of gravity can be derived from the following action

$$S = \int_M \sqrt{-g}\, d^4x \left(\frac{f(R)}{16\pi} + \mathcal{L}_{matter} + \mathcal{L}_{electromagnetism} + \cdots \right) \quad (25)$$

However, in the current study for simplicity, we will not be including electromagnetic fields or any other 'exotic' fields. The field equations can be derived by varying the action with respect to the metric, and its higher derivatives, and by enforcing all variations vanish at the boundaries of the integration, which is well suited to study the classical problem at hand. The field equations so obtained are as follows[21]

$$f'(R) R_{\mu\nu} - \frac{1}{2} f(R) g_{\mu\nu} - [\nabla_\mu \nabla_\nu - g_{\mu\nu} \Box] f'(R) = 8\pi T_{\mu\nu} \quad (26)$$

$$f'(R) = \frac{df(R)}{dR} \quad (27)$$

where ∇_μ, as usual, is the covariant derivative associated with the metric $g_{\mu\nu}$. The above field equations can be written in two different forms (if one intends to use the machinery of GR): one modifies the Newtonian constant (which has been put to unity in the current study), and the other preserves it. The former is written as[21]

$$G_{\mu\nu} = \frac{8\pi}{f'} \left(T_{\mu\nu} + T^{eff}_{\mu\nu} \right) \quad (28)$$

$$T^{eff}_{\mu\nu} \equiv \frac{1}{2}(f - Rf') g_{\mu\nu} + (\nabla_\mu \nabla_\nu - g_{\mu\nu} \Box) f' \quad (29)$$

where $\Box \equiv g^{\alpha\beta} \nabla_\alpha \nabla_\beta$. The latter version has the following form

$$G_{\mu\nu} = 8\pi T_{\mu\nu} + \tilde{T}^{eff}_{\mu\nu} \quad (30)$$

$$\tilde{T}^{eff}_{\mu\nu} = (1 - f') R_{\mu\nu} + \frac{1}{2}(R - f) g_{\mu\nu} + (\nabla_\mu \nabla_\nu - g_{\mu\nu} \Box) f'. \quad (31)$$

In this study, only the former, that is Eqs. (28)-(29) will be considered because of convenience, and the extra terms are less in number. There is also another differential equation that is satisfied by the scalar function f', which is independent of whatever form is chosen for the effective energy-momentum-stress density tensor, and is obtained by taking the trace of either Eqs. (28) or (30). It's given by

$$3 g^{\mu\nu} \nabla_\mu \nabla_\nu f' + f' R - 2 f = 8 \pi T \tag{32}$$

and can be regarded as the dynamics of some effective scalar field. The transition of f' from an 'effective' to an actual scalar degree of freedom will be made clear in a few paragraphs.

Before trying to obtain an equivalent of Eq. (10) one must be made aware of a particular conformal property of $f(R)$ theories of gravity, that is under a general conformal transformation of the metric tensor

$$\tilde{g}_{\mu\nu} = \Omega^2 g_{\mu\nu} \tag{33}$$

$f(R)$ theories can be written as an *Einstein + massive scalar* system. The $f(R)$ action without matter, for example transforms as[26-30]

$$S = \int_M d^4 x \sqrt{-g} \left(\frac{\tilde{R}}{16\pi} + \frac{1}{2} \tilde{g}^{\mu\nu} \phi_{,\mu} \phi_{,\nu} - V(\phi) \right) \tag{34}$$

$$\phi \equiv \sqrt{\frac{3}{16\pi}} \ln \Omega \tag{35}$$

$$V(\phi) \equiv \frac{1}{16\pi} \frac{f - R f'}{(f')^2} \tag{36}$$

$$\Omega \equiv f' \tag{37}$$

Where $\tilde{R}$ is the Ricci scalar of the conformally transformed metric $\tilde{g}_{\mu\nu}$. This confirms the presence of an extra massive scalar degree of freedom in $f(R)$ theories of gravity. In the literature of $f(R)$ and scalar-tensor theories of gravity, the 'vanilla' metric $g_{\mu\nu}$ is known as the Jordan frame, whereas the conformally transformed metric $\tilde{g}_{\mu\nu}$ is called the Einstein frame. From this motivation, one can define a new gothic metric (in the Jordan frame) $\tilde{\mathfrak{g}}^{\mu\nu}$ given by

$$\tilde{\mathfrak{g}}^{\mu\nu} = f'(R) \sqrt{-g} g^{\mu\nu} \tag{38}$$

which frames the field equations (28) in the following form

$$\partial_{\alpha\beta} \tilde{H}^{\alpha\mu\beta\nu} = -16 \pi (-g) f'(R) \left(T^{\mu\nu} + t^{\mu\nu}_{eff} + \tilde{t}^{\mu\nu}_{LL} \right), \tag{39}$$

$$16 \pi (-g) f' t^{\mu\nu}_{eff} = \sqrt{-g} (f - R f') \tilde{\mathfrak{g}}^{\mu\nu} + \frac{3}{(f')^2} \left(\tilde{\mathfrak{g}}^{\mu\alpha} \tilde{\mathfrak{g}}^{\nu\beta} - \frac{1}{2} \tilde{\mathfrak{g}}^{\mu\nu} \tilde{\mathfrak{g}}^{\alpha\beta} \right)$$
$$\times \partial_\alpha f' \partial_\beta f' \tag{40}$$

where $\tilde{H}^{\alpha\mu\beta\nu}$ and $\tilde{t}_{LL}^{\mu\nu}$ has the same form as that of $H^{\alpha\mu\beta\nu}$ and $t_{LL}^{\mu\nu}$, respectively, but with $\mathfrak{g}$ replaced by $\tilde{\mathfrak{g}}$. The newly appeared tensor $t_{eff}^{\mu\nu}$ contains products of only quadratic forms of first derivatives of f', as seen in Eq. (40). Owing to the conformal transformation, all the double derivatives of f' in the tensor field equations cancel away, making $t_{eff}^{\mu\nu}$ a perfectly usable source for the perturbative post Newtonian expansion. Curiously, the definition Eq. (38) appears as an identity of Palatini formalism of $f(R)$ theories of gravity as well, for example in Eq. (17) of.[31]

Now before a post Newtonian sequence of solutions can be found, one needs to choose a particular form of the function $f(R)$, which consequently fixes the form of the function $f'(R)$ as well, and can be taken for simplicity as

$$f(R) = R + \frac{f''(0)}{2} R^2 \qquad (41)$$

$$f'(R) = 1 + f''(0) R \qquad (42)$$

where the coefficients of expansion $f'(0)$ is taken to be unity to recover GR at the $R = 0$ limit, and $f''(0)$ will be taken to be negative for the course of this article, following.[32–35] One defines a tensor field $\tilde{\mathfrak{h}}^{\mu\nu}$, similar to Eq. (14), that propagates on the Minkowski background. One can define that as follows

$$\tilde{\mathfrak{h}}^{\mu\nu} = \eta^{\mu\nu} - \tilde{\mathfrak{g}}^{\mu\nu}. \qquad (43)$$

In order to obtain wave like equations of motion where the coordinate variable functions comprising the coordinate 4-vectors follow the conditions

$$\Box x^\mu = 0, \qquad (44)$$

one must choose the following gauge/coordinate condition similar to Eq. (15)

$$\partial_\mu \tilde{\mathfrak{h}}^{\mu\nu} = 0 \qquad (45)$$

which will be called as the conformal harmonic gauge. Now similar to the conformally transformed new metric density $\tilde{\mathfrak{g}}^{\mu\nu}$, one must also define a scalar variable corresponding to a scalar density, say $\mathfrak{R}$, that follows a massive wave equation (to model the dynamics of the massive scalar degree of freedom), and maintains the $(-g)$ relationship with the trace of the net energy-momentum-stress density tensor $\tilde{\Lambda}^{\mu\nu}$ as well, as in Eq. (16). One may define that as follows

$$\mathfrak{R} = \sqrt{-g}\, R. \qquad (46)$$

Substituting Eq. (43), (46), and (45) in the reduced field equations (39), one obtains the following

$$\Box \tilde{\mathfrak{h}}^{\mu\nu} = -16\pi \tilde{\Lambda}^{\mu\nu} \qquad (47)$$

$$\tilde{\Lambda}^{\mu\nu} = (-g)\left[T_m^{\mu\nu}\left(1 - \frac{f''\mathfrak{R}}{\sqrt{-g}}\right) + t_{LL}^{\mu\nu} + t_H^{\mu\nu} + t_{eff}^{\mu\nu} \right]. \qquad (48)$$

$t^{\mu\nu}_{eff}$ is comprised of various products of $\tilde{\mathfrak{h}}^{\mu\nu}$, $\mathfrak{R}$, and first derivatives of $\tilde{\mathfrak{h}}^{\mu\nu}$ and $\mathfrak{R}$; whose truncated form till the quadratic order of $f''(0)$ is given as follows

$$16\pi(-g)\, t^{\mu\nu}_{eff} = \frac{f''\,\mathfrak{R}^2}{\sqrt{-g}}\,\eta^{\mu\nu} + \frac{3\,(f'')^2}{4\,(-g)}\bigg[2\left(\eta^{\mu\alpha}\eta^{\nu\beta} + \eta^{\mu\beta}\eta^{\nu\alpha}\right.$$
$$\left. - \eta^{\mu\nu}\eta^{\alpha\beta}\right)\mathfrak{R}\partial_\alpha\mathfrak{R}\partial_\beta\tilde{\mathfrak{h}} + \left(\eta^{\mu\alpha}\eta^{\nu\beta} - \frac{1}{2}\eta^{\mu\nu}\eta^{\alpha\beta}\right)\left(4\partial_\alpha\mathfrak{R}\partial_\beta\mathfrak{R} + \mathfrak{R}^2\partial_\alpha\tilde{\mathfrak{h}}\partial_\beta\tilde{\mathfrak{h}}\right)\bigg]$$
$$+ \mathcal{O}\left[\left(\frac{f''}{\sqrt{-g}}\right)^3\right] \tag{49}$$

$$\tilde{\mathfrak{h}} \equiv \eta_{\mu\nu}\tilde{\mathfrak{h}}^{\mu\nu} \tag{50}$$

with the following conservation law being satisfied by $\tilde{\Lambda}^{\mu\nu}$

$$\partial_\mu \tilde{\Lambda}^{\mu\nu} = 0\,, \tag{51}$$

whereas the new scalar dynamical variable $\mathfrak{R}$ satisfies the following, as obtained by substituting Eq. (43), (46), and (45) in Eq. (32)

$$\Box \mathfrak{R} + \sqrt{-g}\,\gamma^2 \mathfrak{R} = -8\pi(-g)\,\gamma^2\,\tilde{\Lambda} \tag{52}$$

$$\gamma^2 \equiv -\frac{1}{3\,f''(0)} \tag{53}$$

$$\tilde{\Lambda} = T_m + f''(0)\left\{\frac{T_m\mathfrak{R}}{3\sqrt{-g}} + \frac{1}{8\pi(-g)}\left(\frac{\mathfrak{R}^2}{3} - \partial_\mu\mathfrak{R}\partial^\mu\tilde{\mathfrak{h}} - \frac{1}{2}\mathfrak{R}\partial_\mu\tilde{\mathfrak{h}}^{\alpha\beta}\partial^\mu\tilde{\mathfrak{h}}_{\alpha\beta}\right.\right.$$
$$\left.\left. - \frac{1}{4}\mathfrak{R}\partial_\mu\tilde{\mathfrak{h}}\partial^\mu\tilde{\mathfrak{h}} - \frac{1}{2}\mathfrak{R}\Box\tilde{\mathfrak{h}}\right)\right\} + \mathcal{O}\left([f''(0)]^2\right) \tag{54}$$

$$\tag{55}$$

$$T_m = \eta_{\mu\nu} T^{\mu\nu}_m\,. \tag{56}$$

Before moving on to finding the equations of motion of compact objects, and to conclude this section one may take the LHS of Eq. (28) to be some modified Einstein tensor $\mathcal{G}_{\mu\nu}$, that is

$$\mathcal{G}_{\mu\nu} \equiv f'(R)\,R_{\mu\nu} - \frac{1}{2}f(R)\,g_{\mu\nu} - \left[\nabla_\mu\nabla_\nu - g_{\mu\nu}\Box\right]f'(R)\,, \tag{57}$$

it can be shown that[32] the modified tensor $\mathcal{G}_{\mu\nu}$ satisfies the same covariant conservation condition as the Einstein tensor $G_{\mu\nu}$, that is

$$\nabla^\mu \mathcal{G}_{\mu\nu} = 0 \tag{58}$$

which further implies

$$\nabla^\mu T_{\mu\nu} = 0. \tag{59}$$

The above leads to the conclusion that the covariant conservation law holds for $f(R)$ theories of gravity in general, and may help in finding a more generalized second Bianchi identity. However, from what is known in the literature (for example in[32, 36]) about the consequence of the covariant conservation law is a peculiar identity on the function $f'(R)$, given by

$$(\Box \nabla_\nu - \nabla_\nu \Box) f' = R_{\mu\nu} \nabla^\mu f' \tag{60}$$

which is similar to the appearance of the Riemann curvature tensor due to covariant derivative of a vector field not commuting, implying curvature or non-flatness of the space-time. However, the above commuting relation is on a scalar field, implying that some unconventional geometry might be at large here.

3. Equations of motion from the covariant conservation law

References 22 and 37 showed that it is possible to obtain the post Newtonian sequence of solutions for beyond the weak field scenario, that is when the post Newtonian parameter squared ϵ^2 is proportional to the compactness (or equivalently, the potential at the surface of an ultra-compact object like Neutron stars and small black holes being proportional to the kinetic energy of either bodies). To be precise, in non-geometrized units when

$$\epsilon^2 \sim \frac{GM}{c^2 a} \tag{61}$$

where M and a are the total mass and radius of the compact object. In order that strong surface gravity (post Minkowskian) can be incorporated within the post Newtonian (relativistic) framework, a series of coordinate transformations can be made that requires the integration of wave equations like (16) or (47) and (52) to be performed in the so-called *body-zone coordinate system*, while not worrying about the effects of strong internal gravity.

In order to maintain the compactness of the body to unity at all times, some temporal+spatial scalings are made, with the temporal scaling defining a proper time s (τ in[37]) given by

$$s = \epsilon t \tag{62}$$

where t is the coordinate time of the inertial observer. Under the above transformation, the Minkowski metric and the corresponding metric determinant scale as follows

$$\eta_{\mu\nu} = diag\left(\epsilon^{-2}, -1, -1, -1\right) \tag{63}$$

$$-\det(\eta_{\mu\nu}) = \epsilon^{-2} \tag{64}$$

which is singular for $\epsilon \to 0$. The spatial scalings that are going to be used for the integration in the body zone of Eq. (47) are given by

$$X_L^i \equiv \frac{x^i - z_L^i(s)}{\epsilon^2}. \tag{65}$$

The scalings in Eq. (62) and (65) lead to any rank two tensor, or in our case, the energy-momentum-stress density tensor, transforming as

$$T_L^{ss} = \epsilon^2 T^{tt} \sim \mathcal{O}(\epsilon^{-2}) \tag{66}$$

$$T_L^{si'} = \epsilon^{-1} T_L^{ti} \sim \mathcal{O}(\epsilon^{-5}) \tag{67}$$

$$T_L^{i'j'} = \epsilon^{-4} T_L^{ij} \sim \mathcal{O}(\epsilon^{-8}), \tag{68}$$

with the un-primed coordinates representing the unscaled coordinates. Now the above scalings, i.e. Eqs. (62)-(65), are made in a coordinate system that is stationary with respect to the origin or the center of mass of the $L-th$ compact body, denoted by an external observer with the position 3-vector $z_L^i(s)$, and the 3-velocity v_L^i defined as

$$v_L^i = \frac{dz_L^i(s)}{ds}. \tag{69}$$

Hence the next (and final) transformation requires the definition of a co-moving frame (but not co-rotating, since boost and rotation in the wrong order may lead to unnecessary Thomas precession), moving along an ultra compact object whose spin can be ignored. The energy-momentum-stress density tensor of just the matter content of the compact object transforms from an inertial frame to the near-zone or the co-moving frame as follows

$$T_L^{ss} = T_L^{ss} \tag{70}$$

$$T_L^{si} = \epsilon^2 T_L^{si'} + v_L^i T_L^{ss} \tag{71}$$

$$T_L^{ij} = \epsilon^4 T_L^{i'j'} + 2\epsilon^2 v_L^{(i} T_L^{j')s} + v_L^i v_L^j T_L^{ss}. \tag{72}$$

Then at the leading order the post Newtonian solutions for both GR and $f(R)$ theories of gravity, as seen by the inertial observer, are given by

$$\mathfrak{h}_\mathcal{B}^{ss} = 4\epsilon^4 \sum_{L=1,2} \left(\frac{P_L^s}{r_L} + \epsilon^2 \frac{D_L^k r_L^k}{r_L^3} \right) + \mathcal{O}(\epsilon^8) \tag{73}$$

$$\mathfrak{h}_\mathcal{B}^{si} = 4\epsilon^4 \sum_{L=1,2} \left(\frac{P_L^i}{r_L} + \epsilon^2 \frac{J_L^{ki} r_L^k}{r_L^3} \right) + \mathcal{O}(\epsilon^8) \tag{74}$$

$$\mathfrak{h}_\mathcal{B}^{ij} = 4\epsilon^2 \sum_{L=1,2} \left(\frac{Z_L^{ij}}{r_L} + \epsilon^2 \frac{Z_L^{kij} r_L^k}{r_L^3} \right) + \mathcal{O}(\epsilon^6) \tag{75}$$

In the current formalism, the above components of the tensor potential are sufficient to obtain equations of motion of the two sources till the first PN order. The monopole and dipole moments, respectively, of various components of $\Lambda^{\mu\nu}$ (or $\tilde{\Lambda}^{\mu\nu}$) are defined as follows

$$P_L^s = \lim_{\epsilon \to 0} \int_{\mathcal{B}_L} d^3 X_L \, \Lambda^{ss} \tag{76}$$

$$P_L^i = \lim_{\epsilon \to 0} \int_{\mathcal{B}_L} d^3 X_L \, \Lambda^{si} \tag{77}$$

$$Z_L^{ij} = \lim_{\epsilon \to 0} \int_{\mathcal{B}_L} d^3 X_L \, \Lambda^{ij} \tag{78}$$

$$D_L^i = \lim_{\epsilon \to 0} \int_{\mathcal{B}_L} d^3 X_L \, \Lambda^{ss} X_L^i \tag{79}$$

$$J_L^{ij} = \lim_{\epsilon \to 0} \int_{\mathcal{B}_L} d^3 X_L \, \Lambda^{si} X_L^j \tag{80}$$

$$Z_L^{ijk} = \lim_{\epsilon \to 0} \int_{\mathcal{B}_L} d^3 X_L \, \Lambda^{ij} X_L^k \tag{81}$$

where $\mathcal{B}_L$ implies the body zone/co-moving+scaled coordinate system of the $L-th$ body zone.

One defines a 4-momentum, by putting together the scalar in Eq. (76) and the 3-vector in Eq. (77), as[22,37–39]

$$P_L^\mu (s) = \epsilon^2 \int_{\mathcal{B}_L} d^3 X_L \, \Lambda^{s\mu} \tag{82}$$

which along with the conservation law (20) or (51), leads to the following 4-force or the 4-momentum evolution formula[22,37,38]

$$\frac{dP_L^\mu}{ds} = -\epsilon^{-4} \oint_{\partial \mathcal{B}_L} dS_k \, \Lambda^{k\mu} + \epsilon^{-4} v_L^k \oint_{\partial \mathcal{B}_L} dS_k \, \Lambda^{s\mu}. \tag{83}$$

When one defines the bare quasi-local mass of the body zone L to be Eq. (76), the 3-momentum to 3-velocity relation is given at the leading order by

$$P_L^i = P_L^s v_L^i + Q_L^i + \mathcal{O}\left(\epsilon^2\right) \tag{84}$$

$$Q_L^i = \epsilon^{-4} \oint_{\partial \mathcal{B}_L} dS_k \left(\Lambda^{sk} - v_L^k \Lambda^{ss}\right) X_L^i. \tag{85}$$

By choosing the origin of the coordinate system to be the center of mass of the body zone L (which is a choice that has already been made), Q_L^i can be shown to vanish at the leading (Newtonian) order, that is $\mathcal{O}(1)$. Therefore, one obtains the 3-velocity evolution relation (or the 3-force on the body zone L) as

$$P_L^s \frac{dv_L^i}{ds} = -\epsilon^{-4} \oint_{\partial \mathcal{B}_L} dS_k \, \Lambda^{ki} + \epsilon^{-4} v_L^k \oint_{\partial \mathcal{B}_L} dS_k \, \Lambda^{si} + \epsilon^{-4} v_L^i \left(\oint_{\partial \mathcal{B}_L} dS_k \, \Lambda^{ks}\right.$$
$$\left. - v_L^k \oint_{\partial \mathcal{B}_L} dS_k \, \Lambda^{ss}\right) + \mathcal{O}\left(\epsilon^2\right). \tag{86}$$

All of the relations in this section (as mentioned along the way) holds both for GR and $f(R)$ theories of gravity, and can be utilized to obtain the 2-body equations of motion of both theories, simply owing to the fact that the second Bianchi identity (or its generalization) holds for both theories of gravity. In GR for example, the equations of motion till 1 PN or $\mathcal{O}(\epsilon^2)$ of Eq. (86) for one of the bodies (say body zone 1) is given by

$$M_1 \frac{dv_1^i}{ds} = -\frac{M_1 M_2}{r_{12}^2} n^i + \epsilon^2 \frac{M_1 M_2}{r_{12}^2} \left[\left(-v_1^2 - 2v_2^2 + \frac{3}{2} (\hat{n} \cdot \mathbf{v}_2)^2 + 4 (\mathbf{v}_1 \cdot \mathbf{v}_2) \right) \right.$$
$$\left. + \frac{5 M_1}{r_{12}} + \frac{4 M_2}{r_{12}} \right) n^i + \{4 (\hat{n} \cdot \mathbf{v}_1) - 3 (\hat{n} \cdot \mathbf{v}_2)\} (v_1^i - v_2^i) \right] + \mathcal{O}(\epsilon^4). \tag{87}$$

4. Post Newtonian sequence of solutions and equations of motion for the quadratic deviation to the Einstein-Hilbert action

4.1. *The curious case of the homogeneous solution*

One may be tempted to immediately go for the particular solution of the differential equation (52), that is by solving for the following inhomogeneous problem using the retarded Green's function $G_\gamma \left(x^\mu, x^{\mu'} \right)$

$$\left(\Box + \sqrt{-g} \gamma^2 \right) G_\gamma \left(x^\mu, x^{\mu'} \right) = \delta \left(x^\mu - x^{\mu'} \right). \tag{88}$$

The support of the corresponding integral problem (that is the limit for $x^{\mu'}$ in the Green's function integral) of the above lies in the past light-cone of the event x^μ. However, one must remember that the homogeneous solution of GR leads to the BH solutions. Hence, one must also consider the homogeneous solution of the Klein-Gordon equation, which must be solved simultaneously along with the homogeneous solution of GR.

The homogeneous Klein-Gordon equation of the current theory under study, under the transformation (62), has an ϵ dependence given as follows

$$\Box \mathfrak{R}_{hom} + \frac{\gamma^2}{\epsilon} \mathfrak{R}_{hom} = 0. \tag{89}$$

While the radiative solutions of the above, under the choice of no-incoming scalar radiation from past null infinity, can be put to zero, the time independent part of the homogeneous solution cannot be ignored. The time independent differential equation is given by

$$\nabla \mathfrak{R}_{hom} - \frac{\gamma^2}{\epsilon} \mathfrak{R}_{hom} = 0 \tag{90}$$

where ∇ is the Laplace operator in Minkowski space-time. In spherical symmetry, for example, the LHS of Eq. (90) is given by

$$\frac{1}{r^2} \left[r^2 \, (\mathfrak{R}_{hom})_{,r} \right]_{,r} - \frac{\gamma^2}{\epsilon} \mathfrak{R}_{hom} = 0 \qquad (91)$$

which has a solution which is both regular at $r = 0$ and $r = \infty$, and is given by

$$\mathfrak{R}_{hom} = \frac{C \, e^{-\frac{\gamma r}{\sqrt{\epsilon}}}}{r} \qquad (92)$$

where C is a real constant of integration yet to be fixed. It is to be noted that the homogeneous solution, which may be part of an extended homogeneous solution of the combined scalar+tensor theory under study (like the Schwarzschild and Kerr solutions of GR), for vanishing post Newtonian or post Minkowskian parameter ϵ, leads to an infinite mass of the scalar field. Which also implies for low energies, the Ricci scalar or the Ricci scalar density considered here is practically un-excitable.

However, it is interesting to look at the effect of $\mathfrak{R}$ on the tensor wave equation (39), and how it modifies the Newtonian order solution, or more specifically, the Newtonian potential. The time-time component of the conformally transformed metric density deviation satisfies the flat-space wave equation with a source, following Eq. (47)

$$\Box \tilde{\mathfrak{h}}^{tt} = 16 \, \pi \, (-g) \, T^{tt} \, (1 - \epsilon \, f'' \, \mathfrak{R}) \qquad (93)$$

where the leading order, or only the terms in Eq. (48) that are proportional to the classical or matter energy-momentum-stress density tensor were used, along with Eq. (64). The above can be solved by using the retarded Green's function for the massless wave operator, with $\tilde{\mathfrak{h}}^{ss}$ given by the body zone integral

$$\tilde{\mathfrak{h}}^{ss} = 4 \, \epsilon^4 \sum_{L=1,2} \int_{\mathcal{B}_L} d^3 X_L \, \frac{T^{ss} \, (1 - \epsilon \, f'' \, \mathfrak{R})}{|Z_L^i - \epsilon^2 \, X_L^i|} \qquad (94)$$

Eq. (64) and (66) was used to obtain the above from Eq. (93). The first integral, and its ϵ expansion of the series is given in Eq. (73), and is the usual Newtonian potential. However, a more curious thing occurs when one considers the extra term coming due to the quadratic modification to the gravitational action

$$\tilde{\mathfrak{h}}^{ss}_{extra} = -4 \, \epsilon^5 \, f'' \sum_{L=1,2} \int_{\mathcal{B}_L} d^3 X_L \, \frac{T^{ss} \, \mathfrak{R}_{hom}}{|Z_L^i - \epsilon^2 \, X_L^i|}. \qquad (95)$$

Considering now the particular form of the homogeneous Ricci density (92), one obtains the following integral using the scaled coordinate (65)

$$\tilde{\mathfrak{h}}^{ss}_{extra} = -4 \, \epsilon^3 \, f'' \sum_{L=1,2} C_L \int_{\mathcal{B}_L} d^3 X_L \, \frac{T^{ss}}{|Z_L^i(s) - \epsilon^2 \, X_L^i| \, |X_L^i|} \, e^{-\gamma \, \epsilon^{\frac{3}{2}} \, |X_L^i|} \qquad (96)$$

which seems to preceed the order at which the gothic metric deviation first appears, that is at $\mathcal{O}(\epsilon^3)$ compared to $\mathcal{O}(\epsilon^4)$. However, expanding the extra term about $\epsilon \to 0$ leads to the following

$$\tilde{\mathfrak{h}}^{ss}_{extra} = -4\,\epsilon^3\,f'' \sum_{L=1,2} \frac{C_L}{|Z^i_L|} \int_{\mathcal{B}_L} d^3 X_L \frac{T^{ss}}{|X^i_L|} \tag{97}$$

$$\tilde{\mathfrak{h}}^{ss}_{extra} = -4\,\epsilon^3\,f'' \sum_{L=1,2} \frac{C_L\,N_L}{|X^i_L|} \tag{98}$$

which is a Newtonian potential like term with negative one multipole moment of the source, denoted by N_L. Therefore, the modified leading order metric deviation $\tilde{\mathfrak{h}}^{ss}$ can be written in the following form

$$\tilde{\mathfrak{h}}^{ss} = 4\,\epsilon^4 \sum_{L=1,2} \left[\frac{\tilde{P}^s_L}{|Z^i_L|} + \mathcal{O}(\epsilon^2) \right] \tag{99}$$

$$\tilde{P}^s_L = P^s_L - \lim_{\epsilon \to 0} \frac{f''\,C_L}{\epsilon} \int_{\mathcal{B}_L} d^3 X_L \frac{T^{ss}}{|X^i_L|} \tag{100}$$

where P^s_L was defined in Eq. (76). It is important to note that while the integral in the second term of the square bracket of the above has a well defined limit for $\epsilon \to 0$, the coefficient multiplying it does not. In fact, due to the ϵ^{-1} nature of the coefficient, the modified mass-energy definition blows up at the $\epsilon \to 0$ limit, leading to the following conclusion

$$C_L = 0, \tag{101}$$

implying that the homogeneous Ricci scalar does not modify the tensor deviation density at all.

4.2. Deviation from the general relativistic equations of motion

The leading order Ricci scalar density deviation occurs at $\mathcal{O}(\epsilon^4)$, and is given by the following

$$_{(4)}\mathfrak{R}_{part} \equiv {}_{(4)}\mathfrak{R} = -8\,\pi\,\gamma^2\,\epsilon^4\,\frac{M_L\,e^{-\frac{\gamma|Z^i_L|}{\sqrt{\epsilon}}}}{|Z^i_L|} \tag{102}$$

whose form is the same as the now extinct homogeneous solution, but instead of the unknown constant, there is just the mass coming as a parameter, as in the definition of Eq. (76). The only unknown in the above equation is the inverse length scale γ, which was related to the coefficient of the quadratic deviation of the GR action in Eq. (53). Derivation of the above has been given in Appendix A.

In GR, the non-vanishing and body zone independent terms in the surface integrals of Eq. (86) lead to the 3-force at different PN orders, and has been well documented in PN literature, for example.[40,41] However, in this study only the leading order modification to the general relativistic equations of motion due to the quadratic deviation to the GR action will be quoted. Such a modification can be found by using the modified conservation law (51) along with the definitions of (83) and (86) with $\Lambda^{\mu\nu}$ replaced by $\tilde{\Lambda}^{\mu\nu}$. In Eq. (86), various components of the modified net energy-momentum-stress density tensor $\tilde{\Lambda}^{\mu\nu}$ will appear as integrand of the surface integrals. However, the components that have a non-vanishing and *body zone boundary radius* independent contribution to the surface integrals of Eq. (86), was found to be coming from the space-space component of $t^{\mu\nu}_{eff}$, or

$$t^{ij}_{eff} = \frac{\epsilon^4}{192\pi\gamma^4}\left[2\left(\eta^{ik}\eta^{jl}+\eta^{il}\eta^{jk}-\eta^{ij}\eta^{kl}\right)\mathfrak{R}\partial_k\mathfrak{R}\partial_l\tilde{\mathfrak{h}}\right.$$
$$\left.+\left(\eta^{ik}\eta^{jl}-\frac{1}{2}\eta^{ij}\eta^{kl}\right)\left(4\partial_k\mathfrak{R}\partial_l\mathfrak{R}+\mathfrak{R}^2\partial_k\tilde{\mathfrak{h}}\partial_l\tilde{\mathfrak{h}}\right)\right] \quad (103)$$

where Eq. (64) was used to replace the metric determinant, or $\frac{1}{(-g)^2}$ multiplying the quadratic f'' part of $t^{\mu\nu}_{eff}$ in Eq. (49), which appear as ϵ^4 above.

Eq. (103) has three different ϵ orders worth of terms inside the square bracket. When one utilizes the scalings of the leading order deviation of either $\tilde{\mathfrak{h}}$ or $\mathfrak{R}$, one notices that $\tilde{\mathfrak{h}} \sim \epsilon^2$ and $\mathfrak{R} \sim \epsilon^4$, following Eqs. (63), (73)-(75), and (102). From the number of times either $\tilde{\mathfrak{h}}$ and $\mathfrak{R}$ appear inside the square bracket in each product of fields, the first term scale as ϵ^{10}, the second as ϵ^8, and the last one as ϵ^{12}. Since the overall factor of ϵ^4 cancels away due to ϵ^{-4} multiplying each surface integral of Eq. (86), the three terms inside the square brackets of Eq. (103) are 5th, 4th, and 6th PN effects on the two body equations of motion. However, not all of them survive the surface integral. Only the last term in the square bracket survives and is a 6th PN effect with the modification to the 3-force on the Lth body given as follows

$$M_L \frac{dv^i_L}{ds} = F^i_{N+PN,GR} - \epsilon^{12}\frac{32\pi M_L M^3_{L'}}{9r^4_{12}}e^{-\frac{2\gamma r_{12}}{\sqrt{\epsilon}}}n^i \quad (104)$$

where M_L is the quasi-local mass enclosed by the Lth body zone boundary, and $M_{L'}$ is the quasi-local mass enclosed by the partner object's body zone boundary in the two-body system. r_{12} is the distance between the origin of the two body zones, whereas n^i is a unit vector pointing from the origin of body zone L to the origin of body zone L'. The negative sign on the modified/extra force imply that the direction of the force is antiparallel to n^i, which is then a repulsive modification to the usual attractive Newtonian and PN forces indicated by the first term in the RHS of the above, that is $F^i_{N+PN,GR}$. Compared to other works in literature on $f(R)$ theories that calculate the conserved potential (or the force) from modifications to the time-time component of the metric tensor, the above has an inverse quartic distance falloff (along with the Yukawa exponential falloff) at 6 PN order, which is an extremely tiny modification to the general relativistic PN equations of motion at the very high energy scales of ultra-compact two-body interactions.

5. Discussions and conclusion

In the current study a particular redefinition of the standard gothic metric was utilized to drastically simplify the field equations of general $f(R)$ theories of gravity. Once the identification was made that $f'(R)$ acts like a massive scalar field, a fourth order system was reduced to two second order system of differential equations. The field equations were framed in the densitized approach following the methods of Landau and Lifshitz, and their redefinition of the field equations of GR. The use of conformal densities to define Landau-Lifshitz like field equations were used in scalar-tensor theories, for example in.[42,43] In this study, it is shown that the redefinition to a conformal density greatly suppresses the actual effect of an extra massive scalar degree of freedom on orbital dynamics.

Following the definition of a tensor density, a scalar density $\mathfrak{R}$, corresponding to the massive scalar degree of freedom was defined, which relates to the trace of the energy-momentum-stress density tensor in the same manner as the conformal metric tensor density relates to the energy-momentum-stress density tensor in the Landau-Lifshitz like tensor field equations of $f(R)$ theories. The differential equation that is satisfied by $\mathfrak{R}$ throws up a static solution that makes the mass-energy definition at the Newtonian/leading order diverge, leading to its removal from further usage. At the leading order, the particular/inhomogeneous $\mathfrak{R}$ is seen to be static as well, and has the Yukawa potential form with a cutoff/inverse length scale that is related to the coefficient of the quadratic modification (with (length)^2 dimensions) to the Einstein-Hilbert action.

However, just finding out the particular form of the leading order deviation of $\mathfrak{R}$ is quite useless, unless one finds its corresponding effect on the conformal tensor density field equations, and then, on the PN equations of motion. The leading order $\mathfrak{R}$ appears as an effective source tensor that drives the behavior of $\tilde{\mathfrak{h}}^{\mu\nu}$, as well as the evolutionary dynamics of the quasi-local four-momentum (83), and correspondingly, the velocity evolution equations (86) through surface integrals of various components of the energy-momentum-stress density tensor. It was found in Eq. (104) that the modification to the GR PN equations of motion, due to quadratic modification at the action level, appear at the sixth PN order. On top of that, the force has an inverse fourth powered dependence on the distance along with a Yukawa falloff, which is a very tiny modification to GR equations of motion. The modified force is dependent on the masses enclosed by the body zone boundaries, and the modification to the equations of motion of one of the objects is independent of the mass enclosed in that object's body zone boundary - implying that the equivalence principle (as far as it holds in the GR PN scheme) is not affected by the quadratic modification to GR. The modified force is also conservative, and hence will not be adding to any extra dissipation (other than GR) of the orbital energy of the binary system, although it might lead to very tiny modifications to the phase evolution of the binary, as encoded in the gravitational waves. More importantly, the force is repulsive, compared to the PN forces that appear on perturbing GR about Minkowski space-times. So in the course of the binary evolution, at length scales comparable to γ^{-1}, if the two objects have not merged into a single object already, they will feel a repulsive force that will compete with the attractive GR PN forces coming out of the *superpotentials* of the PN expansion of GR, which are themselves progressively short ranged. Putting a constraint on the new length scale γ^{-1} is beyond the scope of this study, mostly because the author is not aware of sixth PN equations of motion appearing in the literature.

Appendix A

The net solution to the Klein-Gordon problem (52) with the boundary condition choice of no incoming scalar radiation from past null Minkowskian infinity is given as follows

$$\Re(x^\mu) = -8\pi\gamma^2 \epsilon^{-2} \int d^4y\, G_{\tilde{\gamma}}(x^\mu, y^\mu)\, T_m(y^\mu) \tag{A.1}$$

$$\tilde{\gamma}^2 \equiv \frac{\gamma^2}{\epsilon} \tag{A.2}$$

where the factor of ϵ^{-2} arises because the metric determinant $(-g)$ multiplying the RHS of Eq. (52), under the transformation (62), scale as ϵ^{-2}, as seen after Eq. (63). $G_{\tilde{\gamma}}(x^\mu, y^\mu)$ is the retarded Green's function of the Klein-Gordon equation, as was given in[32] with the $(+,-,-,-)$ metric signature as

$$G_{\tilde{\gamma}}(t, q; x^i, y^i) = \int_{-\infty,\tilde{\gamma}}^{-\tilde{\gamma},\infty} \frac{d\omega}{2\pi} e^{-i\omega(t-q)} \frac{e^{i\sqrt{\omega^2-\tilde{\gamma}^2}\,|x^i-y^i|}}{4\pi\,|x^i-y^i|}$$
$$+ \int_{-\tilde{\gamma}}^{\tilde{\gamma}} \frac{d\omega}{2\pi} e^{-i\omega(t-q)} \frac{e^{-\sqrt{\tilde{\gamma}^2-\omega^2}\,|x^i-y^i|}}{4\pi\,|x^i-y^i|}. \tag{A.3}$$

The notation $\int_{-\infty,\tilde{\gamma}}^{-\tilde{\gamma},\infty}$ involve two integrals, one from $-\infty$ to $-\tilde{\gamma}$, and the other from $\tilde{\gamma}$ to ∞. It is to be noted that the three integrals whose domains encompass all of ω space must be evaluated simultaneously in order for the solution to converge. $T_m(q, y^i)$, the trace of the classical matter energy-momentum tensor, which being a scalar, does not transform under any of the coordinate scalings.

Due to the the coordinate scalings in Eq. (65), the infinitesimal 4-volume element d^4y transform from the asymptotic observer's frame to either of the body zones $\mathscr{B}_L$ in the following manner

$$d^4y \equiv dt \wedge d^3y \tag{A.4}$$
$$\to \epsilon^{-1} ds \wedge \epsilon^6\, d^3X_L \tag{A.5}$$

where $\wedge$ denotes the wedge product between 1-form dt and 3-form d^3y. In the current operational context $\wedge$ is effectively scalar multiplication.

Substituting Eq. (A.3) in Eq. (A.1), and transforming into the body zone coordinates by substituting Eq. (A.5) as the infinitesimal covariant volume element in Eq. (A.1), one obtains the following integral for the particular solution $\mathfrak{R}_{part}$ for the inhomogeneous Klein-Gordon equation

$$\mathfrak{R}_{part}\left(t,\, x^i\right) = -\epsilon^3\, 8\pi\gamma^2 \int_{-\infty}^{\infty} ds' \int_{\mathscr{B}_L} d^3 X_L \int_{-\infty,\tilde{\gamma}}^{-\tilde{\gamma},\infty} \frac{d\omega}{2\pi}\, e^{-i\omega\left(t-s'/\epsilon\right)}$$

$$\times\; \frac{e^{i\sqrt{\omega^2-\tilde{\gamma}^2}\,\left|Z_L^i-\epsilon^2 X_L^i\right|}}{4\pi\,\left|Z_L^i-\epsilon^2 X_L^i\right|}\, \left[\epsilon^4 T_m\left(s'/\epsilon,\, X_L^i\right)\right]$$

$$-\,\epsilon^3\, 8\pi\gamma^2 \int_{-\infty}^{\infty} ds' \int_{\mathscr{B}_L} d^3 X_L \int_{-\tilde{\gamma}}^{\tilde{\gamma}} \frac{d\omega}{2\pi}\, e^{-i\omega\left(t-s'/\epsilon\right)}$$

$$\times\; \frac{e^{-\sqrt{\tilde{\gamma}^2-\omega^2}\,\left|Z_L^i-\epsilon^2 X_L^i\right|}}{4\pi\,\left|Z_L^i-\epsilon^2 X_L^i\right|}\, \left[\epsilon^4 T_m\left(s'/\epsilon,\, X_L^i\right)\right]. \qquad\text{(A.6)}$$

In the body zones that surround each of the objects, the energy-momentum tensor of classical matter $\left(T_{\mathscr{B}_L} = \lim_{\epsilon\to 0} \epsilon^4 T_m\right)$ will be assumed to have a quasi-stationary/adiabatic initial condition for solving the relaxed system of equations, in the absence of any other time dependent driving force inside the compact object, and is given by

$$T_{\mathscr{B}_L}\left(X^i\right) = \sum_{n=-\infty}^{\infty} \mathfrak{T}_n\left(\left|X_L^i\right|,\, X_L^\theta\right) e^{in\mathscr{X}} \qquad\text{(A.7)}$$

$$\mathscr{X}\left(s/\epsilon,\, X_L^\phi\right) \equiv \mathscr{X} = X_L^\phi - \Omega s/\epsilon + \phi_0 \qquad\text{(A.8)}$$

where an axial+time symmetry was assumed for the initial condition, such that the time dependence of the source body in the body zone coordinate system repeats after every $T = \frac{2\pi}{\Omega}$, with a constant phase parameter ϕ_0. The weighing factors $\mathfrak{T}_n$ are coefficients in the series expansion of the trace T_m (or $T_{\mathscr{B}_L}$) using stationary functions $e^{in\mathscr{X}}$, and are functions of the radial and azimuthal coordinates. Eq. (A.7) physically implies that the variations in the energy-momentum tensor sourcing $\mathfrak{R}$ in the body zone of the first object is purely generated by the effect of the motion of the second object around it. The body zone coordinates $\left(X_L^i\right)$ were defined in Eq. (65), in which $\left|X_L^i\right|$ is the distance from the center of mass of the body L to any point in the body zone coordinates, as viewed in the respective body zones. The choice in Eq. (A.7) has a simplifying effect on the subsequent calculations and is justified by the adiabatic and stationarity in the co-moving frame approximations, as found in the literature on PN expansions.

Assuming quasi-periodicity for the source tensor, as in Eq. (A.7), one can substitute it into Eq. (A.6), to obtain

$$\mathfrak{R}_{part}\left(t, x^i\right) = -\epsilon^3 \frac{8\pi\gamma^2}{2\pi} \sum_{n=-\infty}^{\infty} \int_{\mathcal{B}_L} d^3 X_L \left(\int_{-\infty,\tilde{\gamma}}^{-\tilde{\gamma},\infty} d\omega\, e^{-i\omega t}\right) e^{in\left(X_L^\phi + \phi_0\right)}$$

$$\times \frac{e^{i\sqrt{\omega^2-\tilde{\gamma}^2}\left|Z_L^i - \epsilon^2 X_L^i\right|}}{4\pi \left|Z_L^i - \epsilon^2 X_L^i\right|} \mathfrak{T}_n\left(\left|X_L^i\right|, X_L^\theta\right) \int_{-\infty}^{\infty} ds'\, e^{i(\omega-n\Omega) s'/\epsilon}$$

$$- \epsilon^3 \frac{8\pi\gamma^2}{2\pi} \sum_{n=-\infty}^{\infty} \int_{\mathcal{B}_L} d^3 X_L \left(\int_{-\tilde{\gamma}}^{\tilde{\gamma}} d\omega\, e^{-i\omega t}\right) e^{in\left(X_L^\phi + \phi_0\right)}$$

$$\times \frac{e^{-\sqrt{\tilde{\gamma}^2-\omega^2}\left|Z_L^i - \epsilon^2 X_L^i\right|}}{4\pi \left|Z_L^i - \epsilon^2 X_L^i\right|} \mathfrak{T}_n\left(\left|X_L^i\right|, X_L^\theta\right) \int_{-\infty}^{\infty} ds'\, e^{i(\omega-n\Omega) s'/\epsilon}. \tag{A.9}$$

Transforming

$$s' \to \epsilon s \tag{A.10}$$

and using the integral representation of the delta function,

$$\int_{-\infty}^{\infty} e^{ik(x-x')} dk = 2\pi \delta(x-x'), \tag{A.11}$$

one obtains

$$\mathfrak{R}_{part}\left(t, x^i\right) = -\epsilon^4\, 8\pi\gamma^2 \sum_{n=-\infty}^{\infty} \int_{\mathcal{B}_L} d^3 X_L \frac{e^{i\sqrt{n^2\Omega^2-\tilde{\gamma}^2}\left|Z_L^i - \epsilon^2 X_L^i\right|}}{4\pi \left|Z_L^i - \epsilon^2 X_L^i\right|}$$

$$\times \mathfrak{T}_n\left(\left|X_L^i\right|, X_L^\theta\right) \times e^{-in\left(\Omega t - X_L^\phi - \phi_0\right)} \tag{A.12}$$

$$-\epsilon^4\, 8\pi\gamma^2 \sum_{n=-\infty}^{\infty} \int_{\mathcal{B}_L} d^3 X_L \frac{e^{-\sqrt{\tilde{\gamma}^2-n^2\Omega^2}\left|Z_L^i - \epsilon^2 X_L^i\right|}}{4\pi \left|Z_L^i - \epsilon^2 X_L^i\right|}$$

$$\times \mathfrak{T}_n\left(\left|X_L^i\right|, X_L^\theta\right) e^{-in\left(\Omega t - X_L^\phi - \phi_0\right)}. \tag{A.13}$$

The Green's function (A.3) can be written as an infinite sum of spherical harmonic functions, that are weighed by functions of the radial coordinates $\left|Z_L^i\right|$ and $\left|X_L^i\right|$, in the following way for $\left|Z_L^i\right| > \left|X_L^i\right|$

$$\frac{e^{ik\left|X^i - Z^i\right|}}{4\pi \left|X^i - Z^i\right|} = ik \sum_{\ell,m} j_\ell\left(k\left|X^i\right|\right) h_\ell^{(1)}\left(k\left|Z^i\right|\right) Y_{\ell m}^*\left(X^\theta, X^\phi\right) Y_{\ell m}\left(Z^\theta, Z^\phi\right) \tag{A.14}$$

$$\frac{e^{-k\left|X^i - Z^i\right|}}{4\pi \left|X^i - Z^i\right|} = \sum_{\ell,m} \frac{I_{\ell+\frac{1}{2}}\left(k\left|X^i\right|\right) K_{\ell+\frac{1}{2}}\left(k\left|Z^i\right|\right)}{\sqrt{\left|X^i\right|\left|Z^i\right|}} Y_{\ell m}^*\left(X^\theta, X^\phi\right) Y_{\ell m}\left(Z^\theta, Z^\phi\right)$$

$$Z_L^i \equiv \frac{x^i - z_L^i(s)}{\epsilon^2}; \quad L = 1, 2. \tag{A.15}$$

The various functions appearing above are as follows

- j_ℓ: Spherical Bessel function of first kind.
- $h_\ell^{(1)}$: Spherical Bessel function of third kind.
- $I_{\ell+\frac{1}{2}}$: Modified Bessel function of the first kind.
- $K_{\ell+\frac{1}{2}}$: Modified Bessel function of the second kind.
- $Y_{\ell m}, Y_{\ell m}^*$: Spherical harmonic functions and their complex conjugates.

After using Eqs. (A.14) and (A.15) in the above, one obtains for $|Z_L^i| > |X_L^i|$

$$\mathfrak{R}_{part}(t, x^i) = -\epsilon^4 \, 8\pi i \gamma^2 \sum_{n,\ell,m}^{|n| > \lfloor\frac{\tilde{\gamma}}{\Omega}\rfloor} \sqrt{n^2 \Omega^2 - \tilde{\gamma}^2} \int_{\mathcal{B}_L} d^3 X_L \, e^{in(X_L^\phi + \phi_0 - \Omega t)}$$

$$\times \; j_\ell\left(\epsilon^2 \sqrt{n^2 \Omega^2 - \tilde{\gamma}^2} \, |X_L^i|\right) h_\ell^{(1)}\left(\sqrt{n^2 \Omega^2 - \tilde{\gamma}^2} \, |Z^i|\right)$$

$$\times \; Y_{\ell m}^*\left(X_L^\theta, X_L^\phi\right) Y_{\ell m}\left(Z^\theta, Z^\phi\right) \mathfrak{I}_n\left(|X_L^i|, X_L^\theta\right)$$

$$-\epsilon^3 \; 8\pi\gamma^2 \sum_{n,\ell,m}^{|n| < \lfloor\frac{\tilde{\gamma}}{\Omega}\rfloor} \int_{\mathcal{B}_L} d^3 X_L \, e^{in(X_L^\phi + \phi_0 - \Omega t)}$$

$$\times \; \frac{I_{\ell+\frac{1}{2}}\left(\epsilon^2 \sqrt{\tilde{\gamma}^2 - n^2 \Omega^2} \, |X_L^i|\right) K_{\ell+\frac{1}{2}}\left(\sqrt{\tilde{\gamma}^2 - n^2 \Omega^2} \, |Z^i|\right)}{\sqrt{|X_L^i|} \; \sqrt{|Z^i|}}$$

$$\times \; Y_{\ell m}^*\left(X_L^\theta, X_L^\phi\right) Y_{\ell m}\left(Z^\theta, Z^\phi\right) \mathfrak{I}_n\left(|X_L^i|, X_L^\theta\right) \quad (A.16)$$

one can substitute the following properties of spherical harmonic functions in Eq. (A.16)

$$Y_{\ell m}^* = (-1)^m Y_{\ell -m} \quad (A.17)$$

$$Y_{\ell -m} = N_{\ell -m} P_{\ell -m}\left(\cos X_L^\theta\right) e^{-imX^\phi} \quad (A.18)$$

$$\int_0^{2\pi} dX_L^\phi Y_{\ell m}^* e^{inX^\phi} = 2\pi (-1)^m N_{\ell -m} P_{\ell -m}\left(X_L^\theta\right) \delta_{mn} \quad (A.19)$$

$$N_{\ell m} = (-1)^m \sqrt{\frac{(2\ell+1)(\ell-m)!}{4\pi (\ell+m)!}} \quad (A.20)$$

where $P_{\ell m}\left(X_L^\theta\right)$ are the associated Legendre polynomials and δ_{mn} is the Kronecker delta distribution. Since m takes values between $-\ell$ to ℓ, application of the Kronecker delta leads to the summation on ℓ in the first term of Eq. (A.16) going from the lower integral part of $\frac{\tilde{\gamma}}{\Omega}$ or $\lfloor\frac{\tilde{\gamma}}{\Omega}\rfloor$ to ∞, whereas the second terms' summation range takes ℓ from zero to $\lfloor\frac{\tilde{\gamma}}{\Omega}\rfloor$. The contributions to the particular solution from above the cutoff energy scale $\tilde{\gamma}$ is highly suppressed (especially at lower PN orders) because of the properties of j_ℓ and $h_\ell^{(1)}$ for asymptotically large values of ℓ, and terms in $\mathfrak{R}$ series containing the same can be approximated to zero at the current orders of calculation. Hence one can safely set the first summation in RHS of Eq. (A.16) to zero and consider only the second summation. Hence it is to be noted that the factors that depend on ϵ in the above are only in the arguments of the Bessel function $I_{\ell+\frac{1}{2}}$.

Hence the only relevant factors that explicitly contain ϵ in both the sums in Eq. (A.16), can be expanded about $\epsilon \to 0$ as follows

$$I_{\ell+\frac{1}{2}}\left(\epsilon^2 \Lambda \left|X_L\right|\right) \approx \epsilon^{2\ell+1} \frac{\Lambda^{\frac{2\ell+1}{2}}}{2^{\ell+\frac{1}{2}} \Gamma\left(\ell+\frac{3}{2}\right)} \left|X_L\right|^{\ell+\frac{1}{2}}. \tag{A.21}$$

The approximation of (A.21), when substituted in for the relevant factors of the RHS of Eq. (A.16), leads to the following polynomial series of ϵ about $\epsilon \to 0$

$$\mathfrak{R}_{part}\left(t, x^i\right) \approx -8\pi\gamma^2 \sum_{L,\ell,m}^{\ell=\infty} \epsilon^{2\ell+4} \frac{\left(\tilde{\gamma}^2 - m^2\Omega^2\right)^{\frac{2\ell+1}{4}}}{2^{\ell+\frac{1}{2}} \tilde{\gamma}\left(\ell+\frac{3}{2}\right)}$$

$$\times e^{im(\phi_0 - \Omega t)} \frac{K_{\ell+\frac{1}{2}}\left(\sqrt{\tilde{\gamma}^2 - m^2\Omega^2}\left|Z_L^i\right|\right)}{\sqrt{\left|Z_L^i\right|}} Y_{\ell m}\left(Z_L^\theta, Z_L^\phi\right)$$

$$\times \mathfrak{M}_{L\ell m} \tag{A.22}$$

$$\mathfrak{M}_{L\ell m} = 2\pi (-1)^m N_{\ell-m} \int_{\mathcal{B}_L} \left|X_L^i\right|^{2+\ell} \sin\left(X_L^\theta\right)$$

$$\times P_{\ell-m}\left(\cos X_L^\theta\right) \mathfrak{I}_m\left(\left|X_L^i\right|, X_L^\theta\right) d\left|X_L^i\right| dX_L^\theta. \tag{A.23}$$

From Eq. (A.22), one can immediately notice that the leading order deviation for the particular solution of the Ricci scalar for the Lth body zone comes at $\mathcal{O}\left(\epsilon^4\right)$ for $\ell = 0$ with $\mathfrak{M}_{L00} \equiv M_L$ being the mass monopole, and was found to be

$$_{(4)}\mathfrak{R}_{part} \equiv {}_{(4)}\mathfrak{R} = -8\pi\gamma^2 \epsilon^4 \frac{M_L\, e^{-\frac{\gamma\left|Z_L^i\right|}{\sqrt{\epsilon}}}}{\left|Z_L^i\right|}. \tag{A.24}$$

References

1. A. Einstein, Explanation of the Perihelion Motion of Mercury from the General Theory of Relativity, *Sitzungsber. Preuss. Akad. Wiss. Berlin (Math. Phys.)* **1915**, 831 (1915).
2. C. M. Will, The 1919 measurement of the deflection of light, *Class. Quant. Grav.* **32**, p. 124001 (2015).
3. A. Einstein, Approximative Integration of the Field Equations of Gravitation, *Sitzungsber. Preuss. Akad. Wiss. Phys. Math. Kl*, 688 (1916).
4. B. P. Abbott et al., Observation of Gravitational Waves from a Binary Black Hole Merger, *Phys. Rev. Lett.* **116**, p. 061102 (2016).
5. B. P. Abbott et al., GW151226: Observation of Gravitational Waves from a 22-Solar-Mass Binary Black Hole Coalescence, *Phys. Rev. Lett.* **116**, p. 241103 (2016).
6. B. P. Abbott et al., GW170814: A Three-Detector Observation of Gravitational Waves from a Binary Black Hole Coalescence, *Phys. Rev. Lett.* **119**, p. 141101 (2017).

7. B. P. Abbott *et al.*, First search for nontensorial gravitational waves from known pulsars, *Phys. Rev. Lett.* **120**, p. 031104 (2018).
8. B. P. Abbott *et al.*, GW170104: Observation of a 50-Solar-Mass Binary Black Hole Coalescence at Redshift 0.2, *Phys. Rev. Lett.* **118**, p. 221101 (2017).
9. K. Akiyama *et al.*, First M87 Event Horizon Telescope Results. I. The Shadow of the Supermassive Black Hole, *Astrophys. J. Lett.* **875**, p. L1 (2019).
10. A. Einstein and L. Infeld, On the motion of particles in general relativity theory, *Canadian Journal of Mathematics* **1**, 209 (1949).
11. L. Infeld and A. Schild, On the Motion of Test Particles in General Relativity, *Reviews of Modern Physics* **21**, 408 (July 1949).
12. S. Chandrasekhar, The Post-Newtonian Equations of Hydrodynamics in General Relativity, **142**, p. 1488 (November 1965).
13. S. Chandrasekhar, The Post-Newtonian Effects of General Relativity on the Equilibrium of Uniformly Rotating Bodies. II. The Deformed Figures of the Maclaurin Spheroids, **147**, p. 334 (January 1967).
14. S. Chandrasekhar and Y. Nutku, The Second Post-Newtonian Equations of Hydrodynamics in General Relativity, **158**, p. 55 (October 1969).
15. S. Chandrasekhar, Conservation Laws in General Relativity and in the Post-Newtonian Approximations, **158**, p. 45 (October 1969).
16. S. Chandrasekhar and F. P. Esposito, The 2andonehalf-POST-NEWTONIAN Equations of Hydrodynamics and Radiation Reaction in General Relativity, **160**, p. 153 (April 1970).
17. A. A. Starobinsky, Disappearing cosmological constant in f(r) gravity, *JETP Letters* **86**, 157 (2007).
18. S. Nojiri and S. D. Odintsov, Introduction to modified gravity and gravitational alternative for dark energy, *eConf* **C0602061**, p. 06 (2006).
19. S. Capozziello, A. Stabile and A. Troisi, Newtonian limit off(r)gravity, *Physical Review D* **76** (November 2007).
20. S. Capozziello, C. Corda and M. F. De Laurentis, Massive gravitational waves from f (R) theories of gravity: Potential detection with LISA, *Physics Letters, Section B: Nuclear, Elementary Particle and High-Energy Physics* **669**, 255 (2008).
21. S. Capozziello, A. Stabile and A. Troisi, The post-minkowskian limit of f(r)-gravity, *International Journal of Theoretical Physics* **49**, 1251 (2010).
22. T. Futamase and Y. Itoh, The post-newtonian approximation for relativistic compact binaries, *Living Reviews in Relativity* **10** (2007).
23. L. LANDAU and E. LIFSHITZ, Chapter 11 - the gravitational field equations, in *The Classical Theory of Fields (Fourth Edition)*, eds. L. LANDAU and E. LIFSHITZ, Course of Theoretical Physics, Vol. 2 (Pergamon, Amsterdam, 1975) pp. 259–294, fourth edition edn.
24. L. LANDAU and E. LIFSHITZ, Chapter 12 - the field of gravitating bodies, in *The Classical Theory of Fields (Fourth Edition)*, eds. L. LANDAU and E. LIFSHITZ, Course of Theoretical Physics, Vol. 2 (Pergamon, Amsterdam, 1975) pp. 295–344, fourth edition edn.
25. L. LANDAU and E. LIFSHITZ, Chapter 13 - gravitational waves, in *The Classical Theory of Fields (Fourth Edition)*, eds. L. LANDAU and E. LIFSHITZ, Course of Theoretical Physics, Vol. 2 (Pergamon, Amsterdam, 1975) pp. 345 – 357, fourth edition edn.
26. S. Nojiri and S. D. Odintsov, Unified cosmic history in modified gravity: from F(R) theory to Lorentz non-invariant models, *Phys. Rept.* **505**, 59 (2011).

27. G. Magnano and L. M. Sokolowski, On physical equivalence between nonlinear gravity theories and a general relativistic selfgravitating scalar field, *Phys. Rev. D* **50**, 5039 (1994).
28. S. Chakraborty, S. Pal and A. Saa, Dynamical equivalence of $f(R)$ gravity in Jordan and Einstein frames, *Phys. Rev. D* **99**, p. 024020 (2019).
29. S. Bahamonde, S. D. Odintsov, V. K. Oikonomou and P. V. Tretyakov, Deceleration versus acceleration universe in different frames of $F(R)$ gravity, *Phys. Lett. B* **766**, 225 (2017).
30. G. G. L. Nashed, W. El Hanafy, S. D. Odintsov and V. K. Oikonomou, Thermodynamical correspondence of $f(R)$ gravity in the Jordan and Einstein frames, *Int. J. Mod. Phys. D* **29**, p. 2050090 (2020).
31. T. P. Sotiriou and V. Faraoni, f(R) Theories Of Gravity, *Rev. Mod. Phys.* **82**, 451 (2010).
32. C. P. L. Berry and J. R. Gair, Linearized f(R) gravity: Gravitational radiation and Solar System tests, *Physical Review D - Particles, Fields, Gravitation and Cosmology* **83** (2011).
33. H.-J. Schmidt, The newtonian limit of fourth-order gravity, *Astronomische Nachrichten* **307**, 339.
34. P. Teyssandier, New solutions in linearized r+r2 gravity, *Astronomische Nachrichten* **311**, 209.
35. G. J. Olmo, The gravity lagrangian according to solar system experiments, *Phys. Rev. Lett.* **95**, p. 261102 (Dec 2005).
36. T. Koivisto, Covariant conservation of energy momentum in modified gravities, *Class. Quant. Grav.* **23**, 4289 (2006).
37. T. Futamase, Strong-field point-particle limit and the equations of motion in the binary pulsar, *Phys. Rev. D* **36**, 321 (Jul 1987).
38. Y. Itoh, T. Futamase and H. Asada, Equation of motion for relativistic compact binaries with the strong field point particle limit: Formulation, the first post-newtonian order, and multipole terms, *Phys. Rev. D* **62**, p. 064002 (Jul 2000).
39. D. Giulini, Laue's theorem revisited: Energy–momentum tensors, symmetries, and the habitat of globally conserved quantities, *Int. J. Geom. Meth. Mod. Phys.* **15**, p. 1850182 (2018).
40. Y. Itoh, T. Futamase and H. Asada, Equation of motion for relativistic compact binaries with the strong field point particle limit: The Second and half postNewtonian order, *Phys. Rev. D* **63**, p. 064038 (2001).
41. Y. Itoh, Equation of motion for relativistic compact binaries with the strong field point particle limit: Third postNewtonian order, *Phys. Rev. D* **69**, p. 064018 (2004).
42. S. Mirshekari and C. M. Will, Compact binary systems in scalar-tensor gravity: Equations of motion to 2.5 post-Newtonian order, *Phys. Rev. D* **87**, p. 084070 (2013).
43. S. M. Kopeikin, Post-Newtonian Lagrangian of an N-body System with Arbitrary Mass and Spin Multipoles, *Phys. Rev. D* **102**, p. 024053 (2020).

Alternatives to Λ: Torsion, generalized couplings, and scale invariance

C. J. A. P. Martins

Centro de Astrofísica da Universidade do Porto, and
Instituto de Astrofísica e Ciências do Espaço, Universidade do Porto,
Rua das Estrelas, 4150-762 Porto, Portugal
E-mail: Carlos.Martins@astro.up.pt

C. M. J. Marques

Faculdade de Ciências e Tecnologia, Universidade Nova de Lisboa,
2829-516 Caparica, Portugal, and
Centro de Astrofísica da Universidade do Porto,
Rua das Estrelas, 4150-762 Porto, Portugal

C. B. D. Fernandes, J. S. J. S. Oliveira, D. A. R. Pinheiro and B. A. R. Rocha

Faculdade de Ciências, Universidade do Porto,
Rua do Campo Alegre, 4150-007 Porto, Portugal, and
Centro de Astrofísica da Universidade do Porto,
Rua das Estrelas, 4150-762 Porto, Portugal

We present a comparative analysis of current observational constraints on three recently discussed alternative models for explaining the low-redshift acceleration of the universe: the so-called steady-state torsion model, the generalized coupling model, and the scale invariant model by Maeder (an example of a broader class which we also briefly study). These are compared to the traditional parameterization of Chevallier, Polarski and Linder. Each of the candidate models is studied under two different assumptions: as genuine alternatives to ΛCDM (where a new degree of freedom would be expected to explain the recent acceleration of the universe without any cosmological constant) and as parametric extensions of ΛCDM (where both a cosmological constant and the new mechanism can coexist, and the relative contributions of both are determined by the data). Our comparative analysis suggests that, from a phenomenological point of view, all such models neatly divide into two classes, with different observational consequences.

Keywords: Cosmology; Dark energy; Torsion; Generalized couplings; Scale invariance.

1. Introduction

The observational evidence for the acceleration of the universe shows that our canonical theories of cosmology and particle physics are at least incomplete, and possibly incorrect. Is dark energy a cosmological constant (i.e. vacuum energy)? If the answer is yes, it is ten to some large power times smaller than our Quantum Field Theory based expectations. If the answer is no, then the Einstein Equivalence Principle must be violated. Either way, new physics is out there, waiting to be discovered; we must search for, identify and characterize this new physics. The CosmoESPRESSO team uses the universe as a laboratory to characterize, with precision spectroscopy and other observational, computational and theoretical tools, the behaviour of the gravitational interaction, with the goal of determining what makes the universe accelerate. In what follows we highlight recent contributions of the CosmoESPRESSO team to this fundamental quest.

The search for the physical mechanism underlying the observed low-redshift acceleration of the universe is the most compelling goal of modern fundamental cosmology, and several theoretical possibilities beyond a cosmological constant can be envisaged in principle, each with its specific observational consequences.

Our goal here is to present a comparative study of the observational constraints on three classes of alternative models: the so-called steady-state torsion model[1] of Kranas et al., the generalized coupling model[2] of Feng and Carloni, and the scale invariant model[3] of Maeder; the latter is an example of a broader class of models[4,5] first proposed by Canuto et al., which we also briefly study. As a benchmark we use the traditional phenomenological parameterization of Chevallier, Polarski and Linder (henceforth CPL).[6,7] All models have common parameters (specifically, the matter density parameter, Ω_m) but also some specific ones, and a comparative analysis using a common data set is therefore interesting.

We take three models at face value and phenomenologically constrain them through a standard likelihood analysis using low-redshift background cosmology data. Specifically, we use the recent Pantheon dataset,[8] including its covariance matrix. We also use a compilation of 38 Hubble parameter measurements.[9] Occasionally we will also use a Planck prior[10] on the matter density, $\Omega_m = 0.0315 \pm 0.007$. The value of the he Hubble constant is always marginalized analytically, following the procedure detailed in Ref. 11. The analysis is done on a grid (since we are only dealing with background cosmology, there is no computational need for a full MCMC analysis), and we have explicitly verified that the grid sizes that have been used are sufficiently large for the results presented in the following sections not to be affected by these sizes. Moreover, the following section will also present an explicit validation test of our code for the supernova data. We will work in units where the speed of light is set to $c = 1$.

2. Preamble: The CPL parameterization

In the CPL parameterization the dark energy equation of state parameter is assumed to have the form[6,7]

$$w(z) = \frac{p(z)}{\rho(z)} = w_0 + w_a \frac{z}{1+z}, \qquad (1)$$

where w_0 is its present value while w_a quantifies its possible evolution. This is manifestly phenomenological: it is not intended to mimic a particular dark energy model, but aims to describe generic departures from the ΛCDM behaviour (which corresponds to $w_0 = -1$ and $w_a = 0$). In principle it allows for both canonical and phantom fields, since there is no restriction on the two model parameters, at least on purely mathematical grounds.

We assume a flat Friedmann-Lemaître-Robertson-Walker model, in which case the Friedmann equation has the form

$$\frac{H^2(z)}{H_0^2} = \Omega_m(1+z)^3 + (1-\Omega_m)(1+z)^{3(1+w_0+w_a)}\exp\left(-\frac{3w_a z}{1+z}\right), \quad (2)$$

where the matter parameter is $\Omega_m \equiv \kappa \rho_0 / 3H_0^2$ and $\kappa = 8\pi G$. This can now be constrained using the aforementioned data.

The case of a constant equation of state parameter (i.e. $w_a = 0$), for the case of the supernova dataset, have been used in Ref. 12 as a validation test of our analysis code, against the results of Ref. 8. In this case the one-sigma constraints on the two model parameters from the combined data sets are

$$\Omega_m = 0.27 \pm 0.02 \quad (3)$$
$$w_0 = -0.92 \pm 0.06, \quad (4)$$

which are compatible with ΛCDM.

For the full three-parameter CPL model, the one-sigma constraints on the three model parameters from the combined data sets are

$$\Omega_m = 0.26^{+0.03}_{-0.05} \quad (5)$$
$$w_0 = -0.92^{+0.09}_{-0.08} \quad (6)$$
$$w_a = 0.86^{+0.14}_{-0.24}; \quad (7)$$

the reduced chi-square at the best fit is $\chi^2_\nu \sim 0.9$, so the model is slightly overfitting the data (a behaviour which is mainly driven by the Hubble parameter data). The first two of these constraints are compatible with the values for the w_0CDM analysis (with naturally larger uncertainties), but there is a clear preference for a positive slope $w_a > 0$. However there are strong degeneracies between the parameters, and the constraints do depend on the choice of priors. In the above we used the uniform prior on the matter density $\Omega_m = [0.05, 0.5]$, the choice being motivated by the aforementioned validation of our code. As an illustration of the sensitivity of our results to this choice, if instead one uses the narrower uniform prior $\Omega_m = [0.15, 0.45]$, one find

$$\Omega_m = 0.26^{+0.03}_{-0.05} \quad (8)$$
$$w_0 = -0.92^{+0.07}_{-0.08} \quad (9)$$
$$w_a = 0.74^{+0.21}_{-0.48}; \quad (10)$$

in other words, there is no impact on the matter density and w_0, but there is a significant impact on w_a. Breaking these degeneracies requires additional data, for example from cosmic microwave background observations. In any case, our purpose here is to set up a benchmark for the constraining power of these data sets, against which to compare the constraints on the alternative models to be discussed in what follows.

3. Steady-state torsion

A possible extension of General Relativity consists in allowing for the presence of spacetime torsion. In such theories there is a further degree of freedom (in addition to the usual metric), which also gravitates. Mathematically, the torsion tensor is defined as the antisymmetric part of the affine connection; the symmetric part of the connection are the usual Christoffel symbols. Physically, this defines relation between the intrinsic angular momentum (i.e., the spin) of matter with the geometric properties of the underlying spacetime. The only non-trivial contraction of the torsion tensor is a torsion vector, and the general field equations including torsion are known as the Einstein-Cartan equations. Nominally the Einstein equations retain the usual form, but the presence of torsion implies that the Ricci tensor and the energy-momentum tensor are not symmetric. The Cartan equations relate the torsion tensor to the spin tensor, and similarly for the torsion and spin vectors.

The form of the underlying torsion tensor can be chosen such that the homogeneity and isotropy of FLRW universes is preserved,[13] and in this case the remaining degree of freedom is a scalar function ϕ which must depend only on time (a spatial dependence would violate the homogeneity assumption), but is otherwise arbitrary. Making the standard assumption of treating the metric and the torsion as independent objects and furhter assuming a flat universe, one finds the following Friedmann, Raychaudhuri and continuity equations[1]

$$H^2 = \frac{1}{3}\kappa\rho \frac{1}{3}\Lambda - 4\phi^2 - 4H\phi \tag{11}$$

$$\frac{\ddot{a}}{a} = -\frac{\kappa}{6}(\rho + 3p) + \frac{1}{3}\Lambda - 2\dot{\phi} - 2H\phi \tag{12}$$

$$\dot{\rho} = -3H\left(1 + 2\frac{\phi}{H}\right)(\rho + p) + 4\phi\left(\rho + \frac{\Lambda}{\kappa}\right). \tag{13}$$

Here the dot denotes a derivative with respect to physical time, $H = \dot{a}/a$ is the Hubble parameter, and ρ and p are the density and pressure. In what follows we will assume barotropic fluids with a constant equation of state $p = w\rho$. It has been recently suggested that such universes may undergo accelerating phases.[1] We can conveniently define a torsion contribution

$$\Omega_\phi = -4\left(\frac{\phi_0}{H_0}\right)\left[1 + \frac{\phi_0}{H_0}\right]. \tag{14}$$

In Ref. 14 these models were constrained under the so-called steady-state torsion assumption of a constant fractional contribution of torsion to the volume expansion, that is $\phi/H = \lambda = const.$.

It is easy to find, in agreement with other recent works, that models without a cosmological constant (where torsion itself would be expected to yield the current acceleration of the universe) are strongly disfavoured by the data. Indeed, in this case, for which the matter density would be given by $\Omega_m = (1 + 2\lambda)^2$, the best fit parameters would have a reduced chi-square of at least 2.7 for the datasets under consideration.

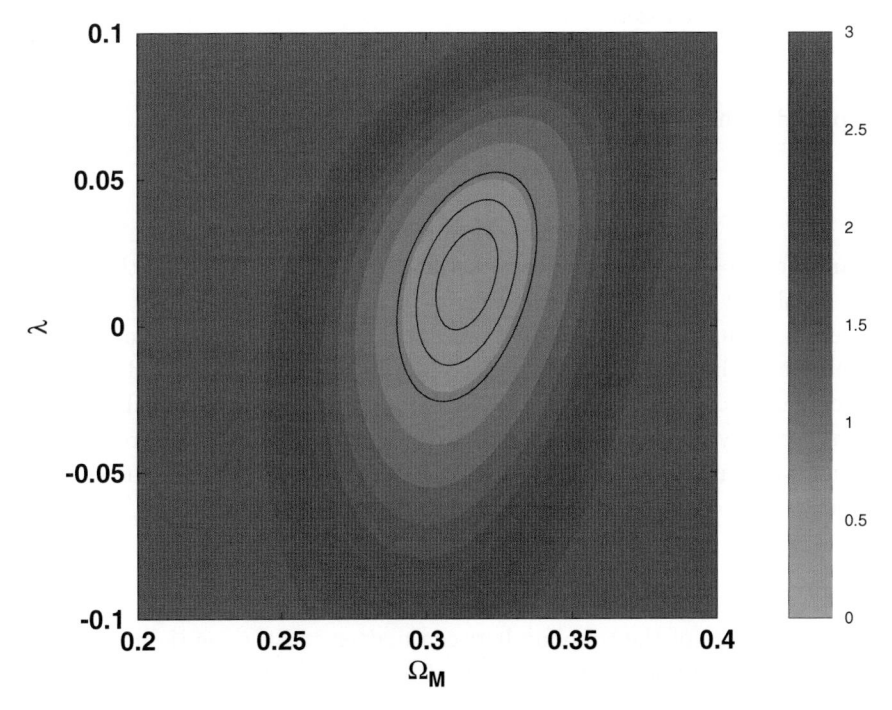

Fig. 1. Constraints on the λ–Ω_m parameter space for $w = 0$. The black lines represent the one, two and three sigma confidence levels, and the colormap depicts the reduced chi-square of the fit, with points with $\chi^2_\nu > 3$ shown in purple. Similar constraints can be found in Figure 2 of Ref. 14.

However, one can also treat these models as one-parameter extensions of ΛCDM, whereby one can constrain the relative contributions of the cosmological constant and of torsion. In this case, if one assumes that that matter has the standard equation of state, $w = 0$. As in the previous subsection will separately consider the cases without and with the aforementioned Planck prior on the matter density. Without the Planck prior, we find the following one-sigma posterior likelihoods for the two free parameters

$$\lambda_{w=0} = -0.07^{+0.05}_{-0.04} \tag{15}$$

$$\Omega_{m,w=0} = 0.18^{+0.06}_{-0.03} ; \tag{16}$$

there is a clear degeneracy between the two parameters, and the preferred value of the matter density is lower. The inclusion of the Planck prior breaks the degeneracy and significantly improves the constraints, as shown in Fig. 1; the one-sigma posterior likelihood for the torsion parameter becomes

$$\lambda_{(w=0,Planck)} = 0.02^{+0.01}_{-0.02}, \tag{17}$$

which is consistent with the null result at just over one sigma.

Allowing for a non-zero (but still constant) equation of state, there is a weak degeneracy between w and the other model parameters, so although the constraints become weaker (as they must), both parameters are still well constrained by the data, provided the Planck prior is included. In this case we have

$$\lambda_{(w \neq 0, Planck)} = -0.01 \pm 0.02 \tag{18}$$
$$w_{Planck} = -0.05 \pm 0.03 \,; \tag{19}$$

compared to the $w = 0$ case the best-fit value has changed sign, and the constraint is now consistent with the null result at one sigma.

Overall, we find no statistically significant preference for the presence of torsion. By itself it can't be responsible for the acceleration of the universe, and even if taken as an extension of the canonical ΛCDM paradigm the overall contribution to the Universe's energy budget is constrained to be no larger than a few percent. We also note that our constraints should be seen as conservative: an analysis including a full treatment of the cosmic microwave background should lead to stronger constraints.

4. Generalized couplings

The precise nature of the coupling between matter and the metric in the Einstein equations is at questionable assumption of the theory. One may therefore explore the possibility that this coupling is nontrivial. On such example is the Feng and Carloni's generalized coupling model,[2] which is equivalent to General Relativity in vacuum, but still allows for a different behaviour within a matter distribution.

In this case the Friedmann and Raychaudhuri equations, assuming a flat universe, can be written[2]

$$3qH^2 = \frac{256\kappa(1-pq)^3(q\rho+1)^2}{[4+q(\rho-3p)]^4} + q\Lambda - \kappa \tag{20}$$

$$6q(\dot{H}+H^2) = \frac{256\kappa(1-pq)^3(q\rho+1)[2-q(\rho+3p)]}{[4+q(\rho-3p)]^4} + 2(q\Lambda - \kappa), \tag{21}$$

where q is a model-specific parameter defined as $q = \kappa/\lambda$ (where λ, not to be confused with the analogous torsion parameter, is interpreted as being akin to the vacuum energy density generated by matter fields) and p is the pressure of a fluid that is assumed to be barotropic, with an equation of state $p = w\rho$, where w is a constant equation of state parameter. The corresponding continuity equation takes the form

$$\dot{\rho} = -\frac{3H\rho(w+1)[q^2\rho^2 w(3w-1) + q\rho(1-7w) + 4]}{q^2\rho^2 w(3w-1) - q\rho(3w^2 + 13w + 2) + 4}. \tag{22}$$

Note the model is effectively a bimetric theory.[2] In what follows we take the model as a phenomenological one and treat q (or a dimensionless version thereof) as a free parameter to be constrained by the data. It is convenient to define the dimensionless parameter $Q = q\rho_0$, where ρ_0 is the present-day critical density.

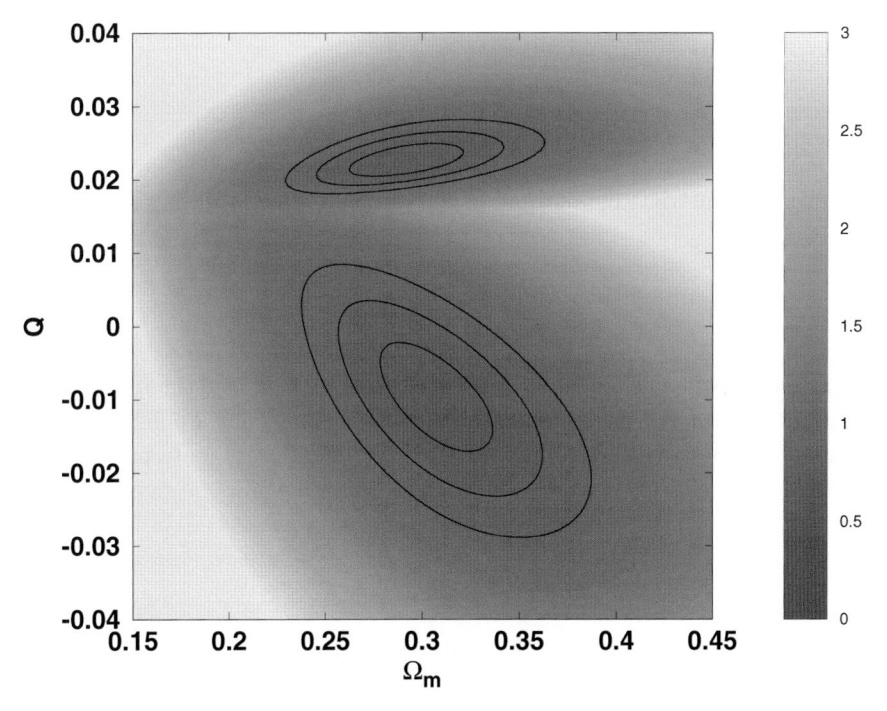

Fig. 2. Two-dimensional constraints on the $w = 0$ generalized coupling model. The $\Delta\chi^2 = 2.3$, $\Delta\chi^2 = 6.17$ and $\Delta\chi^2 = 11.8$ confidence levels are shown in black lines, and the color map depicts the reduced chi-square at each point in the parameter space, with points with $\chi^2_\nu > 3$ shown in yellow. Similar constraints can be found in Figure 3 of Ref. 12.

Since the model effectively has two types of vacuum energy, viz. the one generated by matter fields as well as the usual cosmological constant, one may wonder if the former is sufficient to yield an accelerating universe without invoking the latter. However, it is again simple to show that this can't be the case,[12] since in that case the minimum density would be $\Omega_m \sim 0.86$; clearly such high matter density universes would be incompatible with observations. Thus in what follows we treat this model as a phenomenological extension of ΛCDM, with the vacuum energy density of matter fields, Q, being an additional model parameter which we now constrain.

In the simpler case where the matter equation of state parameter has the standard value, $w = 0$, and agnostically allowing both positive and negative values of the model parameter Q, we find that while non-zero values of Q are preferred, the standard value is not significantly excluded, as shown in Fig. 2. We note the existence of two branches of the solution, one with $Q > 0$ and the other with $Q < 0$, with the former branch being slightly preferred. If we restrict the analysis to the range $Q \leq 0$, the one-sigma constraints on the two model parameters are

$$\Omega_{m-} = 0.31 \pm 0.02 \tag{23}$$

$$Q_{-} = -0.010 \pm 0.006 ; \tag{24}$$

conversely, if we restrict the analysis to the range $Q \geq 0$ we find

$$\Omega_{m+} = 0.29 \pm 0.02 \tag{25}$$

$$Q_{+} = 0.023 \pm 0.003 . \tag{26}$$

In all cases the reduced chi-square at the best fit is $\chi^2_\nu \sim 0.6$, so the model is clearly overfitting the data. All in all, there is no strong evidence for a non-zero Q.

In the general case, allowing the dark energy equation of state parameter w to become a further free parameter, one obtains the following one-sigma constraints on the parameters

$$\Omega_m = 0.29^{-0.09}_{+0.07} \tag{27}$$

$$Q = -0.018^{+0.005}_{-0.004} \tag{28}$$

$$w = -0.06^{+0.17}_{-0.08} . \tag{29}$$

The constraints on the matter density are now significantly weaker, but the two Q branches of the solution are still manifest, as are the degeneracies between the model parameters, as can be seen in Ref. 12. In this case the negative branch is also the preferred one. However, we should also point out that the matter equation of state parameter is already more tightly constrained than this (and this comment also applies to the above constraints on the torsion model). Recent analyses[15, 16] constrain it, conservatively, to $|w| < 0.003$. Using this as a Gaussian prior and repeating the analysis, we recover the constraints on Q and Ω_m reported above for the $w = 0$ case, while the posterior for w itself simply recovers the prior.

5. Scale invariance: The specific Maeder model

Maeder's proposed scale invariant model[3] is a specific case of the scale-covariant theory of Canuto et al.[4, 5] It is well known that the effects of scale invariance disappear upon the presence of matter; the assumption underlying scale invariant models is that at large (i.e., cosmological) scales empty space should still be scale invariant. This again leads to a bimetric theory, with a function λ (not to be confused with the parameters introduced in previous sections) playing the role of a scale transformation factor relating the ordinary matter frame to another frame which one assumes to still be scale invariant.

In this case, and with the further assumption of a flat homogeneous and isotropic universe, the Friedmann, Raychaudhuri, and continuity equations are[4,5]

$$\left(\frac{\dot{a}}{a}+\frac{\dot{\lambda}}{\lambda}\right)^2 + \frac{k}{a^2} = \frac{1}{3}(\kappa\rho + \Lambda\lambda^2) \tag{30}$$

$$\frac{\ddot{a}}{a}+\frac{\ddot{\lambda}}{\lambda}+\frac{\dot{\lambda}\dot{a}}{\lambda a}-\frac{\dot{\lambda}^2}{\lambda^2} = -\frac{\kappa}{6}(\rho + 3p - 2\Lambda\lambda^2) \tag{31}$$

$$\dot{\rho}+3(\rho+p)\frac{\dot{a}}{a} = -(\rho+3p)\frac{\dot{\lambda}}{\lambda}, \tag{32}$$

which match the standard equations if one chooses $\lambda = 1$. Note that for a homogeneous and isotropic model λ depends only on time, as does the scale factor.

The recent work of Maeder further postulates that the Minkowski metric is a solution of these Einstein equations, which leads to the following consistency conditions[3]

$$3\frac{\dot{\lambda}^2}{\lambda^2} = \Lambda\lambda^2 \tag{33}$$

$$2\frac{\ddot{\lambda}}{\lambda}-\frac{\dot{\lambda}^2}{\lambda^2} = \Lambda\lambda^2, \tag{34}$$

and further imply that

$$\lambda(t) = \sqrt{\frac{3}{\Lambda}}\frac{1}{t}. \tag{35}$$

We are again using $c = 1$, and constant equations of state, $p = w\rho$. Together with the solution for λ, the continuity equation yields

$$\rho \propto (1+z)^{3(1+w)} t^{1+3w}. \tag{36}$$

For a cosmological constant equation of state ($w = -1$) this becomes $\rho \propto t^{-2}$; in other words, this is effectively a model with a time-dependent cosmological constant, but no parametric ΛCDM limit. The author claims,[3] from a simple qualitative comparison, that with the choice $\Omega_m = 0.3$ the model is in good agreement with Hubble parameter data. In Ref. 12 this claim was assessed with a more thorough statistical analysis, and we summarize the results here.

With the aforementioned assumptions, the Friedmann equation for the Maeder model can be written

$$E^2(z,x) = \Omega_m(1+z)^{3(1+w)}x^{1+3w} + \frac{\Omega_\lambda}{x}E(z,x), \tag{37}$$

where we have defined an effective parameter

$$\Omega_\lambda = \frac{2}{t_0 H_0}, \tag{38}$$

which effectively quantifies the present age of the universe (in dimensionless units) and for convenience also introduced a dimensionless time $x = t/t_0$, with t_0 being

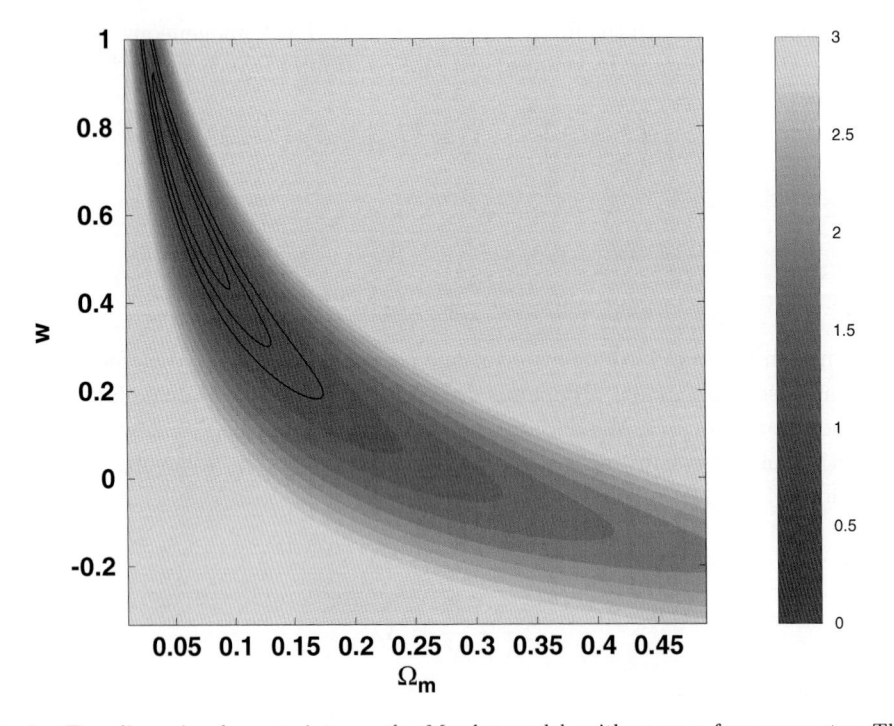

Fig. 3. Two-dimensional constraints on the Maeder model, with w as a free parameter. The black lines represent the one, two and three sigma confidence levels, and the color map depicts the reduced chi-square at each point in the parameter space, with points with $\chi_\nu^2 > 3$ shown in yellow. Similar constraints can be found in Figure 6 of Ref. 12.

the current age of the universe. With these definitions the Friedmann equation can be re-written in the simpler form

$$E(z,x) = \frac{\Omega_\lambda}{2x}\left[1 + \sqrt{1 + M(z,x)}\right] \quad (39)$$

$$M(z,x) = \frac{4\Omega_m}{\Omega_\lambda^2}(1+z)^{3(1+w)}x^{3(1+w)}, \quad (40)$$

with the relation between redshift and (dimensionless) time being given by

$$\frac{dx}{dz} = -\frac{x}{1+z} \times \frac{1}{1 + \sqrt{1 + M(z,x)}} \quad (41)$$

and the initial condition $x = 1$ at $z = 0$.

In the $w = 0$ case we can write $\Omega_\lambda = 1 - \Omega_m$. and the one-sigma posterior constraint in the matter density is

$$\Omega_m = 0.26 \pm 0.02, \quad \chi_\nu^2 = 1.3; \quad (42)$$

the inclusion of curvature as an additional parameter[12] slightly increases the preferred matter density but provides an equally poor fit. On the other hand, allowing

w as a further free parameter, one obtains the result shown in in Fig. 3. In this case the one sigma constraints are

$$\Omega_m = 0.06 \pm 0.02 \qquad (43)$$
$$w = 0.60^{+0.16}_{-0.15}; \qquad (44)$$

again the inclusion of curvature does not significantly change this.[12] In both cases the reduced chi-square is now $\chi_\nu^2 = 0.8$, so the model is now slightly overfitting the data. Clearly there is a strong degeneracy between the matter density and the equation of state parameter (which are anticorrelated), and the best fit values of both parameters are very far from the standard ΛCDM ones.

6. Scale invariance: the general model

The previous section shows that the Maeder model is ruled out. One may therefore ask whether this conclusion extends to the more general model of Canute et al., also introduced in the previous section. Here we present a very preliminary analysis of this issue. We will assume a generic power-law behaviour, $\lambda(t) \propto t^p$, choosing $\lambda_0 = 1$, and further assuming flat models[a]. This choice of λ also ensures that ΛCDM is recovered for $p = 0$.

Note that in the Maeder model there is no explicit cosmological constant Λ. In the general case it is still there, so we may again expect two classes of solutions. One has the usual Λ providing the acceleration, with the λ field providing a further contribution; in other words, this will be an extension of ΛCDM. The other has $\Lambda = 0$, meaning that the model will not have a ΛCDM limit, and the question is then whether the field λ can provide an alternative to acceleration in that case.

In this case the continuity equation gives

$$\rho \propto (1+z)^{3(1+w)} t^{-p(1+3w)}, \qquad (45)$$

while the Friedmann equation gives

$$\left(E(z,x) + \frac{p}{2x}\Omega_\lambda\right)^2 = \Omega_m(1+z)^{3(1+w)} x^{-p(1+3w)} + \Omega_\Lambda x^{2p}. \qquad (46)$$

For $p = -1$ the Maeder model is recovered with the further assumption that

$$\Omega_\Lambda = \frac{1}{4}\Omega_\lambda^2 = \frac{1}{(t_0 H_0)^2}. \qquad (47)$$

In the general case the Friedmann equation can be re-written

$$E(z,x) = \frac{\Omega_\lambda}{2x}\left[-p + \sqrt{N(z,x)}\right] \qquad (48)$$

$$N(z,x) = \frac{4}{\Omega_\lambda^2}\left[\Omega_m(1+z)^{3(1+w)} x^{2-p(1+3w)} + \Omega_\Lambda x^{2(1+p)}\right], \qquad (49)$$

---

[a]We will report on a more detailed analysis, relaxing some of these assumptions and exploring various scenarios, elsewhere.

and the relation between redshift and (dimensionless) time is now given by

$$\frac{dx}{dz} = -\frac{x}{1+z} \times \frac{1}{\sqrt{N(z,x)} - p}, \qquad (50)$$

with the initial condition still being $x = 1$ at $z = 0$. One can easily check that the Maeder model equations are recovered in the appropriate limit. Note that Ω_λ is a dimensionless measure of the current age of the universe, and it must therefore be a positive quantity.

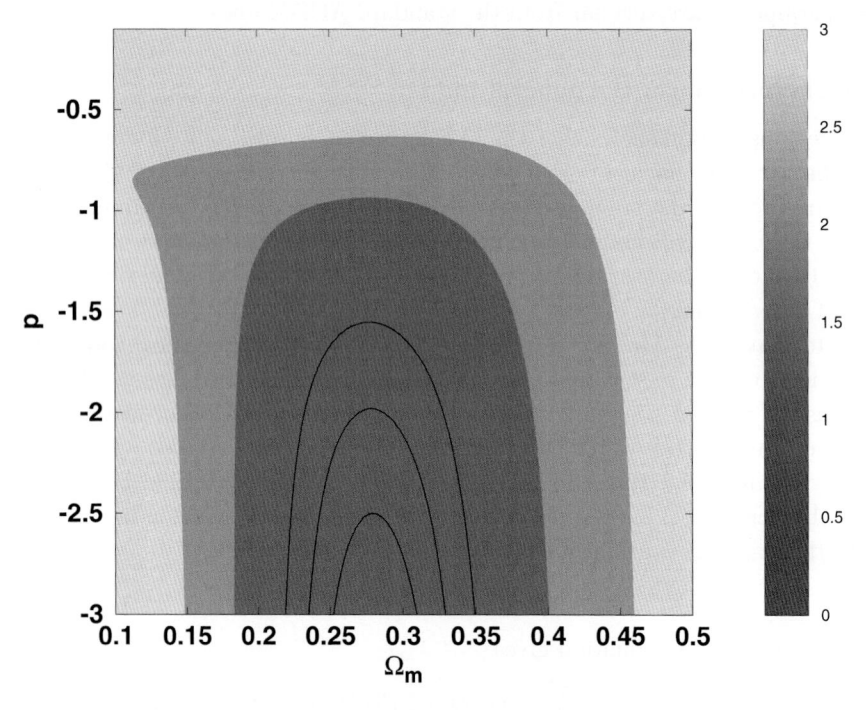

Fig. 4. Two-dimensional constraints on the Canuto et al. model, with $w = 0$ and $\Omega_\Lambda = 0$. The black lines represent the one, two and three sigma confidence levels, and the color map depicts the reduced chi-square at each point in the parameter space, with points with $\chi_\nu^2 > 3$ shown in yellow.

Several different scenarios can now be considered. In what follows we only consider the simplest one. If we assume that $\Omega_\Lambda = 0$ and ordinary matter with an $w = 0$ equation of state we have two free parameters (Ω_m, p) and

$$-p\Omega_\lambda = 2(1 - \sqrt{\Omega_m}); \qquad (51)$$

thus $p = 0$ corresponds to an $\Omega_m = 1$ universe, In this case we again find that this model does not provide a good fit to the data, cf. Fig. 4: while a matter density of around $\Omega_m \sim 0.28$ is preferred, the reduced chi-square of the best fit is quite poor, being always larger than $\chi_\nu^2 = 1.25$. An exploration of the wider parameter space, allowing for a cosmological constant, a non-zero equation of state, and curvature, will be reported elsewhere.

7. Outlook

We have briefly presented a comparison of three classes of models for the low-redshift acceleration of the universe against background low-redshift cosmological observations, further using the traditional CPL phenomenological parameterization as a benchmark. Each of these models contains, in principle, an additional mechanism, in addition to the cosmological constant, that could account for the recent acceleration of the universe.

We find that the steady-state torsion and generalized couplings have similar behaviours. The specific physical mechanism therein are ruled out as unique source of acceleration, but small (e.g. percent level) deviations from ΛCDM are still allowed by the data that we have considered. Constraints can of course be tightened by including further data. The scale invariant model provides an interesting contrast. Assuming the standard equation of state parameter, $w = 0$, the best-fit value is similar to the CPL one. However, these fits have a poor (specifically, high) reduced chi-square, indicating that the model does not provide a good fit to the data. An observationally viable model of this kind would require a highly non-standard 'matter' density (including a non-standard equation of state), which would conflict with other cosmological datasets. In passing, we also mention that another interesting phenomenological class is that of energy-momentum-powered models recently constrained in Ref. 17 and also discussed elsewhere in these proceedings.

Overall, we therefore conclude that ΛCDM is a remarkably robust paradigm. While it is clearly a phenomenological approximation to a still unknown more fundamental model, it is clearly a good one, and any plausible alternative model must be able to closely reproduce its behaviour in a broad range of cosmological settings.

Acknowledgments

This work was financed by FEDER—Fundo Europeu de Desenvolvimento Regional funds through the COMPETE 2020—Operational Programme for Competitiveness and Internationalisation (POCI), and by Portuguese funds through FCT - Fundação para a Ciência e a Tecnologia in the framework of the project POCI-01-0145-FEDER-028987 and PTDC/FIS-AST/28987/2017.

References

1. D. Kranas, C. Tsagas, J. Barrow and D. Iosifidis, Friedmann-like universes with torsion, *Eur. Phys. J. C* **79**, p. 341 (2019).
2. J. C. Feng and S. Carloni, New class of generalized coupling theories, *Phys. Rev. D* **101**, p. 064002 (2020).

3. A. Maeder, An alternative to the ΛCDM model: The case of scale invariance, *Astrophys. J.* **834**, p. 194 (2017).
4. V. Canuto, S. Hsieh and P. Adams, Scale-Covariant Theory of Gravitation and Astrophysical Applications, *Phys. Rev. Lett.* **39**, 429 (1977).
5. V. Canuto, P. Adams, S. Hsieh and E. Tsiang, Scale Covariant Theory of Gravitation and Astrophysical Applications, *Phys. Rev. D* **16**, 1643 (1977).
6. M. Chevallier and D. Polarski, Accelerating universes with scaling dark matter, *Int. J. Mod. Phys. D* **10**, 213 (2001).
7. E. V. Linder, Exploring the expansion history of the universe, *Phys. Rev. Lett.* **90**, p. 091301 (2003).
8. A. G. Riess *et al.*, Type Ia Supernova Distances at Redshift >1.5 from the Hubble Space Telescope Multi-cycle Treasury Programs: The Early Expansion Rate, *Astrophys. J.* **853**, p. 126 (2018).
9. O. Farooq, F. R. Madiyar, S. Crandall and B. Ratra, Hubble Parameter Measurement Constraints on the Redshift of the Deceleration-acceleration Transition, Dynamical Dark Energy, and Space Curvature, *Astrophys. J.* **835**, p. 26 (2017).
10. N. Aghanim *et al.*, Planck 2018 results. VI. Cosmological parameters, *Astron. Astrophys.* **641**, p. A6 (2020), [Erratum: Astron.Astrophys. 652, C4 (2021)].
11. F. K. Anagnostopoulos and S. Basilakos, Constraining the dark energy models with $H(z)$ data: An approach independent of H_0, *Phys. Rev.* **D97**, p. 063503 (2018).
12. C. B. D. Fernandes, C. J. A. P. Martins and B. A. R. Rocha, Constraining alternatives to a cosmological constant: Generalized couplings and scale invariance, *Phys. Dark Univ.* **31**, p. 100761 (2021).
13. M. Tsamparlis, Methods for Deriving Solutions in Generalized Theories of Gravitation: The Einstein-Cartan Theory, *Phys. Rev.* **D24**, 1451 (1981).
14. C. Marques and C. Martins, Low-redshift constraints on homogeneous and isotropic universes with torsion, *Phys. Dark Univ.* **27**, p. 100416 (2020).
15. D. B. Thomas, M. Kopp and C. Skordis, Constraining the Properties of Dark Matter with Observations of the Cosmic Microwave Background, *Astrophys. J.* **830**, p. 155 (2016).
16. I. Tutusaus, B. Lamine, A. Blanchard, A. Dupays, Y. Rousset and Y. Zolnierowski, Dark sectors of the Universe: A Euclid survey approach, *Phys. Rev. D* **94**, p. 123515 (2016).
17. M. C. F. Faria, C. J. A. P. Martins, F. Chiti and B. S. A. Silva, Low redshift constraints on energy-momentum-powered gravity models, *Astron. Astrophys.* **625**, p. A127 (2019).

Model-independent test of scalar-tensor gravity theory by reconstructing scalar mode of GW170817

Yuya Gushima[*] and Kazuhiro Hayama[†]

Department of Applied Physics, Fukuoka University,
Fukuoka, 814-0180, Japan
[*] *E-mail: sd211004@cis.fukuoka-u.ac.jp*
[†] *E-mail: hayama@fukuoka-u.ac.jp*

Einstein's general relativity predicts that a gravitational wave is allowed to have two polarizations called tensor-modes: plus and cross modes. On the other hand, the general metric theory of gravity predicts that a gravitational wave is allowed to have up to six polarizations: two scalar and two vector modes in addition to the tensor-modes. In case the number of laser-interferometric gravitational wave telescopes is larger than the one of the polarizations the gravitational waves have, all the polarizations can be reconstructed separately. Since it depends on theories of gravity which polarizations the gravitational waves have, the investigation of polarizations is important for the test of theories of gravity. In this paper, in order to test the scalar-tensor gravity theory, one of important alternative theories of gravity, we search for the scalar-mode of GW170817 observed by LIGO Livingstone, Hanford and Virgo without prior information about any tensor-scalar gravity theories. As a result, we found the maximum SNR of the scalar-mode of GW170817 was 2.77, the p-value was 0.01, and the band-limited root sum square of h was $1.55 \times 10^{-21} [1/\sqrt{Hz}]$ with the time window of 2[s] and frequency window of 60~120[Hz].

Keywords: Gravitational wave; polarization; scalar-mode; test of gravity theory; GW170817.

1. Introduction

Since the gravitational wave (GW) was observed in 2015, many gravitational waves have been detected.[1] The observation of GWs will provide an opportunity to unveil the mystery of the early universe,[2] black holes[1] and dark matter. Einstein's general relativity predicts that a GW is allowed to have two polarization modes, plus mode and cross mode, which are called tensor modes. On the other hand, the general metric theory of gravity predicts that a gravitational wave is allowed to have up to six polarizations, two scalar and two vector modes in addition to the tensor modes.[3,4] This suggests, if either the scalar or the vector modes are found, it is necessary to modify the general relativity.

E. Hubble observed that the universe was expanding,[5] and George Gamow proposed the big bang cosmology.[6] However, the proposed theory could not explain the flatness problem and the horizon problem. Inflation universe theories were proposed to solve these problems.[7] Direct evidence of inflation has not been found yet, but if inflation theories are correct, a scalar field may be necessary for inflation to occur.

Instead of the general relativity, the general metric theory of gravity has been proposed, and the theory of gravity has been tested using the GWs detected so far.[8,9] Among the proposed theories of gravity, the scalar-tensor gravity theory predicts the gravitation is given through not only the tensor field but also by the scalar field. It is possible to reconstruct the tensor and scalar modes from GW observations when the GW is observed by three or more laser-interferometric gravitational wave telescopes and the direction to the GW is known.[10] In this paper, in order to test the scalar-tensor gravity theory, we search for a scalar mode of GW170817[11] observed by LIGO-Livingston, LIGO-Hanford[12] and Virgo.[13] The direction to GW170817 is known by the multi-messenger observation.[14] Normally, when exploring GWs, the correlation between the predicted waveform and the observed data is examined, which is called the matched filter method. For this purpose, we must assume a specific theory model. In this paper, we take a different way to test the gravity theories. We reconstruct the polarizations without any prior information about waveform. Since our method of reconstruction does not rely on any specific gravity theory, it is possible to test theory of gravity with high generality. In Sec. 2, we describe how reconstruct each polarization. In Sec. 3, we show the analysis result. Section 4 is devoted to the summary of this paper.

2. Reconstruction of polarization modes

2.1. *Polarization modes of a gravitational wave*

The GW propagating in the z direction, the bases of the six polarizations are defined by following tensors in which time, x, y, z component from the left to the right or the top to the bottom,

$$e^+_{ij} = \begin{pmatrix} 0 & 0 & 0 & 0 \\ 0 & 1 & 0 & 0 \\ 0 & 0 & -1 & 0 \\ 0 & 0 & 0 & 0 \end{pmatrix}, \quad e^\times_{ij} = \begin{pmatrix} 0 & 0 & 0 & 0 \\ 0 & 0 & 1 & 0 \\ 0 & 1 & 0 & 0 \\ 0 & 0 & 0 & 0 \end{pmatrix},$$

$$e^b_{ij} = \begin{pmatrix} 0 & 0 & 0 & 0 \\ 0 & 1 & 0 & 0 \\ 0 & 0 & 1 & 0 \\ 0 & 0 & 0 & 0 \end{pmatrix}, \quad e^l_{ij} = \sqrt{2} \begin{pmatrix} 0 & 0 & 0 & 0 \\ 0 & 0 & 0 & 0 \\ 0 & 0 & 0 & 0 \\ 0 & 0 & 0 & 1 \end{pmatrix}, \quad (1)$$

$$e^x_{ij} = \begin{pmatrix} 0 & 0 & 0 & 0 \\ 0 & 0 & 0 & 1 \\ 0 & 0 & 0 & 0 \\ 0 & 1 & 0 & 0 \end{pmatrix}, \quad e^y_{ij} = \begin{pmatrix} 0 & 0 & 0 & 0 \\ 0 & 0 & 0 & 0 \\ 0 & 0 & 0 & 1 \\ 0 & 0 & 1 & 0 \end{pmatrix},$$

where $+, \times, b, l, x$ and y denote plus, cross, breathing, longitudinal, vector-x, vector-y modes. Figure 1 shows that how each polarization affects test masses placed in a circle. Using Eq. (1) and amplitude of each polarization $h_\alpha(\alpha = +, \times, b, l, x, y)$, the GW h_{ij} is given by

$$h_{ij} = h_+ e_{ij}^+ + h_\times e_{ij}^\times + h_b e_{ij}^b + h_l e_{ij}^l + h_x e_{ij}^x + h_y e_{ij}^y. \tag{2}$$

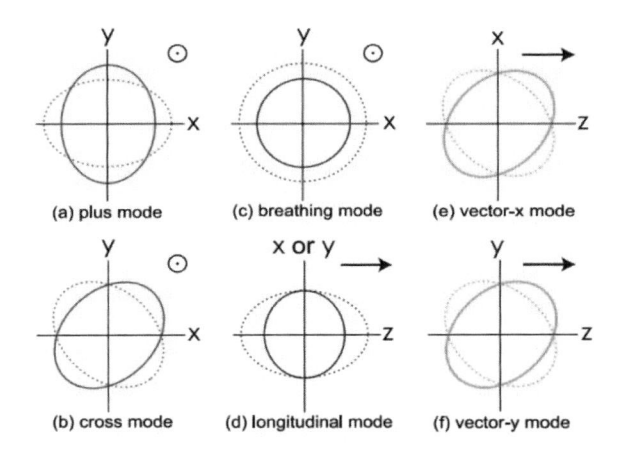

Fig. 1. Six gravitational wave polarizations in a general metric theory of gravity.[15]

2.2. Antenna pattern function

Suppose that a normal orthogonal system $(\hat{u}, \hat{v}, \hat{w})$ in which the unit vector $\hat{u}, \hat{v}$ are directed to each detector arm. The coordination systems $(\hat{m}, \hat{n}, \hat{\Omega})$ are given by the rotation angle (θ, ϕ, ψ) (Fig. 2). $\hat{\Omega}$ is unit vector directed the direction to the GW, and the angle ψ around the $\hat{\Omega}$ is an arbitrary angle. Using vector $\hat{m}, \hat{n}, \hat{\Omega}$, the

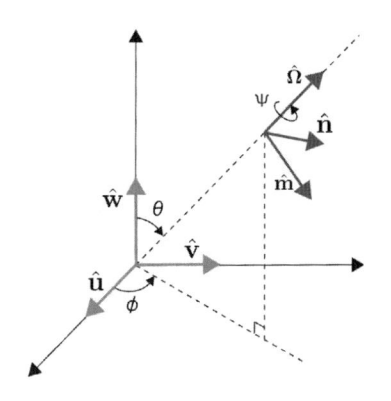

Fig. 2. Coordinate systems.[15]

polarization tensors are given by

$$\tilde{e}_+ = \hat{m} \otimes \hat{m} - \hat{n} \otimes \hat{n}, \qquad \tilde{e}_\times = \hat{m} \otimes \hat{n} + \hat{n} \otimes \hat{m}$$

$$\tilde{e}_b = \hat{m} \otimes \hat{m} + \hat{n} \otimes \hat{n}, \qquad \tilde{e}_l = \sqrt{2}\hat{\Omega} \otimes \hat{\Omega} \qquad (3)$$

$$\tilde{e}_x = \hat{m} \otimes \hat{\Omega} + \hat{\Omega} \otimes \hat{m}, \qquad \tilde{e}_y = \hat{n} \otimes \hat{\Omega} + \hat{\Omega} \otimes \hat{n}$$

where the symbol $\otimes$ denotes a tensor product. The antenna pattern function $F_\alpha(\alpha = +, \times, b, l, x, y)$ of a detector is defined as

$$F_\alpha(\hat{\Omega}) = \mathbf{D} : \tilde{e}_\alpha(\hat{\Omega}), \qquad (4)$$

where the symbol : denotes contraction between tensors. $\mathbf{D}$ is a detector tensor and defined as

$$\mathbf{D} = \frac{1}{2}[\hat{u} \otimes \hat{u} - \hat{v} \otimes \hat{v}]. \qquad (5)$$

The antenna pattern function depends on the position of detectors and the direction to the GW.

2.3. Coherent network analysis

Data from i-th detector are

$$x_i = h_i + \eta_i, \qquad (6)$$

where h_i are the i-th detector response to the GW and η_i are the i-th detector noise. h_i is written as

$$h_i = F_{i+}h_+ + F_{i\times}h_\times + F_{is}h_s, \qquad (7)$$

where $F_{i\alpha}(\alpha = +, \times, s)$ is the antenna pattern function of i-th detector. Here s denotes a scalar-mode. h_α are the amplitude of each polarization. As the antenna pattern function of the breathing-mode and the longitudinal-mode are degenerated, we can't decompose these scalar modes. In this paper, we suppose that the GW has two tensor modes and one scalar mode and the amplitude of vector modes is small enough to be ignored. If there are three detectors, from Eq. (6,7)

$$\begin{bmatrix} x_1 \\ x_2 \\ x_3 \end{bmatrix} = \begin{bmatrix} F_{1+} & F_{1\times} & F_{1s} \\ F_{2+} & F_{2\times} & F_{2s} \\ F_{3+} & F_{3\times} & F_{3s} \end{bmatrix} \begin{bmatrix} h_+ \\ h_\times \\ h_s \end{bmatrix} + \begin{bmatrix} \eta_1 \\ \eta_2 \\ \eta_3 \end{bmatrix}. \qquad (8)$$

Equation (8) is written in a matrix as

$$x = Fh + \eta. \qquad (9)$$

F is not a square matrix and doesn't have its inverse matrix in general. But if we use Moore-Penrose pseudo-inverse matrix we can reconstruct each polarization. We consider the reconstruction without noise for simplicity. Multiplying Eq. (9) by transpose matrix F^T, we get

$$F^T F h = F^T x. \tag{10}$$

Since $F^T F$ is a square matrix, we can find the inverse matrix. We finally get

$$h = M^{-1} F^T x, \qquad M := F^T F, \tag{11}$$

where $M^{-1} F^T$ is the Moore-Penrose pseudo-inverse matrix.

3. Analysis method and results

Figure 3 shows spectrograms of three modes(plus, cross and scalar) reconstructed from GW170817.

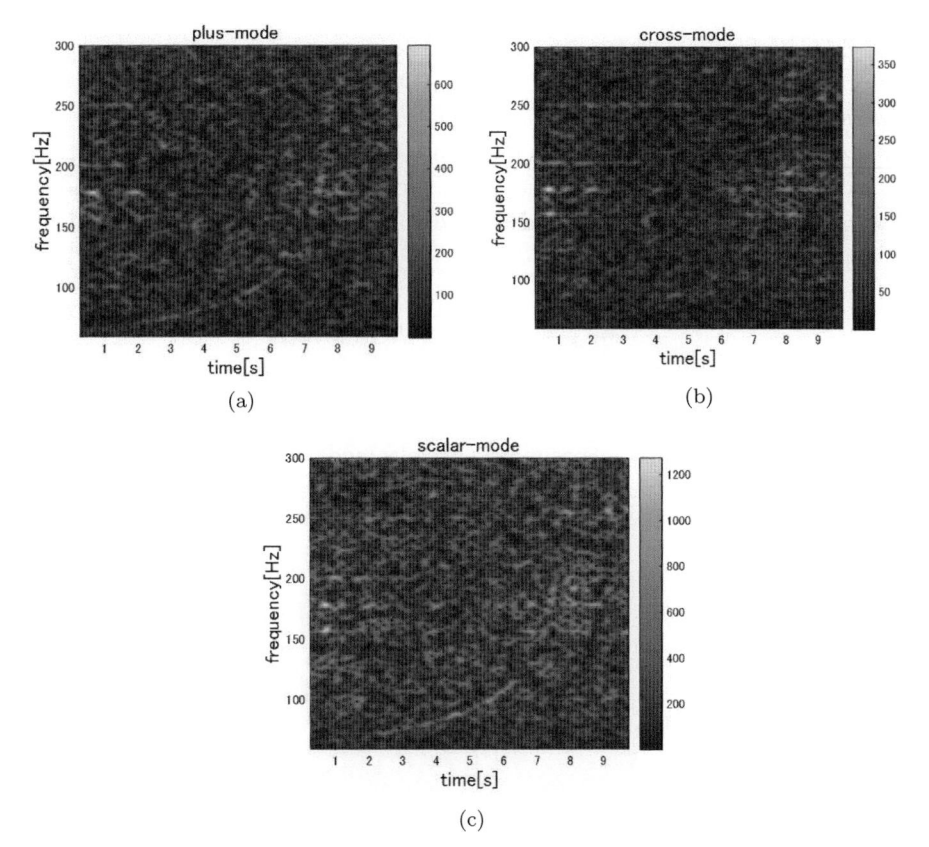

Fig. 3. Spectrograms of the reconstructed plus-mode (a), cross-mode (b) and scalar-mode (c). The horizontal axis is time[s] since GPS time 1187008874[s]. The vertical axis is frequency [Hz].

Next, we describe the statistical evaluation method.

(1) Divide the data into 2, 3.5 or 5[s], and divide the frequency band of the data into 60[Hz] each from 60[Hz] to 300[Hz]. Figure 4 is the spectrogram on which red and black lines are drawn. The black lines are drawn at every 60[Hz] from 60[Hz]. The red lines are drawn at every 2[s] from 0[s].

(2) In each region, calculate the power of signal p, and create a histogram.

$$p = \Sigma h_s^2, \tag{12}$$

where h_s is the reconstructed scalar mode. Figure 5 is a histogram of the reconstructed scalar mode. The data used is divided into 2[s] and the frequency band is limited in 60~120[Hz].

(3) Assuming that the probability distribution of p follows a normal distribution, find the mean μ and standard deviation σ from the distribution.

(4) Calculate the P-value and the signal-to-noise ratio(SNR).

$$\text{P-value} = \frac{n}{N}, \tag{13}$$

$$SNR = \frac{p_{gw} - \mu}{\sigma}, \tag{14}$$

where p_{GW} is the p in the region where GW170817 is in, n is the number of the p larger than p_{GW} and N is the total number of the p.

(5) Calculate the band limited root sum square of h_{rss} in the time-frequency domain with the highest SNR. The band limited root sum square of h, h_{rss}^{BL}, which we defined as follows

$$h_{rss}^{BL} = \sqrt{\sum_{t=t_1}^{t_2} \sum_{f=f_1}^{f_2} h_s(t,f)^2 dt}. \tag{15}$$

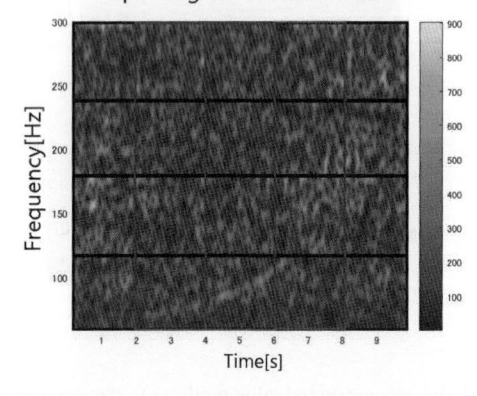

Fig. 4. Spectrogram of the reconstructed scalar-mode. The black lines are drawn at every 60[Hz] from 60[Hz]. The red lines are drawn at every 2[s] from 0[s].

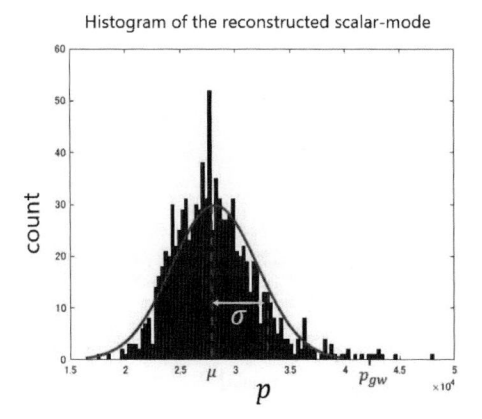

Fig. 5. Histogram of the reconstructed scalar-mode. The data used is divided into the 2[s] and the frequency band is limited in 60~120[Hz]. μ is the mean value and σ is standard deviation of the p. p_{gw} is the p in the region where GW170817 is contained. n is the number of the p larger than p_{GW}.

Table 1. SNRs and P-values. The data used is divided into 2[s] and the frequency band is limited in 60~120[Hz], 120~180[Hz], 180~240[Hz] and 240~300[Hz].

frequency[Hz]	time[s]	2~4	4~6	6~8
60~120	P-value	0.13	0.01	0.60
	SNR	1.07	2.77	-0.308
120~180	P-value	0.40	0.06	0.09
	SNR	0.0150	-0.453	1.39
180~240	P-value	0.87	0.94	0.06
	SNR	-1.01	-1.33	1.59
240~300	P-value	0.62	0.85	0.40
	SNR	-0.477	-0.897	0.0198

Figures 6, 7, 8, 9 shows spectrograms of the reconstructed scalar modes, and Tables 1, 2, 3 shows the SNRs and the P-values. In the Figs. 6, 7, 8, 9, the black lines are drawn at every 60[Hz] from 60[Hz], and the red lines are starting GPS time 1187008878~1187008880[s], 1187008877~1187008880.5[s], 1187008878~1187008881.5[s], 1187008876~1187008881[s], respectively.

The largest SNR was 2.77 with the time window of 2[s]. The P-value of the corresponding time-frequency region was 0.01. In the Fig. 6, the yellow frame is the region with the largest SNR. In case of the time window of 3.5[s], there are two regions where the SNR is larger than 2. The largest SNR was 2.54 with the time window of 3.5[s]. The P-value of the corresponding time-frequency region was 0.01. In the Fig. 7, the yellow frame is the region with the largest SNR. Also, The second

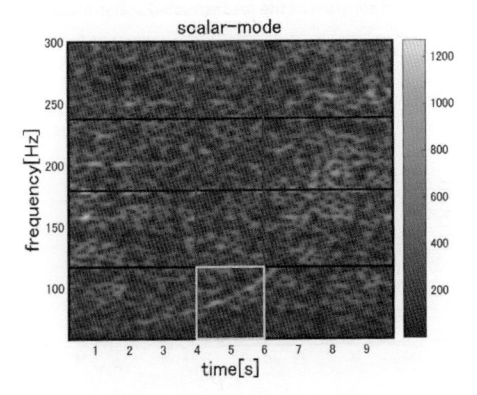

Fig. 6. Spectrogram of the reconstructed scalar-mode. The yellow frame is the region with highest SNR larger than 2.

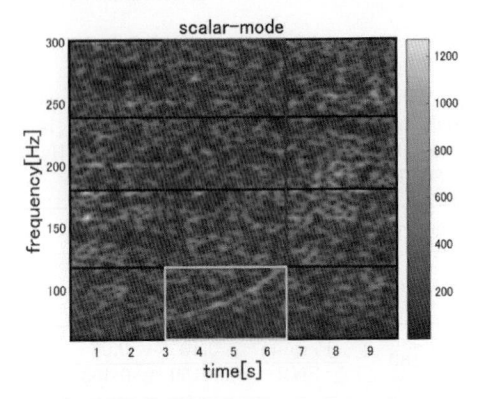

Fig. 7. Spectrogram of the reconstructed scalar-mode. The yellow frame is the region with highest SNR larger than 2.

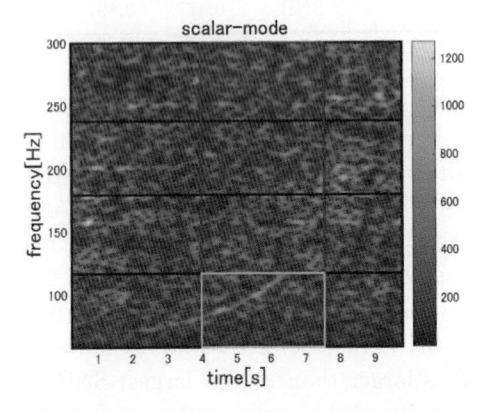

Fig. 8. Spectrogram of the reconstructed scalar-mode. The orange frame is the region with second highest SNR larger than 2.

Table 2. SNRs and P-values. The data used is divided into 3.5[s] and the frequency band is limited in 60~120[Hz], 120~180[Hz], 180~240[Hz] and, 240~300[Hz].

frequency[Hz]	time[s]	2~5.5	3~6.5	4~7.5	5~8.5
60~120	P-value	0.03	0.01	0.03	0.23
	SNR	1.99	2.54	2.10	0.669
120~180	P-value	0.61	0.67	0.25	0.09
	SNR	-0.377	-0.505	0.460	1.51
180~240	P-value	0.96	0.97	0.734	0.04
	SNR	-1.59	-1.69	-0.790	1.94
240~300	P-value	0.84	0.84	0.80	0.40
	SNR	-0.890	-0.887	-0.804	0.017

Table 3. SNRs and P-values. The data used is divided into 5[s] and the frequency band is limited in 60~120[Hz], 120~180[Hz], 180~240[Hz] and 240~300[Hz].

frequency[Hz]	time[s]	2~7	3~8
60~120	P-value	0.02	0.06
	SNR	2.38	1.61
120~180	P-value	0.44	0.27
	SNR	-0.0251	0.44
180~240	P-value	0.96	0.58
	SNR	-1.50	-0.239
240~300	P-value	0.81	0.71
	SNR	-0.860	-0.658

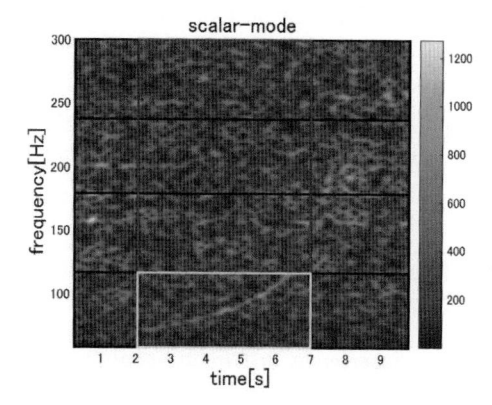

Fig. 9. Spectrogram of the reconstructed scalar-mode. The yellow frame is the region with highest SNR larger than 2.

largest SNR was 2.10. The P-value of the corresponding time-frequency region was 0.03. In the Fig. 8, the orange frame is the region with the second largest SNR. In case of the time window of 5[s], there is one region where the SNR is larger than 2. The largest SNR was 2.38 with the time window of 5[s]. The P-value of the corresponding time-frequency region was 0.02. In the Fig. 9, the yellow frame is the region with the largest SNR. Additionally, the h_{rss}^{BL} in the region with the maximum SNR was $1.55 \times 10^{-21}[1/\sqrt{Hz}]$.

4. Summary

We performed the model-independent test of the scalar-tensor gravity theory using GW170817 by reconstructing the tensor and scalar modes without any information about the waveform. We found the maximum SNR was 2.77 with the time window of 2[s] and the frequency band of 60~120[Hz]. The P-value of the corresponding time-frequency region was 0.01, and the h_{rss}^{BL} of the same region was $1.55 \times 10^{-21}[1/\sqrt{Hz}]$. The SNR was small compared to threshold value of the GW detection by the matched filter analysis in recent years. In order to claim the detection of the scalar-mode, it is necessary to further increase the sensitivity of GW telescope and/or detect larger GWs. There are some future issues. First, we need evaluate the error that occurs in the process of the waveform reconstruction. Next, the method of reconstruction needs to be optimal for the scalar-mode. Our recent studies have shown that different locations have different amounts of leakage from the tensor mode. Therefore, by investigating it in detail, it will be possible to test the scalar-tensor gravity theory with high generality.

Acknowledgments

This work was supported by JSPS KAKENHI Grant Number JP19K03896. This research has made use of data, software and/or web tools obtained from Gravitational Wave Open Science Center (https://www.gw-openscience.org), a service of LIGO Laboratory, the LIGO Scientific Collaboration and the Virgo Collaboration. LIGO is funded by the U.S. National Science Foundation. Virgo is funded by the French Center National de Recherche Scientifique (CNRS), the Italian Istituto Nazionaledella Fisica Nucleare (INFN) and the Dutch Nikhef, with contributions by Polish and Hungarian institutes.

References

1. B. P. Abbott, *et al.*, Phys. Rev. **X9**, 031040 (2019).
2. B. P. Abbott, *et al.*, Nature, **460**, 990 (2009).
3. D. M. Eardley, *et al.*, Phys. Rev. Lett. **30**, 884 (1973).
4. C. M. Will, *Theory and Experiment in Gravitational Physics* (Cambridge University Press, 1993).
5. E. P. Hubble, Proc. National Academy of Science of the USA, **15**, 168 (1929).
6. R. A. Alpher, H. Bethe, G. Gamow, Phys. Rev. **73**, 803 (1948).

7. K. Sato, Monthly Notices of Royal Astronomical Society, **195**, 467 (1981).
8. B. P. Abbott *et al.*, Phys. Rev. Lett. **123**, 011102 (2019).
9. B. P. Abbott *et al.*, Phys. Rev. Lett. **126**, 221101 (2016).
10. K. Hayama, A. Nishizawa, Phys. Rev. D **87**, 062003 (2013).
11. B. P. Abbott *et al.*, Phys. Rev. Lett. **119**, 161101 (2017).
12. LIGO Web page, https://www.ligo.caltech.edu/MIT
13. Virgo Web page, https://www.virgo-gw.eu/
14. LIGO Collab. *et al.*, Apj Lett. **848**, L13 (2017).
15. A. Nishizawa, *et al.*, Phys. Rev. D**79**, 082002 (2009).

Cosmology in the novel scalar-tensor representation of $f(R,T)$ gravity

Tiago B. Gonçalves

Instituto de Astrofísica e Ciências do Espaço, Faculdade de Ciências da Universidade de Lisboa,
Edifício C8, Campo Grande,
P-1749-016 Lisbon, Portugal
E-mail: tgoncalves@alunos.fc.ul.pt

João Luís Rosa

Institute of Physics, University of Tartu, W. Ostwaldi 1,
50411 Tartu, Estonia
E-mail: joaoluis92@gmail.com

Francisco S. N. Lobo

Instituto de Astrofísica e Ciências do Espaço, Faculdade de Ciências da Universidade de Lisboa,
Edifício C8, Campo Grande,
P-1749-016 Lisbon, Portugal
E-mail: fslobo@fc.ul.pt

We apply cosmological reconstruction methods to the $f(R,T)$ modified gravity, in its recently developed scalar-tensor representation. We do this analysis assuming a perfect fluid in a Friedmann-Lemaître-Robsertson-Walker (FLRW) universe. In this contribution we show the equations of motion obtained and we present the solutions found for one of the particular cases we analysed: an exponential evolution of the cosmological scale factor.

Keywords: Cosmology; modified gravity; scalar-tensor theories; accelerated expansion.

1. Introduction

The late-time universe is observed to be expanding in an accelerated way.[1,2] This behaviour can be modelled by introducing a dark energy component, often identified as a cosmological constant. However, we still lack the understanding for the dark energy mechanism at the fundamental level. Alternatively, it is possible to explain the accelerated expansion by modifying the theory of gravity. Many such modifications have been proposed to extend Einstein's General Relativity (GR) (e.g. see Refs. 3–9). For instance, one can modify the gravitational Lagrangian, which depends linearly on the Ricci curvature scalar R, to instead depend on a *general function* of R – thus, referred to as $f(R)$ gravity.[10] Resulting in modified Friedmann equations, $f(R)$ gravity can allow for the accelerated expansion without the need for dark energy.[11]

It is natural, then, to explore further extensions, such as $f(R,T)$ gravity[12] where the action depends on a general function of the curvature scalar R *and* of the trace of the stress-energy tensor T. Because of this explicit coupling between curvature and matter, the stress-energy tensor is not necessarily conserved, allowing the appearance of a fifth force. Since its proposal, the $f(R,T)$ gravity has sparked a lot of interest leading, in some cases, to the study of its cosmological applications (e.g. see Refs. 13–19).

Recently, the original geometrical representation of the $f(R,T)$ gravity was reformulated into an equivalent scalar-tensor representation,[20] where the two extra degrees of freedom of the theory are expressed by means of two scalar fields. So far, this scalar-tensor theory was used to find thin shells' junction conditions[20] and thick brane solutions.[21] Since in scalar-tensor theories it is often easier to find analytical solutions, it calls for further study also of cosmological models in this representation of the $f(R,T)$ gravity. This study is undertaken in our work, modelling a Friedmann-Lemaître-Robsertson-Walker (FLRW) universe. We used reconstruction methods,[13–15, 23, 24] whereby the function $f(R,T)$ is not defined *a priori*, and instead we start from known cosmological solutions such as the time evolution of the spatial scale factor which seem to model well the observations. Here we give simply a preview of this work and some of its preliminary results. A more complete analysis is being incorporated into a paper under preparation.

2. The theory of the $f(R,T)$ gravity

We first introduce briefly the theory of $f(R,T)$ gravity, showing the main equations without detailing all of the steps. For further details we point to the main references. In its original geometrical formulation (see Ref. 12), the action of the $f(R,T)$ gravity is

$$S = \frac{1}{2\kappa^2} \int \sqrt{-g}\, f(R,T) d^4x + \int \sqrt{-g}\, \mathcal{L}_m d^4x, \quad (1)$$

where $\kappa^2 = 8\pi G/c^4$, G is the gravitational constant and c is the speed of light, g is the determinant of the metric $g_{\mu\nu}$, $f(R,T)$ is an arbitrary well-behaved function of the Ricci curvature scalar R and the trace of the stress-energy tensor T, and $\mathcal{L}_m$ is the matter Lagrangian. More explicitly, $R = g^{\mu\nu} R_{\mu\nu}$, where $R_{\mu\nu}$ is the Ricci tensor, and $T = g^{\mu\nu} T_{\mu\nu}$, where the stress-energy tensor $T_{\mu\nu}$ is defined in terms of the variation of the matter Lagrangian $\mathcal{L}_m$ as

$$T_{\mu\nu} = -\frac{2}{\sqrt{-g}} \frac{\delta(\sqrt{-g}\mathcal{L}_m)}{\delta g^{\mu\nu}}. \quad (2)$$

When reformulating into the dynamically equivalent scalar tensor representation (see Ref. 20 for further details), one defines two scalar fields

$$\varphi \equiv \frac{\partial f}{\partial R}, \quad \psi \equiv \frac{\partial f}{\partial T}, \quad (3)$$

with the associated potential

$$V(\varphi,\psi) \equiv -f(R,T) + \varphi R + \psi T. \quad (4)$$

With these definitions, the action (1) can equivalently be written as

$$S = \frac{1}{2\kappa^2} \int_\Omega \sqrt{-g}\, [\varphi R + \psi T - V(\varphi,\psi)]\, d^4x + \int_\Omega \sqrt{-g}\mathcal{L}_m d^4x. \quad (5)$$

The variation of this action with respect to the metric $g_{\mu\nu}$ yields the modified field equations

$$\varphi R_{\mu\nu} - \frac{1}{2}g_{\mu\nu}\left(\varphi R + \psi T - V\right) - (\nabla_\mu \nabla_\nu - g_{\mu\nu}\Box)\varphi = \kappa^2 T_{\mu\nu} - \psi(T_{\mu\nu} + \Theta_{\mu\nu}), \quad (6)$$

where ∇_μ is the covariant derivative and $\Box \equiv \nabla^\sigma \nabla_\sigma$ is the D'Alembert operator, both defined in terms of the metric $g_{\mu\nu}$, and the tensor $\Theta_{\mu\nu}$ is defined as

$$\Theta_{\mu\nu} \equiv g^{\rho\sigma}\frac{\delta T_{\rho\sigma}}{\delta g^{\mu\nu}}. \quad (7)$$

On the other hand, the variation of the action (5) with respect to the scalar fields φ and ψ gives, respectively,

$$V_\varphi = R, \quad (8)$$

$$V_\psi = T, \quad (9)$$

where the subscripts in V_φ and V_ψ denote the partial derivatives of the potential $V(\varphi, \psi)$ with respect to the variables φ and ψ, respectively.

A general conservation equation can be found by taking the divergence of Eq. (6),

$$(\kappa^2 - \psi)\nabla^\mu T_{\mu\nu} = (T_{\mu\nu} + \Theta_{\mu\nu})\nabla^\mu \psi + \psi \nabla^\mu \Theta_{\mu\nu} - \frac{1}{2}g_{\mu\nu}\left[R\nabla^\mu \varphi + \nabla^\mu(\psi T - V)\right]. \quad (10)$$

Even though it is not a requirement of the theory, in this work we will impose the conservation of the stress-energy tensor, i.e. $\nabla^\mu T_{\mu\nu} = 0$, a condition that is automatically assured in GR. As detailed in the following section, for our cosmological model we use a FLRW metric and a perfect fluid approach in order to find the modified equations of motion.

In the following, we adopt a system of geometrized units in such a way that $G = c = 1$, and thus $\kappa^2 = 8\pi$.

3. Cosmology in the scalar-tensor representation

3.1. Assumptions and equations of motion

Let us first state the assumptions of our cosmological model with which we derived the equations of motion that are the focus of our study. We take the metric to be of the FLRW form, i.e., in spherical coordinates (t, r, θ, ϕ),

$$ds^2 = -dt^2 + a^2(t)\left[\frac{dr^2}{1 - kr^2} + r^2\left(d\theta^2 + \sin^2\theta d\phi^2\right)\right], \quad (11)$$

where $a(t)$ is the scale factor and k is the curvature parameter which can take the values $k = \{-1, 0, 1\}$ corresponding to a hyperbolic, spatially flat, or hyperspherical universe, respectively.

We assume the stress-energy tensor $T_{\mu\nu}$ to be well described by that of an isotropic perfect fluid,

$$T_{\mu\nu} = (\rho + p)u_\mu u_\nu + pg_{\mu\nu}, \tag{12}$$

where ρ is the energy density, p is the isotropic pressure, and u^μ is the fluid 4-velocity satisfying the normalization condition $u_\mu u^\mu = -1$. We take the matter Lagrangian to be $\mathcal{L}_m = p$.[22] Under these considerations, the tensor $\Theta_{\mu\nu}$ takes the form

$$\Theta_{\mu\nu} = -2T_{\mu\nu} + pg_{\mu\nu}. \tag{13}$$

With these assumptions, and with all physical quantities depending only on the time coordinate t (which guarantees the homogeneity and isotropy of the solutions $\rho(t)$, $p(t)$, $\varphi(t)$, $\psi(t)$, etc.), the following equations of motion were obtained. From the two independent components of Eq. (6), we obtained the modified Friedmann equation and the modified Raychaudhuri equation,

$$\dot{\varphi}\left(\frac{\dot{a}}{a}\right) + \varphi\left(\frac{\dot{a}^2 + k}{a^2}\right) = \frac{8\pi}{3}\rho + \frac{\psi}{2}\left(\rho - \frac{1}{3}p\right) + \frac{1}{6}V, \tag{14}$$

$$\ddot{\varphi} + 2\dot{\varphi}\left(\frac{\dot{a}}{a}\right) + \varphi\left(\frac{2\ddot{a}}{a} + \frac{\dot{a}^2 + k}{a^2}\right) = -8\pi p + \frac{\psi}{2}(\rho - 3p) + \frac{1}{2}V, \tag{15}$$

respectively, where overdots denote derivatives with respect to time. From Eqs. (8) and (9) we obtained

$$V_\varphi = 6\left(\frac{\ddot{a}}{a} + \frac{\dot{a}^2 + k}{a^2}\right), \tag{16}$$

$$V_\psi = 3p - \rho, \tag{17}$$

respectively. By our choice, we imposed $\nabla_\mu T^{\mu\nu} = 0$ that leads to the usual continuity equation,

$$\dot{\rho} = -3\frac{\dot{a}}{a}(\rho + p). \tag{18}$$

Consequently, from the general conservation equation (Eq. (10)) we obtained

$$2\dot{\psi}(\rho + p) = -\psi(\dot{\rho} - \dot{p}). \tag{19}$$

Finally, we impose an equation of state of the form

$$p = w\rho, \tag{20}$$

where w is a dimensionless parameter.

These equations of motion are the framework with which we searched for cosmological solutions in the $f(R,T)$ gravity. There is a redundancy in the equations obtained, since they are not all linearly independent, and one can be discarded without loss of generality. We chose to work with Eqs. (14), (16), (17), (18), (19), and (20) which form a system of six independent equations. This system is still underdetermined since we have nine degrees of freedom: a, k, w, ρ, p, φ, ψ and V which contributes with two degrees of freedom (because it is a function of two variables, φ and ψ). In a first instance, we solved as much as it was possible without further constraining the system, obtaining some general solutions for $\rho(t)$, $p(t)$, $\psi(t)$, and the $V(\varphi,\psi)$ dependence on ψ. Only subsequently, did we provide further constraints to close the system and analyse particular cases.

3.2. General solutions

Taking the system of equations we have derived, Eqs. (14), (16), (17), (18), (19), and (20), we first found some general results. Beginning in a similar way that we would in GR, we used the equation of state (20) in the continuity equation (18) to find the general forms of the energy density and pressure as a function of a,

$$\rho = \rho_0 \left(\frac{a}{a_0}\right)^{-3(1+w)}, \qquad (21)$$

$$p = w\rho_0 \left(\frac{a}{a_0}\right)^{-3(1+w)}, \qquad (22)$$

respectively, where ρ_0 and a_0 are arbitrary constants from integration, and usually the subscript 0 denotes the value of the quantity today, at $t = t_0$. These solutions are identical to those in GR. This is only so because we required $\nabla_\mu T^{\mu\nu} = 0$ which, again, does not have to be generally true in modified gravity. Yet, it seems sensible to assume the validity of the continuity equation, at least on a first analysis.

Equipped with the results in Eqs. (21) and (22), we then solved Eq. (19) by integration and obtained

$$\psi = \psi_0 \left(\frac{a}{a_0}\right)^{\frac{3}{2}(1-w)}, \qquad (23)$$

where ψ_0 is an integration constant. At this point, we were able to make the following considerations. The partial derivative V_ψ in Eq. (17) depends on ρ and p. We have the forms of $\rho(a)$ and $p(a)$ in Eqs. (21) and (22), and we can find a function $a(\psi)$ by inverting Eq. (23) (which we can do for $w \neq 1$, so, in what follows we will not be considering stiff matter). Thus, we combined these results to write the partial derivative V_ψ in Eq. (17) as depending only on ψ. We integrated the partial derivative to obtain a separable potential $V(\varphi,\psi) = V_0 + V_1(\varphi) + V_2(\psi)$, where V_0 is an arbitrary constant, $V_1(\varphi)$ is an arbitrary function of φ, and $V_2(\psi)$ is a function of ψ given by

$$V_2(\psi) = \frac{(1-3w)(1-w)}{(1+3w)} \rho_0 \psi_0^{\frac{2(1+w)}{(1-w)}} \psi^{-\frac{(1+3w)}{(1-w)}}, \qquad (24)$$

which is undefined when $w = \{-1/3, 1\}$ and vanishes when $w = 1/3$ (corresponding to the case when the stress-energy tensor is traceless $T = 0$, such as for radiation).

This is as far as we were able to go without imposing further constraints. Up to this point, from the system of equations we are considering we have already used Eqs. (17), (18), (19), and (20), so we have only Eqs. (14) and (16) remaining . In balance, there are still five degrees of freedom at the moment: a, k, w, φ and $V_1(\varphi)$. Hence, we have to impose three further constraints in order to fully determine the system. We note that, as it stands, making a choice of the curvature and equation of state parameters, k and w, is not sufficient to determine the evolution of the universe modelled by $a(t)$. This is in contrast with GR where to each equation of state corresponds a unique evolution of the scale factor $a(t)$. Therefore, in this work we took the approach of first specifying the form of the scale factor, and then explored the parameter space of k and w in each particular case. The forms of the scale factor we chose are those known to model well different epochs of the universe: $a(t)$ given by an exponential or by a power law. By way of example, we present here only the particular case with an exponential scale factor, which can model the accelerated expansion observed in the present era.

3.3. The particular case of an exponential expansion

The universe is seen to be undergoing a phase of accelerated expansion. So, one of the particular cases we analysed was the de-Sitter solution that one obtains in GR, i.e., we impose in our system of equations an exponentially evolving scale factor of the form

$$a(t) = a_0 e^{\sqrt{\Lambda}(t-t_0)}, \qquad (25)$$

where a_0, t_0 and Λ are constants. Once again, this particular choice does not require a unique value of w in $f(R,T)$ gravity and the solutions for ρ and ψ from Eqs. (21) and (23) become

$$\rho(t) = \rho_0 e^{-3\sqrt{\Lambda}(t-t_0)(1+w)}, \qquad (26)$$

$$\psi(t) = \psi_0 e^{\frac{3}{2}\sqrt{\Lambda}(t-t_0)(1-w)}, \qquad (27)$$

respectively. The pressure is simply given by $p(t) = w\rho(t)$.

To make further progress in order to find analytical solutions for $\varphi(t)$ and $V_1(\varphi)$, we set $k = 0$ (flat geometry) and left w arbitrary. With this choice of the curvature parameter and with the scale factor given by Eq. (25) the computation of Eq. (16) yields simply $V_\varphi = 12\Lambda$. Given that this is equivalent to having $dV_1/d\varphi = 12\Lambda$, we integrated it to obtain $V_1(\varphi) = 12\Lambda\varphi$. By doing so, we absorbed the arbitrary integration constant into V_0 in the full expression of the potential, which in this case reads as

$$V(\varphi, \psi) = V_0 + 12\Lambda\varphi + \frac{(1-3w)(1-w)}{(1+3w)}\rho_0 \psi_0^{\frac{2(1+w)}{(1-w)}} \psi^{-\frac{(1+3w)}{(1-w)}}. \qquad (28)$$

Having determined the form of the potential, we solved Eq. (14) to obtain $\varphi(t)$,

$$\varphi(t) = \varphi_0 e^{\sqrt{\Lambda}(t-t_0)} - \frac{V_0}{6\Lambda} - \frac{\rho_0}{3\Lambda}\left[\frac{8\pi e^{-3(1+w)\sqrt{\Lambda}(t-t_0)}}{(4+3w)} + \frac{4(1+w)\psi_0 e^{-\frac{3}{2}(1+3w)\sqrt{\Lambda}(t-t_0)}}{(1+3w)(5+9w)}\right], \tag{29}$$

where φ_0 is an integration constant. This solution $\varphi(t)$ is undefined at $w = \{-4/3, -5/9, -1/3\}$, and, from before, we were already not considering the $w = 1$ case. Apart from these discontinuities, the system does not pose further constraints to the equation of state. In the paper under preparation, we include a more complete analysis of this parameter space. However, here we show the solutions only for three particular choices of w.

A natural choice was to take $w = -1$, which in GR is the equation of state of constant dark energy density that drives an exponential expansion, corresponding to a cosmological constant. Given that we have the freedom to do so, we also set $w = 0$, i.e. the case in which pressureless (or dust-like) matter dominates. Alternatively, we also set $w = 1/3$ to model the case in which the energy density is dominated by radiation (remembering, for instance, that the stress-energy tensor of the electromagnetic field is traceless, i.e. $T = 3p - \rho = 0$ in the case of isotropic perfect fluid considered, corresponding to $w = 1/3$). That we tried different values for the equation of state, e.g. for matter and radiation, may be confusing at first given that we are considering an exponential growth of the universe, but we need only to remember that due to the extra degrees of freedom in $f(R,T)$ gravity, this cases can still be consistent within the system of equations we derived.

For each of these three values of the equation of state, $w = \{-1, 0, 1/3\}$, the energy density as given by Eq. (26) is plotted in Fig. 1. When space expands exponentially, the energy density is constant for $w = -1$ (cosmological constant), and undergoes exponential decay for $w = 0$ (dust) and $w = 1/3$ (radiation) — the decay is faster for radiation than for dust (due to the redshift of radiation). For each of the same three values of w, the scalar field $\psi(t)$ as given by Eq. (27) is plotted in Fig. 2. In the three cases, the field ψ grows exponentially with time — in descending order, it grows faster with the cosmological constant than with dust and than with radiation. Likewise, we plot the scalar field $\varphi(t)$ as given by Eq. (29) in Fig. 3. When $t \gg t_0$, all of the plotted $\varphi(t)$ solutions grow exponentially (in fact, they can all be approximated by $\varphi(t) \sim \varphi_0 \exp(\sqrt{\Lambda}t)$ in this limit). On the other hand, when $t < t_0$ the $\varphi(t)$ solutions show different behaviour between them. The two scalar fields do not have a straightforward physical interpretation; as a reminder, they were defined as the partial derivatives of the function $f(R,T)$, i.e. $\varphi = \partial f/\partial R$ and $\psi = \partial f/\partial T$. Finally, to each value of the equation of state corresponds a different form of the potential $V(\varphi, \psi)$ as given by Eq. (28),

$$w = -1: \quad V(\varphi, \psi) = V_0 + 12\Lambda\varphi - 4\rho_0\psi, \tag{30}$$

$$w = 0: \quad V(\varphi, \psi) = V_0 + 12\Lambda\varphi + \frac{\rho_0\psi_0^2}{\psi}, \tag{31}$$

$$w = 1/3: \quad V(\varphi, \psi) = V_0 + 12\Lambda\varphi. \tag{32}$$

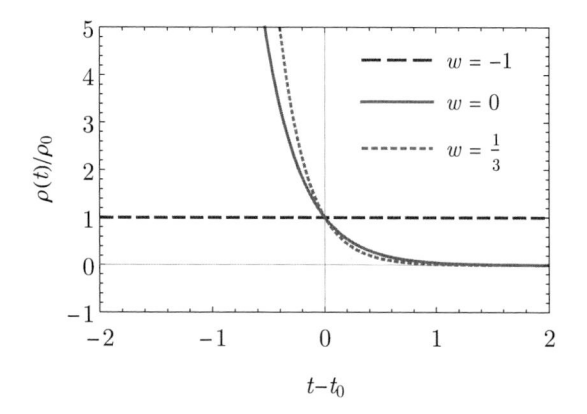

Fig. 1. Energy density $\rho(t)/\rho_0$ from Eq. (26) in the particular case where $a(t)$ is given by Eq. (25), setting $\Lambda = 1$, with the equation of state forced to be each of these values $w = \{-1, 0, 1/3\}$.

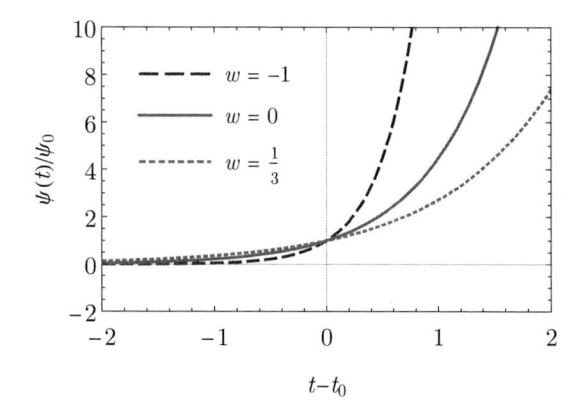

Fig. 2. Scalar field $\psi(t)/\psi_0$ from Eq. (27) in the particular case where $a(t)$ is given by Eq. (25), setting $\Lambda = 1$, with the equation of state forced to be each of these values $w = \{-1, 0, 1/3\}$.

As exemplified here, we were able to find solutions for all the variables in our system: $\rho(t)$, $p(t)$, $\varphi(t)$, $\psi(t)$ and $V(\varphi, \psi)$, for particular choices of $a(t)$, k and w. The next question we addressed in our work was: what form(s) of the function $f(R, T)$ generate these cosmologies?

3.4. *Reconstructing the function* $f(R, T)$

Given that we were able to obtain consistent solutions, one may hope that it is possible to reconstruct the explicit form of the function $f(R, T)$ that can lead to those solutions. For instance, we have found the form of the potential $V(\varphi, \psi)$ and, by definition, the potential is related to the function $f(R, T)$, as per Eq. (4) which

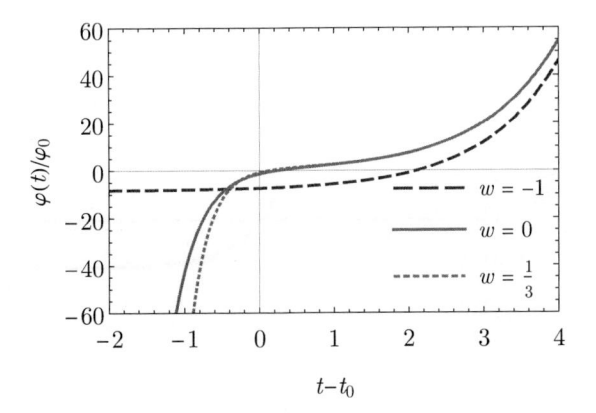

Fig. 3. Scalar field $\varphi(t)/\varphi_0$ from Eq. (29), setting $\varphi_0 = \rho_0 = \psi_0 = 1$, in the particular case where $a(t)$ is given by Eq. (25), setting $\Lambda = 1$, with the equation of state forced to be each of these values $w = \{-1, 0, 1/3\}$.

can be rewritten as

$$f(R, T) = -V(f_R, f_T) + f_R R + f_T T, \tag{33}$$

where we have changed the notation using $\varphi = f_R$ and $\psi = f_T$, with the subscripts R and T denoting the partial derivatives. Taking the partial derivatives of this equation with respect to R and T, we obtained a system of two PDEs which are satisfied for an arbitrary $f(R, T)$ if $V_\varphi = R$ and $V_\psi = T$. These two conditions are the equations of motion we obtained for the fields φ and ψ, in Eqs. (8) and (9), and so are always satisfied. It can be seen, e.g. from Eq. (28), that

$$V_\psi = T = (3w - 1)\rho_0 \left(\frac{f_T}{\psi_0}\right)^{-\frac{2(1+w)}{(1-w)}}, \tag{34}$$

which is not defined for $w = 1$. If $w = \{-1, 1/3\}$, this equation does not give a relation between f_T and T. On the other hand, if $w = 0$, for instance, then $T = -\rho_0 \psi_0^2/f_T^2$. This relation can be inverted and integrated to give

$$f(R, T) = g(R) \pm 2\psi_0 \sqrt{-\rho_0 T}, \tag{35}$$

where $g(R)$ is an arbitrary function of R. In the case of a flat universe ($k = 0$) with an exponentially evolving scale factor as given by Eq. (25), $V_\varphi = R = 12\Lambda$ which does not provide a direct relation between f_R and R, and so it does constrain the form of $g(R)$. Other particular cases are studied in our work and will be presented in the upcoming paper.

4. Summary and concluding remarks

Modified gravity has the potential to solve some of the remaining questions in cosmology, such as the current accelerated expansion. With this motivation, we took the recently developed scalar-tensor representation of the $f(R,T)$ gravity to explore allowed FLRW cosmologies. To keep our contribution short, we presented here only one particular case: that of an exponential expansion. As opposed to GR, in $f(R,T)$ gravity there is not a one-to-one relation between the evolution of the scale factor and the equation of state. For instance, we were able to find a solution by choosing a flat, dust dominated, exponentially expanding universe, which would not have been possible in GR. The extra degrees of freedom in modified gravity may contribute to an effective dark energy, thus allowing an exponential expansion to occur even when the equation of state is that of matter or radiation. In the paper under preparation, we include other particular cases, such as power law evolution of the scale factor, non flat geometries, and other equations of state. We are also already working on testing whether finite time singularities can appear in $f(R,T)$ gravity.

Acknowledgments

TBG is funded by a PhD Research Fellowship in the context of the Fundação para a Ciência e Tecnologia (FCT) project "DarkRipple" with reference PTDC/FIS-OUT/29048/2017. JLR was supported by the European Regional Development Fund and the programme Mobilitas Pluss (MOBJD647). FSNL acknowledges support from the Fundação para a Ciência e a Tecnologia (FCT) Scientific Employment Stimulus contract with reference CEECINST/00032/2018, and funding from the research grants No. UIDB/FIS/04434/2020, UIDP/FIS/04434/2020, No. PTDC/FIS-OUT/29048/2017 and No. CERN/FIS-PAR/0037/2019.

References

1. S. Perlmutter et al. [Supernova Cosmology Project], "Measurements of Ω and Λ from 42 high redshift supernovae," Astrophys. J. **517**, 565-586 (1999) [arXiv:astro-ph/9812133 [astro-ph]].
2. A. G. Riess et al. [Supernova Search Team], "Observational evidence from supernovae for an accelerating universe and a cosmological constant," Astron. J. **116**, 1009-1038 (1998) [arXiv:astro-ph/9805201 [astro-ph]].
3. S. Nojiri and S. D. Odintsov, "Introduction to modified gravity and gravitational alternative for dark energy," eConf **C0602061**, 06 (2006) [arXiv:hep-th/0601213 [hep-th]].
4. F. S. N. Lobo, "The Dark side of gravity: Modified theories of gravity," [arXiv:0807.1640 [gr-qc]].
5. S. Nojiri and S. D. Odintsov, "Unified cosmic history in modified gravity: From F(R) theory to Lorentz non-invariant models," Phys. Rept. **505**, 59-144 (2011) [arXiv:1011.0544 [gr-qc]].
6. T. Clifton, P. G. Ferreira, A. Padilla and C. Skordis, "Modified Gravity and Cosmology," Phys. Rept. **513**, 1-189 (2012) [arXiv:1106.2476 [astro-ph.CO]].
7. S. Capozziello and M. De Laurentis, "Extended Theories of Gravity," Phys. Rept. **509**, 167-321 (2011) [arXiv:1108.6266 [gr-qc]].
8. E. N. Saridakis et al. [CANTATA], "Modified Gravity and Cosmology: An Update by the CANTATA Network," [arXiv:2105.12582 [gr-qc]].

9. P. Avelino, T. Barreiro, C. S. Carvalho, A. da Silva, F. S. N. Lobo, P. Martin-Moruno, J. P. Mimoso, N. J. Nunes, D. Rubiera-Garcia and D. Saez-Gomez, *et al.* "Unveiling the Dynamics of the Universe," Symmetry **8**, no. 8, 70 (2016) [arXiv:1607.02979 [astro-ph.CO]].
10. T. P. Sotiriou and V. Faraoni, "f(R) Theories Of Gravity," Rev. Mod. Phys. **82**, 451-497 (2010) [arXiv:0805.1726 [gr-qc]].
11. S. Capozziello, "Curvature quintessence," Int. J. Mod. Phys. D **11**, 483-492 (2002) [arXiv:gr-qc/0201033 [gr-qc]].
12. T. Harko, F. S. N. Lobo, S. Nojiri and S. D. Odintsov, "$f(R,T)$ gravity," Phys. Rev. D **84**, 024020 (2011) [arXiv:1104.2669 [gr-qc]].
13. M. Jamil, D. Momeni, M. Raza and R. Myrzakulov, "Reconstruction of some cosmological models in f(R,T) gravity," Eur. Phys. J. C **72**, 1999 (2012) [arXiv:1107.5807 [physics.gen-ph]].
14. M. J. S. Houndjo and O. F. Piattella, "Reconstructing $f(R,T)$ gravity from holographic dark energy," Int. J. Mod. Phys. D **21**, 1250024 (2012) [arXiv:1111.4275 [gr-qc]].
15. M. J. S. Houndjo, "Reconstruction of f(R, T) gravity describing matter dominated and accelerated phases," Int. J. Mod. Phys. D **21**, 1250003 (2012) [arXiv:1107.3887 [astro-ph.CO]].
16. F. G. Alvarenga, A. de la Cruz-Dombriz, M. J. S. Houndjo, M. E. Rodrigues and D. Sáez-Gómez, "Dynamics of scalar perturbations in $f(R,T)$ gravity," Phys. Rev. D **87**, no. 10, 103526 (2013) [erratum: Phys. Rev. D **87**, no. 12, 129905 (2013)] [arXiv:1302.1866 [gr-qc]].
17. H. Shabani and M. Farhoudi, "$f(R,T)$ Cosmological Models in Phase Space," Phys. Rev. D **88**, 044048 (2013) [arXiv:1306.3164 [gr-qc]].
18. H. Shabani and M. Farhoudi, "Cosmological and Solar System Consequences of f(R,T) Gravity Models," Phys. Rev. D **90**, no. 4, 044031 (2014) [arXiv:1407.6187 [gr-qc]].
19. P. H. R. S. Moraes, "Cosmological solutions from Induced Matter Model applied to 5D $f(R,T)$ gravity and the shrinking of the extra coordinate," Eur. Phys. J. C **75**, no. 4, 168 (2015) [arXiv:1502.02593 [gr-qc]].
20. J. L. Rosa, "Junction conditions and thin shells in perfect-fluid $f(R,T)$ gravity," Phys. Rev. D **103**, no. 10, 104069 (2021) [arXiv:2103.11698 [gr-qc]].
21. J. L. Rosa, M. A. Marques, D. Bazeia and F. S. N. Lobo, "Thick branes in the scalar-tensor representation of $f(R,T)$ gravity," [arXiv:2105.06101 [gr-qc]].
22. O. Bertolami, F. S. N. Lobo and J. Paramos, "Non-minimum coupling of perfect fluids to curvature," Phys. Rev. D **78**, 064036 (2008) [arXiv:0806.4434 [gr-qc]].
23. S. Capozziello, V. F. Cardone and A. Troisi, "Reconciling dark energy models with f(R) theories," Phys. Rev. D **71**, 043503 (2005) [arXiv:astro-ph/0501426 [astro-ph]].
24. T. Multamaki and I. Vilja, "Cosmological expansion and the uniqueness of gravitational action," Phys. Rev. D **73**, 024018 (2006) [arXiv:astro-ph/0506692 [astro-ph]].

On the interaction between electromagnetic, gravitational, and plasma related perturbations on LRS class II spacetimes

P. Semrén

Department of Physics, Umeå University,
Umeå, SE-901 87, Sweden
E-mail: philip.semren@umu.se

We consider first order perturbations on locally rotationally symmetric (LRS) class II spacetimes. In particular, we investigate the interactions between electromagnetic, gravitational, and plasma related perturbations when allowing for a non-zero magnetic field on the background spacetime. In doing so we focus on mechanisms for generating and magnifying the magnetic fields, as these kinds of mechanisms may have some relevance when trying to explain the origin of the observed large scale cosmic magnetic fields. The equations governing the behavior of the perturbations are gathered from the Ricci identities for certain preferred vector fields, the Bianchi identities, Maxwell's equations, and from relations describing energy-momentum conservation and particle conservation for the cosmological plasma. After employing a simplified cold magnetohydrodynamic (MHD) description, and harmonically decomposing the spatial dependencies, we arrive at a closed set of ordinary differential equations in time. On analyzing this system, which decouples into an even and an odd subsector, we indeed observe possible mechanisms for generating magnetic field perturbations to first order.

Keywords: Cosmological perturbations; LRS Class II; plasma; MHD.

1. Introduction

Using the standard ΛCDM model of cosmology, assumed to be homogeneous and isotropic on average, most of our current observations can be explained. However, as the bounds on a possible anisotropy in our universe still remains quite unrestrictive,[1,2] it is still interesting to study more general anisotropic models. These models have a special relevance when considering electromagnetic perturbations in a cosmological context. When using the standard models as background spacetimes in a perturbative approach, the isotropy of these models make it is essentially impossible to have a non-zero magnetic field on the zeroth order level, since such a field would define a preferred spatial direction. Therefore, when considering electromagnetic perturbations on a FLRW background, previous works have often found it necessary to employ a non-linear perturbation theory to maintain gauge invariance and to be able to see any interesting interactions between the electromagnetic fields and the variables related to gravitational effects.[3–5] However, using an anisotropic model as background spacetime, there is no fundamental problem of having a non-zero magnetic field to zeroth order.

In this work, we take a first step towards a more general anisotropic model by using a $1 + 1 + 2$ covariant split of spacetime to investigate linear perturbations on homogenous and hypersurface orthogonal locally rotationally symmetric (LRS) class II spacetimes. Since these spacetimes have a preferred spatial direction around which they are locally rotationally symmetric, we are able to include a magnetic field to zeroth order in a perturbative approach. The aim is then to investigate if this allows for interesting interactions between the electromagnetic fields and the gravitational variables already to first order in the perturbations.

As for linear perturbations on LRS class II cosmologies, these have been studied extensively before for perfect fluids, with and without vorticity.[6–8] A study of more general and dissipative perturbations can be found in Ref. 9 and in a forthcoming paper. Regarding electromagnetic perturbations, these have also been considered before, but, as far as we know, only when treating these perturbations as test fields or in rather restrictive cases.[10,11] This work therefore seeks to present a more general treatment of electromagnetic perturbations on LRS class II cosmologies when using a cold magnetohydrodynamic (MHD) approximation to describe the details of the cosmological plasma. However, in doing so, we will only outline the main steps and results. For more details, the reader is referred to Ref. 12 or a forthcoming paper to be published elsewhere.

2. Governing Equations

The studied LRS spacetimes are assumed to have two preferred directions, specified by a time-like vector field, u^a, and a space-like vector field n^a. These vector fields are assumed to be normalized as $u^a u_a = -1$ and $n^a n_a = 1$. The time-like direction could represent the 4-velocity of the cosmological fluid or some congruence of fundamental observers, whilst the spatial direction is the direction around which the spacetimes are locally rotationally symmetric.

2.1. *Spacetime Dynamics*

The characteristic directions u^a and n^a play a crucial role when describing the spacetime dynamics, as we will get many of our equations from the Ricci identities for these vector fields, namely

$$2\nabla_{[a}\nabla_{b]}u_c - R_{abcd}u^d = 0, \quad (1)$$

$$2\nabla_{[a}\nabla_{b]}n_c - R_{abcd}n^d = 0. \quad (2)$$

In addition to these equations, we will also make use of the contracted Bianchi identities

$$2\nabla_{[e}R_{d]b} + \nabla_a R^a{}_{bde} = 0, \quad (3)$$

$$\nabla^a G_{ab} = 0, \quad (4)$$

where $G_{ab} \equiv R_{ab} - g_{ab}R/2$ is the Einstein tensor. We will also implicitly enforce Einstein's field equations

$$G_{ab} = T_{ab} - \Lambda g_{ab}, \quad (5)$$

by using them to write the Ricci tensor and Ricci scalar in terms of the energy momentum tensor T_{ab} and the cosmological constant Λ.

Although the relations stated above will give us many of the equations that we need, they will in general not result in a closed set. To get the remaning relations, we also need to specify the detailed properties of the energy-momentum tensor.

2.2. Plasma Dynamics

In our case, where we want to describe a cosmological plasma together with its associated electromagnetic fields, we can divide the energy-momentum tensor as

$$T^{ab} = T_{(F)}{}^{ab} + T_{(EM)}{}^{ab}, \qquad (6)$$

where $T_{(F)}{}^{ab}$ is due to the fluid whilst $T_{(EM)}{}^{ab}$ is due to the electromagnetic fields. The electromagnetic part can be written as

$$T_{(EM)}{}^{ab} = F^a{}_c F^{bc} - \frac{1}{4} g^{ab} F^{cd} F_{cd}, \qquad (7)$$

in terms of the Faraday tensor F_{ab}, which in turn is assumed to satisfy Maxwell's equations

$$\nabla_{[a} F_{bc]} = 0, \qquad (8)$$

$$\nabla_b F^{ab} = j^a. \qquad (9)$$

Here j^a is the 4-current density, which can be written as $j^a = \rho u^a + J^a$ in terms of the charge density ρ and the 3-current density J^a, where $u^a J_a = 0$.

Following the formalism in Ref. 13, the behavior of the fluid contribution can be deduced by first treating the cosmological plasma as a charged multi-component fluid, where the ith component is assumed to have the 4-velocity

$$u_{(i)}{}^a = \gamma_{(i)} \left(u^a + v_{(i)}{}^a \right), \qquad (10)$$

with the properties

$$u^a v_{(i)a} = 0, \quad \gamma_{(i)} = \frac{1}{\sqrt{1 - v_{(i)}{}^2}}, \quad v_{(i)}{}^2 \equiv v_{(i)a} v_{(i)}{}^a. \qquad (11)$$

The dynamics of the ith component is then determined by imposing the following equations, describing conservation of energy-momentum and particles

$$\nabla_b T_{(i)}{}^{ab} = F^{ab} j_{(i)b} + I_{(i)}{}^a, \qquad (12)$$

$$\nabla_a \left(\mathcal{N}_{(i)} u_{(i)}{}^a \right) = 0. \qquad (13)$$

Here, $\mathcal{N}_{(i)}$ is the number density for the ith component relative to its own rest frame, whilst $T_{(i)}{}^{ab}$ is the energy-momentum contribution from this component, so that

$$T_{(F)}{}^{ab} = \sum_{(i)} T_{(i)}{}^{ab}. \qquad (14)$$

As for the right hand side in Eq. (12), $I_{(i)}{}^a$ includes interactions, such as collisions, between the fluid components, whilst $j_{(i)}{}^a$ is the 4-current density of the ith component, which satisfies the relations

$$j_{(i)}{}^a = q_{c(i)} \mathcal{N}_{(i)} u_{(i)}{}^a, \tag{15}$$

$$j^a = \sum_{(i)} j_{(i)}{}^a. \tag{16}$$

Here $q_{c(i)}$ is the charge of the ith species. Furthermore, we will also assume that the ith component is a perfect fluid, so that

$$T_{(i)}{}^{ab} = \left(\mu_{(i)} + p_{(i)}\right) u_{(i)}{}^a u_{(i)}{}^b + p_{(i)} g^{ab}, \tag{17}$$

where $\mu_{(i)}$ is the energy density and $p_{(i)}$ is the isotropic pressure relative to the rest frame of the fluid component. After specifying some reasonable equations of state $p_{(i)} = p_{(i)}(\mu_{(i)}, \mathcal{N}_{(i)})$, Eqs. (1)-(17) are enough to be able to get a closed system in the end. To simplify this system, we will in the following employ a cold MHD description. Instead of working directly with the individual fluid components, we then want to rewrite the system in terms of some collective variables. For this purpose, we will first assume that the plasma is sufficiently cold, so that the components can be seen as dust-like fluids with negligible pressures $p_{(i)}$. We will then, after having linearized the equations as described later on, rewrite the equations in terms of the following collective variables

$$\mu_{(F)} \equiv \sum_i \mu_{(i)},$$

$$\mu_{(F)} v_{(F)}{}^a \equiv \sum_i \mu_{(i)} v_{(i)}{}^a,$$

where $\mu_{(F)}$ is the total energy density of the fluid and $v_{(F)}{}^a$ is an average plasma 3-velocity. In the following we will assume that the plasma consists of an electron component and a much more massive ion counterpart. Then, on following the usual approximations of the resistive MHD description, it is possible to derive an Ohm's law of the form[a]

$$J^a = \frac{1}{\eta} \left(E^a + \epsilon^{abc} v_{(F)b} B_c \right),$$

which will be used to describe the 3-current density. Here, η is the electrical resistivity whilst E^a and B^a are the electric and magnetic fields as defined by the relation

$$F_{ab} = \epsilon_{abc} B^c + 2 u_{[a} E_{b]},$$

where $\epsilon_{abc} \equiv \eta_{dabc} u^d \equiv 4!\sqrt{-g}\delta^0{}_{[d}\delta^1{}_a\delta^2{}_b\delta^3{}_{c]} u^d$ is the 3-dimensional Levi-Civita volume element. As for the charge density, total charge neutrality is assumed on

---

[a] A simplified derivation starting from the linearized and harmonically decomposed multi-component equations can be found in Ref. 12.

the background spacetime, where the plasma velocities $u_{(i)}{}^a$ are assumed to coincide with the fundamental observers u^a. To first order, however, the charge density will be allowed to be non-zero, and is determined by the electromagnetic fields through Maxwell's equations in the MHD description.

Before delving deeper into the perturbations, however, we first break the relevant equations down into smaller pieces by using covariant splits of spacetime.

3. Covariant Splits of Spacetime

Since the studied background spacetimes are equipped with two preferred directions, it is natural to decompose our variables with respect to the vector fields u^a and n^a. We start by performing a $1+3$ split with respect to u^a, after which the 3-dimensional hypersurfaces orthogonal to u^a are decomposed with respect to n^a, yielding a $1+1+2$ covariant split of spacetime.[14]

3.1. $1+3$

Starting with the $1+3$ split, we first write the metric as

$$g_{ab} = U_{ab} + h_{ab}, \qquad (18)$$

where $U_{ab} = -u_a u_b$ is a projection tensor along u^a, whilst h_{ab} projects onto the 3-dimensional hypersurfaces orthogonal to u^a. Using Eq. (18) we may then decompose every other quantity with respect to u^a. This has already been done for the electromagnetic and plasma-related variables in the previous section, but we note the following new variables which emerge as projections of the total energy-momentum tensor and the Weyl tensor

$$\mu \equiv T^{cd} u_c u_d,$$
$$q_a \equiv -T^{cd} u_c h_{da},$$
$$p \equiv \frac{1}{3} T^{cd} h_{cd},$$
$$\pi_{ab} \equiv \left(h_{(a}{}^c h_{b)}{}^d - \frac{1}{3} h^{cd} h_{ab} \right) T_{cd} \equiv T_{\langle ab \rangle},$$
$$E_{ab} \equiv C_{acbd} u^c u^d,$$
$$H_{ab} \equiv \frac{1}{2} \epsilon_a{}^{ef} C_{efbd} u^d.$$

Here μ is the total energy density, q_a is the total energy flow relative to u^a, p is the total isotropic pressure, and π_{ab} is the total anisotropic pressure, whilst E_{ab} and H_{ab} are the electric and magnetic parts of the Weyl tensor C_{abcd}. When defining the anisotropic pressure, we have introduced a notation with angular brackets to denote the Projected Symmetric and Trace-Free (PSTF) part of a tensor with respect to h_{ab}.

To describe the spacetime dynamics, we also have to decompose the covariant derivatives. For this purpose we define a time derivative
$$\dot{T}^{ab...}{}_{cd...} \equiv u^e \nabla_e T^{ab...}{}_{cd...},$$
and a spatial derivative that is fully projected onto the 3-dimensional hypersurfaces
$$D_e T^{ab...}{}_{cd...} \equiv h^a{}_f h^b{}_g \cdots h_c{}^h h_d{}^i \cdots h_e{}^j \nabla_j T^{fg...}{}_{hi...}.$$
Using these definitions, we may write the covariant derivative of u^a as
$$\nabla_a u_b = -u_a \dot{u}_b + \frac{1}{3} \Theta h_{ab} + \omega_{ab} + \sigma_{ab},$$
where $\Theta \equiv D^a u_a$ is the expansion rate, $\omega_{ab} \equiv D_{[a} u_{b]}$ is the vorticity, and $\sigma_{ab} \equiv D_{\langle a} u_{b \rangle}$ is the shear. When dealing with the vorticity we will in the following use the vorticity 3-vector
$$\omega^a \equiv \frac{1}{2} \epsilon^{abc} \omega_{bc},$$
rather than the vorticity tensor.

3.2. 1+1+2

Having decomposed the relevant quantities with respect to u^a, we perform an additional decomposition with respect to n^a. After writing the projection tensor h_{ab} as
$$h_{ab} = N_{ab} + n_a n_b,$$
we may then write the relevant 3-vectors as
$$q^a = Q n^a + \mathcal{Q}^a, \qquad B^a = \mathcal{B} n^a + \mathcal{B}^a,$$
$$\omega^a = \Omega n^a + \Omega^a, \qquad E^a = \mathfrak{E} n^a + \mathfrak{E}^a,$$
$$\dot{u}^a = \mathcal{A} n^a + \mathcal{A}^a, \qquad J^a = \mathfrak{J} n^a + \mathfrak{J}^a,$$
$$\dot{n}^a = \mathcal{A} u^a + \alpha^a, \qquad v_{(F)}{}^a = \mathcal{V}_{(F)} n^a + \mathcal{V}_{(F)}{}^a,$$
where the rightmost vectors in each relation are orthogonal to both u^a and n^b. As for PSTF 3-tensors ψ_{ab}, we decompose these as
$$\psi_{ab} = \Psi \left(n_a n_b - \frac{1}{2} N_{ab} \right) + 2 n_{(a} \Psi_{b)} + \Psi_{ab},$$
where $n^a \Psi_a = 0$ and
$$\Psi_{ab} = \left(N_{(a}{}^c N_{b)}{}^d - \frac{1}{2} N_{ab} N^{cd} \right) \psi_{cd} \equiv \psi_{\{ab\}}.$$
Here we have introduced a notation with curly brackets to denote the PSTF part of a tensor with respect to N_{ab}. For the tensors relevant to us, we can therefore write
$$\pi_{ab} = \Pi \left(n_a n_b - \frac{1}{2} N_{ab} \right) + 2 n_{(a} \Pi_{b)} + \Pi_{ab},$$

$$E_{ab} = \mathcal{E}\left(n_a n_b - \frac{1}{2}N_{ab}\right) + 2n_{(a}\mathcal{E}_{b)} + \mathcal{E}_{ab},$$

$$H_{ab} = \mathcal{H}\left(n_a n_b - \frac{1}{2}N_{ab}\right) + 2n_{(a}\mathcal{H}_{b)} + \mathcal{H}_{ab},$$

$$\sigma_{ab} = \Sigma\left(n_a n_b - \frac{1}{2}N_{ab}\right) + 2n_{(a}\Sigma_{b)} + \Sigma_{ab}.$$

Finally, we also need to decompose the spatial derivatives. For this purpose we define a spatial derivative along n^a

$$\hat{T}^{ab\ldots}{}_{cd\ldots} \equiv n^e D_e T^{ab\ldots}{}_{cd\ldots},$$

and a spatial derivative fully projected onto the 2-sheets orthogonal to both u^a and n^a

$$\delta_e T^{ab\ldots}{}_{cd\ldots} \equiv N^a{}_f N^b{}_g \cdots N_c{}^h N_d{}^i \cdots N_e{}^j D_j T^{fg\ldots}{}_{hi\ldots}.$$

With these definitions, we may write the spatial derivative of n^a as

$$D_a n_b = n_a a_b + \frac{1}{2}\phi N_{ab} + \xi \epsilon_{ab} + \zeta_{ab},$$

where $\epsilon_{ab} \equiv \epsilon_{abc} n^c$, $\phi \equiv \delta^c n_c$ describes an expansion of the 2-sheets, $\xi \epsilon_{ab} \equiv \delta_{[a} n_{b]}$ describes a twist of these sheets, $\zeta_{ab} \equiv \delta_{\{a} n_{b\}}$ is the distortion, and $a_a \equiv \hat{n}_a$.

4. Background Spacetimes

Having decomposed the equations using the $1 + 1 + 2$ covariant split of spacetime, we move on to consider these equations perturbatively, starting with the zeroth order background spacetime. We will assume that this spacetime is a homogeneous and hypersurface orthogonal member of LRS class II, which is characterized by that $\mathcal{H}_{ab}$, ω_{ab} and ξ are all identically zero. To be able to use the same type of harmonics for all of the studied spacetimes, we will also assume that $\phi = 0$. These spacetimes can be described with the line element

$$ds^2 = -dt^2 + a_1^2(t)\,dz^2 + a_2^2(t)\left(d\vartheta^2 + f_\kappa(\vartheta)d\varphi^2\right),$$

where the scale factors a_1 and a_2 satisfy the relations

$$\Theta = \frac{\dot{a}_1}{a_1} + 2\frac{\dot{a}_2}{a_2},$$

$$\Sigma = \frac{2}{3}\left(\frac{\dot{a}_1}{a_1} - \frac{\dot{a}_2}{a_2}\right).$$

The function $f_\kappa(\vartheta)$ is determined by the 2D-curvature scalar

$$\mathcal{R} = \frac{2\kappa}{a_2^2} = 2(\mu + \Lambda) + \frac{3\Sigma^2}{2} - \frac{2\Theta^2}{3}.$$

When $\kappa = 1$, the sheets are 2-spheres with $f_1(\vartheta) = \sin^2 \vartheta$. If $\kappa = 0$ the 2-sheets are flat and $f_0(\vartheta) = 1$ (or ϑ^2). Lastly, if $\kappa = -1$, the 2-sheets are pseudo-spheres with $f_{-1}(\vartheta) = \sinh^2 \vartheta$.

As previously mentioned, we will to zeroth order assume charge neutrality and that the plasma velocities coincide with the fundamental observers. We will also assume that interactions between the plasma components, as described by the last term in Eq. (12), vanish to zeroth order. With these assumptions, our choice of background spacetimes implies that the only relevant non-zero dynamical quantities to zeroth order are

$$S^{(0)} = \{\Theta, \Sigma, \mu_{(F)}, \mathcal{B}, \mathcal{E}, \mu, p, \Pi\},$$

which are found to satisfy the equations

$$\dot{\Theta} = -\frac{\Theta^2}{3} - \frac{3\Sigma^2}{2} - \frac{1}{2}(\mu + 3p) + \Lambda,$$

$$\dot{\Sigma} = \frac{2}{3}(\mu + \Lambda) + \frac{\Sigma^2}{2} - \Sigma\Theta - \frac{2\Theta^2}{9} + \Pi,$$

$$\dot{\mu}_{(F)} = -\mu_{(F)}\Theta,$$

$$\dot{\mathcal{B}} = \left(\Sigma - \frac{2\Theta}{3}\right)\mathcal{B},$$

where

$$3\mathcal{E} = -2(\mu + \Lambda) - 3\Sigma^2 + \frac{2\Theta^2}{3} + \Sigma\Theta - \frac{3\Pi}{2},$$

$$\mu = \mu_{(F)} + \frac{\mathcal{B}^2}{2},$$

$$p = \frac{\mathcal{B}^2}{6},$$

$$\Pi = -\frac{2\mathcal{B}^2}{3}.$$

5. Perturbations

With the behavior of the background determined, we now move on to consider first order perturbations in the gravitational, electromagnetic and plasma-related variables. To ensure gauge invariance, we will use quantities which are zero on the background spacetime to describe the perturbations, as these are gauge invariant in accordance with the Stewart–Walker lemma.[15] However, since there are some non-zero variables on the background, we have to define some new variables to describe the perturbations in these quantities. For this purpose we take advantage of the background homogeneity and let the perturbations of the non-zero background variables be described by spatial gradients of these variables. Therefore, we define the following first order quantities[b]

$$X_a \equiv \delta_a \mathcal{E}, \quad V_a \equiv \delta_a \Sigma, \quad W_a \equiv \delta_a \Theta, \quad \mu_{(F)a} \equiv \delta_a \mu_{(F)},$$
$$Y_a \equiv \delta_a \Pi, \quad \mu_a \equiv \delta_a \mu, \quad p_a \equiv \delta_a p, \quad \mathcal{B}_a \equiv \delta_a \mathcal{B}.$$

Collecting these variables with those that are naturally zero on the background, the complete set of gauge invariant first order quantities are

$$S^{(1)} \equiv \{X_a, V_a, W_a, \mu_a, p_a, Y_a, \mathcal{A}, \mathcal{A}_a, \Sigma_a, \Sigma_{ab}, \mathcal{E}_a, \mathcal{E}_{ab},$$
$$\mathcal{H}, \mathcal{H}_a, \mathcal{H}_{ab}, \alpha_a, a_a, \xi, \phi, \zeta_{ab}, \Omega, \Omega_a, Q, Q_a, \Pi_a,$$
$$\mu_{(F)a}, \mathcal{V}_{(F)}, \mathcal{V}_{(F)a}, \mathfrak{E}, \mathfrak{E}_a, \mathfrak{B}_a, B_a, \rho, \mathfrak{J}, \mathfrak{J}_a\}.$$

To obtain the equations governing these variables to first order, we first rewrite the equations from Sec. 2 in terms of the variables in $S^{(1)}$ by using some commutation relations between the derivatives in the $1+1+2$ formalism. After removing terms which are of second order or higher in the variables in $S^{(1)}$, we arrive at a large set of coupled linear partial differential equations. To simplify the analysis of this system, we now perform a harmonic decomposition, whereby the system can be reduced to a closed set of ordinary differential equations in time.

6. Harmonic Decomposition

When performing the aforementioned harmonic decomposition, we will follow Ref. 7 and make use of the eigenfunctions $P^{k_\parallel}$ and $Q^{k_\perp}$, which are defined as functions satisfying

$$\hat{\Delta} P^{k_\parallel} = -\frac{k_\parallel^2}{a_1^2} P^{k_\parallel}, \quad \delta_a P^{k_\parallel} = 0, \quad \dot{P}^{k_\parallel} = 0,$$

$$\delta^2 Q^{k_\perp} = -\frac{k_\perp^2}{a_2^2} Q^{k_\perp}, \quad \hat{Q}^{k_\perp} = 0, \quad \dot{Q}^{k_\perp} = 0,$$

where $\hat{\Delta} \equiv n^a \nabla_a n^b \nabla_b$, and $\delta^2 = \delta_a \delta^a$, whilst $k_\parallel$ and $k_\perp$ are comoving dimensionless wave numbers along n^a and in the 2-sheets respectively. Using these harmonics, we may also define even and odd vector and tensor harmonics

$$Q^{k_\perp}{}_a = a_2 \delta_a Q^{k_\perp}, \quad Q^{k_\perp}{}_{ab} = a_2^2 \delta_{\{a} \delta_{b\}} Q^{k_\perp},$$
$$\bar{Q}^{k_\perp}{}_a = a_2 \epsilon_{ab} \delta^b Q^{k_\perp}, \quad \bar{Q}^{k_\perp}{}_{ab} = a_2^2 \epsilon_{c\{a} \delta^c \delta_{b\}} Q^{k_\perp},$$

where the odd harmonics are denoted with bars. Equipped with these harmonics, we decompose scalars Ψ, 2-vectors Ψ_a, and PSTF 2-tensors Ψ_{ab} as

$$\Psi = \sum_{k_\parallel, k_\perp} \Psi^S_{k_\parallel k_\perp} P^{k_\parallel} Q^{k_\perp},$$

---

[b]Instead of using the $\delta_a G$ gradients to describe perturbations of a variable G that is non-zero on the background, we could have defined our perturbations using the spatial $\hat{G}$ derivatives. However, after performing a harmonic decomposition, it can be shown that $\hat{G}$ can be written in terms of $\delta_a G$ and the vorticity.[8]

$$\Psi_a = \sum_{k_\|,k_\perp} P^{k_\|} \left(\Psi^V_{k_\| k_\perp} Q^{k_\perp}{}_a + \overline{\Psi}^V_{k_\| k_\perp} \overline{Q}^{k_\perp}{}_a \right),$$

$$\Psi_{ab} = \sum_{k_\|,k_\perp} P^{k_\|} \left(\Psi^T_{k_\| k_\perp} Q^{k_\perp}{}_{ab} + \overline{\Psi}^T_{k_\| k_\perp} \overline{Q}^{k_\perp}{}_{ab} \right),$$

where the coefficients $\{\Psi^{S,V,T}_{k_\| k_\perp}, \overline{\Psi}^{V,T}_{k_\| k_\perp}\}$ now only depend on time. In the following we will omit the wave number indices on these coefficients when there is no risk of ambiguity.

7. Final System

After performing the harmonic decompositions described in the previous section, the first order linearized partial differential equations reduce to a set of constraints and ordinary differential equations in time for the harmonic coefficients. On using the constraints to solve for some of the coefficients in terms of the others, the system can be reduced significantly. In doing so, we also use the remaining freedom of specifying the dyad $\{u^a, n^a\}$ to first order to set a_a, $\mathcal{A}_a$, and $\mathcal{A}$ to zero. We are then left with two separate sectors, one so-called odd sector and one even sector, which decouple from each other. The odd sector consists of the coefficients

$$\{\Omega^S, \overline{\mathcal{E}}^T, \mathcal{H}^T, \overline{\mathcal{V}}_{(F)}{}^V, \mathcal{E}^S, \mathcal{E}^V, \overline{\mathcal{B}}^V\},$$

whilst the even sector contains the coefficients

$$\{\overline{\Omega}^V, \overline{\mathcal{H}}^T, \mathcal{E}^T, \Sigma^T, \mu_{(F)}{}^V, \mathcal{V}_{(F)}{}^S, \mathcal{V}_{(F)}{}^V, \mathcal{B}^V, \overline{\mathcal{E}}^V\}.$$

These sectors form closed sets in the sense that we have evolution equations for all of the coefficients above. As for the remaining coefficients, these can be given algebraically in terms of the ones above.

7.1. *Odd Sector*

The coefficients in the odd sector are found to satisfy the equations

$$\dot{\Omega}^S = \tilde{F}\Omega^S,$$

$$\dot{\overline{\mathcal{E}}}^T = -\frac{3}{2}(F + \Sigma D)\overline{\mathcal{E}}^T + \frac{ik_\|}{a_1}(1-D)\mathcal{H}^T$$
$$+ P\Omega^S + \frac{1}{a_2}(1+D)\left(\mu_{(F)}\overline{\mathcal{V}}_{(F)}{}^V + \mathcal{B}\mathcal{E}^V\right),$$

$$\mathcal{H}^T = \left(\frac{3ia_1\Pi}{k_\| k_\perp^2}\left(\Sigma + \frac{\Theta}{3}\right) + S\right)\Omega^S + \frac{1}{a_2}\mathcal{B}\overline{\mathcal{B}}^V$$
$$+ \frac{ia_1}{a_2 k_\| B}\left(\left(\Sigma + \frac{\Theta}{3}\right)\left(3\Pi + \frac{k_\perp^2}{a_2^2}\right) - \frac{k_\|^2}{a_1^2}\tilde{F}\right)\left(\mu_{(F)}\overline{\mathcal{V}}_{(F)}{}^V + \mathcal{B}\mathcal{E}^V\right)$$
$$+ \frac{ia_1}{2k_\|}\left(\frac{2k_\|^2}{a_1^2} - CB + 9\Sigma E + 3\Pi\right)\overline{\mathcal{E}}^T - \frac{3}{2}(2E + F)\mathcal{H}^T,$$

$$\dot{\mathcal{V}}_{(F)}^{V} = \frac{\mathcal{B}}{\eta\mu_{(F)}}\left(\mathcal{E}^{V} - \mathcal{B}\overline{\mathcal{V}}_{(F)}^{V}\right) + \frac{1}{2}\left(\Sigma - \frac{2\Theta}{3}\right)\overline{\mathcal{V}}_{(F)}^{V},$$

$$\dot{\mathcal{E}}^{S} = \frac{k_{\perp}^{2}}{a_{2}}\overline{\mathcal{B}}^{V} - \frac{2ia_{1}}{k_{\parallel}}\mathcal{B}\left(\Sigma + \frac{\Theta}{3}\right)\Omega^{S} + \left(\Sigma - \frac{2\Theta}{3} - \frac{1}{\eta}\right)\mathcal{E}^{S}, \tag{19}$$

$$\dot{\mathcal{E}}^{V} = \frac{ik_{\parallel}}{a_{1}}\overline{\mathcal{B}}^{V} - \frac{1}{2}\left(\Sigma + \frac{4\Theta}{3}\right)\mathcal{E}^{V} - \frac{1}{\eta}\left(\mathcal{E}^{V} - \mathcal{B}\overline{\mathcal{V}}_{(F)}^{V}\right) - \frac{2a_{2}\dot{\mathcal{B}}}{k_{\perp}^{2}}\Omega^{S}, \tag{20}$$

$$\dot{\mathcal{B}}^{V} = \left(\frac{ik_{\parallel}}{a_{1}}\mathcal{E}^{V} - \frac{1}{a_{2}}\mathcal{E}^{S}\right) - \frac{1}{2}\left(\Sigma + \frac{4\Theta}{3}\right)\overline{\mathcal{B}}^{V}$$

$$- \frac{ia_{1}}{k_{\parallel}}\mathcal{B}\left[\frac{2\left(\mathcal{R}a_{2}^{2} - k_{\perp}^{2}\right)}{a_{2}B}\left(\frac{3\Sigma}{2}\overline{\mathcal{E}}^{T} + \frac{ik_{\parallel}}{a_{1}}\mathcal{H}^{T}\right)\right.$$

$$- \frac{2}{B}\left(3\Sigma\left(\Sigma + \frac{\Theta}{3}\right) + \frac{2k_{\parallel}^{2}}{a_{1}^{2}}\right)\left(\mu_{(F)}\overline{\mathcal{V}}_{(F)}^{V} + \mathcal{B}\mathcal{E}^{V}\right)$$

$$\left. - \frac{a_{2}}{k_{\perp}^{2}}\left(\mu + p - \frac{\Pi}{2} - 3\mathcal{E} + 2N + 3\Sigma\left(\Sigma + \frac{\Theta}{3}\right) + \frac{2k_{\parallel}^{2}}{a_{1}^{2}}\right)\Omega^{S}\right], \tag{21}$$

where we have defined the following auxiliary variables

$$\tilde{k}^{2} = \frac{k_{\perp}^{2}}{a_{2}^{2}} + \frac{2k_{\parallel}^{2}}{a_{1}^{2}},$$

$$B = \tilde{k}^{2} + \frac{9}{2}\Sigma^{2} + 3\left(\mathcal{E} + \frac{1}{2}\Pi\right),$$

$$CB = \Sigma\left(\Theta - \frac{3\Sigma}{2}\right) - \frac{k_{\perp}^{2}}{a_{2}^{2}},$$

$$F = \Sigma + \frac{2\Theta}{3},$$

$$\tilde{F} = \Sigma - \frac{2\Theta}{3},$$

$$D = C + \frac{\mu + p - 2\Pi}{B},$$

$$P = \frac{2}{k_{\perp}^{2}B}\left(\mu + p - \frac{1}{2}\Pi\right)\left(B + 3\mathcal{E} + \mu + p - \frac{1}{2}\Pi + \mathcal{R} - \frac{k_{\perp}^{2}}{a_{2}^{2}}\right),$$

$$S = \frac{2ia_{1}}{3k_{\parallel}k_{\perp}^{2}B}\left(\mu + p - \frac{1}{2}\Pi\right)\left(3\Sigma\left(\frac{k_{\perp}^{2}}{a_{2}^{2}} - \frac{k_{\parallel}^{2}}{a_{1}^{2}} + 3\Pi\right) + \Theta\left(\tilde{k}^{2} + 3\Pi\right)\right),$$

$$EB = \frac{\Sigma}{2}\left(CB - \mathcal{E} - \frac{5}{2}\Pi\right) + \frac{\Theta}{3}\left(\mathcal{E} - \frac{1}{2}\Pi\right),$$

$$N = \left(\mu + p - \frac{1}{2}\Pi\right)\left(1 + \frac{2}{a_{2}^{2}B}\left(\mathcal{R}a_{2}^{2} - k_{\perp}^{2}\right)\right).$$

7.2. Even Sector

As for the even sector, its coefficients satisfy the equations

$$\dot{\mu}_{(F)}^V = \left(\frac{\Sigma}{2} - \frac{4\Theta}{3} - \frac{3\Sigma\mu_{(F)}}{2B}\right)\mu_{(F)}^V - \frac{3\Sigma\mu_{(F)}\mathcal{B}}{2B}\mathcal{B}^V$$
$$+ \frac{ia_1\mu_{(F)}}{2a_2 k_\|}\left(\left(1 - \frac{3\Sigma}{B}\left(\Sigma + \frac{\Theta}{3}\right)\right)\mu_{(F)} - \frac{2k_\|^2}{a_1^2}\right)\mathcal{V}_{(F)}{}^S$$
$$- \mu_{(F)}\left(\left(1 + \frac{3\Sigma}{2B}\left(\Sigma - \frac{2\Theta}{3}\right)\right)\mu_{(F)} - \frac{k_\perp^2}{a_2^2}\right)\mathcal{V}_{(F)}{}^V$$
$$+ \frac{3a_2\Sigma\mu_{(F)}}{2}(C-1)\mathcal{E}^T - \frac{a_2 B\mu_{(F)}}{2}(C-1)\Sigma^T$$
$$- \frac{ia_2 k_\| \mu_{(F)}}{2a_1}(J-2)\overline{\mathcal{H}}^T - \frac{ia_1\mu_{(F)}}{k_\|}\left(\frac{G}{B} + \frac{2k_\|^2}{a_1^2}\right)\overline{\Omega}^V$$
$$+ \frac{\mathcal{B}\mu_{(F)}}{2B}\left(2B + 3\Sigma\left(\Sigma - \frac{2\Theta}{3}\right)\right)\overline{\mathcal{E}}^V,$$

$$\dot{\mathcal{B}}^V = \frac{ia_1\mathcal{B}\mu_{(F)}}{a_2 k_\| B}\left(B - 3\Sigma\left(\Sigma + \frac{\Theta}{3}\right)\right)\mathcal{V}_{(F)}{}^S$$
$$- \frac{3\mathcal{B}\Sigma}{B}\mu_{(F)}{}^V + 3a_2\mathcal{B}\Sigma C\mathcal{E}^T - a_2 \mathcal{B}BC\Sigma^T - \frac{ia_2 k_\| \mathcal{B}J}{a_1}\overline{\mathcal{H}}^T \quad (22)$$
$$- \frac{2ia_1 \mathcal{B} G}{k_\| B}\overline{\Omega}^V + \left(\frac{3\Sigma\mathcal{B}^2}{B}\left(\Sigma - \frac{2\Theta}{3}\right) - \frac{k_\perp^2}{a_2^2}\right)\overline{\mathcal{E}}^V$$
$$+ \frac{3}{2}\left(\Sigma - \frac{2\Theta}{3} - \frac{2\Sigma\mathcal{B}^2}{B}\right)\mathcal{B}^V - \frac{3\mathcal{B}\Sigma\mu_{(F)}}{B}\left(\Sigma - \frac{2\Theta}{3}\right)\mathcal{V}_{(F)}{}^V,$$

$$\dot{\overline{\mathcal{E}}}^V = \frac{2a_2^2 k_\|^2 \mathcal{B}}{a_1^2 k_\perp^2 B}\mu_{(F)}{}^V + \frac{2ia_2 k_\| \mathcal{B}\mu_{(F)}}{a_1 k_\perp^2 B}\left(\Sigma + \frac{\Theta}{3}\right)\mathcal{V}_{(F)}{}^S$$
$$+ \left(\frac{2a_2^2 k_\|^2 \mu_{(F)}}{a_1^2 k_\perp^2 B}\left(\Sigma - \frac{2\Theta}{3}\right) - \frac{1}{\eta}\right)\mathcal{B}\mathcal{V}_{(F)}{}^V$$
$$+ \left(\frac{Ra_2^2 - k_\perp^2}{a_2 B} - \frac{a_2^3 \Sigma L}{k_\perp^2}\right)\mathcal{B}\mathcal{E}^T + \frac{a_2^3 \mathcal{B}BL}{3k_\perp^2}\Sigma^T + \frac{2ia_2^3 k_\| \mathcal{B}L}{3a_1 k_\perp^2}\overline{\mathcal{H}}^T \quad (23)$$
$$+ \frac{4ia_2^2 k_\| \mathcal{B}}{a_1 k_\perp^2 B}(\mu + p + \Pi)\left(\Sigma + \frac{\Theta}{3}\right)\overline{\Omega}^V$$
$$- \left(\frac{\Sigma}{2} + \frac{2\Theta}{3} + \frac{1}{\eta} + \frac{2a_2^2 k_\|^2 \mathcal{B}^2}{a_1^2 k_\perp^2 B}\left(\Sigma - \frac{2\Theta}{3}\right)\right)\overline{\mathcal{E}}^V$$
$$+ \left(1 + \frac{a_2^2 k_\|^2}{a_1^2 k_\perp^2}\left(1 + \frac{2\mathcal{B}^2}{B}\right)\right)\mathcal{B}^V,$$

$$\dot{\overline{\Omega}}^V = -\left(\frac{2\Theta}{3} + \frac{\Sigma}{2}\right)\overline{\Omega}^V,$$

$$\dot{\mathcal{V}}_{(F)}^S = -\left(\Sigma + \frac{\Theta}{3}\right)\mathcal{V}_{(F)}^S,$$

$$\dot{\mathcal{V}}_{(F)}^V = \frac{1}{2}\left(\Sigma - \frac{2\Theta}{3} - \frac{2\mathcal{B}^2}{\eta\mu_{(F)}}\right)\mathcal{V}_{(F)}^V - \frac{\mathcal{B}}{\eta\mu_{(F)}}\overline{\mathcal{E}}^V,$$

$$\dot{\Sigma}^T = \left(\Sigma - \frac{2\Theta}{3}\right)\Sigma^T - \mathcal{E}^T,$$

$$\dot{\mathcal{H}}^T = -\frac{ik_\parallel}{a_1 a_2 B}\left(1 - \frac{2a_2^2\mathcal{B}^2}{k_\perp^2}\right)\left(\mu_{(F)}^{\,V} + \mathcal{B}\mathcal{B}^V\right) + \frac{ia_2 k_\parallel}{a_1 k_\perp^2}\mathcal{B}\mathcal{B}^V$$

$$+ \frac{2}{a_2 B}(\mu + p + \Pi)\left(\Sigma + \frac{\Theta}{3}\right)\left(1 - \frac{2a_2^2\mathcal{B}^2}{k_\perp^2}\right)\overline{\Omega}^V$$

$$+ \frac{1}{a_2^2 B}\left(1 - \frac{2a_2^2\mathcal{B}^2}{k_\perp^2}\right)\left(\Sigma + \frac{\Theta}{3}\right)\mu_{(F)}\mathcal{V}_{(F)}^S$$

$$- \frac{ik_\parallel}{a_1 a_2 B}\left(1 - \frac{2a_2^2\mathcal{B}^2}{k_\perp^2}\right)\left(\Sigma - \frac{2\Theta}{3}\right)\left(\mu_{(F)}\mathcal{V}_{(F)}^V - \mathcal{B}\overline{\mathcal{E}}^V\right)$$

$$+ \frac{ia_1}{k_\parallel}\left(\frac{a_2^2\mathcal{B}^2 BL}{3k_\perp^2} + \frac{3\Pi}{2}\left(\Sigma + \frac{\Theta}{3}\right)\right)\Sigma^T$$

$$- \frac{ia_1}{k_\parallel}\left(\frac{3\Pi}{2} + (1-C)\frac{k_\parallel^2}{a_1^2} - \frac{\mathcal{B}^2}{a_2}\left(\frac{\mathcal{R}a_2^2 - k_\perp^2}{a_2 B} - \frac{a_2^3 \Sigma L}{k_\perp^2}\right)\right)\mathcal{E}^T$$

$$- \left(\frac{2a_2^2 \mathcal{B}^2 L}{3k_\perp^2} + \frac{3}{2}\left(F + \frac{M}{B}\right)\right)\mathcal{H}^T,$$

$$\dot{\mathcal{E}}^T = -\frac{3}{2}(F + \Sigma C)\mathcal{E}^T + \frac{ik_\parallel}{2a_1}(J - 2)\overline{\mathcal{H}}^T$$

$$- \frac{1}{2}(\mu + p - 2\Pi)\Sigma^T + \frac{3\Sigma}{2a_2 B}\left(\mu_{(F)}^{\,V} + \mathcal{B}\mathcal{B}^V\right) + \frac{ia_1 G}{a_2 k_\parallel B}\overline{\Omega}^V$$

$$- \frac{ia_1}{2a_2^2 k_\parallel B}\left(B - 3\Sigma\left(\Sigma + \frac{\Theta}{3}\right)\right)\mu_{(F)}\mathcal{V}_{(F)}^S$$

$$- \frac{1}{a_2 B}\left(B - \frac{3\Sigma}{2}\left(\Sigma - \frac{2\Theta}{3}\right)\right)\left(\mu_{(F)}\mathcal{V}_{(F)}^V - \mathcal{B}\overline{\mathcal{E}}^V\right),$$

where we have introduced the additional auxiliary variables

$$M = 2\left(\varepsilon + \frac{\Pi}{2}\right)\left(\Sigma + \frac{\Theta}{3}\right) + \frac{\Sigma}{a_2^2}\left(\mathcal{R}a_2^2 - k_\perp^2\right),$$

$$JB = \frac{a_1^2 k_\perp^2}{a_2^2 k_\parallel^2}\left(\mathcal{R} - \tilde{k}^2\right) - 3\Sigma\left(\Sigma - \frac{2\Theta}{3}\right),$$

$$G = (\mu + p + \Pi)\left(\mathcal{R} - \tilde{k}^2\right),$$

$$LB = 3\Sigma\left(\frac{k_\perp^2}{a_2^2} - \frac{k_\parallel^2}{a_1^2}\right) + \Theta \tilde{k}^2.$$

8. Discussion and Outlook

From Eqs. (19)-(23), which describe the evolution of the electromagnetic fields, we see that mechanisms for generating magnetic fields from perturbations in variables related to gravitational effects, such as the magnetic part of the Weyl tensor, indeed seem to exist. These mechanisms can be explicitly seen when solving the system numerically.[12] However, the mechanisms depend fundamentally on $\mathfrak{B}$ being non-zero, since the electromagnetic evolution equations decouple completely from the other first order equations when $\mathfrak{B} = 0$. Since a background anisotropy is needed to have a non-zero B-field, these mechanisms are therefore crucially dependent on the LRS nature of the zeroth order solution, at least to first order in the perturbations.

As we were, in the end, able to observe mechanisms for generating magnetic field perturbations, an interesting question is whether or not these results can be used to shed some light on the origin of the observed large scale cosmic magnetic fields. However, determining the viability of these mechanisms as candidates for amplifying primordial magnetic seeds would require a deeper investigation regarding the initial conditions and the primordial seed spectra, and is therefore left for future work.

References

1. D. L. Wiltshire, P. R. Smale, T. Mattsson and R. Watkins, Hubble flow variance and the cosmic rest frame, *Phys. Rev. D* **88**, p. 083529 (2013).
2. R.-G. Cai and Z.-L. Tuo, Direction Dependence of the Deceleration Parameter, *JCAP* **02**, p. 004 (2012).
3. G. Betschart, C. Zunckel, P. Dunsby and M. Marklund, Primordial magnetic seed field amplification by gravitational waves, *Phys. Rev. D* **72**, p. 123514 (2005).
4. C. Zunckel, G. Betschart, P. K. S. Dunsby and M. Marklund, On inhomogeneous magnetic seed fields and gravitational waves within the MHD limit, *Phys. Rev. D* **73**, p. 103509 (2006).
5. B. Mongwane, P. K. S. Dunsby and B. Osano, Cosmic Electromagnetic Fields due to Perturbations in the Gravitational Field, *Phys. Rev. D* **86**, p. 083533 (2012).
6. Z. Keresztes, M. Forsberg, M. Bradley, P. K. Dunsby and L. Gergely, Gravitational, shear and matter waves in Kantowski-Sachs cosmologies, *JCAP* **11**, p. 042 (2015).
7. M. Bradley, M. Forsberg and Z. Keresztes, Gravitational Waves in Locally Rotationally Symmetric (LRS) Class II Cosmologies, *Universe* **3**, p. 69 (2017).
8. R. Törnkvist and M. Bradley, General Perfect Fluid Perturbations of Homogeneous and Orthogonal Locally Rotationally Symmetric Class II Cosmologies, *Phys. Rev. D* **100**, p. 124043 (2019).
9. P. Semrén, Dissipative perturbations on LRS class II cosmologies using the 1+1+2 covariant split of spacetime, Master's thesis, Umeå University (2020).
10. G. Betschart and C. A. Clarkson, Scalar and electromagnetic perturbations on LRS class II space-times, *Class. Quant. Grav.* **21**, 5587 (2004).
11. M. Marklund and C. Clarkson, The General relativistic MHD dynamo, *Mon. Not. Roy. Astron. Soc.* **358**, p. 892 (2005).
12. P. Semrén, On the Interaction Between Electromagnetic, Gravitational, and Plasma Related Perturbations on LRS Class II Spacetimes, Master's thesis, Umeå University (2021).

13. M. Marklund, P. K. S. Dunsby, M. Servin, G. Betschart and C. Tsagas, Charged multifluids in general relativity, *Class. Quant. Grav.* **20**, 1823 (2003).
14. C. Clarkson, A Covariant approach for perturbations of rotationally symmetric spacetimes, *Phys. Rev. D* **76**, p. 104034 (2007).
15. J. M. Stewart and M. Walker, Perturbations of space-times in general relativity, *Proceedings of the Royal Society of London. A. Mathematical and Physical Sciences* **341**, 49 (1974).

Condition for expansion-collapse duality between Einstein and Jordan frames

Dipayan Mukherjee[*], H. K. Jassal[†] and Kinjalk Lochan[‡]

Indian Institute of Science Education and Research Mohali,
SAS Nagar, Mohali-140306, Punjab, India
E-mails: [*]ph17011@iisermohali.ac.in, [†]hkjassal@iisermohali.ac.in, [‡]kinjalk@iisermohali.ac.in

Quintessence fields, or scalar fields minimally coupled to gravity, are considered to be viable candidates for dark energy. It is well-known that some classes of modified theories of gravity can be recast as Einstein's general relativity with a minimally coupled scalar field, through conformal transformation. The 'universe' described by the initial and the final actions are referred to as the Jordan and Einstein frames, respectively. Although these conformally connected frames are mathematically equivalent, the equations of motion in these two frames may describe drastically different physical scenarios. Depending upon the choice of the Jordan frame action (or equivalently the scalar field potential in Einstein frame) it is possible that while the Einstein frame expands, the Jordan frame collapses. We classify quintessence models in the Einstein frame that are dual to $f(R)$ gravity theories in the Jordan frame, based on whether they possess such expansion-collapse duality. We derive a general condition for expansion-collapse duality, applicable to quintessence models with arbitrary time-dependent equations of state. The condition also takes into account the presence of other components in the Einstein frame universe. Such expansion-collapse duality between these conformally connected frames can lead to an effective description of a collapsing universe in terms of an expanding one, which is a topic of further exploration.

Keywords: $f(R)$ theories; quintessence; dark energy; Einstein and Jordan frames

1. Introduction

The quintessence model, or scalar fields minimally coupled to gravity, is a widely used implementation of dark energy in Einstein's gravity.[1-5] As an alternative to the cosmological constant model, quintessence fields (φ) can provide a simple dynamical description of the late-time acceleration of the universe. The equation of state of quintessence (w_φ) can violate the strong energy condition if the potential term ($V(\varphi)$) is set to be sufficiently flat. In general, w_φ can vary with time. One can introduce the time-dependence in w_φ by postulating a parameterization of the form $w_\varphi(a; w_0, w_1, \ldots)$,[6-10] where a is the scale factor and $w_0, w_1 \ldots$ are constant parameters of the model, usually constrained from different cosmological observations.

It is also well-known that some classes of modified theories of gravity can provide a dual description of minimally coupled scalar fields in Einstein gravity, in a conformally connected frame.[11-14] $f(R)$ theory is a simple modification of Einstein gravity, where the Ricci scalar (R) in the Einstein–Hilbert action is replaced with an arbitrary function of the Ricci scalar ($f(R)$) (for reviews, see [11, 12]). The 'universe' governed by the $f(R)$ theory is referred to as the *Jordan frame universe*. A conformal transformation allows for the Jordan frame action to be written as the Einstein–Hilbert action with a quintessence field (for reviews, see [11, 14, 15]). The 'universe' described by the latter action is referred to as the *Einstein frame universe*. Thus, one may consider that dark energy, as implemented by a quintessence field in Einstein gravity, has an equivalent description in terms of a pure $f(R)$ gravity theory in the conformally connected Jordan frame.

Although Einstein and Jordan frames are mathematically equivalent, the field equations in these two frames may describe drastically different universes. In this paper, we are interested in quintessence–$f(R)$ pairs for which, while the Einstein frame universe expands, the Jordan frame universe collapses. We derive a simple condition for such expansion-collapse duality for quintessence models with arbitrary, time-varying equation of state parameters. The condition is general enough to accommodate any other components in the Einstein frame, such as dust or radiation. As an example, we study the quintessence model with logarithmic equation of state[6, 10, 16] ($w_\varphi(a) = w_0 - w' \ln a$) and discuss the possibility of the expansion-collapse duality in the presence of non-relativistic matter and spatial curvature component.

A quintessence model–$f(R)$ theory pair with the expansion-collapse duality essentially provides a description of an expanding universe in terms of a collapsing one. This map between expanding and collapsing geometries may lead to potentially interesting results; for example, introducing perturbation in the background of FRW metric one can study how the evolution of perturbations in the expanding frame corresponds to the perturbations in the collapsing one. This will be pursued elsewhere.

This paper is organized as follows. In Sec. 2 we start with a brief review of the Jordan frame–Einstein frame correspondence in the context of $f(R)$ gravity. Our main result, the expansion-collapse duality condition is presented in Sec. 3. In Sec. 4 we conclude with a summary and discussion.

2. $f(R)$ gravity and quintessence: Einstein and Jordan frames

Let us consider that the Jordan frame universe is governed by the action of an $f(R)$ theory,

$$S_J = \frac{1}{2\kappa^2} \int d^4x \sqrt{-g} f(R), \tag{1}$$

where $\kappa = 8\pi G$, R is the Ricci scalar in Jordan frame, $f(R)$ is an arbitrary function of R. The Jordan frame metric $g_{\mu\nu}$ is the spatially flat FRW metric, i.e., $g_{\mu\nu} \equiv \mathrm{diag}(-1, a^2, a^2, a^2)$, and $a(t)$ is the scale factor in the Jordan frame (see [11, 12] for general reviews on $f(R)$ theories). One can then define a new metric using a conformal transformation,

$$\tilde{g}_{\mu\nu} = \Omega^2(x) g_{\mu\nu}. \tag{2}$$

If the conformal parameter Ω^2 is taken to be $\Omega^2 = \partial f/\partial R = F(R)$, then the same Jordan frame action can be recast in terms of the new metric $\tilde{g}_{\mu\nu}$ as,

$$S_E = \int d^4x \sqrt{-\tilde{g}} \frac{1}{2\kappa^2} \tilde{R} - \int d^4x \sqrt{-\tilde{g}} \left[\frac{1}{2} \tilde{g}^{\mu\nu} \partial_\mu \varphi \partial_\nu \varphi + V(\varphi) \right], \quad (3)$$

where $\tilde{R}$ is the Ricci scalar in Einstein frame[17] and

$$\varphi = \frac{\sqrt{6}}{2\kappa} \ln F, \quad (4a)$$

$$V = \frac{1}{2\kappa^2} \frac{FR - f}{F^2}. \quad (4b)$$

The first part of the action in (3) is the Einstein–Hilbert action with respect to the metric $\tilde{g}_{\mu\nu}$, the second part is the action of a minimally coupled scalar field φ, with potential V. Equation (3) is the action in the Einstein frame universe.

On the other hand, if we consider the Einstein frame to be the physical frame, then the scalar field action in (3) can play the role of the quintessence model of dark energy. The equation of state parameter of φ can be computed as[5,9]

$$w_\varphi = \frac{P_\varphi}{\rho_\varphi} = \frac{\frac{1}{2}\dot{\varphi}^2 - V}{\frac{1}{2}\dot{\varphi}^2 + V}, \quad (5)$$

where P_φ and ρ_φ are the pressure and energy density associated with the quintessence field φ. As we can see from (5), for sufficiently flat potential ($V \gg \dot{\varphi}^2$) w_φ can become $w_\varphi < -1/3$, allowing for the scalar field to drive the acceleration in the Einstein frame.

As a simple example, let us consider a quintessence model with constant equation of state parameter w_φ. The quintessence potential in this case takes the form[16]

$$V(\varphi) = \frac{1}{2}(1-w)\rho_0 \exp\left(-\sqrt{3\kappa^2(1+w)}(\varphi)\right). \quad (6)$$

One can then solve the differential equation (4b), using (4a) and (6), and reconstruct the correspond $f(R)$ action in the Jordan frame as (see [18] for details)

$$f(R) = C_1 R - A_1 C_1^b \text{ or} \quad (7a)$$

$$f(R) = \frac{b-1}{b(A_1 b)^{\frac{1}{b-1}}} R^{\frac{b}{b-1}}, \quad (7b)$$

where, $A_1 = \kappa^2 \rho_0 (1-w)$, $b = -\frac{3}{\sqrt{2}}\sqrt{1+w} + 2$.

In general, the equation of state of the quintessence field can be a function of time. One usually starts with a parameterized time-dependent ansatz for w_φ and then constrains the parameters of the model from cosmological observations (for different parameterizations of equation of state see [6–10]). In this work, we consider the logarithmic parameterization as an example of time-dependent equation of state ([6, 16]), given by

$$w_\varphi(\tilde{a}) = w_0 - w' \ln \tilde{a}, \quad (8)$$

where $\tilde{a}$ is the scale factor in Einstein frame, (w_0, w') are two constant parameters of the model. The values of (w_0, w') are constrained from different cosmological observations in [10, 16]. The quintessence field Φ for this model can be solved as a function of the scale factor as,[16]

$$\varphi(\tilde{a}) = \Phi(\tilde{a}) - \Phi_0 = \frac{2}{\sqrt{3}} \frac{1}{\kappa w'} \left[(1+w_0)^{\frac{3}{2}} - (1 + w_0 - w' \ln \tilde{a})^{\frac{3}{2}} \right], \qquad (9)$$

where Φ_0 is the value of the scalar field at current Einstein frame, i.e. at $\tilde{a} = 1$. We take $w' < 0$ to ensure that the field remains real valued in the late time limit of the Einstein frame $\tilde{a} \to \infty$. In the paper,[18] we used analytical approximations to reconstruct $F(R)$ corresponding to this quintessence model in two parts. First, we derived a perturbative solution in the small R limit, which is applicable in the near future of the Einstein frame. Second, we also obtained a non-perturbative, asymptotic form of $F(R)$ in the late time limit of the Einstein frame. However, as we will see later, the condition for the expansion-collapse duality does not directly depend on the form of the $f(R)$ function. We will hence not discuss the reconstruction of the Jordan frame action here. More details in this regard can be found in [18].

Having summarized the key features of the Einstein-Jordan frame correspondence, we now discuss the main results in the following section.

3. Expansion-collapse duality

A pure $f(R)$ action in the Jordan frame (1) gives rise to only a quintessence field in Einstein gravity in the Einstein frame (3). In order to incorporate the presence of any other matter components in the Einstein frame, the Jordan frame action (3) must be modified. Moreover, since we consider the Einstein frame to be the physical frame, we want the field equations in the Einstein frame to lead to the usual Friedmann equations. Essentially, we want the Einstein frame action to have the form

$$S_E = \int d^4x \sqrt{-\tilde{g}} \frac{1}{2\kappa^2} \tilde{R} - \int d^4x \sqrt{-\tilde{g}} \left[\frac{1}{2} \tilde{g}^{\mu\nu} \partial_\mu \varphi \partial_\nu \varphi + V(\varphi) \right]$$
$$+ \int d^4x \sqrt{-\tilde{g}} \mathcal{L}_M(\psi_M; \tilde{g}_{\mu\nu}), \qquad (10)$$

where $\mathcal{L}_M(\psi_M; \tilde{g}_{\mu\nu})$ is the Lagrangian density of some matter field ψ_M, which is independent of the quintessence field φ. In order to arrive at the Einstein frame action (10), we postulate the following Jordan frame action in the presence of matter,

$$S_J = \frac{1}{2\kappa^2} \int d^4x \sqrt{-g} f(R) + \int d^4x \sqrt{-g} F^2(R) \mathcal{L}_M(\psi_M; F(R) g_{\mu\nu}). \qquad (11)$$

It can be easily verified that the conformal transformation $\tilde{g}_{\mu\nu} = F g_{\mu\nu}$ gives back the desired Einstein frame action (10). It is to be noted that in the modified Jordan frame action (11), the matter field ψ_M is now non-minimally coupled to gravity through the term $F(R)$. However, as we will see now, the exact form of the Jordan frame action is not required in order to predict the expansion-collapse duality.

The Einstein frame action of the form (10) leads to the Friedmann equation

$$\tilde{H}^2 = \frac{\kappa^2}{3}\left(\rho_\varphi + \sum \rho_I\right), \tag{12}$$

where $\tilde{H} = (d\tilde{a}/d\tilde{t})/\tilde{a}$ is the Einstein frame Hubble parameter, $\tilde{t}$ is the coordinate time in the Einstein frame, $\sum \rho_I$ denotes the summation of energy densities of all the component in the Einstein frame apart from φ. Noting that the Einstein frame metric is also a spatially flat FRW metric, $\tilde{g}_{\mu\nu} \equiv \mathrm{diag}(-1, \tilde{a}^2, \tilde{a}^2, \tilde{a}^2)$, one can relate the scale factors in the Jordan frame (a) and Einstein frame $(\tilde{a})$ as (see, for example, [11])

$$a = \frac{\tilde{a}}{\Omega} = \frac{\tilde{a}}{\sqrt{F}}. \tag{13}$$

Using (12) in (13), we find derivative of a with respect to $\tilde{a}$ to be (see [18] for details),

$$\frac{da}{d\tilde{a}} = \frac{d}{d\tilde{a}}\left(\frac{\tilde{a}}{\sqrt{F}}\right) = F^{-1/2}\left(1 - \kappa\sqrt{1 + w_\varphi(\tilde{a})}\sqrt{\frac{\rho_\varphi}{6\tilde{H}^2}}\right). \tag{14}$$

As it can be seen from above, the sign of $da/d\tilde{a}$ is determined by the term inside the parenthesis. The condition for $da/d\tilde{a} < 0$, or expansion-collapse duality becomes

$$w_\varphi(\tilde{a}) > \mathcal{C}(\tilde{a}) \tag{15a}$$

$$\mathcal{C}(\tilde{a}) = \frac{6\tilde{H}^2}{\kappa^2 \rho_\varphi(\tilde{a})} - 1. \tag{15b}$$

Thus, the condition of expansion-collapse duality between Einstein-Jordan frames can be written as a threshold imposed on the equation of state of the quintessence field φ, even when there are other components in the Einstein frame. The Hubble parameter $(\tilde{H})$ incorporates the contribution from all the other components present in the Einstein frame universe. Depending upon whether (15a) is satisfied, there might be a range of $\tilde{a}$, or possibly multiple ranges of $\tilde{a}$, during which the Jordan frame collapses while the Einstein frame expands. The possible 'turn around' of the Jordan frame $(da/d\tilde{a} = 0)$ can be determined by setting

$$w_\varphi(\tilde{a}) = \mathcal{C}(\tilde{a}), \tag{16}$$

provided such a solution does exist. Starting with the relation between Hubble parameters in the Jordan (H) and Einstein $(\tilde{H})$ frames (see [11]),

$$H = \sqrt{F}\tilde{H} - \frac{1}{2\sqrt{F}}\frac{dF}{d\tilde{t}}, \tag{17}$$

one can explicitly show that at the 'turn-around' of the Jordan frame, the Jordan frame Hubble parameter indeed vanishes, $H_{\text{turn-around}} = 0$.

It is also to be noted that the condition for expansion-collapse duality has a significantly simple form. Given an equation of state parameter w_φ, one only requires the knowledge of the energy densities of the components in the Einstein frame in order to check whether the condition is satisfied. The form of the Jordan frame action, even the solution of the field $\varphi(\tilde{a})$ or potential $V(\varphi)$ do not appear explicitly in the condition. Thus, as mentioned before, the reconstruction of Jordan frame action is not required in order to predict the expansion-collapse duality for a quintessence-$f(R)$ pair.

Let us now consider the example of quintessence model with logarithmic equation of state (8), where the Einstein frame universe also contains non-relativistic matter or dust. The condition (15) in this case becomes (see [18])

$$w_\varphi(\tilde{a}) > \mathcal{C}(\tilde{a}), \text{ where} \tag{18a}$$

$$w_\varphi(\tilde{a}) = w_0 - w' \ln \tilde{a}, \tag{18b}$$

$$\mathcal{C}(\tilde{a}) = 1 + 2\frac{\Omega_{m0}}{\Omega_{\varphi 0}} \exp\left(3w_0 \ln \tilde{a} - \frac{3}{2}w'(\ln \tilde{a})^2\right), \tag{18c}$$

Ω_{m0}, $\Omega_{\varphi 0}$ are the density parameters of dust and φ at $\tilde{a} = 1$. The evolution of the Jordan frame scale factor $a(\tilde{a})$ is plotted in Fig. 1(a). In the absence of dust ($\Omega_{m0} = 0$), the Jordan frame initially expands with the Einstein frame. The 'turn around' in the Jordan frame occurs at $\tilde{a} = \exp\left((w_0 - 1)/w'\right)$. In the late time limit of the Einstein frame ($\tilde{a} \to \infty$), the Jordan frame universe completely collapses ($a \to 0$). However, as the fraction of dust in the Einstein frame increases, the Jordan frame collapse staggers. For a realistic value of dust to dark energy ratio ($\Omega_{m0}/\Omega_{\varphi 0} \sim 0.3/0.7$), the Jordan frame does not collapse and the Jordan frame scale factor always increases monotonically with respect to that of the Einstein frame. In fact, it can be argued that in the presence of dust, quintessence model with observationally consistent logarithmic equation of state does not lead to the expansion-collapse duality (see [18]).

Finally, let us consider the effect of spatial curvature in the Jordan frame collapse for the same quintessence model. In the presence of positive spatial curvature and dust, the condition (15) becomes (see [18])

$$w_\varphi(\tilde{a}) > \mathcal{C}(\tilde{a}), \text{ where} \tag{19a}$$

$$w_\varphi(\tilde{a}) = w_0 - w' \ln \tilde{a}, \tag{19b}$$

$$\mathcal{C}(\tilde{a}) = 1 + 2\frac{\Omega_{m0}}{\Omega_{\varphi 0}} \exp\left(3w_0 \ln \tilde{a} - \frac{3}{2}w'(\ln \tilde{a})^2\right)$$

$$+ 2\frac{\Omega_{K0}}{\Omega_{\varphi 0}} \exp\left((1 + 3w_0) \ln \tilde{a} - \frac{3}{2}w'(\ln \tilde{a})^2\right), \tag{19c}$$

where $\Omega_K = -K/(\tilde{a}\tilde{H})^2 = \Omega_{K0}\tilde{a}^{-2}$, K is the spatial curvature parameter in the FRW metric. The expansion-collapse duality condition in this case is plotted in Fig. 2. We can see from (19c), the contribution from positive spatial curvature,[19] or negative Ω_{K0}, brings down the threshold $\mathcal{C}$, allowing for w_φ to eventually

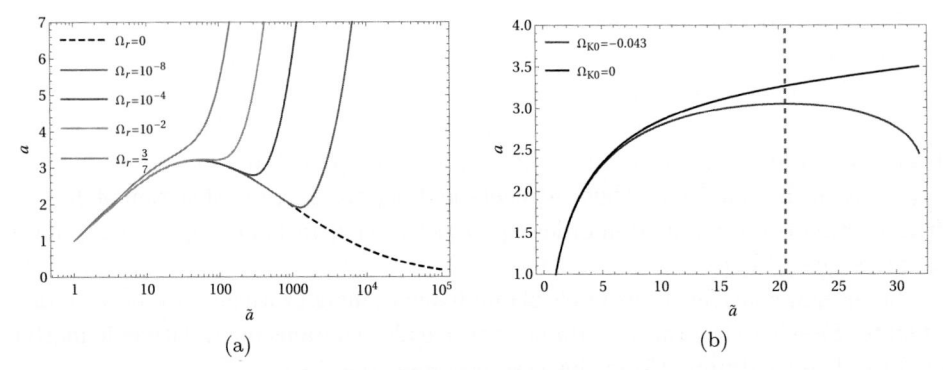

Fig. 1. The scale factor in the Jordan frame (a) is plotted as a function of the scale factor in the Einstein frame ($\tilde{a}$). The quintessence parameters are taken to be $(w_0, w') = (-0.87, -0.48)$, from [16]. (a) Jordan frame collapse in the presence of dust, without spatial curvature. $\Omega_r = \Omega_{m0}/\Omega_{\varphi 0}$ is the ratio of the density parameter of dust to that of the quintessence field, at current Einstein frame universe. In the absence of dust ($\Omega_r = 0$), the Jordan frame scale factor $a \to 0$ while the Einstein frame scale factor $\tilde{a} \to \infty$. However, in the presence of dust ($\Omega_r \neq 0$), the Jordan frame collapse eventually comes to a stop and the Jordan frame starts to expand again. For a realistic value of $\Omega_r = \Omega_{m0}/\Omega_{\varphi 0} \sim 0.3/0.7$, the Jordan frame does not go through a collapsing phase, it always expands monotonically with the Einstein frame. (b) Jordan frame collapse in the presence of dust and spatial curvature. In the presence of a small positive spatial curvature ($\Omega_{K0} = -0.043, \Omega_{m0} = 0.315, \Omega_{\varphi 0} = .728$), the Jordan frame collapse can be recovered (blue curve). The Jordan frame universe goes through a turn-around at $\tilde{a} \sim 20.52$ (represented by the vertical dashed line) after which the Jordan frame scale factor starts to decrease.

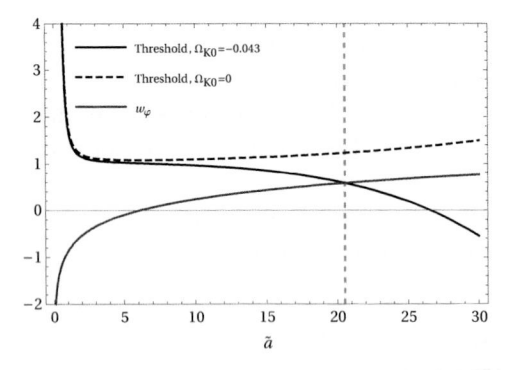

Fig. 2. The equation of state parameter w_φ and the threshold $\mathcal{C}$ (as in (19c)) are plotted as functions of the Einstein frame scale factor. The choice of parameters are: $(w_0, w') = (-0.87, -0.48)$ (from [16]), $\Omega_{m0} = 0.315$, $\Omega_{\varphi 0} = .728$, $\Omega_{K0} = -.043$ (from [19]). The 'turn-around' in the Jordan frame occurs at $w_\varphi(\tilde{a}) = \mathcal{C}(\tilde{a})$ (represented by the vertical dashed line), after which ($w_\varphi > \mathcal{C}$) the Jordan frame collapses. The plots demonstrate that in the absence of spatial curvature Ω_{K0}, w_φ (blue plot) never reaches $\mathcal{C}$ (black dashed plot), hence the Jordan frame collapse never begins. However, even a small positive spatial curvature ($\Omega_{K0} = -.043$) brings down the threshold $\mathcal{C}$ (black plot) enough for w_φ to overcome it eventually. For this case the 'turn-around' ($w_\varphi = \mathcal{C}$) occurs at $\tilde{a} \sim 20.52$, the Jordan frame starts to collapse afterwards.

overcome it. Therefore, the positive spatial curvature may recover the Jordan frame collapse in the presence of dust, at least for a finite duration. The evolution of the Jordan frame scale factor in this case is plotted in Fig. 1(b).

4. Summary and discussion

Dark energy, implemented by a quintessence field in the Einstein frame, can effectively be described by an $f(R)$ gravity theory in the Jordan frame. In this paper we classify quintessence models based on whether they lead to expansion-collapse duality between Einstein and Jordan frames, i.e., while the Einstein frame expands, the Jordan frame collapses or *vice versa*. We show that in order for the quintessence–$f(R)$ gravity pair to have such a feature, the equation of state of the quintessence must overcome a certain threshold. We derive a general condition for the expansion-collapse duality which is applicable to quintessence models with arbitrary, time-dependent equation of state parameters. The condition also holds true in the presence of any other components in the Einstein frame.

As an example, we consider the quintessence model with logarithmic equation of state parameter. We show that if the quintessence field is the sole component in the Einstein frame, this model does lead to the expansion-collapse duality, in fact the Jordan frame universe completely collapses in the late time limit of the Einstein frame. However, even the subdominant presence of dust in the Einstein frame prevents the Jordan frame collapse. If we also consider a small positive spatial curvature in the universe, the Jordan frame collapse can be recovered for a finite duration.

In general, the map between expanding and collapsing geometries at the field equation level may have potentially interesting implications on the cosmological perturbations in these frames. Further studies can reveal how perturbation in a collapsing universe corresponds to the perturbations in an expanding universe.

References

1. B. Ratra and P. J. E. Peebles, Cosmological consequences of a rolling homogeneous scalar field, *Phys. Rev. D* **37**, 3406 (Jun 1988).
2. I. Zlatev, L. Wang and P. J. Steinhardt, Quintessence, cosmic coincidence, and the cosmological constant, *Phys. Rev. Lett.* **82**, 896 (Feb 1999).
3. P. Brax and J. Martin, Robustness of quintessence, *Phys. Rev. D* **61**, p. 103502 (Apr 2000).
4. T. Barreiro, E. J. Copeland and N. J. Nunes, Quintessence arising from exponential potentials, *Phys. Rev. D* **61**, p. 127301 (May 2000).
5. S. Tsujikawa, Quintessence: A Review, *Classical and Quantum Gravity* **30**, p. 214003 (November 2013).
6. G. Efstathiou, Constraining the equation of state of the universe from distant type ia supernovae and cosmic microwave background anisotropies, *Monthly Notices of the Royal Astronomical Society* **310**, 842 (Dec 1999).
7. M. Chevallier and D. Polarski, Accelerating Universes with Scaling Dark Matter, *International Journal of Modern Physics D* **10**, 213 (January 2001).

8. H. K. Jassal, J. S. Bagla and T. Padmanabhan, Observational constraints on low redshift evolution of dark energy: How consistent are different observations?, *Physical Review D* **72** (Nov 2005).
9. E. J. Copeland, M. Sami and S. Tsujikawa, Dynamics of dark energy, *International Journal of Modern Physics D* **15**, 1753 (November 2006).
10. A. Tripathi, A. Sangwan and H. K. Jassal, Dark Energy Equation of State Parameter and Its Variation at Low Redshifts, *Journal of Cosmology and Astroparticle Physics* **2017**, 012 (June 2017).
11. A. De Felice and S. Tsujikawa, F(R) Theories, *Living Reviews in Relativity* **13** (December 2010).
12. T. P. Sotiriou and V. Faraoni, $f(R)$ Theories of gravity, *Reviews of Modern Physics* **82**, 451 (March 2010).
13. S. Capozziello and M. De Laurentis, Extended theories of gravity, *Physics Reports* **509**, 167 (Dec 2011).
14. S. Nojiri, S. Odintsov and V. Oikonomou, Modified gravity theories on a nutshell: Inflation, bounce and late-time evolution, *Physics Reports* **692**, p. 1–104 (Jun 2017).
15. V. Faraoni, Nine Years of f(R) Gravity and Cosmology, in *Accelerated Cosmic Expansion*, eds. C. Moreno González, J. E. Madriz Aguilar and L. M. Reyes Barrera (Springer International Publishing, Cham, 2014) pp. 19–32.
16. A. Sangwan, A. Mukherjee and H. K. Jassal, Reconstructing the Dark Energy Potential, *Journal of Cosmology and Astroparticle Physics* **2018**, 018 (January 2018).
17. R. M. Wald, *General Relativity*, repr. edn. (Univ. of Chicago Press, Chicago, 2009), OCLC: 554287751.
18. D. Mukherjee, H. K. Jassal and K. Lochan, $f(R)$ Dual Theories of Quintessence: Expansion-Collapse Duality (2021), https://arxiv.org/abs/2105.10521.
19. E. Di Valentino, A. Melchiorri and J. Silk, Planck evidence for a closed universe and a possible crisis for cosmology, *Nature Astronomy* **4**, 196 (Nov 2019).

The model of dark energy based on the quantum-mechanical uncertainty relation

Yu. V. Dumin

Sternberg Astronomical Institute (GAISh), Lomonosov Moscow State University,
Universitetskii prosp. 13, Moscow, 119234, Russia
E-mail: dumin@yahoo.com

Space Research Institute (IKI), Russian Academy of Sciences
Profsoyuznaya str. 84/32, Moscow, 117997, Russia

The Dark Energy became now a commonly-accepted paradigm of cosmology, but its physical essence remains absolutely unknown, and its numerical values are drastically different in the early and modern Universe. The Dark Energy is usually introduced in the contemporary literature either by postulating some additional terms in the Lagrangians or by employing the empirical equations of state. In the present work, we try to look at this problem from a more general point of view, namely, employing the quantum-mechanical uncertainty relation between the time and energy in the Mandelstam–Tamm form, which is appropriate for the long-term evolution of quantum systems. This leads us to the time-dependent effective Lambda-term, decaying as $1/t$. The corresponding cosmological model possesses a number of quite appealing features: (1) While in the standard cosmology there are a few very different expansion stages (governed by the Lambda-term, radiation, dust-like matter, and Lambda-term again), our model provides a universal description of the entire evolution of the Universe by the same "quasi-exponential" function. (2) As follows from the analysis of causal structure, the present-day cosmological horizon comprises a single domain developing from the Big Bang. Therefore, the problems of homogeneity and isotropy of the matter, the absence of topological defects, etc. should be naturally resolved. (3) At last, our model naturally explains the observed approximately flat 3D space, i.e., solution with zero curvature is formed "dynamically", starting from the arbitrary initial conditions.

Keywords: Dark Energy; Inflation; Uncertainty relation.

1. Introduction

The concept of Dark Energy (or the effective Λ-term in Einstein equations) represents now a commonly-accepted paradigm both in the cosmology of early and present-day Universe. A crucial role of the effective Λ-term in the early Universe was recognized in the early 1980s, when it was introduced as a driving force of the inflationary stage of the cosmological evolution;[1] while its significance at the present time was recognized in the very end of 1990s, when the accelerated expansion of the Universe was observed.[2] However, despite an active involvement into a huge number of theoretical works, a physical nature of the Dark Energy remains unknown. Besides, it is unclear why densities of the Dark Energy in the early and modern Universe are absolutely different.

In fact, the first inflationary models of the early Universe, discussed in the 1980s, were formulated on the quite solid physical basis steaming from the elementary-particle physics. Namely, it was assumed that the effective Λ-term was associated with a nonzero value of the potential energy of the Higgs field in its symmetry-broken state formed after a phase transition in the expanding and cooling Universe.[3] Unfortunately, a further research in this direction failed to derive a reasonable value of the Λ-term from the existing models of elementary particles, such as the electroweak or Grand Unification theories. As a result, a subsequent development of the inflationary concept of the early Universe was based mostly on the empirical Lagrangians, where some additional terms with a scalar field (the so-called inflaton) were added quite arbitrarily, without any attempts to associate them with the underlying theory of elementary particles. At last, when the accelerated expansion of the contemporary Universe was observed in the late 1990s, and it became necessary to introduce the Λ-term (or Dark Energy) into the "standard" cosmological model, this was done again only in terms of the empirical equations of state of the cosmological matter or, in a more elaborate theoretical approach, by means of the empirical Lagrangians similar to the inflationary ones.

In view of the above circumstances, there is now a clear need for a more solid conceptual basis for explanation of the Λ-term, i.e., stemming from other well-established physical laws and theories. One such approach is well known: this is the so-called Sakharov induced gravity,[4] going back to 1960s. The cornerstone of this concept is that the vacuum modes of the fundamental quantum fields (e.g., electroweak, chromodynamic, etc.) are perturbed if the space–time is curved. As a result, the effective Lagrangian acquires the additional terms, which are proportional to the various degrees of the curvature $\mathcal{R}$.[a] Thereby, the first-order term will represent the standard Einstein–Hilbert part of the Lagrangian (apart from the Λ-term); the term of zero order will be just the effective ("induced") Λ-term; and there should be also the higher-order terms of $\mathcal{R}$. About a decade later, this idea was implemented in the inflationary model by Starobinsky[5] and later evolved into a wide range of the so-called $f(\mathcal{R})$ theories. (However, it should be kept in mind that the ingredient responsible for the inflation in such theories is usually the quadratic rather than zero-order term of the curvature.) Unfortunately, since we do not have the ultimate theory of elementary particles, the exact form of the function f cannot be derived, and it is commonly specified "by hand", so that the required cosmological predictions can be obtained. From this point of view, the most of $f(\mathcal{R})$ theories are based on the same type of Lagrangians with arbitrary additional terms (but without the additional scalar fields); for a review, see Refs. 6 and 7.

The aim of the present paper is to discuss yet another conceivable universal approach to the emergence of the effective Λ-term, namely, based on the quantum-mechanical uncertainty relation between the time and energy. Let us mention that

---

[a]Strictly speaking, the Lagrangian can contain also a number of other invariants composed of the curvature tensor.

some qualitative ideas about a probable role of the uncertainty relation in cosmology were put forward some time ago by Coe,[8] but the corresponding quantitative treatment looked unreasonable. Here, we shall discuss another development of this idea, performed in our recent works.[9–11]

2. Basic Equations

2.1. *Uncertainty Relations*

As is known, the uncertainty relations are one of cornerstones of quantum mechanics. In the case of canonically conjugate variables (e.g., the coordinate x and momentum p_x), they can be derived in the rigorous and universal way by averaging the corresponding quantum commutators. This leads to the inequalities like $\Delta p_x \Delta x \geq \hbar/2$, and similarly for other pairs of conjugate quantities. The uncertainty relations are most widely employed in the problem of quantum measurements. However, they can be sometimes useful also in dealing with other properties of the quantum systems: a well-known example—which is considered in many textbooks—is estimating parameters of the ground state of a hydrogen atom.

Meanwhile, it should be kept in mind that the uncertainty relation between the time t and energy E is a quite exceptional case, because the time and energy are not the canonically conjugate operators in the non-relativistic quantum mechanics (instead, t is the independent variable in Schrödinger equation). So, the time–energy uncertainty relation is commonly derived by various "Gedankenexperiments"; and the resulting coefficients in the right-hand side, in general, can be different:

$$\Delta E \Delta t \geq C_{\text{UR}} \hbar/2, \qquad (1)$$

where C_{UR} is the numerical coefficient on the order of unity ('UR' implies here the uncertainty relation). In the standard Heisenberg's case, pertinent to the problem of measurements, $C_{\text{UR}} = 1$. On the other hand, the case of the long-term evolution of a quantum system was considered by Mandelstam and Tamm[12] in 1945, and it was found that in this situation $C_{\text{UR}} = \pi$. It is interesting that this work remained almost unknown for a few decades and attracted considerable attention of the scientific community only in the recent time; for more details, see Ref. 13. So, it is widely used now in such branches of physics as quantum optics, quantum information processing, etc.; and it was the aim of our recent studies[9–11] to employ it in cosmology.

2.2. *The Modified Friedmann Equation*

The starting point of our consideration is the standard Robertson–Walker cosmological metric:

$$ds^2 = c^2 dt^2 - R^2(t)\left[\frac{dr^2}{1-kr^2} + r^2(d\theta^2 + \sin^2\theta\, d\varphi^2)\right], \qquad (2)$$

where t is time, r, θ, and φ are the dimensionless spherical coordinates, R is the scale factor of the Universe, c is the speed of light, and the coefficient k equals 1, 0, and –1 for the closed, flat, and open Universe.

Temporal evolution of this metric is governed by the well-known Friedmann equation (e.g., Ref. 14):

$$H^2 \equiv \left(\frac{\dot{R}}{R}\right)^2 = \frac{8\pi G}{3c^2}\rho - kc^2\frac{1}{R^2} + \frac{c^2}{3}\Lambda, \qquad (3)$$

where H is the Hubble parameter, ρ is the energy density of matter in the Universe (both visible and dark), G and Λ are the gravitational and cosmological constants.

It is well known that Λ-term in the right-hand side of Eq. (3) can be formally attributed to the vacuum energy density ρ_v:

$$\Lambda = \frac{8\pi G \rho_v}{c^4}; \qquad (4)$$

and then it becomes reasonable to estimate the vacuum energy from the uncertainty relation (1) with the equality sign, assuming that Δt is the total period of the cosmological evolution t. However, since the uncertainty relation should be applied to the energy rather than the energy density, it is necessary to specify the characteristic spatial volume; the most evident choice being the Planck volume l_P^3 (where $l_P = \sqrt{G\hbar/c^3}$ is the Planck length).[b]

Consequently, we arrive at the following effective Λ-term:

$$\Lambda(t) = \frac{4\pi C_{UR}}{c\, l_P}\frac{1}{t}; \qquad (5)$$

and its substitution into Eq. (3) leads to the modified Friedmann equation:

$$H^2 \equiv \left(\frac{\dot{R}}{R}\right)^2 = \frac{8\pi G}{3c^2}\rho - kc^2\frac{1}{R^2} + \frac{4\pi C_{UR}}{3\tau}\frac{1}{t}, \qquad (6)$$

where $\tau = l_P/c = \sqrt{G\hbar/c^5}$ is the Planck time.

A very unusual feature of this equation is the explicit dependence on time in the right-hand side. As far as we know, such situation was never considered in cosmology. However, as will be seen from the subsequent treatment, this time dependence does not result in any anomalous behavior.

The numerical coefficient C_{UR} remains essentially unknown. Since the uncertainty relation (1) was used with the equality sign, this coefficient can actually take the values from π up to infinity (but it cannot be less than π).

---

[b] As was pointed out by Starobinsky (private communication), yet another conceivable choice for the characteristic spatial scale might be the size of the cosmological horizon. However, as will be discussed below in Sec. 5, this option looks less reasonable.

3. The Simplest Solution and Its Main Properties

To get the simplest solution of Eq. (6), let us assume that the three-dimensional space is perfectly flat (i.e., $k \equiv 0$), and the energy density of ordinary matter is negligible (i.e., $\rho = 0$). Then, the resulting equation is easily integrated, and the solution can be written as

$$R(t) = R^* \exp\left[\sqrt{\frac{16\pi C_{\text{UR}}}{3}} \sqrt{\frac{t}{\tau}}\right], \qquad (7)$$

where $R^* = R(0)$ is the constant of integration; and we consider only the case of $R(t)$ increasing with time, i.e., corresponding to the expanding Universe. (In principle, there may be also a contracting solution, with minus sign in the argument of the exponential function.)

So, even the simplest solution (7) suggests us an interesting version of the cosmological model, outlined in Fig. 1. Instead of the standard model, composed of the four very different stages (namely, the inflationary one with exponential expansion, then the stages dominated by radiation and non-relativistic matter with power-like expansion, and finally the modern exponential stage), the uncertainty-mediated model describes everything by the universal "quasi-exponential" function (7). The corresponding Hubble parameter gradually decays with time as $1/\sqrt{t}$.

The age of the Universe T (i.e., the period from $t = 0$ to the present time) can be easily found from Eq. (6), remembering that $k \equiv 0$ and $\rho = 0$:

$$H_0^2 = \frac{4\pi C_{\text{UR}}}{3\tau} \frac{1}{T}. \qquad (8)$$

Next, taking into account that age of the Universe in the standard cosmological model T^* is commonly estimated as $1/H_0$, we get:

$$T \approx (T^*/\tau)\, T^*, \qquad (9)$$

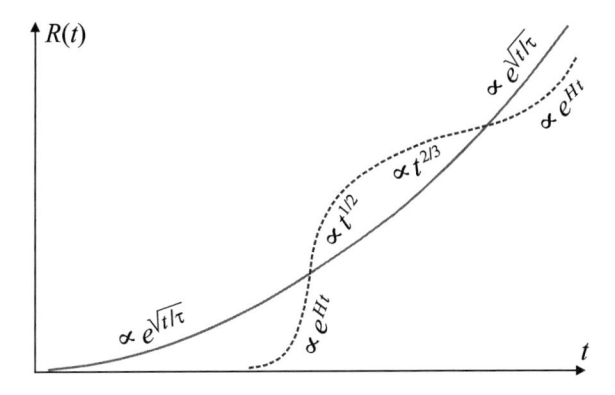

Fig. 1. Temporal variation of the scale factor of the Universe $R(t)$ in the standard cosmological model (dashed blue curve) and in the proposed uncertainty-mediated model (solid red curve).

if the numerical coefficient C_{UR} is assumed to be on the order of unity. Since $T^* \approx 4 \cdot 10^{17}$ s and $\tau = 5 \cdot 10^{-44}$ s, this age in the proposed model will be greater than in the standard cosmology by the huge factor $(T^*/\tau) \approx 10^{61}$.

Nevertheless, this disagreement should not be a crucial failure of our model. Really, the "standard" age of the Universe T^* is measured from the onset of the hot Big Bang. If its evolution is supplemented by the preceding inflationary stage, this age will formally tend to infinity (because the expansion function e^{Ht} starts at $t \to -\infty$). So, the huge age of the Universe in the uncertainty-mediated model, described by the "universal" function (7), is not surprising.

4. The Model of Inflation

As is known, emergence of the inflationary paradigm in the early 1980s was caused by the inability of the "old" cosmological model—governed by radiation and ordinary matter—to resolve a few conceptual problems, such as a homogeneity and isotropy of the observed Universe, the absence of the topological defects, a surprising flatness of the three-dimensional space, etc. A presence of the early stage with very fast expansion (usually, the exponential one) was postulated as a universal remedy to treat all these issues.[1,3] So, it is interesting to check if the "quasi-exponential" expansion (7) can resolve the above-listed problems.

4.1. Causal Structure of the Space–Time

The problems of homogeneity and isotropy, as well as the absence of topological defects are closely related to the causal structure of the space–time under consideration. From our point of view, the most convenient way to analyze this issue is using the conformal diagrams.[15] Namely, in terms of the conformal time

$$\eta = \int dt/R(t) \quad (10)$$

the light rays in the curved Universe will be presented by the straight lines inclined at $\pm\pi/4$; and the causality (light) cones will look like the regular triangles, as shown in Fig. 2.

As distinct from the previous formulas, the null point of time was shifted here to the instant of observation; $\eta = -\eta_0$ corresponds to the "birth" of the Universe; and $\eta = -\eta^*$ is the instant at which the Universe is observed. Particularly, this may be the instant of plasma recombination—when the matter became transparent—if we speak about the observations in electromagnetic waves; or this may be the instant of symmetry-breaking phase transition of Higgs fields—when the ordinary matter was formed—if we speak about formation of the topological defects (such as the domain walls, cosmic strings, or monopoles, depending on the symmetry group involved). Accordingly, x_p is the size of the domain observable at the present time, and x_f is the size of the domain whose state can be "equilibrated" (causally connected) during the preceding cosmological evolution.

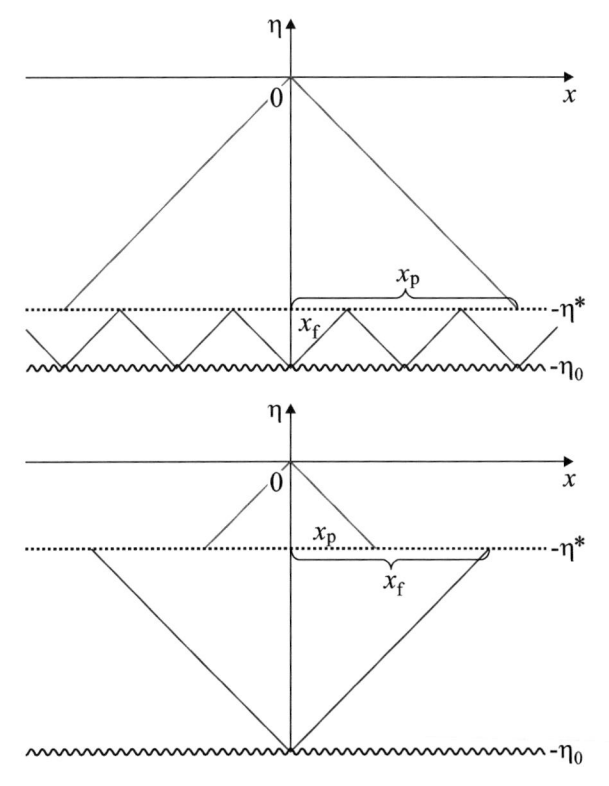

Fig. 2. Causal structure of space–time in the old "pre-inflationary" models (top panel) and in the inflationary models of the Universe (bottom panel). The lower (blue) triangles are the future causality cones developing from the birth of the Universe, and the upper (red) triangle is the past causality cone, representing the part of the Universe observed at the present time.

As is seen in the top panel of Fig. 2, a crucial drawback of the old "pre-inflationary" cosmology was that the observable region of space x_p (e.g., by the instant of recombination or by the instant of phase transition) comprised a large number of domains N developing independently from the birth of the Universe. This is because a difference between the conformal times η_0 and η^* in the case of power-like expansion of the Universe is rater small. As follows from the detailed calculations,[10]

$$N \approx \left\{\left[1 - \left(\frac{T-t^*}{T}\right)^{\frac{1+3w}{3(1+w)}}\right]^{-1} - 1\right\}^{-3} \gg 1, \qquad (11)$$

where w parameterizes the effective equation of state of the cosmological matter, $p = w\rho$ ($w = 0$ for the non-relativistic matter, and $w = 1/3$ for the radiation); and $T(\eta_0)$ is the age of the Universe. As a result, one should expect that, for example, the observed CMB radiation will be strongly anisotropic (if t^* is associated with the instant of recombination), or a large number of topological defects will be formed at the boundaries between the domains[16–19] (if t^* is associated with the instant of phase transition).

The situation changes radically if the inflationary stage with exponential expansion is present. Really, if $R(t) \propto e^{Ht}$, then

$$\eta(t) \propto -e^{-Ht} \to -\infty \quad \text{at} \quad t \to -\infty. \tag{12}$$

In other words, there will be a huge interval of conformal time before the instant η^*, corresponding to the observable structure. Consequently, the entire observable region x_p will be well within a single domain of causality x_f or, more exactly,[10]

$$N \approx \exp\left[-\sqrt{3\Lambda}\,c\,(T-t^*)\right] \ll 1, \tag{13}$$

as is seen in the bottom panel of Fig. 2. This is, in fact, the main reason why the inflationary model easily resolved the crucial problems of the "old" cosmology.

At last, what should we expect in the uncertainty-mediated cosmological model? Will the quasi-exponential expansion law (7) be a reasonable alternative to the pure exponential expansion? A quite straightforward but cumbersome calculation[10] results in

$$N \approx \left(\frac{16\pi C_{UR}}{3}\right)^{3/2} \left(\frac{T-t^*}{\tau}\right)^{3/2} \exp\left[-4\sqrt{3\pi C_{UR}}\left(\frac{T-t^*}{\tau}\right)^{1/2}\right] \ll 1, \tag{14}$$

i.e., the corresponding conformal diagram will be qualitatively the same as in the bottom panel of Fig. 2. In other words, the problems of homogeneity and isotropy of matter distribution, the absence of topological defects, etc. can be resolved by the uncertainty-mediated approach as efficiently as by the standard inflationary scenario.

4.2. The Problem of Singularity

A presence of the initial singularity in the power-like solution of the Friedmann equation with ordinary matter was also considered for a long time as a serious drawback of the cosmological model, but a considerably less attention is usually paid to this issue nowadays. Anyway, the quasi-exponential solution (7) of the uncertainty-mediated model evidently avoids the problem of singularity. However, this is achieved in a different way than in the standard inflationary model: in our case, the function $R(t)$ takes a finite value at $t = 0$ and becomes indefinite at $t < 0$; while in the standard exponential inflation the singularity is actually shifted to minus infinity.

Besides, let us mention that the uncertainty-mediated solution (7), in principle, if favorable for constructing a bounce-type model of the Universe, when a contraction at $t < 0$ is followed by the expansion at $t > 0$. Really, since the modified solution (7) with a minus sign in the argument of exponential function also satisfies the Friedmann equation, the decreasing and increasing branches can be fit to each other at $t = 0$.

4.3. Formation of the Flat Three-Dimensional Space

Yet another important conceptual problem of the old "pre-inflationary" cosmology was why the observed three-dimensional space is approximately flat with a high degree of accuracy. If we do not assume *a priori* that $k \equiv 0$ in the Friedmann equation (3), but the Λ-term is absent and the ordinary matter is described by the equation of state $p = w\rho$, then its energy density ρ will depend on the scale factor as $1/R^{3(1+w)}$, i.e., $1/R^3$ in the case of non-relativistic (dust-like) substance and $1/R^4$ in the case of radiation.[14] On the other hand, the curvature term decays as $1/R^2$ and, therefore, it will inevitably dominate after some time if the evolution begins from the arbitrary (generic) initial conditions. In other words, the approximately flat three-dimensional space cannot be formed "dynamically", and it is necessary to impose the artificial constraint $k \equiv 0$.

This problem is naturally resolved in the framework of classical inflationary scenario: if Λ is non-zero and approximately constant, then the second (curvature) term in the right-hand side of Eq. (3) becomes negligible as compared to the third (vacuum energy) term in the course of time and, therefore, the approximately flat three-dimensional space will be formed starting from the generic initial conditions.

Finally, what is the situation in the uncertainty-mediated cosmological model, described by the modified Friedmann equation (6)? In this case, it is not so easy to compare the magnitudes of the various terms in the right-hand side, because one of them depends immediately on t, while others depend on the function $R(t)$. However, assuming in the first approximation that $\rho = 0$ and utilizing the simplest solution (7), we get:

$$\lim_{t \to \infty} \frac{1/t}{1/R^2(t)} = \lim_{t \to \infty} \frac{R^2(t)}{t} = \infty, \qquad (15)$$

as can be proved, for example, applying the L'Hôpital's rule two times. Consequently, we should expect that the role of the curvature term will become negligible in the course of time. Strictly speaking, this argumentation is not a rigorous mathematical proof, because the above-mentioned solution (7) was obtained under assumption $k \equiv 0$. However, a more accurate treatment in Ref. 11 leads to the same result. Therefore, the uncertainty-mediated model resolves the problem of flatness as efficiently as the standard inflationary scenario.

5. Discussion and Conclusions

1. As follows from the above consideration, the uncertainty-mediated cosmological model provides a unified description of the entire evolution of the Universe on the basis of the well-established physical principle—the quantum-mechanical uncertainty relation. Besides, it resolves all major problems of the early Universe and, therefore, can serve as a reasonable alternative to other inflationary scenarios.

2. Unfortunately, a few conceptual issues still remain questionable. Firstly, this is the basic idea of estimating the vacuum energy density from the uncertainty

relation. Secondly, it is not sufficiently clear what is the physical scale at which the uncertainty relation should be applied. We assumed above that this is the Planck volume. However, as was pointed out by Starobinsky (private communication), this might be also the cosmological horizon. In this case, the vacuum energy derived from the uncertainty relation would be extremely small and insignificant for the cosmological evolution. Nevertheless, from our point of view, the Planck volume is a more reasonable choice because the uncertainty relation should be applied to a fixed physical system, while the horizon is evidently an object changing with time.

3. It is also unclear how the ordinary matter can be created in the framework of the uncertainty-mediated scenario, since it was completely ignored in the simplest solution (7). So, it might be necessary to introduce the additional field(s) whose decay will produce the ordinary substance, as it is commonly postulated in other inflationary models. On the other hand, if the presence of ordinary matter is assumed *a priori*, it is unclear if it will destroy the inflationary stage (i.e., if the scale factor $R(t)$ will collapse into a singularity) under extrapolation backwards in time. To answer this question, it is necessary to obtain more general solutions of the modified Friedmann equation (6).

4. At last, a number of the additional physical effects, such as leptogenesis, bariosynthesis, formation of the large-scale structure, the spectrum of CMB fluctuations, etc. should be considered in more detail to draw the ultimate conclusion on viability of the uncertainty-mediated cosmological model.

References

1. A. H. Guth, The inflationary Universe: A possible solution to the horizon and flatness problems, *Phys. Rev. D* **23**, p. 347 (1981).
2. M. J. Mortonson, D. H. Weinberg and M. White, Dark Energy, *Chin. Phys. C* **40 (100001)**, p. 402 (2016), in *Review of Particle Physics* by C. Patrignani, et al. (Particle Data Group).
3. A. D. Linde, The inflationary Universe, *Rep. Prog. Phys.* **47**, p. 925 (1984).
4. A. D. Sakharov, Vacuum quantum fluctuations in curved space and the theory of gravitation, *Sov. Phys. Dokl.* **12**, p. 1040 (1968).
5. A. A. Starobinsky, A new type of isotropic cosmological models without singularity, *Phys. Lett. B* **91**, p. 99 (1980).
6. J. Martin, C. Ringeval and V. Vennin, Encyclopædia inflationaris, *Phys. Dark Universe* **5–6**, p. 75 (2014).
7. J. Ellis and D. Wands, Inflation, *Chin. Phys. C* **40 (100001)**, p. 367 (2016), in *Review of Particle Physics* by C. Patrignani, et al. (Particle Data Group).
8. A. Coe, *Observable Universe Topology and Heisenberg Uncertainty Principle*, Preprint viXra: 1710.0143 (2017).
9. Y. V. Dumin, A unified model of Dark Energy based on the Mandelstam–Tamm uncertainty relation, *Grav. Cosmol.* **25**, p. 169 (2019).
10. Y. V. Dumin, Cosmological inflation based on the uncertainty-mediated Dark Energy, *Grav. Cosmol.* **26**, p. 259 (2020).

11. Y. V. Dumin, The problem of flatness of the Universe in the uncertainty-mediated inflationary model, *Grav. Cosmol.* **27**, p. 302 (2021).
12. L. I. Mandelstam and I. E. Tamm, The energy–time uncertainty relation in non-relativistic quantum mechanics, *Izv. Akad. Nauk SSSR (Ser. Fiz.)* **9**, p. 122 (1945), in Russian.
13. S. Deffner and S. Campbell, Quantum speed limits: from Heisenberg's uncertainty principle to optimal quantum control, *J. Phys. A: Math. Theor.* **50**, p. 453001 (2017).
14. K. A. Olive and J. A. Peacock, Big-Bang cosmology, *Chin. Phys. C* **40 (100001)**, p. 355 (2016), in *Review of Particle Physics* by C. Patrignani, et al. (Particle Data Group).
15. C. W. Misner, Mixmaster Universe, *Phys. Rev. Lett.* **22**, p. 1071 (1969).
16. N. N. Bogoliubov, Field-theoretical methods in physics, *Suppl. Nuovo Cimento (Ser. prima)* **4**, p. 346 (1966).
17. T. W. B. Kibble, Topology of cosmic domains and strings, *J. Phys. A: Math. Gen.* **9**, p. 1387 (1976).
18. W. H. Zurek, Cosmological experiments in superfluid helium?, *Nature* **317**, p. 505 (1985).
19. Y. V. Dumin, Nonlocal quantum effects in cosmology, *Adv. High Energy Phys.* **2014**, p. 241831 (2014).

Conformal dilaton gravity, antipodal mapping and black hole physics on a warped spacetime

R. J. Slagter

ASFYON, Astronomisch Fysisch Onderzoek Nederland,
former: University of Amsterdam, Dept. Theor. Phys., The Netherlands
E-mail: info@asfyon.com

An exact time-dependent solution of a black hole is found in a conformally invariant gravity model on a warped Randall-Sundrum spacetime, by writing the metric $g_{\mu\nu} = \omega^{\frac{4}{n-2}} \tilde{g}_{\mu\nu}$. Here $\tilde{g}_{\mu\nu}$ represents the "un-physical" spacetime and ω the dilaton field, which will be treated on equal footing as any renormalizable scalar field. It is remarkable that the 5D and 4D effective field equations for the metric components and dilaton fields can be written in general dimension $n = 4, 5$. The location of the horizon(s) are determined by a quintic polynomial. This polynomial is related to the symmetry group of the icosahedron, isomorphic with the Galois group A_5. We applied the antipodal mapping on the axially symmetric black hole spacetime and make some connection with the information and firewall paradoxes. The dilaton field can be used to describe the different notion the in-going and outside observers have of the Hawking radiation by using different conformal gauge freedom. The disagreement about the interior of the black hole is explained by the antipodal map of points on the horizon. The free parameters of the solution can be chosen in such a way that $\tilde{g}_{\mu\nu}$ is singular-free and topologically regular, even for $\omega \to 0$.

Keywords: Conformal Invariance; Dilaton Field; Black Holes; Brane World Models; Antipodal Map; Quintic Polynomial

1. Introduction

One of the greatest challenges of modern physics will be the construction of a quantum-gravity model. In the vicinity of a horizon of a black hole and in the very early universe, these quantum gravity effects will come into play. The quantum features of a black hole were investigated, decades ago, by Hawking in his epic work on radiation effects of a black hole[1] by vacuum polarization. This radiation would be thermal and would contain no information. The black hole will eventually evaporate, and one could say that information is lost, because the anti-particles will fall into the black hole. This would violate quantum mechanics (QM). Related to this issue, is the holographic principle,[2] which states that the interior volume of spacetime of a black hole containing the information of the in-going particles is dual to the surface of the horizon. Could it be that the information is still at the horizon? The idea was extended to the well-known Anti-de Sitter/Conformal Field Theory (AdS/CFT) correspondence: is some way, the information must be present in the Hawking radiation. This model relies heavily on string theory, but would solve the information paradox, by introduction the notion of complementarity of the in- and outside of the black hole. The in-going and out-going particles are entangled and the information of the in-going particle is also reflected back. However, this viewpoint conflict causality.[3] The previously emitted Hawking radiation and the corresponding in-going particles are independent systems and at the same time indirect entangled. Another solution for the information paradox, which don't rely on string theory, is the introduction of a firewall.[4] The entanglement between the in-going and out-going particles is broken by a high energetic shield. The freely in-falling observer encounters high-energy particles at the horizon. This viewpoint conflicts general relativity, i.e., violation of the equivalence principle. Free falling observers, when falling through the horizon, perceive spacetime as Minkowski, so will not notice the horizon at all. A fundamental issue which is omitted in all the treatments as described above, is the time-dependency of the spacetime structure near the horizon. The emitted Hawking particle will have a back-reaction effect on the spacetime.[5,6] Could it be possible, that the topology of the black hole must be revised? It is well know, that quantum field theory on a curved spacetime opens the possibility that a field theory can have different vacuum states. It can have intrinsic statistical features from a change in topology and not from from a priori statistical description of the matter fields. A spacetime with a given local geometry admits in principle, different possible global topologies. One can consider the modification of the spacetime topology of the form $\widehat{\mathcal{M}}/\Gamma$, where Γ is a discrete subgroup of isometries of $\mathcal{M}$,[7–10] without fixed points. $\widehat{\mathcal{M}}$ is non-singular and is obtained from its universal covering $\mathcal{M}$ by identifying points equivalent under Γ. A particular interesting case is obtained, when Γ is the antipodal transformation on $\mathcal{M}$

$$J: \quad P(X) \to \widehat{P}(\widehat{X}). \tag{1}$$

where the light-cone of the antipode of $P(X)$ intersects the light-cone of $P(X)$ only in two point (at the boundary of the spacetime). This is the so-called "elliptic interpretation"[11] of spacetime, where antipodal points represents in fact the same world-point or event. The future and past event horizon intersect each other as a projected cylinder $\mathbb{R}_1 \times \mathbb{S}_1/\mathbb{Z}_2$.[a] At the intersection one then identifies antipodal points. One must realize that the antipodal map is a boundary condition at the horizon, only observable by the outside observer. On a black hole spacetime, the inside is removed. So nothing can escape the interior, since there is no interior. The field theories formulated on $\mathcal{M}$ and $\widehat{\mathcal{M}}$ are globally different, while locally $\mathcal{M}$ and $\widehat{\mathcal{M}}$ are identically. The emitted radiation is only locally thermal. Antipodal identification, however, destroys the thermal features in the Fock space construction. In the construction, one needs unitary evolution operators for the in-going and out-going particles.[5,12] In order to avoid wormhole constellations or demanding "an other universe" in the construction of the Penrose diagram, it is essential that the asymptotic domain of $\mathcal{M}$ maps one-to-one onto the ordinary spacetime in order

---

[a]We work here in polar coordinates, because the spinning black hole we will consider, has a preferred spin axis. The antipodal identification is then $(U, V, z, \varphi) \to (-U, -V, -z, \pi + \varphi)$.

to preserve the metric. In fact, one deals with one black hole. A consequence is that time-inversion take place in region II of the Penrose diagram, so interchange of the creation and annihilation operators and entangling positive energy particles at the horizon with positive energy antiparticles at the antipodes. So the antipodal identification is not in conflict with the general CPT invariance of our world. Further, for the outside observer, the thermodynamically mixed state is replaced by a pure state. So the Hawking particles at opposite sides of the black hole are entangled. The former representation that observers has no access to the inside of the black hole is no longer valid. One arrives by this new geometrical description at pure quantum states for the black hole. It will solve, moreover, the information paradox and firewall problem as well.[b] The gravitational back-reaction as proposed by 't Hooft,[13,14] suggests a cut-off of high momenta, which avoids the firewall. The in-going particle has a back-reaction on the other particles, leading to an unitary S-matrix. The gravitational interaction between the in-going and out-going particles will be strong, because we are dealing here with a strongly curved spacetime near the horizon. Using a "cut-and-paste" procedure, one replaces the high-energy particles ("hard"), i.e., mass or momentum of the order of the Planck mass, by low-energy ("soft") particles far away. These hard particles just caused the firewall problem. Hard particles will also influence the local spacetime (to become non-Schwarzschild) and causes the Shapiro effect. The interaction with the soft particles is described by the Shapiro delay. Effectively, all hard particles are quantum clones of all soft particles. By this "firewall-transformation", we look only at the soft particle clones. They define the Hilbert space and leads to a unitary scattering matrix. The net result is that the black hole is actually in a pure state, invalidating the entanglement arguments in the firewall paradox. The entanglement issue can be reformulated by considering the two regions I and II in the maximally extended Penrose diagram of the black hole, as representing two "hemispheres" of the same black hole. It turns out that the antipodal identification keeps the wave functions pure[6] and the central $r = 0$ singularity has disappeared. This gravitational deformation will cause transitions from region I to II in the Penrose diagram. The fundamental construction then consist of the exchange of the position operator with the momentum operator of the in-going particles, which turn them into out-particles. Hereby, 't Hooft expands the moment distributions and position variables in partial waves in (θ, φ).[5] So the Hawking particles emerging from I are entangled with the particles emerging from II. An important new aspect is the way particles transmit the information they carry across the horizon. In the new model, the Hawking particles emerging from I are maximally entangled with the particles emerging from II. The particles form a pure state, which solves the information paradox. In order to describe the more realistic black holes, such as the axially symmetric Kerr black hole, it is not possible

---

[b]The technical aspects in constructing the unitary S-matrix can be found in the literature, as provided by the references.

to ignore the dynamics of the horizon. Moreover, one must incorporate gravitation waves. There is another reason to consider axially symmetry. A spherical symmetric system cannot emit gravitation waves.[15] Astronomers conjecture that most of the black holes in the center of galaxies are of the Kerr type. A linear approximation is, of course, inadequate in high-curvature situations. In the linear approximation, the waves don't carry enough energy and momentum to affect their own propagation. The notion of the "classical" Hartle-Hawking vacuum thermal state, with a temperature $T \sim \frac{1}{M} \sim \kappa$ and the luminosity $\frac{dM}{dt} \sim -\frac{1}{M^2}$ must also be revised when the mass reaches the order of the Planck mass. On the Kerr black hole spacetime no analog of the Hartle-Hawking vacuum state exists. The Killing field ξ^μ generates a bifurcate Killing horizon ($\xi^\mu \xi_\mu = -1$ at infinity) and possesses spacelike orbits near infinity.[16] Another aspect of the huge curvature in the vicinity of the horizon, will be the problem of constructing a renormalizable (and maintaining unitarity) quantum gravity model of the Standard Model fields, which must be incorporated in the Lagrangian. Up till now, no convincing theory of quantum gravity is available. Many attempts were made in order to make a renormalizable and unitary quantum gravity model. One also can try to construct a renormalizable model, by adding fourth order derivative terms of the curvature tensor (Euler-term). However, one looses unitarity. Also the "old" effective field theory (EFT) has its problems. One ignores what is going on at high energy. In order to solve the anomalies one encounters in calculating the effective action, one can apply the so-called conformal dilaton gravity (CDG) model.[5,6,17] CDG is a promising route to tackle the problems arising in quantum gravity model, such as the loss of unitarity close to the horizon. One assumes local conformal symmetry, which is spontaneously broken (for example by a quartic self-coupling of the Higgs field). Changing the symmetry of the action was also successful in the past, i.e., in the SM of particle physics. A numerical investigation of a black hole solution of a non-vacuum CDG model, was recently performed.[18] The key feature in CDG, is the splitting of the metric tensor $g_{\mu\nu} = \omega^{\frac{4}{n-2}} \tilde{g}_{\mu\nu}$, with ω the dilaton field. Applying perturbation techniques (and renormalization/dimensional regularization), in order to find the effective action and its divergencies, one first integrate over ω (shifted to the complex contour), considered as a conventional renormalizable scalar field and afterwards over $\tilde{g}_{\mu\nu}$ and matter fields. The dilaton field is locally unobservable. It is fixed when we choose the global spacetime and coordinate system. If one applies this principle to a black hole spacetime, then the energy-momentum tensor of ω influences the Hawking radiation. When $\tilde{g}_{\mu\nu}$ is flat, then the handling of the anomalies simplifies considerably.[14] When $\tilde{g}_{\mu\nu}$ is non-flat, the problems are more deep-seated. It is well known, that the antipodal transformation, or inversion, is part of the conformal group.[19] So conformal invariant gravity models could fit very well the models of antipodal mapping as described above. In this context, the modification of GRT by an additional spacetime dimension could be an alternative compromise, because Einstein gravity on the brane will be modified by the very embedding itself and opens up a possible new way to address the dark energy problem.[20,c] These models can be applied to the standard Friedmann-Lemaître-Robertson-Walker (FLRW) spacetime and the modification on the Friedmann equations can be investigated.[21] Recently, Maldacena, et al.,[22] applies the RS model to two black hole spacetimes and could construct a traversable macroscopic wormhole solution by adding only a 5D U(1) gauge field (see also Maldacena[23]). However, an empty bulk would be preferable. In stead, one can investigate the contribution of the projected 5D Weyl tensor on the 4D brane. It carries information of the gravitational field outside the brane. If one writes the 5D Einstein equation in CDG setting, it could be possible that an effective theory can be constructed without an UV cutoff, because the fundamental scale M_5 can be much less than the effective scale M_{Pl} due to the warp factor. The physical scale is therefore not determined by M_{Pl}. In this manuscript we will apply the antipodal map on a spinning black hole spacetime in conformal dilaton gravity applied to a warped 5D spacetime.

2. Conformal Transformations and Antipodal Mapping

2.1. *The origin of the antipodal mapping*

The antipodal map originates from the so-called "elliptic" interpretation.[11] If one considers the hyperboloid H, $-t^2+x^2+y^2+z^2+w^2 = R^2$, then the space-like sections through the origin are ellipses and the time-like sections are hyperbola branches. Since the de Sitter spacetime can be isometrically embedded as a hyperboloid in $\mathbb{R}^5$, one can take $R^2 = -\frac{3}{\Lambda}$. If one suppresses the coordinates (z, w), we have the $\mathbb{R}^3$ Minkowski metric. Lorentz transformations (LT's) around the origin transforms H into itself. Circles on H represent space at different epochs. The bottle-neck parallel is a spatial geodesic, while the others are not. Further, the circumferences contract from $z = -\infty$ to $z = 0$ and then expand. A LT of $\mathbb{R}^3$ turns the bottle-neck into an ellipse, cut out of H with an angle $< 45°$ with the (x, y)-plane. See figure 1. All the ellipses are equivalent space-like geodesics since each of them is transferred by a suitable automorphism into the bottle-neck, which is one of them. One defines the antipodal map

$$J : P(t, x, y) \to \widehat{P}(-t, -x, -y), \qquad (2)$$

on H. The antipodicity is Lorentz invariant. When the angle approaches $45°$, then the ellipses degenerate into a couple of parallel generators (g_1, g_2) (null geodesics). The other plane of $45°$ delivers the set (g_3, g_4). The sets (g_1, g_4) and (g_2, g_3) form, for example, the light-cones at the points M and $\widehat{M}$. If one moves upwards along t, the inner angles of the light-cones decrease. Note that the light-cones at P and $\widehat{P}$ has no point in common and the antipodes are joined by a space-like geodesic. Now Schrödinger proposed to identify P and $\widehat{P}$ with the same physical world-point or

---

[c]There is another argument in favor of a (warped) 5D spacetime. It turns out, as we shall see, that a surface in 4D can be immersed to 5D, like a Klein bottle.

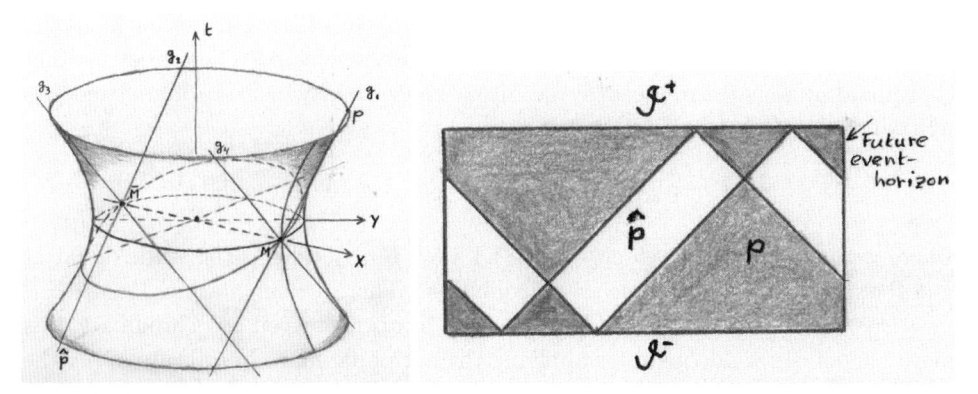

Fig. 1. Hyperboloid H representing the $\mathbb{R}^3$ spacetime of the compactified de Sitter universe $\mathbb{R}^5$ ((z,w) suppressed). Right: the Penrose diagram. The antipodal points P and $J(P)$ are spacelike separated. An observer moving in de Sitter spacetime cannot meet both P and $J(P)$. He cannot receive a message from $P, J(P)$. Moreover, he cannot receive a message from P and send a message to $J(P)$.

event. One half of H, containing no antipodal points, represents the "whole world". Thereafter, Schrödinger argues in a clever way that the total potential of experiences of any observer is complete and embraces the same events for any two observers, whatever their world lines be. But there is a price we have to pay for.[d] The direction of the arrow of time is lost (or the distinction between the "fore-cone" and "after-cone" is lost). The allotment of past and future is undecidable. The elliptic model is time-reversible. This can open perspective to the general CPT invariance of our world. The real problems arise, when one considers thermodynamical systems, as is the case for the Hawking effect in the vicinity of the horizon of a black hole. Then the entropy comes into play. Note, quoting Schrödinger, "the irreversible laws of thermodynamics can only be based on the statistical microscopically reversible systems on condition that statistical theory be autonomous in defining the arrow of time. If any other law of nature determines this arrow, the statistical theory collapses."

In a pseudo-polar frame $(\chi, T, \theta, \varphi)$ we can write the line element

$$ds^2 = -R^2 dT^2 + R^2 \cosh^2 T \left[d\chi^2 + \sin^2 \chi (d\theta^2 + \sin^2 \theta d\varphi^2) \right], \quad (3)$$

where $0 < \chi < 2\pi$. The antipodal map becomes now

$$J : (T, \chi, \theta, \varphi) \to (-T, \pi + \chi, \pi - \theta, \pi + \varphi). \quad (4)$$

---

[d]This price is worth paying in the black hole situation, when the information paradox will be solved by the antipodal map. The antipodal half is not time orientable. There is a breakdown of the global distinction between past and future in the interior of the black hole.

We already mentioned that de Sitter can be embedded as a hyperboloid in 5D Minkowski. We then say that $J : X^\mu \to -X^\mu$ is an inversion.[e] There exist another coordinate system (introduced by de Sitter himself) in which the line element is written as

$$ds^2 = -\left(1 - \frac{\rho^2}{R^2}\right) dT'^2 + \frac{1}{(1 - \frac{\rho^2}{R^2})} d\rho^2 + \rho^2(d\theta'^2 + \sin^2 \theta' d\varphi'^2), \quad (5)$$

where we have taken the velocity of the LT $\tanh T = \frac{t}{y}$. This is the static de Sitter and the spaces of constant time are all equivalent. There are singularities for $x = \pm R$ ($\chi = \pm 90°$), i.e., the points $(M, \widehat{M})$. However, as also observed by Schrödinger, this static model is not adequate for applying the antipodal map. In order to apply the antipodal map on a black hole spacetime in a more general setting, one needs a time dependent spacetime.

2.2. The "classical" Hawking effect and its problems

The famous result of Hawking states, that a black hole will radiate at "sufficiently" late times like a black body at a temperature

$$kT \sim \frac{\kappa}{2\pi} = \frac{\hbar c^3}{8\pi GM}, \quad (6)$$

with κ the surface gravity and M the mass. The entropy should then be $S_{bh} = \frac{kc^3}{4\hbar} A$, with A the area of the horizon. However, one runs into problems by the back-reaction effect of the particle creation, which will alter the area. It is questionable if the ordinary laws of thermodynamics can be applied to a black hole. It is clear that these laws must be constrained to form quantum states with orthonormality and unitarity conditions. Suppose that an isolated black hole completely evaporate within a finite time. Loss of quantum coherence should then occur i.e., an initially pure quantum state should evolve to a mixed state. In general, in the classical picture, a black hole cannot causally influence its exterior, so it is hard to understand the mechanism by which thermal equilibrium could be achieved. Observe that the state of the field at late times in the region I of the Penrose diagram (and so the particles flux reaching infinity) is described by a density matrix by the S-matrix analysis. The particles present in region I are strongly correlated with the particles which entered the black hole at earlier times. Consider now in figure 2 the evolution of two Cauchy surfaces ("time" Σ_1 to "time" Σ_2). When the black hole disappears from the spacetime, then at late times, the entire state of the field is mixed. If one takes the "out" Hilbert space to be the Fock space of the particles propagating out to infinity at late times, one cannot describe particle creation and scattering by an ordinary S-matrix. The initial pure state will evolve to a final density matrix.

---

[e]The inversion $X_\mu \to -\frac{X_\mu}{X^2}$ (as well as the dilatations) is part of the conformal group.[19] We shall see in the next sections that in general the conformal group is a projective group from 5D. The fifth "degree of freedom" is a sort of gauge space.

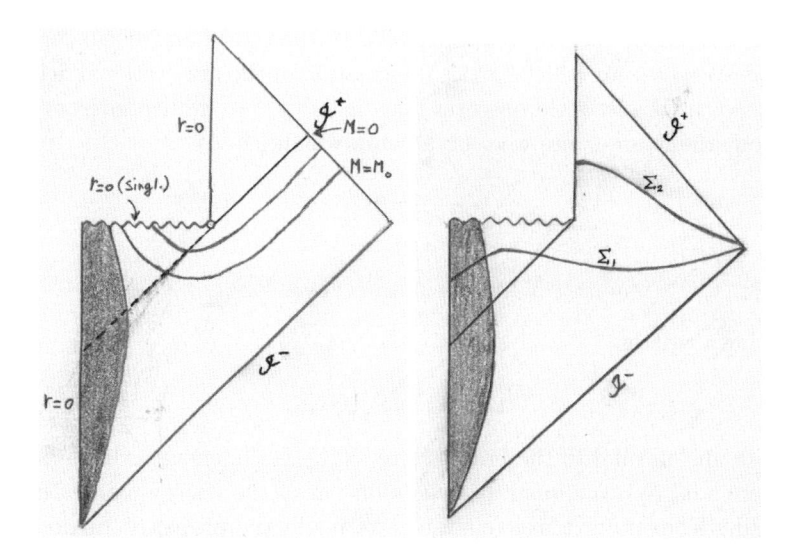

Fig. 2. Left: formation and evaporation of the Schwarschild black hole. The contour $M = 0$ lies at the retarded time corresponding to the final evaporation. The geometry is flat above this contour. Right: Loss of quantum coherence: evolution from a pure state to a mixed state.[16]

So we have a breakdown of quantum theory. The antipodal model, however, could "repair" this breakdown.

3. The Black Hole Solution on a 5D Warped Spacetime in Conformal Dilaton Gravity

3.1. *The 5D warped spacetime*

Let us consider the 5D spacetime warped spacetime[21, 24]

$$ds^2 = \omega(t,r,y)^2 \left[-N(t,r)^2 dt^2 + \frac{1}{N(t,r)^2} dr^2 + dz^2 + r^2(d\varphi + N^\varphi(t,r)dt)^2 + dy^2\right], \quad (7)$$

where y is the extra dimension and ω a warp factor in the formulation of Randall-Sundrum's (RS) 5D warped spacetime with one large extra dimension and negative bulk tension Λ_5. The Standard Model (SM) fields are confined to the 4D brane, while gravity acts also in the fifth dimension. Originally, the RS model was applied to a 5-dimensional anti-de Sitter (AdS) spacetime with a positive brane tension. This is the so-called RS-1 model, with one brane. The RS-2 model treats two branes with $\mathbb{Z}_2$ symmetry. However, the effective cosmological constant on the brane can be zero by fine tuning with the negative Λ_5. In the RS model there is a bound state of the graviton confined to the wall as well as a continuum of Kaluza-Klein (KK) states. Four dimensional gravity is then recovered on the brane and the hierarchy problem seems to be solved. Since the pioneering publication of RS, many investigation were done in diverge domains. In particular, Shiromizu et.al.,[24, 25] extended the RS model to a fully covariant curvature formalism. It this extended model, an effective

Einstein equation is found on the brane, with on the right-hand side a contribution from the 5D Weyl tensor which carries information of the gravitational field outside the brane. So the brane world observer may be subject to influences from the bulk. The field equations are (were we took an empty bulk)[18]

$$^{(5)}G_{\mu\nu} = -\Lambda_5 {}^{(5)}g_{\mu\nu}, \qquad (8)$$

$$^{(4)}G_{\mu\nu} = -\Lambda_{eff}{}^{(4)}g_{\mu\nu} + \kappa_4^{2\,(4)}T_{\mu\nu} + \kappa_5^4 S_{\mu\nu} - \mathcal{E}_{\mu\nu}, \qquad (9)$$

where we have written

$$^{(5)}g_{\mu\nu} = {}^{(4)}g_{\mu\nu} + n_\mu n_\nu, \qquad (10)$$

with n^μ the unit normal to the brane. Here $^{(4)}T_{\mu\nu}$ is the energy-momentum tensor on the brane and $\mathcal{S}_{\mu\nu}$ the quadratic contribution of the energy-momentum tensor $^{(4)}T_{\mu\nu}$ arising from the extrinsic curvature terms in the projected Einstein tensor. Further,

$$\mathcal{E}_{\mu\nu} = {}^{(5)}C^\alpha_{\beta\rho\sigma} n_\alpha n^{\rho\,(4)} g_\mu^{\beta\,(4)} g_\nu^\sigma, \qquad (11)$$

represents the projection of the bulk Weyl tensor orthogonal to n^μ. The effective gravitational filed equations on the brane are not closed. One must solve at the same time the 5D gravitation field in the bulk.

3.2. *The conformal dilaton gravity (CDG) model on a 5D warped spacetime*

One can distinguish several possible "routes" to the unification of GR and QFT. One can start, for example, with a given classical theory and applies heuristic quantization rules. One then can make a division in canonical and covariant approaches, i.e., uses a Hamiltonial formalism or employs covariance at some stage. The CDG model we consider here, is part of the covariant approach to quantum gravity. The key feature in CDG, is the splitting of the metric tensor[5, 17]

$$g_{\mu\nu} = \omega^{\frac{4}{n-2}} \tilde{g}_{\mu\nu}, \qquad (12)$$

with ω the dilaton field and $\tilde{g}_{\mu\nu}$ the "un-physical" spacetime. At high energy, ω will be treated as a (renormalizable) quantum field. One can prove that the action (without matter terms for the time being)

$$S = \int d^n x \sqrt{-\tilde{g}} \left[\frac{1}{2}\xi\omega^2 \tilde{R} + \frac{1}{2}\tilde{g}^{\mu\nu}\partial_\mu\omega\partial_\nu\omega + \Lambda\kappa^{\frac{4}{n-2}}\xi^{\frac{n}{n-2}}\omega^{\frac{2n}{n-2}} \right], \qquad (13)$$

is conformal invariant under

$$\tilde{g}_{\mu\nu} \to \Omega^{\frac{4}{n-2}}\tilde{g}_{\mu\nu}, \quad \omega \to \Omega^{-\frac{n-2}{2}}\omega. \qquad (14)$$

The covariant derivative is taken with respect to $\tilde{g}_{\mu\nu}$. For details, see Slagter.[18] Now we implement the 5D warped spacetime Eq. (7). So

$$^{(5)}g_{\mu\nu} = \omega^{4/3}\,{}^{(5)}\tilde{g}_{\mu\nu}, \qquad ^{(5)}\tilde{g}_{\mu\nu} = {}^{(4)}\tilde{g}_{\mu\nu} + n_\mu n_\nu, \tag{15}$$

and write again

$$^{(4)}\tilde{g}_{\mu\nu} = \bar{\omega}^2 \bar{g}_{\mu\nu}. \tag{16}$$

Variation of the action leads to the field equations

$$\xi\omega\tilde{R} - \tilde{g}^{\mu\nu}\tilde{\nabla}_\mu\tilde{\nabla}_\nu\omega - \frac{2n}{n-2}\Lambda\kappa^{\frac{4}{n-2}}\xi^{\frac{n}{n-2}}\omega^{\frac{n+2}{n-2}} = 0 \tag{17}$$

and

$$\omega^2 \tilde{G}_{\mu\nu} = T^\omega_{\mu\nu} - \Lambda\tilde{g}_{\mu\nu}\kappa^{\frac{4}{n-2}}\xi^{\frac{2}{n-2}}\omega^{\frac{2n}{n-2}}, \tag{18}$$

with

$$T^\omega_{\mu\nu} = \tilde{\nabla}_\mu\tilde{\nabla}_\nu\omega^2 - \tilde{g}_{\mu\nu}\tilde{\nabla}^2\omega^2 + \frac{1}{\xi}\left(\frac{1}{2}\tilde{g}_{\alpha\beta}\tilde{g}_{\mu\nu} - \tilde{g}_{\mu\alpha}\tilde{g}_{\nu\beta}\right)\partial^\alpha\omega\partial^\beta\omega. \tag{19}$$

From the 5D Einstein equations Eq. (8) one obtains $\omega(t,r,y) = \omega_1(t,r)\omega_2(y)$, with $\omega_2(y) = l =$ constant (the length scale of the extra dimension). The dilaton equations Eq. (17) is superfluous. Note that the effective Einstein equations Eq. (9) contains the $\mathcal{E}_{\mu\nu}$, while $\mathcal{T}_{\mu\nu}$ and $\mathcal{S}_{\mu\nu}$ are taken zero in our case. The dilaton equation is again superfluous.

It turns out that one can write the field equations for ω and N in the form ($n = 4, 5$)

$$\ddot{\omega} = -N^4\omega'' + \frac{n}{\omega(n-2)}\left(N^4\omega'^2 + \dot{\omega}^2\right), \tag{20}$$

$$\ddot{N} = \frac{3\dot{N}^2}{N} - N^4\left(N'' + \frac{3N'}{r} + \frac{N'^2}{N}\right)$$
$$-\frac{n-1}{(n-3)\omega}\left[N^5\left(\omega'' + \frac{\omega'}{r} + \frac{n}{2-n}\frac{\omega'^2}{\omega}\right) + N^4\omega'N' + \dot{\omega}\dot{N}\right]. \tag{21}$$

One can solve these equations exact (we took $\Lambda_{eff} = 0$):

$$\omega = \left(\frac{a_1}{(r+a_2)t + a_3 r + a_4}\right)^{\frac{1}{2}n-1},$$

$$N^2 = \frac{1}{5r^2}\frac{10a_2^3 r^2 + 20a_2^2 r^3 + 15a_2 r^4 + 4r^5 + C_1}{C_2(a_3+t)^4 + C_3}, \tag{22}$$

with a_i some constants. There is a constraint equation

$$\bar{\omega}'' = -\frac{2n}{n-2}\frac{\Lambda l\kappa^{\frac{4}{(n-2)}}\xi^{\frac{n-2}{4(n-1)}}\bar{\omega}^{\frac{n+2}{n-2}}}{N^2} - \frac{\omega'N'}{N} - \frac{\omega'}{2r} + \frac{4}{n-2}\frac{\dot{\bar{\omega}}^2}{\bar{\omega}N^4} - \frac{\dot{\bar{\omega}}\dot{N}}{N^5}, \tag{23}$$

which l the dimension of y. The solution for the two dilaton fields ω and $\bar{\omega}$ differs only by the different exponent $\frac{3}{2}$ and 1 respectively. The solution For the metric component is the same (apart from the constants). The solution for the angular momentum component is

$$N^\varphi = F_n(t) + \int \frac{1}{r^3 \bar{\omega}^{\frac{n-1}{n-3}}} dr. \tag{24}$$

The Ricci scalar for $\bar{g}_{\mu\nu}$ ($\Lambda = 0$) is given by

$$\bar{R} = \frac{12}{N^2}\left[\dot{\bar{\omega}}^2 - N^4 \bar{\omega}'^2\right], \tag{25}$$

with is consistent with the null condition for the two-dimensional (t,r) line element, when $\bar{R} = 0$. One can easily check that the trace of the Einstein equations is zero. Note that N^2 can be written as

$$N^2 = \frac{4\int r(r+a_2)^3 dr}{r^2[C_2(a_3+t)^4 + C_3]}. \tag{26}$$

So the spacetime seems to have two poles. However, the $r = 0$ is questionable. The conservation equations become

$$\bar{\nabla}^\mu \mathcal{E}_{\mu\nu} = \bar{\nabla}^\mu \left[\frac{1}{\bar{\omega}^2}\left(-\Lambda \kappa^{2(4)}\bar{g}_{\mu\nu}\bar{\omega}^4 + {}^{(4)}T_{\mu\nu}^{(\bar{\omega})}\right)\right], \tag{27}$$

which yields differential equations for $\ddot{N}'$ and $\dot{N}$ as boundary conditions at the brane. It can be described as the non-local conservation equation. In the high energy case close to the horizon, one must include the $\mathcal{S}_{\mu\nu}$ term. So the divergence of $\mathcal{E}_{\mu\nu}$ is constrained. In the non-conformal case, Eq. (27) contains on the right hand side also the quadratic correction $\mathcal{S}_{\mu\nu}$ of the matter fields on the brane. The effective field equations, Eq. (9), are then not a closed system. One needs the Bianchi equations. In fact, $\mathcal{E}_{\mu\nu}$ encodes corrections from the 5D graviton effects and are for the brane observer non-local. In our model under consideration, we have only the $T_{\mu\nu}^{(\omega)}$ term and no source terms (only the 5D Λ_5). But it still sources the KK modes. The dilaton ω plays the role of a "scalar field". But we don't need the 5D equations themselves, because the solution for N is the same! It is only the $\omega^{4/3}$ which represents the 5D contribution. There is no exchange of energy-momentum between the bulk and brane. If one applies the model to a FLRW model,[26] then the evolution equations are very complicated. Inhomogeneous and anisotropic effects from the 4D matter radiation distribution on the brane are sources for the 5D Weyl tensor $\mathcal{E}_{\mu\nu}$ and cause non-local back-reaction on the brane. One needs an approximation scheme in order to find the missing evolution equation for $\mathcal{E}_{\mu\nu}$.

The locations of the horizon's and ergo-spheres are found by solving $N^2 = 0$ and $\bar{g}_{tt} = 0$ respectively. N^2 becomes singular at coordinate time $t = t_H = -b_3 + \sqrt[4]{-\frac{C_3}{C_2}}$. However, $\bar{g}_{\mu\nu}$ can be made regular everywhere and singular free by suitable choices of the parameters b_i, c_i and C_i. For $C_1 = 0$, $\bar{g}_{\mu\nu}$ has one real zero $r_H =\sim |1.606 b_2|$ and two complex zero's $\sim (0.178 \pm 0.638 I)b_2$. In figure 3 we plotted the possible graphs. If one ignores the contribution from the bulk, then N^2 has for $C_1 = 0$ no real roots, so only naked singularities. The contribution from the bulk then generates at least one horizon.

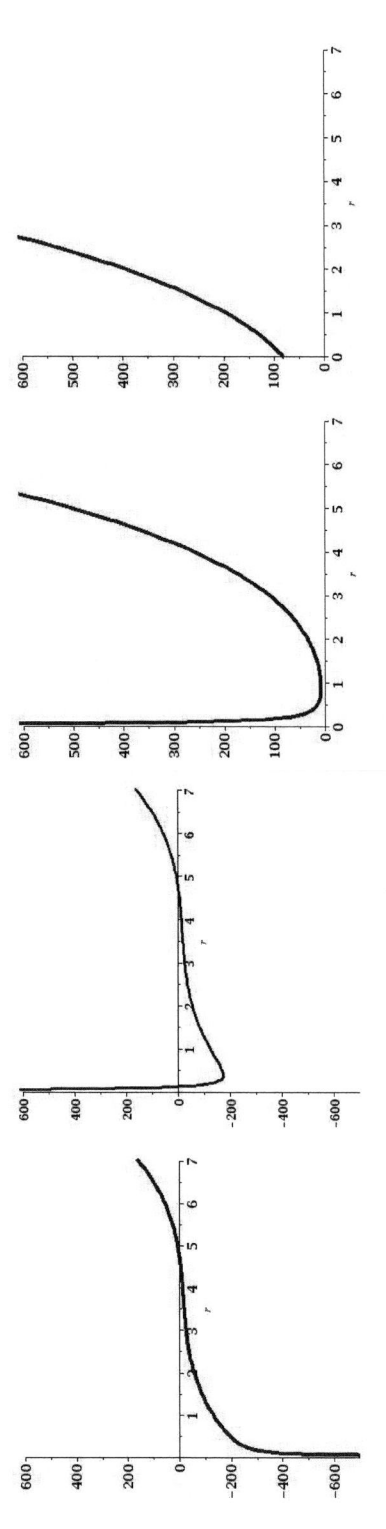

Fig. 3. Four possible plots of N^2 as function of r.

3.3. Penrose diagram

If we define the coordinates, $dr^* \equiv \frac{1}{N_1(r)^2}dr$ and $dt^* \equiv N_2(t)^2 dt$, then our induced spacetime can be written as

$$ds^2 = \omega^{4/3}\bar{\omega}^2\left[\frac{N_1^2}{N_2^2}\left(-dt^{*2}+dr^{*2}\right)+dz^2+r^2\left(d\varphi+\frac{N^\varphi}{N_2^2}dt^*\right)^2\right], \tag{28}$$

with

$$N_1^2 = \frac{10b_2^3 r^2 + 20b_2^2 r^3 + 15b_2 r^4 + 4r^5 + C_1}{5r^2}, \quad N_2^2 = \frac{1}{C_2(t+b_3)^4 + C_3} \tag{29}$$

and

$$r^* = \frac{1}{4}\sum_{r_i^H}\frac{r_i^H \log(r-r_i^H)}{(r_i^H+b_2)^3}, \quad t^* = \frac{1}{4C_2}\sum_{t_i^H}\frac{\log(t-t_i^H)}{(t_i^H+b_3)^3}. \tag{30}$$

The sum it taken over the roots of $(10b_2^3 r^2 + 20b_2^2 r^3 + 15b_2 r^4 + 4r^5 + C_1)$ and $C_2(t+b_3)^4 + C_3$, i. e., r_i^H and t_i^H. This polynomial in r defining the roots of N_1^2, is a quintic equation, which has some interesting connection with Klein's icosahedral solution (see appendix). Further, one can define the azimuthal angular coordinate $d\varphi^* \equiv (d\varphi + \frac{N^\varphi}{N_2^2}dt^*)$, which can be used when an incoming null geodesic falls into the event horizon. φ^* is the azimuthal angle in a coordinate system rotating about the z-axis relative to the Boyer-Lindquist coordinates. Next, we define the coordinates[28] (in the case of $C_1 = C_3 = 0$ and 1 horizon, for the time being)

$$\begin{array}{ll} U_+ = e^{\kappa(r^*-t^*)}, & V_+ = e^{\kappa(r^*+t^*)} \quad r > r_H \\ U_- = -e^{\kappa(r^*-t^*)}, & V_- = -e^{\kappa(r^*+t^*)} \quad r < r_H, \end{array} \tag{31}$$

with κ a constant. The spacetime becomes

$$ds^2 = \omega^{4/3}\bar{\omega}^2\left[\frac{N_1^2}{N_2^2}\log(UV)^{\frac{1}{2\kappa}}dUdV + dz^2 + r^2 d\varphi^{*2}\right]. \tag{32}$$

In figure 4 we plotted the Penrose diagram (left). The antipodal points $P(X)$ and $\bar{P}(\bar{X})$ are physically identified. If we compactify the coordinates,

$$\tilde{U} = \tanh U, \quad \tilde{V} = \tanh V, \tag{33}$$

then the spacetime can be written as

$$ds^2 = \omega^{4/3}\bar{\omega}^2\left[H(\tilde{U},\tilde{V})d\tilde{U}d\tilde{V} + dz^2 + r^2 d\varphi^{*2}\right], \tag{34}$$

with

$$H = \frac{N_1^2}{N_2^2}\frac{1}{\kappa^2 \arctanh\tilde{U} \arctanh\tilde{V}(1-\tilde{U}^2)(1-\tilde{V}^2)}. \tag{35}$$

We can write r and t as

$$r = r_H + \left(\arctanh\tilde{U} \arctanh\tilde{V}\right)^{\frac{1}{2\kappa\alpha}}, \quad t = t_H + \left(\frac{\arctanh\tilde{V}}{\arctanh\tilde{U}}\right)^{\frac{1}{2\kappa\beta}}, \tag{36}$$

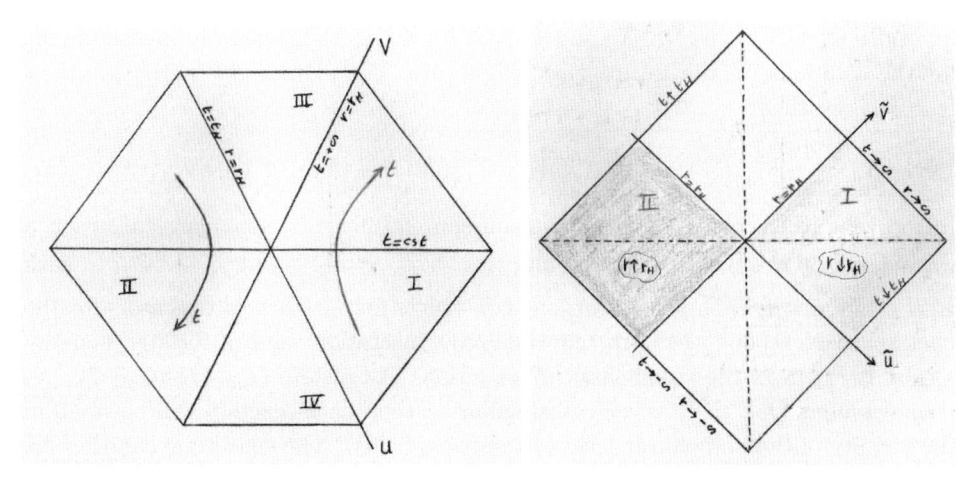

Fig. 4. Left: Kruskal diagram for $\bar{g}_{\mu\nu}$ in (U,V)- coordinates. If one approaches the horizon from the outside and passes the horizon, one approaches from the "otherside" the horizon. Right: Kruskal diagram for $\tilde{g}_{\mu\nu}$ in $(\tilde{U},\tilde{V})$- coordinates.

with

$$\alpha = \frac{r_H}{4(r_H+b_2)^3}, \qquad \beta = \frac{1}{4C_2(t_H+b_3)^3}. \tag{37}$$

Observe that N_1 and N_2 can be expressed in $(\tilde{U},\tilde{V})$. The Penrose diagram is drawn in figure 4 (right). Note that ds^2 and H are invariant under $\tilde{U} \to -\tilde{U}$ and $\tilde{U} \to -\tilde{U}$. $\tilde{g}_{\mu\nu}$ is regular everywhere and conformally flat. The "scale-term" H is consistent with the features of the Penrose diagram. Now we have still the φ dependency. We assume no z-dependency. It is expected that the differential equation for ω can be separated in a (U,V) part and a φ part. The method of 't Hooft can then be applied. In the next sections, we will briefly come back to this issue.

4. Related Issues of the New Black Hole Solution

4.1. *Treatment of the quantum fields*

The physical identification in the de Sitter spacetime of $P(X)$ and $\widehat{P}(\widehat{X})$ are considered as different representations in Kruskal space of one and the same Schwarzschild event. There is only one world with one singularity and one exterior region. Fields which are symmetric under J are identified as

$$\Psi_{JS} = \frac{1}{2}\Big[\Psi(X) + \widehat{\Psi}(\widehat{X})\Big]. \tag{38}$$

One then builds these fields from fields with arguments specified in I.[8] Each of these fields, positive or negative frequency in I, can be extended to global spacetime surfaces. However, due to the time reversal, the inner product on the full Hilbert space have zero norm for the symmetric fields. One then defines negative frequency functions $\Psi^\uparrow_{(-)}(X) = \Psi^\downarrow_{(+)}(JX)$ and $\Psi^\downarrow_{(-)}(X) = \Psi^\uparrow_{(+)}(JX)$, where the arrows stands for the solutions on the future/past singularity. The symmetric (anti-) solutions ($\epsilon = \pm 1$) are then

$$\Psi^{(1)}_{JS}(X) = \frac{1}{2}\left[\Psi^\uparrow_{(+)}(X) + \epsilon\Psi^\downarrow_{(-)}(X)\right], \quad \Psi^{(2)}_{JS}(X) = \frac{1}{2}\left[\Psi^\downarrow_{(+)}(X) + \epsilon\Psi^\uparrow_{(-)}(X)\right]. \quad (39)$$

Introducing then reflection and transmission coefficients, one can construct a wave function regular at the singularities, $\Psi^{(r)}_{JS} = \frac{\epsilon K}{(K+\epsilon)^2}\left[\Psi^{(1)}_{JS} + \epsilon\Psi^{(2)}_{JS}\right]$, with $K = e^{\pi\omega/\kappa}$, $\kappa = 1/4M$. Thereafter, one constructs hermitian field operators for the Fock space. Next, one needs the renormalized expectation value of the stress-energy tensor $<T_{\mu\nu}>$ in the "semiclassical" equations of Einstein $G_{\mu\nu} = 8\pi G <T_{\mu\nu}>$. If one assumes that there is a $r=0$ singularity, then back-reaction will be small in the vicinity of the horizon (at least for massless fields). The spacetime can then be approximated by Schwarzschild geometry. The mass will decrease slowly with time and evaporates. In a flat spacetime, this is easily done, because the vacuum is well defined. One can calculate the zero-energy state and can construct finite quantum operators. In curved spacetime, the vacuum state is dependent of the boundary condition for the propagators (positive frequency modes). In principle, we can follow the method of Sanchez (for the de Sitter spacetime) for the dilaton field and our "un-physical" spacetime $\bar{g}_{\mu\nu}$ ($\Lambda = 0$),

$$<\bar{\omega}^2>\bar{G}_{\mu\nu} = <T^{(\omega)}_{\mu\nu}(\bar{\omega},\bar{g}_{\mu\nu})> - <\bar{\omega}^2>\mathcal{E}_{\mu\nu}, \quad (40)$$

where $T^{(\omega)}_{\mu\nu}$ depends on the geometry and boundary conditions (see Eq. (19)). Further, $<T^{(\omega)}> = -<\bar{\omega}^2>\bar{R}$, because $\mathcal{E}_{\mu\nu}$ is traceless. We have now contributions from the antipode:

$$<T^{(\omega)}_{\mu\nu}> \to <T^{(\omega)}_{\mu\nu}> \pm <\widehat{T}^{(\omega)}_{\mu\nu}>, \quad <\bar{\omega}^2> \to <\bar{\omega}^2> \pm <\widehat{\bar{\omega}^2}>. \quad (41)$$

In the simplified de Sitter space, one then easily construct Green functions[9]

$$G_{\alpha JS}(X,X') = e^{2\alpha}\left[G(X.X') + G(X,JX')\right],$$

$$G_{\alpha JA}(X,X') = e^{2\alpha}\left[G(X.X') - G(X,JX')\right], \quad (42)$$

with α labels the one parameter family of the de Sitter vacua. The expectation values for a scalar field and the energy momentum tensor can then be calculated. One obtain, for example,[8]

$$<\widehat{\Phi^2_{JS,JA}}> = \frac{1}{16\pi\cos\pi\nu}\left[m^2 + \left(\xi - \frac{1}{6}\right)R\right], \quad (43)$$

with $\nu = (9/4 - M^2/H^2)^{1/2}$, $M^2 = m^2 + \xi R$, m the mass of the field and $H \sim \Lambda$. In our case we have no scalar field, but instead ω. The expression for $T_{\tilde{U}\tilde{U}}$ becomes[30]

$$T^{(\omega)}_{UU} = \frac{c_1 e^{-2c_1 U}}{c_3^2 c_4^2 (c_2\rho + c_3)^2}(c_2 c_3 \rho^2 F(U) - c_1^2 c_2^2 \rho^2 + c_1 c_3^2), \quad (44)$$

which can be used to evaluate the expectation value. In order to apply the full antipodal map, one includes the φ-dependency in the dilaton equation. The relevant operator (d'Alembertian) can be separated in the used coordinate system. The relevant φ contribution comes from periodic Mathieu functions (in variable φ). They converge uniformly on all compact sets in the z-plane. Next, one applies the method of 't Hooft, by expanding the position variables $u^\pm(z,\varphi)$ and momentum distributions $p^\pm(z,\varphi)$ in the partial waves of Mathieu functions.[f] Further, one then calculates the gravitational shift $\delta\tilde{U}(z,\varphi)$, in order to carry a particle over from I to II, or back,[6] using the Shapiro delay.

4.2. The surface gravity and the conformal gauge

Since we have now the description of the antipodal map in our black hole spacetime, we will look more closely at the conformal invariance. First of all, one should rely in the dynamical situation on (conformal) Killing vectors in order to describe the spacetime symmetries. Our Lagrangian is conformal invariant under Eq. (14), so we can use the freedom of the conformal factor Ω. Remember, different ω means different notion of the vacuum state for the in-going and outside observer, so they will use different conformal gauge freedom. It is desirable that for the out-going observer, the surface gravity of the horizon is conformal invariant. Further, conformal transformations must preserve affinely parameterized null geodesics. This will deliver Ω for the in-going observer. We can define out-going and in-going null normals[18] for $\bar{g}_{\mu\nu}$

$$\bar{l}^\mu = (1, N\sqrt{N^2 - r^2 N^{\varphi 2}}, 0, 0),$$

$$\bar{m}^\mu = \left(-\frac{1}{2r^2 N^{\varphi 2} - 2N^2}, -\frac{N}{2\sqrt{N^2 - r^2 N^{\varphi 2}}}, 0, 0\right). \quad (45)$$

with $\bar{l}^\mu \bar{l}_\mu = \bar{m}^\mu \bar{m}_\mu = 0$, $\bar{l}^\mu \bar{m}_\mu = -1$. The surface gravity then becomes

$$\kappa = 2N\left(\partial_r(\sqrt{N^2 - r^2 N^{\varphi 2}}) + \partial_t\left(\frac{1}{N}\right)\right) = 2N\left(\partial_t \sqrt{\bar{g}_{rr}} - \partial_r \sqrt{\bar{g}_{tt}}\right). \quad (46)$$

This is consistent with the metric definition of κ.

4.3. The meaning of the warped spacetime

Let us now return to $g_{\mu\nu} = \omega^{4/3} \bar{\omega}^2 \bar{g}_{\mu\nu}$. In the CDG setting, the evaporation of the black hole is also determined by the complementarity transformation of ω between the in-going and outside observer. Our spacetime is now ($b_4 = b_3 b_2$)

$$ds^2 = \omega^{4/3}\bar{\omega}^2 \left[(C_2(t+b_3)^4 + C_3) \frac{(10b_2^3 r^2 + 20b_2^2 r^3 + 15b_2 r^4 + 4r^5 + C_1)}{5r^2} \right.$$
$$\left. \left(-dt^{*2} + dr^{*2}\right) + dz^2 + r^2\left(d\varphi + \frac{N^\varphi}{N_2^2}dt^*\right)^2 \right], \quad (47)$$

---

[f]So the spherical harmonics are replaced by the Mathieu harmonics

with

$$\omega^{4/3}\bar{\omega}^2 = \frac{1}{(r+c_2)^2(t+c_3)^2(r+b_2)^2(t+b_3)^2}, \quad (48)$$

We observe that $\omega^{4/3}\bar{\omega}^2$ approaches zero for coordinate time $t \to \infty$, so $g_{\mu\nu}$ shrinks to zero, so the distant observer sees a gradually shrinking black hole when the metric time runs to infinity. Further, the only contribution from the 5D spacetime is the $\omega^{4/3}$. Remarkable, the projected Weyl component is necessary in order to obtain the same form of N^2 and to avoid naked singularities. So $\omega^{4/3} = [(r+c_2)^2(t+c_3)^2]^{-1}$ is the "scale" term from the 5D warped spacetime (the warpfactor in the RS model is the product of y-dependent part and ω part). Suppose one wants combine the conformal transformation with an internal symmetry transformation, i.e., a spacetime transformation. In particular, the scale transformations. One can proof in that case, $\Box \log \Omega = 0$,[19] which is consistent with our 2D null hypersurface of Eq. (32). Further, in dimension $n \neq 4$ only the scale-invariant theories based upon scalar fields (so ω from 5D) are conformally invariant. Conclusion: $\bar{\omega}$ of our $\bar{g}_{\mu\nu}$ can be used in non-vacuum models. An additional advantage of the warped spacetime in connection with cosmology and hierarchy problem, was already mentioned in the introduction. A new aspect will be the embedding of the 5D in the 4D spacetime and the relation with the 3D BTZ blackhole solution.

4.4. *The relation with the 3D Baňados-Teitelboim-Zanelli black hole*

In the spacetime under consideration, the dz^2 term can be omitted. One obtains then the 3D Baňados-Teitelboim-Zanelli (BTZ) black hole spacetime. It solves the Einstein equations with a negative cosmological constant.[29] The BTZ solution is related to the AdS/CFT correspondence and intensively studies in connection with black hole entropy issues. However, we should like to take the cosmological constant zero. In a former study,[30] an exact solution was found in a CDG setting in Eddington-Finkelstein retarded coordinates (U, ρ) (or advanced V) where the antipodal map $(U, V, \varphi) \to (-U, -V, \varphi + \pi)$ is applicable:

$$ds^2 = \frac{e^{-2c_1 U}}{(c_2\rho + c_3)^2}\left[\pm\frac{c_1(c_3^2 - c_2^2\rho^2)}{c_2 c_3}dU^2 - 2dU\,d\rho + dz^2 + \rho^2\left(d\xi + F(U)dU\right)^2\right], \quad (49)$$

which is Ricci flat, while $\tilde{R}^{(4)} = \frac{6c_1 c_2}{c_3}$. The function $F(U)$ will be fixed when matter terms are incorporated (i.e. for example, a scalar gauge field). The metric Eq. (49) will then contain a term $b(U,\rho)^2 d\varphi^2$ and a relation like $(N^\xi)' = \frac{b}{\eta^2 X^2 + \omega^2}$ will be obtained. It has no curvature singularity. The location of the apparent horizon in U:

$$\rho_{AH} = \pm\frac{c_3}{\sqrt{c_2(c_2 + \frac{c_3}{c_1}F(U)^2)}}, \quad (50)$$

with

$$\frac{d\rho}{dU} = \frac{1}{2}e^{-2c_1 U} \cdot \begin{cases} -\frac{c_1}{c_2 c_3} & \ldots\ldots\ldots \rho \to 0 \\ \frac{c_3 F(U)^2 + c_1 c_2}{c_2^2 c_3} & \ldots \rho \to \infty \\ 0 & \ldots\ldots\ldots \rho = \rho_{AH} \end{cases} \quad (51)$$

which is independent of ω. Here C_i are constants and $F(U)$ a function determined by the non-diagonal contribution. Further, we have

$$\lim_{\rho \to 0} g_{UU} \to \pm \frac{c_1}{c_2 c_3 e^{2c_1 U}}, \quad (52)$$

So when the evaporation speeds up, it approaches zero. We are dealing here with null-radiation in the (ρ, z)-plane. One could compare this solution with that found by Chan[32] in standard GR of a spinning black hole. They also find a solution for $F(U)$ which is determined by an energy-momentum tensor of null spinning dust. It is again curious that the "uplifted" BTZ has the same solution, comparable with the "up-lifting" 5D[30]

5. Metric Fluctuation and Hawking Radiation

In the original deviation of the Hawking radiation, one uses the propagation of a linear quantized field in a classical background metric. However, near the horizon, high-frequencies metric fluctuations can contribute to the vacuum polarization and the impact of gravitational back reactions can be large. These zero-point fluctuations result in a modification of the Hawking radiation by gravitational waves.[31] One could question what the effect is of these waves in our CDG model, where we have instead the dilaton field. Of course, one should need a quantum gravitational approach, which is not available yet. So need some approximation. However, effect of the scattering of these quanta at the horizon can be investigated in the context of the antipodal mapping considered here.[g] Without the contribution of the metric fluctuations, the mean number of quanta reaching $\mathcal{J}^+$ takes the form

$$<\bar{n}_\lambda>_0 \sim \frac{1}{e^{2\pi E_+/\kappa} - 1}, \quad (53)$$

with E_+ the energy measured at $\mathcal{J}^+$ for the out modes. This is the Planck distribution with temperature $T = \kappa/2\pi = (8\pi M)^{-1}$. The correction terms can then be calculated by using the s-modes of a quantum massless scalar field and by using the fact that the in-going and out-going modes decouple.[31] One makes use of the mean energy flux, by calculating $dE/dU = 4\pi r^2 <T_{UU}>_{ren}$, where the renormalized surface gravity is used. However, in this approximation, the reflection conditions are at r=0, with in our antipodal map must be revised (we have no inside). We can

---

[g]A suitable approximation is the high-frequency approximation applied to a Vaidya spacetime, where the not-flat background spacetime is distorted by the gravitational waves.[33] A recent application was provided by Slagter.[34, 35]

use the (U,U) energy-momentum component of our model and can apply Eq. (41) for the antipodal contribution.

Notice that the meaning of the local dilaton $\bar\omega$, is twofold. First, it determines the metric fluctuations (one also must incorporate in the dilaton equation the φ-dependency). Secondly, The in-going observer will use a different conformal gauge freedom Ω on $\bar\omega$ to describe the vacuum. Further, $\bar\omega$ is locally unobservable, unless we include metric fluctuations (gravitational waves. It will be necessary to compare this with the usual contribution using the Bunch-Davies method (and to taken into count the antipodal contribution). Note that the outside observer will use a different gauge and he/she experiences a mass $\sim \omega^2 N^2$ and Hawking radiation $\sim \partial_U(\omega^2 N^2)$, while for the in-going observer it is part of his vacuum. On the other hand, the outside observer is not aware of the antipodal identification. One could also say that they disagree about the observed scales. Or differently stated, they disagree about the back reaction from the Hawking radiation.

6. Conclusion and Outlook

We find an exact time dependent solution in the conformal dilaton gravity model on a warped 5D spacetime. The spacetime is written as $^{(5)}g_{\mu\nu} = \omega^{4/3}\,^{(5)}\tilde g_{\mu\nu}$ and $^{(4)}\tilde g_{\mu\nu} = \bar\omega^{2}\,^{(4)}\bar g_{\mu\nu}$. In our model, ω can be seen as the contribution from the bulk, while $\bar\omega$ is the brane component. It is conjectured that the different conformal gauge freedom, Ω, the in-going and outside observers possess, can be calculated by demanding a conformal invariant surface gravity and the preservation of affinely parameterized null geodesics. This means that the complementarity is expressed by the different notion of the vacuum state. The solution guarantees regularity of the action when $\omega \to 0$. We don't need a Weyl term in the action (generates negative metric states). In stead, we have a contribution from the bulk, i.e., the electric part of the 5D Weyl tensor. It is remarkable that the 5D field equations and the effective 4D equations can be written for general dimension n, with $n = 4, 5$. The energy-momentum tensor of the time-dependent dilaton, determining also the Hawking radiation, can be calculated exactly. By suitable choice of the parameters, the spacetime $\bar g_{\mu\nu}$ can be regular and singular free. This exact solution, nonetheless without mass terms, can be used to tackle the deep-seated problem of the black hole complementarity: the infalling and outside observer experience different ω by the choice of Ω. The next task is to incorporate mass into our model and investigate the dilaton-scalar field interaction. The conformal invariance will then spontaneously be broken.

Appendix: The Quintic Horizon Equation and Related Issues

Our quintic polynomial, determining the horizons,

$$f = r^5 + \frac{15}{4}b_2 r^4 + 5b_2^2 r^3 + \frac{5}{2}b_2^3 r^2 + \frac{C_1}{4} = 0, \tag{54}$$

can be written by a, so-called Tschirnhaus transformation, in the form

$$r^5 - \frac{15b_2}{16}(C_1 + b_2^5)r^2 - \frac{125b_2^3}{256}(C_1 + b_2^5)r - \frac{1}{16}(C_1 + b_2^5)^2 = 0 \qquad (55)$$

By scaling, this form can be reduced to the Bring-Jerrard form $r^5 + r - c$, with c a function of b_2 and C_1.[27] There is an interesting relation between the symmetry group of the icosahedron and our quintic equation. The symmetry group is isomorphic with the Galois group A_5 (of an irreducible quintic polynomial). The icosahedron is dual to the dodecahedron, i.e., their symmetries are isomorphic. The A_5 is interesting in physics, because it is a simple group having no invariant subgroups. It has three orbits, which are invariant under the antipodal map. So the connection with the Möbius group is clear. For details, we refer to Toth.[27] It is conjectured that our quintic polynomial (Eq. (54)) has a deep-seated relation with the 5D spacetime solution. Further, it is remarkable that the resulting quintic equation is independent of the dimension of our manifold ($n = 4, 5$). Moreover, the nice fitting of the antipodal map in our model cannot be a coincident. From Eq. (26) we observe that the derivative of f is $5r(r + b_2)^3$. So it is expected that our quintic equation results from a immersion[h] of a closed surface S in $\mathbb{R}^3$ into $\mathbb{R}^4$. This is currently under investigation by the author.

References

1. Hawking, S. (1975) *Particle Creation by Black Holes*. Comm. Math. Phys. **43**, 199.
2. 't Hooft, G. (1993) *Dimensional Reduction in Quantum Gravity*. Conference on Highlights of Particle and Condensed Matter Physics (SALAMFEST). C930308, 184.
3. Page, D. N. (1993) *Informatgion in black hole radiation*. Phys. Rev. Lett. **71**, 3743.
4. Almheiri, A., Marolf, D., Polchinski, J. and Sully, J. (2013) *Black Holes: Complementarity or Firewalls?*. JHEP **02**, 62.
5. 't Hooft, G. (2016) *Black Hole Unitarity and Antipodal Entanglement*. Found. Phys. **46**, 1185.
6. 't Hooft, G. (2018) *The Firewall Transformation for Black Holes and Some of its Implications*. arXiv: gr-qc/161208640v3.
7. 't Hooft, G. (1984) *Ambiguity of the Equivalence Princple and Hawking's Temperature*. J. Geom. and Physics **Volume 1, Issue 1**, 45.
8. Sanchez, N. and Whiting, B. F. (1987) *Quantum Field Theory and the Antipodal Identification of Black Holes*. Nucl. Phys. **B283**, 605.
9. Sanchez, N. (1986) *Two- and Four-Dimensional Semi-Classical Gravity and Conformal Mappings*. Cern-Th.4592/86.
10. Folacci, A. and Sanchez, N. (1987) *Quantum Field Theory and the Antipodal Identification of de Sitter Space. Elliptic inflation*.
11. Schrödinger, E. (1957) *Expanding Universe*. Cambridge Univ. Press, Cambridge.
12. 't Hooft, G. (2018) *Discreteness of Black Hole Microstates*. arXiv: gr-qc/180905367v2.
13. 't Hooft, G. (2018) *Virtual Black Holes and Spacetime Structure*. Found. Phys. **48**, 1149.

---

[h]An immersion is a differentiable function between differentiable manifold whose derivative is everywhere injective. It is also a topological embedding.

14. 't Hooft, G. (2015) *Diagonalizing the Black Hole Information Retrieval Process.* arXiv: gr-qc/150901695.
15. Zakharov, V. D. (1973) *Gravitational Waves in Einstein's Theory.* John Wiley & Sons, Inc., New York.
16. Wald, R. M. (1994) *Quantum Field Theory in Curved Spacetime and Black Hole Thermodynamics.* The Univ. of Chicago Press, Chicago.
17. Alvarez, E., Herrero-Valea, M. and Martin, C. P. (2014) *Conformal and Non Conformal Dilaton Gravity* JHEP **10**, 214.
18. Slagter, R. J. (2021) *Conformal Dilaton Gravity and Warped Spacetimes in 5D* arXiv: 2012.00409.
19. Felsager, B. (1998) *Geometry, Particles and Fields.* Springer, New York.
20. Mannheim P. D. (2005) *Alternatives to dark matter and dark energy.* Prog. Part. Nucl. Phys. **56**, 340, arXiv: astro-ph/0505266v2.
21. Slagter, R. J. and Pan, S. (2016) *A new fate of a warped 5D FLRW model with a U(1) scalar gauge field.* Found. of Phys. **46**, 1075.
22. Maldacena, J., Milekhin, A. (2021) *Humanly traversable wormholes.* Phys. Rev. D **103**, 066007.
23. Maldacena, J. (2011) *Einstein Gravity from conformal gravity.* arXiv: hep-th/11055632.
24. Shiromizu, T., Maeda, K., Sasaki, M. (2000) *The Einstein equations on the 3-brane world.* Phys. Rev. D **62**, 024012.
25. Shiromizu, T., Maeda, K., Sasaki, M. (2003) *Low Energy Effective Theory for Two Branes System-Covariant Curvature Formulation.* Phys. Rev. D **7** 084022.
26. Maartens, R. (2010) it Brane-World Gravity. arXiv: hep-th/10043962V2.
27. Toth, G. (2002) *Finite Möbius Groups, Minimal Immersions of Spheres and Moduli.* Springer, Heidelberg.
28. Strauss, N. A., Whiting, B. F. and Franzen, A. T. (2020) *Classical Tools for Antipodal Identification in Reissner-Nordstrom Spacetime.* arXiv: gr-qc/200202501.
29. Compère, G. (2019) *Advanced lectures on General Relativity.* Lecture notes in Physics 952, Springer, Heidelberg.
30. Slagter, R. J. (2019) *On the Dynamical BTZ Black Hole in Conformal Gravity.* In Spacetime 1909-2019, Proc. Second H. Minkowski Meeting, Bulgaria, Albena.
31. Barrabès, C. and Hogan, P. A. (2013) *Advanced General Relativity.* Oxford Univ. Press, Oxford.
32. Chan, J. S. F., Chan, K. C. H. and Mann, R. B. (1996) *Interior Structure of a Spinning Black Hole in 2+1 Dimensions.* Phys. Rev. D **54** 1535 (arXiv: gr-qc/9406049).
33. Choquet-Bruhat, Y. and Geroch, R. P. (1969) *Global Aspects of the Cauchy Problem in General Relativity.* Commun. Math. Phys. **14**, 329.
34. Slagter, R. J. and Miedema, P. G. (2020) *On the Azimuthal Alignment of Quasars Spin Vector in Large Quasar Groups and Cosmic Strings.* Mon. Not. R. Astron. Soc., **459** 3054.
35. Slagter, R. J. (2021) *New Evidence of the Azimuthal Alignment of Quasars Spin Vector in the LQG U1.28, U1.27, U1.11, Cosmologically Explained.* arXiv: gr-qc/210212805.

From neutrino masses to the full size of the universe — Some intriguing aspects of the tetron model

B. Lampe

Theoretical Physics, Universität Hamburg,
Hamburg, Germany
E-mail: Lampe.Bodo@web.de

The universe according to the tetron model consists of invisible tiny constituents, elastically bound with bond length about the Planck length and binding energy the Planck energy. A tetron transforms as the fundamental fermion(=octonion) representation **8** of SO(6,1). With respect to the decomposition $SO(6,1) \to SO(3,1) \times SO(3)$ it possesses spin 1/2 and isospin 1/2, i.e. a tetron represents an isospin doublet of Dirac spinors. The 24 known quarks and leptons arise as eigenmode excitations of a tetrahedral fiber structure, which is made up from 4 tetrons (plus 4 antitetrons) and extends into 3 additional 'internal' dimensions. While the laws of gravity are due to the elastic properties of the tetron bonds, particle physics interactions take place within the internal fibers. I will concentrate on two of the most intriguing features of the model:
- understanding small neutrino masses from the conservation of isospin, and, more in general, calculating the spectrum of quark and lepton masses. This is obtained from the tetron model's interpretation of the Higgs mechanism.
- the possibility to determine the full size of the universe from future dark energy measurements. This is obtained from the tetron model's interpretation of the dark energy phenomenon.

Finally, the dark energy equation of state, i.e. the equation of state of the tetron background will be derived.

Keywords: Tetron model; quark and lepton masses and mixings; neutrino masses; full size of the universe; dark energy equation of state.

1. Introduction

In the following sections some implications of the tetron model[1–4] of particle physics and cosmology will be presented.

In this model the universe itself is an elastic medium composed of invisible constituents which are bound at Planck energy. While the laws of gravity are due to the elastic properties of the medium, particle physics interactions take place within internal fibers, with the characteristic internal energy being the Fermi scale. All ordinary matter quarks and leptons are constructed as quasiparticle excitations of this internal fiber structure. Since the quasiparticles fulfill Lorentz covariant wave equations, they perceive the universe as a 3+1 dimensional spacetime continuum lacking a preferred rest system. Any type of mass/energy induces curvature on the spacetime continuum as determined by the Einstein equations.

Now in the following I want to explain some details of these statements.

2. Quark and Lepton Masses from Excitations of Internal Tetrahedrons

In the tetron model the ground state of our universe looks like illustrated in Figure 1. In this figure the large horizontal arrow stands for the 3 dimensions of physical space, while the tetrahedrons extend into 3 additional internal dimensions. The picture is a little misleading because in the tetron model physical space and internal dimensions are assumed to be completely orthogonal. This means the whole game is actually played within a large altogether 6 dimensional space, 3 physical dimensions and 3 internal ones.

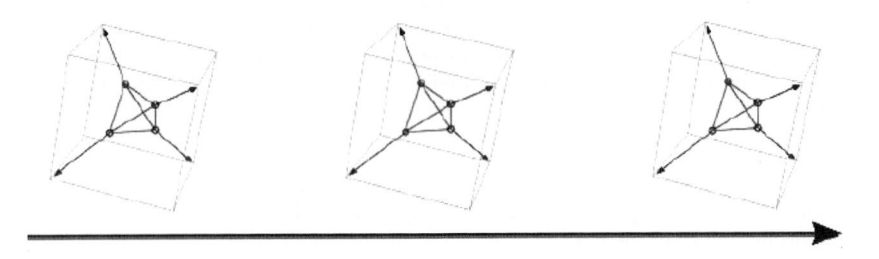

Fig. 1. The global ground state of the tetron model after the electroweak symmetry breaking.

If you ask: why this structure?, I can say at this point that the tetrahedral structure is introduced in order to explain the observed quark and lepton spectrum, which means to get exactly 24 excitation states with the correct multiplet structure.

Before discussing the excitations, let us first consider the ground state Figure 1 in some more detail. As you can see, each tetrahedron is made up from 4 constituents called 'tetrons', depicted as the white dots[a]. The white arrows denote the 'isospins', i.e. internal spin vectors of the tetrons. This means the tetrons have a spin in physical space and in addition an internal spin in internal space. As turns out, the interactions of the internal spins play an important role for particle physics and for electroweak symmetry breaking.

It is important to note, that the 4 isospin vectors in Figure 1 define tetrahedrons, too. Due to the pseudovector property of these vectors their tetrahedral symmetry group actually is a Shubnikov group.[5–7] This means, while the coordinate symmetry is S_4, the arrangement of isospin vectors respects the tetrahedral Shubnikov symmetry

$$G_4 := A_4 + CPT(S_4 - A_4) \tag{1}$$

where $A_4(S_4)$ is the (full) tetrahedral symmetry group and CPT the usual CPT operation except that P is the parity transformation in physical space only. Since

---

[a] Actually, antitetrons are needed as well. For details see the review.[3]

the elements of $S_4 - A_4$ contain an implicit factor of internal parity, the symmetry (1) certifies CPT invariance of the local ground state in the full of R^{6+1}.

2.1.

In the situation depicted in Figure 1 a symmetry breaking has already taken place, because the isospins are aligned between all the tetrahedrons.

Before the symmetry breaking, which means above a certain temperature, isospins are distributed randomly, corresponding to a local $SU(2) \times U_1$ symmetry[b], but when the universe cools down, there is a phase transition, and the isospins freeze into the aligned structure, breaking the symmetry from $SU(2) \times U_1$ to the discrete 'family group' G_4. And the important point to note is, this temperature can be identified with the Fermi scale.[2]

How does this work out in detail? Mathematically, a tetron is assumed to transform as the fundamental spinor representation of SO(6,1). This representation is 8-dimensional and sometimes called the octonion representation.

With respect to the decomposition of $SO(6,1) \to SO(3,1) \times SO(3)$ into the 3-dimensional base space and the 3-dimensional internal space, a tetron possesses spin 1/2 and isospin 1/2. This means it can rotate both in physical space and in internal space, and corresponds to the fact that a tetron Ψ decomposes into an isospin doublet $\Psi = (U, D)$ of two ordinary SO(3,1) Dirac fields U and D.

$$8 \to (1,2,2) + (2,1,2) = ((1,2) + (2,1), 2) \tag{2}$$

Using this, one can now rigorously define the isospin vectors used and drawn in Figure 1:

$$\vec{Q} = \Psi^\dagger \vec{\tau} \Psi \tag{3}$$

where τ are the internal spin Pauli matrices. Actually one has to distinguish chiral isospin vectors

$$\vec{Q}_L = \frac{1}{2}\Psi^\dagger (1 - \gamma_5) \vec{\tau} \Psi \qquad \vec{Q}_R = \frac{1}{2}\Psi^\dagger (1 + \gamma_5) \vec{\tau} \Psi \tag{4}$$

and for tetrons and antitetrons, but this complication will not be discussed in the present talk.[3]

A typical interaction Hamiltonian between such isospin vectors of 2 tetrons a and b looks like this

$$H_H = -J \vec{Q}_a \vec{Q}_b \tag{5}$$

So it has the form of a Heisenberg interaction - but for isospins, not for spins. The coupling J is called the 'isomagnetic exchange coupling'.

The mathematical treatment of the excitations arising from (5) is similar to that of magnons in ordinary magnetism, but the physics here is much different. Since

---

[b]Weak parity violation, i.e. the appearance of $SU(2)_L$, is discussed in.[3]

the isospin vibrations take place in internal space, they are pointlike in physical space. Furthermore, they inherit their fermion nature from the fermion property of the vibrating tetron.

In reality, the Hamiltonian is somewhat more complicated than (5) due to the appearance of antitetrons and of the fact that inner- and inter-tetrahedral interactions are present, the inner ones with 'exchange coupling' $j = -O(1)$ GeV (strong interaction scale) and the inter ones with $J = O(100)$ GeV (weak interaction scale). j and J have different sign, because j leads to the frustrated 'antiferromagnetic' ground state of a single tetrahedron, while J is responsible for the 'ferromagnetic'[c] alignment of neighboring tetrahedrons.[1]

This alignment can be shown to be the microscopic origin of the electroweak symmetry breaking, and furthermore it allows to calculate the quark and lepton masses. I refer here to references[1] and[2]. In these papers you can find all the details - how to construct the electroweak order parameter, the Higgs field and how to calculate the quark and lepton masses and mixings from the isospin couplings.

At this point it must be enough to show that among the 24 isospin excitations which are the quarks and leptons, there are 3 almost massless modes which correspond to the neutrinos. This has to do with the conservation of total isospin. Namely, the masses of the neutrinos are particularly suppressed because the 3 neutrino modes correspond to the vibrations of the 3 components of the total internal angular momentum vector in one tetrahedron

$$\vec{\Sigma} := \sum_{a=1}^{4} \vec{Q}_a = \sum_{a=1}^{4} \Psi_a^\dagger \vec{\tau} \Psi_a \qquad (6)$$

Whenever this quantity is conserved

$$d\vec{\Sigma}/dt = 0 \qquad (7)$$

the neutrino masses will strictly vanish. In fact, the Heisenberg type of interactions (5) conserve total internal angular momentum. Therefore, they fulfill (7) and give no contribution to the neutrino masses. Further details can be found in.[1]

So $\vec{\Sigma}$ is the total internal angular momentum (total isospin), and the conservation equation for the 3 components of $\vec{\Sigma}$ leads to 3 of the 24 eigenmodes being massless. Contributions to the neutrino masses come from tiny torsional interactions which violate the conservation of isospin.[1]

3. The Full Size of the Universe from a Simple Spring Model

From this point on, I do not want to give more details on the particle physics implications, but want to concentrate on gravity and cosmological aspects. In order to include gravity in the tetron model, it is assumed that there is not only an interaction among the isospin vectors in internal space, but also a binding among tetrons

---

[c]I am using the language of magnetism, although interactions of isospins and not of spins are considered here.

in physical space, and that this binding is elastic. In other words, our universe is a 3-dimensional elastic medium expanding within some larger 6-dimensional space, and it can acquire curvature both in space and time.

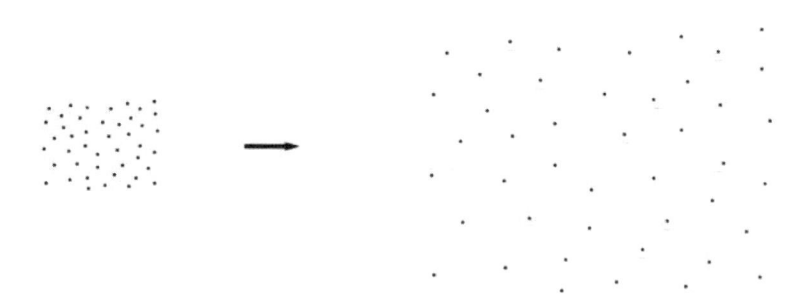

Fig. 2. Expansion of the empty universe consisting of tetrahedrons which look pointlike in physical space.

In 3-dimensional physical space, the expansion looks as shown in Figure 2. Note that in physical space the tetrahedrons are pointlike because they extend only into the internal dimensions. This means, you do not see the tetrahedral structure, you only see points which are bound with bond length about the Planck length and binding energy the Planck energy.

In the beginning, that means before the expansion started, the universe was created in a sudden so to say inflationary condensation process from an ultrahot tetron gas and afterwards was pushed to expansion by the condensation energy. Quark and matter particles were created as quasiparticle excitations of the tetrons gliding on the elastic medium. Since the quasiparticles fulfill Lorentz covariant wave equations, they perceive the universe as a 3+1 dimensional spacetime continuum lacking a preferred rest system. Any type of mass/energy induces curvature on the spacetime continuum as determined by the Einstein equations.

Now in the next step I want to draw a connection between the smallest and the largest scales of the universe, namely between the tetron binding structure at Planck length and the size of the universe as a whole. For that purpose, let us consider the binding energy of 2 tetrahedrons as a function of the bond length L, so this means the binding energy of 2 dots in Figure 3 as a function of their distance. It is assumed, that this function has a minimum at some bond length L_s and that at present we are at bond length L_0 roughly equal to the Planck length. Then the function looks like in Figure 3.

From this figure one concludes that the universe is expanding towards an equilibrium corresponding to an average bond length L_s. So the whole universe is carrying out an extremely low frequency breathing vibration $\omega \ll 10^{-10} yrs^{-1}$ around L_s, and all the tetron bonds on average are vibrating in accord with the universe. One

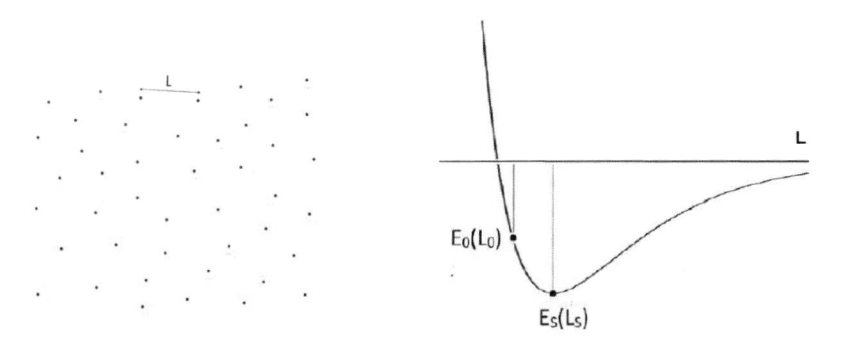

Fig. 3. Binding energy E of 2 neighboring tetrahedrons as a function of their distance L.

can work out the details of this picture and indeed show that this effect accounts for the present accelerated expansion as given by the dark energy observations.[4]

An important point to note is that in future more precise dark energy measurements may allow to extract the breathing frequency ω of the universe, and from ω one can determine the full size radius a of the universe according to the simple formula

$$a = \frac{L}{L_s}\frac{c}{\omega} \qquad (8)$$

where c is the speed of light.

3.1.

The remainder of this section is devoted to the proof of (8) within a simple spring type model, and to carry the idea of the universe as an extremely low frequency oscillatory system to the end.

In addition, these considerations will allow to derive the dark energy equation of state,[11] i.e. the equation of state of the invisible tetron background substrate. The relation between tetron density and pressure is a characteristic property of the bound tetron system. Actually, the elastic tetron universe resembles a fluid with elastic bonds among its constituents rather than an ordered solid, and so the fluid equation seems an appropriate way of description[d].

By 'full size' is meant the diameter of the 3-dimensional elastic medium which according to the tetron model is our universe. As a measure of this size I shall take $a(t)$ as appears in the standard FLRW line element

$$ds^2 = -c^2 dt^2 + a(t)^2 \left[\frac{dr^2}{1-kr^2} + \cdots \right] \qquad (9)$$

$a(t)$ is assumed to have dimension of length and dr^2 to be dimensionless.

---

[d]But note, the stiffness $\zeta = \frac{c^7}{\hbar G^2} \approx 10^{112} \frac{kg}{ms^2}$ of the tetron bonds is large enough, that this fluid pours out into only 3 of the 6 dimensions.

Following reference[4] a harmonic oscillatory term $\sim \omega^2(a - a_s)$ appears in the modified FLRW equations in addition to the cosmological constant Λ

$$\ddot{a} = -\frac{4\pi}{3}G\rho a - \omega^2(a - a_s) + \frac{\Lambda}{3}c^2 a \qquad (10)$$

The assumption of a breathing vibration with $a(t) \sim L(t)$ then leads to an identical equation for L(t):

$$\ddot{L} = -\frac{4\pi}{3}G\rho L - \omega^2(L - L_s) + \frac{\Lambda}{3}c^2 L \qquad (11)$$

The interpretation of the cosmological constant term within the tetron model will be postponed to later sections. For the moment, let us simply forget about Λ. Then the empty universe behaves harmonic with frequency ω, the reason being that its tetrahedral constituents follow a harmonic elastic interaction, i.e. the binding energy among the internal tetrahedrons in the neighborhood of the minimum at L_s can be approximated by a parabola, see Figure 3.

While characteristic frequencies ω and H_0(=Hubble constant) of the universe are tiny, the frequency $f_s = f(t_s)$ of a single tetron spring is extremely large and given by

$$f(t) = \frac{1}{T(t)} = \frac{c}{L(t)} \qquad (12)$$

where $T(t) = L(t)/c$ is the time dependent Planck time.

In accordance with reference[4] I have introduced time dependent Planck quantities

$$L(t) = \sqrt{\frac{\hbar(t)G(t)}{c^3}} \qquad T(t) = \sqrt{\frac{\hbar(t)G(t)}{c^5}} \qquad M(t) = \sqrt{\frac{\hbar(t)c}{G(t)}} \qquad (13)$$

with present day values at t=0:

$$L_0 = 1.6 \times 10^{-35} m \qquad M_0 = 2.2 \times 10^{-8} kg \qquad T_0 = 5.4 \times 10^{-44} s \qquad (14)$$

Inverting (13), a time dependent Planck and Newton constant is induced

$$\hbar(t)c = E(t)L(t) \qquad (15)$$
$$G(t) = c^4 L(t)/E(t) \qquad (16)$$

No time dependence of c is indicated, because in the present model there is none - at least if one uses the so-called cosmic coordinates t and r appearing in the line element (9).

3.2.

Coming to the details of the spring model, it is assumed that at each point of the elastic universe each direction can be approximated as a serial connection of N harmonic springs which connect N+1 constituents (= internal tetrahedrons). These can be thought to lie approximately on a straight line running from one end of the universe to the other. The spatial extension of the universe is then given by

$$a(t) = NL(t) \tag{17}$$

Clearly, this includes the additional very simplifying assumption that the expanding universe has the approximate form of a cube.

The mass μ of any one of the spring chains is given by the sum of all constituent rest masses M_{rest} in the chain, i.e.

$$\mu = NM_{rest} \tag{18}$$

where M_{rest} is the rest mass of one internal tetrahedron. The value of M_{rest} is unknown but should be typically of the order of the Planck mass.

Since in the neighborhood of L_s the binding energy $E(t) = E(L(t))$ is assumed to be quadratic in L, it must have the form

$$E(L) = E_s + \frac{d}{2}(L - L_s)^2 = M_{rest}c^2 - E_{bind} + \frac{1}{2}M_{rest}c^2\left(1 - \frac{L}{L_s}\right)^2 \tag{19}$$

i.e. E(L) is a sum of a constant energy E_s plus a variable component, which vanishes at $L(t_s) = L_s$. E_s comprises the binding energy of 2 tetrahedrons at L_s as well as their possible rest mass

$$E_s = E_{rest} - E_{bind} = M_{rest}c^2 - E_{bind} \tag{20}$$

It is to be noted that (19) does not meet the condition $E(L = \infty) = M_{rest}c^2$, so it holds only in the neighborhood of $L = L_s$. Note further that M_{rest} could in principle be any value, even much larger than E_{bind}. To have a bound state one needs a local minimum of $E(L)$ at L_s but not necessarily a negative $E(L_s)$, i.e. the condition

$$E_{bind} > E_{rest} \tag{21}$$

is not compelling - although present dark energy data seem to give a hint this inequality is true and furthermore in the simple spring model it will be needed for consistency of energy conservation eq. (27).

3.3.

The spring constant of a single spring is $d = M_{rest}f(t_s)^2$ with $f(t)$ from eq. (12). The basic reason why the breathing frequency ω of the universe is so small whereas the fundamental frequency $f = 1/T$ of its tetron constituents is so large, arises from the following fact: Consider one chain of strings stretching from one end of the universe to the other, each spring with a constant d. Then the serial connection of N springs is itself a harmonic oscillator with a much smaller combined spring constant

$$D = d/N \tag{22}$$

Note that the springs connected in parallel belong to different chains and do not contribute to the effective overall chain constant D.

Using $D = \mu \omega^2$ one can express the (extremely small) frequency ω of the universe in terms of the (extremely large) Planck frequency $f_s = f(t_s)$:

$$\omega^2 = \frac{D}{\mu} = \frac{d/N}{NM_{rest}} = \frac{1}{N^2} f_s^2 = \frac{c^2}{N^2 L_s^2} \tag{23}$$

Thus, the full extension (17) of the universe at equilibrium can be given as

$$a_s = NL_s = \frac{c}{\omega} \tag{24}$$

in a similar way as the observable(=Hubble) radius is given as c/H_0.

The present size of the universe is somewhat smaller than a_s and given by (8). These equations show that a precise enough measurement of the dark energy effect (i.e. of ω) can lead to an estimate for the full size of the universe.

3.4.

The spring model is also of use to better understand the FLRW theory within the general elasticity ansatz. The essence of the FLRW model is contained in the following equations
(i) the Friedmann equation for the Hubble parameter $\dot{a}/a$ and
(ii) the 'fluid equations' for the densities ρ_{tet} and ρ_{mat} of tetrons and (ordinary and dark) matter, respectively. Both, the tetron substrate and the matter content of the universe are assumed to be separate uniformly distributed perfect fluids with mass energy densities $\rho_{tet}(t)$ and $\rho_{mat}(t)$ and pressure $p_{tet}(t)$ and $p_{mat}(t)$.

3.4.1.

In the present model one can write down an equation for the conservation of energy in a matter-free spacially flat tetron universe

$$N^3 \frac{M_{rest}}{2} \dot{a}^2 + 3N^3 \frac{M_{rest} c^2}{2} \left(1 - \frac{a}{a_s}\right)^2 = -N^3 E_s \tag{25}$$

the conserved energy being the kinetic plus potential energy of the system of N^3 masses M_{rest} and $3N^3$ springs which make up the empty universe. The system is furthermore assumed to be in a breathing mode. Then, the difference in neighboring spring positions $x_{n+1}(t) - x_n(t)$ within one of the spring chains is n-independent and given by $L(t) - L_s$ for each spring n, and the velocity difference by $\dot{x}_{n+1} - \dot{x}_n = \dot{L}(t)$.

Comparing (25) to the corresponding matter-free FLRW equation

$$\frac{1}{2}\dot{a}^2 + \frac{3c^2}{2}\left(1 - \frac{a}{a_s}\right)^2 - \frac{1}{6}\Lambda c^2 a^2 = 0 \tag{26}$$

one finds 3 differences:

- There is no Λ-term in (25). Any cosmological constant contribution from tetrons has been removed in (25), because for the matter free elastic tetron substrate the binding forces do not drive the universe with Λa^2 to infinity, but with $\omega^2(a-a_s)^2$ to a_s. As will turn out later in section 3.4.3, in the presence of matter a cosmological constant reappears because the time dependent[4] Newton constant (16) implies a time dependent matter contribution to the cosmological constant.[8–10]

- There is a nonvanishing constant contribution $\sim E_s$ on the rhs, where there is 0 in FLRW. This has to do with the fact that the Friedmann equation only counts contributions to the spacetime curvature, where a constant binding energy of the tetron constituents does not matter. The FLRW model does not know about the cosmic constituents and uses the freedom to put their background binding energy to zero. In other words, a constant (like the binding energy $E_s = E(L_s)$ at equilibrium $a = a_s$) does not contribute to any cosmic expansion. E_s is the background tetron binding energy which leads to the flat elastic substrate being built from free tetrons, but does not at all contribute to its possible curvature or expansion.

- In order to have consistency with aforegoing formulas, in (26) I have pulled out a factor of 3 from the definition of the cosmic frequency ω.

3.4.2.

So far we have considered an empty universe built up from an elastic substrate of bound tetrons (or, more precisely, of bound internal tetrahedrons). If, in addition, matter is present in the universe, the modified Friedmann equation becomes

$$\frac{1}{2}\dot{a}^2 + \frac{3}{2}\omega^2(a - a_s)^2 = \frac{4\pi}{3c^2}G\rho_{mat}a^2 + \frac{1}{6}\Lambda_{mat}c^2 a^2 - \frac{E_s}{M_{rest}} \quad (27)$$

where ρ_{mat}/c^2 denotes the mass density of ordinary plus dark matter. As before in (25), the constant term $\sim E_s$ is not relevant when forming the time derivative of (27) in order to obtain the equation for the curvature/acceleration $\ddot{a}$.

Equation (27) includes a cosmological constant contribution Λ_{mat} due to ordinary and dark matter. This contribution derives from the time dependence of the Newton constant $G = c^4 L(t)/E(L(t))$ and will now be proven to be time dependent, too.

3.4.3.

In order to determine Λ_{mat} and its time dependence, we turn to the cosmological fluid equations. Both the expanding tetron background and the matter distribution will be approximated as separate fluids distributed homogeneously over the universe with energy densities $\rho_{tet}(t)$, $\rho_{mat}(t)$ and pressure $p_{tet}(t)$ and $p_{mat}(t)$.

For the tetronic fluid the appropriate form of the fluid equation is the ordinary one

$$\dot{\rho}_{tet} + 3(\rho_{tet} + p_{tet})\frac{\dot{a}}{a} = 0 \quad (28)$$

because the spring coupling d is constant and the time dependent Newton coupling not involved. In terms of a single tetrahedron with physical volume L^3 around it the density of the tetronic 'dark energy' fluid is

$$\rho_{tet}(t) = \frac{E}{V} = \frac{E_s}{L^3} + \frac{E_{rest}}{2L_s^3}\left(1 - \frac{L(t)}{L_s}\right)^2 \qquad (29)$$

where $E_s = E(L_s)$ is the Planck energy at equilibrium and $M_{rest} = E_{rest}/c^2$ is the tetrahedral rest mass, cf. eq. (20).

Similarly, the dark energy pressure is obtained to be

$$p_{tet} = -\frac{\partial E}{\partial V} = \frac{E_{rest}}{3L_s^3}\left(1 - \frac{L}{L_s}\right) + O(L - L_s)^2 \qquad (30)$$

and it can be checked that (29) and (30) indeed fulfill eq. (28).

These equations correspond to an equation of state parameter

$$w = \frac{p_{tet}}{\rho_{tet}} = \frac{E_{rest}}{3E_s}\left(1 - \frac{L}{L_s}\right) + O(L - L_s)^2 \qquad (31)$$

To compare this with various other dark energy equations of state suggested in the literature one may consult.[11]

3.4.4.

For matter and dark matter the suitable form of the fluid equation can be derived from the Bianchi identity

$$T^\mu_{\nu;\mu} = 0 \qquad (32)$$

for the energy-momentum tensor in general relativity. In case of a time dependent Newton and cosmological constant one has[8–10]

$$\frac{d}{dt}\left[G\rho_{mat} + \frac{c^4}{8\pi}\Lambda_{mat}\right] + 3G(p_{mat} + \rho_{mat})\frac{\dot{a}}{a} = 0 \qquad (33)$$

On the other hand, for the late time cosmology under consideration, matter can be approximated in the standard way as uniformly distributed dust. Ordinary and dark matter should then fulfill the ordinary fluid equation

$$\dot{\rho}_{mat} + 3(p_{mat} + \rho_{mat})\frac{\dot{a}}{a} = 0 \qquad (34)$$

by means of

$$p_{mat} = 0 \qquad (35)$$

$$\rho_{mat}(a) = \rho_{mat}(a_s)\frac{a_s^3}{a^3} \qquad (36)$$

Comparing (33) and (34) one concludes, that any imbalance coming from the time dependency of G must be cancelled by a time dependence of Λ_{mat} according to[8–10]

$$\dot{G}\rho_{mat} + \frac{c^4}{8\pi}\dot{\Lambda}_{mat} = 0 \qquad (37)$$

In the present approach all time dependencies arise only through $a(t) = NL(t)$. Therefore using

$$\frac{d}{dt} = \dot{a}\frac{d}{da} = \dot{L}\frac{d}{dL} \qquad (38)$$

one can calculate Λ_{mat} from the scale dependence of G eq. (16)

$$\Lambda_{mat}(a) = \Lambda_{mat}(a_s) + 8\pi \int_a^{a_s} da \, \rho_{mat}(a)\frac{d}{da}\frac{L}{|E(L)|} \qquad (39)$$

with $L = a/N$. In the quadratic approximation used throughout this paper, where one considers the neighborhood of $a = a_s$, one can carry out the integral in (39) to obtain the a(t) dependence of Λ_{mat}:

$$\Lambda_{mat}(a) = \Lambda_{mat}(a_s) + \frac{8\pi\rho_{mat}(a_s)}{|E_s|}(L_s - L) + O(L - L_s)^2 \qquad (40)$$

Here, $\rho_{mat}(a_s)L_s^3/|E_s|$ is the ratio of average energy of matter within a Planck volume L_s^3 over one tetrahedral binding energy E_s. Since there are much more bound tetrons than matter particles in the universe, the cosmological constant due to (40) is extremely small. This can be seen more explicitly by rewriting (40) as

$$\Lambda_{mat}(a) - \Lambda_{mat}(a_s) = 8\pi \frac{\rho_{mat}(a_s)}{\rho_{tet}(a_s)}\frac{L_s - L}{L_s^3} \approx 8\pi \frac{\rho_{mat}(a_0)}{\rho_{tet}(a_0)}\frac{L_0 - L}{L_0^3} \qquad (41)$$

and using approximate values $L_0 - L \approx -L_0$ and

$$\rho_{mat}(a_0)/c^2 = 2.6 \cdot 10^{-27}\frac{kg}{m^3} \qquad (42)$$

$$\rho_{tet}(a_0)/c^2 = \frac{M_0}{L_0^3} = 0.54 \cdot 10^{97}\frac{kg}{m^3} \qquad (43)$$

3.5.

In the literature one often finds the argument that there should be enormous contributions to the cosmological constant from zero point fluctuations of the matter fields. This is 'proven' by summing up the zero point energies $\hbar\omega_k/2$ of all existing fields over all modes with wave vectors k

$$\rho_{quant} = \frac{\hbar}{2}\int\frac{d^3k}{(2\pi)^3}\omega_k \qquad (44)$$

and using the Planck scale as UV cutoff. This leads to an enormous number of the order of $\rho_{quant} \sim E_s/L_s^3$ - actually the same order as ρ_{tet} eqs. (29) and (43) which is no wonder, because both the claimed quantum effects and the tetron properties are derived from the Planck scale.

If true, such a huge contribution ρ_{quant} to the cosmological constant would immediately tear the universe into pieces. This then is usually considered a fundamental unsolved problem and runs under the name 'cosmological constant problem'. The suggested solutions often lead to a cascade of fine tuning problems.

In the tetron model the situation is much simpler. As discussed before, the Planck energy $E_0 \sim E_s$ contained in the neighborhood volume L_0^3 of one bound constituent is the binding energy of tetrons in an empty flat spacetime and does not affect the curvature(=accelerated expansion), because it is a constant contribution in the conservation of energy law (27). Furthermore, quantum fluctuations do not exist by themselves at any point in the universe, but are an artefact of the discreteness of the universe[3] and arise only in the process of detecting and measuring a matter field gliding as quasiparticle excitation on the discrete tetron background.

For these reasons the cosmological constant does not get a contribution from quantum fluctuations.

4. Remark on the Strong Interaction

In the preceeding sections we have obtained an understanding of gravity as well as of the electroweak symmetry breaking. How does the strong interaction among quarks fit into the tetron picture?

The dominant features of the strong interaction are the linear attractive potential at low energies and asymptotic freedom at high energies. In the tetron model the strong interaction is related to disturbances by the triplet isospin excitations(=quarks) of the local frustrated ground state which is formed by a single tetrahedron of isospin vectors. As triplet states of G_4, quarks disturb the ground state's isomagnetism, whereas leptons are G_4-singlets, i.e. 'isomagnetically' neutral. They do not disturb the ground state and therefore do not take part in the strong interaction. As shown in,[1,3] the isomagnetic ground state energy of a single tetrahedron is roughly $E_{QCD} \approx 1$ GeV corresponding to a characteristic length scale $L_{QCD} \approx 10^{-15}$m.

The linear potential between two G_4-triplets, vulgo a quark Q and an antiquark $\bar Q$, arises as follows: Since the inner-tetrahedral exchange energy $j = E_{QCD}$ is relatively small, the 'antiferromagnetic' effects leading to the local frustrated tetrahedral state have a much longer range L_{QCD} than the weak interactions which are induced by the 'ferromagnetic' inter-tetrahedral exchange energies $J = O(100)$ GeV. The triplet excitations corresponding to the two quarks are characterized by small vibrations $\vec\Delta_Q$ and $\vec\Delta_{\bar Q}$ of the isospin vectors $\vec S$. When the distance between the two excitations becomes larger than L_{QCD}, an additional pair $\vec\Delta_q$ and $\vec\Delta_{\bar q}$ is excited on intermediate tetrahedrons in order to reduce the original 'antiferromagnetic' suspense between $\vec\Delta_Q$ and $\vec\Delta_{\bar Q}$. (I am using the language of magnetism, although interactions of isospins and not of spins are considered here.) The associated cost in energy is proportional to the number of $q\bar q$ pairs created, and the potential V between Q and $\bar Q$ therefore increases linearly with distance:

$$V = F|x| \qquad F \approx -j < \vec\Delta_Q \vec\Delta_{\bar Q} > /L_Q \qquad (45)$$

where $< \vec\Delta_Q \vec\Delta_{\bar Q} >$ is the isospin correlation between the sites, on which the isospins vibrate, and L_{QCD} the length where all this becomes relevant. The confinement energy is hence proportional to the original 'antiferromagnetic' exchange energy j induced on the disturbances Q and $\bar{Q}$. The ratio x/L_{QCD} is the number of times, an additional pair of excitations has to be created from the 'sea'.

In summary, a single quark Q increases the energy of the system in its neighborhood L_{QCD} not only by its flavor-dependent mass(=excitation energy) but by an additional energy necessary to 'pick up a $q\bar{q}$ pair from the sea'. This energy is flavor independent, because it does not depend on the flavor Q, which flavors q are excited. The flavors q correspond to an average of the light quarks u, d and s. So when a Q and a $\bar{Q}$ are torn apart, at some distance $x \approx L_{QCD}$ a light $q\bar{q}$ pair is formed, because otherwise the single quark Q could not endure the disturbance of the ground state. In the end a sort of string appears obtained by $Q\bar{q}q\bar{q}'...\bar{Q}$ pairs. Any time a new $q\bar{q}$ pair is created, energy is to be taken from the environment, so the associated cost in energy is proportional to the number of $q\bar{q}$ pairs and the potential between quark and antiquark therefore increases linearly with distance as indicated in (45).

Readers familiar with the quark model, will recognize that one is led directly to the classic ideas of the quark model. For example, using the linear potential (45) masses of mesons and baryons can be estimated just as in the quark model. Since mesons and baryons are G_4-singlets, the 'isomagnetic' disturbances induced by quarks get neutralized in these bound states, i.e. mesons and baryons do not disturb the frustrated 'antiferromagnetic' ground state of a single tetrahedron.

The role of the length L_{QCD} (and the energy E_{QCD}), below (above) which the creation of a light quark-antiquark is enforced, therefore is the same as in the Standard Model. At distances above L_{QCD} one has confinement, while below L_{QCD} the strong force diminishes. Virtual bound quark-antiquark pairs are formed which as gluons mediate an interaction of the original $Q\bar{Q}$ pair which effectively can be described by the QCD Lagrangian. As well known, this interaction dies out when the energies involved go to infinity, i.e. one has asymptotic freedom.

5. Summary

Introducing an additional level of matter, the tetron model offers a unified understanding of particle physics and gravitation. While particle physics processes are induced by 'isomagnetic' interactions in internal fibers with a tetrahedral substructure, gravity arises from elastic forces among the tetrons.

The internal tetrahedral structure is introduced in order to explain the elementary particle spectrum of quarks and leptons (6 singlets and 6 triplets after the spontaneous electroweak symmetry breaking). The 24 states of the 3 quark/lepton families are not truly fundamental particles but can be identified as quasi particle wave excitations of a tetrahedron formed by isospin vectors.

Since the quasiparticles fulfill Lorentz covariant wave equations, they perceive the universe as a 3+1 dimensional spacetime continuum lacking a preferred rest system. Any type of mass/energy induces curvature on this continuum as determined by the Einstein equations.

The tetron model stands for a material understanding of the hitherto abstract particle symmetries $SU(3) \times SU(2)_L \times U(1)$ of the Standard Model of particle physics as well as of their breaking. In the tetron model the Higgs mechanism arises from the alignment of internal isospin vectors of neighboring tetrahedrons, and the Higgs field corresponds to a joint excitation of a neighboring tetron-antitetron pair. One may draw an analogy between particle physics and superconductivity. In this analogy the tetron model corresponds to the BCS theory of superconductivity, whereas the analog of the particle physics Standard Model in this comparison would be the Landau-Ginzberg approach.

References

1. B. Lampe, Int. J. Mod. Phys. A30 (2015)1550025.
2. B. Lampe, Mod. Phys. Lett. A 28 (2013) 1350018.
3. see the review B. Lampe, arXiv:1505.03477 [hep-ph] (2015).
4. B. Lampe, Progr. of Phys. 69 (2021) 2000072.
5. A.P. Cracknell, Progr. Theor. Phys. 35 (1966) 196.
6. A.S. Borovik-Romanov and H. Grimmer, International Tables for Crystallography D (2006) 105.
7. R.M. White, Quantum Theory of Magnetism, Springer Verlag, ISBN-10 3-540-65116-0.
8. H. Fritzsch and J. Sola, Class. Quant. Grav. 29 (2012) 215002.
9. H. Fritzsch and J. Sola, Mod. Phys. Lett. A, Vol. 30, No. 22 (2015) 1540034.
10. H. Fritzsch, J. Sola and Rafael C. Nunes, Eur. Phys. J. C77 (2017) 193.
11. R. Silva, R. S. Goncalves, J. S. Alcaniz and H. H. B. Silva, Astron. and Astrophys. A11 (2012) 537.

Summary parallel session AT5

Reinoud Jan Slagter

Astronomisch Fysisch Onderzoek Nederland (ASFYON),
University of Amsterdam (on leave)
E-mail: info@asfyon.com

Keywords: Conformal dilaton gravity.

It is believed that the understanding of the quantum mechanical properties of gravity at very high energy is one of the major challenges of modern physics. This circumstance occurs, for example, close to the horizon of a black hole or just after the big bang at the Planck scale. There are many ways to attack the problems. One can modify General Relativity rigorously or moderately. One can try to construct a renormalizable model, by adding fourth order derivatives of the curvature tensor to the Lagrangian, try to construct an effective field theory, apply superstring models and many more. However, all these modifications cause problems, such as the appearance of anomalies, loss of unitarity, loss of renormalizability, or one needs ghost fields and gauge-fixing terms. One could also use conformal dilaton gravity models. Conformal invariance is an exact symmetry and spontaneously broken, comparable with the Higgs mechanism.

In the parallel session diverse alternative models pass the review.

Beckwith uses information from a paper deriving a Lorentz-violating energy-momentum relation entailing an exact momentum cutoff as stated by G. Salesi. Salesi in his work allegedly defines Pre Planckian physics, whereas Beckwith restricts himself to an application to GW generation and DE formation in the first $10^{-39}s$ to $10^{-33}s$ or so in the early universe. This procedure is inacted due to an earlier work whereas referees exhibited puzzlement as to the physical mechanism for release of Gravitons in the very early universe. The calculation is meant to be complementary to work done in the Book "Dark Energy" by M. Li, X-D. Li, and Y. Wang, and also a calculation for Black hole destruction as outlined by Karen Freeze, et. al. The GW generation will be when there is sufficient early universe density so as to break apart Relic Black holes but he claims that this destruction is directly linked to a Lorentz violating energy-momentum G. Salesi derived, which he adopts, with a mass m added in the G. Salesi energy momentum results proportional to a tiny graviton mass, times the number of gravitons in the first 10^{-43} seconds.

Slagter presents an exact time-dependent solution of a black hole is found in a conformally invariant gravity model on a warped Randall-Sundrum spacetime, by writing the metric $g_{\mu\nu} = \omega^{\frac{4}{n-2}} \tilde{g}_{\mu\nu}$. Here $\tilde{g}_{\mu\nu}$ represents the "un-physical" spacetime and ω the dilaton field, which will be treated on equal footing as any renormalizable scalar field. In the case of a five-dimensional warped spacetime, he thereafter writes $^{(4)}\tilde{g}_{\mu\nu} = \bar{\omega}^{2\,(4)}\bar{g}_{\mu\nu}$. The dilaton field $\bar{\omega}$ can be used to describe the different notion the in-going and outside observers have of the Hawking radiation by using different conformal gauge freedom. The disagreement about the interior of the black hole is explained by the antipodal map of points on the horizon. The free parameters of the solution can be chosen in such a way that $\bar{g}_{\mu\nu}$ is singular-free and topologically regular, even for $\omega \to 0$. It is remarkable that the 5D and 4D effective field equations for the metric components and dilaton fields can be written in general dimension $n = 4, 5$. From the exact energy-momentum tensor in Eddington-Finkelstein coordinates, he is able to determine the gravitational wave contribution in the process of evaporation of the black hole. It is conjectured that, in context of quantization procedures in the vicinity of the horizon, unitarity problems only occur in the bulk at large extra-dimension scale.

Jain starts his presentation with the proposition that the zero modes can contribute towards divergence in the entanglement entropy and the nature of the divergent term can be either log or log(log). However, a clear understanding of what leads to these two different forms of zero mode divergence is still lacking. So, in order to throw some light along this direction, he investigates how these two different divergent behaviours can be seen as a signature of a crossover in the zero mode limit for the ground state entanglement.

Hartmann investigates an old hypothesis that there exists an intimate connection between weak interaction and gravity, symbolized by the relationship between the Fermi and Newton's constants. He analyzes the hypothesis that the effect of matter upon the metric that represents gravitational interaction in General Relativity is an effective one. He concludes that this leads to consider gravitation to be the result of the interaction of two neutral spinorial fields (g-neutrinos) with all kinds of matter and energy. He presents three examples with only one g-neutrino: two static and spherically symmetric configurations and a cosmological framework for an isotropic dynamical universe. Without self-interaction, the associated effective geometry is precisely the Schwarzschild metric. On the other hand, a self-interacting g-neutrino generates a new gravitational black-hole.

Lampe applies the tetron model of invisible tiny constituents in a cosmological model, elastically bound with bond length about the Planck length and binding energy the Planck energy. A tetron transforms as the fundamental fermion(=octonion) representation 8 of $SO(6,1)$. With respect to the decomposition $SO(6,1) \to SO(3,1) \otimes SO(3)$ a tetron possesses spin 1/2 and isospin 1/2, i.e. it represents an isospin doublet of Dirac spinors. The 24 known quarks and leptons arise as eigenmode excitations of a tetrahedral fiber structure, which is made up from 4 tetrons and extends into 3 additional 'internal' dimensions. While the laws of gravity are due to the elastic properties of the tetron bonds, particle physics interactions take place within the internal fibers. He concentrates on two of the most intriguing features of the model: - understanding small neutrino masses from the conservation of isospin, and, more in general, calculating the spectrum of quark and lepton masses. This is obtained from the tetron model's interpretation of the Higgs mechanism. The possibility to determine the full size of the universe from future dark energy measurements. This is obtained from the tetron model's interpretation of the dark energy phenomenon.

Lapponi applies the model of a perfectly reflecting accelerating mirror to the null-shell of a collapsing black hole. He then investigates an extension of this model to mirror semi-transparency and derive a general expression for the corresponding Bogoliubov coefficients. He introduces the concept of "impulsive accelerated mirrors", corresponding to those mirrors that are accelerated via an impulsive force. He shows that this treatment guarantees analytic solutions of Bogolubov coefficients. In particular, he evaluates the corresponding particle production from the so-obtained Bogoliubov coefficients. Finally, he recognizes that the mirror, as a Gaussian quantum channel, acts between the spacetime regions of left-past and right-future. As a consequence he studies the loss/amplification properties of this quantum channel, alongside the noise it creates and evaluates its capacities in transmitting classical and quantum information.

Boundary conditions for the Klein-Gordon field on Lifshitz spacetimes

Lissa de Souza Campos

Physics Department, University of Pavia,
Pavia, PV 27100, Italy
E-mail: lissa.desouzacampos01@universitadipavia.it

Boundary conditions have physical consequences. On Lifshitz spacetimes, the Klein-Gordon equation gives rise to an initial-boundary value problem that admits a plethora of physically-sensible boundary conditions. Considering a free, scalar, massive quantum field theory on a four-dimensional Lifshitz spacetime with critical exponent $z = 2$, I layout how to construct two-point functions for ground and thermal states, of local Hadamard form, satisfying the canonical commutation relations, and compatible with Robin and mode-dependent boundary conditions. Each one relates to an inequivalent dynamics, but they are all equivalently physically-sensible—only an experiment could single one out. The results I present here are part of a joint work with C. Dappiaggi and D. Sina.[1]

Keywords: Klein-Gordon equation; Robin boundary conditions; Lifshitz spacetime.

Introduction

In this paper I outline part of a joint work with C. Dappiaggi and D. Sina presented in Ref. 1, elaborating on the talk I have given on the Sixteenth Marcel Grossmann Meeting.[2] The goal is to bring awareness to the fact that on Lifshitz spacetimes there are infinitely many physically-sensible boundary conditions naturally arising within a free, scalar quantum field theoretical framework. In particular, I show how to construct two-point functions for ground and thermal states on a four-dimensional Lifshitz spacetime Lif with dynamical critical exponent $z = 2$ compatible with Robin and mode-dependent boundary conditions.

Lif is a metric-solution of Hořava-Lifshitz gravity.[3] This gravity theory provides an alternative to General Relativity by breaking Lorentz invariance with a Lifshitz scaling between time t and space $\underline{x}$ of the form:

$$t \mapsto \delta^z t \quad \text{and} \quad \underline{x} \mapsto \delta \underline{x} \quad \text{with} \quad z > 1. \tag{1}$$

Although the goal of introducing Lifshitz scaling in the theory was to allow its quantization, i.e. to be a theory of quantum gravity, such anisotropic scaling has manifold applications, from cosmology, through AdS/CFT correspondence, to condensed matter physics.[4] Since its initial proposition by Hořava in 2009,[5] it has gone through several developments,[6] and examples relating the dynamical critical exponent z with "real world" quantum critical systems have been elaborated.[7] Hořava-Lifshitz gravity itself lies beyong the scope of this work; here, the focus is on the quantization of a free scalar field on the background solution Lif.

Let us endow Lif with polar coordinates (t, r, θ, φ), where $t \in \mathbb{R}$, $r \in (0, \infty)$, $\theta \in [0, \pi)$ and $\varphi \in [0, 2\pi)$; its line-element reads

$$ds^2 = -\frac{r^4}{L^4}dt^2 + \frac{L^2}{r^2}dr^2 + r^2 d\theta^2 + r^2 \theta^2 d\varphi^2, \tag{2}$$

where $L > 0$ is a length scale. The time coordinate t identifies a global, timelike, irrotational, Killing vector field ∂_t, making Lif a static spacetime. The Lifshitz horizon at $r = 0$ corresponds to a singularity of coordinate type, since neither the Ricci scalar, given by

$$\mathcal{R} = -\frac{22}{L^2}, \tag{3}$$

nor the Kretschmann scalars diverges there. The Lifshitz boundary at $r = \infty$ can be seen as an anisotropic conformal infinity,[8] but it also admits other definitions, see e.g. Ref. 9. I avoid going into details in this regard since I take $r \to \infty$ to be merely an asymptotic radial infinity for the bulk theory, as in Ref. 10. The crucial impact of this asymptotic behavior in the analysis performed here is that it results on Lif being non-globally hyperbolic.

Next, let us consider a free, scalar field $\Psi : \text{Lif} \to \mathbb{R}$ with mass m_0 and coupled to the scalar curvature $\mathcal{R}$ through a parameter $\xi \in \mathbb{R}$. Its dynamics is governed by the Klein-Gordon equation:

$$(\Box - m_0^2 - \xi \mathcal{R})\Psi = 0, \tag{4}$$

where $\Box = g^{\mu\nu} \nabla_\mu \nabla_\nu$ is the D'Alembertian operator, while g is the metric tensor associated to Equation (2). On Lif, the Klein-Gordon equation gives rise to an initial-boundary value problem. Given suitable initial data on a spacelike surface, corresponding solutions might not exist; if they exist, then each boundary condition selects a different solution, identifying an inequivalent dynamics. To guarantee such initial-boundary value problem is well-posed and physically meaningful, I follow the standard approach of looking for self-adjoint extensions of the radial part of the Klein-Gordon operator. This restriction guarantees the dynamics obtained are physically-sensible, as specified by the work of Ishibashi and Wald.[11, 12]

For some boundary conditions, depending on the value of the effective mass, the two-point functions possess bound state contributions: *bound states* are poles of the two-point function. In our case, the set of bound states coincide with the set of poles of the Green function of the radial part of the Klein-Gordon equation. Since we impose self-adjointness on the radial part, they are, in fact, elements of the point spectrum of the radial Green function. Accordingly, they are a subset of the quasi-normal modes. Withall, since the physical meaning of bound state contributions is not well-understood, I rule them out by delineating the boundary conditions for which no bound states arise. Subsequently, by employing a prescription applicable on an static spacetime, as performed in Refs. 13–19, I obtain two-point functions that solve the Klein-Gordon equation in each entry, satisfy the canonical commutation relations and are of local Hadamard form. The analysis I present is consistent with previous works regarding the scalar field on Lifshitz spacetimes[10, 20–23] and it generalizes them in different aspects: first, it takes into account more general boundary conditions; second, it specifies which of these boundary conditions yields physically sensible two-point functions; third, it provides explicit (though not in closed-form) expressions for the two-point functions.

The layout of this paper mirrors my talk.[2] First, in Section 1, taking into account the symmetries of the spacetime, I show that the Klein-Gordon equation reduces to a radial equation, I find the radial solutions and I study their square-integrability. Second, in Section 2, I construct the radial Green function. Then, in Section 3, I show how we can rule out the bound states and focus on physically-sensible boundary conditions. With all these ingredients in hands, in Section 4, I turn to spectral theory of differential operators and to algebraic quantum field theory to write down well-defined, physically-sensible, explicitly expressions for the two-point functions for the ground and thermal states.

1. Solving the Klein-Gordon equation

Let $Y_\ell^m(\theta, \varphi)$ be the eigenfunctions of the Laplacian operator on $\mathbb{R}^2$ in polar coordinates, with eigenvalues λ_ℓ^m. Since Lif is a static spacetime, consider the following ansatz

$$\Psi(t, r, \theta, \varphi) = e^{-i\omega t} R(r) Y_\ell^m(\theta, \varphi). \tag{5}$$

Substituting Equation (5) in the Klein-Gordon equation (4) entails that $R(r)$ is a solution of the radial equation:

$$AR(r) := R''(r) + \frac{5}{r} R'(r) + \left(\frac{L^6}{r^6} \omega^2 + \frac{L^2}{r^4} \lambda_\ell^m - \frac{L^2}{r^2} \right) R(r) = 0. \tag{6}$$

By applying transformations on both the independent and dependent variables,

$$r \mapsto u = \frac{iL^3 \omega}{r^2} \in i(0, \infty) \quad \text{and} \quad R(u) = e^{-u/2} \left(\frac{u}{iL^3 \omega} \right)^{\frac{1}{2}(2+\nu)} w(u), \tag{7}$$

the radial equation (6) yields a confluent hypergeometric equation

$$uw''(u) + (b_0 - u)w'(u) - a_0 w(u) = 0, \quad \text{with} \quad \begin{cases} a_0 := \frac{1+\nu}{2} + \frac{i\lambda}{4L\omega}, \\ b_0 := 1 + \nu, \\ \nu := \sqrt{4 + L^2 \mu^2}. \end{cases} \tag{8}$$

Therefore, the radial solutions are given in terms of the confluent hypergeometric functions M and U.[24] Numerically satisfactory bases of solutions of Equations (6) and (8), close to the point u_0, are respectively given by $\{R_{1(u_0)}(u), R_{2(u_0)}(u)\}$ and $\{w_{1(u_0)}(u), w_{2(u_0)}(u)\}$, with $w_{j(u_0)}$ as in Table 1 and

$$R_{j(u_0)}(u) = e^{-u/2} \left(\frac{u}{iL^3 \omega} \right)^{\frac{1}{2}(2+\nu)} w_{j(u_0)}(u), \quad \text{for } j \in \{1, 2\}. \tag{9}$$

Table 1. Suitable bases of the confluent hypergeometric equation (8).

Endpoint	Suitable Basis
$u = 0 \equiv r = \infty$	$\begin{cases} w_{1(0)}(u) = M(a_0, b_0; u) \\ w_{2(0)}(u) = (iL^3\omega)^\nu u^{1-b_0} M(a_0 - b_0 + 1, 2 - b_0; u) \end{cases}$
$u = i\infty \equiv r = 0$	$\begin{cases} w_{1(\infty)}(u) = U(a_0, b_0; u) \\ w_{2(\infty)}(u) = e^u U(b_0 - a_0, b_0; -u) \end{cases}$

To obtain self-adjoint extensions of the radial part of the Klein-Gordon operator, we turn to Sturm-Liouville theory. Rewriting the radial equation as a Sturm-Liouville problem gives

$$AR(r) =: (L_{\omega^2} - \omega^2)R(r) = -\frac{1}{r^{-1}}\left(\frac{d}{dr}\left(\frac{r^5}{L^6}\frac{d}{dr}\right) + \frac{r}{L^4}\left(-\mu^2 r^2 + \lambda_\ell^m\right)\right)R(r) = 0. \tag{10}$$

Taking Equation (10) into account, we look for solutions $R(r)$ in the space of square-integrable functions with respect to the measure $r^{-1}dr$. In addition, the radial operator A is positive and symmetric on the Hilbert space $L^2((0, \infty), r^{-1}dr)$ when we take its domain to be $C_0^\infty((0, \infty))$.

Since the endpoints $r = 0$ and $r = \infty$ are singular, we perform an asymptotic analysis to check square-integrability of the radial solutions, as follows. As $r \to 0$ the radial solutions defined in Equation (9) together with Table 1 behave like

$$|R_{1(0)}(r)|^2 \sim e^{+\frac{L^3}{r^2}\,\mathrm{Im}(\omega)}, \tag{11a}$$

$$|R_{2(0)}(r)|^2 \sim e^{-\frac{L^3}{r^2}\,\mathrm{Im}(\omega)}. \tag{11b}$$

As $r \to \infty$, we have instead

$$R_{1(\infty)}(r) \sim r^{-2-\nu}, \tag{11c}$$

$$R_{2(\infty)}(r) \sim r^{-2+\nu}. \tag{11d}$$

According to Weyl's endpoint classification,[25] it follows that $r = 0$ is limit point, and that, if $\nu \in (0, 1) \cup (1, 2)$, then $r = \infty$ is limit circle. That is, the unique solution $R_0(r)$ that belongs to $L^2((0, r_0), r^{-1}dr)$ for all $r_0 < \infty$ is given by

$$R_0(r) = \Theta(-\mathrm{Im}(\omega))R_{1(0)}(r) + \Theta(\mathrm{Im}(\omega))R_{2(0)}(r). \tag{12}$$

Contrastingly, if $\nu \in (0, 1) \cup (1, 2)$, there is a one-parameter family of solutions $R_\gamma(r)$, with $\gamma \in [0, \pi)$, belonging to $L^2((r_0, \infty), r^{-1}dr)$ for all $r_0 < \infty$, given by

$$R_\gamma(r) = \cos(\gamma)R_{1(\infty)}(r) + \sin(\gamma)R_{2(\infty)}(r). \tag{13}$$

Define the Wronskian W for differentiable functions $f_1(x)$ and $f_2(x)$ as $W_x[f_1(x), f_2(x)] := f_1(x)\frac{df_2(x)}{dx} - \frac{df_1(x)}{dx}f_2(x)$. The solutions of Equation (13) satisfy the (generalized) Robin boundary conditions parametrized by γ:

$$\lim_{r\to\infty}\left(\cos(\gamma)W_r[R_\gamma(r), R_{1(\infty)}(r)] + \sin(\gamma)W_r[R_\gamma(r), R_{2(\infty)}(r)]\right) = 0. \quad (14)$$

When $\nu \notin (0,1)\cup(1,2)$, $r = \infty$ is also limit point and the only square-integrable solution to be considered is given by the principal solution, which coincides with (13) for $\gamma = 0$. This corresponds to imposing Dirichlet boundary condition and yields a unique dynamics. On this account, from now on let us focus on the more interesting scenario, where alternative boundary conditions give inequivalent dynamics, and consider only effective masses such that $\nu \in (0,1)\cup(1,2)$. In the latter case, given that $r = 0$ is limit point and that $r = \infty$ is limit circle, from standard singular Sturm-Liouville theory[25] follows that A admits a one-parameter family of self-adjoint extensions in one-to-one correspondence with the (generalized) Robin boundary conditions.

2. Constructing the radial Green function

For R_0, R_γ and L_{ω^2} as obtained in the previous section, let $\mathcal{G}_\omega(r,r')$ be a Green function of the radial equation. It satisfies

$$((L_{\omega^2} - \omega^2)\otimes \mathbb{1})\mathcal{G}_\omega(r,r') = (\mathbb{1}\otimes(L_{\omega^2} - \omega^2))\mathcal{G}_\omega(r,r') = \frac{\delta(r-r')}{r^{-1}} \quad (15)$$

and it can be written as[26]

$$\mathcal{G}_\omega(r,r') = \frac{1}{\mathcal{N}_\omega}\left(\Theta(r'-r)R_0(r)R_\gamma(r') + \Theta(r-r')R_0(r')R_\gamma(r)\right). \quad (16)$$

For $\mathrm{Im}\,\omega < 0$, the normalization $\mathcal{N}_\omega$ reads:

$$\mathcal{N}_\omega = 4\nu\{B_0\cos(\gamma) - A_0\sin(\gamma)\}, \text{ with } \begin{cases} A_0 := \frac{\Gamma(1-b_0)}{\Gamma(a_0-b_0+1)}, \\ B_0 := \frac{\Gamma(b_0-1)}{\Gamma(a_0)}(iL^3\omega)^{-\nu}. \end{cases} \quad (17)$$

As shown in Ref. 1, the radial solutions defined above satisfy useful properties with respect to complex conjugation:

$$R_0(r,\bar\omega) = \overline{R_0(r,\omega)} \quad \text{and} \quad R_\gamma(r,\bar\omega) = \overline{R_\gamma(r,\omega)}. \quad (18a)$$

As a consequence, the radial Green function and its normalization are such that

$$\mathcal{N}_{\bar\omega} = \overline{\mathcal{N}_\omega} \quad \text{and} \quad \mathcal{G}_{\bar\omega} = \overline{\mathcal{G}_\omega}. \quad (19)$$

In the next section, we study the poles of $\mathcal{G}_\omega(r,r')$ in the ω-complex plane. The properties above, in Equation (19), simplify our analysis since they imply that we can restrict our attention to either the upper or lower half of the ω-complex plane, and by conjugation, understand the behavior on the other half.

3. Rulying out the poles

The poles of the radial Green function are the frequencies ω for which

$$\mathcal{N}_\omega = 0. \tag{20}$$

As mentioned in the introduction, we refer to these frequencies as bound states; and in the scope of obtaining well-defined two-point functions, we exclude the boundary conditions for which they arise. Given the symmetry properties of the radial Green function with respect to complex conjugation, let us set $\text{Im}(\omega) < 0$.

For Dirichlet and Neumann boundary conditions the analysis is straightforward. One just needs to take into account Equation (20) together with Equations (17) and the fact that the Euler Gamma function $\Gamma(z)$ satisfy $1/\Gamma(z) = 0 \iff z \in \mathbb{Z}_0^-$. We find that for Dirichlet boundary condition, $\gamma = 0$, the frequencies for which Equation (20) holds all lie in the upper half of the complex plane. That is, no bound states occur. For Neumann boundary condition, $\gamma = \pi/2$, bound states are also absent if $\nu \in (0,1)$; however, if $\nu \in (1,2)$, then for each λ_ℓ^m there is a unique pole with negative imaginary part at

$$\omega_p = -i\frac{\lambda_\ell^m}{2L(1-\nu)}. \tag{21}$$

For Robin boundary conditions, $\gamma \in (0, \pi/2) \cup (\pi/2, \pi)$, the analysis is less direct. First, we view Equation (20) as the following transcendental equation

$$\chi(\omega) := \tan(\gamma) - \Xi(\omega) = 0, \text{ with } \Xi(\omega) := \frac{B_0}{A_0}. \tag{22}$$

Then, by noting that Equation (22) admits a solution for all frequencies such that $\Xi(\omega) \in \mathbb{R}$, and by studying the function $\Xi(\omega)$, one can show that there is a one-to-one correspondence between the the boundary conditions for which bound states arise and the image $\mathbf{I} \subset \mathbb{R}$ of $\Xi(\omega)$ for $\omega = -i|\text{Im}(\omega)|$. As a result, the physically-sensible boundary conditions are given by $\gamma \in \mathbb{R} \setminus \mathbf{I}$. Details of this analysis can be found in Ref. 1, but the distilled results are collected in the following table.

Table 2. Boundary conditions for which no bound states arise.

ν	mode-independent	mode-dependent
$(0,1)$	$\gamma \in [0, \pi/2]$	$\gamma \in \left[0, \arctan\left(\left(\frac{-\lambda_\ell^m L^2}{4}\right)^{-\nu} \frac{\Gamma(\nu)}{\Gamma(-\nu)}\right)\right]$
$(1,2)$	$\gamma = 0$	

4. Constructing the two-point functions

Analogously to the ansatz for the solutions to the Klein-Gordon equation, as in Equation (5), consider the following ansatz for the integral kernel of a positive bisolution of the Klein-Gordon equation $G^+ \in \mathcal{D}'(\mathsf{Lif}^2)$, for $x = (t, r, \theta, \varphi) \in \mathsf{Lif}$,

$$G^+(x,x') = \lim_{\varepsilon \to 0^+} \int_{\sigma(\Delta)} d\Sigma(\ell, m) \int_0^\infty d\omega\, e^{-i\omega(t-t'-i\varepsilon)} \widehat{G}_\omega(r, r') Y_\ell^m(\theta, \varphi) Y_\ell^m(\theta', \varphi'),$$ (23)

where $Y_\ell^m(\theta, \varphi)$ are the real-valued eigenfunctions of the Laplacian operator Δ with spectrum $\sigma(\Delta)$ and associated measure $d\Sigma(\ell, m)$, while $i\varepsilon$ implements the standard regularization.

To obtain an explicit expression for the radial component $\widehat{G}_\omega(r, r')$, in the following I employ the same steps as performed on other static spacetimes in Refs. 13–19. On one hand, imposing the canonical commutation relations on the antisymmetric part of Equation (23) entails that $\widehat{G}_\omega(r, r')$ is symmetric with respect to $r \leftrightarrow r'$ and gives the following identity

$$\int_\mathbb{R} \omega d\omega \widehat{G}_\omega(r, r') = \frac{\delta(r-r')}{r^{-1}}.$$ (24)

On the other hand, consider the radial Green function $\mathcal{G}_\omega(r, r')$ constructed in Section 2. Recalling that $\mathcal{G}_\omega(r, r')$ is not defined when $\mathrm{Im}(\omega) = 0$, let $\mathcal{C}^\infty$ be the infinite radius limit of a two semi-disks centered on the ω-complex plane and not touching the real axis, as illustrated in Ref. 1. For the boundary conditions for which the radial Green function has no poles, its spectral resolution[25,26] reads

$$\frac{1}{2\pi i} \oint_{\mathcal{C}^\infty} d(\omega^2) \mathcal{G}_\omega(r, r') = -\frac{\delta(r-r')}{r^{-1}}.$$ (25)

By performing the contour integral of Equation (25) and comparing it with Equation (24) we find the radial component of ansatz given in Equation (23):

$$\widehat{G}_\omega(r,r') = \frac{1}{4\pi\nu} \frac{\mathrm{Im}\,(B_0\overline{A_0})}{|B_0\cos(\gamma) - A_0\sin(\gamma)|^2} R_\gamma(r) R_\gamma(r').$$ (26)

Alltogether, with respect to the Killing field ∂_t and for $\widehat{G}_\omega(r, r')$ given by Equation (26), a two-point function with integral kernel given by Equation (23) identifies the unique ground-state of a free, scalar, massive Klein-Gordon field on a Lifshitz spacetime. For a thermal-state at inverse-temperature β, its integral kernel reads instead

$$G_\beta^+(x,x') = \lim_{\varepsilon \to 0^+} \int_{\sigma(\Delta)} d\Sigma(\ell, m) \int_0^\infty d\omega\, T_\omega(t,t') \widehat{G}_\omega(r,r') Y_\ell^m(\theta,\varphi) Y_\ell^m(\theta',\varphi'),$$ (27)

with

$$T_\omega(t,t') := \left[\frac{e^{-i\omega(t-t'-i\varepsilon)}}{1-e^{-\beta\omega}} + \frac{e^{+i\omega(t-t'+i\varepsilon)}}{e^{\beta\omega}-1} \right].$$ (28)

Two-point functions with integral kernel given either by Equation (23) or Equation (27) identify Gaussian states of local Hadamard form[27] that satisfy the canonical commutation relations—they are physically-sensible two-point functions. Last, but most importantly, note that each boundary condition identifies a different two-point function.

5. Conclusions

The results presented here are part of the work in Ref. 1, where also generalizations to a hyperbolic and to a spherical Lifshitz topological black hole were considered. We demonstrated that on a Lifshitz spacetime, a Klein-Gordon field with effective mass $m^2 \in \left(-\frac{4}{L^2}, -\frac{3}{L^2}\right)$ admits a one-parameter family of Robin boundary conditions at $r \to \infty$ parametrized by $\gamma \in [0, \pi/2]$. In turn, each $\gamma \in [0, \pi/2]$ identifies a distinct two-point function. In addition, we found that for $m^2 \in \left(-\frac{4}{L^2}, -\frac{3}{L^2}\right) \cup \left(-\frac{3}{L^2}, -\frac{2}{L^2}\right)$, λ-mode dependent boundary conditions are also admissible. We call attention to the fact that, in the absence of a reason to justify selecting Dirichlet boundary condition over the others, all of these boundary conditions are of equal relevance—they all yield physically-sensible quantizations. Since these generalized quantizations arise naturally within the quantum field theoretical framework, we hope our results stimulates research in the direction of understanding their physical significance.

The analysis outlined here applies straightforwardly to higher dimensional Lifshitz spacetimes of critical exponent $z = 2$. That is not the case for $z > 2$, however, given that the choice of critical value affects drastically the classification, and hence the solutions, of the radial part of the Klein-Gordon equation. In Ref. 1, we constructed two-point functions not only on this spacetime, but also on Lifshitz topological black holes.[28] With this in mind, an interesting follow up work would be to perform a numerical analysis to understand how the topology and the choice of a boundary condition affects vacuum fluctuations, as performed for topological black holes of Einstein gravity in Ref. 29. Moreover, in this framework one can further directly obtain the transition rate of a static Unruh-DeWitt detector in the infinite interaction time limit, following the same prescription of Ref. 14, and study the effects of different boundary conditions and topologies in the perspective of a particle detector.

Acknowledgments

This work was part of a collaboration[1] with C.Dappiaggi and D.Sina, whom I thank and gratefully acknowledge; and it was partially based on the MSc thesis of D.S. submitted to the University of Pavia on March 2021. My work was supported by a PhD scholarship of the University of Pavia.

References

1. L. De Souza Campos, C. Dappiaggi and D. Sina, [arXiv:2103.15391 [hep-th]].
2. L. De Souza Campos, Talk: Boundary conditions for the Klein-Gordon field on Lifshitz Spacetimes, Sixteenth Marcel Grossmann Meeting, https://indico.icranet.org/event/1/, available on YouTube https://youtu.be/5z7zhpiDOpw?list=PLr5RLbSWSonsaOnZukBDsOqsNIWM8AvRF&t=4007.
3. S. A. Hartnoll, A. Lucas and S. Sachdev, [arXiv:1612.07324] (Pg.27).
4. P. Hořava, Class. Quant. Grav. **28**, 114012 (2011), [arXiv:1101.1081].
5. P. Hořava, Phys. Rev. D **79**, 084008 (2009), [arXiv:0901.3775].
6. A. Wang, Int. J. Mod. Phys. D **26**, no. 7, 1730014 (2017), [arXiv:1701.06087].
7. S. A. Hartnoll, Class. Quant. Grav. **26**, 224002 (2009), [arXiv:0903.3246].
8. P. Hořava and C. M. Melby-Thompson, Gen. Rel. Grav. **43**, 1391-1400 (2011) [arXiv:0909.3841].
9. S. F. Ross, Class. Quant. Grav. **28**, 215019 (2011) [arXiv:1107.4451].
10. S. Kachru, X. Liu and M. Mulligan, Phys. Rev. D **78**, 106005 (2008), [arXiv:0808.1725].
11. A. Ishibashi and R. M. Wald, Class. Quant. Grav. **20**, 3815-3826 (2003), [arXiv:gr-qc/0305012].
12. A. Ishibashi and R. M. Wald, Class. Quant. Grav. **21** (2004), 2981-3014, [arXiv:0402184].
13. C. Dappiaggi and H. Ferreira, Phys. Rev. D **94** (2016) no. 12, 125016, [arXiv:1610.01049].
14. L. Campos and C. Dappiaggi, Phys. Rev. D **103**, no. 2, 025021 (2021), [arXiv:2011.03812].
15. C. Dappiaggi, H. R. C. Ferreira and B. A. Juárez-Aubry, Phys. Rev. D **97** (2018) no. 8, 085022, [arXiv:1802.00283].
16. C. Dappiaggi and H. Ferreira, Rev. Math. Phys. **30** (2017) no. 02, 1850004, [arXiv:1701.07215].
17. C. Dappiaggi, H. Ferreira and A. Marta, Phys. Rev. D **98** (2018) no. 2, 025005, [arXiv:1805.03135].
18. F. Bussola, C. Dappiaggi, H. R. C. Ferreira and I. Khavkine, Phys. Rev. D **96** (2017) no. 10, 105016, [arXiv:1708.00271].
19. F. Bussola and C. Dappiaggi, Class. Quant. Grav. **36** (2019) no. 1, 015020, [arXiv:1806.00427].
20. A. Giacomini, G. Giribet, M. Leston, J. Oliva and S. Ray, Phys. Rev. D **85**, 124001 (2012), [arXiv:1203.0582].
21. G. M. Quinta, A. Flachi and J. P. S. Lemos, Phys. Rev. D **93**, no. 12, 124073 (2016) [arXiv:1604.00495].
22. C. Keeler, JHEP **01**, 067 (2014), [arXiv:1212.1728].
23. T. Andrade and S. F. Ross, Class. Quant. Grav. **30**, 065009 (2013), [arXiv:1212.2572].
24. NIST Digital Library of Mathematical Functions, Ch.13, https://dlmf.nist.gov/13, Accessed: 2021-03-28.
25. A. Zettl, *Sturm-Liouville Theory*, American Mathematical Society, (2005), 328p.
26. I. Stakgold and M.J. Holst, *Green's functions and boundary value problems*, John Wiley & Sons, 99 (2011).
27. H. Sahlmann and R. Verch, Commun. Math. Phys. **214** (2000), 705-731 [arXiv:0002021].
28. R. B. Mann, JHEP **06**, 075 (2009), [arXiv:0905.1136].
29. T. Morley, P. Taylor and E. Winstanley, [arXiv:2010.01562].

Dynamical system analysis of Bianchi-I spacetimes in $f(R)$ gravity

Saikat Chakraborty

Center for Gravitation and Cosmology, College of Physical Science and Technology, Yangzhou University, Yangzhou 225009, China,
and
International Center for Cosmology, Charusat University, Anand 388421, Gujrat, India
E-mail: saikatnilch@gmail.com; snilch@yzu.edu.cn

Kazuharu Bamba

Division of Human Support System, Faculty of Symbiotic Systems Science, Fukushima University, Fukushima 960-1296, Japan
E-mail: bamba@sss.fukushima-u.ac.jp

Alberto Saa

Department of Applied Mathematics, University of Campinas, 13083-859 Campinas, SP, Brazil
E-mail: asaa@ime.unicamp.br

Based on our original work published in Ref.[1], we investigate an autonomous system analysis in terms of new expansion-normalized variables for homogeneous and anisotropic Bianchi-I spacetimes in $f(R)$ gravity in the presence of anisotropic matter. It is demonstrated that with a suitable choice of the evolution parameter, the Einstein's equations are reduced to an autonomous 5-dimensional system of ordinary differential equations for the new variables. Furthermore, for a large class of functions $f(R)$, which includes several cases commonly considered in the literature, all the fixed points are polynomial roots, and thus they can be determined with good accuracy and classified for stability. In addition, typically for these cases, any fixed point corresponding to isotropic solutions in the presence of anisotropic matter will be unstable. The assumption of a perfect fluid as source and or the vacuum cases imply some dimensional reductions and even more simplifications. In particular, it is found that the vacuum solutions of $f(R) = R^{\delta+1}$ with δ a constant are governed by an effective bi-dimensional phase space which can be constructed analytically, leading to an exactly soluble dynamics. It is also shown that several results already reported in the literature can be re-obtained in a more direct and easy way by exploring our dynamical formulation.

Keywords: Modified gravity theories; autonomous system analysis

1. Introduction

According to recent various cosmological observations including Type Ia Supernovae, cosmic microwave background (CMB) radiation and large scale structure, in addition to inflation[2-4] in the early universe, the current expansion of the universe is also accelerating. This is the so-called dark energy problem. There are two representative approaches to study the issue of dark energy. One is to introduce some unknown matter called dark energy with the negative pressure in general relativity.

The other is to modify gravity at large scales (for reviews of dark energy and modified gravity theories, see, e.g., Refs.[5-17]). As one of the popular modified gravity theories, $f(R)$ gravity has been proposed.[18-20]

In this article, based on our original reference[1], we extend the so-called expansion-normalized variables[21] to write down the dynamical equations of $f(R)$ gravity for a homogeneous and anisotropic Bianchi-I metric in the presence of an anisotropic fluid, as a 5-dimensional system of ordinary differential equations. We show that some further assumptions may lead to considerable simplifications in the equations, and for several examples we end up with analytically soluble systems. For the sake of illustration, we consider explicitly the case of $f(R) = R^{1+\delta}$. We demonstrate that the formulation of[22, 23] is recovered in the isotropic matter limit. Moreover, in a simpler and more direct way, we re-derive some uniqueness and stability properties of the Starobinsky's isotropic inflationary scenario in R^2 gravity,[24-26] which is consistent with the Planck 2018 results.[27, 28]

The article is organized as follows. In section 2, we describe the dynamical equations for a Bianchi-I cosmology in $f(R)$ gravity in the presence of an anisotropic fluid. We discuss the isotropic fluid limit and introduce the new expansion-normalized variables for the system. In Section 3, we present cosmological applications. Finally, we summarize our results in Section 4.

2. Bianchi-I cosmology in $f(R)$ gravity with anisotropic fluid

The action describing $f(R)$ gravity is expressed as

$$S = \frac{1}{2\kappa} \int d^4x \sqrt{-g} f(R) + S_M, \qquad (1)$$

where $\kappa = 8\pi G$, $c = \hbar = 1$, and S_M stands for the usual matter contributions to the totalaction.

We consider the homogeneous and anisotropic Bianchi-I metric, which can be conveniently cast for our purposes in the following form[29-31]

$$ds^2 = -dt^2 + a^2(t) \sum_{i=1}^{3} e^{2\beta_i(t)} (dx^i)^2, \qquad (2)$$

where $a(t)$ is the average scale factor and the three functions β_i, which characterize the anisotropies, are such that $\beta_1 + \beta_2 + \beta_3 = 0$. It is more convenient to employ the variables

$$\beta_\pm = \beta_1 \pm \beta_2. \qquad (3)$$

The total amount of anisotropy in the metric (2) is given by the quantity

$$\sigma^2 = \dot\beta_1^2 + \dot\beta_2^2 + \dot\beta_3^2 = \frac{3}{2}\dot\beta_+^2 + \frac{1}{2}\dot\beta_-^2. \qquad (4)$$

For $\sigma = 0$, one can show that the spatial coordinates x^i can be suitably rescaled to recast the Bianchi-I metric in the standard Friedmann-Lemaitre-Robertson-Walker

(FLRW) form. The Ricci scalar for the metric (2) reads
$$R = 6\dot{H} + 12H^2 + \sigma^2, \tag{5}$$
where the average Hubble parameter H is given by the standard expression
$$H = \frac{\dot{a}}{a}. \tag{6}$$
We assume the presence of an anisotropic barotropic fluid with energy momentum tensor parametrized as[32]
$$T^\nu_\mu = \text{diag}\,(-\rho, p_1, p_2, p_3) = \text{diag}\,(-\rho, \omega_1\rho, \omega_2\rho, \omega_3\rho), \tag{7}$$
and we define the anisotropic equation of state as
$$p_i = (\omega + \mu_i)\rho, \tag{8}$$
with $i = 1, 2, 3$, where ω is the average barotropic parameter and $\omega_i = \omega + \mu_i$, with $\mu_1 + \mu_2 + \mu_3 = 0$ by construction. We parameterize our fluid by the constants ω and $\mu_\pm = \mu_1 \pm \mu_2$.[31]

The dynamics of the Bianchi-I metric (2) under $f(R)$ gravity action (1), in the presence of and anisotropic barotropic fluid with energy-momentum tensor (7), can be described by the following set of equations,[31]

$$3H^2 = \frac{\kappa}{f'}\left(\rho + \frac{Rf' - f}{2\kappa} - \frac{3Hf''\dot{R}}{\kappa}\right) + \frac{\sigma^2}{2}, \tag{9}$$

$$2\dot{H} + 3H^2 = -\frac{\kappa}{f'}\left(\omega\rho + \frac{\dot{R}^2 f''' + \left(2H\dot{R} + \ddot{R}\right)f''}{\kappa}\right.$$
$$\left. - \frac{Rf' - f}{2\kappa}\right) - \frac{\sigma^2}{2}, \tag{10}$$

$$\ddot{\beta}_\pm + \left(3H + \frac{\dot{R}f''}{f'}\right)\dot{\beta}_\pm = \frac{\kappa\rho}{F}\mu_\pm, \tag{11}$$

$$\dot{\rho} + \left(3H(1+\omega) + \boldsymbol{\delta}\cdot\dot{\boldsymbol{\beta}}\right)\rho = 0, \tag{12}$$

where $i = 1, 2, 3$, and

$$\boldsymbol{\delta}\cdot\dot{\boldsymbol{\beta}} = \mu_1\dot{\beta}_1 + \mu_2\dot{\beta}_2 + \mu_3\dot{\beta}_3 = \frac{3}{2}\mu_+\dot{\beta}_+ + \frac{1}{2}\mu_-\dot{\beta}_-. \tag{13}$$

Notice that in the presence of a perfect fluid, we have $\mu_+ = \mu_- = 0$ and the two equations (11) for β_+ and β_- can be substituted with

$$\dot{\sigma} + \left(3H + \frac{\dot{R}f''}{f'}\right)\sigma = 0. \tag{14}$$

In this case, there is no anisotropy in the matter sector and the single variable σ is sufficient to describe the total amount of metric anisotropy in the system.

In general, we have four functions of time $H(t)$, $\rho(t)$, $\beta_\pm(t)$ governing the dynamics. The existence of the constraint equation (9) implies that only three of them are indeed independent. Without loss of generality, we can choose them to be, for instance, $H(t)$ and $\beta_\pm(t)$. Given some specific form of the function $f(R)$, they can be determined by solving equations (10) and (11). The fluid energy density $\rho(t)$ can then be found using the energy constraint (9).

The traditional expansion-normalized variables were initially introduced for a better dynamical analysis of the standard FLRW model, see, e.g., Ref.[21]. Here, we expand the variables already introduced in[22, 23] to include the case of the anisotropic barotropic fluid (7). In this regard, let us introduce the monotonically increasing variable

$$N = \epsilon \ln a, \tag{15}$$

known as the logarithmic time, where ϵ is defined to be $+1$ for expanding universe and -1 for a contracting one. Without loss of generality, we choose the scale factor at $t = 0$ to be $a_0 = 1$. Therefore, as time progresses in the forward (positive) direction, the logarithmic time N becomes positive and goes towards $+\infty$ in case of both expanding and contracting universes. One can notice that

$$\dot{N} = \epsilon H, \tag{16}$$

so that $\dot{N}$ is effectively always positive, justifying the use of N as the dimensionless evolution variable for both expanding and contracting universes. On the other hand, around a bounce or a turnaround point, this argument is not valid though and the expanding and contracting branches must be considered separately.

The expansion-normalized dynamical variables suitable for the equations (9) - (12) are the following dimensionless combinations

$$u_1 = \frac{\dot{R} f''}{f' H}, \quad u_2 = \frac{R}{6H^2}, \quad u_3 = \frac{f}{6 f' H^2}, \tag{17}$$

$$u_4^+ = \frac{\dot{\beta}_+^2}{4H^2}, \quad u_4^- = \frac{\dot{\beta}_-^2}{12 H^2}, \quad u_5 = \frac{\kappa \rho}{3 f' H^2}.$$

in terms of which the energy constraint (9) reads simply

$$g = 1 + u_1 - u_2 + u_3 - u_4^+ - u_4^- - u_5 = 0, \tag{18}$$

from where we have that one of the expansion-normalized variables can always be eliminated. Unless otherwise stated, we always choose the matter content variable u_5 to be expressed in terms of the others dynamical variables. The variable

$$u_4 = u_4^+ + u_4^- = \frac{\sigma^2}{6H^2} \tag{19}$$

is also relevant for our purposes. It is important to stress that the variables u_4^+ and u_4^- are both non-negative by construction. Now, let us introduce the quantity

$$\gamma(R) = \frac{f'}{R f''}, \tag{20}$$

which contains the information about the form of $f(R)$. Knowing the form of $f(R)$, γ can be determined in terms of the dynamical variables u_2, u_3 by inverting the relation

$$\frac{u_2}{u_3} = \frac{Rf'}{f}. \tag{21}$$

We return to the question of the invertibility of (21) in the last section. The 5-dimensional system of autonomous first order differential equations fully equivalent to (10) - (12) is given by

$$\epsilon \frac{du_1}{dN} = 1 + u_2 - 3u_3 - u_4 - 3\omega u_5$$
$$- u_1 (u_1 + u_2 - u_4), \tag{22}$$

$$\epsilon \frac{du_2}{dN} = u_1 u_2 \gamma \left(\frac{u_2}{u_3}\right) - 2u_2 (u_2 - u_4 - 2), \tag{23}$$

$$\epsilon \frac{du_3}{dN} = u_1 u_2 \gamma \left(\frac{u_2}{u_3}\right) - u_3 (u_1 + 2u_2 - 2u_4 - 4), \tag{24}$$

$$\epsilon \frac{du_4^+}{dN} = -2u_4^+ (1 + u_1 + u_2 - u_4) + 3\mu_+ \sqrt{u_4^+} u_5, \tag{25}$$

$$\epsilon \frac{du_4^-}{dN} = -2u_4^- (1 + u_1 + u_2 - u_4) + \mu_- \sqrt{3u_4^-} u_5, \tag{26}$$

$$\epsilon \frac{du_5}{dN} = -u_5 \left(3\omega - 1 + u_1 + 2u_2 - 2u_4 \right.$$
$$\left. + 3\mu_+ \sqrt{u_4^+} + \mu_- \sqrt{3u_4^-}\right). \tag{27}$$

Notice that differentiating (18) with respect to N and using the equations (22)-(27), we have

$$\epsilon \frac{dg}{dN} = -(u_1 + 2u_2 - 2u_4^+ - 2u_4^- - 1)g, \tag{28}$$

showing that the constraint $g = 0$ is indeed conserved along the solutions of our equations and the system (22) - (27) is effectively 5-dimensional.

The case of $f(R) = R^{1+\delta}$, with $\delta \neq 0$, is particularly important in our next examples. For this choice of $f(R)$, one has simply

$$\gamma = \delta^{-1}, \tag{29}$$

and the equations (23) and (24) can be considerably simplified. In this case, the right-handed side of the equations (22) - (27) involves only second degree polynomials in u_1, u_2, and u_3, and forth degree in $\sqrt{u_4^-}$ and $\sqrt{u_4^+}$. Hence, the task of finding the fixed points of our system reduce to finding polynomial roots, which may be performed in general with good accuracy. Notice that there are other relevant choices for $f(R)$ leading to polynomial fixed points. Besides of the trivial extension $f(R) = \alpha R^{1+\delta} + \Lambda$, with α and Λ constants, for which (29) also holds. For $f(R) = R^a + \alpha R^b$, with $a \neq b$ constants, we have

$$\gamma = \frac{u_2}{(b+a-1)u_2 - abu_3}. \tag{30}$$

Notice that, as in the exponential case, the function γ does not depend on the parameter α. This, of course, does not mean that the dynamics in insensitive to the value of α, since the expansion-normalized variables (17) depend explicitly on α. The case $a = 1$ and $b = 2$ is the original Starobinsky inflationary scenario,[4] and for the vacuum case our approach reduces to that one considered recently in.[33]

3. Applications to cosmology

In the following, we consider the expanding universes ($\epsilon = 1$). We investigate the case $f(R) = R^{1+\delta}$, whose main motivations from a cosmological perspective can be found in,[22, 23, 34, 35] for instance. The case with $\delta = 0$ is obviously pure GR, for which the corresponding system is lower-dimensional, and our approach simply does not apply. The case logarithmic case $f(R) = \ln R$ must be treated separately. Hence, we start considering $\delta \neq 0$ and $\delta \neq -1$. Since we will deal with vacuum solutions, we set $u_5 = 0$ in the equations (18) and (22) - (27). In this case, notice that (25) and (26) can be combined in only one equation for u_4. We can use (18) to write u_3 as

$$u_3 = u_2 - u_1 + u_4 - 1, \tag{31}$$

and we are left with only three dynamical variables $u_1, u_2,$ and u_4. Now, there is an interesting point to notice[36] about the specific choice $f(R) = R^{1+\delta}$, with $\delta \neq -1$, namely that

$$\frac{u_2}{u_3} = \frac{Rf'}{f} = 1 + \delta, \tag{32}$$

which combined with the constraint (31) implies

$$\delta u_2 = (1+\delta)(u_1 - u_4 + 1), \tag{33}$$

and we are left in fact with a two-dimensional phase space spanned by the variables u_1 and u_4. The corresponding dynamical equations in this case are

$$\frac{du_1}{dN} = \phi_1(u_1, u_4) \tag{34}$$
$$= -\delta^{-1}(1+2\delta)(u_1 - u_1^*)(u_1 - u_4 + 1),$$
$$\frac{du_4}{dN} = \phi_4(u_1, u_4) \tag{35}$$
$$= -2\delta^{-1}(1+2\delta)u_4(u_1 - u_4 + 1),$$

where

$$u_1^* = \frac{2(\delta-1)}{1+2\delta}. \tag{36}$$

The phase space (u_1, u_4) associated with the system (34) - (35) has some interesting features. For instance, it has an one-dimensional invariant subspace (a continuous line of fixed points) corresponding to the straight line $u_1 - u_4 = -1$. However, from (31) we have that $u_3 = u_2$ on this line, which implies from (17) and (32) that $R = 0$ on $u_1 - u_4 = -1$. Besides of this invariant straight line, we find the isolated fixed point $(u_1^*, 0)$, for $\delta \neq -\frac{1}{2}$. The case $\delta = -\frac{1}{2}$ is also discussed separately.

The stability of the isolated fixed point can be inferred from the linearization of (34) - (35). The Jacobian matrix of (34) - (35) at the point $(u_1^*, 0)$ reads

$$\left(\frac{\partial(\phi_1, \phi_4)}{\partial(u_1, u_4)}\right) = -\delta^{-1}(4\delta - 1)\begin{pmatrix} 1 & 0 \\ 0 & 2 \end{pmatrix}, \qquad (37)$$

from where we see that such fixed point is stable for $\delta > \frac{1}{4}$ or for $\delta < 0$. For the stability of the invariant straight line, we can consider the divergence of the vector field (ϕ_1, ϕ_2). One has

$$\nabla \cdot \phi = \frac{\partial \phi_1}{\partial u_1} + \frac{\partial \phi_4}{\partial u_4} = \delta^{-1}((1 + 2\delta)u_4 + 4\delta - 1) \qquad (38)$$

on the invariant line. Recalling that $u_4 \geq 0$, we find that the invariant line is entirely repulsive (positive divergence) for $\delta > \frac{1}{4}$ or for $\delta \leq -\frac{1}{2}$. For $-\frac{1}{2} < \delta \leq \frac{1}{4}$, we can obtain some attractive segments, depending on the value of u_4. We return to the physical interpretation of this $R = 0$ invariant line in a following sub-section. The case $\delta = -\frac{1}{2}$ is particularly curious, since the isolated fixed point is absent and we get a second one-dimensional invariant line, namely $u_1 = 0$, which is also entirely repulsive. On the other hand, the case $f(R) = \ln R$ cannot be incorporated in the present analysis since (32) is not valid for $\delta \to -1$, and in fact we have a three-dimensional phase space for such case.

The solutions of (34) and (35) are curves on the plane (u_1, u_4), and it turns out that such curves can be determined analytically. Notice that the solutions are such that

$$\frac{u_4'}{u_1'} = \frac{2u_4}{u_1 - u_1^*}, \qquad (39)$$

which can be integrated as

$$u_4 = c(u_1 - u_1^*)^2, \qquad (40)$$

with arbitrary c. Thus, the phase space trajectories of all solutions of (34) and (35) are simply parabolas centered in the isolated fixed point, irrespective of the value of δ, provided the fixed point exists. Since we know the trajectories graphs, one can infer the dynamics direction and, consequently, the dynamical properties of the fixed point and the invariant line, directly form the equations (34) and (35) as follows. Consider the phase space function $L = u_1 - u_4 + 1$. It is clear that $L = 0$ is the invariant line. On the other hand, $L = c$ constant is a parallel line located below the invariant line if $c > 0$, or above if $c < 0$. The invariant line is the boundary between two semiplanes with reverse dynamics direction, and the dynamical properties of the

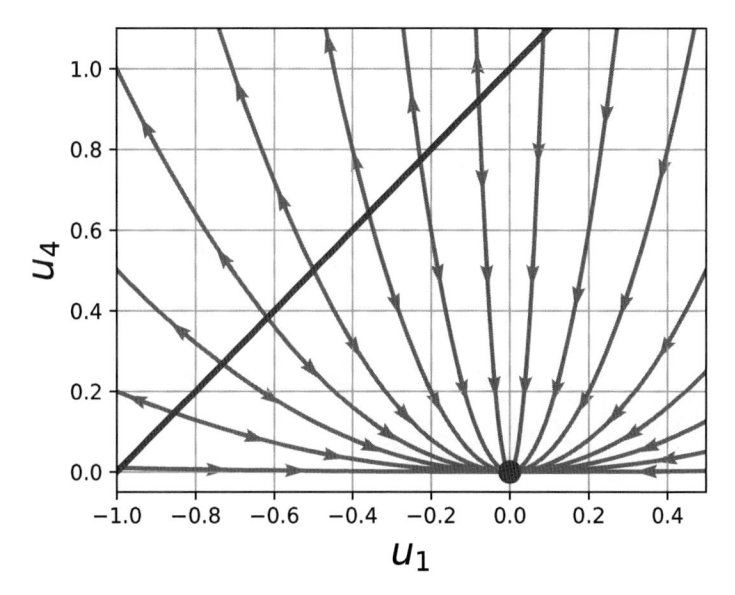

Fig. 1. Phase space for the system (34) - (35), for $\delta = 1$. The fixed point $(0,0)$ is located in the semiplane below the critical line. The solutions are restricted to parabolas centered in the attractive fixed point. The region below the invariant line corresponds to the attraction basin of the fixed point. Any solution starting there tends to the fixed point asymptotically. All solutions starting in the region above the critical line will diverge to infinity. Notice that the critical line is entirely repulsive. Such phase space is rather generic, it is essentially the same for all theories of the type $f(R) = R^{1+\delta}$ such that the fixed point is attractive and is located below the invariant line.

fixed point and of the invariant line depend on the relative position between then, see Figs 1 and 2, which correspond, respectively, to the cases $\delta = 1$ and $\delta = \frac{1}{10}$. The former is the important case of the Starobinsky's inflationary scenario with $f(R) = R^2$.

We note that the solutions are constrained to the parabolas (40), the exact solutions of (34) and (35) boils down to a simple quadrature of a rational function

$$\frac{d\bar{u}_1}{c\bar{u}_1^3 - \bar{u}_1^2 - (u_1^* + 1)\bar{u}_1} = -\delta^{-1}(1 + 2\delta)dN, \tag{41}$$

with $u_1 = \bar{u}_1 + u_1^*$. For the case $\delta = -\frac{1}{2}$, u_4 is a constant and (34) also reduces to a simple rational quadrature. It has been shown that the vacuum solutions for the $f(R) = R^{1+\delta}$ case, for $\delta \neq -1$, are exactly soluble.

Since the stable fixed points of a cosmological model correspond to the cosmological histories which dominate the asymptotic evolution of the system, it worth to look more closely on them. By using (31) and (32), we see that the isolated fixed points are given by

$$u_3 = \frac{4\delta - 1}{\delta(1 + 2\delta)}, \tag{42}$$

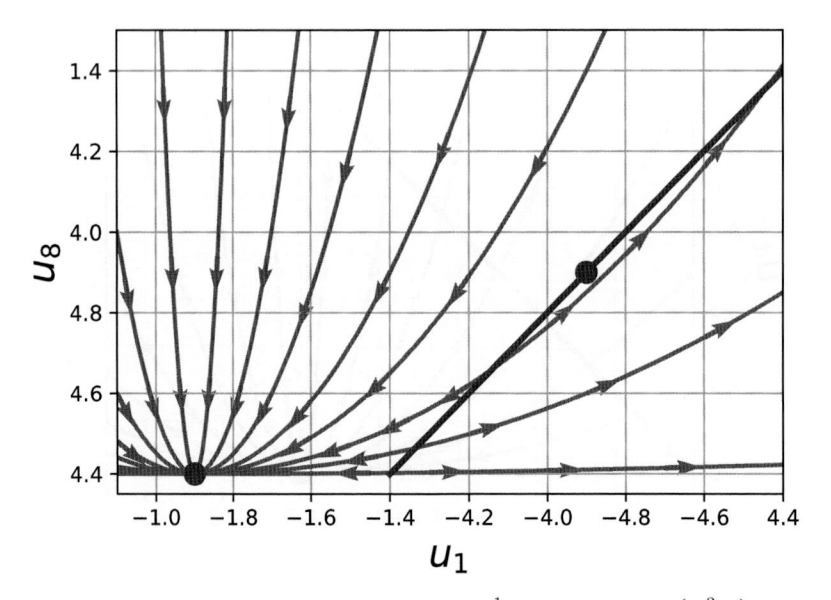

Fig. 2. Phase space for the system (34) - (35), for $\delta = \frac{1}{10}$. The fixed point $\left(-\frac{3}{2}, 0\right)$ is now located in the semiplane above the critical line. The solutions are also restricted to parabolas centered in the attractive fixed point. However, the attraction basin of the fixed point is now in the region above the critical line. Notice that the invariant line in this case has an attractive and a repulsive segment located, respectively, above and below the depicted point $\left(-\frac{1}{2}, \frac{1}{2}\right)$. The divergence (38) always vanishes in limit points between attractive and repulsive segments like this one.

with $\delta > \frac{1}{4}$ or $\delta < 0$. From the definition of u_3 and (5), we have that (42) implies that

$$\dot{H} = \Delta H^2, \tag{43}$$

where

$$\Delta = \frac{\delta - 1}{\delta(1 + 2\delta)}. \tag{44}$$

It is clear that for $\delta = 1$, the stable fixed point corresponds to de Sitter solution with $a(t) = e^{Ht}$, with constant H. (The case $H = 0$ corresponds to the flat Minkowski spacetime). This is namely the well known Starobinsky's inflationary solution. For $\delta \neq 1$, the solutions are

$$H(t) = \frac{H_0}{1 - \Delta H_0 (t - t_0)}, \tag{45}$$

where $H(t_0) = H_0$, which interpretation is straightforward. For $\Delta > 0$, which corresponds to $-\frac{1}{2} < \delta < 0$ or $\delta > 1$, we have a future finite time big rip singularity, while for $\Delta < 0$ ($\delta < -\frac{1}{2}$ or $0 < \delta < 1$), the Hubble parameter H decreases as t^{-1} for large t, i.e., the solution asymptotically tends to a power law expansion.

The Starobinsky's R^2 inflationary scenario is unique among the $F(R) = R^{1+\delta}$ theories of gravity, since only for $\delta = 1$ the stable de Sitter fixed point $(0,0)$ is available, a result indeed known for a long time, see,[24–26] for example. We can, however, easily prove a stronger result for generic $f(R)$ theories. The de Sitter solution $a(t) = e^{Ht}$, with constant and arbitrary H, implies $u_1 = u_4 = 0$, and also

$$R = 12H^2, \qquad (46)$$

which, on the other hand, determine that $u_2 = 2$ and $u_3 = \frac{2f}{Rf'}$ and, hence, the constraint (18) reads

$$Rf'(R) = 2f(R). \qquad (47)$$

Since we assume that de Sitter solution exists for arbitrary H, we have from (46) that it should exist for any $R > 0$, and hence equation (47) can be seen as a ordinary differential equation for $f(R)$, which unique solution is $f(R) = \alpha R^2$, establishing in this way a stronger result: the case R^2 is unique among all vacuum $f(R)$ theories with respect to the existence of a de Sitter solution with arbitrary H. The condition (47) was first obtained by Barrow and Ottewill in[24] by using a more intricate approach, but here we see that it appears from a very simple analysis of fixed points.

It is noted that in the case with anisotropic fluids, all isotropic fixed points are unstable (there is no asymptotically stable isotropic solutions in the presence of anisotropic matter). It is also mentioned that several known results as the existence of vacuum Kasner-like solutions for $-\frac{1}{2} \leq \delta \leq \frac{1}{4}$ [34, 35] are found. Moreover, for the case of exponential gravity,[37–40] $f(R) = e^{\alpha R}$, all isotropic fixed points in the presence of an anisotropic barotropic fluid are unstable.

4. Summary

In this article, we have introduced a new set of expansion-normalized variables for homogeneous and anisotropic Bianchi-I spacetimes in $f(R)$ gravity in the presence of anisotropic matter. In terms of these new dynamical variables, the full set of Einstein's equations boils down to a 5-dimensional phase space. As applications of the proposed dynamical approach, we have explicitly explored the $f(R) = R^{1+\delta}$ modified theory of gravity, and shown that its vacuum dynamics is exactly solvable. Furthermore, in a easier and more direct way, we have re-obtained several well known results for this particular choice of $f(R)$ such as Bleyer and Schmidt isotropic solutions.[41–43] We have also extended a uniqueness result for Starobisnki inflationary scenario, namely that the case R^2 is unique among all vacuum $f(R)$ theories with respect to the existence of a de Sitter solution with arbitrary H, a result obtained previously by Barrow and Ottewill by using a more intricate approach.[24]

Acknowledgments

The work of KB was supported in part by the JSPS KAKENHI Grant Number JP21K03547.

References

1. S. Chakraborty, K. Bamba and A. Saa, Phys. Rev. D **99**, 064048 (2019) [arXiv:1805.03237 [gr-qc]].
2. A. H. Guth, Phys. Rev. D **23**, 347 (1981).
3. A. D. Linde, Phys. Lett. **108B**, 389 (1982).
4. A. A. Starobinsky, Phys. Lett. **91B**, 99 (1980).
5. E. J. Copeland, M. Sami and S. Tsujikawa, Int. J. Mod. Phys. D **15**, (2006) 1753-1936. doi:10.1142/S021827180600942X [arXiv:hep-th/0603057 [hep-th]].
6. T. Padmanabhan, Gen. Rel. Grav. **40**, (2008) 529-564. doi:10.1007/s10714-007-0555-7 [arXiv:0705.2533 [gr-qc]].
7. R. Durrer and R. Maartens, Gen. Rel. Grav. **40**, (2008) 301-328. doi:10.1007/s10714-007-0549-5 [arXiv:0711.0077 [astro-ph]].
8. T. Clifton, P. G. Ferreira, A. Padilla and C. Skordis, Phys. Rept. **513**, (2012) 1-189. doi:10.1016/j.physrep.2012.01.001 [arXiv:1106.2476 [astro-ph.CO]].
9. K. Bamba, S. Capozziello, S. Nojiri and S.D. Odintsov, Astrophys. Space Sci. **342**, 155 (2012) [arXiv:1205.3421].
10. A. de Felice and S. Tsujikawa, Living Rev. Rel. **13**, 3 (2010) [arXiv:1002.4928].
11. T.P. Sotiriou and V. Faraoni, Rev. Mod. Phys. **82**, 451 (2010) [arXiv:0805.1726].
12. V. Faraoni and S. Capozziello, Fundam. Theor. Phys. **170** (2010).
13. S. Nojiri and S. Odintsov, Phys. Rep. **505**, 59 (2011) [arXiv:1011.0544].
14. S. Capozziello and M. De Laurentis, Phys. Rept. **509**, 167 (2011) [arXiv:1108.6266].
15. Y. F. Cai, S. Capozziello, M. De Laurentis and E. N. Saridakis, Rept. Prog. Phys. **79**, 106901 (2016) [arXiv:1511.07586].
16. S. Nojiri, S. Odintsov, and V.K. Oikonomou, Phys. Rep. **692**, 1 (2017) [arXiv:1705.11098].
17. K. Bamba and S. D. Odintsov, Symmetry **7**, 220 (2015) [arXiv:1503.00442].
18. S. Capozziello, S. Carloni and A. Troisi, Recent Res. Dev. Astron. Astrophys. **1**, 625 (2003) [astro-ph/0303041].
19. S. Nojiri and S. D. Odintsov, Phys. Rev. D **68**, 123512 (2003) [hep-th/0307288].
20. S. M. Carroll, V. Duvvuri, M. Trodden and M. S. Turner, Phys. Rev. D **70**, 043528 (2004) [astro-ph/0306438].
21. J. Wainwright and G.F.R. Ellis, *Dynamical systems in cosmology*, Cambridge University Press (1997).
22. J. A. Leach, S. Carloni and P. K. S. Dunsby, Class. Quant. Grav. **23**, 4915 (2006) [gr-qc/0603012].
23. N. Goheer, J. A. Leach and P. K. S. Dunsby, Class. Quant. Grav. **24**, 5689 (2007) [arXiv:0710.0814].
24. J.D. Barrow. and A.C. Ottewill, J. Phys. A**16**, 2757 (1983).
25. K. Maeda, Phys. Rev. D **37**, 858 (1988).
26. J. D. Barrow and S. Hervik, Phys. Rev. D **74**, 124017 (2006) [gr-qc/0610013].
27. N. Aghanim et al. [Planck], Astron. Astrophys. **641**, A6 (2020) [erratum: Astron. Astrophys. **652**, C4 (2021)] doi:10.1051/0004-6361/201833910 [arXiv:1807.06209 [astro-ph.CO]].
28. Y. Akrami et al. [Planck], Astron. Astrophys. **641**, A10 (2020) doi:10.1051/0004-6361/201833887 [arXiv:1807.06211 [astro-ph.CO]].
29. T. S. Pereira, C. Pitrou and J. P. Uzan, JCAP **0709**, 006 (2007) [arXiv:0707.0736].
30. S. Chakraborty, Phys. Rev. D **98**, 024009 (2018) [arXiv:1803.01594].
31. S. Chakraborty, S. Pal, and A. Saa, Phys. Rev. D **99**, 024020 (2019) [arXiv:1812.01694].

32. O. Akarsu and C.B. Kilinc, Astr. Sp. Science, **326**, 315 (2010) [arXiv:1001.0550].
33. D. Muller, A. Ricciardone, A.A. Starobinsky, A. Toporensky, Eur. Phys. J. C **78**, 311 (2018) [arXiv:1710.08753].
34. J. D. Barrow and T. Clifton, Class. Quant. Grav. **23**, L1 (2006) [gr-qc/0509085].
35. T. Clifton and J. D. Barrow, Class. Quant. Grav. **23**, 2951 (2006) [gr-qc/0601118].
36. S. Carloni, P. K. S. Dunsby, S. Capozziello and A. Troisi, Class. Quant. Grav. **22**, 4839 (2005) [gr-qc/0410046].
37. M. Abdelwahab, S. Carloni, and P.K.S. Dunsby, Class. Quantum Grav. **25**, 135002 (2008) [arXiv:0706.1375].
38. E.V. Linder, Phys. Rev. D **80**, 123528 (2009) [arXiv:0905.2962].
39. S. I. Kruglov, Int. J. Mod. Phys. A **28**, 13501194 (2013) [arXiv:1204.6709].
40. S. D. Odintsov, D. Saez-Chillon Gomez, G.S. Sharov, Eur. Phys. J. C **77**, 862 (2017) [arXiv:1709.06800].
41. U. Bleyer and H.J. Schmidt, Int. J. Mod. Phys. A**5**, 4671 (1990).
42. H. J. Schmidt, Astron. Nachr. **311**, 165 (1990) [arXiv:gr-qc/0109004].
43. H. J. Schmidt, *Lectures on Mathematical Cosmology* [arXiv:gr-qc/0407095].

Cosmological implications in modified Hořava-Lifshitz gravity

Abdul Jawad

Department of Mathematics, COMSATS University Islamabad,
Lahore-Campus, Lahore-54000, Pakistan
E-mail: jawadab181@yahoo.com; abduljawad@cuilahore.edu.pk

Kazuharu Bamba

Division of Human Support System, Faculty of Symbiotic Systems Science, Fukushima
University, Fukushima 960-1296, Japan
E-mail: bamba@sss.fukushima-u.ac.jp

Farwa Khurshid

Department of Mathematics, COMSATS University Islamabad,
Lahore-Campus, Lahore-54000, Pakistan
E-mail: farwakhursheed1@gmail.com

We imvestigate the cosmological implications for the Sharma-Mittal holographic dark energy such as some cosmological parameters and thermodynamic analysis. Taking into account the apparent horizon with interacting scenario of dark energy and dark matter, the framework of deformed Hořava-Lifshitz gravity is considered. The cosmological parameters include the Hubble parameter, equation of state parameter for the accelerating/deceleratng phases, deceleration parameter to explore the expansion rate and squared speed of sound for stability analysis.

Keywords: Modified gravity theories; autonomous system analysis

1. Introduction

Observational data reveals that the expansion of our cosmos is currently accelerating.[1,2] If Einstein's law of gravity is valid on cosmological scales, this acceleration indicates that our cosmos is governed by a mystery type of energy. This unknown energy component known as dark energy (DE) which has some peculiar characteristics, such as the fact that it is not concentrated on massive distances and that its pressure must be negative in order to cause the universe's current acceleration. DE has appeared among the most major challenges in modern cosmology and in theoretical physics. Dark energy makes up 68 percent of the entire content of the universe, whereas mass energies in the form of dark matter (DM) and ordinary matter make up 27 percent and 5%, respectively, according to the standard model of cosmology. Cosmological investigations of thermodynamics in modified gravity theories have been executed in Refs.[4–10] (for a recent review on thermodynamic properties of modified gravity theories, see, e.g.,[11]).

The accelerated expansion is currently under the limelight of modern research. One of the most challenging problems in modern physics is to find a physical mechanism that may explain this accelerating universe. This acceleration can be easily accommodated within the scope of general relativity (GR) by adding DE. One of the most significant obstacles to achieving this goal is that GR is not a renormalizable theory in the high-energy limit, the ultraviolet (UV) limit and so there is no control over the theory along with its predictions.[12] Hořava-Lifshitz gravity is a new class of UV-complete gravity theories that attempts to solve this major issue. In the high-energy limit, the Hořava-Lifshitz theory of gravity is derived by rejecting the Lorentz symmetry using a Lifshitz-type re-scaling[13]

$$t \to b^z t^i, \quad x^i \to b x^i, \quad (i = 1, 2, 3, \ldots, d), \quad (1)$$

here z represents the exponent of dynamical scaling, d is a spacetime dimension that expresses a spatial dimension and b is any constant term. The Lorentz symmetry broken when $z \neq 1$ and recovered only when $z = 1$. Hořava-Lifshitz gravity[14] is nonrelativistic at high energies and it's expected that in the low-energy limit, the four-dimensional general covariance may be reconstituted. A lot of research has been done in the literature on modified Hořava-Lifshitz gravity. The deformed Hořava-Lifshitz[15] gravity model has been studied to investigate black hole quasinormal modes.

In this paper, we discuss some cosmological parameters in the framework of deformed Hořava-Lifshitz gravity with Sharma-Mittal holographic DE (SMHDE) model. We discuss the basic equations of SMHDE and deformed Hořava-Lifshitz gravity in the section **2**. In section **3**, we evaluate the cosmological parameters such as Hubble parameter, EoS parameter, deceleration parameter and squared speed of sound parameter. In the last, we discuss the final results.

2. The Deformed Hořava-Lifshitz Modified Gravity and SMHDE Model

The deformed Hořava-Lifshitz theory is a power-counting, renormalizable and ultraviolet total gravity theory. The total action of this gravity can be described as[12]

$$I = \int (\mathcal{L}_0 + \mathcal{L}_1 + \mathcal{L}_m) dt dx^3. \quad (2)$$

From the above expression $\mathcal{L}_m$ is a matter Lagrangian and $\mathcal{L}_1$, $\mathcal{L}_0$ are given by

$$\mathcal{L}_1 = \sqrt{g} N \left[\frac{k^2 \mu^2 (1-4\lambda)}{32(1-3\lambda)} R^2 - \frac{k^2}{2E^2} (C_{ij} - \frac{\mu E^2}{2} R_{ij})(C^{ij} - \frac{\mu E^2}{2} R^{ij}) \right], \quad (3)$$

$$\mathcal{L}_0 = \sqrt{g} N \left[\frac{k^2 \mu^2 (\Lambda_E R - 3\Lambda_E^2)}{8(1-3\lambda)} + \frac{2}{k^2} (K_{ij} K^{ij} - \lambda K^2) \right], \quad (4)$$

where g and N are the determinant of metric tensor and Lapse function respectively, μ, Λ_E are mass dimension parameters whereas dimensionless parameters are E, λ, k^2. In aditios, R, R_{ij} are Ricci scalar and Ricci tensor respectively while the extrinsic curvature K_{ij} and the Cotton tensor C^{ij} are defined as

$$K_{ij} = \frac{1}{2N}(\partial_t g_{ij} - \nabla_i N_j - \nabla_j N_i), C^{ij} = \frac{\nabla_k}{\sqrt{g}} \epsilon^{ikl}\left(-\frac{1}{4}R\delta_l^j + R_l^j\right). \quad (5)$$

here ϵ^{ikl} is the antisymmetric unit tensor. The total action of Hořava-Liftshitz gravity takes the form[12]

$$I = \int \left[\frac{k^2\mu^2(1-4\lambda)}{32(1-3\lambda)\mu^4 R + R^2} + \frac{k^2\mu}{2E^2}\epsilon^{ijk}R_{il}\nabla_j R_k^l - \frac{\mu^2 k^2}{8}R^{ij}R_{ij} \right.$$
$$\left. - \frac{k^2}{2E^4}C_{ij}C^{ij} + \frac{2}{8\pi G}(K^{ij}K_{ij} - K^2\lambda)\right]dtdx^3. \quad (6)$$

If $c^2 = \frac{k^2\mu^2}{2}$, $G = \frac{k^2}{32\pi C}$ and $\lambda = 1$, the Einstein-Hilbert action in anti de Sitter form can be constructed from the aforementioned action. For the flat FRW universe model, the Friedmann equation of deformed Hořava-Lifshitz gravity can be written as

$$H^2 + \frac{H^4}{2E} = \frac{\rho_D + \rho_m}{3M_p^2}. \quad (7)$$

In the above equation, we can define $\frac{H^2}{2E} = \gamma$, $\frac{\rho_m}{3M_p^2} = \Omega_m$ and $\frac{\rho_D}{3M_p^2} = \Omega_D$. Therefore, the above equation can be re-written as

$$1 + \gamma = \Omega_D + \Omega_m. \quad (8)$$

Also, $\dot{\rho} + 3H(p+\rho) = 0$ is the equation of continuity where ρ and p represent the total energy density and pressure respectively. Interacting of DE and cold DM leads to the following conservation equation

$$\dot{\rho}_D + 3H\rho_D(1+\omega_D) = -\Gamma, \quad (9)$$
$$\dot{\rho}_m + 3H\rho_m = \Gamma. \quad (10)$$

The coupling parameter Γ shows the mutual exchange rate between DM and DE. The energy exchange from DM to DE when $\Gamma < 0$ and corresponds to reverse scenario for $\Gamma > 0$. In the literature the various models have been proposed for parameter interaction to understand the universe's dynamics. We consider following expression for Γ as

$$\Gamma = 3Hd^2\rho_m, \quad (11)$$

here the coupling constant d exchange the energy between cold DM and DE. Inserting the value of Γ in Eq. (10), we get

$$\rho_m = a^{3(d^2-1)}\rho_{m0}, \quad (12)$$

where ρ_{m0} is an integration constant.

Now we will discuss the SMHDE model. SMHDE model is the new form of HDE model which is proposed due to the inspiration of holographic principle.[16] The Renyi and Tsallis entropies are formulations in which probability distributions are replaced with power-law distributions, yielding generalized entropies. Tsallis and Renyi entropies are combined in the Sharma-Mittal (SM) entropy. This entropy[17] leads to useful conclusions in cosmological scenarios, such as a description of the present accelerating universe that makes use of vacuum energy. The energy density of SMHDE is given by

$$\rho_D = \frac{3c^2 H^4}{8\pi R}\left[\left(1+\frac{\delta\pi}{H^2}\right)^{\frac{R}{\delta}}-1\right], \quad (13)$$

where c^2 is the unknown free parameter, R, δ are constants which provide Renyi and Tsallis HDE models under appropriate limits and IR cutoff is taken as Hubble horizon. We attain the following expression by taking the derivative of Eq. (13) w.r.t to t as

$$\dot{\rho}_D = 4\frac{\dot{H}}{H}\rho_D - \frac{3}{4}c^2 H\dot{H}\left(1+\frac{\delta\pi}{H^2}\right)^{\frac{R}{\delta}-1}. \quad (14)$$

3. Cosmological Parameters

In this section, we discuss the cosmological parameters in the frame work of SMHDE with apparent horizon, such that the Hubble, EoS, deceleration and squared speed of sound parameters.

3.1. Hubble Parameter

Taking into account Eqs. (7), (10), (11), (12) and (14), we obtain

$$\dot{H} = \left(9(d^2-1)HH_0^2\Omega_{m0}M_{p0}^2 a^{3(d^2-1)} * E\right)\left[6M_p^2 H^2(E+H^2)-E\right.$$
$$\left.\times\left(\frac{3c^2 H^3}{2\pi R}\left[\left(\frac{\delta\pi}{H^2}+1\right)^{\frac{R}{\delta}}-1\right]-\frac{3c^2 H}{4}\left(\frac{\delta\pi}{H^2}+1\right)^{\frac{R}{\delta}-1}\right)\right]^{-1} \quad (15)$$

The Hubble parameter H versus redshift function $(1+z)$ trajectories are shown in **Figure 1** for different values of $d^2 = 0.4, 0.6, 0.8$ and $M_{p0}^2 = 1$, $E = 80$, $\delta = 0.5$, $c = 1$, $R = 0.1$, $\Omega_{m0} = 0.5$, $H_0 = 74$. are the other constant parameters. The values of Hubble parameter lie within the range 74.010^{+10}_{-10} for all epochs.

3.2. Equation of State Parameter

For the identification of universe at different phases of acceleration and deceleration, we examine the EoS parameter. It is ratio of pressure to density i.e $\omega = \frac{p}{\rho}$. If we take $\omega = 0$, it is a non-relativistic matter while radiation period as decelerated phase of the universe corresponds to $0 < \omega < \frac{1}{3}$ and stiff fluid is for $(\omega = 1)$. During acceleration phase, it represents the phantom epoch for $(\omega < -1)$, quintessence epoch for $(-1 < \omega < \frac{-1}{3})$, and cosmological constant for $(\omega = -1)$. For SMHDE

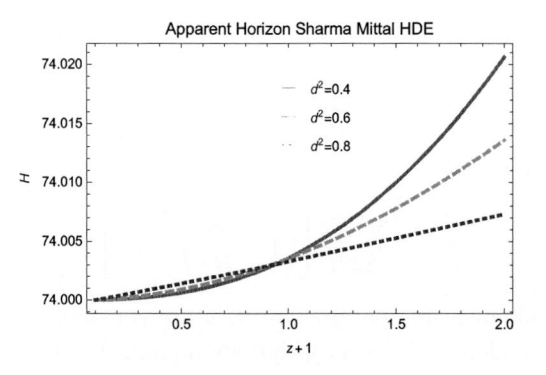

Fig. 1. (Color online) Plot of Hubble parameter H versus $1+z$ for Hubble horizon by choosing $d^2 = 0.4$ (solid red), 0.6 (dashed green), 0.8 (dotted blue).

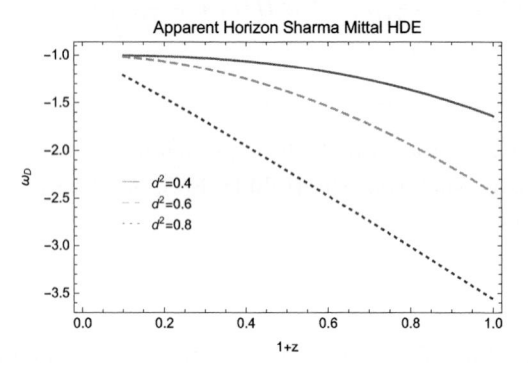

Fig. 2. (Color online) Plot of ω_{DE} versus $1+z$ for Hubble horizon by choosing $d^2 = 0.4$ (solid red), 0.6 (dashed green), 0.8 (dotted blue).

model we check the behavior of EoS parameter by using Eqs. (9), (11), (12) and (14), we get

$$\omega_D = \frac{-3d^2 H_0^2 M_{p0}^2 \Omega_{m0} a^{3(d^2-1)}}{\frac{3c^2 H^4}{8\pi R}[(1+\frac{\delta\pi}{H^2})^{\frac{R}{\delta}} - 1]} - 1 - \left[\frac{4}{3H^2} - \frac{c^2(1+\frac{\delta\pi}{H^2})^{\frac{R}{\delta}-1}}{\frac{3c^2 H^2}{2\pi R}\left((1+\frac{\delta\pi}{H^2})^{\frac{R}{\delta}} - 1\right)}\right]$$

$$\times \left(9(d^2-1)HH_0^2 \Omega_{m0} M_{p0}^2 a^{3(d^2-1)}E\right)\left[6M_p^2 H^2(E+H^2) - E\right.$$

$$\times \left.\left(\frac{3c^2 H^3}{2\pi R}\left[\left(\frac{\delta\pi}{H^2}+1\right)^{\frac{R}{\delta}} - 1\right] - \frac{3c^2 H}{4}\left(\frac{\delta\pi}{H^2}+1\right)^{\frac{R}{\delta}-1}\right)\right]^{-1}. \qquad (16)$$

In **Figure 2**, we plot ω_D versus $1+z$ by taking same values of constants. The EoS parameter (ω_D) trajectories lie in the phantom regime which follow the cosmological constant behavior at $z = -1$.

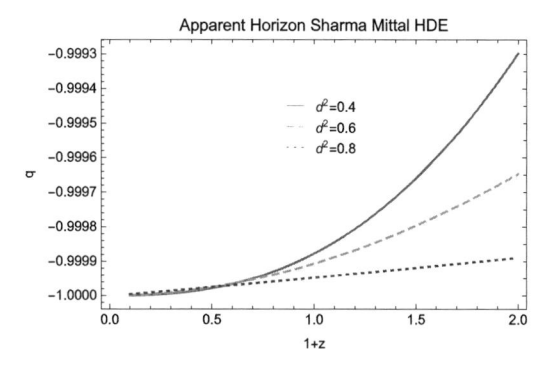

Fig. 3. Plot of q versus $1+z$ for Hubble horizon by choosing $d^2 = 0.4$ (solid red), 0.6 (dashed green), 0.8 (dotted blue).

3.3. Deceleration Parameter

We can analyze the accelerating and decelerating rate in different phases of the universe by using deceleration parameter. In terms of Hubble parameter, it is given by

$$q = -\frac{\ddot{a}}{aH^2} = -1 - \frac{\dot{H}}{H^2}. \tag{17}$$

The positive values of this parameter represent decelerated phase and expansion rate as constant when this parameter vanishes. The region described by $q < (-1, 0)$ is accelerating phase with power law expansion, $q = -1$ shows exponential expansion while and $q < -1$ describe super-exponential expansion of the accelerated phase of the expanding universe. In the underlying case, it takes the form

$$q = -1 - \frac{1}{H^2}\left[\left(9(d^2-1)HH_0^2\Omega_{m0}M_{p0}^2 a^{3(d^2-1)}E\right)\left(6M_p^2H^2(E+H^2)\right.\right.$$
$$\left.\left. - E\left(\frac{3c^2H^3}{2\pi R}\left[\left(\frac{\delta\pi}{H^2}+1\right)^{\frac{R}{\delta}}-1\right]-\frac{3c^2H}{4}\left(\frac{\delta\pi}{H^2}+1\right)^{\frac{R}{\delta}-1}\right)\right)^{-1}\right]. \tag{18}$$

Considering same values of constants, we plot q versus redshift $(1+z)$ as shown in **Figure 3**. The plot shows the expansion rate at power law level of the accelerating universe for all values of redshift parameter as well as d^2.

3.4. Squared Speed of Sound Parameter

In order to check the stability of model, we use squared speed of sound parameter for the underlying case. It is given by

$$v_s^2 = \frac{\dot{p}_D}{\dot{\rho}_D}, \tag{19}$$

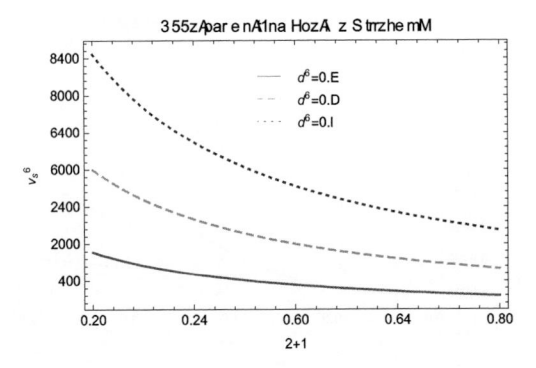

Fig. 4. Plot of v_s^2 versus $1+z$ for Hubble horizon by choosing $d^2 = 0.4$ (solid red), 0.6 (dashed green), 0.8 (dotted blue).

If v_s^2 is greater than zero then model is stable, otherwise unstable. For SMHDE model, v_s^2 becomes

$$v_s^2 = \left(8RH_0^2\Omega_{m0}M_{p0}^2 a^{3(d^2-1)\pi}(2(\delta\pi + H^2)(4d^2 M_{p0}^2 ER\pi + Ec^2 H \right.$$
$$+ 4d^2 M_{p0}^2 H^2 R\pi) - c^2\left(1 + \frac{\delta\pi}{H^2}\right)^{\frac{R}{\delta}} H(-ER\pi + d^2 R\pi(1+E)$$
$$+ 2E\delta\pi + 2EH^2))\left.\right)\left(c^2\left(-1 + \left(1 + \frac{\delta\pi}{H^2}\right)^{\frac{R}{\delta}} H^4(-2(\delta\pi + H^2)\right.$$
$$\times (4M_{p0}^2 ER\pi + Ec^2 H + 4M_{p0}^2 H^2 R\pi) + c^2\left(1 + \frac{\delta\pi}{H^2}\right)^{\frac{R}{\delta}} H$$
$$\left.\left.\times (R\pi + 2E\delta\pi + 2EH^2))\right)\right)^{-1} + \dot{\omega}_D\left(\frac{4\dot{H}}{H} - \frac{3c^2 H\dot{H}}{4\rho_D}\right)$$
$$\times \left(1 + \frac{\delta\pi}{H^2}\right)^{\frac{R}{\delta}-1}\right)^{-1} - 1 \tag{20}$$

Figure 4 describes the plot of $v_s^2 > 0$ versus redshift parameter for same constant values as in previous cases. The plot expresses positive behavior for all the trajectories which lead to the stable behavior of the model.

4. Conclusions

In this paper, we have considered deformed Hořava-Lifshitz gravity with interaction of dark sector constituents of the universe. The SMHDE model with Hubble horizon is taken into account in order to discuss some cosmological parameters. These parameters are Hubble, EoS, deceleration and squared speed of sound. For different values of interaction parameter, we have investigated the behavior of these parameters graphically for some arbitrary values of model constants. The Hubble parameter represents consistent results as 74.010^{+10}_{-10} for all trajectories while EoS parameter expresses phantom behavior of the universe. The deceleration parameter indicates the accelerating universe with power law expansion which leads to exponential expansion and squared speed of sound parameter gives the stable behavior of SMHDE models in the framework of deformed Hořava-Lifshitz gravity for all values of interaction parameter.

Acknowledgments

The work of KB was supported in part by the JSPS KAKENHI Grant Number JP21K03547.

References

1. Perlmutter, S., et al., Astrophy. J **517**, 565 (1999).
2. Spergel, D. N., et al., Astrophys. J **170**, 377 (2007).
3. Jawad, A. and Majeed, A.: Astrophy. Space Sci. **356**(2015)375; Jawad, A.: Eur. Phys. J. C **75**(2015)206; Jawad, A., Chattopadhyay, S. and Pasqua, A.: Astrophy. Space Sci. **346**, 273 (2013); Jawad, A., Chattopadhyay, S. and Pasqua, A.: Eur. Phys. J. Plus **128**, 88 (2013); Jawad, A., Chattopadhyay, S. and Pasqua, A.: Eur. Phys. J. Plus **129**, 54 (2014); Jawad, A., Pasqua, A. and Chattopadhyay, S.: Astrophy. Space Sci. **344**, 489 (2013); Jawad, A., Pasqua, A. and Chattopadhyay, S.: Eur. Phys. J. Plus **128**, 156 (2013); Jawad, A.: Astrophy. Space Sci. **353**, 691 (2014); Jawad, A.: Eur. Phys. J. Plus **129**, 207 (2014).
4. K. Bamba and C. Q. Geng, Phys. Lett. B **679**, 282 (2009).
5. K. Bamba, C. Q. Geng and S. Tsujikawa, Phys. Lett. B **688**, 101 (2010).
6. K. Bamba, C. Q. Geng, S. Nojiri and S. D. Odintsov, EPL **89**, 50003 (2010).
7. K. Bamba and C. Q. Geng, JCAP **1006**, 014 (2010).
8. K. Bamba and C. Q. Geng, JCAP **1111**, 008 (2011).
9. K. Bamba, R. Myrzakulov, S. Nojiri and S. D. Odintsov, Phys. Rev. D **85**, 104036 (2012).
10. K. Bamba, M. Jamil, D. Momeni and R. Myrzakulov, Astrophys. Space Sci. **344**, 259 (2013).
11. K. Bamba, Int. J. Geom. Meth. Mod. Phys. **13**, 1630007 (2016).
12. Horava, P., Phys. Rev. D **79**, 084008 (2009).
13. Minamitsuji, M., Phys. Lett. B **684**, 194-198 (2010).
14. Mukohyama, S., Phys. Rev. D **80**, 064005 (2009).
15. Chen, S., Jing, J., Phys. Lett. B **687**, 124-128 (2010).
16. Sharma, U.K., Dubey, V.C., Eur. Phys J. Plus **135**, 1-20 (2020).
17. Jawad, A., Bamba, K., Younas, M., Qummer, S., Rani, S, Symmetry **10**, 635 (2018).

Finite action principle and wormholes

Jan Chojnacki[1]

[1] *Faculty of Physics, University of Warsaw, ul. Pasteura 5, 02-093 Warsaw, Poland*

Jan Kwapisz[1,2]

[1] *Faculty of Physics, University of Warsaw, ul. Pasteura 5, 02-093 Warsaw, Poland*
[2] *CP3-Origins, University of Southern Denmark, Campusvej 55, DK-5230 Odense M, Denmark*

In this work, we elaborate on the finite action for wormholes in higher derivative theories as well as for wormholes. Both non-traversable and traversable wormholes in theories with higher curvature invariants posses finite action.

Keywords: Horava gravity; Wormholes; finite action

1. Introduction

The Finite Action Principle (FAP) proposes that the physical spacetimes are those for which the action is finite. This reasoning comes from the fact that in Euclidian path integral the weighting factor is $e^{-S[\Phi]}$. Hence lesser the action the more it contributes to the path integral. On the other hand, in the Lorentztian signature the more varying actions contribute less. For an infinitely varying action, one expects a distructive interference with the neighboring fields in such a configuration, see.[1]

This notion has recently received significant attention in the literature, see[2–4] for the cosmological considerations and[1,4] for the investigation of the black holes. Since it is expected that the quantum gravity should resolve the black-hole singularity problem, one may ask which of the microscopic actions remain finite for non-singular black holes and conversely interfere destructively for the singular ones. This we shall call the finite action selection principle. Only after the inclusion of higher-curvature operators, beyond the Einstein-Hilbert term, such selection principle can be satisfied.[1] Furthermore, in asymptotic safety, the quantum corrections to the Newtonian potential eliminate the classical-singularity.[5]

These findings suggest that by taking into account the higher curvatures one can resolve the singularities in black holes. Yet, an issue with the higher-curvature theory of quantum gravity is the existence of the particles with the negative mass-squared spectrum, known as *ghosts*, which makes the theory non-unitary. In this article, we explore possible resolution, namely, we investigate Horava-Lifshitz (H-L) gravity,[6] where the Lorentz Invariance (LI) is broken at the fundamental level (see[7] for a comprehensive progress report on this subject). Kinetic terms are first order in the time derivatives, while higher spatial curvature scalars regulate the UV behavior of the gravity. In our investigation we follow Horava[6] and assume that Wick rotation is well defined. This can be motivated by the lack of the higher time-like curvature invariants. In the usual higher derivative constructions the existence of massive poles in the propagator makes the Wick rotation troublesome.[8] Conversely to the latter, the new poles are massless and non-tachyonic for suitable choice of parameters.[9] Furthermore, the existence of the foliation supports that claim. For the discussion of Minkowski path integral and FAP, see.[1]

In the previous article, we discussed the possibility that the Finite Action arguments applied to the projectable H-L gravity result in a flat, homogeneous, UV-complete, and ghost-free beginning of the universe.[4] However there is no known regular black hole solutions in HL gravity. Here we discuss the wormholes solutions in the context of the Finite Action Principle in HL gravity, as well as in the $f(R)$ theories. Interestingly the stable and traversable wormholes solutions are known only in the higher derivative gravities[10] (without exotic matter), so there seems to be a wormhole/non-singular BH trade-off after taking into account the Finite Action Principle.

2. Horava-Lifshitz gravity

In the Horava-Lifshitz gravity, space and time are scaled in a non-equivalent way. Diffeomorphism invariance is broken by the foliation of the 4-dimensional spacetime into 3-dimensional hypersurfaces of constant time, called leaves, making the theory power-counting renormalizable (see also the renormalization group studies of the subject[11–13]). The remaining symmetry respects transformations:

$$t \to \xi_0(t), \quad x^i \to \xi^i(t, x^k), \tag{1}$$

and is often referred to as the foliation-preserving diffeomorphism, denoted by $\text{Diff}(M, \mathcal{F})$. The diffeomorphism invariance is still present on the leaves. The four-dimensional metric may be expressed in the Arnowitt-Deser-Misner (ADM)[14] variables:

$$(N, N^i, {}^{(3)}g_{ij}), \tag{2}$$

where N, N^i, ${}^{(3)}g_{ij}$ denote respectively the lapse function, shift vector, and 3-dimensional induced metric on the leaves. The theory is constructed from the following quantities:

$${}^{(3)}R_{ij}, \quad K_{ij}, \quad a_i, \quad {}^{(3)}\nabla_i, \tag{3}$$

where ${}^{(3)}R_{ij}$ is the 3-dimensional Ricci curvature tensor, ${}^{(3)}\nabla_i$ is the covariant derivative constructed from the 3-dimensional metric ${}^{(3)}g_{ij}$, and $a_i := \frac{N_{,i}}{N}$. Extrinsic curvature K_{ij} is the only object, invariant under general spatial diffeomorphisms containing exactly one time derivative of the metric tensor ${}^{(3)}g_{ij}$:

$$K_{ij} = \frac{1}{2N}\left(\frac{\partial {}^{(3)}g_{ij}}{\partial t} - {}^{(3)}\nabla_i N_j - {}^{(3)}\nabla_j N_i\right). \tag{4}$$

Quantities (2) are tensor/vectors with respect to Diff($M, \mathcal{F}$) possessing the following mass dimensions:

$$[^{(3)}R_{ij}] = 2, \quad [K_{ij}] = 3, \quad [a_i] = 1, \quad [^{(3)}\nabla_i] = 1. \tag{5}$$

One may use (2) to construct, order by order, scalar terms appearing in the Lagrangian of the theory. Following[7,15] the action of the Horava gravity takes the form:

$$S_g = \zeta^2 \int dt dx^3 N \sqrt{^{(3)}g} \left(\mathcal{K} - V \right), \tag{6}$$

where $\mathcal{K} = K_{ij}K^{ij} - \lambda K^2$ with $K = K_{ij}\,^{(3)}g^{ij}$, $^{(3)}g$ denotes the determinant of the 3-dimensional metric and $\zeta^2 = 1/16\pi G$. It may be expressed as the difference of the kinetic and potential part $\mathcal{L} = \mathcal{K} - V$ with $\mathcal{K} = \left(K_{ij}K^{ij} - \lambda K^2 \right)$. At the 6th order, the potential part of the lagrangian contains over 100 terms.[7] The immense number of invariants is limited by imposing further symmetries. One possible restriction for the potential comes from the projectability condition $N = N(t)$, then terms proportional to $a_i \equiv 0$ vanish. Up to the sixth order (compatible with power counting renormalizability), the potential V restricted by the projectability condition is given by:

$$V = 2\Lambda\zeta^2 - {}^{(3)}R + \frac{1}{\zeta^2}\left(g_2\,^{(3)}R^2 + g_3\,^{(3)}R^{ij}\,^{(3)}R_{ij}\right)$$

$$+ \frac{1}{\zeta^4}\left(g_4\,^{(3)}R^3 + g_5\,^{(3)}R\,^{(3)}R^{ij}\,^{(3)}R_{ij} + g_6\,^{(3)}R^i_j\,^{(3)}R^j_k\,^{(3)}R^k_i\right),$$

$$+ \frac{1}{\zeta^4}\left(g_7\,^{(3)}R\nabla^{2(3)}R + g_8(\nabla_i\,^{(3)}R_{jk})(\nabla^{i(3)}R^{jk})\right), \tag{7}$$

where Λ is the cosmological constant and α_{ij} are the coupling constants. For our purposes, we drop terms containing covariant derivatives $^{(3)}\nabla_i$. One should also mention that this *minimal theory*[16] suffers from the existence of spin 0 graviton, which is unstable in the IR. Various solutions to this problem have been proposed. One can add the additional local $U(1)$ symmetry.[7,17] Then by the introduction of new fields prevents the zero-mode from propagating. On the other hand, one can drop the projectability condition $a_i = 0$ and include the terms containing a_i in the potential term:

$$V = 2\Lambda\zeta^2 - {}^{(3)}R - \beta_0 a_i a^i + \sum_{n=3}^{6}\mathcal{L}_V^{(n)}, \tag{8}$$

then for the spin-0 mode to be stable one requires $0 < \beta_0 < 2$.[18,19]

3. Wormholes and finite action principle

Here, we take the first step in the direction of the investigations of the consequences of the Finite Action Principle in the context of wormholes (WH). The wormholes may be characterized in two classes: traversable and non-traversable.

The traversable WH, colloquially speaking, are such that one can go through it to the other side, see[20] for specific conditions. The pioneering Einstein-Rosen bridge has been found originally as a non-static, non-traversable solution to GR. The traversable solutions are unstable, however, they might be stabilized by an exotic matter or inclusion of the higher curvature scalar gravity.[10] This is important in the context of finite action since usually the divergences of black holes do appear in the curvature squared terms. Hence, due to the inclusion of the higher-order terms in the actions, the traversable wormholes are solutions to the equations of motions without the exotic matter. The exemplary wormhole spacetimes investigated here are the Einstein-Rosen bridge proposed in,[21] the Morris-Thorne (MT) wormhole,[20] the traversable exponential metric wormhole[22] and the wormhole solution discussed in the H-L gravity.[23] All of them have a finite action. Here, we shall discuss the exponential metric WH. For the exponential metric WH, the line element is given by:

$$ds^2 = -e^{-\frac{2M}{r}} dt^2 + e^{\frac{2M}{r}} \left(dr^2 + r^2 d\Omega^2\right). \qquad (9)$$

This spacetime consists two regions: "our universe" with $r > M$ and the "other universe" with $r < M$. $r = M$ corresponds to the wormhole's throat. The spacial volume of the "other universe" is infinite when $r \to 0$. Such volume divergence is irrelevant to our discussion since it describes large distances in the "other universe". Hence, we further consider only $r \geq M$. The resulting Ricci and Kretschmann scalars have been calculated in[22] and the measure are non-singular everywhere:

$$R = -\frac{2M^2}{r^4} e^{-\frac{2M}{r}},$$
$$R_{\mu\nu\sigma\rho} R^{\mu\nu\sigma\rho} = \frac{4M^2(12r^2 - 16Mr + 7M^2)}{r^8} e^{-4\frac{M}{r}}, \qquad (10)$$

resulting in the finite action for the Stelle gravity. Similarly for the H-L gravity:

$$^{(3)}R = R, \quad K^2 = K_{ij}K^{ij} = 0,$$
$$^{(3)}R_{ij}\,^{(3)}R^{ij} = \frac{2M^2(M^2 - 2Mr + 3r^2)}{r^8} e^{-\frac{4M}{r}}. \qquad (11)$$

Einstein-Rosen bridge The Einstein-Rosen (E-R) bridge smoothly glues together two copies of the Schwarzschild spacetime: the black hole and the white hole solutions corresponding to the positive and negative coordinate u. The metric tensor of the Einstein-Rosen wormhole proposed in[21] and discussed in e.g.[24] is given by:

$$ds^2 = \frac{-u^2}{u^2 + 4M} dt^2 + (u^2 + 4M) du^2 + \frac{1}{4}(u^2 + 4M) d\Omega^2. \qquad (12)$$

The E-R bridge is non-traversable and geodesically incomplete in $u = 0$. This fact, however, does not impact the regularity of the curvature scalars. The 4-dimensional

Ricci scalar is:
$$R = \frac{2\left(64M^2 + 32Mu^2 + 4u^4 + u^2\right)}{(4M + u^2)^3}. \tag{13}$$

The second order curvature scalar $R_{\mu\nu}R^{\mu\nu}$ is:

$$\frac{4\left(48M^2 + 8\left(4M + u^2\right)^4 + (32M - 1)\left(4M + u^2\right)^2\right)}{(4M + u^2)^6}. \tag{14}$$

Both of which integrated with the measure are non-singular:

$$\sqrt{g} = \frac{1}{4}u(4M + u^2). \tag{15}$$

The wormhole solutions analyzed in this paper generally yield the finite action in both GR and H-L. The finite Action Principle suggests, that in the quantum UV regime, singular black-hole spacetimes may be replaced with the regular wormhole solutions.

Morris-Thorne wormhole The MT wormhole is defined in the spherically symmetric, Lorentzian spacetime by the line element:

$$ds^2 = -e^{2\Phi(r)}dt^2 + \frac{dr^2}{1 - \frac{b(r)}{r}} + r^2 d\Omega^2 \tag{16}$$

where $\Phi(r)$ is known as the redshift and there are no horizons if it is finite. Function $b(r)$ determines the wormhole's shape. We choose $\Phi(r)$, $b(r)$ to be:

$$\Phi(r) = 0, \quad b(r) = 2M\left(1 - e^{r_0 - r}\right) + r_0 e^{r_0 - r}, \tag{17}$$

where r_0 is the radius of the throat of the wormhole, such that $b(r_0) = r_0$. 4-dimensional curvature scalars for this spacetime have been calculated in.[25] The Ricci curvature scalar is singular at $r = 0$, however, the radial coordinate r varies between $r_0 > 0$ and infinity:

$$R = -2\left(2M - r_0\right)\frac{e^{r_0 - r}}{r^2}. \tag{18}$$

The resulting $S_s = \int_{r_{UV} = r_0}^{r_{IR}} \sqrt{g} R$ function is divergent as $r_{UV} \to r_0$ and cannot be expressed in terms of simple functions:

$$2(2M - r_0)\int_{r_{UV}=r_0}^{r_{IR}} \sqrt{\frac{r}{r - 2M(1 - e^{r_0 - r}) + r_0 e^{r_0 - r}}} e^{r_0 - r} dr. \tag{19}$$

However, this is only a coordinate singularity and one may get rid of it with a proper transformation.

Higher-order curvature scalars for Morris-Thorne wormhole are:

$$^{(3)}R = \frac{2b'(r)}{r^2}$$

$$^{(3)}R_{ij}{}^{(3)}R^{ij} = \frac{3r^2b'(r)^2 - 2rb(r)b'(r) + 3b(r)^2}{2r^6},$$

$$^{(3)}R^i_j{}^{(3)}R^j_k{}^{(3)}R^k_i = \frac{-9r^2b(r)b'(r)^2 + 5r^3b'(r)^3 + 15rb(r)^2b'(r) - 3b(r)^3}{4r^9}, \quad (20)$$

and integrated give action that is finite.

H-L wormhole Static spherically traversable symmetric wormholes have been constructed in[23] in the H-L theory through the modification of the Rosen-Einstein spacetime:

$$ds^2 = -N^2(\rho)dt^2 + \frac{1}{f(\rho)}d\rho^2 + (r_0 + \rho^2)^2 d\Omega^2, \quad (21)$$

with additional Z_2 symmetry with respect to the wormhole's throat. There are solutions with $\lambda = 1$ asymptotically corresponding to the Minkowski vacuum. Explicitly we have:

$$f = N^2 = 1 + \omega(r_0 + \rho^2)^2$$
$$- \sqrt{(r_0 + \rho^2)(\omega^2(r_0 + \rho^2)^3 + 4\omega M)}. \quad (22)$$

The radius of the wormhole's throat is given by r_0. The parameters ω, and M are connected to the coupling constants in H-L action. See[23] for their explicit form. Ricci scalar of the H-L wormhole invariants are given by

$$^{(3)}R = -\frac{1}{(\rho^2 + r_0)^2}\Big[2(-10\rho^2\sqrt{\omega(\rho^2 + r_0)(4M + \omega(r_0 + \omega^2)^3)}$$
$$- 4r_0\sqrt{\omega(\rho^2 + r_0)(4M + \omega(r_0 + \omega^2)^3)} + 16\rho^6\omega + 8\rho^2$$
$$+ 36\rho^4 r_0\omega + 24\rho^2 r_0^2\omega + 4r_0^3\omega + 4r_0 - 1)\Big],$$

$$^{(3)}R_{ij}{}^{(3)}R^{ij} = \frac{1}{(\rho^2 + r_0)^4}\Big\{2(-7\rho^2\sqrt{\omega(\rho^2 + r_0)(4M + \omega(r_0 + \omega^2)^3)}$$
$$- 2r_0\sqrt{\omega(\rho^2 + r_0)(4M + \omega(r_0 + \omega^2)^3)}$$
$$+ 10\rho^6\omega + 6\rho^2 + 22\rho^4 r_0\omega + 14\rho^2 r_0^2\omega + 2r_0^3\omega + 2r_0 - 1)^2 + 4M$$
$$+ \frac{4(\rho^2 + r_0)}{\omega(4M + \omega(r_0 + \omega^2)^3)}\Big[\rho^2\omega(-4(\rho^2 + r_0)$$
$$\times \sqrt{\omega(\rho^2 + r_0)(4M + \omega(r_0 + \omega^2)^3)} + \omega(r_0 + \omega^2)^3)\Big]$$
$$- 2\sqrt{\omega(\rho^2 + r_0)(4M + \omega(r_0 + \omega^2)^3)}$$
$$\times \Big[-\sqrt{\omega(\rho^2 + r_0)(4M + \omega(r_0 + \omega^2)^3)} + \omega(\rho^2 + r_0)^2 + 1\Big]^2\Big\} \quad (23)$$

The kinetic terms with $K_{ij} = 0$ are vanishing, while the spacial Ricci scalar and higher curvature terms are finite.

From the point of view of the Finite Action Principle, all of the investigated wormhole spacetimes are included in the gravitational path integral.

4. Conclusions and discussion

The Finite Action Principle is a powerful tool to study quantum gravity theories and also QFTs in general. From the point of view of finite action selection principle[1,4] they are equally good theories, resolving the black holes singularities, assuming that ghost issue is resolved in the latter case. Yet none of the regular B-H solutions have been found in the context of H-L gravity[26] and the ones found for $f(R)$ suffer from mass inflation issue.[27–29] Hence, it is a strong suggestion that wormholes may appear in the UV regime of H-L gravity and can serve as a "cure" for singularities.[30–32]

Moreover, both the traversable and the non-traversable wormholes are on equal footing in the case of the Finite Action Principle, yet maybe the finite amplitude principle could distinguish between those,[3] since the amplitude to cross non-traversable wormhole should be different than the traversable one. However, this principle suggests that there is a trade-off between the resolution of black-hole singularities and the appearance of wormhole spacetimes due to higher curvature invariants. The wormhole solutions will remain in both the LI and H-L path integrals. The higher-order curvature scalars, generically present in the quantum gravity, stabilise the wormhole solutions without the need for an exotic matter.

Acknowledgements

We thank J. N. Borrisova, A. Eichhorn and A. Wang for inspiring discussions and careful reading of the manuscript. J.H.K. was supported by the Polish National Science Centre grant 2020/39/B/ST2/01279. J.H.K. would like to thank the CP3-Origins for the extended hospitality during this work. J.H.K acknowledges the NAWA Iwanowska scholarship PPN/IWA/2019/1/00048.

References

1. J. N. Borissova and A. Eichhorn, Universe **7**, 48 (2021), arXiv:2012.08570 [gr-qc].
2. J. D. Barrow and F. J. Tipler, Nature **331**, 31 (1988).
3. C. Jonas, J.-L. Lehners, and J. Quintin, Phys. Rev. D **103**, 103525 (2021), arXiv:2102.05550 [hep-th].
4. J. Chojnacki and J. Kwapisz, (2021), arXiv:2102.13556 [gr-qc].
5. L. Bosma, B. Knorr, and F. Saueressig, Phys. Rev. Lett. **123**, 101301 (2019), arXiv:1904.04845 [hep-th].
6. P. Hořava, Physical Review D **79** (2009), 10.1103/physrevd.79.084008.
7. A. Wang, International Journal of Modern Physics D **26**, 1730014 (2017).
8. J. F. Donoghue and G. Menezes, Phys. Rev. D **100**, 105006 (2019), arXiv:1908.02416 [hep-th].
9. F. S. Bemfica and M. Gomes, Phys. Rev. D **84**, 084022 (2011), arXiv:1108.5979 [hep-th].

10. F. Duplessis and D. A. Easson, Physical Review D **92** (2015), 10.1103/physrevd.92.043516.
11. G. D'Odorico, F. Saueressig, and M. Schutten, Phys. Rev. Lett. **113**, 171101 (2014), arXiv:1406.4366 [gr-qc].
12. G. D'Odorico, J.-W. Goossens, and F. Saueressig, JHEP **10**, 126 (2015), arXiv:1508.00590 [hep-th].
13. A. O. Barvinsky, D. Blas, M. Herrero-Valea, S. M. Sibiryakov, and C. F. Steinwachs, Phys. Rev. Lett. **119**, 211301 (2017), arXiv:1706.06809 [hep-th].
14. R. Arnowitt, S. Deser, and C. W. Misner, General Relativity and Gravitation **40**, 1997–2027 (2008).
15. R. Maier and I. D. Soares, Physical Review D **96** (2017), 10.1103/physrevd.96.103532.
16. P. Horava, Class. Quant. Grav. **28**, 114012 (2011), arXiv:1101.1081 [hep-th].
17. P. Horava and C. M. Melby-Thompson, Phys. Rev. D **82**, 064027 (2010), arXiv:1007.2410 [hep-th].
18. D. Blas, O. Pujolas, and S. Sibiryakov, JHEP **04**, 018 (2011), arXiv:1007.3503 [hep-th].
19. S. Carloni, E. Elizalde, and P. J. Silva, Class. Quant. Grav. **28**, 195002 (2011), arXiv:1009.5319 [hep-th].
20. M. S. Morris and K. S. Thorne, Am. J. Phys. **56**, 395 (1988).
21. A. Einstein and N. Rosen, Phys. Rev. **48**, 73 (1935).
22. P. Boonserm, T. Ngampitipan, A. Simpson, and M. Visser, Physical Review D **98** (2018), 10.1103/physrevd.98.084048.
23. M. Botta Cantcheff, N. E. Grandi, and M. Sturla, Physical Review D **82** (2010), 10.1103/physrevd.82.124034.
24. M. O. Katanaev, Modern Physics Letters A **29**, 1450090 (2014).
25. B. Mattingly, A. Kar, W. Julius, M. Gorban, C. Watson, M. Ali, A. Baas, C. Elmore, B. Shakerin, E. Davis, and et al., Universe **6**, 11 (2020).
26. A. Wang, "private communication".
27. R. Carballo-Rubio, F. Di Filippo, S. Liberati, C. Pacilio, and M. Visser, JHEP **07**, 023 (2018), arXiv:1805.02675 [gr-qc].
28. A. Bonanno, A.-P. Khosravi, and F. Saueressig, Phys. Rev. D **103**, 124027 (2021), arXiv:2010.04226 [gr-qc].
29. M. Bertipagani, M. Rinaldi, L. Sebastiani, and S. Zerbini, Phys. Dark Univ. **33**, 100853 (2021), arXiv:2012.15645 [gr-qc].
30. F. S. N. Lobo, Int. J. Mod. Phys. D **25**, 1630017 (2016), arXiv:1604.02082 [gr-qc].
31. G. J. Olmo, D. Rubiera-Garcia, and A. Sanchez-Puente, in *14th Marcel Grossmann Meeting on Recent Developments in Theoretical and Experimental General Relativity, Astrophysics, and Relativistic Field Theories*, Vol. 2 (2017) pp. 1391–1396, arXiv:1601.00161 [gr-qc].
32. C. Bambi, A. Cardenas-Avendano, G. J. Olmo, and D. Rubiera-Garcia, Phys. Rev. D **93**, 064016 (2016), arXiv:1511.03755 [gr-qc].

Strange quark stars in Hořava gravity

Grigoris Panotopoulos

Departamento de Ciencias Físicas, Universidad de la Frontera, Casilla 54-D, 4811186 Temuco, Chile
grigorios.panotopoulos@ufrontera.cl

Non-rotating strange quark stars made of isotropic matter in Lorentz-violating theories of gravity are studied. In particular, Hořava gravity and Einstein-æther theory are considered. For quark matter we adopt both linear and non-linear equations-of-state, corresponding to the MIT bag model and color flavor locked phase, respectively. The new, modified structure equations generalize the usual Tolman-Oppenheimer-Volkoff equations valid in Einstein's General Relativity. A dimensionless parameter ν measures the deviation from the standard TOV equations, which are recovered in the appropriate limit. We compute some properties, such as masses, radii as well as the factor of compactness of the stars, and we show pictorially the impact of the parameter ν on the mass-to-radius relationships for several different equations-of-state. Other physical considerations, such as stability criteria, causality and energy conditions, are also considered, and they are all found to be fulfilled.

Keywords: Relativistic stars; Composition of astronomical objects; Theories of gravity other than GR.

1. Introduction

Einstein's General Relativity (GR)[1] is a relativistic, geometric theory of gravitation, which not only is beautiful but also very successful.[2,3] The classical tests and solar system tests,[4] and recently the direct detection of gravitational waves by the LIGO/VIRGO Collaborations[5] have confirmed a series of remarkable predictions of GR.

Despite its success, however, it it believed that GR must be somehow extended for several different reasons. One may mention, for example, the current cosmic acceleration,[6,7] one of the most dramatic discoveries in Cosmology in the end of the 90's. If a modified theory of gravity is assumed, correction terms to GR on cosmological scales are expected to appear, and those terms of geometrical origin could play the role of dark energy,[8] the fluid component that dominates the expansion of the Universe at late time. In this class of models one finds for instance $f(R)$ theories of gravity,[9–12] brane models[13–15] and scalar-tensor theories of gravity.[16–18]

Moreover, it has been known for a long time that GR is a classical, non-renormalizable theory of gravitation. A theory of gravity incorporating quantum mechanics in a consistent way is still one of the biggest challenges in Modern Theoretical Physics. In 2009 Hořava gravity[19,20] was proposed as a new candidate theory for quantum gravity which explicitly breaks Lorentz invariance at any energy scale by introducing a preferred foliation of spacetime. Since then a lot of work has been done to prove, very successfully, its renormalizability by means of both power-counting arguments[21–26] and quantum field theory approaches.[27–30] Besides, a lot of effort has been made in order to investigate its phenomenological implications, e.g. concerning late-time Cosmology,[31,32] black hole physics,[33–39] binary systems,[40–42] and interior solutions of anisotropic stars.[43–45] In particular, after the multiple detections of gravitational waves by the LIGO-VIRGO Collaboration, and in particular the first merger observed from a binary of neutron stars,[46] a new era for gravitational astronomy get started. Very interestingly, Hořava gravity passes with flying colors all the theoretical and observational constraints which are available to date.[47] It is worth noticing that in the low-energy limit of Hořava gravity, its action written in a covariant form becomes equivalent to Einstein-æther theory[48] once the æther vector is restricted to be hypersurface-orthogonal at the level of the action.[49] In spherical symmetry it can be shown that the two theories share the same solutions.[50]

Therefore, it has become even more urgent to investigate the astrophysical implications and predictions of viable alternative theories of gravity, in order to explore non-standard scenarios and the possible signatures of deviations from GR to be observed in the forthcoming missions/space-based detectors. In this respect, compact objects,[51–53] such as neutron stars and white dwarfs, are relativistic stars of astrophysical and astronomical interest, which are characterized by ultra dense matter content and strong gravitational fields. Thanks to their properties, naturally they serve as ideal cosmic laboratories to study, test and constrain non-standard physics as well as non-conventional theories of gravity.

A new class of theoritized compact objects, that may be an alternative to neutron stars, are some as of today hypothetical objects which are supposed to be made of quark matter, and for that reason they are called strange quark stars.[54–59] Quark matter is by assumption absolutely stable,[60,61] and so it could be the true ground state of hadrons. That property provides us with a plausible explanation of some puzzling super-luminous supernovae,[62,63] which occur in about one out of every 1000 supernovae explosions, and which are more than 100 times more luminous than regular supernovae.

Our work is organized as follows. In Sec. 2 we briefly review the basics of Hořava gravity, and its connection to Einstein-æther theory, while in Sec. 3 we present the field equations as well as the structure equations describing hydrostatic equilibrium of static, spherically symmetric relativistic stars made of isotropic matter. In Sec. 4 we obtain and discuss our numerical results for quark stars. Finally, we finish our work with some concluding remarks in Sec. 5. We adopt the mostly negative metric signature $+,-,-,-$, and we work in natural units where $\hbar = 1 = c$. In those units all dimensionful quantities are measured in GeV $= 10^3$ MeV, and we make use of the conversion rules: 1 m $= 5.068 \times 10^{15}$ GeV^{-1} and 1 kg $= 5.610 \times 10^{26}$ GeV.[64]

2. Hořava gravity and Einstein-æther theory

The action of Hořava gravity[19,20] can be written in the preferred foliation as

$$S_H = \frac{1}{16\pi G_H} \int dT d^3x \sqrt{-g} \left(K_{ij}K^{ij} - \lambda K^2 + \xi \mathcal{R} + \eta a_i a^i + \frac{L_4}{M_*^2} + \frac{L_6}{M_*^4} \right) + S_m[g_{\mu\nu}, \psi], \tag{1}$$

where G_H is the effective gravitational constant; g is the determinant of the metric $g_{\mu\nu}$; $\mathcal{R}$ is the Ricci scalar of the three-dimensional constant-T hypersurfaces; K_{ij} is the extrinsic curvature and K is its trace; and $a_i = \partial_i \ln N$, where N is the lapse function and S_m is the matter action where ψ collectively denotes the matter fields. The constant couplings $\{\lambda, \xi, \eta\}$ are dimensionless, and GR is identically recovered when they take the values $\{1, 1, 0\}$, respectively. Furthermore, L_4 and L_6 stand for the fourth-order and sixth-order operators respectively, which are suppressed by a characteristic mass scale M_*.

In the following, we consider the covariantized version of the low-energy limit of Hořava gravity, named the *khronometric* model, that is obtained by keeping only the operators up to second-order derivatives, which amounts to discarding L_4 and L_6 which instead contain the higher-order operators.

In order to write the action covariantly, let us first take the action of Einstein-æther theory:[48]

$$S_\ae = \frac{1}{16\pi G_\ae} \int d^4x \sqrt{-g} \left(-R + L_\ae \right) + S_m[g_{\mu\nu}, \psi], \tag{2}$$

where $G_\ae$ is the "bare" gravitational constant; R is the four-dimensional Ricci scalar; u^a is a timelike vector field of unit norm, *i.e.*, $g_{\mu\nu}u^\mu u^\nu = 1$, from now on referred to as the "æther"; and

$$L_\ae = -M^{\alpha\beta}{}_{\mu\nu} \nabla_\alpha u^\mu \nabla_\beta u^\nu, \tag{3}$$

with $M^{\alpha\beta}{}_{\mu\nu}$ defined as

$$M^{\alpha\beta}{}_{\mu\nu} = c_1 g^{\alpha\beta} g_{\mu\nu} + c_2 \delta^\alpha_\mu \delta^\beta_\nu + c_3 \delta^\alpha_\nu \delta^\beta_\mu + c_4 u^\alpha u^\beta g_{\mu\nu}, \tag{4}$$

where c_i's are dimensionless coupling constants.

Once the æther vector is taken to be hypersurface-orthogonal at the level of the action, that is

$$u_\alpha = \frac{\partial_\alpha T}{\sqrt{g^{\mu\nu} \partial_\mu T \partial_\nu T}}, \tag{5}$$

where the preferred time T is a scalar field (the *khronon*) which defines the preferred foliation, then the two actions in Eqs. (1) and (2) become equivalent if the parameters of the two theories are mapped into each other as[49]

$$\frac{G_H}{G_\ae} = \xi = \frac{1}{1 - c_{13}}, \qquad \frac{\lambda}{\xi} = 1 + c_2, \qquad \frac{\eta}{\xi} = c_{14}, \tag{6}$$

where $c_{ij} = c_i + c_j$. Moreover $G_æ = G_N(1 - \eta/2\xi)$, where G_N is the Newton's constant, which is needed to recover the Newtonian limit.[20,65] In what follows, we will thus consider the covariant formulation of the low-energy limit of Hořava gravity.

The variation of the action in Eq. (2) with respect to $g^{\alpha\beta}$ and T yields, respectively,[42]

$$G_{\alpha\beta} - T^{æ}_{\alpha\beta} = 8\pi G_æ T^{m}_{\alpha\beta}, \tag{7}$$

$$\partial_\mu \left(\frac{1}{\sqrt{\nabla^\alpha T \nabla_\alpha T}} \sqrt{-g} Æ^\mu \right) = 0, \tag{8}$$

where $G_{\alpha\beta} = R_{\alpha\beta} - R g_{\alpha\beta}/2$ is the Einstein tensor,

$$T^{æ}_{\alpha\beta} = \nabla_\mu \left(J_{(\alpha}{}^\mu u_{\beta)} - J^\mu{}_{(\alpha} u_{\beta)} - J_{(\alpha\beta)} u^\mu \right) + c_1 \left[(\nabla_\mu u_\alpha)(\nabla^\mu u_\beta) - (\nabla_\alpha u_\mu)(\nabla_\beta u^\mu) \right]$$
$$+ \left[u_\nu(\nabla_\mu J^{\mu\nu}) - c_4 \dot{u}^2 \right] u_\alpha u_\beta + c_4 \dot{u}_\alpha \dot{u}_\beta - \frac{1}{2} L_æ g_{\alpha\beta} + 2Æ_{(\alpha} u_{\beta)} \tag{9}$$

is the khronon stress-energy tensor,

$$J^\alpha{}_\mu = M^{\alpha\beta}{}_{\mu\nu} \nabla_\beta u^\nu, \quad \dot{u}_\nu = u^\mu \nabla_\mu u_\nu, \quad Æ_\mu = (\nabla_\alpha J^{\alpha\nu} - c_4 \dot{u}_\alpha \nabla^\nu u^\alpha)(g_{\mu\nu} - u_\mu u_\nu), \tag{10}$$

and $T^m_{\alpha\beta}$ is the matter stress-energy tensor, defined as

$$T^m_{\alpha\beta} = \frac{2}{\sqrt{-g}} \frac{\delta S_m}{\delta g^{\alpha\beta}}. \tag{11}$$

3. Field equations

The most general static, spherically symmetric geometry, in Schwarzschild-like coordinates, may be written down as follows

$$ds^2 = e^{A(r)} dt^2 - B(r) dr^2 - r^2 \left(d\theta^2 + \sin^2\theta d\phi^2 \right). \tag{12}$$

In addition, let us consider an interior spacetime filled by an isotropic fluid whose stress-energy tensor is

$$T^m_{\alpha\beta} = (\rho + p) v_\alpha v_\beta - p g_{\alpha\beta}, \tag{13}$$

where ρ is the density and p is the pressure of the fluid, and its 4-velocity v^α is given by

$$v^\alpha = \left(e^{-A(r)/2}, 0, 0, 0 \right). \tag{14}$$

The æther vector field, which is by definition a unit timelike vector, in spherical symmetry is always hypersurface-orthogonal and takes the following general form:

$$u^\alpha = \left(F(r), \sqrt{\frac{e^{A(r)} F(r)^2 - 1}{B(r)}}, 0, 0 \right). \tag{15}$$

However, in the following we will consider the case of a static aether which is aligned with the interior matter fluid 4-velocity v^α, i.e. when $F(r) = e^{-A(r)/2}$, which leads to

$$u^\alpha = \left(e^{-A(r)/2}, 0, 0, 0\right). \tag{16}$$

The field equations that we have to consider are the modified Einstein equations (0-0), (1-1) and (2-2) in Eq. (7), which can be written respectively as:

$$-\nu\left[4r^2 A''(r) - \frac{2r^2 A'(r)B'(r)}{B(r)} + r^2 A'(r)^2 + 8rA'(r)\right] + \frac{rB'(r)}{B(r)} + B(r) - 1$$
$$= 8\pi G_\text{æ} r^2 B(r)\rho(r), \tag{17}$$

$$\nu r^2 A'(r)^2 + rA'(r) - B(r) + 1 = 8\pi G_\text{æ} r^2 B(r) p(r), \tag{18}$$

$$\frac{1}{2}r^2 A''(r) - \frac{r^2 A'(r)B'(r)}{4B(r)} - \nu r^2 A'(r)^2 + \frac{1}{4}r^2 A'(r)^2 + \frac{1}{2}rA'(r) - \frac{rB'(r)}{2B(r)}$$
$$= 8\pi G_\text{æ} r^2 B(r) p(r), \tag{19}$$

where $\nu = \frac{\eta}{8\xi}$. Furthermore, Eq. (8) is identically satisfied. In the following we shall set $8\pi G_\text{æ} = 1$. Finally, the conservation equation for the energy-momentum tensor takes the form

$$p'(r) + \frac{1}{2}A'(r)\left[\rho(r) + p(r)\right] = 0. \tag{20}$$

Notice that the standard Tolman-Oppenheimmer-Volkoff (TOV) equations,[66-69] which hold in GR,[1] are recovered setting $\nu = 0$ in the equations above.

Despite the fact that there are four equations in total, it turns out that only three of them are independent. Furthermore, since spherically symmetric solutions in Hořava gravity are identical to those of Einstein-æther theory, all of our conclusions will hold for both theories.[50]

In order to derive the modified TOV equations that will be used for the numerical integration, one can obtain $A'(r)$ from Eq. (18):

$$A'(r) = -\frac{r - r\sqrt{4\nu r^2 B(r)p(r) + 4\nu B(r) - 4\nu + 1}}{2\nu r^2}, \tag{21}$$

which corresponds to the only branch which admits the proper GR limit when $\nu \to 0$. Then, one has to substitute the latter in Eq. (17) and Eq. (20), that for brevity we do not show here. However, one can immediately notice the difference with respect to GR, since here the parameter ν (which in GR is identically zero) enters non-linearly in the resulting equations.

4. Properties of strange quark stars: Numerical treatment

In this section we investigate the properties of strange quark stars within the Lorentz-violating theories of gravity at hand. We integrate numerically the generalized structure equations, and after that we present and discuss the results.

4.1. *Vacuum solution*

In order to compute the radius and the mass of the objects, we need to match the solutions at the surface of the stars. For that we need to know the exterior (vacuum) solution first, and so we set the stress-energy tensor (i.e. both the pressure and the energy density of the matter content) to zero.

In order to calculate the total gravitational mass M of the fluid star appearing in the Newtonian potential, we will make use of the general vacuum solution found in Ref. 70 and summarized below:

$$e^A = \left(\frac{1 - Y/Y_-}{1 - Y/Y_+}\right)^{\frac{-Y_+}{2+Y_+}}, \tag{22}$$

$$B = \nu(Y - Y_-)(Y - Y_+), \tag{23}$$

$$\frac{r_{\min}}{r} = \left(\frac{Y}{Y - Y_-}\right)\left(\frac{Y - Y_-}{Y - Y_+}\right)^{\frac{1}{2+Y_+}}, \tag{24}$$

where $Y = rA'$, $Y_\pm = (-1 \pm \sqrt{1 - 4\nu})/(2\nu)$, and $r_{\min}$ is an integration constant which is related to the gravitational radius $r_g = 2G_N M$ by

$$r_{\min}/r_g = (-Y_+)^{-1}(-1 - Y_+)^{(1+Y_+)/(2+Y_+)}. \tag{25}$$

The above solution agrees with the Schwarzschild solution[71] of GR to leading order in $1/r$.

4.2. *Equation-of-state*

Before we start integrating the structure equations, we must specify the matter content first, or in other words pick up a certain equation-of-state. Quark matter inside stars is commobly described by the MIT bag model.[72,73] In the simplest version there is a linear analytic function relating the energy density to the pressure of the fluid, which reads

$$p = k(\rho - \rho_s), \tag{26}$$

where k is a dimensionless numerical factor, while ρ_s is the surface energy density. The MIT bag model is characterized by 3 parameters, namely i) the QCD coupling constant, α_c, ii) the mass of the strange (s) quark, m_s, and iii) the bag constant, B_0. In this work we shall consider the following 3 models:[74]

- The extreme model SQSB40 where $m_s = 100$ MeV, $\alpha_c = 0.6$ and $B_0 = 40$ MeV fm^{-3}. In this model $k = 0.324$ and $\rho_s = 3.0563 \times 10^{14}$ g cm^{-3}.

- The standard model SQSB56 where $m_s = 200$ MeV, $\alpha_c = 0.2$ and $B_0 = 56$ MeV fm^{-3}. In this model $k = 0.301$ and $\rho_s = 4.4997 \times 10^{14}$ g cm^{-3}.
- The simplified model SQSB60 where $m_s = 0 = \alpha_c$ and $B_0 = 60$ MeV fm^{-3}. In this model $k = 1/3$ and $\rho_s = 4.2785 \times 10^{14}$ g cm^{-3}.

Furthermore, at asymptotically large densities color superconductivity effects[75,76] become important. Quark matter is found to be in the so called color flavor locked (CFL) state,[77,78] in which quarks form Cooper pairs of different color and flavor, and where all quarks have the same Fermi momentum and electrons cannot be present. That quark state is described by a slightly more complicated equation of state (EoS), although still an analytic function, and it is given by the following non-linear relation[79-81]

$$\rho = 3p + 4B_0 - \frac{9\gamma\mu^2}{\pi^2}, \tag{27}$$

where γ and μ^2 are given by

$$\gamma = \frac{2\Delta^2}{3} - \frac{m_s^2}{6}, \tag{28}$$

and

$$\mu^2 = -3\gamma + \left(9\gamma^2 + \frac{4}{3}\pi^2(B_0 + p)\right)^{1/2}, \tag{29}$$

with Δ being the non-vanishing energy gap.

In the CFL state there are 19 viable models, but here we shall consider two, namely CFL4 and CFL10, characterized by the following parameters (look at table I in Ref. 81):

$$\Delta = 100 \text{ MeV}, \tag{30}$$
$$m_s = 150 \text{ MeV}, \tag{31}$$
$$B_0 = 60 \text{ MeV fm}^{-3}, \tag{32}$$

for CFL4, and

$$\Delta = 150 \text{ MeV}, \tag{33}$$
$$m_s = 150 \text{ MeV}, \tag{34}$$
$$B_0 = 80 \text{ MeV fm}^{-3}, \tag{35}$$

for CFL10.

4.3. *Numerical solution of structure equations*

The radius of the stars, R, is determined from the requirement that $p(r = R) = 0$, while the mass of the stars, M, is computed numerically using the vacuum solution presented before, and requiring that $B_{int}(r = R) = B_{ext}(r = R)$. Finally, the compactness of the object is computed by $C = G_N M/R$.

Our main numerical results are summarized in the figures below. At this point it should be mentioned that the 3 observed super-massive pulsars J1614-2230 $((1.928 \pm 0.017)\ M_\odot)$,[82,83] J0348+0432 $((2.01 \pm 0.04)\ M_\odot)$[84] and J0740+6620 $((2.14^{+0.20}_{-0.18})\ M_\odot)$,[85] with masses $M \sim 2 M_\odot$ have put stringent constraints on compact object modelling, since any EoS that does not cross the 2 solar mass strip must be ruled out. Furthermore, the recent observation of the highly massive pulsar in the binary J2215 + 5135 $((2.27^{+0.17}_{-0.15})\ M_\odot)$[86] has put an even more tight constraint to be satisfied. However, our results will also depend on the assumed EoS, as the predicted mass-to-radius profiles are affected. For that reason, our goal is not to show that the models discussed here are able to pass all current tests, but just to study the general features of quark stars in the framework of Hořava gravity and Einstein-æther theory, and the impact of the modifications that they induce on the resulting mass-radius relationships. Moreover, the reader should also keep in mind that electrically charged stars or compact objects with anisotropic matter can have higher masses compared to their isotropic neutral counterparts, see e.g. Refs. 87, 88 and references therein.

In Fig. 1 we show the mass-to-radius (M_R) relations (left panel) and the compactness (right panel) of the quark stars with a linear EoS. Similarly, Fig. 2 shows the same properties of the stars with a non-linear EoS. We see that the M_R profiles are shifted downwards as the parameter ν increases. Therefore, if the highest star mass that a given EoS can support is lower than the 2 solar mass limit in GR, it will become even worse in Hořava gravity and Einstein-æther theory.

The speed of sound, defined by $c_s^2 \equiv dp/d\rho$, is shown in Fig. 3 for the models CFL4 and CFL10, while when the EoS is linear the sound speed is just a constant, $c_s^2 = k$. We have considered the cases where $\nu = 0.01, 0.02$, while for GR the speed of sound for the 19 CFL viable models can be seen in Fig. 2 (panel (b)) of Ref. 81. Clearly, throughout the object the speed of sound takes values in the range $0 < c_s^2 < 1$, as it should, and therefore causality is not violated. It should be stated that for each model the 2 curves corresponding to a different value of the parameter ν are indistinguishable.

The solutions obtained here should be able to describe realistic astrophysical configurations. Therefore, as a final check we investigate i) stability criteria, and ii) if the energy conditions are fulfilled or not. For the latter, we require that[89–93]

$$\rho \geq 0, \tag{36}$$

$$\rho - p \geq 0, \tag{37}$$

$$\rho - 3p \geq 0. \tag{38}$$

In Fig. 4 we show the normalized pressure, $\bar{p} \equiv p/B_0$, $3\bar{p}$, and normalized energy density, $\bar{\rho} \equiv \rho/B_0$ (from bottom to top) versus the normalized radial coordinate r/R for $\nu = 0.01, 0.02$ and $p_c(0) = 1.5\ B_0$ for the models CFL4 and CFL10. Notice that the lower curves corresponding to $\bar{p}$ and $3\bar{p}$ are indistinguishable for all four

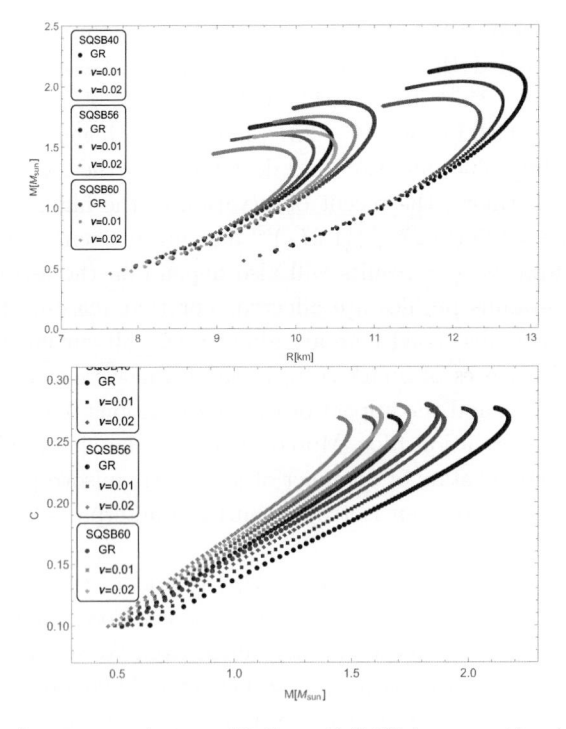

Fig. 1. Properties of strange quark stars with linear EoS. We have considered 3 MIT bag models, SQSB40 (in black), SQSB56 (in blue) and SQSB60 (in red) (see text) and $\nu = 0.01, 0.02$. The curves corresponding to GR ($\nu = 0$) are also shown for comparison reasons. **TOP:** M_R profiles (mass in solar masses and radius in km). **BOTTOM:** Compactness $C = G_N M/R$ vs mass (in solar masses).

cases, while the upper curves corresponding to the normalized energy density are clearly different for the two models. However, within each model the two curves corresponding to the two values of ν cannot be told apart. Regarding the models with a linear EoS we have obtained qualitatively very similar curves, which we do not show here. Clearly, all energy conditions are fulfilled throughout the star, and therefore we conclude that the solutions obtained here are realistic one, capable of describing realistic astrophysical configurations.

Regarding stability criteria, Bondi[94] suggested that for a stable Newtonian sphere the adiabatic index defined by

$$\Gamma \equiv c_s^2 \left[1 + \frac{\rho}{p}\right] \tag{39}$$

should be larger than 4/3. Moreover, the Harrison-Zeldovich-Novikov criterion requires that[95,96]

$$\frac{dM}{d\rho_c} > 0 \tag{40}$$

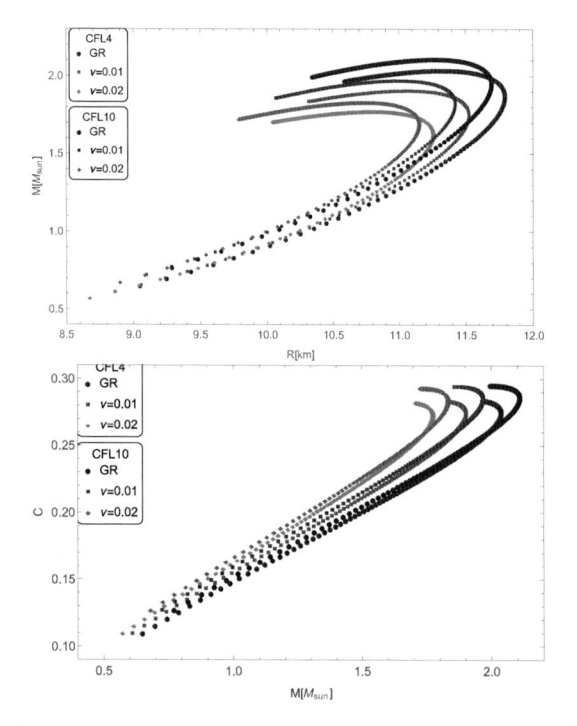

Fig. 2. Properties of strange quark stars with a non-linear EoS. We have considered 2 CFL models, CFL4 (in blue) and CFL10 (in black) (see text) and $\nu = 0.01, 0.02$. The curves corresponding to GR ($\nu = 0$) are also shown for comparison reasons. **TOP:** M_R profiles (mass in solar masses and radius in km). **BOTTOM:** Compactness $C = G_N M/R$ vs mass (in solar masses).

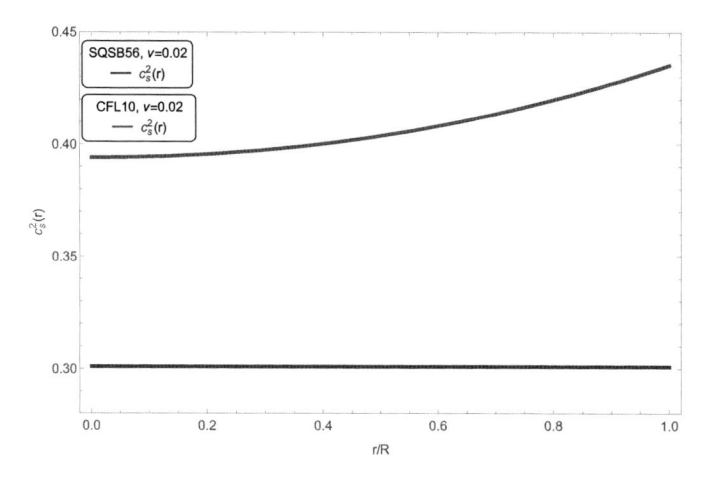

Fig. 3. Speed of sound, $c_s^2 = dp/d\rho$, vs normalized radial coordinate r/R for $\nu = 0.01, 0.02$ and for 2 color flavor locked states, CFL4 model (lower curves) and CFL10 model (upper curves) and for $\nu = 0.01, 0.02$.

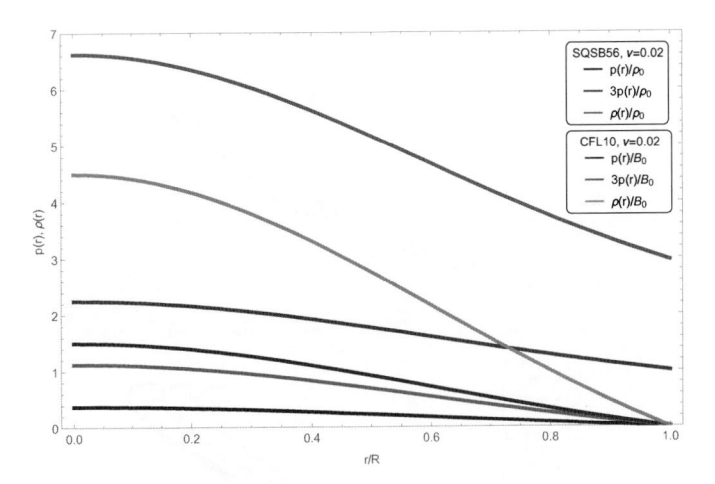

Fig. 4. Normalized pressure $\bar{p} \equiv p/B_0$, $3\bar{p}$ and energy density $\bar{\rho} \equiv \rho/B_0$ vs normalized radial coordinate r/R for $p_c = 1.5\,B_0$, $\nu = 0.01, 0.02$ and for 2 color flavor locked states, CFL4 model and CFL10 model. Shown are from bottom to top: i) Pressure (blue), ii) 3 times pressure (green), and iii) energy density (orange) for CFL 4 (upper) and for CFL10 (lower).

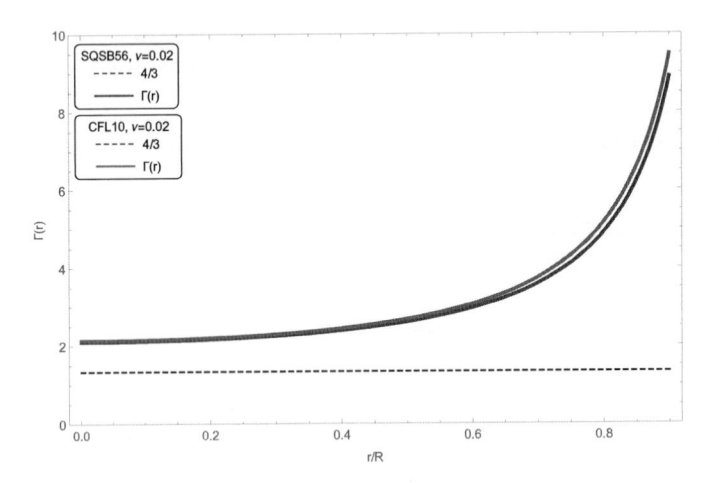

Fig. 5. Adiabatic index Γ vs normalized radial coordinate r/R for the model SQSB56 (linear EoS) and $\nu = 0.02$. The dashed horizontal line represents the Newtonian bound corresponding to 4/3.

Fig. 5 shows that $\Gamma > 4/3$, as it should be. In Fig. 5 we have shown the adiabatic index only for one particular case, but we have checked that we have obtained almost identical figures for all the cases considered in the present work.

5. Conclusions

In summary, we have investigated in detail the properties of non-rotating, isotropic strange quark stars in Lorentz-violating theories of gravity. To be more precise, we have studied quark stars both in Hořava gravity and Einstein-æther theory, where a single dimensionless parameter ν measures the deviations from GR. As far as the EoS for the matter content is concerned, we adopted analytic functions, both linear and non-linear. The former corresponds to simple versions of the MIT bag model, while the latter corresponds to the CFL phase, where color superconductivity effects become important at very high densities. We numerically integrated the generalized structure equations, and we computed the factor of compactness, the radii and the masses of the objects upon matching the interior and the exterior solutions at the surface of the stars. We have presented graphically the mass-to-radius profiles for several different EoSs as well as for two distinct values of the parameter ν. The case $\nu = 0$ corresponding to GR is shown as well for comparison reasons. Our results show that the $M - R$ relationships are shifted downwards as ν increases, which implies a lower highest mass supported by a given EoS in comparison with the one obtained in GR for the same EoS. Finally, we have checked that causality is not violated, stability criteria are met, and energy conditions are fulfilled. Therefore we conclude that within the framework of the gravitational theories considered here, we have obtained well behaved solutions capable of describing realistic astrophysical configurations.

Acknowledgements

I wish to thank professor A. Wang for inviting me to MG-16, and the organizers for an excellent organization. I thank my colleagues I. Lopes and D. Vernieri for a fruitful collaboration. The work was financially supported by the Fundação para a Ciência e Tecnologia (FCT), Portugal, through the Project No. UIDB/FIS/00099/2020 and grant No. PTDC/FIS-AST/28920/2017.

References

1. A. Einstein, Annalen Phys. **49**, no. 7, 769 (1916).
2. S. G. Turyshev, Ann. Rev. Nucl. Part. Sci. **58** (2008) 207.
3. C. M. Will, Living Rev. Rel. **17** (2014) 4.
4. E. Asmodelle, arXiv:1705.04397 [gr-qc].
5. B. P. Abbott et al. [LIGO Scientific and Virgo Collaborations], Phys. Rev. Lett. **116** (2016) no. 6, 061102 [arXiv:1602.03837 [gr-qc]].
6. A. G. Riess et al. Astron. J. 116, 1009 (1998).
7. S. Perlmutter et al., Astrophys. J. 517, 565 (1999).
8. E. J. Copeland, M. Sami and S. Tsujikawa, Int. J. Mod. Phys. D **15** (2006) 1753 [hep-th/0603057].
9. T. P. Sotiriou and V. Faraoni, Rev. Mod. Phys. **82** (2010) 451 [arXiv:0805.1726 [gr-qc]].
10. A. De Felice and S. Tsujikawa, Living Rev. Rel. **13** (2010) 3 [arXiv:1002.4928 [gr-qc]].

11. W. Hu and I. Sawicki, Phys. Rev. D **76** (2007) 064004 [arXiv:0705.1158 [astro-ph]].
12. A. A. Starobinsky, JETP Lett. **86** (2007) 157.
13. D. Langlois, Prog. Theor. Phys. Suppl. **148** (2003) 181 [hep-th/0209261].
14. R. Maartens, Living Rev. Rel. **7** (2004) 7 [gr-qc/0312059].
15. G. R. Dvali, G. Gabadadze and M. Porrati, Phys. Lett. B **485** (2000) 208 [hep-th/0005016].
16. C. Brans and R. H. Dicke, Phys. Rev. **124** (1961) 925.
17. C. H. Brans, Phys. Rev. **125**, 2194 (1962).
18. J. C. B. Sanchez and L. Perivolaropoulos, Phys. Rev. D **81** (2010) 103505 [arXiv:1002.2042 [astro-ph.CO]].
19. P. Horava, Phys. Rev. D **79**, 084008 (2009) [arXiv:0901.3775 [hep-th]].
20. D. Blas, O. Pujolas and S. Sibiryakov, Phys. Rev. Lett. **104**, 181302 (2010) [arXiv:0909.3525 [hep-th]].
21. M. Visser, Phys. Rev. D **80**, 025011 (2009) [arXiv:0902.0590 [hep-th]].
22. T. P. Sotiriou, M. Visser and S. Weinfurtner, Phys. Rev. Lett. **102**, 251601 (2009) [arXiv:0904.4464 [hep-th]].
23. T. P. Sotiriou, M. Visser and S. Weinfurtner, JHEP **0910**, 033 (2009) [arXiv:0905.2798 [hep-th]].
24. D. Vernieri and T. P. Sotiriou, Phys. Rev. D **85**, 064003 (2012) [arXiv:1112.3385 [hep-th]].
25. D. Vernieri and T. P. Sotiriou, J. Phys. Conf. Ser. **453**, 012022 (2013) [arXiv:1212.4402 [hep-th]].
26. D. Vernieri, Phys. Rev. D **91**, no. 12, 124029 (2015) [arXiv:1502.06607 [hep-th]].
27. G. D'Odorico, F. Saueressig and M. Schutten, Phys. Rev. Lett. **113**, no. 17, 171101 (2014) [arXiv:1406.4366 [gr-qc]].
28. A. O. Barvinsky, D. Blas, M. Herrero-Valea, S. M. Sibiryakov and C. F. Steinwachs, Phys. Rev. D **93**, no. 6, 064022 (2016) [arXiv:1512.02250 [hep-th]].
29. A. O. Barvinsky, D. Blas, M. Herrero-Valea, S. M. Sibiryakov and C. F. Steinwachs, JHEP **1807**, 035 (2018) [arXiv:1705.03480 [hep-th]].
30. A. O. Barvinsky, M. Herrero-Valea and S. M. Sibiryakov, Phys. Rev. D **100**, no. 2, 026012 (2019) [arXiv:1905.03798 [hep-th]].
31. B. Audren, D. Blas, M. M. Ivanov, J. Lesgourgues and S. Sibiryakov, JCAP **1503**, no. 03, 016 (2015) [arXiv:1410.6514 [astro-ph.CO]].
32. N. Frusciante, M. Raveri, D. Vernieri, B. Hu and A. Silvestri, Phys. Dark Univ. **13**, 7 (2016) [arXiv:1508.01787 [astro-ph.CO]].
33. D. Blas and S. Sibiryakov, Phys. Rev. D **84**, 124043 (2011) [arXiv:1110.2195 [hep-th]].
34. E. Barausse, T. Jacobson and T. P. Sotiriou, Phys. Rev. D **83**, 124043 (2011) [arXiv:1104.2889 [gr-qc]].
35. P. Berglund, J. Bhattacharyya and D. Mattingly, Phys. Rev. D **85**, 124019 (2012) [arXiv:1202.4497 [hep-th]].
36. E. Barausse and T. P. Sotiriou, Phys. Rev. D **87**, 087504 (2013) [arXiv:1212.1334 [gr-qc]].
37. A. Wang, Phys. Rev. Lett. **110**, no. 9, 091101 (2013) [arXiv:1212.1876 [hep-th]].
38. E. Barausse and T. P. Sotiriou, Class. Quant. Grav. **30**, 244010 (2013) [arXiv:1307.3359 [gr-qc]].
39. T. P. Sotiriou, I. Vega and D. Vernieri, Phys. Rev. D **90**, no. 4, 044046 (2014) [arXiv:1405.3715 [gr-qc]].
40. K. Yagi, D. Blas, N. Yunes and E. Barausse, Phys. Rev. Lett. **112**, no. 16, 161101 (2014) [arXiv:1307.6219 [gr-qc]].

41. K. Yagi, D. Blas, E. Barausse and N. Yunes, Phys. Rev. D **89**, no. 8, 084067 (2014) Erratum: [Phys. Rev. D **90**, no. 6, 069902 (2014)] Erratum: [Phys. Rev. D **90**, no. 6, 069901 (2014)] [arXiv:1311.7144 [gr-qc]].
42. O. Ramos and E. Barausse, Phys. Rev. D **99**, no. 2, 024034 (2019) [arXiv:1811.07786 [gr-qc]].
43. D. Vernieri and S. Carloni, EPL **121**, no. 3, 30002 (2018) [arXiv:1706.06608 [gr-qc]].
44. D. Vernieri, Phys. Rev. D **98**, no. 2, 024051 (2018) [arXiv:1808.00974 [gr-qc]].
45. D. Vernieri, Phys. Rev. D **100**, no. 10, 104021 (2019) [arXiv:1906.07738 [gr-qc]].
46. B. P. Abbott *et al.* [LIGO Scientific and Virgo and Fermi-GBM and INTEGRAL Collaborations], Astrophys. J. **848**, no. 2, L13 (2017) [arXiv:1710.05834 [astro-ph.HE]].
47. A. Emir Gümrükçüoğlu, M. Saravani and T. P. Sotiriou, Phys. Rev. D **97**, no. 2, 024032 (2018) [arXiv:1711.08845 [gr-qc]].
48. T. Jacobson and D. Mattingly, Phys. Rev. D **64**, 024028 (2001) [gr-qc/0007031].
49. T. Jacobson, Phys. Rev. D **81**, 101502 (2010) Erratum: [Phys. Rev. D **82**, 129901 (2010)] [arXiv:1001.4823 [hep-th]].
50. D. Blas, O. Pujolas and S. Sibiryakov, JHEP **1104**, 018 (2011) [arXiv:1007.3503 [hep-th]].
51. S. L. Shapiro and S. A. Teukolsky, *Black holes, white dwarfs, and neutron stars: The physics of compact objects*, New York, USA: Wiley, 645 p. (1983).
52. D. Psaltis, Living Rev. Rel. **11**, 9 (2008) [arXiv:0806.1531 [astro-ph]].
53. D. R. Lorimer, Living Rev. Rel. **11**, 8 (2008) [arXiv:0811.0762 [astro-ph]].
54. C. Alcock, E. Farhi and A. Olinto, Astrophys. J. **310**, 261 (1986).
55. C. Alcock and A. Olinto, Ann. Rev. Nucl. Part. Sci. **38**, 161 (1988).
56. J. Madsen, Lect. Notes Phys. **516**, 162 (1999) [astro-ph/9809032].
57. F. Weber, Prog. Part. Nucl. Phys. **54**, 193 (2005) [astro-ph/0407155].
58. Y. L. Yue, X. H. Cui and R. X. Xu, Astrophys. J. **649**, L95 (2006) [astro-ph/0603468].
59. D. Leahy and R. Ouyed, Mon. Not. Roy. Astron. Soc. **387**, 1193 (2008) [arXiv:0708.1787 [astro-ph]].
60. E. Witten, Phys. Rev. D **30**, 272 (1984).
61. E. Farhi and R. L. Jaffe, Phys. Rev. D **30**, 2379 (1984).
62. E. O. Ofek *et al.*, Astrophys. J. **659**, L13 (2007) [astro-ph/0612408].
63. R. Ouyed, D. Leahy and P. Jaikumar, arXiv:0911.5424 [astro-ph.HE].
64. A. H. Guth, Phys. Rev. D **23**, 347 (1981) [Adv. Ser. Astrophys. Cosmol. **3**, 139 (1987)].
65. S. M. Carroll and E. A. Lim, Phys. Rev. D **70**, 123525 (2004) [hep-th/0407149].
66. R. C. Tolman, Phys. Rev. **55**, 364 (1939).
67. J. R. Oppenheimer and G. M. Volkoff, Phys. Rev. **55**, 374 (1939).
68. S. Carloni and D. Vernieri, Phys. Rev. D **97**, no. 12, 124056 (2018) [arXiv:1709.02818 [gr-qc]].
69. S. Carloni and D. Vernieri, Phys. Rev. D **97**, no. 12, 124057 (2018) [arXiv:1709.03996 [gr-qc]].
70. C. Eling and T. Jacobson, Class. Quant. Grav. **23**, 5625 (2006) Erratum: [Class. Quant. Grav. **27**, 049801 (2010)] [gr-qc/0603058].
71. K. Schwarzschild, Sitzungsber. Preuss. Akad. Wiss. Berlin (Math. Phys.) **1916**, 189 (1916) [physics/9905030].
72. A. Chodos, R. L. Jaffe, K. Johnson, C. B. Thorn and V. F. Weisskopf, Phys. Rev. D **9**, 3471 (1974).
73. A. Chodos, R. L. Jaffe, K. Johnson and C. B. Thorn, Phys. Rev. D **10**, 2599 (1974).
74. D. Gondek-Rosinska and F. Limousin, arXiv:0801.4829 [gr-qc].
75. M. G. Alford, K. Rajagopal and F. Wilczek, Phys. Lett. B **422**, 247 (1998) [hep-ph/9711395].

76. M. G. Alford, K. Rajagopal and F. Wilczek, Nucl. Phys. A **638**, 515C (1998) [hep-ph/9802284].
77. M. G. Alford, K. Rajagopal and F. Wilczek, Nucl. Phys. B **537**, 443 (1999) [hep-ph/9804403].
78. K. Rajagopal and F. Wilczek, Phys. Rev. Lett. **86**, 3492 (2001) [hep-ph/0012039].
79. G. Lugones and J. E. Horvath, Phys. Rev. D **66**, 074017 (2002) [hep-ph/0211070].
80. C. Vasquez Flores and G. Lugones, Phys. Rev. D **82**, 063006 (2010) [arXiv:1008.4882 [astro-ph.HE]].
81. C. V. Flores and G. Lugones, Phys. Rev. C **95**, no. 2, 025808 (2017) [arXiv:1702.02081 [astro-ph.HE]].
82. P. Demorest, T. Pennucci, S. Ransom, M. Roberts and J. Hessels, Nature **467**, 1081 (2010) [arXiv:1010.5788 [astro-ph.HE]].
83. E. Fonseca et al., Astrophys. J. **832**, no. 2, 167 (2016) [arXiv:1603.00545 [astro-ph.HE]].
84. J. Antoniadis et al., Science **340**, 6131 (2013) [arXiv:1304.6875 [astro-ph.HE]].
85. H. T. Cromartie et al., Nature Astronomy Letters (2019) [arXiv:1904.06759 [astro-ph.HE]].
86. M. Linares, T. Shahbaz and J. Casares, Astrophys. J. **859**, no. 1, 54 (2018) doi:10.3847/1538-4357/aabde6 [arXiv:1805.08799 [astro-ph.HE]].
87. G. Panotopoulos and Á. Rincón, Eur. Phys. J. C **79**, no. 6, 524 (2019).
88. I. Lopes, G. Panotopoulos and Á. Rincón, Eur. Phys. J. Plus **134**, no. 9, 454 (2019) [arXiv:1907.03549 [gr-qc]].
89. M. K. Mak and T. Harko, Chin. J. Astron. Astrophys. **2**, 248 (2002).
90. D. Deb, S. R. Chowdhury, S. Ray, F. Rahaman and B. K. Guha, Annals Phys. **387**, 239 (2017) [arXiv:1606.00713 [gr-qc]].
91. D. Deb, S. Roy Chowdhury, S. Ray and F. Rahaman, Gen. Rel. Grav. **50**, no. 9, 112 (2018) [arXiv:1509.00401 [gr-qc]].
92. P. Bhar, M. Govender and R. Sharma, Eur. Phys. J. C **77**, no. 2, 109 (2017) [arXiv:1607.06664 [gr-qc]].
93. G. Panotopoulos and Á. Rincón, Eur. Phys. J. Plus **134**, no. 9, 472 (2019) [arXiv:1907.03545 [gr-qc]].
94. H. Bondi, Proc. R. Soc. Lond. A **281** (1964) 39.
95. B. K. Harrison, *Gravitational Theory and Gravitational Collapse*, University of Chicago Press, Chicago, 1965.
96. Y. B. Zeldovich, and I. D. Novikov, *Relativistic Astrophysics, Vol. I: Stars and Relativity*, University of Chicago Press, Chicago, 1971.

Shadows of Kerr-like black holes in $4D$ Einstein–Gauss–Bonnet gravity and constraints from EHT observations

Sushant G. Ghosh

Centre for Theoretical Physics, Jamia Millia Islamia, New Delhi 110025, India
Astrophysics Research Centre, School of Mathematics, Statistics and Computer Science, University of KwaZulu-Natal, Private Bag 54001, Durban 4000, South Africa
E-mail: sghosh2@jmi.ac.in

Rahul Kumar Walia

Astrophysics Research Centre, School of Mathematics, Statistics and Computer Science, University of KwaZulu-Natal, Private Bag 54001, Durban 4000, South Africa
E-mail: rahul.phy3@gmail.com

The M87* black hole shadow observation by the Event Horizon Telescope (EHT) has enabled us to test the modified gravity theories in the extreme-field regime and estimating the black hole parameters. Having this assertion, we investigate the Kerr-like rotating black holes in $4D$ Einstein-Gauss-Bonnet (EGB) gravity and deduce their shadows. Considering the inclination angle $\theta_0 = 17^\circ$, we show that the EGB black hole shadows are smaller and more distorted than for the Kerr black holes. Modelling the M87* black hole as the EGB black hole, we predict the shadow angular size $35.7888\mu as \leq \theta_d \leq 39.6192\mu as$. The M87* black hole shadow angular size $\theta_d = 42\pm3\mu as$, within the 1σ region, constrains the GB coupling parameter and the black hole spin parameter. Interestingly, the circularity deviation of the EGB black hole shadows is smaller than the bounded deduced for the M87* black hole.

Keywords: EGB gravity, Shadows, Astrophysical black holes, Parameter Estimation, EHT, M87* black hole shadow

1. Introduction

The uniqueness of the Einstein tensor to describe gravity in the four-dimensional ($4D$) spacetime is dictated by the Lovelock theorem.[1] However, if one or more conditions in the Lovelock theorem are relaxed, then modifications to the Einstein-Hilbert action exist that lead to covariant, conserved, and second-order field equations and propagate only gravitational degrees of freedom and thus are free from the ghost instabilities. One such Lagrangian-based theory of gravity is Einstein-Gauss-Bonnet (EGB) gravity that exists in the $D \geq 5$ and is motivated by the heterotic string theory.[2,3] EGB gravity supplements the Einstein-Hilbert action with quadratic corrections terms constructed from the curvature tensors invariants and reads as follows

$$\mathcal{I}_{\text{EGB}} = \frac{1}{16\pi G_D} \int d^D x \sqrt{-g}(\mathcal{L}_{\text{EH}} + \alpha \mathcal{L}_{\text{GB}}), \tag{1}$$

with

$$\mathcal{L}_{\text{EH}} = R, \quad \mathcal{L}_{\text{GB}} = R^{\mu\nu\rho\sigma}R_{\mu\nu\rho\sigma} - 4R^{\mu\nu}R_{\mu\nu} + R^2. \tag{2}$$

Here, α is identified as the GB coupling constant and is related to the inverse string tension, making it positive-definite. The GB Lagrangian is a unique quadratic combination of the Riemann tensor that naturally emerges as a leading-order correction term in low-energy effective actions of heterotic string theory and $10D$ gauged supergravity. Boulware and Deser, in their seminal paper,[4] obtained the first spherically symmetric and static black hole solution for the EGB theory, afterward several intriguing black hole solutions are obtained.[5–7] It is worth mentioning that for $D < 5$ GB Lagrangian $\mathcal{L}_{GB}$ turns into a total derivative, and thereby its contribution to the gravitational dynamics vanishes, rendering the theory indistinguishable from general relativity. However, in the presence of an additional non-minimally coupled scalar field dilaton with the canonical kinetic term, $\mathcal{L}_{GB}$ leads to the non-trivial gravitational dynamics[8–11] and the resulting theory is Horndeski or Galilean.

Ever since the formulation of the EGB gravity theory, its $4D$ regularization has been a topic of great interest. In this line of research, Tomozawa[12] showed for the first time that the quantum corrections to gravity in a conformally flat metric in $4D$ appears as GB quadratic curvature forms, and the $4D$ black hole solution shows repulsive nature at $r \to 0$. In another attempt of regularization procedure, Cognolo et al.[13] used an "entropic" dimensional reduction of EGB gravity to $D \to 4$ within the classical Lagrangian formulation. Lately, the interest in the $4D$ EGB gravity theory is re-surged due to the regularization approach proposed by Glavan and Lin;[14] the GB coupling is re-scaled as $\alpha \to \alpha/(D-4)$ and the $4D$ EGB theory was obtained as the limit $D \to 4$ at the level of field equations. The aim for introducing this re-scaling is to generate a divergence that exactly cancels the vanishing contribution that the GB term makes to the field equations in $4D$. The extension to higher-order Lovelock gravity is presented in Refs.[15,16] Likewise, EGB theory is obtained in lower dimensions.[17,18] Interestingly, the Glavan and Lin's static and spherically symmetric black hole solution[14] matched with that obtained using the quantum correction by Tomozawa,[12] and Cognolo et al.[13]

However, Glavan and Lin's claim[14] that the resulting theory is of pure graviton was later proven to be spurious on several grounds. The covariant approach proposed in Ref.[14] is largely speculated to be valid only for specific higher-dimensional spacetimes with high degrees of symmetries, particularly maximally symmetric or spherically symmetric spacetimes. Recently, some studies have called into question the Glavan and Lin[14] regularization procedure for the less-symmetric spacetimes and also reported several other inconsistencies Refs.[17,19–22] Following that, the GB contribution arising in higher dimensions could be renormalized in such a way as to yield a non-trivial contribution also in $4D$, even without re-scaling the GB coupling.[16–18,23–26] Hennigar et al.[17] proposed another well defined $D \to 4$ limit of EGB gravity generalizing the previous work of Mann and Ross[27] in establishing the $D \to 2$ limit of general relativity and this regularization is applicable not only in $4D$ but also to $D < 4$. These alternate regularization procedures of EGB theory, leading to a divergence-free $4D$ action, describe the scalar-tensor theory of gravity of the Horndeski type. These scalar-tensor models propagate the supplementary scalar mode in addition to the gravitational degree of freedom. Thus these alternate regularized theories are in line with Lovelock's theorem, as they introduce another dynamical field. Nevertheless, the spherically symmetric $4D$ black hole solution obtained in Ref.[14] remains valid for these regularised scalar-tensor theories.[16–18,23,28] This means that $4D$ EGB gravity can be viewed as both a dimensionally reduced theory and as a gravitational theory that displays known quantum corrections. As a result, both the Glavan and Lin theory[14] and scalar-tensor regularizations have received remarkable attention and more then 100 papers have been reported on $4D$ EGB gravity and its various solutions including their charged extension,[29,30] rotating counterparts,[31,32] Vaidya-like radiating black holes,[33,34] regular black holes.[35,36] The gravitational lensing of $4D$ EGB black holes have also been studied.[37–40]

The black hole shadow observations by the Event Horizon Telescope (EHT) Collaboration have unprecedentedly opened up an exciting arena to make a precision test of the gravitational theory in the strong and relativistic field regimes (in the vicinity of the unstable bound orbits around black holes).[41,42] The EHT analysis suggested that, based on *a priori* known estimates for the mass and distance from stellar dynamics, the M87* shadow size is consistent within 17% for a 68% confidence interval of the size predicted from the Kerr black hole general-relativistic-magneto-hydrodynamics (GRMHD) image.[43] However, several other studies altogether have not entirely precluded the possibility of non-Kerr black holes.[44–46] Using the M87* shadow angular size, constraints are placed on the second post-Newtonian metric coefficients, which were inaccessible in the earlier weak-field tests at the Solar-scale.[43] Therefore, it is both legitimate and timely to test the viability of the $4D$ EGB gravity theory using the M87* black hole shadow observations. This paper aims to present the detailed study of the rotating $4D$ EGB black hole shadow, parameter estimation of the black hole using the shadow observables, and constraining them using the M87* black hole shadow observed by the Event Horizon Telescope (EHT).

2. Rotating $4D$ EGB black hole shadows

Finding an exact analytic and rotating axially symmetric black hole solution of the EGB gravity is a notorious task due to the non-linearity involved in the field equations. However, there exists the rotating solution generating mechanisms such as the Newman-Janis algorithm[47] and the gravitational-decoupling method,[48] which have been widely used to construct rotating black hole solutions from their non-rotating counterparts. The Azreg-Aïnou's non-complexification procedure[49,50] for the modified Newman-Janis algorithm generates a unique imperfect fluid rotating solution from the seed spherically symmetric static solution. It has been applied to generate rotating solutions in several modified gravity theories.[32,51–56] The rotating

4D EGB black hole metric, in Boyer-Lindquist coordinates, reads[31,32]

$$ds^2 = -\frac{\Delta}{\Sigma}\left(dt - a\sin^2\theta\, d\phi\right)^2 + \frac{\Sigma}{\Delta}dr^2 + \Sigma\, d\theta^2 + \frac{\sin^2\theta}{\Sigma}\left((r^2+a^2)\, d\phi - a\, dt\right)^2 \tag{3}$$

with

$$\Delta = r^2 + a^2 + \frac{r^4}{32\pi\alpha}\left[1 - \sqrt{1 + \frac{128\pi\alpha M}{r^3}}\right], \quad \Sigma = r^2 + a^2\cos^2\theta. \tag{4}$$

Thus rotating 4D EGB black holes are characterized by three parameters, mass (M), spin (a), and GB coupling parameter α, which also gives potential deviation from the Kerr solution. In the limit $\alpha \to 0$ or large r, the metric Eq. (3) smoothly recovers the Kerr black hole.[57] Because the static black hole solution of Ref.[14] is identical to that of regularized scalar-tensor theories and other quantum-corrected theories of gravity,[12–17,58,59] the rotating black hole metric (3) also corresponds to these theories. The rotating black hole admits up to two distinct horizons whose radii $r_- \leq r_+$ can be identified as real positive roots of the $\Delta = 0$. The variation of both horizon radii with GB coupling is shown in Fig. 1, it is evident that the event horizon radius decreases and Cauchy horizon radius increase with α. For a given value of spin a, there exists a extremal value of GB coupling $\alpha = \alpha_E$ for which degenerate horizons $r_- = r_+$ exists, such that for $\alpha > \alpha_E$ horizons disappear and the central singularity becomes globally naked. Similarly, for a given value of α, one can find the extremal value of spin $a = a_E$ which leads to degenerate horizons $r_- = r_+$. In this paper, we will only consider the black hole case viz., $\alpha \leq \alpha_E$.

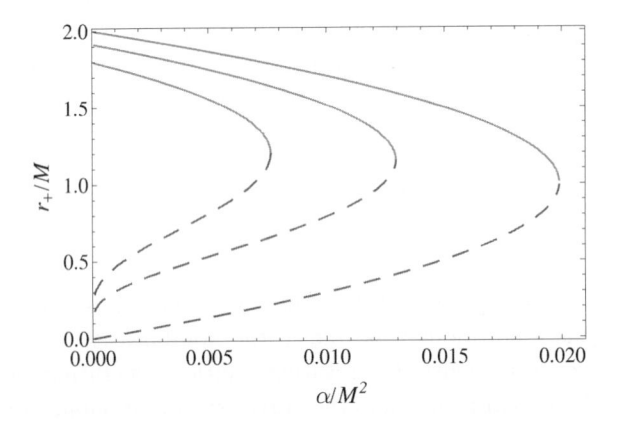

Fig. 1. Event horizon (solid green) and Cauchy horizon (dashed red) radii variation with α for different values of $a = 0, 0.40M, 0.60M$ (from outside to inside).

The optical appearance of the black hole in the presence of a bright background or the illuminated matter accretion flow is known as the shadow. The light from the source gets strongly lensed by the black hole in the vicinity of the horizon and receive by a faraway observer on the opposite side of the source. Synge,[60] and Luminet[61] led the study of black hole shadow and calculated the capturing angle of the Schwarzschild black hole. For the first time, the shadow of the Kerr black hole was reported by Bardeen[62] in his pioneering work in 1973. The rotating EGB metric (3) belongs to Petrov type-D spacetimes, and thus the geodesics equations are completely integrable. The metric (3) carries two Killing vectors ∂_t and ∂_ϕ, associated with the time translational and rotational invariance of the spacetime geometry. The components of photon four-momentum p^μ projected along these Killing vectors are constant of motion, which in this case can be identified as the energy E and axial angular momentum magnitude L_z. We follow the Hamilton-Jacobi formalism to determine the null geodesics equations of motion around the rotating black hole, which read as follows[32,63]

$$\Sigma \frac{dt}{d\tau} = \frac{r^2 + a^2}{\Delta} \left(E(r^2 + a^2) - aL_z \right) - a(aE\sin^2\theta - L_z), \tag{5}$$

$$\Sigma \frac{dr}{d\tau} = \pm\sqrt{\mathcal{R}(r)}, \tag{6}$$

$$\Sigma \frac{d\theta}{d\tau} = \pm\sqrt{\Theta(\theta)}, \tag{7}$$

$$\Sigma \frac{d\phi}{d\tau} = \frac{a}{\Delta} \left(E(r^2 + a^2) - aL_z \right) - \left(aE - \frac{L_z}{\sin^2\theta} \right), \tag{8}$$

where τ is the affine parameter along the null geodesics and

$$\mathcal{R}(r) = \left((r^2 + a^2)E - aL_z \right)^2 - \Delta((aE - L_z)^2 + K), \tag{9}$$

$$\Theta(\theta) = K - \left(\frac{L_z^2}{\sin^2\theta} - a^2 E^2 \right) \cos^2\theta. \tag{10}$$

The constant K is the separability constant related to the Carter constant $\mathcal{Q}$ through $\mathcal{Q} = K + (aE - L_z)^2$. Carter constant appears as a conserved quantity associated with the hidden symmetry described by the second-rank Killing tensor. We introduce the impact parameters for the photons geodesics, which are constant along geodesics and defined in dimensionless form as follows[63]

$$\xi = \frac{L_z}{E}, \quad \eta = \frac{K}{E^2}. \tag{11}$$

Photons may get scattered, captured, or follow bound orbits around the black hole depending on the values of (xi, eta). Because of the black hole rotation, photons can either co-rotate or counter-rotate along with the black hole, whose radii vary differently with black hole spin. At $\theta = \pi/2$, Carter's constant vanishes, and the photons follow the circular orbits with radii $r_p^\pm$, which can be determined by solving $Y = 0$. Whereas for $\theta \neq \pi/2$ the Carter constant is positive definite and the photons follow the non-planar orbits with radii $r_p^- < r_p < r_p^+$. The photons following the spherical orbits of constant coordinate radii r_p around the black hole are characterized by $\dot{r} = 0$ and $\ddot{r} = 0$. This results into the critical values of impact parameters

(ξ_{crit}, η_{crit}) for the unstable orbits[32]

$$\xi_{crit} = \frac{\left(a^2 + r^2\right) \Delta'(r) - 4r\Delta(r)}{a\Delta'(r)},$$
$$\eta_{crit} = \frac{r^2 \left(8\Delta(r)\left(2a^2 + r\Delta'(r)\right) - r^2\Delta'(r)^2 - 16\Delta(r)^2\right)}{a^2\Delta'(r)^2}, \quad (12)$$

where $'$ stands for the derivative with the radial coordinate r. Furthermore, these spherical photons orbits are the non-planar orbits that periodically cross the equatorial plane and construct a photon region around the black hole. As a result, the photons following the spherical orbits, beside having a motion along the ϕ direction also move along the θ-direction. For visualizing the black hole shadow, we consider a distant observer at position (r_0, θ_0). The coordinates (X, Y) define the observer image plane, such that the stereographic projection of the shadow from the celestial sphere to the image plane is defined as follow

$$X = \lim_{r_0 \to \infty} \left(-r_0^2 \sin\theta_0 \frac{d\phi}{dr}\right),$$
$$Y = \lim_{r_0 \to \infty} \left(r_0^2 \frac{d\theta}{dr}\right). \quad (13)$$

For an asymptotically far observer, Eq. (13) leads to

$$X = -\xi_{crit} \csc\theta_0,$$
$$Y = \pm\sqrt{\eta_{crit} + a^2\cos^2\theta_0 - \xi_{crit}^2 \cot^2\theta_0}. \quad (14)$$

and satisfy

$$X^2 + Y^2 = \eta_{crit} + \xi_{crit}^2 + a^2\cos^2\theta_0. \quad (15)$$

The parametric curve Y vs X delineates the shadow's boundary of the rotating EGB black hole. It is clear that the non-rotating black hole ($a = 0$) cast a perfectly circular shadow silhouette. For $\theta_0 \neq 0$ or π the rotating black hole shadow shifts in the direction perpendicular to the black hole rotation and appears distorted, whereas for $\theta_0 = 0, \pi$ shadows is centered at $(0,0)$ and is perfectly circular for all values of a. The maximum off-center displacement of shadow appears for $\theta_0 = \pi/2$.

In April 2019, the EHT collaboration using the VLBI technology unveiled the first-ever horizon-scaled image of the supermassive black hole M87*.[41,42] The M87* image shows powerful relativistic jets, which could be emerged from magnetohydrodynamic interactions between the accretion disk and the rotating black hole. Considering the orientation of these jets in M87*, the inclination angle (angle between the rotational axis and the line of sight) is estimated to be 17°.[64] Hereafter, for our analysis of EGB black hole shadows, we will consider the inclination angle $\theta_0 = 17^o$. The rotating EGB black holes shadows with varying a and α are depicted in Fig. 2. It is evident that the shadow size decreases with increasing α, such that

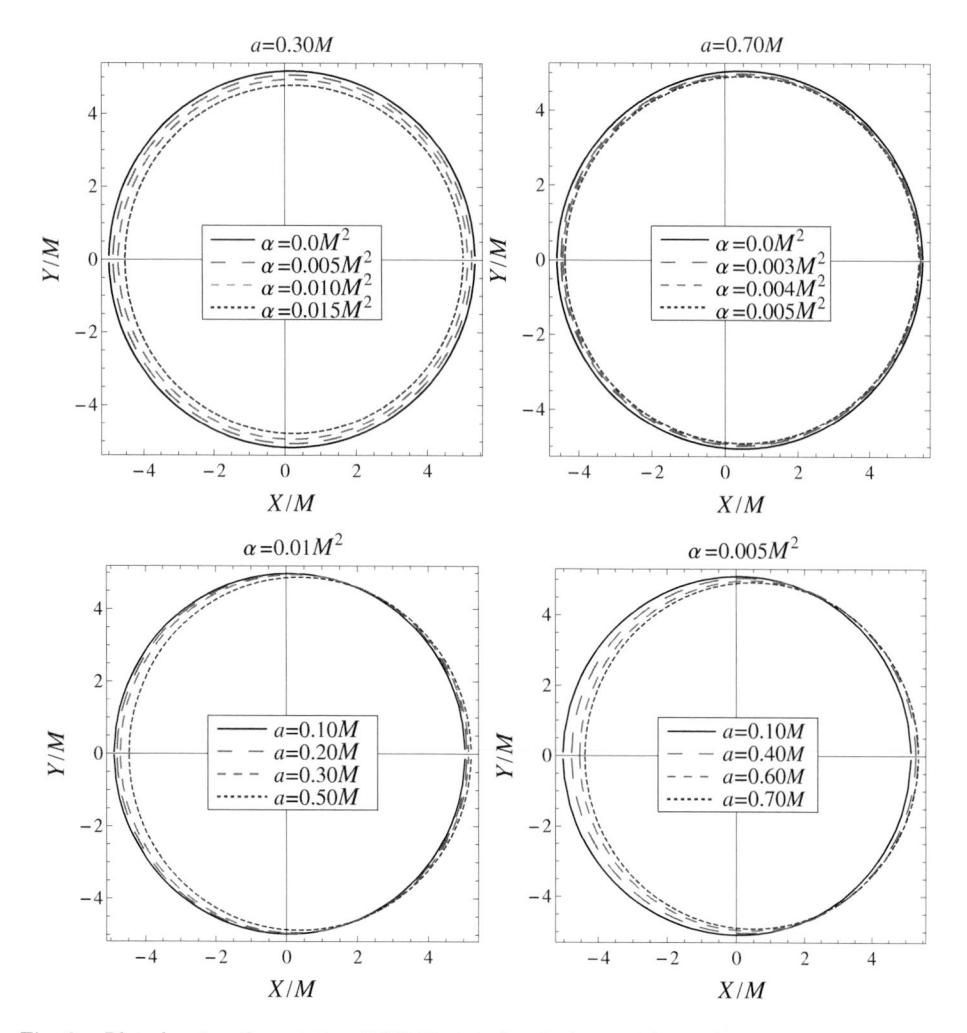

Fig. 2. Plot showing the rotating EGB black holes shadows with varying parameters a and α. Solid black curves in the upper panel are for the Kerr black holes.

the rotating EGB black hole shadows are smaller than the Kerr black hole shadows. Furthermore, the rotating black holes shadows are not perfectly circular. To characterize the shadow size and the deviation from the circularity, we introduce the shadow observables, namely, shadow area A and oblateness D as follows[65,66]

$$A = 2\int Y dX = 2\int_{r_p^-}^{r_p^+} \left(Y\frac{dX}{dr_p}\right) dr_p, \tag{16}$$

$$D = \frac{X_r - X_l}{Y_t - Y_b}, \tag{17}$$

where the points on the right, left, top, and bottom of the shadow boundary are designated by subscripts r, l, t and b. The shadow boundary, defined by (X, Y), is a function of spherical photon orbits radii r_p. Interestingly, photons with different orbit radii construct the different parts of the shadow boundary. Therefore, as one moves along the Y-axis in the shadow image, one sees deeper or far away from the black hole. The behavior of the shadow observables A and D with varying a and α is shown in Fig. 3. The shadow area monotonically decreases with α and a, and the oblateness increases with increasing a. To estimate the rotating EGB black hole parameters, we make a contour plot of observables A and D as functions of a and α in Fig. 4. Therein each solid red curve corresponds to constant values of A and dashed blue curve to D. The intersection point of observables A and D determines the unique and precise values of the black hole parameters a and α. Hence, from Fig. 4, it is clear that for a given set of 4D EGB black hole shadow observables, A and D, we can determine information about black hole spin and GB coupling parameter.

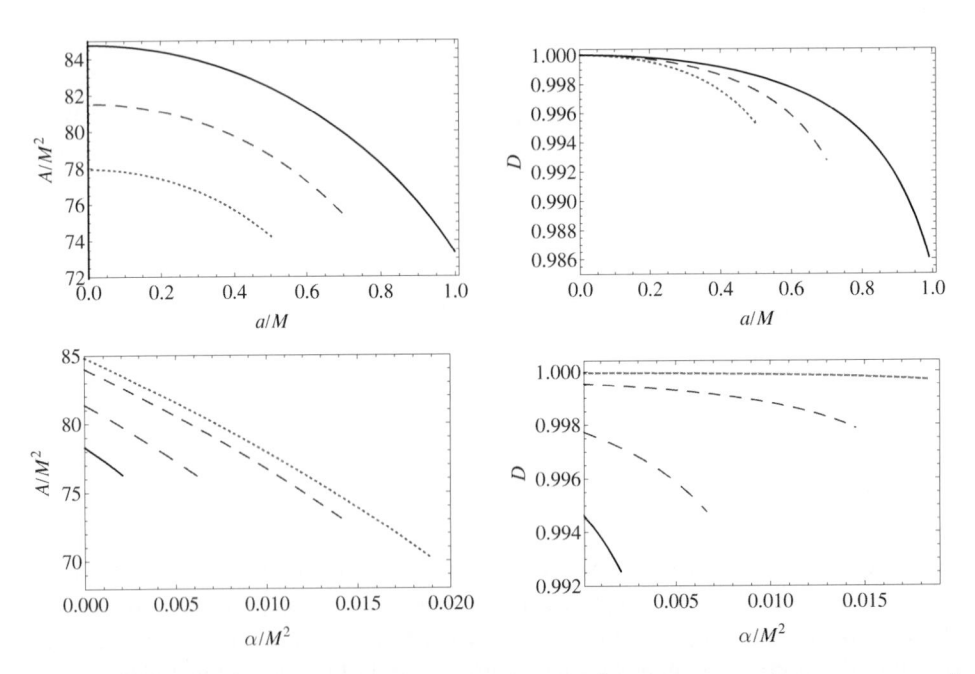

Fig. 3. *Upper*: The observables A and D vs a for $\alpha = 0.0M^2$ (solid black curve), for $\alpha = 0.005M^2$ (dashed blue curve), and for $\alpha = 0.01M^2$ (dotted magenta curve). *Bottom*: The observables A and D vs α for $a = 0.0M$ (dotted magenta curve), for $a = 0.1M$ (dotted green curve), for $a = 0.3M$ (dashed blue curve), for $a = 0.6M$ (long-dashed brown curve), and for $a = 0.8M$ (solid black curve).

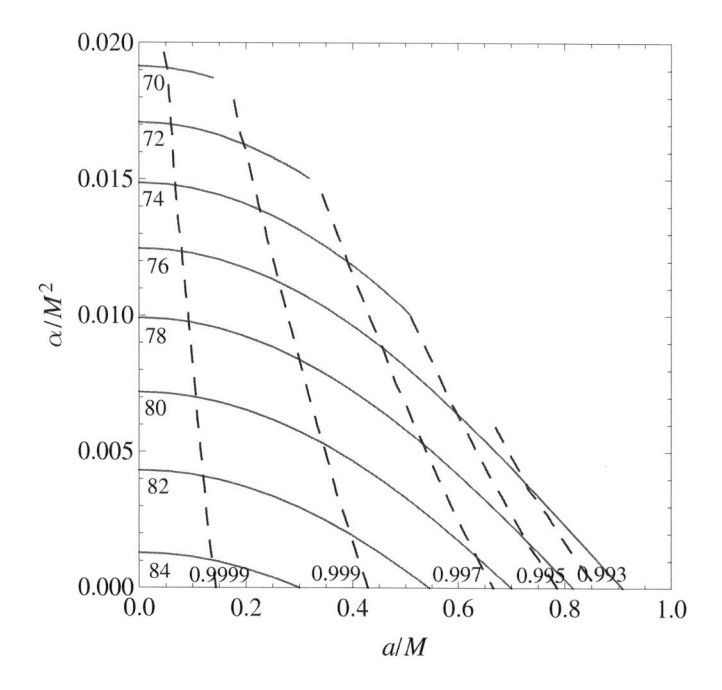

Fig. 4. Contour plots of the observables A and D in the plane (a, α) for the rotating EGB black holes. Each curve is labeled with the corresponding values of A and D. Solid red curves correspond to the A, and dashed blue curves are for the oblateness parameter D.

3. Constraints from the M87* shadow

Although the M87* black hole shadow is found to be consistent with the Kerr black hole image as predicted in the general relativity, the non-Kerr black holes are also not ruled out. Very recently, the EHT collaboration team has set stringent constraints on the physical charges of a large variety of modified gravity black holes by using the M87* shadow.[67] The M87* shadow is of crescent shape with the circularity deviation $\Delta C \leq 0.10$ (10%) in terms of root-mean-square deviation from average shadow radius, axis ratio $\lesssim 4/3$, whereas the angular diameter θ_d is $42 \pm 3 \mu as$.[41,42] Here, we will model the M87* black hole as the rotating 4D EGB black hole and use the M87* shadow observables to place constraints on the black hole parameters.

For this, we define the shadow boundary with polar coordinates $(R(\varphi), \varphi)$ such that the origin is at the shadow center (X_O, Y_O). Figure (2) infers that the rotating black hole shadow is always $\mathcal{Z}_2$ symmetric around $Y = 0$. However, due to black hole rotation, the shadow center shifts from $X = 0$, and as a result, the shadow is asymmetric along the Y axis. It ascertains that the shadow center is $(X_O = |X_r + X_l|/2, Y_O = 0)$, where X_r and X_l are the maximum and minimum abscissas of the shadow boundary in the image plane. The radial coordinate of shadow boundary from its center reads as

$$R(\varphi) = \sqrt{(X - X_O)^2 + (Y - Y_O)^2}, \quad \varphi \equiv \tan^{-1}\left(\frac{Y}{X - X_O}\right),$$

whereas shadow average radius $\bar{R}$ is defined as[68]

$$\bar{R}^2 = \frac{1}{2\pi} \int_0^{2\pi} R^2(\varphi) d\varphi. \tag{18}$$

We describe the circularity deviation ΔC to quantifies the shadow deviation from a perfect circle as a measure of the root-mean-square deviation of $R(\varphi)$ from the shadow average radius[68–70]

$$\Delta C = \frac{1}{\bar{R}} \sqrt{\frac{1}{2\pi} \int_0^{2\pi} \left(R(\varphi) - \bar{R}\right)^2 d\varphi}, \tag{19}$$

clearly, for a circular shadow of spherically symmetric black hole $\Delta C = 0$. Second observable is the shadow angular diameter θ_d, which for a far distant observer, at a distance r_0 from the black hole, is defined as

$$\theta_d = 2\frac{R_s}{r_0}, \quad R_s = \sqrt{A/\pi}, \tag{20}$$

and the third observable is the axis ratio

$$D_x = \frac{\Delta Y}{\Delta X}, \tag{21}$$

which is just the inverse of oblateness observable $D_x = 1/D$. We have calculated these three observable $\Delta C, \theta_d$, and D_x for the rotating $4D$ EGB black hole with $M = 6.5 \times 10^9 M_\odot$ and $r_0 = 16.8$ Mpc and plotted them in Fig. 5. The EHT bound for the M87* black hole shadow angular diameter $\theta_d = 39\,\mu$as within the 1σ region, shown as the black solid line, constrained the a and α. The shadow angular size for the non-rotating extremal EGB black hole with $a = 0, \alpha = 0.019894367M^2$ is $\theta_d = 35.7888\mu$as and for extremal Kerr black hole with $a = M, \alpha = 0$ is $\theta_d = 36.8632\mu$as. For comparison, at the inclination angle $\theta_o = 90°$, the extremal Kerr black hole shadow angular size is 37.3534μas. The relative difference in shadow angular diameter $\delta\theta_d \equiv (\theta_d|_{Kerr} - \theta_d|_{EGB})/\theta_d|_{Kerr}$ is shown in Fig. 6. Clearly, $\delta\theta_d \leq 17\%$ and thus it is consistent with the Psaltis et al.[43] findings. Furthermore, the axis ratio and the circularity deviation for the M87* black hole shadow allow all parameter space of the EGB black hole.

4. Conclusions

The underlying theory of gravity in the extreme-field regime is currently unknown, and insights into it are likely to be gained through observations. In this paper, we have investigated the rotating $4D$ EGB black hole. The EGB gravity theory has been of great interest and importance due to second-order field equations and being

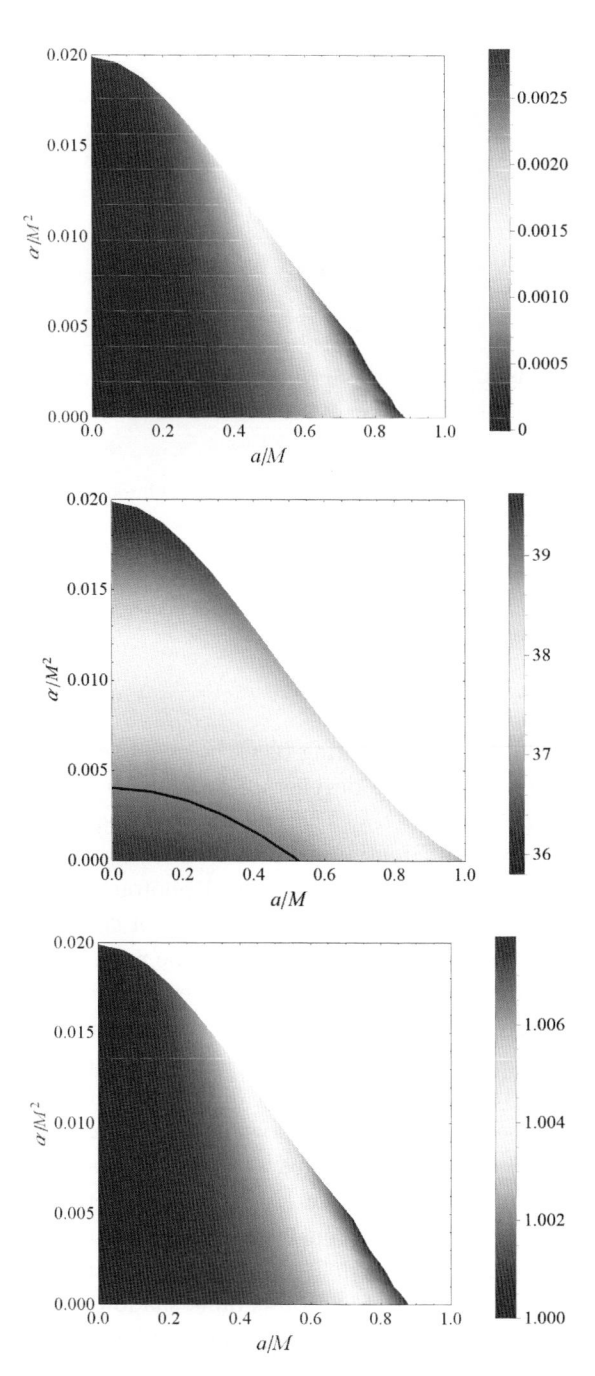

Fig. 5. Circularity deviation observable ΔC (*top*), the angular diameter θ_d (*middle*), and axis ratio D_x (*bottom*) as a function of (a, α) for the rotating EGB black holes. Black solid lines correspond to the M87* black hole shadow bounds $\theta_d = 39\mu as$ within the 1σ region, such that the region above the black line is excluded by the EHT bounds.

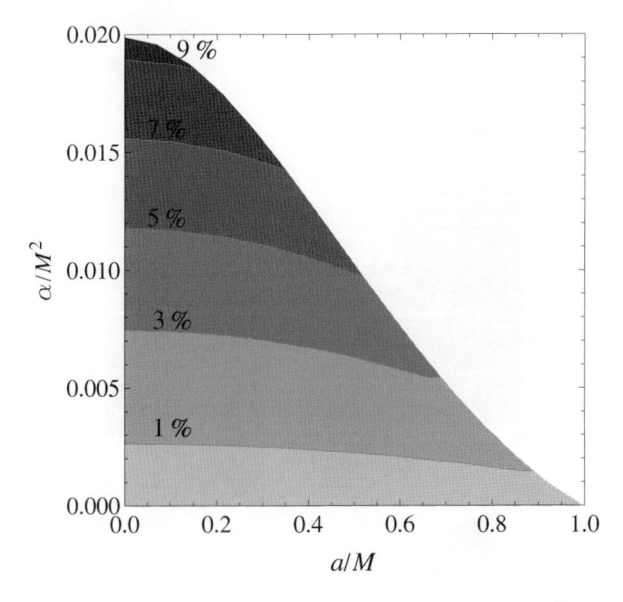

Fig. 6. Relative difference between the shadow angular diameter size of a rotating EGB black hole and a Kerr black hole with the same mass.

free from ghost instabilities. The rotating black holes possess two distinct horizons that eventually merge to form the degenerate horizon for the extremal values of the GB coupling parameter $\alpha = \alpha_E$. The null geodesics equations of motion were obtained in the first-order differential form, and the analytical expressions of the critical impact parameters for unstable spherical photon orbits are derived. The shadow contours are drawn for the rotating black hole for $\theta_0 = 17°$ inclination angle and compared with those for the Kerr black hole. The rotating black hole shadows deviate from the circularity. The shadow observables A and D are calculated, and it is shown that the EGB black hole shadows are smaller and more distorted than those for the Kerr black hole. Furthermore, these observables are used to estimate the black hole parameters. We modeled the M87* black hole as the rotating 4D EGB black hole and used the deduced shadow observables ΔC, θ_d, and D_x for the M87* to constrain the EGB black hole parameters. We have found that only θ_d within 1σ region placed stringent bound the EGB parameters. Whereas ΔC and D_x allows all parameter space. The constraints deduced for $\theta_0 = 17°$ are weaker than those deduced for $\theta_0 = 90°$ in Ref.[32] However, it is important to account for systematic uncertainty when identifying observable shadow characteristics like the emission ring and center brightness depression, especially when using low-resolution data, to gravitational qualities like the size and shape of the critical curve. Future observations utilizing an improved ground or space-based array might significantly reduce these systematic errors, and we anticipate better constraints on the GB coupling parameter.

Acknowledgments

S.G.G. would like to thank DST INDO-SA bilateral project DST/INT/South Africa/P-06/2016, SERB-DST for the ASEAN project IMRC/AISTDF/CRD/2018/000042 and also IUCAA, Pune for the hospitality while this work was being done. R.K. would like to thanks UKZN and NRF for the post-doctoral fellowship.

References

1. D. Lovelock, J. Math. Phys. **13** 874 (1972).
2. C. Lanczos, Annals Math. **39** 842 (1938).
3. D. Lovelock, J. Math. Phys. **12** 498 (1971).
4. D. G. Boulware and S. Deser, Phys. Rev. Lett. **55**, 2656 (1985); J. T. Wheeler, Nucl. Phys. B **268**, 737 (1986).
5. S. Nojiri and S. D. Odintsov, Phys. Lett. B **521** 87 (2001); Erratum: [Phys. Lett. B **542** 301 (2002)]; Y. M. Cho and I. P. Neupane, Phys. Rev. D **66**, 024044 (2002); M. Cvetic, S. Nojiri and S. D. Odintsov, Nucl. Phys. B **628**, 295 (2002); R. G. Cai, Phys. Rev. D **65**, 084014 (2002); I. P. Neupane, Phys. Rev. D **67**, 061501(R) (2003); **69**, 084011 (2004); A. Padilla, Class. Quant. Grav. **20**, 3129 (2003); N. Deruelle, J. Katz, and S. Ogushi, Class. Quant. Grav. **21**, 1971 (2004); M. H. Dehghani, Phys. Rev. D **69**, 064024 (2004); R. G. Cai and Q. Guo, Phys. Rev. D **69**, 104025 (2004); T. Torii and H. Maeda, Phys. Rev. D **71**, 124002 (2005); M. H. Dehghani and R. B. Mann, Phys. Rev. D **72**, 124006 (2005); M. H. Dehghani and S. H. Hendi, Phys. Rev. D **73**, 084021 (2006); M. H. Dehghani, G. H. Bordbar, and M. Shamirzaie, Phys. Rev. D **74**, 064023 (2006).
6. S. Jhingan and S. G. Ghosh, Phys. Rev. D **81**, 024010 (2010); S. G. Ghosh, M. Amir and S. D. Maharaj, Eur. Phys. J. C **77**, 530 (2017); S. G. Ghosh, Class. Quant. Grav. **35**, 085008 (2018).
7. S. Mignemi and N. R. Stewart, Phys. Rev. D **47**, 5259 (1993); P. Kanti, N. E. Mavromatos, J. Rizos, K. Tamvakis and E. Winstanley, Phys. Rev. D **54**, 5049 (1996); S. O. Alexeev and M. V. Pomazanov, Phys. Rev. D **55**, 2110 (1997); T. Torii, H. Yajima and K. i. Maeda, Phys. Rev. D **55**, 739 (1997); R. Konoplya, Phys. Rev. D **71**, 024038 (2005); B. Kleihaus, J. Kunz and E. Radu, Phys. Rev. Lett. **106**, 151104 (2011); A. Maselli, P. Pani, L. Gualtieri and V. Ferrari, Phys. Rev. D **92**, 083014 (2015).
8. T. P. Sotiriou and S. Y. Zhou, Phys. Rev. Lett. **112**, 251102 (2014).
9. T. P. Sotiriou and S. Y. Zhou, Phys. Rev. D **90**, 124063 (2014).
10. D. D. Doneva and S. S. Yazadjiev, Phys. Rev. Lett. **120**, 131103 (2018).
11. P. V. P. Cunha, C. A. R. Herdeiro and E. Radu, Phys. Rev. Lett. **123**, 011101 (2019).
12. Y. Tomozawa, arXiv:1107.1424 [gr-qc].
13. G. Cognola, R. Myrzakulov, L. Sebastiani and S. Zerbini, Phys. Rev. D **88**, 024006 (2013).
14. D. Glavan and C. Lin, Phys. Rev. Lett. **124**, 081301 (2020).
15. R. A. Konoplya and A. Zhidenko, Phys. Rev. D **101**, 084038 (2020).
16. A. Casalino, A. Colleaux, M. Rinaldi and S. Vicentini, Phys. Dark Univ. **31**, 100770 (2021).
17. R. A. Hennigar, D. Kubiznak, R. B. Mann and C. Pollack, JHEP **07**, 027 (2020).
18. L. Ma and H. Lu, Eur. Phys. J. C **80**, 1209 (2020).
19. W. Ai, Commun. Theor. Phys. **72**, 095402 (2020).
20. F. Shu, Phys. Lett. B **811**, 135907 (2020).

21. M. Gurses, T. C. Sisman and B. Tekin, Eur. Phys. J. C **80** 647 (2020).
22. S. Mahapatra, Eur. Phys. J. C **80**, 992 (2020).
23. H. Lu and Y. Pang, Phys. Lett. B **809**, 135717 (2020).
24. T. Kobayashi, JCAP **07**, 013 (2020).
25. J. Arrechea, A. Delhom and A. Jiménez-Cano, Chin. Phys. C **45**, 013107 (2021).
26. K. Aoki, M. A. Gorji and S. Mukohyama, Phys. Lett. B **810**, 135843 (2020).
27. R. B. Mann and S. F. Ross, Class. Quant. Grav. **10**, 1405 (1993).
28. P. G. S. Fernandes, P. Carrilho, T. Clifton and D. J. Mulryne, Phys. Rev. D **102**, 024025 (2020).
29. P. G. S. Fernandes, Phys. Lett. B **805**, 135468 (2020).
30. D. V. Singh, S. G. Ghosh and S. D. Maharaj, Phys. Dark Univ. **30**, 100730 (2020).
31. S. W. Wei and Y. X. Liu, Eur. Phys. J. Plus **136**, 436 (2021).
32. R. Kumar and S. G. Ghosh, JCAP **07**, 053 (2020).
33. S. G. Ghosh and S. D. Maharaj, Phys. Dark Univ. **30**, 100687 (2020).
34. S. G. Ghosh and R. Kumar, Class. Quant. Grav. **37**, 245008 (2020).
35. A. Kumar and S. G. Ghosh, arXiv:2004.01131 [gr-qc].
36. A. Kumar and R. Kumar, arXiv:2003.13104 [gr-qc].
37. S. U. Islam, R. Kumar and S. G. Ghosh, JCAP **09**, 030 (2020).
38. M. Heydari-Fard, M. Heydari-Fard and H. R. Sepangi, EPL **133**, 50006 (2021).
39. X. H. Jin, Y. X. Gao and D. J. Liu, Int. J. Mod. Phys. D **29**, 2050065 (2020).
40. R. Kumar, S. U. Islam and S. G. Ghosh, Eur. Phys. J. C **80**, 1128 (2020).
41. K. Akiyama *et al.*, Astrophys. J. **875**, L1 (2019).
42. K. Akiyama *et al.*, Astrophys. J. **875**, L6 (2019).
43. D. Psaltis *et al.*, Phys. Rev. Lett. **125**, 141104 (2020).
44. Y. Mizuno, *et al.*, Nature Astron. **2**, 585 (2018).
45. F. H. Vincent, M. Wielgus, M. A. Abramowicz, E. Gourgoulhon, J. P. Lasota, T. Paumard and G. Perrin, Astron. Astrophys. **646**, A37 (2021).
46. H. C. D. Lima, Junior, L. B. Crispino, P. P. Cunha and C. R. Herdeiro, Phys. Rev. D **103**, 084040 (2021).
47. E. Newman and A. Janis, J. Math. Phys. **6**, 915 (1965).
48. E. Contreras, J. Ovalle and R. Casadio, Phys. Rev. D **103**, 044020 (2021).
49. M. Azreg-Aïnou, Phys. Rev. D **90**, 064041 (2014).
50. M. Azreg-Aïnou, Eur. Phys. J. C **74**, 2865 (2014).
51. T. Johannsen and D. Psaltis, Phys. Rev. D **83**, 124015 (2011).
52. C. Bambi and L. Modesto, Phys. Lett. B **721**, 329 (2013).
53. S. G. Ghosh, Eur. Phys. J. C **75**, 532 (2015).
54. J. W. Moffat, Eur. Phys. J. C **75**, 175 (2015).
55. R. Kumar, S. G. Ghosh and A. Wang, Phys. Rev. D **101**, 104001 (2020).
56. R. Kumar and S. G. Ghosh, Eur. Phys. J. C **78**, 750 (2018).
57. R. P. Kerr, Phys. Rev. Lett. **11**, 237 (1963).
58. R. G. Cai, L. M. Cao and N. Ohta, JHEP **1004**, 082 (2010); R. G. Cai, Phys. Lett. B **733**, 183 (2014).
59. A. Kehagias and K. Sfetsos, Phys. Lett. B **678**, 123 (2009).
60. J. L. Synge, Mon. Not. R. Astron. Soc. **131**, 463 (1966).
61. J. P. Luminet, Astron. Astrophys. **75**, 228 (1979).
62. J. M. Bardeen, *Black Holes*, Edited by C. DeWitt and B. S. DeWitt (Gordon and Breach, New York, 1973, p. 215).
63. S. Chandrasekhar, *The Mathematical Theory of Black Holes* (Oxford University Press, New York, 1992).

64. R. Craig Walker, P. E. Hardee, F. B. Davies, C. Ly and W. Junor, Astrophys. J. **855**, 128 (2018).
65. R. Kumar and S. G. Ghosh, Astrophys. J. **892**, 78 (2020).
66. O. Y. Tsupko, Phys. Rev. D **95**, 104058 (2017).
67. P. Kocherlakota *et al.*, Phys. Rev. D **103**, 104047 (2021).
68. C. Bambi, K. Freese, S. Vagnozzi and L. Visinelli, Phys. Rev. D **100**, 044057 (2019).
69. T. Johannsen and D. Psaltis, Astrophys. J. **718**, 446 (2010).
70. T. Johannsen, Astrophys. J. **777**, 170 (2013).

Wormhole interaction in 2d Horăva-Lifshitz quantum gravity

Jan Ambjørn[a]

The Niels Bohr Institute, Copenhagen University,
Blegdamsvej 17, DK-2100 Copenhagen, Denmark
and
IMPP, Radboud University,
Heyendaalseweg 135, 6525 AJ, Nijmegen, The Netherlands
[a] *E-mail: ambjorn@nbi.dk*

Yuki Hiraga[b], Yoshiyasu Ito[c] and Yuki Sato[d]

Department of Physics, Nagoya University,
Chikusaku, Nagoya 464-8602, Japan
[b] *E-mail: hiraga@eken.phys.nagoya-u.ac.jp*
[c] *E-mail: ito@eken.phys.nagoya-u.ac.jp*
and
Institute for Advanced Research, Nagoya University,
Chikusaku, Nagoya 464-8602, Japan
[d] *E-mail: ysato@th.phys.nagoya-u.ac.jp*

A lattice regularization for the 2d projectable Horăva-Lifshitz (HL) quantum gravity is known to be the 2d causal dynamical triangulations (CDT), and the 2d CDT can be generalized so as to include all possible genus contributions non-perturbatively. We show that in the context of HL gravity, effects coming from such a non-perturbative sum over topologies can be successfully taken into account, if we quantize the 2d projectable HL gravity with a simple bi-local wormhole interaction. This conference paper is based on the article, Phys. Lett. B **816** (2021), 136205.[1]

Keywords: Wormholes; Low dimensional quantum gravity; Canonical quantization

1. Introduction

Two-dimensional models of quantum gravity are useful for understanding some aspects of non-perturbative physics, since they can be examined beyond the framework of perturbation theory by analytic computations in many cases. One of such models is the two-dimensional causal dynamical triangulations (2d CDT),[2] which is a lattice toy model of quantum gravity with a global time foliation. Global hyperbolicity imposed at the quantum level do not allow for any topology change in the CDT model, and the continuum limit can be described by quantum mechanics of a 1d universe.[2]

Yet another toy model for quantum gravity that has a global time foliation is 2d Horăva-Lifshitz (HL) quantum gravity that was introduced first in higher dimensions to resolve the issue of perturbative renormalizability by breaking the diffeomorphisms down to the foliation-preserving diffeomorphisms,[3,4] and so the model has a preferred foliation structure. The projectable version of the 2d HL quantum gravity was discussed in the articles,[5,6] and in particular it was shown that the canonical quantization of the model yields exactly the same quantum Hamiltonian as the one obtained by the continuum limit of 2d CDT.[5] Therefore, one can interpret 2d CDT as a lattice regularization for the 2d projectable HL quantum gravity.

Although the creation of baby universes and wormholes (handles) is not allowed to occur in the original setup of CDT, one can generalize the 2d model to include such configurations in a manner consistent with the scaling limit,[7] and such a generalized model can be fully described by a string field theory for CDT[8a]. Here the word "string" refers to the 1d spatial universe. Based on the string field theory, one can take into account all genera (handles) as well as all baby universes of the two-dimensional spacetime. In addition, as long as one only asks for the amplitude between the states describing connected spatial universes separated a proper time t, this sum over topologies and baby universes can effectively be described by a one-body Hamiltonian.[11,12]

Having the equivalence between the continuum limit of 2d CDT and the 2d projectable HL quantum gravity, we discussed in the article[1] what kind of effective interaction should be added to the classical Lagrangian of the 2d projectable HL gravity when canonically quantized, in order to obtain the above mentioned one-body quantum Hamiltonian that includes all wormholes and baby universes obtained in 2d CDT. The answer is that it is enough to include a simple bi-local and spatial wormhole interaction that is compatible with the foliation-preserving diffeomorphisms.

This article is organized as follows. In Section 2, we give a brief introduction to 2d CDT and 2d HL quantum gravity, and explain the relation between the two. In Section 3 the string field theory for CDT is described and we introduce the one-body quantum Hamiltonian that includes all possible topologies. In Section 4, we introduce a simple wormhole interaction to the 2d projectable HL gravity and show that one can precisely recover the one-body Hamiltonian when canonically quantizing the model. Section 5 is devoted to discussions.

2. CDT and Horǎva-Lifshitz gravity in two dimensions

In this Section, we review causal dynamical triangulations (CDT) and Horǎva-Lifshitz gravity (HL) in two dimension, and explain the relation between the two.

2.1. *2d CDT*

The starting point is a globally hyperbolic manifold equipped with a global time foliation:

$$\mathcal{M} = \bigcup_{t\in\mathbb{R}} \Sigma_t \,, \qquad (1)$$

---

[a]The time-independent amplitudes can be also computed by the matrix model for CDT[9] and by the new scaling limit of the Hermitian one-matrix model.[10]

where each leaf Σ_t is a Cauchy "surface". 2d CDT is a model which quantizes 2d geometries with such a proper-time foliation. The geometries in the path integral are regularized by piecewise linear geometries constructed by gluing together special kinds of triangles.[2] Each triangle consists of one space-like edge and two time-like edges such that a square of the space-like edge is positive, $a_s^2 = \varepsilon^2$, while it is negative for the time-like edge, $a_t^2 = -\alpha\varepsilon^2$ with positive α.

If we prohibit a creation of baby universes, a reasonable choice of the action is the cosmological constant term that is regularized as follows:

$$S[g_{ij}] = -\lambda_0 \int d^2x \sqrt{-\det(g_{ij})},$$
$$\to \quad S_R[T;\alpha] = -\frac{\mu}{\varepsilon^2} \times \left(\frac{\sqrt{4\alpha+1}}{4}\varepsilon^2 \times n(T)\right), \qquad (2)$$

where the bare cosmological constant λ_0 is replaced by the dimensionless cosmological constant μ, and the quantity in the parentheses is the discretized area of the triangulation T, i.e. the area of each triangle times the number of triangles $n(T)$. The lattice action S_R in eq. (2) is called the Regge action.[13]

For computational convenience we implement a rotation to the Euclidean signature which can be done by replacing α with $-\alpha$:

$$iS_R[T;\alpha] \to -S_R^{(e)}[-\alpha;T] = -\mu\frac{\sqrt{4\alpha-1}}{4}n(T) =: -\mu\, n(T), \qquad (3)$$

where we have absorbed a numerical factor into the dimensionless cosmological constant. Note that this map is a bijection between individual Lorentzian and Euclidean geometries.

In CDT, the integration over diffeomorphism equivalent classes of metric g keeping both initial and final geometries fixed can be regularized by the sum over "all" triangulations. Therefore, the 2d Euclidean path-integral regularized by CDT is

$$G^{(0)}_{\text{lattice}}(l_1,l_2;\tau) = \sum_{T\in\mathcal{T}(l_1,l_2;\tau)} e^{-\mu n(T)}, \qquad (4)$$

where $\mathcal{T}(l_1,l_2;\tau)$ is a set of triangulations such that the initial and final boundaries whose lengths are kept fixed to l_1 and l_2 are separated by τ Euclidean time steps.

One can compute the amplitude (4) analytically through the use of the generating function for the numbers $G^{(0)}_{\text{lattice}}(l_1,l_2;\tau)$.[2] As in the case of lattice QCD, tuning the UV relevant coupling constant μ/ε^2 to its critical value μ_c/ε^2 and taking $\varepsilon \to 0$ in a correlated manner, one can transmute the dimension of the lattice spacing to the renormalized coupling constant:

$$\lambda := \lim_{\substack{\varepsilon\to 0 \\ \mu\to\mu_c}} \frac{\mu - \mu_c}{\varepsilon^2}, \qquad (5)$$

where λ is the renormalized cosmological constant. Introducing the renormalized quantities, boundary lengths and a proper time such that

$$\ell_1 := \varepsilon l_1 , \quad \ell_2 := \varepsilon l_2 , \quad t := \varepsilon \tau , \qquad (6)$$

one can obtain the renormalized amplitude $G^{(0)}(\ell_1, \ell_2; t)$ that is known to satisfy the differential equation:[2,5]

$$-\frac{\partial}{\partial t} G^{(0)}(\ell_1, \ell_2; t) = H_a^{(0)}(\ell_1) G^{(0)}(\ell_1, \ell_2; t) , \qquad (7)$$

where $H_a^{(0)}$ is the quantum Hamiltonian defined as

$$H_0^{(0)}(\ell) = -\frac{\partial}{\partial \ell} \ell \frac{\partial}{\partial \ell} + \lambda \ell , \quad H_{-1}^{(0)}(\ell) = -\ell \frac{\partial^2}{\partial \ell^2} + \lambda \ell , \quad H_{+1}^{(0)}(\ell) = -\frac{\partial^2}{\partial \ell^2} \ell + \lambda \ell . \quad (8)$$

Here the label a in eq. (7) specifies the ordering of the Hamiltonian. If we define a quantum state of the one-dimensional universe whose length is ℓ as $|\ell\rangle$, the amplitude $G^{(0)}(\ell_1, \ell_2; t)$ can be rewritten as

$$G^{(0)}(\ell_1, \ell_2; t) = \langle \ell_2 | e^{-t H_a^{(0)}(\ell_1)} | \ell_1 \rangle . \qquad (9)$$

In fact, each ordering specifies the geometry of the quantum state $|\ell\rangle$, i.e. if $a = 0, -1, +1$, then the geometry of the one-dimensional universe is open, closed with a mark, and closed, respectively.[2,5] Marking a point on a closed universe is analogous to introducing a coordinate. The Hamiltonian is hermitian with respect to the following inner product:

$$\langle \phi | H_a^{(0)} | \psi \rangle = \int_0^\infty \phi^*(\ell) H_a^{(0)}(\ell) \psi(\ell) \, d\mu_a(\ell) , \quad \text{with} \quad d\mu_a(\ell) = \ell^a d\ell . \qquad (10)$$

As a result, the physics of 2d CDT can be described by the quantum mechanics of a one-dimensional universe.

2.2. 2d projectable HL gravity

The starting point is the same as that of CDT, i.e. a globally hyperbolic manifold equipped with a global time foliation (1). A natural parametrization for the metric on such a geometry is given by the Arnowitt-Deser-Misner metric:

$$g = -N^2 ds^2 + h_{11}(dx + N^1 ds)(dx + N^1 ds) , \qquad (11)$$

where h_{11} is the spatial metric on the leaf; N and N^1 called lapse and shift functions, quantify the normal and tangential directions of the proper time to the leaf, respectively.

The 2d HL gravity is introduced as a theory that keeps the foliation structure,[3] or in other words, it is invariant under the foliation preserving diffeomorphisms (FPD):

$$s \to s + \xi^0(s) , \quad x \to x + \xi^1(s, x) . \qquad (12)$$

Under the FPD, the fields transform as

$$\delta_\xi h_{11} = \xi^0 \partial_0 h_{11} + \xi^1 \partial_1 h_{11} + 2 h_{11} \partial_1 \xi^1 , \quad (13)$$
$$\delta_\xi N_1 = \xi^\mu \partial_\mu N_1 + N_1 \partial_\mu \xi^\mu + h_{11} \partial_0 \xi^1 , \quad (14)$$
$$\delta_\xi N = \xi^\mu \partial_\mu N + N \partial_0 \xi^0 , \quad (15)$$

where $N_1 = h_{11} N^1$.

Note that if the lapse function N is a function of time, $N = N(t)$, it stays as a function of time under the FPD. The 2d projectable HL gravity satisfies this condition on N, and it is defined by the following action:

$$I = \frac{1}{\kappa} \int ds dx \, N \sqrt{h} \left((1-\eta) K^2 - 2\tilde{\lambda} \right) , \quad (16)$$

where η, $\tilde{\lambda}$ and κ are a dimensionless parameter, the cosmological constant and the dimensionless gravitational coupling constant, respectively; h is the determinant of the metric h_{11}, i.e. $h = h_{11}$; K is the trace of the extrinsic curvature K_{11} defined as

$$K_{11} = \frac{1}{2N} (\partial_0 h_{11} - 2 \nabla_1 N_1) , \quad \text{with} \quad \nabla_1 N_1 := \partial_1 N_1 - \Gamma^1_{11} N_1 . \quad (17)$$

Here Γ^1_{11} is the spatial Christoffel symbol:

$$\Gamma^1_{11} = \frac{1}{2} h^{11} \partial_1 h_{11} . \quad (18)$$

In principle, one can add higher spatial derivative terms to the action (16), but they are not needed since 2d gravity is renormalizable without such terms and we will omit such terms.

The quantization of 2d projectable HL gravity was discussed in,[5,6] and in particular, it was shown that the quantum Hamiltonian coincides with the continuum Hamiltonian of 2d CDT when the following identification of the parameters is made:[5]

$$\lambda = \frac{\tilde{\lambda}}{2(1-\eta)} , \quad \eta < 1 , \quad \tilde{\lambda} > 0 , \quad \kappa = 4(1-\eta) . \quad (19)$$

where λ is the renormalized cosmological constant in 2d CDT (5)[b].

Let us briefly explain how to recover the quantum Hamiltonian (8) from the quantization of 2d HL gravity. Introducing the conjugate momentum of $\sqrt{h}$ as π, we have in the canonical formalism the Poisson bracket

$$\left\{ \sqrt{h(s,x)}, \pi(s,x') \right\} = \delta(x-x') , \quad (20)$$

and corresponding to the Lagrangian (16) we have the Hamiltonian

$$H = \int dx \left[N_1 \left(-\frac{\partial_1 \pi}{\sqrt{h}} \right) + N \left(\frac{\kappa}{4(1-\eta)} \pi^2 \sqrt{h} + \frac{2}{\kappa} \tilde{\lambda} \sqrt{h} \right) \right] . \quad (21)$$

---

[b] We have set unimportant dimensionless gravitational constant as $\kappa = 4(1-\eta)$.

If we solve the momentum constraint at the classical level, i.e.

$$-\frac{\partial_1 \pi}{\sqrt{h}} = 0, \quad \Rightarrow \quad \pi = \pi(s), \tag{22}$$

the system reduces to a one-dimensional model with the Hamiltonian

$$H = N(s)\left(\frac{\kappa}{4(1-\eta)}\pi^2(s)\ell(s) + \frac{2}{\kappa}\tilde{\lambda}\ell(s)\right), \quad \text{with} \quad \ell(s) := \int dx \sqrt{h(s,x)}. \tag{23}$$

Hereafter choosing the correct sign for the kinetic term, i.e. $\eta < 1$, we use the parametrization (19) with positive λ in order to discuss the relation to 2d CDT.

The classical 1d system with the Hamiltonian (23) can be alternatively described by the following action:

$$S = \int_0^1 ds \left(\frac{\dot{\ell}^2}{4N\ell} - \lambda N\ell\right), \tag{24}$$

where $\dot{\ell} := d\ell/ds$. This system is invariant under the time reparametrization, $s \to s + \xi^0(t)$, which is ensured by the lapse function. In fact, the proper time,

$$t := \int_0^1 ds\, N(s), \tag{25}$$

and the length, $\ell = \ell(t)$, are invariant under the time reparametrization, and so it makes sense to discuss the probability amplitude for a 1d universe to propagate in the proper time $t(>0)$, starting from the state with the length ℓ_1 and ending up in the one with length ℓ_2.[5] Such an amplitude can be computed based on the path-integral, and we evaluate it by a rotation to the Euclidean signature for convenience. In our foliated spacetime, for $\eta < 1$, we can implement this procedure by a formal rotation, $s \to is$, which yields the amplitude:

$$G^{(0)}(\ell_2, \ell_1; t) = \int \frac{\mathcal{D}N(s)}{\text{Diff}[0,1]} \int_{\ell(0)=\ell_1}^{\ell(1)=\ell_2} \mathcal{D}\ell(s) e^{-S_E[N(s),\ell(s)]}, \tag{26}$$

where $\text{Diff}[0,1]$ is the volume of the time reparametrization; S_E is the Euclidean action given by

$$S_E = \int_0^1 ds \left(\frac{\dot{\ell}^2}{4N\ell} + \lambda N\ell\right), \tag{27}$$

where $\dot{\ell} := d\ell/ds$.

We set $N = 1$ as a gauge choice. One can show that the corresponding Faddeev-Popov determinant only gives an overall constant, which we will omit in the following. The amplitude (26) then becomes

$$G^{(0)}(\ell_2, \ell_1; t) = \int_{\ell(0)=\ell_1}^{\ell(t)=\ell_2} \mathcal{D}\ell(s) \exp\left[-\int_0^t ds \left(\frac{\dot{\ell}^2}{4\ell} + \lambda\ell\right)\right], \tag{28}$$

which can be expressed in terms of the quantum Hamiltonian H that is unknown at the moment:

$$G^{(0)}(\ell_2, \ell_1; t) = \langle \ell_2 | e^{-tH} | \ell_1 \rangle , \qquad (29)$$

where $|\ell\rangle$ is a quantum state of the 1d universe with the length ℓ. By standard methods (see e.g. the article[5]), one can determine the quantum Hamiltonian from eq. (28) and eq. (29). One obtains precisely the 2d CDT quantum Hamiltonians given by eq. (8) if the integral measures are chosen as

$$\mathcal{D}\ell(s) = \prod_{s=0}^{s=t} \ell^a(s) d\ell(s) , \qquad (30)$$

where $a = 0, \pm 1$. The measures (30) are consistent with eq. (10) introduced in 2d CDT.

Therefore, we can conclude that 2d CDT is a lattice regularization for the 2d projectable HL quantum gravity.

3. Sum over all genera in 2d CDT

One can generalize the 2d CDT model so as to include spatial topology changes (splitting and joining interactions of 1d universe) in keeping with the foliation structure, and this is described by promoting the 1d quantum mechanics to a field theory of 1d universes, which is called the string field theory for CDT.[8] Here the word "string" means a 1d closed spatial universe.

We introduce an operator that creates a marked closed string with the length ℓ, $\Psi^\dagger(\ell)$, and an operator that annihilates a length ℓ closed string without a mark, $\Psi(\ell)$. They satisfy the commutation relation:

$$[\Psi(\ell), \Psi^\dagger(\ell')] = \delta(\ell - \ell'), \quad [\Psi(\ell), \Psi(\ell')] = [\Psi^\dagger(\ell), \Psi^\dagger(\ell')] = 0. \qquad (31)$$

The vacuum $|\text{vac}\rangle$ is defined by $0 = \Psi(\ell)|\text{vac}\rangle = \langle \text{vac}|\Psi^\dagger(\ell)$.

The CDT amplitude (9) can be written in terms of the string field Hamiltonian obtained by sandwiching the one-body Hamiltonian:

$$G^{(0)}(\ell_1, \ell_2; t) = \langle \text{vac}| \Psi(\ell_2) \, e^{-t\hat{H}^{(0)}} \Psi^\dagger(\ell_1) |\text{vac}\rangle , \qquad (32)$$

where

$$\hat{H}^{(0)} = \int_0^\infty \frac{d\ell}{\ell} \Psi^\dagger(\ell) H^{(0)}_{-1} \Psi(\ell) . \qquad (33)$$

In order to incorporate topology change, one has to include suitable interactions, and the full string field Hamiltonian is given by:[8]

$$\hat{H} = \hat{H}^{(0)} - \int_0^\infty d\ell \, \delta(\ell) \Psi(\ell) - g_s \int_0^\infty d\ell_1 \int_0^\infty d\ell_2 \, \Psi^\dagger(\ell_1) \Psi^\dagger(\ell_2)(\ell_1 + \ell_2) \Psi(\ell_1 + \ell_2)$$

$$- \alpha g_s \int_0^\infty d\ell_1 \int_0^\infty d\ell_2 \, \Psi^\dagger(\ell_1 + \ell_2) \ell_1 \Psi(\ell_1) \ell_2 \Psi(\ell_2) , \qquad (34)$$

where the second, third and fourth terms mean a string vanishing into the vacuum, the splitting interaction with the string coupling g_s, and the joining interaction with the coupling αg_s, respectively; α is a constant introduced for counting handles. In general one can compute the following amplitude:

$$A(\ell_1, \cdots, \ell_m; \ell'_1, \cdots, \ell'_n; t) = \langle \text{vac} | \Psi(\ell'_1) \cdots \Psi(\ell'_n) e^{-t\hat{H}} \Psi^\dagger(\ell_1) \cdots \Psi^\dagger(\ell_m) | \text{vac} \rangle . \tag{35}$$

From now on, we focus on the full propagator $G(\ell_1, \ell_2; t)(:= A(\ell_1; \ell_2; t))$ that includes the sum over all genera (handles) and baby universes, and so we simply set $\alpha = 1$. In this case, somewhat miraculously, the full propagator in the multi-body system can be described by an effective one-body system:[11,12]

$$G(\ell_1, \ell_2; t) = \langle \ell_2 | e^{-tH_{-1}} | \ell_1 \rangle , \quad \text{with} \quad H_{-1} = -\ell \frac{\partial^2}{\partial \ell^2} + \lambda \ell - g_s \ell^2 . \tag{36}$$

All the contributions coming from the sum over all genera and baby universes can be effectively described by the last term $-g_s \ell^2$. Although the Hamiltonian (36) is not bounded from below, it belongs to a class of Hamiltonians which are called "classical incomplete", where the Hamiltonians have discrete energy spectra and square integrable eigenfunctions.

The effective one-body system given by eq. (36) can be also described by the path-integral:[1,14]

$$G(\ell_1, \ell_2; t) = \int_{\ell(0)=\ell_1}^{\ell(t)=\ell_2} \mathcal{D}\ell(s) \, \exp\left[-\int_0^t ds \left(\frac{\dot{\ell}^2(s)}{4\ell(s)} + \lambda \ell(s) - g_s \ell^2(s) \right) \right] . \tag{37}$$

If we choose the integral measure such that

$$\mathcal{D}\ell(s) = \prod_{s=0}^{s=t} \ell^a(s) d\ell(s) , \tag{38}$$

where $a = 0, \pm 1$, all possible orderings of the full one-body Hamiltonian (36) can be realized. As explained in the article,[14] in order for the functional integral to be well defined, the boundary conditions on $\ell(s)$ at infinity have to be chosen such that the kinetic term counteracts the unboundedness of the potential. As we will see, the information about the boundary conditions also appears in the classical Hamiltonian constraint (42) of 2d projectable HL gravity with a wormhole interaction.

In the next section, we will show that the path-integral (37) can be obtained quantizing the 2d projectable HL gravity with a wormhole interaction.

4. Wormhole interaction in 2d projectable HL gravity

We consider 2d projectable HL gravity with a space-like wormhole interaction given by the action:

$$I_w = \frac{1}{\kappa} \int ds dx N(s) \sqrt{h(s,x)} \left((1-\eta) K^2(s,x) - 2\tilde{\lambda} \right)$$

$$+ \beta \int ds N(s) \int dx_1 dx_2 \sqrt{h(s,x_1)} \sqrt{h(s,x_2)} , \tag{39}$$

where β is a dimensionfull coupling constant. One can show that the action (39) is invariant under the FPD (12) with the projectable lapse function, $N = N(t)$. The bi-local interaction in eq. (39) relates two distinct points at an equal time. The action is a simplified version of the general bi-local action suggested in the article,[15] made possible because HL gravity is invariant only under the FPD (12) and not the full set of diffeomorphisms.

Following the same procedure explained in the section 2.2, we quantize the system with the action (39). Introducing a conjugate momentum of $\sqrt{h}$ as π as before, we move on to the canonical formalism, and the Hamiltonian is

$$H = \int dx \left[N_1 \mathcal{C}^1(s,x) + N\mathcal{C}(s,x) \right] , \tag{40}$$

where

$$\mathcal{C}^1(s,x) = -\frac{\partial_1 \pi(s,x)}{\sqrt{h(s,x)}} , \tag{41}$$

$$\mathcal{C}(s,x) = \frac{\kappa}{4(1-\eta)} \pi^2(s,x)\sqrt{h(s,x)} + \frac{2}{\kappa}\tilde{\lambda}\sqrt{h(s,x)} - \beta\sqrt{h(s,x)}\int dx_2 \sqrt{h(s,x_2)} . \tag{42}$$

If we solve the momentum constraint (41) at the classical level, the system again reduces to the 1d system with the Hamiltonian:

$$H = N(s)\left(\frac{\kappa}{4(1-\eta)} \pi^2(s)\ell(s) + \frac{2}{\kappa}\tilde{\lambda}\ell(s) - \beta\ell^2(s) \right) , \tag{43}$$

where $\ell(s) := \int dx \sqrt{h(s,x)}$. Hereafter choosing the correct sign for the kinetic term, i.e. $\eta < 1$, we use the parametrization (19) with positive λ as before.

The classical Hamiltonian constraint (42) can be solved as

$$\pi^2 = -\lambda + \beta\ell \geq 0 , \tag{44}$$

for $\sqrt{\lambda}\ell \geq 1/\xi$ with $\xi := \beta/\lambda^{3/2}$, and otherwise, the classical Hamiltonian constraint (42) requires $\ell = 0$ on the constraint surface. As in the $\beta = 0$ case, when quantizing the system based on the path-integral, we don't have any problem with respect to the quantization around $\ell(s) = 0$.

Simply repeating the procedure in the section 2.2, one can show that the amplitude (37) can be precisely recovered by quantizing the 2d projectable HL gravity with the bi-local interaction based on the path-integral, if $\beta = g_s$.

5. Discussions

We have canonically quantized the 2d projectable HL gravity with a simple space-like wormhole interaction, and shown that the quantum Hamiltonian is equivalent to the one-body quantum Hamiltonian that includes contributions coming from all wormholes and baby universes obtained in the string field theory for CDT, if $g_s = \beta$ and $\lambda = \tilde{\lambda}/(2(1-\eta))$ where $\beta > 0$, $\lambda > 0$ and $\eta < 1$.

Let us consider the classical Hamiltonian constraint $\mathcal{C}$ (42) in the parameter region above. When $\sqrt{\lambda}\ell \geq 1/\xi$ where ξ is a dimensionless quantity defined by $\xi := g_s/\lambda^{3/2}$, the constraint surface is given by $\pi^2 = -\lambda + g_s\ell \geq 0$. However, when $\sqrt{\lambda}\ell < 1/\xi$, the only allowed solution is $\ell = 0$. In the case of the 2d projectable HL gravity ($\beta = g_s = 0$), with the parameter region corresponding to 2d CDT, i.e. $\lambda > 0$, the only solution to the classical Hamiltonian constraint is $\ell = 0$. Therefore, when $\sqrt{\lambda}\ell < 1/\xi$, the classical solution of the 2d projectable HL with the wormhole interaction will be close to that of the 2d projectable HL gravity, if one sits in the parameter region above; they can be quite different when $\sqrt{\lambda}\ell \geq 1/\xi$. Such a relation also holds at the quantum level. As shown in the article,[14] when $\sqrt{\lambda}\ell < 1/\xi$ the eigenfunctions of the one-body quantum Hamiltonian including all wormholes and baby universes, H_{-1} (36), can be well approximated by the eigenfunctions of the quantum Hamiltonian of 2d CDT without wormholes and baby universes, $H_{-1}^{(0)}$ (8). On the other hand, when $\sqrt{\lambda}\ell \geq 1/\xi$, their behaviors are quite different, and in this case, in order for the theory to be well-defined, the unbounded nature of the potential in H_{-1} will be counteracted by the kinetic term. This balance between the kinetic and potential terms is precisely what is reflected in the classical Hamiltonian constraint (42). This is also consistent with the boundary conditions on ℓ at infinity in the path-integral (38).

The picture of creation and annihilation of baby universes and wormholes is conceptually straightforward in the string field theory for CDT.[8] Nevertheless it is somewhat surprising that one from this can derive an effective one-body Hamiltonian which can describe propagation of a single spatial universe, i.e. the propagation where the spatial universe starts with the topology of a circle and at a later time t has the same topology, but where it in the intermediate times is allowed to split in two and either one part disappears in the vacuum (a baby universe), or the two parts join again at a later time (then changing the spacetime topology). This process of joining and splitting can be iterated at intermediate times and using string field theory we can perform the summation of all iterations and derive the effective one-body Hamiltonian (36). From the point of view of unitary evolution (or using Euclidean time, semigroup evolution, to be more precise), as given in eq. (29), it is difficult to understand how a complete set of intermediate states can both be given by the one spatial universe states $|\ell\rangle$ and by the complete multi-universe Fock states of the string field theory (for a recent discussion of this issue see i.e.[16]). However, this seems to be the case by explicit calculation, and we find it even more surprising that the simplest wormhole interaction term added to the classical action as in eq. (39) leads to precisely the same single universe quantum Hamiltonian as found in the string field theory for CDT.

References

1. J. Ambjørn, Y. Hiraga, Y. Ito and Y. Sato, "Wormholes in 2d Hořava-Lifshitz quantum gravity," Phys. Lett. B **816** (2021), 136205 doi:10.1016/j.physletb.2021.136205 [arXiv:2101.07401 [hep-th]].

2. J. Ambjørn and R. Loll, "Nonperturbative Lorentzian quantum gravity, causality and topology change," Nucl. Phys. B **536** (1998), 407-434 doi:10.1016/S0550-3213(98)00692-0 [arXiv:hep-th/9805108 [hep-th]].
3. P. Hořava, "Quantum gravity at a Lifshitz point," Phys. Rev. D **79** (2009) 084008, [arXiv:0901.3775, hep-th].
4. P. Hořava and C.M. Melby-Thompson, "General covariance in quantum gravity at a Lifshitz point," Phys. Rev. D **82** (2010) 064027, [arXiv:1007.2410, hep-th].
5. J. Ambjørn, L. Glaser, Y. Sato and Y. Watabiki, "2d CDT is 2d Hořava–Lifshitz quantum gravity," Phys. Lett. B **722** (2013), 172-175 doi:10.1016/j.physletb.2013.04.006 [arXiv:1302.6359 [hep-th]].
6. B. F. Li, A. Wang, Y. Wu and Z. C. Wu, "Quantization of (1+1)-dimensional Hořava-Lifshitz theory of gravity," Phys. Rev. D **90** (2014) no. 12, 124076 doi:10.1103/PhysRevD.90.124076 [arXiv:1408.2345 [hep-th]].
7. J. Ambjørn, R. Loll, W. Westra and S. Zohren, "Putting a cap on causality violations in CDT," JHEP **12** (2007), 017 doi:10.1088/1126-6708/2007/12/017 [arXiv:0709.2784 [gr-qc]].
8. J. Ambjørn, R. Loll, Y. Watabiki, W. Westra and S. Zohren, "A String Field Theory based on Causal Dynamical Triangulations," JHEP **05** (2008), 032 doi:10.1088/1126-6708/2008/05/032 [arXiv:0802.0719 [hep-th]].
9. J. Ambjørn, R. Loll, Y. Watabiki, W. Westra and S. Zohren, "A Matrix Model for 2D Quantum Gravity defined by Causal Dynamical Triangulations," Phys. Lett. B **665** (2008), 252-256 doi:10.1016/j.physletb.2008.06.026 [arXiv:0804.0252 [hep-th]].
10. J. Ambjørn, R. Loll, Y. Watabiki, W. Westra and S. Zohren, "A New continuum limit of matrix models," Phys. Lett. B **670** (2008), 224-230 doi:10.1016/j.physletb.2008.11.003 [arXiv:0810.2408 [hep-th]].
11. J. Ambjørn, R. Loll, W. Westra and S. Zohren, "Summing over all Topologies in CDT String Field Theory," Phys. Lett. B **678** (2009), 227-232 doi:10.1016/j.physletb.2009.06.031 [arXiv:0905.2108 [hep-th]].
12. J. Ambjørn, R. Loll, W. Westra and S. Zohren, "Stochastic quantization and the role of time in quantum gravity," Phys. Lett. B **680** (2009), 359-364 doi:10.1016/j.physletb.2009.09.016 [arXiv:0908.4224 [hep-th]].
13. T. Regge, "General Relativity without Coordinates," Nuovo Cim. **19** (1961), 558-571 doi:10.1007/BF02733251
14. J. Ambjørn, Y. Sato and Y. Watabiki, "Wormholes, a fluctuating cosmological constant and the Coleman mechanism," Phys. Lett. B **815** (2021), 136152 doi:10.1016/j.physletb.2021.136152 [arXiv:2101.00478 [hep-th]].
15. S. W. Hawking, "The Effective action for wormholes," Nucl. Phys. B **363** (1991), 117-131 doi:10.1016/0550-3213(91)90237-R
16. D. Marolf and H. Maxfield, "Transcending the ensemble: Baby universes, spacetime wormholes, and the order and disorder of black hole information," JHEP **08** (2020), 044, doi:10.1007/JHEP08(2020)044 [arXiv:2002.08950 [hep-th]].

Nature of singularities in vector-tensor theories of gravity

V. H. Satheeshkumar

Departamento de Física, Universidade Federal do Estado do Rio de Janeiro (UNIRIO),
Rio de Janeiro, RJ 22290-240, Brazil
vhsatheeshkumar@gmail.com

The Vector-Tensor (VT) theories of gravity are a class of alternative theories to General Relativity (GR) that are characterized by the presence of a dynamical vector field besides the metric. They are studied in attempts to understand spontaneous Lorentz violation, to generate massive gravitons, and as models of dark matter and dark energy. In this article, I outline how the nature of singularities and horizons in VT theories differ greatly from GR even under the same ordinary conditions. This is illustrated with Einstein-aether theory where vacuum black hole solutions have naked singularities and vacuum cosmological solutions have new singularities that are otherwise absent in GR. It would be interesting to explore these deviations using gravitational waves.

Keywords: Vector-tensor theories of gravity, Modified theories of gravity, Lorentz violation, Spacetime singularities, Naked singularities, Event horizon, Universal horizon

1. Introduction

In the 1960s and early 1970s Roger Penrose, Stephen Hawking and Robert Geroch proved, independently and often in collaboration, a series of theorems on global features of spacetimes in GR. These theorems implied that singularities are inevitable in physically important situations of gravitational collapse and cosmology. The unpreventable existence of singularities for wide classes of rather general models in GR (and other classical theories of gravitation) marks the breakdown of the theory. That is why understanding singularities is crucial for us to find a replacement of GR at very high energies. Even after decades of work, very little is known about the structure and properties of spacetime singularities. For the latest developments on these issues, I refer the reader to the recent reviews by Witten,[1] and Penrose,[2] and also an accessible introduction to the subject by Joshi.[3]

In this paper, we are interested in studying how the presence of a dynamical vector field present in VT theories affects the nature of singularities in comparison to GR. There are many VT theories, but of them the Einstein-aether (EA) theory has the most general diffeomorphism-invariant action involving a spacetime metric and a vector field with the field equations being the second-order differential equations in terms of not only the metric but also the aether field. We study both timelike and spacelike singularities in EA theory. To this end, we consider both black hole and cosmological singularities. In both cases, by computing the Kretschmann scalar, we guarantee that we are dealing with curvature singularities, not conical or caustic singularities.

The paper is organized as follows. The Section 2 presents a quick overview of VT theories. Section 3, briefly outlines the EA theory. In Section 4 and 5, we present future and past singularities respectively. We end with a short summary in Section 6.

2. Vector-Tensor Theories of Gravity

One simple and straightforward extension of GR involves an introduction of a dynamical, timelike four-vector field in addition to the dynamical metric. This class of theories is referred to as Vector-Tensor theories of gravity. In some models, the four-vector is unconstrained, while in others it is constrained to have unit norm. The examples of unconstrained theories are Will-Nordtvedt theory[4,5] (1972), Hellings-Nordtvedt theory[6] (1973) and General vector-tensor theory[7] (1981). The constrained theories include Kostelecky-Samuel theory[8] (1989), Einstein-Aether theory[9] (2001) and Khronometric theory[10] (2010).

The most general action for such a theory which is Lagrangian-based and whose equations of motion involving the vector-field are linear and at most of second order is given by,

$$S = \frac{1}{16\pi G} \int \left[(1+\omega\, g_{ab}u^a u^b)R - K^{ab}{}_{mn}\nabla_a u^m \nabla_b u^n + \lambda(g_{ab}u^a u^b + 1)\right]\sqrt{-g}\,d^4x, \quad (1)$$

where

$$K^{ab}{}_{mn} = c_1 g^{ab} g_{mn} + c_2 \delta^a_m \delta^b_n + c_3 \delta^a_n \delta^b_m - c_4 u^a u^b g_{mn}, \quad (2)$$

the c_i being dimensionless coupling constants, and λ is a Lagrange multiplier enforcing the unit timelike constraint on the aether. The parameter ω is taken to be zero in constrained theories, while λ is set to zero in unconstrained theories.[11] Below, we give the conditions under which different VT theories can be obtained from the general action given above.

- Will-Nordtvedt theory: $\lambda = 0$, $c_1 = -1$ and $c_2 = c_3 = c_4 = 0$
- Hellings-Nordtvedt theory: $\lambda = 0$, $c_1 = 2$, $c_2 = 2\omega$, $c_1 + c_2 + c_3 = 0$ and $c_4 = 0$
- General vector-tensor theory: $\lambda = 0$, $c_1 = 2\epsilon - \tau$, $c_2 = -\eta$, $c_1 + c_2 + c_3 = -\tau$ and $c_4 = 0$
- Kostelecky-Samuel theory: $\omega = 0$ and u^a is not necessarily timelike.
- Einstein-Aether theory: $\omega = 0$ and u^a is always timelike unit vector.
- Khronometric theory: $\omega = 0$, $c_1 = -\epsilon$, $c_2 = \lambda_K$, $c_3 = \beta_K + \epsilon$ and $c_4 = \alpha_K + \epsilon$ where the limit $\epsilon \to \infty$ is to be taken.

Although a lot of work is done on VT theories, there are few reviews on the subject.[12] From the latest phenomenological studies,[13–15] it is evident that EA theory is the most representative of the VT theories and observationally relevant. For this reason, we shall restrict our discussion to EA theory.

3. Einstein-Aether Theory

The general action[9] of the EA theory is given by

$$S = \frac{1}{16\pi G} \int \left[R - K^{ab}{}_{mn} \nabla_a u^m \nabla_b u^n + \lambda(g_{ab} u^a u^b + 1) \right] \sqrt{-g} \, d^4 x + S_{matter}, \quad (3)$$

where

$$K^{ab}{}_{mn} = c_1 g^{ab} g_{mn} + c_2 \delta^a_m \delta^b_n + c_3 \delta^a_n \delta^b_m - c_4 u^a u^b g_{mn}, \quad (4)$$

the c_i being dimensionless coupling constants, and λ is a Lagrange multiplier enforcing the unit timelike constraint on the aether, and $\delta^a_m \delta^b_n = g^{a\alpha} g_{\alpha m} g^{b\beta} g_{\beta n}$. In the weak-field, slow-motion limit EA theory reduces to Newtonian gravity with a value of Newton's constant G_N related to the parameter G in the action (3) by,

$$G = G_N \left(1 - \frac{c_{14}}{2} \right). \quad (5)$$

Here, the constant c_{14} is defined as

$$c_{14} = c_1 + c_4. \quad (6)$$

Note that if $c_{14} = 0$ the EA coupling constant G becomes the Newtonian coupling constant G_N, without necessarily imposing $c_1 = c_4 = 0$. For $c_{14} > 2$ the coupling constant G becomes negative, implying that the gravity is repulsive. The coupling constant vanishes when $c_{14} = 2$ which renders the action undefined. Thus, physically interesting region is $0 \leq c_{14} < 2$. These free parameters have been severely constrained using many observational/experimental tests, including gravitational waves.[16]

The field equations are obtained by extremizing the action with respect to independent variables of the system. The variation with respect to the Lagrange multiplier λ imposes the condition that u^a is a unit timelike vector, thus

$$g_{ab} u^a u^b = -1, \quad (7)$$

while the variation of the action with respect u^a, leads to

$$\nabla_a K^{am}{}_{bn} \nabla_m u^n + c_4 u^m \nabla_m u_a \nabla_b u^a + \lambda u_b = 0, \quad (8)$$

the variation of the action with respect to the metric g_{mn} gives the dynamical equations,

$$G^{Einstein}_{ab} = T^{aether}_{ab} + 8\pi G T^{matter}_{ab}, \quad (9)$$

where

$$G^{Einstein}_{ab} = R_{ab} - \frac{1}{2} g_{ab} R,$$

$$T^{aether}_{ab} = \nabla_c [J^c{}_{(a} u_{b)} + u^c J_{(ab)} - J_{(a}{}^c u_{b)}] - \frac{1}{2} g_{ab} J^c_d \nabla_c u^d + \lambda u_a u_b$$
$$+ c_1 [\nabla_a u_c \nabla_b u^c - \nabla^c u_a \nabla_c u_b] + c_4 u^c \nabla_c u_a u^d \nabla_d u_b,$$

$$T^{matter}_{ab} = \frac{-2}{\sqrt{-g}} \frac{\delta(\sqrt{-g} L_{matter})}{\delta g_{ab}}, \quad (10)$$

with

$$J^a{}_m = K^{ab}{}_{mn}\nabla_b u^n. \tag{11}$$

In a more general situation, the Lagrangian of GR is recovered, if and only if, the coupling constants are identically zero, i.e., $c_1 = c_2 = c_3 = c_4 = 0$.

4. Naked Singularities in Einstein-Aether Theory

In this section, I show that naked singularities appear in EA theory which are otherwise covered by event (Killing) horizons in GR. For this, we start with the most general spherically symmetric static metric,

$$ds^2 = -e^{2A(r)}dt^2 + e^{2B(r)}dr^2 + r^2 d\theta^2 + r^2 \sin^2\theta d\phi^2. \tag{12}$$

In accordance with equation (7), the aether vector is taken to be unitary and timelike,

$$u^a = (e^{-A(r)}, 0, 0, 0). \tag{13}$$

This choice is not the most general and is restricted to the scenario where aether is static. The aether must tip in a black hole solution as it cannot be timelike to be aligned with the null Killing vector on the horizon. As that is not the case with our choice, our solutions are valid only outside the Killing horizon. However, this is not going to be problematic for the solutions presented here.

The timelike Killing vector of the metric (12) is giving by

$$\chi^a = (-1, 0, 0, 0). \tag{14}$$

The Killing and the universal horizon[17] are obtained finding the largest root of

$$\chi^a \chi_a = 0, \tag{15}$$

and

$$\chi^a u_a = 0, \tag{16}$$

respectively, where χ^a is the timelike Killing vector. Thus

$$\chi^a \chi_a = -e^{2A(r)}, \tag{17}$$

$$\chi^a u_a = e^{A(r)}. \tag{18}$$

For the metric in Eq. (12), the tt, rr and $\theta\theta$ components of the vacuum field equations (10) are given by,

$$-\frac{e^{2(A-B)}}{2r^2}\left[c_{14}(-2r^2 A'B' + r^2 A'^2 + 2r^2 A'' + 4rA') - 4rB' - 2e^{2B} + 2\right] = 0, \tag{19}$$

$$-\frac{1}{2r^2}\left(c_{14}r^2 A'^2 + 4rA' - 2e^{2B} + 2\right) = 0, \tag{20}$$

$$\frac{r}{2e^{2B}}\left(2rA'' - 2rA'B' + 2A' - 2B' - (c_{14} - 2)rA'^2\right) = 0. \tag{21}$$

The Kretschmann scalar for the metric (12), is given by

$$K = \frac{4}{r^4 e^{4B}} \left(2B'^2 r^2 + e^{4B} - 2e^{2B} + 1 + 2A'^2 r^2 + r^4 A''^2 + \right.$$
$$\left. 2r^4 A'' A'^2 - 2r^4 A'' B' A' + r^4 A'^4 - 2r^4 A'^3 B' + r^4 B'^2 A'^2 \right). \quad (22)$$

It is not possible to solve these equations analytically for a general case. However, there exist closed form solutions for $c_{14} = 16/9$ and $c_{14} = 48/25$, both of which are within the permitted range. More details about the method employed to obtain these solutions are found in our papers.[18,19]

For $c_{14} = 16/9$, the metric functions and Kretschmann scalar are given by,

$$A = -\frac{3}{4}\ln(r) + \frac{3}{4}\ln\left[r + 4 + \sqrt{(r+8)r}\right], \quad (23)$$

$$B = -\frac{1}{2}\ln(2) + \frac{1}{2}\ln\left(\sqrt{\frac{r}{r+8}} + \frac{r}{r+8}\right), \quad (24)$$

$$K = \frac{768\sqrt{r+8}\left[2r(r+8)^2 + (384 + 104r + 7r^2)\sqrt{(r+8)r}\right]}{\left[r^{11/2}\left(r + 8 + \sqrt{(r+8)r}\right)^4\right]}. \quad (25)$$

From the above equation, we can see that there exists a curvature singularity at $r = 0$. The Killing and universal horizons for this case are obtained by finding the roots of the following,

$$\chi^a \chi_a = -r^{-\frac{3}{2}}\left(r + 4 + \sqrt{(r+8)r}\right)^{\frac{3}{2}} = 0, \quad (26)$$

$$\chi^a u_a = r^{-\frac{3}{4}}\left(r + 4 + \sqrt{(r+8)r}\right)^{\frac{3}{4}} = 0. \quad (27)$$

We can see easily that these equations do not have any real root. Thus, there exists neither Killing horizon nor universal horizon.

For $c_{14} = 48/25$, we see the same behavior as in the previous case, but the mathematical expressions are quite lengthy. So, instead of presenting them here, I refer the reader to our paper.[18]

5. Cosmological Singularities in Einstein-Aether Theory

In this section, I show that initial singularities appear in EA theory which are otherwise absent in GR. For this, we start with the most general isotropic and homogeneous universe is described by a Friedmann-Lemaître-Robertson-Walker (FLRW) metric,

$$ds^2 = -dt^2 + B(t)^2\left[\frac{dr^2}{1 - kr^2} + r^2 d\theta^2 + r^2 \sin^2\theta d\phi^2\right], \quad (28)$$

where, $B(t)$ is the scale factor and k is a Gaussian curvature of the spacial slice at a given time. The appropriate aether vector for this metric is given by,

$$u^a = (1, 0, 0, 0). \tag{29}$$

The standard definitions of the Hubble parameter $H(t)$ and the deceleration parameter $q(t)$ are given by,

$$H(t) = \frac{\dot{B}(t)}{B(t)}, \tag{30}$$

$$q(t) = -\frac{\ddot{B}(t)B(t)}{\dot{B}(t)^2}, \tag{31}$$

where the symbol dot denotes the differentiation with respect to the time coordinate. The Friedmann-Lemaître equations are given by,

$$\left(1 + \frac{\beta}{2}\right)\left(\frac{\dot{B}(t)}{B(t)}\right)^2 = \frac{\Lambda}{3} - \frac{k}{B(t)^2}, \tag{32}$$

$$\left(1 + \frac{\beta}{2}\right)\frac{\ddot{B}(t)}{B(t)} = \frac{\Lambda}{3}, \tag{33}$$

where Λ is the cosmological constant. The Kretschmann scalar for FLRW metric is given by,

$$K = \frac{12}{B^4}\left[k^2 + 2k\dot{B}(t)^2 + \dot{B}(t)^4 + \ddot{B}(t)^2 B(t)^2\right]. \tag{34}$$

We can solve the above equations for nine different combinations of Λ and k. However, here I present only the three cases involving $k = -1$, because these solutions are non-singular in GR but are singular in EA theory. The theoretical consistency requires $\beta \equiv c_1 + 3c_2 + c_3 > -2$. A detailed discussion on other cases can be found in our article.[20]

For $\Lambda > 0, k = -1$, the Friedmann-Lemaître equations have two solutions that exist for $\beta + 2 > 0$,

$$B_1(t) = \frac{1}{2\sqrt{\Lambda}}\left[-\frac{3\,e^{\sqrt{\frac{2\Lambda}{3(\beta+2)}}(t_0-t)}}{\epsilon\sqrt{\Lambda+3}+\sqrt{\Lambda}} + \frac{\epsilon\sqrt{\Lambda+3}+\sqrt{\Lambda}}{e^{\sqrt{\frac{2\Lambda}{3(\beta+2)}}(t_0-t)}}\right], \tag{35}$$

$$B_2(t) = \frac{1}{2\sqrt{\Lambda}}\left[-\frac{3\,e^{\sqrt{\frac{2\Lambda}{3(\beta+2)}}(t-t_0)}}{\epsilon\sqrt{\Lambda+3}+\sqrt{\Lambda}} + \frac{\epsilon\sqrt{\Lambda+3}+\sqrt{\Lambda}}{e^{\sqrt{\frac{2\Lambda}{3(\beta+2)}}(t-t_0)}}\right]. \tag{36}$$

Both are singular at,

$$t_{sing}(B_1) = t_0 - \sqrt{\frac{3(\beta+2)}{8\Lambda}}\ln\left[\frac{2}{3}\Lambda + \frac{2}{3}\epsilon\sqrt{\Lambda(\Lambda+3)} + 1\right], \tag{37}$$

$$t_{sing}(B_2) = t_0 + \sqrt{\frac{3(\beta+2)}{8\Lambda}}\ln\left[\frac{2}{3}\Lambda + \frac{2}{3}\epsilon\sqrt{\Lambda(\Lambda+3)} + 1\right]. \tag{38}$$

The metric is not singular for $\beta = 0$ as the curvature invariant being $\frac{8\Lambda^2}{3}$. But, the metric is singular for $\beta + 2 > 0$ with $\beta \neq 0$. This means it exists only in EA theory but not in GR.

For $\Lambda = 0, k = -1$, we have two solutions satisfying $\beta + 2 > 0$,

$$B_1(t) = 1 + \sqrt{\frac{2}{2+\beta}}(t_0 - t) \tag{39}$$

$$B_2(t) = 1 + \sqrt{\frac{2}{2+\beta}}(t - t_0) \tag{40}$$

Both are singular at

$$t_{sing}(B_1) = t_0 + \sqrt{\frac{2+\beta}{2}}, \tag{41}$$

$$t_{sing}(B_2) = t_0 - \sqrt{\frac{2+\beta}{2}}. \tag{42}$$

For $\beta = 0$ which corresponds to GR, the solution exists and is never singular with the curvature invariant being zero. But, the metric is singular for $\beta + 2 > 0$ such that $\beta \neq 0$. This means it is a new singularity that exists only in EA theory but not GR.

For $\Lambda < 0, k = -1$, there exists two solutions satisfying $\beta + 2 > 0$,

$$B_1(t) = \sqrt{\frac{3}{|\Lambda|}} \sin\left(\sqrt{\frac{2|\Lambda|}{3(\beta+2)}}(t-t_0) + \sin^{-1}\sqrt{\frac{|\Lambda|}{3}}\right) \tag{43}$$

$$B_2(t) = \sqrt{\frac{3}{|\Lambda|}} \sin\left(\sqrt{\frac{2|\Lambda|}{3(\beta+2)}}(t_0-t) + \sin^{-1}\sqrt{\frac{|\Lambda|}{3}}\right) \tag{44}$$

Both are singular at

$$t_{sing}(B_1) = t_0 - \sqrt{\frac{3(\beta+2)}{2|\Lambda|}} \sin^{-1}\sqrt{\frac{|\Lambda|}{3}} \tag{45}$$

$$t_{sing}(B_2) = t_0 + \sqrt{\frac{3(\beta+2)}{2|\Lambda|}} \sin^{-1}\sqrt{\frac{|\Lambda|}{3}} \tag{46}$$

For $\beta = 0$ the solution exists but is never singular with the curvature invariant being $\frac{8|\Lambda|^2}{3}$. But, the metric is singular for $\beta + 2 > 0$ with $\beta \neq 0$. This means it is a new singularity that exists only in EA theory.

The above results are independently confirmed by studying the focusing of congruence of timelike geodesics using the Raychaudhuri equation.[20]

6. Conclusions

Many of the deep conceptual issues related to gravity are closely connected with the very existence spacetime singularities. The singularity theorems predict only the existence of spacetime singularities under a set of physically reasonable conditions, but not say much else about them. In principle, spacetime singularities and event horizons are two totally different and independent concepts in gravitational physics. However, the Cosmic Censorship Conjecture (CCC) suggests that whenever a spacetime singularity occurs it always stays hidden within an event horizon. But, the mathematically rigorous formulation of the CCC, let alone its proof, is still an open problem. We have attempted to understand these issues in VT theories of gravity with the hope that we might look at GR from a fresh perspective.

In this paper, we investigated how the presence of timelike vector field in EA theory affects the nature of singularities in comparison to GR theory. Firstly, I have illustrated with two analytical solutions ($c_{14} = 16/9$ and $48/25$) that the Schwarzschild metric in EA theory is singular at $r = 0$ but it is not covered by neither Killing horizon nor universal horizon, whereas the corresponding case in GR has horizons. Thus we have naked singularities. Astrophysically, a naked singularity is distinguishable from a black hole of the same mass from the the luminosity of the accretion disk as it extends very close to the naked singularity.[21] Secondly, I have shown that for three different cases with $k = -1$, the FLRW vacuum solutions in EA theory are singular, but non-singular in GR. All these solutions are within the experimentally allowed parameter space. Initial singularity is in principle visible. However, from the data we know that our universe has $k = 0$, thus making this result observationally not viable. The important take away is that the new singular solutions show that GR and EA theories have different global structures even for the simple situations.

Acknowledgments

It is my pleasure to thank Roberto Chan and Maria de Fátima Alves da Silva for several useful discussions and collaboration on the works that produced some of the key results presented here. I am grateful to the organizers of MG16, especially Anzong Wang, for the invitation to give this talk. Finally, I would like to dedicate this article to T. Padmanabhan (1957–2021) who has significantly influenced me before and since I got to be in his orbit when I participated in the *IUCAA Vacation Students' Programme* during the summer of 2003.

References

1. E. Witten, Rev. Mod. Phys. **92**, no. 4, 045004 (2020) [arXiv:1901.03928 [hep-th]].
2. R. Penrose, "Singularity theorems," in *Topology and Physics*, Editors, Chen Ning Yang, Mo-Lin Ge, Yang-Hui He (World Scientific, Singapore, 2019) pp. 135 –171.
3. P. S. Joshi, "The Story of Collapsing Stars: Black Holes, Naked Singularities, and the Cosmic Play of Quantum Gravity," (Oxford University Press, USA, 2015).

4. C. M. Will and K. Nordtvedt, Jr., Astrophys. J. **177**, 757 (1972).
5. K. Nordtvedt, Jr. and C. M. Will, Astrophys. J. **177**, 775-792 (1972).
6. R. W. Hellings and K. Nordtvedt, Phys. Rev. D **7**, 3593-3602 (1973).
7. C. M. Will, *Theory and experiment in gravitational physics*, (Cambridge University Press, First Edition, UK, 1981). pp 126–130
8. V. A. Kostelecky and S. Samuel, Phys. Rev. D **40**, 1886-1903 (1989).
9. T. Jacobson and D. Mattingly, Phys. Rev. D **64**, 024028 (2001) [arXiv:gr-qc/0007031 [gr-qc]].
10. D. Blas, O. Pujolas and S. Sibiryakov, JHEP **04**, 018 (2011) [arXiv:1007.3503 [hep-th]].
11. C. M. Will, *Theory and experiment in gravitational physics*, (Cambridge University Press, Second Edition, UK, 2018). pp 118–121
12. A. Petrov, "Introduction to Modified Gravity" (Springer, Switzerland, 2020). pp 37–46
13. J. Oost, M. Bhattacharjee and A. Wang, Gen. Rel. Grav. **50**, no. 10, 124 (2018) [arXiv:1804.01124 [gr-qc]].
14. K. Lin, X. Zhao, C. Zhang, T. Liu, B. Wang, S. Zhang, X. Zhang, W. Zhao, T. Zhu and A. Wang, Phys. Rev. D **99**, no. 2, 023010 (2019) [arXiv:1810.07707 [astro-ph.GA]].
15. C. Zhang, X. Zhao, A. Wang, B. Wang, K. Yagi, N. Yunes, W. Zhao and T. Zhu, Phys. Rev. D **101**, no. 4, 044002 (2020) [erratum: Phys. Rev. D **104**, no. 6, 069905 (2021)] [arXiv:1911.10278 [gr-qc]].
16. J. Oost, S. Mukohyama and A. Wang, Phys. Rev. D **97**, no. 12, 124023 (2018) [arXiv:1802.04303 [gr-qc]].
17. K. Lin, O. Goldoni, M. F. da Silva and A. Wang, Phys. Rev. D **91**, no. 2, 024047 (2015) [arXiv:1410.6678 [gr-qc]].
18. R. Chan, M. F. A. Da Silva and V. H. Satheeshkumar, Eur. Phys. J. C **81**, no. 4, 317 (2021) [arXiv:2003.00227 [gr-qc]].
19. M. Campista, R. Chan, M. F. A. da Silva, O. Goldoni, V. H. Satheeshkumar and J. F. V. da Rocha, Can. J. Phys. **98**, no. 10, 917-928 (2020) [arXiv:1807.07553 [gr-qc]].
20. R. Chan, M. F. A. da Silva and V. H. Satheeshkumar, JCAP **05**, 025 (2020) [arXiv:1912.12845 [gr-qc]].
21. P. S. Joshi, D. Malafarina and R. Narayan, Class. Quant. Grav. **31**, 015002 (2014) [arXiv:1304.7331 [gr-qc]].

Hořava-Lifshitz and Einstein-Æther gravity in the light of Event Horizon Telescope observations of M87*

Emmanuel N. Saridakis

National Observatory of Athens, Lofos Nymfon, 11852 Athens, Greece
E-mail: msaridak@noa.gr

We investigate Hořava-Lifshitz and Einstein-Æther gravity in light of the Event Horizon Telescope (EHT) observations of the M87*. We calculate the corresponding photon effective potential, the unstable photon sphere radius, and finally the induced angular size, which combined with the mass and the distance can lead to a single prediction that quantifies the black hole shadow, namely the diameter per unit mass d. Since d_{M87*} is observationally known from the EHT Probe, we extract the corresponding parameter regions in order to obtain consistency. We find that Einstein-Æther black hole solutions agree with the shadow size of EHT M87*, if the involved Æther parameters are restricted within specific ranges, along with an upper bound on the dimensionless spin parameter a, which is verified by a full scan of the parameter space within 1σ-error.

Keywords: M87* observations; Event Horizon Telescope; Einstein-Æther gravity; Hořava-Lifshitz gravity.

1. Introduction

In the light of recording the first stunning new radio images of the supermassive black hole (BH) that exists at the center of nearby galaxy M87* by *"Event Horizon Telescope"* (EHT),[1,2] the black-hole shadow has become one of the most exciting events in observational astronomy. Historically the concept of the black hole shadow comes from the 70's with the seminal works.[3] In these studies it was found that the non-rotating BH has a perfect circular shadow, while by taking the rotation into account the shape of shadow is elongated due to the dragging effect.[4]

The dark area over a brighter background in the center of the image is termed as *"BH's shadow"*, and it is predicted by general relativity as the null geodesics in the strong gravity area.[5,6] In particular, photons with some critical angular momentum, will swirl around the BH one ring by one ring which makes the unstable boundary of the shadow, which is the same as the shining halo observed in EHT image. Nevertheless, given that the shape and size of the shadow contains traces of the geometry vicinity of the BH, and similarly to the quasinormal modes approach, one can consider the shadow as a potential probe to investigate the BH structure within different gravitational theories.

Horava-Lifshitz[7-10] and Einstein-Æther (EA) theory[11-14] are generally covariant theories of gravity, which violate the Lorentz invariance locally, and the latter possesses a dynamical, unit-norm and timelike vector field, called *"æther field"*, which defines a preferred timelike direction at each spacetime point. EA gravity includes a number of coupling constants called æther parameters. In the present work we are interested in investigating Horava-Lifshitz and Einstein-Æther theory using the EHT observations of the M87*, based on.[15] Throughout the manuscript we adopt natural units where $\hbar = k_B = c = 1$.

2. Rotating black-hole solutions in Einstein-Æther gravity

The action of the EA theory is[11]

$$S = S_{EH} + S_{AE} = \frac{1}{16\pi G_{AE}} \int d^4x \sqrt{-g}\left(R + \mathcal{L}_{AE}\right), \quad (1)$$

which includes the standard Einstein-Hilbert action S_{EH} plus the æther action S_{AE}. In the above action, R, G_{EA} and $\mathcal{L}_{AE}$ refer respectively to the Ricci scalar, the Æther gravitational constant and the Lagrangian of the Æther field u^μ, which is defined as

$$\mathcal{L}_{AE} \equiv -\left(c_1 g^{\alpha\beta} g_{\mu\nu} + c_2 \delta^\alpha_\mu \delta^\beta_\nu + c_3 \delta^\alpha_\nu \delta^\beta_\mu - c_4 u^\alpha u^\beta g_{\mu\nu}\right)(\nabla_\alpha u^\mu)(\nabla_\beta u^\nu) + \lambda_0(u^2 + 1). \quad (2)$$

Here, λ_0 is a Lagrangian multiplier, ensuring that the Æther four-velocity u^α is always timelike (i.e. $u^2 = -1$). All of four coupling constants (c_1, c_2, c_3, c_4) in the above expression are dimensionless, and thus G_{AE} is linked to the Newtonian constant G_N via two of them, namely $G_{AE} = \frac{2G_N}{2-c_1-c_4}$.[16] As usual, variations of the total action with respect to $g_{\mu\nu}$, u^α, λ_0 yield, respectively, the field equations.[15]

There exists a corresponding slowly rotating black hole solution, with a spherically symmetric æther field configuration $(\lambda(r) = 0)$, namely[15]

$$ds^2 = -e(r)dt^2 + \frac{dr^2}{e(r)} + r^2(d\theta^2 + \sin^2\theta d\phi^2) - \frac{4Ma}{r}\sin^2\theta dt d\phi, \quad (3)$$

with

$$e(r) = 1 - \frac{2M}{r} - \frac{27c_{13}}{256(1-c_{13})}\left(\frac{2M}{r}\right)^4. \quad (4)$$

Note that for convenience we have replaced the angular momentum J by introducing the rotation parameter[17] a through $a \equiv \frac{J}{M}$.

3. Black hole shadow

As usual, in order to study the geodesics structure of the photon trajectories, we begin with the Hamilton-Jacobi equation

$$\frac{\partial S}{\partial \lambda} = -\frac{1}{2}g^{\mu\nu}\frac{\partial S}{\partial x^\mu}\frac{\partial S}{\partial x^\nu}, \quad (5)$$

where S and λ denote respectively the Jacobi action of the particle (here photon) moving in the black hole spacetime, and the affine parameter of the null geodesic. Concerning the massless photon propagating on the null geodesics, the Jacobi action S can be separated as

$$S = -Et + J\phi + S_r(r) + S_\theta(\theta), \quad (6)$$

where E and J respectively address the energy and angular momentum of the photon in the direction of the rotation axis. Furthermore, the functions $S_r(r)$ and $S_\theta(\theta)$ have only r and θ dependencies, respectively.

By inserting the Jacobi action (6) into the Hamilton-Jacobi equation (5), using also the metric components (3), we find that the photon trajectories are expressed in terms of the radial geodesics and the effective potential $U_{eff}(r)$ as:[15]

$$\left(\frac{dr}{d\lambda}\right)^2 + U_{eff}(r) = 0 \tag{7}$$

with

$$U_{eff}(r) = -1 + \frac{e(r)}{r^2}(\xi^2 + \eta) + \frac{4M\eta a}{r^3}, \tag{8}$$

where $\xi = \frac{J}{E}$, $\eta = \frac{K}{E^2}$. The above two impact parameters ξ and η are actually the principle quantities for determining the photon motion. We can extract the geometric shape of the shadow via the allowed values of ξ and η that satisfy the above conditions. Thus, we arrive at

$$2(\eta + \xi^2)re(r) - (\eta + \xi^2)r^2 e'(r) + 12M\xi a = 0 . \tag{9}$$

By solving this equation one acquires the radius r_{ps} of the photon sphere, which since we have taken the rotation effect into account is expected to be between the two values $r_{ps}^{\mp}$.

For slowly rotating BHs we immediately find that for the spherical-orbit photon motion the two parameters ξ and η have the form

$$\xi(r) = \frac{r^3[re'(r) - 2e(r)]}{4Ma[e(r) + re'(r)]}, \tag{10}$$

$$\eta(r) = \frac{-r^6[-2e(r) + re'(r)]^2 + 48M^2 a^2 r^2 [e(r) + re'(r)]}{16M^2 a^2 [e(r) + e'(r)]^2}. \tag{11}$$

As usual, to describe the shadow as seen by a distant observer, one introduces the following two celestial coordinates X and Y:[6]

$$X = \lim_{r_* \to \infty} \left(-r_*^2 \sin\theta_0 \frac{d\phi}{dr}\right), \tag{12}$$

$$Y = \lim_{r_* \to \infty} r_*^2 \frac{d\theta}{dr}, \tag{13}$$

where r_* and θ_0 are respectively the distance between the observer and the black hole, and the inclination angle between the line of sight of the observer and the rotational axis of the black hole. By applying the geodesics equations along with the expressions $\frac{d\phi}{dr} = \frac{d\phi/d\lambda}{dr/d\lambda}$ and $\frac{d\theta}{dr} = \frac{d\theta/d\lambda}{dr/d\lambda}$ we obtain

$$X = -\xi(r_{ps})\csc\theta_0 , \tag{14}$$

$$Y = \sqrt{\eta(r_{ps}) - \xi^2(r_{ps})\cot^2\theta_0} , \tag{15}$$

and therefore these two celestial coordinates fulfill
$$X^2 + Y^2 = \xi^2(r_{ps}) + \eta_{\mathbf{ps}}(r_{ps}) ,\qquad(16)$$
where r_{ps} is the aforementioned radius of the unstable photon sphere. This is the expression of the EA BHs shadow in the slow rotation limit. As a self-consistency check, we can see that in the Schwarzschild limit, namely $a \to 0$, the above equation becomes $X^2 + Y^2 = 27M^2$, as expected.

3.1. *Einstein-Æther black hole solution*

In order to draw the shadow of the BH solution we need to calculate two essential quantities, namely the event horizon radius r_e and the radius of the unstable photon sphere r_{ps}. In order to find the even horizon of metric (3) we have to solve
$$r^4 - 2Mr^3 - \frac{27c_{13}}{16(1-c_{13})} M^4 = 0 ,\qquad(17)$$
where $c_{13} \equiv c_1 + c_3$. This leads to
$$r_{e_{1,2}} = \frac{3M^2}{2} - s \pm \frac{1}{2}\sqrt{-4s^2 + 3M^2 - \frac{M^2}{s}} ,\qquad(18)$$
$$r_{e_{3,4}} = \frac{3M^2}{2} + s \pm \frac{1}{2}\sqrt{-4s^2 + 3M^2 + \frac{M^2}{s}} ,\qquad(19)$$
where
$$s = \sqrt{\frac{3M^2 Q + Q^2 + \Delta_0}{12Q}}, \quad Q = \left(\frac{\Delta_1 + \sqrt{\Delta_1^2 - 4\Delta_0^3}}{2}\right)^{1/3} ,\qquad(20)$$
$$\Delta_0 = -\frac{81c_{13}}{4(1-c_{13})}M^4, \quad \Delta_1 = \frac{729c_{13}}{2(1-c_{13})}M^7 .\qquad(21)$$

Solutions $r_{1,2}$ are imaginary and thus not physically interesting. Nevertheless, by setting c_{13} to zero the third solution becomes $r_3 = 2M$, as expected from Schwarzschild background. Thus, we deduce that r_3 addresses the event horizon radius r_e of the Einstein-Æther BH solution.

We proceed by setting $\eta = 0$, and inserting the ξ_{ps} from $U_{eff} = 0$
$$\xi_{ps} = \frac{2Ma}{e(r_{ps})r_{ps}} \left[-1 + \sqrt{1 + \frac{r_{ps}^4 e(r_{ps})}{4M^2 a^2}}\right] ,\qquad(22)$$
into (9). Then, using $e(r)$ from Eq. (4) we finally result to the following equation
$$a^2 (\alpha_1 - 8)(c_{13} - 1)r_{ps}^3 \left[81\alpha_1 c_{13} + 16(\alpha_1 + 16)(c_{13} - 1)r_{ps}^4 \right.$$
$$\left. -48(\alpha_1 + 8)(c_{13} - 1)r_{ps}^3\right] = 0 ,\qquad(23)$$
with
$$\alpha_1 = \sqrt{\frac{64a^2(c_{13} - 1)(r_{ps} - 2)r_{ps}^3 + 16(c_{13} - 1) + 27c_{13}}{(c_{13} - 1)a^2}} .\qquad(24)$$
The solution of Eq. (23) will provide the radius of the photon sphere r_{ps}.

4. Confrontation with and M87* observations

We can now proceed to the investigation of the constraints on the æther parameter c_{13} that arise from the EHT Observations of the shadow of M87*. In particular, the size of the resulting shadow is sensitive on the æther parameter c_{13}, and hence the image of M87* is able to impose bounds on them.

In light of the report released by EHT collaboration for the shadow of M87* in,[1,2] for the angular size of the shadow, the mass and the distance to M87* one respectively has the values

$$\delta = (42 \pm 3)\,\mu\text{arcsec}, \qquad (25)$$
$$M = (6.5 \pm 0.9) \times 10^9\, M_\odot, \qquad (26)$$
$$D = 16.8^{+0.8}_{-0.7}\,\text{Mpc}, \qquad (27)$$

where $M_\odot$ is the Sun mass. One can merge this information by introducing the single number d_{M87*}, which quantifies the size of M87*'s shadow in unit mass, defined as[17]

$$d_{M87*} \equiv \frac{D\delta}{M} \approx 11.0 \pm 1.5. \qquad (28)$$

This combination can be used in order to confront with the theoretically predicted shadows (e.g. the above number is in agreement within 1σ-error with what we theoretically expect for the Schwarzschild BH, namely $d_{Schw} \simeq 10.4^6$).

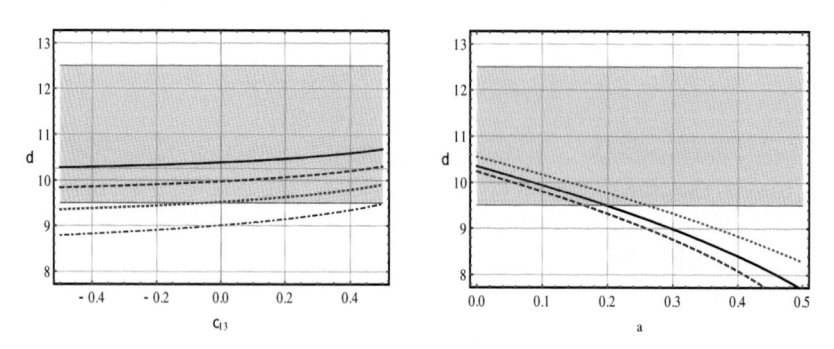

Fig. 1. **Left graph:** The predicted diameter per unit mass d for the Einstein-Æther black hole solution (3) with (4), as a function of the æther parameter c_{13}, for several values of the rotational parameter: $a = 0$ (black - solid), $a = 0.1$ (blue - dashed), $a = 0.2$ (red - dotted), $a = 0.3$ (purple - dashed-dotted). **Right graph:** d as a function of the rotational parameter a, for $c_{13} = -0.5$ (blue - dashed), $c_{13} = 0$ (black- solid), $c_{13} = 0.5$ (red- dotted). In both graphs the shaded area mark the observationally determined diameter per unit mass of M87*'s shadow, namely d_{M87*}, within 1σ-error.

In order to confront Einstein-Æther solutions with the above observational number, all we need is to calculate the angular size δ as a function of the Einstein-Æther parameters. The angular size can be immediately extracted from the profile (16), as long as we know the radius of the unstable photon sphere r_{ps} (as a function of the Einstein-Æther parameter). Knowing δ can then easily lead to the predicted diameter per unit mass d. Note that in agreement with EHT, from now on we fix the value $\theta_0 = 17$ for the inclination angle.

In Fig. 1 we depict the diameter of the predicted shadow d as a function of c_{13} and a, on top of the observed one from M87* within 1σ. As we observe, the Æther BH solution is able to quantitatively describe the shadow size of M87*, provided that the dimensionless spin parameter a is constrained to specific values, dependent on c_{13}. Note that since our whole analysis has been restricted to the slow rotation case, the extracted upper bounds on a are perfectly consistent and justify our approximation. The curves in Fig. 1 imply that within these ranges of c_{13} it is possible to distinguish a naked singularity ($c_{13} < 0$) from BH ($c_{13} > 0$). Furthermore, in order to present the bounds on spin parameter a in a more transparent way, we perform a full scan of the two-dimensional parameter space and in Fig. 2 we depict the region which corresponds to a d in agreement with the observed value d_{M87*}. As it is clear from it as well as from the right panel in Fig. 1, by moving from negative to positive values of æther parameter c_{13}, the upper bound on the a grows. This may be useful in distinguishing between BH and naked singularity.

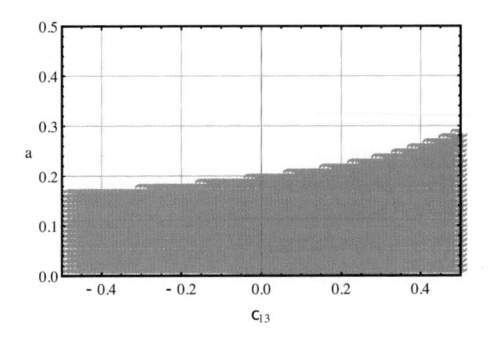

Fig. 2. The allowed parameter region (green) in the $c_{13} - a$ plane, for fixed BH mass ($M = 6 \times 10^9 M_\odot$), for the Einstein-Æther black hole solution (3) with (4), that leads to diameter per unit mass d in agreement with the observationally determined one d_{M87*} within 1σ-error.

We mention here that in order to create the allowed parameter space plots on the $c_{13} - a$ plane, we have fixed the BH mass to $M = 6 \times 10^9 M_\odot$. Nevertheless, one can also perform a similar parameter scan for the case of non-fixed BH mass, namely within the two-dimensional parameter space (c_{13}, M), for different fixed values of the rotation parameter a. In Fig. 3 we present such a graph. As we observe, for reasonable c_{13} values, the BH mass lies within the range we expect from EHT for M87*, i.e. $M = (6.5 \pm 0.9) \times 10^9 M_\odot$. Furthermore, Fig. 3 shows the role of rotation on the allowed region of the $c_{13} - M$ plane, namely by increasing the rotation parameter we are led to larger region for the c_{13} parameter and still be consistent with EHT data within 1-σ error. In summary, Einstein-Æther BH solution is in agreement with M87* observation, and moreover we obtain a restriction to low rotational values.

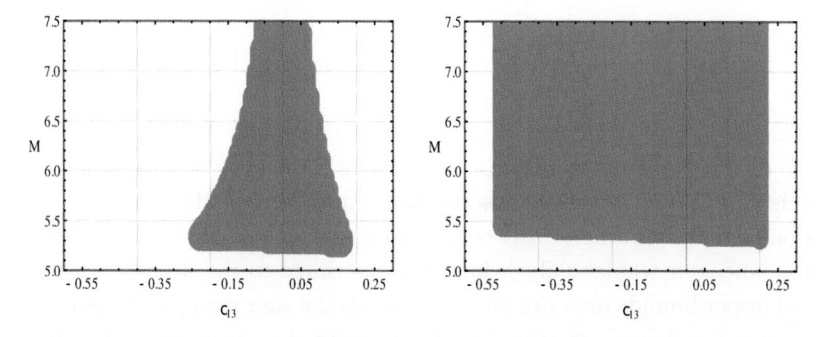

Fig. 3. The allowed parameter region (green) in the $c_{13} - M(10^9 M_\odot)$ plane, for fixed rotation parameter values $a = 0$ (left graph) and $a = 0.2$ (right graph), for the Einstein-Æther black hole solution (3) with (4), that leads to diameter d in agreement with the observationally determined one d_{M87*} within 1σ-error.

5. Conclusions

In the present work we investigated Hořava-Lifshitz and Einstein-Æther gravity in light of the recent Event Horizon Telescope (EHT) observations of the M87*. In particular, the EHT provided the first visual evidence indicating directly the existence of a compact object such as a supermassive black hole candidate at the center of the M87* galaxy. Since the shape and size of the observed BH shadow contains information of the geometry in the vicinity of the BH, one can consider the shadow as a potential probe to investigate the BH structure within different gravitational theories, due to the fact that in modified gravity one obtain black holes which deviate from those of general relativity.[18] Hence, allowing for a modified gravity as the underlying theory enriches the calculation framework with different size-rotation features as well as with extra model parameters.

We first extracted the black hole solutions for EA gravity, and we calculated the corresponding effective potential $U_{eff}(r)$ for the photons, the resulting event horizon radius r_e and the radius of the unstable photon sphere r_{ps}. Then we straightforwardly calculated the induced angular size δ, which combined with the mass and the distance can lead to a single prediction that quantifies the black hole shadow size, namely the diameter per unit mass d. Since d_{M87*} is observationally known from the EHT Probe, we extracted the corresponding parameter regions of Einstein-Æther theory in order to obtain consistency.

Apart from the restriction of the æther parameter c_{13} to specific ranges, we found some constraints on the dimensionless spin parameter a in slow rotation limit, dependent on the values of æther parameters, which was verified by a full scan of the parameter space. Furthermore, our analysis has indicated that in the Einstein-Æther theory is possible to distinguish a naked singularity from BH. This is indeed a verification of the fact that in modified gravity one obtains different size-rotation features, depending on the extra model parameters, and hence the M87* observation can be in principle described in different ways comparing to general relativity, especially in theories which possess various corrections on the Kerr-metric solutions, such is the case in Hořava-Lifshitz and Einstein-Æther gravity. In summary, Einstein-Æther black hole solutions are in agreement with EHT M87* observation.

References

1. K. Akiyama *et al.* [Event Horizon Telescope Collaboration], *First M87 Event Horizon Telescope Results. I. The Shadow of the Supermassive Black Hole*, Astrophys. J. Lett. **875**, L1 (2019).
2. K. Akiyama *et al.* [Event Horizon Telescope Collaboration], *First M87 Event Horizon Telescope Results. VI. The Shadow and Mass of the Central Black Hole*, Astrophys. J. Lett. **875**, no. 1, L6 (2019).
3. J. L. Synge, *The Escape of Photons from Gravitationally Intense Stars*, Mon. Not. Roy. Astron. Soc. **131**, no. 3, 463 (1966).
4. R. Narayan, M. D. Johnson and C. F. Gammie, *The Shadow of a Spherically Accreting Black Hole*, Astrophys. J. Lett. **885**, no. 2, L33 (2019).
5. P. V. P. Cunha and C. A. R. Herdeiro, *Shadows and strong gravitational lensing: a brief review*, Gen. Rel. Grav. **50**, no. 4, 42 (2018).
6. S. Chandrasekhar, *The mathematical theory of black holes*, Oxford classic texts in the physical sciences, Oxford Univ. Press, Oxford (2002).
7. P. Horava, *Quantum Gravity at a Lifshitz Point*, Phys. Rev. D **79**, 084008 (2009).
8. E. N. Saridakis, *Horava-Lifshitz Dark Energy*, Eur. Phys. J. C **67**, 229-235 (2010).
9. S. Dutta and E. N. Saridakis, *Observational constraints on Horava-Lifshitz cosmology*, JCAP **01**, 013 (2010).
10. R. Garattini and E. N. Saridakis, *Gravity's Rainbow: A bridge towards Hořava–Lifshitz gravity*, Eur. Phys. J. C **75**, no. 7, 343 (2015).
11. T. Jacobson and D. Mattingly, *Gravity with a dynamical preferred frame*, Phys. Rev. D **64**, 024028 (2001).
12. T. Jacobson, *Extended Horava gravity and Einstein-aether theory*, Phys. Rev. D **81**, 101502 (2010) [erratum: Phys. Rev. D **82**, 129901 (2010)].
13. K. Yagi, D. Blas, E. Barausse and N. Yunes, *Constraints on Einstein-Æther theory and Hořava gravity from binary pulsar observations*, Phys. Rev. D **89**, no. 8, 084067 (2014) [erratum: Phys. Rev. D **90**, no. 6, 069902 (2014); erratum: Phys. Rev. D **90**, no. 6, 069901 (2014)].
14. C. Eling and T. Jacobson, *Spherical solutions in Einstein-aether theory: Static aether and stars*, Class. Quant. Grav. **23**, 5625-5642 (2006) [erratum: Class. Quant. Grav. **27**, 049801 (2010)].
15. M. Khodadi and E. N. Saridakis, *Einstein-Æther gravity in the light of event horizon telescope observations of M87**, Phys. Dark Univ. **32**, 100835 (2021).
16. S. M. Carroll and E. A. Lim, *Lorentz-violating vector fields slow the universe down*, Phys. Rev. D **70**, 123525 (2004).
17. C. Bambi, K. Freese, S. Vagnozzi and L. Visinelli, *Testing the rotational nature of the supermassive object M87* from the circularity and size of its first image*, Phys. Rev. D **100**, no. 4, 044057 (2019).
18. E. N. Saridakis *et al.* [CANTATA], *Modified Gravity and Cosmology: An Update by the CANTATA Network*, [arXiv:2105.12582 [gr-qc]].

Hořava-Lifshitz gravity in (3 + 1) dimensions coupled with anisotropic matter and possible constraints from GRB 170817A

Tao Zhang[1,2,3] and Fu-Wen Shu[2,3,4,*]

[1]*School of Electrical Engineering, Jiujiang Vocational and Technical College, Jiujiang, Jiangxi 332007, China*
[2]*Department of Physics, Nanchang University, Nanchang, 330031, China*
[3]*Center for Relativistic Astrophysics and High Energy Physics, Nanchang University, Nanchang 330031, China*
[4]*GCAP-CASPER, Physics Department, Baylor University, Waco, TX 76798-7316, USA*
*E-mail: shufuwen@ncu.edu.cn

This paper is a summary of a talk given in the proceedings of Sixteenth Marcel Grossmann Meeting (MG16). We study a (3+1)-dimensional Hořava-Lifshitz (HL) gravity which coupling with an anisotropic electromagnetic (EM) field which is obtained from a (4+1)-dimensional HL gravity. The model has a noticeable feature that gravitational and electromagnetic waves have the same velocity in the Minkowski background and the Friedman-Robertson-Walker (FRW) background. Based on this characteristic we put forward a new way to restrict the parameter of the HL gravity by considering the possible Lorentz violation effect of the GRB 170817A. It turns out that in this way we can place a stringent constraint on the parameter of (4+1)-dimensional HL gravity.

Keywords: Hořava-Lifshitz gravity; Lorentz violation effect; GRB 170817A.

1. Introduction

The first gravitational wave (GW) event from a binary neutron star merger, GW170817, was detected by LIGO and Virgo Collaboration,[1] opened the era of multi-messenger astronomy, which create an opportunity to study gravity and cosmology by multiple observations. At the same time, its EM counterpart—GRB 170817A— was observed by Fermi-GBM with a time delay $\Delta t = (1.74 \pm 0.05)s$.[2] Analyzing the time delay between GW170817 and GRB 170817A, one can impose a stringent constraint on the speed deviation between GWs and the GRBs. This in turn may put restrictions on certain models of modified gravity. However, due to the lack of more similar GW events and the way of direct detection of the speed of GWs, it is necessary to develop new methods to restrict the GWs velocity. In view of this, we turn to consider the GW's counterpart: the gamma ray bursts (GRBs). It is of great interest to investigate whether we can limit the velocity of GWs from the GRB data. If this is possible, it may provide an independent approach in restricting the parameter of some modified models of gravity.

On the other hand, Lorentz invariance has been confirmed rigorously in low energy and the light speed is a constancy in General Relativity (GR). However, the viewpoint that the possible Lorentz violation (LV) will happen at energies comparable with the Planck scale ($E_{pl} \approx 1.22 \times 10^{19}$ GeV) has been proposed in many quantum gravity theories. This possible LV effect may have been observed in some high-energy astrophysical phenomena such as gamma-ray bursts, active galactic nuclei (AGN) and Crab pulsars, etc., and the LV energy scale can be estimated by analyzing the observed time delay or spectra delay of the gamma rays.[3] Then we wonder if the possible LV is common in these high-energy astrophysical phenomena, the GRB 170817A would have the similar LV behavior. It can be then used to study GWs and restrict the parameter of some modified theories of gravity.

For this reason, in this work we consider a special modified model of gravity: a (3+1)-dimensional HL gravity couple with the electromagnetic field which is obtained from a $(4+1)$−dimensions HL gravity through a Kaluza-Klein (KK) reduction. The wave equations for gravitational and EM fields can be obtained by linear perturbations. One of the most significant characteristics of this model is that the speeds of gravitational and EM waves are the same, no matter it is in the Minkowski background or the Friedman-Robertson-Walker (FRW) background. Based on this feature, we can impose restrictions on the propagation velocity of GWs by considering the possible LV effect of the accompanied GRB, which in turn can be applied to limit the parameter of some gravity theories.

2. The (4+1)-dimensional Hořava-Lifshitz gravity

We begin with a (4+1)-dimensional HL gravity. The action of the non-projectable HL gravity in (4+1) dimensions is,[4]

$$S(g_{\mu\nu}, N_\rho, N) = \int dt d^4 x N \sqrt{g} \Big[K_{\mu\nu} K^{\mu\nu} - \lambda K^2 + \beta\, ^{(4)}R + \alpha a_\mu a^\mu + V(g_{\mu\nu}, N) \Big], \quad (1)$$

where μ, ν=1, 2, 3, 4. $V(g_{\mu\nu}, N)$ expresses the higher terms, we can ignore these terms because the most energetic particles of the GRB events are much less than the HL energy scale.

The Hamiltonian density $\mathcal{H}$ can be expressed as

$$\mathcal{H} = \sqrt{g} N \left[\frac{\pi_{\mu\nu} \pi^{\mu\nu}}{g} + \frac{\lambda}{1-4\lambda} \frac{\pi^2}{g} - \beta\, ^{(4)}R - \alpha a_\mu a^\mu \right] + 2\pi^{\mu\nu} \nabla_\mu N_\nu + \sigma P_N, \quad (2)$$

where $\pi^{\mu\nu}$ is the conjugate momentum to $g_{\mu\nu}$ and we have added the the primary constraints by multiplying the Lagrange multipliers σ and N_ν.

In Eq.(2), we notice that $\lambda = 1/4$ is a kinetic conformal point which will eliminate a scalar mode, but it has no influence on gravity and electromagnetic modes which we are interest. In order to analyze the couplings between gravity modes and electromagnetic modes, we can perform a KK reduction and reduce the theory to (3+1) dimensions. The specific approach is to decompose the 4-dimensional Riemannian metric $g_{\mu\nu}$ in the following way[4]

$$g_{\mu\nu} = \begin{pmatrix} \gamma_{ij} + \phi A_i A_j & \phi A_j \\ \phi A_i & \phi \end{pmatrix}, \quad (3)$$

where γ_{ij} is a 3-dimensional Riemannian metric, A_i, A_j are the anti-symmetric electromagnetism vectors, and ϕ is a scalar field. After a canonical transformation, the Hamiltonian density (2) can be rewritten by γ_{ij}, A_i, ϕ and their conjugate momenta p_{ij}, p_i and p. Variations with respect to variables γ_{ij}, A_i, ϕ, p^{ij}, p^i, p generate the equations of motion.[4]

For the scalar field ϕ and its conjugate momenta p, we can get their solutions from the equations of motion and find they are constants, regardless of whether it is in the Minkowski background or in the FRW background. As a consequence, one can assume $\bar{\phi} = 1$ and $\bar{p} = 0$ without loss of generality. Under this condition, for the Minkowski background we have

$$\bar{\gamma}_{ij} = \delta_{ij}, \bar{p}_{ij} = 0, \bar{N} = 1, \bar{A}_i = \bar{p}_i = 0, \bar{N}_i = \bar{N}_4 = 0. \tag{4}$$

and for the FRW background it becomes

$$\bar{\gamma}_{ij} = a(t)^2 \delta_{ij}, \ \bar{p}_{ij} = 0, \ \bar{p} = -a(t)^2 \dot{a}(t), \ \bar{N} = 1, \ \bar{A}_i = \bar{p}_i = 0, \ \bar{N}_i = \bar{N}_4 = 0, \ \bar{\phi} = 1. \tag{5}$$

In order to get the wave equations of gravitational tensor and electromagnetic vectors, we can perform perturbations in both two backgrounds. The perturbations of the Minkowski background are

$$\gamma_{ij} = \delta_{ij} + \epsilon h_{ij}, \ p_{ij} = \epsilon \Omega_{ij}, \ N_i = \epsilon n_i, \ N_4 = \epsilon n_4,$$
$$N = 1 + \epsilon n, \ A_i = \epsilon \xi_i, \ p_i = \epsilon \zeta_i, \ \phi = 1 + \epsilon \tau, \ p = \epsilon \chi, \tag{6}$$

and for the FRW background we have

$$\gamma_{ij} = a(t)^2 (\delta_{ij} + \epsilon h_{ij}), \ p_{ij} = \epsilon \Omega_{ij}, \ p = -a(t)^2 \dot{a} + \epsilon \chi,$$
$$N_i = \epsilon n_i, \ N_4 = \epsilon n_4, \ N = 1 + \epsilon n, \ A_i = \epsilon \xi_i, \ p_i = \epsilon \zeta_i, \ \phi = 1 + \epsilon \tau. \tag{7}$$

where h_{ij}, Ω_{ij}, n_i, n_4, n, ξ_i, ζ_i, τ, χ are linear perturbations for each field.

Inputting these perturbations into the equations of motion, the equations of motion at the linear order of ϵ can be obtained. Imposing the transverse traceless (TT) gauge conditions of tensors and vectors, and combining the constraint conditions, the wave equations of the EM vectors and the gravitational tensors in the Minkowski background are

$$\ddot{\xi}_i^T - \beta c^2 \Delta \xi_i^T = 0, \tag{8}$$
$$\ddot{h}_{ij}^{TT} - \beta c^2 \Delta h_{ij}^{TT} = 0. \tag{9}$$

Similarly, the wave equations in the FRW background can be obtained in the same way, they are

$$\ddot{\xi}_i^T + H \dot{\xi}_i^T - \beta c^2 \Delta \xi_i^T = 0, \tag{10}$$
$$\ddot{h}_{ij}^{TT} + 3H \dot{h}_{ij}^{TT} - \beta c^2 \Delta h_{ij}^{TT} = 0, \tag{11}$$

where $H = \dot{a}(t)/a(t)$ is the Hubble parameter.

From these wave equations, we can find that the propagation velocity of the EM waves and the GWs are the same, that is, $\sqrt{\beta} c$, no matter whether it is in the Minkowski background or in the FRW spacetime. In other words, in this model the speed of GWs is exactly identified with the one of the EM waves. This remarkable feature allows us to examine possible LV of the model (and in turn place possible constraints on the parameter of the model) by detecting the deviation of the speed of the EM waves from the usual speed of light. In what follows we will present how can one get the deviation of the speed of the EM waves by analyzing the observed GRBs data.

3. Lorentz violation from GRB photons

Considering possible LV, the dispersion relation of a particle with energy E can be phenomenologically written as[3]

$$E^2 = p^2c^2 + m^2c^4 - \Sigma_n s_n E^2 \left(\frac{E}{E_{LV,n}}\right)^n, \qquad (12)$$

where n is an integer, which corresponds to linear or higher-order dependence of the energy in question. $s_n = \pm 1$ is the sign factor of the LV correction, which indicates that the high-energy photons spread slower than the low-energy photons or vice versa. All GRB data we adopt in this paper have the sign $s_n = 1$. $E_{LV,n}$ is the nth-order LV energy scale which can be obtained from the time delay or the spectra lag of the high-energy particles generated from astrophysical sources such as the GRBs, the active galactic nuclei(AGN) and the Crab pulsars, etc.

In this paper, the GRB 170817A is a photon event which has the mass $m = 0$. Consider only the linear effect $n = 1$, Eq. (12) then becomes

$$E^2 = \left(1 - s_1 \frac{E}{E_{LV,1}}\right) p^2 c^2. \qquad (13)$$

The propagation velocity will be modified by the relation $v = \partial E/\partial P$. Comparing to the speed of EM waves in the previous section, the parameter β has the relation

$$\beta = \left[1 - s_1 \left(\frac{E}{E_{LV,1}}\right)\right]^2. \qquad (14)$$

From the relation (14), we can find that the propagation velocity of the GRBs $\sqrt{\beta}c$ depends on the energy of photons and LV energy scale $E_{LV,1}$, that is to say, the LV effect will lead to $\beta \neq 1$. The expression of $E_{LV,1}$ turns out to be

$$E_{LV,1} = s_1 \frac{1}{H_0} \frac{E_h - E_1}{\Delta t_{LV}} \int_0^z \frac{(1+z')dz'}{h(z')}, \qquad (15)$$

where $h(z) = \sqrt{\Omega_\Lambda + \Omega_K(1+z)^2 + \Omega_m(1+z)^3 + \Omega_R(1+z)^4}$ and H_0, z, E_h are the Hubble parameter, the redshift and the energy of the high-energy photons, respectively. E_1 is the energy of the low energy photon that the energy is low and we can neglect it.

Removing the intrinsic emission time lag in the source, we can get the value of $E_{LV,1}$ from the time delay or spectral lag of GRB 170817A under ideal conditions. However, due to the lack of the data of high-energy photons (the GRB 170817A was only observed by Fermi-GBM), the explicit time delay or spectral lag of the GRB 170817A was not detected.[5] Our strategy is to assume that the possible LV observed from other GRBs[6] is generic, that is to say, the GRB 170817A would have the similar LV behavior. We therefore take the value of $E_{LV,1}$ obtained from these GRB data. It turns out that $E_{LV,1}$ has the following characteristics: Firstly, using different GRB data will get different constraints on $E_{LV,1}$. Secondly, different analysis methods, energy sections or cosmological models will effect the result even if the same event such as GRB 090510. The full list of the restrictions on $E_{LV,1}$ can be found in our previous work,[7] which indicates that $E_{LV,1}$ ranges from 10^{17} GeV to 10^{20} GeV from the time lag of the GRBs (the newest GRB events,[8] where $E_{LV,1} \sim 10^{17}$ GeV, is also in this range).

As for the highest energy of the photon of the GRB 170817A, we estimate it by gamma-gamma absorption with the bulk Lorentz factors Γ in the early phase. The specific method is presented in Ref.[9]

$$E_{high} = \frac{\Gamma^2(m_e c^2)^2}{E_{high,an}(1+z)^2}, \qquad (16)$$

where z is the redshift of the GRBs, m_e is the mass of electron, $E_{high,an}$ is the spectral break/cutoff energy and E_{high} is the corresponding highest energy of photons. Generally speaking, one can assume $E_{high,an} = E_{peak}$ (the peak energy of the Band fit of the GBM data), which implies those photons have the maximum probabilities to undergo the absorption with the highest-energy photons (E_{high}). As to the value of the Lorentz factor, we apply the estimated values ($100 - 10^{2.5}$) as suggested in the literatures,[10,11] combining the observations data of the GRB 170817A ($E_{peak} = (185 \pm 62)$ keV and $z \simeq 0.01$ in[2]), we can have an estimation $E_{high} \sim (10 - 200)$ GeV.

Based on these two estimations, we can find that the speed of the GRB 170817A has a tiny deviation with the light speed c due to the possible LV effect, and the deviation depends on the highest energy photons E_{high} and LV energy scale $E_{LV,1}$. In the most stringent constraint $E_{LV,1} \sim 10^{20}$ GeV,[12] the deviation can be restricted in the range

$$|\Delta v/c| < (10^{-19} - 10^{-18}). \qquad (17)$$

4. Result

With the constraint (17), now we can turn to discuss the constraint on the HL gravity. Recalling that the speed of electromagnetic and gravitational waves are the same as discussed in the previous sections. Therefore the speed of GW respects the same constraint as Eq. (17). This, in turn, puts a constraints on the parameter β of the model

$$|1 - \sqrt{\beta}| < (10^{-19} - 10^{-18}). \qquad (18)$$

This is the main result of the paper. Some points should be addressed in what follows. Firstly, due to the lack of direct observation on the time delay of the GRB 170817A, we do not have direct value of $E_{LV,1}$ of this event. Instead, we estimate it by using values obtained from other GRB events. Therefore, the above result (18) depends on which GRB events we adopt. Secondly, up to date, the lack of more GW event companying EM counterpart makes it difficult to implement a statistic analysis. Hence, the system error of our result expect to be obvious. Moreover, this result has the limitation that it is only valid for the present HL gravity model which has the feature that the speed of EM waves and GWs are the same. In spite of these, our result is meaningful since it provide a new way to constraint the model parameter from the properties of matter (the LV effect of GRBs for example as what we did in this work). Meanwhile, with the development of detectors, the first two flaws will be wiped since we can expect with more events it is possible to directly observe the time lag of the EM counterpart.

5. Conclusion

In this talk we present a (3+1)-dimensional HL gravity couple to an anisotropic EM field, which can be obtained by a KK reduction from a (4+1)-dimensional HL gravity. The most remarkable feature of this model is that the electromagnetic and gravitational waves have the same speed, both in the Minkowski background and the FRW spacetime. Then we can use this feature to restrict the speed of gravitational wave and the parameter of model by analyzing the LV effect of the companying EM event, the GRB 170817A. We find, up to some estimations, the parameter β of the model can be received a more stringent constraint than the one obtained from GW analysis itself.

Acknowledgments

This work was supported in part by the National Natural Science Foundation of China under Grant No. 11975116, and Jiangxi Science Foundation for Distinguished Young Scientists under grant number 20192BCB23007.

References

1. B. P. Abbott *et al.* [LIGO Scientific and Virgo Collaborations], "GW170817: Observation of Gravitational Waves from a Binary Neutron Star Inspiral," Phys. Rev. Lett. **119**, no. 16, 161101 (2017) [arXiv:1710.05832 [gr-qc]].
2. B. P. Abbott *et al.* [LIGO Scientific and Virgo and Fermi-GBM and INTEGRAL Collaborations], "Gravitational Waves and Gamma-rays from a Binary Neutron Star Merger: GW170817 and GRB 170817A," Astrophys. J. **848**, no. 2, L13 (2017) [arXiv:1710.05834 [astro-ph.HE]].
3. G. Amelino-Camelia, J. R. Ellis, N. E. Mavromatos, D. V. Nanopoulos and S. Sarkar, "Tests of quantum gravity from observations of gamma-ray bursts," Nature **393**, 763 (1998) [astro-ph/9712103].

4. J. Bellorin, A. Restuccia and F. Tello-Ortiz, "Anisotropic coupling of gravity and electromagnetism in Hořava-Lifshitz theory," Phys. Rev. D **98**, no. 10, 104018 (2018) [arXiv:1807.01629 [hep-th]].
5. A. Goldstein, P. Veres, E. Burns, M. S. Briggs, R. Hamburg, D. Kocevski, C. A. Wilson-Hodge, R. D. Preece, S. Poolakkil and O. J. Roberts, *et al.* "An Ordinary Short Gamma-Ray Burst with Extraordinary Implications: Fermi-GBM Detection of GRB 170817A," Astrophys. J. Lett. **848**, no.2, L14 (2017) [arXiv:1710.05446 [astro-ph.HE]].
6. J. R. Ellis, N. E. Mavromatos, D. V. Nanopoulos, A. S. Sakharov and E. K. G. Sarkisyan, "Robust limits on Lorentz violation from gamma-ray bursts," Astropart. Phys. **25**, 402-411 (2006) [erratum: Astropart. Phys. **29**, 158-159 (2008)] [arXiv:0712.2781 [astro-ph]].
7. T. Zhang, F. W. Shu, Q. W. Tang and D. H. Du, "Constraints on Hořava–Lifshitz gravity from GRB 170817A," Eur. Phys. J. C **80**, no.11, 1062 (2020) [arXiv:2011.00816 [gr-qc]].
8. J. Zhu and B. Q. Ma, "Pre-burst events of gamma-ray bursts with light speed variation," Phys. Lett. B **820**, 136518 (2021) [arXiv:2108.05804 [astro-ph.HE]].
9. Q. W. Tang, F. K. Peng, X. Y. Wang and P. H. T. Tam, "Measuring the bulk Lorentz factors of gamma-ray bursts with Fermi," Astrophys. J. **806**, no. 2, 194 (2015) [arXiv:1412.3342 [astro-ph.HE]].
10. G. P. Lamb *et al.*, "The optical afterglow of GW170817 at one year post-merger," Astrophys. J. **870**, no. 2, L15 (2019) [arXiv:1811.11491 [astro-ph.HE]].
11. R. Gill, J. Granot, F. De Colle and G. Urrutia, "Numerical Simulations of an Initially Top-Hat Jet and the Afterglow of GW170817 / GRB170817A," Astrophys. J. **883**, no. 1, 15(2019) arXiv:1902.10303 [astro-ph.HE].
12. Z. Chang, Y. Jiang and H. Lin, "A unified constraint on the Lorentz invariance violation from both short and long GRBs," Astropart. Phys. **36**, 47 (2012) [arXiv:1201.3413 [astro-ph.HE]].

Summary of the parallel session AT6

Anzhong Wang

GCAP-CASPER, Physics Department, Baylor University, Waco, Texas, 76798-7316, USA
E-mail: Anzhong_Wang@baylor.edu

In this brief report, as the session convener of Hořava-Lifshitz (HL) Gravity (AT6), I summarize the main results of the 15 talks presented in the 16th Marcel Grossmann Meeting, July 5–10, 2021. This session mainly focused on classical and quantum aspects of HL gravity and some related theories, such as Einstein-aether theory and khronometric gravity, as well as their applications to cosmology and astrophysics.

Keywords: Anisotropic scaling; breaking Lorentz symmetry; quantizations; black holes; cosmology

1. A Brief Introduction to Hořava-Lifshitz gravity

Hořava-Lifshitz (HL) gravity is a theory proposed by Hořava in 2009.[1] To avoid Ostrogradsky's ghosts,[2,3] a problem that has been plaguing quantization of general relativity (GR) since the middle of 1970's,[4] Hořava chose to break the Lorentz invariance (LI) by a Lifshitz-type of anisotropic scaling between space and time at the ultra-high energy,[5,6] $t \to b^{-z}t$, $x^i \to b^{-1}x'^i$, $(i = 1, 2, ..., d)$, where z denotes the dynamical critical exponent, and d the spatial dimension of the spacetime. LI requires $z = 1$, while power-counting renomalizibality requires $z \geq d$. With the above scalings, the time and space have, respectively, the dimensions, $[t] = -z$, $[x^i] = -1$. Clearly, such a scaling breaks explicitly the LI and hence the diffeomorphism invariance. Hořava assumed that it is broken only down to the level

$$t \to \xi_0(t), \quad x^i \to \xi^i\left(t, x^k\right), \tag{1}$$

so the spatial diffeomorphism still remains. The above symmetry is often referred as to *the foliation-preserving diffeomorphism*, denoted by Diff(M, $\mathcal{F}$). Introducing the Arnowitt-Deser-Misner (ADM) variables (N, N^i, g_{ij}),[7] where N, N^i and g_{ij}, denote, respectively, the lapse function, shift vector, and d-dimensional metric of the leaves $t =$ constant, it is found that they are scaling, respectively, as,[1] $N \to N$, $N^i \to b^{z-1}N^i$, $g_{ij} \to g_{ij}$, so that their dimensions are $N = 0$, $[N^i] = z - 1$, $[g_{ij}] = 0$. With the above symmetry, one can construct the basic operators of the fundamental ADM variables and their derivatives, which turn out to be,

$$R_{ij}, \quad K_{ij}, \quad a_i, \quad \nabla_i, \tag{2}$$

where $a_i \equiv N_{,i}/N$, and ∇_i denotes the covariant derivative with respect to g_{ij}, while R_{ij} and K_{ij} are the d-dimensional Ricci tensor, and the extrinsic curvature tensor of the leaves $t=$ constant, respectively, constructed from the g_{ij} and g^{ij} where

$g_{ij}g^{ik} = \delta_j^k$, and $K_{ij} \equiv (-\dot{g}_{ij} + \nabla_i N_j + \nabla_j N_i)/(2N)$, with $\dot{g}_{ij} \equiv \partial g_{ij}/\partial t$. These basic quantities are vectors/tensors under the coordinate transformations (1), and have the dimensions, $[K_{ij}] = z$, $[R_{ij}] = 2$, $[a_i] = 1$, $[\nabla_i] = 1$. With the basic blocks of Eq.(2), we can build scalar operators order by order, so the total Lagrangian will take the form,[1]

$$\mathcal{L}_g = \sum_{n=0}^{2z} \mathcal{L}_g^{(n)}\left(N, N^i, g_{ij}\right), \qquad (3)$$

where $\mathcal{L}_g^{(n)}$ denotes the part of the Lagrangian that contains operators of the nth-order only. Including all the terms that are allowed by the symmetry, it was found that there are about 100 terms appearing in the above action in the case $d = z = 3$.

To reduce the number of independent coupling terms, Hořava introduced *the projectability condition*,[1] which requires that the lapse function be a function of t only, $N = N(t)$, so that all the terms proportional to a_i and its derivatives will be dropped out. This will reduce the total number of the independent terms in Eq.(3) to 14 (including the cosmological constant and parity-violated terms).[8] However, despite of various desired features, this condition leads to several problems, including that the Newtonian limit does not exist, and the six-order derivative operators are eliminated, so the theory is still not power-counting renormalizable. In addition, it is not clear if this symmetry is still respected by radiative corrections. Even more fundamentally, the foliation-preserving diffeomorphism (1) allows one more degree of freedom in the gravitational sector, in comparing with that of general diffeomorphism. As a result, a spin-0 mode of gravitons appears generically. This mode is potentially dangerous and may cause ghosts and instability problems, which lead the constraint algebra dynamically inconsistent.

To solve these problems, various modifications have been proposed.[8] In some of these models the Einstein-aether theory[9] and khronometric gravity[10] are particular cases. For a recent review on these models, we refer readers to Ref. 8.

2. Summary of the 15 Talks

In this section, I summarize the main results of the 15 talks in a chronological order.

- Sato presented a joint work with Ambjorn, Hiraga and Ito. In particular, they quantized the 2D projectable HL gravity with a bi-local as well as spacelike wormhole interaction, and found that the resulting quantum Hamiltonian coincides with the one obtained through summing over all genus in the string field theory for 2D causal dynamical triangulations. This implies that the wormhole interaction can be interpreted as a splitting or joining interaction of 1D strings.
- Bellorín presented a joint work with Droguett, and showed that the Batalin-Fradkin-Vilkovisky (BFV) quantization scheme can be implemented in the nonprojectable 3D HL theory. The BFV quantization is based on the canonical formalism and suitable to incorporate the measure associated to the second-class constraints

that the theory has. They presented the Becchi-Rouet-Stora-Tyutin symmetry transformations in the canonical variables, and found that the theory is of rank one in the classification introduced by Fradkin and Fradkina. In particular, they found that the nonlocal gauge condition introduced in the projectable theory can be included among these gauges.

• Satheeshkumar presented a talk on how the nature of singularities and horizons in vector-tensor theories differ significantly from GR. In particular, by considering Einstien-aether theory, based on a joint work with Chan and da Silva, he showed that, due to the presence of the aether field, vacuum black holes in GR are replaced by naked singularities, while new singularities appear in some cosmological models of GR.

• Lappicy presented a joint work with Hell and Uggla on bifurcations and chaos in HL cosmology. In particular, they considered the initial singularity in spatially homogeneous Bianchi type VIII and IX vacuum models, where relativistic first principles are replaced with anisotropic scalings of Lifshitz type. Within this class of models, GR is shown to be a bifurcation where chaos becomes generic. To describe the chaotic features of generic singularities in HL cosmology, they introduced symbolic dynamics within Cantor sets and iterated function systems, and obtained the general properties of various cases.

• Shu presented his joint work with Zhang, Tang and Du on constraining HL gravity from GRB 170817A observations. In particular, they considered the HL gravity coupling with an anisotropic electromagnetic field, generated through a Kaluza-Klein reduction of a $(4+1)$-dimensional HL gravity, and found that the model has the same velocity for both gravitational and electromagnetic waves. By analyzing the possible Lorentz invariance violation effect of the GRB 170817A, they found a stringent constraint on a parameter β of the theory with $|1-\sqrt{\beta}| < (10^{-19} - 10^{-18})$.

• Saridakis presented his joint work with Khodadi on Einstein-aether gravity in the light of Event Horizon Telescope (EHT) observations of M87, and calculated the photon effective potential, the unstable photon sphere radius, and the induced angular size of two analytical black hole solutions in the theory. Since d_{M87*} is observationally known from the EHT Probe, they extracted the corresponding parameter regions in order to obtain consistency, and found that the Einstien-aether black hole solutions agree with the shadow size of EHT $M87*$, if the involved aether parameters are restricted within specific ranges, along with an upper bound on the dimensionless spin parameter a, which is verified by a full scan of the parameter space within 1σ-error.

• Ajith presented a joint work with Yagi and Yunes on testing HL gravity with I-Love-Q. The authors studied how the I-Love-Q relations depend on the parameters of the theory, and found that the only un-constrained parameter disappears from the field equations in HL gravity. Therefore, the I-Love-Q relations are universal against not only the nuclear physics uncertainty but also the gravitational physics uncertainty within HL gravity.

- Ghosh presented a joint work with Kumar on the Einstein-Gauss-Bonnet (EGB) gravity under the limit $D \to 4$, and studied rotating black holes in regularized 4D EGB gravity and their horizon properties and shadows. In particular, they found that the $4D$ non-relativistic Horava-Lifshitz theory of gravity also admits the identical black hole solution. The effects of the GB coupling parameter on the shape and size of shadows were investigated and analyzed in recent M87 observations from EHT. They estimated the parameters associated with the 4D EGB gravity Kerr black holes using the shadow observables, and found that the inferred circularity deviation $\Delta C \leq 0.1$ for the M87 black hole, whereas shadow angular diameter $\theta_d = 42 \pm 3 \mu as$ within the 1σ region on the GB parameter. Interestingly, the shadow axial ratio obeying undefined control sequence is in agreement with the EHT results and thus eventuates in the 4D EGB gravity black holes being suitable candidates for astrophysical black holes.

- Bamba presented a joint work with Chakraborty and Saa on dynamical system analysis of the homogeneous and anisotropic Bianchi-I spacetimes in $f(R)$ gravity coupled with an anisotropic matter. It was demonstrated that with a suitable choice of the evolution parameter, Einstein's equations are reduced to an autonomous 5D system of ordinary differential equations. Furthermore, for a large class of functions $f(R)$, which includes several cases commonly considered in the literature, all the fixed points are polynomial roots, and thus they can be determined with a good accuracy and classified for stability. In addition, any fixed point corresponding to isotropic solutions in the presence of anisotropic matter will be unstable. The assumption of a perfect fluid as source and or the vacuum cases imply some dimensional reductions and even more simplifications. In particular, it was found that the vacuum solutions of $f(R) = R^{\delta+1}$ (with $\delta =$ constant) are governed by an effective 2D phase space which can be constructed analytically, leading to an exactly solvable dynamics.

- Jawad presented various solutions of Einstein-aether gravity through a reconstruction approach. In order to discuss the current cosmic acceleration corresponding to his reconstructed models, he evaluated different cosmological parameters, and discussed the consistency of his results of cosmological parameters with current observational data.

- de Souza Campos presented her joint work with Dappiaggi and Sina on boundary conditions for the Klein-Gordon field in Lifshitz spacetimes. In particular, she considered a free, scalar, massive quantum field theory on a 4D Lifshitz spacetime with a critical exponent $z = 2$ and showed that there are two-point functions for ground and thermal states of the local Hadamard form and satisfying the canonical commutation relations, compatible with Robin's boundary conditions and with mode-dependent boundary conditions, depending on the value of the effective mass. Each of these generalized boundary conditions determine an inequivalent dynamics, but they are all equivalently physically sensible.

- Panotopoulos presented his recent work on non-rotating and isotropic strange quark stars in HL gravity and Einstein-æther theory. For quark matter he adopted both linear and non-linear equations of state (EoS), corresponding to the MIT bag model and color flavor locked state, respectively. The new structure equations describe the generalization of the hydrostatic equilibrium of the usual Tolman-Oppenheimer-Volkoff (TOV) equations of GR, parameterized by a dimensionless deviation parameter v. He computed the mass, radius and compactness of the stars, and showed graphically the impact of v on the mass-to-radius profiles for different EoS describing quark matter. The energy conditions and stability criteria were also considered, and found that they are all fulfilled.

• Lin presented a joint work with Wang, Zhang, Zhao and Zhu on testing Einstein-aether theory by gravitational wave (GW) observations. In particular, he presented their recent studies of GWs produced by massive and compact objects, including the GW waveforms, polarizations, response function, Fourier transform, and energy loss rate through three different channels of radiation - the scalar, vector and tensor modes, and showed that combination of such theoretical predictions with future observations of GWs can bring severe constraints on the theory.

• Kwapisz presented a joint work with Chojnacki on finite action principle and black holes in HL gravity, and showed that the finite action selection principle works well for HL gravity in the context of black holes. In addition, wormholes possess a finite action and hence contribute to the path-integral of quantum gravity.

• Chojnacki presented a joint work with Kwapisz on their studies of the finite action principle and the beginning of the universe in HL gravity, and showed that field configurations with finite classical action describe a flat universe with a homogeneous and isotropic beginning without the ghost particles.

References

1. P. Horava, *Quantum gravity at a Lifshitz point*, Phys. Rev. D**79** (2009) 084008.
2. M. Ostrogradsky, Mem. Ac. St. Petersbourg, VI**4** (1850) 385.
3. R. P. Woodard, *The Theorem of Ostrogradsky*, Scholarpedia **10** (2015) 32243.
4. K. S. Stelle, *Renormalization of higher-derivative quantum gravity*, Phys. Rev. D**16** (1977) 953.
5. E. M. Lifshitz, *On the theory of second-order phase transitions I*, Zh. Eksp. Teor. Fiz. **11** (1941) 255.
6. E. M. Lifshitz, *On the theory of second-order phase transitions II*, Zh. Eksp. Teor. Fiz. **11** (1941) 269.
7. R. Arnowitt, S. Deser, and C. W. Misner, *The Dynamics of General Relativity*, Gen. Relativ. Gravit. **40**, 1997 (2008).
8. A. Wang, *Hořava gravity at a Lifshitz point: A progress report*, Inter. J. Mod. Phys. D**26** (2017) 1730014.
9. T. Jacobson, *Extended Horava gravity and Einstein-aether theory*, Phys. Rev. D**81** (2010) 101502; *ibid.*, D**82** (2010) 129901(E); *Undoing the twist: the Hořava limit of Einstein-aether*, *ibid.*, D**89** (2013) 081501.
10. D. Blas, O. Pujolas, and S. Sibiryakov, *Models of non-relativistic quantum gravity: The good, the bad and the healthy*, JHEP **04** (2011).

Non-local R^2-like inflation, gravitational waves and Non-Gaussianities

K. Sravan Kumar

Department of Physics, Tokyo Institute of Technology
1-12-1 Ookayama, Meguro-ku, Tokyo 152-8551, Japan
E-mail: sravan.k.aa@m.titech.ac.jp,
www.titech.ac.jp/english

The emergence of R^2 (Starobinsky) inflation from the semi-classical modification of gravity due to matter quantum fields (trace anomaly) clearly points out the importance of fundamental physics and the first principles in the construction of successful cosmological models. Along with the observational success, R^2 gravity is also an important step beyond general relativity (GR) towards quantum gravity. Furthermore, several approaches of quantum gravity to date are strongly indicating the presence of non-locality at small time and length scales. In this regard, ultraviolet (UV) completion of R^2 inflation has been recently studied in a string theory-inspired ghost-free analytic non-local gravity. We discuss the promising theoretical predictions of non-local R^2-like inflation with respect to the key observables such as tensor-to-scalar ratio, tensor tilt which tell us about the spectrum of primordial gravitational waves, and scalar Non-Gaussianities which tell us about the three-point correlations in the CMB fluctuations. Any signature of non-local physics in the early Universe will significantly improve our understanding of fundamental physics at UV energy scales and quantum gravity.

Keywords: Quantum gravity, Inflation, CMB, Gravitational Waves

1. Status of inflation and the quests for UV-completion

Inflationary cosmology has become the most important field of study in theoretical higher energy physics (THEP) in the recent years not only because of its success with respect to the data of Cosmic Microwave Background (CMB)[1–3] but also it gives a best chance to test our approaches to build physics at the fundamental scales such as Planck energy or length scales. Recent detection of Gravitational Waves from binary black hole merger events further corroborated to build new hopes and strategies to probe the physics of early Universe.[4,5]

Inflationary cosmology is so far developed in two equivalent ways. One is by geometrical modification i.e., by extension of General Relativity (GR) by higher curvature terms (for example "$R + R^2$ gravity which is also known as Starobinsky theory[6–9]). Second way is by the addition of hypothetical (scalar) matter fields which result in modification of right hand side of Einstein equations.[10,11] This second way motivated in the view of particle physics beyond the standard model and several ultraviolet (UV) complete approaches such as string theory and supergravity (SUGRA).[12] In this regard, inflationary cosmology is so far studied from the point of view of beyond the standard model of particle physics and as a low-energy limit of UV-complete approaches such as string theory/M-theory (see left panel of Fig. 1).

In the last decades plethora of inflationary models have been constructed with different scalar fields emerging from simplest set ups to all the way up to the most general scalar tensor theories[13,14] (see left panel of Fig. 1). However the latest data from Planck satellite[1] has found out Starobinsky and Higgs inflation be the most compatible models with the following predictions of spectral index and the tensor to scalar ratio

$$n_s = 1 - \frac{2}{N}, \qquad r = \frac{12}{N^2}, \qquad (1)$$

where $N = 50 - 60$ number of e-folds before the end of inflation. The recent Planck data[1,2] has constrained $n_s = 0.9649 \pm 0.0042$ at $68\%\mathrm{CL}, r < 0.036$ at 95% CL. The success of Starobinsky and Higgs inflation has lead to the emergence of equivalent frameworks of inflation in string theory and SUGRA.[12]

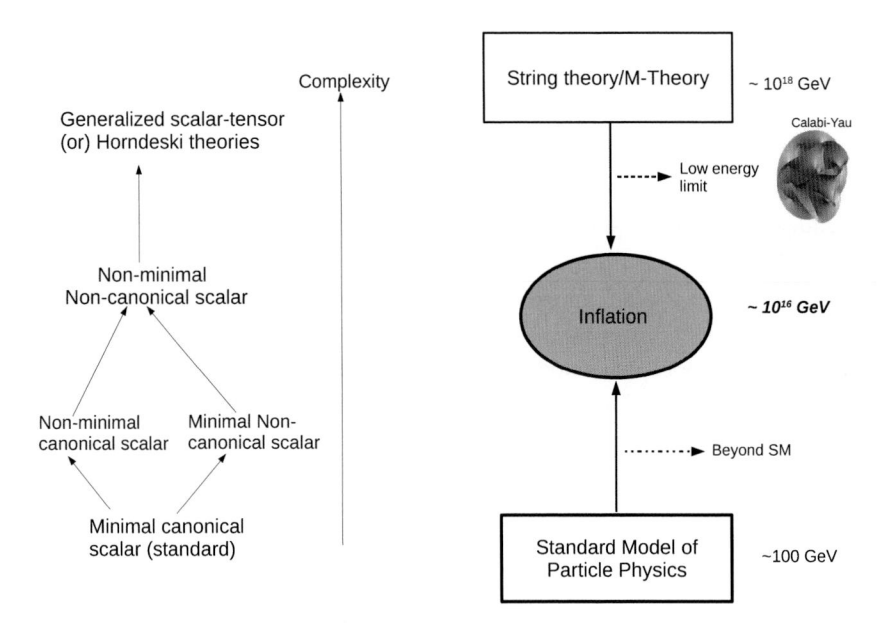

Fig. 1. In the right panel, arrow of complexity shows how one can start with a simplest scalar field Lagrangian and generalized all the way up to most general scalar-tensor theories whose equations of motion are second order in field derivative. In the right panel we can see that inflationary cosmology can be understood well either from beyond the standard model of particle physics or from low-energy limit of a UV-complete approaches such as string theory (This Figure taken from[13]).

The challenging problem of the current status of inflationary cosmology is to break several degeneracies in the frameworks of inflation and find definitive clues towards achieving quantum gravity and UV-completion. For this purpose, from observational point of view, one must go beyond the two observables (n_s, r). In this regard there are two more important observational parameters known as tensor tilt

(n_t) which is the tilt of the tensor power-spectrum and non-Gaussianity parameter (f_{NL}) which is related to the 3-point scalar correlations. If inflation is driven by single (canonical) scalar field with standard slow-roll then the tensor consistency relation[13] and the Maldacena consistency relation[15] given by

$$r = -8n_t \quad f_{NL}^{sq} = \frac{5}{12}(1 - n_s) \qquad (2)$$

serves as a crucial test. Here f_{NL}^{sq} is so-called squeezed shape of non-Gaussianity. If inflation is driven by multiple fields then the above consistency relations are understood to be violated.[16] If inflation is driven by non-canonical scalar fields and if non-standard quantum initial conditions are assumed we will find a strong signal in the equilateral (f_{NL}^{eq}) and orthogonal (f_{NL}^{ortho}) shapes of non-Gaussianities. These shapes are constrained by the latest Planck data as

$$f_{NL}^{loc} = 0.8 \pm 5.0, \quad f_{NL}^{equi} = -4 \pm 43, \quad f_{NL}^{ortho} = -26 \pm 21, \quad \text{at } 68\% \text{CL}. \qquad (3)$$

Violation of consistency relations (2) and any detection of $f_{NL} \sim O(1)$ is definitely a new physics in the context of early Universe cosmology which will be crucial for further advancements in THEP. Moreover, in a quest to find signatures of new physics, recently a new program of research has gained significant attention known as "cosmological collider physics"[17] whose aim is to find signatures of higher energy particles interacting with primordial fields during inflation.

Despite numerous phenomenological approaches in understanding inflation and find new observables to probe physics of inflation, it is very vital to focus on consistency of our theoretical endeavors. The success of Starobinsky and Higgs inflationaris (which are almost identical during inflation) covey us a very crucial property that at the scale of inflation approximate "scale invariance" symmetry of the Lagrangian is important. The fact that various setups of SUGRA leading to Starobinsky-like or R^2-like inflation[12] indicate that $R + R^2$ is an important modification of GR. In the next section, we will discuss in detail about the foundations of Starobinsky inflation and how a very straightforward procedure from geoemertric modification of gravity lead us a UV-complete framework.[18–21]

2. From Starobinsky inflation to Stelle gravity and the emergence of ghost-free UV-non-local gravity

$R + R^2$ gravity should not be viewed as a toy model in the class of f(R) gravity. The theory naturally emerges from generic considerations and important questions about UV-completion which dates back the discovery of trace anomaly.[22] The trace anomaly comes from 1-loop quantum corrections to the graviton propagator due to matter conformal fields leading to an anomalous non-zero trace of energy momentum tensor which is proportional to curvature square term.

$$M_p^2 R = g^{\mu\nu} \langle T_{\mu\nu} \rangle = aF + bG + c\Box R, \qquad (4)$$

where $F = W_{\mu\nu\rho\sigma}W^{\mu\nu\rho\sigma}$ is the the Weyl tensor square and $G = R_{\mu\nu\rho\sigma}R^{\mu\nu\rho\sigma} - 4R_{\mu\nu}R^{\mu\nu} + R^2$ is the so-called Gauss-Bonnet term and $R_{\mu\nu\rho\sigma}$, $R_{\mu\nu}$, R Riemann tensor, Ricci tensor and Ricci scalar respectively. Here a, b, c are dimensionless coefficients quantified by the number of conformal fields. Trace anomaly has been widely studied and applied in various fundamental theories including anticipated UV complete theories such as string theory and supergravity (SUGRA).[22] Neglecting the coefficients a, b the trace anomaly equation reduces to the trace equation of the $R + R^2$ given by the action[6, 23]

$$S_{R^2} = \int d^4x \sqrt{-g} \left[\frac{M_p^2}{2} R + \frac{M_p^2}{12M^2} R^2 \right], \qquad (5)$$

where $M \ll M_p$ becomes the mass of a propagating scalar in this model, named scalaron. Independent of what is the right framework of UV-completion R^2 term is very natural term that appears as a classical addition to the GR and it naturally leads to a quasi-de Sitter evolution (which is "cosmic inflation") in the high curvature regime $R \gg M^2$. Therefore it is a matter of fact that $R + R^2$ gravity indeed an unavoidable and very important extension of GR. Further more if we add Weyl square term to the action of $R + R^2$ gravity (5) the resultant gravity theory becomes renormalizable (which is an important property to achieve quantum gravity) as it was proven by K. S. Stelle long ago[24]

$$S_{\text{Stelle}} = S_{R^2} = \int d^4x \sqrt{-g} \left[\frac{M_p^2}{2} R + \frac{M_p^2}{12M^2} R^2 + \frac{M_p^2}{M_g^2} W_{\mu\nu\rho\sigma}W^{\mu\nu\rho\sigma} \right]. \qquad (6)$$

However, Stelle gravity unfortunately falls short in becoming a consistent theory of quantum gravity because of the presence of a massive tensor ghost in the spectrum which spoils Unitarity. A natural question one can ask is that whether this ghost can be removed by any higher derivative extension of Stelle gravity. Due to Ostrogradsky theorem any finite derivative extension of Stelle gravity results in further introduction of ghosts in the spectrum and it becomes not a viable option. However, Krasnikov has shown that analytic infinite derivative extension of Stelle gravity (i.e., analytic non-local gravity) can give a ghost-free theory.[25]

$$S = \int d^4x \sqrt{-g} \left(\frac{M_p^2}{2} R + \frac{1}{2} \left[R \mathcal{F}_R(\Box_s) R + W_{\mu\nu\rho\sigma} \mathcal{F}_W(\Box_s) W^{\mu\nu\rho\sigma} \right] \right), \qquad (7)$$

where $\Box_s = \frac{\Box}{M_s^2}$ with $\Box$ is being the d'Alembertian and $\mathcal{F}_R, \mathcal{F}_W$ analytic infinite derivative operators or non-local form factors. This theory (7) has been studied over the years and understood to have good properties of UV-completion with respect to renormalizability and Unitarity (See[21] and the references therein). In a nutshell, the action (7) is a very logical extension of Stelle gravity and we very much straightforwardly end up with introducing non-locality in the gravity sector. Note that "Non-locality" is a very important common concept that appears in several approaches to quantum gravity such as string theory, loop quantum gravity, causal sets and non-commutative gravity. Therefore, (7) is a culmination of various approaches which allow us to give a consistent UV-completion for Starobinsky inflation[a]. Further note that (7) should not be understood as an effective theory but rather a consistent part of a UV-complete theory. We do not have any cut off scales in the theory and the scale $\mathcal{M}_s$ represents the scale at which non-local nature of gravity is prominent. In the next section, we will discuss the cosmological application of (7) and identify the specific features of non-local gravity which can be probed in the future observations.

3. Non-local R^2-like inflation and future targets for CMB and gravitational wave observations

In this section, we apply UV non-local quadratic curvature gravity in the context of inflationary cosmology. The first and foremost difficulty is associated with solving equations of motion of an infinite derivative theory which perhaps appears to be an impossible task. However, this was consistency achieved[18] and it was also quite rigorously shown in[19] that the theory contains an inflationary attractor solution exactly same as the local $R + R^2$ or Starobinsky theory. To see this explicitly let us write down the background equations of motion for (7) Friedmann-Lemaître-Robertson-Walker background for which the Weyl tensor is zero

$$\bar{E}^\mu_\nu \equiv -\left[M_p^2 + 2\lambda \mathcal{F}\left(\frac{\Box}{\mathcal{M}_s^2}\right)\bar{R}\right]\bar{G}^\mu_\nu \delta^\mu_\nu - \frac{1}{2}\bar{R}\mathcal{F}\left(\frac{\Box}{\mathcal{M}_s^2}\right)\bar{R}\delta^\mu_\nu$$
$$+ 2\left(\nabla^\mu \partial_\nu - \delta^\mu_\nu \Box\right)\mathcal{F}\left(\frac{\Box}{\mathcal{M}_s^2}\right)R + \bar{\mathcal{K}}^\mu_\nu - \frac{\lambda}{2}\delta^\mu_\nu\left(\bar{\mathcal{K}}^\sigma_\sigma + \bar{\mathcal{K}}\right) = 0\,,$$

where

$$\bar{\mathcal{K}}^\mu_\nu = \frac{1}{\mathcal{M}_s^2}\sum_{n=1}^\infty f_n \sum_{l=0}^{n-1} \partial^\mu \frac{\Box^l}{\mathcal{M}_s^{2l}} \bar{R} \partial_\nu \left(\frac{\Box}{\mathcal{M}_s^2}\right)^{n-l-1} \bar{R}\,,$$

$$\bar{\mathcal{K}} = \sum_{n=1}^\infty f_n \sum_{l=0}^{n-1} \frac{\Box^l}{\mathcal{M}_s^{2l}} \bar{R} \left(\frac{\Box}{\mathcal{M}_s^2}\right)^{n-l} \bar{R}\,.$$

The trace equation is

$$\bar{E} = M_p^2 \bar{R} - 6\bar{\Box}\mathcal{F}\left(\frac{\bar{\Box}}{\mathcal{M}_s^2}\right)\bar{R} - \bar{\mathcal{K}}^\mu_\mu - 2\bar{\mathcal{K}} = 0\,. \tag{8}$$

It was showed in[19] that the only solution of the above equations is $\bar{\Box}\bar{R} = M^2 \bar{R}$ given the following Unique conditions on the form factor are satisfied.

$$\mathcal{F}'_R\left(\frac{M^2}{\mathcal{M}_s^2}\right) = 0,\quad \frac{M_P^2}{2\lambda} = 3M^2 \mathcal{F}_1,\quad \text{where } \mathcal{F}_1 \equiv \mathcal{F}_R\left(\frac{M^2}{\mathcal{M}_s^2}\right) \tag{9}$$

---

[a]Worth to metion that Starobinsky inflation has also been embedded in SUGRA which gives an interesting route for UV-completion.[26] Here we focus on non-supersymmetric aspects of UV-completion.

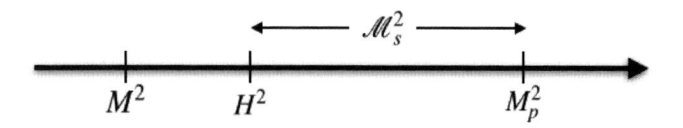

Fig. 2. We depict here the hierarchy of mass scales in non-local R^2-like inflation.

where $'$ denotes derivative with respect to argument. Note that $\bar{\Box}\bar{R} = M^2\bar{R}$ is the trace equation of local $R + R^2$ which gives Starobinsky inflationary solutions. Here given the conditions (9) are met we can solve exactly the full non-local gravity equations of motion and also we have good inflationary solution. Now it is important to see how non-local effects of gravity appear through inflationary perturbations. Before we go this step we can draw a heuristic bound on the scale of non-locality shown in Fig. 2 based on the fact that we require near scale invariance at the scale of inflation. This can be seen heuristically by expanding the quadratic Ricci scalar part of the action as

$$S = \int d^4x \sqrt{-g} \left[\frac{M_p^2}{2} R + \frac{M_p^2}{12M^2} R^2 + \mathcal{O}\left(\frac{M_p^2 R \Box R}{M^2 \mathcal{M}_s^2}\right) \right].$$

In the high curvature regime $R \gg M^2$ local quadratic curvature term is naturally dominant and it is known to be scale invariance.

3.1. *Scalar and tensor power spectrum*

To study perturbations around quasi-de Sitter we take the perturbed metric of the form

$$ds^2 = a^2(\eta) \left[-(1 + 2\Phi) d\eta^2 + ((1 - 2\Psi)\delta_{ij} + 2h_{ij}) dx^i dx^j \right], \quad (10)$$

where Φ, Ψ are Bardeen potentials and h_{ij} is tensor fluctuation. The study of non-local perturbed equations of motion[19] has revealed that $\Phi + \Psi \approx 0$ during inflation. Since $\delta W_{\mu\nu\rho\sigma} \propto (\Phi + \Psi)$ the Weyl tensor part in (7) does not contribute to the scalar perturbations during inflation. Following the computations in[19,20] the second order action of scalar degree of freedom in de Sitter approximation becomes

$$\delta^2 S_{(s)} = \frac{1}{2\mathcal{F}_1 \bar{R}} \int d\tau d^3 x \sqrt{-\bar{g}} \Upsilon \frac{\mathcal{W}\left(\frac{\bar{\Box}}{M^2}\right)}{\mathcal{F}_R\left(\frac{\bar{\Box}}{M^2}\right)} (\bar{\Box} - M^2) \Upsilon, \quad (11)$$

where $\Upsilon \approx 2\bar{R}\Psi$. In order not to have any more ghost degrees of freedom we choose the structure of form factor as

$$\mathcal{F}_R(\Box_s) = \mathcal{F}_1 \frac{3e^{\gamma_S(\Box_s)}\left(\Box_s - \frac{M^2}{\mathcal{M}_s^2}\right) + \left(\frac{\bar{R}}{\mathcal{M}_s^2} + 3\frac{M^2}{\mathcal{M}_s^2}\right)}{3\Box_s + \frac{\bar{R}}{\mathcal{M}_s^2}}, \quad (12)$$

where $\bar{R} \approx$ constant and γ_S is an entire function. Therefore, the theory now has only one scalar(on) degree of freedom similar to local $R + R^2$ theory but however, the the scalar field here is non-local in nature.

Computation of the power spectrum and the scalar spectral index of curvature perturbation $\mathcal{R} = \Psi + H\frac{\delta R}{\dot{\bar{R}}} = \Psi + \frac{24H^3}{24H\dot{H}}\Phi \approx -\frac{1}{\epsilon}\Psi$ we get

$$\mathcal{P}_\mathcal{R} = \frac{H^2}{16\pi^2\epsilon^2}\frac{1}{3\lambda\mathcal{F}_1\bar{R}}\bigg|_{k=aH}, \quad n_s \equiv \frac{d\ln\mathcal{P}_\mathcal{R}}{d\ln k}\bigg|_{k=aH} \approx 1 - \frac{2}{N}. \quad (13)$$

Similarly the computation of the second order action of tensor perturbations gives (with addition of the non-trivial contributions from the Weyl tensor part in (7))

$$\delta^2 S_{(T)} = \frac{1}{2}\int d^4x\sqrt{-\bar{g}}h_{ij}^\perp e^{2\gamma_T\left(\Box_s - \frac{2\bar{R}}{3\mathcal{M}_s^2}\right)}\left(\bar{\Box} - \frac{\bar{R}}{6}\right)h^{\perp ij}, \quad (14)$$

where

$$\mathcal{F}_W(\Box_s) = \frac{\mathcal{F}_1\bar{R}\,e^{\gamma_T\left(\Box_s - \frac{2}{3}\frac{\bar{R}}{\mathcal{M}_s^2}\right)} - 1}{\mathcal{M}_s^2\quad\Box_s - \frac{2\bar{R}}{3\mathcal{M}_s^2}}. \quad (15)$$

which fixes the tensor degree of freedom to be just massless graviton.

Computing the tensor power spectrum in the leading order in slow-roll we obtain

$$\mathcal{P}_T|_{k=aH} = \frac{H^2}{\pi^2\mathcal{F}_1\bar{R}}e^{-2\gamma_T\left(\frac{\bar{R}}{6\mathcal{M}_s^2}\right)}. \quad (16)$$

As a result the key inflationary parameter called tensor-to-scalar ratio becomes

$$r = \frac{12}{N^2}e^{-2\gamma_T\left(\frac{-\bar{R}}{2\mathcal{M}_s^2}\right)}\bigg|_{k=aH}. \quad (17)$$

The tilt of the tensor power spectrum can be obtained as

$$n_t \equiv \frac{d\ln\mathcal{P}_T}{d\ln k}\bigg|_{k=aH} \approx -\frac{d\ln\mathcal{P}_T}{dN}\left(1 + \frac{1}{2N}\right)\bigg|_{k=aH} \\ \approx -\frac{3}{2N^2} - \left(\frac{2}{N} + \frac{3}{2N^2}\right)\frac{\bar{R}}{2\mathcal{M}_s^2}\gamma_T^{(\prime)}\left(-\frac{\bar{R}}{2\mathcal{M}_s^2}\right)\bigg|_{k=aH}, \quad (18)$$

where $'$ denotes derivative with respect to the argument.

4. Primordial (scalar) non-Gaussianities

Beyond two point correlations it is interesting to see if there will be non-Gaussianities in non-local R^2-like inflation. As we discussed before the scalar(on) in the non-local R^2-like inflation is non-local in nature. Therefore, we generally expect the non-local interactions to play a role in predicting inflationary 3-point correlations different from the local theories. The primordial (scalar) non-Gaussianities in

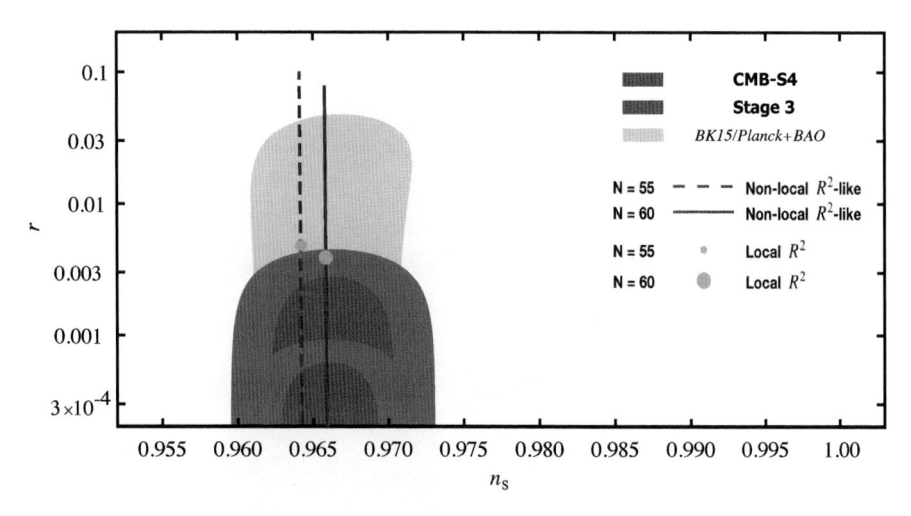

Fig. 3. We depict the predictions of non-local R^2-like inflation in the (n_s, r) plane of the latest CMB S-4 science paper about future forecast of detecting B-modes.[19, 21, 27]

the non-local R^2-like inflation are computed in[20] and here we briefly review the main results. The 3-point correlations and the parameter f_{NL} are defined by

$$\langle \mathcal{R}(\mathbf{k_1}) \mathcal{R}(\mathbf{k_2}) \mathcal{R}(\mathbf{k_3}) \rangle = (2\pi)^3 \delta^3 (\mathbf{k_1} + \mathbf{k_2} + \mathbf{k_3}) \mathcal{B}_\mathcal{R}(k_1, k_2, k_3),$$

and

$$B_\mathcal{R}(k_1, k_2, k_3) = (2\pi)^4 \frac{1}{\prod_i k_i^3} \mathcal{P}_\mathcal{R}^{*2} f_{NL}(k_1, k_2, k_3),$$

where

$$f_{NL} = -\frac{5}{6} \frac{A_\mathcal{R}(k_1, k_2, k_3)}{\sum_i k_i^3}. \tag{19}$$

The interactions of the curvature perturbations in the non-local R^2-like inflation can be schematically explained as in Fig. 5.

To calculate bi-spectrum, first we expand our action to cubic order to the leading order in slow-roll parameter. Then we compute the correlations using the following definition

$$\langle \mathcal{R}(\mathbf{k_1}) \mathcal{R}(\mathbf{k_2}) \mathcal{R}(\mathbf{k_3}) \rangle = -i \int_{-\infty}^{\tau_e} ad\tau \langle 0| [\mathcal{R}(\tau_e, \mathbf{k_1}) \mathcal{R}(\tau_e, \mathbf{k_2}) \mathcal{R}(\tau_e, \mathbf{k_3}), H_{int}] |0\rangle, \tag{20}$$

where $\mathbf{k}_i$ are wave vectors and H_{int} is the interaction Hamiltonian. It is related to a perturbation of the Lagrangian (7) expanded up to the 3rd order in curvature perturbations ($\mathcal{L}_3$) as $H_{int} \approx -\mathcal{L}_3$. We consider the mode functions as

$$\mathcal{R} \approx -\Psi/\epsilon, \quad \bar{\Box}\mathcal{R} = M^2 \mathcal{R}. \tag{21}$$

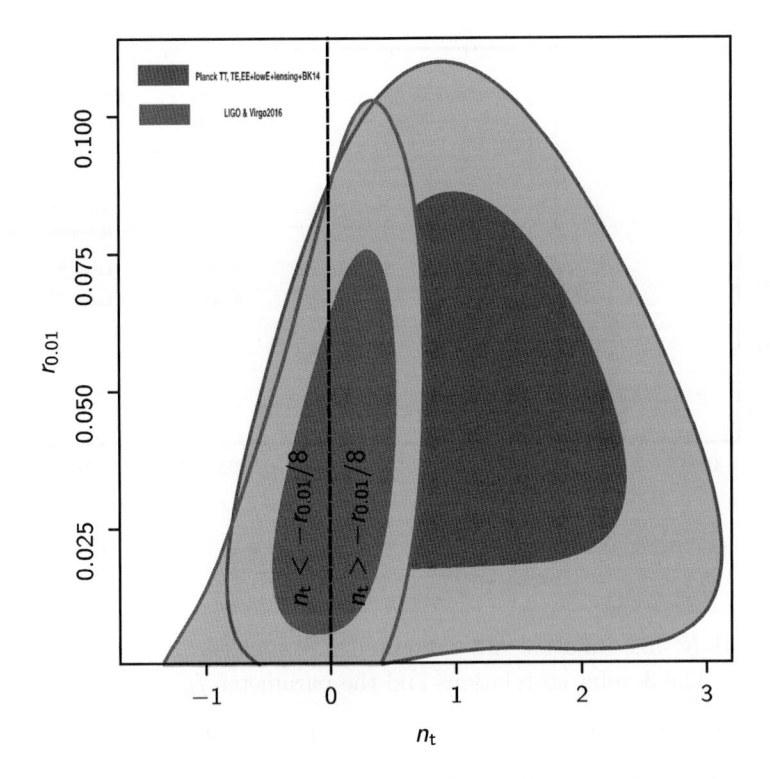

Fig. 4. We note that the predictions of non-local R^2-like inflation can be anywhere within the likelihood projected (n_t, r) plane of latest Planck 2018.[19,21,28]

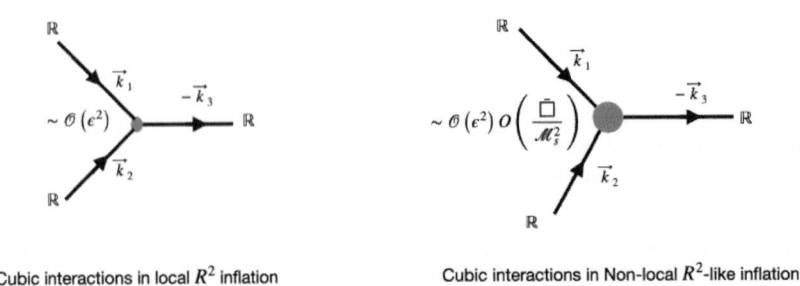

Fig. 5. In the above plot $\mathbb{R} = \{\mathcal{R}, \partial \mathcal{R}, \mathcal{D}^\mu \partial \mathcal{R}\}$ imply various tree level interactions of different modes of the curvature perturbation in the local R^2 and the non-local R^2-like inflation. $O\left(\frac{\Box}{\mathcal{M}_s^2}\right)$ is some analytic non-local operator.

New Interactions arise via the commutation relation in de Sitter approximation

$$\Box \nabla_\mu \mathcal{R} = \nabla_\mu \Box \mathcal{R} + \frac{\bar{R}}{4} \nabla_\mu \mathcal{R}. \tag{22}$$

After numerous steps of computation the cubic order action in $\mathcal{R}$ of (7) in the leading order slow-roll approximation is obtained as[20]

$$\delta^{(3)}S_{(S)} = 4\epsilon M_p^2 \int d\tau d^3x \Big\{ T_1^* \mathcal{R} \nabla \mathcal{R} \cdot \nabla \mathcal{R} + T_2^* \mathcal{R} \mathcal{R}'^2 + T_3^* \mathcal{H}^2 \mathcal{R}^3$$
$$+ T_4^* \mathcal{H} \mathcal{R} \mathcal{R} \mathcal{R}' + T_5^* \mathcal{H}^{-1} \nabla \mathcal{R} \cdot \nabla \mathcal{R} \mathcal{R}' + T_6^* \mathcal{H}^{-1} \mathcal{R}'^3$$
$$+ T_7^* \mathcal{H}^{-2} \mathcal{R}' \nabla \mathcal{R} \cdot \nabla \mathcal{R}' \Big\},$$

where T_i's are dimensionless constants whose can be found in[20]

Computing different shapes of f_{NL} parameter when $k = aH$ we get[20]

$$f_{NL}^{sq}\Big|_{k=aH} \approx \frac{5}{12}(1-n_s) - 23\epsilon^2 \left[e^{\gamma_S\left(\frac{\bar{R}}{4\mathcal{M}_s^2}\right)} - 1 \right] - \frac{4\bar{R}}{\mathcal{M}_s^2} \epsilon^3 e^{\gamma_S\left(\frac{\bar{R}}{4\mathcal{M}_s^2}\right)} \gamma_S'\left(\frac{\bar{R}}{4\mathcal{M}_s^2}\right)$$

$$f_{NL}^{eq}\Big|_{k=aH} \approx \frac{5}{12}(1-n_s) - 49\epsilon^2 \left[e^{\gamma_S\left(\frac{\bar{R}}{4\mathcal{M}_s^2}\right)} - 1 \right] - \frac{9\bar{R}}{\mathcal{M}_s^2} \epsilon^3 e^{\gamma_S\left(\frac{\bar{R}}{4\mathcal{M}_s^2}\right)} \gamma_S'\left(\frac{\bar{R}}{4\mathcal{M}_s^2}\right)$$

$$f_{NL}^{ortho}\Big|_{k=aH} \approx \frac{5}{12}(1-n_s) - 43\epsilon^2 \left[e^{\gamma_S\left(\frac{\bar{R}}{4\mathcal{M}_s^2}\right)} - 1 \right] - \frac{22\bar{R}_*}{3\mathcal{M}_s^2} \epsilon^3 e^{\gamma_S\left(\frac{\bar{R}}{4\mathcal{M}_s^2}\right)} \gamma_S'\left(\frac{\bar{R}}{4\mathcal{M}_s^2}\right).$$
(23)

These characterize the non-local interactions of curvature perturbation. Clearly from the above expressions single field Maldacena consistency relation is violated in non-local theories and one can obtain detectable level of non-Gaussianities due to non-local nature of interactions (See Fig. 6). This is totally non-trivial effect in comparison with all the known mechanisms of producing large non-Gaussianities in the local theories.

5. Concluding remarks

We conclude here with highlighting the notable results of early Universe cosmology in the context of UV-non-local ghost-free theories of gravity. First of all we note that the UV non-local gravity action (7) is a consistent and necessary extension of Stelle gravity in order to achieve UV-completion based on the first principles. Another point to note here is "non-locality" is an important concept that is needed for building a consistent theory of quantum gravity. We have discussed how one can have a successful realization of inflation with the action action (7) and how non-local nature of gravity can be seen through inflationary observables. These are the important conclusions we can draw here to probe non-local nature of gravity in the scope of future CMB and gravitational wave observations.[5, 16, 27–29]

- In the non-local R^2-like inflation the primordial scalar power spectrum remains same as in the case of local $R + R^2$ inflation. However the tensor power spectrum is modified and one can have any value of tensor-to-scalar

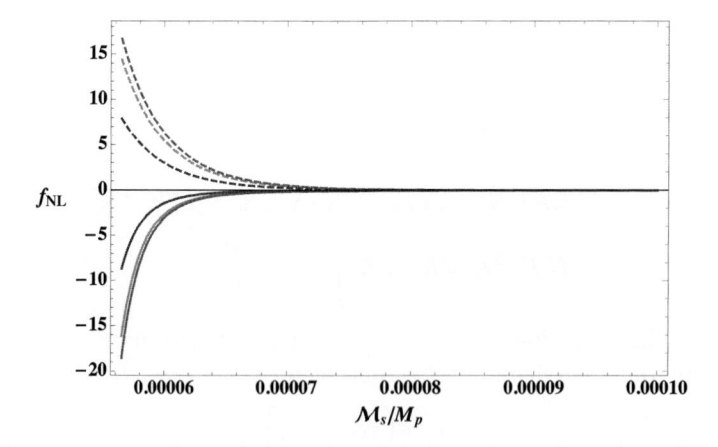

Fig. 6. In the above plots, f_{NL} versus the scale of non-locality $\mathcal{M}_s$ (in the units of M_p) is depicted for squeezed (blue), equilateral (red), and orthogonal (green) configurations for the polynomial entire functions γ_T given by eqs. (4.19) and (4.20) of arXiv:2003.00629 and represented by solid and dashed lines respectively. Here $N = 55$ of e-foldings is assumed. In the limit $\mathcal{M}_s \to M_p$ the predictions of the local R^2 model are recovered.

ratio[2,20,21] $r < 0.036$. As a result of modification of tensor power spectrum the tensor tilt in this theory is modified and ultimately tensor consistency relation $r = -8n_t$ is violated. Note that the violation of consistency relation is purely a non-local effect, the sound speed of primordial fluctuations are unity in this theory.

- The blue tensor tilt $n_t > 0$ is possible with non-local R^2-like inflation. Since not many frameworks of inflation can predict blue tilt any detection of it automatically favours non-local theory. Also $n_t < 0$ can also equally possible too.
- Non-local nature of gravity leads to detectable range of non-Gaussianities especial one can have squeezed limit of $f_{NL}^{\text{eq}} \sim O(1)$ despite there is only one scalar degree of freedom and nature of inflation is standard-slow-roll. Further more, other shapes of f_{NL} can also be large despite the sound speed of primordial scalar field is unity.

In summary, non-local nature of gravity brings very unique predictions which are indeed very interesting in the view of future observations as well as further theoretical investigations.

Acknowledgments

KSK acknowledges financial support from JSPS and KAKENHI Grant-in-Aid for Scientific Research No. JP20F20320.

References

1. Planck, Y. Akrami *et al.*, (2018), 1807.06211.
2. BICEP, Keck, P. A. R. Ade *et al.*, Phys. Rev. Lett. **127**, 151301 (2021), 2110.00483.
3. Planck, Y. Akrami *et al.*, (2019), 1905.05697.
4. LIGO Scientific, Virgo, B. P. Abbott *et al.*, Phys. Rev. Lett. **116**, 061102 (2016), 1602.03837.
5. A. Ricciardone, J. Phys. Conf. Ser. **840**, 012030 (2017), 1612.06799.
6. A. A. Starobinsky, Phys. Lett. **B91**, 99 (1980).
7. A. A. Starobinsky, Nonsingular Model of the Universe with the Quantum Gravitational De Sitter Stage and its Observational Consequences, in *Moscow 1981, Proceedings of the second seminar "Quantum Theory of Gravity"*, 58-72, 1981.
8. A. A. Starobinsky, JETP Lett. **34**, 438 (1981).
9. A. A. Starobinsky, Reheating in R^2 gravity, in *Fundamental Interactions, MGPI Press, Moscow, 1984, p. 55-79*, 1984.
10. A. H. Guth, Phys. Rev. **D23**, 347 (1981).
11. A. D. Linde, Phys. Lett. **B129**, 177 (1983).
12. A. Linde, Inflationary Cosmology after Planck 2013, in *Proceedings, 100th Les Houches Summer School: Post-Planck Cosmology: Les Houches, France, July 8 - August 2, 2013*, pp. 231–316, 2015, 1402.0526.
13. S. K. Korumilli, *Inflaton candidates: from string theory to particle physics*, PhD thesis, UBI, Covilha, 2017, 1808.03701.
14. J. Martin, C. Ringeval, and V. Vennin, Phys. Dark Univ. **5-6**, 75 (2014), 1303.3787.
15. J. M. Maldacena, JHEP **05**, 013 (2003), astro-ph/0210603.
16. P. D. Meerburg *et al.*, (2019), 1903.04409.
17. N. Arkani-Hamed and J. Maldacena, (2015), 1503.08043.
18. A. S. Koshelev, L. Modesto, L. Rachwal, and A. A. Starobinsky, JHEP **11**, 067 (2016), 1604.03127.
19. A. S. Koshelev, K. Sravan Kumar, and A. A. Starobinsky, JHEP **03**, 071 (2018), 1711.08864.
20. A. S. Koshelev, K. Sravan Kumar, A. Mazumdar, and A. A. Starobinsky, JHEP **06**, 152 (2020), 2003.00629.
21. A. S. Koshelev, K. S. Kumar, and A. A. Starobinsky, Int. J. Mod. Phys. D **29**, 2043018 (2020), 2005.09550.
22. M. J. Duff, Class. Quant. Grav. **11**, 1387 (1994), hep-th/9308075.
23. S. W. Hawking, T. Hertog, and H. S. Reall, Phys. Rev. **D63**, 083504 (2001), hep-th/0010232.
24. K. S. Stelle, Phys. Rev. **D16**, 953 (1977).
25. N. V. Krasnikov, Theor. Math. Phys. **73**, 1184 (1987), [Teor. Mat. Fiz.73,235(1987)].
26. S. V. Ketov and A. A. Starobinsky, Phys. Rev. **D83**, 063512 (2011), 1011.0240.
27. K. Abazajian *et al.*, (2019), 1907.04473.
28. CMB-S4, K. N. Abazajian *et al.*, (2016), 1610.02743.
29. P. D. Meerburg, M. Munchmeyer, J. B. Muñoz, and X. Chen, JCAP **1703**, 050 (2017), 1610.06559.

Palatini kinetic scalar-tensor theory: Analytical and numerical solutions

D. V. Gal'tsov* and D. S. Bushuev[†]

Faculty of Physics, Moscow State University, 119899, Moscow, Russia
* E-mail: galtsov@phys.msu.ru
[†] E-mail:bushuev.ds16@physics.msu.ru

We investigate static spherically symmetric solutions in the Palatini kinetically coupled scalar-tensor theory, which reduces to gravity minimally coupled to a scalar field in Einstein frame. Using the fact that the Jordan and Einstein frame are related by a reversible disformal transformation, which can be solved in closed form, we derive the general solution in the Jordan frame and show that it does not contain black holes. There is a wormhole branch and a naked singularity branch between which lies a non-singular asymptotically flat solution with kernel $M_{1,1} \times S^2$. This theory strongly violates the null energy condition.

Keywords: Black holes, wormholes, Palatini scalar-tensor theories

1. Introduction

Recently[1] was discovered a particularly simple, albeit nontrivial, example of scalar-tensor theory with kinetic coupling, which strongly violates the null energy condition. This theory is a Palatini version of the well-known model with a scalar field coupled to Ricci tensor and Ricci scalar through derivatives.[2] With a certain ratio of the two coupling constants, the metric version of this theory belongs to Horndeski class,[3–5] and has an attractive feature to generate inflationary cosmological solutions without scalar potentials.[6–9]

The situation is different in the Palatini version of this theory, what is typical for scalar-tensor theories in general.[10–14] In this case, another ratio of the two coupling constants gives a theory admitting an Einstein frame in which the scalar coupling is minimally coupled. Moreover, the Einstein metric turns out to be the metric, the Levi-Civita connection of which is the Palatini connection of the original theory. The two metrics are related by an invertible disformal transformation.[15–17] The reversibilty of the disformal transformations ensures classical equivalence of the theories in two frames,[18–20] which probably extends to the quantum level.[21] It also opens a way to use disformal transformations as a generating tool to construct exact solutions of new theories.[1,22] Some examples of solutions of Palatini kinetic theory were presented in[1] demonstrating desingularization of solutions which are singular in the Einstein frame. For deeper discussion of singularities of general relativity in the context of modified gravity theories see.[23,24]

Further investigation of[25] showed a connection between this theory and the metric conformally coupled theory, both of which demonstrate a strong violation of the null energy condition. The natural question is whether our theory allows for wormhole solutions.[26,27] Here we show that this is indeed the case.

2. The setup

We consider the action with two independent couplings of the derivatives of the scalar field $\phi_\mu \equiv \phi_{,\mu}$ to the Ricci tensor and the Ricci scalar[2,6–8]

$$S = \int d^4x \sqrt{-g}\,[R - (g_{\mu\nu} + \kappa_1 g_{\mu\nu} R + \kappa_2 R_{\mu\nu})\,\phi^\mu \phi^\nu], \tag{1}$$

where $\phi^\mu = \phi_\nu g^{\mu\nu}$. In the metric formalism, an interesting case is $\kappa_1 = -\kappa_2/2$ when the Ricci tensor and Ricci scalar are combined into the Einstein tensor, which has zero covariant divergence. This case belongs to the Horndeski ghost-free class.

In the Palatini version, the action will read

$$S = \int d^4x\sqrt{-g}\,[(\hat{R}_{\mu\nu} - \phi_\mu\phi_\nu)g^{\mu\nu} - \hat{R}_{\alpha\beta}\phi_\mu\phi_\nu(\kappa_1 g^{\alpha\beta}g^{\mu\nu} + \kappa_2 g^{\alpha\mu}g^{\beta\nu})], \tag{2}$$

where $\hat{R}_{\alpha\beta}$ is the Ricci-tensor constructed with the Palatini connection $\hat{\Gamma}$. The corresponding Einstein equations are

$$\lambda \hat{R}_{\mu\nu} - \phi_\mu \phi_\nu (1 + \kappa_1 \hat{R}) - 2\kappa_2 \hat{R}_{\alpha(\mu} \phi_{\nu)} \phi^\alpha - g_{\mu\nu} L/2 = 0, \tag{3}$$

where the Lagrangian and the factor λ are

$$L = \hat{R}_{\mu\nu} Z^{\mu\nu} - \phi_\mu \phi_\nu g^{\mu\nu}, \quad Z^{\mu\nu} = \lambda g^{\mu\nu} - \kappa_2 \phi^\mu \phi^\nu, \quad \lambda = (1 - \kappa_1 X), \tag{4}$$

and $X = \phi_\alpha \phi_\beta g^{\alpha\beta}$. Variation over ϕ gives rise to a scalar equation

$$\partial_\mu \left[\sqrt{-g}\left(\phi^\mu + \kappa_1 \hat{R}\phi^\mu + \kappa_2 \hat{R}_{\alpha\beta} g^{\beta\mu}\phi^\alpha\right)\right] = 0, \tag{5}$$

and variation over an independent connection gives:

$$\hat{\nabla}_\lambda \left(\sqrt{-g} Z^{\mu\nu}\right) = 0, \tag{6}$$

where the covariant derivative refers to the $\hat{\Gamma}$-connection.

Direct solution of the Einstein-scalar equations (3,5) does not seem possible. But as was shown in,[1] the Palatini equation (6) can be solved giving the Levi-Civita connection

$$\hat{\Gamma}^\lambda_{\mu\nu} = \hat{g}^{\lambda\tau}\left(\partial_\mu \hat{g}_{\lambda\nu} + \partial_\mu \hat{g}_{\mu\lambda} - \partial_\lambda \hat{g}_{\mu\nu}\right)/2 \tag{7}$$

of the second metric

$$\hat{g}_{\mu\nu} = \sqrt{\Lambda\lambda}\left(g_{\mu\nu} + \kappa_2 \Lambda^{-1}\phi_\mu \phi_\nu\right), \quad \Lambda = 1 - (\kappa_1 + \kappa_2)X. \tag{8}$$

This is a disformal transformation, which can be inverted (for details see[1]). It is clear that setting $\kappa_1 + \kappa_2 = 0$, will greatly simplify the above relation, and we assume that from now on. Then, remarkably, when expressed in the second metric, the action (2) is transformed into an Einstein-Hilbert action plus a minimally coupled scalar:

$$S_E = \int \sqrt{-\hat{g}}\,[R_{\mu\nu}(\hat{g}) - \phi_\mu \phi_\nu]\,\hat{g}^{\mu\nu} d^4x. \tag{9}$$

This action gives (setting torsion to zero) the same equations in the Palatini version and in the metric version:

$$R_{\mu\nu} = \phi_\mu \phi_\nu, \qquad \hat{\Box}\phi = 0. \tag{10}$$

So our strategy will be first to integrate the system (10) and then to use an inverse of the disformal transformation (8) to obtain the desired metric $g_{\mu\nu}$. To be sure that we get the general solutions in the Jordan frame we need a general solution in the Einstein frame.

3. Einstein frame: Complete integration

Static solutions of the minimally coupled scalar-tensor gravity were investigated in the past in various contexts.[28–31] The most popular solution belongs to Fisher.[28] To make sure that it is unique in the class of static spherically symmetric solutions, we repeat the derivation here.

It is convenient to present the metric ansatz as

$$ds^2 = Adt^2 + \frac{dr^2}{A} + R(d\theta^2 + \sin^2\theta d\phi^2), \tag{11}$$

where A and R are functions of r only, and it is assumed that $R > 0$ (note that we are using R and not R^2 in the angular part). The non-zero components of the Ricci tensor are

$$R_{tt} = \frac{A}{2R}(A'R)', \tag{12}$$

$$R_{rr} = -\frac{1}{2AR^2}(2ARR'' + A'RR' - AR'^2 + A''R^2), \tag{13}$$

$$R_{\theta\theta} = \frac{1}{\sin^2\theta}R_{\phi\phi} = -\frac{1}{2}(AR')' + 1, \tag{14}$$

where the prime denotes the radial derivative. The scalar field satisfies the simple divergence equation

$$(AR\phi')' = 0. \tag{15}$$

With our choice of the action, the Einstein equations read $R_{\mu\nu} = \phi_\mu \phi_\nu$, so the equations for (tt) and $(\theta\theta)$ components of the Ricci tensor are sourceless and can be integrated once, giving

$$A'R = C = \text{const}; \quad AR' = 2(r+a), \quad a = \text{const}.$$

Similarly, integrating the scalar equation we get

$$\phi' = \frac{q}{AR},$$

where the integration constant q represents the scalar charge.

From the (rr) component of the Einstein equation we obtain a constraint

$$(2R - CR')A - 2(r+a)^2 + q^2 = 0,$$

Finally, we derive a separate equation for R:
$$\frac{2}{R'} - \frac{2(r+a)R''}{R'^2} = \frac{C}{R}.$$

To solve it, we put $R = e^u$, obtaining a non-linear equation for u:
$$u'' + u'^2 - \frac{u'}{x} + \frac{Cu'^2}{2x} = 0,$$

where $x = r + a$. This equation can be integrated once, giving
$$u' = \frac{2x}{x^2 + Cx + 2C_1}$$

with some new integration constant C_1. This constant, using the constraint equation, is reduced to $C_1 = -q^2/4$. Further integration gives
$$u = \ln\left(2x^2 + 2Cx - q^2\right) + \frac{2C}{\sqrt{C^2 + 2q^2}} \tanh^{-1} \frac{2x + C}{\sqrt{C^2 + 2q^2}} + u_0,$$

where u_0 is a trivial integration constant which can be changed by angular coordinates rescaling, so we put $u_0 = -\ln 2$. Rewriting the quadratic function under logarithm as
$$x^2 + Cx - \frac{q^2}{2} = (x - x_+)(x - x_-), \quad x_\pm = -\frac{1}{2}\left(C \pm \sqrt{C^2 + 2q^2}\right).$$

To get the metric function R, one has to take the power that leads to:
$$R = e^u = (x - x_-)(x - x_+)\left(\frac{x - x_-}{x - x_+}\right)^\gamma = r^2\left(1 - \frac{b}{r}\right)^{1-\gamma}, \tag{16}$$

where we have introduced two new parameters instead of C, q^2:
$$\gamma = \frac{C}{\sqrt{C^2 + 2q^2}} \quad b = \sqrt{C^2 + 2q^2}, \tag{17}$$

and a new radial coordinate $r = x - x_-$. The metric function A in the new variables reads
$$A = \frac{2(r + x_-)}{R'}.$$

Differentiating (16), we find
$$A = \left(1 - \frac{b}{r}\right)^\gamma. \tag{18}$$

Summarizing, we obtained the famous Fisher-Janis-Newman-Winicour (FJNW) solution, proving its uniqueness within the static spherically symmetric class:
$$ds^2 = -\left(1 - \frac{b}{r}\right)^\gamma dt^2 + \left(1 - \frac{b}{r}\right)^{-\gamma} dr^2 + r^2\left(1 - \frac{b}{r}\right)^{1-\gamma} d\Omega. \tag{19}$$

The derivative of the scalar field in terms of b, γ reads:

$$\phi' = \frac{b\sqrt{1-\gamma^2}}{\sqrt{2}\,r(r-b)}. \tag{20}$$

Note that the range of the radial variable is chosen $r \in (b, \infty)$ to ensure positivity of the function R. The region $r < b$ corresponds to cosmological solution.[32]

4. Disformal transformation

To pass to the Jordan frame, it is necessary to carry out the inverse disformal transformation

$$g_{\mu\nu} = \hat{g}_{\mu\nu}\lambda^{-1/2} - \kappa\phi_\mu\phi_\nu, \tag{21}$$

where

$$\lambda = (g_{rr}/w)^{-2/3}, \quad w = A = \left(1 - \frac{b}{r}\right)^{-\gamma}, \tag{22}$$

and g_{rr} obeys the following equation:

$$\left(g_{rr} - \frac{2x}{3\sqrt{3}}\right)^3 = wg_{rr}, \quad x = \frac{3\sqrt{3}\kappa q^2}{2r^2(r-b)^2}. \tag{23}$$

A real solution of this equation reads

$$g_{rr} = \frac{2x}{3\sqrt{3}} + \frac{1}{\sqrt{3}}\begin{cases} 2w\cos\left(\frac{1}{3}\arccos x/w\right), & x < w, \\ w^{2/3}B + w^{1/3}B^{-1}, & x > w, \end{cases} \tag{24}$$

where

$$B = \left(x + \sqrt{x^2 - w^2}\right)^{1/3}.$$

Two other Jordan frame metric components are

$$g_{tt} = \hat{g}_{tt}\lambda^{-1/2} \qquad g_{\theta\theta} \equiv Q = \hat{g}_{\theta\theta}\lambda^{-1/2} = R\lambda^{-1/2}. \tag{25}$$

It is easy to see that the above transformation to the Jordan frame preserves asymptotic flatness. Indeed, when $r \to \infty$, the variables $x \to 0$, $w \to 1$, so that

$$g_{rr} \sim 1 + x/\sqrt{3} \Rightarrow \lambda = 1 + O(1/r^4),$$

and we get as $r \to \infty$:

$$g_{tt} \simeq -1 + \frac{\gamma b}{r} \quad g_{rr} \simeq 1 - \frac{\gamma b}{r} \quad g_{\theta\theta} \sim r^2. \tag{26}$$

5. Wormholes

Consider first an asymptotic behavior of the Jordan metric as $r \to b$. Without loss of generality, let the dimensionless parameter $\kappa q^2/b^4$ be equal to one. Then a careful analysis of the behavior of various terms for $x \to \infty$, $w \to 0$ assuming arbitrary values $0 < \gamma < 1$ gives the following leading approximation for small $u = (r/b - 1)$:

$$ds^2 = -u^{2(2\gamma-1)/3}dt^2 + \frac{b^2 du^2}{u^2} + b^2 u^{(1-2\gamma)/3} d\Omega. \tag{27}$$

As $r \to b$, the metric component $g_{\theta\theta} = Q(r)$ explodes if $\gamma > 1/2$, while it goes to zero for $\gamma < 1/2$. One can suspect that in the first case the intrinsic volume of a region close to $r = b$, namely $r \in [b + \delta, r_0]$, such that $\delta \ll r_0 - b \ll b$, will be infinite as $\delta \to 0$. Indeed,

$$V_\delta = 4\pi \int_{b+\delta}^{r_0} \sqrt{h} dr = \frac{12\pi}{2\gamma - 1} b^3 \left(\frac{\delta}{b}\right)^{(1-2\gamma)/3}.$$

Thus, for $\gamma > 1/2$ one has the second infinite region of three-space. This region is not flat, and not Ricci flat. It is not asymptotically flat as $r \to b$ either, moreover the scalar field diverges there. But one can suspect the existence of an asymmetric wormhole, connecting our AF-region with the second sheet to the left of the local minimum of $Q(r)$ (a turning point) at some point $r_t > b$, if exists:

$$\left.\frac{dQ}{dr}\right|_{r=r_t} = 0, \quad \left.\frac{d^2Q}{dr^2}\right|_{r=r_t} > 0, \tag{28}$$

which could correspond to a wormhole throat.

Numerical analysis shows that for $\gamma < 1/2$, $g_{\theta\theta}$ does not have a local minimum for all positive values of the coupling constant κ. For $\gamma > 1/2$ a local minimum arises, with r_t depending on γ and κ.

5.1. Numerical solutions

Though we obtained solutions in the Jordan frame analytically, the algebraic functions involved are difficult for understanding the nature of the metric, so we undertake numerical plotting. On Fig. 1, 2 we plot the metric functions for various values of $1/2 < \gamma < 1$. In this case a local minimum of $Q(r)$ arises at $r = r_t$, whose position depends on γ and κ. This corresponds to the throat radius of an asymmetric wormhole. The values r_t can be found numerically with any desired accuracy. For $\kappa = 2$, the radii of the throat for some selected γ are

γ	3/5	3/4	0,95	0,99
r_t/b	1.041	1.078	1.072	1.041

With growing κ, the throat radius increases, as can be seen from the left panel of Fig. 1. Left to the minimum, the radial function Q increases again and tends to

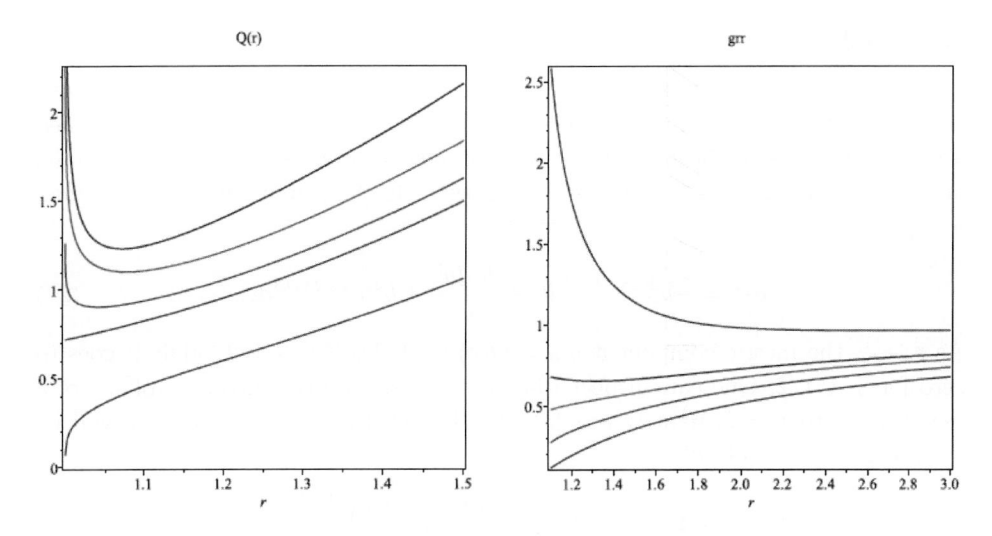

Fig. 1. Metric functions $g_{\theta\theta}$ and g_{tt} for various values of γ: $\gamma = 0.1$ (purple), $\gamma = 0.5$ (red), $\gamma = 0.6$ (light blue), $\gamma = 0.75$ (green), $\gamma = 0.95$ (blue).

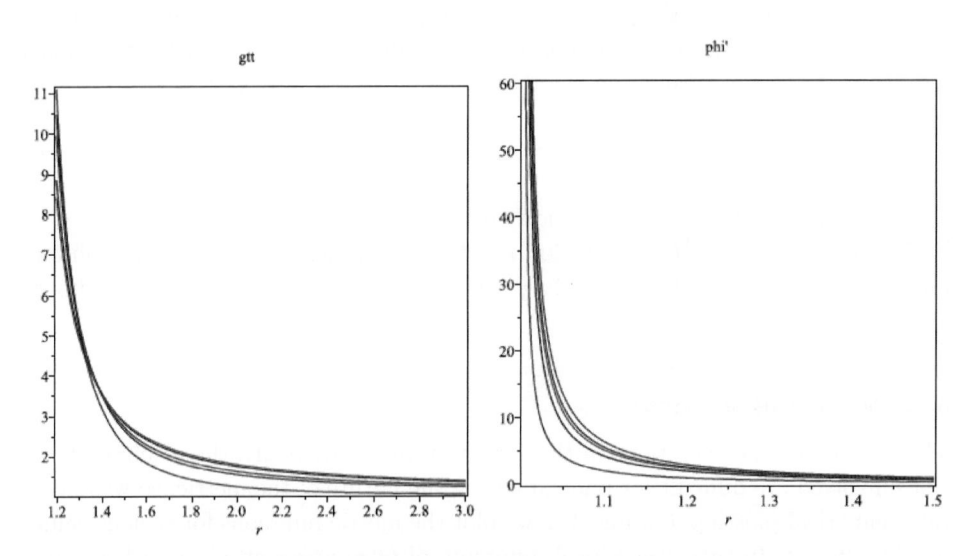

Fig. 2. Metric function g_{rr} and the derivative of the scalar field (ϕ') for various values of γ: $\gamma = 0.1$ (purple), $\gamma = 0.5$ (red), $\gamma = 0.6$ (light blue), $\gamma = 0.75$ (green), $\gamma = 0.95$ (blue).

infinity as $r \to b$ for $\gamma > 1/2$. From Fig. 2 (left panel) one can also see that $g_{tt} > 0$ for all $r > b$, so the solutions do not have horizons.

It can be shown that our wormhole is traversable: radial time-like and null geodesics freely pass through the throat. The tidal forces remain finite.

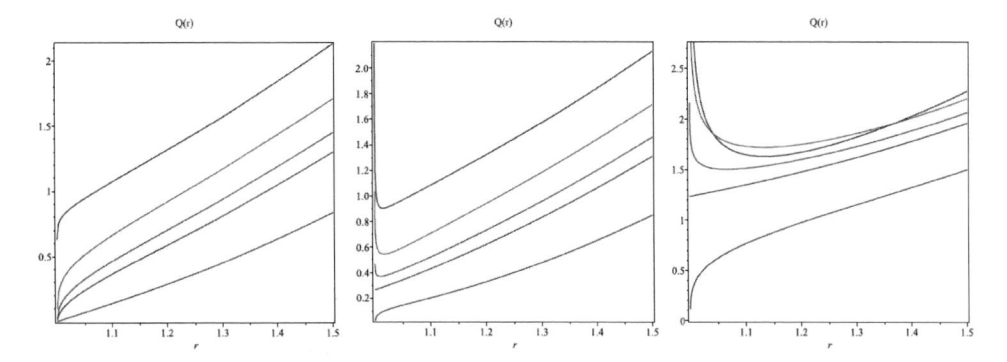

Fig. 3. Metric function ($g_{\theta\theta}$) for various values of κ: $\kappa = 0$ (left figure), $\kappa = 0.01$ (center), $\kappa = 10$ (right); and γ: $\gamma = 0.1$ (purple), $\gamma = 0.5$ (red), $\gamma = 0.6$ (light blue), $\gamma = 0.75$ (green), $\gamma = 0.95$ (blue).

5.2. Geometry of the second sheet

To investigate the geometry of the second leaf of the wormhole $r < r_t$, we first calculate the asymptotic behavior of the Ricci tensor and the Ricci scalar constructed from the Jordan metric (which is not the Palatini Ricci tensor):

$$R_{\mu\nu}(g)dx^\mu dx^\nu = -\frac{(1-2\gamma)^2}{6u^2}du^2 + d\Omega, \tag{29}$$

$$R(g) = \frac{2u^{(2\gamma-1)/3}}{b^2} - \frac{(1-2\gamma)^2}{6\mu^2}. \tag{30}$$

The rr-component of the Ricci tensor diverges as $u \to 0$, but the square of the Ricci tensor is finite for $\gamma > 1/2$:

$$R_{\mu\nu}R^{\mu\nu} = \frac{2u^{2(2\gamma-1)/3}}{b^4} + \frac{(2\gamma-1)^2}{36\,b^4}. \tag{31}$$

We then calculate the effective energy density and pressure by defining them in terms of the mixed components of the (diagonal) Einstein tensor, again constructed using the Jordan metric:

$$G^\nu_\mu(g) = (-\epsilon,\, p_r,\, p_\theta,\, p_\varphi). \tag{32}$$

This is not the physical energy density and pressure in Palatini's theory (see below), but only the effective ones used to illustrate geometry in terms of the notions of the Riemann geometry. The calculation gives for the energy density and radial pressure:

$$\epsilon = \frac{u^{(2\gamma-1)/3}}{b^2} - \frac{(2\gamma-1)^2}{12b^2}, \quad p_r = -\frac{u^{(2\gamma-1)/3}}{b^2} - \frac{(2\gamma-1)^2}{12b^2}. \tag{33}$$

Their sum is negative, demonstrating violation of NEC in our theory. The tangential pressure is positive and finite

$$p_\theta = p_\varphi = (2\gamma-1)^2/12b^2. \tag{34}$$

In the sense of the Palatini theory, the Ricci scalar must be computed by contracting the Ricci tensor built from the Palatini connection, which is the Levi-Civita connection of Einstein's frame (i.e. $R_{\mu\nu}(\hat{g})$), with the Jordan contravariant metric tensor. Near the boundary $r = b$ the leading behavior of this quantity will be:

$$R_P = R_{\mu\nu}(\hat{g})\, g^{\mu\nu} = \frac{(1-2\gamma)^2}{6\, b^2}\, \frac{1}{u^{2-\gamma}}, \tag{35}$$

which diverges as $u \to 0$ for any $0 < \gamma < 1$. The question arises whether an observer will see the second sheet as a regular or a singular space. In fact, with independent connection, the curves of minimum length do not coincide with the curves along which the tangent vector is parallel transported. More generally, the matter action can depend only on the metric, or on the metric and the connection. The point particle action belongs to the first type, so the particle will move along the curves of minimal length. Such an observer will not see singularities on the internal sheet of the wormhole. If the notion of geodesic completeness is attributed to curves of minimal length, then this spacetime should be regarded as nonsingular indeed.

5.3. *Isotropic coordinates*

The asymptotic metric of the second sheet can be presented in isotropic coordinates t, ρ, θ, ϕ changing the radial variable as

$$\rho = b\exp\left(\nu^{-1} u^\nu\right), \quad \nu = (2\gamma - 1)/6.$$

The resulting metric reads

$$ds^2 = -\left(\nu \ln \frac{\rho}{b}\right)^4 dt^2 + f^2 dl_3^2, \quad dl_3^2 = d\rho^2 + \rho^2 d\Omega. \tag{36}$$

The conformal factor $f = \frac{b}{\rho\nu}\left(\ln \rho/b\right)^{-1}$, shown in Fig. 4 as a function of ρ, clearly demonstrates two asymptotic behavior of a wormhole:

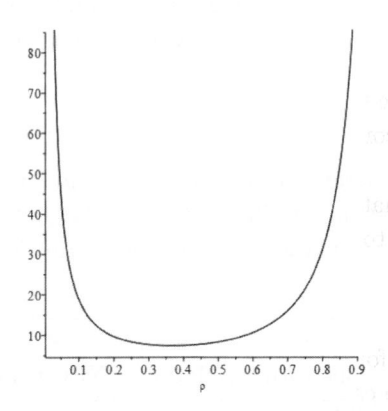

Fig. 4. The radial scale factor in isotropic coordinates.

5.4. The soliton $\gamma = 1/2$

In the Einstein frame the FJNW solution for $\gamma = 1/2$ satisfies the condition $g_{rr} = 1/|g_{tt}|$:

$$ds^2 = -\sqrt{1 - \frac{b}{r}} dt^2 + \frac{dr^2}{\sqrt{1 - \frac{b}{r}}} + r^2 \sqrt{1 - \frac{b}{r}} d\Omega. \tag{37}$$

It has curvature invariants divergent as $r \to b$. But its Jordan frame counterpart turns out to be non-singular, namely

$$ds^2 = -dt^2 + \xi^{-2} dr^2 + b^2 (d\theta^2 + \sin^2\theta d\varphi^2). \tag{38}$$

Passing to a new radial coordinate $z = b \ln \xi$, we transform the domain $r \in (b, \infty)$ into the complete real line $-\infty < z < \infty$

$$ds^2 = -dt^2 + dz^2 + b^2 (d\theta^2 + \sin^2\theta d\varphi^2). \tag{39}$$

Therefore the manifold is isomorphic to the product of the two-dimensional Minkowski space and a sphere of radius b: $M_{1,1} \times S^2$. This manifold is geodesically complete in the Riemannian geometry sense. Thus, our solution can be regarded as a regular scalar-tensor soliton. Its striking feature is that, within the framework of our theory, it is supported by a singular scalar. The singularity now is transfered to the Palatini connection.

5.5. Naked singularities

The range of the power index $0 < \gamma < 1/2$ corresponds to Jordan metrics singular in the Riemannian sense. This can be seen already from inspection of the Ricci scalar constructed with the Jordan metric:

$$R(g) = \frac{2u^{(2\gamma-1)/3}}{b^2} - \frac{(1-2\gamma)^2}{6b^2}. \tag{40}$$

The constant term is due to the two-sphere sector of the metris, while the first term originates from radial component of the Ricci tensor and it tends to infinity for $\gamma < 1/2$.

Also, one can see that the three-volume of the region between $r = b - \delta$ and $r = b$ for $\gamma < 1/2$ tends to zero when $\delta \to 0$:

$$V_\delta = 12\pi b^3 (\delta/b)^{(1-2\gamma)/3}. \tag{41}$$

The metric function $g_{\theta\theta}$ for various κ and γ is plotted in Fig. 3. From these plots one can see that in all three cases the metric has no horizons. More general numerical tests show that the static spherical sector of our theory does not contain black holes indeed.

5.6. *Classification of solutions*

Since our solution in the Einstein frame is generic in its class, we conclude that the above three types of static spherically symmetric solutions in the Jordan frame exhaust all possibilities, namely:

a) $\gamma > 1/2$ — asymmetric wormholes,
b) $\gamma = 1/2$ — regular soliton with the $M_{1,1} \times S_2$ core,
c) $\gamma < 1/2$ — asymptotically flat spacetime with a naked sigularity.

No solutions contain horizons.

Finally, we have two options for introducing the Kretschman scalar to investigate non-Ricci singularities. The Riemannian type scalar is simply $K_R = R_{\mu\nu\lambda\tau}(g)R^{\mu\nu\lambda\tau}(g)$. The Palatini-type Kretschmann scalar reads

$$K_P = R^{\mu}{}_{\nu\lambda\tau}(\hat{g}) R^{\alpha}{}_{\beta\gamma\delta}(\hat{g})\, g_{\mu\alpha}\, g^{\nu\beta}\, g^{\lambda\gamma}\, g^{\tau\delta}.$$

In the asymptotic region of the second sheet (small u) the first one is:

$$K_R = \frac{1}{9\,b^4}\left(36u^{2(2\gamma-1)/3} - 2(2\gamma-1)^2 u^{(2\gamma-1)/3} + 12\gamma^2(\gamma-1)^2 + 6\gamma(\gamma-1) + 3/4\right). \tag{42}$$

It is finite in the cases a, b and singular in the case c as expected. The Palatini Kretschmann scalar always diverges as $u \to 0$:

$$K_P = \frac{(\gamma-1)^2(5\gamma^2 - 2\gamma + 2)}{4b^4\, u^{4(2-\gamma)/3}}, \tag{43}$$

reflecting singular nature of the Palatini connection.

6. Conclusion

To summarize: we have found that Palatini scalar-tensor theory with a scalar field kinetically coupled to the Ricci tensor and the Ricci scalar is an example of theory that does not admit solutions with an event horizon at least in the static case.

The theory has Palatini connection which is the Levi-Civita connection of the Einstein frame metic. The general static spherically symmetric solution in the Einstein frame is given by the Fisher family of metrics, specified by the power index $0 < \gamma < 1$. We have shown that for $1/2 < \gamma < 1$ the Jordan metric describes wormholes, interpolating between an asymptotically flat space and a Ricci non-flat second space of an infinite volume. The second sheet of the wormholes is not asymptotically flat. Its spacetime metric is regular, and the Riemannian Einstein tensor corresponds to an effective matter violating the null energy condition.

For $\gamma < 1/2$ the Jordan solutions are one-sheeted and represent naked singularities in asymptotically flat space. In the intermediate case $\gamma = 1/2$ the Jordan metric is non-singular, and have a core of cylindrical topology.

The work is supported by the Russian Foundation for Basic Research on the project 20-52-18012Bulg-a, and the Scientific and Educational School of Moscow State University "Fundamental and Applied Space Research".

References

1. D. Gal'tsov and S. Zhidkova, "Ghost-free Palatini derivative scalar-tensor theory: Desingularization and the speed test," Phys. Lett. B **790** (2019) 453 [arXiv:1808.00492 [hep-th]].
2. L. Amendola, "Cosmology with nonminimal derivative couplings," Phys. Lett. B **301**, 175 (1993).
3. G. W. Horndeski, "Second-order scalar-tensor field equations in a four-dimensional space," Int. J. Theor. Phys. **10**, 363-384 (1974).
4. T. Kobayashi, "Horndeski theory and beyond: a review," Rept. Prog. Phys. **82**, no. 8, 086901 (2019) [arXiv:1901.07183 [gr-qc]].
5. C. Deffayet, X. Gao, D. A. Steer and G. Zahariade, "From k-essence to generalised Galileons," Phys. Rev. D **84** (2011), 064039 [arXiv:1103.3260 [hep-th]].
6. S. Capozziello and G. Lambiase, "Nonminimal derivative coupling and the recovering of cosmological constant," Gen. Rel. Grav. **31** (1999) 1005 [gr-qc/9901051].
7. S. V. Sushkov, "Exact cosmological solutions with nonminimal derivative coupling," Phys. Rev. D **80** (2009), 103505 [arXiv:0910.0980 [gr-qc]].
8. L. N. Granda and W. Cardona, "General Non-minimal Kinetic coupling to gravity," JCAP **1007**, 021 (2010). [arXiv:1005.2716 [hep-th]].
9. L. N. Granda and D. F. Jimenez, "Dynamical analysis for a scalar-tensor model with kinetic and nonminimal couplings," Int. J. Mod. Phys. D **27** (2017) no. 03, 1850030 [arXiv:1710.07273 [gr-qc]].
10. T. P. Sotiriou, "Unification of inflation and cosmic acceleration in the Palatini formalism," Phys. Rev. D **73**, 063515 (2006). [gr-qc/0509029].
11. T. Harko, T. S. Koivisto and F. S. N. Lobo, "Palatini formulation of modified gravity with a nonminimal curvature-matter coupling," Mod. Phys. Lett. A **26**, 1467 (2011). [arXiv:1007.4415 [gr-qc]].
12. X. Luo, P. Wu and H. Yu, "Non-minimal derivatively coupled quintessence in the Palatini formalism," Astrophys. Space Sci. **350**, no. 2, 831 (2014).
13. T. Helpin and M. S. Volkov, "Varying the Horndeski Lagrangian within the Palatini approach," arXiv:1906.07607 [hep-th].
14. N. Kaewkhao and B. Gumjudpai, "Cosmology of non-minimal derivative coupling to gravity in Palatini formalism and its chaotic inflation," Phys. Dark Univ. **20**, 20 (2018).
15. J. D. Bekenstein, "The Relation between physical and gravitational geometry," Phys. Rev. D **48**, 3641 (1993). [gr-qc/9211017].
16. D. Bettoni and S. Liberati, "Disformal invariance of second order scalar-tensor theories: Framing the Horndeski action," Phys. Rev. D **88**, 084020 (2013). [arXiv:1306.6724 [gr-qc]].
17. J. Sakstein and S. Verner, "Disformal Gravity Theories: A Jordan Frame Analysis," Phys. Rev. D **92**, no. 12, 123005 (2015). [arXiv:1509.05679 [gr-qc]].
18. G. Domenech, S. Mukohyama, R. Namba, A. Naruko, R. Saitou and Y. Watanabe, "Derivative-dependent metric transformation and physical degrees of freedom," Phys. Rev. D **92**, no. 8, 084027 (2015). [arXiv:1507.05390 [hep-th]].
19. K. Takahashi, H. Motohashi, T. Suyama and T. Kobayashi, "General invertible transformation and physical degrees of freedom," Phys. Rev. D **95**, no. 8, 084053 (2017). [arXiv:1702.01849 [gr-qc]].
20. E. Babichev, K. Izumi, N. Tanahashi and M. Yamaguchi, "Invertible field transformations with derivatives: necessary and sufficient conditions," [arXiv:1907.12333 [hep-th]].

21. A. Y. Kamenshchik and C. F. Steinwachs, "Question of quantum equivalence between Jordan frame and Einstein frame," Phys. Rev. D **91**, no. 8, 084033 (2015) [arXiv:1408.5769 [gr-qc]].
22. J. Ben Achour, H. Liu and S. Mukohyama, "Hairy black holes in DHOST theories: Exploring disformal transformation as a solution-generating method," JCAP **02** (2020), 023 [arXiv:1910.11017 [gr-qc]].
23. C. J. Fewster and G. J. Galloway, "Singularity theorems from weakened energy conditions," Class. Quant. Grav. **28** (2011) 125009 [arXiv:1012.6038 [gr-qc]].
24. C. J. Fewster and E. A. Kontou, "A new derivation of singularity theorems with weakened energy hypotheses," Class. Quant. Grav. **37** (2020) no. 6, 065010 [arXiv:1907.13604 [gr-qc]].
25. D. V. Gal'tsov, "Conformal and kinetic couplings as two Jordan frames of the same theory: Conformal and kinetic couplings," Eur. Phys. J. C **80** (2020) no. 5, 443 [arXiv:2001.03221 [gr-qc]].
26. V. A. Rubakov, "The Null Energy Condition and its violation," Phys. Usp. **57**, 128 (2014) [Usp. Fiz. Nauk **184**, no. 2, 137 (2014)] [arXiv:1401.4024 [hep-th]].
27. Mandal, S. "Revisiting Laws of Black Hole Mechanics and Violation of Null Energy Condition". Journal of High Energy Physics, Gravitation and Cosmology, 5, 82-111 (2019) arXiv:1907.12333 [hep-th].
28. I. Z. Fisher, "Scalar mesostatic field with regard for gravitational effects" Zh. Exp. Teor. Fiz., v. 18, 636-640 (1948), translated in arXiv: gr-qc/9911008.
29. O. Bergmann and R. Leipnik, *Space-Time Structure of a Static Spherically Symmetric Scalar Field*, Phys. Rev. **107** (1957) 1157.
30. A. I. Janis, E. T. Newman, J. Winicour, "Reality of the Schwarzschild singularity" Phys. Rev. Lett. **20**, 878 (1968).
31. K. A. Bronnikov, "Scalar-tensor theory and scalar charge," Acta Phys. Polon. B **4**, 251 (1973).
32. S. Abdolrahimi and A. A. Shoom, "Analysis of the Fisher solution," Phys. Rev. D **81** (2010), 024035 [arXiv:0911.5380 [gr-qc]].